BASEBALL CARD

PRICE GUIDE
1995

Other **CONFIDENT COLLECTOR** *Titles*
by Allan Kaye and Michael McKeever
from Avon Books

BASKETBALL CARD PRICE GUIDE 1994
FOOTBALL CARD PRICE GUIDE 1994
HOCKEY CARD PRICE GUIDE 1994

Coming Soon

BASKETBALL CARD PRICE GUIDE 1995
FOOTBALL CARD PRICE GUIDE 1995
HOCKEY CARD PRICE GUIDE 1995

BASEBALL CARD

PRICE GUIDE
1995

ALLAN KAYE
AND
MICHAEL McKEEVER

The CONFIDENT COLLECTOR™

AVON BOOKS ◆ NEW YORK

THE CONFIDENT COLLECTOR: BASEBALL CARD PRICE GUIDE (1995) is an original publication of Avon Books. This edition has never before appeared in book form.

AVON BOOKS
A division of
The Hearst Corporation
1350 Avenue of the Americas
New York, New York 10019

First Avon Books Printing: April 1994

AVON TRADEMARK REG. U.S. PAT. OFF. AND IN OTHER COUNTRIES, MARCA REGISTRADA, HECHO EN U.S.A.

Printed in the U.S.A.

OPM 10 9 8 7 6 5 4 3 2 1

Important Notice: All of the information, including valuations, in this book has been compiled from the most reliable sources, and every effort has been made to eliminate errors and questionable data. Nevertheless, the possibility of error always exists in a work of such immense scope. The publisher and the author will not be held responsible for losses which may occur in the purchase, sale, or other transaction of property because of information contained herein. Readers who feel they have discovered errors are invited to *write* the authors in care of Avon Books, so that the errors may be corrected in subsequent editions.

TABLE OF CONTENTS

Acknowledgements

This book would not have been possible without the contributions of dozens of people whose imput and expertise in the areas of card evaluations, research and technical support have significantly enhanced this edition. We sincerely appreciate their efforts and want to thank each of them for their time, dedication and hard work.

Betty and Jonathan Abraham, Cape Coral Cards; Darren Adams, West Coast SportsCards; Michael Balser, Classic Games; Bill Boake, Hall Of Fame Cards; Tim Boyle, Lesnik Public Relations; Rich Bradley, The Upper Deck Company; Scott Bradshaw, Centerfield; John Brenner; Joie Casey, Field Of Dreams; Ken Cicola, Lou Costanza, Champion Sports; Mike Cramer; Pacific Trading Cards; Dick DeCourcy; Georgia Music & Sports; Larry Dluhy, Sports Collectibles of Houston; Lewis Early, Early Entertainment; Chris Eberheart; Joe Esposito, B & E Collectibles; Eddie Fisher, Batter's Box; Larry Fritsch, Larry Fritsch Cards; Richard Galasso, Home Plate Collectibles; Tony Galovich, American Card Exchange; Richard Gelman, Card Collector's Company; Dawn Marie Giargiari, Graphic Designer; Dick Gilkeson; Bill Goepner, San Diego Sports Collectibles; David Greenhill, New York Card Company; Wayne Grove, First Base Sports Nostalgia; Bill Goodwin, St. Louis Baseball Cards; Walter Hall, Hall's Nostalgia; Eric Handler, Lapin Public Relations; Don Harrison, The Tenth Inning; Bill Henderson (King Of The Commons); Neil Hoppenworth; Peter Hughes; NFL Properties; Bob Ibach, Lesnik Public Relations; Toby Johnson; Donn Jennings, Donn Jennings Cards; Bill Karaman; Bill Kennedy, No Gum Just Cards; Tim Kilbane, Ron Klasnick, JW International; Rick Kohl, The Strike Zone; David Kohler, SportsCards Plus; Chuck LaPaglia, The SportsCard Report Radio Show; Don Lepore; Lew Lipset; Kay Longmire, O-Pee-Chee of Canada; Greg Manning; Jane McKeever; Katherine McKeever; Jim Mayfield; Blake Meyer, Lone Star SportsCards; Chuck Miller; The SportsCard Report Radio Show; Mike Miller; Dick Millerd; Richard Morris; Steve Myland; Vince Nauss, Leaf/Donruss; Donovan Niemi; Joe Pasternack, Card Collectors Company; Frank and Steve Pemper, Ball Four Cards; Jack and Patti Petruzzelli, 59 Innings; Warren Power; Andy Rapoza; Peter Reeves (Our computer guru); Gavin Riley; Alan "Mr. Mint" Rosen; Steve Rotman, Rotman Productions; Murray Rubenfeld, The SportsCard Report Radio Show; Robert Rusnak; Ben Runyan; Kevin Savage, The Sports Gallery; Duke and Smokey Scheinman, Smokey's Baseball Cards; Michelle Serrio; Eric Slutsky, Edelman Public Relations Worldwide; Nigel Spill, Oldies And Goodies; Clifford Spohn, Jim Stevens; Ted Taylor, Fleer Corp.; Bud Tompkins, Minnesota Connection; Joe Valle, Cardboard Dreams; Eddie Vidal; Tom Wall; Virginia Webster; Bill Wesslund, Portland SportsCards; Katherine Wilkins, Del Mar Broadcasting and Publishing; Dean Winskill, Argyle SportsCards; Matt Wozniak, Kit Young. We especially want to thank our Editor, Dorothy Harris and all of the staff at Avon Books.

Introduction

Over the past several years baseball card collecting has surged in popularity and baseball card prices have soared in value. When we first started collecting cards there was only one company, Topps. When we published our first hobby magazine there were only three card companies, Donruss, Fleer and Topps. Today more than a dozen companies manufacture cards on an annual basis and collecting has grown from a passive, fun-filled hobby to a huge industry with investment grade cards selling for hundreds, even thousands of dollars.

The purpose of this edition is to provide you with an accurate, up-to-date listing of baseball card values. These prices don't reflect our opinions but are the result of extensive research throughout the marketplace. The prices listed in this volume are actual retail prices obtained by monitoring retail sports card shops, baseball card shows, memorabilia conventions and auctions, hobby publications and mail order catalogues. The card values were then entered in the book just prior to the press run.

We have also tried to make this edition as easy to use as possible. Since rookie cards are among the most popular in the hobby, and are usually a player's most valuable card, we've provided rookie card designations for thousands of players. Look for the (R) symbol next to the player's name.

Since bonus cards and limited edition inserts are among the hottest cards in the hobby we have provided a checklist and values for these special cards following the regular checklist for the set in which they were issued.

Finally, we have provided a complete card grading and conditioning guide to help you analyze the condition of your collection and a glossary with definitions to help you better understand the terminology of the hobby.

Over the past decade card collecting and sports memorabilia has grown from a cottage industry to a $5 billion a year business. It is estimated that 20 million people actively participate in what has become the most popular hobby in America. We sincerely hope this edition will enhance your enjoyment of the hobby and will serve as your official reference guide to the exciting world of baseball cards.

Glossary Of Terms

AS- All-Star. Cards with the AS designation are usually part of a subset and mean the player was chosen for the All-Star team the previous year.

AW-Award Winners. Cards that are usually part of a subset that honor a player's achievements from the previous season.

BC-Bonus card. Cards that are not part of a regular set but are often issued in conjunction with the set. Bonus cards are often issued in limited quantities and randomly inserted into selected wax or foil packs.

CL-Checklist. Cards that contain a numerical list of all the cards in a set.

Commons-Applies to the typical card in a set. A card that is not in demand. Most cards in any particular set are commons and have no significant value above the listing for all the common cards in a set.

COR-A card that's been reissued with corrections after an error was discovered on the original.

CY-Cy Young Award Winner

DP-Draft Pick

DK-Diamond King. Art cards of popular baseball stars found in Donruss issues and produced by Perez-Steele.

DS-Diamond Skills. A popular subset produced by Upper Deck.

DT-Dream Team. The title of a popular subset produced by Score.

EP-Elite Performers. A subset found in Fleer Ultra sets.

ER-Error Card. Signifies that an error exists on a baseball card. Covers such mistakes as misspelling, erroneous statistics or biographical information, wrong photograph or other graphics. The card has no significant value unless a corrected card is issued creating a variation. (See Variation)

FRAN-The Franchise. A popular subset produced by Score.

HL-Highlight Cards. These cards appear in various sets, primarily Topps, as part of subsets that depict selected players who are honored for special achievements.

IA-In-Action Cards. Usually appears as part of a subset and features an action photo of a player that differs from the player's regular card in the set.

INSERT-A card that's not part of a regular edition but usually produced in conjunction with that issue. Some insert cards are produced in limited quantities and packed randomly in wax or foil packs.

LL-League Leaders. A card in a subset that depicts leaders in various hitting, pitching and stolen base categories from the previous year.

MB-Master Blaster. A popular baseball subset produced by Score.

MVP-Most Valuable Player.

PV-Pro Visions. A popular subset produced by Fleer

R-Rookie Card. Indicates the player's first appearance on a card in a regular annual baseball card set, including update, traded and rookie sets. Rookie cards are usually a player's most valuable card.

RB-Record Breaker. A card that's usually part of a subset that honors a player for a particular milestone or record set the previous season.

RR-Rated Rookies. A subset found in Donruss issues that features promising prospects.

ROY-Rookie Of The Year.

SR-Star Rookies. A popular subset produced by Upper Deck.

TL-Team Leaders. The name of a popular subset or insert set.

UMP-Umpires. Part of a subset found in selected Topps sets.

USA-A card that's part of a subset that depicts players who performed for Team USA Baseball and the US Olympic team.

VAR-Variations. This symbol means that at least two versions of the same card exist. This usually happens when an error card is corrected in future print runs and then put in circulation by the card company.

WS-World Series cards.

Grading And Conditioning Guide

All prices quoted in this edition are retail prices, the price the card would sell for in established sports card stores. Buy prices, the price the dealer would pay for a card, range from about one-third of the price listed for common cards to one-half or more for higher valued cards. Regional interest and other factors may cause the value of a card to vary from one part of the country to another.

The values appearing in this edition are intended only to serve as an aid in evaluating your cards. They are not a solicitation to buy or sell on the part of the publisher or any other party.

Mint (MT): A perfect card. Well-centered, with equal borders. Four sharp, square corners. No nicks, creases, scratches, yellowing or fading. The printing must be flawless. No miscut cards or out of register photos. Cards with gum or wax stains cannot be considered truly mint, even when removed from brand new packs.

Near Mint (NR MT): A nearly perfect card that contains a minor flaw upon close inspection. Must be well-centered and three of the four corners must be perfectly sharp. A slightly off-centered card with four perfect corners would fit this grade. No creases, scratches, yellowing or fading. Card is valued at 50% to 60% of a mint card depending on the scarcity of the card and the demand for the player.

Excellent (EX): Moderate wear, corners still fairly sharp. Card borders might be off-center. No creases, scratches, gum or wax stains on front or back. Surface may show some lack of luster. Card is valued at 40% of mint.

Very Good (VG): Corners rounded or showing minor wear or light creases. Loss of surface luster. All printing must be perfect. No gum or wax stains, no major creases, no writing or markings on the card. Card is valued at 30% to 40% of mint.

Good (G): A well-worn card with rounded corners and a major crease. Could have a small tear, pencil, tape or glue marks on the back. Printing must be intact, but overall, the card shows excessive wear. Card is valued at 20% to 30% of mint.

Fair (F): Card shows major damage such as creases that break the cardboard or pin holes along the border. Shows tape and glue marks. May have a tear or missing a bit of paper. Could have writing or other markings on the back. Card has very little value, less than 10% of mint.

Poor (P): Card fronts have been defaced with pen and ink marks. Corners may be torn off or paper may be missing or ripped-off. Card may have pin holes, glue and tape marks and major cracks through the cardboard. Cards have little or no value, less than 10% of the good (G) value.

Hank Aaron. All Time Home Run King

Hank Aaron is one of baseball's all-time greats. He owns three of the most coveted records in baseball history, all-time leader in home runs (755), RBI's (2,297) and total bases (6,856). In his 23 year career Aaron covered over 51 miles running out his homers. He was elected to the Hall of Fame in 1982. His rookie 1954 Topps card is currently valued at around $1,900. In this exclusive interview Aaron talks about his baseball cards and career.

Q. Hank, are you surprised at how fast the sports card hobby is growing?

A. It certainly is surprising yes. I've seen it from the beginning I guess. I was one of the first ball players in this business to sign autographs at card shows. I remember flying from Atlanta to San Francisco for a friend of mine and signing autographs for four hours. It wasn't very crowded and we barely met expenses. That was in the late '70's. Today, these young players can make as much money as they want to make in this hobby.

Q. Your rookie Topps card is approaching $2,000 in mint condition. Do you have any of your cards?

A. Yes. I have a few but I'm not much of a collector. I have some of my own momentos but that's about it. I don't keep up with the value of my baseball cards but it doesn't surprise me. They didn't make as many cards of the players back then like they do now so I imagine it's pretty tough finding one in good condition. Baseball is like everything else, it keeps growing in popularity. New kids are coming into the game and the hobby. The interest in cards is higher now that at any time than I can remember.

Q. Your 1957 Topps card is valued at over $225 because it shows you batting lefthanded. It's one of the most famous error cards in the hobby. Are you familiar with that card?

A. Yes, very fimilar. I did it intentionally. A lot of people see a reverse negative but I actually posed for the picture lefthanded. I was joking around with the photographer and when he was ready to take the picture for Topps I turned around and deliberately put the bat on the other side and acted like a left handed hitter. No one at Topps caught the mistake until after the cards were distributed.

Q. In your book "I had a Hammer", you described the pressure you felt leading up to breaking Babe Ruth's all-time home run record. What was that like?

A. It was very difficult at the time because it was big news. There were a few people who didn't want to see the record broken. There were threats and it was hard to find any privacy. The fact that I had to go an entire off-season two home runs shy of the record complicated matters. It made for the longest winter of my life.

Q. Do you think your all-time home run record will ever be broken?

A. I think it's possible. You know records are made to be broken. But I don't think it will happen. Today's players make so much money they don't have to put in the time that it would take to break the record. They can retire in comfort without playing 20 years or more and for that reason I think the record will stand for a long time.

Q. As an executive with the Atlanta Braves you see a lot of today's players. Are there any out there that you think are capable of approaching your record?

A. Well, there are a lot of good players around today with home run power. Ken Griffey Jr. comes to mind. There's Frank Thomas in Chicago. Barry Bonds and our own David Justice and Fred McGriff. Then there's the kid in Texas, Juan Gonzalez. These player's are capable of 40 plus homers a year but can they do it over 20 years? They have the talent but it comes down to longevity.

Q. You played along side some of the game's all-time greats. Who was the best you ever played against?

A. There were so many great players from that era it's hard to choose just one. Certainly Willie (Mays) would be at the top of anyone's list. Stan Musial was a great hitter. So was Ernie Banks. Roberto Clemente was as good as anyone who ever played. I saw Frank Robinson come up with the Reds. He was a great hitter. I didn't get to see player's from the other league much except during All-Star games so I can't comment on them.

Q. How about pitchers. Who were some of the toughest pitchers you had to face?

A. Bob Gibson was as tough as they come. He wasn't afraid to challenge you. Drysdale was like that too. Sal Maglie of the Giants was a little guy who never gave you a good pitch to hit. And the Pirates had a relief pitcher, Roy Face, who threw a fork ball. When it was on he was virtually unhittable. There were a lot of great pitchers back then. Robin Roberts, Don Newcombe, (Juan) Marichal and Koufax were four of the best. So was Fergie Jenkins. I'm sure I'm leaving a lot of others out.

Q. Your Milwaukee Braves teams in the late 1950's won two National League Pennants and a World Series. How does that team compare with some of the other great teams?

A. I don't think that team ever got the recognition it deserved. Maybe it was because we played in Milwaukee and not in the spotlight of New York. But we had everything it takes to be a great club. Hitting, pitching and defense. Warren Spahn and Lew Burdette were our aces. We were strong at the corners with (Joe) Adcock and (Eddie) Mathews. And strong up the middle with (Del) Crandell, Johnny Logan and Felix Mantilla had just come up at the time. Spahn and Mathews are in the Hall of Fame. Several other players deserve more recognition from that team. It was a great team.

Q. Looking back on your own Hall of Fame career do you have any regrets?

A. No, not really. At the time I played I thought I deserved more recognition and probably would have gotten more if I played in New York. But over time, I felt I didn't have to prove myself to anybody. It was a struggle just to get to the Major Leagues when I was coming up. I've documented that in my book. Today things are a lot easier for the players. Baseball has made a lot of progress and it's grown in popularity. I think the kids make the game grow and baseball has to continue to focus on the kids if it wants to maintain its popularity.

1948 Bowman

This 48-card black and white set was the first major set issued after World War II. Cards measured 2-1/16" by 2-1/2". A dozen cards in the set were short printed and are considered scarce (7,8,13,16,20, 22,24,26,28,29,30,34).

	NR/MT	EX
Complete Set (48)	3,800.00	1,900.00
Commons (1-36)	22.00	9.50
Commons (37-48)	32.00	15.00

		NR/MT	EX
1	Bob Elliott	110.00	25.00
2	Ewell Blackwell (R)	48.00	22.00
3	Ralph Kiner (R)	180.00	85.00
4	Johnny Mize	100.00	45.00
5	Bob Feller	250.00	115.00
6	Yogi Berra (R)	575.00	275.00
7	Pete Reiser	65.00	30.00
8	Phil Rizzuto (R)	275.00	125.00
9	Walker Cooper	22.00	9.50
10	Buddy Rosar	22.00	9.50
11	Johnny Lindell	22.00	9.50
12	Johnny Sain (R)	50.00	22.50
13	Willard Marshall	35.00	15.00
14	Allie Reynolds (R)	50.00	22.50
15	Eddie Joost	22.00	9.50
16	Jack Lohrke	35.00	15.00
17	Enos Slaughter	110.00	48.00
18	Warren Spahn (R)	340.00	160.00
19	Tommy Henrich	35.00	15.00
20	Buddy Kerr	35.00	15.00
21	Ferris Fain (R)	28.00	12.00
22	Floyd Bevins (Er)	28.00	12.00
23	Larry Jansen (R)	28.00	12.00
24	Dutch Leonard	40.00	18.00
25	Barney McCosky	22.00	9.50
26	Frank Shea	35.00	15.00
27	Sid Gordon	22.00	9.50
28	Emil Verban	35.00	15.00
29	Joe Page (R)	55.00	25.00
30	Whitey Lockman (R)	45.00	20.00
31	Bill McCahan	22.00	9.50
32	Bill Rigney	28.00	12.00
33	Bill Johnson	22.00	9.50
34	Sheldon Jones	35.00	15.00
35	George Stirnweiss	25.00	10.00
36	Stan Musial (Π)	900.00	425.00
37	Clint Hartung (R)	35.00	15.00
38	Red Schoendienst (R)	175.00	75.00
39	Augie Galan	32.00	15.00
40	Marty Marion (R)	90.00	40.00
41	Rex Barney (R)	35.00	15.00
42	Ray Poat	32.00	15.00
43	Bruce Edwards	32.00	15.00
44	Johnny Wyrostek	32.00	15.00
45	Hank Sauer (R)	45.00	20.00
46	Herman Wehmeier	32.00	15.00
47	Bobby Thomson (R)	85.00	38.00
48	George "Dave" Kosio	75.00	35.00

1949 Bowman

In this 240-card set, Bowman tinted black and white photographs in various pastel shades to add color to the cards. The set consists of posed player shots with the player's name printed in a horizontal box in the bottom center of the card front. Some names were printed on the card backs, others used script. Numerous variations exist and are noted in the checklist. Cards measure 2-1/16" by 2-1/2".

	NR/MT	EX
Complete Set (240)	16,750.00	8,250.00
Commons (1-36)	18.00	8.00
Commons (37-73)	20.00	9.00
Commons (74-144)	16.00	7.00
Commons (145-240)	75.00	35.00

1	Vernon Bickford	85.00	40.00
2	Whitey Lockman	18.00	8.00
3	Bob Porterfield	18.00	8.00
4a	Jerry Priddy (no name on front)	18.00	8.00
4b	Jerry Priddy (name on front)	35.00	15.00
5	Hank Sauer	25.00	10.00
6	Phil Cavarretta	25.00	10.00
7	Joe Dobson	18.00	8.00
8	Murry Dickson	22.00	9.00
9	Ferris Fain	25.00	10.00
10	Ted Gray	18.00	8.00
11	Lou Boudreau	70.00	32.00
12	Cass Michaels	18.00	8.00
13	Bob Cesnes	18.00	8.00
14	Curt Simmons (R)	32.00	14.00
15	Ned Garver	18.00	8.00
16	Al Kozar	18.00	8.00
17	Earl Torgeson	18.00	8.00
18	Bobby Thomson	35.00	15.00
19	Bobby Brown (R)	50.00	22.50
20	Gene Hermanski	18.00	8.00
21	Frank Baumholtz	18.00	8.00
22	Harry Lowrey	18.00	8.00
23	Bobby Doerr	70.00	32.00
24	Stan Musial	600.00	275.00
25	Carl Scheib	18.00	8.00
26	George Kell	50.00	22.50
27	Bob Feller	175.00	75.00
28	Don Kolloway	18.00	8.00
29	Ralph Kiner	120.00	55.00
30	Andy Seminick	18.00	8.00
31	Dick Kokos	18.00	8.00
32	Eddie Yost (R)	25.00	10.00
33	Warren Spahn	190.00	90.00
34	Dave Koslo	18.00	8.00
35	Vic Raschi (R)	50.00	22.50
36	"Pee Wee" Reese	225.00	100.00
37	John Wyrostek	20.00	9.00
38	Emil Verban	20.00	9.00
39	Bill Goodman	25.00	10.00
40	George Munger	20.00	9.00
41	Lou Brissie	20.00	9.00
42	Walter Evers	20.00	9.00
43	Dale Mitchell	25.00	10.00
44	Dave Philley	20.00	9.00
45	Wally Westlake	20.00	9.00
46	Robin Roberts (R)	275.00	125.00
47	Johnny Sain	35.00	15.00
48	Willard Marshall	20.00	9.00
49	Frank Shea	20.00	9.00
50	Jackie Robinson	950.00	425.00
51	Herman Wehmeier	20.00	9.00
52	Johnny Schmitz	20.00	9.00
53	Jack Kramer	20.00	9.00
54	Marty Marion	30.00	12.50
55	Eddie Joost	20.00	9.00
56	Pat Mullin	20.00	9.00
57	Gene Bearden	20.00	9.00
58	Bob Elliott	20.00	9.00
59	Jack Lohrke	20.00	9.00
60	Yogi Berra	325.00	150.00
61	Rex Barney	20.00	9.00
62	Grady Hatton	20.00	9.00
63	Andy Pafko	25.00	10.00
64	Dom DiMaggio	30.00	12.50
65	Enos Slaughter	90.00	40.00
66	Elmer Valo	25.00	10.00
67	Alvin Dark	35.00	15.00
68	Sheldon Jones	20.00	9.00
69	Tommy Henrich	35.00	15.00
70	Carl Furillo (R)	75.00	35.00
71	Vern Stephens	25.00	10.00
72	Tommy Holmes	25.00	10.00
73	Billy Cox (R)	35.00	15.00
74	Tom McBride	16.00	7.00
75	Eddie Mayo	16.00	7.00
76	Bill Nicholson	25.00	10.00
77	Ernie Bonham	16.00	7.00
78a	Sam Zoldak (no name on front)	16.00	7.00
78b	Sam Zoldak (name on front)	38.00	16.50
79	Ron Northey	16.00	7.00
80	Bill McCahan	16.00	7.00
81	Virgil Stallcup	16.00	7.00
82	Joe Page	28.00	12.00
83a	Bob Scheffing (no name on front)	16.00	7.00
83b	Bob Scheffing (name on front)	38.00	16.50
84	Roy Campanella (R)	775.00	350.00
85a	Johnny Mize (no name on front)	100.00	45.00
85b	Johnny Mize (name on front)	175.00	100.00
86	Johnny Pesky	28.00	12.00
87	Randy Gumpert	16.00	7.00
88a	Bill Salkeld (no name on front)	16.00	7.00
88b	Bill Salkeld (name on front)	38.00	16.50
89	Mizell Platt	16.00	7.00
90	Gil Coan	16.00	7.00
91	Dick Wakefield	16.00	7.00
92	Willie Jones	16.00	7.00
93	Ed Stevens	16.00	7.00
94	Mickey Vernon (R)	35.00	15.00
95	Howie Pollett (R)	20.00	8.50
96	Taft Wright	16.00	7.00
97	Danny Litwhiler	16.00	7.00
98a	Phil Rizzuto (no name on front)	140.00	65.00

98b	Phil Rizzuto (name on front)	210.00	90.00
99	Frank Gustine	16.00	7.00
100	Gil Hodges (R)	260.00	125.00
101	Sid Gordon	16.00	7.00
102	Stan Spence	16.00	7.00
103	Joe Tinton	16.00	7.00
104	Ed Stanky (R)	35.00	14.00
105	Bill Kennedy	16.00	7.00
106	Jake Early	16.00	7.00
107	Eddie Lake	16.00	7.00
108	Ken Heintzelman	16.00	7.00
109a	Ed Fitzgerald (Script)	16.00	7.00
109b	Ed Fitzgerald (Print)	35.00	15.00
110	Early Wynn (R)	140.00	65.00
111	Red Schoendienst	80.00	35.00
112	Sam Chapman	16.00	7.00
113	Ray Lamanno	16.00	7.00
114	Allie Reynolds	35.00	15.00
115	Dutch Leonard	16.00	7.00
116	Joe Hatten	16.00	7.00
117	Walker Cooper	16.00	7.00
118	Sam Mele	16.00	7.00
119	Floyd Baker	16.00	7.00
120	Cliff Fannin	16.00	7.00
121	Mark Christman	16.00	7.00
122	George Vico	16.00	7.00
123	Johnny Blatnick	16.00	7.00
124a	Danny Murtaugh (Script)	20.00	8.50
124b	Danny Murtaugh (Print)	45.00	20.00
125	Ken Keltner	16.00	7.00
126a	Al Brazie (Script)	16.00	7.00
126b	Al Brazie (Print)	35.00	15.00
127a	Henry Majeski (Script)	16.00	7.00
127b	Henry Majeski (Print)	35.00	15.00
128	Johnny Vander Meer	30.00	12.50
129	Bill Johnson	16.00	7.00
130	Harry Walker	16.00	7.00
131	Paul Lehner	16.00	7.00
132a	Al Evans (Script)	16.00	7.00
132b	Al Evans (Print)	35.00	15.00
133	Aaron Robinson	16.00	7.00
134	Hank Borowy	16.00	7.00
135	Stan Rojek	16.00	7.00
136	Henry Edwards	16.00	7.00
137	Ted Wilks	16.00	7.00
138	Warren Rosar	16.00	7.00
139	Hank Arft	16.00	7.00
140	Rae Scarborough	16.00	7.00
141	Ulysses Lupien	16.00	7.00
142	Eddie Waitkus	18.00	8.00
143a	Bob Dillinger (Script)	16.00	7.00
143b	Bob Dillinger (Print)	35.00	15.00
144	Milton Haefner	16.00	7.00
145	Sylvester Donnelly	85.00	40.00
146	Myron McCormick	75.00	35.00
147	Elmer Singleton	75.00	35.00
148	Bob Swift	85.00	40.00
149	Roy Partee	85.00	40.00
150	Alfred Clark	85.00	40.00
151	Maurice Harris	75.00	35.00
152	Clarence Maddern	85.00	40.00
153	Phil Masi	75.00	35.00
154	Clint Hartung	90.00	42.00
155	Fermin Guerra	75.00	35.00
156	Al Zarilla	85.00	40.00
157	Walt Masterson	85.00	40.00
158	Harry Brecheen	100.00	45.00
159	Glen Moulder	75.00	35.00
160	Jim Blackburn	75.00	35.00
161	John Thompson	75.00	35.00
162	Preacher Roe (R)	160.00	75.00
163	Clyde Mccullough	85.00	40.00
164	Vic Wertz (R)	110.00	50.00
165	George Stirnweiss	90.00	42.00
166	Mike Tresh	85.00	45.00
167	Boris Martin	75.00	35.00
168	Doyle Lade	75.00	35.00
169	Jeff Heath	75.00	35.00
170	Bill Rigney	100.00	45.00
171	Dick Fowler	85.00	40.00
172	Eddie Pelagrini	85.00	40.00
173	Eddie Stewart	75.00	35.00
174	Terry Moore (R)	125.00	60.00
175	Luke Appling	160.00	75.00
176	Ken Raffensberger	75.00	35.00
177	Stan Lopata	85.00	40.00
178	Tommy Brown	75.00	35.00
179	Hugh Casey	90.00	42.00
180	Connie Berry	75.00	35.00
181	Gus Niarhos	75.00	35.00
182	Hal Peck	75.00	35.00
183	Lou Stringer	75.00	35.00
184	Bob Chipman	75.00	35.00
185	Pete Reiser	100.00	45.00
186	John Kerr	75.00	35.00
187	Phil Marchildon	75.00	35.00
188	Karl Drews	75.00	35.00
189	Earl Wooten	75.00	35.00
190	Jim Hearn	75.00	35.00
191	Joe Haynes	75.00	35.00
192	Harry Gumbert	75.00	35.00
193	Ken Trinkle	75.00	35.00
194	Ralph Branca (R)	125.00	60.00
195	Eddie Bockman	75.00	35.00
196	Fred Hutchinson	90.00	42.00
197	Johnny Lindell	75.00	35.00
198	Steve Gromek	75.00	35.00
199	Cecil Hughson	75.00	35.00
200	Jess Dobernic	75.00	35.00
201	Sibby Sisti	75.00	35.00

202	Larry Jansen	100.00	45.00
203	Barney McCosky	75.00	35.00
204	Bob Savage	75.00	35.00
205	Dick Sisler	90.00	42.00
206	Bruce Edwards	75.00	35.00
207	Johnny Hopp	85.00	40.00
208	Dizzy Trout	100.00	45.00
209	Charlie Keller	100.00	45.00
210	Joe Gordon	100.00	45.00
211	Dave Ferris	75.00	35.00
212	Ralph Hamner	75.00	35.00
213	Charles Barrett	75.00	35.00
214	Richie Ashburn (R)	500.00	240.00
215	Kirby Higbe	75.00	35.00
216	Lynwood Rowe	90.00	42.00
217	Marino Pieretti	75.00	35.00
218	Dick Kryhoski	75.00	35.00
219	Virgil Trucks	100.00	45.00
220	Johnny McCarthy	75.00	35.00
221	Bob Muncrief	75.00	35.00
222	Alex Kellner	75.00	35.00
223	Bob Hofman	75.00	35.00
224	"Satchel" Paige (R)	1,350.00	650.00
225	Jerry Coleman (R)	110.00	50.00
226	"Duke" Snider (R)	1,250.00	600.00
227	Fritz Ostermueller	75.00	35.00
228	Jackie Mayo	75.00	35.00
229	Ed Lopat (R)	150.00	70.00
230	Augie Galan	75.00	35.00
231	Earl Johnson	75.00	35.00
232	George McQuinn	75.00	35.00
233	Larry Doby	190.00	90.00
234	Rip Sewell	85.00	40.00
235	Jim Russell	75.00	35.00
236	Fred Sanford	75.00	35.00
237	Monte Kennedy	75.00	35.00
238	Bob Lemon (R)	275.00	125.00
239	Frank McCormick	85.00	40.00
240	Norman Young (Wrong Photo)	160.00	70.00

1950 Bowman

The 252-cards in this set feature beautiful color portraits made from each player's black and white photograph. Cards measure 2-1/16" by 2-1/2". Card backs are horizontal. Cards 1-72 are considered scarce.

	NR/MT	EX
Complete Set (252)	9,875.00	4,650.00
Commons (1-72)	50.00	22.50
Commons (73-252)	16.00	7.00

1	Mel Parnell (R)	185.00	85.00
2	Vern Stephens	50.00	22.50
3	Dom DiMaggio	70.00	32.00
4	Gus Zernial (R)	70.00	32.00
5	Bob Kuzava	50.00	22.50
6	Bob Feller	225.00	100.00
7	Jim Hegan	50.00	22.50
8	George Kell	100.00	45.00
9	Vic Wertz	65.00	30.00
10	Tommy Henrich	70.00	32.00
11	Phil Rizzuto	200.00	90.00
12	Joe Page	70.00	32.00
13	Ferris Fain	65.00	30.00
14	Alex Kellner	50.00	22.50
15	Al Kozar	50.00	22.50
16	Roy Sievers (R)	70.00	32.00
17	Sid Hudson	50.00	22.50
18	Eddie Robinson	50.00	22.50
19	Warren Spahn	225.00	100.00
20	Bob Elliott	50.00	22.50
21	Pee Wee Reese	225.00	100.00
22	Jackie Robinson	775.00	340.00
23	Don Newcombe (R)	175.00	85.00
24	Johnny Schmitz	50.00	22.50
25	Hank Sauer	65.00	30.00
26	Grady Hatton	50.00	22.50
27	Herman Wehmeier	50.00	22.50
28	Bobby Thomson	75.00	35.00
29	Ed Stanky	65.00	30.00
30	Eddie Waitkus	50.00	22.50

31	Del Ennis	70.00	32.00
32	Robin Roberts	160.00	75.00
33	Ralph Kiner	130.00	60.00
34	Murry Dickson	60.00	28.00
35	Enos Slaughter	140.00	65.00
36	Eddie Kazak	50.00	22.50
37	Luke Appling	80.00	38.00
38	Bill Wright	50.00	22.50
39	Larry Doby	75.00	35.00
40	Bob Lemon	100.00	45.00
41	Walter Evers	50.00	22.50
42	Art Houtterman	50.00	22.50
43	Bobby Doerr	95.00	42.00
44	Joe Dobson	50.00	22.50
45	Al Zarilla	50.00	22.50
46	Yogi Berra	425.00	200.00
47	Jerry Coleman	70.00	32.00
48	Leland Brissie	50.00	22.50
49	Elmer Valo	65.00	30.00
50	Dick Kokos	50.00	22.50
51	Ned Garver	50.00	22.50
52	Sam Mele	50.00	22.50
53	Clyde Vollmer	50.00	22.50
54	Gil Coan	50.00	22.50
55	John Kerr	50.00	22.50
56	Del Crandall (R)	75.00	35.00
57	Vernon Bickford	50.00	22.50
58	Carl Furillo	75.00	35.00
59	Ralph Branca	65.00	30.00
60	Andy Pafko	65.00	30.00
61	Bob Rush	50.00	22.50
62	Ted Kluszewski	100.00	45.00
63	Ewell Blackwell	65.00	30.00
64	Alvin Dark	70.00	32.00
65	Dave Koslo	50.00	22.50
66	Larry Jansen	65.00	30.00
67	Willie Jones	50.00	22.50
68	Curt Simmons	65.00	30.00
69	Wally Westlake	50.00	22.50
70	Bob Chesnes	50.00	22.50
71	Al Schoendienst	100.00	45.00
72	Howie Pollet	50.00	22.50
73	Willard Mashall	16.00	7.00
74	Johnny Antonelli (R)	30.00	12.50
75	Roy Campanella	325.00	150.00
76	Rex Barney	20.00	8.50
77	Duke Snider	325.00	150.00
78	Mickey Owen	25.00	10.00
79	Johnny Vander Meer	30.00	12.50
80	Howard Fox	16.00	7.00
81	Ron Northey	20.00	8.50
82	Whitey Lockman	20.00	8.50
83	Sheldon Jones	16.00	7.00
84	Richie Ashburn	100.00	45.00
85	Ken Heintzelman	16.00	7.00
86	Stan Rojek	16.00	7.00
87	Bill Werle	16.00	7.00
88	Marty Marion	25.00	10.00
89	George Munger	16.00	7.00
90	Harry Brecheen	16.00	7.00
91	Cass Michaels	16.00	7.00
92	Hank Majeski	16.00	7.00
93	Gene Bearden	16.00	7.00
94	Lou Boudreau	60.00	28.00
95	Aaron Robinson	16.00	7.00
96	Virgil Trucks	20.00	8.50
97	Maurice McDermott	16.00	7.00
98	Ted Williams	875.00	400.00
99	Billy Goodman	18.00	8.00
100	Vic Raschi	30.00	12.50
101	Bobby Brown	35.00	15.00
102	Billy Johnson	16.00	7.00
103	Eddie Joost	16.00	7.00
104	Sam Chapman	18.00	8.00
105	Bob Dillinger	16.00	7.00
106	Cliff Fannin	16.00	7.00
107	Sam Dente	16.00	7.00
108	Rae Scarborough	16.00	7.00
109	Sid Gordon	16.00	7.00
110	Tommy Holmes	16.00	7.00
111	Walker Cooper	20.00	8.50
112	Gil Hodges	125.00	60.00
113	Gene Hermanski	16.00	7.00
114	Wayne Terwilliger	20.00	8.50
115	Roy Smalley	16.00	7.00
116	Virgil Stallcup	16.00	7.00
117	Bill Rigney	20.00	8.50
118	Clint Hartung	16.00	7.00
119	Dick Sisler	20.00	8.50
120	John Thompson	16.00	7.00
121	Andy Seminick	18.00	8.00
122	Johnny Hopp	16.00	7.00
123	Dino Restelli	16.00	7.00
124	Clyde Mccullough	16.00	7.00
125	Del Rice	20.00	8.50
126	Al Brazle	16.00	7.00
127	Dave Philley	16.00	7.00
128	Phil Masi	16.00	7.00
129	Joe Gordon	20.00	8.50
130	Dale Mitchell	20.00	8.50
131	Steve Gromek	16.00	7.00
132	Mickey Vernon	25.00	10.00
133	Don Kolloway	16.00	7.00
134	Paul Trout	16.00	7.00
135	Pat Mullin	16.00	7.00
136	Warren Rosar	16.00	7.00
137	Johnny Pesky	20.00	8.50
138	Allie Reynolds	35.00	15.00
139	Johnny Mize	80.00	38.00
140	Pete Suder	16.00	7.00
141	Joe Coleman	20.00	8.50
142	Sherman Lollar (R)	28.00	12.00
143	Eddie Stewart	16.00	7.00
144	Al Evans	16.00	7.00

145	Jack Graham	16.00	7.00
146	Floyd Baker	16.00	7.00
147	Mike Garcia (R)	25.00	10.00
148	Early Wynn	75.00	35.00
149	Bob Swift	16.00	7.00
150	George Vico	16.00	7.00
151	Fred Hutchinson	20.00	8.50
152	Ellis Kinder	18.00	8.00
153	Walt Masterson	16.00	7.00
154	Gus Niarhos	16.00	7.00
155	Frank Shea	16.00	7.00
156	Fred Sanford	16.00	7.00
157	Mike Guerra	16.00	7.00
158	Paul Lehner	16.00	7.00
159	Joe Tipton	16.00	7.00
160	Mickey Harris	16.00	7.00
161	Sherry Robertson	16.00	7.00
162	Eddie Yost	20.00	8.50
163	Earl Torgeson	20.00	8.50
164	Sibby Sisti	16.00	7.00
165	Bruce Edwards	16.00	7.00
166	Joe Hatten	16.00	7.00
167	Preacher Roe	35.00	15.00
168	Bob Scheffing	16.00	7.00
169	Hank Edwards	16.00	7.00
170	Dutch Leonard	20.00	8.50
171	Harry Gumbert	16.00	7.00
172	Harry Lowrey	20.00	8.50
173	Lloyd Merriman	16.00	7.00
174	Henry Thompson (R)	25.00	10.00
175	Monte Kennedy	16.00	7.00
176	Sylvester Donnelly	16.00	7.00
177	Hank Borowy	16.00	7.00
178	Ed Fitzgerald	16.00	7.00
179	Charles Diering	16.00	7.00
180	Harry Walker	20.00	8.50
181	Marino Pieretti	16.00	7.00
182	Sam Zoldak	16.00	7.00
183	Mickey Haefner	16.00	7.00
184	Randy Gumpert	16.00	7.00
185	Howie Judson	16.00	7.00
186	Ken Keltner	20.00	8.50
187	Lou Stringer	16.00	7.00
188	Earl Johnson	16.00	7.00
189	Owen Friend	16.00	7.00
190	Ken Wood	16.00	7.00
191	Dick Starr	16.00	7.00
192	Bob Chipman	16.00	7.00
193	Pete Reiser	25.00	10.00
194	Billy Cox	25.00	10.00
195	Phil Cavaretta (Er)	25.00	10.00
196	Doyle Lade	16.00	7.00
197	Johnny Wyrostek	16.00	7.00
198	Danny Litwhiler	16.00	7.00
199	Jack Kramer	16.00	7.00
200	Kirby Higbe	16.00	7.00
201	Pete Castiglione	16.00	7.00
202	Cliff Chambers	16.00	7.00
203	Danny Murtaugh	20.00	8.50
204	Granville Hamner (R)	25.00	10.00
205	Mike Goliat	16.00	7.00
206	Stan Lopata	20.00	8.50
207	Max Lanier	16.00	7.00
208	Jim Hearn	16.00	7.00
209	Johnny Lindell	16.00	7.00
210	Ted Gray	16.00	7.00
211	Charlie Keller	20.00	8.50
212	Gerry Priddy	16.00	7.00
213	Carl Scheib	16.00	7.00
214	Dick Fowler	16.00	7.00
215	Ed Lopat	35.00	15.00
216	Bob Porterfield	16.00	7.00
217	Casey Stengel	160.00	75.00
218	Cliff Mapes	16.00	7.00
219	Hank Bauer (R)	80.00	38.00
220	Leo Durocher	75.00	35.00
221	Don Mueller (R)	30.00	12.50
222	Bobby Morgan	16.00	7.00
223	Jimmy Russell	16.00	7.00
224	Jack Banta	16.00	7.00
225	Eddie Sawyer	20.00	8.50
226	Jim Konstanty (R)	35.00	15.00
227	Bob Miller	16.00	7.00
228	Bill Nicholson	16.00	7.00
229	Frank Frisch	50.00	22.50
230	Bill Serena	16.00	7.00
231	Preston Ward	16.00	7.00
232	Al Rosen (R)	75.00	35.00
233	Allie Clark	16.00	7.00
234	Bobby Shantz (R)	40.00	18.00
235	Harold Gilbert	16.00	7.00
236	Bob Cain	16.00	7.00
237	Bill Salkeld	16.00	7.00
238	Vernal Jones	16.00	7.00
239	Bill Howerton	16.00	7.00
240	Eddie Lake	16.00	7.00
241	Neil Berry	16.00	7.00
242	Dick Kryhoski	16.00	7.00
243	Johnny Groth	16.00	7.00
244	Dale Coogan	16.00	7.00
245	Al Papal	16.00	7.00
246	Walt Dropo (R)	28.00	12.00
247	Irv Noren (R)	25.00	10.00
248	Sam Jethroe (R)	20.00	8.50
249	George Stirnweiss	20.00	8.50
250	Ray Coleman	16.00	7.00
251	John Moss	16.00	7.00
252	Billy DeMars (R)	80.00	35.00

1951 Bowman

Bowman enlarged the size of their cards to 2-1/16" by 3-1/8" and increased the size of their set to 324-cards. Card fronts depict colorful portraits drawn from actual player photos. High numbered cards(#253-324) are considered scarce. This set contains the true rookie cards of Mickey Mantle and Willie Mays.

		NR/MT	EX
Complete Set (324)		21,500.00	10,000.00
Commons (1-36)		18.00	8.00
Commons (37-252)		15.00	6.00
Commons (253-324)		60.00	25.00

1	Whitey Ford (R)	1,350.00	650.00
2	Yogi Berra	480.00	225.00
3	Robin Roberts	90.00	40.00
4	Del Ennis	25.00	10.00
5	Dale Mitchell	18.00	8.00
6	Don Newcombe	50.00	22.00
7	Gil Hodges	90.00	40.00
8	Paul Lehner	18.00	8.00
9	Sam Chapman	18.00	8.00
10	Al Schoendienst	80.00	38.00
11	George Munger	18.00	8.00
12	Hank Majeski	18.00	8.00
13	Ed Stanky	25.00	10.00
14	Alvin Dark	28.00	12.00
15	Johnny Pesky	25.00	10.00
16	Maurice McDermott	18.00	8.00
17	Pete Castiglione	18.00	8.00
18	Gil Coan	18.00	8.00
19	Sid Gordon	18.00	8.00
20	Del Crandall	25.00	10.00
21	George Stirnweiss	22.00	9.00
22	Hank Sauer	25.00	10.00
23	Walter Evers	18.00	8.00
24	Ewell Blackwell	25.00	10.00
25	Vic Raschi	30.00	12.50
26	Phil Rizzuto	125.00	60.00
27	Jim Konstanty	25.00	10.00
28	Eddie Waitkus	18.00	8.00
29	Allie Clark	18.00	8.00
30	Bob Feller	150.00	70.00
31	Roy Campanella	280.00	130.00
32	Duke Snider	275.00	125.00
33	Bob Hooper	18.00	8.00
34	Marty Marion	25.00	10.00
35	Al Zarilla	18.00	8.00
36	Joe Dobson	18.00	8.00
37	Whitey Lockman	20.00	8.50
38	Al Evans	15.00	6.00
39	Ray Scarborough	15.00	6.00
40	Gus Bell (R)	25.00	10.00
41	Eddie Yost	18.00	7.00
42	Vern Bickford	15.00	6.00
43	Billy DeMars	15.00	6.00
44	Roy Smalley	15.00	6.00
45	Art Houtteman	15.00	6.00
46	George Kell	50.00	22.50
47	Grady Hatton	15.00	6.00
48	Ken Raffensberger	15.00	6.00
49	Jerry Colemen	25.00	10.00
50	Johnny Mize	65.00	30.00
51	Andy Seminick	15.00	6.00
52	Dick Sisler	18.00	7.00
53	Bob Lemon	55.00	25.00
54	Ray Boone (R)	28.00	12.00
55	Gene Hermanski	15.00	6.00
56	Ralph Branca	30.00	12.50
57	Alex Kellner	15.00	6.00
58	Enos Slaughter	60.00	28.00
59	Randy Gumpert	15.00	6.00
60	Chico Carrasquel (R)	22.00	9.00
61	Jim Hearn	15.00	6.00
62	Lou Boudreau	50.00	22.50
63	Bob Dillinger	15.00	6.00
64	Bill Werle	15.00	6.00
65	Mickey Vernon	20.00	8.50
66	Bob Elliott	18.00	7.00
67	Roy Sievers	20.00	8.50
68	Dick Kokos	15.00	6.00
69	Johnny Schmitz	15.00	6.00
70	Ron Northey	15.00	6.00
71	Jerry Priddy	15.00	6.00
72	Lloyd Merriman	15.00	6.00
73	Tommy Byrne	15.00	6.00
74	Billy Johnson	15.00	6.00
75	Russ Meyer	16.00	7.00
76	Stan Lopata	15.00	6.00
77	Mike Goliat	15.00	6.00
78	Early Wynn	55.00	25.00
79	Jim Hegan	15.00	6.00
80	Pee Wee Reese	160.00	75.00
81	Carl Furillo	40.00	18.00
82	Joe Tipton	15.00	6.00
83	Carl Scheib	15.00	6.00

84	Barney McCosky	15.00	6.00
85	Eddie Kazak	15.00	6.00
86	Harry Drechccn	15.00	6.00
87	Floyd Baker	15.00	6.00
88	Eddie Robinson	15.00	6.00
89	Hank Thompson	15.00	6.00
90	Dave Koslo	15.00	6.00
91	Clyde Vollmer	15.00	6.00
92	Vern Stephens	15.00	6.00
93	Danny O'Connell	15.00	6.00
94	Clyde McCullough	15.00	6.00
95	Sherry Robertson	15.00	6.00
96	Sandy Consuegra	15.00	6.00
97	Bob Kuzava	15.00	6.00
98	Willard Marshall	15.00	6.00
99	Earl Torgeson	15.00	6.00
100	Sherman Lollar	18.00	7.00
101	Owen Friend	15.00	6.00
102	Dutch Leonard	18.00	7.00
103	Andy Pafko	18.00	7.00
104	Virgil Trucks	18.00	7.00
105	Don Kolloway	15.00	6.00
106	Pat Mullin	15.00	6.00
107	Johnny Wyrostek	15.00	6.00
108	Virgil Stallcup	15.00	6.00
109	Allie Reynolds	35.00	15.00
110	Bobby Brown	28.00	12.00
111	Curt Simons	20.00	8.50
112	Willie Jones	15.00	6.00
113	Bill Nicholson	15.00	6.00
114	Sam Zoldak	15.00	6.00
115	Steve Gromek	15.00	6.00
116	Bruce Edwards	15.00	6.00
117	Eddie Miksis	15.00	6.00
118	Preacher Roe	28.00	12.00
119	Eddie Joost	15.00	6.00
120	Joe Coleman	15.00	6.00
121	Gerry Staley	15.00	6.00
122	Joe Garagiola (R)	125.00	55.00
123	Howie Judson	15.00	6.00
124	Gus Niarhos	15.00	6.00
125	Bill Rigney	18.00	7.00
126	Bobby Thomson	35.00	15.00
127	Sal Maglie (R)	50.00	22.50
128	Ellis Kinder	15.00	6.00
129	Matt Batts	15.00	6.00
130	Tom Saffell	15.00	6.00
131	Cliff Chambers	15.00	6.00
132	Cass Michaels	15.00	6.00
133	Sam Dente	15.00	6.00
134	Warren Spahn	135.00	65.00
135	Walker Cooper	15.00	6.00
136	Ray Coleman	15.00	6.00
137	Dick Starr	15.00	6.00
138	Phil Cavarretta	20.00	8.50
139	Doyle Lade	15.00	6.00
140	Eddie Lake	15.00	6.00
141	Fred Hutchinson	18.00	7.00
142	Aaron Robinson	15.00	6.00
143	Ted Kluszewski	40.00	18.00
144	Herman Wehmeier	15.00	6.00
145	Fred Sanford	15.00	6.00
146	Johnny Hopp	15.00	6.00
147	Ken Heintzelman	15.00	6.00
148	Granny Hamner	15.00	6.00
149	Emory Church	15.00	6.00
150	Mike Garcia	18.00	7.00
151	Larry Doby	35.00	16.00
152	Cal Abrams	15.00	6.00
153	Rex Barney	15.00	6.00
154	Pete Suder	15.00	6.00
155	Lou Brissie	15.00	6.00
156	Del Rice	18.00	7.00
157	Al Brazle	15.00	6.00
158	Chuck Diering	15.00	6.00
159	Eddie Stewart	15.00	6.00
160	Phil Masi	15.00	6.00
161	Wes Westrum (R)	20.00	8.50
162	Larry Jansen	18.00	7.00
163	Monte Kennedy	15.00	6.00
164	Bill Wight	15.00	6.00
165	Ted Williams	780.00	350.00
166	Stan Rojek	15.00	6.00
167	Murry Dickson	15.00	6.00
168	Sam Mele	15.00	6.00
169	Sid Hudson	15.00	6.00
170	Sibby Sisti	15.00	6.00
171	Buddy Kerr	15.00	6.00
172	Ned Garver	15.00	6.00
173	Hank Arft	15.00	6.00
174	Mickey Owen	18.00	7.00
175	Wayne Terwilliger	15.00	6.00
176	Vic Wertz	18.00	7.00
177	Charlie Keller	18.00	7.00
178	Ted Gray	15.00	6.00
179	Danny Litwhiler	15.00	6.00
180	Howie Fox	15.00	6.00
181	Casey Stengel	110.00	48.00
182	Tom Ferrick	15.00	6.00
183	Hank Bauer	32.00	14.00
184	Eddie Sawyer	15.00	6.00
185	Jimmy Bloodworth	15.00	6.00
186	Richie Ashburn	65.00	30.00
187	Al Rosen	28.00	12.00
188	Roberto Avila (R)	22.00	9.00
189	Erv Palica	15.00	6.00
190	Joe Hatten	15.00	6.00
191	Billy Hitchcock	15.00	6.00
192	Hank Wyse	15.00	6.00
193	Ted Wilks	15.00	6.00
194	Harry Lowrey	15.00	6.00
195	Paul Richards	18.00	7.00
196	Bill Pierce (R)	28.00	12.00
197	Bob Cain	15.00	6.00

198	Monte Irvin (R)	110.00	50.00
199	Sheldon Jones	15.00	6.00
200	Jack Kramer	15.00	6.00
201	Steve O'Neill	15.00	6.00
202	Mike Guerra	15.00	6.00
203	Vernon Law (R)	28.00	12.00
204	Vic Lombardi	15.00	6.00
205	Mickey Brasso	15.00	6.00
206	Conrado Marrero	15.00	6.00
207	Billy Southworth	15.00	6.00
208	Blix Donnelly	15.00	6.00
209	Ken Wood	15.00	6.00
210	Les Moss	15.00	6.00
211	Hal Jeffcoat	15.00	6.00
212	Bob Rush	15.00	6.00
213	Neil Berry	15.00	6.00
214	Bob Swift	15.00	6.00
215	Kent Peterson	15.00	6.00
216	Connie Ryan	15.00	6.00
217	Joe Page	20.00	8.50
218	Ed Lopat	32.00	14.00
219	Gene Woodling (R)	38.00	18.00
220	Bob Miller	15.00	6.00
221	Dick Whitman	15.00	6.00
222	Thurman Tucker	15.00	6.00
223	Johnny Vander Meer	28.00	12.00
224	Billy Cox	18.00	7.00
225	Dan Bankhead	15.00	6.00
226	Jimmy Dykes	18.00	7.00
227	Bobby Schantz (Er)	20.00	8.50
228	Cloyd Boyer	18.00	7.00
229	Bill Howerton	15.00	6.00
230	Max Lanier	15.00	6.00
231	Luis Aloma	15.00	6.00
232	Nelson Fox (R)	160.00	75.00
233	Leo Durocher	50.00	22.50
234	Clint Hartung	15.00	6.00
235	Jack Lohrke	15.00	6.00
236	Warren Rosar	15.00	6.00
237	Billy Goodman	15.00	6.00
238	Pete Reiser	20.00	8.50
239	Bill MacDonald	15.00	6.00
240	Joe Haynes	15.00	6.00
241	Irv Noren	18.00	7.00
242	Sam Jethroe	15.00	6.00
243	John Antonelli	18.00	7.00
244	Cliff Fannin	15.00	6.00
245	John Berardino (R)	25.00	10.00
246	Bill Serena	15.00	6.00
247	Bob Ramazotti	15.00	6.00
248	Johnny Klippstein	15.00	6.00
249	Johnny Groth	15.00	6.00
250	Hank Borowy	15.00	6.00
251	Willard Ramsdell	15.00	6.00
252	Dixie Howell	15.00	6.00
253	Mickey Mantle (R)	9,500.00	4,600.00
254	Jackie Jensen (R)	150.00	70.00
255	Milo Candini	60.00	25.00
256	Ken Silvestri	60.00	25.00
257	Birdie Tebbetts (R)	75.00	35.00
258	Luke Easter (R)	75.00	35.00
259	Charlie Dressen	70.00	30.00
260	Carl Erskine (R)	130.00	60.00
261	Wally Moses	70.00	30.00
262	Gus Zernial	70.00	30.00
263	Howie Pollett (Er)	60.00	25.00
264	Don Richmond	60.00	25.00
265	Steve Bilko	60.00	25.00
266	Harry Dorish	60.00	25.00
267	Ken Holcombe	60.00	25.00
268	Don Mueller	65.00	28.00
269	Ray Noble	60.00	25.00
270	Willard Nixon	60.00	25.00
271	Tommy Wright	60.00	25.00
272	Billy Meyer	60.00	25.00
273	Danny Murtaugh	70.00	30.00
274	George Metkovich	60.00	25.00
275	Bucky Harris	70.00	30.00
276	Frank Quinn	60.00	25.00
277	Roy Hartsfield	60.00	25.00
278	Norman Roy	60.00	25.00
279	Jim Delsing	60.00	25.00
280	Frank Overmire	60.00	25.00
281	Al Widmar	60.00	25.00
282	Frank Frisch	100.00	45.00
283	Walt Dubiel	60.00	25.00
284	Gene Bearden	60.00	25.00
285	Johnny Lipon	60.00	25.00
286	Bob Usher	60.00	25.00
287	Jim Blackburn	60.00	25.00
288	Bobby Adams	60.00	25.00
289	Cliff Mapes	60.00	25.00
290	Bill Dickey	180.00	80.00
291	Tommy Henrich	80.00	38.00
292	Eddie Pellagrini	60.00	25.00
293	Ken Johnson	60.00	25.00
294	Jocko Thompson	60.00	25.00
295	Al Lopez	125.00	60.00
296	Bob Kennedy	60.00	25.00
297	Dave Philley	60.00	25.00
298	Joe Astroth	60.00	25.00
299	Clyde King	60.00	25.00
300	Hal Rice	60.00	25.00
301	Tommy Galviano	60.00	25.00
302	Jim Busby	60.00	25.00
303	Marv Rotblatt	60.00	25.00
304	Allen Gettel	60.00	25.00
305	Willie Mays (R)	4,000.00	1,950.00
306	Jim Piersall (R)	125.00	60.00
307	Walt Masterson	60.00	25.00
308	Ted Beard	60.00	25.00
309	Mel Queen	60.00	25.00
310	Erv Dusak	60.00	25.00
311	Mickey Harris	60.00	25.00

312	Gene Mauch (R)	75.00	35.00
313	Ray Mueller	60.00	25.00
314	Johnny Sain	75.00	35.00
315	Zack Taylor	60.00	25.00
316	Duane Pillette	60.00	25.00
317	Smoky Burgess (R)	80.00	38.00
318	Warren Hacker	60.00	25.00
319	Red Rolfe	75.00	35.00
320	Hal White	60.00	25.00
321	Earl Johnson	60.00	25.00
322	Luke Sewell	75.00	35.00
323	Joe Adcock (R)	95.00	45.00
324	Johnny Pramesa (R)	110.00	50.00

1952 Bowman

Bowman cut back to 252-cards and employed a fascimile autograph on the card fronts in 1952. The card size remained the same as the previous year, 2-1/16" by 3-1/8", and the pictures were colorful art renditions of black and white photographs.

		NR/MT	EX
	Complete Set (252)	9,250.00	4,500.00
	Commons (1-36)	20.00	8.50
	Commons (37-216)	16.00	6.00
	Commons (217-252)	32.00	15.00

1	Yogi Berra	625.00	300.00
2	Bobby Thomson	35.00	15.00
3	Fred Hutchinson	22.00	9.00
4	Robin Roberts	75.00	35.00
5	Minnie Minoso (R)	110.00	48.00
6	Virgil Stallcup	20.00	8.50
7	Mike Garcia	22.00	9.00
8	Pee Wee Reese	110.00	48.00
9	Vern Stephens	20.00	8.50
10	Bob Hooper	20.00	8.50

11	Ralph Kiner	75.00	35.00
12	Max Surkont	20.00	8.50
13	Cliff Mapes	20.00	8.50
14	Cliff Chambers	20.00	8.50
15	Sam Mele	20.00	8.50
16	Omar Lown	20.00	8.50
17	Ed Lopat	38.00	18.00
18	Don Mueller	20.00	8.50
19	Bob Cain	20.00	8.50
20	Willie Jones	20.00	8.50
21	Nelson Fox	50.00	22.50
22	Willard Ramsdell	20.00	8.50
23	Bob Lemon	60.00	28.00
24	Carl Furillo	38.00	18.00
25	Mickey McDermott	20.00	8.50
26	Eddie Joost	20.00	8.50
27	Joe Garagiola	70.00	30.00
28	Roy Hartsfield	20.00	8.50
29	Ned Garver	20.00	8.50
30	Al Schoendienst	70.00	30.00
31	Eddie Yost	20.00	8.50
32	Eddie Miksis	20.00	8.50
33	Gil McDougald (R)	75.00	35.00
34	Al Dark	25.00	10.00
35	Granny Hamner	20.00	8.50
36	Cass Michaels	20.00	8.50
37	Vic Raschi	22.00	9.00
38	Whitey Lockman	20.00	8.50
39	Vic Wertz	20.00	8.50
40	Emory Church	16.00	6.00
41	Chico Carrasquel	20.00	8.50
42	Johnny Wyrostek	16.00	6.00
43	Bob Feller	130.00	65.00
44	Roy Campanella	250.00	115.00
45	Johnny Pesky	22.00	9.00
46	Carl Scheib	16.00	6.00
47	Pete Castiglione	16.00	6.00
48	Vern Bickford	16.00	6.00
49	Jim Hearn	16.00	6.00
50	Gerry Staley	16.00	6.00
51	Gil Coan	16.00	6.00
52	Phil Rizzuto	110.00	48.00
53	Richie Ashburn	60.00	28.00
54	Billy Pierce	25.00	10.00
55	Ken Raffensberger	16.00	6.00
56	Clyde King	16.00	6.00
57	Clyde Vollmer	16.00	6.00
58	Hank Majeski	16.00	6.00
59	Murray Dickson (Er)	16.00	6.00
60	Sid Gordon	16.00	6.00
61	Tommy Byrne	16.00	6.00
62	Joe Presko	16.00	6.00
63	Irv Noren	16.00	6.00
64	Roy Smalley	16.00	6.00
65	Hank Bauer	28.00	12.00
66	Sal Maglie	25.00	15.00
67	Johnny Groth	16.00	6.00

68	Jim Busby	20.00	8.50
69	Joe Adcock	25.00	10.00
70	Carl Erskine	35.00	15.00
71	Vernon Law	25.00	10.00
72	Earl Torgeson	16.00	6.00
73	Jerry Coleman	20.00	8.50
74	Wes Westrum	10.00	6.00
75	George Kell	42.00	20.00
76	Del Ennis	20.00	9.00
77	Eddie Robinson	16.00	6.00
78	Lloyd Merriman	16.00	6.00
79	Lou Brissie	16.00	6.00
80	Gil Hodges	90.00	40.00
81	Billy Goodman	16.00	6.00
82	Gus Zernial	16.00	6.00
83	Howie Pollet	16.00	6.00
84	Sam Jethroe	16.00	6.00
85	Marty Marion	20.00	8.50
86	Cal Abrams	16.00	6.00
87	Mickey Vernon	20.00	8.50
88	Bruce Edwards	16.00	6.00
89	Billy Hitchcock	16.00	6.00
90	Larry Jansen	20.00	8.50
91	Don Kolloway	16.00	6.00
92	Eddie Waitkus	16.00	6.00
93	Paul Richards	20.00	8.50
94	Luke Sewell	20.00	8.50
95	Luke Easter	20.00	8.50
96	Ralph Branca	20.00	8.50
97	Willard Marshall	16.00	6.00
98	Jimmy Dykes	20.00	8.50
99	Clyde McCullough	16.00	6.00
100	Sibby Sisti	16.00	6.00
101	Mickey Mantle	2,800.00	1,650.00
102	Peanuts Lowrey	16.00	6.00
103	Joe Haynes	16.00	6.00
104	Hal Jeffcoat	16.00	6.00
105	Bobby Brown	22.00	9.00
106	Randy Gumpert	16.00	6.00
107	Del Rice	16.00	6.00
108	George Metkovich	16.00	6.00
109	Tom Morgan	16.00	6.00
110	Max Lanier	16.00	6.00
111	Walter Evers	16.00	6.00
112	Smoky Burgess	20.00	8.50
113	Al Zarilla	16.00	6.00
114	Frank Hiller	16.00	6.00
115	Larry Doby	28.00	12.00
116	Duke Snider	225.00	100.00
117	Bill Wright	18.00	7.00
118	Ray Murray	16.00	6.00
119	Bill Howerton	16.00	6.00
120	Chet Nichols	16.00	6.00
121	Al Corwin	16.00	6.00
122	Billy Johnson	16.00	6.00
123	Sid Hudson	16.00	6.00
124	Birdie Tebbetts	20.00	8.50
125	Howie Fox	16.00	6.00
126	Phil Cavarretta	20.00	8.50
127	Dick Sisler	16.00	6.00
128	Don Newcombe	32.00	14.00
129	Gus Niarhos	16.00	6.00
130	Allie Clark	16.00	6.00
131	Bob Swift	16.00	6.00
132	Dave Cole	16.00	6.00
133	Dick Kryhoski	16.00	6.00
134	Al Brazle	16.00	6.00
135	Mickey Harris	16.00	6.00
136	Gene Hermanski	16.00	6.00
137	Stan Rojek	16.00	6.00
138	Ted Wilks	16.00	6.00
139	Jerry Priddy	16.00	6.00
140	Ray Scarborough	16.00	6.00
141	Hank Edwards	16.00	6.00
142	Early Wynn	50.00	22.50
143	Sandy Consuegra	16.00	6.00
144	Joe Hatten	16.00	6.00
145	Johnny Mize	65.00	30.00
146	Leo Durocher	45.00	20.00
147	Marlin Stuart	16.00	6.00
148	Ken Heintzelman	16.00	6.00
149	Howie Judson	16.00	6.00
150	Herman Wehmeier	16.00	6.00
151	Al Rosen	25.00	10.00
152	Billy Cox	20.00	8.50
153	Fred Hatfield	16.00	6.00
154	Ferris Fain	16.00	6.00
155	Billy Meyer	16.00	6.00
156	Warren Spahn	120.00	55.00
157	Jim Delsing	16.00	6.00
158	Bucky Harris	25.00	10.00
159	Dutch Leonard	16.00	6.00
160	Eddie Stanky	20.00	8.50
161	Jackie Jensen	35.00	15.00
162	Monte Irvin	50.00	22.50
163	Johnny Lipon	16.00	6.00
164	Connie Ryan	16.00	6.00
165	Saul Rogovin	16.00	6.00
166	Bobby Adams	16.00	6.00
167	Bob Avila	20.00	8.50
168	Preacher Roe	25.00	10.00
169	Walt Dropo	16.00	6.00
170	Joe Astroth	16.00	6.00
171	Mel Queen	16.00	6.00
172	Ebba St. Claire	16.00	6.00
173	Gene Bearden	16.00	6.00
174	Mickey Grasso	16.00	6.00
175	Ransom Jackson	16.00	6.00
176	Harry Brecheen	16.00	6.00
177	Gene Woodling	25.00	10.00
178	Dave Williams	18.00	8.00
179	Pete Suder	16.00	6.00
180	Ed Fitzgerald	16.00	6.00
181	Joe Collins (R)	20.00	8.50

182	Dave Koslo	16.00	6.00
183	Pat Mullin	16.00	6.00
184	Curt Simmons	16.00	6.00
185	Eddie Stewart	16.00	6.00
186	Frank Smith	16.00	6.00
187	Jim Hegan	16.00	6.00
188	Charlie Dressen	16.00	6.00
189	Jim Piersall	20.00	8.50
190	Dick Fowler	16.00	6.00
191	Bob Friend (R)	25.00	10.00
192	John Cusick	16.00	6.00
193	Bobby Young	16.00	6.00
194	Bob Porterfield	16.00	6.00
195	Frank Baumholtz	16.00	6.00
196	Stan Musial	580.00	300.00
197	Charlie Silvera	18.00	8.00
198	Chuck Diering	16.00	6.00
199	Ted Gray	16.00	6.00
200	Ken Silvestri	16.00	6.00
201	Ray Coleman	16.00	6.00
202	Harry Perkowski	16.00	6.00
203	Steve Gromek	16.00	6.00
204	Andy Pafko	20.00	8.50
205	Walt Masterson	16.00	6.00
206	Elmer Valo	16.00	6.00
207	George Strickland	16.00	6.00
208	Walker Cooper	16.00	6.00
209	Dick Littlefield	16.00	6.00
210	Archie Wilson	16.00	6.00
211	Paul Minner	16.00	6.00
212	Solly Hemus	16.00	6.00
213	Monte Kennedy	16.00	6.00
214	Ray Boone	20.00	8.50
215	Sheldon Jones	16.00	6.00
216	Matt Batts	16.00	6.00
217	Casey Stengel	175.00	80.00
218	Willie Mays	1,450.00	750.00
219	Neil Berry	32.00	15.00
220	Russ Meyer	32.00	15.00
221	Lou Kretlow	32.00	15.00
222	Dixie Howell	32.00	15.00
223	Harry Simpson	32.00	15.00
224	Johnny Schmitz	32.00	15.00
225	Del Wilber	32.00	15.00
226	Alex Kellner	32.00	15.00
227	Clyde Sukeforth	32.00	15.00
228	Bob Chipman	32.00	15.00
229	Hank Arft	32.00	15.00
230	Frank Shea	32.00	15.00
231	Dee Fondy	32.00	15.00
232	Enos Slaughter	100.00	45.00
233	Bob Kuzava	32.00	15.00
234	Fred Fitzsimmons	32.00	15.00
235	Steve Souchock	32.00	15.00
236	Tommy Brown	32.00	15.00
237	Sherman Lollar	32.00	15.00
238	Roy McMillan (R)	38.00	18.00

239	Dale Mitchell	32.00	15.00
240	Billy Loes (R)	38.00	18.00
241	Mel Parnell	32.00	15.00
242	Evert Kell	32.00	15.00
243	George Munger	32.00	15.00
244	Lew Burdette (R)	65.00	30.00
245	George Schmees	32.00	15.00
246	Jerry Snyder	32.00	15.00
247	John Pramesa	32.00	15.00
248	Bill Werle	32.00	15.00
249	Hank Thompson	32.00	15.00
250	Ivan Delock	32.00	15.00
251	Jack Lohrke	32.00	15.00
252	Frank Crosetti	160.00	70.00

1953 Bowman Color

Bowman increased the size of their cards to 2-1/2" by 3-3/4" and, for the first time, used actual color photographs on the card fronts. No player names, team names or autographs appeared on the front making this one of the most desirable sets of all-time.

		NR/MT	EX
Complete Set (160)		11,250.00	5,200.00
Commons (1-112)		30.00	14.00
Commons (113-128)		55.00	25.00
Commons (129-160)		50.00	22.00

1	Davey Williams	90.00	35.00
2	Vic Wertz	38.00	18.00
3	Sam Jethroe	30.00	14.00
4	Art Houtteman	30.00	14.00
5	Sid Gordon	30.00	14.00
6	Joe Ginsberg	30.00	14.00
7	Harry Chiti	30.00	14.00
8	Al Rosen	50.00	22.50
9	Phil Rizzuto	125.00	60.00

10	Richie Ashburn	100.00	45.00
11	Bobby Shantz	38.00	18.00
12	Carl Erskine	45.00	20.00
13	Gus Zernial	35.00	16.50
14	Billy Loes	38.00	18.00
15	Jim Busby	30.00	14.00
16	Bob Friend	38.00	18.00
17	Gerry Staley	30.00	14.00
18	Nelson Fox	80.00	38.00
19	Al Dark	38.00	18.00
20	Don Lenhardt	30.00	14.00
21	Joe Garagiola	70.00	38.00
22	Bob Porterfield	30.00	14.00
23	Herman Wehmeier	30.00	14.00
24	Jackie Jensen	45.00	20.00
25	Walter Evers	30.00	14.00
26	Roy McMillan	30.00	14.00
27	Vic Raschi	38.00	18.00
28	Smoky Burgess	38.00	18.00
29	Roberto Avila	35.00	16.50
30	Phil Cavarretta	38.00	18.00
31	Jimmy Dykes	35.00	16.50
32	Stan Musial	575.00	275.00
33	Pee Wee Reese	550.00	250.00
34	Gil Coan	30.00	14.00
35	Maury McDermott	30.00	14.00
36	Minnie Minoso	60.00	28.00
37	Jim Wilson	30.00	14.00
38	Harry Byrd	30.00	14.00
39	Paul Richards	35.00	16.50
40	Larry Doby	48.00	20.00
41	Sammy White	30.00	14.00
42	Tommy Brown	30.00	14.00
43	Mike Garcia	35.00	16.50
44	H. Bauer, Y. Berra, M. Mantle	550.00	250.00
45	Walt Dropo	38.00	18.00
46	Roy Campanella	290.00	140.00
47	Ned Garver	30.00	14.00
48	Hank Sauer	35.00	16.50
49	Eddie Stanky	35.00	16.50
50	Lou Kretlow	30.00	14.00
51	Monte Irvin	60.00	28.00
52	Marty Marion	38.00	18.00
53	Del Rice	30.00	14.00
54	Chico Carrasquel	30.00	14.00
55	Leo Durocher	65.00	30.00
56	Bob Cain	30.00	14.00
57	Lou Boudreau	50.00	22.50
58	Willard Marshall	30.00	14.00
59	Mickey Mantle	2,750.00	1,500.00
60	Granny Hamner	30.00	14.00
61	George Kell	65.00	30.00
62	Ted Kluszewski	65.00	30.00
63	Gil McDougald	60.00	28.00
64	Curt Simmons	38.00	18.00
65	Robin Roberts	90.00	40.00
66	Mel Parnell	35.00	16.50
67	Mel Clark	30.00	14.00
68	Allie Reynolds	50.00	22.50
69	Charlie Grimm	35.00	16.50
70	Clint Courtney	30.00	14.00
71	Paul Minner	30.00	14.00
72	Ted Gray	30.00	14.00
73	Billy Pierce	38.00	18.00
74	Don Mueller	35.00	16.50
75	Saul Rogovin	30.00	14.00
76	Jim Hearn	30.00	14.00
77	Mickey Grasso	30.00	14.00
78	Carl Furillo	55.00	25.00
79	Ray Boone	38.00	18.00
80	Ralph Kiner	90.00	40.00
81	Enos Slaughter	90.00	40.00
82	Joe Astroth	30.00	14.00
83	Jack Daniels	30.00	14.00
84	Hank Bauer	50.00	22.00
85	Solly Hemus	30.00	14.00
86	Harry Simpson	30.00	14.00
87	Harry Perkowski	30.00	14.00
88	Joe Dobson	30.00	14.00
89	Sandy Consuegra	30.00	14.00
90	Joe Nuxhall	45.00	20.00
91	Steve Souchock	30.00	14.00
92	Gil Hodges	165.00	80.00
93	Billy Martin, Phil Rizzuto	280.00	135.00
94	Bob Addis	30.00	14.00
95	Wally Moses	35.00	16.50
96	Sal Maglie	45.00	20.00
97	Eddie Mathews	200.00	90.00
98	Hector Rodriquez	30.00	14.00
99	Warren Spahn	225.00	100.00
100	Bill Wright	30.00	14.00
101	Al Schoendienst	90.00	40.00
102	Jim Hegan	35.00	16.50
103	Del Ennis	38.00	18.00
104	Luke Easter	38.00	18.00
105	Eddie Joost	30.00	14.00
106	Ken Raffensberger	30.00	14.00
107	Alex Kellner	30.00	14.00
108	Bobby Adams	30.00	14.00
109	Ken Wood	30.00	14.00
110	Bob Rush	30.00	14.00
111	Jim Dyck	30.00	14.00
112	Toby Atwell	30.00	14.00
113	Karl Drews	55.00	25.00
114	Bob Feller	340.00	160.00
115	Cloyd Boyer	65.00	30.00
116	Eddie Yost	60.00	28.00
117	Duke Snider	650.00	300.00
118	Billy Martin	310.00	150.00
119	Dale Mitchell	65.00	30.00
120	Martin Stuart	55.00	25.00
121	Yogi Berra	600.00	275.00

122	Bill Serena	55.00	25.00
123	Johnny Lipon	55.00	25.00
124	Charle Dressen	60.00	28.00
125	Fred Hatfield	55.00	25.00
126	Al Corwin	55.00	25.00
127	Dick Kryhoski	55.00	25.00
128	Whitey Lockman	65.00	30.00
129	Russ Meyer	50.00	22.00
130	Cass Michaels	50.00	22.00
131	Connie Ryan	50.00	22.00
132	Fred Hutchinson	50.00	22.00
133	Willie Jones	50.00	22.00
134	Johnny Pesky	50.00	22.50
135	Bobby Morgan	50.00	22.00
136	Jim Brideweser	50.00	22.00
137	Sam Dente	50.00	22.00
138	Bubba Church	50.00	22.00
139	Pete Runnels	50.00	22.50
140	Al Brazle	50.00	22.00
141	Frank Shea	50.00	22.00
142	Larry Miggins	50.00	22.00
143	Al Lopez	65.00	30.00
144	Warren Hacker	50.00	22.00
145	George Shuba	50.00	22.00
146	Early Wynn	125.00	60.00
147	Clem Koshorek	50.00	22.00
148	Billy Goodman	50.00	22.00
149	Al Corwin	50.00	22.00
150	Carl Scheib	50.00	22.00
151	Joe Adcock	55.00	25.00
152	Clyde Vollmer	50.00	22.00
153	Whitey Ford	550.00	250.00
154	Omar Lown	50.00	22.00
155	Allie Clark	50.00	22.00
156	Max Surkont	50.00	22.00
157	Sherman Lollar	50.00	22.50
158	Howard Fox	50.00	22.00
159	Mickey Vernon (Er)	50.00	22.50
160	Cal Abrams	90.00	35.00

1953 Bowman Black & White

The design of this set is identical to the 1953 Bowman color set except the cards were printed in black and white. Cards measure 2-1/2" by 3-3/4".

		NR/MT	EX
Complete Set (64)		2,600.00	1,200.00
Commons		32.00	15.00

1	Gus Bell	125.00	50.00
2	Willard Nixon	32.00	15.00
3	Bill Rigney	32.00	15.00
4	Pat Mullin	32.00	15.00
5	Dee Fondy	32.00	15.00
6	Ray Murray	32.00	15.00
7	Andy Seminick	32.00	15.00
8	Pete Suder	32.00	15.00
9	Walt Masterson	32.00	15.00
10	Dick Sisler	32.00	15.00
11	Dick Gernert	32.00	15.00
12	Randy Jackson	32.00	15.00
13	Joe Tipton	32.00	15.00
14	Bill Nicholson	32.00	15.00
15	Johnny Mize	125.00	60.00
16	Stu Miller (R)	45.00	20.00
17	Virgil Trucks	38.00	18.00
18	Billy Hoeft	38.00	18.00
19	Paul LaPalme	32.00	15.00
20	Eddie Robinson	32.00	15.00
21	Clarence Podbielan	32.00	15.00
22	Matt Batts	32.00	15.00
23	Wilmer Mizell	40.00	18.00
24	Del Wilber	32.00	15.00
25	John Sain	60.00	28.00
26	Preacher Roe	50.00	22.50
27	Bob Lemon	140.00	65.00
28	Hoyt Wilheim	125.00	60.00
29	Sid Hudson	32.00	15.00

30	Walker Cooper	32.00	15.00
31	Gene Wooding	45.00	20.00
32	Rocky Bridges	35.00	16.50
33	Bob Kuzava	32.00	15.00
34	Ebba St. Clair (Er)	32.00	15.00
35	Johnny Wyrostek	32.00	15.00
36	Jim Piersall	50.00	22.50
37	Hal Jeffcoat	32.00	15.00
38	Dave Cole	32.00	15.00
39	Casey Stengel	340.00	150.00
40	Larry Jansen	35.00	16.50
41	Bob Ramazotti	32.00	15.00
42	Howie Judson	32.00	15.00
43	Hal Bevan	32.00	15.00
44	Jim Delsing	32.00	15.00
45	Irv Noren	32.00	15.00
46	Bucky Harris	50.00	22.50
47	Jack Lohrke	32.00	15.00
48	Steve Ridzik	32.00	15.00
49	Floyd Baker	32.00	15.00
50	Dutch Leonard	35.00	16.50
51	Lew Burdette	50.00	22.50
52	Ralph Branca	45.00	20.00
53	Morris Martin	32.00	15.00
54	Bill Miller	32.00	15.00
55	Don Johnson	32.00	15.00
56	Roy Smalley	32.00	15.00
57	Andy Pafko	32.00	15.00
58	Jim Konstanty	38.00	18.00
59	Duane Pillette	32.00	15.00
60	Billy Cox	38.00	18.00
61	Tom Gorman	32.00	15.00
62	Keith Thomas	32.00	15.00
63	Steve Gromek	32.00	15.00
64	Andy Hansen	45.00	20.00

1954 Bowman

This full-color set contains 224 cards which measure 2-1/2" by 3-3/4". Card #66, Ted Williams, was pulled from the set shortly after it's release and replaced by Jimmy Piersall. The set includes a number of variations involving statistical errors on the card backs which are noted in the checklist. In most cases, the variations are worth no more than the original. The complete set price below does not include the scarce Ted Williams card.

	NR/MT	EX
Complete Set (224)	4,300.00	2,000.00
Commons (1-128)	10.00	5.00
Commons (129-224)	14.00	7.00

1	Phil Rizzuto	135.00	60.00
2	Jackie Jensen	18.00	8.00
3	Marion Fricano	10.00	5.00
4	Bob Hooper	10.00	5.00
5	William Hunter	10.00	5.00
6	Nelson Fox	28.00	13.00
7	Walter Dropo	12.50	6.50
8	Jim Busby	10.00	5.00
9	Davey Williams	10.00	5.00
10	Carl Erskine	15.00	7.00
11	Sid Gordon	10.00	5.00
12	Roy McMillan (Var)	12.50	6.50
13	Paul Minner	10.00	5.00
14	Gerald Staley	10.00	5.00
15	Richie Ashburn	38.00	18.00
16	Jim Wilson	10.00	5.00
17	Tom Gorman	10.00	5.00
18	Walter Evers	10.00	5.00
19	Bobby Shantz	12.00	6.00
20	Artie Houtteman	10.00	5.00
21	Vic Wertz	12.50	6.50
22	Sam Mele (Var)	10.00	5.00
23	Harvey Kuenn (R)	38.00	18.00
24	Bob Porterfield	10.00	5.00
25	Wes Westrum (Var)	10.00	5.00
26	Billy Cox (Var)	12.50	6.50
27	Richard Cole	10.00	5.00
28	Jim Greengrass (Var)	10.00	5.00
29	Johnny Klippstein	10.00	5.00
30	Del Rice Jr.	10.00	5.00
31	Smoky Burgess	15.00	7.00
32	Del Crandall	12.50	6.50
33a	Vic Raschi (No trade)	25.00	12.00
33b	Vic Raschi (Traded)	35.00	16.50
34	Sammy White	10.00	5.00
35	Eddie Joost (Var)	10.00	5.00
36	George Strickland	10.00	5.00
37	Dick Kokos	10.00	5.00
38	Minnie Minoso (Var)	25.00	12.00
39	Ned Garver	10.00	5.00
40	Gil Coan	10.00	5.00

41	Alvin Dark (Var)	15.00	7.00
42	Billy Loes	12.50	6.50
43	Bob Friend (Var)	12.50	6.50
44	Harry Perkowski	10.00	5.00
45	Ralph Kiner	50.00	22.50
46	Rip Repulski	10.00	5.00
47	Granny Hamner (Var)	10.00	5.00
48	Jack Dittmer	10.00	5.00
49	Harry Byrd	10.00	5.00
50	George Kell	30.00	14.00
51	Alex Kellner	10.00	5.00
52	Myron Ginsberg	10.00	5.00
53	Don Lenhardt (Var)	10.00	5.00
54	Chico Carrasquel	10.00	5.00
55	Jim Delsing	10.00	5.00
56	Maurice McDermott	10.00	5.00
57	Hoyt Wilhelm	32.00	15.00
58	Pee Wee Reese	80.00	38.00
59	Bob Schultz	10.00	5.00
60	Fred Baczewski	10.00	5.00
61	Eddie Miksis (Var)	10.00	5.00
62	Enos Slaughter	50.00	22.50
63	Earl Torgeson	10.00	5.00
64	Ed Mathews	75.00	35.00
65	Mickey Mantle	1,250.00	600.00
66a	Ted Williams	4,850.00	2,500.00
66b	Jimmy Piersall	90.00	40.00
67	Carl Scheib (Var)	10.00	5.00
68	Bob Avila	10.00	5.00
69	Clinton Courtney	10.00	5.00
70	Willard Marshall	10.00	5.00
71	Ted Gray	10.00	5.00
72	Ed Yost	10.00	5.00
73	Don Mueller	10.00	5.00
74	Jim Gilliam	25.00	12.00
75	Max Surkont	10.00	5.00
76	Joe Nuxhall	12.50	6.50
77	Bob Rush	10.00	5.00
78	Sal Yvars	10.00	5.00
79	Curt Simmons	12.00	6.00
80	John Logan (Var)	15.00	7.00
81	Jerry Coleman (Var)	12.50	6.50
82	Bill Goodman (Var)	10.00	5.00
83	Ray Murray	10.00	5.00
84	Larry Doby	18.00	8.00
85	Jim Dyck (Var)	10.00	5.00
86	Harry Dorish	10.00	5.00
87	Don Lund	10.00	5.00
88	Tommy Umphlett	10.00	5.00
89	Willie Mays (Er)	500.00	250.00
90	Roy Campanella	185.00	90.00
91	Cal Abrams	10.00	5.00
92	Ken Raffensberger	10.00	5.00
93	Bill Serena (Var)	10.00	5.00
94	Solly Hemus (Var)	10.00	5.00
95	Robin Roberts	45.00	20.00
96	Joe Adcock	15.00	7.00
97	Gil McDougald	22.00	10.00
98	Ellis Kinder	10.00	5.00
99	Peter Suder (Var)	10.00	5.00
100	Mike Garcia	12.00	6.00
101	Don Larsen (R)	50.00	24.00
102	Bill Pierce	12.50	6.50
103	Steve Souchock (Var)	10.00	5.00
104	Frank Shea	10.00	5.00
105	Sal Maglie (Var)	15.00	7.00
106	Clem Labine	12.50	6.50
107	Paul LaPalme	10.00	5.00
108	Bobby Adams	10.00	5.00
109	Roy Smalley	10.00	5.00
110	Al Schoendienst	38.00	18.00
111	Murry Dickson	10.00	5.00
112	Andy Pafko	12.50	6.50
113	Allie Reynolds	20.00	8.50
114	Williard Nixon	10.00	5.00
115	Don Bollweg	10.00	5.00
116	Luke Easter	10.00	5.00
117	Dick Kryhoski	10.00	5.00
118	Robert Boyd	10.00	5.00
119	Fred Hatfield	10.00	5.00
120	Mel Hoderlein	10.00	5.00
121	Ray Katt	10.00	5.00
122	Carl Furillo	20.00	8.50
123	Toby Atwell	10.00	5.00
124	Gus Bell (Var)	12.50	6.50
125	Warren Hacker	10.00	5.00
126	Cliff Chambers	10.00	5.00
127	Del Ennis	10.00	5.00
128	Ebba St. Claire	10.00	5.00
129	Hank Bauer	22.00	10.00
130	Milt Bolling	14.00	7.00
131	Joe Astroth	14.00	7.00
132	Bob Feller	100.00	50.00
133	Duane Pillette	14.00	7.00
134	Luis Aloma	14.00	7.00
135	Johnny Pesky	15.00	7.00
136	Clyde Vollmer	14.00	7.00
137	Al Corwin Jr.	14.00	7.00
138	Gil Hodges (Var)	75.00	35.00
139	Preston Ward (Var)	14.00	7.00
140	Saul Rogovin (Var)	14.00	7.00
141	Joe Garagiola	50.00	22.50
142	Al Brazle	14.00	7.00
143	Willie Jones	14.00	7.00
144	Ernie Johnson	22.00	10.00
145	Billy Martin (Var)	80.00	38.00
146	Dick Gernert	14.00	7.00
147	Joe DeMaestri	14.00	7.00
148	Dale Mitchell	15.00	7.00
149	Bob Young	14.00	7.00
150	Cass Michaels	14.00	7.00
151	Patrick Mullin	14.00	7.00
152	Mickey Vernon	15.00	7.00
153	Whitey Lockman (Var)	15.00	7.00

154	Don Newcombe	28.00	13.00
155	Frank Thomas (R)	22.00	10.00
156	Rocky Bridges (Var)	14.00	7.00
157	Omar Lown	14.00	7.00
158	Stu Miller	15.00	7.00
159	John Lindell	14.00	7.00
160	Danny O'Connell	14.00	7.00
161	Yogi Berra	200.00	100.00
162	Ted Lepcio	14.00	7.00
163a	Dave Philley (No Trade)	18.00	8.00
163b	Dave Philley (Trade)	30.00	14.00
164	Early Wynn	50.00	22.50
165	Johnny Groth	14.00	7.00
166	Sandy Consuegra	14.00	7.00
167	Bill Hoeft	14.00	7.00
168	Ed Fitzgerald	14.00	7.00
169	Larry Jansen	15.00	7.00
170	Duke Snider	175.00	80.00
171	Carlos Bernier	14.00	7.00
172	Andy Seminick	14.00	7.00
173	Dee Fondy Jr.	14.00	7.00
174	Pete Castiglione (Var)	14.00	7.00
175	Melvin Clark	14.00	7.00
176	Vernon Bickford	14.00	7.00
177	Whitey Ford	125.00	60.00
178	Del Wilber	14.00	7.00
179	Morris Martin (Var)	14.00	7.00
180	Joe Tipton	14.00	7.00
181	Les Moss	14.00	7.00
182	Sherman Lollar	15.00	7.00
183	Matt Batts	14.00	7.00
184	Mickey Grasso	14.00	7.00
185	Daryl Spencer (Var)	14.00	7.00
186	Russell Meyer	14.00	7.00
187	Verne Law (Er)	20.00	8.50
188	Frank Smith	14.00	7.00
189	Ransom Jackson	14.00	7.00
190	Joe Presko	14.00	7.00
191	Karl Drews	14.00	7.00
192	Lew Burdette	20.00	8.50
193	Eddie Robinson	14.00	7.00
194	Sid Hudson	14.00	7.00
195	Bob Cain	14.00	7.00
196	Bob Lemon	45.00	20.00
197	Lou Kretlow	14.00	7.00
198	Virgil Trucks	15.00	7.00
199	Steve Gromek	14.00	7.00
200	Conrad Marrero	14.00	7.00
201	Bobby Thomson	20.00	8.50
202	George Shuba	14.00	7.00
203	Vic Janowicz	20.00	8.50
204	Jack Collum	14.00	7.00
205	Hal Jeffcoat	14.00	7.00
206	Steve Bilko	14.00	7.00
207	Stan Lopata	14.00	7.00
208	Johnny Antonelli	20.00	8.50
209	Gene Woodling (Er)	20.00	8.50
210	Jimmy Piersall	20.00	8.50
211	Al Robertson	14.00	7.00
212	Owen Friend (Var)	14.00	7.00
213	Dick Littlefield	14.00	7.00
214	Ferris Fain	15.00	7.00
215	Johnny Bucha	14.00	7.00
216	Jerry Snyder (Var)	14.00	7.00
217	Hank Thompson (Var)	15.00	7.00
218	Preacher Roe	20.00	8.50
219	Hal Rice	14.00	7.00
220	Hobie Landrith	14.00	7.00
221	Frank Baumholtz	14.00	7.00
222	Memo Luna	14.00	7.00
223	Steve Ridzik	14.00	7.00
224	Bill Bruton	40.00	15.00

1955 Bowman

This set proved to be one of Bowman's most popular issues primarily due to the design which featured player photos inside a television screen. Known as the "TV Set", the cards measure 2-1/2" by 3-3/4".

		NR/MT	EX
Complete Set (320)		5,250.00	2,600.00
Commons (1-224)		7.50	3.50
Commons (225-320)		20.00	8.50

1	Hoyt Wilhelm	100.00	45.00
2	Al Dark	12.50	6.50
3	Joe Coleman	7.50	3.50
4	Eddie Waitkus	7.50	3.50
5	Jim Robertson	7.50	3.50
6	Pete Suder	7.50	3.50
7	Gene Baker	7.50	3.50
8	Warren Hacker	7.50	3.50
9	Gil McDougald	20.00	8.50

10	Phil Rizzuto	65.00	32.00
11	Billy Bruton	7.50	3.50
12	Andy Pafko	10.00	5.00
13	Clyde Vollmer	7.50	3.50
14	Gus Keriazakos	7.50	3.50
15	Frank Sullivan	7.50	3.50
16	Jim Piersall	12.00	6.00
17	Del Ennis	8.50	4.00
18	Stan Lopata	7.50	3.50
19	Bobby Avila	8.50	4.00
20	Al Smith	7.50	3.50
21	Don Hoak	10.00	5.00
22	Roy Campanella	140.00	65.00
23	Al Kaline	160.00	75.00
24	Al Aber	7.50	3.50
25	Minnie Minoso	20.00	8.50
26	Virgil Trucks	10.00	5.00
27	Preston Ward	7.50	3.50
28	Dick Cole	7.50	3.50
29	Red Schoendienst	30.00	14.00
30	Bill Sarni	7.50	3.50
31	Johnny Temple (R)	12.00	6.00
32	Wally Post	10.00	5.00
33	Nelson Fox	27.00	13.00
34	Clint Courtney	7.50	3.50
35	Bill Tuttle	7.50	3.50
36	Wayne Belardi	7.50	3.50
37	Pee Wee Reese	80.00	38.00
38	Early Wynn	30.00	14.00
39	Bob Darnell	7.50	3.50
40	Vic Wertz	8.50	4.00
41	Mel Clark	7.50	3.50
42	Bob Greenwood	7.50	3.50
43	Bob Buhl	8.50	4.00
44	Danny O'Connell	7.50	3.50
45	Tom Umphlett	7.50	3.50
46	Mickey Vernon	8.50	4.00
47	Sammy White	7.50	3.50
48a	Milt Bolling (Er)	8.50	4.00
48b	Milt Bolling (Cor)	20.00	8.50
49	Jim Greengrass	7.50	3.50
50	Hobie Landrith	7.50	3.50
51	Elvin Tappe	7.50	3.50
52	Hal Rice	7.50	3.50
53	Alex Kellner	7.50	3.50
54	Don Bollweg	7.50	3.50
55	Cal Abrams	7.50	3.50
56	Billy Cox	8.50	4.00
57	Bob Friend	7.50	3.50
58	Frank Thomas	10.00	5.00
59	Whitey Ford	85.00	42.00
60	Enos Slaughter	30.00	14.00
61	Paul LaPalme	7.50	3.50
62	Royce Lint	7.50	3.50
63	Irv Noren	7.50	3.50
64	Curt Simmons	8.50	4.00
65	Don Zimmer (R)	30.00	14.00
66	George Shuba	7.50	3.50
67	Don Larsen	20.00	8.50
68	Elston Howard (R)	75.00	35.00
69	Bill Hunter	7.50	3.50
70	Lew Burdette	12.00	6.00
71	Dave Jolly	7.50	3.50
72	Chet Nichols	7.50	3.50
73	Eddie Yost	7.50	3.50
74	Jerry Snyder	7.50	3.50
75	Brooks Lawrence	8.50	4.00
76	Tom Poholsky	7.50	3.50
77	Jim McDonald	7.50	3.50
78	Gil Coan	7.50	3.50
79	Willie Miranda	7.50	3.50
80	Lou Limmer	7.50	3.50
81	Bob Morgan	7.50	3.50
82	Lee Walls	7.50	3.50
83	Max Surkont	7.50	3.50
84	George Freese	7.50	3.50
85	Cass Michaels	7.50	3.50
86	Ted Gray	7.50	3.50
87	Randy Jackson	7.50	3.50
88	Steve Bilko	7.50	3.50
89	Lou Boudreau	25.00	12.00
90	Art Ditmar	7.50	3.50
91	Dick Marlowe	7.50	3.50
92	George Zuverink	7.50	3.50
93	Andy Seminick	7.50	3.50
94	Hank Thompson	7.50	3.50
95	Sal Maglie	12.00	6.00
96	Ray Narleski (R)	12.00	6.00
97	John Podres	20.00	8.50
98	Junior Gilliam	20.00	8.50
99	Jerry Coleman	8.50	4.00
100	Tom Morgan	7.50	3.50
101a	Don Johnson Wrong Photo)	8.50	4.00
101b	Don Johnson (Cor)	20.00	8.50
102	Bobby Thomson	12.00	6.00
103	Eddie Mathews	60.00	28.00
104	Bob Porterfield	7.50	3.50
105	Johnny Schmitz	7.50	3.50
106	Del Rice	7.50	3.50
107	Solly Hemus	7.50	3.50
108	Lou Kretlow	7.50	3.50
109	Vern Stephens	7.50	3.50
110	Bob Miller	7.50	3.50
111	Steve Ridzik	7.50	3.50
112	Granny Hamner	7.50	3.50
113	Bob Hall	7.50	3.50
114	Vic Janowicz	8.50	4.00
115	Roger Bowman	7.50	3.50
116	Sandy Consuegra	7.50	3.50
117	Johnny Groth	7.50	3.50
118	Bobby Adams	7.50	3.50
119	Joe Astroth	7.50	3.50
120	Ed Brutschy	7.50	3.50

121	Rufus Crawford	7.50	3.50
122	Al Corwin	7.50	3.50
123	Marv Grissom	7.50	3.50
124	Johnny Antonelli	10.00	5.00
125	Paul Giel	7.50	3.50
126	Billy Goodman	7.50	3.50
127	Hank Majeski	7.50	3.50
128	Mike Garcia	7.50	3.50
129	Hal Naragon	7.50	3.50
130	Richie Ashburn	30.00	14.00
131	Willard Marshall	7.50	3.50
132a	Harvey Kueen (Er)	12.00	6.00
132b	Harvey Kuenn (Cor)	28.00	13.00
133	Charles King	7.50	3.50
134	Bob Feller	70.00	30.00
135	Lloyd Merriman	7.50	3.50
136	Rocky Bridges	7.50	3.50
137	Bob Talbot	7.50	3.50
138	Davey Williams	7.50	3.50
139	Wil & Bobby Shantz	10.00	5.00
140	Bobby Shantz	8.50	4.00
141	Wes Westrum	7.50	3.50
142	Rudy Regalado	7.50	3.50
143	Don Newcombe	20.00	8.50
144	Art Houtteman	7.50	3.50
145	Bob Nieman	7.50	3.50
146	Don Liddle	7.50	3.50
147	Sam Mele	7.50	3.50
148	Bob Chakales	7.50	3.50
149	Cloyd Boyer	8.50	4.00
150	Bill Klaus	7.50	3.50
151	Jim Brideweser	7.50	3.50
152	Johnny Klippstein	7.50	3.50
153	Eddie Robinson	7.50	3.50
154	Frank Lary (R)	12.00	6.00
155	Gerry Staley	7.50	3.50
156	Jim Hughes	7.50	3.50
157a	Ernie Johnson (Wrong Photo)	8.50	4.00
157b	Ernie Johnson (Cor)	20.00	8.50
158	Gil Hodges	45.00	20.00
159	Harry Byrd	7.50	3.50
160	Bill Skowron	25.00	12.00
161	Matt Batts	7.50	3.50
162	Charlie Maxwell	7.50	3.50
163	Sid Gordon	7.50	3.50
164	Toby Atwell	7.50	3.50
165	Maurice McDermott	7.50	3.50
166	Jim Busby	7.50	3.50
167	Bob Grim (R)	12.00	6.00
168	Yogi Berra	125.00	60.00
169	Carl Furillo	20.00	8.50
170	Carl Erskine	18.00	7.50
171	Robin Roberts	30.00	14.00
172	Willie Jones	7.50	3.50
173	Chico Carrasquel	7.50	3.50
174	Sherman Lollar	8.50	4.00
175	Wilmer Shantz	7.50	3.50
176	Joe DeMaestri	7.50	3.50
177	Willard Nixon	7.50	3.50
178	Tom Brewer	7.50	3.50
179	Hank Aaron	285.00	140.00
180	Johnny Logan	8.50	4.00
181	Eddie Miksis	7.50	0.00
182	Bob Rush	7.50	3.50
183	Ray Katt	7.50	3.50
184	Willie Mays	285.00	140.00
185	Vic Raschi	10.00	5.00
186	Alex Grammas	7.50	3.50
187	Fred Hatfield	7.50	3.50
188	Ned Garver	7.50	3.50
189	Jack Collum	7.50	3.50
190	Fred Baczewski	7.50	3.50
191	Bob Lemon	30.00	14.00
192	George Strickland	7.50	3.50
193	Howie Judson	7.50	3.50
194	Joe Nuxhall	8.50	4.00
195a	Erv Palica (No Trade)	8.50	4.00
195b	Erv Palica (Traded)	25.00	12.00
196	Russ Meyer	7.50	3.50
197	Ralph Kiner	30.00	14.00
198	Dave Pope	7.50	3.50
199	Vernon Law	8.50	4.00
200	Dick Littlefield	7.50	3.50
201	Allie Reynolds	15.00	7.00
202	Mickey Mantle	675.00	330.00
203	Steve Gromek	7.50	3.50
204a	Frank Bolling (Er)	8.50	4.00
204b	Frank Bolling (Cor)	20.00	8.50
205	Rip Repulski	7.50	3.50
206	Ralph Beard	7.50	3.50
207	Frank Shea	7.50	3.50
208	Ed Fitzgerald	7.50	3.50
209	Smoky Burgess	8.50	4.00
210	Earl Torgeson	7.50	3.50
211	John Dixon	7.50	3.50
212	Jack Dittmer	7.50	3.50
213	George Kell	22.00	10.00
214	Billy Pierce	10.00	5.00
215	Bob Kuzava	7.50	3.50
216	Preacher Roe	12.00	6.00
217	Del Crandall	8.50	4.00
218	Joe Adcock	10.00	5.00
219	Whitey Lockman	8.50	4.00
220	Jim Hearn	7.50	3.50
221	Hector Brown	7.50	3.50
222	Russ Kemmerer	7.50	3.50
223	Hal Jeffcoat	7.50	3.50
224	Dee Fondy	7.50	3.50
225	Paul Richards	20.00	8.50
226	W.F. McKinley (Ump)	28.00	13.00
227	Frank Baumholtz	20.00	8.50
228	John Phillips	20.00	8.50
229	Jim Brosnan (R)	22.00	10.00

230	Al Brazle	20.00	8.50
231	Jim Konstanty	24.00	12.00
232	Birdie Tebbetts	20.00	8.50
233	Bill Serena	20.00	8.50
234	Dick Bartell	20.00	8.50
235	J.A. Paparella (Ump)	28.00	13.00
236	Murray Dickson (Er)	20.00	8.50
237	Johnny Wyrostek	20.00	8.50
238	Eddie Stanky	22.00	10.00
239	Edwin Rommel (Ump)	28.00	13.00
240	Billy Loes	20.00	8.50
241	John Pesky	22.00	10.00
242	Ernie Banks	475.00	235.00
243	Gus Bell	20.00	8.50
244	Duane Pillette	20.00	8.50
245	Bill Miller	20.00	8.50
246	Hank Bauer	38.00	18.00
247	Dutch Leonard	20.00	8.50
248	Harry Dorish	20.00	8.50
249	Billy Gardner	20.00	8.50
250	Larry Napp (Ump)	28.00	13.00
251	Stan Jok	20.00	8.50
252	Roy Smalley	20.00	8.50
253	Jim Wilson	20.00	8.50
254	Bennett Flowers	20.00	8.50
255	Pete Runnels	22.00	10.00
256	Owen Friend	20.00	8.50
257	Tom Alston	20.00	8.50
258	John W. Stevens (Ump)	28.00	13.00
259	Don Mossi (R)	28.00	13.00
260	Edwin Hurley (Ump)	28.00	13.00
261	Walt Moryn	20.00	8.50
262	Jim Lemon	22.00	10.00
263	Eddie Joost	20.00	8.50
264	Bill Henry	20.00	8.50
265	Albert Barlick (Ump)	80.00	38.00
266	Mike Fornieles	20.00	8.50
267	Jim Honochick (Ump)	75.00	35.00
268	Roy Lee Hawes	20.00	8.50
269	Joe Amalfitano (R)	22.00	10.00
270	Chico Fernandez	20.00	8.50
271	Bob Hooper	20.00	8.50
272	John Flaherty (Ump)	28.00	13.00
273	Emory Church	20.00	8.50
274	Jim Delsing	20.00	8.50
275	William Grieve (Ump)	28.00	13.00
276	Ivan Delock	20.00	8.50
277	Ed Runge (Ump)	30.00	14.00
278	Charles Neal (R)	32.00	15.00
279	Hank Soar (Ump)	25.00	12.00
280	Clyde McCullough	20.00	8.50
281	Charles Berry (Ump)	25.00	12.00
282	Phil Cavarretta	22.00	10.00
283	Nestor Chylak (Ump)	30.00	14.00
284	Wm. Jackowski (Ump)	25.00	12.00
285	Walt Dropo	20.00	8.50
286	Frank Secory (Ump)	30.00	14.00
287	Ron Mrozinski	20.00	8.50
288	Dick Smith	20.00	8.50
289	Arthur Gore (Ump)	25.00	12.00
290	Hershell Freeman	20.00	8.50
291	Frank Dascoli (Ump)	30.00	14.00
292	Marv Blaylock	20.00	8.50
293	Thomas Gorman (Ump)	30.00	14.00
294	Wally Moses	20.00	8.50
295	Lee Ballanfant (Ump)	25.00	12.00
296	Bill Virdon (R)	38.00	18.00
297	Dusty Boggess (Ump)	30.00	14.00
298	Charlie Grimm	20.00	8.50
299	Lonnie Warneke (Ump)	30.00	14.00
300	Tommy Byrne	20.00	8.50
301	William Engeln (Ump)	25.00	12.00
302	Frank Malzone (R)	30.00	14.00
303	Jocko Conlan (Ump)	100.00	45.00
304	Harry Chiti	20.00	8.50
305	Frank Umont (Ump)	30.00	14.00
306	Bob Cerv	22.00	10.00
307	Babe Pinelli (Ump)	30.00	14.00
308	Al Lopez	48.00	22.50
309	Hal Dixon (Ump)	25.00	12.00
310	Ken Lehman	20.00	8.50
311	Lawrence Goetz (Ump)	25.00	12.00
312	Bill Wight	20.00	8.50
313	A.J. Donatelli (Ump)	38.00	18.00
314	Dale Mitchell	20.00	8.50
315	Cal Hubbard (Ump)	100.00	45.00
316	Marion Fricano	20.00	8.50
317	Wm. Summers (Ump)	28.00	13.00
318	Sid Hudson	20.00	8.50
319	Albert Schroll	20.00	8.50
320	George Susce, Jr.	50.00	20.00

1989 Bowman

After a 33 year layoff, Bowman returned under the Topps banner. The 484-card set was patterned after the 1953 Bowman set with full-color photos and a fascimile autograph on the card fronts. Cards measure 2-1/2" by 3-3/4".

		MINT	NR/MT
Complete Set (484)		13.00	7.50
Commons		.04	.02

1	Oswald Peraza	.04	.02
2	Brian Holton	.04	.02
3	Jose Bautista	.04	.02
4	Pete Harnisch (R)	.15	.08
5	Dave Schmidt	.04	.02
6	Gregg Olson (R)	.20	.12
7	Jeff Ballard	.07	.04
8	Bob Melvin	.04	.02
9	Cal Ripken	.45	.28
10	Randy Milligan	.10	.06
11	Juan Bell (R)	.08	.05
12	Billy Ripken	.04	.02
13	Jim Trabor	.04	.02
14	Pete Stanicek	.04	.02
15	Steve Finley (R)	.20	.12
16	Larry Sheets	.04	.02
17	Phil Bradley	.04	.02
18	Brady Anderson (R)	.50	.30
19	Lee Smith	.10	.06
20	Tom Fischer	.04	.02
21	Mike Boddicker	.04	.02
22	Rob Murphy	.04	.02
23	Wes Gardner	.04	.02
24	John Dopson	.04	.02
25	Bob Stanley	.04	.02
26	Roger Clemens	.40	.25
27	Rich Gedman	.04	.02
28	Marty Barrett	.04	.02
29	Luis Rivera	.04	.02
30	Jody Reed	.06	.03
31	Nick Esasky	.04	.02
32	Wade Boggs	.20	.12
33	Jim Rice	.07	.04
34	Mike Greenwell	.08	.05
35	Dwight Evans	.08	.05
36	Ellis Burks	.10	.06
37	Chuck Finley	.10	.06
38	Kirk McCaskill	.06	.03
39	Jim Abbott (R)	.80	.50
40	Bryan Harvey (R)	.40	.25
41	Bert Blyleven	.10	.06
42	Mike Witt	.08	.05
43	Bob McClure	.04	.02
44	Bill Schroeder	.04	.02
45	Lance Parrish	.08	.05
46	Dick Schofield	.04	.02
47	Wally Joyner	.10	.06
48	Jack Howell	.04	.02
49	Johnny Ray	.04	.02
50	Chili Davis	.07	.04
51	Tony Armas	.04	.02
52	Claudell Washington	.04	.02
53	Brian Downing	.06	.03
54	Devon White	.07	.04
55	Bobby Thigpen	.08	.05
56	Bill Long	.04	.02
57	Jerry Reuss	.04	.02
58	Shawn Hillegas	.04	.02
59	Melido Perez	.08	.05
60	Jeff Bittiger	.04	.02
61	Jack McDowell	.40	.25
62	Carlton Fisk	.15	.08
63	Steve Lyons	.04	.02
64	Ozzie Guillen	.07	.04
65	Robin Ventura (R)	1.00	.70
66	Fred Manrique	.04	.02
67	Dan Pasqua	.04	.02
68	Ivan Calderon	.07	.04
69	Ron Kittle	.04	.02
70	Daryl Boston	.04	.02
71	Dave Gallagher	.04	.02
72	Harold Baines	.08	.05
73	Charles Nagy (R)	.30	.18
74	John Farrell	.04	.02
75	Kevin Wickander	.04	.02
76	Greg Swindell	.08	.05
77	Mike Walker	.06	.03
78	Doug Jones	.04	.02
79	Rich Yett	.04	.02
80	Tom Candiotti	.07	.04
81	Jesse Orosco	.04	.02
82	Bud Black	.07	.03
83	Andy Allanson	.04	.02
84	Pete O'Brien	.04	.02
85	Jerry Browne	.04	.02
86	Brook Jacoby	.04	.02
87	Mark Lewis (R)	.20	.12
88	Luis Aguayo	.04	.02

89	Cory Snyder	.07	.04
90	Oddibe McDowell	.04	.02
91	Joe Carter	.35	.20
92	Frank Tanana	.07	.04
93	Jack Morris	.15	.10
94	Doyle Alexander	.04	.02
95	Steve Searcy	.07	.04
96	Randy Bockus	.04	.02
97	Jeff Robinson	.04	.02
98	Mike Henneman	.04	.02
99	Paul Gibson	.04	.02
100	Frank Williams	.04	.02
101	Matt Nokes	.08	.05
102	Rico Brogna (R)	.20	.12
103	Lou Whitaker	.07	.04
104	Al Pedrique	.04	.02
105	Alan Trammell	.08	.05
106	Chris Brown	.04	.02
107	Pat Sheridan	.04	.02
108	Garry Pettis	.04	.02
109	Keith Moreland	.04	.02
110	Mel Stottlemyre, Jr.	.07	.04
111	Bret Saberhagen	.12	.07
112	Floyd Bannister	.04	.02
113	Jeff Montgomery	.07	.04
114	Steve Farr	.04	.02
115	Tom Gordon (R)	.10	.06
116	Charlie Leibrandt	.06	.03
117	Mike Gubicza	.07	.04
118	Mike MacFarlane (R)	.10	.06
119	Bob Boone	.07	.04
120	Kurt Stillwell	.04	.02
121	George Brett	.20	.12
122	Frank White	.04	.02
123	Keven Seitzer	.08	.05
124	Willie Wilson	.04	.02
125	Pat Tabler	.04	.02
126	Bo Jackson	.20	.12
127	Hugh Walker (R)	.10	.06
128	Danny Tartabull	.12	.07
129	Teddy Higuera	.04	.02
130	Don August	.04	.02
131	Juan Nieves	.04	.02
132	Mike Birkbeck	.04	.02
133	Dan Plesac	.04	.02
134	Chris Bosio	.08	.05
135	Bill Wegman	.04	.02
136	Chuck Crim	.04	.02
137	B.J. Surhoff	.07	.04
138	Joey Meyer	.04	.02
139	Dale Sveum	.04	.02
140	Paul Molitor	.20	.12
141	Jim Gantner	.04	.02
142	Gary Sheffield (R)	2.00	1.25
143	Greg Brock	.04	.02
144	Robin Yount	.25	.15
145	Glenn Braggs	.04	.02
146	Rob Deer	.08	.05
147	Fred Toliver	.04	.02
148	Jeff Reardon	.10	.06
149	Allan Anderson	.04	.02
150	Frank Viola	.08	.05
151	Shane Rawley	.04	.02
152	Juan Berenguer	.04	.02
153	Johnny Ard (R)	.08	.05
154	Tim Laudner	.04	.02
155	Brian Harper	.07	.04
156	Al Newman	.04	.02
157	Kent Hrbek	.07	.04
158	Gary Gaetti	.07	.04
159	Wally Backman	.04	.02
160	Gene Larkin	.04	.02
161	Greg Gagne	.08	.05
162	Kirby Puckett	.35	.20
163	Danny Gladden	.04	.02
164	Randy Bush	.04	.02
165	Dave LaPoint	.04	.02
166	Andy Hawkins	.04	.02
167	Dave Righetti	.07	.04
168	Lance McCullers	.04	.02
169	Jimmy Jones	.04	.02
170	Al Leiter	.04	.02
171	John Candelaria	.04	.02
172	Don Slaught	.04	.02
173	Jamie Quirk	.04	.02
174	Rafael Santana	.04	.02
175	Mike Pagliarulo	.04	.02
176	Don Mattingly	.20	.12
177	Ken Phelps	.04	.02
178	Steve Sax	.08	.05
179	Dave Winfield	.20	.12
180	Stan Jefferson	.04	.02
181	Rickey Henderson	.25	.15
182	Bob Brower	.04	.02
183	Roberto Kelly	.20	.12
184	Curt Young	.04	.02
185	Gene Nelson	.04	.02
186	Bob Welch	.07	.04
187	Rick Honeycutt	.04	.02
188	Dave Stewart	.08	.05
189	Mike Moore	.07	.03
190	Dennis Eckersley	.20	.12
191	Eric Plunk	.04	.02
192	Storm Davis	.04	.02
193	Terry Steinbach	.08	.05
194	Ron Hassey	.04	.02
195	Stan Royer (R)	.10	.06
196	Walt Weiss	.07	.04
197	Mark McGwire	.40	.25
198	Carney Lansford	.07	.04
199	Glenn Hubbard	.04	.02
200	Dave Henderson	.07	.04
201	Jose Canseco	.40	.25
202	Dave Parker	.07	.04

203	Scott Bankhead	.04	.02
204	Tom Niedenfuer	.04	.02
205	Mark Langston	.10	.06
206	Erik Hanson (R)	.25	.15
207	Mike Jackson	.07	.03
208	Dave Valle	.04	.02
209	Scott Bradley	.04	.02
210	Harold Reynolds	.07	.04
211	Tino Martinez (R)	.30	.18
212	Rich Renteria	.04	.02
213	Rey Quinones	.04	.02
214	Jim Presley	.04	.02
215	Alvin Davis	.04	.02
216	Edgar Martinez	.20	.12
217	Darnell Coles	.04	.02
218	Jeffrey Leonard	.04	.02
219	Jay Buhner	.12	.07
220	Ken Griffey, Jr. (R)	4.50	3.00
221	Drew Hall	.04	.02
222	Bobby Witt	.08	.05
223	Jamie Moyer	.04	.02
224	Charlie Hough	.04	.02
225	Nolan Ryan	.60	.35
226	Jeff Russell	.07	.03
227	Jim Sundberg	.04	.02
228	Julio Franco	.10	.06
229	Buddy Bell	.04	.02
230	Scott Fletcher	.04	.02
231	Jeff Kunkel	.04	.02
232	Steve Buechele	.06	.03
233	Monty Fariss (R)	.15	.08
234	Rich Leach	.04	.02
235	Ruben Sierra	.30	.18
236	Cecil Espy	.04	.02
237	Rafael Palmeiro	.20	.12
238	Pete Incaviglia	.07	.04
239	Dave Steib	.08	.05
240	Jeff Musselman	.04	.02
241	Mike Flanagan	.04	.02
242	Todd Stottlemyre	.12	.07
243	Jimmy Key	.08	.05
244	Tony Castillo	.04	.02
245	Alex Sanchez	.04	.02
246	Tom Henke	.06	.03
247	John Cerutti	.04	.02
248	Ernie Whitt	.04	.02
249	Bob Brenly	.04	.02
250	Rance Mulliniks	.04	.02
251	Kelly Gruber	.08	.05
252	Ed Sprague (R)	.20	.12
253	Fred McGriff	.40	.25
254	Tony Fernandez	.07	.04
255	Tom Lawless	.04	.02
256	George Bell	.10	.06
257	Jesse Barfield	.07	.04
258	R. Alomar/Dad	.30	.18
259	Ken Griffey Jr & Sr	1.25	.80
260	Cal Ripken Jr & Sr	.20	.12
261	Mel Stottlemyre Jr & Sr	.08	.05
262	Zane Smith	.07	.04
263	Charlie Puleo	.04	.02
264	Derek Lilliquist (R)	.08	.05
265	Paul Assenmacher	.04	.02
266	John Smoltz (R)	.75	.45
267	Tom Glavine	.70	.40
268	Steve Avery (R)	1.40	.85
269	Pete Smith	.12	.07
270	Jody Davis	.04	.02
271	Bruce Benedict	.04	.02
272	Andres Thomas	.04	.02
273	Gerald Perry	.04	.02
274	Ron Gant	.35	.20
275	Darrell Evans	.07	.03
276	Dale Murphy	.10	.06
277	Dion James	.04	.02
278	Lonnie Smith	.04	.02
279	Geronimo Berroa	.04	.02
280	Steve Wilson	.07	.04
281	Rick Sutcliffe	.07	.04
282	Kevin Coffman	.04	.02
283	Mitch Williams	.04	.02
284	Greg Maddux	.35	.20
285	Paul Kilgus	.04	.02
286	Mike Harkey (R)	.12	.07
287	Lloyd McClendon	.04	.02
288	Damon Berryhill	.06	.03
289	Ty Griffin (R)	.07	.03
290	Ryne Sandberg	.35	.20
291	Mark Grace	.30	.18
292	Curt Wilkerson	.04	.02
293	Vance Law	.04	.02
294	Shawon Dunston	.08	.05
295	Jerome Walton (R)	.08	.05
296	Mitch Webster	.04	.02
297	Dwight Smith (R)	.12	.07
298	Andre Dawson	.15	.08
299	Jeff Sellers	.04	.02
300	Jose Rijo	.08	.05
301	John Franco	.04	.02
302	Rich Mahler	.04	.02
303	Ron Robinson	.04	.02
304	Danny Jackson	.07	.03
305	Rob Dibble (R)	.15	.10
306	Tom Browning	.07	.04
307	Bo Diaz	.04	.02
308	Manny Trillo	.04	.02
309	Chris Sabo (R)	.25	.15
310	Ron Oester	.04	.02
311	Barry Larkin	.15	.08
312	Todd Benzinger	.04	.02
313	Paul O'Neill	.08	.05
314	Kal Daniels	.04	.02
315	Joel Youngblood	.04	.02
316	Eric Davis	.10	.06

317	Dave Smith	.04	.02	374	Randy Myers	.04	.02
318	Mark Portugal	.04	.02	375	David Cone	.15	.10
319	Brian Meyer	.07	.04	376	Doc Gooden	.15	.10
320	Jim Deshales	.04	.02	377	Sid Fernandez	.07	.04
321	Juan Agosto	.04	.02	378	Dave Proctor (R)	.08	.05
322	Mike Scott	.04	.02	379	Gary Carter	.08	.05
323	Rick Rhoden	.04	.02	380	Keith Miller	.04	.02
324	Jim Clancy	.04	.02	381	Gregg Jefferies (R)	.40	.25
325	Larry Andersen	.04	.02	382	Tim Teufel	.04	.02
326	Alex Trevino	.04	.02	383	Kevin Elster	.04	.02
327	Alan Ashby	.04	.02	384	Dave Magaden	.07	.04
328	Craig Reynolds	.04	.02	385	Keith Hernandez	.07	.04
329	Bill Doran	.04	.02	386	Mookie Wilson	.04	.02
330	Rafael Ramirez	.04	.02	387	Darryl Strawberry	.20	.12
331	Glenn Davis	.07	.04	388	Kevin McReynolds	.07	.04
332	Willie Ansley (R)	.15	.08	389	Mark Carreon	.04	.02
333	Gerald Young	.04	.02	390	Jeff Parrett	.04	.02
334	Cameron Drew	.04	.02	391	Mike Maddux	.04	.02
335	Jay Howell	.04	.02	392	Don Carman	.04	.02
336	Tim Belcher	.07	.04	393	Bruce Ruffin	.04	.02
337	Fernando Valenzuela	.08	.05	394	Ken Howell	.04	.02
338	Ricky Horton	.04	.02	395	Steve Bedrosian	.07	.04
339	Tim Leary	.04	.02	396	Floyd Youmans	.04	.02
340	Bill Bene	.04	.02	397	Larry McWilliams	.04	.02
341	Orel Hershiser	.08	.05	398	Pat Combs (R)	.10	.06
342	Mike Scioscia	.04	.02	399	Steve Lake	.04	.02
343	Rick Dempsey	.04	.02	400	Dickie Thon	.04	.02
344	Willie Randolph	.07	.04	401	Ricky Jordan (R)	.08	.05
345	Alfredo Griffin	.04	.02	402	Mike Schmidt	.35	.20
346	Eddie Murray	.12	.07	403	Tom Herr	.04	.02
347	Mickey Hatcher	.04	.02	404	Chris James	.04	.02
348	Mike Sharperson	.04	.02	405	Juan Samuel	.04	.02
349	John Shelby	.04	.02	406	Von-Hayes	.04	.02
350	Mike Marshall	.04	.02	407	Ron Jones	.07	.04
351	Kirk Gibson	.07	.04	408	Curt Ford	.04	.02
352	Mike Davis	.04	.02	409	Bob Walk	.04	.02
353	Bryn Smith	.04	.02	410	Jeff Robinson	.04	.02
354	Pascual Perez	.04	.02	411	Jim Gott	.04	.02
355	Kevin Gross	.04	.02	412	Scott Medvin	.07	.04
356	Andy McGaffigan	.04	.02	413	John Smiley	.10	.06
357	Brian Holman (R)	.12	.07	414	Bob Kipper	.04	.02
358	Dave Wainhouse (R)	.10	.06	415	Brian Fisher	.04	.02
359	Denny Martinez	.10	.06	416	Doug Drabek	.10	.06
360	Tim Burke	.04	.02	417	Mike Lavalliere	.04	.02
361	Nelson Santovenia	.04	.02	418	Ken Oberkfell	.04	.02
362	Tim Wallach	.08	.05	419	Sid Bream	.04	.02
363	Spike Owen	.04	.02	420	Austin Manahan (R)	.10	.06
364	Rex Hudler	.04	.02	421	Jose Lind	.04	.02
365	Andres Galarraga	.20	.12	422	Bobby Bonilla	.12	.07
366	Otis Nixon	.04	.02	423	Glenn Wilson	.04	.02
367	Hubie Brooks	.07	.04	424	Andy Van Slyke	.12	.07
368	Mike Aldrete	.04	.02	425	Gary Redus	.04	.02
369	Tim Raines	.08	.05	426	Barry Bonds	.60	.35
370	Dave Martinez	.04	.02	427	Don Heinkel	.04	.02
371	Bob Ojeda	.04	.02	428	Ken Dayley	.04	.02
372	Ron Darling	.04	.02	429	Todd Worrel	.07	.04
373	Wally Whitehurst (R)	.07	.04	430	Brad DuVall	.07	.04

431	Jose DeLeon	.04	.02
432	Joe Magrane	.07	.04
433	John Ericks (R)	.12	.07
434	Frank DiPino	.04	.02
435	Tony Pena	.06	.03
436	Ozzie Smith	.15	.08
437	Terry Pendleton	.15	.08
438	Jose Oquendo	.04	.02
439	Tim Jones	.08	.05
440	Pedro Guerrero	.07	.04
441	Milt Thompson	.04	.02
442	Willie McGee	.08	.05
443	Vince Coleman	.07	.04
444	Tom Brunansky	.07	.04
445	Walt Terrell	.04	.02
446	Eric Show	.04	.02
447	Mark Davis	.07	.04
448	Andy Benes (R)	.50	.30
449	Eddie Whitson	.04	.02
450	Dennis Rasmussen	.04	.02
451	Bruce Hurst	.07	.04
452	Pat Clements	.04	.02
453	Benito Santiago	.10	.06
454	Sandy Alomar, Jr. (R)	.15	.08
455	Garry Templeton	.04	.02
456	Jack Clark	.07	.04
457	Tim Flannery	.04	.02
458	Roberto Alomar	.75	.45
459	Carmelo Martinez	.04	.02
460	John Kruk	.08	.05
461	Tony Gwynn	.25	.15
462	Jerald Clark (R)	.08	.05
463	Don Robinson	.04	.02
464	Craig Lefferts	.04	.02
465	Kelly Downs	.04	.02
466	Rick Rueschel	.04	.02
467	Scott Garrelts	.04	.02
468	Wil Tejada	.04	.02
469	Kirt Manwaring	.04	.02
470	Terry Kennedy	.04	.02
471	Jose Uribe	.04	.02
472	Royce Clayton (R)	.60	.35
473	Robby Thompson	.06	.03
474	Kevin Mitchell	.10	.06
475	Ernie Riles	.04	.02
476	Will Clark	.40	.25
477	Donnell Nixon	.04	.02
478	Candy Maldonado	.04	.02
479	Tracy Jones	.04	.02
480	Brett Butler	.08	.05
481	Checklist	.04	.02
482	Checklist	.04	.02
483	Checklist	.04	.02
484	Checklist	.04	.02

1990 Bowman

In this 528-card set Bowman reverted to the current standard card size of 2-1/2" by 3-1/2". Card fronts feature full-color player photos surrounded by white borders.

The checklist is organized by teams, in alphabetical order beginning with the National League.

		MINT	NR/MT
Complete Set (528)		17.50	9.00
Commons		.05	.02

1	Tommy Greene (R)	.70	.40
2	Tom Glavine	.35	.20
3	Andy Nezelek	.05	.02
4	Mike Stanton (R)	.15	.10
5	Rick Lueken	.08	.05
6	Kent Mercker (R)	.12	.07
7	Derek Lilliquist	.05	.02
8	Charlie Liebrandt	.05	.02
9	Steve Avery	.70	.40
10	John Smoltz	.25	.15
11	Mark Lemke	.05	.02
12	Lonnie Smith	.05	.02
13	Oddibe McDowell	.05	.02
14	Tyler Houston (R)	.12	.07
15	Jeff Blauser	.05	.02
16	Ernie Whitt	.05	.02
17	Alexis Infante	.07	.04
18	Jim Presley	.05	.02
19	Dale Murphy	.10	.06
20	Nick Esasky	.05	.02
21	Rick Sutcliffe	.07	.04
22	Mike Bielecki	.05	.02
23	Steve Wilson	.05	.02
24	Kevin Blankenship	.05	.02
25	Mitch Williams	.05	.02
26	Dean Wilkins	.05	.02
27	Greg Maddux	.25	.15
28	Mike Harkey	.08	.05

29	Mark Grace	.15	.10
30	Ryne Sandberg	.30	.18
31	Greg Smith (R)	.08	.05
32	Dwight Smith	.07	.04
33	Damon Berryhill	.05	.02
34	Earl Cunningham (R)	.12	.07
35	Jerome Walton	.07	.04
36	Lloyd McClendon	.05	.02
37	Ty Griffin	.05	.02
38	Shawon Dunston	.08	.05
39	Andre Dawson	.12	.07
40	Luis Salazar	.05	.02
41	Tim Layana	.07	.04
42	Rob Dibble	.08	.05
43	Tom Browning	.07	.04
44	Danny Jackson	.06	.03
45	Jose Rijo	.08	.05
46	Scott Scudder (R)	.10	.06
47	Randy Myers	.05	.02
48	Brian Lane (R)	.10	.06
49	Paul O'Neill	.08	.05
50	Barry Larkin	.10	.06
51	Reggie Jefferson (R)	.25	.15
52	Jeff Branson (R)	.10	.06
53	Chris Sabo	.10	.06
54	Joe Oliver	.07	.04
55	Todd Benzinger	.05	.02
56	Rolando Roomes	.05	.02
57	Hal Morris	.20	.12
58	Eric Davis	.08	.05
59	Scott Bryant (R)	.12	.07
60	Ken Griffey	.07	.04
61	Darryl Kile (R)	1.25	.70
62	Dave Smith	.05	.02
63	Mark Portugal	.05	.02
64	Jeff Juden (R)	.30	.18
65	Bill Gullickson	.05	.02
66	Danny Darwin	.05	.02
67	Larry Andersen	.05	.02
68	Jose Cano	.07	.04
69	Dan Schatzeder	.05	.02
70	Jim Deshaies	.05	.02
71	Mike Scott	.05	.02
72	Gerald Young	.05	.02
73	Ken Caminiti	.07	.04
74	Ken Oberkfell	.05	.02
75	Dave Rhode	.07	.04
76	Bill Doran	.05	.02
77	Andujar Cedeno (R)	.35	.20
78	Craig Biggio	.07	.04
79	Karl Rhodes	.12	.07
80	Glenn Davis	.08	.05
81	Eric Anthony (R)	.35	.20
82	John Wetteland	.20	.12
83	Jay Howell	.05	.02
84	Orel Hershiser	.07	.04
85	Tim Belcher	.07	.04
86	Kiki Jones (R)	.10	.06
87	Mike Hartley (R)	.10	.06
88	Ramon Martinez	.15	.08
89	Mike Scioscia	.05	.02
90	Willie Randolph	.05	.02
91	Juan Samuel	.05	.02
92	Jose Offerman (R)	.25	.15
93	Dave Hansen (R)	.12	.07
94	Jeff Hamilton	.05	.02
95	Alfredo Griffin	.05	.02
96	Tom Goodwin (R)	.12	.07
97	Kirk Gibson	.06	.03
98	Jose Vizcaino (R)	.12	.07
99	Kal Daniels	.05	.02
100	Hubie Brooks	.07	.04
101	Eddie Murray	.10	.06
102	Dennis Boyd	.05	.02
103	Tim Burke	.05	.02
104	Bill Sampen	.05	.02
105	Brett Gideon	.07	.04
106	Mark Gardner (R)	.12	.07
107	Howard Farmer	.08	.05
108	Mel Rojas (R)	.10	.06
109	Kevin Gross	.05	.02
110	Dave Schmidt	.05	.02
111	Denny Martinez	.08	.05
112	Jerry Goff	.05	.02
113	Andres Galarraga	.20	.12
114	Tim Welch	.07	.04
115	Marquis Grissom (R)	.75	.45
116	Spike Owen	.05	.02
117	Larry Walker (R)	.80	.50
118	Tim Raines	.07	.04
119	Delino DeShields (R)	.60	.35
120	Tom Foley	.05	.02
121	Dave Martinez	.05	.02
122	Frank Viola	.07	.04
123	Julio Valera (R)	.12	.07
124	Alejandro Pena	.05	.02
125	David Cone	.12	.07
126	Doc Gooden	.12	.07
127	Kevin Brown	.08	.05
128	John Franco	.05	.02
129	Terry Bross	.10	.06
130	Blaine Beatty	.10	.06
131	Sid Fernandez	.05	.02
132	Mike Marshall	.05	.02
133	Howard Johnson	.08	.05
134	Jaime Roseboro	.08	.05
135	Alan Zinter (R)	.10	.06
136	Keith Miller	.05	.02
137	Kevin Elster	.05	.02
138	Kevin McReynolds	.07	.04
139	Barry Lyons	.05	.02
140	Gregg Jefferies	.20	.12
141	Darryl Strawberry	.20	.12
142	Todd Hundley (R)	.12	.07

143	Scott Service	.05	.02
144	Chuck Malone	.08	.05
145	Steve Ontiveros	.05	.02
146	Roger McDowell	.05	.02
147	Ken Howell	.05	.02
148	Pat Combs	.08	.05
149	Jeff Parrett	.05	.02
150	Chuck McElroy (R)	.10	.06
151	Jason Grimsley (R)	.12	.07
152	Len Dykstra	.20	.12
153	Mickey Morandini (R)	.15	.08
154	John Kruk	.07	.04
155	Dickie Thon	.05	.02
156	Ricky Jordan	.05	.02
157	Jeff Jackson (R)	.12	.07
158	Darren Daulton	.20	.12
159	Tom Herr	.05	.02
160	Von Hayes	.05	.02
161	Dave Hollins (R)	1.00	.60
162	Carmelo Martinez	.05	.02
163	Bob Walk	.05	.02
164	Doug Drabek	.10	.06
165	Walt Terrell	.05	.02
166	Bill Landrum	.05	.02
167	Scott Ruskin	.10	.06
168	Bob Patterson	.05	.02
169	Bobby Bonilla	.10	.06
170	Jose Lind	.05	.02
171	Andy Van Slyke	.10	.06
172	Mike Lavalliere	.05	.02
173	Willie Greene (R)	.25	.15
174	Jay Bell	.05	.02
175	Sid Bream	.05	.02
176	Tom Prince	.05	.02
177	Wally Backman	.05	.02
178	Moises Alou (R)	.60	.35
179	Steve Carter	.10	.06
180	Gary Redus	.05	.02
181	Barry Bonds	.40	.25
182	Don Slaught	.05	.02
183	Joe Magrane	.05	.02
184	Bryn Smith	.05	.02
185	Todd Worrell	.05	.02
186	Jose Deleon	.05	.02
187	Frank DiPino	.05	.02
188	John Tudor	.05	.02
189	Howard Hilton (R)	.08	.05
190	John Ericks	.10	.06
191	Ken Dayley	.05	.02
192	Ray Lankford (R)	.40	.25
193	Todd Zeile (R)	.15	.08
194	Willie McGee	.07	.04
195	Ozzie Smith	.12	.07
196	Milt Thompson	.05	.02
197	Terry Pendleton	.10	.06
198	Vince Coleman	.07	.04
199	Paul Coleman (R)	.10	.06
200	Jose Oquendo	.05	.02
201	Pedro Guerrero	.05	.02
202	Tom Brunansky	.06	.03
203	Roger Smithberg (R)	.08	.05
204	Ed Whitson	.05	.02
205	Dennis Rasmusen	.05	.02
206	Craig Lefferts	.05	.02
207	Andy Benes	.20	.12
208	Bruce Hurst	.07	.04
209	Eric Show	.05	.02
210	Rafael Valdez (R)	.12	.07
211	Joey Cora	.05	.02
212	Thomas Howard (R)	.10	.06
213	Rob Nelson	.05	.02
214	Jack Clark	.07	.04
215	Garry Templeton	.05	.02
216	Fred Lynn	.07	.04
217	Tony Gwynn	.20	.12
218	Benny Santiago	.08	.05
219	Mike Pagliarulo	.05	.02
220	Joe Carter	.25	.15
221	Roberto Alomar	.50	.30
222	Bip Roberts	.05	.02
223	Rick Reuschel	.05	.02
224	Russ Swan (R)	.08	.05
225	Eric Gunderson (R)	.08	.05
226	Steve Bedrosian	.05	.02
227	Mike Remlinger (R)	.07	.04
228	Scott Garrelts	.05	.02
229	Ernie Camacho	.05	.02
230	Andres Santana (R)	.15	.08
231	Will Clark	.25	.15
232	Kevin Mitchell	.08	.05
233	Robby Thompson	.05	.02
234	Bill Bathe	.05	.02
235	Tony Perezchica	.05	.02
236	Gary Carter	.07	.04
237	Brett Butler	.07	.04
238	Matt Williams	.15	.10
239	Ernie Riles	.05	.02
240	Kevin Bass	.05	.02
241	Terry Kennedy	.05	.02
242	Steve Hosey (R)	.35	.20
243	Ben McDonald (R)	.60	.35
244	Jeff Ballard	.05	.02
245	Joe Price	.05	.02
246	Curt Schilling (R)	.40	.25
247	Pete Harnisch	.10	.06
248	Mark Williamson	.05	.02
249	Gregg Olson	.08	.05
250	Chris Myers (R)	.08	.05
251	David Segui (R)	.12	.07
252	Joe Orsulak	.05	.02
253	Craig Worthington	.05	.02
254	Mickey Tettleton	.07	.04
255	Cal Ripken	.35	.20
256	Billy Ripken	.05	.02

257 Randy Milligan	.06	.03
258 Brady Anderson	.12	.07
259 Chris Hoiles (R)	.30	.18
260 Mike Devereaux	.07	.04
261 Phil Bradley	.05	.02
262 Leo Gomez (R)	.30	.18
263 Lee Smith	.08	.05
264 Mike Rockford	.05	.02
265 Jeff Reardon	.07	.04
266 Wes Gardner	.05	.02
267 Mike Boddicker	.05	.02
268 Roger Clemens	.30	.18
269 Rob Murphy	.05	.02
270 Mickey Pina (R)	.07	.04
271 Tony Pena	.05	.02
272 Jody Reed	.05	.02
273 Kevin Romine	.05	.02
274 Mike Greenwell	.07	.04
275 Maurice Vaughn (R)	1.25	.70
276 Danny Heep	.05	.02
277 Scott Cooper (R)	.40	.25
278 Greg Blosser (R)	.40	.25
279 Dwight Evans	.07	.04
280 Ellis Burks	.08	.05
281 Wade Boggs	.20	.12
282 Marty Barrett	.05	.02
283 Kirk McCaskill	.05	.02
284 Mark Langston	.07	.04
285 Bert Blyleven	.08	.05
286 Mike Fetters (R)	.08	.05
287 Kyle Abbott (R)	.12	.07
288 Jim Abbott	.20	.12
289 Chuck Finley	.08	.05
290 Gary DiSarcina (R)	.15	.08
291 Dick Schofield	.05	.02
292 Devon White	.05	.02
293 Bobby Rose (R)	.10	.06
294 Brian Downing	.05	.02
295 Lance Parrish	.05	.02
296 Jack Howell	.05	.02
297 Claudell Washington	.05	.02
298 John Orton (R)	.08	.05
299 Wally Joyner	.10	.06
300 Lee Stevens (R)	.12	.07
301 Chili Davis	.07	.04
302 Johnny Ray	.05	.02
303 Greg Hibbard (R)	.15	.08
304 Eric King	.05	.02
305 Jack McDowell	.30	.18
306 Bobby Thigpen	.07	.04
307 Adam Peterson	.05	.02
308 Scott Radinsky (R)	.15	.08
309 Wayne Edwards	.07	.04
310 Melido Perez	.06	.03
311 Robin Ventura	.50	.30
312 Sammy Sosa (R)	.75	.45
313 Dan Pasqua	.05	.02

314 Carlton Fisk	.10	.06
315 Ozzie Guillen	.07	.04
316 Ivan Calderon	.07	.04
317 Daryl Boston	.05	.02
318 Craig Grebeck (R)	.12	.07
319 Scott Fletcher	.05	.02
320 Frank Thomas (R)	4.00	2.50
321 Steve Lyons	.05	.02
322 Carlos Martinez	.07	.04
323 Joe Skalski	.07	.04
324 Tom Candiotti	.05	.02
325 Greg Swindell	.07	.04
326 Steve Olin (R)	.12	.07
327 Kevin Wickander	.05	.02
328 Doug Jones	.05	.02
329 Jeff Shaw	.08	.05
330 Kevin Bearse	.07	.04
331 Dion James	.05	.02
332 Jerry Browne	.05	.02
333 Albert Belle (R)	1.50	.90
334 Felix Fermin	.05	.02
335 Candy Maldonado	.05	.02
336 Cory Snyder	.05	.02
337 Sandy Alomar	.10	.06
338 Mark Lewis	.10	.06
339 Carlos Baerga (R)	2.00	1.25
340 Chris James	.05	.02
341 Brook Jacoby	.05	.02
342 Keith Hernandez	.06	.03
343 Frank Tanana	.05	.02
344 Scott Aldred (R)	.12	.07
345 Mike Henneman	.05	.02
346 Steve Wapnick	.07	.04
347 Greg Gohr (R)	.15	.10
348 Eric Stone (R)	.10	.06
349 Brian DuBois	.07	.04
350 Kevin Ritz	.07	.04
351 Rico Brogna	.10	.06
352 Mike Heath	.05	.02
353 Alan Trammell	.08	.05
354 Chet Lemon	.05	.02
355 Dave Bergman	.05	.02
356 Lou Whitaker	.07	.04
357 Cecil Fielder	.20	.12
358 Milt Cuyler (R)	.15	.10
359 Tony Phillips	.05	.02
360 Travis Fryman (R)	1.25	.70
361 Ed Romero	.05	.02
362 Lloyd Moseby	.05	.02
363 Mark Gubicza	.05	.02
364 Bret Saberhagen	.07	.04
365 Tom Gordon	.05	.02
366 Steve Farr	.05	.02
367 Kevin Appier (R)	.35	.20
368 Storm Davis	.05	.02
369 Mark Davis	.05	.02
370 Jeff Montgomery	.05	.02

371	Frank White	.05	.02
372	Brent Mayne (R)	.10	.06
373	Bob Boone	.08	.05
374	Jim Eisenreich	.05	.02
375	Danny Tartabull	.10	.06
376	Kurt Stillwell	.05	.02
377	Bill Pecota	.05	.02
378	Bo Jackson	.20	.12
379	Bob Hamelin (R)	.10	.06
380	Kevin Seitzer	.05	.02
381	Rey Palacios	.05	.02
382	George Brett	.20	.12
383	Gerald Perry	.05	.02
384	Teddy Higuera	.05	.02
385	Tom Filer	.05	.02
386	Dan Plesac	.05	.02
387	Cal Eldred (R)	.80	.50
388	Jaime Navarro (R)	.25	.15
389	Chris Bosio	.50	.02
390	Randy Veres	.07	.04
391	Gary Sheffield	.50	.30
392	George Canale	.08	.05
393	B.J. Surhoff	.05	.02
394	Tim McIntosh (R)	.12	.07
395	Greg Brock	.05	.02
396	Greg Vaughn (R)	.35	.20
397	Darryl Hamilton (R)	.20	.12
398	Dave Parker	.07	.04
399	Paul Molitor	.15	.10
400	Jim Gantner	.05	.02
401	Rob Deer	.05	.02
402	Billy Spiers	.05	.02
403	Glenn Braggs	.05	.02
404	Robin Yount	.20	.12
405	Rick Aguilera	.07	.04
406	Johnny Ard	.07	.04
407	Kevin Tapani (R)	.20	.12
408	Park Pittman	.08	.05
409	Allan Anderson	.05	.02
410	Juan Berenguer	.05	.02
411	Willie Banks (R)	.25	.15
412	Rich Yett	.05	.02
413	Dave West	.05	.02
414	Greg Gagne	.05	.02
415	Chuck Knoblauch (R)	.70	.40
416	Randy Bush	.05	.02
417	Gary Gaetti	.05	.02
418	Kent Hrbek	.05	.02
419	Al Newman	.05	.02
420	Danny Gladden	.05	.02
421	Paul Sorrento (R)	.25	.15
422	Derek Parks (R)	.10	.06
423	Scott Leius (R)	.20	.12
424	Kirby Puckett	.30	.18
425	Willie Smith	.10	.06
426	Dave Righetti	.05	.02
427	Jeff Robinson	.05	.02
428	Alan Mills (R)	.12	.07
429	Tim Leary	.05	.02
430	Pascual Perez	.05	.02
431	Alvaro Espinoza	.05	.02
432	Dave Winfield	.20	.12
433	Jesse Barfield	.05	.02
434	Randy Velarde	.05	.02
435	Rick Cerone	.05	.02
436	Steve Balboni	.05	.02
437	Mel Hall	.05	.02
438	Bob Geren	.05	.02
439	Bernie Williams (R)	.25	.15
440	Kevin Maas (R)	.15	.10
441	Mike Blowers	.07	.04
442	Steve Sax	.07	.04
443	Don Mattingly	.15	.10
444	Roberto Kelly	.15	.08
445	Mike Moore	.05	.02
446	Reggie Harris (R)	.10	.06
447	Scott Sanderson	.05	.02
448	Dave Otto	.05	.02
449	Dave Stewart	.07	.04
450	Rick Honeycutt	.05	.02
451	Dennis Eckersley	.10	.06
452	Carney Lansford	.05	.02
453	Scott Hemond (R)	.08	.05
454	Mark McGwire	.25	.15
455	Felix Jose	.15	.08
456	Terry Steinbach	.07	.04
457	Rickey Henderson	.20	.12
458	Dave Henderson	.06	.03
459	Mike Gallego	.05	.02
460	Jose Canseco	.25	.15
461	Walt Weiss	.05	.02
462	Ken Phelps	.05	.02
463	Darren Lewis (R)	.35	.20
464	Ron Hassey	.05	.02
465	Roger Salkeld (R)	.30	.18
466	Scott Bankhead	.05	.02
467	Keith Comstock	.05	.02
468	Randy Johnson	.35	.20
469	Erik Hanson	.10	.06
470	Mike Schooler	.08	.05
471	Gary Eave	.07	.04
472	Jeffrey Leonard	.05	.02
473	Dave Valle	.05	.02
474	Omar Vizquel	.05	.02
475	Pete O'Brien	.05	.02
476	Henry Cotto	.05	.02
477	Jay Buhner	.08	.05
478	Harold Reynolds	.05	.02
479	Alvin Davis	.05	.02
480	Darnell Coles	.05	.02
481	Ken Griffey, Jr.	2.00	1.25
482	Greg Briley	.07	.04
483	Scott Bradley	.05	.02
484	Tino Martinez	.15	.10

485	Jeff Russell	.05	.02
486	Nolan Ryan	.50	.30
487	Robb Nen (R)	.15	.10
488	Kevin Brown	.12	.07
489	Brian Bohanon (R)	.08	.05
490	Ruben Sierra	.20	.12
491	Pete Incaviglia	.05	.02
492	Juan Gonzalez (R)	3.50	2.00
493	Steve Buechele	.05	.02
494	Scott Coolbaugh	.05	.02
495	Geno Petralli	.05	.02
496	Rafael Palmeiro	.15	.10
497	Julio Franco	.10	.06
498	Gary Pettis	.05	.02
499	Donald Harris (R)	.12	.07
500	Monty Fariss	.07	.04
501	Harold Baines	.07	.04
502	Cecil Espy	.05	.02
503	Jack Daugherty	.07	.04
504	Willie Blair	.10	.06
505	Dave Steib	.07	.04
506	Tom Henke	.05	.02
507	John Cerutti	.05	.02
508	Paul Kilgus	.05	.02
509	Jimmy Key	.05	.02
510	John Olerud (R)	2.50	1.50
511	Ed Sprague	.08	.05
512	Manny Lee	.05	.02
513	Fred McGriff	.25	.15
514	Glenallen Hill	.08	.05
515	George Bell	.07	.04
516	Mookie Wilson	.05	.02
517	Luis Sojo (R)	.12	.07
518	Nelson Liriano	.05	.02
519	Kelly Gruber	.07	.04
520	Greg Myers	.05	.02
521	Pat Borders	.07	.04
522	Junior Felix	.05	.02
523	Eddie Zosky (R)	.15	.08
524	Tony Fernandez	.05	.02
525	Checklist	.05	.02
526	Checklist	.05	.02
527	Checklist	.05	.02
528	Checklist	.05	.02

1991 Bowman

The 1991 Bowman set is similar in design to the 1990 set and features 704 cards compared to 528 in 1990. Special subsets honor Hall of Famer Rod Carew and the winners of the NL and AL Silver Slugger Awards. A factory set was also issued and is valued $2.00 higher than the complete set price below. The standard size cards measure 2-1/2" by 3-1/2" with full-color action and portrait photos on the card fronts.

		MINT	NR/MT
Complete Set (704)		23.00	15.00
Commons		.05	.02

1	Rod Carew	.15	.08
2	Rod Carew	.15	.08
3	Rod Carew	.15	.08
4	Rod Carew	.15	.08
5	Rod Carew	.15	.08
6	Willie Fraser	.05	.02
7	John Olerud	.60	.35
8	William Suero (R)	.10	.06
9	Roberto Alomar	.20	.12
10	Todd Stottlemyre	.07	.04
11	Joe Carter	.15	.08
12	Steve Karsay (R)	.75	.45
13	Mark Whiten	.40	.25
14	Pat Borders	.05	.02
15	Mike Timlin (R)	.10	.06
16	Tom Henke	.05	.02
17	Eddie Zosky	.07	.04
18	Kelly Gruber	.07	.04
19	Jimmy Key	.07	.04
20	Jerry Schunk (R)	.10	.06
21	Manny Lee	.05	.02
22	Dave Steib	.07	.04
23	Pat Hentgen (R)	.80	.50
24	Glenallen Hill	.08	.05
25	Rene Gonzales	.05	.02

26	Ed Sprague	.15	.08
27	Ken Dayley	.05	.02
28	Pat Tabler	.05	.02
29	Denis Boucher (R)	.10	.06
30	Devon White	.05	.02
31	Dante Bichette	.05	.02
32	Paul Molitor	.15	.08
33	Greg Vaughn	.15	.08
34	Dan Plesac	.05	.02
35	Chris George (R)	.10	.06
36	Tim McIntosh	.07	.04
37	Franklin Stubbs	.05	.02
38	Bo Dodson (R)	.15	.08
39	Ron Robinson	.05	.02
40	Ed Nunez	.05	.02
41	Greg Brock	.05	.02
42	Jaime Navarro	.08	.05
43	Chris Bosio	.07	.04
44	B.J. Surhoff	.05	.02
45	Chris Johnson (R)	.10	.06
46	Willie Randolph	.05	.02
47	Narciso Elvira (R)	.08	.05
48	Jim Gantner	.05	.02
49	Kevin Brown	.05	.02
50	Julio Machado	.05	.02
51	Chuck Crim	.05	.02
52	Gary Sheffield	.35	.20
53	Angel Miranda (R)	.15	.08
54	Teddy Higuera	.05	.02
55	Robin Yount	.15	.08
56	Cal Eldred	.25	.15
57	Sandy Alomar	.07	.04
58	Greg Swindell	.07	.04
59	Brook Jacoby	.05	.02
60	Efrain Valdez	.08	.05
61	Ever Magallanes (R)	.10	.06
62	Tom Candiotti	.05	.02
63	Eric King	.05	.02
64	Alex Cole	.07	.04
65	Charles Nagy	.25	.15
66	Mitch Webster	.05	.02
67	Chris James	.05	.02
68	Jim Thome (R)	.35	.20
69	Carlos Baerga	.35	.20
70	Mark Lewis	.10	.06
71	Jerry Browne	.05	.02
72	Jesse Orosco	.05	.02
73	Mike Huff	.05	.02
74	Jose Escobar (R)	.08	.05
75	Jeff Manto	.07	.04
76	Turner Ward (R)	.12	.07
77	Doug Jones	.05	.02
78	Bruce Egloff (R)	.10	.06
79	Tim Costo (R)	.20	.12
80	Beau Allred	.08	.05
81	Albert Belle	.25	.15
82	John Farrell	.05	.02
83	Glenn Davis	.07	.04
84	Joe Orsulak	.05	.02
85	Mark Williamson	.05	.02
86	Ben McDonald	.12	.07
87	Billy Ripken	.05	.02
88	Leo Gomez	.12	.07
89	Bob Melvin	.05	.02
90	Jeff Robinson	.05	.02
91	Jose Mesa	.05	.02
92	Gregg Olson	.07	.04
93	Mike Devereaux	.10	.06
94	Luis Mercedes (R)	.20	.12
95	Arthur Rhodes (R)	.25	.15
96	Juan Bell	.05	.02
97	Mike Mussina (R)	1.75	1.00
98	Jeff Ballard	.05	.02
99	Chris Hoiles	.12	.07
100	Brady Anderson	.20	.12
101	Bob Milacki	.05	.02
102	David Segui	.07	.04
103	Dwight Evans	.07	.04
104	Cal Ripken	.25	.15
105	Mike Linskey (R)	.08	.05
106	Jeff Tackett (R)	.10	.06
107	Jeff Reardon	.07	.04
108	Dana Kiecker	.05	.02
109	Ellis Burks	.07	.04
110	Dave Owen (R)	.08	.05
111	Danny Darwin	.05	.02
112	Mo Vaughn	.35	.20
113	Jeff McNeely (R)	.40	.25
114	Tom Bolton	.05	.02
115	Greg Blosser	.15	.08
116	Mike Greenwell	.08	.05
117	Phil Plantier (R)	.75	.45
118	Roger Clemens	.20	.12
119	John Marzano	.05	.02
120	Jody Reed	.05	.02
121	Scott Taylor (R)	.08	.05
122	Jack Clark	.07	.04
123	Derek Livernois (R)	.08	.05
124	Tony Pena	.05	.02
125	Tom Brunansky	.05	.02
126	Carlos Quintana	.07	.04
127	Tim Naehring	.10	.06
128	Matt Young	.05	.02
129	Wade Boggs	.15	.08
130	Kevin Morton (R)	.10	.06
131	Pete Incaviglia	.05	.02
132	Rob Deer	.05	.02
133	Bill Gullickson	.05	.02
134	Rico Brogna	.10	.06
135	Lloyd Moseby	.05	.02
136	Cecil Fielder	.15	.08
137	Tony Phillips	.05	.02
138	Mark Leiter (R)	.10	.06
139	John Cerutti	.05	.02

140	Mickey Tettleton	.05	.02
141	Milt Cuyler	.08	.05
142	Greg Gohr	.07	.04
143	Tony Bernazard	.05	.02
144	Dan Gakeler (R)	.08	.05
145	Travis Fryman	.40	.25
146	Dan Petry	.05	.02
147	Scott Aldred	.05	.02
148	John DeSilva (R)	.10	.06
149	Rusty Meacham (R)	.10	.06
150	Lou Whitaker	.05	.02
151	Dave Haas (R)	.08	.05
152	Luis de los Santos	.05	.02
153	Ivan Cruz (R)	.10	.06
154	Alan Trammell	.07	.04
155	Pat Kelly (R)	.15	.08
156	Carl Everett (R)	.30	.18
157	Greg Cadaret	.05	.02
158	Kevin Maas	.10	.06
159	Jeff Johnson (R)	.12	.07
160	Willie Smith	.07	.04
161	Gerald Williams (R)	.20	.12
162	Mike Humphreys (R)	.10	.06
163	Alvaro Espinoza	.05	.02
164	Matt Nokes	.05	.02
165	Wade Taylor	.10	.06
166	Roberto Kelly	.10	.06
167	John Habyan	.05	.02
168	Steve Farr	.05	.02
169	Jesse Barfield	.05	.02
170	Steve Sax	.07	.04
171	Jim Leyritz	.07	.04
172	Robert Eenhoorn (R)	.10	.06
173	Bernie Williams	.12	.07
174	Scott Lusader	.05	.02
175	Torey Lovullo	.05	.02
176	Chuck Cary	.05	.02
177	Scott Sanderson	.05	.02
178	Don Mattingly	.15	.08
179	Mel Hall	.07	.04
180	Juan Gonzalez	.75	.45
181	Hensley Meulens	.05	.02
182	Jose Offerman	.10	.06
183	Jeff Bagwell (R)	2.00	1.25
184	Jeff Conine (R)	.60	.35
185	Henry Rodriguez (R)	.20	.12
186	Jimmie Reese	.08	.05
187	Kyle Abbott	.08	.05
188	Lance Parrish	.05	.02
189	Rafael Montaivo (R)	.08	.05
190	Floyd Bannister	.05	.02
191	Dick Schofield	.05	.02
192	Scott Lewis (R)	.08	.05
193	Jeff Robinson	.05	.02
194	Kent Anderson	.05	.02
195	Wally Joyner	.07	.04
196	Chuck Finley	.07	.04
197	Luis Sojo	.05	.02
198	Jeff Richardson (R)	.08	.05
199	Dave Parker	.05	.02
200	Jim Abbott	.12	.07
201	Junior Felix	.05	.02
202	Mark Langston	.07	.04
203	Tim Salmon (R)	5.00	3.00
204	Cliff Young	.05	.02
205	Scott Bailes	.05	.02
206	Bobby Rose	.07	.04
207	Gary Gaetti	.05	.02
208	Ruben Amaro (R)	.12	.07
209	Luis Polonia	.05	.02
210	Dave Winfield	.12	.07
211	Bryan Harvey	.08	.05
212	Mike Moore	.05	.02
213	Rickey Henderson	.15	.08
214	Steve Chitren (R)	.10	.06
215	Bob Welch	.05	.02
216	Terry Steinbach	.05	.02
217	Ernie Riles	.05	.02
218	Todd Van Poppel (R)	.75	.45
219	Mike Gallego	.05	.02
220	Curt Young	.05	.02
221	Todd Burns	.05	.02
222	Vance Law	.05	.02
223	Eric Show	.05	.02
224	Don Peters (R)	.10	.06
225	Dave Stewart	.07	.04
226	Dave Henderson	.05	.02
227	Jose Canseco	.20	.12
228	Walt Weiss	.05	.02
229	Dann Howitt	.12	.07
230	Willie Wilson	.05	.02
231	Harold Baines	.05	.02
232	Scott Hemond	.05	.02
233	Joe Slusarski	.08	.05
234	Mark McGwire	.20	.12
235	Kirk Dressendorfer (R)	.10	.06
236	Craig Paquette (R)	.20	.12
237	Dennis Eckersley	.10	.06
238	Dana Allison (R)	.08	.05
239	Scott Bradley	.05	.02
240	Brian Holman	.05	.02
241	Mike Schooler	.05	.02
242	Rich Delucia	.08	.05
243	Edgar Martinez	.15	.08
244	Henry Cotto	.05	.02
245	Omar Vizquel	.05	.02
246	Ken Griffey, Jr.	.80	.50
247	Jay Buhner	.07	.04
248	Bill Krueger	.05	.02
249	Dave Fleming (R)	.80	.50
250	Patrick Lennon (R)	.20	.12
251	Dave Valle	.05	.02
252	Harold Reynolds	.05	.02
253	Randy Johnson	.15	.08

254	Scott Bankhead	.05	.02	
255	Ken Griffey	.07	.04	
256	Greg Briley	.05	.02	
257	Tino Martinez	.10	.06	
258	Alvin Davis	.05	.02	
259	Pete O'Brien	.05	.02	
260	Erik Hanson	.08	.05	
261	Bret Boone (R)	.75	.45	
262	Roger Salkeld	.12	.07	
263	Dave Burba (R)	.10	.06	
264	Kerry Woodson (R)	.10	.06	
265	Julio Franco	.07	.04	
266	Dan Peltier (R)	.15	.08	
267	Jeff Russell	.05	.02	
268	Steve Buechele	.05	.02	
269	Donald Harris	.07	.04	
270	Robb Nen	.07	.04	
271	Rich Gossage	.05	.02	
272	Ivan Rodriguez (R)	1.00	.70	
273	Jeff Huson	.05	.02	
274	Kevin Brown	.08	.05	
275	Dan Smith (R)	.10	.06	
276	Gary Pettis	.05	.02	
277	Jack Daugherty	.05	.02	
278	Mike Jeffcoat	.05	.02	
279	Brad Arnsbarg	.05	.02	
280	Nolan Ryan	.60	.35	
281	Eric McCray (R)	.08	.05	
282	Scott Chiamparino	.07	.04	
283	Ruben Sierra	.15	.08	
284	Geno Petralli	.05	.02	
285	Monty Fariss	.05	.02	
286	Rafael Palmeiro	.15	.08	
287	Bobby Witt	.07	.04	
288	Dean Palmer (R)	.35	.20	
289	Tony Scruggs (R)	.10	.06	
290	Kenny Rogers	.05	.02	
291	Bret Saberhagen	.07	.04	
292	Brian McRae (R)	.25	.15	
293	Storm Davis	.05	.02	
294	Danny Tartabull	.07	.04	
295	David Howard (R)	.08	.05	
296	Mike Boddicker	.05	.02	
297	Joel Johnston (R)	.10	.06	
298	Tim Spehr (R)	.08	.05	
299	Hector Wagner	.07	.04	
300	George Brett	.20	.12	
301	Mike Macfarlane	.05	.02	
302	Kirk Gibson	.05	.02	
303	Harvey Pulliam (R)	.10	.06	
304	Jim Eisenreich	.05	.02	
305	Kevin Seitzer	.07	.04	
306	Mark Davis	.05	.02	
307	Kurt Stillwell	.05	.02	
308	Jeff Montgomery	.05	.02	
309	Kevin Appier	.15	.08	
310	Bob Hamelin	.07	.04	
311	Tom Gordon	.07	.04	
312	Kerwin Moore (R)	.12	.07	
313	Hugh Walker	.07	.04	
314	Terry Shumpert	.07	.04	
315	Warren Cromartie	.05	.02	
316	Gary Thurman	.05	.02	
317	Steve Bedrosian	.05	.02	
318	Danny Gladden	.05	.02	
319	Jack Morris	.10	.06	
320	Kirby Puckett	.25	.15	
321	Kent Hrbek	.05	.02	
322	Kevin Tapani	.07	.04	
323	Denny Neagle (R)	.10	.06	
324	Rich Garces (R)	.10	.06	
325	Larry Casian	.07	.04	
326	Shane Mack	.07	.04	
327	Allan Anderson	.05	.02	
328	Junior Ortiz	.05	.02	
329	Paul Abbott (R)	.08	.05	
330	Chuck Knoblauch	.30	.18	
331	Chili Davis	.05	.02	
332	Todd Ritchie (R)	.10	.06	
333	Brian Harper	.05	.02	
334	Rick Aguilera	.05	.02	
335	Scott Erickson (R)	.25	.15	
336	Pedro Munoz (R)	.20	.12	
337	Scott Leuis	.05	.02	
338	Greg Gagne	.05	.02	
339	Mike Pagliarulo	.05	.02	
340	Terry Leach	.05	.02	
341	Willie Banks	.08	.05	
342	Bobby Thigpen	.05	.02	
343	Roberto Hernandez (R)	.25	.15	
344	Melido Perez	.05	.02	
345	Carlton Fisk	.10	.06	
346	Norberto Martin (R)	.08	.05	
347	Johnny Ruffin (R)	.15	.08	
348	Jeff Carter (R)	.08	.05	
349	Lance Johnson	.05	.02	
350	Sammy Sosa	.15	.08	
351	Alex Fernandez (R)	.50	.30	
352	Jack McDowell	.20	.12	
353	Bob Wickman (R)	.60	.35	
354	Wilson Alvarez (R)	.50	.30	
355	Charlie Hough	.05	.02	
356	Ozzie Guillen	.05	.02	
357	Cory Snyder	.05	.02	
358	Robin Ventura	.20	.12	
359	Scott Fletcher	.05	.02	
360	Cesar Bernhardt (R)	.08	.05	
361	Dan Pasqua	.05	.02	
362	Tim Raines	.05	.02	
363	Brian Drahman (R)	.08	.05	
364	Wayne Edwards	.05	.02	
365	Scott Radinsky	.07	.04	
366	Frank Thomas	2.50	1.50	
367	Cecil Fielder (Slugger)	.10	.06	

368	Julio Franco (Slugger)	.06	.03
369	Kelly Gruber (Slugger)	.06	.03
370	Alan Trammell (Slugger)	.06	.03
371	Rickey Henderson (Slugger)	.10	.06
372	Jose Canseco (Slugger)	.12	.07
373	Ellis Burks (Slugger)	.06	.03
374	Lance Parrish (Slugger)	.06	.03
375	Dave Parker (Slugger)	.06	.03
376	Eddie Murray (Slugger)	.06	.03
377	Ryne Sandberg (Slugger)	.10	.06
378	Matt Williams (Slugger)	.08	.05
379	Barry Larkin (Slugger)	.06	.03
380	Barry Bonds (Slugger)	.15	.08
381	Bobby Bonilla (Slugger)	.06	.03
382	D. Strawberry (Slugger)	.10	.06
383	Benny Santiago (Slugger)	.06	.03
384	Don Robinson (Slugger)	.05	.02
385	Paul Coleman	.07	.04
386	Milt Thompson	.05	.02
387	Lee Smith	.07	.04
388	Ray Lankford	.25	.15
389	Tom Pagnozzi	.05	.02
390	Ken Hill	.05	.02
391	Jamie Moyer	.05	.02
392	Greg Carmona (R)	.08	.05
393	John Ericks	.07	.04
394	Bob Tewksbury	.05	.02
395	Jose Oquendo	.05	.02
396	Rheal Cormier (R)	.15	.08
397	Mike Milchin (R)	.15	.08
398	Ozzie Smith	.12	.07
399	Aaron Holbert (R)	.15	.08
400	Jose DeLeon	.05	.02
401	Felix Jose	.07	.04
402	Juan Agosto	.05	.02
403	Pedro Guerrero	.05	.02
404	Todd Zeile	.10	.06
405	Gerald Perry	.05	.02
406	Donovan Osborne (R)	.40	.25
407	Bryn Smith	.05	.02
408	Bernard Gilkey (R)	.20	.12
409	Rex Hudler	.05	.02
410	Thomson/Branca	.10	.06
411	Lance Dickson (R)	.12	.07
412	Danny Jackson	.05	.02
413	Jerome Walton	.05	.02
414	Sean Cheetham (R)	.08	.05
415	Joe Girardi	.05	.02
416	Ryne Sandberg	.20	.12
417	Mike Harkey	.07	.04
418	George Bell	.07	.04
419	Rick Wilkins (R)	.60	.35
420	Earl Cunningham	.08	.05
421	Heathcliff Slocumb (R)	.10	.06
422	Mike Bieleci	.05	.02
423	Jessie Hollins (R)	.12	.07
424	Shawon Dunston	.05	.02
425	Dave Smith	.05	.02
426	Greg Maddux	.15	.08
427	Jose Vizcaino	.05	.02
428	Luis Salazar	.05	.02
429	Andre Dawson	.12	.07
430	Rick Sutcliffe	.05	.02
431	Paul Assenmacher	.05	.02
432	Erik Pappas	.07	.04
433	Mark Grace	.10	.06
434	Denny Martinez	.08	.05
435	Marquis Grissom	.20	.12
436	Wilfredo Cordero (R)	.60	.35
437	Tim Wallach	.07	.04
438	Brian Barnes (R)	.15	.08
439	Barry Jones	.05	.02
440	Ivan Calderon	.05	.02
441	Stan Spencer (R)	.08	.05
442	Larry Walker	.20	.12
443	Chris Haney (R)	.12	.07
444	Hector Rivera (R)	.08	.05
445	Delino DeShields	.15	.08
446	Andres Galarraga	.15	.08
447	Gilberto Reyes	.05	.02
448	Willie Greene	.10	.06
449	Greg Colbrunn (R)	.15	.08
450	Rondell White (R)	.75	.45
451	Steve Frey	.05	.02
452	Shane Andrews (R)	.15	.08
453	Mike Fitzgerald	.05	.02
454	Spike Owen	.05	.02
455	Dave Martinez	.05	.02
456	Dennis Boyd	.05	.02
457	Eric Bullock	.05	.02
458	Reid Cornelius (R)	.12	.07
459	Chris Nabholz (R)	.15	.08
460	David Cone	.08	.05
461	Hubie Brooks	.05	.02
462	Sid Fernandez	.05	.02
463	Doug Simons	.07	.04
464	Howard Johnson	.08	.05
465	Chris Donnels (R)	.08	.05
466	Anthony Young (R)	.20	.12
467	Todd Hundley	.08	.05
468	Rick Cerone	.05	.02
469	Kevin Elster	.05	.02
470	Wally Whitehurst	.05	.02
471	Vince Coleman	.05	.02
472	Doc Gooden	.10	.06
473	Charlie O'Brien	.05	.02
474	Jeromy Burnitz (R)	.60	.35
475	John Franco	.05	.02
476	Daryl Boston	.05	.02
477	Frank Viola	.07	.04
478	D.J. Dozier	.10	.06

479	Kevin McReynolds	.05	.02
480	Tom Herr	.05	.02
481	Gregg Jefferies	.12	.07
482	Pete Schourek (R)	.10	.06
483	Ron Darling	.05	.02
484	Dave Magadan	.05	.02
485	Andy Ashby (R)	.10	.06
486	Dale Murphy	.10	.06
487	Von Hayes	.05	.02
488	Kim Batiste (R)	.12	.07
489	Tony Longmire (R)	.10	.06
490	Wally Backman	.05	.02
491	Jeff Jackson	.08	.05
492	Mickey Morandini	.08	.05
493	Darrel Akerfelds	.05	.02
494	Ricky Jordan	.05	.02
495	Randy Ready	.05	.02
496	Darrin Fletcher	.05	.02
497	Chuck Malone	.07	.04
498	Pat Combs	.07	.04
499	Dickie Thon	.05	.02
500	Roger McDowell	.05	.02
501	Len Dykstra	.15	.08
502	Joe Boever	.05	.02
503	John Kruk	.05	.02
504	Terry Mulholland	.05	.02
505	Wes Chamberlain (R)	.20	.12
506	Mike Lieberthal (R)	.25	.15
507	Darren Daulton	.15	.08
508	Charlie Hayes	.05	.02
509	John Smiley	.08	.05
510	Gary Varsho	.05	.02
511	Curt Wilkerson	.05	.02
512	Orlando Merced (R)	.25	.15
513	Barry Bonds	.35	.20
514	Mike Lavalliere	.05	.02
515	Doug Drabek	.08	.05
516	Gary Redus	.05	.02
517	William Pennyfeather (R)	.15	.08
518	Randy Tomlin (R)	.15	.08
519	Mike Zimmerman (R)	.08	.05
520	Jeff King	.07	.04
521	Kurt Miller (R)	.20	.12
522	Jay Bell	.05	.02
523	Bill Landrum	.05	.02
524	Zane Smith	.05	.02
525	Bobby Bonilla	.10	.06
526	Bob Walk	.05	.02
527	Austin Manahan	.07	.04
528	Joe Ausanio (R)	.08	.05
529	Andy Van Slyke	.10	.06
530	Jose Lind	.05	.02
531	Carlos Garcia (R)	.50	.30
532	Don Slaught	.05	.02
533	Colin Powell	.10	.06
534	Frank Bolick	.12	.07
535	Gary Scott (R)	.12	.07
536	Nikco Riesgo (R)	.12	.07
537	Reggie Sanders (R)	1.00	.70
538	Tim Howard (R)	.12	.07
539	Ryan Bowen (R)	.15	.08
540	Eric Anthony	.15	.08
541	Jim Deshaies	.05	.02
542	Tom Nevers (R)	.10	.06
543	Ken Caminiti	.07	.04
544	Karl Rhodes	.07	.04
545	Xavier Hernandez	.07	.04
546	Mike Scott	.05	.02
547	Jeff Juden	.10	.06
548	Darryl Kile	.15	.08
549	Willie Ansley	.10	.06
550	Luis Gonzalez (R)	.30	.18
551	Mike Simms (R)	.08	.05
552	Mark Portugal	.05	.02
553	Jimmy Jones	.05	.02
554	Jim Clancy	.05	.02
555	Pete Harnisch	.07	.04
556	Craig Biggio	.10	.06
557	Eric Yelding	.07	.04
558	Dave Rohde	.05	.02
559	Casey Candaele	.05	.02
560	Curt Schilling	.12	.07
561	Steve Finley	.05	.02
562	Javier Ortiz	.05	.02
563	Andujar Cedeno	.15	.08
564	Rafael Ramirez	.05	.02
565	Kenny Lofton (R)	1.50	.90
566	Steve Avery	.20	.12
567	Lonnie Smith	.05	.02
568	Kent Mercker	.05	.02
569	Chipper Jones (R)	1.25	.70
570	Terry Pendleton	.10	.06
571	Otis Nixon	.05	.02
572	Juan Berenguer	.05	.02
573	Charlie Leibrandt	.05	.02
574	David Justice (R)	.60	.35
575	Keith Mitchell (R)	.10	.06
576	Tom Glavine	.20	.12
577	Greg Olson	.05	.02
578	Rafael Belliard	.05	.02
579	Ben Rivera (R)	.15	.08
580	John Smoltz	.12	.07
581	Tyler Houston	.07	.04
582	Mark Wohlers (R)	.20	.12
583	Ron Gant	.15	.08
584	Ramon Caraballo (R)	.10	.06
585	Sid Bream	.05	.02
586	Jeff Treadway	.05	.02
587	Javier Lopez (R)	1.50	.90
588	Deion Sanders	.25	.15
589	Mike Heath	.05	.02
590	Ryan Klesko (R)	.80	.50
591	Bob Ojeda	.05	.02
592	Alfredo Griffin	.05	.02

593	Raul Mondesi (R)	.60	.35
594	Greg Smith	.05	.02
595	Orel Hershiser	.07	.04
596	Juan Samuel	.05	.02
597	Brett Butler	.07	.04
598	Gary Carter	.08	.05
599	Stan Javier	.05	.02
600	Kal Daniels	.05	.02
601	Jamie McAndrew (R)	.10	.06
602	Mike Sharperson	.05	.02
603	Jay Howell	.05	.02
604	Eric Karros (R)	1.00	.60
605	Tim Belcher	.07	.04
606	Dan Opperman (R)	.08	.05
607	Lenny Harris	.05	.02
608	Tom Goodwin	.08	.05
609	Darryl Strawberry	.12	.07
610	Ramon Martinez	.08	.05
611	Kevin Gross	.05	.02
612	Zakary Shinall (R)	.15	.08
613	Mike Scioscia	.05	.02
614	Eddie Murray	.12	.07
615	Ronnie Walden (R)	.10	.06
616	Will Clark	.20	.12
617	Adam Hyzdu (R)	.15	.08
618	Matt Williams	.12	.07
619	Don Robinson	.05	.02
620	Jeff Brantley	.08	.05
621	Greg Litton	.05	.02
622	Steve Decker (R)	.10	.06
623	Robby Thompson	.05	.02
624	Mark Leonard (R)	.08	.05
625	Kevin Bass	.05	.02
626	Scott Garrelts	.05	.02
627	Jose Uribe	.05	.02
628	Eric Gunderson	.05	.02
629	Steve Hosey	.15	.08
630	Trevor Wilson	.07	.04
631	Terry Kennedy	.05	.02
632	Dave Righetti	.05	.02
633	Kelly Downs	.05	.02
634	Johnny Ard	.05	.02
635	Eric Christopherson (R)	.12	.07
636	Kevin Mitchell	.08	.05
637	John Burkett	.05	.02
638	Kevin Rogers (R)	.20	.12
639	Bud Black	.05	.02
640	Willie McGee	.05	.02
641	Royce Clayton	.15	.08
642	Tony Fernandez	.05	.02
643	Ricky Bones (R)	.10	.06
644	Thomas Howard	.07	.04
645	Dave Staton (R)	.20	.12
646	Jim Presley	.05	.02
647	Tony Gwynn	.15	.08
648	Marty Barrett	.05	.02
649	Scott Coolbaugh	.05	.02
650	Craig Lefferts	.05	.02
651	Eddie Whitson	.05	.02
652	Oscar Azocar	.05	.02
653	Wes Gardner	.05	.02
654	Bip Roberts	.05	.02
655	Robbie Beckett (R)	.15	.08
656	Benny Santiago	.07	.04
657	Greg W. Harris	.05	.02
658	Jerald Clark	.05	.02
659	Fred McGriff	.25	.15
660	Larry Andersen	.05	.02
661	Bruce Hurst	.07	.04
662	Steve Martin (R)	.08	.05
663	Rafael Valdez	.07	.04
664	Paul Faries	.05	.02
665	Andy Benes	.12	.07
666	Randy Myers	.05	.02
667	Rob Dibble	.07	.04
668	Glenn Sutko (R)	.08	.05
669	Glenn Braggs	.05	.02
670	Billy Hatcher	.05	.02
671	Joe Oliver	.05	.02
672	Freddie Benavides	.05	.02
673	Barry Larkin	.10	.06
674	Chris Sabo	.07	.04
675	Mariano Duncan	.05	.02
676	Chris Jones	.12	.07
677	Gino Minutelli (R)	.10	.06
678	Reggie Jefferson	.12	.07
679	Jack Armstrong	.05	.02
680	Chris Hammond (R)	.12	.07
681	Jose Rijo	.07	.04
682	Bill Doran	.05	.02
683	Terry Lee (R)	.10	.06
684	Tom Browning	.07	.04
685	Paul O'Neill	.08	.05
686	Eric Davis	.08	.05
687	Dan Wilson (R)	.15	.08
688	Ted Power	.05	.02
689	Tim Layana	.05	.02
690	Norm Charlton	.05	.02
691	Hal Morris	.10	.06
692	Rickey Henderson	.15	.08
693	Sam Militello (R)	.40	.25
694	Matt Mieske (R)	.20	.12
695	Paul Russo (R)	.10	.06
696	Domingo Mota (R)	.10	.06
697	Todd Guggiana (R)	.08	.05
698	Marc Newfield (R)	.60	.35
699	Checklist	.05	.02
700	Checklist	.05	.02
701	Checklist	.05	.02
702	Checklist	.05	.02
703	Checklist	.05	.02
704	Checklist	.05	.02

1992 Bowman

The cards in this 705-card set measure 2-1/2" by 3-1/2" and feature full color photos on the card fronts. The quality of the 1992 set has been upgraded over previous years and uses a premium UV coated glossy card stock. The set includes 45-special Gold Foil insert cards and a group of 1991 Minor League MVP's and First Round Draft Picks.

		MINT	NR/MT
Complete Set (705)		340.00	160.00
Commons		.25	.15

1	Ivan Rodriquez	1.75	1.00
2	Kirk McCaskill	.25	.15
3	Scott Livingstone	.25	.15
4	Solomon Torres (R)	3.50	2.00
5	Carlos Hernandez	.30	.18
6	Dave Hollins	3.00	1.75
7	Scott Fletcher	.25	.15
8	Jorge Fabregas	.35	.20
9	Andujar Cedeno	.40	.25
10	Howard Johnson	.30	.18
11	Trevor Hoffman (R)	.35	.20
12	Roberto Kelly	.40	.25
13	Gregg Jefferies	1.00	.70
14	Marquis Grissom	1.00	.70
15	Mike Ignasiak (R)	.35	.20
16	Jack Morris	.30	.18
17	William Penneyfeather	.30	.18
18	Todd Stottlemyre	.30	.18
19	Chito Martinez	.30	.18
20	Roberto Alomar	3.50	2.00
21	Sam Militello	.60	.35
22	Hector Fajardo (R)	.35	.20
23	Paul Quantrill	.35	.20
24	Chuck Knoblauch	.60	.35
25	Reggie Jefferson	.70	.40
26	Jeremy McGarity (R)	.35	.20
27	Jerome Walton	.25	.15
28	Chipper Jones	6.50	3.75
29	Brain Barber	1.75	1.00
30	Ron Darling	.30	.18
31	Roberto Petragine (R)	1.50	.90
32	Chuck Finley	.30	.18
33	Edgar Martinez	.40	.25
34	Napoleon Robinson (R)	.35	.20
35	Andy Van Slyke	.45	.28
36	Bobby Thigpen	.30	.18
37	Travis Fryman	4.00	2.50
38	Eric Christopherson	.30	.18
39	Terry Mulholland	.25	.15
40	Darryl Strawberry	.45	.28
41	Manny Alexander	.40	.25
42	Tracy Sanders (R)	.45	.28
43	Pete Incaviglia	.25	.15
44	Kim Batiste	.30	.18
45	Frank Rodriquez (R)	2.50	1.50
46	Gregg Swindell	.30	.18
47	Delino DeShields	.70	.40
48	John Ericks	.30	.18
49	Franklin Stubbs	.25	.15
50	Tony Gwynn	.90	.60
51	Clifton Garrett (R)	.35	.20
52	Mike Gardella (R)	.30	.18
53	Scott Erickson	.45	.28
54	Gary Cababallo (R)	.30	.18
55	Jose Oliva (R)	.60	.35
56	Brook Fordyce (R)	.40	.25
57	Mark Whiten	.80	.50
58	Joe Slusarski	.30	.18
59	J. R. Phillips (R)	1.75	1.00
60	Barry Bonds	4.50	2.75
61	Bob Milacki	.25	.15
62	Keith Mitchell	.30	.18
63	Angel Miranda	.35	.20
64	Raul Mondesi	2.50	1.50
65	Brian Koelling (R)	.50	.30
66	Brian McRae	.50	.30
67	John Patterson	.30	.18
68	John Wetteland	.50	.30
69	Wilson Alvarez	1.00	.70
70	Wade Boggs	.90	.60
71	Darryl Ratliff (R)	.30	.18
72	Jeff Jackson	.35	.20
73	Jeremy Hernandez (R)	.35	.20
74	Darryl Hamilton	.40	.25
75	Rafeal Belliard	.25	.15
76	Ricky Talicek (R)	.30	.18
77	Felipe Crespo (R)	.60	.35
78	Carney Lansford	.30	.18
79	Ryan Long (R)	.40	.25
80	Kirby Puckett	2.50	1.50
81	Earl Cunningham	.30	.18
82	Pedro Martinez (R)	1.25	.80
83	Scott Hatteberg (R)	.60	.35

84	Juan Gonzalez	14.00	9.00
85	Robert Nutting (R)	.30	.18
86	Calvin Reese (R)	.50	.30
87	Dave Silvestri	.30	.18
88	Scott Ruffcorn (R)	2.50	1.50
89	Rick Aguilera	.25	.15
90	Cecil Fielder	1.50	.90
91	Kirk Dressendorfer	.30	.18
92	Jerry DiPoto (R)	.35	.20
93	Mike Fielder	.25	.15
94	Craig Paquette	.50	.30
95	Elvin Paulino (R)	.30	.18
96	Donovan Osborne	1.00	.70
97	Hubie Brooks	.25	.15
98	Derek Lowe (R)	.60	.35
99	David Zancanaro (R)	.35	.20
100	Ken Griffey Jr.	15.00	10.00
101	Todd Hundley	.30	.18
102	Mike Trombley (R)	.30	.18
103	Ricky Gutierrez (R)	.70	.40
104	Braulio Castillo	.30	.18
105	Craig Lefferts	.25	.15
106	Rick Sutcliffe	.25	.15
107	Dean Palmer	2.00	1.25
108	Henry Rodriquez	.35	.20
109	Mark Clark (R)	.50	.30
110	Kenny Lofton	4.00	2.50
111	Mark Carreon	.25	.15
112	J.T. Bruett (R)	.30	.18
113	Gerald Williams	.40	.25
114	Frank Thomas	18.00	12.00
115	Kevin Reimer	.30	.18
116	Sammy Sosa	1.25	.80
117	Mickey Tettleton	.30	.18
118	Reggie Sanders	1.75	1.00
119	Trevor Wilson	.35	.20
120	Cliff Brantley (R)	.30	.18
121	Spike Owen	.25	.15
122	Jeff Montgomery	.25	.15
123	Alex Sutherland (R)	.30	.18
124	Brien Taylor (R)	7.50	4.50
125	Brian Williams (R)	.60	.35
126	Kevin Seitzer	.30	.18
127	Carlos Delgado (R)	10.00	6.50
128	Gary Scott	.30	.18
129	Scott Cooper	.80	.50
130	Domingo Jean (R)	2.50	1.50
131	Pat Mahomes (R)	1.00	.70
132	Mike Boddicker	.25	.15
133	Roberto Hernandez	.70	.40
134	Dave Valle	.25	.15
135	Kurt Stillwell	.25	.15
136	Brad Pennington (R)	.45	.28
137	Jermaine Swifton (R)	.35	.20
138	Ryan Hawblitzel (R)	.50	.30
139	Tito Navarro (R)	.35	.20
140	Sandy Alomar	.35	.20
141	Todd Benzinger	.25	.15
142	Danny Jackson	.25	.15
143	Melvin Nieves (R)	3.00	1.75
144	Jim Campanis (R)	.40	.25
145	Luis Gonzalez	.40	.25
146	Dave Doorneweerd (R)	.35	.20
147	Charlie Hayes	.30	.18
148	Greg Maddux	1.25	.80
149	Brian Harper	.25	.15
150	Brent Miller (R)	.35	.20
151	Shawn Estes (R)	.50	.30
152	Mike Williams (R)	.35	.20
153	Charlie Hough	.25	.15
154	Randy Myers	.25	.15
155	Kevin Young (R)	2.50	1.50
156	Rick Wilkins	1.50	.90
157	Terry Schumpert	.25	.15
158	Steve Karsay	3.50	2.00
159	Gary DiSarcina	.30	.18
160	Deion Sanders	.80	.50
161	Tom Browning	.25	.15
162	Dickie Thon	.25	.15
163	Luis Mercedes	.30	.18
164	Riccardo Ingram (R)	.35	.20
165	Tavo Alvarez (R)	.80	.50
166	Rickey Henderson	.90	.60
167	Jaime Navarro	.35	.20
168	Billy Ashley (R)	3.00	1.75
169	Phil Dauphin (R)	.40	.25
170	Ivan Cruz	.30	.18
171	Harold Baines	.25	.15
172	Bryan Harvey	.35	.20
173	Alex Cole	.30	.18
174	Curtis Shaw (R)	.30	.18
175	Matt Williams	.80	.50
176	Felix Jose	.30	.18
177	Sam Horn	.25	.15
178	Randy Johnson	1.00	.70
179	Ivan Calderon	.30	.18
180	Steve Avery	1.75	1.00
181	William Suero	.30	.18
182	Bill Swift	.40	.25
183	Howard Battle (R)	.75	.45
184	Ruben Amaro	.30	.18
185	Jim Abbott	.80	.50
186	Mike Fitzgerald	.25	.15
187	Bruce Hurst	.30	.18
188	Jeff Juden	.60	.35
189	Jeromy Burnitz	1.75	1.00
190	Dave Burba	.30	.18
191	Kevin Brown	.35	.20
192	Patrick Lennon	.35	.20
193	Jeffrey McNeely	.50	.30
194	Wil Cordero	1.75	1.00
195	Chili Davis	.25	.15
196	Milt Cuyler	.30	.18
197	Von Hayes	.25	.15

198	Todd Revenig (R)	.30	.18
199	Joel Johnson	.30	.18
200	Jeff Bagwell	3.00	1.75
201	Alex Fernandez	2.00	1.25
202	Todd Jones (R)	.60	.35
203	Charles Nagy	.70	.40
204	Tim Haines	.30	.18
205	Kevin Maas	.30	.18
206	Julio Franco	.30	.18
207	Randy Velarde	.25	.15
208	Lance Johnson	.25	.15
209	Scott Leius	.30	.18
210	Derek Lee (R)	.35	.20
211	Joe Sondrini (R)	.30	.18
212	Royce Clayton	1.25	.80
213	Chris George	.30	.18
214	Gary Sheffield	1.75	1.00
215	Mark Gubicza	.30	.18
216	Mike Moore	.25	.15
217	Rick Huisman (R)	.40	.25
218	Jeff Russell	.25	.15
219	D.J. Dozier	.25	.15
220	Dave Martinez	.25	.15
221	Alan Newman (R)	.30	.18
222	Nolan Ryan	10.00	6.50
223	Teddy Higuera	.25	.15
224	Damon Buford (R)	.45	.28
225	Ruben Sierra	.75	.45
226	Tom Nevers	.25	.15
227	Tommy Greene	1.00	.70
228	Nigel Wilson	5.00	3.00
229	John DeSilva	.30	.18
230	Bobby Witt	.30	.18
231	Greg Cadaret	.25	.15
232	John VanderWal (R)	.30	.18
233	Jack Clark	.25	.15
234	Bill Doran	.25	.15
235	Bobby Bonilla	.40	.25
236	Steve Olin	.30	.18
237	Derek Bell	1.50	.90
238	David Cone	.30	.18
239	Victor Cole (R)	.30	.18
240	Rod Bolton (R)	.45	.28
241	Tom Pagnozzi	.25	.15
242	Rob Dibble	.30	.18
243	Michael Carter (R)	.35	.20
244	Don Peters (R)	.40	.25
245	Mike LaValliere	.25	.15
246	Joe Perona (R)	.30	.18
247	Mitch Williams	.25	.15
248	Jay Buhner	.40	.25
249	Andy Benes	.60	.35
250	Alex Ochoa (R)	1.25	.80
251	Greg Blosser	1.00	.70
252	Jack Armstrong	.25	.15
253	Juan Samuel	.25	.15
254	Terry Pendleton	.60	.35
255	Ramon Martinez	.35	.20
256	Rico Brogna	.35	.20
257	John Smiley	.30	.18
258	Carl Everett	.80	.50
259	Tim Salmon	18.00	11.00
260	Will Clark	1.50	.90
261	Ugueth Urbina (R)	1.75	1.00
262	Jason Wood (R)	.35	.20
263	Dave Magadan	.25	.15
264	Dante Bichette	.35	.20
265	Jose DeLeon	.25	.15
266	Mike Neill (R)	.90	.60
267	Paul O'Neill	.35	.20
268	Anthony Young	.30	.18
269	Greg Harris	.25	.15
270	Todd Van Poppel	2.00	1.25
271	Pete Castellano (R)	.45	.28
272	Tony Phillips	.25	.15
273	Mike Gallego	.25	.15
274	Steve Cooke (R)	1.25	.80
275	Robin Ventura	1.25	.80
276	Kevin Mitchell	.30	.18
277	Doug Linton (R)	.30	.18
278	Robert Eenhorne	.30	.18
279	Gabe White (R)	1.50	.90
280	Dave Stewart	.30	.18
281	Mo Sanford	.30	.18
282	Greg Perschke (R)	.30	.18
283	Kevin Flora (R)	.35	.20
284	Jeff Williams (R)	.30	.18
285	Keith Miller	.25	.15
286	Andy Ashby	.25	.15
287	Doug Dascenzo	.25	.15
288	Eric Karros	3.00	1.75
289	John Murray (R)	1.75	1.00
290	Troy Percival (R)	.40	.25
291	Orlando Merced	.80	.50
292	Peter Hoy (R)	.30	.18
293	Tony Fernandez	.25	.15
294	Juan Guzman	2.50	1.50
295	Jesse Barfield	.25	.15
296	Sid Fernandez	.30	.18
297	Scott Cepicky (R)	.35	.20
298	Garret Anderson (R)	.40	.25
299	Cal Eldred	2.00	1.25
300	Ryne Sandberg	2.75	1.60
301	Jim Gantner	.25	.15
302	Mariano Rivera (R)	.30	.18
303	Ron Lockett (R)	.30	.18
304	Jose Offerman	.40	.25
305	Denny Martinez	.30	.18
306	Luis Ortiz (R)	.70	.40
307	David Howard	.30	.18
308	Russ Springer (R)	.80	.50
309	Chris Howard (R)	.30	.18
310	Kyle Abbott	.30	.18
311	Aaron Sele (R)	10.00	6.50

312	David Justice	4.00	2.50
313	Pete O'Brien	.25	.15
314	Greg Hansell (R)	.40	.25
315	Dave Winfield	2.00	1.25
316	Lance Dickson	.40	.25
317	Eric King	.25	.15
318	Vaughn Eshelman (R)	.30	.18
319	Tim Belcher	.30	.18
320	Andres Galarraga	.70	.40
321	Scott Bullett (R)	.35	.20
322	Doug Strange	.25	.15
323	Jerald Clark	.25	.15
324	Greg Hibbard	.25	.15
326	Eric Dillman (R)	.30	.18
327	Shane Reynolds (R)	.35	.20
328	Chris Hammond	.30	.18
329	Albert Belle	4.00	2.50
330	Rich Becker (R)	1.00	.70
331	Eddie Williams	.25	.15
332	Donald Harris	.40	.25
333	Dave Smith	.25	.15
334	Steve Fireovid	.30	.18
335	Steve Buechele	.25	.15
336	Mike Schooler	.25	.15
337	Kevin McReynolds	.25	.15
338	Hensley Meulens	.30	.18
339	Benji Gil (R)	2.00	1.25
340	Don Mattingly	1.25	.80
341	Alvin Davis	.25	.15
342	Alan Mills	.30	.18
343	Kelly Downs	.25	.15
344	Leo Gomez	.35	.20
345	Tarrik Brock (R)	.35	.20
346	Ryan Turner (R)	.60	.35
347	John Smoltz	.80	.50
348	Bill Sampen	.25	.15
349	Paul Byrd (R)	.60	.35
350	Mike Bordick	.30	.18
351	Jose Lind	.25	.15
352	David Wells	.25	.15
353	Barry Larkin	.50	.30
354	Bruce Ruffin	.25	.15
355	Luis Rivera	.25	.15
356	Sid Bream	.25	.15
357	Julain Vasquez (R)	.30	.18
358	Jason Bere (R)	7.50	4.50
359	Ben McDonald	.45	.28
360	Scott Stahoviak (R)	.40	.25
361	Kirt Manwaring	.25	.15
362	Jeff Johnson	.25	.15
363	Rob Deer	.25	.15
364	Tony Pena	.25	.15
365	Melido Perez	.25	.15
366	Clay Parker	.25	.15
367	Dale Sveum	.25	.15
368	Mike Scioscia	.25	.15
369	Roger Salkeld	.60	.35
370	Mike Stanley	.25	.15
371	Jack McDowell	2.00	1.25
372	Tim Wallach	.30	.18
373	Billy Ripken	.25	.15
374	Mike Christopher (R)	.30	.18
375	Paul Molitor	1.50	.90
376	Dave Stieb	.30	.18
377	Pedro Guerrero	.25	.15
378	Russ Swan	.25	.15
379	Bob Ojeda	.25	.15
380	Donn Pall	.25	.15
381	Eddie Zosky	.30	.18
382	Darnell Coles	.25	.15
383	Tom Smith (R)	.30	.18
384	Mark McGwire	1.25	.80
385	Gary Carter	.30	.18
386	Rich Amarel	.40	.25
387	Alan Embree (R)	.60	.35
388	Jonathan Hurst (R)	.35	.20
389	Bobby Jones (R)	2.50	1.50
390	Rico Rossy (R)	.30	.18
391	Dan Smith (R)	.35	.20
392	Terry Steinbach	.30	.18
393	Jon Farrell (R)	.60	.35
394	Dave Anderson	.25	.15
395	Benito Santiago	.30	.18
396	Mark Wohlers	.35	.20
397	Mo Vaughn	2.50	1.50
398	Randy Kramer	.30	.18
399	John Jaha (R)	1.00	.70
400	Cal Ripken	3.00	1.75
401	Ryan Bowen	.30	.18
402	Tim McIntosh	.30	.18
403	Bernard Gilkey	.50	.30
404	Junior Felix	.25	.15
405	Cris Colon (R)	.30	.18
406	Marc Newfield	3.00	1.75
407	Bernie Williams	.60	.35
408	Jay Howell	.25	.15
409	Zane Smith	.25	.15
410	Jeff Shaw	.30	.18
411	Kerry Woodson	.30	.18
412	Wes Chamberlain	.45	.28
413	Dave Mlicki	.30	.18
414	Benny Distefano	.25	.15
415	Kevin Rogers	.35	.20
416	Tim Naehring	.30	.18
417	Clemente Nunez (R)	.60	.35
418	Luis Sojo	.25	.15
419	Kevin Ritz	.25	.15
420	Omar Olivares	.25	.15
421	Manuel Lee	.25	.15
422	Julio Valera	.25	.15
423	Omar Vizquel	.25	.15
424	Darren Burton (R)	.50	.30
425	Mel Hall	.30	.18
426	Dennis Powell	.30	.18

#	Player	Price 1	Price 2
427	Lee Stevens	.30	.18
428	Glenn Davis	.25	.15
429	Willie Greene	.90	.60
430	Kevin Wickander	.25	.15
431	Dennis Eckersley	.50	.30
432	Joe Orsulak	.25	.15
433	Eddie Murray	.70	.40
434	Matt Stairs	.30	.18
435	Wally Joyner	.30	.18
436	Rondell White	5.00	3.00
437	Rob Mauer (R)	.35	.20
438	Joe Redfield (R)	.30	.18
439	Mark Lewis	.30	.18
440	Darren Daulton	1.00	.70
441	Mike Henneman	.25	.15
442	John Cangelosi	.25	.15
443	Vince Moore (R)	1.25	.80
444	John Wehner	.30	.18
445	Kent Hrbek	.30	.18
446	Mark McLemore	.25	.15
447	Bill Wegman	.25	.15
448	Robby Thompson	.35	.20
449	Mark Anthony (R)	.30	.18
450	Archi Cianfrocco (R)	.45	.28
451	Johnny Ruffin	.40	.25
452	Javier Lopez	7.00	4.00
453	Greg Gohr	.35	.20
454	Tim Scott (R)	.30	.18
455	Stan Belinda	.25	.15
456	Darrin Jackson	.25	.15
457	Chris Gardner (R)	.30	.18
458	Esteban Beltre (R)	.35	.20
459	Phil Plantier	1.50	.90
460	Jim Thome (R)	3.00	1.75
461	Mike Piazza (R)	32.00	20.00
462	Matt Sinatro	.25	.15
463	Scott Servais	.25	.15
464	Brian Jordan (R)	1.75	1.00
465	Doug Drabek	.35	.20
466	Carl Willis	.25	.15
467	Bret Barberie	.30	.18
468	Hal Morris	.30	.18
469	Steve Sax	.30	.18
470	Jerry Willard	.25	.15
471	Dan Wilson	.30	.18
472	Chris Hoiles	.40	.25
473	Rheal Cormier	.35	.20
474	John Morris	.25	.15
475	Jeff Reardon	.30	.18
476	Mark Leiter	.25	.15
477	Tom Gordon	.25	.15
478	Kent Bottenfield (R)	.30	.18
479	Gene Larkin	.25	.15
480	Dwight Gooden	.35	.20
481	B.J. Surhoff	.25	.15
482	Andy Stankiewicz (R)	.30	.18
483	Tino Martinez	.30	.18
484	Craig Biggio	.30	.18
485	Denny Neagle	.30	.18
486	Rusty Meacham	.25	.15
487	Kal Daniels	.25	.15
488	Dave Henderson	.25	.15
489	Tim Costo	.60	.35
490	Doug Davis	.25	.15
491	Frank Viola	.30	.18
492	Cory Snyder	.25	.15
493	Chris Martin (R)	.30	.18
494	Dion James	.25	.15
495	Randy Tomlin	.30	.18
496	Greg Vaughn	.70	.40
497	Dennis Cook	.25	.15
498	Rosario Rodriguez	.25	.15
499	Dave Staton	.60	.35
500	George Brett	2.50	1.50
501	Brian Barnes	.35	.20
502	Butch Henry (R)	.30	.18
503	Harold Reynolds	.25	.15
504	Dave Nied (R)	3.50	2.00
505	Lee Smith	.40	.25
506	Steve Chitren	.25	.15
507	Ken Hill	.35	.20
508	Robbie Beckett	.35	.20
509	Tony Afenir (R)	.35	.20
510	Kelly Gruber	.30	.18
511	Bret Boone (R)	1.50	.90
512	Jeff Branson	.35	.20
513	Mike Jackson	.30	.18
514	Pete Harnisch	.30	.18
515	Chad Kreuter	.25	.15
516	Joe Vitko (R)	.30	.18
517	Orel Hershiser	.30	.18
518	John Doherty (R)	.70	.40
519	Jay Bell	.30	.18
520	Mark Langston	.35	.20
521	Dann Howitt	.35	.20
522	Bobby Reed (R)	.30	.18
523	Roberto Munoz (R)	.35	.20
524	Todd Ritchie	.30	.18
525	Bip Roberts	.25	.15
526	Pat Listach	.80	.50
527	Scott Brosius	.30	.18
528	John Roper (R)	.70	.40
529	Phil Hiatt (R)	2.00	1.25
530	Denny Walling	.25	.15
531	Carlos Baerga	5.00	3.00
532	Manny Ramirez (R)	12.00	7.50
533	Pat Clements	.25	.15
534	Ron Gant	.80	.50
535	Pat Kelly	.30	.18
536	Billy Spiers	.25	.15
537	Darren Reid	.25	.15
538	Ken Caminiti	.25	.15
539	Butch Huskey (R)	1.75	1.00
540	Matt Nokes	.25	.15

541	John Kruk	.70	.40
542	John Jaha (Foil)	2.50	1.50
543	Justin Thompson (R)	.80	.50
544	Steve Hosey	1.00	.70
545	Joe Kmak (R)	.30	.18
546	John Franco	.25	.15
547	Devon White	.30	.18
548	Elston Hansen (Foil)	1.25	.80
549	Ryan Klesko	3.50	2.00
550	Danny Tartabull	.30	.18
551	Frank Thomas (Foil)	45.00	30.00
552	Kevin Tapani	.30	.18
553	Willie Banks	.40	.25
554	B.J. Wallace (R)(Foil)	3.50	2.00
555	Orlando Miller (R)	.60	.35
556	Mark Smith (R)	1.25	.80
557	Tim Wallach (Foil)	.50	.30
558	Bill Gullickson	.25	.15
559	Derek Bell (Foil)	2.00	1.25
560	Joe Randa (R)(Foil)	1.00	.70
561	Frank Seminara (R)	.35	.20
562	Mark Gardner (R)	.35	.20
563	Rick Greene (R)(Foil)	.80	.50
564	Gary Gaetti	.25	.15
565	Ozzie Guillen	.25	.15
566	Charles Nagy (Foil)	1.00	.70
567	Mike Milchin (R)	.45	.28
568	Ben Shelton (R)	.60	.35
569	Chris Roberts (Foil)	1.25	.80
570	Ellis Burks	.30	.18
571	Scott Scudder	.25	.15
572	Jim Abbott (Foil)	1.25	.80
573	Joe Carter	1.75	1.00
574	Steve Finley	.25	.15
575	Jim Olander (Foil)	.50	.30
576	Carlos Garcia	1.00	.70
577	Greg Olson	.25	.15
578	Greg Swindell (Foil)	.60	.35
579	Matt Williams (Foil)	1.50	.90
580	Mark Grace	.75	.45
581	Howard House (R)(Foil)	.60	.35
582	Luis Polonia	.30	.18
583	Erik Hanson	.35	.20
584	Salomon Torres (Foil)	3.50	2.00
585	Carlton Fisk	.70	.40
586	Bret Saberhagen	.30	.18
587	Chad McDonnell (R) (Foil)	1.50	.90
588	Jimmy Key	.30	.18
589	Mike MacFarlane	.30	.18
590	Barry Bonds (Foil)	7.50	4.50
591	Jamie McAndrew	.35	.20
592	Shane Mack	.30	.18
593	Kerwin Moore	.50	.30
594	Joe Oliver	.25	.15
595	Chris Sabo	.30	.18
596	Alex Gonzalez (R)	2.50	1.50
597	Bret Butler	.30	.18
598	Mark Hutton	1.25	.80
599	Andy Benes (Foil)	.80	.50
600	Jose Canseco	1.25	.80
601	Darryl Kile	2.00	1.25
602	Matt Stairs (Foil)	.80	.50
603	Robert Butler (R)(Foil)	1.00	.70
604	Willie McGee	.30	.18
605	Jack McDowell (Foil)	2.50	1.50
606	Tom Candiotti	.25	.15
607	Ed Martel (R)	.30	.18
608	Matt Mieske (R)	.80	.50
609	Darrin Fletcher	.25	.15
610	Rafael Palmeiro	1.00	.70
611	Bill Swift (Foil)	1.00	.70
612	Mike Mussina	3.50	2.00
613	Vince Coleman	.25	.15
614	Scott Cepicky (Foil)	.60	.35
615	Mike Greenwell	.30	.18
616	Kevin McGehee (R)	.40	.25
617	Jeffrey Hammonds (Foil)	12.00	7.50
618	Scott Taylor	.30	.18
619	Dave Otto	.25	.15
620	Mark McGwire (Foil)	1.75	1.00
621	Kevin Tatar (R)	.30	.18
622	Steve Farr	.25	.15
623	Ryan Klesko (Foil)	5.00	3.00
624	Dave Fleming	1.75	1.00
625	Andre Dawson	.75	.45
626	Tino Martinez (Foil)	1.25	.80
627	Chad Curtis (R)	3.00	1.75
628	Mickey Morandini	.35	.20
629	Gregg Olson (Foil)	.70	.40
630	Lou Whitaker	.30	.18
631	Arthur Rhodes	.35	.20
632	Brandon Wilson (R)	.45	.28
633	Lance Jennings (R)	.30	.18
634	Allen Watson (R)	4.00	2.50
635	Len Dykstra	1.00	.70
636	Joe Girardi	.25	.15
637	Kiki Hernandez (R)(Foil)	1.00	.70
638	Mike Hampton (R)	.45	.28
639	Al Osuna	.25	.15
640	Kevin Appier	.80	.50
641	Rick Helling (Foil)	3.00	1.75
642	Jody Reed	.25	.15
643	Ray Lankford	.60	.35
644	John Olerud	4.50	2.75
645	Paul Molitor (Foil)	5.00	3.00
646	Pat Borders	.25	.15
647	Mike Morgan	.25	.15
648	Larry Walker	1.25	.80
649	Pete Castellano (Foil)	1.25	.80
650	Fred McGriff	2.50	1.50
651	Walt Weiss	.25	.15
652	Calvin Murray (R)(Foil)	3.50	2.00

653	Dave Nilsson	.35	.20
654	Greg Pirkl	.70	.40
655	Robin Ventura (Foil)	3.00	1.75
656	Mark Portugal	.25	.15
657	Roger McDowell	.25	.15
658	Rick Hirtensteiner (Foil)	1.25	.80
659	Glenallen Hill	.30	.18
660	Greg Gagne	.25	.15
661	Charles Johnson (Foil)	4.50	2.75
662	Brian Hunter	.30	.18
663	Mark Lemke	.25	.15
664	Tim Belcher (Foil)	.75	.45
665	Rich DeLucia	.25	.15
666	Bob Walk	.25	.15
667	Joe Carter (Foil)	5.00	3.00
668	Jose Guzman	.30	.18
669	Otis Nixon	.30	.18
670	Phil Nevin (Foil)	6.00	3.50
671	Eric Davis	.30	.18
672	Damion Easley (R)	1.50	.90
673	Will Clark (Foil)	2.50	1.50
674	Mark Keifer	.30	.18
675	Ozzie Smith	.80	.50
676	Manny Ramirez (Foil)	10.00	6.50
677	Gregg Olson	.30	.18
678	Cliff Floyd (R)	24.00	15.00
679	Duane Singleton (R)	.35	.20
680	Jose Rijo	.30	.18
681	Willie Randolph	.30	.18
682	Michael Tucker (Foil)	5.00	3.00
683	Darren Lewis	.35	.20
684	Dale Murphy	.30	.18
685	Mike Pagliarulo	.25	.15
686	Paul Miller (R)	.30	.18
687	Mike Robertson (R)	.45	.28
688	Mike Devereaux	.30	.18
689	Pedro Astacio (R)	1.25	.80
690	Alan Trammell	.35	.20
691	Roger Clemens	2.50	1.50
692	Bud Black	.25	.15
693	Turk Wendell (R)	.50	.30
694	Barry Larkin (Foil)	3.00	1.75
695	Todd Zeile	.30	.18
696	Pat Hentgen	4.00	2.50
697	Eddie Taubensee	.35	.20
698	Guillermo Vasquez (R)	.45	q.28
699	Tom Glavine	1.25	.80
700	Robin Yount	2.00	1.25
701	Checklist 1	.25	.15
702	Checklist 2	.25	.15
703	Checklist 3	.25	.15
704	Checklist 4	.25	.15
705	Checklist 5	.25	.15

1993 Bowman

The cards in this set contain full-color action photos on the card fronts framed by a white border and printed on a glossy card stock with UV coating. The player's name appears in the lower corner of the card in white type. The horizontal card backs consist of another color photo and, as in the previous years, a statistical breakdown of how the player performed against each of the other teams in his league. The set contains 48 foil cards (339-374, 693-704) which were distributed one per wax pack. All cards measure 2-1/2" by 3-1/2".

		MINT	NR/MT
Complete Set (708)		190.00	115.00
Commons		.15	.10
Common Foil Cards		.25	.15

1	Glenn Davis	.15	.10
2	Hector Roa (R)	.25	.15
3	Ken Ryan (R)	.40	.25
4	Derek Wallace (R)	.50	.30
5	Jorge Fabregas	.25	.15
6	Joe Oliver	.15	.10
7	Brandon Wilson	.45	.28
8	Mark Thompson (R)	.60	.35
9	Tracy Sanders	.15	.10
10	Rich Renteria	.15	.10
11	Lou Whitaker	.20	.12
12	Brian Hunter (R)	.40	.25
13	Joe Vitiello	.70	.40
14	Eric Karros	.60	.35
15	Joe Kmak	.15	.10
16	Tavo Alvarez	.20	.12
17	Steve Dunn (R)	.40	.25
18	Tony Fernandez	.15	.10
19	Melido Perez	.15	.10
20	Mike Lieberthal	.25	.15
21	Terry Steinbach	.15	.10

22	Stan Belinda	.15	.10
23	Jay Buhner	.20	.12
24	Allen Watson	1.50	.90
25	Daryl Henderson (R)	.25	.15
26	Ray McDavid (R)	.80	.50
27	Shawn Green	.80	.50
28	Bud Black	.15	.10
29	Sherman Obando (R)	.40	.25
30	Mike Hostetler (R)	.25	.15
31	Nate Minchey (R)	.75	.45
32	Randy Myers	.15	.10
33	Brian Grebeck (R)	.30	.18
34	John Roper	.20	.12
35	Larry Thomas	.25	.15
36	Alex Cole	.15	.10
37	Tom Kramer (R)	.50	.30
38	Matt Whisenant (R)	.25	.15
39	Chris Gomez (R)	.35	.20
40	Luis Gonzalez	.20	.12
41	Kevin Appier	.30	.18
42	Omar Daal (R)	.35	.20
43	Duane Singleton	.20	.12
44	Bill Risley	.20	.12
45	Pat Meares (R)	.30	.18
46	Butch Huskey	.80	.50
47	Bobby Munoz	.20	.12
48	Juan Bell	.15	.10
49	Scott Lydy (R)	.40	.25
50	Dennis Moeller	.20	.12
51	Marc Newfield	1.00	.70
52	Tripp Cromer (R)	.25	.15
53	Kurt Miller	.25	.15
54	Jim Pena	.15	.10
55	Juan Guzman	.60	.35
56	Matt Williams	.25	.15
57	Harold Reynolds	.15	.10
58	Donnie Elliott (R)	.40	.25
59	Jon Shave (R)	.25	.15
60	Kevin Roberson (R)	.80	.50
61	Hilly Hathaway (R)	.50	.30
62	Jose Rijo	.20	.12
63	Kerry Taylor (R)	.35	.20
64	Ryan Hawblitzel	.20	.12
65	Glenallen Hill	.20	.12
66	Ramon D. Martinez (R)	.25	.15
67	Travis Fryman	1.00	.70
68	Tom Nevers	.15	.10
69	Phil Hiatt	.60	.35
70	Tim Wallach	.15	.10
71	B.J. Surhoff	.15	.10
72	Rondell White	1.50	.90
73	Denny Hocking (R)	.25	.15
74	Mike Oquist (R)	.25	.15
75	Paul O'Neill	.20	.12
76	Willie Banks	.15	.10
77	Bob Welch	.15	.10
78	Jose Sandoval (R)	.25	.15
79	Bill Haselman	.15	.10
80	Rheal Cormier	.15	.10
81	Dean Palmer	.50	.30
82	Pat Gomez (R)	.35	.20
83	Steve Karsey	1.25	.75
84	Carl Hanselman (R)	.20	.12
85	T.R. Lewis (R)	.40	.25
86	Chipper Jones	2.00	1.25
87	Scott Hatteberg	.25	.15
88	Greg Hibbard	.15	.10
89	Lance Painter (R)	.30	.18
90	Chad Mottola (R)	3.50	2.00
91	Jason Bere	1.75	1.00
92	Dante Bichette	.15	.10
93	Sandy Alomar	.15	.10
94	Carl Everett	.25	.15
95	Danny Bautista (R)	.40	.25
96	Steve Finley	.15	.10
97	David Cone	.20	.12
98	Todd Hollandsworth	.50	.30
99	Matt Mieske	.20	.12
100	Larry Walker	.40	.25
101	Shane Mack	.15	.10
102	Aaron Ledesma (R)	.40	.25
103	Andy Pettitte (R)	.70	.40
104	Kevin Stocker	2.50	1.50
105	Mike Mohler (R)	.20	.12
106	Tony Menendez (R)	.15	.10
107	Derek Lowe	.20	.12
108	Basil Shabazz (R)	.40	.25
109	Dan Smith	.20	.12
110	Scott Sanders (R)	.30	.18
111	Todd Stottlemyre	.15	.10
112	Benji Simonton (R)	.60	.35
113	Rick Sutcliffe	.15	.10
114	Lee Heath (R)	.30	.18
115	Jeff Russell	.15	.10
116	Dave Stevens (R)	.25	.15
117	Mark Holzemer (R)	.25	.15
118	Tim Belcher	.15	.10
119	Bobby Thigpen	.15	.10
120	Roger Bailey (R)	.25	.15
121	Tony Mitchell (R)	.25	.15
122	Junior Felix	.15	.10
123	Rich Robertson (R)	.25	.15
124	Andy Cook (R)	.25	.15
125	Brian Bevil (R)	.35	.20
126	Darryl Strawberry	.25	.15
127	Cal Eldred	.50	.30
128	Cliff Floyd	8.00	5.00
129	Alan Newman	.15	.10
130	Howard Johnson	.15	.10
131	Jim Abbott	.30	.18
132	Chad McConnell	.40	.25
133	Miguel Jimenez (R)	.75	.45
134	Brett Backlund (R)	.80	.50
135	John Cummings (R)	.50	.30

136	Brian Barber	.75	.45	193	Doug Dascenzo	.15	.10
137	Rafael Palmeiro	.25	.15	194	Ray Holbert (R)	.30	.18
138	Tim Worrell (R)	.35	.20	195	Howard Battle	.20	.12
139	Jose Pett (R)	1.50	.90	196	Willie McGee	.15	.10
140	Barry Bonds	1.75	1.00	197	John O'Donoghue (R)	.35	.20
141	Damon Buford	.20	.12	198	Steve Avery	.75	.45
142	Jeff Blauser	.15	.10	199	Greg Blosser	.50	.30
143	Frank Rodriguez	.75	.45	200	Ryne Sandberg	1.00	.70
144	Mike Morgan	.15	.10	201	Joe Grahe	.15	.10
145	Gary DiSarcina	.15	.10	202	Dan Wilson	.20	.12
146	Calvin Reese	.20	.12	203	Domingo Martinez (R)	.30	.18
147	Johnny Ruffin	.20	.12	204	Andres Galarraga	.20	.12
148	David Nied	1.75	1.00	205	Jamie Taylor (R)	.25	.15
149	Charles Nagy	.25	.15	206	Darrell Whitmore (R)	1.50	.90
150	Mike Myers (R)	.30	.18	207	Ben Blomdahl (R)	.25	.15
151	Kenny Carlyle (R)	.30	.18	208	Doug Drabek	.20	.12
152	Eric Anthony	.20	.12	209	Keith Miller	.15	.10
153	Jose Lind	.15	.10	210	Billy Ashley	1.25	.75
154	Pedro Martinez	.25	.15	211	Mike Farrell (R)	.25	.15
155	Mark Kiefer	.15	.10	212	John Wetteland	.15	.10
156	Tim Laker (R)	.30	.18	213	Randy Tomlin	.15	.10
157	Pat Mahomes	.20	.12	214	Sid Fernandez	.15	.10
158	Bobby Bonilla	.20	.12	215	Quilvio Veras (R)	.75	.45
159	Domingo Jean	.90	.60	216	Dave Hollins	.35	.20
160	Darren Daulton	.30	.18	217	Mike Neill	.40	.25
161	Mark McGwire	.35	.20	218	Andy Van Slyke	.25	.15
162	Jason Kendall (R)	1.00	.70	219	Bret Boone	.50	.30
163	Desi Relaford	.25	.15	220	Tom Pagnozzi	.15	.10
164	Ozzie Canseco	.15	.10	221	Mike Welch (R)	.30	.18
165	Rick Helling	.75	.45	222	Frank Seminara	.15	.10
166	Steve Pegues (R)	.30	.18	223	Ron Villone	.50	.30
167	Paul Molitor	.25	.15	224	D.J. Thielen (R)	.50	.30
168	Larry Carter (R)	.25	.15	225	Cal Ripken	1.25	.75
169	Arthur Rhodes	.20	.12	226	Pedro Borbon (R)	.40	.25
170	Damon Hollins (R)	.25	.15	227	Carlos Quintana	.15	.10
171	Frank Viola	.15	.10	228	Tommy Shields (R)	.25	.15
172	Steve Trachsel (R)	.40	.25	229	Tim Salmon	5.00	3.00
173	J.T. Snow (R)	3.50	2.00	230	John Smiley	.15	.10
174	Keith Gordon (R)	.25	.15	231	Ellis Burks	.15	.10
175	Carlton Fisk	.20	.12	232	Pedro Castellano	.15	.10
176	Jason Bates (R)	.25	.15	233	Paul Byrd	.15	.10
177	Mike Crosby (R)	.20	.12	234	Bryan Harvey	.20	.12
178	Benito Santiago	.15	.10	235	Scott Livingstone	.15	.10
179	Mike Moore	.15	.10	236	James Mouton (R)	1.00	.70
180	Jeff Juden	.20	.12	237	Joe Randa	.20	.12
181	Darren Burton	.20	.12	238	Pedro Astacio	.40	.25
182	Todd Williams (R)	.25	.15	239	Darryl Hamilton	.25	.15
183	John Jaha	.20	.12	240	Joey Eischen (R)	.50	.30
184	Mike Lansing (R)	.75	.45	241	Edgar Herrera (R)	.35	.20
185	Pedro Grifol (R)	.25	.15	242	Doc Gooden	.20	.12
186	Vince Coleman	.15	.10	243	Sam Militello	.20	.12
187	Pat Kelly	.15	.10	244	Ron Blazier (R)	.25	.15
188	Clemente Alvarez (R)	.25	.15	245	Ruben Sierra	.35	.20
189	Ron Darling	.15	.10	246	Al Martin	.30	.18
190	Orlando Merced	.20	.12	247	Mike Felder	.15	.10
191	Chris Bosio	.15	.10	248	Bob Tewksbury	.15	.10
192	Steve Dixon (R)	.25	.15	249	Craig Lefferts	.15	.10

250	Luis Lopez	.25	.15
251	Devon White	.15	.10
252	Will Clark	.75	.45
253	Mark Smith	.50	.30
254	Terry Pendleton	.25	.15
255	Aaron Sele	4.50	2.75
256	Jose Viera (R)	.25	.15
257	Damion Easley	.20	.12
258	Rod Lofton (R)	.30	.18
259	Chris Snopek (R)	.50	.30
260	Quinton McCracken (R)	.30	.18
261	Mike Matthews (R)	.35	.20
262	Hector Carrasco (R)	.25	.15
263	Rick Greene	.20	.12
264	Chris Holt (R)	.30	.18
265	George Brett	.70	.40
266	Rick Gorecki (R)	.40	.25
267	Francisco Gamez (R)	.20	.12
268	Marquis Grissom	.30	.18
269	Kevin Tapani	.15	.10
270	Ryan Thompson	.30	.18
271	Gerald Williams	.20	.12
272	Paul Fletcher (R)	.20	.12
273	Lance Blankenship	.15	.10
274	Marty Neff (R)	.30	.18
275	Shawn Estes	.50	.30
276	Rene Arocha (R)	1.00	.70
277	Scott Eyre (R)	.50	.30
278	Phil Plantier	.40	.25
279	Paul Spoljaric (R)	1.00	.70
280	Chris Gambs	.20	.12
281	Harold Baines	.15	.10
282	Jose Oliva	.20	.12
283	Matt Whiteside (R)	.40	.25
284	Brant Brown (R)	.60	.35
285	Russ Springer	.20	.12
286	Chris Sabo	.15	.10
287	Ozzie Guillen	.15	.10
288	Marcus Moore (R)	.40	.25
289	Chad Ogea	.60	.35
290	Walt Weiss	.15	.10
291	Brian Edmondson	.20	.12
292	Jimmy Gonzalez	.20	.12
293	Danny Miceli (R)	.50	.30
294	Jose Offerman	.20	.12
295	Greg Vaughn	.25	.15
296	Frank Bolick	.15	.10
297	Mike Maksudian (R)	.25	.15
298	John Franco	.15	.10
299	Danny Tartabull	.20	.12
300	Len Dykstra	.30	.18
301	Bobby Witt	.15	.10
302	Trey Beamon (R)	1.00	.70
303	Tino Martinez	.20	.12
304	Aaron Holbert	.20	.12
305	Juan Gonzalez	5.00	3.00
306	Billy Hall (R)	.25	.15
307	Duane Ward	.15	.10
308	Rod Beck	.35	.20
309	Jose Mercedes (R)	.20	.12
310	Otis Nixon	.15	.10
311	Gettys Glaze (R)	.35	.20
312	Candy Maldonado	.15	.10
313	Chad Curtis	.40	.25
314	Tim Costo	.25	.15
315	Mike Robertson	.20	.12
316	Nigel Wilson	2.50	1.50
317	Greg McMichael (R)	1.00	.70
318	Scott Posey (R)	.35	.20
319	Ivan Cruz	.20	.12
320	Greg Swindell	.15	.10
321	Kevin McReynolds	.15	.10
322	Tom Candiotti	.15	.10
323	Rob Wishnevski (R)	.20	.12
324	Ken Hill	.20	.12
325	Kirby Puckett	1.50	.90
326	Tim Bogar (R)	.40	.25
327	Mariano Rivera	.20	.12
328	Mitch Williams	.15	.10
329	Craig Paquette	.20	.12
330	Jay Bell	.15	.10
331	Jose Martinez (R)	.60	.35
332	Rob Deer	.15	.10
333	Brook Fordyce	.25	.15
334	Matt Nokes	.15	.10
335	Derek Lee	.25	.15
336	Paul Ellis (R)	.25	.15
337	Desi Wilson (R)	.25	.15
338	Roberto Alomar	1.25	.75
339	Jim Tatum (R)(Foil)	.40	.25
340	J.T. Snow (Foil)	3.50	2.00
341	Tim Salmon (Foil)	8.00	5.00
342	Russ Davis (R)(Foil)	1.25	.75
343	Javy Lopez (Foil)	3.00	1.75
344	Troy O'Leary (R)(Foil)	.60	.35
345	Marty Cordova (R)(Foil)	.75	.45
346	Bubba Smith (R)(Foil)	.40	.25
347	Chipper Jones (Foil)	3.00	1.75
348	Jessie Hollins (Foil)	.30	.18
349	Willie Greene (Foil)	.50	.30
350	Mark Thompson (Foil)	.60	.35
351	Nigel Wilson (Foil)	3.50	2.00
352	Todd Jones (Foil)	.25	.15
353	Raul Mondesi (Foil)	.80	.50
354	Cliff Floyd (Foil)	10.00	6.50
355	Bobby Jones (Foil)	1.00	.70
356	Kevin Stocker (Foil)	3.50	2.00
357	Midre Cummings (Foil)	1.75	1.00
358	Allen Watson (Foil)	2.50	1.50
359	Ray McDavid (Foil)	1.00	.70
360	Steve Hosey (Foil)	.60	.35
361	Brad Pennington (Foil)	.25	.15
362	Frank Rodriguez (Foil)	1.00	.70
363	Troy Percival (Foil)	.30	.18

364	Jason Bere (Foil)	3.00	1.75
365	Manny Ramirez (Foil)	4.00	2.75
366	Justin Thompson (Foil)	.30	.18
367	Joe Vitiello (Foil)	1.25	.75
368	Tyrone Hill (Foil)	.60	.35
369	David McCarty (Foil)	2.50	1.50
070	Drion Taylor (Foil)	1.00	0.76
371	Todd Van Poppel (Foil)	1.00	.70
372	Marc Newfield (Foil)	1.25	.75
373	Terrell Lowery (R)(Foil)	.75	.45
374	Alex Gonzalez (Foil)	.75	.45
375	Ken Griffey Jr.	6.00	3.75
376	Donovan Osborne	.35	.20
377	Ritchie Moody (R)	.30	.18
378	Shane Andrews	.35	.20
379	Carlos Delgado	3.00	1.75
380	Bill Swift	.25	.15
381	Leo Gomez	.15	.10
382	Ron Gant	.25	.15
383	Scott Fletcher	.15	.10
384	Matt Walbeck (R)	.35	.20
385	Chuck Finley	.15	.10
386	Kevin Mitchell	.20	.12
387	Wilson Alvarez	.20	.12
388	John Burke (R)	.75	.45
389	Alan Embree	.20	.12
390	Trevor Hoffman	.25	.15
391	Alan Trammell	.20	.12
392	Todd Jones	.20	.12
393	Felix Jose	.15	.10
394	Orel Hershiser	.20	.12
395	Pat Listach	.30	.18
396	Gabe White	.50	.30
397	Dan Serafini (R)	.60	.35
398	Todd Hundley	.15	.10
399	Wade Boggs	.40	.25
400	Tyler Green	.20	.12
401	Mike Bordick	.15	.10
402	Scott Bullett	.25	.15
403	LaGrande Russell (R)	.25	.15
404	Ray Lankford	.30	.18
405	Nolan Ryan	3.50	2.00
406	Robbie Beckett	.25	.15
407	Brent Bowers (R)	.35	.20
408	Adell Davenport (R)	.40	.25
409	Brady Anderson	.15	.10
410	Tom Glavine	.50	.30
411	Doug Hecker (R)	.30	.18
412	Jose Guzman	.15	.10
413	Luis Polonia	.15	.10
414	Brian Williams	.20	.12
415	Bo Jackson	.30	.18
416	Eric Young	.30	.18
417	Kenny Lofton	.60	.35
418	Orestes Destrade	.15	.10
419	Tony Phillips	.15	.10
420	Jeff Bagwell	.75	.45
421	Mark Gardner	.15	.10
422	Brett Butler	.15	.10
423	Graeme Lloyd (R)	.30	.18
424	Delino DeShields	.25	.15
425	Scott Erickson	.20	.12
426	Jeff Kent	.20	.12
427	Jimmy Key	.15	.10
428	Mickey Morandini	.20	.12
429	Marcos Armas (R)	.75	.45
430	Don Slaught	.15	.10
431	Randy Johnson	.25	.15
432	Omar Olivares	.15	.10
433	Charlie Leibrandt	.15	.10
434	Kurt Stillwell	.15	.10
435	Scott Brow (R)	.30	.18
436	Robby Thompson	.15	.10
437	Ben McDonald	.25	.15
438	Deion Sanders	.40	.25
439	Tony Pena	.15	.10
440	Mark Grace	.35	.20
441	Eduardo Perez	2.50	1.50
442	Tim Pugh (R)	.40	.25
443	Scott Ruffcorn	.80	.50
444	Jay Gainer (R)	.40	.25
445	Albert Belle	1.25	.75
446	Bret Barberie	.15	.10
447	Justin Mashore	.25	.15
448	Pete Harnisch	.15	.10
449	Greg Gagne	.15	.10
450	Eric Davis	.20	.12
451	Dave Mlicki	.15	.10
452	Moises Alou	.30	.18
453	Rick Aguilera	.15	.10
454	Eddie Murray	.20	.12
455	Bob Wickman	.40	.25
456	Wes Chamberlain	.20	.12
457	Brent Gates	1.25	.75
458	Paul Wagner	.20	.12
459	Mike Hampton	.20	.12
460	Ozzie Smith	.40	.25
461	Tom Henke	.15	.10
462	Ricky Gutierrez	.20	.12
463	Jack Morris	.20	.12
464	Joel Chimelis (R)	.25	.15
465	Gregg Olson	.15	.10
466	Javy Lopez	1.75	1.00
467	Scott Cooper	.20	.12
468	Willie Wilson	.15	.10
469	Mark Langston	.20	.12
470	Barry Larkin	.35	.20
471	Rod Bolton	.15	.10
472	Freddie Benavides	.15	.10
473	Ken Ramos (R)	.20	.12
474	Chuck Carr	.25	.15
475	Cecil Fielder	.60	.35
476	Eddie Taubensee	.15	.10
477	Chris Eddy (R)	.25	.15

478 Greg Hansell	.15	.10
479 Kevin Reimer	.15	.10
480 Denny Martinez	.20	.12
481 Chuck Knoblauch	.25	.15
482 Mike Draper	.15	.10
483 Spike Owen	.15	.10
484 Terry Mulholland	.15	.10
485 Dennis Eckersley	.25	.15
486 Blas Minor	.15	.10
487 Dave Fleming	.40	.25
488 Dan Cholowsky	.25	.15
489 Ivan Rodriguez	.60	.35
490 Gary Sheffield	.60	.35
491 Ed Sprague	.15	.10
492 Steve Hosey	.40	.25
493 Jimmy Haynes (R)	.40	.25
494 John Smoltz	.25	.15
495 Andre Dawson	.30	.18
496 Rey Sanchez	.15	.10
497 Ty Van Burkleo (R)	.20	.18
498 Bobby Ayala (R)	.35	.20
499 Tim Raines	.20	.12
500 Charlie Hayes	.15	.10
501 Paul Sorrento	.15	.10
502 Richie Lewis (R)	.30	.18
503 Jason Pfaff (R)	.20	.12
504 Ken Caminiti	.15	.10
505 Mike MacFarlane	.15	.10
506 Jody Reed	.15	.10
507 Bobby Hughes (R)	.30	.18
508 Wil Cordero	.40	.25
509 George Tsamis (R)	.25	.15
510 Bret Saberhagen	.15	.10
511 Derek Jeter (R)	2.50	1.50
512 Gene Schall	.60	.35
513 Curtis Shaw	.15	.10
514 Steve Cooke	.40	.25
515 Edgar Martinez	.20	.12
516 Mike Milchin	.25	.15
517 Billy Ripken	.15	.10
518 Andy Benes	.25	.15
519 Juan de la Rosa (R)	.30	.18
520 John Burkett	.15	.10
521 Alex Ochoa	.30	.18
522 Tony Tarasco (R)	1.50	.90
523 Luis Ortiz	.30	.18
524 Rick Wilkins	.15	.10
525 Chris Turner (R)	.25	.15
526 Rob Dibble	.15	.10
527 Jack McDowell	.75	.45
528 Daryl Boston	.15	.10
529 Bill Wertz (R)	.25	.15
530 Charlie Hough	.15	.10
531 Sean Bergman	.20	.12
532 Doug Jones	.15	.10
533 Jeff Montgomery	.15	.10
534 Roger Cedeno (R)	.80	.50

535 Robin Yount	.60	.35
536 Mo Vaughn	.50	.30
537 Brian Harper	.15	.10
538 Juan Castillo	.15	.10
539 Steve Farr	.15	.10
540 John Kruk	.20	.12
541 Troy Neel	.60	.35
542 Danny Clyburn (R)	.60	.35
543 Jim Converse (R)	.40	.25
544 Gregg Jefferies	.30	.18
545 Jose Canseco	.40	.25
546 Julio Bruno (R)	.25	.15
547 Rob Butler	.20	.12
548 Royce Clayton	.30	.18
549 Chris Hoiles	.20	.12
550 Greg Maddux	.50	.30
551 Joe Ciccarella (R)	.25	.15
552 Ozzie Timmons	.30	.18
553 Chili Davis	.15	.10
554 Brian Koelling	.20	.12
555 Frank Thomas	7.50	4.50
556 Vinny Castilla	.15	.10
557 Reggie Jefferson	.20	.12
558 Rob Natal	.20	.12
559 Mike Henneman	.15	.10
560 Craig Biggio	.15	.10
561 Billy Brewer (R)	.25	.15
562 Dan Melendez	.30	.18
563 Kenny Felder (R)	.80	.50
564 Miguel Batista (R)	.40	.25
565 Dave Winfield	.60	.35
566 Al Shirley	.30	.18
567 Robert Eenhoorn	.20	.12
568 Mike Williams	.15	.10
569 Tanyon Sturtze (R)	.40	.25
570 Tim Wakefield	.20	.12
571 Greg Pirkl	.20	.12
572 Sean Lowe (R)	.60	.35
573 Terry Burrows (R)	.25	.15
574 Kevin Higgins (R)	.25	.15
575 Joe Carter	.60	.35
576 Kevin Rogers	.15	.10
577 Manny Alexander	.15	.10
578 David Justice	1.25	.75
579 Brian Conroy (R)	.25	.15
580 Jessie Hollins	.20	.12
581 Ron Watson (R)	.25	.15
582 Bip Roberts	.15	.10
583 Tom Urbani (R)	.25	.15
584 Jason Hutchins (R)	.25	.15
585 Carlos Baerga	1.25	.75
586 Jeff Mutis	.15	.10
587 Justin Thompson	.20	.12
588 Orlando Miller	.20	.12
589 Brian McRae	.20	.12
590 Ramon Martinez	.20	.12
591 Dave Nilsson	.20	.12

592	Jose Vidro (R)	.30	.18
593	Rich Becker	.20	.12
594	Preston Wilson (R)	1.75	1.00
595	Don Mattingly	.50	.30
596	Tony Longmire	.15	.10
597	Kevin Seitzer	.15	.10
598	Midre Cummings (R)	1.25	.75
599	Omar Vizquel	.15	.10
600	Lee Smith	.20	.12
601	David Hulse (R)	.50	.30
602	Darrell Sherman (R)	.50	.30
603	Alex Gonzalez	.60	.35
604	Geronimo Pena	.15	.10
605	Mike Devereaux	.15	.10
606	Sterling Hitchcock (R)	1.25	.75
607	Mike Greenwell	.20	.12
608	Steve Buechele	.15	.10
609	Troy Percival	.20	.12
610	Bobby Kelly	.20	.12
611	James Baldwin (R)	.75	.45
612	Jerald Clark	.15	.10
613	Albie Lopez (R)	.40	.25
614	Dave Magadan	.15	.10
615	Mickey Tettleton	.20	.12
616	Sean Runyan (R)	.25	.15
617	Bob Hamelin	.25	.15
618	Raul Mondesi	.40	.25
619	Tyrone Hill	.25	.15
620	Darren Fletcher	.15	.10
621	Mike Trombley	.15	.10
622	Jeromy Burnitz	.60	.35
623	Bernie Williams	.25	.15
624	Mike Farmer (R)	.20	.12
625	Rickey Henderson	.35	.20
626	Carlos Garcia	.25	.15
627	Jeff Darwin (R)	.35	.20
628	Todd Zeile	.15	.10
629	Benji Gil	.60	.35
630	Tony Gwynn	.40	.25
631	Aaron Small (R)	.30	.18
632	Joe Rosselli (R)	.25	.15
633	Mike Mussina	1.25	.75
634	Ryan Klesko	1.50	.90
635	Roger Clemens	1.25	.75
636	Sammy Sosa	.20	.12
637	Orlando Palmeiro (R)	.25	.15
638	Willie Greene	.20	.12
639	George Bell	.15	.10
640	Garvin Alston (R)	.25	.15
641	Pete Janicki (R)	.60	.35
642	Chris Sheff (R)	.25	.15
643	Felipe Lira (R)	.30	.18
644	Roberto Petagine	.60	.35
645	Wally Joyner	.20	.12
646	Mike Piazza	10.00	6.50
647	Jaime Navarro	.15	.10
648	Jeff Hartsock (R)	.20	.12
649	David McCarty	1.25	.75
650	Bobby Jones	.75	.45
651	Mark Hutton	.20	.12
652	Kyle Abbott	.15	.10
653	Steve Cox (R)	.30	.18
654	Jeff King	.15	.10
655	Norm Charlton	.15	.10
656	Mike Gulan (R)	.30	.18
657	Julio Franco	.15	.10
658	Cameron Cairncross (R)	.40	.25
659	John Olerud	1.50	.90
660	Salomon Torres	1.25	.75
661	Brad Pennington	.20	.12
662	Melvin Nieves	1.25	.75
663	Ivan Calderon	.15	.10
664	Turk Wendell	.20	.12
665	Chris Pritchett	.20	.12
666	Reggie Sanders	.35	.20
667	Robin Ventura	.60	.35
668	Joe Girardi	.15	.10
669	Manny Ramirez	4.00	2.75
670	Jeff Conine	.20	.12
671	Greg Gohr	.20	.12
672	Andujar Cedeno	.20	.12
673	Les Norman (R)	.40	.25
674	Mike James (R)	.25	.15
675	Marshall Boze (R)	.80	.50
676	B.J. Wallace	1.00	.70
677	Kent Hrbek	.15	.10
678	Jack Voight (R)	.30	.18
679	Brien Taylor	2.75	1.60
680	Curt Schilling	.20	.12
681	Todd Van Poppel	.60	.35
682	Kevin Young	.50	.30
683	Tommy Adams	.20	.12
684	Bernard Gilkey	.15	.10
685	Kevin Brown	.15	.10
686	Fred McGriff	.80	.50
687	Pat Borders	.15	.10
688	Kirt Manwaring	.15	.10
689	Sid Bream	.15	.10
690	John Valentin	.20	.12
691	Steve Olsen (R)	.25	.15
692	Roberto Mejia (R)	1.00	.70
693	Carlos Delgado (Foil)	4.50	2.75
694	Steve Gibralter (R)(Foil)	.75	.45
695	Gary Mota (R)(Foil)	.50	.30
696	Jose Malave (R)(Foil)	.60	.35
697	Larry Sutton (R)(Foil)	.50	.30
698	Dan Frye (R)(Foil)	.50	.30
699	Tim Clark (R)(Foil)	.80	.50
700	Brian Rupp (R)(Foil)	.75	.45
701	Felipe/Moises Alou (Foil)	.50	.30
702	Barry/Bobby Bonds(Foil)	1.00	.70
703	Ken Griffey Jr/Sr(Foil)	1.75	1.00
704	Hal/Brian McRae (Foil)	.40	.25
705	Checklist	.15	.10

		MINT	NR/MT
706	Checklist	.15	.10
707	Checklist	.15	.10
708	Checklist	.15	.10

CLASSIC

1987 Classic

This inaugural set was part of a baseball trivia board game produced by GameTime Ltd of Marietta, Georgia. The 100-card set features full-color player photos framed by green borders on the front with career statistics and trivia questions of the card backs. Cards measured 2-1/2" by 3-1/2".

		MINT	NR/MT
Complete Set (100)		200.00	120.00
Commons		.15	.10
1	Pete Rose	3.00	1.75
2	Len Dykstra	2.50	1.50
3	Darryl Strawberry	2.00	1.25
4	Keith Hernandez	.35	.20
5	Gary Carter	.50	.35
6	Wally Joyner	1.00	.70
7	Andres Thomas	.15	.10
8	Pat Dobson	.15	.10
9	Kirk Gibson	.35	.20
10	Don Mattingly	4.50	2.75
11	Dave Winfield	1.25	.80
12	Rickey Henderson	7.50	4.50
13	Dan Pasqua	.15	.10
14	Don Baylor	.20	.12
15	Bo Jackson	28.00	16.00
16	Pete Incaviglia	.25	.15
17	Kevin Bass	.15	.10
18	Barry Larkin	5.00	3.00
19	Dave Magadan	.35	.20
20	Steve Sax	.25	.15
21	Eric Davis	1.00	.80
22	Mike Pagliarulo	.15	.10
23	Fred Lynn	.25	.15
24	Reggie Jackson	4.00	2.50
25	Lance Parrish	.15	.10
26	Tony Gwynn	5.00	3.00
27	Steve Garvey	.75	.45
28	Glenn Davis	.15	.10
29	Tim Raines	.35	.20
30	Vince Coleman	.15	.10
31	Willie McGee	.25	.15
32	Ozzie Smith	1.25	.80
33	Dave Parker	.25	.15
34	Tony Pena	.15	.10
35	Ryne Sandberg	7.50	4.50
36	Brett Butler	.15	.10
37	Dale Murphy	.60	.35
38	Bob Horner	.15	.10
39	Pedro Guerrero	.20	.12
40	Brook Jacoby	.15	.10
41	Carlton Fisk	2.50	1.50
42	Harold Baines	.25	.15
43	Rob Deer	.15	.10
44	Robin Yount	7.00	4.00
45	Paul Molitor	1.00	.70
46	Jose Canseco	30.00	18.00
47	George Brett	7.00	4.00
48	Jim Presley	.15	.10
49	Rich Gedman	.15	.10
50	Lance Parrish	.20	.12
51	Eddie Murray	2.00	1.25
52	Cal Ripken Jr.	20.00	12.50
53	Kent Hrbek	.30	.18
54	Gary Gaetti	.20	.12
55	Kirby Puckett	12.00	7.50
56	George Bell	.50	.30
57	Tony Fernandez	.20	.12
58	Jesse Barfield	.15	.10
59	Jim Rice	.50	.30
60	Wade Boggs	3.50	2.00
61	Marty Barrett	.15	.10
62	Mike Schmidt	6.00	3.50
63	Von Hayes	.20	.12
64	Jeffrey Leonard	.15	.10
65	Chris Brown	.15	.10
66	Dave Smith	.15	.10
67	Mike Krukow	.15	.10
68	Ron Guidry	.30	.18
69	Rob Woodward	.15	.10
70	Rob Murphy	.15	.10
71	Andres Galarraga	.75	.45
72	Dwight Gooden	1.50	.90
73	Bob Ojeda	.15	.10
74	Sid Fernandez	.20	.12

75	Jesse Orosco	.15	.10
76	Roger McDowell	.15	.10
77	John Tudor (Er)	.15	.10
78	Tom Browning	.20	.12
79	Rick Aguilera	.15	.10
80	Lance McCullers	.15	.10
81	Mike Scott	.25	.15
82	Nolan Ryan	18.00	10.00
83	Bruce Hurst	.20	.12
84	Roger Clemens	10.00	6.50
85	Dennis "Oil Can" Boyd	.15	.10
86	Dave Righetti	.15	.10
87	Dennis Rasmussen	.15	.10
88	Bret Saberhagen (Er)	.30	.18
89	Mark Langston	.35	.20
90	Jack Morris	.40	.25
91	Fernando Valenzuela	.30	.18
92	Orel Hershiser	.35	.20
93	Rick Honeycutt	.15	.10
94	Jeff Reardon	.25	.15
95	John Habyan	.15	.10
96	Rich "Goose" Gossage	.20	.12
97	Todd Worrell	.20	.12
98	Floyd Youmans	.15	.10
99	Don Aase	.15	.10
100	John Franco	.15	.10

101	Mike Schmidt	2.75	1.50
102	Eric Davis	1.00	.70
103	Pete Rose	1.25	.80
104	Don Mattingly	1.75	1.00
105	Wade Boggs	1.50	.90
106	Dale Murphy	.50	.30
107	Glenn Davis	.10	.06
108	Wally Joyner	1.00	.70
109	Bo Jackson	1.75	1.00
110	Cory Snyder	.25	.15
111	Jim Lindeman	.10	.06
112	Kirby Puckett	3.50	2.00
113	Barry Bonds	8.50	5.00
114	Roger Clemens	4.50	2.75
115	Oddibe McDowell	.10	.06
116	Bret Saberhagen	.30	.18
117	Joe Magrane	.25	.15
118	Scott Fletcher	.10	.06
119	Mark McLemore	.10	.06
120	Joe Niekro (Who Me?)	.30	.18
121	Mark McGwire	5.00	3.00
122	Darryl Strawberry	.75	.45
123	Mike Scott	.25	.15
124	Andre Dawson	.60	.35
125	Jose Canseco	3.50	2.00
126	Kevin McReynolds	.25	.15
127	Joe Carter	2.50	1.50
128	Casey Candaele	.10	.06
129	Matt Nokes	.40	.25
130	Kal Daniels	.15	.10
131	Pete Incaviglia	.20	.12
132	Benito Santiago	.80	.50
133	Barry Larkin	1.50	.90
134	Gary Pettis	.10	.06
135	B.J. Surhoff	.25	.15
136	Juan Nieves	.10	.06
137	Jim Deshaies	.12	.07
138	Pete O'Brien	.15	.10
139	Kevin Seitzer	.20	.12
140	Devon White	.30	.25
141	Rob Deer	.10	.06
142	Kurt Stillwell	.15	.10
143	Edwin Correa	.10	.06
144	Dion James	.10	.06
145	Danny Tartabull	.80	.50
146	Jerry Browne	.10	.06
147	Ted Higuera	.25	.15
148	Jack Clark	.25	.15
149	Ruben Sierra	3.50	2.00
150	E. Davis/M. McGwire	1.50	.90

1987 Classic Travel Edition

This 50-card set is an update to the original Classic Baseball Trivia board game. The card fronts feature yellow borders while the backs consist of all new trivia questions. The cards in this set were issued without the game board and measure 2-1/2" by 3-1/2".

	MINT	NR/MT
Complete Set (50)	28.00	18.00
Commons	.10	.06

1988 Classic Travel Edition
Red Series

This 50-card update set is the second extension of Classic's original Baseball Trivia board game. Numbered from 151-200, the card fronts feature red borders while the backs contain all new trivia questions. All cards measure 2-1/2" by 3-1/2".

		MINT	NR/MT
Complete Set (50)		16.50	9.50
Commons		.10	.06
151	D. Mattingly/ M. McGwire	2.50	1.50
152	Don Mattingly	1.25	.80
153	Mark McGwire	2.50	1.50
154	Eric Davis	.80	.50
155	Wade Boggs	1.00	.70
156	Dale Murphy	.50	.30
157	Andre Dawson	.35	.20
158	Roger Clemens	2.50	1.50
159	Kevin Seitzer	.10	.06
160	Benito Santiago	.25	.15
161	Kal Daniels	.15	.10
162	John Kruk	.25	.15
163	Billy Ripkin (Er)	.10	.06
164	Kirby Puckett	2.50	1.50
165	Jose Canseco	2.50	1.50
166	Matt Nokes	.15	.10
167	Mike Schmidt	1.00	.70
168	Tim Raines	.40	.25
169	Ryne Sandberg	1.75	1.00
170	Dave Winfield	.80	.50
171	Dwight Gooden	.75	.45
172	Bret Saberhagen	.25	.15
173	Willie McGee	.20	.12
174	Jack Morris	.25	.15
175	Jeff Leonard	.10	.06
176	Cal Ripkin Jr. (Er)	3.50	2.00
177	Pete Incaviglia	.10	.06
178	Devon White	.15	.10
179	Nolan Ryan	3.00	1.75
180	Ruben Sierra	.80	.50
181	Todd Worrell	.10	.06
182	Glenn Davis	.10	.06
183	Frank Viola	.25	.15
184	Cory Snyder	.10	.06
185	Tracy Jones	.10	.06
186	Terry Steinbach	.20	.12
187	Julio Franco	.25	.15
188	Larry Sheets	.10	.06
189	John Marzano	.10	.06
190	Kevin Elster	.15	.10
191	Vincente Palacios	.12	.07
192	Kent Hrbek	.25	.15
193	Eric Bell	.10	.06
194	Kelly Downs	.15	.10
195	Jose Lind	.25	.15
196	Dave Stewart	.40	.25
197	J. Canseco/ 3.00	1.75	
	M. McGwire (Er) (No card number)		
198	Phil Niekro (Indians)	.40	.25
199	Phil Niekro (Blue Jays)	.40	.25
200	Phil Niekro (Braves)	.40	.25

1988 Classic Travel Edition
Blue Series

This 50-card blue bordered set is an update of the Classic Travel Edition Red Series. The card backs feature new baseball trivia questions and a box for player's autographs. The cards measure 2-1/2" by 3-1/2".

		MINT	NR/MT
Complete Set (50)		15.00	9.00
Commons		.12	.07
201	E. Davis/D. Murphy	.50	.35
202	B.J. Surhoff	.15	.10
203	John Kruk	.40	.25
204	Sam Horn	.20	.12
205	Jack Clark	.25	.15
206	Wally Joyner	.30	.18
207	Matt Nokes	.20	.12
208	Bo Jackson	2.50	1.50
209	Darryl Strawberry	.75	.45
210	Ozzie Smith	.30	.18
211	Don Mattingly	1.00	.70
212	Mark McGwire	2.25	1.40
213	Eric Davis	.30	.18
214	Wade Boggs	1.00	.70
215	Dale Murphy	.25	.15
216	Andre Dawson	.35	.20
217	Roger Clemens	2.00	1.25
218	Kevin Seitzer	.12	.07
219	Benito Santiago	.25	.15
220	Tony Gwynn	1.25	.80
221	Mike Scott	.15	.10
222	Steve Bedrosian	.15	.10
223	Vince Coleman	.20	.12
224	Rick Sutcliffe	.20	.12
225	Will Clark	6.00	3.75
226	Pete Rose	1.50	.90
227	Mike Greenwell	.60	.35
228	Ken Caminiti	.20	.12
229	Ellis Burks	.50	.30
230	Dave Magadan	.15	.10
231	Alan Trammell	.50	.30
232	Paul Molitor	.75	.45
233	Gary Gaetti	.20	.12
234	Rickey Henderson	1.50	.90
235	Danny Tartabull	.75	.45
236	Bobby Bonilla	1.00	.70
237	Mike Dunne	.12	.07
238	Al Leiter	.12	.07
239	John Farrell	.12	.07
240	Joe Magrane	.15	.10
241	Mike Henneman	.15	.10
242	George Bell	.30	.18
243	Gregg Jefferies	1.25	.80
244	Jay Buhner	.35	.20
245	Todd Benzinger	.15	.10
246	Matt Williams	1.75	1.00
247	Mattingly/McGwire (Er)	2.50	1.50
	(No Card Number)		
248	George Brett	.75	.45
249	Jimmy Key	.25	.15
250	Mark Langston	.25	.15

1989 Classic

This 100-card set featured light blue borders and full color player photos on the fronts. The card backs include all new trivia questions. Card sets were packaged with a baseball trivia board game. All cards measure 2-1/2" by 3-1/2".

		MINT	NR/MT
Complete Set (100)		32.00	20.00
Commons		.10	.06
1	Orel Hershiser	.35	.20
2	Wade Boggs	.75	.45
3	Jose Canseco	2.50	1.50
4	Mark McGwire	2.00	1.25
5	Don Mattingly	1.00	.70
6	Gregg Jefferies	1.00	.70
7	Dwight Gooden	.70	.40
8	Darryl Strawberry	.50	.30
9	Eric Davis	.40	.25
10	Joey Meyer	.10	.06
11	Joe Carter	1.25	.80
12	Paul Molitor	.80	.50
13	Mark Grace	1.25	.80
14	Kurt Stillwell	.10	.06
15	Kirby Puckett	2.50	1.50
16	Keith Miller	.10	.06
17	Glenn Davis	.10	.06
18	Will Clark	2.00	1.25
19	Cory Snyder	.12	.07
20	Jose Lind	.10	.06
21	Andres Thomas	.10	.06
22	Dave Smith	.10	.06
23	Mike Scott	.10	.06
24	Kevin McReynolds	.15	.10
25	B.J. Surhoff	.15	.10
26	Mackey Sasser	.10	.06
27	Chad Kreuter	.12	.07
28	Hal Morris	.80	.50
29	Wally Joyner	.20	.12
30	Tony Gwynn	1.00	.70

31	Kevin Mitchell	.60	.35
32	Dave Winfield	.80	.50
33	Billy Bean	.10	.06
34	Steve Bedrosian	.10	.06
35	Ron Gant	1.25	.80
36	Len Dykstra	.60	.35
37	Andre Dawson	.25	.15
38	Brett Butler	.20	.12
39	Rob Deer	.12	.07
40	Tommy John	.15	.10
41	Gary Gaetti	.15	.10
42	Tim Raines	.20	.12
43	George Bell	.25	.15
44	Dwight Evans	.20	.12
45	Dennis Martinez	.12	.07
46	Andres Galarraga	.40	.25
47	George Brett	1.75	1.00
48	Mike Schmidt	2.00	1.25
49	Dave Steib	.25	.15
50	Rickey Henderson	1.50	.90
51	Craig Biggio	.60	.35
52	Mark Lemke	.25	.15
53	Chris Sabo	.60	.35
54	Jeff Treadway	.10	.06
55	Kent Hrbek	.20	.12
56	Cal Ripken Jr.	3.00	1.75
57	Tim Belcher	.25	.15
58	Ozzie Smith	.60	.35
59	Keith Hernandez	.20	.12
60	Pedro Guerrero	.15	.10
61	Greg Swindell	.25	.15
62	Bret Saberhagen	.35	.20
63	John Tudor	.10	.06
64	Gary Carter	.20	.12
65	Kevin Seitzer	.15	.10
66	Jesse Barfield	.15	.10
67	Luis Medina	.10	.06
68	Walt Weiss	.25	.15
69	Terry Steinbach	.30	.18
70	Barry Larkin	.75	.45
71	Pete Rose	1.25	.80
72	Luis Salazar	.12	.07
73	Benito Santiago	.35	.20
74	Kal Daniels	.10	.06
75	Kevin Elster	.10	.06
76	Rob Dibble	.50	.30
77	Bobby Witt	.40	.25
78	Steve Searcy	.15	.10
79	Sandy Alomar Jr.	.80	.50
80	Chili Davis	.25	.15
81	Alvin Davis	.12	.07
82	Charlie Leibrandt	.12	.07
83	Robin Yount	1.75	1.00
84	Mark Carreon	.25	.15
85	Pascual Perez	.10	.06
86	Dennis Rasmussen	.10	.06
87	Ernie Riles	.10	.06

88	Melido Perez	.20	.12
89	Doug Jones	.15	.10
00	Donnie Eokoroloy	.80	.50
91	Bob Welch	.20	.12
92	Bob Milacki	.15	.10
93	Jeff Robinson	.12	.07
94	Mike Henneman	.12	.07
95	Randy Johnson	.80	.50
96	Ron Jones	.12	.07
97	Jack Armstrong	.20	.12
98	Willie McGee	.12	.07
99	Ryne Sandberg	2.50	1.50
100	D. Cone/D. Jackson	.75	.45

1989 Classic Travel Edition
Orange Series

Andy Van Slyke

First update of the 1989 Classic Baseball Trivia board game. This 50-card set featured orange borders and was sold without the game board. Cards measure 2-1/2" by 3-1/2".

		MINT	NR/MT
Complete Set (50)		20.00	12.00
Commons		.10	.06

101	Gary Sheffield	2.75	1.60
102	Wade Boggs	.60	.35
103	Jose Canseco	1.25	.80
104	Mark McGwire	1.00	.70
105	Orel Hershiser	.30	.18
106	Don Mattingly	1.00	.70
107	Dwight Gooden	.60	.35
108	Darryl Strawberry	.40	.25
109	Eric Davis	.30	.18
110	Bam Bam Meulens	.30	.18
111	Andy Van Slyke	.35	.20
112	Al Leiter	.12	.07

113	Matt Nokes	.15	.10
114	Mike Krukow	.10	.06
115	Tony Fernandez	.25	.15
116	Fred McGriff	1.75	1.00
117	Barry Bonds	2.00	1.25
118	Gerald Perry	.10	.06
119	Roger Clemens	1.00	.60
120	Kirk Gibson	.15	.10
121	Greg Maddux	1.50	.90
122	Bo Jackson	1.00	.70
123	Danny Jackson	.15	.10
124	Dale Murphy	.25	.15
125	David Cone	.40	.25
126	Tom Browning	.15	.10
127	Roberto Alomar	7.50	4.50
128	Alan Trammell	.20	.12
129	Rickey Jordan	.15	.10
130	Ramon Martinez	1.00	.70
131	Ken Griffey Jr.	15.00	10.00
132	Gregg Olson	.50	.30
133	Carlos Quintana	.25	.15
134	Dave West	.25	.15
135	Cameron Drew	.10	.06
136	Ted Higuera	.20	.12
137	Sil Campusano	.10	.06
138	Mark Gubicza	.25	.15
139	Mike Boddicker	.10	.06
140	Paul Gibson	.10	.06
141	Jose Rijo	.35	.20
142	John Costello	.10	.06
143	Cecil Espy	.10	.06
144	Frank Viola	.25	.15
145	Erik Hanson	.35	.20
146	Juan Samuel	.10	.06
147	Harold Reynolds	.20	.12
148	Joe Magrane	.12	.07
149	Mike Greenwell	.25	.15
150	W. Clark/D. Strawberry	1.25	.80

1989 Classic
Travel Edition
Purple Series

Bruce Hurst

This purple bordered set is the second update to the 1989 Classic Baseball Trivia board game. Also known as Travel Edition II, the card fronts feature purple borders along with special cards of Bo Jackson and Deion Sanders as two-sport stars. All cards measure 2-1/2" by 3-1/2".

		MINT	NR/MT
Complete Set (50)		14.00	9.00
Commons		.10	.06
151	Jim Abbott	1.00	.70
152	Ellis Burks	.25	.15
153	Mike Schmidt	1.25	.80
154	Gregg Jefferies	.50	.30
155	Mark Grace	.50	.30
156	Jerome Walton	.15	.10
157	Bo Jackson	1.00	.70
158	Jack Clark	.10	.06
159	Tom Glavine	2.00	1.25
160	Eddie Murray	.25	.15
161	John Dopson	.10	.06
162	Ruben Sierra	.70	.40
163	Rafael Palmeiro	.60	.35
164	Nolan Ryan	2.50	1.50
165	Barry Larkin	.50	.30
166	Tommy Herr	.10	.06
167	Roberto Kelly	.80	.50
168	Glenn Davis	.10	.06
169	Glenn Braggs	.10	.06
170	Juan Bell	.25	.15
171	Todd Burns	.10	.06
172	Derek Lilliquist	.10	.06
173	Orel Hershiser	.25	.15
174	John Smoltz	1.50	.90
175	E. Burks/O. Guillen	.30	.18

176	Kirby Puckett	1.00	.70
177	Robin Ventura	1.50	.90
178	Allan Anderson	.10	.06
179	Steve Sax	.15	.10
180	Will Clark	1.00	.70
181	Mike Devereaux	.50	.30
182	Tom Gordon	.35	.20
183	Rob Murphy	.10	.06
184	Pete O'Brien	.10	.06
185	Cris Carpenter	.15	.10
186	Tom Brunansky	.12	.07
187	Bob Boone	.15	.10
188	Lou Whitaker	.10	.06
189	Dwight Gooden	.40	.25
190	Mark McGwire	.80	.50
191	John Smiley	.20	.12
192	Tommy Gregg	.10	.06
193	Ken Griffey Jr.	5.00	3.00
194	Bruce Hurst	.10	.06
195	Greg Swindell	.25	.15
196	Nelson Liriano	.10	.06
197	Randy Myers	.15	.10
198	Kevin Mitchell	.40	.25
199	Dante Bichette	.15	.10
200	Deion Sanders	1.25	.80

1990 Classic Baseball

John Smiley

The 1990 version of the Classic Baseball Trivia Game features 150 new cards with five new trivia questions on the card backs. Border colors are blue with colorful burgandy waves around the frame. All cards measure 2-1/2" by 3-1/2".

Game features 150 new cards with five new trivia.

		MINT	NR/MT
Complete Set (150)		18.00	12.00
Commons		.06	.03

1	Nolan Ryan	2.00	1.25
2	Bo Jackson	.90	.60
3	Gregg Olson	.35	.20
4	Tom Gordon	.40	.25
5	Robin Ventura	.75	.45
6	Will Clark	.75	.45
7	Ruben Sierra	.35	.20
8	Mark Grace	.25	.15
9	Luis de los Santos	.06	.03
10	Bernie Williams	.50	.30
11	Eric Davis	.12	.07
12	Carney Lansford	.10	.06
13	John Smoltz	.20	.12
14	Gary Sheffield	.80	.50
15	Kent Merker	.30	.18
16	Don Mattingly	.50	.30
17	Tony Gwynn	.40	.25
18	Ozzie Smith	.20	.12
19	Fred McGriff	.50	.30
20	Ken Griffey Jr.	2.50	1.50
21a	Prime Time (Deion Sanders)	5.00	3.00
21b	Deion "Prime Time" Sanders	1.75	1.00
22	Jose Canseco	.70	.40
23	Mitch Williams	.15	.10
24	Cal Ripken Jr.	1.50	.90
25	Bob Geren	.10	.06
26	Wade Boggs	.30	.18
27	Ryne Sandberg	.80	.50
28	Kirby Puckett	1.00	.70
29	Mike Scott	.06	.03
30	Dwight Smith	.15	.10
31	Craig Worthington	.06	.03
32	Ricky Jordan	.15	.10
33	Darryl Strawberry	.20	.12
34	Jerome Walton	.08	.05
35	John Olerud	2.50	1.50
36	Tom Glavine	1.00	.70
37	Rickey Henderson	.50	.30
38	Rolando Roomes	.06	.03
39	Mickey Tettleton	.12	.07
40	Jim Abbott	.50	.30
41	Dave Righetti	.06	.03
42	Mike LaValliere	.08	.05
43	Rob Dibble	.35	.20
44	Pete Harnisch	.30	.18
45	Jose Offerman	.80	.50
46	Walt Weiss	.08	.05
47	Mike Greenwell	.25	.15
48	Barry Larkin	.25	.15
49	Dave Gallagher	.06	.03
50	Junior Felix	.20	.12
51	Roger Clemens	.80	.50
52	Lonnie Smith	.06	.03
53	Jerry Browne	.06	.03
54	Greg Briley	.20	.12

55	Delino DeShields	1.00	.70
56	Carmelo Martinez	.06	.03
57	Craig Biggio	.20	.12
58	Dwight Gooden	.20	.12
59a	Bo, Ruben, Mark (Bo Jackson, Ruben Sierra, Mar McGwire)	5.00	3.00
59b	A.L. Fence Busters (Bo Jackson, Ruben Sierra, Mark McGwire)	1.75	1.00
60	Greg Vaughn	.75	.45
61	Roberto Alomar	1.75	1.00
62	Steve Bedrosian	.06	.03
63	Devon White	.06	.03
64	Kevin Mitchell	.30	.18
65	Marquis Grissom	.80	.50
66	Brian Holman	.10	.06
67	Julio Franco	.20	.12
68	Dave West	.08	.05
69	Harold Baines	.12	.07
70	Eric Anthony	.80	.50
71	Glenn Davis	.07	.04
72	Mark Langston	.20	.12
73	Matt Williams	.50	.30
74	Rafael Palmeiro	.35	.20
75	Pete Rose Jr.	.25	.15
76	Ramon Martinez	.50	.30
77	Dwight Evans	.10	.06
78	Mackey Sasser	.06	.03
79	Mike Schooler	.10	.06
80	Dennis Cook	.08	.05
81	Orel Hershiser	.20	.15
82	Barry Bonds	1.25	.80
83	Geronimo Berroa	.06	.03
84	George Bell	.12	.07
85	Andre Dawson	.15	.10
86	John Franco	.10	.06
87a	W. Clark/T. Gwynn	3.00	1.75
87b	N.L. Hit Kings (Will Clark, Tony Gwynn)	.80	.50
88	Glenallen Hill	.30	.18
89	Jeff Ballard	.12	.07
90	Todd Zeile	.80	.50
91	Frank Viola	.20	.12
92	Ozzie Guillen	.12	.07
93	Jeff Leonard	.06	.03
94	Dave Smith	.06	.03
95	Dave Parker	.15	.10
96	Jose Gonzalez	.12	.07
97	Dave Steib	.15	.10
98	Charlie Hayes	.12	.07
99	Jesse Barfield	.08	.05
100	Joey Belle	1.50	.90
101	Jeff Reardon	.12	.07
102	Bruce Hurst	.08	.05
103	Luis Medina	.06	.03
104	Mike Moore	.08	.05
105	Vince Coleman	.10	.06
106	Alan Trammell	.12	.07
107	Randy Myers	.12	.07
108	Frank Tanana	.10	.06
109	Craig Lefferts	.08	.05
110	John Wetteland	.50	.30
111	Chris Gwynn	.10	.06
112	Mark Carreon	.10	.06
113	Von Hayes	.08	.05
114	Doug Jones	.08	.05
115	Andres Galarraga	.35	.20
116	Carlton Fisk	.20	.12
117	Paul O'Neill	.12	.07
118	Tim Raines	.10	.06
119	Tom Brunansky	.10	.06
120	Andy Benes	.50	.30
121	Mark Portugal	.06	.03
122	Willie Randolph	.10	.06
123	Jeff Blauser	.08	.05
124	Don August	.06	.03
125	Chuck Cary	.06	.03
126	John Smiley	.12	.07
127	Terry Mullholland	.10	.06
128	Harold Reynolds	.07	.04
129	Hubie Brooks	.08	.05
130	Ben McDonald	1.00	.70
131	Kevin Ritz	.15	.10
132	Luis Quinones	.06	.03
133	Bam Bam Meulens	.25	.15
134	Bill Spiers	.15	.10
135	Andy Hawkins	.06	.03
136	Alvin Davis	.08	.05
137	Lee Smith	.10	.06
138	Joe Carter	.50	.30
139	Bret Saberhagen	.12	.07
140	Sammy Sosa	.35	.20
141	Matt Nokes	.08	.05
142	Bert Blyleven	.12	.07
143	Bobby Bonilla	.30	.18
144	Howard Johnson	.15	.10
145	Joe Magrane	.06	.03
146	Pedro Guerrero	.08	.05
147	Robin Yount	.60	.35
148	Dan Gladden	.08	.05
149	Steve Sax	.10	.06
150a	W. Clark/K. Mitchell	4.00	2.50
150b	Bay Bombers (W. Clark, K. Mitchell)	.60	.35

1990 Classic II

This 50-card update set features all new trivia questions. Border colors are the reverse of Series I. Card numbers carry the "T" designation on the card backs. All cards measure 2-1/2" by 3-1/2".

		MINT	NR/MT
Complete Set (50)		12.50	7.50
Commons		.06	.03

1	Gregg Jefferies	.30	.18
2	Steve Adkins	.08	.05
3	Sandy Alomar Jr.	.20	.12
4	Steve Avery	2.50	1.50
5	Mike Blowers	.08	.05
6	George Brett	.20	.12
7	Tom Browning	.08	.05
8	Ellis Burks	.10	.06
9	Joe Carter	.25	.15
10	Jerald Clark	.10	.06
11	Hot Corners (W. Clark, M. Williams)	.40	.25
12	Pat Combs	.15	.10
13	Scott Cooper	.40	.25
14	Mark Davis	.06	.03
15	Storm Davis	.06	.03
16	Larry Walker	2.50	1.50
17	Brian DuBois	.08	.05
18	Len Dykstra	.20	.12
19	John Franco	.10	.06
20	Kirk Gibson	.08	.05
21	Juan Gonzalez	6.00	3.75
22	Tommy Greene	.35	.20
23	Kent Hrbek	.10	.06
24	Mike Huff	.40	.25
25	Bo Jackson	.90	.60
26	Nolan Knows Bo Nolan Ryan	3.50	2.00
27	Roberto Kelly	.15	.10
28	Mark Langston	.10	.06
29	Ray Lankford	1.25	.80
30	Kevin Maas	.35	.20

31	Julio Machado	.20	.12
32	Greg Maddux	.50	.30
33	Mark McGwire	.50	.30
34	Paul Molitor	.20	.12
35	Hal Morris	.50	.30
36	Dale Murphy	.10	.06
37	Eddie Murray	.10	.06
38	Jaime Navarro	.15	.10
39	Dean Palmer	.80	.50
40	Derek Parks	.25	.15
41	Bobby Rose	.25	.15
42	Wally Joyner	.08	.05
43	Chris Sabo	.08	.05
44	Benito Santiago	.08	.05
45	Mike Stanton	.08	.05
46	Terry Steinbach	.10	.06
47	Dave Stewart	.10	.06
48	Greg Swindell	.10	.06
49	Jose Vizcaino	.15	.10
50	Royal Flush (M. Davis B. Saberhagen) (No number on card back)	.20	.12

1990 Classic III

Lance Dickson

This 100-card update set is Classic's third 1990 series. Cards feature yellow borders with blue highlights. Cards backs consist of all-new trivia questions to go with Classic's Baseball Trivia board game. Card numbers 51 and 57 were never issued. All cards measure 2-1/2" by 3-1/2".

		MINT	NR/MT
Complete Set (100)		15.00	9.50
Commons		.06	.03

1	Ken Griffey Jr.	2.50	1.50
2	John Tudor	.06	.03
3	John Kruk	.25	.15

4	Mark Gardner	.15	.10
5	Scott Radinsky	.15	.10
6	John Burkett	.20	.12
7	Will Clark	.50	.30
8	Gary Carter	.10	.06
9	Ted Higuera	.09	.05
10	Dave Parker	.10	.06
11	Dante Bichette	.06	.03
12	Don Mattingly	.30	.18
13	Greg Harris	.12	.07
14	Dave Hollins	.80	.50
15	Matt Nokes	.06	.03
16	Kevin Tapani	.12	.07
17	Shane Mack	.25	.15
18	Randy Myers	.10	.06
19	Greg Olson	.12	.07
20	Shawn Abner	.08	.05
21	Jim Presley	.06	.03
22	Randy Johnson	.25	.15
23	Edgar Martinez	.20	.12
24	Scott Coolbaugh	.06	.03
25	Jeff Treadway	.06	.03
26	Joe Klink	.06	.03
27	Rickey Henderson	.35	.20
28	Sam Horn	.08	.05
29	Kurt Stillwell	.06	.03
30	Andy Van Slyke	.12	.07
31	Willie Banks	.35	.20
32	Jose Canseco	.50	.30
33	Felix Jose	.15	.10
34	Candy Maldonado	.06	.03
35	Carlos Baerga	3.50	2.00
36	Keith Hernandez	.06	.03
37	Frank Viola	.08	.05
38	Pete O'Brien	.06	.03
39	Pat Borders	.06	.03
40	Mike Heath	.06	.03
41	Kevin Brown	.20	.12
42	Chris Bosio	.08	.05
43	Shawn Boskie	.15	.10
44	Carlos Quintana	.08	.05
45	Juan Samuel	.06	.03
46	Tim Layana	.12	.07
47	Mike Harkey	.12	.07
48	Gerald Perry	.06	.03
49	Mike Witt	.06	.03
50	Joe Orsulak	.06	.03
51	Never Issued	.00	.00
52	Willie Blair	.08	.05
53	Gene Larkin	.06	.03
54	Jody Reed	.06	.03
55	Jeff Reardon	.08	.05
56	Kevin McReynolds	.06	.03
57	Never Issued	.00	.00
58	Eric Yelding	.08	.05
59	Fred Lynn	.06	.03
60	Jim Leyritz	.10	.06

61	John Orton	.08	.05
62	Mike Leiberthal	.75	.45
63	Mike Hartley	.10	.06
64	Kal Daniels	.06	.03
65	Terry Shumpert	.15	.10
66	Sil Campusano	.06	.03
67	Tony Pena	.06	.03
68	Barry Bonds	1.00	.70
69	Oddibe McDowell	.06	.03
70	Kelly Gruber	.08	.05
71	Willie Randolph	.06	.03
72	Rick Parker	.08	.05
73	Bobby Bonilla	.12	.07
74	Jack Armstrong	.08	.05
75	Hubie Brooks	.08	.05
76	Sandy Alomar Jr.	.10	.06
77	Ruben Sierra	.15	.10
78	Erik Hanson	.08	.05
79	Tony Phillips	.06	.03
80	Rondell White	1.25	.80
81	Bobby Thigpen	.10	.06
82	Ron Walden	.15	.10
83	Don Peters	.20	.2
84	Nolan Ryan's 6th	1.75	1.00
85	Lance Dickson	.35	.20
86	Ryne Sandberg	.40	.25
87	Eric Christopherson	.25	.15
88	Shane Andrews	.20	.12
89	Marc Newfield	1.75	1.00
90	Adam Hyzdu	.40	.25
91	Texas Heat (Nolan and Reid Ryan)	2.50	1.50
92	Chipper Jones	2.00	1.25
93	Frank Thomas	8.50	5.00
94	Cecil Fielder	.50	.30
95	Delino DeShields	.35	.20
96	John Olerud	.75	.45
97	Dave Justice	1.50	.90
98	Joe Oliver	.12	.07
99	Alex Fernandez	.75	.45
100	Todd Hundley	.25	.15
___	Mike Marshall (Game instructions on back. No number)	.06	.03
___	Frank Viola (Micro)	.20	.12
___	Texas Heat (Micro)	.35	.20
___	Chipper Jones (Micro)	.50	.30
___	Don Mattingly (Micro)	.25	.15

1990 Classic Draft Picks

This set is not related to Classic's Baseball Trivia Game. Only 150,000 sets were issued featuring the first round draft picks from 1990. Card fronts consist of players photographed wearing their college or high school uniforms. Card numbers 2 and 22 were never issued. All cards measure 2-1/2" by 3-1/2".

		MINT	NR/MT
	Complete Set (25)	20.00	12.50
	Commons	.20	.12
1	Chipper Jones	4.00	2.75
2	Never Issued	.00	.00
3	Mike Lieberthal	.40	.25
4	Alex Fernandez	2.00	1.25
5	Kurt Miller	.40	.25
6	Marc Newfield	1.50	.90
7	Dan Wilson	.50	.30
8	Tim Costo	.75	.45
9	Ron Walden	.25	.15
10	Carl Everett	.75	.45
11	Shane Andrews	.40	.25
12	Todd Richie	.40	.25
13	Donovan Osborne	1.00	.70
14	Todd Van Poppel	2.00	1.25
15	Adam Hyzdu	.35	.20
16	Dan Smith	.20	.12
17	Jeromy Burnitz	1.75	1.00
18	Aaron Holbert	.20	.12
19	Eric Christopherson	.25	.15
20	Mike Mussina	4.00	2.75
21	Tom Nevers	.20	.12
22	Never Issued	.00	.00
23	Lance Dickson	.25	.15
24	Rondell White	4.00	2.75
25	Robbie Beckett	.25	.15
26	Don Peters	.25	.15

	Checklist (Chipper Jones, Rondell White)	2.00	1.25

1991 Classic

The 1991 Classic set was issued with a game board and included all new baseball trivia questions on the card backs. Border colors are blue with red highlights. All cards measure 2-1/2" by 3-1/2".

		MINT	NR/MT
	Complete Set (100)	11.00	7.00
	Commons	.07	.04
1	John Olerud	.35	.20
2	Tino Martinez	.30	.18
3	Ken Griffey Jr.	1.00	.70
4	Jeromy Burnitz	.90	.60
5	Ron Gant	.30	.18
6	Mike Benjamin	.07	.04
7	Steve Decker	.12	.07
8	Matt Williams	.25	.15
9	Rafael Novoa	.10	.06
10	Kevin Mitchell	.10	.06
11	Dave Justice	.70	.40
12	Leo Gomez	.25	.15
13	Chris Hoiles	.35	.20
14	Ben McDonald	.25	.15
15	David Segui	.15	.10
16	Anthony Telford	.25	.15
17	Mike Mussina	1.75	1.00
18	Roger Clemens	.60	.35
19	Wade Boggs	.30	.18
20	Tim Naehring	.20	.12
21	Joe Carter	.30	.18
22	Phil Plantier	.80	.50
23	Rob Dibble	.20	.12
24	Maurice Vaughn	1.00	.70
25	Lee Stevens	.10	.06
26	Chris Sabo	.20	.12

27	Mark Grace	.20	.12
28	Derrick May	.25	.15
29	Ryne Sandberg	.50	.30
30	Matt Stark	.20	.12
31	Bobby Thigpen	.10	.06
32	Frank Thomas	2.00	1.25
33	Don Mattingly	.40	.25
34	Eric Davis	.20	.12
35	Reggie Jefferson	.30	.18
36	Alex Cole	.25	.15
37	Mark Lewis	.25	.15
38	Tim Costo	.40	.25
39	Sandy Alomar Jr.	.20	.12
40	Travis Fryman	1.75	1.00
41	Cecil Fielder	.40	.25
42	Milt Cuyler	.30	.18
43	Andujar Cedeno	.25	.15
44	Danny Darwin	.07	.04
45	Randy Hennis	.10	.06
46	George Brett	.25	.15
47	Jeff Conine	.25	.15
48	Bo Jackson	.50	.30
49	Brian McRae	.30	.18
50	Brent Mayne	.20	.12
51	Eddie Murray	.20	.12
52	Ramon Martinez	.20	.12
53	Jim Neidlinger	.07	.04
54	Jim Poole	.07	.04
55	Tim McIntosh	.20	.12
56	Randy Veres	.07	.04
57	Kirby Puckett	.70	.40
58	Todd Ritchie	.15	.10
59	Rich Garces	.20	.12
60	Moises Alou	.25	.15
61	Delino DeShields	.30	.18
62	Oscar Azocar	.15	.10
63	Kevin Maas	.20	.12
64	Alan Mills	.10	.06
65	John Franco	.08	.05
66	Chris Jelic	.10	.06
67	Dave Magadan	.10	.06
68	Darryl Strawberry	.25	.15
69	Hensley Meulens	.15	.10
70	Juan Gonzalez	2.00	1.25
71	Reggis Harris	.15	.10
72	Rickey Henderson	.35	.20
73	Mark McGwire	.40	.25
74	Willie McGee	.15	.10
75	Todd Van Poppel	.80	.50
76	Bob Welch	.10	.06
77	Future Aces (T. Van Poppel, K. Dressendorfer, D. Peters, D. Zancanaro)	.75	.45
78	Len Dykstra	.20	.12
79	Mickey Morandini	.15	.10
80	Wes Chamberlain	.20	.12
81	Barry Bonds	.60	.35

82	Doug Drabek	.15	.10
83	Randy Tomlin	.15	.10
84	Scott Chiamparino	.15	.10
85	Rafael Palmiero	.20	.12
86	Nolan Ryan	.80	.50
87	Bobby Witt	.10	.06
88	Fred McGriff	.25	.15
89	Dave Stieb	.12	.07
90	Ed Sprague	.15	.10
91	Vince Coleman	.10	.06
92	Rod Brewer	.07	.04
93	Bernard Gilkey	.25	.15
94	Roberto Alomar	.80	.50
95	Chuck Finley	.15	.10
96	Dale Murphy	.15	.10
97	Jose Rijo	.15	.10
98	Hal Morris	.20	.12
99	Friendly Foes (D. Gooden, D. Strawberry)	.25	.15
__	Micro (D. Justice, K. Maas, R. Sandberg, T. Van Poppel)	.80	.50

1991 Classic II

Jose Rijo

Classic doubled the size of their second series in 1991 to 100-cards compared to 50-cards in 1990. Card fronts sport burgandy borders while the card backs contain five new trivia questions to go along with Classic's Baseball Trivia board game. All cards measure 2-1/2" by 3-1/2".

	MINT	NR/MT
Complete Set (100)	12.00	7.50
Commons	.07	.04
1 Ken Griffey Jr.	1.00	.70
2 Wilfredo Cordero	1.00	.70

3	Cal Ripken, Jr.	.80	.50
4	D.J. Dozier	.15	.10
5	Darrin Fletcher	.07	.04
6	Glenn Davis	.10	.06
7	Alex Fernandez	.20	.12
8	Cory Snyder	.07	.04
9	Tim Raines	.07	.04
10	Greg Swindell	.12	.07
11	Mark Lewis	.20	.12
12	Rico Brogna	.30	.18
13	Gary Sheffield	.75	.45
14	Paul Molitor	.20	.12
15	Kent Hrbek	.07	.04
16	Scott Erickson	.30	.18
17	Steve Sax	.10	.06
18	Dennis Eckersley	.20	.12
19	Jose Canseco	.35	.20
20	Kirk Dressendorfer	.20	.12
21	Ken Griffey, Sr.	.07	.04
22	Erik Hanson	.10	.06
23	Dan Peltier	.20	.12
24	John Olerud	.25	.15
25	Eddie Zosky	.12	.07
26	Steve Avery	.35	.20
27	John Smoltz	.15	.10
28	Frank Thomas	2.00	1.25
29	Jerome Walton	.07	.04
30	George Bell	.10	.06
31	Jose Rijo	.10	.06
32	Randy Myers	.07	.04
33	Barry Larkin	.12	.07
34	Eric Anthony	.15	.10
35	Dave Hanson	.08	.05
36	Eric Karros	1.00	.70
37	Jose Offerman	.10	.06
38	Marquis Grissom	.15	.10
39	Dwight Gooden	.10	.06
40	Greg Jefferies	.10	.06
41	Pat Combs	.10	.06
42	Todd Zeile	.10	.06
43	Benito Santiago	.10	.06
44	Dave Staton	.12	.07
45	Tony Fernandez	.07	.04
46	Fred McGriff	.20	.12
47	Jeff Brantley	.07	.04
48	Junior Felix	.07	.04
49	Jack Morris	.10	.06
50	Chris George	.07	.04
51	Henry Rodriguez	.40	.25
52	Paul Marak	.12	.07
53	Ryan Klesko	2.00	1.25
54	Darren Lewis	.15	.10
55	Lance Dickson	.15	.10
56	Anthony Young	.15	.10
57	Willie Banks	.15	.10
58	Mike Bordick	.35	.20
59	Roger Salkeld	.40	.25
60	Steve Karsay	.25	.15
61	Bernie Williams	.20	.12
62	Mickey Tettleton	.10	.06
63	Dave Justice	.25	.15
64	Steve Decker	.10	.06
65	Roger Clemens	.60	.35
66	Phil Plantier	.50	.30
67	Ryne Sandberg	.40	.25
68	Sandy Alomar Jr.	.10	.06
69	Cecil Fielder	.15	.10
70	George Brett	.12	.07
71	Delino DeShields	.12	.07
72	Dave Magadan	.07	.04
73	Darryl Strawberry	.12	.07
74	Juan Gonzalez	2.50	1.50
75	Rickey Henderson	.12	.07
76	Willie McGee	.07	.04
77	Todd Van Poppel	.80	.50
78	Barry Bonds	.50	.30
79	Doug Drabek	.10	.06
80	Nolan Ryan (300)	.50	.30
81	Roberto Alomar	.30	.18
82	Ivan Rodriguez	1.00	.70
83	Dan Opperman	.15	.10
84	Jeff Bagwell	1.75	1.00
85	Braulio Castillo	.10	.06
86	Doug Simons	.10	.06
87	Wade Taylor	.10	.06
88	Gary Scott	.25	.15
89	Dave Stewart	.10	.06
90	Mike Simms	.10	.06
91	Luis Gonzalez	.20	.12
92	Bobby Bonilla	.12	.07
93	Tony Gwynn	.20	.12
94	Will Clark	.40	.25
95	Rich Rowland	.08	.05
96	Alan Trammell	.10	.06
97	Strikeout Kings (N.Ryan R. Clemens)	.80	.50
98	Joe Carter	.20	.12
99	Jack Clark	.07	.04
100	Micro (S. Decker)	.10	.06

1991 Classic III

This is the third series of Classic's 1991 Baseball Trivia board game. The set features gray borders with green accents. Card backs contain five new baseball trivia questions. All cards measure 2-1/2" by 3-1/2".

		MINT	NR/MT
	Complete Set (100)	10.00	6.50
	Commons	.07	.04
1	Jim Abbott	.25	.15
2	Craig Biggio	.15	.10
3	Wade Boggs	.30	.18
4	Bobby Bonilla	.25	.15
5	Ivan Calderon	.07	.04
6	Jose Canseco	.35	.20
7	Andy Benes	.20	.12
8	Wes Chamberlain	.20	.12
9	Will Clark	.40	.25
10	Royce Clayton	.50	.30
11	Gerald Alexander	.08	.05
12	Chili Davis	.10	.06
13	Eric Davis	.12	.07
14	Andre Dawson	.20	.12
15	Rob Dibble	.15	.10
16	Chris Donnels	.15	.10
17	Scott Erickson	.30	.18
18	Monty Fariss	.15	.10
19	Ruben Amaro Jr.	.25	.15
20	Chuck Finley	.10	.06
21	Carlton Fiks	.15	.10
22	Carlos Baerga	1.75	1.00
23	Ron Gant	.25	.15
24	D. Justice/R. Gant	.50	.30
25	Mike Gardiner	.10	.06
26	Tom Glavine	.60	.35
27	Joe Grahe	.10	.06
28	Derek Bell	.35	.20
29	Mike Greenwell	.10	.06
30	Ken Griffey Jr.	.90	.60
31	Leo Gomez	.12	.07
32	Tom Goodwin	.20	.12
33	Tony Gwynn	.30	.18
34	Mel Hall	.10	.06
35	Brian Harper	.07	.04
36	Dave Henderson	.10	.06
37	Albert Belle	.50	.30
38	Orel Hershiser	.12	.07
39	Brian Hunter	.15	.10
40	Howard Johnson	.15	.10
41	Felix Jose	.15	.10
42	Wally Joyner	.15	.10
43	Jeff Juden	.25	.15
44	Pat Kelly	.25	.15
45	Jimmy Key	.08	.05
46	Chuck Knoblauch	.30	.18
47	John Kruk	.15	.10
48	Ray Lankford	.25	.15
49	Cedric Landrum	.08	.05
50	Scott Livingstone	.15	.10
51	Kevin Maas	.12	.07
52	Greg Maddux	.25	.15
53	Dennis Martinez	.10	.06
54	Edgar Martinez	.15	.10
55	Pedro Martinez	.80	.50
56	Don Mattingly	.30	.18
57	Orlando Merced	.20	.12
58	Keith Mitchell	.10	.06
59	Kevin Mitchell	.10	.06
60	Paul Molitor	.15	.10
62	Hal Morris	.15	.10
63	Kevin Morton	.07	.04
64	Pedro Munoz	.30	.18
65	Eddie Murray	.15	.10
66	Jack McDowell	.50	.30
67	Jeff McNeely	.35	.20
68	Brian McRae	.15	.10
69	Kevin McReynolds	.08	.05
70	Gregg Olson	.10	.06
71	Rafael Palmeiro	.20	.12
72	Dean Palmer	.30	.18
73	Tony Phillips	.07	.04
74	Kirby Puckett	.60	.35
75	Carlos Quintana	.10	.06
76	Pat Rice	.10	.06
77	Cal Ripken Jr.	.60	.35
78	Ivan Rodriquez	.70	.40
79	Nolan Ryan (7th)	.70	.40
80	Bret Saberhagen	.10	.06
81	Tim Salmon	1.75	1.00
82	Juan Samuel	.07	.04
83	Ruben Sierra	.25	.15
84	Heathcliff Slocumb	.10	.06
85	Joe Slusarski	.15	.10
86	John Smiley	.15	.10
87	Dave Smith	.07	.04
88	Ed Sprague	.10	.06

89	Todd Stottlemyre	.10	.06
90	Mike Timlin	.10	.06
91	Greg Vaughn	.20	.12
92	Frank Viola	.12	.07
93	Chico Walker	.10	.06
94	Devon White	.07	.04
95	Matt Williams	.20	.12
96	Rick Wilkins	.10	.06
97	Bernie Williams	.20	.12
98	N. Ryan/G. Gossage	.40	.25
99	Gerald Williams	.25	.15
___	Micro (B. Bonilla, W. Clark, S. Erickson, C. Ripken Jr.)	.35	.20

1991 Classic Collectors Edition

Limited to just 100,000 individually numbered sets, this edition was packaged in a special collector's box and came with a game board, game pieces, spinner, scoreboard and a booklet offering baseball tips. Card fronts feature purple borders. Card backs include baseball trivia questions. All cards measure 2-1/2" by 3-1/2".

		MINT	NR/MT
Complete Set (200)		32.00	20.00
Commons		.08	.05
1	Frank Viola	.10	.06
2	Tim Wallach	.10	.06
3	Lou Whitaker	.08	.05
4	Bret Butler	.10	.06
5	Jim Abbott	.15	.10
6	Jack Armstrong	.08	.05
7	Craig Biggio	.10	.06

8	Brian Barnes	.15	.10
9	Dennis "Oil Can" Boyd	.08	.05
10	Tom Browning	.08	.05
11	Tom Brunansky	.08	.05
12	Ellis Burks	.10	.06
13	Harold Baines	.10	.06
14	Kal Daniels	.08	.05
15	Mark Davis	.08	.05
16	Storm Davis	.08	.05
17	Tom Glavine	.60	.35
18	Mike Greenwell	.15	.10
19	Kelly Gruber	.15	.10
20	Mark Gubicza	.10	.06
21	Pedro Guerrero	.10	.06
22	Mike Harkey	.10	.06
23	Orel Hershiser	.15	.10
24	Ted Higuera	.10	.06
25	Von Hayes	.08	.05
26	Andre Dawson	.20	.12
27	Shawon Dunston	.15	.10
28	Roberto Kelly	.20	.12
29	Joe Magrane	.08	.05
30	Dennis Martinez	.15	.10
31	Kevin McReynolds	.12	.07
32	Matt Nokes	.12	.07
33	Dan Plesac	.08	.05
34	Dave Parker	.12	.07
35	Randy Johnson	.30	.18
36	Bret Saberhagen	.20	.12
37	Mackey Sasser	.08	.05
38	Mike Scott	.08	.05
39	Ozzie Smith	.20	.12
40	Kevin Seitzer	.10	.06
41	Ruben Sierra	.20	.12
42	Kevin Tapani	.10	.06
43	Danny Tartabull	.20	.12
44	Robby Thompson	.10	.06
45	Andy Van Slyke	.20	.12
46	Greg Vaughn	.20	.12
47	Harold Reynolds	.10	.06
48	Will Clark	.50	.30
49	Gary Gaetti	.08	.05
50	Joe Grahe	.10	.06
51	Carlton Fisk	.20	.12
52	Robin Ventura	.40	.25
53	Ozzie Guillen	.15	.10
54	Tom Candiotti	.12	.07
55	Doug Jones	.10	.06
56	Eric King	.10	.06
57	Kirk Gibson	.10	.06
58	Tim Costo	.30	.18
59	Robin Yount	.50	.30
60	Sammy Sosa	.25	.15
61	Jesse Barfield	.10	.06
62	Marc Newfield	.75	.45
63	Jimmy Key	.10	.06
64	Felix Jose	.20	.12

65	Mark Whiten	.60	.35	122	Juan Gonzalez	2.00	1.25
66	Tommy Greene	.20	.12	123	Ron Gant	.25	.15
67	Kent Mercker	.10	.06	124	Travis Fryman	.80	.50
68	Greg Maddux	.50	.30	125	John Franco	.08	.05
69	Danny Jackson	.10	.06	126	Dennis Eckersley	.20	.12
70	Reggie Sanders	.60	.35	127	Cecil Fielder	.25	.15
71	Eric Yelding	.12	.07	128	Phil Plantier	.60	.50
72	Karl Rhodes	.15	.10	129	Kevin Mitchell	.12	.07
73	Fernando Valenzuela	.12	.07	130	Kevin Maas	.15	.10
74	Chris Nabholz	.15	.10	131	Mark McGwire	.40	.25
75	Andres Galarraga	.20	.12	132	Ben McDonald	.30	.18
76	Howard Johnson	.20	.12	133	Lenny Dykstra	.20	.12
77	Hubie Brooks	.12	.07	134	Delino DeShields	.25	.15
78	Terry Mulholland	.12	.07	135	Jose Canseco	.60	.35
79	Paul Molitor	.20	.12	136	Eric Davis	.15	.10
80	Roger McDowell	.08	.05	137	George Brett	.20	.12
81	Darren Daulton	.20	.12	138	Steve Avery	.50	.30
82	Zane Smith	.10	.06	139	Eric Anthony	.20	.12
83	Ray Lankford	.25	.15	140	Bobby Thigpen	.12	.07
84	Bruce Hurst	.12	.07	141	Ken Griffey Sr.	.10	.06
85	Andy Benes	.25	.15	142	Barry Larkin	.20	.12
86	John Burkett	.10	.06	143	Jeff Brantley	.10	.06
87	Dave Righetti	.10	.06	144	Bobby Bonilla	.20	.12
88	Steve Karsay	.20	.12	145	Jose Offerman	.20	.12
89	D.J. Dozier	.20	.12	146	Mike Mussina	.80	.50
90	Jeff Bagwell	1.75	1.00	147	Erik Hanson	.20	.12
91	Joe Carter	.35	.20	148	Dale Murphy	.20	.12
92	Wes Chamberlain	.25	.15	149	Roger Clemens	.60	.35
93	Vince Coleman	.10	.06	150	Tino Martinez	.25	.15
94	Pat Combs	.15	.10	151	Todd Van Poppel	1.25	.80
95	Jerome Walton	.08	.05	152	Maurice Vaughn	.80	.50
96	Jeff Conine	.20	.12	153	Derrick May	.25	.15
97	Alan Trammell	.10	.06	154	Jack Clark	.10	.06
98	Don Mattingly	.30	.18	155	Dave Hansen	.15	.10
99	Ramon Martinez	.25	.15	156	Tony Gwynn	.35	.20
100	Dave Magadan	.10	.06	157	Brian McRae	.25	.15
101	Greg Swindell	.12	.07	158	Matt Williams	.25	.15
102	Dave Stewart	.12	.07	159	Kirk Dressendorfer	.25	.15
103	Gary Sheffield	.80	.50	160	Scott Erickson	.30	.18
104	George Bell	.15	.10	161	Tony Fernandez	.10	.06
105	Mark Grace	.20	.12	162	Willie McGee	.10	.06
106	Steve Sax	.15	.10	163	Fred McGriff	.30	.18
107	Ryne Sandberg	.40	.25	164	Leo Gomez	.20	.12
108	Chris Sabo	.15	.10	165	Bernard Gilkey	.25	.15
109	Jose Rijo	.15	.10	166	Bobby Witt	.08	.05
110	Cal Ripken Jr.	.75	.45	167	Doug Drabek	.12	.07
111	Kirby Puckett	.60	.35	168	Rob Dibble	.15	.10
112	Eddie Murray	.20	.12	169	Glenn Davis	.08	.05
113	Roberto Alomar	.50	.30	170	Danny Darwin	.08	.05
114	Randy Myers	.08	.05	171	Eric Karros	1.00	.70
115	Rafael Palmeiro	.25	.15	172	Eddie Zosky	.20	.12
116	John Olerud	.40	.25	173	Todd Zeile	.20	.12
117	Gregg Jefferies	.20	.12	174	Tim Raines	.10	.06
118	Kent Hrbek	.12	.07	175	Benito Santiago	.15	.10
119	Marquis Grissom	.30	.18	176	Dan Peltier	.20	.12
120	Ken Griffey Jr	1.50	.90	177	Darryl Strawberry	.25	.15
121	Dwight Gooden	.15	.10	178	Hal Morris	.20	.12

179	Hensley Meulens	.20	.12
180	John Smoltz	.15	.10
181	Frank Thomas	2.50	1.50
182	Dave Staton	.25	.15
183	Scott Chiamparino	.15	.10
184	Alex Fernandez	.50	.30
185	Mark Lewis	.20	.12
186	Bo Jackson	.75	.45
187	Mickey Morandini	.15	.10
188	Cory Snyder	.08	.05
189	Rickey Henderson	.40	.25
190	Junior Felix	.15	.10
191	Milt Cuyler	.25	.15
192	Wade Boggs	.35	.20
193	Justice Prevails (Dave Justice)	1.25	.80
194	Sandy Alomar Jr.	.15	.10
195	Barry Bonds	.60	.35
196	Nolan Ryan	1.25	.80
197	Rico Brogna	.35	.20
198	Steve Decker	.10	.06
199	Bob Welch	.10	.06
200	Andujar Cedeno	.50	.30

1991 Classic Draft Picks

This edition features the top selections from the 1991 amateur baseball draft. Only 330,000 sets were produced, each shipped with a numbered certificate. Border colors are gray and burgundy. One-half of the sets contained a Frankie Rodriguez bonus card. All cards measure 2-1/2" by 3-1/2".

	MINT	NR/MT
Complete Set (51)	12.00	7.50
Commons	.07	.04

1	Brien Taylor	1.25	.80
2	Mike Kelly	.80	.50
3	David McCarty	1.00	.70
4	Dmitri Young	1.00	.70
5	Joe Vitiello	.50	.30
6	Mark Smith	.50	.30
7	Tyler Green	.30	.18
8	Shawn Estes	.20	.12
9	Doug Glanville	.20	.12
10	Manny Ramirez	1.25	.80
11	Cliff Floyd	2.50	1.50
12	Tyrone Hill	.25	.15
13	Eduardo Perez	1.25	.80
14	Al Shirley	.15	.10
15	Benji Gil	.50	.30
16	Calvin Reese	.12	.07
17	Allen Watson	.80	.50
18	Brian Barber	.50	.30
19	Aaron Sele	1.50	.90
20	John Farrell	.20	.12
21	Scott Ruffcorn	.35	.20
22	Brent Gates	.60	.35
23	Scott Stahoviak	.15	.10
24	Tom McKinnon	.12	.07
25	Shawn Livsey	.20	.12
26	Jason Pruitt	.12	.07
27	Greg Anthony	.12	.07
28	Justin Thompson	.25	.15
29	Steve Whitaker	.12	.07
30	Jorge Fabregas	.15	.10
31	Jeff Ware	.10	.07
32	Bobby Jones	.40	.25
33	J.J. Johnson	.25	.15
34	Mike Rossiter	.10	.06
35	Dan Chowlowsky	.20	.12
36	Jimmy Gonzalez	.10	.06
37	Trevor Miller	.10	.06
38	Scott Hatteberg	.30	.18
39	Mike Groppuso	.15	.10
40	Ryan Long	.15	.10
41	Eddie Williams	.10	.06
42	Mike Durant	.10	.06
43	Buck McNabb	.07	.04
44	Jimmy Lewis	.10	.06
45	Eddie Ramos	.10	.06
46	Terry Horn	.07	.04
47	Jon Barnes	.10	.06
48	Shawn Curran	.10	.06
49	Tommy Adams	.12	.07
50	Trevor Mallory	.07	.04
___	Bonus Card (Frankie Rodriquez)	1.00	.70

1992 Classic

The 1992 edition of Classic's Baseball Trivia board game features all new trivia questions and is packaged with a game board. Cards are printed on a glossy stock with white borders on the front. All cards measure 2-1/2" by 3-1/2".

		MINT	NR/MT
Complete Set (100)		12.00	7.00
Commons		.07	.04

1	Jim Abbott	.25	.15
2	Kyle Abbott	.15	.10
3	Scott Aldred	.12	.07
4	Roberto Alomar	.35	.20
5	Wilson Alvarez	.12	.07
6	Andy Ashby	.07	.04
7	Steve Avery	.30	.18
8	Jeff Bagwell	.75	.45
9	Bret Barberie	.25	.15
10	Kim Batiste	.20	.12
11	Derek Bell	.25	.15
12	Jay Bell	.10	.06
13	Albert Belle	.25	.15
14	Andy Benes	.15	.10
15	Sean Berry	.10	.06
16	Barry Bonds	.40	.25
17	Ryan Bowen	.15	.10
18	Trifecta (A. Pena, K. Mercker, M. Wohlers)	.12	.07
19	Scott Brosius		
20	Jay Buhner	.12	.07
21	David Burba	.10	.06
22	Jose Canseco	.40	.25
23	Andujar Cedeno	.20	.12
24	Will Clark	.30	.18
25	Royce Clayton	.25	.15
26	Roger Clemens	.40	.25
27	David Cone	.15	.10
28	Scott Cooper	.15	.10
29	Chris Cron	.10	.06
30	Len Dykstra	.15	.10
31	Cal Eldred	.50	.30
32	Hector Fajardo	.12	.07
33	Cecil Fielder	.25	.15
34	Dave Fleming	.40	.25
35	Steve Foster	.10	.06
36	Julio Franco	.15	.10
37	Carlos Garcia	.50	.30
38	Tom Glavine	.30	.18
39	Tom Goodwin	.20	.12
40	Ken Griffey Jr.	.80	.50
41	Chris Haney	.12	.07
42	Bryan Harvey	.12	.07
43	Rickey Henderson	.30	.18
44	Carlos Hernandez	.12	.07
45	Roberto Hernandez	.12	.07
46	Brook Jacoby	.07	.04
47	Howard Johnson	.15	.10
48	Pat Kelly	.12	.07
49	Darryl Kile	.25	.15
50	Chuck Knoblauch	.30	.18
51	Ray Lankford	.20	.12
52	Mark Leiter	.12	.07
53	Darren Lewis	.12	.07
54	Scott Livingstone	.12	.07
55	Shane Mack	.12	.07
56	Chito Martinez	.20	.12
57	Dennis Martinez	.12	.07
58	Don Mattingly	.30	.18
59	Paul McCellan	.12	.07
60	Chuck McElroy	.10	.06
61	Fred McGriff	.25	.15
62	Orlando Merced	.15	.10
63	Luis Mercedes	.20	.12
64	Kevin Mitchell	.12	.07
65	Hal Morris	.15	.10
66	Jack Morris	.12	.07
67	Mike Mussina	.40	.25
68	Denny Naegle	.15	.10
69	Tom Pagnozzi	.12	.07
70	Terry Pendleton	.15	.10
71	Phil Plantier	.30	.18
72	Kirby Puckett	.40	.25
73	Carlos Quintana	.12	.07
74	Willie Randolph	.10	.06
75	Arthur Rhodes	.25	.15
76	Cal Ripken Jr.	.35	.20
77	Ivan Rodriquez	.35	.20
78	Nolan Ryan	.50	.30
79	Ryne Sandberg	.40	.25
80	Deion Sanders	.35	.20
81	Reggie Sanders	.35	.20
82	Mo Sanford	.10	.06
83	Terry Shumpert	.07	.04
84	Tim Spehr	.07	.04
85	Lee Stevens	.07	.04
86	Darryl Strawberry	.25	.15
87	Kevin Tapani	.12	.07

		MINT	NR/MT
88	Danny Tartabull	.20	.12
89	Frank Thomas	1.75	1.00
90	Jim Thome	.40	.25
91	Todd Van Poppel	.35	.20
92	Andy Van Slyke	.20	.12
93	John Wehner	.10	.06
94	John Wetteland	.15	.10
95	Devon White	.10	.06
96	Brian Williams	.35	.20
97	Mark Wohlers	.15	.10
98	Robin Yount	.40	.25
99	Eddie Zosky	.12	.07
___	Micro (S. Avery, B. Bonds, R. Clemens, N. Ryan)	.75	.45

1992 Classic Draft Picks

Steve Rodriguez

The cards in this 125-card set feature the top draft picks from baseball's 1992 amateur draft. The cards measure 2-1/2" by 3-1/2". Card fronts include full color photos framed by a white border with the player's name printed in a color bar under his photo. 20-limited foil stamped bonus cards were issued in conjunction with the set. Those cards are listed at the end of this checklist but are not included in the complete set price below.

		MINT	NR/MT
	Complete Set (125)	12.00	7.50
	Commons	.05	.02
1	Phil Nevin	1.25	.80
2	Paul Shuey	.40	.25
3	B.J. Wallace	.50	.30
4	Jeffrey Hammonds	2.50	1.50

5	Chad Mottola	1.00	.70
6	Derek Jeter	.75	.45
7	Michael Tucker	1.25	.80
8	Derek Wallace	.25	.15
9	Kenny Felder	.30	.18
10	Chad McConnell	.25	.15
11	Sean Lowe	.20	.12
12	Ricky Greene	.20	.12
13	Chris Roberts	.30	.18
14	Shannon Stewart	.15	.10
15	Benji Grigsby	.25	.15
16	Jamie Arnold	.15	.10
17	Rick Helling	.40	.25
18	Jason Kendall	.40	.25
19	Todd Steverson	.20	.12
20	Dan Serafini	.25	.15
21	Jeff Schmidt	.10	.06
22	Sherard Clinkscales	.10	.06
23	Ryan Luzinski	.40	.25
24	Shon Walker	.25	.15
25	Brandon Cromer	.12	.07
26	Dave Landaker	.15	.10
27	Michael Mathews	.12	.07
28	Brian Sackinsky	.12	.07
29	Jon Lieber	.20	.12
30	Jim Rosenbohm	.10	.06
31	DeShawn Warren	.12	.07
32	Danny Clyburn	.25	.15
33	Chris Smith	.15	.10
34	Dwain Bostic	.12	.07
35	Bobby Hughes	.15	.10
36	Rick Magdellano	.10	.06
37	Bob Wolcott	.12	.07
38	Mike Gulan	.20	.12
39	Yuri Sanchez	.08	.05
40	Tony Sheffield	.12	.07
41	Dan Melendez	.20	.12
42	Jason Giambi	.35	.20
43	Ritchie Moody	.08	.05
44	Trey Beamon	.20	.12
45	Tim Crabtree	.08	.05
46	Chad Roper	.15	.10
47	Mark Thompson	.12	.07
48	Marquis Riley	.15	.10
49	Tom Krauss	.08	.05
50	Chris Holt	.15	.10
51	Jonathan Nunnally	.10	.06
52	Everett Stull	.08	.05
53	Billy Owens	.25	.15
54	Todd Etler	.08	.05
55	Benji Simonton	.20	.12
56	Dwight Maness	.15	.10
57	Chris Eddy	.12	.07
58	Brant Brown	.15	.10
59	Trevor Humphrey	.08	.05
60	Chris Widger	.15	.10
61	Steve Montgomery	.08	.05

62	Chris Gomez	.30	.18
63	Jared Baker	.12	.07
64	Doug Hecker	.08	.05
65	David Spykstra	.08	.05
66	Scott Miller	.08	.05
67	Carey Paige	.10	.06
68	Dave Manning	.08	.05
69	James Keefe	.08	.05
70	Levon Largusa	.12	.07
71	Roger Bailey	.10	.06
72	Rich Ireland	.10	.06
73	Matt Williams	.08	.05
74	Scott Gentile	.12	.07
75	Hut Smith	.12	.07
76	Rodney Henderson	.20	.12
77	Mike Buddie	.05	.02
78	Stephen Lyons	.07	.04
79	John Burke	.60	.35
80	Jim Pittsley	.20	.12
81	Donnie Leshnock	.20	.12
82	Cory Pearson	.07	.04
83	Kurt Ehmann	.05	.02
84	Bobby Bonds, Jr.	.25	.15
85	Steven Cox	.07	.04
86	Brien Taylor	.50	.30
87	Mike Kelly	.25	.15
88	David McCarty	.25	.15
89	Dmitri Young	.20	.12
90	Joey Hamilton	.15	.10
91	Mark Smith	.20	.12
92	Doug Glanville	.12	.07
93	Mike Lieberthal	.12	.07
94	Joe Vitiello	.12	.07
95	Mike Mussina	.40	.25
96	Derek Hacopian	.25	.15
97	Ted Corbin	.07	.04
98	Carlton Fleming	.05	.02
99	Aaron Rounsifer	.08	.05
100	Chad Fox	.05	.02
101	Chris Sheff	.12	.07
102	Ben Jones	.10	.06
103	David Post	.05	.02
104	Jonnie Gendron	.05	.02
105	Bob Juday	.10	.06
106	David Becker	.05	.02
107	Brandon Pico	.07	.04
108	Tom Evans	.05	.02
109	Jeff Faino	.07	.04
110	Shawn Wills	.10	.06
111	Derrick Cantrell	.10	.06
112	Steve Rodriquez	.15	.10
113	Ray Suplee	.10	.06
114	Pat Leahy	.05	.02
115	Matt Luke	.08	.05
116	Jon McMullen	.05	.02
117	Preston Wilson	.75	.45
118	Gus Gandarillas	.15	.10

119	Pete Janicki	.30	.18
120	Byron Mathews	.08	.05
121	Eric Owens	.12	.07
122	John Lynch	.15	.10
123	Mike Hickey	.07	.04
124	Checklist I	.05	.02
125	Checklist 2	.05	.02
BC1	Phil Nevin	1.50	.90
BC2	Paul Shuey	.30	.18
BC3	B.J. Wallace	.60	.35
BC4	Jeffrey Hammonds	3.00	1.75
BC5	Chad Mottola	1.25	.80
BC6	Derek Jeter	.80	.50
BC7	Michael Tucker	1.50	.90
BC8	Derek Wallace	.50	.30
BC9	Kenny Felder	.40	.25
BC10	Chad McConnell	.40	.25
BC11	Sean Lowe	.30	.18
BC12	Chris Roberts	.50	.30
BC13	Shannon Stewart	.25	.15
BC14	Benji Grigsby	.40	.25
BC15	Jamie Arnold	.25	.15
BC16	Ryan Luzinski	.60	.35
BC17	Bobby Bonds, Jr.	.25	.15
BC18	Brien Taylor	1.75	1.00
BC19	Mike Kelly	.75	.45
BC20	Mike Mussina	1.75	1.00

1993 Classic

This 99-card set is used as part of Classic Games Baseball Trivia Board Game. The card fronts feature full color action photos while the backs contain trivia questions. All cards measure 2-1/2" by 3-1/2".

	MINT	NR/MT
Complete Set (99)	11.00	7.50
Commons	.07	.04

1	Jim Abbott	.15	.10
2	Roberto Alomar	.30	.18
3	Moises Alou	.15	.10
4	Brady Anderson	.10	.06
5	Eric Anthony	.10	.06
6	Alex Arias	.10	.06
7	Pedro Astacio	.30	.18
8	Steve Avery	.25	.15
9	Carlos Baerga	.30	.18
10	Jeff Bagwell	.30	.18
11	George Bell	.10	.06
12	Albert Belle	.20	.12
13	Craig Biggio	.07	.04
14	Barry Bonds	.25	.15
15	Bobby Bonilla	.12	.07
16	Mike Bordick	.12	.07
17	George Brett	.15	.10
18	Jose Canseco	.35	.20
19	Joe Carter	.20	.12
20	Royce Clayton	.12	.07
21	Roger Clemens	.20	.12
22	Greg Colbrunn	.15	.10
23	David Cone	.10	.06
24	Darren Daulton	.15	.10
25	Delino DeShields	.12	.07
26	Rob Dibble	.07	.04
27	Dennis Eckersley	.15	.10
28	Cal Eldred	.50	.30
29	Scott Erickson	.15	.10
30	Junior Felix	.07	.04
31	Tony Fernandez	.08	.05
32	Cecil Fielder	.15	.10
33	Steve Finley	.07	.04
34	Dave Fleming	.40	.25
35	Travis Fryman	.20	.12
36	Tom Glavine	.25	.15
37	Juan Gonzalez	.75	.45
38	Ken Griffey, Jr.	.60	.35
39	Marquis Grissom	.15	.10
40	Juan Guzman	.25	.15
41	Tony Gwynn	.15	.10
42	Rickey Henderson	.15	.10
43	Felix Jose	.07	.04
44	Wally Joyner	.08	.05
45	David Justice	.25	.15
46	Eric Karros	.35	.20
47	Roberto Kelly	.12	.07
48	Ryan Klesko	.60	.35
49	Chuck Knoblauch	.25	.15
50	John Kruk	.15	.10
51	Ray Lankford	.15	.10
52	Barry Larkin	.12	.07
53	Pat Listach	.25	.15
54	Kenny Lofton	.30	.18
55	Shane Mack	.08	.05
56	Greg Maddux	.25	.15
57	Dave Magadan	.07	.04
58	Edgar Martinez	.12	.07
59	Don Mattingly	.20	.12
60	Ben McDonald	.12	.07
61	Jack McDowell	.20	.12
62	Fred McGriff	.20	.12
63	Mark McGwire	.25	.15
64	Kevin McReynolds	.07	.04
65	Sam Militello	.35	.20
66	Paul Molitor	.15	.10
67	Jeff Montgomery	.07	.04
68	Jack Morris	.12	.07
69	Eddie Murray	.12	.07
70	Mike Mussina	.40	.25
71	Otis Nixon	.08	.05
72	Donovan Osborne	.25	.15
73	Terry Pendleton	.12	.07
74	Mike Piazza	2.50	1.50
75	Kirby Puckett	.25	.15
76	Cal Ripken, Jr.	.25	.15
77	Bip Roberts	.07	.04
78	Ivan Rodriquez	.30	.18
79	Nolan Ryan	.50	.30
80	Ryne Sandberg	.30	.18
81	Deion Sanders	.25	.15
82	Reggie Sanders	.25	.15
83	Frank Seminara	.10	.06
84	Gary Sheffield	.20	.12
85	Ruben Sierra	.20	.12
86	John Smiley	.08	.05
87	Lee Smith	.10	.06
88	Ozzie Smith	.12	.07
89	John Smoltz	.10	.06
90	Danny Tartabull	.10	.06
91	Frank Thomas	1.50	.90
92	Bob Tewksbury	.07	.04
93	Andy Van Slyke	.10	.06
94	Mo Vaughn	.20	.12
95	Robin Ventura	.15	.10
96	Tim Wakefield	.15	.10
97	Larry Walker	.20	.12
98	Dave Winfield	.15	.10
99	Robin Yount	.20	.12

DONRUSS

1981 Donruss

JOHNNY BENCH

This 605-card set marks the first baseball edition from Donruss. The standard-size cards feature four-color photos on the fronts and career highlights in a vertical format on the card backs. The set contains more than three dozen errors which were corrected in later print runs. Those variations are noted in the checklist but are not reflected in the set price.

		MINT	NR/MT
Complete Set (605)		60.00	38.00
Commons		.10	.05
1	Ozzie Smith	3.50	2.00
2	Rollie Fingers	1.00	.70
3	Rick Wise	.10	.05
4	Gene Richards	.10	.05
5	Alan Trammell	1.25	.80
6	Tom Brookens	.10	.05
7	Duffy Dyer (Var)	.10	.06
8	Mark Fidrych	.15	.08
9	Dave Rozema	.10	.05
10	Ricky Peters	.10	.05
11	Mike Schmidt	3.50	2.00
12	Willie Stargell	1.00	.70
13	Tim Foli	.10	.05
14	Manny Sanguillen	.10	.05
15	Grant Jackson	.10	.05
16	Eddie Solomon	.10	.05
17	Omar Moreno	.10	.05
18	Joe Morgan	1.00	.70
19	Rafael Landestoy	.10	.05
20	Bruce Bochy	.10	.05
21	Joe Sambito	.10	.05
22	Manny Trillo	.10	.05
23	Dave Smith (R) (Var)	.25	.15
24	Terry Puhl	.10	.05
25	Bump Wills	.10	.05
26a	John Ellis (Wrong photo)	.40	.25
26b	John Ellis (Cor)	.10	.05
27	Jim Kern	.10	.05
28	Richie Zisk	.10	.05
29	John Mayberry	.10	.05
30	Bob Davis	.10	.05
31	Jackson Todd	.10	.05
32	Al Woods	.10	.05
33	Steve Carlton	2.50	1.50
34	Lee Mazzilli	.10	.05
35	John Stearns	.10	.05
36	Roy Jackson	.10	.05
37	Mike Scott	.20	.12
38	Lamar Johnson	.10	.05
39	Kevin Bell	.10	.05
40	Ed Farmer	.10	.05
41	Ross Baumgarten	.10	.05
42	Leo Sutherland	.10	.05
43	Dan Meyer	.10	.05
44	Ron Reed	.10	.05
45	Mario Mendoza	.10	.05
46	Rick Honeycutt	.10	.05
47	Glenn Abbott	.10	.05
48	Leon Roberts	.10	.05
49	Rod Carew	2.00	1.25
50	Bert Campaneris	.12	.07
51a	Tom Donahue (Er)	.10	.06
51b	Tom Donohue (Cor)	.10	.05
52	Dave Frost	.10	.05
53	Ed Halicki	.10	.05
54	Dan Ford	.10	.05
55	Garry Maddox	.10	.05
56a	Steve Garvey (25 Hr)	1.25	.80
56b	Steve Garvey (21 Hr)	.80	.50
57	Bill Russell	.12	.07
58	Don Sutton	.70	.40
59	Reggie Smith	.10	.06
60	Rick Monday	.12	.07
61	Ray Knight	.10	.05
62	Johnny Bench	2.50	1.50
63	Mario Soto	.10	.05
64	Doug Bair	.10	.05
65	George Foster	.25	.15
66	Jeff Burroughs	.12	.07
67	Keith Hernandez	.25	.15
68	Tom Herr	.10	.05
69	Bob Forsch	.10	.05
70	John Fulgham	.10	.05
71a	Bobby Bonds (lifetime HR 986)	.35	.20

71b Bobby Bonds(lifetime HR 326)	.12	.07	
72 Rennie Stennett (Var)	.12	.07	
73 Joe Strain	.10	.05	
74 Ed Whitson	.10	.05	
75 Tom Griffin	.10	.05	
76 Bill North	.10	.05	
77 Gene Garber	.10	.05	
78 Mike Hargrove	.10	.06	
79 Dave Rosello	.10	.05	
80 Ron Hassey	.10	.06	
81 Sid Monge	.10	.05	
82 Joe Charboneau (R)	.10	.06	
83 Cecil Cooper	.12	.07	
84 Sal Bando	.15	.08	
85 Moose Haas	.10	.05	
86 Mike Caldwell	.10	.05	
87a Larry Hisle(28 RBI)	.12	.07	
87b Larry Hisle(28 Hr)	.10	.05	
88 Luis Gomez	.10	.05	
89 Larry Parrish	.10	.05	
90 Gary Carter	1.25	.80	
91 Bill Gullickson (R)	.80	.50	
92 Fred Norman	.10	.05	
93 Tommy Hutton	.10	.05	
94 Carl Yastrzemski	2.50	1.50	
95 Glenn Hoffman	.10	.05	
96 Dennis Eckersley	1.50	.90	
97a Tom Burgmeier (Throws:Right)	.12	.07	
97b Tom Burgmeier (Throws:Left)	.10	.05	
98 Win Remmerswaal	.10	.05	
99 Bob Horner	.12	.07	
100 George Brett	4.50	2.50	
101 Dave Chalk	.10	.05	
102 Dennis Leonard	.10	.05	
103 Renie Martin	.10	.05	
104 Amos Otis	.10	.06	
105 Graig Nettles	.15	.08	
106 Eric Soderholm	.10	.05	
107 Tommy John	.20	.12	
108 Tom Underwood	.10	.05	
109 Lou Piniella	.20	.12	
110 Mickey Klutts	.10	.05	
111 Bobby Murcer	.15	.08	
112 Eddie Murray	3.00	2.00	
113 Rick Dempsey	.10	.05	
114 Scott McGregor	.10	.05	
115 Ken Singleton	.10	.05	
116 Gary Roenicke	.10	.05	
117 Dave Revering	.10	.05	
118 Mike Norris	.10	.05	
119 Rickey Henderson	12.00	7.00	
120 Mike Heath	.10	.05	
121 Dave Cash	.10	.05	
122 Randy Jones	.10	.05	
123 Eric Rasmussen	.10	.05	
124 Jerry Mumphrey	.10	.05	
125 Richie Hebner	.12	.07	
126 Mark Wagner	.10	.05	
127 Jack Morris	1.25	.80	
128 Dan Petry	.10	.06	
129 Bruce Robbins	.10	.05	
130 Champ Summers	.10	.05	
131a Pete Rose("see card 251.")	3.00	2.00	
131b Pete Rose ("see card 371.")	2.00	1.25	
132 Willie Stargell	.80	.50	
133 Ed Ott	.10	.05	
134 Jim Bibby	.10	.05	
135 Bert Blyleven	.50	.30	
136 Dave Parker	.40	.25	
137 Bill Robinson	.12	.07	
138 Enos Cabell	.10	.05	
139 Dave Bergman	.10	.05	
140 J.R. Richard	.12	.07	
141 Ken Forsch	.10	.05	
142 Larry Bowa	.10	.06	
143 Frank LaCorte (Wrong photo)	.10	.05	
144 Dennis Walling	.10	.05	
145 Buddy Bell	.12	.07	
146 Ferguson Jenkins	.60	.35	
147 Danny Darwin	.10	.06	
148 John Grubb	.10	.05	
149 Alfredo Griffin	.12	.07	
150 Jerry Garvin	.10	.05	
151 Paul Mirabella (R)	.12	.07	
152 Rick Bosetti	.10	.05	
153 Dick Ruthven	.10	.05	
154 Frank Taveras	.10	.05	
155 Craig Swan	.10	.05	
156 Jeff Reardon (R)	5.00	3.00	
157 Steve Henderson	.10	.05	
158 Jim Morrison	.10	.05	
159 Glenn Borgmann	.10	.05	
160 LaMarr Hoyt (R)	.12	.07	
161 Rich Wortham	.10	.05	
162 Thad Bosley	.10	.05	
163 Julio Cruz	.10	.05	
164 Del Unser (Var)	.12	.07	
165 Jim Anderson	.10	.05	
166 Jim Beattie	.10	.05	
167 Shane Rawley	.10	.05	
168 Joe Simpson	.10	.05	
169 Rod Carew	2.00	1.25	
170 Fred Patek	.10	.05	
171 Frank Tanana	.12	.07	
172 Alfredo Martinez	.10	.05	
173 Chris Knapp	.10	.05	
174 Joe Rudi	.10	.06	
175 Greg Luzinski	.20	.12	

176	Steve Garvey	.80	.50
177	Joe Ferguson	.10	.05
178	Bob Welch	.35	.20
179	Dusty Baker	.12	.07
180	Rudy Law	.10	.05
181	Dave Concepcion	.25	.15
182	Johnny Bench	2.50	1.50
183	Mike LaCoss	.10	.05
184	Ken Griffey	.30	.18
185	Dave Collins	.10	.05
186	Brian Asselstine	.10	.05
187	Garry Templeton	.12	.07
188	Mike Phillips	.10	.05
189	Pete Vukovich	.10	.05
190	John Urrea	.10	.05
191	Tony Scott	.10	.05
192	Darrell Evans	.20	.12
193	Milt May	.10	.05
194	Bob Knepper	.10	.05
195	Randy Moffitt	.10	.05
196	Larry Herndon	.10	.05
197	Rick Camp	.10	.05
198	Andre Thornton	.12	.07
199	Tom Veryzer	.10	.05
200	Gary Alexander	.10	.05
201	Rick Waits	.10	.05
202	Rick Manning	.10	.05
203	Paul Molitor	3.50	2.00
204	Jim Gantner	.12	.07
205	Paul Mitchell	.10	.05
206	Reggie Cleveland	.10	.05
207	Sixto Lezcano	.10	.05
208	Bruce Benedict	.10	.05
209	Rodney Scott	.10	.05
210	John Tamargo	.10	.05
211	Bill Lee	.10	.05
212	Andre Dawson	2.00	1.25
213	Rowland Office	.10	.05
214	Carl Yastrzemski	2.50	1.50
215	Jerry Remy	.10	.05
216	Mike Torrez	.10	.05
217	Skip Lockwood	.10	.05
218	Fred Lynn	.25	.15
219	Cris Chambliss	.10	.06
220	Willie Aikens	.10	.05
221	John Wathan	.10	.06
222	Dan Quisenberry	.20	.12
223	Willie Wilson	.25	.15
224	Clint Hurdle	.12	.07
225	Bob Watson	.12	.07
226	Jim Spencer	.10	.05
227	Ron Guidry	.30	.18
228	Reggie Jackson	3.50	2.00
229	Oscar Gamble	.12	.07
230	Jeff Cox	.10	.05
231	Luis Tiant	.12	.07
232	Rich Dauer	.10	.05
233	Dan Graham	.10	.05
234	Mike Flanagan	.12	.07
235	John Lowenstein	.10	.05
236	Benny Ayala	.10	.05
237	Wayne Gross	.10	.05
238	Rick Langford	.10	.06
239	Tony Armas	.10	.05
240	Bob Lacy(Er)	.12	.07
240	Bob Lacey(Cor)	.10	.05
241	Gene Tenace	.10	.06
242	Bob Shirley	.10	.05
243	Gary Lucas	.10	.05
244	Jerry Turner	.10	.05
245	John Wockenfuss	.10	.05
246	Stan Papi	.10	.05
247	Milt Wilcox	.10	.05
248	Dan Schatzeder	.10	.05
249	Steve Kemp	.10	.05
250	Jim Lentine	.10	.05
251	Pete Rose	2.75	1.75
252	Bill Madlock	.20	.12
253	Dale Berra	.10	.05
254	Kent Tekulve	.10	.06
255	Enrique Romo	.10	.05
256	Mike Easler	.10	.05
257	Chuck Tanner	.10	.05
258	Art Howe	.12	.07
259	Alan Ashby	.10	.05
260	Nolan Ryan	9.00	5.50
261a	Vern Ruhle(Wrong photo)	.35	.20
261b	Vern Ruhle(Cor)	.10	.05
262	Bob Boone	.20	.12
263	Cesar Cedeno	.15	.08
264	Jeff Leonard	.10	.06
265	Pat Putnam	.10	.05
266	Jon Matlack	.10	.05
267	Dave Rajsich	.10	.05
268	Billy Sample	.10	.05
269	Damaso Garcia	.10	.05
270	Tom Buskey	.10	.05
271	Joey McLaughlin	.10	.05
272	Barry Bonnell	.10	.05
273	Tug McGraw	.20	.12
274	Mike Jorgensen	.10	.05
275	Pat Zachry	.10	.05
276	Neil Allen	.10	.05
277	Joel Youngblood	.10	.05
278	Greg Pryor	.10	.05
279	Britt Burns (R)	.10	.06
280	Rich Dotson (R)	.15	.08
281	Chet Lemon	.10	.05
282	Rusty Kuntz	.10	.05
283	Ted Cox	.10	.05
284	Sparky Lyle	.10	.06
285	Larry Cox	.10	.05
286	Floyd Bannister	.10	.05

287 Byron McLaughlin	.10	.05
288 Rodney Craig	.10	.05
289 Bobby Grich	.12	.07
290 Dickie Thon	.12	.07
291 Mark Clear	.10	.05
292 Dave Lemanczyk	.10	.05
293 Jason Thompson	.10	.05
294 Rick Miller	.10	.05
295 Lonnie Smith	.20	.12
296 Ron Cey	.12	.07
297 Steve Yeager	.10	.05
298 Bobby Castillo	.10	.05
299 Manny Mota	.10	.06
300 Jay Johnstone	.12	.07
301 Dan Driessen	.12	.07
302 Joe Nolan	.10	.05
303 Paul Householder	.10	.05
304 Harry Spilman	.10	.05
305 Cesar Geronimo	.10	.05
306a Gary Mathews (Er)	.12	.07
306b Gary Mathews (Cor)	.10	.05
307 Ken Reitz	.10	.05
308 Ted Simmons	.15	.08
309 John Littlefield	.10	.05
310 George Frazier	.10	.05
311 Dane Iorg	.10	.05
312 Mike Ivie	.10	.05
313 Dennis Littlejohn	.10	.05
314 Gary Lavelle	.10	.05
315 Jack Clark	.25	.15
316 Jim Wohlford	.10	.05
317 Rick Matula	.10	.05
318 Toby Harrah	.10	.05
319a Dwane Kuiper (Er)	.12	.07
319b Duane Kuiper(Cor)	.10	.05
320 Len Barker	.10	.05
321 Victor Cruz	.10	.05
322 Dell Alston	.10	.05
323 Robin Yount	3.50	2.50
324 Charlie Moore	.10	.05
325 Lary Sorensen	.10	.05
326a Gorman Thomas (30 Hr 4th on back)	.25	.15
326b Gorman Thomas (30 Hr 3rd on back)	.10	.06
327 Bob Rodgers	.10	.05
328 Phil Niekro	.75	.45
329 Chris Speier	.10	.05
330a Steve Rodgers (Er)	.15	.08
330b Steve Rogers(Cor)	.10	.05
331 Woodie Fryman	.10	.05
332 Warren Cromartie	.10	.05
333 Jerry White	.10	.05
334 Tony Perez	.70	.40
335 Carlton Fisk	2.00	1.25
336 Dick Drago	.10	.05
337 Steve Renko	.10	.05

338 Jim Rice	.25	.15
339 Jerry Royster	.10	.05
340 Frank White	.12	.07
341 Jamie Quirk	.10	.05
342a Paul Spittorff (Er)	.10	.06
342b Paul Splittorff (Cor)	.10	.05
343 Marty Pattin	.10	.05
344 Pete LaCock	.10	.05
345 Willie Randolph	.15	.08
346 Rick Cerone	.10	.05
347 Rich Gossage	.25	.15
348 Reggie Jackson	3.00	1.75
349 Ruppert Jones	.10	.05
350 Dave McKay	.10	.05
351 Yogi Berra	.35	.20
352 Doug DeCinces	.10	.05
353 Jim Palmer	2.00	1.25
354 Tippy Martinez	.10	.05
355 Al Bumbry	.10	.05
356 Earl Weaver	.15	.08
357a Bob Picciolo (Er)	.12	.07
357b Rob Picciolo (Cor)	.10	.05
358 Matt Keough	.10	.05
359 Dwayne Murphy	.10	.05
360 Brian Kingman	.10	.05
361 Bill Fahey	.10	.05
362 Steve Mura	.10	.05
363 Dennis Kinney	.10	.05
364 Dave Winfield	4.50	2.75
365 Lou Whitaker	.80	.50
366 Lance Parrish	.25	.15
367 Tim Corcoran	.10	.05
368 Pat Underwood	.10	.05
369 Al Cowens	.10	.05
370 Sparky Anderson	.10	.06
371 Pete Rose	2.50	1.50
372 Phil Garner	.12	.07
373 Steve Nicosia	.10	.05
374 John Candelaria	.15	.08
375 Don Robinson	.10	.05
376 Lee Lacy	.10	.05
377 John Milner	.10	.05
378 Craig Reynolds	.10	.05
379a Luis Pujols (Er)	.12	.07
279b Luis Pujols (Cor)	.10	.05
380 Joe Niekro	.12	.07
381 Joaquin Andujar	.10	.06
382 Keith Moreland (R)	.12	.07
383 Jose Cruz	.15	.08
384 Bill Virdon	.10	.05
385 Jim Sundberg	.10	.05
386 Doc Medich	.10	.05
387 Al Oliver	.12	.07
388 Jim Norris	.10	.05
389 Bob Bailor	.10	.05
390 Ernie Whitt	.10	.05
391 Otto Velez	.10	.05

392	Roy Howell	.10	.05	447	Jim Slaton	.10	.05
393	Bob Walk (R)	.50	.30	448	Doyle Alexander	.10	.05
394	Doug Flynn	.10	.05	449	Tony Bernazard	.10	.05
395	Pete Falcone	.10	.05	450	Scott Sanderson	.12	.07
396	Tom Hausman	.10	.05	451	Dave Palmer	.10	.05
397	Elliott Maddox	.10	.05	452	Stan Bahnsen	.10	.05
398	Mike Squires	.10	.05	453	Dick Williams	.10	.05
399	Marvis Foley	.10	.05	454	Rick Burleson	.12	.07
400	Steve Trout	.10	.05	455	Gary Allenson	.10	.05
401	Wayne Nordhagen	.10	.05	456	Bob Stanley	.10	.05
402	Tony LaRussa	.12	.07	457	John Tudor(R)	.30	.18
403	Bruce Bochte	.10	.05	458	Dwight Evans	.35	.20
404	Bake McBride	.10	.05	459	Glenn Hubbard	.10	.05
405	Jerry Narron	.10	.05	460	U. L. Washington	.10	.05
406	Rob Dressler	.10	.05	461	Larry Gura	.10	.05
407	Dave Heaverlo	.10	.05	462	Rich Gale	.10	.05
408	Tom Paciorek	.10	.05	463	Hal McRae	.20	.12
409	Carney Lansford	.15	.10	464	Jim Frey	.10	.05
410	Brian Downing	.12	.07	465	Bucky Dent	.10	.06
411	Don Aase	.10	.05	466	Dennis Werth	.10	.05
412	Jim Barr	.10	.05	467	Ron Davis	.10	.05
413	Don Baylor	.20	.12	468	Reggie Jackson	3.00	2.00
414	Jim Fregosi	.10	.05	469	Bobby Brown	.10	.05
415	Dallas Green	.10	.05	470	Mike Davis (R)	.12	.07
416	Dave Lopes	.12	.07	471	Gaylord Perry	.60	.35
417	Jerry Reuss	.10	.05	472	Mark Belanger	.12	.07
418	Rick Sutcliffe	.30	.18	473	Jim Palmer	2.00	1.25
419	Derrel Thomas	.10	.05	474	Sammy Stewart	.10	.05
420	Tommy Lasorda	.12	.07	475	Tim Stoddard	.10	.05
421	Charlie Leibrandt (R)	.75	.45	476	Steve Stone	.10	.05
422	Tom Seaver	2.50	1.50	477	Jeff Newman	.10	.05
423	Ron Oester	.10	.05	478	Steve McCatty	.10	.05
424	Junior Kennedy	.10	.05	479	Billy Martin	.25	.15
425	Tom Seaver	2.50	1.50	480	Mitchell Page	.10	.05
426	Bobby Cox	.10	.05	481	Steve Carlton (Cy)	1.00	.70
427	Leon Durham (R)	.12	.07	482	Bill Buckner	.12	.07
428	Terry Kenndey	.12	.07	483	Ivan DeJesus(Var)	.10	.05
429	Silvio Martinez	.10	.05	484	Cliff Johnson	.10	.05
430	George Hendrick	.12	.07	485	Lenny Randle	.10	.05
431	Red Schoendienst	.12	.07	486	Larry Milbourne	.10	.05
432	John LeMaster	.10	.05	487	Roy Smalley	.10	.05
433	Vida Blue	.12	.07	488	John Castino	.10	.05
434	John Montefusco	.10	.05	489	Ron Jackson	.10	.05
435	Terry Whitfield	.10	.05	490	Dave Roberts (Var)	.10	.05
436	Dave Bristol	.10	.05	491	George Brett (MVP)	2.75	1.75
437	Dale Murphy	1.25	.80	492	Mike Cubbage	.10	.05
438	Jerry Dybzinski	.10	.05	493	Rob Wilfon	.10	.05
439	Jorge Orta	.10	.05	494	Danny Goodwin	.10	.05
440	Wayne Garland	.10	.05	495	Jose Morales	.10	.05
441	Miguel Dilone	.10	.05	496	Mickey Rivers	.10	.06
442	Dave Garcia	.10	.05	497	Mike Edwards	.10	.05
443	Don Money	.10	.05	498	Mike Sadek	.10	.05
444a	Buck Martinez (Photo reversed)	.10	.06	499	Lenn Sakata	.10	.05
				500	Gene Michael	.10	.05
444b	Buck Martinez (Cor)	.10	.05	501	Dave Roberts	.10	.05
445	Jerry Augustine	.10	.05	502	Steve Dillard	.10	.05
446	Ben Oglivie	.10	.05	503	Jim Essian	.10	.05

504 Rance Mulliniks	.10	.05
505 Darrell Porter	.10	.05
500 Joe Torre	.15	.08
507 Terry Crowley	.10	.05
508 Bill Travers	.10	.05
509 Nelson Norman	.10	.05
510 Bob McClure	.10	.05
511 Steve Howe (R)	.10	.06
512 Dave Rader	.10	.05
513 Mick Kelleher	.10	.05
514 Kiko Garcia	.10	.05
515 Larry Biittner	.10	.05
516 Willie Norwood (Var)	.10	.05
517 Bo Diaz	.10	.05
518 Juan Beniquez	.10	.05
519 Scot Thompson	.10	.05
520 Jim Tracy	.10	.05
521 Carlos Lezcano	.10	.05
522 Joe Amalfitano	.10	.05
523 Preston Hanna	.10	.05
524 Ray Burris (Var)	.12	.07
525 Broderick Perkins	.10	.05
526 Mickey Hatcher	.10	.05
527 John Goryl	.10	.05
528 Dick Davis	.10	.05
529 Butch Wynegar	.10	.05
530 Sal Butera	.10	.05
531 Jerry Koosman	.12	.07
532 Jeff Zahn (Var)	.10	.05
533 Dennis Martinez	.40	.25
534 Gary Thomasson	.10	.05
535 Steve Macko	.10	.05
536 Jim Kaat	.25	.15
537 Best Hitters(George Brett, Rod Carew	3.00	2.00
538 Tim Raines (R)	6.00	3.75
539 Keith Smith	.10	.05
540 Ken Macha	.10	.05
541 Burt Hooton	.10	.05
542 Butch Hobson	.12	.07
543 Bill Stein	.10	.05
544 Dave Stapleton	.10	.05
545 Bob Pate	.10	.05
546 Doug Corbett	.10	.05
547 Darrell Jackson	.10	.05
548 Pete Redfern	.10	.05
549 Roger Erickson	.10	.05
550 Al Hrabosky	.10	.05
551 Dick Tidrow	.10	.05
552 Dave Ford	.10	.05
553 Dave Kingman	.15	.08
554 Mike Vail (Var)	.10	.05
555 Jerry Martin (Var)	.10	.05
556 Jesus Figueroa (Var)	.10	.05
557 Don Stanhouse	.10	.05
558 Barry Foote	.10	.05
559 Tim Blackwell	.10	.05

560 Bruce Sutter	.15	.08
561 Rick Reuschel	.15	.08
562 Lynn McGlothen	.10	.05
563 Bob Owchinko (Var)	.10	.05
564 John Verhoeven	.10	.05
565 Ken Landreaux	.10	.05
566 Glenn Adams (Var)	.10	.05
567 Hosken Powell	.10	.05
568 Dick Noles	.10	.05
569 Danny Ainge (R)	3.00	2.00
570 Bobby Mattick	.10	.05
571 Joe LeFebvre	.10	.05
572 Bobby Clark	.10	.05
573 Dennis Lamp	.10	.05
574 Randy Lerch	.10	.05
575 Mookie Wilson (R)	.40	.25
576 Ron LeFlore	.12	.07
577 Jim Dwyer	.10	.05
578 Bill Castro	.10	.05
579 Greg Minton	.10	.05
580 Mark Littell	.10	.05
581 Andy Hassler	.10	.05
582 Dave Stieb	.40	.25
583 Ken Oberkfell	.10	.05
584 Larry Bradford	.10	.05
585 Fred Stanley	.10	.05
586 Bill Caudill	.10	.05
587 Doug Capilla	.10	.05
588 George Riley	.10	.05
589 Willie Hernandez	.12	.07
590 Mike Schmidt (MVP)	1.75	1.00
591 Steve Stone (CY)	.12	.07
592 Rick Sofield	.10	.05
593 Bombo Rivera	.10	.05
594 Gary Ward	.10	.05
595 Dave Edwards (Var)	.10	.05
596 Mike Proly	.10	.05
597 Tommy Boggs	.10	.05
598 Greg Gross	.10	.05
599 Elias Sosa	.10	.05
600 Pat Kelly	.10	.05
___ Checklist (Er) (Tom Donohue)	1.00	.70
___ Checklist (Cor) (Tom Donahue)	.15	.08
___ Checklist (Er) (Gary Mathews)	.25	.15
___ Checklist (Cor) (Gary Matthews)	.15	.08
___ Checklist (Er) (Luis Pujols)	.25	.15
___ Checklist (Cor) (Luis Pujols)	.15	.08
___ Checklist (Er) Glen Adams)	.25	.15
___ Checklist (Cor) (Glenn Adams)	.15	.08

1982 Donruss

The second Donruss baseball set consists of 660-cards and marks the debut of the Donruss Diamond Kings subset (DK). Donruss upgraded the quality of the paper stock over the previous year and included puzzle pieces instead of bubble gum in each pack. The cared feature full color photos on the front with the team name in a small baseball in the lower corner of the card while the player's name appears in a baseball bat design under his photograph. Cards measure 2-1/2" by 3-1/2".

		MINT	NR/MT
Complete Set (660)		110.00	75.00
Commons		.10	.05
1	Pete Rose (DK)	2.50	1.50
2	Gary Carter (DK)	.50	.30
3	Steve Garvey (DK)	.50	.30
4	Vida Blue (DK)	.15	.08
5a	Alan Trammel (DK) (Er)	1.25	.80
5b	Alan Trammell (DK) (Cor)	.50	.30
6	Len Barker (DK)	.12	.07
7	Dwight Evans (DK)	.20	.12
8	Rod Carew (DK)	.80	.50
9	George Hendrick (DK)	.15	.08
10	Phil Niekro (DK)	.40	.25
11	Richie Zisk (DK)	.12	.07
12	Dave Parker (DK)	.20	.12
13	Nolan Ryan (DK)	5.00	3.00
14	Ivan DeJesus (DK)	.12	.07
15	George Brett (DK)	1.75	1.00
16	Tom Seaver (DK)	1.50	.90
17	Dave Kingman (DK)	.15	.08
18	Dave Winfield (DK)	2.00	1.25
19	Mike Norris (DK)	.12	.07
20	Carlton Fisk (DK)	1.00	.70
21	Ozzie Smith (DK)	1.50	.90
22	Roy Smalley (DK)	.12	.07
23	Buddy Bell (DK)	.12	.07
24	Ken Singleton (DK)	.12	.07
25	John Mayberry (DK)	.12	.07
26	Gorman Thomas (DK)	.12	.07
27	Earl Weaver	.12	.07
28	Hollie Fingers	.90	.60
29	Sparky Anderson	.12	.07
30	Dennis Eckersley	1.50	.90
31	Dave Winfield	3.50	2.00
32	Burt Hooton	.10	.05
33	Rick Waits	.10	.05
34	George Brett	3.00	2.00
35	Steve McCatty	.10	.05
36	Steve Rogers	.10	.05
37	Bill Stein	.10	.05
38	Steve Renko	.10	.05
39	Mike Squires	.10	.05
40	George Hendrick	.10	.05
41	Bob Knepper	.10	.05
42	Steve Carlton	2.00	1.25
43	Larry Biittner	.10	.05
44	Chris Welsh	.10	.05
45	Steve Nicosia	.10	.05
46	Jack Clark	.15	.08
47	Chris Chambliss	.12	.07
48	Ivan DeJesus	.10	.05
49	Lee Mazzilli	.10	.05
50	Julio Cruz	.10	.05
51	Pete Redfern	.10	.05
52	Dave Stieb	.20	.12
53	Doug Corbett	.10	.05
54	Jorge Bell (R)	4.00	2.50
55	Joe Simpson	.10	.05
56	Rusty Staub	.15	.08
57	Hector Cruz	.10	.05
58	Claudell Washington	.10	.05
59	Enrique Romo	.10	.05
60	Gary Lavelle	.10	.05
61	Tim Flannery	.10	.05
62	Joe Nolan	.10	.05
63	Larry Bowa	.12	.07
64	Sixto Lezcano	.10	.05
65	Joe Sambito	.10	.05
66	Bruce Kison	.10	.05
67	Wayne Nordhagen	.10	.05
68	Woodie Fryman	.10	.05
69	Billy Sample	.10	.05
70	Amos Otis	.10	.05
71	Matt Keough	.10	.05
72	Toby Harrah	.10	.05
73	Dave Righetti(R)	.50	.30
74	Carl Yastrzemski	2.00	1.25
75	Bob Welch	.20	.12
76a	Alan Trammell(Er)	1.50	.90
76b	Alan Trammell(Cor)	1.00	.70
77	Rick Dempsey	.10	.05

78	Paul Molitor	3.00	2.00	135	Lou Piniella	.12	.07
79	Dennis Martinez	.30	.18	136	Pedro Guerrero	.25	.15
80	Jim Slaton	.10	.05	137	Len Barker	.10	.05
81	Champ Summers	.10	.05	138	Richard Gale	.10	.05
82	Carney Lansford	.12	.07	139	Wayne Gross	.10	.05
83	Barry Foote	.10	.05	140	Tim Wallach (R)	.80	.50
84	Steve Garvey	.70	.40	141	Gene Mauch	.12	.07
85	Rick Manning	.10	.05	142	Doc Medich	.10	.05
86	John Wathan	.10	.05	143	Tony Bernazard	.10	.05
87	Brian Kingman	.10	.05	144	Bill Virdon	.10	.05
88	Andre Dawson	2.00	1.25	145	John Littlefield	.10	.05
89	Jim Kern	.10	.05	146	Dave Bergman	.10	.05
90	Bobby Grich	.12	.07	147	Dick Davis	.10	.05
91	Bob Forsch	.10	.05	148	Tom Seaver	2.00	1.25
92	Art Howe	.10	.05	149	Matt Sinatro	.10	.05
93	Marty Bystrom	.10	.05	150	Chuck Tanner	.10	.05
94	Ozzie Smith	2.50	1.50	151	Leon Durham	.10	.05
95	Dave Parker	.30	.18	152	Gene Tenace	.10	.05
96	Doyle Alexander	.10	.05	153	Al Bumbry	.10	.05
97	Al Hrabosky	.10	.05	154	Mark Brouhard	.10	.05
98	Frank Taveras	.10	.05	155	Rick Peters	.10	.05
99	Tim Blackwell	.10	.05	156	Jerry Remy	.10	.05
100	Floyd Bannister	.10	.05	157	Rick Reuschel	.10	.05
101	Alfredo Griffin	.10	.05	158	Steve Howe	.10	.05
102	Dave Engle	.10	.05	159	Alan Bannister	.10	.05
103	Mario Soto	.10	.05	160	U.L. Washington	.10	.05
104	Ross Baumgarten	.10	.05	161	Rick Langford	.10	.05
105	Ken Singleton	.10	.05	162	Bill Gullickson	.15	.08
106	Ted Simmons	.12	.07	163	Mark Wagner	.10	.05
107	Jack Morris	1.00	.70	164	Geoff Zahn	.10	.05
108	Bob Watson	.12	.07	165	Ron LeFlore	.10	.05
109	Dwight Evans	.25	.15	166	Dane Iorg	.10	.05
110	Tom Lasorda	.15	.08	167	Joe Niekro	.10	.05
111	Bert Blyleven	.35	.20	168	Pete Rose	2.50	1.50
112	Dan Quisenberry	.12	.07	169	Dave Collins	.10	.05
113	Rickey Henderson	5.00	3.00	170	Rick Wise	.10	.05
114	Gary Carter	.80	.50	171	Jim Bibby	.10	.05
115	Brian Downing	.10	.05	172	Larry Herndon	.10	.05
116	Al Oliver	.12	.07	173	Bob Horner	.12	.07
117	LaMarr Hoyt	.10	.05	174	Steve Dillard	.10	.05
118	Cesar Cedeno	.12	.07	175	Mookie Wilson	.10	.05
119	Keith Moreland	.10	.05	176	Dan Meyer	.10	.05
120	Bob Shirley	.10	.05	177	Fernando Arroyo	.10	.05
121	Terry Kennedy	.10	.05	178	Jackson Todd	.10	.05
122	Frank Pastore	.10	.05	179	Darrell Jackson	.10	.05
123	Gene Garber	.10	.05	180	Al Woods	.10	.05
124	Tony Pena	.25	.15	181	Jim Anderson	.10	.05
125	Allen Ripley	.10	.05	182	Dave Kingman	.12	.07
126	Randy Martz	.10	.05	183	Steve Henderson	.10	.05
127	Richie Zisk	.10	.05	184	Brian Asselstine	.10	.05
128	Mike Scott	.20	.12	185	Rod Scurry	.10	.05
129	Lloyd Moseby	.12	.07	186	Fred Breining	.10	.05
130	Rob Wilfong	.10	.05	187	Danny Boone	.10	.05
131	Tim Stoddard	.10	.05	188	Junior Kennedy	.10	.05
132	Gorman Thomas	.12	.07	189	Sparky Lyle	.12	.07
133	Dan Petry	.10	.05	190	Whitey Herzog	.12	.07
134	Bob Stanley	.10	.05	191	Dave Smith	.10	.05

192	Ed Ott	.10	.05
193	Greg Luzinski	.12	.07
194	Bill Lee	.10	.05
195	Don Zimmer	.10	.05
196	Hal McRae	.12	.07
197	Mike Norris	.10	.05
198	Duane Kuiper	.10	.05
199	Rick Cerone	.10	.05
200	Jim Rice	.25	.15
201	Steve Yeager	.10	.05
202	Tom Brookens	.10	.05
203	Jose Morales	.10	.05
204	Roy Howell	.10	.05
205	Tippy Martinez	.10	.05
206	Moose Haas	.10	.05
207	Al Cowens	.10	.05
208	Dave Stapleton	.10	.05
209	Bucky Dent	.12	.07
210	Ron Cey	.12	.07
211	Jorge Orta	.10	.05
212	Jamie Quirk	.10	.05
213	Jeff Jones	.10	.05
214	Tim Raines	2.00	1.25
215	Jon Matlack	.10	.05
216	Rod Carew	1.50	.90
217	Jim Kaat	.15	.08
218	Joe Pittman	.10	.05
219	Larry Christenson	.10	.05
220	Juan Bonilla	.10	.05
221	Mike Easler	.10	.05
222	Vida Blue	.12	.07
223	Rick Camp	.10	.05
224	Mike Jorgensen	.10	.05
225	Jody Davis (R)	.12	.07
226	Mike Parrott	.10	.05
227	Jim Clancy	.10	.05
228	Hosken Powell	.10	.05
229	Tom Hume	.10	.05
230	Britt Burns	.10	.05
231	Jim Palmer	1.50	.90
232	Bob Rodgers	.10	.05
233	Milt Wilcox	.10	.05
234	Dave Revering	.10	.05
235	Mike Torrez	.10	.05
236	Robert Castillo	.10	.05
237	Von Hayes (R)	.25	.15
238	Renie Martin	.10	.05
239	Dwayne Murphy	.10	.05
240	Rodney Scott	.10	.05
241	Fred Patek	.10	.05
242	Mickey Rivers	.10	.05
243	Steve Trout	.10	.05
244	Jose Cruz	.12	.07
245	Manny Trillo	.10	.05
246	Lary Sorensen	.10	.05
247	Dave Edwards	.10	.05
248	Dan Driessen	.10	.05
249	Tommy Boggs	.10	.05
250	Dale Berra	.10	.05
251	Ed Whitson	.10	.05
252	Lee Smith (R)	9.00	6.00
253	Tom Paciorek	.10	.05
254	Pat Zachry	.10	.05
255	Luis Leal	.10	.05
256	John Castino	.10	.05
257	Rich Dauer	.10	.05
258	Cecil Cooper	.12	.07
259	Dave Rozema	.10	.05
260	John Tudor	.10	.05
261	Jerry Mumphrey	.10	.05
262	Jay Johnstone	.10	.05
263	Bo Diaz	.10	.05
264	Dennis Leonard	.10	.05
265	Jim Spencer	.10	.05
266	John Milner	.10	.05
267	Don Aase	.10	.05
268	Jim Sundberg	.10	.05
269	Lamar Johnson	.10	.05
270	Frank LaCorte	.10	.05
271	Barry Evans	.10	.05
272	Enos Cabell	.10	.05
273	Del Unser	.10	.05
274	George Foster	.15	.08
275	Brett Butler (R)	2.00	1.25
276	Lee Lacy	.10	.05
277	Ken Reitz	.10	.05
278	Keith Hernandez	.20	.12
279	Doug DeCinces	.10	.05
280	Charlie Moore	.10	.05
281	Lance Parrish	.25	.15
282	Ralph Houk	.10	.06
283	Rich Gossage	.25	.15
284	Jerry Reuss	.10	.05
285	Mike Stanton	.10	.05
286	Frank White	.10	.05
287	Bob Owchinko	.10	.05
288	Scott Sanderson	.10	.05
289	Bump Wills	.10	.05
290	Dave Frost	.10	.05
291	Chet Lemon	.10	.05
292	Tito Landrum	.10	.05
293	Vern Ruhle	.10	.05
294	Mike Schmidt	3.00	2.00
295	Sam Mejias	.10	.05
296	Gary Lucas	.10	.05
297	John Candelaria	.10	.05
298	Jerry Martin	.10	.05
299	Dale Murphy	1.00	.70
300	Mike Lum	.10	.05
301	Tom Hausman	.10	.05
302	Glenn Abbott	.10	.05
303	Roger Erickson	.10	.05
304	Otto Velez	.10	.05
305	Danny Goodwin	.10	.05

306	John Mayberry	.10	.05
307	Lenny Randle	.10	.05
308	Bob Bailor	.10	.05
309	Jerry Morales	.10	.05
310	Rufino Linares	.10	.05
311	Kent Tekulve	.10	.05
312	Joe Morgan	.75	.45
313	John Urrea	.10	.05
314	Paul Householder	.10	.05
315	Garry Maddox	.10	.05
316	Mike Ramsey	.10	.05
317	Alan Ashby	.10	.05
318	Bob Clark	.10	.05
319	Tony LaRussa	.12	.07
320	Charlie Lea	.10	.05
321	Danny Darwin	.10	.05
322	Cesar Geronimo	.10	.05
323	Tom Underwood	.10	.05
324	Andre Thornton	.12	.07
325	Rudy May	.10	.05
326	Frank Tanana	.10	.05
327	Davey Lopes	.12	.07
328	Richie Hebner	.10	.05
329	Mike Flanagan	.10	.05
330	Mike Caldwell	.10	.05
331	Scott McGregor	.10	.05
332	Jerry Augustine	.10	.05
333	Stan Papi	.10	.05
334	Rick Miller	.10	.05
335	Graig Nettles	.20	.12
336	Dusty Baker	.15	.10
337	Dave Garcia	.10	.05
338	Larry Gura	.10	.05
339	Cliff Johnson	.10	.05
340	Warren Cromartie	.10	.05
341	Steve Comer	.10	.05
342	Rick Burleson	.10	.05
343	John Martin	.10	.05
344	Craig Reynolds	.10	.05
345	Mike Proly	.10	.05
346	Ruppert Jones	.10	.05
347	Omar Moreno	.10	.05
348	Greg Minton	.10	.05
349	Rick Mahler (R)	.12	.07
350	Alex Trevino	.10	.05
351	Mike Krukow	.10	.05
352a	Shane Rawley (Wrong photo)	.50	.30
352b	Shane Rawley (Cor)	.10	.05
353	Garth Iorg	.10	.05
354	Pete Mackanin	.10	.05
355	Paul Moskau	.10	.05
356	Richard Dotson	.10	.05
357	Steve Stone	.10	.05
358	Larry Hisle	.10	.05
359	Aurelio Lopez	.10	.05
360	Oscar Gamble	.10	.05
361	Tom Burgmeier	.10	.05
362	Terry Forster	.10	.05
363	Joe Charboneau	.10	.05
364	Ken Brett	.10	.05
365	Tony Armas	.10	.05
366	Chris Speier	.10	.05
367	Fred Lynn	.15	.08
368	Buddy Bell	.10	.05
369	Jim Essian	.10	.05
370	Terry Puhl	.10	.05
371	Greg Gross	.10	.05
372	Bruce Sutter	.15	.08
373	Joe Lefebvre	.10	.05
374	Ray Knight	.10	.05
375	Bruce Benedict	.10	.05
376	Tim Foli	.10	.05
377	Al Holland	.10	.05
378	Ken Kravec	.10	.05
379	Jeff Burroughs	.10	.05
380	Pete Falcone	.10	.05
381	Ernie Whitt	.10	.05
382	Brad Havens	.10	.05
383	Terry Crowley	.10	.05
384	Don Money	.10	.05
385	Dan Schatzeder	.10	.05
386	Gary Allenson	.10	.05
387	Yogi Berra	.35	.20
388	Ken Landreaux	.10	.05
389	Mike Hargrove	.10	.05
390	Darryl Motley	.10	.05
391	Dave McKay	.10	.05
392	Stan Bahnsen	.10	.05
393	Ken Forsch	.10	.05
394	Mario Mendoza	.10	.05
395	Jim Morrison	.10	.05
396	Mike Ivie	.10	.05
397	Broderick Perkins	.10	.05
398	Darrell Evans	.12	.07
399	Ron Reed	.10	.05
400	Johnny Bench	1.75	1.00
401	Steve Bedrosian (R)	.25	.15
402	Bill Robinson	.10	.05
403	Bill Buckner	.12	.07
404	Ken Oberkfell	.10	.05
405	Cal Ripken, Jr. (R)	60.00	45.00
406	Jim Gantner	.10	.05
407	Kirk Gibson	.80	.50
408	Tony Perez	.40	.25
409	Tommy John	.20	.12
410	Dave Stewart (R)	3.50	2.00
411	Dan Spillner	.10	.05
412	Willie Aikens	.10	.05
413	Mike Heath	.10	.05
414	Ray Burris	.10	.05
415	Leon Roberts	.10	.05
416	Mike Witt (R)	.20	.12
417	Bobby Molinaro	.10	.05

418	Steve Braun	.10	.05	473	Randy Niemann	.10	.05
419	Nolan Ryan	8.50	5.00	474	Tom Griffin	.10	.05
420	Tug McGraw	.20	.12	475	Phil Niekro	.50	.30
421	Dave Concepcion	.15	.08	476	Hubie Brooks	.30	.18
422a	Juan Eickelberger (Er)	.50	.30	477	Dick Tidrow	.10	.05
	Wrong photo)			478	Jim Beattie	.10	.05
422b	Juan Eickelberger (Cor)	.10	.05	479	Damaso Garcia	.10	.05
423	Rick Rhoden	.10	.05	480	Mickey Hatcher	.10	.05
424	Frank Robinson	.25	.15	481	Joe Price	.10	.05
425	Eddie Miller	.10	.05	482	Ed Farmer	.10	.05
426	Bill Caudill	.10	.05	483	Eddie Murray	2.00	1.25
427	Doug Flynn	.10	.05	484	Ben Oglivie	.10	.05
428	Larry Anderson (Er)	.10	.05	485	Kevin Saucier	.10	.05
429	Al Williams	.10	.05	486	Bobby Murcer	.12	.07
430	Jerry Garvin	.10	.05	487	Bill Campbell	.10	.05
431	Glenn Adams	.10	.05	488	Reggie Smith	.10	.05
432	Barry Bonnell	.10	.05	489	Wayne Garland	.10	.05
433	Jerry Narron	.10	.05	490	Jim Wright	.10	.05
434	John Stearns	.10	.05	491	Billy Martin	.25	.15
435	Mike Tyson	.10	.05	492	Jim Fanning	.10	.05
436	Glenn Hubbard	.10	.05	493	Don Baylor	.20	.12
437	Eddie Solomon	.10	.05	494	Rick Honeycutt	.10	.05
438	Jeff Leonard	.10	.05	495	Carlton Fisk	1.75	1.00
439	Randy Bass	.10	.05	496	Denny Walling	.10	.05
440	Mike LaCoss	.10	.05	497	Bake McBride	.10	.05
441	Gary Matthews	.10	.05	498	Darrell Porter	.10	.05
442	Mark Littell	.10	.05	499	Gene Richards	.10	.05
443	Don Sutton	.50	.30	500	Ken Dayley (R)	.12	.07
444	John Harris	.10	.05	502	Jason Thompson	.10	.05
445	Vada Pinson	.10	.05	503	Milt May	.10	.05
446	Elias Sosa	.10	.05	504	Doug Bird	.10	.05
447	Charlie Hough	.10	.05	505	Bruce Bochte	.10	.05
448	Willie Wilson	.12	.07	506	Neil Allen	.10	.05
449	Fred Stanley	.10	.05	507	Joey McLaughlin	.10	.05
450	Tom Veryzer	.10	.05	508	Butch Wynegar	.10	.05
451	Ron Davis	.10	.05	509	Gary Roenicke	.10	.05
452	Mark Clear	.10	.05	510	Robin Yount	3.50	2.00
453	Bill Russell	.12	.07	511	Dave Tobik	.10	.05
454	Lou Whitaker	.40	.25	512	Rich Gedman (R)	.12	.07
455	Dan Graham	.10	.05	513	Gene Nelson (R)	.10	.05
456	Reggie Cleveland	.10	.05	514	Rick Monday	.10	.05
457	Sammy Stewart	.10	.05	515	Miguel Dilone	.10	.05
458	Pete Vuckovich	.10	.05	516	Clint Hurdle	.10	.05
459	John Wockenfuss	.10	.05	517	Jeff Newman	.10	.05
460	Glenn Hoffman	.10	.05	518	Grant Jackson	.10	.05
461	Willie Randolph	.15	.08	519	Andy Hassler	.10	.05
462	Fernando Valenzuela	.35	.20	520	Pat Putnam	.10	.05
463	Ron Hassey	.10	.05	521	Greg Pryor	.10	.05
464	Paul Splittorff	.10	.05	522	Tony Scott	.10	.05
465	Rob Picciolo	.10	.05	523	Steve Mura	.10	.05
466	Larry Parrish	.12	.07	524	Johnnie LeMaster	.10	.05
467	Johnny Grubb	.10	.05	525	Dick Ruthven	.10	.05
468	Dan Ford	.10	.05	526	John McNamara	.10	.05
469	Silvio Martinez	.10	.05	527	Larry McWilliams	.10	.05
470	Kiko Garcia	.10	.05	528	Johnny Ray (R)	.12	.07
471	Bob Boone	.12	.07	529	Pat Tabler (R)	.20	.12
472	Luis Salazar	.10	.05	530	Tom Herr	.10	.05

531	San Diego Chicken (Var)	1.50	.90
532	Sal Butera	.10	.05
533	Mike Griffin	.10	.05
534	Kelvin Moore	.10	.05
535	Reggie Jackson	2.50	1.50
536	Ed Romero	.10	.05
537	Derrel Thomas	.10	.05
538	Mike O'Berry	.10	.05
539	Jack O'Connor	.10	.05
540	Bob Ojeda (R)	.35	.20
541	Roy Lee Jackson	.10	.05
542	Lynn Jones	.10	.05
543	Gaylord Perry	.50	.30
544a	Phil Garner(Photo reversed)	.50	.30
544b	Phil Garner (Cor)	.10	.05
545	Garry Templeton	.10	.05
546	Rafael Ramirez	.10	.05
547	Jeff Reardon	1.50	.90
548	Ron Guidry	.25	.15
549	Tim Laudner (R)	.12	.07
550	John Henry Johnson	.10	.05
551	Chris Bando	.10	.05
552	Bobby Brown	.10	.05
553	Larry Bradford	.10	.05
554	Scott Fletcher (R)	.35	.20
555	Jerry Royster	.10	.05
556	Shooty Babbitt	.10	.05
557	Kent Hrbek (R)	2.50	1.50
558	Yankee Winners(Ron Guidry, Tommy John)	.20	.12
559	Mark Bomback	.10	.05
560	Julio Valdez	.10	.05
561	Buck Martinez	.10	.05
562	Mike Marshall (R)	.15	.08
563	Rennie Stennett	.10	.05
564	Steve Crawford	.10	.05
565	Bob Babcock	.10	.05
566	Johnny Podres	.12	.07
567	Paul Serna	.10	.05
568	Harold Baines	1.00	.70
569	Dave LaRoche	.10	.05
570	Lee May	.10	.05
571	Gary Ward	.10	.05
572	John Denny	.10	.05
573	Roy Smalley	.10	.05
574	Bob Brenly (R)	.15	.08
575	Bronx Bombers(Reggie Jackson, Dave Winfield)	2.50	1.50
576	Luis Pujols	.10	.05
577	Butch Hobson	.10	.05
578	Harvey Kuenn	.12	.07
579	Cal Ripken, Sr.	.12	.07
580	Juan Berenguer	.10	.05
581	Benny Ayala	.10	.05
582	Vance Law	.10	.05
583	Rick Leach (R)	.10	.05
584	George Frazier	.10	.05
585	Phillies Finest(Pete Rose, Mike Schmidt)	2.00	1.25
586	Joe Rudi	.12	.07
587	Juan Beniquez	.10	.05
588	Luis DeLeon (R)	.10	.05
589	Craig Swan	.10	.05
590	Dave Chalk	.10	.05
591	Billy Gardner	.10	.05
592	Sal Bando	.12	.07
593	Bert Campaneris	.10	.05
594	Steve Kemp	.10	.05
595a	Randy Lerch(Braves)	.50	.30
595b	Randy Lerch(Brewers)	.10	.05
596	Bryan Clark	.10	.05
597	Dave Ford	.10	.05
598	Mike Scioscia	.35	.20
599	John Lowenstein	.10	.05
600	Rene Lachemann	.10	.05
601	Mick Kelleher	.10	.05
602	Ron Jackson	.10	.05
603	Jerry Koosman	.12	.07
604	Dave Goltz	.10	.05
605	Ellis Valentine	.10	.05
606	Lonnie Smith	.12	.07
607	Joaquin Andujar	.10	.05
608	Garry Hancock	.10	.05
609	Jerry Turner	.10	.05
610	Bob Bonner	.10	.05
611	Jim Dwyer	.10	.05
612	Terry Bulling	.10	.05
613	Joel Youngblood	.10	.05
614	Larry Milbourne	.10	.05
615	Phil Roof (Er)(Gene)	.10	.05
616	Keith Drumright	.10	.05
617	Dave Rosello	.10	.05
618	Rickey Keeton	.10	.05
619	Dennis Lamp	.10	.05
620	Sid Monge	.10	.05
621	Jerry White	.10	.05
622	Luis Aguayo (R)	.10	.05
623	Jamie Easterly	.10	.05
624	Steve Sax (R)	1.75	1.00
625	Dave Roberts	.10	.05
626	Rick Bosetti	.10	.05
627	Terry Francona (R)	.12	.07
628	Pride of the Reds (Johnny Bench, Tom Seaver)	2.00	1.25
629	Paul Mirabella	.10	.05
630	Rance Mulliniks	.10	.05
631	Kevin Hickey	.10	.05
632	Reid Nichols	.10	.05
633	Dave Geisel	.10	.05
634	Ken Griffey	.20	.12
635	Bob Lemon	.15	.08

636	Orlando Sanchez	.10	.05
637	Bill Almon	.10	.05
638	Danny Ainge	1.00	.70
639	Willie Stargell	.75	.45
640	Bob Sykes	.10	.05
641	Ed Lynch	.10	.05
642	John Ellis	.10	.05
643	Fergie Jenkins	.50	.30
644	Lenn Sakata	.10	.05
645	Julio Gonzales	.10	.05
646	Jesse Orosco	.10	.05
647	Jerry Dybzinski	.10	.05
648	Tommy Davis	.12	.07
649	Ron Gardenhire	.10	.05
650	Felipe Alou	.12	.07
651	Harvey Haddix	.10	.05
652	Willie Upshaw	.10	.05
653	Bill Madlock	.12	.07
___	Checklist (Er) (Alan trammel)	.50	.30
___	Checklist (Cor) (Alan Trammell)	.15	.08
___	Checklist 27-130	.15	.08
___	Checklist 131-234	.15	.08
___	Checklist 235-338	.15	.08
___	Checklist 339-442	.15	.08
___	Checklist 443-544	.15	.08
___	Checklist 545-653	.15	.08

1983 Donruss

The 1983 Donruss set features 660 standard-size cards including seven unnumbered checklist cards. The first 26 cards in the set are Diamond Kings (DK). The card design is similar to the 1982 set with full color player photos on the front with the player's name appearing in a bat design under his photograph and the team name located inside a small baseball glove in the lower corner of the card. The backs consist of black type on a yellow and white background. The cards were sold with puzzle pieces featuring Ty Cobb.

		MINT	NR/MT
Complete Set (660)		140.00	100.00
Commons		.10	.05
1	Fernando Valenzuela (DK)	.25	.15
2	Rollie Fingers(DK)	.40	.25
3	Reggie Jackson(DK)	1.00	.70
4	Jim Palmer(DK)	.50	.30
5	Jack Morris(DK)	.30	.18
6	George Foster(DK)	.12	.07
7	Jim Sundberg(DK)	.12	.07
8	Willie Stargell(DK)	.35	.20
9	Dave Stieb(DK)	.12	.07
10	Joe Niekro(DK)	.12	.07
11	Rickey Henderson(DK)	2.00	1.25
12	Dale Murphy(DK)	.35	.20
13	Toby Harrah(DK)	.12	.07
14	Bill Buckner(DK)	.12	.07
15	Willie Wilson(DK)	.12	.07
16	Steve Carlton(DK)	.75	.45
17	Ron Guidry(DK)	.15	.08
18	Steve Rogers(DK)	.12	.07
19	Kent Hrbek(DK)	.15	.08
20	Keith Hernandez(DK)	.15	.08
21	Floyd Bannister(DK)	.12	.07
22	Johnny Bench (DK)	.75	.45
23	Britt Burns(DK)	.12	.07
24	Joe Morgan (DK)	.40	.25
25	Carl Yastrzemski (DK)	.75	.45
26	Terry Kenndey (DK)	.12	.07
27	Gary Roenicke	.10	.05
28	Dwight Bernard	.10	.05
29	Pat Underwood	.10	.05
30	Gary Allenson	.10	.05
31	Ron Guidry	.15	.08
32	Burt Hooton	.10	.05
33	Chris Bando	.10	.05
34	Vida Blue	.12	.07
35	Rickey Henderson	3.00	2.00
36	Ray Burris	.10	.05
37	John Butcher	.10	.05
38	Don Aase	.10	.05
39	Jerry Koosman	.10	.06
40	Bruce Sutter	.12	.07
41	Jose Cruz	.12	.07
42	Pete Rose	2.00	1.25
43	Cesar Cedeno	.10	.06
44	Floyd Chiffer	.10	.05
45	Larry McWilliams	.10	.05

46	Alan Fowlkes	.10	.05	102	Robert Castillo	.10	.05
47	Dale Murphy	.75	.45	103	Bruce Berenyi	.10	.05
48	Doug Bird	.10	.05	104	Carlton Fisk	1.50	.90
49	Hubie Brooks	.15	.08	105	Mike Flanagan	.10	.05
50	Floyd Bannister	.10	.05	106	Cecil Cooper	.10	.05
51	Jack O'Connor	.10	.05	107	Jack Morris	.60	.35
52	Steve Senteney	.10	.05	108	Mike Morgan	.30	.18
53	Gary Gaetti (R)	.30	.18	109	Luis Aponte	.10	.05
54	Damaso Garcia	.10	.05	110	Pedro Guerrero	.25	.15
55	Gene Nelson	.10	.05	111	Len Barker	.10	.05
56	Mookie Wilson	.10	.05	112	Willie Wilson	.10	.05
57	Allen Ripley	.10	.05	113	Dave Beard	.10	.05
58	Bob Horner	.10	.06	114	Mike Gates	.10	.05
59	Tony Pena	.10	.05	115	Reggie Jackson	2.50	1.50
60	Gary Lavelle	.10	.05	116	George Wright	.10	.05
61	Tim Lollar	.10	.05	117	Vance Law	.10	.05
62	Frank Pastore	.10	.05	118	Nolan Ryan	8.50	5.00
63	Garry Maddox	.10	.05	119	Mike Krukow	.10	.05
64	Bob Forsch	.10	.05	120	Ozzie Smith	1.75	1.00
65	Harry Spilman	.10	.05	121	Broderick Perkins	.10	.05
66	Geoff Zahn	.10	.05	122	Tom Seaver	1.75	1.00
67	Salome Barojas	.10	.05	123	Chris Chambliss	.10	.06
68	David Palmer	.10	.05	124	Chuck Tanner	.10	.05
69	Charlie Hough	.10	.05	125	Johnnie LeMaster	.10	.05
70	Dan Quisenberry	.10	.05	126	Mel Hall (R)	.80	.50
71	Tony Armas	.10	.05	127	Bruce Bochte	.10	.05
72	Rick Sutcliffe	.12	.07	128	Charlie Puleo (R)	.10	.05
73	Steve Balboni	.10	.05	129	Luis Leal	.10	.05
74	Jerry Remy	.10	.05	130	John Pacella	.10	.05
75	Mike Scioscia	.12	.07	131	Glenn Gulliver	.10	.05
76	John Wockenfuss	.10	.05	132	Don Money	.10	.05
77	Jim Palmer	1.25	.80	133	Dave Rozema	.10	.05
78	Rollie Fingers	.80	.50	134	Bruce Hurst	.40	.25
79	Joe Nolan	.10	.05	135	Rudy May	.10	.05
80	Pete Vuckovich	.10	.05	136	Tom Lasorda	.10	.06
81	Rick Leach	.10	.05	137	Dan Spillner (Er)	.10	.05
82	Rick Miller	.10	.05		(Wrong Photo)		
83	Graig Nettles	.12	.07	138	Jerry Martin	.10	.05
84	Ron Cey	.10	.06	139	Mike Norris	.10	.05
85	Miguel Dilone	.10	.05	140	Al Oliver	.12	.07
86	John Wathan	.10	.05	141	Daryl Sconiers	.10	.05
87	Kelvin Moore	.10	.05	142	Lamar Johnson	.10	.05
88a	Byrn Smith(Er)	.50	.30	143	Harold Baines	.40	.25
88b	Bryn Smith(Cor)	.10	.06	144	Alan Ashby	.10	.05
89	Dave Hostetler	.10	.05	145	Garry Templeton	.10	.05
90	Rod Carew	1.25	.80	146	Al Holland	.10	.05
91	Lonnie Smith	.10	.05	147	Bo Diaz	.10	.05
92	Bob Knepper	.10	.05	148	Dave Concepcion	.12	.07
93	Marty Bystrom	.10	.05	149	Rick Camp	.10	.05
94	Chris Welsh	.10	.05	150	Jim Morrison	.10	.05
95	Jason Thompson	.10	.05	151	Randy Martz	.10	.05
96	Tom O'Malley	.10	.05	152	Keith Hernandez	.20	.12
97	Phil Niekro	.60	.35	153	John Lowenstein	.10	.05
98	Neil Allen	.10	.05	154	Mike Caldwell	.10	.05
99	Bill Buckner	.10	.06	155	Milt Wilcox	.10	.05
100	Ed VandeBerg (R)	.10	.05	156	Rich Gedman	.10	.05
101	Jim Clancy	.10	.05	157	Rich Gossage	.15	.10

158	Jerry Reuss	.10	.05
159	Ron Hassey	.10	.05
160	Larry Gura	.10	.05
161	Dwayne Murphy	.10	.05
162	Woodie Fryman	.10	.05
163	Steve Comer	.10	.05
164	Ken Forsch	.10	.06
165	Dennis Lamp	.10	.05
166	David Green	.10	.05
167	Terry Puhl	.10	.05
168	Mike Schmidt	2.50	1.50
169	Eddie Milner (R)	.10	.05
170	John Curtis	.10	.05
171	Don Robinson	.10	.05
172	Richard Gale	.10	.05
173	Steve Bedrosian	.10	.05
174	Willie Hernandez	.10	.05
175	Ron Gardenhire	.10	.05
176	Jim Beattie	.10	.05
177	Tim Laudner	.10	.05
178	Buck Martinez	.10	.05
179	Kent Hrbek	.40	.25
180	Alfredo Griffin	.10	.05
181	Larry Andersen	.10	.05
182	Pete Falcone	.10	.05
183	Jody Davis	.10	.05
184	Glenn Hubbard	.10	.05
185	Dale Berra	.10	.05
186	Greg Minton	.10	.05
187	Gary Lucas	.10	.05
188	Dave Van Gorder	.10	.05
189	Bob Dernier	.10	.05
190	Willie McGee (R)	3.50	2.25
191	Dickie Thon	.10	.05
192	Bob Boone	.12	.07
193	Britt Burns	.10	.05
194	Jeff Reardon	1.00	.70
195	Jon Matlack	.10	.05
196	Don Slaught (R)	.75	.45
197	Fred Stanley	.10	.05
198	Rick Manning	.10	.05
199	Dave Righetti	.15	.08
200	Dave Stapleton	.10	.05
201	Steve Yeager	.10	.05
202	Enos Cabell	.10	.05
203	Sammy Stewart	.10	.05
204	Moose Haas	.10	.05
205	Lenn Sakata	.10	.05
206	Charlie Moore	.10	.05
207	Alan Trammell	.90	.60
208	Jim Rice	.25	.15
209	Roy Smalley	.10	.05
210	Bill Russell	.10	.06
211	Andre Thornton	.10	.05
212	Willie Aikens	.10	.05
213	Dave McKay	.10	.05
214	Tim Blackwell	.10	.05
215	Buddy Bell	.10	.05
216	Doug DeCinces	.10	.05
217	Tom Herr	.10	.05
218	Frank LaCorte	.10	.05
219	Steve Carlton	1.50	.90
220	Terry Kennedy	.10	.05
221	Mike Easler	.10	.05
222	Jack Clark	.15	.08
223	Gene Garber	.10	.05
224	Scott Holman	.10	.05
225	Mike Proly	.10	.05
226	Terry Bulling	.10	.05
227	Jerry Garvin	.10	.05
228	Ron Davis	.10	.05
229	Tom Hume	.10	.05
230	Marc Hill	.10	.05
231	Dennis Martinez	.15	.10
232	Jim Gantner	.10	.05
233	Larry Pashnick	.10	.05
234	Dave Collins	.10	.05
235	Tom Burgmeier	.10	.05
236	Ken Landreaux	.10	.05
237	John Denny	.10	.05
238	Hal McRae	.12	.07
239	Matt Keough	.10	.05
240	Doug Flynn	.10	.05
241	Fred Lynn	.12	.07
242	Billy Sample	.10	.05
243	Tom Paciorek	.10	.05
244	Joe Sambito	.10	.05
245	Sid Monge	.10	.05
246	Ken Oberkfell	.10	.05
247	Joe Pittman (Er) (Wrong Photo)	.10	.05
248	Mario Soto	.10	.05
249	Claudell Washington	.10	.05
250	Rick Rhoden	.10	.05
251	Darrell Evans	.10	.06
252	Steve Henderson	.10	.05
253	Manny Castillo	.10	.05
254	Craig Swan	.10	.05
255	Joey McLaughlin	.10	.05
256	Pete Redfern	.10	.05
257	Ken Singleton	.10	.05
258	Robin Yount	2.50	1.50
259	Elias Sosa	.10	.05
260	Bob Ojeda	.12	.07
261	Bobby Murcer	.12	.07
262	Candy Maldonado (R)	.50	.30
263	Rick Waits	.10	.05
264	Greg Pryor	.10	.05
265	Bob Owchinko	.10	.05
266	Chris Speier	.10	.05
267	Bruce Kison	.10	.05
268	Mark Wagner	.10	.05
269	Steve Kemp	.10	.05
270	Phil Garner	.10	.05

271	Gene Richards	.10	.05
272	Renie Martin	.10	.05
273	Dave Roberts	.10	.05
274	Dan Driessen	.10	.05
275	Rufino Linares	.10	.05
276	Lee Lacy	.10	.05
277	Ryne Sandberg (R)	40.00	28.00
278	Darrell Porter	.10	.05
279	Cal Ripken	18.00	11.00
280	Jamie Easterly	.10	.05
281	Bill Fahey	.10	.05
282	Glenn Hoffman	.10	.05
283	Willie Randolph	.10	.06
284	Fernando Valenzuela	.12	.07
285	Alan Bannister	.10	.05
286	Paul Splittorff	.10	.05
287	Joe Rudi	.10	.06
288	Bill Gullickson	.12	.07
289	Danny Darwin	.10	.05
290	Andy Hassler	.10	.05
291	Ernesto Escarrega	.10	.05
292	Steve Mura	.10	.05
293	Tony Scott	.10	.05
294	Manny Trillo	.10	.05
295	Greg Harris	.10	.06
296	Luis DeLeon	.10	.05
297	Kent Tekulve	.10	.05
298	Atlee Hammaker	.10	.05
299	Bruce Benedict	.10	.05
300	Fergie Jenkins	.50	.30
301	Dave Kingman	.12	.07
302	Bill Caudill	.10	.05
303	John Castino	.10	.05
304	Ernie Whitt	.10	.05
305	Randy Johnson	.10	.05
306	Garth Iorg	.10	.05
307	Gaylord Perry	.50	.30
308	Ed Lynch	.10	.05
309	Keith Moreland	.10	.05
310	Rafael Ramirez	.10	.05
311	Bill Madlock	.12	.07
312	Milt May	.10	.05
313	John Montefusco	.10	.05
314	Wayne Krenchicki	.10	.05
315	George Vukovich	.10	.05
316	Joaquin Andujar	.10	.06
317	Craig Reynolds	.10	.05
318	Rick Burleson	.10	.05
319	Richard Dotson	.10	.05
320	Steve Rogers	.10	.05
321	Dave Schmidt	.10	.06
322	Bud Black (R)	.40	.25
323	Jeff Burroughs	.10	.05
324	Von Hayes	.10	.05
325	Butch Wynegar	.10	.05
326	Carl Yastrzemski	2.00	1.25
327	Ron Roenicke	.10	.05
328	Howard Johnson (R)	3.50	2.25
329	Rick Dempsey	.10	.05
330	Jim Slaton	.10	.05
331	Benny Ayala	.10	.05
332	Ted Simmons	.10	.05
333	Lou Whitaker	.35	.20
334	Chuck Rainey	.10	.05
335	Lou Piniella	.12	.07
336	Steve Sax	.30	.18
337	Toby Harrah	.10	.05
338	George Brett	2.75	1.60
339	Davey Lopes	.10	.06
340	Gary Carter	.75	.45
341	John Grubb	.10	.05
342	Tim Foli	.10	.05
343	Jim Kaat	.15	.08
344	Mike LaCoss	.10	.05
345	Larry Christenson	.10	.05
346	Juan Bonilla	.10	.05
347	Omar Moreno	.10	.05
348	Chili Davis	.80	.50
349	Tommy Boggs	.10	.05
350	Rusty Staub	.12	.07
351	Bump Wills	.10	.05
352	Rick Sweet	.10	.05
353	Jim Gott (R)	.30	.18
354	Terry Felton	.10	.05
355	Jim Kern	.10	.05
356	Bill Almon	.10	.05
357	Tippy Martinez	.10	.05
358	Roy Howell	.10	.05
359	Dan Petry	.10	.05
360	Jerry Mumphrey	.10	.05
361	Mark Clear	.10	.05
362	Mike Marshall	.10	.05
363	Lary Sorensen	.10	.05
364	Amos Otis	.10	.06
365	Rick Langford	.10	.05
366	Brad Mills	.10	.05
367	Brian Downing	.10	.05
368	Mike Richardt	.10	.05
369	Aurelio Rodriguez	.10	.05
370	Dave Smith	.10	.05
371	Tug McGraw	.12	.07
372	Doug Bair	.10	.05
373	Ruppert Jones	.10	.05
374	Alex Trevino	.10	.05
375	Ken Dayley	.10	.05
376	Rod Scurry	.10	.05
377	Bob Brenly	.10	.05
378	Scot Thompson	.10	.05
379	Julio Cruz	.10	.05
380	John Stearns	.10	.05
381	Dale Murray	.10	.05
382	Frank Viola (R)	3.50	2.25
383	Al Bumbry	.10	.05
384	Ben Oglivie	.10	.05

385	Dave Tobik	.10	.05
386	Bob Stanley	.10	.05
387	Andre Robertson	.10	.05
388	Jorge Orta	.10	.05
389	Ed Whitson	.10	.05
390	Don Hood	.10	.05
391	Tom Underwood	.10	.06
392	Tim Wallach	.20	.12
393	Steve Renko	.10	.05
394	Mickey Rivers	.10	.05
395	Greg Luzinski	.12	.07
396	Art Howe	.10	.05
397	Alan Wiggins	.10	.05
298	Jim Barr	.10	.05
399	Ivan DeJesus	.10	.05
400	Tom Lawless (R)	.10	.05
401	Bob Walk	.10	.05
402	Jimmy Smith	.10	.05
403	Lee Smith	2.75	1.60
404	George Hendrick	.10	.05
405	Eddie Murray	2.00	1.25
406	Marshall Edwards	.10	.05
407	Lance Parrish	.12	.07
408	Carney Lansford	.12	.07
409	Dave Winfield	2.75	1.60
410	Bob Welch	.15	.08
411	Larry Milbourne	.10	.05
412	Dennis Leonard	.10	.05
413	Dan Meyer	.10	.05
414	Charlie Lea	.10	.05
415	Rick Honeycutt	.10	.05
416	Mike Witt	.10	.05
417	Steve Trout	.10	.05
418	Glenn Brummer	.10	.05
419	Denny Walling	.10	.05
420	Gary Matthews	.10	.05
421	Charlie Liebrandt (Er)	.10	.05
422	Juan Eichelberger	.10	.05
423	Matt Guante (R) (Er) (Cecilio)	.10	.05
424	Bill Laskey	.10	.05
425	Jerry Royster	.10	.05
426	Dickie Noles	.10	.05
427	George Foster	.12	.07
428	Mike Moore (R)	.70	.40
429	Gary Ward	.10	.05
430	Barry Bonnell	.10	.05
431	Ron Washington	.10	.05
432	Rance Mulliniks	.10	.05
433	Mike Stanton	.10	.05
434	Jesse Orosco	.10	.05
435	Larry Bowa	.10	.06
436	Biff Pocoroba	.10	.05
437	Johnny Ray	.10	.05
438	Joe Morgan	.75	.45
439	Eric Show	.10	.05
440	Larry Biittner	.10	.05
441	Greg Gross	.10	.05
442	Gene Tenace	.10	.06
443	Danny Heep	.10	.05
444	Bobby Clark	.10	.05
445	Kevin Hickey	.10	.05
446	Scott Sanderson	.10	.05
447	Frank Tanana	.10	.06
448	Cesar Geronimo	.10	.05
449	Jimmy Sexton	.10	.05
450	Mike Hargrove	.10	.05
451	Doyle Alexander	.10	.05
452	Dwight Evans	.25	.15
453	Terry Forster	.10	.05
454	Tom Brookens	.10	.05
455	Rich Dauer	.10	.05
456	Rob Picciolo	.10	.05
457	Terry Crowley	.10	.05
458	Ned Yost	.10	.05
459	Kirk Gibson	.40	.25
460	Reid Nichols	.10	.05
461	Oscar Gamble	.10	.05
462	Dusty Baker	.10	.06
463	Jack Perconte	.10	.05
464	Frank White	.10	.05
465	Mickey Klutts	.10	.05
466	Warren Cromartie	.10	.05
467	Larry Parrish	.10	.05
468	Bobby Grich	.10	.06
469	Dane Iorg	.10	.05
470	Joe Niekro	.10	.05
471	Ed Farmer	.10	.05
472	Tim Flannery	.10	.05
473	Dave Parker	.30	.18
474	Jeff Leonard	.10	.05
475	Al Hrabosky	.10	.05
476	Ron Hodges	.10	.05
477	Leon Durham	.10	.05
478	Jim Essian	.10	.05
479	Roy Lee Jackson	.10	.05
480	Brad Havens	.10	.05
481	Joe Price	.10	.05
482	Tony Bernazard	.10	.05
483	Scott McGregor	.10	.05
484	Paul Molitor	2.75	1.60
485	Mike Ivie	.10	.05
486	Ken Griffey	.15	.08
487	Dennis Eckersley	1.00	.70
488	Steve Garvey	.50	.30
489	Mike Fischlin	.10	.05
490	U.L. Washington	.10	.05
491	Steve McCatty	.10	.05
492	Roy Johnson	.10	.05
493	Don Baylor	.12	.07
494	Bobby Johnson	.10	.05
495	Mike Squires	.10	.05
496	Bert Roberge	.10	.05
497	Dick Ruthven	.10	.05

498	Tito Landrum	.10	.05
499	Sixto Lezcano	.10	.05
500	Johnny Bench	1.50	.90
501	Larry Whisenton	.10	.05
502	Manny Sarmiento	.10	.05
503	Fred Breining	.10	.05
504	Bill Campbell	.10	.05
505	Todd Cruz	.10	.05
506	Bob Bailor	.10	.05
507	Dave Stieb	.15	.08
508	Al Williams	.10	.05
509	Dan Ford	.10	.05
510	Gorman Thomas	.10	.05
511	Chet Lemon	.10	.05
512	Mike Torrez	.10	.05
513	Shane Rawley	.10	.05
514	Mark Belanger	.10	.06
515	Rodney Craig	.10	.05
516	Onix Concepcion	.10	.05
517	Mike Heath	.10	.05
518	Andre Dawson	2.00	1.25
519	Luis Sanchez	.10	.05
520	Terry Bogener	.10	.05
521	Rudy Law	.10	.05
522	Ray Knight	.10	.05
523	Joe Lefebvre	.10	.05
524	Jim Wohlford	.10	.05
525	Julio Franco (R)	5.00	3.00
526	Ron Oester	.10	.05
527	Rick Mahler	.10	.05
528	Steve Nicosia	.10	.05
529	Junior Kenndey	.10	.05
530	Whitey Herzog (Var)	.10	.06
531	Don Sutton (Var)	.40	.25
532	Mark Brouhard	.10	.05
533	Sparky Anderson (Var)	.10	.06
534	Roger LaFrancois	.10	.05
535	George Frazier	.10	.05
536	Tom Niedenfuer	.10	.05
537	Ed Glynn	.10	.05
538	Lee May	.10	.05
539	Bob Kearney	.10	.05
540	Tim Raines	.70	.40
541	Paul Mirabella	.10	.05
542	Luis Tiant	.10	.06
543	Ron LeFlore	.10	.05
544	Dave LaPoint (R)	.10	.06
545	Randy Moffitt	.10	.05
546	Luis Aguayo	.10	.05
547	Brad Lesley	.10	.05
548	Luis Salazar	.10	.05
549	John Candelaria	.10	.05
550	Dave Bergman	.10	.05
551	Bob Watson	.10	.06
552	Pat Tabler	.10	.05
553	Brent Gaff	.10	.05
554	Al Cowens	.10	.05
555	Tom Brunansky	.35	.20
556	Lloyd Moseby	.10	.05
557a	Pascual Perez (Twins)	1.00	.70
557b	Pascual Perez (Braves)	.25	.15
558	Willie Upshaw	.10	.05
559	Richie Zisk	.10	.05
560	Pat Zachry	.10	.05
561	Jay Johnstone	.10	.05
562	Carlos Diaz	.10	.05
563	John Tudor	.10	.05
564	Frank Robinson	.25	.15
565	Dave Edwards	.10	.05
566	Paul Householder	.10	.05
567	Ron Reed	.10	.05
568	Mike Ramsey	.10	.05
569	Kiko Garcia	.10	.05
570	Tommy John	.15	.08
571	Tony LaRussa	.10	.06
572	Joel Youngblood	.10	.05
573	Wayne Tolleson (R)	.10	.05
574	Keith Creel	.10	.05
575	Billy Martin	.15	.08
576	Jerry Dybzinski	.10	.05
577	Rick Cerone	.10	.05
578	Tony Perez	.40	.25
579	Greg Brock (R)	.10	.06
580	Glenn Wilson (R)	.10	.05
581	Tim Stoddard	.10	.05
582	Bob McClure	.10	.05
583	Jim Dwyer	.10	.05
584	Ed Romero	.10	.05
585	Larry Herndon	.10	.05
586	Wade Boggs (R)	25.00	16.00
587	Jay Howell	.12	.07
588	Dave Stewart	.80	.50
589	Bert Blyleven	.40	.25
590	Dick Howser	.10	.05
591	Wayne Gross	.10	.05
592	Terry Francona	.10	.05
593	Don Werner	.10	.05
594	Bill Stein	.10	.05
595	Jesse Barfield	.25	.15
596	Bobby Molinaro	.10	.05
597	Mike Vail	.10	.05
598	Tony Gwynn (R)	28.00	18.00
599	Gary Rajsich	.10	.05
600	Jerry Ujdur	.10	.05
601	Cliff Johnson	.10	.05
602	Jerry White	.10	.05
603	Bryan Clark	.10	.05
604	Joe Ferguson	.10	.05
605	Guy Sularz	.10	.05
606	Ozzie Virgil (Var)	.10	.05
607	Terry Harper	.10	.05
608	Harvey Kuenn	.10	.06
609	Jim Sundberg	.10	.05
610	Willie Stargell	.60	.35

611	Reggie Smith	.10	.05
612	Rob Wilfong	.10	.05
613	Niekro Brothers	.25	.15
614	Lee Elia	.10	.05
615	Mickey Hatcher	.10	.05
616	Jerry Hairston	.10	.05
617	John Martin	.10	.05
618	Wally Backman	.10	.06
619	Storm Davis (R)	.15	.08
620	Alan Knicely	.10	.05
621	John Stuper	.10	.05
622	Matt Sinatro	.10	.05
623	Gene Petralli (R)	.10	.06
624	Duane Walker	.10	.05
625	Dick Williams	.10	.05
626	Pat Corrales	.10	.05
627	Vern Ruhle	.10	.05
628	Joe Torre	.10	.06
629	Anthony Johnson	.10	.05
630	Steve Howe	.10	.05
631	Gary Woods	.10	.05
632	LaMarr Hoyt	.10	.05
633	Steve Swisher	.10	.05
634	Terry Leach	.10	.05
635	Jeff Newman	.10	.05
636	Brett Butler	.75	.45
637	Gary Gray	.10	.05
638	Lee Mazzilli	.10	.05
639a	Ron Jackson (A's)(Er)	12.00	7.50
639b	Ron Jackson (Angels)	.10	.06
640	Juan Beniquez	.10	.05
641	Dave Rucker	.10	.05
642	Luis Pujols	.10	.05
643	Rick Monday	.10	.05
644	Hosken Powell	.10	.05
645	San Diego Chicken	.25	.15
646	Dave Engle	.10	.05
647	Dick Davis	.10	.05
648	MVP's(Vida Blue,Joe Morgan,Frank Robinson)	.40	.25
649	Al Chambers	.10	.05
650	Jesus Vega	.10	.05
651	Jeff Jones	.10	.05
652	Marvis Foley	.10	.05
653	Ty Cobb Puzzle Card	.10	.05
___	Checklist (DK)	.15	.08
___	Checklist (27-130)	.15	.08
___	Checklist (131-234)	.15	.08
___	Checklist (235-338)	.15	.08
___	Checklist (339-442)	.15	.08
___	Checklist (443-546)	.15	.08
___	Checklist (547-653)	.15	.08

1984 Donruss

Donruss changed the design of their card fronts for 1984 but maintained the horizontal style of the card backs which feature black type over a green and white background. The set includes 26 Diamond Kings (DK) and a new 20-card subset called Rated Rookies (27-46). Two "Living Legends" cards were randomly inserted into wax packs. Those cards marked A (Gaylord Perry and Rollie Fingers) and B (Johnny Bench and Carl Yastzremsky) are listed at the end of this checklist. A lower print run has created a scarcity of 1984 Donruss cards. All cards measure 2-1/2" by 3-1/2".

		MINT	NR/MT
Complete Set (660)		375.00	250.00
Commons		.20	.12

1a	Robin Yount(DK)	5.00	3.00
	(Perez-Steel on back)		
1b	Robin Yount(DK)	6.50	3.75
	(Perez-Steel on back)		
2a	Dave Concepcion(DK)	.35	.20
	(Perez-Steel on back)		
2b	Dave Concepcion(DK)	.50	.30
	(Perez-Steele on back)		
3a	Dwayne Murphy(DK)	.25	.15
	(Perez-Steel on back)		
3b	Dwayne Murphy(DK)	.35	.20
	(Perez-Steele on back)		
4a	John Castino(DK)	.25	.15
	(Perez-Steel on back)		
4b	John Castino(DK)	.35	.20
	(Perez-Steele on back)		
5a	Leon Durham(DK)	.25	.15
	(Perez-Steel on back)		
5b	Leon Durham(DK)	.35	.20
	(Perez-Steele on back)		
6a	Rusty Staub(DK)	.40	.25

6b	Rusty Staub(DK) (Perez-Steele on back)	.55	.28
7a	Jack Clark(DK)(Perez Steel on back)	.30	.18
7b	Jack Clark(DK)(Perez Steele on back)	.40	.25
8a	Dave Dravecky(DK) (Perez-Steel on back)	.30	.18
8b	Dave Dravecky(DK) (Perez-Steele on back)	.40	.25
9a	Al Oliver(DK)(Perez Steel on back)	.30	.18
9b	Al Oliver(DK)(Perez Steele on back)	.40	.25
10a	Dave Righetti(DK) (Perez-Steel on back)	.30	.18
10b	Dave Righetti(DK) (Perez-Steele on back)	.40	.25
11a	Hal McRae(DK)(Perez Steel on back)	.40	.25
11b	Hal McRae(DK)(Perez Steele on back)	.55	.28
12a	Ray Knight(DK)(Perez Steel on back)	.30	.18
12b	Ray Knight(DK)(Perez Steele on back)	.40	.25
13a	Bruce Sutter(DK) (Perez-Steel on back)	.30	.18
13b	Bruce Sutter(DK) (Perez-Steele on back)	.40	.25
14a	Bob Horner(DK)(Perez Steel on back)	.30	.18
14b	Bob Horner(DK)(Perez Steele on back)	.40	.25
15a	Lance Parrish(DK) (Perez-Steel on back)	.30	.18
15b	Lance Parrish(DK) (Perez-Steele on back)	.40	.25
16a	Matt Young(DK)(Perez Steel on back)	.25	.15
16b	Matt Young(DK)(Perez Steele on back)	.35	.20
17a	Fred Lynn(DK)(Perez Steel on back)	.30	.18
17b	Fred Lynn(DK)(Perez Steele on back)	.40	.25
18a	Ron Kittle(DK)(Perez Steel on back)(FC)	.25	.15
18b	Ron Kittle(DK)(Perez Steele on back)(FC)	.35	.20
19a	Jim Clancy(DK)(Perez Steel on back)	.25	.15
19b	Jim Clancy(DK)(Perez Steele on back)	.35	.20
20a	Bill Madlock(DK) (Perez-Steel on back)	.30	.18
20b	Bill Madlock(DK) (Perez-Steele on back)	.40	.25
21a	Larry Parrish(DK) (Perez-Steel on back)	.30	.18
21b	Larry Parrish(DK) (Perez-Steele on back)	.40	.25
22a	Eddie Murray(DK) (Perez-Steel on back)	1.75	1.00
22b	Eddie Murray(DK) (Perez-Steele on back)	2.50	1.50
23a	Mike Schmidt(DK) (Perez-Steel on back)	4.00	2.50
23b	Mike Schmidt(DK) (Perez-Steele on back)	5.00	3.00
24a	Pedro Guerrero(DK) (Perez-Steel on back)	.30	.18
24b	Pedro Guerrero(DK) (Perez-Steele on back)	.40	.25
25a	Andre Thornton(DK) (Perez-Steel on back)	.30	.18
25b	Andre Thornton(DK) (Perez-Steele on back)	.40	.25
26a	Wade Boggs(DK) (Perez-Steel on back)	4.00	2.50
26b	Wade Boggs(DK) (Perez-Steele on back)	5.00	3.00
27	Joel Skinner (R)	.30	.18
28	Tom Dunbar (R)	.30	.18
29a	Mike Stenhouse (R) (No number on back)	.30	.18
29b	Mike Stenhouse (R) (29 on back)	3.00	2.00
30a	Ron Darling (R) (No number on back)	1.50	.90
30b	Ron Darling (R) (30 on back)	10.00	6.50
31	Dion James (R)	.30	.18
32	Tony Fernandez (R)	6.00	3.75
33	Angel Salazar (R)	.30	.18
34	Kevin McReynolds (R)	2.00	1.25
35	Dick Schofield (R)	.50	.30
36	Brad Kimminsk (R)	.30	.18
37	Tim Teufel (R)	.35	.20
38	Doug Frobel (R)	.30	.18
39	Greg Gagne (R)	1.25	.80
40	Mike Fuentes (R)	.30	.18
41	Joe Carter (R)	70.00	40.00
42	Mike Brown (R)	.30	.18
43	Mike Jeffcoat (R)	.30	.18
44	Sid Fernandez (R)	3.50	2.25
45	Brian Dayett (R)	.30	.18
46	Chris Smith (R)	.30	.18
47	Eddie Murray	7.50	4.50
48	Robin Yount	10.00	6.50
49	Lance Parrish	.35	.20
50	Jim Rice	.40	.25
51	Dave Winfield	14.00	9.00

No.	Player	Value	Value
52	Fernando Valenzuela	.30	.18
53	George Brett	15.00	10.00
54	Rickey Henderson	14.00	9.00
55	Gary Carter	2.00	1.25
56	Buddy Bell	.20	.12
57	Reggie Jackson	8.00	5.00
58	Harold Baines	1.00	.70
59	Ozzie Smith	6.50	3.75
60	Nolan Ryan	35.00	20.00
61	Pete Rose	6.00	3.75
62	Ron Oester	.20	.12
63	Steve Garvey	1.50	.90
64	Jason Thompson	.20	.12
65	Jack Clark	.25	.15
66	Dale Murphy	2.50	1.50
67	Leon Durham	.20	.12
68	Darryl Strawberry(R)	30.00	18.00
69	Richie Zisk	.20	.12
70	Kent Hrbek	.80	.50
71	Dave Stieb	.40	.25
72	Ken Schrom	.20	.12
73	George Bell	2.00	1.25
74	John Moses	.20	.12
75	Ed Lynch	.20	.12
76	Chuck Rainey	.20	.12
77	Biff Pocoroba	.20	.12
78	Cecilio Guante	.20	.12
79	Jim Barr	.20	.12
80	Kurt Bevacqua	.20	.12
81	Tom Foley	.20	.12
82	Joe Lefebvre	.20	.12
83	Andy Van Slyke (R)	12.00	8.50
84	Bob Lillis	.20	.12
85	Rick Adams	.20	.12
86	Jerry Hairston	.20	.12
87	Bob James	.20	.12
88	Joe Altobelli	.20	.12
89	Ed Romero	.20	.12
90	John Grubb	.20	.12
91	John Henry Johnson	.20	.12
92	Juan Espino	.20	.12
93	Candy Maldonado	.25	.15
94	Andre Thornton	.20	.12
95	Onix Concepcion	.20	.12
96	Donnie Hill (R)	.20	.12
97	Andre Dawson	6.50	4.00
98	Frank Tanana	.25	.15
99	Curt Wilkerson (R)	.20	.12
100	Larry Gura	.20	.12
101	Dwayne Murphy	.20	.12
102	Tom Brennan	.20	.12
103	Dave Righetti	.25	.15
104	Steve Sax	.80	.50
105	Dan Petry	.20	.12
106	Cal Ripken	35.00	25.00
107	Paul Molitor	8.00	5.00
108	Fred Lynn	.25	.15
109	Neil Allen	.20	.12
110	Joe Niekro	.20	.12
111	Steve Carlton	6.00	3.75
112	Terry Kennedy	.20	.12
113	Bill Madlock	.25	.15
114	Chili Davis	.60	.35
115	Jim Gantner	.20	.12
116	Tom Seaver	8.00	5.00
117	Bill Buckner	.25	.15
118	Bill Caudill	.20	.12
119	Jim Clancy	.20	.12
120	John Castino	.20	.12
121	Dave Concepcion	.25	.15
122	Greg Luzinski	.25	.15
123	Mike Broddicker	.25	.15
124	Pete Ladd	.20	.12
125	Juan Berenguer	.20	.12
126	John Montefusco	.20	.12
127	Ed Jurak	.20	.12
128	Tom Niedenfuer	.20	.12
129	Bert Blyleven	1.00	.70
130	Bud Black	.20	.12
131	Gorman Heimueller	.20	.12
132	Dan Schatzeder	.20	.12
133	Ron Jackson	.20	.12
134	Tom Henke (R)	2.00	1.25
135	Kevin Hickey	.20	.12
136	Mike Scott	.25	.15
137	Bo Diaz	.20	.12
138	Glenn Brummer	.20	.12
139	Sid Monge	.20	.12
140	Rich Gale	.20	.12
141	Brett Butler	.80	.50
142	Brian Harper (R)	3.50	2.50
143	John Rabb	.20	.12
144	Gary Woods	.20	.12
145	Pat Putnam	.20	.12
146	Jim Acker (R)	.20	.12
147	Mickey Hatcher	.20	.12
148	Todd Cruz	.20	.12
149	Tom Tellmann	.20	.12
150	John Wockenfuss	.20	.12
151	Wade Boggs	15.00	10.00
152	Don Baylor	.25	.15
153	Bob Welch	.40	.25
154	Alan Bannister	.20	.12
155	Willie Aikens	.20	.12
156	Jeff Burroughs	.20	.12
157	Bryan Little	.20	.12
158	Bob Boone	.30	.18
159	Dave Hostetler	.20	.12
160	Jerry Dybzinski	.20	.12
161	Mike Madden	.20	.12
162	Luis DeLeon	.20	.12
163	Willie Hernandez	.20	.12
164	Frank Pastore	.20	.12
165	Rick Camp	.20	.12

166	Lee Mazzilli	.20	.12
167	Scot Thompson	.20	.12
168	Bob Forsch	.20	.12
169	Mike Flanagan	.20	.12
170	Rick Manning	.20	.12
171	Chet Lemon	.20	.12
172	Jerry Remy	.20	.12
173	Ron Guidry	.35	.20
174	Pedro Guerrero	.30	.18
175	Willie Wilson	.20	.12
176	Carney Lansford	.25	.15
177	Al Oliver	.25	.15
178	Jim Sundberg	.20	.12
179	Bobby Grich	.25	.15
180	Richard Dotson	.20	.12
181	Joaquin Andujar	.20	.12
182	Jose Cruz	.20	.12
183	Mike Schmidt	18.50	12.00
184	Gary Redus (R)	.40	.25
185	Garry Templeton	.20	.12
186	Tony Pena	.20	.12
187	Greg Minton	.20	.12
188	Phil Niekro	1.75	1.00
189	Ferguson Jenkins	1.50	.90
190	Mookie Wilson	.20	.12
191	Jim Beattie	.20	.12
192	Gary Ward	.20	.12
193	Jesse Barfield	.30	.18
194	Pete Filson	.20	.12
195	Roy Lee Jackson	.20	.12
196	Rick Sweet	.20	.12
197	Jesse Orosco	.20	.12
198	Steve Lake (R)	.20	.12
199	Ken Dayley	.20	.12
200	Manny Sarmiento	.20	.12
201	Mark Davis	.25	.15
202	Tim Flannery	.20	.12
203	Bill Scherrer	.20	.12
204	Al Holland	.20	.12
205	David Von Ohlen	.20	.12
206	Mike LaCoss	.20	.12
207	Juan Beniquez	.20	.12
208	Juan Agosto (R)	.25	.15
209	Bobby Ramos	.20	.12
210	Al Bumbry	.20	.12
211	Mark Brouhard	.20	.12
212	Howard Bailey	.20	.12
213	Bruce Hurst	.30	.18
214	Bob Shirley	.20	.12
215	Pat Zachry	.20	.12
216	Julio Franco	2.50	1.50
217	Mike Armstrong	.20	.12
218	Dave Beard	.20	.12
219	Steve Rogers	.20	.12
220	John Butcher	.20	.12
221	Mike Smithson (R)	.20	.12
222	Frank White	.20	.12
223	Mike Heath	.20	.12
224	Chris Bando	.20	.12
225	Roy Smalley	.20	.12
226	Dusty Baker	.25	.15
227	Lou Whitaker	2.00	1.25
228	John Lowenstein	.20	.12
229	Ben Oglivie	.20	.12
230	Doug DeCinces	.20	.12
231	Lonnie Smith	.25	.15
232	Ray Knight	.20	.12
233	Gary Matthews	.20	.12
234	Juan Bonilla	.20	.12
235	Rod Scurry	.20	.12
236	Atlee Hammaker	.20	.12
237	Mike Caldwell	.20	.12
238	Keith Hernandez	.30	.18
239	Larry Bowa	.25	.15
240	Tony Bernazard	.20	.12
241	Damaso Garcia	.20	.12
242	Tom Brunansky	.25	.15
243	Dan Driessen	.20	.12
244	Ron Kittle	.20	.12
245	Tim Stoddard	.20	.12
246	Bob Gibson	.20	.12
247	Marty Castillo	.20	.12
248	Don Mattingly (R)	60.00	38.00
249	Jeff Newman	.20	.12
250	Alejandro Pena (R)	.70	.40
251	Toby Harrah	.20	.12
252	Cesar Geronimo	.20	.12
253	Tom Underwood	.20	.12
254	Doug Flynn	.20	.12
255	Andy Hassler	.20	.12
256	Odell Jones	.20	.12
257	Rudy Law	.20	.12
258	Harry Spilman	.20	.12
259	Marty Bystrom	.20	.12
260	Dave Rucker	.20	.12
261	Ruppert Jones	.20	.12
262	Jeff Jones	.20	.12
263	Gerald Perry (R)	.30	.18
264	Gene Tenace	.25	.15
265	Brad Wellman	.20	.12
266	Dickie Noles	.20	.12
267	Jamie Allen	.20	.12
268	Jim Gott	.20	.12
269	Ron Davis	.20	.12
270	Benny Ayala	.20	.12
271	Ned Yost	.20	.12
272	Dave Rozema	.20	.12
273	Dave Stapleton	.20	.12
274	Lou Piniella	.30	.18
275	Jose Morales	.20	.12
276	Broderick Perkins	.20	.12
277	Butch Davis	.30	.18
278	Tony Phillips (R)	5.00	3.00
279	Jeff Reardon	2.00	1.25

280	Ken Forsch	.20	.12	337	Joe Beckwith	.20	.12
281	Pete O'Brien (R)	.60	.35	338	Rick Sutcliffe	.30	.18
282	Tom Paciorek	.20	.12	339	Mark Huismann (R)	.20	.12
283	Frank LaCorte	.20	.12	340	Tim Conroy (R)	.20	.12
284	Tim Lollar	.20	.12	341	Scott Sanderson	.20	.12
285	Greg Gross	.20	.12	342	Larry Biittner	.20	.12
286	Alex Trevino	.20	.12	343	Dave Stewart	1.25	.80
287	Gene Garber	.20	.12	344	Darryl Motley	.20	.12
288	Dave Parker	.90	.60	345	Chris Codiroli	.20	.12
289	Lee Smith	4.00	2.50	346	Rick Behenna	.20	.12
290	Dave LaPoint	.20	.12	347	Andre Robertson	.20	.12
291	John Shelby (R)	.25	.15	348	Mike Marshall	.20	.12
292	Charlie Moore	.20	.12	349	Larry Herndon	.20	.12
293	Alan Trammell	2.50	1.50	350	Rich Dauer	.20	.12
294	Tony Armas	.20	.12	351	Cecil Cooper	.20	.12
295	Shane Rawley	.20	.12	352	Rod Carew	5.00	3.00
296	Greg Brock	.20	.12	353	Willie McGee	1.00	.70
297	Hal McRae	.30	.18	354	Phil Garner	.20	.12
298	Mike Davis	.20	.12	355	Joe Morgan	1.75	1.00
299	Tim Raines	2.50	1.50	356	Luis Salazar	.20	.12
300	Bucky Dent	.25	.15	357	John Candelaria	.20	.12
301	Tommy John	.30	.18	358	Bill Laskey	.20	.12
302	Carlton Fisk	5.00	3.00	359	Bob McClure	.20	.12
303	Darrell Porter	.20	.12	360	Dave Kingman	.25	.15
304	Dickie Thon	.20	.12	361	Ron Cey	.25	.15
305	Garry Maddox	.20	.12	362	Matt Young (R)	.25	.15
306	Cesar Cedeno	.25	.15	363	Lloyd Moseby	.20	.12
307	Gary Lucas	.20	.12	364	Frank Viola	1.50	.90
308	Johnny Ray	.20	.12	365	Eddie Milner	.20	.12
309	Andy McGaffigan	.20	.12	366	Floyd Bannister	.20	.12
310	Claudell Washington	.20	.12	367	Dan Ford	.20	.12
311	Ryne Sandberg	32.00	20.00	368	Moose Haas	.20	.12
312	George Foster	.25	.15	369	Doug Bair	.20	.12
313	Spike Owen (R)	.70	.40	370	Ray Fontenot (R)	.20	.12
314	Gary Gaetti	.25	.15	371	Luis Aponte	.20	.12
315	Willie Upshaw	.20	.12	372	Jack Fimple	.20	.12
316	Al Williams	.20	.12	373	Neal Heaton (R)	.25	.15
317	Jorge Orta	.20	.12	374	Greg Pryor	.20	.12
318	Orlando Mercado	.20	.12	375	Wayne Gross	.20	.12
319	Junior Ortiz (R)	.20	.12	376	Charlie Lea	.20	.12
320	Mike Proly	.20	.12	377	Steve Lubratich	.20	.12
321	Randy Johnson	.20	.12	378	Jon Matlack	.20	.12
322	Jim Morrison	.20	.12	379	Julio Cruz	.20	.12
323	Max Venable	.20	.12	380	John Mizerock	.20	.12
324	Tony Gwynn	18.50	12.00	381	Kevin Gross (R)	.50	.30
325	Duane Walker	.20	.12	382	Mike Ramsey	.20	.12
326	Ozzie Virgil	.20	.12	383	Dough Gwosdz	.20	.12
327	Jeff Lahti	.20	.12	384	Kelly Paris	.20	.12
328	Bill Dawley (R)	.20	.12	385	Pete Falcone	.20	.12
329	Rob Wilfong	.20	.12	386	Milt May	.20	.12
330	Marc Hill	.20	.12	387	Fred Breining	.20	.12
331	Ray Burris	.20	.12	388	Craig Lefferts (R)	.50	.30
332	Allan Ramirez	.20	.12	389	Steve Henderson	.20	.12
333	Chuck Porter	.20	.12	390	Randy Moffitt	.20	.12
334	Wayne Krenchicki	.20	.12	391	Ron Washington	.20	.12
335	Gary Allenson	.20	.12	392	Gary Roenicke	.20	.12
336	Bob Meacham (R)	.20	.12	393	Tom Candiotti (R)	1.25	.80

394 Larry Pashnick	.20	.12
395 Dwight Evans	.75	.45
396 Goose Gossage	.50	.30
397 Derrel Thomas	.20	.12
398 Juan Eichelberger	.20	.12
399 Leon Roberts	.20	.12
400 Davey Lopes	.25	.15
401 Bill Gullickson	.20	.12
402 Geoff Zahn	.20	.12
403 Billy Sample	.20	.12
404 Mike Squires	.20	.12
405 Craig Reynolds	.20	.12
406 Eric Show	.20	.12
407 John Denny	.20	.12
408 Dann Bilardello	.20	.12
409 Bruce Benedict	.20	.12
410 Kent Tekulve	.20	.12
411 Mel Hall	.50	.30
412 John Stuper	.20	.12
413 Rich Dempsey	.20	.12
414 Don Sutton	1.75	1.00
415 Jack Morris	2.00	1.25
416 John Tudor	.20	.12
417 Willie Randolph	.25	.15
418 Jerry Reuss	.20	.12
419 Don Slaught	.35	.20
420 Steve McCatty	.20	.12
421 Tim Wallach	.35	.20
422 Larry Parrish	.20	.12
423 Brian Downing	.20	.12
424 Britt Burns	.20	.12
425 David Green	.20	.12
426 Jerry Mumphrey	.20	.12
427 Ivan DeJesus	.20	.12
428 Mario Soto	.20	.12
429 Gene Richards	.20	.12
430 Dale Berra	.20	.12
431 Darrell Evans	.25	.15
432 Glenn Hubbard	.20	.12
433 Jody Davis	.20	.12
434 Danny Heep	.20	.12
435 Ed Nunez (R)	.30	.18
436 Bobby Castillo	.20	.12
437 Ernie Whitt	.20	.12
438 Scott Ullger	.20	.12
439 Doyle Alexander	.20	.12
440 Domingo Ramos	.20	.12
441 Craig Swan	.20	.12
442 Warren Brusstar	.20	.12
443 Len Barker	.20	.12
444 Mike Easler	.20	.12
445 Renie Martin	.20	.12
446 Dennis Rasmussen (R)	.30	.18
447 Ted Power	.20	.12
448 Charlie Hudson (R)	.20	.12
449 Danny Cox (R)	.40	.25
450 Kevin Bass	.25	.15
451 Daryl Sconiers	.20	.12
452 Scott Fletcher	.20	.12
453 Bryn Smith	.20	.12
454 Jim Dwyer	.20	.12
455 Rob Picciolo	.20	.12
456 Enos Cabell	.20	.12
457 Dennis "Oil Can" Boyd (R))	.25	.15
458 Butch Wynegar	.20	.12
459 Burt Hooton	.20	.12
460 Ron Hassey	.20	.12
461 Danny Jackson (R)	.80	.50
462 Bob Kearney	.20	.12
463 Terry Francona	.20	.12
464 Wayne Tolleson	.20	.12
465 Mickey Rivers	.20	.12
466 John Wathan	.20	.12
467 Bill Almon	.20	.12
468 George Vukovich	.20	.12
469 Steve Kemp	.20	.12
470 Ken Landreaux	.20	.12
471 Milt Wilcox	.20	.12
472 Tippy Martinez	.20	.12
473 Ted Simmons	.30	.18
474 Tim Foli	.20	.12
475 George Hendrick	.20	.12
476 Terry Puhl	.20	.12
477 Von Hayes	.20	.12
478 Bobby Brown	.20	.12
479 Lee Lacy	.20	.12
480 Joel Youngblood	.20	.12
481 Jim Slaton	.20	.12
482 Mike Fitzgerald (R)	.20	.12
483 Keith Moreland	.20	.12
484 Ron Roenicke	.20	.12
485 Luis Leal	.20	.12
486 Bryan Oelkers	.20	.12
487 Bruce Berenyi	.20	.12
488 LaMarr Hoyt	.20	.12
489 Joe Nolan	.20	.12
490 Marshall Edwards	.20	.12
491 Mike Laga	.20	.12
492 Rick Cerone	.20	.12
493 Mike Miller (Rick)	.20	.12
494 Rick Honeycutt	.20	.12
495 Mike Hargrove	.20	.12
496 Joe Simpson	.20	.12
497 Keith Atherton (R)	.20	.12
498 Chris Welsh	.20	.12
499 Bruce Kison	.20	.12
500 Bob Johnson	.20	.12
501 Jerry Koosman	.30	.18
502 Frank DiPino	.20	.12
503 Tony Perez	1.25	.80
504 Ken Oberkfell	.20	.12
505 Mark Thurmond (R)	.20	.12
506 Joe Price	.20	.12

507	Pascual Perez	.20	.12
508	Marvell Wynne (R)	.20	.12
509	Mike Krukow	.20	.12
510	Dick Ruthven	.20	.12
511	Al Cowens	.20	.12
512	Cliff Johnson	.20	.12
513	Randy Bush	.25	.15
514	Sammy Stewart	.20	.12
515	Bill Schroeder (R)	.20	.12
516	Aurelio Lopez	.20	.12
517	Mike Brown	.20	.12
518	Graig Nettles	.25	.15
519	Dave Sax	.20	.12
520	Gerry Willard	.20	.12
521	Paul Splittorff	.20	.12
522	Tom Burgmeier	.20	.12
523	Chris Speier	.20	.12
524	Bobby Clark	.20	.12
525	George Wright	.20	.12
526	Dennis Lamp	.20	.12
527	Tony Scott	.20	.12
528	Ed Whitson	.20	.12
529	Ron Reed	.20	.12
530	Charlie Puleo	.20	.12
531	Jerry Royster	.20	.12
532	Don Robinson	.20	.12
533	Steve Trout	.20	.12
534	Bruce Sutter	.35	.20
535	Bob Horner	.25	.15
536	Pat Tabler	.20	.12
537	Chris Chambliss	.20	.12
538	Bob Ojeda	.25	.15
539	Alan Ashby	.20	.12
540	Jay Johnstone	.20	.12
541	Bob Dernier	.20	.12
542	Brook Jacoby (R)	.40	.25
543	U.L. Washington	.20	.12
544	Danny Darwin	.20	.12
545	Kiko Garcia	.20	.12
546	Vance Law	.20	.12
547	Tug McGraw	.20	.12
548	Dave Smith	.20	.12
549	Len Matuszek	.20	.12
550	Tom Hume	.20	.12
551	Dave Dravecky	.35	.20
552	Rick Rhoden	.20	.12
553	Duane Kuiper	.20	.12
554	Rusty Staub	.25	.15
555	Bill Campbell	.20	.12
556	Mike Torrez	.20	.12
557	Dave Henderson	.80	.50
558	Len Whitehouse	.20	.12
559	Barry Bonnell	.20	.12
560	Rick Lysander	.20	.12
561	Garth Iorg	.20	.12
562	Bryan Clark	.20	.12
563	Brian Giles	.20	.12
564	Vern Ruhle	.20	.12
565	Steve Bedrosian	.20	.12
566	Larry McWilliams	.20	.12
567	Jeff Leonard	.20	.12
568	Alan Wiggins	.20	.12
569	Jeff Russell (R)	1.00	.70
570	Salome Barojas	.20	.12
571	Dane Iorg	.20	.12
572	Bob Knepper	.20	.12
573	Gary Lavelle	.20	.12
574	Gorman Thomas	.20	.12
575	Manny Trillo	.20	.12
576	Jim Palmer	5.00	3.00
577	Dale Murray	.20	.12
578	Tom Brookens	.20	.12
579	Rich Gedman	.20	.12
580	Bill Doran (R)	.50	.30
581	Steve Yeager	.20	.12
582	Dan Spillner	.20	.12
583	Dan Quisenberry	.20	.12
584	Rance Mulliniks	.20	.12
585	Storm Davis	.20	.12
586	Dave Schmidt	.20	.12
587	Bill Russell	.25	.15
588	Pat Sheridan (R)	.25	.15
589	Rafael Ramirez	.20	.12
590	Bud Anderson	.20	.12
591	George Frazier	.20	.12
592	Lee Tunnell (R)	.20	.12
593	Kirk Gibson	.80	.50
594	Scott McGregor	.20	.12
595	Bob Bailor	.20	.12
596	Tom Herr	.20	.12
597	Luis Sanchez	.20	.12
598	Dave Engle	.20	.12
599	Craig McMurtry (R)	.20	.12
600	Carlos Diaz	.20	.12
601	Tom O'Malley	.20	.12
602	Nick Esasky (R)	.25	.15
603	Ron Hodges	.20	.12
604	Ed Vande Berg	.20	.12
605	Alfredo Griffin	.20	.12
606	Glenn Hoffman	.20	.12
607	Hubie Brooks	.25	.15
608	Richard Barnes (Er) (Wrong Photo)	.20	.12
609	Greg Walker (R)	.20	.12
610	Ken Singleton	.20	.12
611	Mark Clear	.20	.12
612	Buck Martinez	.20	.12
613	Ken Griffey	.25	.15
614	Reid Nichols	.20	.12
615	Doug Sisk (R)	.20	.12
616	Bob Brenly	.20	.12
617	Joey McLaughlin	.20	.12
618	Glenn Wilson	.20	.12

619	Bob Stoddard	.20	.12
620	Lenn Sakata	.20	.12
621	Mike Young (R)	.20	.12
622	John Stefero	.20	.12
623	Carmelo Martinez (R)	.25	.15
624	Dave Bergman	.20	.12
625	Runnin' Reds(David	1.25	.80
	Green, Willie McGee,		
	Lonnie Smith, Ozzie		
	Smith)		
626	Rudy May	.20	.12
627	Matt Keough	.20	.12
628	Jose DeLeon (R)	.35	.20
629	Jim Essian	.20	.12
630	Darnell Coles (R)	.50	.30
631	Mike Warren	.20	.12
632	Del Crandall	.20	.12
633	Dennis Martinez	.30	.18
634	Mike Moore	.40	.25
635	Lary Sorensen	.20	.12
636	Ricky Nelson	.20	.12
637	Omar Moreno	.20	.12
638	Charlie Hough	.20	.12
639	Dennis Eckersley	4.00	2.50
640	Walt Terrell (R)	.30	.18
641	Denny Walling	.20	.12
642	Dave Anderson (R)	.25	.15
643	Jose Oquendo (R)	.35	.20
644	Bob Stanley	.20	.12
645	Dave Geisel	.20	.12
646	Scott Garrelts (R)	.25	.15
647	Gary Pettis (R)	.40	.25
648	Duke Snider Puzzle	.35	.20
649	Johnnie LeMaster	.20	.12
650	Dave Collins	.20	.12
651	San Diego Chicken	.40	.25
___	Checklist (DK)	.25	.10
___	Checklist 27-130	.25	.10
___	Checklist 131-234	.25	.10
___	Checklist 235-338	.25	.10
___	Checklist 339-442	.25	.10
___	Checklist 443-546	.25	.10
___	Checklist 547-651	.25	.10
___	Living Legends (A)	6.00	3.75
	(Fingers/Perry)		
___	Living Legends (B)	12.00	8.50
	(Bench/Yastrzemski)		

1985 Donruss

This 660-card set features full color photos with black borders on the card fronts. Card backs are horizontal and contain player stats and personal data. Subsets include Diamond Kings (DK) and Rated Rookies (27-46). The cards were issued with a Lou Gehrig puzzle. All cards measure 2-1/2" by 3-1/2".

	MINT	NR/MT
Complete Set (660)	200.00	135.00
Commons	.10	.06

1	Ryne Sandberg (DK)	3.50	2.25
2	Doug DeCinces (DK)	.12	.07
3	Rich Dotson (DK)	.12	.07
4	Bert Blyleven (DK)	.15	.10
5	Lou Whitaker (DK)	.25	.15
6	Dan Quisenberry (DK)	.12	.05
7	Don Mattingly (DK)	3.50	2.25
8	Carney Lansford (DK)	.12	.07
9	Frank Tanana (DK)	.12	.07
10	Willie Upshaw (DK)	.12	.07
11	Claudell Washington	.12	.07
	(DK)		
12	Mike Marshall (DK)	.12	.07
13	Joaquin Andujar (DK)	.12	.07
14	Cal Ripken, Jr. (DK)	5.00	3.00
15	Jim Rice (DK)	.20	.12
16	Don Sutton (DK)	.25	.15
17	Frank Viola (DK)	.20	.12
18	Alvin Davis (DK)	.15	.10
19	Mario Soto (DK)	.12	.07
20	Jose Cruz (DK)	.15	.10
21	Charlie Lea (DK)	.12	.07
22	Jesse Orosco (DK)	.12	.07
23	Juan Samuel (DK)	.15	.10
24	Tony Pena (DK)	.12	.07
25	Tony Gwynn (DK)	2.50	1.50
26	Bob Brenly (DK)	.12	.07
27	Danny Tartabull (R)	7.00	4.00
28	Mike Bielecki (R)	.35	.20

29	Steve Lyons (R)	.15	.08
30	Jeff Reed(R)	.12	.07
31	Tony Brewer (R)	.10	.06
32	John Morris (R)	.10	.06
33	Daryl Boston (R)	.40	.25
34	Alfonso Pulido (R)	.10	.06
35	Steve Kiefer (R)	.10	.06
36	Larry Sheets (R)	.12	.07
37	Scott Bradley (R)	.12	.07
38	Calvin Schiraldi (R)	.12	.07
39	Shawon Dunston (R)	1.50	.90
40	Charlie Mitchell (R)	.10	.06
41	Billy Hatcher (R)	.75	.45
42	Russ Stephans (R)	.10	.06
43	Alejandro Sanchez (R)	.10	.06
44	Steve Jeltz (R)	.12	.07
45	Jim Traber (R)	.12	.07
46	Doug Loman (R)	.10	.06
47	Eddie Murray	2.00	1.25
48	Robin Yount	3.50	2.25
49	Lance Parrish	.12	.07
50	Jim Rice	.20	.12
51	Dave Winfield	4.50	2.75
52	Fernando Valenzuela	.15	.08
53	George Brett	4.00	2.50
54	Dave Kingman	.12	.07
55	Gary Carter	.50	.30
56	Buddy Bell	.10	.06
57	Reggie Jackson	2.50	1.50
58	Harold Baines	.50	.30
59	Ozzie Smith	2.00	1.25
60	Nolan Ryan	12.00	8.00
61	Mike Schmidt	6.00	3.75
62	Dave Parker	.30	.18
63	Tony Gwynn	7.00	4.00
64	Tony Pena	.10	.06
65	Jack Clark	.12	.07
66	Dale Murphy	.80	.50
67	Ryne Sandberg	10.00	6.50
68	Keith Hernandez	.15	.10
69	Alvin Davis (R)	.30	.18
70	Kent Hrbek	.40	.25
71	Willie Upshaw	.10	.06
72	Dave Engle	.10	.06
73	Alfredo Griffin	.10	.06
74	Jack Perconte (Var)	.10	.06
75	Jesse Orosco	.10	.06
76	Jody Davis	.10	.06
77	Bob Horner	.12	.07
78	Larry McWilliams	.10	.06
79	Joel Youngblood	.10	.06
80	Alan Wiggins	.10	.06
81	Ron Oester	.10	.06
82	Ozzie Virgil	.10	.06
83	Ricky Horton (R)	.12	.07
84	Bill Doran	.12	.07
85	Rod Carew	2.00	1.25
86	LaMarr Hoyt	.10	.06
87	Tim Wallach	.15	.08
88	Mike Flanagan	.10	.06
89	Jim Sundberg	.10	.06
90	Chet Lemon	.10	.06
91	Bob Stanley	.10	.06
92	Willie Randolph	.12	.07
93	Bill Russell	.12	.07
94	Julio Franco	.90	.60
95	Dan Quisenberry	.10	.06
96	Bill Caudill	.10	.06
97	Bill Gullickson	.10	.06
98	Danny Darwin	.10	.06
99	Curtis Wilkerson	.10	.06
100	Bud Black	.12	.07
101	Tony Phillips	.80	.50
102	Tony Bernazard	.10	.06
103	Jay Howell	.12	.07
104	Burt Hooton	.10	.06
105	Milt Wilcox	.10	.06
106	Rich Dauer	.10	.06
107	Don Sutton	.60	.35
108	Mike Witt	.10	.06
109	Bruce Sutter	.12	.07
110	Enos Cabell	.10	.06
111	John Denny	.10	.06
112	Dave Dravecky	.10	.06
113	Marvell Wynne	.10	.06
114	Johnnie LeMaster	.10	.06
115	Chuck Porter	.10	.06
116	John Gibbons	.10	.06
117	Keith Moreland	.10	.06
118	Darnell Coles	.10	.06
119	Dennis Lamp	.10	.06
120	Ron Davis	.10	.06
121	Nick Esasky	.10	.06
122	Vance Law	.10	.06
123	Gary Roenicke	.10	.06
124	Bill Schroeder	.10	.06
125	Dave Rozema	.10	.06
126	Bobby Meacham	.10	.06
127	Marty Barrett	.12	.07
128	R.J. Reynolds (R)	.10	.06
129	Ernie Camacho	.10	.06
130	Jorge Orta	.10	.06
131	Lary Sorensen	.10	.06
132	Terry Francona	.10	.06
133	Fred Lynn	.12	.07
134	Bobby Jones	.10	.06
135	Jerry Hairston	.10	.06
136	Kevin Bass	.12	.07
137	Garry Maddox	.10	.06
138	Dave LaPoint	.10	.06
139	Kevin McReynolds	.35*	.20
140	Wayne Krenchicki	.10	.06
141	Rafael Ramirez	.10	.06
142	Rod Scurry	.10	.06

143	Greg Minton	.10	.06
144	Tim Stoddard	.10	.06
145	Steve Henderson	.10	.06
146	George Bell	.50	.30
147	Dave Meier	.10	.06
148	Sammy Stewart	.10	.06
149	Mark Brouhard	.10	.06
150	Larry Herndon	.10	.06
151	Oil Can Boyd	.10	.06
152	Brian Dayett	.10	.06
153	Tom Niedenfuer	.10	.06
154	Brook Jacoby	.12	.07
155	Onix Concepcion	.10	.06
156	Tim Conroy	.10	.06
157	Joe Hesketh	.20	.12
158	Brian Downing	.10	.06
159	Tommy Dunbar	.10	.06
160	Marc Hill	.10	.06
161	Phil Garner	.10	.06
162	Jerry Davis	.10	.06
163	Bill Campbell	.10	.06
164	John Franco (R)	1.25	.80
165	Len Barker	.10	.06
166	Benny Distefano (R)	.10	.06
167	George Frazier	.10	.06
168	Tito Landrum	.10	.06
169	Cal Ripken	12.00	8.00
170	Cecil Cooper	.10	.06
171	Alan Trammell	.75	.45
172	Wade Boggs	6.00	3.75
173	Don Baylor	.15	.10
174	Pedro Guerrero	.12	.07
175	Frank White	.10	.06
176	Rickey Henderson	4.00	2.75
177	Charlie Lea	.10	.06
178	Pete O'Brien	.10	.06
179	Doug DeCinces	.10	.06
180	Ron Kettle	.10	.06
181	George Hendrick	.10	.06
182	Joe Niekro	.10	.06
183	Juan Samuel	.20	.12
184	Mario Soto	.10	.06
185	Goose Gossage	.12	.07
186	Johnny Ray	.10	.06
187	Bob Brenly	.10	.06
188	Craig McMurtry	.10	.06
189	Leon Durham	.10	.06
190	Dwight Gooden (R)	8.50	5.00
191	Barry Bonnell	.10	.06
192	Tim Teufel	.10	.06
193	Dave Stieb	.15	.08
194	Mickey Hatcher	.10	.06
195	Jesse Barfield	.12	.07
196	Al Cowens	.10	.06
197	Hubie Brooks	.12	.07
198	Steve Trout	.10	.06
199	Glenn Hubbard	.10	.06
200	Bill Madlock	.12	.07
201	Jeff Robinson (R)	.15	.10
202	Eric Show	.10	.06
203	Dave Concepcion	.12	.07
204	Ivan DeJesus	.10	.06
205	Neil Allen	.10	.06
206	Jerry Mumphrey	.10	.06
207	Mike Brown	.10	.06
208	Carlton Fisk	1.75	1.00
209	Bryn Smith	.10	.06
210	Tippy Martinez	.10	.06
211	Dion James	.10	.06
212	Willie Hernandez	.10	.06
213	Mike Easler	.10	.06
214	Ron Guidry	.15	.08
215	Rick Honeycutt	.10	.06
216	Brett Butler	.40	.25
217	Larry Gura	.10	.06
218	Ray Burris	.10	.06
219	Steve Rogers	.10	.06
220	Frank Tanana	.10	.06
221	Ned Yost	.10	.06
222	Bret Saberhagen (R)	3.50	2.25
223	Mike Davis	.10	.06
224	Bert Blyleven	.30	.18
225	Steve Kemp	.10	.06
226	Jerry Reuss	.10	.06
227	Darrell Evans	.12	.07
228	Wayne Gross	.10	.06
229	Jim Gantner	.10	.06
230	Bob Boone	.15	.08
231	Lonnie Smith	.12	.07
232	Frank DePino	.10	.06
233	Jerry Koosman	.12	.07
234	Graig Nettles	.12	.07
235	John Tudor	.10	.06
236	John Rabb	.10	.06
237	Rick Manning	.10	.06
238	Mike Fitzgerald	.10	.06
239	Gary Matthews	.10	.06
240	Jim Presley (R)	.12	.07
241	Dave Collins	.10	.06
242	Gary Gaetti	.12	.07
243	Dann Bilardello	.10	.06
244	Rudy Law	.10	.06
245	John Lowenstein	.10	.06
246	Tom Tellmann	.10	.06
247	Howard Johnson	1.25	.80
248	Ray Fontenot	.10	.06
249	Tony Armas	.10	.06
250	Candy Maldonado	.10	.06
251	Mike Jeffcoat	.10	.06
252	Dane Iorg	.10	.06
253	Bruce Bochte	.10	.06
254	Pete Rose	2.50	1.50
255	Don Aase	.10	.06
256	George Wright	.10	.06

257	Britt Burns	.10	.06
258	Mike Scott	.15	.08
259	Len Matuszek	.10	.06
260	Dave Rucker	.10	.06
261	Craig Lefferts	.10	.06
262	Jay Tibbs (R)	.10	.06
263	Bruce Benedict	.10	.06
264	Don Robinson	.10	.06
265	Gary Lavelle	.10	.06
266	Scott Sanderson	.10	.06
267	Matt Young	.10	.06
268	Ernie Whitt	.10	.06
269	Houston Jimenez	.10	.06
270	Ken Dixon	.10	.06
271	Peter Ladd	.10	.06
272	Juan Berenguer	.10	.06
273	Roger Clemens (R)	55.00	35.00
274	Rick Cerone	.10	.06
275	Dave Anderson	.10	.06
276	George Vukovich	.10	.06
277	Greg Pryor	.10	.06
278	Mike Warren	.10	.06
279	Bob James	.10	.06
280	Bobby Grich	.12	.07
281	Mike Mason (R)	.10	.06
282	Ron Reed	.10	.06
283	Alan Ashby	.10	.06
284	Mark Thurmond	.10	.06
285	Joe Lefebvre	.10	.06
286	Ted Power	.10	.06
287	Chris Chambliss	.10	.06
288	Lee Tunnell	.10	.06
289	Rich Bordi	.10	.06
290	Glenn Brummer	.10	.06
291	Mike Boddicker	.10	.06
292	Rollie Fingers	.70	.40
293	Lou Whitaker	.75	.45
294	Dwight Evans	.20	.12
295	Don Mattingly	8.00	5.00
296	Mike Marshall	.10	.06
297	Willie Wilson	.10	.06
298	Mike Heath	.10	.06
299	Tim Raines	.50	.30
300	Larry Parrish	.10	.06
301	Geoff Zahn	.10	.06
302	Rich Dotson	.10	.06
303	David Green	.10	.06
304	Jose Cruz	.12	.07
305	Steve Carlton	1.75	1.00
306	Gary Redus	.10	.06
307	Steve Garvey	.50	.30
308	Jose DeLeon	.10	.06
309	Randy Lerch	.10	.06
310	Claudell Washington	.10	.06
311	Lee Smith	1.50	.90
312	Darryl Strawberry	3.50	2.25
313	Jim Beattie	.10	.06
314	John Butcher	.10	.06
315	Damaso Garcia	.10	.06
316	Mike Smithson	.10	.06
317	Luis Leal	.10	.06
318	Ken Phelps	.12	.07
319	Wally Backman	.10	.06
320	Ron Cey	.12	.07
321	Brad Komminsk	.10	.06
322	Jason Thompson	.10	.06
323	Frank Williams (R)	.10	.06
324	Tim Lollar	.10	.06
325	Eric Davis (R)	8.00	5.00
326	Von Hayes	.10	.06
327	Andy Van Slyke	2.00	1.25
328	Craig Reynolds	.10	.06
329	Dick Schofield	.10	.06
330	Scott Fletcher	.10	.06
331	Jeff Reardon	.70	.40
332	Rick Dempsey	.10	.06
333	Ben Oglivie	.10	.06
334	Dan Petry	.10	.06
335	Jackie Gutierrez	.10	.06
336	Dave Righetti	.12	.07
337	Alejandro Pena	.10	.06
338	Mel Hall	.15	.08
339	Pat Sheridan	.10	.06
340	Keith Atherton	.10	.06
341	David Palmer	.10	.06
342	Gary Ward	.10	.06
343	Dave Stewart	.50	.30
344	Mark Gubicza (R)	.60	.35
345	Carney Lansford	.12	.07
346	Jerry Willard	.10	.06
347	Ken Griffey	.12	.07
348	Franklin Stubbs (R)	.20	.12
349	Aurelio Lopez	.10	.06
350	Al Bumbry	.10	.06
351	Charlie Moore	.10	.06
352	Luis Sanchez	.10	.06
353	Darrell Porter	.10	.06
354	Bill Dawley	.10	.06
355	Charlie Hudson	.10	.06
356	Garry Templeton	.10	.06
357	Cecilio Guante	.10	.06
358	Jeff Leonard	.10	.06
359	Paul Molitor	2.75	1.60
360	Ron Gardenhire	.10	.06
361	Larry Bowa	.10	.06
362	Bob Kearney	.10	.06
363	Garth Iorg	.10	.06
364	Tom Brunansky	.12	.07
265	Brad Gulden	.10	.06
366	Greg Walker	.10	.06
367	Mike Young	.10	.06
368	Rick Waits	.10	.06
369	Doug Bair	.10	.06
370	Bob Shirley	.10	.06

371	Bob Ojeda	.12	.07
372	Bob Welch	.15	.08
373	Neal Heaton	.10	.06
374	Danny Jackson(Er) (Wrong Photo)	.12	.07
375	Donnie Hill	.10	.06
376	Mike Stenhouse	.10	.06
377	Bruce Kison	.10	.06
378	Wayne Tolleson	.10	.06
379	Floyd Bannister	.10	.06
380	Vern Ruhle	.10	.06
381	Tim Corcoran	.10	.06
382	Kurt Kepshire	.10	.06
383	Bobby Brown	.10	.06
384	Dave Van Gorder	.10	.06
385	Rick Mahler	.10	.06
386	Lee Mazzilli	.10	.06
387	Bill Laskey	.10	.06
388	Thad Bosley	.10	.06
389	Al Chambers	.10	.06
390	Tony Fernandez	.80	.50
391	Ron Washington	.10	.06
392	Bill Swaggerty	.10	.06
393	Bob Gibson	.10	.06
394	Marty Castillo	.10	.06
395	Steve Crawford	.10	.06
396	Clay Christiansen	.10	.06
397	Bob Bailor	.10	.06
398	Mike Hargrove	.10	.06
399	Charlie Leibrandt	.10	.06
400	Tom Burgmeier	.10	.06
401	Razor Shines	.10	.06
402	Rob Wilfong	.10	.06
403	Tom Henke	.50	.30
404	Al Jones	.10	.06
405	Mike LaCoss	.10	.06
406	Luis DeLeon	.10	.06
407	Greg Gross	.10	.06
408	Tom Hume	.10	.06
409	Rick Camp	.10	.06
410	Milt May	.10	.06
411	Henry Cotto (R)	.12	.07
412	Dave Von Ohlen	.10	.06
413	Scott McGregor	.10	.06
414	Ted Simmons	.12	.07
415	Jack Morris	.90	.60
416	Bill Buckner	.12	.07
417	Butch Wynegar	.10	.06
418	Steve Sax	.50	.30
419	Steve Balboni	.10	.06
420	Dwayne Murphy	.10	.06
421	Andre Dawson	2.00	1.25
422	Charlie Hough	.10	.06
423	Tommy John	.15	.10
424a	Tom Seaver (Er) (Wrong Photo)	2.50	1.50
424b	Tom Seaver (Cor)	30.00	20.00
425	Tom Herr	.10	.06
426	Terry Puhl	.10	.06
427	Al Holland	.10	.06
428	Eddie Milner	.10	.06
429	Terry Kennedy	.10	.06
430	John Candelaria	.10	.06
431	Manny Trillo	.10	.06
432	Ken Oberkfell	.10	.06
433	Rick Sutcliffe	.10	.06
434	Ron Darling	.30	.18
435	Spike Owen	.10	.06
436	Frank Viola	.50	.30
437	Lloyd Moseby	.10	.06
438	Kirby Puckett (R)	65.00	40.00
439	Jim Clancy	.10	.06
440	Mike Moore	.30	.18
441	Doug Sisk	.10	.06
442	Dennis Eckersley	1.00	.70
443	Gerald Perry	.10	.06
444	Dale Berra	.10	.06
445	Dusty Baker	.12	.07
446	Ed Whitson	.10	.06
447	Cesar Cedeno	.12	.07
448	Rick Schu (R)	.10	.06
449	Joaquin Andujar	.10	.06
450	Mark Bailey (R)	.10	.06
451	Ron Romanick (R)	.10	.06
452	Julio Cruz	.10	.06
453	Miguel Dilone	.10	.06
454	Storm Davis	.10	.06
455	Jaime Cocanower	.10	.06
456	Barbaro Garbey	.10	.06
457	Rich Gedman	.10	.06
458	Phil Niekro	.70	.40
459	Mike Scioscia	.15	.08
460	Pat Tabler	.10	.06
461	Darryl Motley	.10	.06
462	Chris Codiroli	.10	.06
463	Doug Flynn	.10	.06
464	Billy Sample	.10	.06
465	Mickey Rivers	.10	.06
466	John Wathan	.10	.06
467	Bill Krueger	.10	.06
468	Andre Thornton	.10	.06
469	Rex Hudler	.12	.07
470	Sid Bream (R)	.50	.30
471	Kirk Gibson	.25	.15
472	John Shelby	.10	.06
473	Moose Haas	.10	.06
474	Doug Corbett	.10	.06
475	Willie McGee	.50	.30
476	Bob Knepper	.10	.06
477	Kevin Gross	.10	.06
478	Carmelo Martinez	.10	.06
479	Kent Tekulve	.10	.06
480	Chili Davis	.15	.10
481	Bobby Clark	.10	.06

482	Mookie Wilson	.10	.06	537	Dave Bergman	.10	.06
483	Dave Owen	.10	.06	538	Mark Clear	.10	.06
484	Ed Nunez	.10	.06	539	Mike Pagliarulo (R)	.20	.12
485	Rance Mulliniks	.10	.06	540	Terry Whitfield	.10	.06
486	Ken Schrom	.10	.06	541	Joe Beckwith	.10	.06
487	Jeff Russell	.12	.07	542	Jeff Burroughs	.10	.06
488	Tom Paciorek	.10	.06	543	Dan Schatzeder	.10	.06
489	Dan Ford	.10	.06	544	Donnie Scott	.10	.06
490	Mike Caldwell	.10	.06	545	Jim Slaton	.10	.06
491	Scottie Earl	.10	.06	546	Greg Luzinski	.12	.07
492	Jose Rijo (R)	4.00	2.75	547	Mark Salas (R)	.10	.06
493	Bruce Hurst	.15	.08	548	Dave Smith	.10	.06
494	Ken Landreaux	.10	.06	549	John Wockenfuss	.10	.06
495	Mike Fischlin	.10	.06	550	Frank Pastore	.10	.06
496	Don Slaught	.10	.06	551	Tim Flannery	.10	.06
497	Steve McCatty	.10	.06	552	Rick Rhoden	.10	.06
498	Gary Lucas	.10	.06	553	Mark Davis	.10	.06
499	Gary Pettis	.10	.06	554	Jeff Dedmon (R)	.10	.06
500	Marvis Foley	.10	.06	555	Gary Woods	.10	.06
501	Mike Squires	.10	.06	556	Danny Heep	.10	.06
502	Jim Pankovits (R)	.10	.06	557	Mark Langston (R)	3.50	2.25
503	Luis Aguayo	.10	.06	558	Darrell Brown	.10	.06
504	Ralph Citarella	.10	.06	559	Jimmy Key (R)	3.50	2.25
505	Bruce Bochy	.10	.06	560	Rick Lysander	.10	.06
506	Bob Owchinko	.10	.06	561	Doyle Alexander	.10	.06
507	Pascual Perez	.12	.07	562	Mike Stanton	.10	.06
508	Lee Lacy	.10	.06	563	Sid Fernandez	.35	.20
509	Atlee Hammaker	.10	.06	564	Richie Hebner	.10	.06
510	Bob Dernier	.10	.06	565	Alex Trevino	.10	.06
511	Ed Vande Berg	.10	.06	566	Brian Harper	.70	.40
512	Cliff Johnson	.10	.06	567	Dan Gladden (R)	.40	.25
513	Len Whitehouse	.10	.06	568	Luis Salazar	.10	.06
514	Dennis Martinez	.25	.15	569	Tom Foley	.10	.06
515	Ed Romero	.10	.06	570	Larry Andersen	.10	.06
516	Rusty Kuntz	.10	.06	571	Danny Cox	.10	.06
517	Rick Miller	.10	.06	572	Joe Sambito	.10	.06
518	Dennis Rasmussen	.10	.06	573	Juan Beniquez	.10	.06
519	Steve Yeager	.10	.06	574	Joel Skinner	.10	.06
520	Chris Bando	.10	.06	575	Randy St. Claire	.10	.06
521	U.L. Washington	.10	.06	576	Floyd Rayford	.10	.06
522	Curt Young (R)	.12	.07	577	Roy Howell	.10	.06
523	Angel Salazar	.10	.06	578	John Grubb	.10	.06
524	Curt Kaufman	.10	.06	579	Ed Jurak	.10	.06
525	Odell Jones	.10	.06	580	John Montefusco	.10	.06
526	Juan Agosto	.10	.06	581	Orel Hershiser (R)	3.50	2.25
527	Denny Walling	.10	.06	582	Tom Waddell	.10	.06
528	Andy Hawkins	.12	.07	583	Mark Huismann	.10	.06
529	Sixto Lezcano	.10	.06	584	Joe Morgan	.60	.35
530	Skeeter Barnes (R)	.15	.10	585	Jim Wohlford	.10	.06
531	Randy Johnson	.10	.06	586	Dave Schmidt	.10	.06
532	Jim Morrison	.10	.06	587	Jeff Kunkel (R)	.10	.06
533	Warren Brusstar	.10	.06	588	Hal McRae	.12	.07
534a	Jeff Pendleton (Er) (Wrong name)	6.50	3.75	589	Bill Almon	.10	.06
				590	Carmen Castillo	.10	.06
534b	Terry Pendleton (R)	24.00	15.00	591	Omar Moreno	.10	.06
535	Vic Rodriguez	.10	.06	592	Ken Howell (R)	.12	.07
536	Bob McClure	.10	.06	593	Tom Brookens	.10	.06

594	Joe Nolan	.10	.06
595	Willie Lozado	.10	.06
596	Tom Nieto	.10	.06
597	Walt Terrell	.10	.06
598	Al Oliver	.12	.07
599	Shane Rawley	.10	.06
600	Denny Gonzalez (R)	.10	.06
601	Mark Grant (R)	.10	.06
602	Mark Armstrong	.10	.06
603	George Foster	.12	.07
604	Davey Lopes	.12	.07
605	Salome Barojas	.10	.06
606	Roy Lee Jackson	.10	.06
607	Pete Filson	.10	.06
608	Duane Walker	.10	.06
609	Glenn Wilson	.10	.06
610	Rafael Santana (R)	.12	.07
611	Roy Smith	.10	.06
612	Ruppert Jones	.10	.06
613	Joe Cowley	.10	.06
614	Al Nipper(Wrong Photo)	.12	.07
615	Gene Nelson	.10	.06
616	Joe Carter	14.00	9.00
617	Ray Knight	.10	.06
618	Chuck Rainey	.10	.06
619	Dan Driessen	.10	.06
620	Daryl Sconiers	.10	.06
621	Bill Stein	.10	.06
622	Roy Smalley	.10	.06
623	Ed Lynch	.10	.06
624	Jeff Stone (R)	.10	.06
625	Bruce Berenyi	.10	.06
626	Kelvin Chapman	.10	.06
627	Joe Price	.10	.06
628	Steve Bedrosian	.10	.06
629	Vic Mata	.10	.06
630	Mike Krukow	.10	.06
631	Phil Bradley (R)	.20	.12
632	Jim Gott	.10	.06
633	Randy Bush	.10	.06
634	Tom Browning (R)	.80	.50
635	Lou Gehrig Puzzle Card	.15	.08
636	Reid Nichols	.10	.06
637	Dan Pasqua (R)	.35	.20
638	German Rivera	.10	.06
639	Don Schulze (R)	.10	.06
640	Mike Jones (Var)	.10	.06
641	Pete Rose	2.50	1.50
642	Wade Rowdon	.10	.06
643	Jerry Narron	.10	.06
644	Darrell Miller (R)	.10	.06
645	Tim Hulett (R)	.12	.07
646	Andy McGaffigan	.10	.06
647	Kurt Bevacqua	.10	.06
648	John Russell (R)	.12	.07
649	Ron Robinson (R)	.12	.07
650	Donnie Moore	.10	.06

651a	Two for the Title (Mattingly/Winfield) (Yellow names)	3.50	2.25
651b	Two for the Title (Mattingly/Winfield) (White names)	10.00	6.00
652	Tim Laudner	.10	.06
653	Steve Farr (R)	.50	.30
___	Checklist (DK)	.15	.10
___	Checklist 27-130	.12	.07
___	Checklist 131-234	.12	.07
___	Checklist 235-338	.12	.07
___	Checklist 339-442	.12	.07
___	Checklist 443-546	.12	.07
___	Checklist 547-653	.12	.07

1986 Donruss

This 660-card set features full color photos with blue borders on the card fronts and horizontal card backs with black type on a blue and white back-ground. Subsets include Diamond Kings (1-26) and Rated Rookies (27-46). The standard-size cards measure 2-1/2" by 3-1/2". Wax packs included puzzle pieces featuring Hank Aaron.

	MINT	NR/MT
Complete Set (660)	135.00	85.00
Commons	.08	.05

1	Kirk Gibson (DK)	.15	.10
2	Goose Gossage (DK)	.15	.10
3	Willie McGee (DK)	.15	.10
4	George Bell (DK)	.15	.10
5	Tony Armas (DK)	.10	.06
6	Chili Davis (DK)	.12	.07
7	Cecil Cooper (DK)	.12	.07
8	Mike Boddicker (DK)	.10	.06
9	Davey Lopes (DK)	.12	.07
10	Bill Doran (DK)	.10	.06
11	Bret Saberhagen (DK)	.15	.10
12	Brett Butler (DK)	.15	.10

13 Harold Baines (DK)	.12	.07
14 Mike Davis (DK)	.10	.06
15 Tony Perez (DK)	.20	.12
16 Willie Randolph (DK)	.12	.07
17 Bob Boone (DK)	.15	.10
18 Orel Hershiser (DK)	.15	.10
19 Johnny Ray (DK)	.10	.06
20 Gary Ward (DK)	.10	.06
21 Rick Mahler (DK)	.10	.06
22 Phil Bradley (DK)	.12	.07
23 Jerry Koosman (DK)	.12	.07
24 Tom Brunansky (DK)	.12	.07
25 Andre Dawson (DK)	.50	.30
26 Dwight Gooden (DK)	.35	.20
27 Kal Daniels (R)	.60	.35
28 Fred McGriff (R)	40.00	28.00
29 Cory Snyder (R)	.50	.30
30 Jose Guzman (R)	.80	.50
31 Ty Gainey (R)	.10	.06
32 Johnny Abrego (R)	.08	.05
33 Andres Galarraga (R)	7.50	4.50
34 Dave Shipanoff (R)	.08	.05
35 Mark McLemore (R)	.40	.25
36 Marty Clary (R)	.10	.06
37 Paul O'Neill (R)	3.50	2.25
38 Danny Tartabull (R)	1.75	1.00
39 Jose Canseco (R)	38.00	25.00
40 Juan Nieves (R)	.15	.10
41 Lance McCullers (R)	.10	.06
42 Rick Surhoff (R)	.10	.06
43 Todd Worrell (R)	.30	.18
44 Bob Kipper (R)	.10	.06
45 John Habyan (R)	.15	.10
46 Mike Woodard (R)	.08	.05
47 Mike Boddicker	.08	.05
48 Robin Yount	2.00	1.25
49 Lou Whitaker	.25	.15
50 "Oil Can" Boyd	.08	.05
51 Rickey Henderson	2.50	1.50
52 Mike Marshall	.08	.05
53 George Brett	2.50	1.50
54 Dave Kingman	.10	.06
55 Hubie Brooks	.10	.06
56 Oddibe McDowell (R)	.10	.06
57 Doug DeCinces	.08	.05
58 Britt Burns	.08	.05
59 Ozzie Smith	1.00	.70
60 Jose Cruz	.10	.06
61 Mike Schmidt	3.00	1.75
62 Pete Rose	1.25	.80
63 Steve Garvey	.40	.25
64 Tony Pena	.08	.05
65 Chili Davis	.10	.06
66 Dale Murphy	.40	.25
67 Ryne Sandberg	5.00	3.00
68 Gary Carter	.40	.25
69 Alvin Davis	.08	.05
70 Kent Hrbek	.15	.10
71 George Bell	.35	.20
72 Kirby Puckett	12.00	8.00
73 Lloyd Moseby	.08	.05
74 Bob Kearney	.08	.05
75 Dwight Gooden	1.25	.80
76 Gary Matthews	.08	.05
77 Rick Mahler	.08	.05
78 Benny Distefano	.08	.05
79 Jeff Leonard	.08	.05
80 Kevin McReynolds	.15	.10
81 Ron Oester	.08	.05
82 John Russell	.08	.05
83 Tommy Herr	.08	.05
84 Jerry Mumphrey	.08	.05
85 Ron Romanick	.08	.05
86 Daryl Boston	.08	.05
87 Andre Dawson	1.25	.80
88 Eddie Murray	1.25	.80
89 Dion James	.08	.05
90 Chet Lemon	.08	.05
91 Bob Stanley	.08	.05
92 Willie Randolph	.10	.06
93 Mike Scioscia	.10	.06
94 Tom Waddell	.08	.05
95 Danny Jackson	.08	.05
96 Mike Davis	.08	.05
97 Mike Fitzgerald	.08	.05
98 Gary Ward	.08	.05
99 Pete O'Brien	.08	.05
100 Bret Saberhagen	.50	.30
101 Alfredo Griffin	.08	.05
102 Brett Butler	.15	.10
103 Ron Guidry	.12	.07
104 Jerry Reuss	.08	.05
105 Jack Morris	.60	.35
106 Rick Dempsey	.08	.05
107 Ray Burris	.08	.05
108 Brian Downing	.08	.05
109 Willie McGee	.20	.12
110 Bill Doran	.08	.05
111 Kent Tekulve	.08	.05
112 Tony Gwynn	3.50	2.25
113 Marvell Wynne	.08	.05
114 David Green	.08	.05
115 Jim Gantner	.08	.05
116 George Foster	.10	.06
117 Steve Trout	.08	.05
118 Mark Langston	.50	.30
119 Tony Fernandez	.20	.12
120 John Butcher	.08	.05
121 Ron Robinson	.08	.05
122 Dan Spillner	.08	.05
123 Mike Young	.08	.05
124 Paul Molitor	1.50	.90
125 Kirk Gibson	.15	.10
126 Ken Griffey	.12	.07

127 Tony Armas	.08	.05
128 Mariano Duncan (R)	.40	.25
129 Pat Tabler	.08	.05
130 Frank White	.08	.05
131 Carney Lansford	.10	.06
132 Vance Law	.08	.05
133 Dick Schofield	.08	.05
134 Wayne Tolleson	.08	.05
135 Greg Walker	.08	.05
136 Denny Walling	.08	.05
137 Ozzie Virgil	.08	.05
138 Ricky Horton	.08	.05
139 LaMarr Hoyt	.08	.05
140 Wayne Krenchicki	.08	.05
141 Glenn Hubbard	.08	.05
142 Cecilio Guante	.08	.05
143 Mike Krukow	.08	.05
144 Lee Smith	.75	.45
145 Edwin Nunez	.08	.05
146 Dave Steib	.12	.07
147 Mike Smithson	.08	.05
148 Ken Dixon	.08	.05
149 Danny Darwin	.08	.05
150 Chris Pittaro	.08	.05
151 Bill Buckner	.10	.06
152 Mike Pagliarulo	.08	.05
153 Bill Russell	.10	.06
154 Brook Jacoby	.08	.05
155 Pat Sheridan	.08	.05
156 Mike Gallego (R)	.15	.10
157 Jim Wohlford	.08	.05
158 Gary Pettis	.08	.05
159 Toby Harrah	.08	.05
160 Richard Dotson	.08	.05
161 Bob Knepper	.08	.05
162 Dave Dravecky	.08	.05
163 Greg Gross	.08	.05
164 Eric Davis	1.00	.70
165 Gerald Perry	.08	.05
166 Rick Rhoden	.08	.05
167 Keith Moreland	.08	.05
168 Jack Clark	.12	.07
169 Storm Davis	.08	.05
170 Cecil Cooper	.08	.05
171 Alan Trammell	.50	.30
172 Roger Clemens	12.00	8.00
173 Don Mattingly	2.75	1.75
174 Pedro Guerrero	.10	.06
175 Willie Wilson	.08	.05
176 Dwayne Murphy	.08	.05
177 Tim Raines	.25	.15
178 Larry Parrish	.08	.05
179 Mike Witt	.08	.05
180 Harold Baines	.15	.10
181 Vince Coleman (R)	.75	.45
182 Jeff Heathcock (R)	.08	.05
183 Steve Carlton	1.25	.80
184 Mario Soto	.08	.05
185 Goose Gossage	.12	.07
186 Johnny Ray	.08	.05
187 Dan Gladden	.08	.05
188 Bob Horner	.10	.06
189 Rick Sutcliffe	.10	.06
190 Keith Hernandez	.12	.07
191 Phil Bradley	.08	.05
192 Tom Brunansky	.10	.06
193 Jesse Barfield	.12	.07
194 Frank Viola	.30	.18
195 Willie Upshaw	.08	.05
196 Jim Beattie	.08	.05
197 Darryl Strawberry	1.75	1.00
198 Ron Cey	.10	.06
199 Steve Bedrosian	.08	.05
200 Steve Kemp	.08	.05
201 Manny Trillo	.08	.05
202 Garry Templeton	.08	.05
203 Dave Parker	.15	.10
204 John Denny	.08	.05
205 Terry Pendleton	1.50	.90
206 Terry Puhl	.08	.05
207 Bobby Grich	.10	.06
208 Ozzie Guillen (R)	.75	.45
209 Jeff Reardon	.60	.35
210 Cal Ripken Jr.	5.00	3.00
211 Bill Schroeder	.08	.05
212 Dan Petry	.08	.05
213 Jim Rice	.15	.10
214 Dave Righetti	.10	.06
215 Fernando Valenzuela	.12	.07
216 Julio Franco	.40	.25
217 Darryl Motley	.08	.05
218 Dave Collins	.08	.05
219 Tim Wallach	.12	.07
220 George Wright	.08	.05
221 Tommy Dunbar	.08	.05
222 Steve Balboni	.08	.05
223 Jay Howell	.08	.05
224 Joe Carter	5.00	3.00
225 Ed Whitson	.08	.05
226 Orel Hershiser	.50	.30
227 Willie Hernandez	.08	.05
228 Lee Lacy	.08	.05
229 Rollie Fingers	.40	.25
230 Bob Boone	.12	.07
231 Joaquin Andujar	.08	.05
232 Craig Reynolds	.08	.05
233 Shane Rawley	.08	.05
234 Eric Show	.08	.05
235 Jose DeLeon	.08	.05
236 Jose Uribe (R)	.15	.10
237 Moose Haas	.08	.05
238 Wally Backman	.08	.05
239 Dennis Eckersley	.75	.45
240 Mike Moore	.12	.07

241	Damaso Garcia	.08	.05
242	Tim Teufel	.08	.05
243	Dave Concepcion	.12	.07
244	Floyd Bannister	.08	.05
245	Fred Lynn	.12	.07
246	Charlie Moore	.08	.05
247	Walt Terrell	.08	.05
248	Dave Winfield	1.75	1.00
249	Dwight Evans	.12	.07
250	Dennis Powell (R)	.08	.05
251	Andre Thornton	.08	.05
252	Onix Concepcion	.08	.05
253	Mike Heath	.08	.05
254a	David Palmer (Er)(2B)	.08	.05
254b	David Palmer (Cor)(P)	.75	.45
255	Donnie Moore	.08	.05
256	Curtis Wilkerson	.08	.05
257	Julio Cruz	.08	.05
258	Nolan Ryan	7.50	4.50
259	Jeff Stone	.08	.05
260	John Tudor (Var)	.08	.05
261	Mark Thurmond	.08	.05
262	Jay Tibbs	.08	.05
263	Rafael Ramirez	.08	.05
264	Larry McWilliams	.08	.05
265	Mark Davis	.08	.05
266	Bob Dernier	.08	.05
267	Matt Young	.08	.05
268	Jim Clancy	.08	.05
269	Mickey Hatcher	.08	.05
270	Sammy Stewart	.08	.05
271	Bob Gibson	.08	.05
272	Nelson Simmons	.08	.05
273	Rich Gedman	.08	.05
274	Butch Wynegar	.08	.05
275	Ken Howell	.08	.05
276	Mel Hall	.15	.10
277	Jim Sundberg	.08	.05
278	Chris Codiroli	.08	.05
279	Herm Winningham (R)	.12	.07
280	Rod Carew	1.00	.70
281	Don Slaught	.08	.05
282	Scott Fletcher	.08	.05
283	Bill Dawley	.08	.05
284	Andy Hawkins	.08	.05
285	Glenn Wilson	.08	.05
286	Nick Esasky	.08	.05
287	Claudell Washington	.08	.05
288	Lee Mazzilli	.08	.05
289	Jody Davis	.08	.05
290	Darrell Porter	.08	.05
291	Scott McGregor	.08	.05
292	Ted Simmons	.10	.06
293	Aurelio Lopez	.08	.05
294	Marty Barrett	.08	.05
295	Dale Berra	.08	.05
296	Greg Brock	.08	.05
297	Charlie Leibrandt	.08	.05
298	Bill Krueger	.08	.05
299	Bryn Smith	.08	.05
300	Burt Hooton	.08	.05
301	Stu Cliburn	.08	.05
302	Luis Salazar	.08	.05
303	Ken Dayley	.08	.05
304	Frank DiPino	.08	.05
305	Von Hayes	.08	.05
306	Gary Redus (Var)	.08	.05
307	Craig Lefferts	.08	.05
308	Sam Khalifa	.08	.05
309	Scott Garrelts	.08	.05
310	Rick Cerone	.08	.05
311	Shawon Dunston	.25	.15
312	Howard Johnson	.40	.25
313	Jim Presley	.08	.05
314	Gary Gaetti	.10	.06
315	Luis Leal	.08	.05
316	Mark Salas	.08	.05
317	Bill Caudill	.08	.05
318	Dave Henderson	.12	.07
319	Rafael Santana	.08	.05
320	Leon Durham	.08	.05
321	Bruce Sutter	.10	.06
322	Jason Thompson	.08	.05
323	Bob Brenly	.08	.05
324	Carmelo Martinez	.08	.05
325	Eddie Milner	.08	.05
326	Juan Samuel	.08	.05
327	Tom Nieto	.08	.05
328	Dave Smith	.08	.05
329	Urbano Lugo (R)	.08	.05
330	Joel Skinner	.08	.05
331	Bill Gullickson	.08	.05
332	Floyd Rayford	.08	.05
333	Ben Oglivie	.08	.05
334	Lance Parrish	.08	.05
335	Jackie Gutierrez	.08	.05
336	Dennis Rasmussen	.08	.05
337	Terry Whitfield	.08	.05
338	Neal Heaton	.08	.05
339	Jorge Orta	.08	.05
340	Donnie Hill	.08	.05
341	Joe Hesketh	.10	.06
342	Charlie Hough	.08	.05
343	Dave Rozema	.08	.05
344	Greg Pryor	.08	.05
345	Mickey Tettleton (R)	3.50	2.25
346	George Vukovich	.08	.05
347	Don Baylor	.10	.06
348	Carlos Diaz	.08	.05
349	Barbaro Garbey	.08	.05
350	Larry Sheets	.08	.05
351	Ted Higuera (R)	.20	.12
352	Juan Beniquez	.08	.05
353	Bob Forsch	.08	.05

354 Mark Bailey	.08	.05
355 Larry Andersen	.08	.05
356 Terry Kennedy	.08	.05
357 Don Robinson	.08	.05
358 Jim Gott	.08	.05
359 Earnest Riles (R)	.12	.07
360 John Christensen (R)	.08	.05
361 Ray Fontenot	.08	.05
362 Spike Owen	.08	.05
363 Jim Acker	.08	.05
364 Ron Davis (Var)	.08	.05
365 Tom Hume	.08	.05
366 Carlton Fisk	1.00	.70
367 Nate Snell	.08	.05
368 Rick Manning	.08	.05
369 Darrell Evans	.10	.06
370 Ron Hassey	.08	.05
371 Wade Boggs	3.50	2.25
372 Rick Honeycutt	.08	.05
373 Chris Bando	.08	.05
374 Bud Black	.08	.05
375 Steve Henderson	.08	.05
376 Charlie Lea	.08	.05
377 Reggie Jackson	1.75	1.00
378 Dave Schmidt	.08	.05
379 Bob James	.08	.05
380 Glenn Davis	.40	.25
381 Tim Corcoran	.08	.05
382 Danny Cox	.08	.05
383 Tim Flannery	.08	.05
384 Tom Browning	.15	.10
385 Rick Camp	.08	.05
386 Jim Morrison	.08	.05
387 Dave LaPoint	.08	.05
388 Davey Lopes	.10	.06
389 Al Cowens	.08	.05
390 Doyle Alexander	.08	.05
391 Tim Laudner	.08	.05
392 Don Aase	.08	.05
393 Jaime Cocanower	.08	.05
394 Randy O'Neal (R)	.08	.05
395 Mike Easler	.08	.05
396 Scott Bradley	.08	.05
397 Tom Niedenfuer	.08	.05
398 Jerry Willard	.08	.05
399 Lonnie Smith	.08	.05
400 Bruce Bochte	.08	.05
401 Terry Francona	.08	.05
402 Jim Slaton	.08	.05
403 Bill Stein	.08	.05
404 Tim Hulett	.08	.05
405 Alan Ashby	.08	.05
406 Tim Stoddard	.08	.05
407 Garry Maddox	.08	.05
408 Ted Power	.08	.05
409 Len Barker	.08	.05
410 Denny Gonzalez	.08	.05
411 George Frazier	.08	.05
412 Andy Van Slyke	.80	.50
413 Jim Dwyer	.08	.05
414 Paul Householder	.08	.05
415 Alejandro Sanchez	.08	.05
416 Steve Crawford	.08	.05
417 Dan Pasqua	.12	.07
418 Enos Cabell	.08	.05
419 Mike Jones	.08	.05
420 Steve Kiefer	.08	.05
421 Tim Burke (R)	.12	.07
422 Mike Mason	.08	.05
423 Ruppert Jones	.08	.05
424 Jerry Hairston	.08	.05
425 Tito Landrum	.08	.05
426 Jeff Calhoun	.08	.05
427 Don Carman (R)	.12	.07
428 Tony Perez	.35	.20
429 Jerry Davis	.08	.05
430 Bob Walk	.08	.05
431 Brad Wellman	.08	.05
432 Terry Forster	.08	.05
433 Billy Hatcher	.08	.05
434 Clint Hurdle	.08	.05
435 Ivan Calderon (R)	.50	.30
436 Pete Filson	.08	.05
437 Tom Henke	.35	.20
438 Dave Engle	.08	.05
439 Tom Filer	.08	.05
440 Gorman Thomas	.08	.05
441 Rick Aguilera (R)	1.25	.80
442 Scott Sanderson	.08	.05
443 Jeff Dedmon	.08	.05
444 Joe Orsulak (R)	.25	.15
445 Atlee Hammaker	.08	.05
446 Jerry Royster	.08	.05
447 Buddy Bell	.08	.05
448 Dave Rucker	.08	.05
449 Ivan DeJesus	.08	.05
450 Jim Pankovits	.08	.05
451 Jerry Narron	.08	.05
452 Bryan Little	.08	.05
453 Gary Lucas	.08	.05
454 Dennis Martinez	.15	.08
455 Ed Romero	.08	.05
456 Bob Melvin (R)	.10	.06
457 Glenn Hoffman	.08	.05
458 Bob Shirley	.08	.05
459 Bob Welch	.10	.06
460 Carmen Castillo	.08	.05
461 Dave Leeper	.08	.05
462 Tim Birtsas (R)	.10	.06
463 Randy St. Claire	.08	.05
464 Chris Welsh	.08	.05
465 Greg Harris	.08	.05
466 Lynn Jones	.08	.05
467 Dusty Baker	.10	.06

No.	Name	Price 1	Price 2
468	Roy Smith	.08	.05
469	Andre Robertson	.08	.05
470	Ken Landreaux	.08	.05
471	Dave Bergman	.08	.05
472	Gary Roenicke	.08	.05
473	Pete Vuckovich	.08	.05
474	Kirk McCaskill (R)	.25	.15
475	Jeff Lahti	.08	.05
476	Mike Scott	.10	.06
477	Darren Daulton (R)	6.00	3.75
478	Graig Nettles	.12	.07
479	Bill Almon	.08	.05
480	Greg Minton	.08	.05
481	Randy Ready	.10	.06
482	Lenny Dykstra (R)	7.00	4.00
483	Thad Bosley	.08	.05
484	Harold Reynolds (R)	.75	.45
485	Al Oliver	.10	.06
486	Roy Smalley	.08	.05
487	John Franco	.12	.07
488	Juan Agosto	.08	.05
489	Al Pardo	.08	.05
490	Bill Wegman (R)	.30	.18
491	Frank Tanana	.10	.06
492	Brian Fisher (R)	.08	.05
493	Mark Clear	.08	.05
494	Len Matuszek	.08	.05
495	Ramon Romero	.08	.05
496	John Wathan	.08	.05
497	Rob Picciolo	.08	.05
498	U.L. Washington	.08	.05
499	John Candelaria	.08	.05
500	Duane Walker	.08	.05
501	Gene Nelson	.08	.05
502	John Mizerock	.08	.05
503	Luis Aguayo	.08	.05
504	Kurt Kepshire	.08	.05
505	Ed Wojna	.08	.05
506	Joe Price	.08	.05
507	Milt Thompson (R)	.25	.15
508	Junior Ortiz	.08	.05
509	Vida Blue	.12	.07
510	Steve Engel	.08	.05
511	Karl Best	.08	.05
512	Cecil Fielder (R)	32.00	20.00
513	Frank Eufemia	.08	.05
514	Tippy Martinez	.08	.05
515	Billy Robidoux (R)	.08	.05
516	Bill Scherrer	.08	.05
517	Bruce Hurst	.12	.07
518	Rich Bordi	.08	.05
519	Steve Yeager	.08	.05
520	Tony Bernazard	.08	.05
521	Hal McRae	.10	.06
522	Jose Rijo	.50	.30
523	Mitch Webster (R)	.20	.12
524	Jack Howell (R)	.10	.06
525	Alan Bannister	.08	.05
526	Ron Kittle	.08	.05
527	Phil Garner	.10	.06
528	Kurt Bevacqua	.08	.05
529	Kevin Gross	.08	.05
530	Bo Diaz	.08	.05
531	Ken Oberkfell	.08	.05
532	Rich Reuschel	.08	.05
533	Ron Meridith	.08	.05
534	Steve Braun	.08	.05
535	Wayne Gross	.08	.05
536	Ray Searage	.08	.05
537	Tom Brookens	.08	.05
538	Al Nipper	.08	.05
539	Billy Sample	.08	.05
540	Steve Sax	.25	.15
541	Dan Quisenberry	.08	.05
542	Tony Phillips	.08	.05
543	Floyd Youmans (R)	.10	.06
544	Steve Buechele (R)	.80	.50
545	Craig Gerber	.08	.05
546	Joe DeSa	.08	.05
547	Brian Harper	.25	.15
548	Kevin Bass	.10	.06
549	Tom Foley	.08	.05
550	Dave Van Gorder	.08	.05
551	Bruce Bochy	.08	.05
552	R.J. Reynolds	.08	.05
553	Chris Brown (R)	.08	.05
554	Bruce Benedict	.08	.05
555	Warren Brusstar	.08	.05
556	Danny Heep	.08	.05
558	Greg Gagne	.10	.06
559	Ernie Whitt	.08	.05
560	Ron Washington	.08	.05
561	Jimmy Key	.40	.25
562	Billy Swift (R)	1.25	.80
563	Ron Darling	.15	.08
564	Dick Ruthven	.08	.05
565	Zane Smith	.30	.18
566	Sid Bream	.10	.06
567a	Joel Youngblood (Er) (P on front)	.10	.06
567b	Joel Youngblood (Cor)	.75	.45
568	Mario Ramirez	.08	.05
569	Tom Runnells	.08	.05
570	Rick Schu	.08	.05
571	Bill Campbell	.08	.05
572	Dickie Thon	.08	.05
573	Al Holland	.08	.05
574	Reid Nichols	.08	.05
575	Bert Roberge	.08	.05
576	Mike Flanagan	.08	.05
577	Tim Leary (R)	.12	.07
578	Mike Laga	.08	.05
579	Steve Lyons	.08	.05
580	Phil Niekro	.35	.20

581	Gilberto Reyes	.10	.06
582	Jamie Easterly	.08	.05
583	Mark Gubicza	.12	.07
584	Stan Javier (R)	.12	.07
585	Bill Laskey	.08	.05
586	Jeff Russell	.10	.06
587	Dickie Noles	.08	.05
588	Steve Farr	.08	.05
589	Steve Ontiveros (R)	.08	.05
590	Mike Hargrove	.08	.05
591	Marty Bystrom	.08	.05
592	Franklin Stubbs	.08	.05
593	Larry Herndon	.08	.05
594	Bill Swaggerty	.08	.05
595	Carlos Ponce	.08	.05
596	Pat Perry (R)	.08	.05
597	Ray Knight	.08	.05
598	Steve Lombardozzi (R)	.08	.05
599	Brad Havens	.08	.05
600	Pat Clements (R)	.10	.06
601	Joe Niekro	.08	.05
602	Hank Aaron Puzzle Card	.15	.10
603	Dwayne Henry (R)	.12	.07
604	Mookie Wilson	.08	.05
605	Buddy Biancalana	.08	.05
606	Rance Mulliniks	.08	.05
607	Alan Wiggins	.08	.05
608	Joe Cowley	.08	.05
609a	Tom Seaver (Green)	1.25	.80
609b	Tom Seaver (Yellow)	3.00	2.00
610	Neil Allen	.08	.05
611	Don Sutton	.35	.20
612	Fred Toliver (R)	.10	.06
613	Jay Baller	.08	.05
614	Marc Sullivan	.08	.05
615	John Grubb	.08	.05
616	Bruce Kison	.08	.05
617	Bill Madlock	.10	.06
618	Chris Chambliss	.08	.05
619	Dave Stewart	.25	.15
620	Tim Lollar	.08	.05
621	Gary Lavelle	.08	.05
622	Charles Hudson	.08	.05
623	Joel Davis (R)	.08	.05
624	Joe Johnson (R)	.10	.06
625	Sid Fernandez	.25	.15
626	Dennis Lamp	.08	.05
627	Terry Harper	.08	.05
628	Jack Lazorko	.08	.05
629	Roger McDowell (R)	.25	.15
630	Mark Funderburk	.08	.05
631	Ed Lynch	.08	.05
632	Rudy Law	.08	.05
633	Roger Mason (R)	.15	.08
634	Mike Felder (R)	.20	.12
635	Ken Schrom	.08	.05
636	Bob Ojeda	.10	.06

637	Ed Vande Berg	.08	.05
638	Bobby Meacham	.08	.05
039	Cliff Johnson	.08	.05
640	Garth Iorg	.08	.05
641	Dan Driessen	.08	.05
642	Mike Brown	.08	.05
643	John Shelby	.08	.05
644	Ty-Breaker (Pete Rose)	.75	.45
645	Knuckle Brothers(Joe Niekro, Phil Niekro)	.20	.12
646	Jesse Orosco	.08	.05
647	Billy Beane (R)	.10	.06
648	Cesar Cedeno	.10	.06
649	Bert Blyleven	.20	.12
650	Max Venable	.08	.05
651	Fleet Feet(Vince Coleman, Willie McGee)	.20	.12
652	Calvin Schiraldi	.08	.05
653	King of Kings(Pete Rose)	1.25	.80
___	Checklist (DK)	.12	.07
___a	Checklist 27-130 (Er) (45 Beane)	.08	.05
___b	Checklist 27-130 (Cor) (45 Habyan)	.40	.15
___	Checklist 131-234	.08	.05
___	Checklist 235-338	.08	.05
___	Checklist 339-442	.08	.05
___	Checklist 443-546	.08	.05
___	Checklist 547-653	.08	.05

1986 Donruss Rookies

This marks the first update set issued by Donruss. The 56-card set is similar to the regular edition except for bluish-green border colors and a small "rookies" logo in the lower left corner of the card front.

The cards measure 2-1/2" by 3-1/2".

		MINT	NR/MT
	Complete Set (56)	55.00	38.00
	Commons	.12	.07
1	Wally Joyner (R)	1.75	1.00
2	Tracy Jones (R)	.15	.08
3	Allan Anderson (R)	.12	.07
4	Ed Correa (R)	.12	.07
5	Reggie Williams (R)	.12	.07
6	Charlie Kerfeld (R)	.12	.07
7	Andres Galarraga (R)	2.50	1.50
8	Bob Tewksbury (R)	.80	.50
9	Al Newman	.12	.07
10	Andres Thomas (R)	.15	.08
11	Barry Bonds (R)	18.00	12.00
12	Juan Nieves	.15	.08
13	Mark Eichhorn (R)	.15	.08
14	Dan Plesac (R)	.20	.12
15	Cory Snyder	.40	.25
16	Kelly Gruber	.50	.30
17	Kevin Mitchell (R)	3.00	1.75
18	Steve Lombardozzi	.12	.07
19	Mitch Williams	.60	.35
20	John Cerutti (R)	.15	.08
21	Todd Worrell	.15	.08
22	Jose Canseco	5.00	3.00
23	Pete Incaviglia (R)	1.00	.70
24	Jose Guzman	.25	.15
25	Scott Bailes (R)	.20	.12
26	Greg Mathews (R)	.15	.08
27	Eric King (R)	.12	.07
28	Paul Assenmacher	.15	.08
29	Jeff Sellers	.12	.07
30	Bobby Bonilla (R)	3.50	2.25
31	Doug Drabek (R)	2.50	1.50
32	Will Clark (R)	12.00	7.50
33	Bip Roberts (R)	.80	.50
34	Jim Deshaies (R)	.15	.08
35	Mike LaValliere (R)	.20	.12
36	Scott Bankhead (R)	.15	.08
37	Dale Sveum (R)	.20	.12
38	Bo Jackson (R)	6.00	4.00
39	Rob Thompson (R)	1.25	.80
40	Eric Plunk (R)	.20	.12
41	Bill Bathe	.12	.07
42	John Kruk (R)	4.50	2.75
43	Andy Allanson (R)	.15	.08
44	Mark Portugal (R)	.75	.45
45	Danny Tartabull	1.50	.90
46	Bob Kipper	.15	.08
47	Gene Walter	.12	.07
48	Rey Quinonez	.15	.08
49	Bobby Witt (R)	.75	.45
50	Bill Mooneyham	.12	.07
51	John Cangelosi (R)	.15	.08
52	Ruben Sierra (R)	8.00	5.00
53	Rob Woodward	.12	.07
54	Ed Hearn	.12	.07
55	Joel McKeon	.12	.07
56	Checklist (1-56)	.15	.08

1987 Donruss

This 660-card set features black borders with gold trim on the card fronts and horizontal card backs with black and gold print on a white card stock. Subsets include Diamond Kings (1-26) and Rated Rookies (28-47). Cards measure 2-1/2" by 3-1/2". The set was issued with puzzle pieces featuring Roberto Clemente.

		MINT	NR/MT
	Complete Set (660)	65.00	42.00
	Commons	.05	.02
1	Wally Joyner (DK)	.35	.20
2	Roger Clemens (DK)	1.00	.70
3	Dale Murphy (DK)	.15	.08
4	Darryl Strawberry(DK)	.20	.12
5	Ozzie Smith (DK)	.20	.12
6	Jose Canseco (DK)	1.00	.70
7	Charlie Hough (DK)	.07	.04
8	Brook Jacoby (DK)	.07	.04
9	Fred Lynn (DK)	.10	.06
10	Rick Rhoden (DK)	.07	.04
11	Chris Brown (DK)	.07	.04
12	Von Hayes (DK)	.07	.04
13	Jack Morris (DK)	.20	.12
14a	Kevin McReynolds (DK) (Er)	.40	.25
14b	Kevin McReynolds (DK) (Cor)	.10	.06
15	George Brett (DK)	.35	.20
16	Ted Higuera (DK)	.07	.04

17 Hubie Brooks (DK)	.07	.04
18 Mike Scott (DK)	.07	.04
19 Kirby Puckett (DK)	.80	.50
20 Dave Winfield (DK)	.40	.25
21 Lloyd Moseby (DK)	.07	.04
22a Eric Davis (DK) (Er)	.80	.50
22b Eric Davis(DK) (Cor)	.20	.12
23 Jim Presley(DK)	.07	.04
24 Keith Moreland (DK)	.07	.04
25a Greg Walker (DK) (Er)	.25	.15
25b Greg Walker (DK)(Cor)	.07	.04
26 Steve Sax (DK)	.10	.06
27 Checklist 1-27	.08	.05
28 B.J. Surhoff (R)	.20	.12
29 Randy Myers (R)	.75	.45
30 Ken Gerhart (R)	.05	.02
31 Benito Santiago (R)	.50	.30
32 Greg Swindell (R)	.80	.50
33 Mike Birkbeck (R)	.07	.04
34 Terry Steinbach (R)	.35	.20
35 Bo Jackson	5.00	3.00
36 Greg Maddux (R)	7.50	4.50
37 Jim Lindeman (R)	.07	.04
38 Devon White (R)	1.50	.90
39 Eric Bell (R)	.07	.04
40 Will Fraser (R)	.07	.04
41 Jerry Browne (R)	.20	.12
42 Chris James (R)	.12	.07
43 Rafael Palmeiro (R)	6.50	3.75
44 Pat Dodson (R)	.07	.04
45 Duane Ward (R)	1.00	.70
46 Mark McGwire (R)	7.50	4.50
47 Bruce Field (R) (Er)	.07	.04
(Wrong Photo)		
48 Eddie Murray	.50	.30
49 Ted Higuera	.05	.02
50 Kirk Gibson	.10	.06
51 Oil Can Boyd	.05	.02
52 Don Mattingly	1.00	.70
53 Pedro Guerrero	.08	.05
54 George Brett	.80	.50
55 Jose Rijo	.20	.12
56 Tim Raines	.20	.12
57 Ed Correa	.05	.02
58 Mike Witt	.05	.02
59 Greg Walker	.05	.02
60 Ozzie Smith	.40	.25
61 Glenn Davis	.10	.06
62 Glenn Wilson	.05	.02
63 Tom Browning	.08	.05
64 Tony Gwynn	1.00	.70
65 R.J. Reynolds	.05	.02
66 Will Clark	8.00	5.00
67 Ozzie Virgil	.05	.02
68 Rick Sutcliffe	.07	.04
69 Gary Carter	.25	.15
70 Mike Moore	.07	.04
71 Bert Blyleven	.20	.12
72 Tony Fernandez	.12	.07
73 Kent Hrbek	.12	.07
74 Lloyd Moseby	.05	.02
75 Alvin Davis	.05	.02
76 Keith Hernandez	.08	.05
77 Ryne Sandberg	1.75	1.00
78 Dale Murphy	.25	.15
79 Sid Bream	.05	.02
80 Chris Brown	.05	.02
81 Steve Garvey	.25	.15
82 Mario Soto	.05	.02
83 Shane Rawley	.05	.02
84 Willie McGee	.10	.06
85 Jose Cruz	.08	.05
86 Brian Downing	.05	.02
87 Ozzie Guillen	.10	.06
88 Hubie Brooks	.10	.06
89 Cal Ripken	2.00	1.25
90 Juan Nieves	.05	.02
91 Lance Parrish	.07	.04
92 Jim Rice	.10	.06
93 Ron Guidry	.10	.06
94 Fernando Valenzuela	.10	.06
95 Andy Allanson	.05	.02
96 Willie Wilson	.05	.02
97 Jose Canseco	4.00	2.50
98 Jeff Reardon	.25	.15
99 Bobby Witt	.35	.20
100 Checklist (28-133)	.08	.05
101 Jose Guzman	.12	.07
102 Steve Balboni	.05	.02
103 Tony Phillips	.12	.07
104 Brook Jacoby	.05	.02
105 Dave Winfield	.75	.45
106 Orel Hershiser	.15	.08
107 Lou Whitaker	.12	.07
108 Fred Lynn	.10	.06
109 Bill Wegman	.12	.08
110 Donnie Moore	.05	.02
111 Jack Clark	.10	.06
112 Bob Knepper	.05	.02
113 Von Hayes	.05	.02
114 Bip Roberts	.40	.25
115 Tony Pena	.05	.02
116 Scott Garrelts	.05	.02
117 Paul Molitor	.40	.25
118 Darryl Strawberry	.80	.50
119 Shawon Dunston	.20	.12
120 Jim Presley	.05	.02
121 Jesse Barfield	.08	.05
122 Gary Gaetti	.07	.04
123 Kurt Stillwell	.08	.05
124 Joel Davis	.05	.02
125 Mike Boddicker	.05	.02
126 Robin Yount	.80	.50
127 Alan Trammell	.25	.15

128	Dave Righetti	.07	.04
129	Dwight Evans	.10	.06
130	Mike Scioscia	.07	.04
131	Julio Franco	.25	.15
132	Bret Saberhagen	.20	.12
133	Mike Davis	.05	.02
134	Joe Hesketh	.05	.02
135	Wally Joyner	1.25	.80
136	Don Slaught	.08	.05
137	Daryl Boston	.05	.02
138	Nolan Ryan	3.00	2.00
139	Mike Schmidt	1.50	.90
140	Tommy Herr	.05	.02
141	Garry Templeton	.05	.02
142	Kal Daniels	.05	.02
143	Billy Sample	.05	.02
144	Johnny Ray	.05	.02
145	Rob Thompson	.50	.30
146	Bob Dernier	.05	.02
147	Danny Tartabull	.40	.25
148	Ernie Whitt	.05	.02
149	Kirby Puckett	2.00	1.25
150	Mike Young	.05	.02
151	Ernest Riles	.05	.02
152	Frank Tanana	.07	.04
153	Rich Gedman	.05	.02
154	Willie Randolph	.07	.04
155	Bill Madlock (Var)	.10	.06
156	Joe Carter (Var)	1.25	.80
157	Danny Jackson	.07	.04
158	Carney Lansford	.07	.04
159	Bryn Smith	.05	.02
160	Gary Pettis	.05	.02
161	Oddibe McDowell	.05	.02
162	John Cangelosi	.07	.04
163	Mike Scott	.07	.04
164	Eric Show	.05	.02
165	Juan Samuel	.05	.02
166	Nick Esasky	.05	.02
167	Zane Smith	.07	.04
168	Mike Brown	.05	.02
169	Keith Moreland	.05	.02
170	John Tudor	.05	.02
171	Ken Dixon	.05	.02
172	Jim Gantner	.05	.02
173	Jack Morris	.30	.18
174	Bruce Hurst	.08	.05
175	Dennis Rasmussen	.05	.02
176	Mike Marshall	.05	.02
177	Dan Quisenberry	.05	.02
178	Eric Plunk	.08	.05
179	Tim Wallach	.08	.05
180	Steve Buechele	.07	.04
181	Don Sutton	.20	.12
182	Dave Schmidt	.05	.02
183	Terry Pendleton	.50	.30
184	Jim Deshaies	.10	.06
185	Steve Bedrosian	.05	.02
186	Pete Rose	.60	.35
187	Dave Dravecky	.05	.02
188	Rick Reuschel	.05	.02
189	Dan Gladden	.05	.02
190	Rick Mahler	.05	.02
191	Thad Bosley	.05	.02
192	Ron Darling	.08	.05
193	Matt Young	.05	.02
194	Tom Brunansky	.08	.05
195	Dave Steib	.10	.06
196	Frank Viola	.15	.08
197	Tom Henke	.05	.02
198	Karl Best	.05	.02
199	Dwight Gooden	.30	.18
200	Checklist (134-239)	.08	.05
201	Steve Trout	.05	.02
202	Rafael Ramirez	.05	.02
203	Bob Walk	.05	.02
204	Roger Mason	.05	.02
205	Terry Kennedy	.05	.02
206	Ron Oester	.05	.02
207	John Russell	.05	.02
208	Greg Mathews	.05	.02
209	Charlie Kerfeld	.05	.02
210	Reggie Jackson	.60	.35
211	Floyd Bannister	.05	.02
212	Vance Law	.05	.02
213	Rich Bordi	.05	.02
214	Dan Plesac	.08	.05
215	Dave Collins	.05	.02
216	Bob Stanley	.05	.02
217	Joe Niekro	.05	.02
218	Tom Niedenfuer	.05	.02
219	Brett Butler	.10	.06
220	Charlie Leibrandt	.05	.02
221	Steve Ontiveros	.05	.02
222	Tim Burke	.05	.02
223	Curtis Wilkerson	.05	.02
224	Pete Incaviglia	.40	.25
225	Lonnie Smith	.05	.02
226	Chris Codiroli	.05	.02
227	Scott Bailes	.05	.02
228	Rickey Henderson	1.00	.70
229	Ken Howell	.05	.02
230	Darnell Coles	.05	.02
231	Don Aase	.05	.02
232	Tim Leary	.05	.02
233	Bob Boone	.10	.06
234	Ricky Horton	.05	.02
235	Mark Bailey	.05	.02
236	Kevin Gross	.05	.02
237	Lance McCullers	.05	.02
238	Cecilio Guante	.05	.02
239	Bob Melvin	.05	.02
240	Billy Jo Robidoux	.05	.02
241	Roger McDowell	.05	.02

242	Leon Durham	.05	.02	299	Franklin Stubbs	.08	.05
243	Ed Nunez	.05	.02	300	Checklist (240-345)	.08	.05
244	Jimmy Key	.20	.12	301	Steve Farr	.07	.04
245	Mike Smithson	.05	.02	302	Bill Mooneyham	.05	.02
246	Bo Diaz	.05	.02	303	Andres Galarraga	.50	.30
247	Carlton Fisk	.50	.30	304	Scott Fletcher	.05	.02
248	Larry Sheets	.05	.02	305	Jack Howell	.05	.02
249	Juan Castillo (R)	.08	.05	306	Russ Morman (R)	.05	.02
250	Eric King	.10	.06	307	Todd Worrell	.08	.05
251	Doug Drabek	1.00	.70	308	Dave Smith	.05	.02
252	Wade Boggs	1.00	.70	309	Jeff Stone	.05	.02
253	Mariano Duncan	.15	.08	310	Ron Robinson	.05	.02
254	Pat Tabler	.05	.02	311	Bruce Bochy	.05	.02
255	Frank White	.05	.02	312	Jim Winn	.05	.02
256	Alfredo Griffin	.05	.02	313	Mark Davis	.05	.02
257	Floyd Youmans	.05	.02	314	Jeff Dedmon	.05	.02
258	Rob Wilfong	.05	.02	315	Jamie Moyer (R)	.15	.08
259	Pete O'Brien	.05	.02	316	Wally Backman	.05	.02
260	Tim Hulett	.05	.02	317	Ken Phelps	.05	.02
261	Dickie Thon	.05	.02	318	Steve Lombardozzi	.05	.02
262	Darren Daulton	.80	.50	319	Rance Mulliniks	.05	.02
263	Vince Coleman	.20	.12	320	Tim Laudner	.05	.02
264	Andy Hawkins	.05	.02	321	Mark Eichhorn	.10	.06
265	Eric Davis	.35	.20	322	Lee Guetterman	.07	.04
266	Andres Thomas	.07	.04	323	Sid Fernandez	.12	.07
267	Mike Diaz (R)	.08	.05	324	Jerry Mumphrey	.05	.02
268	Chili Davis	.07	.04	325	David Palmer	.05	.02
269	Jody Davis	.05	.02	326	Bill Almon	.05	.02
270	Phil Bradley	.05	.02	327	Candy Maldonado	.07	.04
271	George Bell	.20	.12	328	John Kruk	2.75	1.60
272	Keith Atherton	.05	.02	329	John Denny	.05	.02
273	Storm Davis	.05	.02	330	Milt Thompson	.05	.02
274	Rob Deer (R)	.25	.15	331	Mike LaValliere	.20	.12
275	Walt Terrell	.05	.02	332	Alan Ashby	.05	.02
276	Roger Clemens	2.00	1.25	333	Doug Corbett	.05	.02
277	Mike Easler	.05	.02	334	Ron Karkovice (R)	.20	.12
278	Steve Sax	.12	.07	335	Mitch Webster	.05	.02
279	Andre Thornton	.05	.02	336	Lee Lacy	.05	.02
280	Jim Sundberg	.05	.02	337	Glenn Braggs (R)	.20	.12
281	Bill Bathe	.05	.02	338	Dwight Lowry	.05	.02
282	Jay Tibbs	.05	.02	339	Don Baylor	.10	.06
283	Dick Schofield	.05	.02	340	Brian Fisher	.05	.02
284	Mike Mason	.05	.02	341	Reggie Williams	.05	.02
285	Jerry Hairston	.05	.02	342	Tom Candiotti	.08	.05
286	Bill Doran	.05	.02	343	Rudy Law	.05	.02
287	Tim Flannery	.05	.02	344	Curt Young	.05	.02
288	Gary Redus	.05	.02	345	Mike Fitzgerald	.05	.02
289	John Franco	.05	.02	346	Ruben Sierra	5.00	3.00
290	Paul Assenmacher	.05	.02	347	Mitch Williams	.40	.25
291	Joe Orsulak	.07	.04	348	Jorge Orta	.05	.02
292	Lee Smith	.30	.18	349	Mickey Tettleton	.20	.12
293	Mike Laga	.05	.02	350	Ernie Camacho	.05	.02
294	Rick Dempsey	.05	.02	351	Ron Kittle	.05	.02
295	Mike Felder	.07	.04	352	Ken Landreaux	.05	.02
296	Tom Brookens	.05	.02	353	Chet Lemon	.05	.02
297	Al Nipper	.05	.02	354	John Shelby	.05	.02
298	Mike Pagliarulo	.05	.02	355	Mark Clear	.05	.02

356 Doug DeCinces	.05	.02
357 Ken Dayley	.05	.02
358 Phil Garner	.08	.05
359 Steve Jeltz	.05	.02
360 Ed Whitson	.05	.02
361 Barry Bonds	13.00	8.00
362 Vida Blue	.07	.04
363 Cecil Cooper	.05	.02
364 Bob Ojeda	.07	.04
365 Dennis Eckersley	.35	.20
366 Mike Morgan	.05	.02
367 Willie Upshaw	.05	.02
368 Allan Anderson (R)	.12	.07
369 Bill Gullickson	.05	.02
370 Bobby Thigpen	.30	.18
371 Juan Beniquez	.05	.02
372 Charlie Moore	.05	.02
373 Dan Petry	.05	.02
374 Rod Scurry	.05	.02
375 Tom Seaver	.50	.30
376 Ed Vande Berg	.05	.02
377 Tony Bernazard	.05	.02
378 Greg Pryor	.05	.02
379 Dwayne Murphy	.05	.02
380 Andy McGaffigan	.05	.02
381 Kirk McCaskill	.05	.02
382 Greg Harris	.08	.05
383 Rich Dotson	.05	.02
384 Craig Reynolds	.05	.02
385 Greg Gross	.05	.02
386 Tito Landrum	.05	.02
387 Craig Lefferts	.05	.02
388 Dave Parker	.12	.07
389 Bob Horner	.08	.05
390 Pat Clements	.05	.02
391 Jeff Leonard	.05	.02
392 Chris Speier	.05	.02
393 John Moses	.05	.02
394 Garth Iorg	.05	.02
395 Greg Gagne	.07	.04
396 Nate Snell	.05	.02
397 Bryan Clutterbuck (R)	.05	.02
398 Darrell Evans	.07	.04
399 Steve Crawford	.05	.02
400 Checklist (346-451)	.08	.05
401 Phil Lombardi (R)	.07	.04
402 Rick Honeycutt	.05	.02
403 Ken Schrom	.05	.02
404 Bud Black	.07	.04
405 Donnie Hill	.05	.02
406 Wayne Krenchicki	.05	.02
407 Chuck Finley (R)	.70	.40
408 Toby Harrah	.05	.02
409 Steve Lyons	.05	.02
410 Kevin Bass	.05	.02
411 Marvell Wynne	.05	.02
412 Ron Roenicke	.05	.02
413 Tracy Jones	.07	.04
414 Gene Garber	.05	.02
415 Mike Bielecki	.07	.04
416 Frank DiPino	.05	.02
417 Andy Van Slyke	.35	.20
418 Jim Dwyer	.05	.02
419 Ben Oglivie	.05	.02
420 Dave Bergman	.05	.02
421 Joe Sambito	.05	.02
422 Bob Tewksbury	.50	.30
423 Len Matuszek	.05	.02
424 Mike Kingery (R)	.08	.05
425 Dave Kingman	.07	.04
426 Al Newman	.05	.02
427 Gary Ward	.05	.02
428 Ruppert Jones	.05	.02
429 Harold Baines	.12	.07
430 Pat Perry	.05	.02
431 Terry Puhl	.05	.02
432 Don Carman	.05	.02
433 Eddie Milner	.05	.02
434 LaMarr Hoyt	.05	.02
435 Rick Rhoden	.05	.02
436 Jose Uribe	.05	.02
437 Ken Oberkfell	.05	.02
438 Ron Davis	.05	.02
439 Jesse Orosco	.05	.02
440 Scott Bradley	.05	.02
441 Randy Bush	.05	.02
442 John Cerutti	.08	.05
443 Roy Smalley	.05	.02
444 Kelly Gruber	.80	.05
445 Bob Kearney	.05	.02
446 Ed Hearn	.05	.02
447 Scott Sanderson	.05	.02
448 Bruce Benedict	.05	.02
449 Junior Ortiz	.05	.02
450 Mike Aldrete	.07	.04
451 Kevin McReynolds	.10	.06
452 Rob Murphy (R)	.10	.06
453 Kent Tekulve	.05	.02
454 Curt Ford (R)	.05	.02
455 Davey Lopes	.07	.04
456 Bobby Grich	.07	.04
457 Jose DeLeon	.05	.02
458 Andre Dawson	.50	.30
459 Mike Flanagan	.05	.02
460 Joey Meyer (R)	.10	.06
461 Chuck Cary (R)	.08	.05
462 Bill Buckner	.07	.04
463 Bob Shirley	.05	.02
464 Jeff Hamilton (R)	.08	.05
465 Phil Niekro	.20	.12
466 Mark Gubicza	.12	.07
467 Jerry Willard	.05	.02
468 Bob Sebra (R)	.07	.04
469 Larry Parrish	.05	.02

470	Charlie Hough	.05	.02	527	Buddy Biancalana	.05	.02
471	Hal McRae	.08	.05	528	Moose Haas	.05	.02
472	Dave Leiper (R)	.07	.04	529	Wilfredo Tejada (R)	.07	.04
473	Mel Hall	.08	.05	530	Stu Cliburn	.05	.02
474	Dan Pasqua	.07	.04	531	Dale Mohorcic (R)	.08	.05
475	Bob Welch	.08	.05	532	Ron Hassey	.05	.02
476	Johnny Grubb	.05	.02	533	Ty Gainey	.05	.02
477	Jim Traber	.05	.02	534	Jerry Royster	.05	.02
478	Chris Bosio (R)	.40	.25	535	Mike Maddux (R)	.07	.04
479	Mark McLemore	.05	.02	536	Ted Power	.05	.02
480	John Morris	.05	.02	537	Ted Simmons	.07	.04
481	Billy Hatcher	.07	.04	538	Rafael Belliard (R)	.20	.12
482	Dan Schatzeder	.05	.02	539	Chico Walker	.08	.05
483	Rich Gossage	.08	.05	540	Bob Forsch	.05	.02
484	Jim Morrison	.05	.02	541	John Stefero	.05	.02
485	Bob Brenly	.05	.02	542	Dale Sveum	.08	.05
486	Bill Schroeder	.05	.02	543	Mark Thurmond	.05	.02
487	Mookie Wilson	.05	.02	544	Jeff Sellers	.07	.04
488	Dave Martinez (R)	.20	.12	545	Joel Skinner	.05	.02
489	Harold Reynolds	.08	.05	546	Alex Trevino	.05	.02
490	Jeff Hearron	.05	.02	547	Randy Kutcher (R)	.07	.04
491	Mickey Hatcher	.05	.02	548	Joaquin Andujar	.05	.02
492	Barry Larkin (R)	3.50	2.25	549	Casey Candaele (R)	.08	.05
493	Bob James	.05	.02	550	Jeff Russell	.08	.05
494	John Habyan	.05	.02	551	John Candelaria	.05	.02
495	Jim Adduci (R)	.05	.02	552	Joe Cowley	.05	.02
496	Mike Heath	.05	.02	553	Danny Cox	.05	.02
497	Tim Stoddard	.05	.02	554	Denny Walling	.05	.02
498	Tony Armas	.05	.02	555	Bruce Ruffin (R)	.10	.06
499	Dennis Powell	.05	.02	556	Buddy Bell	.05	.02
500	Checklist (452-557)	.08	.05	557	Jimmy Jones (R)	.15	.08
501	Chris Bando	.05	.02	558	Bobby Bonilla	2.50	1.50
502	David Cone (R)	3.00	1.75	559	Jeff Robinson	.08	.05
503	Jay Howell	.05	.02	560	Ed Olwine	.05	.02
504	Tom Foley	.05	.02	561	Glenallen Hill (R)	.35	.20
505	Ray Chadwick (R)	.05	.02	562	Lee Mazzilli	.05	.02
506	Mike Loynd (R)	.05	.02	563	Mike Brown	.05	.02
507	Neil Allen	.05	.02	564	George Frazier	.05	.02
508	Danny Darwin	.05	.02	565	Mike Sharperson (R)	.10	.06
509	Rick Schu	.05	.02	566	Mark Portugal	.40	.25
510	Jose Oquendo	.05	.02	567	Rick Leach	.05	.02
511	Gene Walter	.05	.02	568	Mark Langston	.25	.15
512	Terry McGriff (R)	.05	.02	569	Rafael Santana	.05	.02
513	Ken Griffey	.08	.05	570	Manny Trillo	.05	.02
514	Benny Distefano	.05	.02	571	Cliff Speck	.05	.02
515	Terry Mulholland (R)	.80	.50	572	Bob Kipper	.05	.02
516	Ed Lynch	.05	.02	573	Kelly Downs (R)	.12	.07
517	Bill Swift	.35	.20	574	Randy Asadoor (R)	.05	.02
518	Manny Lee (R)	.08	.05	575	Dave Magadan (R)	.35	.20
519	Andre David	.05	.02	576	Marvin Freeman (R)	.08	.05
520	Scott McGregor	.05	.02	577	Jeff Lahti	.05	.02
521	Rick Manning	.05	.02	578	Jeff Calhoun	.05	.02
522	Willie Hernandez	.05	.02	579	Gus Polidor (R)	.05	.02
523	Marty Barrett	.05	.02	580	Gene Nelson	.05	.02
524	Wayne Tolleson	.05	.02	581	Tim Teufel	.05	.02
525	Jose Gonzalez (R)	.08	.05	582	Odell Jones	.05	.02
526	Cory Snyder	.10	.06	583	Mark Ryal	.05	.02

584	Randy O'Neal	.05	.02
585	Mike Greenwell (R)	1.50	.90
586	Ray Knight	.05	.02
587	Ralph Bryant (R)	.07	.04
588	Carmen Castillo	.05	.02
589	Ed Wojna	.05	.02
590	Stan Javier	.07	.04
591	Jeff Musselman (R)	.07	.04
592	Mike Stanley (R)	.80	.50
593	Darrell Porter	.05	.02
594	Drew Hall (R)	.07	.04
595	Rob Nelson (R)	.07	.04
596	Bryan Oelkers	.05	.02
597	Scott Nielsen (R)	.07	.04
598	Brian Holton (R)	.08	.05
599	Kevin Mitchell	1.25	.80
600	Checklist (558-660)	.08	.05
601	Jackie Gutierrez	.05	.02
602	Barry Jones (R)	.10	.06
603	Jerry Narron	.05	.02
604	Steve Lake	.05	.02
605	Jim Pankovits	.05	.02
606	Ed Romero	.05	.02
607	Dave LaPoint	.05	.02
608	Don Robinson	.05	.02
609	Mike Krukow	.05	.02
610	Dave Valle (R)	.12	.07
611	Len Dykstra	.60	.35
612	Roberto Clemente Puzzle	.15	.08
613	Mike Trujillo (R)	.05	.02
614	Damaso Garcia	.05	.02
615	Neal Heaton	.05	.02
616	Juan Berenguer	.05	.02
617	Steve Carlton	.60	.35
618	Gary Lucas	.05	.02
619	Geno Petralli	.05	.02
620	Rick Aguilera	.20	.12
621	Fred McGriff	5.00	3.00
622	Dave Henderson	.10	.06
623	Dave Clark (R)	.10	.06
624	Angel Salazar	.05	.02
625	Randy Hunt	.05	.02
626	John Gibbons	.05	.02
627	Kevin Brown (R)	2.00	1.25
628	Bill Dawley	.05	.02
629	Aurelio Lopez	.05	.02
630	Charlie Hudson	.05	.02
631	Ray Soff	.05	.02
632	Ray Hayward (R)	.05	.02
633	Spike Owen	.05	.02
634	Glenn Hubbard	.05	.02
635	Kevin Elster (R)	.12	.07
636	Mike LaCoss	.05	.02
637	Dwayne Henry	.05	.02
638	Rey Quinones	.05	.02
639	Jim Clancy	.05	.02

640	Larry Andersen	.05	.02
641	Calvin Schiraldi	.05	.02
642	Stan Jefferson (R)	.07	.04
643	Marc Sullivan	.05	.02
644	Mark Grant	.05	.02
645	Cliff Johnson	.05	.02
646	Howard Johnson	.25	.15
647	Dave Sax	.05	.02
648	Dave Stewart	.15	.08
649	Danny Heep	.05	.02
650	Joe Johnson	.05	.02
651	Bob Brower (R)	.05	.02
652	Rob Woodward	.05	.02
653	John Mizerock	.05	.02
654	Tim Pyznarski (R)	.05	.02
655	Luis Aquino (R)	.08	.05
656	Mickey Brantley (R)	.08	.05
657	Doyle Alexander	.05	.02
658	Sammy Stewart	.05	.02
659	Jim Acker	.05	.02
660	Pete Ladd	.05	.02

1987 Donruss Rookies

This 56-card update set features green borders on the card fronts with a small "rookies" logo in the lower corner of the card. Cards measure 2-1/2" by 3-1/2".

		MINT	NR/MT
Complete Set (56)		20.00	12.50
Commons		.08	.05
1	Mark McGwire	3.50	2.25
2	Eric Bell	.08	.05
3	Mark Williamson (R)	.12	.07
4	Mike Greenwell	.80	.50

5	Ellis Burks (R)	.90	.60
6	DeWayne Buice (R)	.08	.05
7	Mark McLemore	.08	.05
8	Devon White	.75	.45
9	Willie Fraser	.08	.05
10	Les Lancaster (R)	.15	.08
11	Ken Williams (R)	.12	.07
12	Matt Nokes (R)	.35	.20
13	Jeff Robinson (R)	.10	.06
14	Bo Jackson	2.00	1.25
15	Kevin Seitzer (R)	.30	.18
16	Billy Ripken (R)	.15	.08
17	B.J. Surhoff	.12	.07
18	Chuck Crim (R)	.10	.06
19	Mike Birbeck	.08	.05
20	Chris Bosio	.20	.12
21	Les Straker (R)	.10	.06
22	Mark Davidson (R)	.10	.06
23	Gene Larkin (R)	.20	.12
24	Ken Gerhart	.08	.05
25	Luis Polonia (R)	.60	.35
26	Terry Steinbach	.30	.18
27	Mickey Brantley	.10	.06
28	Mike Stanley	.50	.30
29	Jerry Browne	.10	.06
30	Todd Benzinger (R)	.20	.12
31	Fred McGriff	4.50	2.75
32	Mike Henneman	.25	.15
33	Casey Candaele	.10	.06
34	Dave Magadan	.20	.12
35	David Cone	2.00	1.25
36	Mike Jackson (R)	.20	.12
37	John Mitchell (R)	.08	.05
38	Mike Dunne (R)	.10	.06
39	John Smiley (R)	.70	.40
40	Joe Magrane (R)	.25	.15
41	Jim Lindeman	.08	.05
42	Shane Mack (R)	.80	.50
43	Stan Jefferson	.10	.06
44	Benito Santiago	.35	.20
45	Matt Williams (R)	6.00	3.75
46	Dave Meads (R)	.10	.06
47	Rafael Palmeiro	4.50	2.75
48	Bill Long (R)	.10	.06
49	Bob Brower	.08	.05
50	James Steels (R)	.08	.05
51	Paul Noce (R)	.08	.05
52	Greg Maddux	5.00	3.00
53	Jeff Musselman	.10	.06
54	Brian Holton	.10	.06
55	Chuck Jackson (R)	.10	.06
56	Checklist (1-56)	.08	.05

1988 Donruss

The cards in this 660-card set feature black borders with blue and red accents. The cards measure 2-1/2" by 3-1/2". Diamond Kings (1-26) and Rated Rookies (28-47) are the two major subsets. 26 MVP insert bonus cards were randomly distributed in Donruss wax packs. Those cards are listed at the end of this checklist but are not included in the complete set price below. Puzzle pieces featuring Stan Musial were distributed with the cards.

	MINT	NR/MT
Complete Set (660)	20.00	14.00
Commons	.05	.02

1	Mark McGwire (DK)	.40	.25
2	Tim Raines (DK)	.08	.05
3	Benito Santiago (DK)	.10	.06
4	Alan Trammell (DK)	.10	.06
5	Danny Tartabull (DK)	.10	.06
6	Ron Darling (DK)	.07	.04
7	Paul Molitor (DK)	.10	.06
8	Devon White (DK)	.08	.05
9	Andre Dawson (DK)	.12	.07
10	Julio Franco (DK)	.10	.06
11	Scott Fletcher (DK)	.05	.02
12	Tony Fernandez (DK)	.07	.04
13	Shane Rawley (DK)	.05	.02
14	Kal Daniels (DK)	.07	.04
15	Jack Clark (DK)	.08	.05
16	Dwight Evans (DK)	.08	.05
17	Tommy John (DK)	.07	.04
18	Andy Van Slyke (DK)	.10	.06
19	Gary Gaetti (DK)	.05	.02
20	Mark Langston (DK)	.10	.06
21	Will Clark (DK)	.35	.20
22	Glenn Hubbard (DK)	.05	.02
23	Billy Hatcher (DK)	.07	.04
24	Bob Welch (DK)	.08	.05
25	Ivan Calderson (DK)	.07	.04
26	Cal Ripken, Jr. (DK)	.40	.25

27 Checklist (1-27)	.05	.02
28 Mackey Sasser (R)	.10	.06
29 Jeff Treadway (R)	.10	.06
30 Mike Campbell (R)	.05	.02
31 Lance Johnson (R)	.35	.20
32 Nelson Liriano (R)	.08	.05
33 Shawn Abner (R)	.07	.04
34 Roberto Alomar (R)	4.50	2.75
35 Shawn Hillegas (R)	.07	.04
36 Joey Meyer	.05	.02
37 Kevin Elster	.07	.04
38 Jose Lind (R)	.12	.07
39 Kirt Manwaring (R)	.15	.10
40 Mark Grace (R)	1.75	1.00
41 Jody Reed (R)	.25	.15
42 John Farrell (R)	.08	.05
43 Al Leiter (R)	.12	.07
44 Gary Thurman (R)	.10	.06
45 Vicente Palacios (R)	.10	.06
46 Eddie Williams (R)	.05	.02
47 Jack McDowell (R)	2.00	1.25
48 Ken Dixon	.05	.02
49 Mike Birkbeck	.05	.02
50 Eric King	.05	.02
51 Roger Clemens	.60	.35
52 Pat Clements	.05	.02
53 Fernando Valenzuela	.08	.05
54 Mark Gubicza	.08	.05
55 Jay Howell	.05	.02
56 Floyd Youmans	.05	.02
57 Ed Correa	.05	.02
58 DeWayne Buice	.05	.02
59 Jose DeLeon	.05	.02
60 Danny Cox	.05	.02
61 Nolan Ryan	.80	.50
62 Steve Bedrosian	.05	.02
63 Tom Browning	.07	.04
64 Mark Davis	.05	.02
65 R.J. Reynolds	.05	.02
66 Kevin Mitchell	.20	.12
67 Ken Oberkfell	.05	.02
68 Rick Sutcliffe	.07	.04
69 Dwight Gooden	.15	.08
70 Scott Bankhead	.05	.02
71 Bert Blyleven	.15	.08
72 Jimmy Key	.10	.06
73 Les Straker	.05	.02
74 Jim Clancy	.05	.02
75 Mike Moore	.08	.05
76 Ron Darling	.08	.05
77 Ed Lynch	.05	.02
78 Dale Murphy	.12	.07
79 Doug Drabek	.12	.07
80 Scott Garrelts	.05	.02
81 Ed Whitson	.05	.02
82 Rob Murphy	.05	.02
83 Shane Rawley	.05	.02
84 Greg Mathews	.05	.02
85 Jim Deshaies	.05	.02
86 Mike Witt	.05	.02
87 Donnie Hill	.05	.02
88 Jeff Reed	.05	.02
89 Mike Boddicker	.05	.02
90 Ted Higuera	.05	.02
91 Walt Terrell	.05	.02
92 Bob Stanley	.05	.02
93 Dave Righetti	.07	.04
94 Orel Hershiser	.10	.06
95 Chris Bando	.05	.02
96 Bret Saberhagen	.15	.08
97 Curt Young	.05	.02
98 Tim Burke	.05	.02
99 Charlie Hough	.05	.02
100a Checklist (28-137)	.05	.02
100b Checklist (28-133)	.05	.02
101 Bobby Witt	.08	.05
102 George Brett	.35	.20
103 Mickey Tettleton	.12	.07
104 Scott Bailes	.05	.02
105 Mike Pagliarulo	.05	.02
106 Mike Scioscia	.05	.02
107 Tom Brookens	.05	.02
108 Ray Knight	.05	.02
109 Dan Plesac	.05	.02
110 Wally Joyner	.15	.08
111 Bob Forsch	.05	.02
112 Mike Scott	.07	.04
113 Kevin Gross	.05	.02
114 Benito Santiago	.10	.06
115 Bob Kipper	.05	.02
116 Mike Krukow	.05	.02
117 Chris Bosio	.10	.06
118 Sid Fernandez	.07	.04
119 Jody Davis	.05	.02
120 Mike Morgan	.05	.02
121 Mark Eichhorn	.05	.02
122 Jeff Reardon	.20	.12
123 John Franco	.05	.02
124 Richard Dotson	.05	.02
125 Eric Bell	.05	.02
126 Juan Nieves	.05	.02
127 Jack Morris	.12	.07
128 Rick Rhoden	.05	.02
129 Rich Gedman	.05	.02
130 Ken Howell	.05	.02
131 Brook Jacoby	.05	.02
132 Danny Jackson	.07	.04
133 Gene Nelson	.05	.02
134 Neal Heaton	.05	.02
135 Willie Fraser	.05	.02
136 Jose Guzman	.07	.04
137 Ozzie Guillen	.08	.05
138 Bob Knepper	.05	.02
139 Mike Jackson	.10	.06

140	Joe Magrane	.12	.07	197	Rance Mulliniks	.05	.02
141	Jimmy Jones	.07	.04	198	Rey Quinones	.05	.02
142	Ted Power	.05	.02	199	Gary Carter	.10	.06
143	Ozzie Virgil	.05	.02	200a	Checklist (138-247)	.05	.02
144	Felix Fermin (R)	.05	.02	200b	Checklist (134-239)	.05	.02
145	Kelly Downs	.07	.04	201	Keith Moreland	.05	.02
146	Shawon Dunston	.12	.07	202	Ken Griffey	.08	.05
147	Scott Bradley	.05	.02	203	Tommy Gregg (R)	.07	.04
148	Dave Stieb	.07	.04	204	Will Clark	.75	.45
149	Frank Viola	.08	.05	205	John Kruk	.20	.12
150	Terry Kennedy	.05	.02	206	Buddy Bell	.05	.02
151	Bill Wegman	.05	.02	207	Von Hayes	.05	.02
152	Matt Nokes	.15	.08	208	Tommy Herr	.05	.02
153	Wade Boggs	.30	.18	209	Craig Reynolds	.05	.02
154	Wayne Tolleson	.05	.02	210	Gary Pettis	.05	.02
155	Mariano Duncan	.05	.02	211	Harold Baines	.07	.04
156	Julio Franco	.12	.07	212	Vance Law	.05	.02
157	Charlie Leibrandt	.05	.02	213	Ken Gerhart	.05	.02
158	Terry Steinbach	.08	.05	214	Jim Gantner	.05	.02
159	Mike Fitzgerald	.05	.02	215	Chet Lemon	.05	.02
160	Jack Lazorko	.05	.02	216	Dwight Evans	.07	.04
161	Mitch Williams	.07	.04	217	Don Mattingly	.30	.18
162	Greg Walker	.05	.02	218	Franklin Stubbs	.05	.02
163	Alan Ashby	.05	.02	219	Pat Tabler	.05	.02
164	Tony Gwynn	.35	.20	220	Bo Jackson	.25	.15
165	Bruce Ruffin	.05	.02	221	Tony Phillips	.05	.02
166	Ron Robinson	.05	.02	222	Tim Wallach	.07	.04
167	Zane Smith	.05	.02	223	Ruben Sierra	.40	.25
168	Junior Ortiz	.05	.02	224	Steve Buechele	.05	.02
169	Jamie Moyer	.05	.02	225	Frank White	.05	.02
170	Tony Pena	.05	.02	226	Alfredo Griffin	.05	.02
171	Cal Ripken	.70	.40	227	Greg Swindell	.12	.07
172	B.J. Surhoff	.07	.04	228	Willie Randolph	.07	.04
173	Lou Whitaker	.08	.05	229	Mike Marshall	.05	.02
174	Ellis Burks	.25	.15	230	Alan Trammell	.10	.06
175	Ron Guidry	.07	.04	231	Eddie Murray	.25	.15
176	Steve Sax	.08	.05	232	Dale Sveum	.05	.02
177	Danny Tartabull	.15	.08	233	Dick Schofield	.05	.02
178	Carney Lansford	.07	.04	234	Jose Oquendo	.05	.02
179	Casey Candaele	.05	.02	235	Bill Doran	.05	.02
180	Scott Fletcher	.05	.02	236	Milt Thompson	.05	.02
181	Mark McLemore	.05	.02	237	Marvell Wynne	.05	.02
182	Ivan Calderon	.07	.04	238	Bobby Bonilla	.25	.15
183	Jack Clark	.07	.04	239	Chris Speier	.05	.02
184	Glenn Davis	.07	.04	240	Glenn Braggs	.05	.02
185	Luis Aguayo	.05	.02	241	Wally Backman	.05	.02
186	Bo Diaz	.05	.02	242	Ryne Sandberg	.50	.30
187	Stan Jefferson	.05	.02	243	Phil Bradley	.05	.02
188	Sid Bream	.05	.02	244	Kelly Gruber	.10	.06
189	Bob Brenly	.05	.02	245	Tom Brunansky	.07	.04
190	Dion James	.05	.02	246	Ron Oester	.05	.02
191	Leon Durham	.05	.02	247	Bobby Thigpen	.07	.04
192	Jesse Orosco	.05	.02	248	Fred Lynn	.07	.04
193	Alvin Davis	.05	.02	249	Paul Molitor	.25	.15
194	Gary Gaetti	.07	.04	250	Darrell Evans	.07	.04
195	Fred McGriff	.60	.35	251	Gary Ward	.05	.02
196	Steve Lombardozzi	.05	.02	252	Bruce Hurst	.08	.05

253	Bob Welch	.07	.04	309	Darren Daulton	.20	.12
254	Joe Carter	.30	.18	310	Tracy Jones	.05	.02
255	Willie Wilson	.05	.02	311	Greg Booker	.05	.02
256	Mark McGwire	.60	.35	312	Mike LaValliere	.05	.02
257	Mitch Webster	.05	.02	313	Chili Davis	.07	.04
258	Brian Downing	.05	.02	314	Glenn Hubbard	.05	.02
259	Mike Stanley	.05	.02	315	Paul Noce	.05	.02
260	Carlton Fisk	.20	.12	316	Keith Hernandez	.07	.04
261	Billy Hatcher	.05	.02	317	Mark Langston	.12	.07
262	Glenn Wilson	.05	.02	318	Keith Atherton	.05	.02
263	Ozzie Smith	.20	.12	319	Tony Fernandez	.08	.05
264	Randy Ready	.05	.02	320	Kent Hrbek	.08	.05
265	Kurt Stillwell	.05	.02	321	John Cerutti	.05	.02
266	David Palmer	.05	.02	322	Mike Kingery	.05	.02
267	Mike Diaz	.05	.02	323	Dave Magadan	.07	.04
268	Robby Thompson	.07	.04	324	Rafael Palmeiro	.35	.20
269	Andre Dawson	.25	.15	325	Jeff Dedmon	.05	.02
270	Lee Guetterman	.05	.02	326	Barry Bonds	.75	.45
271	Willie Upshaw	.05	.02	327	Jeffrey Leonard	.05	.02
272	Randy Bush	.05	.02	328	Tim Flannery	.05	.02
273	Larry Sheets	.05	.02	329	Dave Concepcion	.07	.04
274	Rob Deer	.07	.04	330	Mike Schmidt	.50	.30
275	Kirk Gibson	.07	.04	331	Bill Dawley	.05	.02
276	Marty Barrett	.05	.02	332	Larry Andersen	.05	.02
277	Rickey Henderson	.30	.18	333	Jack Howell	.05	.02
278	Pedro Guerrero	.05	.02	334	Ken Williams	.05	.02
279	Brett Butler	.08	.05	335	Bryn Smith	.05	.02
280	Kevin Seitzer	.07	.04	336	Billy Ripken	.07	.04
281	Mike Davis	.05	.02	337	Greg Brock	.05	.02
282	Andres Galarraga	.20	.12	338	Mike Heath	.05	.02
283	Devon White	.15	.08	339	Mike Greenwell	.10	.06
284	Pete O'Brien	.05	.02	340	Claudell Washington	.05	.02
285	Jerry Hairston	.05	.02	341	Jose Gonzalez	.05	.02
286	Kevin Bass	.05	.02	342	Mel Hall	.07	.04
287	Carmelo Martinez	.05	.02	343	Jim Eisenreich	.05	.02
288	Juan Samuel	.05	.02	344	Tony Bernazard	.05	.02
289	Kal Daniels	.07	.04	345	Tim Raines	.08	.05
290	Albert Hall	.05	.02	346	Bob Brower	.05	.02
291	Andy Van Slyke	.10	.06	347	Larry Parrish	.05	.02
292	Lee Smith	.20	.12	348	Thad Bosley	.05	.02
293	Vince Coleman	.07	.04	349	Dennis Eckersley	.20	.12
294	Tom Niedenfuer	.05	.02	350	Cory Snyder	.07	.04
295	Robin Yount	.35	.20	351	Rick Cerone	.05	.02
296	Jeff Robinson	.05	.02	352	John Shelby	.05	.02
297	Todd Benzinger	.12	.07	353	Larry Herndon	.05	.02
298	Dave Winfield	.30	.18	354	John Habyan	.05	.02
299	Mickey Hatcher	.05	.02	355	Chuck Crim	.05	.02
300a	Checklist (248-357)	.05	.02	356	Gus Polidor	.05	.02
300b	Checklist (240-345)	.05	.02	357	Ken Dayley	.05	.02
301	Bud Black	.05	.02	358	Danny Darwin	.07	.04
302	Jose Canseco	.60	.35	359	Lance Parrish	.05	.02
303	Tom Foley	.05	.02	360	James Steels	.05	.02
304	Pete Incaviglia	.08	.05	361	Al Pedrique (R)	.05	.02
305	Bob Boone	.07	.04	362	Mike Aldrete	.05	.02
306	Bill Long	.05	.02	363	Juan Castillo	.05	.02
307	Willie McGee	.07	.04	364	Len Dykstra	.20	.12
308	Ken Caminiti (R)	.25	.15				

365	Luis Quinones	.05	.02
366	Jim Presley	.05	.02
367	Lloyd Moseby	.05	.02
368	Kirby Puckett	.50	.30
369	Eric Davis	.15	.08
370	Gary Redus	.05	.02
371	Dave Schmidt	.05	.02
372	Mark Clear	.05	.02
373	Dave Bergman	.05	.02
374	Charles Hudson	.05	.02
375	Calvin Schiraldi	.05	.02
376	Alex Trevino	.05	.02
377	Tom Candiotti	.05	.02
378	Steve Farr	.05	.02
279	Mike Gallego	.05	.02
380	Andy McGaffigan	.05	.02
381	Kirk McCaskill	.05	.02
382	Oddibe McDowell	.05	.02
383	Floyd Bannister	.05	.02
384	Denny Walling	.05	.02
385	Don Carman	.05	.02
386	Todd Worrell	.08	.05
387	Eric Show	.05	.02
388	Dave Parker	.07	.04
389	Rick Mahler	.05	.02
390	Mike Dunne	.05	.02
391	Candy Maldonado	.05	.02
392	Bob Dernier	.05	.02
393	Dave Valle	.05	.02
394	Ernie Whitt	.05	.02
395	Juan Berenguer	.05	.02
396	Mike Young	.05	.02
397	Mike Felder	.05	.02
398	Willie Hernandez	.05	.02
399	Jim Rice	.07	.04
400a	Checklist (358-467)	.05	.02
400b	Checklist (346-451)	.05	.02
401	Tommy John	.07	.04
402	Brian Holton	.05	.02
403	Carmen Castillo	.05	.02
404	Jamie Quirk	.05	.02
405	Dwayne Murphy	.05	.02
406	Jeff Parrett (R)	.07	.04
407	Don Sutton	.12	.07
408	Jerry Browne	.05	.02
409	Jim Winn	.05	.02
410	Dave Smith	.05	.02
411	Shane Mack	.15	.08
412	Greg Gross	.05	.02
413	Nick Esasky	.05	.02
414	Damaso Garcia	.05	.02
415	Brian Fisher	.05	.02
416	Brian Dayett	.05	.02
417	Curt Ford	.05	.02
418	Mark Williamson	.08	.05
419	Bill Schroeder	.05	.02
420	Mike Henneman	.15	.08
421	John Marzano (R)	.07	.04
422	Ron Kittle	.05	.02
423	Matt Young	.07	.04
424	Steve Balboni	.05	.02
425	Luis Polonia	.25	.15
426	Randy St. Claire	.05	.02
427	Greg Harris	.07	.04
428	Johnny Ray	.05	.02
429	Ray Searage	.05	.02
430	Ricky Horton	.05	.02
431	Gerald Young (R)	.10	.06
432	Rick Schu	.05	.02
433	Paul O'Neill	.12	.07
434	Rich Gossage	.07	.04
435	John Cangelosi	.05	.02
436	Mike LaCoss	.05	.02
437	Gerald Perry	.05	.02
438	Dave Martinez	.05	.02
439	Darryl Strawberry	.25	.15
440	John Moses	.05	.02
441	Greg Gagne	.05	.02
442	Jesse Barfield	.07	.04
443	George Frazier	.05	.02
444	Garth Iorg	.05	.02
445	Ed Nunez	.05	.02
446	Rick Aguilera	.08	.05
447	Jerry Mumphrey	.05	.02
448	Rafael Ramirez	.05	.02
449	John Smiley	.25	.15
450	Atlee Hammaker	.05	.02
451	Lance McCullers	.05	.02
452	Guy Hoffman (R)	.05	.02
453	Chris James	.05	.02
454	Terry Pendleton	.20	.12
455	Dave Meads	.05	.02
456	Bill Buckner	.07	.04
457	John Pawlowski (R)	.05	.02
458	Bob Sebra	.05	.02
459	Jim Dwyer	.05	.02
460	Jay Aldrich (R)	.05	.02
461	Frank Tanana	.07	.04
462	Oil Can Boyd	.05	.02
463	Dan Pasqua	.07	.04
464	Tim Crews (R)	.10	.06
465	Andy Allanson	.05	.02
466	Bill Pecota (R)	.10	.06
467	Steve Ontiveros	.05	.02
468	Hubie Brooks	.08	.05
469	Paul Kilgus (R)	.07	.04
470	Dale Mohorcic	.05	.02
471	Dan Quisenberry	.05	.02
472	Dave Stewart	.08	.05
473	Dave Clark	.05	.02
474	Joel Skinner	.05	.02
475	Dave Anderson	.05	.02
476	Dan Petry	.05	.02
477	Carl Nichols (R)	.05	.02

478	Ernest Riles	.05	.02	534	Eric Nolte (R)	.07	.04
479	George Hendrick	.05	.02	535	Kent Tekulve	.05	.02
480	John Morris	.05	.02	536	Pat Pacillo (R)	.05	.02
481	Manny Hernandez (R)	.05	.02	537	Charlie Puleo	.05	.02
482	Jeff Stone	.05	.02	538	Tom Prince (R)	.08	.05
483	Chris Brown	.05	.02	539	Greg Maddux	.50	.30
484	Mike Bielecki	.07	.04	540	Jim Lindeman	.05	.02
485	Dave Dravecky	.05	.02	541	Pete Stanicek (R)	.05	.02
486	Rick Manning	.05	.02	542	Steve Kiefer	.05	.02
487	Bill Almon	.05	.02	543	Jim Morrison	.05	.02
488	Jim Sundberg	.05	.02	544	Spike Owen	.05	.02
489	Ken Phelps	.05	.02	545	Jan Buhner (R)	.50	.30
490	Tom Henke	.07	.04	546	Mike Devereaux (R)	.60	.35
491	Dan Gladden	.05	.02	547	Jerry Don Gleaton	.05	.02
492	Barry Larkin	.20	.12	548	Jose Rijo	.12	.07
493	Fred Manrique (R)	.07	.04	549	Dennis Martinez	.10	.06
494	Mike Griffin	.05	.02	550	Mike Loynd	.05	.02
495	Mark Knudson (R)	.08	.05	551	Darrell Miller	.05	.02
496	Bill Madlock	.08	.05	552	Dave LaPoint	.05	.02
497	Tim Stoddard	.05	.02	553	John Tudor	.05	.02
498	Sam Horn (R)	.15	.08	554	Rocky Childress (R)	.07	.04
499	Tracy Woodson (R)	.10	.06	555	Wally Ritchie (R)	.08	.05
500a	Checklist (468-577)	.05	.02	556	Terry McGriff	.05	.02
500b	Checklist (452-557)	.05	.02	557	Dave Leiper	.05	.02
501	Ken Schrom	.05	.02	558	Jeff Robinson	.05	.02
502	Angel Salazar	.05	.02	559	Jose Uribe	.05	.02
503	Eric Plunk	.07	.04	560	Ted Simmons	.07	.04
504	Joe Hesketh	.05	.02	561	Les Lancaster	.07	.04
505	Greg Minton	.05	.02	562	Keith Miller (R)	.10	.06
506	Geno Petralli	.05	.02	563	Harold Reynolds	.07	.04
507	Bob James	.05	.02	564	Gene Larkin	.08	.05
508	Robbie Wine (R)	.05	.02	565	Cecil Fielder	.35	.20
509	Jeff Calhoun	.05	.02	566	Roy Smalley	.05	.02
510	Steve Lake	.05	.02	567	Duane Ward	.08	.05
511	Mark Grant	.05	.02	568	Bill Wilkinson (R)	.07	.04
512	Frank Williams	.05	.02	569	Howard Johnson	.15	.08
513	Jeff Blauser (R)	.50	.30	570	Frank DiPino	.05	.02
514	Bob Walk	.05	.02	571	Pete Smith (R)	.20	.12
515	Craig Lefferts	.05	.02	572	Darnell Coles	.05	.02
516	Manny Trillo	.05	.02	573	Don Robinson	.05	.02
517	Jerry Reed	.05	.02	574	Rob Nelson	.05	.02
518	Rick Leach	.05	.02	575	Dennis Rasmussen	.05	.02
519	Mark Davidson	.07	.04	576	Steve Jeltz (Er)	.05	.02
520	Jeff Ballard (R)	.10	.06		(Wrong Photo)		
521	Dave Stapleton (R)	.07	.04	577	Tom Pagnozzi (R)	.30	.18
522	Pat Sheridan	.05	.02	578	Ty Gainey	.05	.02
523	Al Nipper	.05	.02	579	Gary Lucas	.05	.02
524	Steve Trout	.05	.02	580	Ron Hassey	.05	.02
525	Jeff Hamilton	.05	.02	581	Herm Winningham	.05	.02
526	Tommy Hinzo (R)	.05	.02	582	Rene Gonzales (R)	.10	.06
527	Lonnie Smith	.05	.02	583	Brad Komminsk	.05	.02
528	Greg Cadaret (R)	.08	.05	584	Doyle Alexander	.05	.02
529	Rob McClure (Bob)	.05	.02	585	Jeff Sellers	.05	.02
530	Chuck Finley	.12	.07	586	Bill Gullickson	.05	.02
531	Jeff Russell	.07	.04	587	Tim Belcher	.15	.08
532	Steve Lyons	.05	.02	588	Doug Jones (R)	.20	.12
533	Terry Puhl	.05	.02	589	Melido Perez (R)	.35	.20

590	Rick Honeycutt	.05	.02
591	Pascual Perez	.05	.02
592	Curt Wilkerson	.05	.02
593	Steve Howe	.05	.02
594	John Davis (R)	.05	.02
595	Storm Davis	.05	.02
596	Sammy Stewart	.05	.02
597	Neil Allen	.05	.02
598	Alejandro Pena	.05	.02
599	Mark Thurmond	.05	.02
600a	Checklist (578-BC26)	.05	.02
600b	Checklist (558-660)	.05	.02
601	Jose Mesa (R)	.15	.08
602	Don August (R)	.07	.04
603	Terry Leach	.05	.02
604	Tom Newell (R)	.05	.02
605	Randall Byers (R)	.05	.02
606	Jim Gott	.05	.02
607	Harry Spilman	.05	.02
608	John Candelaria	.05	.02
609	Mike Brumley (R)	.07	.04
610	Mickey Brantley	.05	.02
611	Jose Nunez (R)	.07	.04
612	Tom Nieto	.05	.02
613	Rick Reuschel	.05	.02
614	Lee Mazzilli	.05	.02
615	Scott Lusader (R)	.07	.04
616	Bobby Meacham	.05	.02
617	Kevin McReynolds	.08	.05
618	Gene Garber	.05	.02
619	Barry Lyons (R)	.10	.06
620	Randy Myers	.08	.05
621	Donnie Moore	.05	.02
622	Domingo Ramos	.05	.02
623	Ed Romero	.05	.02
624	Greg Myers (R)	.10	.06
625	Ripken Family	.30	.18
626	Pat Perry	.05	.02
627	Andres Thomas	.05	.02
628	Matt Williams	2.50	1.50
629	Dave Hengel (R)	.05	.02
630	Jeff Musselman	.05	.02
631	Tim Laudner	.05	.02
632	Bob Ojeda	.07	.04
633	Rafael Santana	.05	.02
634	Wes Gardner (R)	.10	.06
635	Roberto Kelly (R)	1.00	.70
636	Mike Flanagan	.05	.02
637	Jay Bell (R)	.75	.45
638	Bob Melvin	.05	.02
639	Damon Berryhill (R)	.15	.08
640	David Wells (R)	.35	.20
641	Stan Musial Puzzle	.15	.08
642	Doug Sisk	.05	.02
643	Keith Hughes (R)	.05	.02
644	Tom Glavine (R)	3.00	1.75
645	Al Newman	.05	.02

646	Scott Sanderson	.05	.02
647	Scott Terry	.05	.02
648	Tim Teufel	.05	.02
649	Garry Templeton	.05	.02
650	Manny Lee	.05	.02
651	Roger McDowell	.05	.02
652	Mookie Wilson	.05	.02
653	David Cone	.40	.25
654	Ron Gant (R)	3.00	1.75
655	Joe Price	.05	.02
656	George Bell	.15	.08
657	Gregg Jefferies (R)	2.50	1.50
658	Todd Stottlemyre (R)	.30	.18
659	Geronimo Berroa (R)	.10	.06
660	Jerry Royster	.05	.02
B1	Cal Ripken (MVP)	.40	.25
B2	Eric Davis (MVP)	.12	.07
B3	Paul Molitor (MVP)	.15	.10
B4	Mike Schmidt (MVP)	.25	.15
B5	Ivan Calderon (MVP	.08	.05
B6	Tony Gwynn (MVP)	.15	.08
B7	Wade Boggs (MVP)	.15	.08
B8	Andy Van Slyke (MVP)	.12	.07
B9	Joe Carter (MVP)	.15	.08
B10	Andre Dawson (MVP)	.15	.08
B11	Alan Trammell (MVP)	.12	.07
B12	Mike Scott (MVP)	.07	.04
B13	Wally Joyner (MVP)	.10	.06
B14	Dale Murphy (MVP)	.12	.07
B15	Kirby Puckett (MVP)	.35	.20
B16	Pedro Guerrero (MVP)	.07	.04
B17	Kevin Seitzer (MVP)	.07	.04
B18	Tim Raines (MVP)	.08	.05
B19	George Bell (MVP)	.12	.07
B20	Darryl Strawberry (MVP)	.25	.15
B21	Don Mattingly (MVP)	.30	.18
B22	Ozzie Smith (MVP)	.15	.08
B23	Mark McGwire (MVP)	.35	.20
B24	Will Clark (MVP)	.35	.20
B25	Alvin Davis (MVP)	.07	.04
B26	Ruben Sierra (MVP)	.35	.20

1988 Donruss Rookies

This 56-card update set is similar to the Donruss regular edition except the black borders feature green and red accents instead of blue and red accents. The standard-size cards measure 2-1/2" by 3-1/2".

	MINT	NR/MT
Complete Set (56)	20.00	14.00
Commons	.08	.05

		MINT	NR/MT
1	Mark Grace	2.75	1.75
2	Mike Campbell	.08	.05
3	Todd Frowirth (R)	.10	.06
4	Dave Stapleton	.08	.05
5	Shawn Abner	.10	.06
6	Jose Cecena (R)	.08	.05
7	Dave Gallagher (R)	.10	.06
8	Mark Parent (R)	.10	.06
9	Cecil Espy (R)	.10	.06
10	Pete Smith	.30	.18
11	Jay Buhner	.80	.50
12	Pat Borders (R)	.50	.30
13	Doug Jennings (R)	.08	.05
14	Brady Anderson (R)	1.00	.70
15	Pete Stanicek	.08	.05
16	Roberto Kelly	1.00	.70
17	Jeff Treadway	.12	.07
18	Walt Weiss (R)	.25	.15
19	Paul Gibson (R)	.08	.05
20	Tim Crews	.12	.07
21	Melido Perez	.20	.12
22	Steve Peters (R)	.10	.06
23	Craig Worthington (R)	.08	.05
24	John Trautwein (R)	.08	.05
25	DeWayne Vaughn (R)	.08	.05
26	David Wells	.35	.20
27	Al Leiter	.10	.06
28	Tim Belcher	.15	.08
29	Johnny Paredes (R)	.08	.05
30	Chris Sabo (R)	.80	.50
31	Damon Berryhill	.10	.06
32	Randy Milligan (R)	.30	.18
33	Gary Thurman	.08	.05
34	Kevin Elster	.12	.07
35	Roberto Alomar	12.00	8.00
36	Edgar Martinez (R)	1.25	.80
37	Todd Stottlemyre	.30	.18
38	Joey Meyer	.10	.06
39	Carl Nichols	.08	.05
40	Jack McDowell	3.50	2.25
41	Jose Bautista (R)	.10	.06
42	Sil Campusano (R)	.10	.06
43	John Dopson (R)	.10	.06
44	Jody Reed	.25	.15
45	Darrin Jackson (R)	.40	.25
46	Mike Capel (R)	.08	.05
47	Ron Gant	2.75	1.60
48	John Davis	.08	.05
49	Kevin Coffman (R)	.08	.05
50	Cris Carpenter (R)	.15	.08
51	Mackey Sasser	.10	.06
52	Luis Alicea (R)	.20	.12
53	Bryan Harvey (R)	1.50	.90
54	Steve Ellsworth (R)	.08	.05
55	Mike Macfarlane (R)	.40	.25
56	Checklist (1-56)	.08	.05

1989 Donruss

This 660-card set is similar to the 1988 Donruss set except for the border colors which are multi-colored at the top and bottom of the card fronts with black stripes on the sides. The card backs are orange and black. Subsets include Diamond Kings (1-26) and Rated Rookies (28-47). A Warren Spahn puzzle was included in the set. For the second straight year Donruss issued Bonus MVP cards which were randomly inserted into wax packs.Those cards are listed at the end of this checklist but not included in the complete set price below. All cards measure 2-1/2" by 3-1/2".

		MINT	NR/MT
	Complete Set (660)	18.50	12.50
	Commons	.05	.02
1	Mike Greenwell (DK)	.08	.05
2	Bobby Bonilla (DK)	.08	.05
3	Pete Incaviglia (DK)	.05	.02
4	Chris Sabo (DK)	.08	.05
5	Robin Yount (DK)	.12	.07
6	Tony Gwynn (DK)	.12	.07
7	Carlton Fisk (DK)	.12	.07
8	Cory Snyder (DK)	.05	.02
9	David Cone (DK)	.10	.06
10	Kevin Seitzer (DK)	.07	.04
11	Rick Reuschel (DK)	.05	.02
12	Johnny Ray (DK)	.05	.02
13	Dave Schmidt (DK)	.05	.02
14	Andres Galarraga (DK)	.10	.06
15	Kirk Gibson (DK)	.08	.05
16	Fred McGriff (DK)	.15	.08
17	Mark Grace (DK)	.10	.06
18	Jeff Robinson (DK)	.05	.02
19	Vince Coleman (DK)	.07	.04
20	Dave Henderson (DK)	.05	.02
21	Harold Reynolds (DK)	.05	.02
22	Gerald Perry (DK)	.05	.02
23	Frank Viola (DK)	.08	.05
24	Steve Bedrosian (DK)	.05	.02
25	Glenn Davis (DK)	.05	.02
26	Don Mattingly (DK)	.12	.07
27	Checklist (1-27)	.05	.02
28	Sandy Alomar, Jr. (R)	.35	.20
29	Steve Searcy (R)	.08	.05
30	Cameron Drew (R)	.05	.02
31	Gary Sheffield (R)	2.00	1.25
32	Erik Hanson (R)	.25	.05
33	Ken Griffey, Jr. (R)	5.00	3.00
34	Greg Harris (R)	.10	.06
35	Gregg Jefferies (R)	.35	.20
36	Luis Medina (R)	.10	.06
37	Carlos Quintana (R)	.12	.07
38	Felix Jose (R)	.30	.18
39	Cris Carpenter (R)	.10	.06
40	Ron Jones (R)	.07	.04
41	Dave West	.10	.06
42	Randy Johnson (R)	.75	.45
43	Mike Harkey (R)	.15	.08
44	Pete Harnisch (R)	.20	.12
45	Tom Gordon (R)	.12	.07
46	Gregg Olson (R)	.25	.15
47	Alex Sanchez (R)	.07	.04
48	Ruben Sierra	.30	.18
49	Rafael Palmeiro	.25	.15
50	Ron Gant	.40	.25
51	Cal Ripken, Jr.	.60	.35
52	Wally Joyner	.10	.06
53	Gary Carter	.08	.05
54	Andy Van Slyke	.10	.06
55	Robin Yount	.30	.18
56	Pete Incaviglia	.05	.02
57	Greg Brock	.05	.02
58	Melido Perez	.07	.04
59	Craig Lefferts	.05	.02
60	Gary Pettis	.05	.02
61	Danny Tartabull	.15	.08
62	Guillermo Hernandez	.05	.02
63	Ozzie Smith	.15	.08
64	Gary Gaetti	.05	.02
65	Mark Davis	.05	.02
66	Lee Smith	.12	.07
67	Dennis Eckersley	.15	.08
68	Wade Boggs	.25	.15
69	Mike Scott	.07	.04
70	Fred McGriff	.35	.20
71	Tom Browning	.05	.02
72	Claudell Washington	.05	.02
73	Mel Hall	.07	.04
74	Don Mattingly	.25	.15
75	Steve Bedrosian	.05	.02
76	Juan Samuel	.05	.02
77	Mike Scioscia	.05	.02
78	Dave Righetti	.05	.02
79	Alfredo Griffin	.05	.02
80	Eric Davis	.12	.07
81	Juan Berenguer	.05	.02
82	Todd Worrell	.07	.04
83	Joe Carter	.25	.15
84	Steve Sax	.07	.04
85	Frank White	.05	.02
86	John Kruk	.15	.10
87	Rance Mulliniks	.05	.02
88	Alan Ashby	.05	.02
89	Charlie Leibrandt	.05	.02
90	Frank Tanana	.05	.02
91	Jose Canseco	.40	.25
92	Barry Bonds	.75	.45
93	Harold Reynolds	.05	.02
94	Mark McLemore	.05	.02
95	Mark McGwire	.35	.20
96	Eddie Murray	.15	.08
97	Tim Raines	.08	.05
98	Robby Thompson	.08	.05
99	Kevin McReynolds	.07	.04
100	Checklist (28-137)	.05	.02
101	Carlton Fisk	.15	.08
102	Dave Martinez	.05	.02
103	Glenn Braggs	.05	.02

104	Dale Murphy	.12	.07
105	Ryne Sandberg	.35	.20
106	Dennis Martinez	.10	.06
107	Pete O'Brien	.05	.02
108	Dick Schofield	.05	.02
109	Henry Cotto	.05	.02
110	Mike Marshall	.05	.02
111	Keith Moreland	.05	.02
112	Tom Brunansky	.07	.04
113	Kelly Gruber	.08	.05
114	Brook Jacoby	.05	.02
115	Keith Brown (R)	.07	.04
116	Matt Nokes	.07	.04
117	Keith Hernandez	.07	.04
118	Bob Forsch	.05	.02
119	Bert Blyleven	.10	.06
120	Willie Wilson	.05	.02
121	Tommy Gregg	.05	.02
122	Jim Rice	.07	.04
123	Bob Knepper	.05	.02
124	Danny Jackson	.05	.02
125	Eric Plunk	.05	.02
126	Brian Fisher	.05	.02
127	Mike Pagliarulo	.05	.02
128	Tony Gwynn	.25	.15
129	Lance McCullers	.05	.02
130	Andres Galarraga	.15	.08
131	Jose Uribe	.05	.02
132	Kirk Gibson	.07	.04
133	David Palmer	.05	.02
134	R.J. Reynolds	.05	.02
135	Greg Walker	.05	.02
136	Kirk McCaskill	.05	.02
137	Shawon Dunston	.10	.06
138	Andy Allanson	.05	.02
139	Rob Murphy	.05	.02
140	Mike Aldrete	.05	.02
141	Terry Kennedy	.05	.02
142	Scott Fletcher	.05	.02
143	Steve Balboni	.05	.02
144	Bret Saberhagen	.12	.07
145	Ozzie Virgil	.05	.02
146	Dale Sveum	.05	.02
147	Darryl Strawberry	.25	.15
148	Harold Baines	.07	.04
149	George Bell	.10	.06
150	Dave Parker	.07	.04
151	Bobby Bonilla	.15	.08
152	Mookie Wilson	.05	.02
153	Ted Power	.05	.02
154	Nolan Ryan	.75	.45
155	Jeff Reardon	.12	.07
156	Tim Wallach	.07	.04
157	Jamie Moyer	.05	.02
158	Rich Gossage	.07	.04
159	Dave Winfield	.25	.15
160	Von Hayes	.05	.02
161	Willie McGee	.08	.05
162	Rich Gedman	.05	.02
163	Tony Pena	.05	.02
164	Mike Morgan	.05	.02
165	Charlie Hough	.05	.02
166	Mike Stanley	.05	.02
167	Andre Dawson	.20	.12
168	Joe Boever (R)	.08	.05
169	Pete Stanicek	.05	.02
170	Bob Boone	.08	.05
171	Ron Darling	.07	.04
172	Bob Walk	.05	.02
173	Rob Deer	.07	.04
174	Steve Buechele	.05	.02
175	Ted Higuera	.05	.02
176	Ozzie Guillen	.07	.04
177	Candy Maldonado	.05	.02
178	Doyle Alexander	.05	.02
179	Mark Gubicza	.07	.04
180	Alan Trammell	.10	.06
181	Vince Coleman	.07	.04
182	Kirby Puckett	.35	.20
183	Chris Brown	.05	.02
184	Marty Barrett	.05	.02
185	Stan Javier	.05	.02
186	Mike Greenwell	.08	.05
187	Billy Hatcher	.05	.02
188	Jimmy Key	.08	.05
189	Nick Esasky	.05	.02
190	Don Slaught	.05	.02
191	Cory Snyder	.07	.04
192	John Candelaria	.05	.02
193	Mike Schmidt	.40	.25
194	Kevin Gross	.05	.02
195	John Tudor	.05	.02
196	Neil Allen	.05	.02
197	Orel Hershiser	.08	.05
198	Kal Daniels	.05	.02
199	Kent Hrbek	.08	.05
200	Checklist (138-247)	.05	.02
201	Joe Magrane	.07	.04
202	Scott Bailes	.05	.02
203	Tim Belcher	.07	.04
204	George Brett	.30	.18
205	Benito Santiago	.10	.06
206	Tony Fernandez	.05	.02
207	Gerald Young	.08	.05
208	Bo Jackson	.25	.15
209	Chet Lemon	.05	.02
210	Storm Davis	.05	.02
211	Doug Drabek	.10	.06
212	Mickey Brantley (Er) (Wrong Photo)	.05	.02
213	Devon White	.08	.05
214	Dave Stewart	.08	.05
215	Dave Schmidt	.05	.02
216	Bryn Smith	.05	.02

217	Brett Butler	.08	.05
218	Bob Ojeda	.05	.02
219	Steve Rosenberg (R)	.08	.05
220	Hubie Brooks	.07	.04
221	B.J. Surhoff	.05	.02
222	Rick Mahler	.05	.02
223	Rick Sutcliffe	.07	.04
224	Neal Heaton	.05	.02
225	Mitch Williams	.07	.04
226	Chuck Finley	.10	.06
227	Mark Langston	.10	.06
228	Jesse Orosco	.05	.02
229	Ed Whitson	.05	.02
230	Terry Pendleton	.15	.08
231	Lloyd Moseby	.05	.02
232	Greg Swindell	.07	.04
233	John Franco	.05	.02
234	Jack Morris	.12	.07
235	Howard Johnson	.12	.07
236	Glenn Davis	.05	.02
237	Frank Viola	.07	.04
238	Kevin Seitzer	.07	.04
239	Gerald Perry	.05	.02
240	Dwight Evans	.07	.04
241	Jim Deshaies	.05	.02
242	Bo Diaz	.05	.02
243	Carney Lansford	.05	.02
244	Mike LaValliere	.05	.02
245	Rickey Henderson	.30	.18
246	Roberto Alomar	.90	.60
247	Jimmy Jones	.05	.02
248	Pasquel Perez	.05	.02
249	Will Clark	.50	.30
250	Fernando Valenzuela	.08	.05
251	Shane Rawley	.05	.02
252	Sid Bream	.05	.02
253	Steve Lyons	.05	.02
254	Brian Downing	.05	.02
255	Mark Grace	.30	.18
256	Tom Candiotti	.05	.02
257	Barry Larkin	.20	.12
258	Mike Krukow	.05	.02
259	Billy Ripken	.05	.02
260	Cecilio Guante	.05	.02
261	Scott Bradley	.05	.02
262	Floyd Bannister	.05	.02
263	Pete Smith	.12	.07
264	Jim Gantner	.05	.02
265	Roger McDowell	.05	.02
266	Bobby Thigpen	.07	.04
267	Jim Clancy	.05	.02
268	Terry Steinbach	.07	.04
269	Mike Dunne	.05	.02
270	Dwight Gooden	.15	.08
271	Mike Heath	.05	.02
272	Dave Smith	.05	.02
273	Keith Atherton	.05	.02
274	Tim Burke	.05	.02
275	Damon Berryhill	.05	.02
276	Vance Law	.05	.02
277	Rich Dotson	.05	.02
278	Lance Parrish	.05	.02
279	Denny Walling	.05	.02
280	Roger Clemens	.50	.30
281	Greg Mathews	.05	.02
282	Tom Niedenfuer	.05	.02
283	Paul Kilgus	.05	.02
284	Jose Guzman	.07	.04
285	Calvin Schiraldi	.05	.02
286	Charlie Puleo	.05	.02
287	Joe Orsulak	.05	.02
288	Jack Howell	.05	.02
289	Kevin Elster	.05	.02
290	Jose Lind	.05	.02
291	Paul Molitor	.20	.12
292	Cecil Espy	.05	.02
293	Bill Wegman	.05	.02
294	Dan Pasqua	.05	.02
295	Scott Garrelts	.05	.02
296	Walt Terrell	.05	.02
297	Ed Hearn	.05	.02
298	Lou Whitaker	.07	.04
299	Ken Dayley	.05	.02
300	Checklist (248-357)	.05	.02
301	Tommy Herr	.05	.02
302	Mike Brumley	.05	.02
303	Ellis Burks	.08	.05
304	Curt Young	.05	.02
305	Jody Reed	.05	.02
306	Bill Doran	.05	.02
307	David Wells	.08	.05
308	Ron Robinson	.05	.02
309	Rafael Santana	.05	.02
310	Julio Franco	.10	.06
311	Jack Clark	.07	.04
312	Chris James	.05	.02
313	Milt Thompson	.05	.02
314	John Shelby	.05	.02
315	Al Leiter	.05	.02
316	Mike Davis	.05	.02
317	Chris Sabo	.25	.15
318	Greg Gagne	.05	.02
319	Jose Oquendo	.05	.02
320	John Farrell	.05	.02
321	Franklin Stubbs	.05	.02
322	Kurt Stillwell	.05	.02
323	Shawn Abner	.05	.02
324	Mike Flanagan	.05	.02
325	Kevin Bass	.05	.02
326	Pat Tabler	.05	.02
327	Mike Henneman	.05	.02
328	Rick Honeycutt	.05	.02
329	John Smiley	.10	.06
330	Rey Quinones	.05	.02

331	Johnny Ray	.05	.02
332	Bob Welch	.07	.04
333	Larry Sheets	.05	.02
334	Jeff Parrett	.05	.02
335	Rick Reuschel	.05	.02
337	Ken Williams	.05	.02
338	Andy McGaffigan	.05	.02
339	Joey Meyer	.05	.02
340	Dion James	.05	.02
341	Les Lancaster	.05	.02
342	Tom Foley	.05	.02
343	Geno Petralli	.05	.02
344	Dan Petry	.05	.02
345	Alvin Davis	.05	.02
346	Mickey Hatcher	.05	.02
347	Marvell Wynne	.05	.02
348	Danny Cox	.05	.02
349	Dave Stieb	.08	.05
350	Jay Bell	.12	.07
351	Jeff Treadway	.05	.02
352	Luis Salazar	.05	.02
353	Lenny Dykstra	.20	.12
354	Juan Agosto	.05	.02
355	Gene Larkin	.05	.02
356	Steve Farr	.05	.02
357	Paul Assenmacher	.05	.02
358	Todd Benzinger	.05	.02
359	Larry Andersen	.05	.02
360	Paul O'Neill	.10	.06
361	Ron Hassey	.05	.02
362	Jim Gott	.05	.02
363	Ken Phelps	.05	.02
364	Tim Flannery	.05	.02
365	Randy Ready	.05	.02
366	Nelson Santovenia (R)	.08	.05
367	Kelly Downs	.05	.02
368	Danny Heep	.05	.02
369	Phil Bradley	.05	.02
370	Jeff Robinson	.05	.02
371	Ivan Calderon	.07	.04
372	Mike Witt	.05	.02
373	Greg Maddux	.35	.20
374	Carmen Castillo	.05	.02
375	Jose Rijo	.08	.05
376	Joe Price	.05	.02
377	Rene Gonzalez	.05	.02
378	Oddibe McDowell	.05	.02
379	Jim Presley	.05	.02
380	Brad Wellman	.05	.02
381	Tom Glavine	.80	.50
382	Dan Plesac	.05	.02
383	Wally Backman	.05	.02
384	Dave Gallagher	.05	.02
385	Tom Henke	.05	.02
386	Luis Polonia	.08	.05
387	Junior Ortiz	.05	.02
388	David Cone	.15	.08
389	Dave Bergman	.05	.02
390	Danny Darwin	.05	.02
391	Dan Gladden	.05	.02
392	John Dopson	.05	.02
393	Frank DiPino	.05	.02
394	Al Nipper	.05	.02
395	Willie Randolph	.07	.04
396	Don Carman	.05	.02
397	Scott Terry	.05	.02
398	Rick Cerone	.05	.02
399	Tom Pagnozzi	.10	.06
400	Checklist (358-467)	.05	.02
401	Mickey Tettleton	.08	.05
402	Curtis Wilkerson	.05	.02
403	Jeff Russell	.05	.02
404	Pat Perry	.05	.02
405	Jose Alvarez (R)	.07	.04
406	Rick Schu	.05	.02
407	Sherman Corbett (R)	.07	.04
408	Dave Magadan	.07	.04
409	Bob Kipper	.05	.02
410	Don August	.05	.02
411	Bob Brower	.05	.02
412	Chris Bosio	.08	.05
413	Jerry Reuss	.05	.02
414	Atlee Hammaker	.05	.02
415	Jim Walewander (R)	.05	.02
416	Mike Macfarlane	.10	.06
417	Pat Sheridan	.05	.02
418	Pedro Guerrero	.07	.04
419	Allan Anderson	.05	.02
420	Mark Parent	.05	.02
421	Bob Stanley	.05	.02
422	Mike Gallego	.05	.02
423	Bruce Hurst	.07	.04
424	Dave Meads	.05	.02
425	Jesse Barfield	.07	.04
426	Rob Dibble (R)	.20	.12
427	Joel Skinner	.05	.02
428	Ron Kittle	.05	.02
429	Rick Rhoden	.05	.02
430	Bob Dernier	.05	.02
431	Steve Jeltz	.05	.02
432	Rick Dempsey	.05	.02
433	Roberto Kelly	.20	.12
434	Dave Anderson	.05	.02
435	Herm Winningham	.05	.02
436	Al Newman	.05	.02
437	Jose DeLeon	.05	.02
438	Doug Jones	.05	.02
439	Brian Holton	.05	.02
440	Jeff Montgomery	.08	.05
441	Dickie Thon	.05	.02
442	Cecil Fielder	.30	.18
443	John Fishel (R)	.05	.02
444	Jerry Don Gleaton	.05	.02
445	Paul Gibson	.05	.02

446	Walt Weiss	.08	.05
447	Glenn Wilson	.05	.02
448	Mike Moore	.05	.02
449	Chili Davis	.07	.04
450	Dave Henderson	.05	.02
451	Jose Bautista	.05	.02
452	Rex Hudler	.05	.02
453	Bob Brenly	.05	.02
454	Mackey Sasser	.05	.02
455	Daryl Boston	.05	.02
456	Mike Fitzgerald	.05	.02
457	Jeffery Leonard	.05	.02
458	Bruce Sutter	.07	.04
459	Mitch Webster	.05	.02
460	Joe Hesketh	.05	.02
461	Bobby Witt	.08	.05
462	Stew Cliburn	.05	.02
463	Scott Bankhead	.05	.02
464	Ramon Martinez (R)	.50	.30
465	Dave Leiper	.05	.02
466	Luis Alicea	.08	.05
467	John Cerutti	.05	.02
468	Ron Washington	.05	.02
469	Jeff Reed	.05	.02
470	Jeff Robinson	.05	.02
471	Sid Fernandez	.07	.04
472	Terry Puhl	.05	.02
473	Charlie Lea	.05	.02
474	Israel Sanchez (R)	.07	.04
475	Bruce Benedict	.05	.02
476	Oil Can Boyd	.05	.02
477	Craig Reynolds	.05	.02
478	Frank Williams	.05	.02
479	Greg Cadaret	.05	.02
480	Randy Kramer (R)	.08	.05
481	Dave Eiland (R)	.10	.06
482	Eric Show	.05	.02
483	Garry Templeton	.05	.02
484	Wallace Johnson (R)	.05	.02
485	Kevin Mitchell	.12	.07
486	Tim Crews	.07	.04
487	Mike Maddux	.05	.02
488	Dave LaPoint	.05	.02
489	Fred Manrique	.05	.02
490	Greg Minton	.05	.02
491	Doug Dascenzo (R)	.10	.06
492	Willie Upshaw	.05	.02
493	Jack Armstrong (R)	.12	.07
494	Kirt Manwaring	.05	.02
495	Jeff Ballard	.05	.02
496	Jeff Kunkel	.05	.02
497	Mike Campbell	.05	.02
498	Gary Thurman	.05	.02
499	Zane Smith	.05	.02
500	Checklist (468-577)	.05	.02
501	Mike Birkbeck	.05	.02
502	Terry Leach	.05	.02
503	Shawn Hillegas	.05	.02
504	Manny Lee	.05	.02
505	Doug Jennings	.05	.02
506	Ken Oberkfell	.05	.02
507	Tim Teufel	.05	.02
508	Tom Brookens	.05	.02
509	Rafael Ramirez	.05	.02
510	Fred Toliver	.05	.02
511	Brian Holman (R)	.12	.07
512	Mike Bielecki	.05	.02
513	Jeff Pico (R)	.07	.04
514	Charles Hudson	.05	.02
515	Bruce Ruffin	.05	.02
516	Larry McWilliams	.05	.02
517	Jeff Sellers	.05	.02
518	John Costello (R)	.08	.05
519	Brady Anderson	.60	.35
520	Craig McMurtry	.05	.02
521	Ray Hayward	.05	.02
522	Drew Hall	.05	.02
523	Mark Lemke (R)	.12	.07
524	Oswald Peraza (R)	.08	.05
525	Bryan Harvey	.40	.25
526	Rick Aguilera	.05	.02
527	Tom Prince	.05	.02
528	Mark Clear	.05	.02
529	Jerry Browne	.05	.02
530	Juan Castillo	.05	.02
531	Jack McDowell	.40	.25
532	Chris Speier	.05	.02
533	Darrell Evans	.07	.04
534	Luis Aquino	.05	.02
535	Eric King	.05	.02
536	Ken Hill (R)	.50	.30
537	Randy Bush	.05	.02
538	Shane Mack	.10	.06
539	Tom Bolton	.08	.05
540	Gene Nelson	.05	.02
541	Wes Gardner	.07	.04
542	Ken Caminiti	.07	.04
543	Duane Ward	.05	.02
544	Norm Charlton (R)	.20	.12
545	Hal Morris (R)	.35	.20
546	Rich Yett	.05	.02
547	Hensley Meulens (R)	.12	.07
548	Greg Harris	.05	.02
549	Darren Daulton	.15	.08
550	Jeff Hamilton	.05	.02
551	Luis Aguayo	.05	.02
552	Tim Leary	.05	.02
553	Ron Oester	.05	.02
554	Steve Lombardozzi	.05	.02
555	Tim Jones (R)	.07	.04
556	Bud Black	.07	.04
557	Alejandro Pena	.05	.02
558	Jose DeJesus (R)	.08	.05
559	Dennis Rasmussen	.05	.02

560	Pat Borders	.15	.08
561	Craig Biggio (R)	.35	.20
562	Luis de los Santos (R)	.07	.04
563	Fred Lynn	.07	.04
564	Todd Burns (R)	.10	.06
565	Felix Fermin	.05	.02
566	Darnell Coles	.05	.02
567	Willie Fraser	.05	.02
568	Glenn Hubbard	.05	.02
569	Craig Worthington	.05	.02
570	Johnny Paredes	.05	.02
571	Don Robinson	.05	.02
572	Barry Lyons	.05	.02
573	Bill Long	.05	.02
574	Tracy Jones	.05	.02
575	Juan Nieves	.05	.02
576	Andres Thomas	.05	.02
577	Rolando Roomes (R)	.08	.05
578	Luis Rivera	.05	.02
579	Chad Kreuter (R)	.15	.08
580	Tony Armas	.05	.02
581	Jay Buhner	.12	.07
582	Ricky Horton	.05	.02
583	Andy Hawkins	.05	.02
584	Sil Campusano	.05	.02
585	Dave Clark	.05	.02
586	Van Snider (R)	.10	.06
587	Todd Frohwirth	.05	.02
588	Warren Spahn Puzzle	.12	.07
589	William Brennan (R)	.07	.04
590	German Gonzalez (R)	.07	.04
591	Ernie Whitt	.05	.02
592	Jeff Blauser	.12	.07
593	Spike Owen	.05	.02
594	Matt Williams	.35	.20
595	Lloyd McClendon	.07	.04
596	Steve Ontiveros	.05	.02
597	Scott Medvin (R)	.08	.05
598	Hipolito Pena (R)	.08	.05
599	Jerald Clark (R)	.12	.07
600	Checklist (578-BC26)	.05	.02
601	Carmelo Martinez	.05	.02
602	Mike LaCoss	.05	.02
603	Mike Devereaux	.12	.07
604	Alex Madrid (R)	.08	.05
605	Gary Redus	.05	.02
606	Lance Johnson (R)	.05	.02
607	Terry Clark (R)	.07	.04
608	Manny Trillo	.05	.02
609	Scott Jordan (R)	.08	.05
610	Jay Howell	.05	.02
611	Francisco Melendez (R)	.07	.04
612	Mike Boddicker	.05	.02
613	Kevin Brown	.25	.15
614	Dave Valle	.05	.02
615	Tim Laudner	.05	.02
616	Andy Nezelek (R)	.08	.05
617	Chuck Crim	.05	.02
618	Jack Savage	.08	.05
619	Adam Peterson	.08	.05
620	Todd Stottlemyre	.08	.05
621	Lance Blankenship (R)	.12	.07
622	Miguel Garcia (R)	.08	.05
623	Keith Miller	.05	.02
624	Ricky Jordan (R)	.15	.08
625	Ernest Riles	.05	.02
626	John Moses	.05	.02
627	Nelson Liriano	.05	.02
628	Mike Smithson	.05	.02
629	Scott Sanderson	.05	.02
630	Dale Mohorcic	.05	.02
631	Marvin Freeman	.05	.02
632	Mike Young	.05	.02
633	Dennis Lamp	.05	.02
634	Dante Bichette (R)	.35	.20
635	Curt Schilling (R)	.75	.45
636	Scott May (R)	.08	.05
637	Mike Schooler (R)	.15	.08
638	Rick Leach	.05	.02
639	Tom Lampkin (R)	.08	.05
640	Brian Meyer (R)	.10	.06
641	Brian Harper	.05	.02
642	John Smoltz (R)	.80	.50
643	Jose Canseco (40/40)	.25	.15
644	Bill Schroeder	.05	.02
645	Edgar Martinez	.25	.15
646	Dennis Cook (R)	.08	.05
647	Barry Jones	.05	.02
648	Orel Hershiser (59)	.12	.07
649	Rod Nichols (R)	.08	.05
650	Jody Davis	.05	.02
651	Bob Milacki (R)	.10	.06
652	Mike Jackson	.05	.02
653	Derek Lilliquist (R)	.10	.06
654	Paul Mirabella	.05	.02
655	Mike Diaz	.05	.02
656	Jeff Musselman	.05	.02
657	Jerry Reed	.05	.02
658	Kevin Blankenship (R)	.08	.05
659	Wayne Tolleson	.05	.02
660	Eric Hetzel (R)	.10	.06
B1	Kirby Puckett	.20	.12
B2	Mike Scott	.07	.04
B3	Joe Carter	.15	.08
B4	Orel Hershiser	.10	.06
B5	Jose Canseco	.20	.12
B6	Darryl Strawberry	.12	.07
B7	George Brett	.15	.08
B8	Andre Dawson	.12	.07
B9	Paul Molitor	.12	.07
B10	Andy Van Slyke	.08	.05
B11	Dave Winfield	.12	.07
B12	Kevin Gross	.07	.04
B13	Mike Greenwell	.08	.05

		MINT	NR/MT
B14	Ozzie Smith	.12	.07
B15	Cal Ripken Jr.	.25	.15
B16	Andres Galarraga	.10	.06
B17	Alan Trammell	.10	.06
B18	Kal Daniels	.07	.04
B19	Fred McGriff	.25	.15
B20	Tony Gwynn	.15	.08
B21	Wally Joyner	.10	.06
B22	Will Clark	.15	.10
B23	Ozzie Guillen	.07	.04
B24	Gerald Perry	.07	.04
B25	Alvin Davis	.07	.04
B26	Ruben Sierra	.15	.08

1989 Donruss Rookies

Green and black borders highlight this 56-card update set from Donruss which is similar to their regular 1989 set. Cards measure 2-1/2" by 3-1/2".

		MINT	NR/MT
	Complete Set (56)	15.00	10.00
	Commons	.07	.04
1	Gary Sheffield	2.50	1.50
2	Gregg Jefferies	.50	.30
3	Ken Griffey, Jr.	10.00	6.50
4	Tom Gordon	.10	.06
5	Billy Spiers (R)	.12	.07
6	Deion Sanders (R)	2.00	1.25
7	Donn Pall (R)	.07	.04
8	Steve Carter (R)	.05	.02
9	Francisco Oliveras (R)	.08	.05
10	Steve Wilson (R)	.08	.05
11	Bob Geren (R)	.10	.06
12	Tony Castillo (R)	.07	.04

		MINT	NR/MT
13	Kenny Rogers (R)	.10	.06
14	Carlos Martinez (R)	.10	.06
15	Edgar Martinez	.30	.18
16	Jim Abbott (R)	1.50	.90
17	Torey Lovullo (R)	.10	.06
18	Mark Carreon (R)	.10	.06
19	Geronimo Berroa	.05	.02
20	Luis Medina	.08	.05
21	Sandy Alomar, Jr.	.25	.15
22	Bob Milacki	.10	.06
23	Joe Girardi (R)	.10	.06
24	German Gonzalez	.05	.02
25	Craig Worthington	.05	.02
26	Jerome Walton (R)	.10	.06
27	Gary Wayne (R)	.08	.05
28	Tim Jones	.07	.04
29	Dante Bichette	.30	.18
30	Alexis Infante (R)	.08	.05
31	Ken Hill	.40	.25
32	Dwight Smith (R)	.20	.12
33	Luis de los Santos	.05	.02
34	Eric Yelding(FC)	.12	.07
35	Gregg Olson	.25	.15
36	Phil Stephenson (R)	.08	.05
37	Ken Patterson (R)	.08	.05
38	Rick Wrona (R)	.08	.05
39	Mike Brumley	.07	.04
40	Cris Carpenter	.10	.06
41	Jeff Brantley (R)	.12	.07
42	Ron Jones	.07	.04
43	Randy Johnson	.70	.40
44	Kevin Brown	.25	.15
45	Ramon Martinez	.50	.30
46	Greg Harris	.10	.06
47	Steve Finley (R)	.25	.15
48	Randy Kramer	.07	.04
49	Erik Hanson	.20	.12
50	Matt Merullo (R)	.12	.07
51	Mike Devereaux	.20	.12
52	Clay Parker (R)	.07	.04
53	Omar Vizquel (R)	.20	.12
54	Derek Lilliquist	.07	.04
55	Junior Felix (R)	.15	.08
56	Checklist	.05	.02

1990 Donruss

Donruss increased the size of their set to 716-cards in 1990 and added a new All-Star subset to go along with Diamond Kings (1-26) and Rated Rookies (28-47). Bonus insert MVP cards were also distributed randomly in was packs. Those cards are listed at the end of this checklist but not included in the complete set price below. The cards measure 2-1/2" by 3-1/2" and feature bright red borders framing full color action photos on the card fronts. There are many variations in this set and only those with significant differences in value are listed in the checklist.

		MINT	NR/MT
Complete Set (716)		16.00	10.00
Commons		.05	.02

		MINT	NR/MT
1	Bo Jackson (DK)	.15	.08
2	Steve Sax (DK)	.08	.05
3	Ruben Sierra (DK)	.25	.15
4	Ken Griffey, Jr. (DK)	.50	.30
5	Mickey Tettleton (DK)	.07	.04
6	Dave Stewart (DK)	.08	.05
7	Jim Deshaies (DK)	.05	.02
8	John Smoltz (DK)	.12	.07
9	Mike Bielecki (DK)	.05	.02
10a	Brian Downing (DK) (Reverse Negative)	.50	.30
10b	Brian Downing (DK) (Corrected)	.07	.04
11	Kevin Mitchell (DK)	.08	.05
12	Kelly Gruber (DK)	.07	.04
13	Joe Magrane (DK)	.07	.04
14	John Franco (DK)	.07	.04
15	Ozzie Guillen (DK)	.07	.04
16	Lou Whitaker (DK)	.08	.05
17	John Smiley (DK)	.08	.05
18	Howard Johnson (DK)	.08	.05
19	Willie Randolph (DK)	.07	.04
20	Chris Bosio (DK)	.07	.04
21	Tommy Herr (DK)	.05	.02
22	Dan Gladden (DK)	.05	.02
23	Ellis Burks (DK)	.08	.05
24	Pete O'Brien (DK)	.05	.02
25	Bryn Smith (DK)	.05	.02
26	Ed Whitson (DK)	.05	.02
27	Checklist (1-27)	.06	.02
28	Robin Ventura (R)	.75	.45
29	Todd Zeile (R)	.20	.12
30	Sandy Alomar, Jr.	.08	.05
31	Kent Mercker (R)	.12	.07
32	Ben McDonald (R)	.50	.30
33a	Juan Gonzalez (R) (Reverse Negative)	5.00	3.00
33b	Juan Gonzalez (R) (Corrected)	3.00	1.75
34	Eric Anthony (R)	.40	.25
35	Mike Fetters (R)	.10	.06
36	Marquis Grissom (R)	.75	.45
37	Greg Vaughn (R)	.40	.25
38	Brian Dubois (R)	.10	.06
39	Steve Avery (R)	.80	.50
40	Mark Gardner (R)	.15	.08
41	Andy Benes (R)	.35	.20
42	Delino Deshields (R)	.70	.40
43	Scott Coolbaugh	.07	.04
44	Pat Combs	.10	.06
45	Alex Sanchez	.07	.04
46	Kelly Mann (R)	.07	.04
47	Julio Machado (R)	.10	.06
48	Pete Incaviglia	.07	.04
49	Shawon Dunston	.08	.05
50	Jeff Treadway	.05	.02
51	Jeff Ballard	.05	.02
52	Claudell Washington	.05	.02
53	Juan Samuel	.05	.02
54	John Smiley	.10	.06
55	Rob Deer	.07	.04
56	Geno Petralli	.05	.02
57	Chris Bosio	.08	.05
58	Carlton Fisk	.10	.06
59	Kirt Manwaring	.05	.02
60	Chet Lemon	.05	.02
61	Bo Jackson	.20	.12
62	Doyle Alexander	.05	.02
63	Pedro Guerrero	.05	.02
64	Allan Anderson	.05	.02
65	Greg Harris	.05	.02
66	Mike Greenwell	.10	.06
67	Walt Weiss	.08	.05
68	Wade Boggs	.20	.12
69	Jim Clancy	.05	.02
70	Junior Felix	.07	.04
71	Barry Larkin	.12	.07
72	Dave LaPoint	.05	.02
73	Joel Skinner	.05	.02
74	Jesse Barfield	.07	.04

#	Name			#	Name		
75	Tommy Herr	.05	.02	132	Mike Morgan	.05	.02
76	Ricky Jordan	.07	.04	133	Steve Jeltz	.05	.02
77	Eddie Murray	.15	.08	134	Jeff Robinson	.05	.02
78	Steve Sax	.08	.05	135	Ozzie Guillen	.07	.04
79	Tim Belcher	.07	.04	136	Chili Davis	.07	.04
80	Danny Jackson	.05	.02	137	Mitch Webster	.05	.02
81	Kent Hrbek	.07	.04	138	Jerry Browne	.05	.02
82	Milt Thompson	.05	.02	139	Bo Diaz	.05	.02
83	Brook Jacoby	.05	.02	140	Robby Thompson	.07	.04
84	Mike Marshall	.05	.02	141	Craig Worthington	.05	.02
85	Kevin Seitzer	.07	.04	142	Julio Franco	.10	.06
86	Tony Gwynn	.20	.12	143	Brian Holman	.05	.02
87	Dave Steib	.08	.05	144	George Brett	.20	.12
88	Dave Smith	.05	.02	145	Tom Glavine	.35	.20
89	Bret Saberhagen	.10	.06	146	Robin Yount	.20	.12
90	Alan Trammell	.10	.06	147	Gary Carter	.08	.05
91	Tony Phillips	.05	.02	148	Ron Kittle	.05	.02
92	Doug Drabek	.10	.06	149	Tony Fernandez	.05	.02
93	Jeffrey Leonard	.05	.02	150	Dave Stewart	.08	.05
94	Wally Joyner	.08	.05	151	Gary Gaetti	.05	.02
95	Carney Lansford	.07	.04	152	Kevin Elster	.05	.02
96	Cal Ripken	.40	.25	153	Gerald Perry	.05	.02
97	Andres Galarraga	.15	.08	154	Jesse Orosco	.05	.02
98	Kevin Mitchell	.08	.05	155	Wally Backman	.05	.02
99	Howard Johnson	.08	.05	156	Dennis Martinez	.08	.05
100	Checklist	.05	.02	157	Rick Sutcliffe	.05	.02
101	Melido Perez	.05	.02	158	Greg Maddux	.25	.15
102	Spike Owen	.05	.02	159	Andy Hawkins	.05	.02
103	Paul Molitor	.20	.12	160	John Kruk	.10	.06
104	Geronimo Berroa	.05	.02	161	Jose Oquendo	.05	.02
105	Ryne Sandberg	.35	.20	162	John Dopson	.05	.02
106	Bryn Smith	.05	.02	163	Joe Magrane	.05	.02
107	Steve Buechele	.05	.02	164	Billy Ripken	.05	.02
108	Jim Abbott	.25	.15	165	Fred Manrique	.05	.02
109	Alvin Davis	.05	.02	166	Nolan Ryan	.75	.45
110	Lee Smith	.10	.06	167	Damon Berryhill	.05	.02
111	Roberto Alomar	.40	.25	168	Dale Murphy	.10	.06
112	Rick Reuschel	.05	.02	169	Mickey Tettleton	.07	.04
113	Kelly Gruber	.07	.04	170	Kirk McCaskill	.05	.02
114	Joe Carter	.20	.12	171	Dwight Gooden	.12	.07
115	Jose Rijo	.08	.05	172	Jose Lind	.05	.02
116	Greg Minton	.05	.02	173	B.J. Surhoff	.05	.02
117	Bob Ojeda	.05	.02	174	Ruben Sierra	.20	.12
118	Glenn Davis	.05	.02	175	Dan Plesac	.05	.02
119	Jeff Reardon	.08	.05	176	Dan Pasqua	.05	.02
120	Kurt Stillwell	.05	.02	177	Kelly Downs	.05	.02
121	John Smoltz	.30	.18	178	Matt Nokes	.05	.02
122	Dwight Evans	.07	.04	179	Luis Aquino	.05	.02
123	Eric Yelding	.07	.04	180	Frank Tanana	.05	.02
124	John Franco	.05	.02	181	Tony Pena	.05	.02
125	Jose Canseco	.35	.20	182	Dan Gladden	.05	.02
126	Barry Bonds	.50	.30	183	Bruce Hurst	.07	.04
127	Lee Guetterman	.05	.02	184	Roger Clemens	.35	.20
128	Jack Clark	.07	.04	185	Mark McGwire	.30	.18
129	Dave Valle	.05	.02	186	Rob Murphy	.05	.02
130	Hubie Brooks	.07	.04	187	Jim Deshaies	.05	.02
131	Ernest Riles	.05	.02	188	Fred McGriff	.30	.18

#	Name			#	Name		
189	Rob Dibble	.08	.05	246	Garry Templeton	.05	.02
190	Don Mattingly	.20	.12	247	Gene Harris	.05	.02
191	Felix Fermin	.05	.02	248	Kevin Gross	.05	.02
192	Roberto Kelly	.15	.08	249	Brett Butler	.08	.05
193	Dennis Cook	.05	.02	250	Willie Randolph	.05	.02
194	Darren Daulton	.15	.08	251	Roger McDowell	.05	.02
195	Alfredo Griffin	.05	.02	252	Rafael Belliard	.05	.02
196	Eric Plunk	.05	.02	253	Steve Rosenberg	.05	.02
197	Orel Hershiser	.08	.05	254	Jack Howell	.05	.02
198	Paul O'Neil	.08	.05	255	Marvell Wynne	.05	.02
199	Randy Bush	.05	.02	256	Tom Candiotti	.05	.02
200	Checklist	.05	.02	257	Todd Benzinger	.05	.02
201	Ozzie Smith	.12	.07	258	Don Robinson	.05	.02
202	Pete O'Brien	.05	.02	259	Phil Bradley	.05	.02
203	Jay Howell	.05	.02	260	Cecil Espy	.05	.02
204	Mark Gibicza	.07	.04	261	Scott Bankhead	.05	.02
205	Ed Whitson	.05	.02	262	Frank White	.05	.02
206	George Bell	.08	.05	263	Andres Thomas	.05	.02
207	Mike Scott	.05	.02	264	Glenn Braggs	.05	.02
208	Charlie Leibrandt	.05	.02	265	David Cone	.10	.06
209	Mike Heath	.05	.02	266	Bobby Thigpen	.07	.04
210	Dennis Eckersley	.12	.07	267	Nelson Liriano	.05	.02
211	Mike LaValliere	.05	.02	268	Terry Steinbach	.05	.02
212	Darnell Coles	.05	.02	269	Kirby Puckett	.30	.18
213	Lance Parrish	.05	.02	270	Gregg Jefferies	.20	.12
214	Mike Moore	.05	.02	271	Jeff Blauser	.07	.04
215	Steve Finley	.07	.04	272	Cory Snyder	.05	.02
216	Tim Raines	.07	.04	273	Roy Smith	.05	.02
217	Scott Garrelts	.05	.02	274	Tom Foley	.05	.02
218	Kevin McReynolds	.07	.04	275	Mitch Williams	.05	.02
219	Dave Gallagher	.05	.02	276	Paul Kilgus	.05	.02
220	Tim Wallach	.07	.04	277	Don Slaught	.05	.02
221	Chuck Crim	.05	.02	278	Von Hayes	.05	.02
222	Lonnie Smith	.05	.02	279	Vince Coleman	.07	.04
223	Andre Dawson	.15	.08	280	Mike Boddicker	.05	.02
224	Nelson Santovenia	.05	.02	281	Ken Dayley	.05	.02
225	Rafael Palmeiro	.15	.08	282	Mike Devereaux	.08	.05
226	Devon White	.08	.05	283	Kenny Rogers	.05	.02
227	Harold Reynolds	.05	.02	284	Jeff Russell	.05	.02
228	Ellis Burks	.08	.05	285	Jerome Walton	.08	.05
229	Mark Parent	.05	.02	286	Derek Lilliquist	.05	.02
230	Will Clark	.30	.18	287	Joe Orsulak	.05	.02
231	Jimmy Key	.08	.05	288	Dick Schofield	.05	.02
232	John Farrell	.05	.02	289	Ron Darling	.07	.04
233	Eric Davis	.10	.06	290	Bobby Bonilla	.15	.08
234	Johnny Ray	.05	.02	291	Jim Gantner	.05	.02
235	Darryl Strawberry	.25	.15	292	Bobby Witt	.08	.05
236	Bill Doran	.05	.02	293	Greg Brock	.05	.02
237	Greg Gagne	.05	.02	294	Ivan Calderon	.07	.04
238	Jim Eisenreich	.05	.02	295	Steve Bedrosian	.05	.02
239	Tommy Gregg	.05	.02	296	Mike Henneman	.05	.02
240	Marty Barrett	.05	.02	297	Tom Gordon	.07	.04
241	Rafael Ramirez	.05	.02	298	Lou Whitaker	.07	.04
242	Chris Sabo	.10	.06	299	Terry Pendleton	.15	.08
243	Dave Henderson	.05	.02	300	Checklist	.05	.02
244	Andy Van Slyke	.12	.07	301	Juan Berenguer	.05	.02
245	Alvaro Espinoza	.05	.02	302	Mark Davis	.05	.02

303	Nick Esasky	.05	.02
304	Rickey Henderson	.20	.12
305	Rick Cerone	.05	.02
306	Craig Biggio	.10	.06
307	Duane Ward	.05	.02
308	Tom Browning	.07	.04
309	Walt Terrell	.05	.02
310	Greg Swindell	.07	.04
311	Dave Righetti	.05	.02
312	Mike Maddux	.05	.02
313	Lenny Dykstra	.15	.08
314	Jose Gonzalez	.05	.02
315	Steve Balboni	.05	.02
316	Mike Scioscia	.05	.02
317	Ron Oester	.05	.02
318	Gary Wayne	.05	.02
319	Todd Worrell	.08	.05
320	Doug Jones	.05	.02
321	Jeff Hamilton	.05	.02
322	Danny Tartabull	.10	.06
323	Chris James	.05	.02
324	Mike Flanagan	.05	.02
325	Gerald Young	.05	.02
326	Bob Boone	.08	.05
327	Frank Williams	.05	.02
328	Dave Parker	.07	.04
329	Sid Bream	.05	.02
330	Mike Schooler	.05	.02
331	Bert Blyleven	.10	.06
332	Bob Welch	.07	.04
333	Bob Milacki	.05	.02
334	Tim Burke	.05	.02
335	Jose Uribe	.05	.02
336	Randy Myers	.07	.04
337	Eric King	.05	.02
338	Mark Langston	.08	.05
339	Ted Higuera	.05	.02
340	Oddibe McDowell	.05	.02
341	Lloyd McClendon	.05	.02
342	Pasqual Perez	.05	.02
343	Kevin Brown	.12	.07
344	Chuck Finley	.08	.05
345	Erik Hanson	.10	.06
346	Rich Gedman	.05	.02
347	Bip Roberts	.05	.02
348	Matt Williams	.20	.12
349	Tom Henke	.05	.02
350	Brad Komminsk	.05	.02
351	Jeff Reed	.05	.02
352	Brian Downing	.05	.02
353	Frank Viola	.08	.05
354	Terry Puhl	.05	.02
355	Brian Harper	.07	.04
356	Steve Farr	.05	.02
357	Joe Boever	.05	.02
358	Danny Heep	.05	.02
359	Larry Andersen	.05	.02
360	Rolando Roomes	.05	.02
361	Mike Gallego	.05	.02
362	Bob Kipper	.05	.02
363	Clay Parker	.05	.02
364	Mike Pagliarulo	.05	.02
365	Ken Griffey, Jr.	2.00	1.25
366	Rex Hudler	.05	.02
367	Pat Sheridan	.05	.02
368	Kirk Gibson	.07	.04
369	Jeff Parrett	.05	.02
370	Bob Walk	.05	.02
371	Ken Patterson	.05	.02
372	Bryan Harvey	.10	.06
373	Mike Bielecki	.05	.02
374	Tom Magrann (R)	.07	.04
375	Rick Mahler	.05	.02
376	Craig Lefferts	.05	.02
377	Gregg Olson	.08	.05
378	Jamie Moyer	.05	.02
379	Randy Johnson	.12	.07
380	Jeff Montgomery	.05	.02
381	Marty Clary	.05	.02
382	Bill Spiers	.07	.04
383	Dave Magadan	.07	.04
384	Greg Hibbard (R)	.15	.08
385	Ernie Whitt	.05	.02
386	Rick Honeycutt	.05	.02
387	Dave West	.05	.02
388	Keith Hernandez	.07	.04
389	Jose Alvarez	.05	.02
390	Joey Belle (R)	1.50	.90
391	Rick Aguilera	.05	.02
392	Mike Fitzgerald	.05	.02
393	Dwight Smith	.08	.05
394	Steve Wilson	.07	.04
395	Bob Geren	.05	.02
396	Randy Ready	.05	.02
397	Ken Hill	.12	.07
398	Jody Reed	.05	.02
399	Tom Brunansky	.07	.04
400	Checklist	.05	.02
401	Rene Gonzales	.05	.02
402	Harold Baines	.07	.04
403	Cecilio Guante	.05	.02
404	Joe Girardi	.07	.04
405	Sergio Valdez (R)	.10	.06
406	Mark Williamson	.05	.02
407	Glenn Hoffman	.05	.02
408	Jeff Innis (R)	.10	.06
409	Randy Kramer	.05	.02
410	Charlie O'Brien	.07	.04
411	Charlie Hough	.05	.02
412	Gus Polidor	.05	.02
413	Ron Karkovice	.05	.02
414	Trevor Wilson (R)	.12	.07
415	Kevin Ritz (R)	.10	.06
416	Gary Thurman	.05	.02

417	Jeff Robinson	.05	.02
418	Scott Terry	.05	.02
419	Tim Laudner	.05	.02
420	Dennis Rasmussen	.05	.02
421	Luis Rivera	.05	.02
422	Jim Corsi	.05	.02
423	Dennis Lamp	.05	.02
424	Ken Caminiti	.07	.04
425	David Wells	.07	.04
426	Norm Charlton	.07	.04
427	Deion Sanders	.40	.25
428	Dion James	.05	.02
429	Chuck Cary	.05	.02
430	Ken Howell	.05	.02
431	Steve Lake	.05	.02
432	Kal Daniels	.05	.02
433	Lance McCullers	.05	.02
434	Lenny Harris	.05	.02
435	Scott Scudder (R)	.12	.07
436	Gene Larkin	.05	.02
437	Dan Quisenberry	.05	.02
438	Steve Olin (R)	.12	.07
439	Mickey Hatcher	.05	.02
440	Willie Wilson	.05	.02
441	Mark Grant	.05	.02
442	Mookie Wilson	.05	.02
443	Alex Trevino	.05	.02
444	Pat Tabler	.05	.02
445	Dave Bergman	.05	.02
446	Todd Burns	.05	.02
447	R.J. Reynolds	.05	.02
448	Jay Buhner	.08	.05
449	Lee Stevens (R)	.10	.06
450	Ron Hassey	.05	.02
451	Bob Melvin	.05	.02
452	Dave Martinez	.05	.02
453	Greg Litton (R)	.10	.06
454	Mark Carreon	.05	.02
455	Scott Fletcher	.05	.02
456	Otis Nixon	.07	.04
457	Tony Fossas (R)	.10	.06
458	John Russell	.05	.02
459	Paul Assenmacher	.05	.02
460	Zane Smith	.05	.02
461	Jack Daugherty (R)	.12	.07
462	Rich Monteleone (R)	.08	.05
463	Greg Briley (R)	.08	.05
464	Mike Smithson	.05	.02
465	Benito Santiago	.08	.05
466	Jeff Brantley	.07	.04
467	Jose Nunez	.05	.02
468	Scott Bailes	.05	.02
469	Ken Griffey Sr.	.07	.04
470	Bob McClure	.05	.02
471	Mackey Sasser	.05	.02
472	Glenn Wilson	.05	.02
473	Kevin Tapani (R)	.20	.12
474	Bill Buckner	.07	.04
475	Ron Gant	.25	.15
476	Kevin Romine	.05	.02
477	Juan Agosto	.05	.02
478	Herm Winningham	.05	.02
479	Storm Davis	.05	.02
480	Jeff Kling (R)	.10	.06
481	Kevin Mmahat (R)	.10	.06
482	Carmelo Martinez	.05	.02
483	Omar Vizquel	.05	.02
484	Jim Dwyer	.05	.02
485	Bob Knepper	.05	.02
486	Dave Anderson	.05	.02
487	Ron Jones	.05	.02
488	Jay Bell	.08	.05
489	Sammy Sosa (R)	.75	.45
490	Kent Anderson (R)	.08	.05
491	Domingo Ramos	.05	.02
492	Dave Clark	.05	.02
493	Tim Birtsas	.05	.02
494	Ken Oberkfell	.05	.02
495	Larry Sheets	.05	.02
496	Jeff Kunkel	.05	.02
497	Jim Presley	.05	.02
498	Mike Macfarlane	.05	.02
499	Pete Smith	.10	.06
500	Checklist	.05	.02
501	Gary Sheffield	.50	.30
502	Terry Bross (R)	.12	.07
503	Jerry Kutzler (R)	.07	.04
504	Lloyd Moseby	.05	.02
505	Curt Young	.05	.02
506	Al Newman	.05	.02
507	Keith Miller	.05	.02
508	Mike Stanton (R)	.15	.08
509	Rich Yett	.05	.02
510	Tim Drummond (R)	.08	.05
511	Joe Hesketh	.05	.02
512	Rick Wrona	.07	.04
513	Luis Salazar	.05	.02
514	Hal Morris	.15	.08
515	Terry Mulholland	.08	.05
516	John Morris	.05	.02
517	Carlos Quintana	.07	.04
518	Frank DePino	.05	.02
519	Randy Milligan	.07	.04
520	Chad Kreuter	.05	.02
521	Mike Jeffcoat	.05	.02
522	Mike Harkey	.08	.05
523	Andy Nezelek	.05	.02
524	Dave Schmidt	.05	.02
525	Tony Armas	.05	.02
526	Barry Lyons	.05	.02
527	Rick Reed (R)	.10	.06
528	Jerry Reuss	.05	.02
529	Dean Palmer (R)	.75	.45
530	Jeff Peterek (R)	.08	.05

531	Carlos Martinez	.05	.02
532	Atlee Hammaker	.05	.02
533	Mike Brumley	.05	.02
534	Terry Leach	.05	.02
535	Doug Strange (R)	.10	.06
536	Jose DeLeon	.05	.02
537	Shane Rawley	.05	.02
538	Joey Cora	.08	.05
539	Eric Hetzel	.05	.02
540	Gene Nelson	.05	.02
541	Wes Gardner	.05	.02
542	Mark Portugal	.07	.04
543	Al Leiter	.05	.02
544	Jack Armstrong	.07	.04
545	Greg Cadaret	.05	.02
546	Rod Nichols	.05	.02
547	Luis Polonia	.05	.02
548	Charlie Hayes	.12	.07
549	Dickie Thon	.05	.02
550	Tim Crews	.05	.02
551	Dave Winfield	.20	.12
552	Mike Davis	.05	.02
553	Ron Robinson	.05	.02
554	Carmen Castillo	.05	.02
555	John Costello	.05	.02
556	Bud Black	.05	.02
557	Rick Dempsey	.05	.02
558	Jim Acker	.05	.02
559	Eric Show	.05	.02
560	Pat Borders	.05	.02
561	Danny Darwin	.05	.02
562	Rick Luecken (R)	.08	.05
563	Edwin Nunez	.05	.02
564	Felix Jose	.15	.08
565	John Cangelosi	.05	.02
566	Bill Swift	.10	.06
567	Bill Schroeder	.05	.02
568	Stan Javier	.05	.02
569	Jim Traber	.05	.02
570	Wallace Johnson	.05	.02
571	Donell Nixon	.05	.02
572	Sid Fernandez	.05	.02
573	Lance Johnson	.05	.02
574	Andy McGaffigan	.05	.02
575	Mark Knudson	.05	.02
576	Tommy Greene (R)	.70	.40
577	Mark Grace	.15	.08
578	Larry Walker (R)	.80	.50
579	Mike Stanley	.05	.02
580	Mike Witt	.05	.02
581	Scott Bradley	.05	.02
582	Greg Harris	.05	.02
583	Kevin Hickey	.05	.02
584	Lee Mazzilli	.05	.02
585	Jeff Pico	.07	.04
586	Joe Oliver (R)	.15	.08
587	Willie Fraser	.05	.02
588	Yaz Puzzle Card	.07	.04
589	Kevin Bass	.05	.02
590	John Moses	.05	.02
591	Tom Pagnozzi	.08	.05
592	Tony Castillo	.05	.02
593	Jerald Clark	.07	.04
594	Dan Schatzeder	.05	.02
595	Luis Quinones	.05	.02
596	Pete Harnisch	.08	.05
597	Gary Redus	.05	.02
598	Mel Hall	.07	.04
599	Rick Schu	.05	.02
600	Checklist	.05	.02
601	Mike Kingery	.05	.02
602	Terry Kennedy	.05	.02
603	Mike Sharperson	.05	.02
604	Don Carman	.05	.02
605	Jim Gott	.05	.02
606	Donn Pall	.05	.02
607	Rance Mulliniks	.05	.02
608	Curt Wilkerson	.05	.02
609	Mike Felder	.05	.02
610	Guillermo Hernandez	.05	.02
611	Candy Maldonado	.05	.02
612	Mark Thurmond	.05	.02
613	Rick Leach	.05	.02
614	Jerry Reed	.05	.02
615	Franklin Stubbs	.05	.02
616	Billy Hatcher	.05	.02
617	Don August	.05	.02
618	Tim Teufel	.05	.02
619	Shawn Hillegas	.05	.02
620	Manny Lee	.05	.02
621	Gary Ward	.05	.02
622	Mark Guthrie (R)	.10	.06
623	Jeff Musselman	.05	.02
624	Mark Lemke	.08	.05
625	Fernando Valenzuela	.08	.05
626	Paul Sorrento (R)	.20	.12
627	Glenallen Hill	.08	.05
628	Les Lancaster	.05	.02
629	Vance Law	.05	.02
630	Randy Velarde	.07	.04
631	Todd Frohwirth	.05	.02
632	Willie McGee	.08	.05
633	Oil Can Boyd	.05	.02
634	Cris Carpenter	.05	.02
635	Brian Holton	.05	.02
636	Tracy Jones	.05	.02
637	Terry Steinbach(AS)	.07	.04
638	Brady Anderson	.10	.06
639a	Jack Morris (Er)	.20	.12
639b	Jack Morris (Cor)	.12	.07
640	Jaime Navarro (R)	.20	.12
641	Darrin Jackson	.05	.02
642	Mike Dyer (R)	.10	.06
643	Mike Schmidt	.30	.18

644	Henry Cotto	.05	.02
645	John Cerutti	.05	.02
646	Francisco Cabrera (R)	.10	.06
647	Scott Sanderson	.05	.02
648	Brian Meyer	.05	.02
649	Ray Searage	.05	.02
650a	Bo Jackson AS (Er) (Major League Performance)	.30	.18
650b	Bo Jackson AS (Cor) (All-Star Performance)	.20	.12
651	Steve Lyons	.05	.02
652	Mike LaCoss	.05	.02
653	Ted Power	.05	.02
654	Howard Johnson(AS)	.08	.05
655	Mauro Gozzo (R)	.08	.05
656	Mike Blowers (R)	.08	.05
657	Paul Gibson	.05	.02
654	Neal Heaton	.05	.02
659a	Nolan Ryan (5000K) (Er)	3.50	2.25
659b	Nolan Ryan (5000K) (Cor)	.50	.30
660a	Harold Baines(AS)(Er)	2.00	1.25
660b	Harold Baines(AS)(Cor)	.08	.05
661	Gary Pettis	.05	.02
662	Clint Zavaras (R)	.10	.06
663	Rick Reuschel	.05	.02
664	Alejandro Pena	.05	.02
665a	Nolan Ryan (King)(Er) (Wrong Card Number)	2.50	1.50
665b	Nolan Ryan (King)(Er) (No Card Number)	1.00	.70
665c	Nolan Ryan (King)(Cor)	.50	.30
666	Ricky Horton	.05	.02
667	Curt Schilling	.20	.12
668	Bill Landrum	.05	.02
669	Todd Stottlemyre	.07	.04
670	Tim Leary	.05	.02
671	John Wetteland (R)	.20	.12
672	Calvin Schiraldi	.05	.02
673	Ruben Sierra(AS)	.12	.07
674	Pedro Guerrero(AS)	.05	.02
675	Ken Phelps	.05	.02
676	Cal Ripken(AS)	.20	.12
677	Denny Walling	.05	.02
678	Goose Gossage	.07	.04
679	Gary Mielke (R)	.08	.05
680	Bill Bathe	.05	.02
681	Tom Lawless	.05	.02
682	Xavier Hernandez (R)	.10	.06
683	Kirby Puckett(AS)	.15	.08
684	Mariano Duncan	.05	.02
685	Ramon Martinez	.20	.12
686	Tim Jones	.05	.02
687	Tom Filer	.05	.02
688	Steve Lombardozzi	.05	.02
689	Bernie Williams (R)	.25	.15
690	Chip Hale (R)	.10	.06
691	Beau Allred (R)	.12	.07
692	Ryne Sandberg(AS)	.15	.08
693	Jeff Huson (R)	.10	.06
694	Curt Ford	.05	.02
695	Eric Davis(AS)	.08	.05
696	Scott Lusader	.05	.02
697	Mark McGwire(AS)	.15	.08
698	Steve Cummings (R)	.10	.06
699	George Canale (R)	.12	.07
700	Checklist	.05	.02
701	Julio Franco(AS)	.10	.06
702	Dave Johnson (R)	.10	.06
703	Dave Stewart(AS)	.08	.05
704	Dave Justice (R)	1.75	1.00
705	Tony Gwynn(AS)	.12	.07
706	Greg Myers	.05	.02
707	Will Clark(AS)	.15	.08
708	Benito Santiago(AS)	.10	.06
709	Larry McWilliams	.05	.02
710	Ozzie Smith(AS)	.10	.06
711	John Olerud (R)	2.00	1.25
712	Wade Boggs(AS)	.10	.06
713	Gary Eave (R)	.10	.06
714	Bob Tewksbury	.07	.04
715	Kevin Mitchell(AS)	.08	.05
716	A. Bartlett Giamatti	.15	.08
B1	Bo Jackson	.20	.12
B2	Howard Johnson	.08	.05
B3	Dave Stewart	.08	.05
B4	Tony Gwynn	.12	.07
B5	Orel Hershiser	.08	.05
B6	Pedro Guerrero	.07	.04
B7	Tim Raines	.07	.04
B8	Kirby Puckett	.20	.12
B9	Alvin Davis	.05	.02
B10	Ryne Sandberg	.20	.12
B11	Kevin Mitchell	.08	.05
B12	John Smoltz	.20	.12
B13	George Bell	.08	.05
B14	Julio Franco	.07	.04
B15	Paul Molitor	.12	.07
B16	Bobby Bonilla	.08	.05
B17	Mike Greenwell	.07	.04
B18	Cal Ripken	.25	.15
B19	Carlton Fisk	.10	.06
B20	Chili Davis	.07	.04
B21	Glenn Davis	.05	.02
B22	Steve Sax	.07	.04
B23	Eric Davis	.08	.05
B24	Greg Swindell	.07	.04
B25	Von Hayes	.05	.02
B26	Alan Trammell	.10	.06

1990 Donruss Rookies

This 56-card update set features green borders and a small "rookies" logo on the card front to distinguish it from the 1990 Donruss regular issue. Cards measure 2-1/2" by 3-1/2".

		MINT	NR/MT
Complete Set (56)		7.00	4.00
Commons		.05	.02

1	Sandy Alomar	.08	.05
2	John Olerud	1.75	1.00
3	Pat Combs	.10	.06
4	Brian Dubois	.08	.05
5	Felix Jose	.25	.15
6	Delino DeShields	.60	.35
7	Mike Stanton	.12	.07
8	Mike Munoz (R)	.08	.05
9	Craig Grebeck (R))	.15	.08
10	Joe Kraemer (R)	.08	.05
11	Jeff Huson	.08	.05
12	Bill Sampen (R)	.15	.08
13	Brian Bohanon (R)	.10	.06
14	Dave Justice	1.25	.80
15	Robin Ventura	.60	.35
16	Greg Vaughn	.30	.18
17	Wayne Edwards (R)	.10	.06
18	Shawn Boskie (R)	.10	.06
19	Carlos Baerga (R)	1.75	1.00
20	Mark Gardner	.12	.07
21	Kevin Appier (R)	.50	.30
22	Mike Harkey	.10	.06
23	Tim Layana (R)	.10	.06
24	Glenallen Hill	.10	.06
25	Jerry Kutzler	.05	.02
26	Mike Blowers	.08	.05
27	Scott Ruskin (R)	.15	.08
28	Dana Kiecker (R)	.15	.08
29	Willie Blair (R)	.20	.12
30	Ben McDonald	.40	.25
31	Todd Zeile	.20	.12
32	Scott Coolbaugh	.05	.02
33	Xavier Hernandez	.07	.04
34	Mike Harley (R)	.08	.05
35	Kevin Tapani	.20	.12
36	Kevin Wickander	.05	.02
37	Carlos Hernandez (R)	.12	.07
38	Brian Traxler (R)	.10	.06
39	Marty Brown (R)	.07	.04
40	Scott Radinsky	.15	.08
41	Julio Machado	.07	.04
42	Steve Avery	.75	.45
43	Mark Lemke	.08	.05
44	Alan Mills	.10	.06
45	Marquis Grissom	.50	.30
46	Greg Olson (R)	.08	.05
47	Dave Hollins (R)	1.00	.70
48	Jerald Clark	.08	.05
49	Eric Anthony	.35	.20
50	Tim Drummond	.08	.05
51	John Burkett (R)	.50	.30
52	Brent Knackert (R)	.10	.06
53	Jeff Shaw (R)	.08	.05
54	John Orton (R)	.12	.07
55	Terry Shumpert	.12	.07
56	Checklist	.05	.02

1991 Donruss

For the first time Donruss issued their set in two series. Card fronts feature blue borders and the cards measure 2-1/2" by 3-1/2". Key subsets include Diamond Kings (1-26) and Rated Rookies (28-47, 413-432), All-Stars (AS) and MVP's. 22 bonus cards were packed randomly in wax packs. Special limited edition Elite Series cards were also randomly distributed in wax packs as were 5,000 autographed Ryne Sandberg Signature Series cards and 7,500 Nolan Ryan Legend Series cards. Those limited inserts are listed at the end of this checklist but are not included in the complete set price below.

	MINT	NR/MT
Complete Set (792)	16.50	10.50
Commons	.05	.02

		MINT	NR/MT
1	Dave Steib (DK)	.07	.04
2	Craig Biggio (DK)	.07	.04
3	Cecil Fielder (DK)	.10	.06
4	Barry Bonds (DK)	.15	.08
5	Barry Larkin (DK)	.08	.05
6	Dave Parker (DK)	.07	.04
7	Len Dykstra (DK)	.08	.05
8	Bobby Thigpen (DK)	.07	.04
9	Roger Clemens (DK)	.12	.07
10	Ron Gant (DK)	.10	.06
11	Delino DeShields (DK)	.10	.06
12	Roberto Alomar (DK)	.15	.08
13	Sandy Alomar (DK)	.08	.05
14	Ryne Sandberg (DK)	.12	.08
15	Ramon Martinez (DK)	.08	.05
16	Edgar Martinez (DK)	.08	.05
17	Dave Magadan (DK)	.06	.03
18	Matt Williams (DK)	.10	.06
19	Rafael Palmeiro (DK)	.10	.06
20	Bob Welch (DK)	.06	.03
21	Dave Righetti (DK)	.06	.03
22	Brian Harper (DK)	.07	.04
23	Gregg Olson (DK)	.07	.04
24	Kurt Stillwell (DK)	.06	.03
25	Pedro Guerrero (DK)	.07	.04
26	Chuck Finley (DK)	.08	.05
27	Checklist (DK)	.05	.02
28	Tino Martinez (R)	.20	.12
29	Mark Lewis (R)	.12	.07
30	Bernard Gilkey (R)	.20	.12
31	Hensley Meulens (R)	.07	.04
32	Derek Bell (R)	.35	.20
33	Jose Offerman (R)	.20	.12
34	Terry Bross	.08	.05
35	Leo Gomez (R)	.15	.08
36	Derrick May	.25	.15
37	Kevin Morton (R)	.10	.06
38	Moises Alou (R)	.25	.15
39	Julio Valera (R)	.12	.08
40	Milt Cuyler (R)	.15	.08
41	Phil Plantier (R)	.70	.40
42	Scott Chiamparino (R)	.10	.06
43	Ray Lankford (R)	.40	.25
44	Mickey Morandini (R)	.15	.07
45	Dave Hansen (R)	.12	.07
46	Kevin Belcher (R)	.08	.05
47	Darrin Fletcher (R)	.08	.05
48	Steve Sax(AS)	.07	.04
49	Ken Griffey, Jr.(AS)	.25	.15
50	Jose Canseco(AS)	.15	.08
51	Sandy Alomar(AS)	.07	.04
52	Cal Ripken(AS)	.20	.12
53	Rickey Henderson(AS)	.12	.07
54	Bob Welch(AS)	.07	.04
55	Wade Boggs(AS)	.10	.06
56	Mark McGwire(AS)	.15	.00
57	Jack McDowell	.20	.12
58	Jose Lind	.05	.02
59	Alex Fernandez (R)	.50	.30
60	Pat Combs	.08	.05
61	Mike Walker (R)	.08	.05
62	Juan Samuel	.05	.02
63	Mike Blowers	.05	.02
64	Mark Guthrie	.05	.02
65	Mark Salas	.05	.02
66	Tim Jones	.05	.02
67	Tim Leary	.05	.02
68	Andres Galarraga	.12	.07
69	Bob Milacki	.05	.02
70	Tim Belcher	.07	.04
71	Todd Zeile	.10	.06
72	Jerome Walton	.07	.04
73	Kevin Seitzer	.07	.04
74	Jerald Clark	.07	.04
75	John Smoltz	.15	.08
76	Mike Henneman	.05	.02
77	Ken Griffey, Jr.	1.00	.70
78	Jim Abbott	.12	.07
79	Gregg Jefferies	.12	.07
80	Kevin Reimer	.08	.05
81	Roger Clemens	.25	.15
82	Mike Fitzgerald	.05	.02
83	Bruce Hurst	.07	.04
84	Eric Davis	.08	.05
85	Paul Molitor	.15	.08
86	Will Clark	.20	.12
87	Mike Bielecki	.05	.02
88	Bret Saberhagen	.08	.05
89	Nolan Ryan	.60	.35
90	Bobby Thigpen	.07	.04
91	Dickie Thon	.05	.02
92	Duane Ward	.05	.02
93	Luis Polonia	.05	.02
94	Terry Kennedy	.05	.02
95	Kent Hrbek	.07	.04
96	Danny Jackson	.05	.02
97	Sid Fernandez	.07	.04
98	Jimmy Key	.08	.05
99	Franklin Stubbs	.05	.02
100	Checklist	.05	.02
101	R.J. Reynolds	.05	.02
102	Dave Stewart	.08	.05
103	Dan Pasqua	.05	.02
104	Dan Plesac	.05	.02
105	Mark McGwire	.20	.12
106	John Farrell	.05	.02

107	Don Mattingly	.15	.08	164	Melido Perez	.05	.02
108	Carlton Fisk	.10	.06	165	Danny Darwin	.05	.02
109	Ken Oberkfell	.05	.02	166	Roger McDowell	.05	.02
110	Darrell Akerfelds	.05	.02	167	Bill Ripken	.05	.02
111	Gregg Olson	.07	.04	168	Mike Sharperson	.05	.02
112	Mike Scioscia	.05	.02	169	Lee Smith	.08	.05
113	Bryn Smith	.05	.02	170	Matt Nokes	.05	.02
114	Bob Geren	.05	.02	171	Jesse Orosco	.05	.02
115	Tom Candiotti	.05	.02	172	Rick Aguilera	.05	.02
116	Kevin Tapani	.08	.05	173	Jim Presley	.05	.02
117	Jeff Treadway	.05	.02	174	Lou Whitaker	.07	.04
118	Alan Trammell	.08	.05	175	Harold Reynolds	.05	.02
119	Pete O'Brien	.05	.02	176	Brook Jacoby	.05	.02
120	Joel Skinner	.05	.02	177	Wally Backman	.05	.02
121	Mike LaValliere	.05	.02	178	Wade Boggs	.12	.07
122	Dwight Evans	.07	.04	179	Chuck Cary	.05	.02
123	Jody Reed	.05	.02	180	Tom Folen	.05	.02
124	Lee Guetterman	.05	.02	181	Pete Harnisch	.08	.05
125	Tim Burke	.05	.02	182	Mike Morgan	.05	.02
126	Dave Johnson	.05	.02	183	Bob Tewksbury	.05	.02
127	Fernando Valenzuela	.07	.04	184	Joe Girardi	.05	.02
128	Jose DeLeon	.05	.02	185	Storm Davis	.05	.02
129	Andre Dawson	.12	.07	186	Ed Whitson	.05	.02
130	Gerald Perry	.05	.02	187	Steve Avery	.25	.15
131	Greg Harris	.05	.02	188	Lloyd Moseby	.05	.02
132	Tom Glavine	.20	.12	189	Scott Bankhead	.05	.02
133	Lance McCullers	.05	.02	190	Mark Langston	.08	.05
134	Randy Johnson	.15	.08	191	Kevin McReynolds	.07	.04
135	Lance Parrish	.05	.02	192	Julio Franco	.08	.05
136	Mackey Sasser	.05	.02	193	John Dopson	.05	.02
137	Geno Petralli	.05	.02	194	Oil Can Boyd	.05	.02
138	Dennis Lamp	.05	.02	195	Bip Roberts	.05	.02
139	Dennis Martinez	.08	.05	196	Billy Hatcher	.05	.02
140	Mike Pagliarulo	.05	.02	197	Edgar Diaz	.08	.05
141	Hal Morris	.10	.06	198	Greg Litton	.05	.02
142	Dave Parker	.07	.04	199	Mark Grace	.12	.07
143	Brett Butler	.07	.04	200	Checklist	.05	.02
144	Paul Assenmacher	.05	.02	201	George Brett	.15	.08
145	Mark Gubicza	.07	.04	202	Jeff Russell	.05	.02
146	Charlie Hough	.05	.02	203	Ivan Calderson	.07	.04
147	Sammy Sosa	.15	.08	204	Ken Howell	.05	.02
148	Randy Ready	.05	.02	205	Tom Henke	.05	.02
149	Kelly Gruber	.07	.04	206	Bryan Harvey	.10	.06
150	Devon White	.08	.05	207	Steve Bedrosian	.05	.02
151	Gary Carter	.10	.06	208	Al Newman	.05	.02
152	Gene Larkin	.05	.02	209	Randy Myers	.07	.04
153	Chris Sabo	.08	.05	210	Daryl Boston	.05	.02
154	David Cone	.10	.06	211	Manny Lee	.05	.02
155	Todd Stottlemyre	.07	.04	212	Dave Smith	.05	.02
156	Glenn Wilson	.07	.04	213	Don Slaught	.05	.02
157	Bob Walk	.07	.04	214	Walt Weiss	.07	.04
158	Mike Gallego	.05	.02	215	Donn Pall	.05	.02
159	Greg Hibbard	.05	.02	216	Jamie Navarro	.08	.05
160	Chris Bosio	.07	.04	217	Willie Randolph	.05	.02
161	Mike Moore	.05	.02	218	Rudy Seanez (R)	.10	.06
162	Jerry Browne	.05	.02	219	Jim Leyritz (R)	.10	.06
163	Steve Sax	.07	.04	220	Ron Karkovice	.05	.02

221	Ken Caminiti	.07	.04
222	Von Hayes	.05	.02
223	Cal Ripken	.30	.18
224	Lenny Harris	.05	.02
225	Milt Thompson	.05	.02
226	Alvaro Espinoza	.05	.02
227	Chris James	.05	.02
228	Dan Gladden	.05	.02
229	Jeff Blauser	.07	.04
230	Mike Heath	.05	.02
231	Omar Vizquel	.05	.02
232	Doug Jones	.05	.02
233	Jeff King	.07	.04
234	Luis Rivera	.05	.02
235	Ellis Burks	.08	.05
236	Greg Cadaret	.05	.02
237	Dave Martinez	.05	.02
238	Mark Williamson	.05	.02
239	Stan Javier	.05	.02
240	Ozzie Smith	.12	.07
241	Shawn Boskie	.05	.02
242	Tom Gordon	.07	.04
243	Tony Gwynn	.15	.08
244	Tommy Gregg	.05	.02
245	Jeff Robinson	.05	.02
246	Keith Comstock	.05	.02
247	Jack Howell	.05	.02
248	Keith Miller	.05	.02
249	Bobby Witt	.07	.04
250	Rob Murphy	.05	.02
251	Spike Owen	.05	.02
252	Garry Templeton	.05	.02
253	Glenn Braggs	.05	.02
254	Ron Robinson	.05	.02
255	Kevin Mitchell	.08	.05
256	Les Lancaster	.05	.02
257	Mel Stottlemyre (R)	.10	.06
258	Kenny Rogers	.05	.02
259	Lance Johnson	.05	.02
260	John Kruk	.10	.06
261	Fred McGriff	.25	.15
262	Dick Schofield	.05	.02
263	Trevor Wilson	.05	.02
264	David West	.05	.02
265	Scott Scudder	.07	.04
266	Dwight Gooden	.12	.07
267	Willie Blair	.10	.06
268	Mark Portugal	.07	.04
269	Doug Drabek	.10	.06
270	Dennis Eckersley	.12	.07
271	Eric King	.05	.02
272	Robin Yount	.15	.08
273	Carney Lansford	.05	.02
274	Carlos Baerga	.40	.25
275	Dave Righetti	.05	.02
276	Scott Fletcher	.05	.02
277	Eric Yelding	.05	.02
278	Charlie Hayes	.05	.02
279	Jeff Ballard	.05	.02
280	Orel Hershiser	.08	.05
281	Jose Oquendo	.05	.02
282	Mike Witt	.05	.02
283	Mitch Webster	.05	.02
284	Greg Gagne	.05	.02
285	Greg Olson	.07	.04
286	Tony Phillips	.07	.04
287	Scott Bradley	.05	.02
288	Cory Snyder	.05	.02
289	Jay Bell	.07	.04
290	Kevin Romine	.05	.02
291	Jeff Robinson	.05	.02
292	Steve Frey	.07	.04
293	Craig Worthington	.05	.02
294	Tim Crews	.05	.02
295	Joe Magrane	.07	.04
296	Hector Villanueva	.07	.04
297	Terry Shumpert	.07	.04
298	Joe Carter	.20	.12
299	Kent Mercker	.07	.04
300	Checklist	.05	.02
301	Chet Lemon	.05	.02
302	Mike Schooler	.05	.02
303	Dante Bichette	.05	.02
304	Kevin Elster	.05	.02
305	Jeff Huson	.05	.02
306	Greg Harris	.05	.02
307	Marquis Grissom	.20	.12
308	Calvin Schiraldi	.05	.02
309	Mariano Duncan	.05	.02
310	Bill Spiers	.05	.02
311	Scott Garrelts	.05	.02
312	Mitch Williams	.05	.02
313	Mike Macfarlane	.05	.02
314	Kevin Brown	.07	.04
315	Robin Ventura	.20	.12
316	Darren Daulton	.15	.08
317	Pat Borders	.05	.02
318	Mark Eichhorn	.05	.02
319	Jeff Brantley	.05	.02
320	Shane Mack	.08	.05
321	Rob Dibble	.07	.04
322	John Franco	.05	.02
323	Junior Felix	.05	.02
324	Casey Candaele	.05	.02
325	Bobby Bonilla	.12	.07
326	Dave Henderson	.05	.02
327	Wayne Edwards	.05	.02
328	Mark Knudson	.05	.02
329	Terry Steinbach	.05	.02
330	Colby Ward (R)	.08	.05
331	Oscar Azocar (R)	.10	.06
332	Scott Radinsky	.07	.04
333	Eric Anthony	.12	.07
334	Steve Lake	.05	.02

335 Bob Melvin	.05	.02
336 Kal Daniels	.05	.02
337 Tom Pagnozzi	.07	.04
338 Alan Mills	.05	.02
339 Steve Olin	.05	.02
340 Juan Berenguer	.05	.02
341 Francisco Cabrera	.07	.04
342 Dave Bergman	.05	.02
343 Henry Cotto	.05	.02
344 Sergio Valdez	.05	.02
345 Bob Patterson	.05	.02
346 John Marzano	.05	.02
347 Dana Kiecker	.07	.04
348 Dion James	.05	.02
349 Hubie Brooks	.05	.02
350 Bill Landrum	.05	.02
351 Bill Sampen	.05	.02
352 Greg Briley	.05	.02
353 Paul Gibson	.05	.02
354 Dave Eiland	.05	.02
355 Steve Finley	.07	.04
356 Bob Boone	.08	.05
357 Steve Buechele	.05	.02
358 Chris Hoiles (R)	.20	.12
359 Larry Walker	.60	.35
360 Frank DiPino	.05	.02
361 Mark Grant	.05	.02
362 Dave Magadan	.05	.02
363 Robby Thompson	.07	.04
364 Lonnie Smith	.05	.02
365 Steve Farr	.05	.02
366 Dave Valle	.05	.02
367 Tim Naehring (R)	.20	.12
368 Jim Acker	.05	.02
369 Jeff Reardon	.08	.05
370 Tim Teufel	.05	.02
371 Juan Gonzalez	.75	.45
372 Luis Salazar	.05	.02
373 Rick Honeycutt	.05	.02
374 Greg Maddux	.15	.08
375 Jose Uribe	.05	.02
376 Donnie Hill	.05	.02
377 Don Carman	.05	.02
378 Craig Grebeck	.07	.04
379 Willie Fraser	.05	.02
380 Glenallen Hill	.08	.05
381 Joe Oliver	.05	.02
382 Randy Bush	.05	.02
383 Alex Cole	.10	.06
384 Norm Charlton	.05	.02
385 Gene Nelson	.05	.02
386 Checklist	.05	.02
387 Rickey Henderson (MVP)	.10	.06
388 Lance Parrish(MVP)	.05	.02
389 Fred McGriff(MVP)	.15	.08
390 Dave Parker(MVP)	.07	.04
391 Candy Maldonado (MVP)	.07	.04
392 Ken Griffey, Jr (MVP)	.50	.30
393 Gregg Olson(MVP)	.07	.04
394 Rafael Palmeiro(MVP)	.08	.05
395 Roger Clemens(MVP)	.12	.07
396 George Brett(MVP)	.12	.07
397 Cecil Fielder(MVP)	.12	.07
398 Brian Harper(MVP)	.05	.02
399 Bobby Thigpen(MVP)	.05	.02
400 Roberto Kelly (MVP)	.08	.05
401 Danny Darwin(MVP)	.05	.02
402 Dave Justice(MVP)	.15	.08
403 Lee Smith(MVP)	.08	.05
404 Ryne Sanberg(MVP)	.12	.07
405 Eddie Murray(MVP)	.10	.06
406 Tim Wallach(MVP)	.07	.04
407 Kevin Mitchell(MVP)	.07	.04
408 Darryl Strawberry (MVP)	.10	.06
409 Joe Carter(MVP)	.12	.07
410 Len Dykstra(MVP)	.10	.06
411 Doug Drabek(MVP)	.08	.05
412 Chris Sabo(MVP)	.07	.04
413 Paul Marak (R)	.10	.06
414 Tim McIntosh (R)	.12	.07
415 Brian Barnes (R)	.15	.08
416 Eric Gunderson (R)	.08	.05
417 Mike Gardiner (R)	.12	.07
418 Steve Carter (R)	.08	.05
419 Gerald Alexander (R)	.08	.05
420 Rich Garces (R)	.12	.07
421 Chuck Knoblauch (R)	.30	.18
422 Scott Aldred (R)	.10	.06
423 Wes Chamberlain (R)	.20	.12
424 Lance Dickson (R)	.15	.08
425 Greg Colbrunn (R)	.20	.12
426 Rich Delucia (R)	.12	.07
427 Jeff Conine (R)	.40	.25
428 Steve Decker (R)	.10	.06
429 Turner Ward (R)	.12	.07
430 Mo Vaughn (R)	.40	.25
431 Steve Chitren (R)	.10	.06
432 Mike Benjamin (R)	.10	.06
433 Ryne Sandberg (AS)	.12	.07
434 Len Dykstra (AS)	.08	.05
435 Andre Dawson (AS)	.10	.06
436 Mike Scioscia (AS)	.05	.02
437 Ozzie Smith (AS)	.10	.06
438 Kevin Mitchell (AS)	.08	.05
439 Jack Armstrong (AS)	.05	.02
440 Chris Sabo (AS	.07	.04
441 Will Clark (AS)	.12	.07
442 Mel Hall	.07	.04
443 Mark Gardner	.05	.02
444 Mike Devereaux	.07	.04
445 Kirk Gibson	.07	.04

446	Terry Pendleton	.12	.07	503	Omar Olivares (R)	.15	.08
447	Mike Harkey	.07	.04	504	Ryne Sandberg	.20	.12
448	Jim Eisenreich	.05	.02	505	Jeff Montgomery	.05	.02
449	Benito Santiago	.08	.05	506	Mark Parent	.05	.02
450	Oddibe McDowell	.05	.02	507	Ron Gant	.15	.08
451	Cecil Fielder	.15	.08	508	Frank Tanana	.05	.02
452	Ken Griffey, Sr.	.07	.04	509	Jay Buhner	.07	.04
453	Bert Blyleven	.08	.05	510	Max Venable	.05	.02
454	Howard Johnson	.07	.04	511	Wally Whitehurst	.05	.02
455	Monty Farris	.12	.07	512	Gary Pettis	.05	.02
456	Tony Pena	.05	.02	513	Tom Brunansky	.07	.04
457	Tim Raines	.07	.04	514	Tim Wallach	.07	.04
458	Dennis Rasmussen	.05	.02	515	Craig Lefferts	.05	.02
459	Luis Quinones	.05	.02	516	Tim Layana	.05	.02
460	B.J. Surhoff	.05	.02	517	Darryl Hamilton	.08	.05
461	Ernest Riles	.05	.02	518	Rick Reuschel	.05	.02
462	Rick Sutcliffe	.07	.04	519	Steve Wilson	.05	.02
463	Danny Tartabull	.10	.06	520	Kurt Stillwell	.05	.02
464	Pete Incaviglia	.05	.02	521	Rafael Palmeiro	.15	.08
465	Carlos Martinez	.05	.02	522	Ken Patterson	.05	.02
466	Ricky Jordan	.07	.04	523	Len Dykstra	.15	.08
467	John Cerutti	.05	.02	524	Tony Fernandez	.05	.02
468	Dave Winfield	.15	.08	525	Kent Anderson	.05	.02
469	Francisco Oliveras	.05	.02	526	Mark Leonard (R)	.10	.06
470	Roy Smith	.05	.02	527	Allan Anderson	.05	.02
471	Barry Larkin	.08	.05	528	Tom Browning	.07	.04
472	Ron Darling	.05	.02	529	Frank Viola	.08	.05
473	David Wells	.05	.02	530	John Olerud	.50	.30
474	Glenn Davis	.05	.02	531	Juan Agosto	.05	.02
475	Neal Heaton	.05	.02	532	Zane Smith	.05	.02
476	Ron Hassey	.05	.02	533	Scott Sanderson	.05	.02
477	Frank Thomas (R)	1.75	1.00	534	Barry Jones	.05	.02
478	Greg Vaughn	.12	.07	535	Mike Felder	.05	.02
479	Todd Burns	.05	.02	536	Jose Canseco	.25	.15
480	Candy Maldonado	.05	.02	537	Felix Fermin	.05	.02
481	Dave LaPoint	.05	.02	538	Roberto Kelly	.10	.06
482	Alvin Davis	.05	.02	539	Brian Holman	.05	.02
483	Mike Scott	.05	.02	540	Mark Davidson	.05	.02
484	Dale Murphy	.10	.06	541	Terry Mulholland	.07	.04
485	Ben McDonald	.12	.07	542	Randy Milligan	.07	.04
486	Jay Howell	.05	.02	543	Jose Gonzalez	.05	.02
487	Vince Coleman	.07	.04	544	Craig Wilson(FC)	.10	.06
488	Alfredo Griffin	.05	.02	545	Mike Hartley	.05	.02
489	Sandy Alomar	.08	.05	546	Greg Swindell	.07	.04
490	Kirby Puckett	.25	.15	547	Gary Gaetti	.05	.02
491	Andres Thomas	.05	.02	548	Dave Justice	.30	.18
492	Jack Morris	.10	.06	549	Steve Searcy	.05	.02
493	Matt Young	.05	.02	550	Erik Hanson	.07	.04
494	Greg Myers	.05	.02	551	Dave Stieb	.07	.04
495	Barry Bonds	.30	.18	552	Andy Van Slyke	.10	.06
496	Scott Cooper (R)	.20	.12	553	Mike Greenwell	.08	.05
497	Dan Schatzeder	.05	.02	554	Kevin Maas	.12	.07
498	Jesse Barfield	.07	.04	555	Delino Deshields	.20	.12
499	Jerry Goff	.07	.04	556	Curt Schilling	.12	.07
500	Checklist	.05	.02	557	Ramon Martinez	.12	.07
501	Anthony Telford (R)	.15	.08	558	Pedro Guerrero	.05	.02
502	Eddie Murray	.12	.07	559	Dwight Smith	.07	.04

560 Mark Davis	.05	.02
561 Shawn Abner	.05	.02
562 Charlie Leibrandt	.05	.02
563 John Shelby	.05	.02
564 Bill Swift	.10	.06
565 Mike Fetters	.05	.02
566 Alejandro Pena	.05	.02
567 Ruben Sierra	.15	.08
568 Carlos Quintana	.07	.04
569 Kevin Gross	.05	.02
570 Derek Lilliquist	.05	.02
571 Jack Armstrong	.05	.02
572 Greg Brock	.05	.02
573 Mike Kingery	.05	.02
574 Greg Smith	.10	.06
575 Brian McRae(FC)	.25	.15
576 Jack Daugherty	.05	.02
577 Ozzie Guillen	.05	.02
578 Joe Boever	.05	.02
579 Luis Sojo	.07	.04
580 Chili Davis	.07	.04
581 Don Robinson	.05	.02
582 Brian Harper	.05	.02
583 Paul O'Neill	.08	.05
584 Bob Ojeda	.05	.02
585 Mookie Wilson	.05	.02
586 Rafael Ramirez	.05	.02
587 Gary Redus	.05	.02
588 Jamie Quirk	.05	.02
589 Shawn Hilligas	.05	.02
590 Tom Edens (R)	.08	.05
591 Joe Klink	.07	.04
592 Charles Nagy (R)	.35	.20
593 Eric Plunk	.05	.02
594 Tracy Jones	.05	.02
595 Craig Biggio	.08	.05
596 Jose DeJesus	.05	.02
597 Mickey Tettleton	.07	.04
598 Chris Gwynn	.05	.02
599 Rex Hudler	.05	.02
600 Checklist	.05	.02
601 Jim Gott	.05	.02
602 Jeff Manto	.10	.06
603 Nelson Liriano	.05	.02
604 Mark Lemke	.07	.04
605 Clay Parker	.05	.02
606 Edgar Martinez	.12	.07
607 Mark Whiten (R)	.40	.25
608 Ted Power	.05	.02
609 Tom Bolton	.05	.02
610 Tom Herr	.05	.02
611 Andy Hawkins	.05	.02
612 Scott Ruskin	.05	.02
613 Ron Kittle	.05	.02
614 John Wetteland	.10	.06
615 Mike Perez (R)	.12	.07
616 Dave Clark	.05	.02

617 Brent Mayne	:10	.06
618 Jack Clark	.07	.04
619 Marvin Freeman	.05	.02
620 Edwin Nunez	.05	.02
621 Russ Swan	.08	.05
622 Johnny Ray	.05	:02
623 Charlie O'Brien	.05	.02
624 Joe Bitker	.08	.05
625 Mike Marshall	.05	.02
626 Otis Nixon	.05	.02
627 Andy Benes	.12	.07
628 Ron Oester	.05	.02
629 Ted Higuera	.05	.02
631 Damon Berryhill	.05	.02
632 Bo Jackson	.20	.12
633 Brad Arnsberg	.05	.02
634 Jerry Willard	.05	.02
635 Tommy Greene	.15	.08
636 Bob MacDonald (R)	.10	.06
637 Kirk McCaskill	.05	.02
638 John Burkett	.07	.04
639 Paul Abbott (R)	.10	.06
640 Todd Benzinger	.05	.02
641 Todd Hundley	.08	.05
642 George Bell	.08	.05
643 Javier Ortiz (R)	.10	.06
644 Sid Bream	.05	.02
645 Bob Welch	.05	.02
646 Phil Bradley	.05	.02
647 Bill Krueger	.05	.02
648 Rickey Henderson	.15	.08
649 Kevin Wickander	.05	.02
650 Steve Balboni	.05	.02
651 Gene Harris	.05	.02
652 Jim Deshaies	.05	.02
653 Jason Grimsley (R)	.12	.07
654 Joe Orsulak	.05	.02
655 Jimmy Poole	.08	.05
656 Felix Jose	.10	.06
657 Dennis Cook	.05	.02
658 Tom Brookens	.05	.02
659 Junior Ortiz	.05	.02
660 Jeff Parrett	.05	.02
661 Jerry Don Gleaton	.05	.02
662 Brent Knackert	.07	.04
663 Rance Mulliniks	.05	.02
664 John Smiley	.08	.05
665 Larry Andersen	.05	.02
666 Willie McGee	.08	.05
667 Chris Nabholz (R)	.20	.12
668 Brady Anderson	.10	.06
669 Darren Holmes (R)	.10	.06
670 Ken Hill	.10	.06
671 Gary Varsho	.05	.02
672 Bill Pecota	.05	.02
673 Fred Lynn	.07	.04
674 Kevin Brown	.10	.06

675	Dan Petry	.05	.02	732	Vicente Palacios	.05	.02
676	Mike Jackson	.05	.02	733	Sam Horn	.05	.02
677	Wally Joyner	.08	.05	734	Howard Farmer	.08	.05
678	Danny Jackson	.05	.02	735	Ken Dayley	.05	.02
679	Bill Haselman	.10	.06	736	Kelly Mann	.05	.02
680	Mike Boddicker	.05	.02	737	Joe Grahe (R)	.15	.08
681	Mel Rojas (R)	.13	.08	738	Kelly Downs	.05	.02
682	Roberto Alomar	.35	.20	739	Jimmy Kremers (R)	.08	.05
683	Dave Justice(R.O.Y.)	.15	.08	740	Kevin Appier	.08	.05
684	Chuck Crim	.05	.02	741	Jeff Reed	.05	.02
685	Matt Williams	.12	.07	742	Jose Rijo (WS)	.07	.04
686	Shawon Dunston	.08	.05	743	Dave Rohde	.08	.05
687	Jeff Schulz (R)	.10	.06	744	Dr. Dirt/Mr. Clean	.08	.05
688	John Barfield	.10	.06		(L.Dykstra/D. Murphy)		
689	Gerald Young	.05	.02	745	Paul Sorrento	.08	.05
690	Luis Gonzalez (R)	.20	.12	746	Thomas Howard	.12	.07
691	Frank Wills	.07	.04	747	Matt Stark (R)	.10	.06
692	Chuck Finley	.08	.05	748	Harold Baines	.07	.04
693	Sandy Alomar(R.O.Y.)	.07	.04	749	Doug Dascenzo	.05	.02
694	Tim Drummond	.05	.02	750	Doug Drabek (Cy)	.08	.05
695	Herm Winningham	.05	.02	751	Gary Sheffield	.30	.18
696	Darryl Strawberry	.15	.08	752	Terry Lee	.08	.05
697	Al Leiter	.05	.02	753	Jim Vatcher	.08	.05
698	Karl Rhodes	.12	.07	754	Lee Stevens	.07	.04
699	Stan Belinda	.10	.06	755	Randy Veres	.07	.04
700	Checklist	.05	.02	756	Bill Doran	.05	.02
701	Lance Blankenship	.05	.02	757	Gary Wayne	.05	.02
702	Puzzle Card (Stargell)	.08	.05	758	Pedro Munoz (R)	.20	.12
703	Jim Gantner	.05	.02	759	Chris Hammond (R)	.15	.08
704	Reggie Harris (R)	.12	.07	760	Checklist	.05	.02
705	Rob Ducey	.07	.04	761	Rickey Henderson	.12	.07
706	Tim Hulett	.07	.04		(MVP)		
707	Atlee Hammaker	.05	.02	762	Barry Bonds (MVP)	.15	.08
708	Xavier Hernandez	.07	.04	763	Billy Hatcher (WS)	.05	.02
709	Chuck McElroy	.08	.05	764	Julio Machado	.05	.02
710	John Mitchell	.05	.02	765	Jose Mesa	.05	.02
711	Carlos Hernandez	.05	.02	766	Willie Randolph (WS)	.05	.02
712	Geronimo Pena	.08	.05	767	Scott Erickson (R)	.25	.15
713	Jim Neidlinger (R)	.10	.06	768	Travis Fryman (R)	.70	.40
714	John Orton	.08	.05	769	Rich Rodriguez (R)	.12	.07
715	Terry Leach	.05	.02	770	Checklist	.05	.02
716	Mike Stanton	.05	.02	B1	Langston/Witt (No-Hit)	.05	.02
717	Walt Terrel	.05	.02	B2	Randy Johnson	.15	.08
718	Luis Aquino	.05	.02		(No-Hit)		
719	Bud Black	.05	.02	B3	Nolan Ryan (No-Hit)	.50	.30
720	Bob Kipper	.05	.02	B4	Dave Stewart (No-Hit)	.07	.04
721	Jeff Gray	.08	.05	B5	Cecil Fielder (50 Hr)	.12	.07
722	Jose Rijo	.08	.05	B6	Carlton Fisk (RB)	.10	.06
723	Curt Young	.05	.02	B7	Ryne Sandberg (RB)	.15	.08
724	Jose Vizcaino	.08	.05	B8	Gary Carter (RB)	.08	.05
725	Randy Tomlin (R)	.15	.08	B9	Mark McGwire (RB)	.12	.07
726	Junior Noboa	.05	.02	B10	Bo Jackson (4 straight	.15	.08
727	Bob Welch (CY)	.07	.04		home runs)		
728	Gary Ward	.05	.02	B11	Fernando Valenzuela	.08	.05
729	Rob Deer	.07	.04		(No-Hit)		
730	David Segui	.08	.05	B12	Andy Hawkins (No-Hit)	.05	.02
731	Mark Carreon	.05	.02	B13	Melido Perez (No-Hit)	.05	.02

		MINT	NR/MT
B14	Terry Mulholland (No-Hit)	.05	.02
B15	Nolan Ryan (300th)	.50	.30
B16	Delino DeShields (4 hits in debut)	.12	.07
B17	Cal Ripken (Errorless)	.25	.15
B18	Eddie Murray (RB)	.10	.06
B19	George Brett (RB)	.12	.07
B20	Bobby Thigpen (RB)	.07	.04
B21	Dave Stieb (No-Hit)	.07	.04
B22	Willie McGee (AW)	.08	.05
E1	Barry Bonds (Elite)	175.00	100.00
E2	George Brett (Elite)	110.00	70.00
E3	Jose Canseco (Elite)	85.00	50.00
E4	Andre Dawson (Elite)	75.00	45.00
E5	Doug Drabek (Elite)	45.00	28.00
E6	Cecil Fielder (Elite)	80.00	48.00
E7	Rickey Henderson (Elite)	80.00	48.00
E8	Matt Williams (Elite)	70.00	40.00
L1	Nolan Ryan (Legends)	375.00	220.00
S1	Ryne Sandberg (Signature)	450.00	325.00

1991 Donruss Rookies

This 56-card rookie update set features red borders with white frame lines around the photos. Card fronts feature a "rookies" logo in the lower corner. Cards measure 2-1/2" by 3-1/2".

	MINT	NR/MT
Complete Set (56)	5.00	3.00
Commons	.05	.02

		MINT	NR/MT
1	Pat Kelly (R)	.25	.15
2	Rich DeLucia	.08	.05
3	Wes Chamberlain	.20	.12
4	Scott Leius (R)	.15	.08
5	Darryl Kile (R)	.30	.18
6	Milt Cuyler	.08	.05
7	Todd Van Poppel (R)	.70	.40
8	Ray Lankford	.25	.15
9	Brian Hunter (R)	.20	.12
10	Tony Perezchica	.05	.02
11	Ced Landrum (R)	.10	.06
12	Dave Burba (R)	.10	.06
13	Ramon Garcia (R)	.08	.05
14	Ed Sprague (R)	.15	.08
15	Warren Newson (R)	.10	.06
16	Paul Faries (R)	.05	.02
17	Luis Gonzalez	.20	.12
18	Charles Nagy	.25	.15
19	Chris Hammond	.10	.06
20	Frank Castillo (R)	.12	.07
21	Pedro Munoz	.20	.12
22	Orlando Merced (R)	.25	.15
23	Jose Melendez (R)	.10	.06
24	Kirk Dressendorfer(R)	.12	.07
25	Heathcliff Slocumb (R)	.10	.06
26	Doug Simons (R)	.10	.06
27	Mike Timlin (R)	.10	.06
28	Jeff Fassero (R)	.20	.12
29	Mark Leiter (R)	.10	.06
30	Jeff Bagwell (R)	1.25	.80
31	Brian McRae	.25	.15
32	Mark Whiten	.25	.15
33	Ivan Rodriguez (R)	.90	.60
34	Wade Taylor (R)	.12	.07
35	Darren Lewis (R)	.15	.08
36	Mo Vaughn	.40	.25
37	Mike Remlinger (R)	.08	.05
38	Rick Wilkins (R)	.40	.25
39	Chuck Knoblauch	.15	.08
40	Kevin Morton	.08	.05
41	Carlos Rodriguez (R)	.10	.06
42	Mark Lewis	.10	.06
43	Brent Mayne	.08	.05
44	Chris Haney (R)	.12	.07
45	Denis Boucher (R)	.10	.06
46	Mike Gardiner	.10	.06
47	Jeff Johnson (R)	.10	.06
48	Dean Palmer	.35	.20
49	Chuck McElroy	.08	.05
50	Chris Jones (R)	.10	.06
51	Scott Kamieniecki (R)	.12	.07
52	Al Osuna (R)	.10	.06
53	Rusty Meacham (R)	.10	.06
54	Chito Martinez (R)	.15	.08
55	Reggie Jefferson (R)	.15	.08
56	Checklist	.05	.02

1992 Donruss

The 1992 Donruss set was issued in two series and included a new anti-counterfeit device on the card backs. The card fronts feature glossy white borders with two shades of blue stripes above and below the player photos. Key subsets include Rated Rookies (1-20, 397-421), All-Stars (AS) and Highlights (HL). Donruss dropped Diamond Kings from the regular edition and randomly inserted them in foil packs. Once again, the company produced a limited Elite Series along with 8 bonus insert cards. 5,000 autographed Cal Ripken cards make up the Signature Series and Rickey Henderson is featured in the 7,500 card Legend Series. All insert cards are listed at the end of this checklist but are not included in the complete set price below. All cards measure 2-1/2" by 3-1/2".

		MINT	NR/MT
Complete Set (784)		17.00	11.00
Commons		.05	.02

1	Mark Wohlers (R)	.15	.08
2	Will Cordero (R)	.20	.12
3	Kyle Abbott (R)	.15	.08
4	Dave Nilsson (R)	.20	.12
5	Kenny Lofton (R)	.50	.30
6	Luis Mercedes (R)	.15	.08
7	Roger Salkeld (R)	.20	.12
8	Eddie Zosky (R)	.12	.08
9	Todd Van Poppel (R)	.30	.18
10	Frank Seminara (R)	.12	.07
11	Andy Ashby (R)	.12	.07
12	Reggie Jefferson (R)	.15	.08
13	Ryan Klesko (R)	.50	.30
14	Carlos Garcia (R)	.20	.12
15	John Ramos (R)	.15	.08
16	Eric Karros (R)	.50	.30
17	Pat Lennon (R)	.25	.15
18	Eddie Taubensee (R)	.12	.07
19	Roberto Hernandez	.12	.07
20	D.J. Dozier (R)	.10	.06
21	Dave Henderson(AS)	.05	.02
22	Cal Ripken(AS)	.20	.12
23	Wade Boggs(AS)	.10	.06
24	Ken Griffey, Jr.(AS)	.05	.02
25	Jack Morris(AS)	.08	.05
26	Danny Tartabull(AS)	.08	.05
27	Cecil Fielder(AS)	.10	.06
28	Roberto Alomar(AS)	.15	.08
29	Sandy Alomar(AS)	.07	.04
30	Rickey Henderson(AS)	.10	.06
31	Ken Hill	.08	.05
32	John Habyan	.05	.02
33	Otis Nixon (HL)	.05	.02
34	Tim Wallach	.07	.04
35	Cal Ripken	.30	.18
36	Gary Carter	.10	.06
37	Juan Agosto	.05	.02
38	Doug Dascenzo	.05	.02
39	Kirk Gibson	.07	.04
40	Benito Santiago	.08	.05
41	Otis Nixon	.05	.02
42	Andy Allanson	.05	.02
43	Brian Holman	.05	.02
44	Dick Schofield	.05	.02
45	Dave Magadan	.05	.02
46	Rafael Palmeiro	.15	.08
47	Jody Reed	.05	.02
48	Ivan Calderon	.07	.04
49	Greg Harris	.05	.02
50	Chris Sabo	.07	.04
51	Paul Molitor	.15	.08
52	Robby Thompson	.07	.04
53	Dave Smith	.05	.02
54	Mark Davis	.05	.02
55	Kevin Brown	.08	.05
56	Donn Pall	.05	.02
57	Lenny Dykstra	.15	.08
58	Roberto Alomar	.25	.15
59	Jeff Robinson	.05	.02
60	Willie McGee	.08	.05
61	Jay Buhner	.07	.04
62	Mike Pagliarulo	.05	.02
63	Paul O'Neill	.08	.05
64	Hubie Brooks	.07	.04
65	Kelly Gruber	.07	.04
66	Ken Caminiti	.07	.04
67	Gary Redus	.05	.02
68	Harold Baines	.07	.04
69	Charlie Hough	.05	.02
70	B.J. Surhoff	.05	.02
71	Walt Weiss	.07	.04
72	Shawn Hillegas	.05	.02
73	Roberto Kelly	.10	.06
74	Jeff Ballard	.05	.02

#	Player			#	Player		
75	Craig Biggio	.07	.04	132	Todd Zeile	.08	.05
76	Pat Combs	.05	.02	133	Dave Winfield	.20	.12
77	Jeff Robinson	.05	.02	134	Wally Whitehurst	.05	.02
78	Tim Belcher	.07	.04	135	Matt Williams	.12	.07
79	Cris Carpenter	.05	.02	136	Tom Browning	.07	.04
80	Checklist	.05	.02	137	Marquis Grissom	.15	.08
81	Steve Avery	.20	.12	138	Erik Hanson	.07	.04
82	Chris James	.05	.02	139	Rob Dibble	.07	.04
83	Brian Harper	.05	.02	140	Don August	.05	.02
84	Charlie Leibrandt	.05	.02	141	Tom Henke	.05	.02
85	Mickey Tettleton	.07	.04	142	Dan Pasqua	.05	.02
86	Pete O'Brien	.05	.02	143	George Brett	.25	.15
87	Danny Darwin	.05	.02	144	Jerald Clark	.07	.04
88	Bob Walk	.05	.02	145	Robin Ventura	.15	.08
89	Jeff Reardon	.08	.05	146	Dale Murphy	.08	.05
90	Bobby Rose	.08	.05	147	Dennis Eckersley	.10	.06
91	Danny Jackson	.05	.02	148	Eric Yelding	.05	.02
92	John Morris	.05	.02	149	Mario Diaz	.05	.02
93	Bud Black	.05	.02	150	Casey Candaele	.05	.02
94	Tommy Greene (HL)	.08	.05	151	Steve Olin	.05	.02
95	Rick Aguilera	.05	.02	152	Luis Salazar	.05	.02
96	Gary Gaetti	.05	.02	153	Kevin Maas	.08	.05
97	David Cone	.10	.06	154	Nolan Ryan (HL)	.30	.18
98	John Olerud	.40	.25	155	Barry Jones	.05	.02
99	Joel Skinner	.05	.02	156	Chris Hoiles	.10	.06
100	Jay Bell	.07	.04	157	Bobby Ojeda	.05	.02
101	Bob Milacki	.05	.02	158	Pedro Guerrero	.05	.02
102	Norm Charlton	.05	.02	159	Paul Assenmacher	.05	.02
103	Chuck Crim	.05	.02	160	Checklist	.05	.02
104	Terry Steinbach	.05	.02	161	Mike Macfarlane	.05	.02
105	Juan Samuel	.05	.02	162	Craig Lefferts	.05	.02
106	Steve Howe	.05	.02	163	Brian Hunter	.08	.05
107	Rafael Belliard	.05	.02	164	Alan Trammell	.10	.06
108	Joey Cora	.05	.02	165	Ken Griffey, Jr.	1.25	.80
109	Tommy Greene	.10	.06	166	Lance Parrish	.05	.02
110	Gregg Olson	.08	.05	167	Brian Downing	.05	.02
111	Frank Tanana	.05	.02	168	John Barfield	.05	.02
112	Lee Smith	.10	.06	169	Jack Clark	.05	.02
113	Greg Harris	.05	.02	170	Chris Nabholz	.08	.05
114	Dwayne Henry	.05	.02	171	Tim Teufel	.05	.02
115	Chili Davis	.07	.04	172	Chris Hammond	.05	.02
116	Kent Mercker	.05	.02	173	Robin Yount	.20	.12
117	Brian Barnes	.05	.02	174	Dave Righetti	.05	.02
118	Rich DeLucia	.05	.02	175	Joe Girardi	.05	.02
119	Andre Dawson	.10	.06	176	Mike Boddicker	.05	.02
120	Carlos Baerga	.25	.15	177	Dean Palmer	.20	.12
121	Mike La Valliere	.05	.02	178	Greg Hibbard	.05	.02
122	Jeff Gray	.05	.02	179	Randy Ready	.05	.02
123	Bruce Hurst	.07	.04	180	Devon White	.07	.04
124	Alvin Davis	.05	.02	181	Mark Eichhorn	.05	.02
125	John Candelaria	.05	.02	182	Mike Felder	.05	.02
126	Matt Nokes	.05	.02	183	Joe Klink	.05	.02
127	George Bell	.10	.06	184	Steve Bedrosian	.05	.02
128	Bret Saberhagen	.08	.05	185	Barry Larkin	.10	.06
129	Jeff Russell	.05	.02	186	John Franco	.05	.02
130	Jim Abbott	.12	.07	187	Ed Sprague	.07	.04
131	Bill Gullickson	.05	.02	188	Mark Portugal	.07	.04

189	Jose Lind	.05	.02
190	Bob Welch	.07	.04
191	Alex Fernandez	.20	.12
192	Gary Sheffield	.25	.15
193	Rickey Henderson	.15	.08
194	Rod Nichols	.05	.02
195	Scott Kamieniecki	.08	.05
196	Mike Flanagan	.05	.02
197	Steve Finley	.05	.02
198	Darren Daulton	.12	.07
199	Leo Gomez	.10	.06
202	Mike Morgan	.05	.02
201	Bob Tewksbury	.05	.02
202	Sid Bream	.05	.02
203	Sandy Alomar	.08	.05
204	Greg Gagne	.05	.02
205	Juan Berenguer	.05	.02
206	Cecil Fielder	.15	.08
207	Randy Johnson	.20	.12
208	Tony Pena	.05	.02
209	Doug Drabek	.08	.05
210	Wade Boggs	.15	.08
211	Bryan Harvey	.08	.05
212	Jose Vizcaino	.05	.02
213	Alonzo Powell (R)	.10	.06
214	Will Clark	.20	.12
215	Rickey Henderson (HL)	.10	.06
216	Jack Morris	.10	.06
217	Junior Felix	.05	.02
218	Vince Coleman	.07	.04
219	Jimmy Key	.08	.05
220	Alex Cole	.05	.02
221	Bill Landrum	.05	.02
222	Randy Milligan	.05	.02
223	Jose Rijo	.07	.04
224	Greg Vaughn	.10	.06
225	Dave Stewart	.08	.05
226	Lenny Harris	.05	.02
227	Scott Sanderson	.05	.02
228	Jeff Blauser	.07	.04
229	Ozzie Guillen	.07	.04
230	John Kruk	.12	.07
231	Bob Melvin	.05	.02
232	Milt Cuyler	.08	.05
233	Felix Jose	.08	.05
234	Ellis Burks	.07	.04
235	Pete Harnisch	.08	.05
236	Kevin Tapani	.07	.04
237	Terry Pendleton	.12	.07
238	Mark Gardner	.05	.02
239	Harold Reynolds	.05	.02
240	Checklist	.05	.02
241	Mike Harkey	.07	.04
242	Felix Fermin	.05	.02
243	Barry Bonds	.50	.30
244	Roger Clemens	.25	.15
245	Dennis Rasmussen	.05	.02
246	Jose DeLeon	.05	.02
247	Orel Hershiser	.08	.05
248	Mel Hall	.07	.04
249	Rick Wilkins	.10	.06
250	Tom Gordon	.07	.04
251	Kevin Reimer	.07	.04
252	Luis Polonia	.05	.02
253	Mike Henneman	.05	.02
254	Tom Pagnozzi	.07	.04
255	Chuck Finley	.07	.04
256	Mackey Sasser	.05	.02
257	John Burkett	.05	.02
258	Hal Morris	.10	.06
259	Larry Walker	.12	.07
260	Billy Swift	.08	.05
261	Joe Oliver	.05	.02
262	Julio Machado	.05	.02
263	Todd Stottlemyre	.07	.04
264	Matt Merullo	.05	.02
265	Brent Mayne	.07	.04
266	Thomas Howard	.07	.04
267	Lance Johnson	.05	.02
268	Terry Mulholland	.05	.02
269	Rick Honeycutt	.05	.02
270	Luis Gonzalez	.12	.07
271	Jose Guzman	.05	.02
272	Jimmy Jones	.05	.02
273	Mark Lewis	.08	.05
274	Rene Gonzales	.05	.02
275	Jeff Johnson	.05	.02
276	Dennis Martinez (HL)	.07	.04
277	Delino DeShields	.15	.08
278	Sam Horn	.05	.02
279	Kevin Gross	.05	.02
280	Jose Oquendo	.05	.02
281	Mark Grace	.10	.06
282	Mark Gubicza	.07	.04
283	Fred McGriff	.20	.12
284	Ron Gant	.12	.07
285	Lou Whitaker	.07	.04
286	Edgar Martinez	.12	.07
287	Ron Tingley	.05	.02
288	Kevin McReynolds	.07	.04
289	Ivan Rodriguez	.25	.15
290	Mike Gardiner	.08	.05
291	Chris Haney	.08	.05
292	Darrin Jackson	.05	.02
293	Bill Doran	.05	.02
294	Ted Higuera	.05	.02
295	Jeff Brantley	.05	.02
296	Les Lancaster	.05	.02
297	Jim Eisenreich	.05	.02
298	Ruben Sierra	.15	.08
299	Scott Radinsky	.05	.02
300	Jose DeJesus	.05	.02
301	Mike Timlin	.08	.05
302	Luis Sojo	.05	.02

303	Kelly Downs	.05	.02
304	Scott Bankhead	.05	.02
305	Pedro Munoz	.08	.05
306	Scott Scudder	.07	.04
307	Kevin Elster	.05	.02
308	Duane Ward	.05	.02
309	Darryl Kile	.08	.05
310	Orlando Merced	.12	.07
311	Dave Henderson	.05	.02
312	Tim Raines	.08	.05
313	Mark Lee	.07	.04
314	Mike Gallego	.05	.02
315	Charles Nagy	.15	.08
316	Jesse Barfield	.05	.02
317	Todd Frohwirth	.05	.02
318	Al Osuna	.05	.02
319	Darrin Fletcher	.05	.02
320	Checklist	.05	.02
321	David Segui	.07	.04
322	Stan Javier	.05	.02
323	Bryn Smith	.05	.02
324	Jeff Treadway	.05	.02
325	Mark Whiten	.15	.08
326	Kent Hrbek	.07	.04
327	David Justice	.25	.15
328	Tony Phillips	.07	.04
329	Rob Murphy	.05	.02
330	Kevin Morton	.07	.04
331	John Smiley	.08	.05
332	Luis Rivera	.05	.02
333	Wally Joyner	.08	.05
334	Heathcliff Slocumb	.05	.02
335	Rick Cerone	.05	.02
336	Mike Remlinger	.07	.04
337	Mike Moore	.05	.02
338	Lloyd McClendon	.05	.02
339	Al Newman	.05	.02
340	Kirk McCaskill	.05	.02
341	Howard Johnson	.10	.06
342	Greg Myers	.05	.02
343	Kal Daniels	.05	.02
344	Bernie Williams	.10	.06
345	Shane Mack	.08	.05
346	Gary Thurman	.05	.02
347	Dante Bichette	.05	.02
348	Mark McGwire	.15	.08
349	Travis Fryman	.25	.15
350	Ray Lankford	.12	.07
351	Mike Jeffcoat	.05	.02
352	Jack McDowell	.15	.08
353	Mitch Williams	.05	.02
354	Mike Devereaux	.07	.04
355	Andres Galarraga	.10	.06
356	Henry Cotto	.05	.02
357	Scott Bailes	.05	.02
358	Jeff Bagwell	.30	.18
359	Scott Leius	.07	.04
360	Zane Smith	.05	.02
361	Bill Pecota	.05	.02
362	Tony Fernandez	.05	.02
363	Glenn Braggs	.05	.02
364	Bill Spiers	.05	.02
365	Vicente Palacios	.05	.02
366	Tim Burke	.05	.02
367	Randy Tomlin	.10	.06
368	Kenny Rogers	.05	.02
369	Brett Butler	.07	.04
370	Pat Kelly	.08	.05
371	Bip Roberts	.05	.02
372	Gregg Jefferies	.10	.06
373	Kevin Bass	.05	.02
374	Ron Karkovice	.05	.02
375	Paul Gibson	.05	.02
376	Bernard Gilkey	.10	.06
377	Dave Gallagher	.05	.02
378	Bill Wegman	.05	.02
379	Pat Borders	.05	.02
380	Ed Whitson	.05	.02
381	Gilberto Reyes	.05	.02
382	Russ Swan	.05	.02
383	Andy Van Slyke	.10	.06
384	Wes Chamberlain	.10	.06
385	Steve Chitren	.05	.02
386	Greg Olson	.05	.02
387	Brian McRae	.10	.06
388	Rich Rodriguez	.05	.02
389	Steve Decker	.08	.05
390	Chuck Knoblauch	.15	.08
391	Bobby Witt	.07	.04
392	Eddie Murray	.10	.06
393	Juan Gonzalez	.80	.50
394	Scott Ruskin	.05	.02
395	Jay Howell	.05	.02
396	Checklist	.05	.02
397	Royce Clayton (R)	.20	.12
398	John Jaha (R)	.20	.12
399	Dan Wilson	.12	.07
400	Archie Corbin (R)	.10	.06
401	Barry Manuel (R)	.10	.06
402	Kim Batiste	.10	.06
403	Pat Mahomes (R)	.25	.15
404	Dave Fleming	.30	.18
405	Jeff Juden	.15	.08
406	Jim Thome	.25	.15
407	Sam Militello	.25	.15
408	Jeff Nelson (R)	.12	.07
409	Anthony Young	.12	.07
410	Tino Martinez	.10	.06
411	Jeff Mutis (R)	.10	.06
412	Rey Sanchez (R)	.12	.07
413	Chris Gardner (R)	.12	.07
414	John VanderWal (R)	.10	.06
415	Reggie Sanders	.30	.18
416	Brian Williams (R)	.20	.12

417	Mo Sanford	.10	.06
418	David Weathers (R)	.15	.08
419	Hector Fajardo (R)	.15	.08
420	Steve Foster (R)	.10	.06
421	Lance Dickson	.10	.06
422	Andre Dawson (AS)	.10	.06
423	Ozzie Smith (AS)	.10	.06
424	Chris Sabo (AS)	.05	.02
425	Tony Gwynn (AS)	.10	.06
426	Tom Glavine (AS)	.10	.06
427	Bobby Bonilla (AS)	.07	.04
428	Will Clark (AS)	.10	.06
429	Ryne Sandberg (AS)	.10	.06
430	Benito Santiago (AS)	.07	.04
431	Ivan Calderon (AS)	.05	.02
432	Ozzie Smith	.12	.07
433	Tim Leary	.05	.02
434	Bret Saberhagen (HL)	.07	.04
435	Mel Rojas	.07	.04
436	Ben McDonald	.12	.07
437	Tim Crews	.05	.02
438	Rex Hudler	.05	.02
439	Chico Walker	.05	.02
440	Kurt Stillwell	.05	.02
441	Tony Gwynn	.15	.08
442	John Smoltz	.12	.07
443	Lloyd Moseby	.05	.02
444	Mike Schooler	.05	.02
445	Joe Grahe	.05	.02
446	Dwight Gooden	.10	.06
447	Oil Can Boyd	.05	.02
448	John Marzano	.05	.02
449	Bret Barberie	.07	.04
450	Mike Maddux	.05	.02
451	Jeff Reed	.05	.02
452	Dale Sveum	.05	.02
453	Jose Uribe	.05	.02
454	Bob Scanlan	.05	.02
455	Kevin Appier	.08	.05
456	Jeff Huson	.05	.02
457	Ken Patterson	.05	.02
458	Ricky Jordan	.05	.02
459	Tom Candiotti	.05	.02
460	Lee Stevens	.07	.04
461	Rod Beck (R)	.25	.15
462	Dave Valle	.05	.02
463	Scott Erickson	.10	.06
464	Chris Jones	.05	.02
465	Mark Carreon	.05	.02
466	Rob Ducey	.05	.02
467	Jim Corsi	.05	.02
468	Jeff King	.07	.04
469	Curt Young	.05	.02
470	Bo Jackson	.15	.08
471	Chris Bosio	.07	.04
472	Jamie Quirk	.05	.02
473	Jesse Orosco	.05	.02
474	Alvaro Espinoza	.05	.02
475	Joe Orsulak	.05	.02
476	Checklist Card	.05	.02
477	Gerald Young	.05	.02
478	Wally Backman	.05	.02
479	Juan Bell	.05	.02
480	Mike Scioscia	.05	.02
481	Omar Olivares	.05	.02
482	Francisco Cabrera	.05	.02
483	Greg Swindell	.07	.04
484	Terry Leach	.05	.02
485	Tommy Gregg	.05	.02
486	Scott Aldred	.05	.02
487	Greg Briley	.05	.02
488	Phil Plantier	.25	.15
489	Curtis Wilkerson	.05	.02
490	Tom Brunansky	.05	.02
491	Mike Fetters	.05	.02
492	Frank Castillo	.07	.04
493	Joe Boever	.05	.02
494	Kirt Manwaring	.05	.02
495	Wilson Alvarez (HL)	.07	.04
496	Gene Larkin	.05	.02
497	Gary DiSarcina	.05	.02
498	Frank Viola	.07	.04
499	Manuel Lee	.05	.02
500	Albert Belle	.25	.15
501	Stan Belinda	.05	.02
502	Dwight Evans	.05	.02
503	Eric Davis	.07	.04
504	Darren Holmes	.05	.02
505	Mike Bordick	.10	.06
506	Dave Hansen	.08	.05
507	Lee Guetterman	.05	.02
508	Keith Mitchell	.08	.05
509	Melido Perez	.07	.04
510	Dickie Thon	.05	.02
511	Mark Williamson	.05	.02
512	Mark Salas	.05	.02
513	Milt Thompson	.05	.02
514	Mo Vaughn	.25	.15
515	Jim Deshaies	.05	.02
516	Rich Garces	.05	.02
517	Lonnie Smith	.05	.02
518	Spike Owen	.05	.02
519	Tracy Jones	.05	.02
520	Greg Maddux	.15	.08
521	Carlos Martinez	.05	.02
522	Neal Heaton	.05	.02
523	Mike Greenwell	.07	.04
524	Andy Benes	.08	.05
525	Jeff Schaefer	.05	.02
526	Mike Sharperson	.05	.02
527	Wade Taylor	.05	.02
528	Jerome Walton	.05	.02
529	Storm Davis	.05	.02
530	Jose Hernandez (R)	.10	.06

531	Mark Langston	.08	.05	588	Bob MacDonald	.05	.02
532	Rob Deer	.05	.02	589	Jose Tolentino (R)	.10	.06
533	Geronimo Pena	.05	.02	590	Bob Patterson	.05	.02
534	Juan Guzman	.30	.18	591	Scott Brosius (R)	.08	.05
535	Pete Schourek	.08	.04	592	Frank Thomas	1.50	.90
536	Todd Benzinger	.05	.02	593	Darryl Hamilton	.07	.04
537	Billy Hatcher	.05	.02	594	Kirk Dressendorfer	.08	.05
538	Tom Foley	.05	.02	595	Jeff Shaw	.05	.02
539	Dave Cochrane	.05	.02	596	Don Mattingly	.20	.12
540	Mariano Duncan	.05	.02	597	Glenn Davis	.05	.02
541	Edwin Nunez	.05	.02	598	Andy Mota	.05	.02
542	Rance Mulliniks	.05	.02	599	Jason Grimsley	.05	.02
543	Carlton Fisk	.10	.06	600	Jimmy Poole	.05	.02
544	Luis Aquino	.05	.02	601	Jim Gott	.05	.02
545	Ricky Bones	.08	.05	602	Stan Royer	.07	.04
546	Craig Grebeck	.05	.02	603	Marvin Freeman	.05	.02
547	Charlie Hayes	.05	.02	604	Denis Boucher	.05	.02
548	Jose Canseco	.25	.15	605	Denny Neagle	.08	.05
549	Andujar Cedeno	.08	.05	606	Mark Lemke	.05	.02
550	Geno Petralli	.05	.02	607	Jerry Don Gleaton	.05	.02
551	Javier Ortiz	.05	.02	608	Brent Knackert	.05	.02
552	Rudy Seanez	.05	.02	609	Carlos Quintana	.07	.04
553	Rich Gedman	.05	.02	610	Bobby Bonilla	.10	.06
554	Eric Plunk	.05	.02	611	Joe Hesketh	.05	.02
555	Nolan Ryan (HL)	.25	.15	612	Daryl Boston	.05	.02
556	Checklist Card	.05	.02	613	Shawon Dunston	.07	.04
557	Greg Colbrunn	.08	.05	614	Danny Cox	.05	.02
558	Chito Martinez	.10	.06	615	Darren Lewis	.07	.04
559	Darryl Strawberry	.12	.07	616	Alejandro Pena (HL)	.08	.05
560	Luis Alicea	.05	.02		Kent Mercker		
561	Dwight Smith	.07	.04		Mark Wohlers		
562	Terry Shumpert	.05	.02	616	Kirby Puckett	.25	.15
563	Jim Vatcher	.05	.02	618	Franklin Stubbs	.05	.02
564	Deion Sanders	.15	.08	619	Chris Donnels	.05	.02
565	Walt Terrell	.05	.02	620	David Wells	.05	.02
566	Dave Burba	.05	.02	621	Mike Aldrete	.05	.02
567	Dave Howard	.05	.02	622	Bob Kipper	.05	.02
568	Todd Hundley	.07	.04	623	Anthony Telford	.05	.02
569	Jack Daugherty	.05	.02	624	Randy Myers	.07	.04
570	Scott Cooper	.10	.06	625	Willie Randolph	.05	.02
571	Bill Sampen	.05	.02	626	Joe Slusarski	.07	.04
572	Jose Melendez	.05	.02	627	John Wetteland	.08	.05
573	Freddie Benavides	.05	.02	628	Greg Cadaret	.05	.02
574	Jim Gantner	.05	.02	629	Tom Glavine	.25	.15
575	Trevor Wilson	.05	.02	630	Wilson Alvarez	.08	.05
576	Ryne Sandberg	.20	.12	631	Wally Ritchie	.05	.02
577	Kevin Seitzer	.07	.04	632	Mike Mussina	.50	.30
578	Gerald Alexander	.05	.02	633	Mark Leiter	.05	.02
579	Mike Huff	.05	.02	634	Gerald Perry	.05	.02
580	Von Hayes	.05	.02	635	Matt Young	.05	.02
581	Derek Bell	.20	.12	636	Checklist Card	.05	.02
582	Mike Stanley	.05	.02	637	Scott Hemond	.05	.02
583	Kevin Mitchell	.08	.05	638	David West	.05	.02
584	Mike Jackson	.05	.02	639	Jim Clancy	.05	.02
585	Dan Gladden	.05	.02	640	Doug Piatt (R)	.07	.04
586	Ted Power	.05	.02	641	Omar Vizquel	.05	.02
587	Jeff Innis	.05	.02	642	Rick Sutcliffe	.05	.02

643	Glenallen Hill	.08	.05
644	Gary Varsho	.05	.02
645	Tony Fossas	.07	.04
646	Jack Howell	.05	.02
647	Jim Campanis (R)	.10	.06
648	Chris Gwynn	.05	.02
649	Jim Leyritz	.05	.02
650	Chuck McElroy	.05	.02
651	Sean Berry	.05	.02
652	Donald Harris	.08	.05
653	Don Slaught	.05	.02
654	Rusty Meacham	.05	.02
655	Scott Terry	.05	.02
656	Ramon Martinez	.08	.05
657	Keith Miller	.05	.02
658	Ramon Garcia	.05	.02
659	Milt Hill (R)	.08	.04
660	Steve Frey	.05	.02
661	Bob McClure	.05	.02
662	Ced Landrum	.08	.05
663	Doug Henry (R)	.20	.12
664	Candy Maldonado	.05	.02
665	Carl Willis	.05	.02
666	Jeff Montgomery	.05	.02
667	Craig Shipley	.07	.04
668	Warren Newson	.05	.02
669	Mickey Morandini	.07	.04
670	Brook Jacoby	.05	.02
671	Ryan Bowen	.08	.05
672	Bill Krueger	.05	.02
673	Rob Mallicoat	.05	.02
674	Doug Jones	.05	.02
675	Scott Livingstone	.08	.05
676	Danny Tartabull	.10	.06
677	Joe Carter (HL)	.15	.08
678	Cecil Espy	.05	.02
679	Randy Velarde	.05	.02
680	Bruce Ruffin	.05	.02
681	Ted Wood	.08	.05
682	Dan Plesac	.05	.02
683	Eric Bullock	.05	.02
684	Junior Ortiz	.05	.02
685	Dave Hollins	.20	.12
686	Dennis Martinez	.07	.04
687	Larry Andersen	.05	.02
688	Doug Simmons	.05	.02
689	Tim Spehr	.05	.02
690	Calvin Jones (R)	.10	.06
691	Mark Guthrie	.05	.02
692	Alfredo Griffin	.05	.02
693	Joe Carter	.25	.15
694	Terry Matthews (R)	.08	.05
695	Pascual Perez	.05	.02
696	Gene Nelson	.05	.02
697	Gerald Williams	.10	.06
698	Chris Cron	.08	.05
699	Steve Buechele	.05	.02
700	Paul McClellan	.05	.02
701	Jim Lindeman	.05	.02
702	Francisco Oliveras	.05	.02
703	Rob Maurer	.12	.07
704	Pat Hentgen	.20	.12
705	Jaime Navarro	.08	.05
706	Mike Magnante (H)	.08	.05
707	Nolan Ryan	.75	.45
708	Bobby Thigpen	.07	.04
709	John Cerrutti	.05	.02
710	Steve Wilson	.05	.02
711	Hensley Meulens	.07	.04
712	Rheal Cormier	.10	.06
713	Scott Bradley	.05	.02
714	Mitch Webster	.05	.02
715	Roger Mason	.05	.02
716	Checklist Card	.05	.02
717	Jeff Fassero	.07	.04
718	Cal Eldred	.25	.15
719	Sid Fernandez	.07	.04
720	Bob Zupcic (R)	.15	.08
721	Jose Offerman	.08	.05
722	Cliff Brantley	.08	.05
723	Ron Darling	.07	.04
724	Dave Stieb	.07	.04
725	Hector Villanueva	.05	.02
726	Mike Hartley	.05	.02
727	Arthur Rhodes	.10	.06
728	Randy Bush	.05	.02
729	Steve Sax	.07	.04
730	Dave Otto	.05	.02
731	John Wehner	.08	.05
732	Dave Martinez	.05	.02
733	Ruben Amaro	.08	.05
734	Billy Ripken	.05	.02
735	Steve Farr	.05	.02
736	Shawn Abner	.05	.02
737	Gil Heredia	.07	.04
738	Ron Jones	.05	.02
739	Tony Castillo	.05	.02
740	Sammy Sosa	.15	.08
741	Julio Franco	.07	.04
742	Tim Naehring	.07	.04
743	Steve Wapnick (R)	.08	.05
744	Craig Wilson	.05	.02
745	Darrin Chapin (R)	.12	.07
746	Chris George (R)	.10	.06
747	Mike Simms	.07	.04
748	Rosario Rodriguez	.05	.02
749	Skeeter Barnes	.05	.02
750	Roger McDowell	.05	.02
751	Dann Howitt	.08	.05
752	Paul Sorrento	.08	.05
753	Braulio Castillo (R)	.12	.07
754	Yorkis Perez (R)	.08	.05
755	Willie Fraser	.05	.02
756	Jeremy Hernandez (R)	.10	.06

757	Curt Schilling	.12	.07
758	Steve Lyons	.05	.02
759	Dave Anderson	.05	.02
760	Willie Banks	.10	.06
761	Mark Leonard	.05	.02
762	Jack Armstrong	.07	.04
763	Scott Servais	.07	.04
764	Ray Stephens	.05	.02
765	Junior Noboa	.05	.02
766	Jim Olander	.07	.04
767	Joe Magrane	.07	.04
768	Lance Blankenship	.05	.02
769	Mike Humphreys	.07	.04
770	Jarvis Brown (R)	.10	.06
771	Damon Berryhill	.05	.02
772	Alejandro Pena	.05	.02
773	Jose Mesa	.05	.02
774	Gary Cooper (R)	.08	.05
775	Carney Lansford	.05	.02
776	Mike Bielecki	.05	.02
777	Charlie O'Brien	.05	.02
778	Carlos Hernandez	.05	.02
779	Howard Farmer	.05	.02
780	Mike Stanton	.05	.02
781	Reggie Harris	.05	.02
782	Xavier Hernandez	.05	.02
783	Bryan Hickerson (R)	.15	.08
784	Checklist Card	.05	.02
BC1	Cal Ripken (MVP)	.60	.35
BC2	Terry Pendleton (MVP)	.15	.08
BC3	Roger Clemens (CY)	.30	.18
BC4	Tom Glavine (CY)	.30	.18
BC5	Chuck Knoblauch (ROY)	.20	.12
BC6	Jeff Bagwell (ROY)	.50	.30
BC7	Colorado Rockies	.50	.30
BC8	Florida Marlins	.50	.30
DK1	Paul Molitor	1.75	1.00
DK2	Will Clark	2.50	1.50
DK3	Joe Carter	2.50	1.50
DK4	Julio Franco	.80	.50
DK5	Cal Ripken	4.50	2.75
DK6	Dave Justice	3.50	2.00
DK7	George Bell	.80	.50
DK8	Frank Thomas	12.00	7.50
DK9	Wade Boggs	2.00	1.25
DK10	Scott Sanderson	.80	.50
DK11	Jeff Bagwell	3.50	2.00
DK12	John Kruk	1.00	.70
DK13	Felix Jose	.80	.50
DK14	Harold Baines	.80	.50
DK15	Dwight Gooden	1.00	.70
DK16	Brian McRae	1.00	.70
DK17	Jay Bell	.80	.50
DK18	Brett Butler	1.00	.70
DK19	Hal Morris	1.00	.70
DK20	Mark Langston	1.00	.80
DK21	Scott Erickson	1.00	.70

DK22	Randy Johnson	1.75	1.00
DK23	Greg Swindell	.80	.50
DK24	Dennis Martinez	.80	.50
DK25	Tony Phillips	.80	.05
DK26	Fred McGriff	3.00	1.75
DK27	Checklist	.40	.25
E9	Wade Boggs (Elite)	75.00	45.00
E10	Joe Carter (Elite)	100.00	70.00
E11	Will Clark (Elite)	100.00	70.00
E12	Doc Gooden (Elite)	50.00	32.00
E13	Ken Griffey Jr. (Elite)	200.00	125.00
E14	Tony Gwynn (Elite)	80.00	50.00
E15	Howard Johnson (Elite)	40.00	25.00
E16	Terry Pendleton (Elite)	50.00	32.00
E17	Kirby Puckett (Elite)	125.00	80.00
E18	Frank Thomas (Elite)	275.00	175.00
L1	Rickey Henderson	175.00	100.00
S1	Cal Ripken (Auto)	450.00	325.00

1992 Donruss Rookies

At 132-cards this is the largest Donruss Rookies set issued to date. The card design is identical to the regular Donruss set except for the green borders at the top and bottom.

The set includes 20 limited Bonus Cards called Phenoms which were randomly inserted in foil packs. Those cards are listed at the end of this checklist but are not included in the complete set price. All cards measure 2-1/2" by 3-1/2".

	MINT	NR/MT
Complete Set (132)	10.00	6.50
Commons	.05	.02

1	Kyle Abbott	.08	.05
2	Troy Afenir	.05	.02
3	Rich Amaral (R)	.15	.10
4	Ruben Amaro	.07	.04
5	Billy Ashley (R)	.50	.30
6	Pedro Astacio (R)	.35	.20
7	Jim Austin (R)	.08	.05
8	Robert Ayrault (R)	.07	.04
9	Kevin Baez (R)	.12	.07
10	Estaban Beltre (R)	.15	.10
11	Brian Bohanon	.05	.02
12	Kent Bottenfield (R)	.15	.10
13	Jeff Branson	.05	.02
14	Brad Brink (R)	.08	.05
15	John Briscoe	.07	.04
16	Doug Brocail (R)	.12	.07
17	Rico Brogna (R)	.15	.10
18	J.T. Bruett (R)	.10	.06
19	Jacob Brumfield (R)	.08	.05
20	Jim Bullinger	.05	.02
21	Kevin Campbell (R)	.10	.06
22	Pedro Castellano (R)	.15	.10
23	Mike Christopher (R)	.12	.07
24	Archi Cianfrocco (R)	.20	.12
25	Mark Clark (R)	.12	.07
26	Craig Colbert (R)	.10	.06
27	Victor Cole (R)	.12	.07
28	Steve Cooke (R)	.20	.12
29	Tim Costo	.15	.10
30	Chad Curtis (R)	.50	.30
31	Doug Davis (R)	.08	.05
32	Gary DiSarcina	.08	.05
33	John Doherty (R)	.12	.07
34	Mike Draper (R)	.08	.05
35	Monty Fariss	.08	.05
36	Bien Figueroa (R)	.08	.05
37	John Flaherty (R)	.08	.05
38	Tim Fortugno (R)	.08	.05
39	Eric Fox (R)	.12	.07
40	Jeff Frye (R)	.10	.06
41	Ramon Garcia	.05	.02
42	Brent Gates (R)	.75	.45
43	Tom Goodwin	.10	.06
44	Buddy Groom (R)	.08	.05
45	Jeff Grotewold (R)	.08	.05
46	Juan Guerrero (R)	.12	.07
47	Johnny Guzman (R)	.12	.07
48	Shawn Hare (R)	.12	.07
49	Ryan Hawblitzel (R)	.25	.15
50	Bert Heffernan (R)	.08	.05
51	Butch Henry (R)	.12	.07
52	Cesar Hernandez (R)	.08	.05
53	Vince Horsman (R)	.15	.10
54	Steve Hosey	.25	.15
55	Pat Howell (R)	.12	.07
56	Peter Hoy (R)	.12	.07
57	Jon Hurst (R)	.10	.06
58	Mark Hutton (R)	.25	.15
59	Shawn Jeter (R)	.10	.06
60	Joel Johnston (R)	.15	.10
61	Jeff Kent (R)	.20	.12
62	Kurt Knudsen (R)	.08	.05
63	Kevin Koslofski (R)	.07	.04
64	Danny Leon (R)	.07	.04
65	Jesse Levis (R)	.08	.05
66	Tom Marsh (R)	.08	.05
67	Ed Martel (R)	.12	.07
68	Al Martin (R)	.50	.30
69	Pedro Martinez (R)	.30	.18
70	Derrick May	.15	.10
71	Matt Maysey (R)	.08	.05
72	Russ McGinnis (R)	.08	.05
73	Tim McIntosh	.10	.06
74	Jim McNamara (R)	.08	.05
75	Jeff McNeely	.15	.10
76	Rusty Meacham	.05	.02
77	Tony Menendez (R)	.08	.05
78	Henry Mercedes (R)	.10	.06
79	Paul Miller (R)	.12	.07
80	Joe Millette (R)	.08	.05
81	Blas Minor (R)	.10	.06
82	Dennis Moeller (R)	.10	.06
83	Raul Mondesi	.40	.25
84	Rob Natal (R)	.08	.05
85	Troy Neel (R)	.40	.25
86	David Nied (R)	1.50	.90
87	Jerry Nielsen (R)	.08	.05
88	Donovan Osborne	.25	.15
89	John Patterson (R)	.12	.07
90	Roger Pavlik (R)	.25	.15
91	Dan Peltier	.08	.05
92	Jim Pena (R)	.08	.05
93	William Pennyfeather	.10	.06
94	Mike Perez	.07	.04
95	Hipolito Pichardo (R)	.20	.12
96	Greg Pirkl (R)	.15	.10
97	Harvey Pulliam	.08	.05
98	Manny Ramirez (R)	1.50	.90
99	Pat Rapp (R)	.15	.10
100	Jeff Reboulet (R)	.10	.06
101	Darren Reed	.05	.02
102	Shane Reynolds (R)	.12	.07
103	Bill Risley (R)	.08	.05
104	Ben Rivera	.08	.05
105	Henry Rodriguez	.15	.10
106	Rico Rossy (R)	.12	.07
107	Johnny Ruffin	.10	.06
108	Steve Scarsone (R)	.10	.06
109	Tim Scott (R)	.15	.10
110	Steve Shifflett (R)	.10	.06
111	Dave Silvestri	.12	.07
112	Matt Stairs (R)	.15	.10
113	William Suero (R)	.10	.06
114	Jeff Tackett	.10	.06

115	Eddie Taubensee	.08	.05
116	Rick Trlicek (R)	.10	.06
117	Scooter Tucker (R)	.08	.05
118	Shane Turner	.05	.02
119	Julio Valera	.07	.04
120	Paul Wagner (R)	.20	.12
121	Tim Wakefield (R)	.35	.20
122	Mike Walker (R)	.08	.05
123	Bruce Walton	.05	.02
124	Lenny Webster	.05	.02
125	Bob Wickman	.25	.15
126	Mike Williams (R)	.12	.07
127	Kerry Woodson	.08	.05
128	Eric Young (R)	.20	.12
129	Kevin Young (R)	.35	.20
130	Pete Young (R)	.08	.05
131	Checklist	.05	.02
132	Checklist	.05	.02
BC1	Moises Alou	2.00	1.25
BC2	Bret Boone	2.50	1.50
BC3	Jeff Conine	2.00	1.25
BC4	Dave Fleming	2.50	1.50
BC5	Tyler Green	1.25	.80
BC6	Eric Karros	4.00	2.50
BC7	Pat Listach	1.50	.90
BC8	Kenny Lofton	5.00	3.00
BC9	Mike Piazza	25.00	15.00
BC10	Tim Salmon	12.00	7.50
BC11	Andy Stankiewicz	.60	.35
BC12	Dan Walters	.80	.50
BC13	Ramon Caraballo	1.25	.80
BC14	Brian Jordan	2.50	1.50
BC15	Ryan Klesko	4.50	2.75
BC16	Sam Militello	1.25	.80
BC17	Frank Seminara	.60	.35
BC18	Salomon Torres	5.00	3.00
BC19	John Valentin	1.50	.90
BC20	Wilfredo Cordero	2.50	1.50

1993 Donruss

This set was issued in two 396-card series with each card measuring 2-1/2" by 3-1/2". Card fronts feature full color action shots. A color stripe reflecting the player's team colors appears below the photo and contains the player's name and position. Card backs include a large photo, stats and personal data. Special inserts include Diamond Kings, Spirit Of The Game, Elite, a Will Clark Signature Series and a Robin Yount Legends Series. Those inserts are listed at the end of this checklist but are not included in the complete set price below.

		MINT	NR/MT
Complete Set (792)		33.00	20.00
Commons		.05	.02

1	Craig Lefferts	.05	.02
2	Kent Mercker	.07	.04
3	Phil Plantier	.30	.18
4	Alex Arias	.08	.05
5	Julio Valera	.05	.02
6	Dan Wilson	.08	.05
7	Frank Thomas	1.50	.90
8	Eric Anthony	.08	.05
9	Derek Lilliquist	.05	.02
10	Rafael Bournigal (R)	.12	.07
11	Manny Alexander	.12	.07
12	Bret Barberie	.07	.04
13	Mickey Tettleton	.05	.02
14	Anthony Young	.08	.05
15	Tim Spehr	.05	.02
16	Bob Ayrault	.08	.05
17	Bill Wegman	.05	.02
18	Jay Bell	.07	.04
19	Rick Aguilera	.05	.02
20	Todd Zeile	.07	.04
21	Steve Farr	.05	.02
22	Andy Benes	.08	.05

23	Lance Blankenship	.05	.02		80	Hector Villanueva	.05	.02
24	Ted Wood	.07	.04		81	Mike Gallego	.05	.02
25	Omar Vizquel	.05	.02		82	Tim Belcher	.07	.04
26	Steve Avery	.15	.10		83	Mike Bordick	.07	.04
27	Brian Bohanon	.05	.02		84	Craig Biggio	.07	.04
28	Rick Wilkins	.08	.05		85	Lance Parrish	.05	.02
29	Devon White	.08	.05		86	Brett Butler	.07	.04
30	Bobby Ayala (R)	.12	.07		87	Mike Timlin	.07	.04
31	Leo Gomez	.07	.04		88	Brian Barnes	.07	.04
32	Mike Simms	.05	.02		89	Brady Anderson	.12	.07
33	Ellis Burks	.07	.04		90	D.J. Dozier	.07	.04
34	Steve Wilson	.05	.02		91	Frank Viola	.07	.04
35	Jim Abbott	.12	.07		92	Darren Daulton	.15	.10
36	Tim Wallach	.05	.02		93	Chad Curtis	.15	.10
37	Wilson Alvarez	.08	.05		94	Zane Smith	.05	.02
38	Daryl Boston	.05	.02		95	George Bell	.08	.05
39	Sandy Alomar, Jr.	.07	.04		96	Rex Hudler	.05	.02
40	Mitch Williams	.05	.02		97	Mark Whiten	.12	.07
41	Rico Brogna	.10	.06		98	Tim Teufel	.05	.02
42	Gary Varsho	.05	.02		99	Kevin Ritz	.07	.04
43	Kevin Appier	.08	.05		100	Jeff Brantley	.05	.02
44	Eric Wedge (R)	.12	.07		101	Jeff Conine	.12	.07
45	Dante Bichette	.07	.04		102	Vinny Castilla	.05	.02
46	Jose Oquendo	.05	.02		103	Greg Vaughn	.10	.06
47	Mike Trombley	.07	.04		104	Steve Buechele	.05	.02
48	Dan Walters	.08	.05		105	Darren Reed	.05	.02
49	Gerald Williams	.08	.05		106	Bip Roberts	.05	.02
50	Bud Black	.05	.02		107	John Habyan	.05	.02
51	Bobby Witt	.07	.04		108	Scott Servais	.05	.02
52	Mark Davis	.05	.02		109	Walt Weiss	.05	.02
53	Shawn Barton (R)	.08	.05		110	J.T. Snow (R)	.75	.45
54	Paul Assenmacher	.05	.02		111	Jay Buhner	.07	.04
55	Kevin Reimer	.07	.04		112	Darryl Strawberry	.15	.10
56	Billy Ashley	.35	.20		113	Roger Pavlik	.07	.04
57	Eddie Zosky	.07	.04		114	Chris Nabholz	.07	.04
58	Chris Sabo	.07	.04		115	Pat Borders	.05	.02
59	Billy Ripken	.05	.02		116	Pat Howell	.05	.02
60	Scooter Tucker	.07	.04		117	Gregg Olson	.07	.04
61	Tim Wakefield	.15	.10		118	Curt Schilling	.10	.06
62	Mitch Webster	.05	.02		119	Roger Clemens	.25	.15
63	Jack Clark	.07	.04		120	Victor Cole	.05	.02
64	Mark Gardner	.05	.02		121	Gary DiSarcina	.07	.04
65	Lee Stevens	.05	.02		122	Checklist	.05	.02
66	Todd Hundley	.05	.02		123	Steve Sax	.07	.04
67	Bobby Thigpen	.05	.02		124	Chuck Carr	.05	.02
68	Dave Hollins	.15	.10		125	Mark Lewis	.07	.04
69	Jack Armstrong	.05	.02		126	Tony Gwynn	.15	.10
70	Alex Cole	.05	.02		127	Travis Fryman	.25	.15
71	Mark Carreon	.05	.02		129	Dave Burba	.05	.02
72	Todd Worrell	.05	.02		130	John Smoltz	.12	.07
73	Steve Shifflett	.05	.02		131	Cal Eldred	.15	.10
74	Jerald Clark	.07	.04		132	Checklist	.05	.02
75	Paul Molitor	.12	.07		133	Arthur Rhodes	.08	.05
76	Larry Carter (R)	.10	.06		134	Jeff Blauser	.07	.04
77	Rich Rowland	.08	.05		135	Scott Cooper	.08	.05
78	Damon Berryhill	.05	.02		136	Doug Strange	.05	.02
79	Willie Banks	.05	.02		137	Luis Sojo	.05	.02

138 Jeff Branson	.05	.02
139 Alex Fernandez	.12	.07
140 Ken Caminiti	.07	.04
141 Charles Nagy	.15	.10
142 Tom Candiotti	.05	.02
143 Willie Green	.12	.07
144 John Vander Wal	.08	.05
145 Kurt Knudsen	.08	.05
146 John Franco	.05	.02
147 Eddie Pierce (R)	.15	.10
148 Kim Batiste	.05	.02
149 Darren Holmes	.05	.02
150 Steve Cooke	.07	.04
151 Terry Jorgensen	.05	.02
152 Mark Clark	.05	.02
153 Randy Velarde	.05	.02
154 Greg Harris	.05	.02
155 Kevin Campbell	.05	.02
156 John Burkett	.05	.02
157 Kevin Mitchell	.08	.05
158 Deion Sanders	.12	.07
159 Jose Canseco	.20	.12
160 Jeff Hartsock (R)	.08	.05
161 Tom Quinlan (R)	.08	.05
162 Tim Pugh (R)	.20	.12
163 Glenn Davis	.05	.02
164 Shane Reynolds	.05	.02
165 Jody Reed	.05	.02
166 Mike Sharperson	.05	.02
167 Scott Lewis	.05	.02
168 Dennis Martinez	.08	.05
169 Scott Radinsky	.05	.02
170 Dave Gallagher	.05	.02
171 Jim Thome	.10	.06
172 Terry Mulholland	.05	.02
173 Milt Cuyler	.07	.04
174 Bob Patterson	.05	.02
175 Jeff Montgomery	.05	.02
176 Tim Salmon	1.50	.90
177 Franklin Stubbs	.05	.02
178 Donovan Osborne	.15	.10
179 Jeff Reboulet	.07	.04
180 Jeremy Hernandez	.07	.04
181 Charlie Hayes	.05	.02
182 Matt Williams	.12	.07
183 Mike Raczka (R)	.08	.05
184 Francisco Cabrera	.05	.02
185 Rich DeLucia	.05	.02
186 Sammy Sosa	.12	.07
187 Ivan Rodriguez	.20	.12
188 Bret Boone	.20	.12
189 Juan Guzman	.25	.15
190 Randy Milligan	.05	.02
191 Ivan Calderon	.07	.04
197 Junior Felix	.05	.02
198 Pete Schourek	.05	.02
199 Craig Grebeck	.05	.02

200 Juan Bell	.05	.02
201 Glenallen Hill	.07	.04
202 Danny Jackson	.05	.02
203 John Kiely	.05	.02
204 Bob Tewksbury	.05	.02
205 Kevin Koslofski	.05	.02
206 Craig Shipley	.05	.02
207 John Jaha	.12	.07
208 Royce Clayton	.12	.07
209 Mike Piazza	3.00	1.75
210 Ron Gant	.12	.07
211 Scott Erickson	.12	.07
212 Doug Dascenzo	.05	.02
213 Andy Stankiewicz	.05	.02
214 Geronimo Berroa	.05	.02
215 Dennis Eckersley	.10	.06
216 Al Osuna	.05	.02
217 Tino Martinez	.07	.04
218 Henry Rodriguez	.08	.05
219 Ed Sprague	.07	.04
220 Ken Hill	.07	.04
221 Chito Martinez	.08	.05
222 Bret Saberhagen	.08	.05
223 Mike Greenwell	.07	.04
224 Mickey Morandini	.07	.04
225 Chuck Finley	.07	.04
226 Denny Neagle	.07	.04
227 Kirk McCaskill	.05	.02
228 Rheal Cormier	.07	.04
229 Paul Sorrento	.10	.06
230 Darrin Jackson	.05	.02
231 Rob Deer	.07	.04
232 Bill Swift	.10	.06
233 Kevin McReynolds	.07	.04
234 Terry Pendleton	.15	.10
235 Dave Nilsson	.10	.06
236 Chuck McElroy	.05	.02
237 Derek Parks	.08	.05
238 Norm Charlton	.05	.02
239 Matt Nokes	.05	.02
240 Juan Guerrero	.07	.04
241 Jeff Parrett	.05	.02
242 Ryan Thompson	.15	.10
243 Dave Fleming	.20	.12
244 Dave Hansen	.05	.02
245 Monty Fariss	.05	.02
246 Archi Cianfrocco	.08	.05
247 Pat Hentgen	.07	.04
248 Bill Pecota	.05	.02
249 Ben McDonald	.15	.10
250 Cliff Brantley	.07	.04
251 John Valentin	.12	.07
252 Jeff King	.08	.05
253 Reggie Williams	.05	.02
254 Checklist	.05	.02
255 Ozzie Guillen	.05	.02
256 Mike Perez	.07	.04

257	Thomas Howard	.07	.04	314	Mike Jackson	.05	.02
258	Kurt Stillwell	.05	.02	315	Rickey Henderson	.15	.10
259	Mike Henneman	.05	.02	316	Mark Lemke	.05	.02
260	Steve Decker	.07	.04	317	Erik Hanson	.05	.02
261	Bret Mayne	.07	.04	318	Derrick May	.10	.06
262	Otis Nixon	.07	.04	319	Geno Petralli	.05	.02
263	Mark Keifer	.08	.05	320	Melvin Nieves	.35	.20
264	Checklist	.05	.02	321	Doug Linton	.08	.05
265	Richie Lewis (R)	.12	.07	322	Rob Dibble	.07	.04
266	Pat Gomez (R)	.10	.06	323	Chris Hoiles	.08	.05
267	Scott Taylor	.05	.02	324	Jimmy Jones	.05	.02
268	Shawon Dunston	.07	.04	325	Dave Staton	.10	.06
269	Greg Myers	.05	.02	326	Pedro Martinez	.20	.12
270	Tim Costo	.08	.05	327	Paul Quantrill	.08	.05
271	Greg Hibbard	.07	.04	328	Greg Colbrunn	.08	.05
272	Pete Harnisch	.07	.04	329	Hilly Hathaway (R)	.15	.10
273	Dave Mlicki	.08	.05	330	Jeff Innis	.05	.02
274	Orel Hershiser	.08	.05	331	Ron Karkovice	.05	.02
275	Sean Berry	.05	.02	332	Keith Shepherd (R)	.10	.06
276	Doug Simons	.05	.02	333	Alan Embree	.10	.06
277	John Doherty	.05	.02	334	Paul Wagner	.07	.04
278	Eddie Murray	.12	.07	335	Dave Haas	.07	.04
279	Chris Haney	.07	.04	336	Ozzie Canseco	.07	.04
280	Stan Javier	.05	.02	337	Bill Sampen	.05	.02
281	Jaime Navarro	.08	.05	338	Rich Rodriguez	.05	.02
282	Orlando Merced	.08	.05	339	Dean Palmer	.15	.10
283	Kent Hrbek	.05	.02	340	Greg Litton	.05	.02
284	Bernard Gilkey	.08	.05	341	Jim Tatum (R)	.15	.10
285	Russ Springer	.12	.07	342	Todd Haney (R)	.12	.07
286	Mike Maddux	.05	.02	343	Larry Casian	.05	.02
287	Eric Fox	.05	.02	344	Ryne Sandberg	.25	.15
288	Mark Leonard	.05	.02	345	Sterling Hitchcock (R)	.30	.18
289	Tim Leary	.05	.02	346	Chris Hammond	.07	.04
290	Brian Hunter	.10	.06	347	Vince Horsman	.08	.05
291	Donald Harris	.10	.06	348	Butch Henry	.07	.04
292	Bob Scanlan	.05	.02	349	Dan Howitt	.08	.05
293	Turner Ward	.05	.02	350	Roger McDowell	.05	.02
294	Hal Morris	.10	.06	351	Jack Morris	.10	.06
295	Jimmy Poole	.05	.02	352	Bill Krueger	.05	.02
296	Doug Jones	.05	.02	353	Cris Colon	.10	.06
297	Tony Pena	.05	.02	354	Joe Vitko	.10	.06
298	Ramon Martinez	.10	.06	355	Willie McGee	.08	.05
299	Tim Fortugno	.07	.04	356	Jay Baller	.05	.02
300	Marquis Grissom	.15	.10	357	Pat Mahomes	.15	.10
301	Lance Johnson	.05	.02	358	Roger Mason	.05	.02
302	Jeff Kent	.07	.04	359	Jerry Nielsen	.05	.02
303	Reggie Jefferson	.08	.05	360	Tom Pagnozzi	.07	.04
304	Wes Chamberlain	.08	.05	361	Kevin Baez	.07	.04
305	Shawn Hare	.08	.05	362	Tim Scott	.07	.04
306	Mike LaValliere	.05	.02	363	Domingo Martinez (R)	.12	.07
307	Gregg Jefferies	.10	.06	364	Kirt Manwaring	.05	.02
308	Troy Neel	.08	.05	365	Rafael Palmeiro	.10	.06
309	Pat Listach	.12	.07	366	Ray Lankford	.15	.10
310	Geronimo Pena	.05	.02	367	Tim McIntosh	.10	.06
311	Pedro Munoz	.08	.05	368	Jessie Hollins	.07	.04
312	Guillermo Pena	.08	.05	369	Scott Leius	.05	.02
313	Roberto Kelly	.10	.06	370	Bill Doran	.05	.02

371 Sam Militello	.12	.07
372 Ryan Bowen	.07	.04
373 Dave Henderson	.07	.04
374 Dan Smith	.08	.05
375 Steve Reed (R)	.10	.06
376 Jose Offerman	.08	.05
377 Kevin Brown	.07	.04
378 Darrin Fletcher	.05	.02
379 Duane Ward	.05	.02
380 Wayne Kirby	.05	.02
381 Steve Scarsone	.07	.04
382 Mariano Duncan	.05	.02
383 Ken Ryan (R)	.12	.07
384 Lloyd McClendon	.05	.02
385 Brian Holman	.07	.04
386 Braulio Castillo	.07	.04
387 Danny Leon	.07	.04
388 Omar Olivares	.05	.02
389 Kevin Wickander	.05	.02
390 Fred McGriff	.20	.12
391 Phil Clark	.08	.05
392 Darren Lewis	.07	.04
393 Phil Hiatt	.15	.10
394 Mike Morgan	.05	.02
395 Shane Mack	.12	.07
396 Checklist	.05	.02
397 David Segui	.08	.05
398 Rafael Belliard	.05	.02
399 Tim Naehring	.08	.05
400 Frank Castillo	.05	.02
401 Joe Grahe	.07	.04
402 Reggie Sanders	.12	.07
403 Roberto Hernandez	.07	.04
404 Luis Gonzalez	.08	.05
405 Carlos Baerga	.25	.15
406 Carlos Hernandez	.10	.06
407 Pedro Astacio	.15	.10
408 Mel Rojas	.05	.02
409 Scott Livingstone	.07	.04
410 Chico Walker	.05	.02
411 Brian McRae	.08	.05
412 Ben Rivera	.07	.04
413 Ricky Bones	.08	.05
414 Andy Van Slyke	.10	.06
415 Chuck Knoblauch	.12	.07
416 Luis Alicea	.05	.02
417 Bob Wickman	.15	.10
418 Doug Brocail	.08	.05
419 Scott Brosius	.05	.02
420 Rod Beck	.08	.05
421 Edgar Martinez	.10	.06
422 Ryan Klesko	.40	.25
423 Nolan Ryan	.60	.35
424 Rey Sanchez	.10	.06
425 Roberto Alomar	.25	.15
426 Barry Larkin	.10	.06
427 Mike Mussina	.35	.20

428 Jeff Bagwell	.25	.15
429 Mo Vaughn	.12	.07
430 Eric Karros	.25	.15
431 John Orton	.05	.02
432 Wil Cordero	.20	.12
433 Jack McDowell	.15	.10
434 Howard Johnson	.08	.05
435 Albert Belle	.25	.15
436 John Kruk	.07	.04
437 Skeeter Barnes	.05	.02
438 Don Slaught	.05	.02
439 Rusty Meacham (R)	.20	.12
440 Tim Laker (R)	.10	.06
441 Robin Yount	.20	.12
442 Brian Jordan	.15	.10
443 Kevin Tapani	.08	.05
444 Gary Sheffield	.20	.12
445 Rich Monteleone	.05	.02
446 Will Clark	.20	.12
447 Jerry Browne	.05	.02
448 Jeff Treadway	.05	.02
449 Mike Schooler	.05	.02
450 Mike Harkey	.08	.05
451 Julio Franco	.07	.04
452 Kevin Young	.25	.15
453 Kelly Gruber	.07	.04
454 Jose Rijo	.08	.05
455 Mike Devereaux	.07	.04
456 Andujar Cedeno	.15	.10
457 Damion Easley (R)	.20	.12
458 Kevin Gross	.05	.02
459 Matt Young	.05	.02
460 Matt Stairs	.08	.05
461 Luis Polonia	.07	.04
462 Dwight Gooden	.10	.06
463 Warren Newson	.07	.04
464 Jose DeLeon	.05	.02
465 Jose Mesa	.10	.06
466 Danny Cox	.05	.02
467 Dan Gladden	.05	.02
468 Gerald Perry	.05	.02
469 Mike Boddicker	.05	.02
470 Jeff Gardner	.05	.02
471 Doug Henry	.07	.04
472 Mike Benjamin	.07	.04
473 Dan Peltier	.10	.06
474 Mike Stanton	.05	.02
475 John Smiley	.08	.05
476 Dwight Smith	.07	.04
477 Jim Leyritz	.05	.02
478 Dwayne Henry	.05	.02
479 Mark McGwire	.15	.10
480 Pete Incaviglia	.05	.02
481 Dave Cochrane (R)	.15	.10
482 Eric Davis	.08	.05
483 John Olerud	.30	.18
484 Ken Bottenfield	.05	.02

485	Mark McLemore	.05	.02
486	Dave Magadan	.07	.04
487	John Marzano	.05	.02
488	Ruben Amaro	.08	.05
489	Rob Ducey	.05	.02
490	Stan Belinda	.05	.02
491	Dan Pasqua	.05	.02
492	Joe Magrane	.07	.04
493	Brook Jacoby	.05	.02
494	Gene Harris	.05	.02
495	Mark Leiter	.05	.02
496	Bryan Hickerson	.07	.04
497	Tom Gordon	.08	.05
498	Pete Smith	.08	.05
499	Chris Bosio	.07	.04
500	Shawn Boskie	.07	.04
501	Dave West	.05	.02
502	Milt Hill	.05	.02
503	Pat Kelly	.08	.05
504	Joe Boever	.05	.02
505	Terry Steinbach	.07	.04
506	Butch Huskey (R)	.25	.15
507	Dave Valle	.05	.02
508	Mike Scioscia	.05	.02
509	Kenny Rogers	.05	.02
510	Moises Alou	.12	.07
511	David Wells	.05	.02
512	Mackey Sasser	.05	.02
513	Todd Frohwirth	.07	.04
514	Ricky Jordan	.07	.04
515	Mike Gardiner	.07	.04
516	Gary Redus	.05	.02
517	Gary Gaetti	.05	.02
518	Checklist	.05	.02
519	Carlton Fisk	.12	.07
520	Ozzie Smith	.15	.10
521	Rod Nichols	.05	.02
522	Benito Santiago	.08	.05
523	Bill Gullickson	.05	.02
524	Robby Thompson	.07	.04
525	Mike Macfarlane	.07	.04
526	Sid Bream	.05	.02
527	Darryl Hamilton	.12	.07
528	Checklist	.05	.02
529	Jeff Tackett	.10	.06
530	Greg Olson	.05	.02
531	Bob Zupcic	.12	.07
532	Mark Grace	.10	.06
533	Steve Frey	.05	.02
534	Dave Martinez	.05	.02
535	Robin Ventura	.20	.12
536	Casey Candaele	.05	.02
537	Kenny Lofton	.25	.15
538	Jay Howell	.05	.02
539	Fernando Ramsey (R)	.10	.06
540	Larry Walker	.12	.07
541	Cecil Fielder	.15	.10
542	Lee Guetterman	.05	.02
543	Keith Miller	.05	.02
544	Lenny Dykstra	.10	.06
545	B.J. Surhoff	.05	.02
546	Bob Walk	.05	.02
547	Brian Harper	.05	.02
548	Lee Smith	.10	.06
549	Danny Tartabull	.08	.05
550	Frank Seminara	.07	.04
551	Henry Mercedes	.08	.05
552	Dave Righetti	.05	.02
553	Ken Griffey, Jr.	1.00	.70
554	Tom Glavine	.20	.12
555	Juan Gonzalez	.80	.50
556	Jim Bullinger	.08	.05
557	Derek Bell	.15	.10
558	Cesar Hernandez	.08	.05
559	Cal Ripken, Jr.	.30	.18
560	Eddie Taubensee	.08	.05
561	John Flaherty	.08	.05
562	Todd Benzinger	.05	.02
563	Hubie Brooks	.07	.04
564	Delino DeShields	.10	.06
565	Tim Raines	.07	.04
566	Sid Fernandez	.07	.04
567	Steve Olin	.07	.04
568	Tommy Greene	.10	.06
569	Buddy Groom	.08	.05
570	Randy Tomlin	.10	.06
571	Hipolito Pichardo	.08	.05
572	Rene Arocha (R)	.25	.15
573	Mike Fetters	.05	.02
574	Felix Jose	.08	.05
575	Gene Larkin	.05	.02
576	Bruce Hurst	.08	.05
577	Bernie Williams	.12	.07
578	Trevor Wilson	.05	.02
579	Bob Welch	.07	.04
580	David Justice	.20	.12
581	Randy Johnson	.12	.07
582	Jose Vizcaino	.05	.02
583	Jeff Huson	.07	.04
584	Rob Maurer	.10	.06
585	Todd Stottlemyre	.05	.02
586	Joe Oliver	.05	.02
587	Bob Milacki	.05	.02
588	Rob Murphy	.05	.02
589	Greg Pirkl	.10	.06
590	Lenny Harris	.05	.02
591	Luis Rivera	.05	.02
592	John Wetteland	.08	.05
593	Mark Langston	.10	.06
594	Bobby Bonilla	.10	.06
595	Este Beltre	.08	.05
596	Mike Hartley	.08	.05
597	Felix Fermin	.05	.02
598	Carlos Garcia (R)	.35	.20

599 Frank Tanana	.05	.02
600 Pedro Guerrero	.08	.05
601 Terry Shumpert	.05	.02
602 Wally Whitehurst	.05	.02
603 Kevin Seitzer	.05	.02
604 Chris James	.05	.02
605 Greg Gohr	.10	.06
606 Mark Wohlers	.10	.06
607 Kirby Puckett	.25	.15
608 Greg Maddux	.20	.12
609 Don Mattingly	.20	.12
610 Greg Cadaret	.05	.02
611 Dave Stewart	.08	.05
612 Mark Portugal	.07	.04
613 Pete O'Brien	.05	.02
614 Bobby Ojeda	.05	.02
615 Joe Carter	.25	.15
616 Pete Young	.08	.05
617 Sam Horn	.05	.02
618 Vince Coleman	.08	.05
619 Wade Boggs	.15	.10
620 Todd Pratt (R)	.12	.07
621 Ron Tingley (R)	.12	.07
622 Doug Drabek	.10	.06
623 Scott Hemond	.07	.04
624 Tim Jones	.10	.06
625 Dennis Cook	.05	.02
626 Jose Melendez	.08	.05
627 Mike Munoz	.08	.05
628 Jim Pena	.08	.05
629 Gary Thurman	.08	.05
630 Charlie Leibrandt	.05	.02
631 Scott Fletcher	.05	.02
632 Andre Dawson	.12	.07
633 Greg Gagne	.05	.02
634 Greg Swindell	.08	.05
635 Kevin Maas	.07	.04
636 Xavier Hernandez	.07	.04
637 Ruben Sierra	.20	.12
638 Dmitri Young (R)	.50	.30
639 Harold Reynolds	.05	.02
640 Tom Goodwin	.08	.05
641 Todd Burns	.05	.02
642 Jeff Fassero	.05	.02
643 Dave Winfield	.15	.10
644 Willie Randolph	.07	.04
645 Luis Mercedes	.08	.05
646 Dale Murphy	.10	.06
647 Danny Darwin	.05	.02
648 Dennis Moeller	.08	.05
649 Chuck Crim	.08	.05
650 Checklist	.05	.02
651 Shawn Abner	.05	.02
652 Tracy Woodson	.05	.02
653 Scott Scudder	.05	.02
654 Tom Lampkin	.05	.02
655 Alan Trammell	.10	.06
656 Cory Snyder	.05	.02
657 Chris Gwynn	.07	.04
658 Lonnie Smith	.05	.02
659 Jim Austin	.08	.05
660 Checklist	.05	.02
661 Tim Hulett	.15	.10
662 Marvin Freeman	.05	.02
663 Greg Harris	.05	.02
664 Heathcliff Slocumb	.05	.02
665 Mike Butcher	.12	.07
666 Steve Foster	.08	.05
667 Donn Paul	.05	.02
668 Darryl Kile	.10	.06
669 Jesse Levis	.08	.05
670 Jim Gott	.05	.02
671 Mark Hutton	.15	.10
672 Brian Drahman	.15	.10
673 Chad Kreuter	.05	.02
674 Tony Fernandez	.07	.04
675 Jose Lind	.05	.02
676 Kyle Abbott	.08	.05
677 Dan Plesac	.05	.02
678 Barry Bonds	.40	.25
679 Chili Davis	.07	.04
680 Stan Royer	.07	.04
681 Scott Kamieniecki	.07	.04
682 Carlos Martinez	.07	.04
683 Mike Moore	.05	.02
684 Candy Maldonado	.07	.04
685 Jeff Nelson	.10	.06
686 Lou Whitaker	.07	.04
687 Jose Guzman	.05	.02
688 Manuel Lee	.05	.02
689 Bob MacDonald	.08	.05
690 Scott Bankhead	.05	.02
691 Alan Mills	.07	.04
692 Brian Williams	.10	.06
693 Tom Brunansky	.05	.02
694 Lenny Webster	.05	.02
695 Greg Briley	.05	.02
696 Paul O'Neill	.10	.06
697 Joey Cora	.05	.02
698 Charlie O'Brien	.05	.02
699 Junior Ortiz	.05	.02
700 Ron Darling	.07	.04
701 Tony Phillips	.05	.02
702 William Pennyfeather	.10	.06
703 Mark Gubicza	.07	.04
704 Steve Hosey	.15	.10
705 Henry Cotto	.05	.02
706 David Hulse (R)	.15	.10
707 Mike Pagliarulo	.05	.02
708 Dave Stieb	.07	.04
709 Melido Perez	.05	.02
710 Jimmy Key	.08	.05
711 Jeff Russell	.05	.02
712 David Cone	.10	.06

713	Russ Swan	.05	.02
714	Mark Guthrie	.05	.02
715	Checklist	.05	.02
716	Al Martin	.20	.12
717	Randy Knorr	.05	.02
718	Mike Stanley	.05	.02
719	Dick Cutcliffe	.05	.02
720	Terry Leach	.05	.02
721	Chipper Jones	.50	.30
722	Jim Eisenrich	.05	.02
723	Tom Henke	.05	.02
724	Jeff Frye	.08	.05
725	Harold Baines	.07	.04
726	Scott Sanderson	.05	.02
727	Tom Foley	.05	.02
728	Bryan Harvey	.07	.04
729	Tom Edens	.10	.06
730	Eric Young	.12	.07
731	Dave Weathers	.08	.05
732	Spike Owen	.05	.02
733	Scott Aldred	.08	.05
734	Cris Carpenter	.07	.04
735	Dion James	.05	.02
736	Joe Girardi	.05	.02
737	Nigel Wilson	.60	.35
738	Scott Chiamparino	.07	.04
739	Jeff Reardon	.08	.05
740	Willie Blair	.08	.05
741	Jim Corsi	.05	.02
742	Ken Patterson	.05	.02
743	Andy Ashby	.07	.04
744	Rob Natal	.08	.05
745	Kevin Bass	.05	.02
746	Freddie Benavides	.05	.02
747	Chris Donnels	.07	.04
748	Kerry Woodson	.10	.06
749	Calvin Jones	.10	.06
750	Joe Scott	.05	.02
751	Joe Orsulak	.05	.02
752	Armondo Reynoso	.07	.04
753	Monty Fariss	.07	.04
754	Billy Hatcher	.05	.02
755	Denis Boucher	.07	.04
756	Walt Weiss	.05	.02
757	Mike Fitzgerald	.05	.02
758	Rudy Seanez	.07	.04
759	Bret Barberie	.08	.05
760	Mo Sanford	.08	.05
761	Pedro Castellano	.08	.05
762	Chuck Carr	.10	.06
763	Steve Howe	.05	.02
764	Andres Galarraga	.10	.06
765	Jeff Conine	.12	.07
766	Ted Power	.05	.02
767	Butch Henry	.08	.05
768	Steve Decker	.07	.04
769	Storm Davis	.05	.02
770	Vinny Castilla	.10	.06
771	Junior Felix	.05	.02
772	Walt Terrell	.05	.02
773	Brad Ausmus (R)	.20	.12
774	Jamie McAndrew	.10	.06
775	Milt Thompson	.05	.02
776	Charlie Hayes	.05	.02
777	Jack Armstrong	.07	.04
778	Dennis Rasmussen	.05	.02
779	Darren Holmes	.08	.05
780	Alex Arias	.08	.05
781	Randy Bush	.05	.02
782	Javy Lopez	.50	.30
783	Dante Bichette	.07	.04
784	John Johnstone (R)	.10	.06
785	Rene Gonzales	.05	.02
786	Alex Cole	.05	.02
787	Jeromy Burnitz	.25	.15
788	Michael Huff	.07	.04
789	Anthony Telford	.08	.05
790	Jerald Clark	.05	.02
791	Joel Johnston	.05	.02
792	David Nied	.60	.35
E19	Fred McGriff	125.00	80.00
E20	Ryne Sandberg	150.00	90.00
E21	Eddie Murray	60.00	38.00
E22	Paul Molitor	80.00	50.00
E23	Barry Larkin	70.00	40.00
E24	Don Mattingly	100.00	70.00
E25	Dennis Eckersley	50.00	28.00
E26	Roberto Alomar	125.00	80.00
E27	Edgar Martinez	40.00	24.00
E28	Gary Sheffield	75.00	48.00
E29	Darren Daulton	75.00	48.00
E30	Larry Walker	70.00	40.00
E31	Barry Bonds	160.00	95.00
E32	Andy Van Slyke	50.00	28.00
E33	Mark McGwire	75.00	48.00
E34	Cecil Fielder	75.00	48.00
E35	Dave Winfield	75.00	48.00
E36	Juan Gonzalez	175.00	110.00
L1	Robin Yount	200.00	125.00
S1	Will Clark (Auto)	300.00	200.00

1993 Donruss Diamond Kings

For the first time Donruss issued Diamond Kings as a limited insert set. The cards were distributed randomly in the company's foil packs. The full-color card fronts feature the artwork of noted Baseball Hall of Fame artist Dick Perez. All cards measure 2-1/2" by 3-1/2".

		MINT	NR/MT
	Complete Set (30)	60.00	38.00
	Commons	1.00	.70
1	Ken Griffey, Jr.	10.00	6.50
2	Ryne Sandberg	4.50	3.00
3	Roger Clemens	4.00	2.75
4	Kirby Puckett	4.50	3.00
5	Bill Swift	1.00	.70
6	Larry Walker	2.00	1.25
7	Juan Gonzalez	8.50	5.00
8	Wally Joyner	1.00	.70
9	Andy Van Slyke	1.00	.70
10	Robin Ventura	2.50	1.50
11	Bip Roberts	1.00	.70
12	Roberto Kelly	1.00	.70
13	Carlos Baerga	3.50	2.00
14	Orel Hershiser	1.00	.70
15	Cecil Fielder	3.00	1.75
16	Robin Yount	3.50	2.00
17	Darren Daulton	2.50	1.50
18	Mark McGwire	3.50	2.00
19	Tom Glavine	2.50	1.50
20	Roberto Alomar	5.00	3.50
21	Gary Sheffield	3.00	1.75
22	Bob Tewksbury	1.00	.70
23	Brady Anderson	1.25	.80
24	Craig Biggio	1.00	.70
25	Eddie Murray	1.50	.90
26	Luis Polonia	1.00	.70
27	Nigel Wilson	4.00	2.75
28	David Nied	3.00	1.75
29	Pat Listach	1.25	.80
30	Eric Karros	2.50	1.50

1993 Donruss Long Ball Leaders

The cards in this limited insert set were distributed randomly in Donruss Jumbo Packs. Card fronts consist of full-color player photos with the player's name located in a color bar under his photo next to a Long Ball Leaders logo. Card numbers contain the prefix LL. All cards measure 2-1/2" by 3-1/2".

		MINT	NR/MT
	Complete Set (18)	85.00	50.00
	Commons	1.50	.90
1	Rob Deer	1.50	.90
2	Fred McGriff	6.00	3.75
3	Albert Belle	5.00	2.75
4	Mark McGwire	3.50	2.00
5	David Justice	5.00	2.75
6	Jose Canseco	3.50	2.00
7	Kent Hrbek	1.50	.90
8	Roberto Alomar	6.00	3.75
9	Ken Griffey Jr	18.00	12.00
10	Frank Thomas	20.00	14.00
11	Darryl Strawberry	2.00	1.25
12	Felix Jose	1.50	.90
13	Cecil Fielder	3.50	2.00
14	Juan Gonzalez	15.00	10.00
15	Ryne Sandberg	6.00	3.75
16	Gary Sheffield	3.50	2.00
17	Jeff Bagwell	5.00	2.75
18	Larry Walker	3.00	1.75

1993 Donruss MVP's

The cards in this set were issued one per Donruss Jumbo pack. The fronts feature full color action photos with the player's name and team appearing in a banner across the bottom of the card. An MVP logo is centered in a circle under the player's photo. Card numbers include the letters MVP. All cards measure 2-1/2" by 3-1/2".

		MINT	NR/MT
	Complete Set (26)	50.00	35.00
	Commons	.75	.45
1	Luis Polonia	.75	.45
2	Frank Thomas	10.00	6.50
3	George Brett	3.00	1.75
4	Paul Molitor	1.75	1.00
5	Don Mattingly	2.00	1.25
6	Roberto Alomar	3.50	2.00
7	Terry Pendleton	1.00	.70
8	Eric Karros	1.75	1.00
9	Larry Walker	1.00	.70
10	Eddie Murray	1.50	.90
11	Darren Daulton	1.25	.80
12	Ray Lankford	1.00	.70
13	Will Clark	2.00	1.25
14	Cal Ripken	3.50	2.00
15	Roger Clemens	2.50	1.50
16	Carlos Baerga	3.00	1.75
17	Cecil Fielder	1.75	1.00
18	Kirby Puckett	3.00	1.75
19	Mark McGwire	1.75	1.00
20	Ken Griffey, Jr.	7.50	4.50
21	Juan Gonzalez	6.00	3.75
22	Ryne Sandberg	3.00	1.75
23	Bip Roberts	.75	.45
24	Jeff Bagwell	2.50	1.50
25	Barry Bonds	4.50	2.75
26	Gary Sheffield	1.75	1.00

1	Winfield/Bordick	1.75	1.00
2	David Justice	2.50	1.50
3	Roberto Alomar	3.50	2.00
4	Dennis Eckersley	1.00	.70
5	Gonzalez/Canseco	6.00	3.50
6	G. Bell/F. Thomas	7.50	4.50
7	Wade Boggs	1.25	.80
8	Will Clark	2.50	1.50
9	Braggs/Berryhill/ Roberts	.75	.45
10	Fielder/Deer/Tettleton	1.50	.90
11	Kenny Lofton	2.00	1.25
12	Sheffield/McGriff	3.00	1.75
13	Gagne/Larkin	1.00	.70
14	Ryne Sandberg	3.50	2.00
15	Baerga/Gaetti	2.50	1.50
16	Danny Tartabull	1.00	.70
17	Brady Anderson	.75	.45
18	Frank Thomas	10.00	6.50
19	Kevin Gross	.75	.45
20	Robin Yount	3.50	2.00

FLEER

1963 Fleer

RABBIT MARANVILLE

This 67-card set was packaged with a cookie rather than bubble gum and was expected to be the first in a series. However, a lawsuit by filed by Topps ended the series at 67 cards. Two cards in the set, #46 Joe Adcock and the unnumbered checklist are considered scarce. Both are included in the complete set price below. Cards measure 2-1/2" by 3-1/2".

1993 Donruss Spirit Of The Game

The cards in this limited insert set were randomly distributed in Donruss foil and jumbo packs. The fronts consist of full-blee, full-color action shots with the headline "Spirit of the Game" printed across the bottom. Card numbers contain the prefix SG. All cards measure 2-1/2" by 3-1/2".

	MINT	NR/MT
Complete Set (20)	36.00	20.00
Commons	.75	.45

	NR/MT	EX
Complete Set (67)	1,500.00	750.00
Commons	12.00	6.00
1 Steve Barber	20.00	8.50
2 Ron Hansen	12.00	6.00
3 Milt Pappas	12.00	6.00
4 Brooks Robinson	75.00	37.50
5 Willie Mays	200.00	110.00
6 Lou Clinton	12.00	6.00
7 Bill Monbouquette	12.00	6.00
8 Carl Yastrzemski	120.00	60.00
9 Ray Herbert	12.00	6.00
10 Jim Landis	12.00	6.00
11 Dick Donovan	12.00	6.00
12 Tito Francona	12.00	6.00
13 Jerry Kindall	12.00	6.00
14 Frank Lary	15.00	7.50
15 Dick Howser	13.00	6.50
16 Jerry Lumpe	12.00	6.00
17 Norm Siebern	12.00	6.00
18 Don Lee	12.00	6.00
19 Albie Pearson	12.00	6.00
20 Bob Rodgers	12.00	6.00
21 Leon Wagner	12.00	6.00
22 Jim Kaat	20.00	10.00
23 Vic Power	12.00	6.00
24 Rich Rollins	12.00	6.00
25 Bobby Richardson	20.00	10.00
26 Ralph Terry	13.00	6.50
27 Tom Cheney	12.00	6.00
28 Chuck Cottier	12.00	6.00
29 Jimmy Piersall	18.00	9.00
30 Dave Stenhouse	12.00	6.00
31 Glen Hobbie	12.00	6.00
32 Ron Santo	22.00	11.00
33 Gene Freese	12.00	6.00
34 Vada Pinson	15.00	7.50
35 Bob Purkey	12.00	6.00
36 Joe Amalfitano	12.00	6.00
37 Bob Aspromonte	12.00	6.00
38 Dick Farrell	12.00	6.00
39 Al Spangler	12.00	6.00
40 Tommy Davis	16.00	8.00
41 Don Drysdale	70.00	35.00
42 Sandy Koufax	190.00	100.00
43 Maury Wills (R)	90.00	45.00
44 Frank Bolling	12.00	6.00
45 Warren Spahn	70.00	35.00
46 Joe Adcock	175.00	90.00
47 Roger Craig	15.00	7.50
48 Al Jackson	12.00	6.00
49 Rod Kanehl	12.00	6.00
50 Ruben Amaro	12.00	6.00
51 John Callison	13.00	6.50
52 Clay Dalrymple	12.00	6.00

53 Don Demeter	12.00	6.00
54 Art Mahaffey	12.00	6.00
55 Smoky Burgess	14.00	7.00
56 Roberto Clemente	190.00	100.00
57 Elroy Face	15.00	7.50
58 Vernon Law	13.00	6.50
59 Bill Mazeroski	22.00	11.00
60 Ken Boyer	22.00	11.00
61 Bob Gibson	75.00	37.50
62 Gene Oliver	12.00	6.00
63 Bill White	20.00	10.00
64 Orlando Cepeda	28.00	14.00
65 Jimmy Davenport	12.00	6.00
66 Billy O'Dell	12.00	6.00
__ Checklist 1-66	500.00	200.00

1981 Fleer

For the first time since 1963 Fleer returned to the baseball card scene with a 660-card set. The standard size cards measure 2-1/2" by 3-1/2". The set is filled with numerous errors which were corrected creating many variations. Those variations are listed below with the lower price included in the complete set price. Players are grouped by team and each team group has it's own border color that frames a full color player photo on the card fronts. Card backs are horizontal and feature statistical information printed in black, yellow and gray.

	MINT	NR/MT
Complete Set (660)	62.00	45.00
Commons	.10	.05
1 Pete Rose	3.00	2.00
2 Larry Bowa	.15	.10

3	Manny Trillo	.10	.05
4	Bob Boone	.20	.12
5	Mike Schmidt	4.50	3.00
6a	Steve Carlton(Date 1066 on back)	2.00	1.25
6b	Steve Carlton(Date 1966 on back)	4.00	2.75
7	Tug McGraw	.30	.18
8	Larry Christenson	.10	.05
9	Bake McBride	.10	.05
10	Greg Luzinski	.20	.12
11	Ron Reed	.10	.05
12	Dickie Noles	.10	.05
13	Keith Moreland (R)	.12	.07
14	Bob Walk (R)	.60	.35
15	Lonnie Smith	.15	.10
16	Dick Ruthven	.10	.05
17	Sparky Lyle	.15	.10
18	Greg Gross	.10	.05
19	Garry Maddox	.10	.05
20	Nino Espinosa	.10	.05
21	George Vukovich	.10	.05
22	John Vukovich	.10	.05
23	Ramon Aviles	.10	.05
24	Kevin Saucier(Ken Saucier on back)	.10	.05
25	Randy Lerch	.10	.05
26	Del Unser	.10	.05
27	Tim McCarver	.15	.10
28	George Brett	4.50	3.50
29	Willie Wilson	.20	.12
30	Paul Splittorff	.10	.05
31	Dan Quisenberry	.20	.12
32	Amos Otis	.20	.12
33	Steve Busby	.10	.05
34	U.L. Washington	.10	.05
35	Dave Chalk	.10	.05
36	Darrell Porter	.10	.05
37	Marty Pattin	.10	.05
38	Larry Gura	.10	.05
39	Renie Martin	.10	.05
40	Rich Gale	.10	.05
41a	Hal McRae(Black "Royals" on front)	.40	.25
41b	Hal McRae(Light blue "Royals" on front)	.20	.12
42	Dennis Leonard	.10	.05
43	Willie Aikens	.10	.05
44	Frank White	.12	.07
45	Clint Hurdle	.10	.05
46	John Wathan	.10	.05
47	Pete LaCock	.10	.05
48	Rance Mulliniks	.10	.05
49	Jeff Twitty	.10	.05
50	Jamie Quirk	.10	.05
51	Art Howe	.12	.07
52	Ken Forsch	.10	.05
53	Vern Ruhle	.10	.05
54	Joe Niekro	.12	.07
55	Frank LaCorte	.10	.05
56	J.R. Richard	.20	.12
57	Nolan Ryan	10.00	6.50
58	Enos Cabell	.10	.05
59	Cesar Cedeno	.15	.10
60	Jose Cruz	.15	.10
61	Bill Virdon	.12	.07
62	Terry Puhl	.10	.05
63	Joaquin Andujar	.10	.05
64	Alan Ashby	.10	.05
65	Joe Sambito	.10	.05
66	Denny Walling	.10	.05
67	Jeff Leonard	.10	.05
68	Luis Pujols	.10	.05
69	Bruce Bochy	.10	.05
70	Rafael Landestoy	.10	.05
71	Dave Smith (R)	.20	.12
72	Danny Heep (R)	.12	.07
73	Julio Gonzalez	.10	.05
74	Craig Reynolds	.10	.05
75	Gary Woods	.10	.05
76	Dave Bergman	.10	.05
77	Randy Niemann	.10	.05
78	Joe Morgan	1.25	.80
79	Reggie Jackson	4.50	3.50
80	Bucky Dent	.12	.07
81	Tommy John	.15	.10
82	Luis Tiant	.15	.10
83	Rick Cerone	.10	.05
84	Dick Howser	.10	.05
85	Lou Piniella	.15	.10
86	Ron Davis	.10	.05
87a	Graig Nettles(Craig on back)	12.00	8.50
87b	Graig Nettles(Graig on back)	.35	.20
88	Ron Guidry	.30	.18
89	Rich Gossage	.30	.18
90	Rudy May	.10	.05
91	Gaylord Perry	.75	.45
92	Eric Soderholm	.10	.05
93	Bob Watson	.12	.07
94	Bobby Murcer	.15	.10
95	Bobby Brown	.10	.05
96	Jim Spencer	.10	.05
97	Tom Underwood	.10	.05
98	Oscar Gamble	.10	.05
99	Johnny Oates	.12	.07
100	Fred Stanley	.10	.05
101	Ruppert Jones	.10	.05
102	Dennis Werth	.10	.05
103	Joe Lefebvre	.10	.05
104	Brian Doyle	.10	.05
105	Aurelio Rodriguez	.10	.05
106	Doug Bird	.10	.05

#	Player	Price 1	Price 2
107	Mike Griffin	.10	.05
108	Tim Lollar	.10	.05
109	Willie Randolph	.12	.07
110	Steve Garvey	.80	.50
111	Reggie Smith	.12	.07
112	Don Sutton	.80	.50
113	Burt Hooton	.10	.05
114a	Dave Lopes (No finger on back)	.12	.07
114b	Dave Lopes (Small finger on back)	.40	.25
115	Dusty Baker	.12	.07
116	Tom Lasorda	.15	.10
117	Bill Russell	.12	.07
118	Jerry Reuss	.12	.07
119	Terry Forster	.10	.05
120	Robert Welch(Bob)	.35	.20
121	Don Stanhouse	.10	.05
122	Rick Monday	.12	.07
123	Derrel Thomas	.10	.05
124	Joe Ferguson	.10	.05
125	Rick Sutcliffe	.30	.18
126a	Ron Cey(No finger on back)	.12	.07
126b	Ron Cey(Small finger on back)	.40	.25
127	Dave Goltz	.10	.05
128	Jay Johnstone	.12	.07
129	Steve Yeager	.10	.05
130	Gary Weiss	.10	.05
131	Mike Scioscia (R)	.60	.35
132	Vic Davalillo	.10	.05
133	Doug Rau	.10	.05
134	Pepe Frias	.10	.05
135	Mickey Hatcher	.10	.05
136	Steve Howe (R)	.15	.10
137	Robert Castillo	.10	.05
138	Gary Thomasson	.10	.05
139	Rudy Law	.10	.05
140	Fernand Valenzuela (R) (Fernando)	2.50	1.50
141	Manny Mota	.12	.07
142	Gary Carter	1.25	.80
143	Steve Roberts	.10	.05
144	Warren Cromartie	.10	.05
145	Andre Dawson	2.50	1.50
146	Larry Parrish	.10	.05
147	Rowland Office	.10	.05
148	Ellis Valentine	.10	.05
149	Dick Williams	.10	.05
150	Bill Gullickson (R)	.75	.45
151	Elias Sosa	.10	.05
152	John Tamargo	.10	.05
153	Chris Speier	.10	.05
154	Ron LeFlore	.12	.07
155	Rodney Scott	.10	.05
156	Stan Bahnsen	.10	.05
157	Bill Lee	.12	.07
158	Fred Norman	.10	.05
159	Woodie Fryman	.10	.05
160	Dave Palmer	.10	.05
161	Jerry White	.10	.05
162	Roberto Ramos	.10	.05
163	John D'Acquisto	.10	.05
164	Tommy Hutton	.10	.05
165	Charlie Lea (R)	.12	.07
166	Scott Sanderson	.15	.10
167	Ken Macha	.10	.05
168	Tony Bernazard	.10	.05
169	Jim Palmer	2.00	1.25
170	Steve Stone	.12	.07
171	Mike Flanagan	.20	.12
172	Al Bumbry	.10	.05
173	Doug DeCinces	.10	.05
174	Scott McGregor	.10	.05
175	Mark Belanger	.20	.12
176	Tim Stoddard	.10	.05
177a	Rick Dempsey(No finger on front)	.10	.06
177b	Rick Dempsey(Small finger on front)	.35	.20
178	Earl Weaver	.12	.07
179	Tippy Martinez	.10	.05
180	Dennis Martinez	.50	.30
181	Sammy Stewart	.10	.05
182	Rich Dauer	.10	.05
183	Lee May	.10	.05
184	Eddie Murray	3.50	2.50
185	Benny Ayala	.10	.05
186	John Lowenstein	.10	.05
187	Gary Roenicke	.10	.05
188	Ken Singleton	.12	.07
189	Dan Graham	.10	.05
190	Terry Crowley	.10	.05
191	Kiko Garcia	.10	.05
192	Dave Ford	.10	.05
193	Mark Corey	.10	.05
194	Lenn Sakata	.10	.05
195	Doug DeCinces	.10	.05
196	Johnny Bench	2.50	1.50
197	Dave Concepcion	.25	.15
198	Ray Knight	.12	.07
199	Ken Griffey	.25	.15
200	Tom Seaver	3.00	2.00
201	Dave Collins	.10	.05
202	George Foster	.20	.12
203	Junior Kennedy	.10	.05
204	Frank Pastore	.10	.05
205	Dan Driessen	.12	.07
206	Hector Cruz	.10	.05
207	Paul Moskau	.10	.05
208	Charlie Leibrandt (R)	.75	.45
209	Harry Spilman	.10	.05
210	Joe Price (R)	.12	.07

211	Tom Hume	.10	.05
212	Joe Nolan	.10	.05
213	Doug Bair	.10	.05
214	Mario Soto	.12	.07
215	Bill Bonham	.10	.05
216	George Foster	.20	.12
217	Paul Householder	.10	.05
218	Ron Oester	.10	.05
219	Sam Mejias	.10	.05
220	Sheldon Burnside	.10	.05
221	Carl Yastrzemski	2.00	1.25
222	Jim Rice	.25	.15
223	Fred Lynn	.25	.15
224	Carlton Fisk	2.50	1.50
225	Rick Burleson	.12	.07
226	Dennis Eckersley	2.00	1.25
227	Butch Hobson	.10	.05
228	Tom Burgmeier	.10	.05
229	Garry Hancock	.10	.05
230	Don Zimmer	.10	.05
231	Steve Renko	.10	.05
232	Dwight Evans	.40	.25
233	Mike Torrez	.10	.05
234	Bob Stanley	.10	.05
235	Jim Dwyer	.10	.05
236	Dave Stapleton	.10	.05
237	Glenn Hoffman	.10	.05
238	Jerry Remy	.10	.05
239	Dick Drago	.10	.05
240	Bill Campbell	.10	.05
241	Tony Perez	.60	.35
242	Phil Niekro	.80	.50
243	Dale Murphy	1.25	.80
244	Bob Horner	.12	.07
245	Jeff Burroughs	.10	.05
246	Rick Camp	.10	.05
247	Bob Cox	.10	.05
248	Bruce Benedict	.10	.05
249	Gene Garber	.10	.05
250	Jerry Royster	.10	.05
251a	Gary Matthews(No finger on back)	.12	.07
251b	Gary Matthews(Small finger on back)	.35	.20
252	Chris Cambliss	.12	.07
253	Luis Gomez	.10	.05
254	Bill Nahorodny	.10	.05
255	Doyle Alexander	.10	.05
256	Brian Asselstine	.10	.05
257	Biff Pocoroba	.10	.05
258	Mike Lum	.10	.05
259	Charlie Spikes	.10	.05
260	Glenn Hubbard	.10	.05
261	Tommy Boggs	.10	.05
262	Al Hrabosky	.12	.07
263	Rick Matula	.10	.05
264	Preston Hanna	.10	.05
265	Larry Bradford	.10	.05
266	Rafael Ramirez (R)	.12	.07
267	Larry McWilliams	.10	.05
268	Rod Carew	2.50	1.50
269	Bobby Grich	.12	.07
270	Carney Lansford	.15	.10
271	Don Baylor	.20	.12
272	Joe Rudi	.12	.07
273	Dan Ford	.10	.05
274	Jim Fregosi	.12	.07
275	Dave Frost	.10	.05
276	Frank Tanana	.12	.07
277	Dickie Thon	.12	.07
278	Jason Thompson	.10	.05
279	Rick Miller	.10	.05
280	Bert Campaneris	.12	.07
281	Tom Donohue	.10	.05
282	Brian Downing	.15	.10
283	Fred Patek	.10	.05
284	Bruce Kison	.10	.05
285	Dave LaRoche	.10	.05
286	Don Aase	.10	.05
287	Jim Barr	.10	.05
288	Alfredo Martinez	.10	.05
289	Larry Harlow	.10	.05
290	Andy Hassler	.10	.05
291	Dave Kingman	.15	.10
292	Bill Buckner	.15	.10
293	Rick Reuschel	.12	.07
294	Bruce Sutter	.20	.12
295	Jerry Martin	.10	.05
296	Scot Thompson	.10	.05
297	Ivan DeJesus	.10	.05
298	Steve Dillard	.10	.05
299	Dick Tidrow	.10	.05
300	Randy Martz	.10	.05
301	Lenny Randle	.10	.05
302	Lynn McGlothen	.10	.05
303	Cliff Johnson	.10	.05
304	Tim Blackwell	.10	.05
305	Dennis Lamp	.10	.05
306	Bill Caudill	.10	.05
307	Carlos Lezcano	.10	.05
308	Jim Tracy	.10	.05
309	Doug Capilla	.10	.05
310	Willie Hernandez	.12	.07
311	Mike Vail	.10	.05
312	Mike Krukow	.10	.05
313	Barry Foote	.10	.05
314	Larry Biittner	.10	.05
315	Mike Tyson	.10	.05
316	Lee Mazzilli	.10	.05
317	John Stearns	.10	.05
318	Alex Trevino	.10	.05
319	Craig Swan	.10	.05
320	Frank Taveras	.10	.05
321	Steve Henderson	.10	.05

322	Neil Allen	.10	.05
323	Mark Bomback	.10	.05
324	Mike Jorgensen	.10	.05
325	Joe Torre	.12	.07
326	Elliott Maddox	.10	.05
327	Pete Falcone	.10	.05
328	Ray Burris	.10	.05
329	Claudell Washington	.10	.05
330	Doug Flynn	.10	.05
331	Joel Youngblood	.10	.05
332	Bill Almon	.10	.05
333	Tom Hausman	.10	.05
334	Pat Zachry	.10	.05
335	Jeff Reardon (R)	5.00	2.75
336	Wally Backman (R)	.15	.10
337	Dan Norman	.10	.05
338	Jerry Morales	.10	.05
339	Ed Farmer	.10	.05
340	Bob Molinaro	.10	.05
341	Todd Cruz	.10	.05
342	Britt Burns (R)	.15	.10
343	Kevin Bell	.10	.05
344	Tony LaRussa	.15	.10
345	Steve Trout	.10	.05
346	Harold Baines (R)	3.50	2.00
347	Richard Wortham	.10	.05
348	Wayne Nordhagen	.10	.05
349	Mike Squires	.10	.05
350	Lamar Johnson	.10	.05
351	Rickey Henderson	8.50	5.50
352	Francisco Barrios	.10	.05
353	Thad Bosley	.10	.05
354	Chet Lemon	.10	.05
355	Bruce Kimm	.10	.05
356	Richard Dotson (R)	.15	.10
357	Jim Morrison	.10	.05
358	Mike Proly	.10	.05
359	Greg Pryor	.10	.05
360	Dave Parker	.40	.25
361	Omar Moreno	.10	.05
362a	Kent Tekulve (1071 on back)	.12	.07
362b	Kent Tekulve (1971 on back)	.10	.05
363	Willie Stargell	1.25	.80
364	Phil Garner	.12	.07
365	Ed Ott	.10	.05
366	Don Robinson	.10	.05
367	Chuck Tanner	.10	.05
368	Jim Rooker	.10	.05
369	Dale Berra	.10	.05
370	Jim Bibby	.10	.05
371	Steve Nicosia	.10	.05
372	Mike Easler	.10	.05
373	Bill Robinson	.12	.07
374	Lee Lacy	.10	.05
375	John Candelaria	.12	.07
376	Manny Sanguillen	.12	.07
377	Rick Rhoden	.10	.05
378	Grant Jackson	.10	.05
379	Tim Foli	.10	.05
380	Rod Scurry (R)	.12	.07
381	Bill Madlock	.15	.10
382a	Kurt Bevacqua (Photo reversed)	.15	.10
382b	Kurt Bevacqua (Cor)	.10	.05
383	Bert Blyleven	.50	.30
384	Eddie Solomon	.10	.05
385	Enrique Romo	.10	.05
386	John Milner	.10	.05
387	Mike Hargrove	.12	.07
388	Jorge Orta	.10	.05
389	Toby Harrah	.10	.05
390	Tom Veryzer	.10	.05
391	Miguel Dilone	.10	.05
392	Dan Spillner	.10	.05
393	Jack Brohamer	.10	.05
394	Wayne Garland	.10	.05
395	Sid Monge	.10	.05
396	Rick Waits	.10	.05
397	Joe Charboneau (R)	.12	.07
398	Gary Alexander	.10	.05
399	Jerry Dybzinski	.10	.05
400	Mike Stanton	.10	.05
401	Mike Paxton	.10	.05
402	Gary Gray	.10	.05
403	Rick Manning	.10	.05
404	Bo Diaz	.10	.05
405	Ron Hassey	.10	.05
406	Ross Grimsley	.10	.05
407	Victor Cruz	.10	.05
408	Len Barker	.12	.07
409	Bob Bailor	.10	.05
410	Otto Velez	.10	.05
411	Ernie Whitt	.10	.05
412	Jim Clancy	.10	.05
413	Barry Bonnell	.10	.05
414	Dave Stieb	.40	.25
415	Damaso Garcia (R)	.12	.07
416	John Mayberry	.12	.07
417	Roy Howell	.10	.05
418	Dan Ainge (R)	3.50	2.00
419a	Jesse Jefferson (Pirates on back)	.10	.05
419b	Jesse Jefferson (Blue Jays on back)	.20	.12
420	Joey McLaughlin	.10	.05
421	Lloyd Moseby (R)	.25	.15
422	Al Woods	.10	.05
423	Garth Iorg	.10	.05
424	Doug Ault	.10	.05
425	Ken Schrom	.10	.05
426	Mike Willis	.10	.05
427	Steve Braun	.10	.05

428	Bob Davis	.10	.05
429	Jerry Garvin	.10	.05
430	Alfredo Griffin	.10	.05
431	Bob Mattick	.10	.05
432	Vida Blue	.15	.10
433	Jack Clark	.20	.12
434	Willie McCovey	1.25	.80
435	Mike Ivie	.10	.05
436a	Darrel Evans(ER)	.50	.30
436b	Darrell Evans(Cor)	.20	.12
437	Terry Whitfield	.10	.05
438	Rennie Stennett	.10	.05
439	John Montefusco	.10	.05
440	Jim Wohlford	.10	.05
441	Bill North	.10	.05
442	Milt May	.10	.05
443	Max Venable	.10	.05
444	Ed Whitson	.10	.05
445	Al Holland (R)	.12	.07
446	Randy Moffitt	.10	.05
447	Bob Knepper	.10	.05
448	Gary Lavelle	.10	.05
449	Greg Minton	.10	.05
450	Johnnie LeMaster	.10	.05
451	Larry Herndon	.10	.05
452	Rich Murray	.10	.05
453	Joe Pettini	.10	.05
454	Allen Ripley	.10	.05
455	Dennis Littlejohn	.10	.05
456	Tom Griffin	.10	.05
457	Alan Hargesheimer	.10	.05
458	Joe Strain	.10	.05
459	Steve Kemp	.10	.05
460	Sparky Anderson	.15	.10
461	Alan Trammell	1.50	.90
462	Mark Fidrych	.15	.10
463	Lou Whitaker	1.00	.60
464	Dave Rozema	.10	.05
465	Milt Wilcox	.10	.05
466	Champ Summers	.10	.05
467	Lance Parrish	.20	.12
468	Dan Petry	.12	.07
469	Pat Underwood	.10	.05
470	Rick Peters	.10	.05
471	Al Cowens	.10	.05
472	John Wockenfuss	.10	.05
473	Tom Brookens	.10	.05
474	Richie Hebner	.10	.05
475	Jack Morris	1.00	.60
476	Jim Lentine	.10	.05
477	Bruce Robbins	.10	.05
478	Mark Wagner	.10	.05
479	Tim Corcoran	.10	.05
480	Stan Papi(P)	.12	.07
480b	Stan Papi (SS)	.10	.05
481	Kirk Gibson (R)	3.00	1.75
482	Dan Schatzeder	.10	.05
483	Amos Otis	.20	.12
484	Dave Winfield	5.00	2.75
485	Rollie Fingers	1.25	.80
486	Gene Richards	.10	.05
487	Randy Jones	.12	.07
488	Ozzie Smith	3.00	1.75
489	Gene Tenace	.12	.07
490	Bill Fahey	.10	.05
491	John Curtis	.10	.05
492	Dave Cash	.10	.05
493a	Tim Flannery(Photo reversed)	.12	.07
493b	Tim Flannery(Cor)	.10	.05
494	Jerry Mumphrey	.10	.05
495	Bob Shirley	.10	.05
496	Steve Mura	.10	.05
497	Eric Rasmussen	.10	.05
498	Broderick Perkins	.10	.05
499	Barry Evans	.10	.05
500	Chuck Baker	.10	.05
501	Luis Salazar (R)	.12	.07
502	Gary Lucas	.10	.05
503	Mike Armstrong	.10	.05
504	Jerry Turner	.10	.05
505	Dennis Kinney	.10	.05
506	Willie Montanez	.10	.05
507	Gorman Thomas	.12	.07
508	Ben Oglivie	.10	.05
509	Larry Hisle	.12	.07
510	Sal Bando	.12	.07
511	Robin Yount	4.50	3.50
512	Mike Caldwell	.10	.05
513	Sixto Lezcano	.10	.05
514a	Jerry Augustine(Billy Travers photo)	.15	.10
514b	Billy Travers(Correct name with photo)	.10	.05
515	Paul Molitor	3.50	2.00
516	Moose Haas	.10	.05
517	Bill Castro	.10	.05
518	Jim Slaton	.10	.05
519	Lary Sorensen	.10	.05
520	Bob McClure	.10	.05
521	Charlie Moore	.10	.05
522	Jim Gantner	.12	.07
523	Reggie Cleveland	.10	.05
524	Don Money	.10	.05
525	Billy Travers	.10	.05
526	Buck Martinez	.10	.05
527	Dick Davis	.10	.05
528	Ted Simmons	.20	.12
529	Garry Templeton	.12	.07
530	Ken Reitz	.10	.05
531	Tony Scott	.10	.05
532	Ken Oberkfell	.10	.05
533	Bob Sykes	.10	.05
534	Keith Smith	.10	.05

535	John Littlefield	.10	.05	589	Steve McCatty	.10	.05
536	Jim Kaat	.30	.18	590	Dwayne Murphy	.10	.05
537	Bob Forsch	.10	.05	591	Mario Guerrero	.10	.05
538	Mike Phillips	.10	.05	592	Dave McKay	.10	.05
539	Terry Landrum (R)	.12	.07	593	Jim Essian	.10	.05
540	Leon Durham (R)	.15	.10	594	Dave Heaverlo	.10	.05
541	Terry Kennedy	.12	.07	595	Maury Wills	.15	.10
542	George Hendrick	.12	.07	596	Juan Beniquez	.10	.05
543	Dane Iorg	.10	.05	597	Rodney Craig	.10	.05
544	Mark Littell	.10	.05	598	Jim Anderson	.10	.05
545	Keith Hernandez	.25	.15	599	Floyd Bannister	.10	.05
546	Silvio Martinez	.10	.05	600	Bruce Bochte	.10	.05
547a	Pete Vuckovich(Don Hood Photo)	.25	.15	601	Julio Cruz	.10	.05
				602	Ted Cox	.10	.05
547b	Don Hood(correct Photo)	.10	.05	603	Dan Meyer	.10	.05
				604	Larry Cox	.10	.05
548	Bobby Bonds	.20	.12	605	Bill Stein	.10	.05
549	Mike Ramsey	.10	.05	606	Steve Garvey	.80	.50
550	Tom Herr	.10	.05	607	Dave Roberts	.10	.05
551	Roy Smalley	.10	.05	608	Leon Roberts	.10	.05
552	Jerry Koosman	.15	.10	609	Reggie Walton	.10	.05
553	Ken Landreaux	.10	.05	610	Dave Edler	.10	.05
554	John Castino	.10	.05	611	Larry Milbourne	.10	.05
555	Doug Corbett	.10	.05	612	Kim Allen	.10	.05
556	Bombo Rivera	.10	.05	613	Mario Mendoza	.10	.05
557	Ron Jackson	.10	.05	614	Tom Paciorek	.10	.05
558	Butch Wynegar	.10	.05	615	Glenn Abbott	.10	.05
559	Hosken Powell	.10	.05	616	Joe Simpson	.10	.05
560	Pete Redfern	.10	.05	617	Mickey Rivers	.12	.07
561	Roger Erickson	.10	.05	618	Jim Kern	.10	.05
562	Glenn Adams	.10	.05	619	Jim Sundberg	.10	.05
563	Rick Sofield	.10	.05	620	Richie Zisk	.10	.05
564	Geoff Zahn	.10	.05	621	Jon Matlack	.12	.07
565	Pete Mackanin	.10	.05	622	Ferguson Jenkins	.75	.45
566	Mike Cubbage	.10	.05	623	Pat Corrales	.10	.05
567	Darrell Jackson	.10	.05	624	Ed Figueroa	.10	.05
568	Dave Edwards	.10	.05	625	Buddy Bell	.10	.05
569	Rob Wilfong	.10	.05	626	Al Oliver	.15	.10
570	Sal Butera	.10	.05	627	Doc Medich	.10	.05
571	Jose Morales	.10	.05	628	Bump Wills	.10	.05
572	Rick Langford	.10	.05	629	Rusty Staub	.15	.10
573	Mike Norris	.10	.05	630	Pat Putnam	.10	.05
574	Rickey Henderson	12.00	7.50	631	John Grubb	.10	.05
575	Tony Armas	.12	.07	632	Danny Darwin	.12	.07
576	Dave Revering	.10	.05	633	Ken Clay	.10	.05
577	Jeff Newman	.10	.05	634	Jim Norris	.10	.05
578	Bob Lacey	.10	.05	635	John Butcher	.10	.05
579	Brian Kingman	.10	.05	636	Dave Roberts	.10	.05
580	Mitchell Page	.10	.05	637	Billy Sample	.10	.05
581	Billy Martin	.20	.12	638	Carl Yastrzemski	2.00	1.00
582	Rob Piciolo	.10	.05	639	Cecil Cooper	.20	.12
583	Mike Heath	.10	.05	640	Mike Schmidt	4.50	3.00
584	Mickey Klutts	.10	.05	641	Checklist (1-50)	.15	.07
585	Orlando Gonzalez	.10	.05	642	Checklist (51-109)	.15	.07
586	Mike Davis (R)	.15	.10	643	Checklist (110-168)	.15	.07
587	Wayne Gross	.10	.05	644	Checklist (169-220)	.15	.07
588	Matt Keough	.10	.05				

645a	Triple Threat(Larry Bowa, Pete Rose, Mike Schmidt)(No card Number)	3.50	2.50
645b	Triple Threat(Larry Bowa, Pete Rose, Mike Schmidt) (Cor)	2.50	1.50
646	Checklist (221-267)	.15	.07
647	Checklist (268-315)	.15	.07
648	Checklist (316-359)	.15	.07
649	Checklist (360-408)	.15	.07
650	Reggie Jackson	4.50	3.00
651	Checklist (409-458)	.15	.07
652	Checklist (459-509)	.15	.07
653	Willie Wilson	.15	.10
654	Checklist (507-550)	.15	.07
655	George Brett	3.50	2.50
656	Checklist (551-593)	.15	.07
657	Tug McGraw	.20	.12
658	Checklist (594-637)	.15	.07
659	Checklist (640-660)	.15	.07
660a	Steve Carlton(Date 1066 on back)	2.00	1.25
660b	Steve Carlton(Date 1966 on back)	3.50	2.50

1982 Fleer

This 660-card set features full color photos with multi-colored borders with each team assigned a different border color. Card backs are horizontal and printed in blue, yellow and white. The set is marked by poor photography and many variations. The lower priced variation is included in the complete set price below. Cards measure 2-1/2" by 3-1/2".

		MINT	NR/MT
Complete Set (660)		100.00	65.00
Commons		.10	.05
1	Dusty Baker	.12	.07
2	Robert Castillo	.10	.05
3	Ron Cey	.12	.07
4	Terry Forster	.10	.05
5	Steve Garvey	.75	.45
6	Dave Goltz	.10	.05
7	Pedro Guerrero	.20	.12
8	Burt Hooton	.10	.05
9	Steve Howe	.15	.10
10	Jay Johnstone	.10	.05
11	Ken Landreaux	.10	.05
12	Davey Lopes	.12	.07
13	Mike Marshall (R)	.12	.07
14	Bobby Mitchell	.10	.05
15	Rick Monday	.12	.07
16	Tom Niedenfuer (R)	.12	.07
17	Ted Power (R)	.15	.10
18	Jerry Reuss	.12	.07
19	Ron Roenicke	.10	.05
20	Bill Russell	.12	.07
21	Steve Sax (R)	1.50	.90
22	Mike Scioscia	.30	.18
23	Reggie Smith	.12	.07
24	Dave Stewart (R)	3.50	2.00
25	Rick Sutcliffe	.25	.15
26	Derrel Thomas	.10	.05
27	Fernando Valenzuela	.20	.12
28	Bob Welch	.25	.15
29	Steve Yeager	.10	.05
30	Bobby Brown	.10	.05
31	Rick Cerone	.10	.05
32	Ron Davis	.10	.05
33	Bucky Dent	.12	.07
34	Barry Foote	.10	.05
35	George Frazier	.10	.05
36	Oscar Gamble	.10	.05
37	Rich Gossage	.25	.15
38	Ron Guidry	.25	.15
39	Reggie Jackson	3.00	2.00
40	Tommy John	.15	.10
41	Rudy May	.10	.05
42	Larry Milbourne	.10	.05
43	Jerry Mumphrey	.10	.05
44	Bobby Murcer	.12	.07
45	Gene Nelson (R)	.12	.07
46	Graig Nettles	.15	.10
47	Johnny Oates	.10	.05
48	Lou Piniella	.12	.07
49	Willie Randolph	.12	.07
50	Rick Reuschel	.12	.07
51	Dave Revering	.10	.05
52	Dave Righetti (R)	.40	.25

53	Aurelio Rodriguez	.10	.05
54	Bob Watson	.12	.07
55	Dennis Werth	.10	.05
56	Dave Winfield	4.00	2.50
57	Johnny Bench	.30	.18
58	Bruce Berenyi	.10	.05
59	Larry Biitner	.10	.05
60	Scott Brown	.10	.05
61	Dave Collins	.10	.05
62	Geoff Combe	.10	.05
63	Dave Concepcion	.20	.12
64	Dan Driessen	.12	.07
65	Joe Edelen	.10	.05
66	George Foster	.15	.10
67	Ken Griffey	.20	.12
68	Paul Householder	.10	.05
69	Tom Hume	.10	.05
70	Junior Kennedy	.10	.05
71	Ray Knight	.12	.07
72	Mike LaCoss	.10	.05
73	Rafael Landestoy	.10	.05
74	Charlie Leibrandt	.12	.07
75	Sam Mejias	.10	.05
76	Paul Moskau	.10	.05
77	Joe Nolan	.10	.05
78	Mike O'Berry	.10	.05
79	Ron Oester	.10	.05
80	Frank Pastore	.10	.05
81	Joe Price	.10	.05
82	Tom Seaver	2.50	1.50
83	Mario Soto	.12	.07
84	Mike Vail	.10	.05
85	Tony Armas	.10	.05
86	Shooty Babitt	.10	.05
87	Dave Beard	.10	.05
88	Rick Bosetti	.10	.05
89	Keith Drumright	.10	.05
90	Wayne Gross	.10	.05
91	Mike Heath	.10	.05
92	Rickey Henderson	4.50	3.50
93	Cliff Johnson	.10	.05
94	Jeff Jones	.10	.05
95	Matt Keough	.10	.05
96	Brian Kingman	.10	.05
97	Mickey Klutts	.10	.05
98	Rick Langford	.10	.05
99	Steve McCatty	.10	.05
100	Dave McKay	.10	.05
101	Dwayne Murphy	.10	.05
102	Jeff Newman	.10	.05
103	Mike Norris	.10	.05
104	Bob Owchinko	.10	.05
105	Mitchell Page	.10	.05
106	Rob Picciolo	.10	.05
107	Jim Spencer	.10	.05
108	Fred Stanley	.10	.05
109	Tom Underwood	.10	.05
110	Joaquin Andujar	.12	.07
111	Steve Braun	.10	.05
112	Bob Forsch	.10	.05
113	George Hendrick	.12	.07
114	Keith Hernandez	.20	.12
115	Tom Herr	.10	.05
116	Dane Iorg	.10	.05
117	Jim Kaat	.15	.10
118	Tito Landrum	.10	.05
119	Sixto Lezcano	.10	.05
120	Mark Littell	.10	.05
121	John Martin	.10	.05
122	Silvio Martinez	.10	.05
123	Ken Oberkfell	.10	.05
124	Darrell Porter	.12	.07
125	Mike Ramsey	.10	.05
126	Orlando Sanchez	.10	.05
127	Bob Shirley	.10	.05
128	Lary Sorensen	.10	.05
129	Bruce Sutter	.15	.10
130	Bob Sykes	.10	.05
131	Garry Templeton	.12	.07
132	Gene Tenace	.12	.07
133	Jerry Augustine	.10	.05
134	Sal Bando	.12	.07
135	Mark Brouhard	.10	.05
136	Mike Caldwell	.10	.05
137	Reggie Cleveland	.10	.05
138	Cecil Cooper	.12	.07
139	Jamie Easterly	.10	.05
140	Marshall Edwards	.10	.05
141	Rollie Fingers	.80	.50
142	Jim Gantner	.10	.05
143	Moose Haas	.10	.05
144	Larry Hisle	.10	.05
145	Roy Howell	.10	.05
146	Rickey Keeton	.10	.05
147	Randy Lerch	.10	.05
148	Paul Molitor	3.00	1.75
149	Don Money	.10	.05
150	Charlie Moore	.10	.05
151	Ben Oglivie	.10	.05
152	Ted Simmons	.15	.10
153	Jim Slaton	.10	.05
154	Gorman Thomas	.12	.07
155	Robin Yount	3.00	2.00
156	Pete Vukovich	.12	.07
157	Benny Ayala	.10	.05
158	Mark Belanger	.12	.07
159	Al Bumbry	.10	.05
160	Terry Crowley	.10	.05
161	Rich Dauer	.10	.05
162	Doug DeCinces	.10	.05
163	Rick Dempsey	.10	.05
164	Jim Dwyer	.10	.05
165	Mike Flanagan	.15	.10
166	Dave Ford	.10	.05

167	Dan Graham	.10	.05
168	Wayne Krenchicki	.10	.05
169	John Lowenstein	.10	.05
170	Dennis Martinez	.30	.18
171	Tippy Martinez	.10	.05
172	Scott McGregor	.10	.05
173	Jose Morales	.10	.05
174	Eddie Murray	2.50	1.50
175	Jim Palmer	1.50	.90
176	Cal Ripken, Jr. (R)	60.00	48.00
177	Gary Roenicke	.10	.05
178	Lenn Sakata	.10	.05
179	Ken Singleton	.10	.05
180	Sammy Stewart	.10	.05
181	Tim Stoddard	.10	.05
182	Steve Stone	.12	.07
183	Stan Bahnsen	.10	.05
184	Ray Burris	.10	.05
185	Gary Carter	1.00	.70
186	Warren Cromartie	.10	.05
187	Andre Dawson	2.50	1.50
188	Terry Francona (R)	.12	.07
189	Woodie Fryman	.10	.05
190	Bill Gullickson	.15	.10
191	Grant Jackson	.10	.05
192	Wallace Johnson	.10	.05
193	Charlie Lea	.10	.05
194	Bill Lee	.10	.05
195	Jerry Manuel	.10	.05
196	Brad Mills	.10	.05
197	John Milner	.10	.05
198	Rowland Office	.10	.05
199	David Palmer	.10	.05
200	Larry Parrish	.10	.05
201	Mike Phillips	.10	.05
202	Tim Raines (R)	2.50	1.50
203	Bobby Ramos	.10	.05
204	Jeff Reardon	1.50	.90
205	Steve Rogers	.10	.05
206	Scott Sanderson	.12	.07
207	Rodney Scott(Wrong Photo)	.15	.10
208	Elias Sosa	.10	.05
209	Chris Speier	.10	.05
210	Tim Wallach (R)	.80	.50
211	Jerry White	.10	.05
212	Alan Ashby	.10	.05
213	Cesar Cedeno	.12	.07
214	Jose Cruz	.12	.07
215	Kiko Garcia	.10	.05
216	Phil Garner	.12	.07
217	Danny Heep	.10	.05
218	Art Howe	.12	.07
219	Bob Knepper	.10	.05
220	Frank LaCorte	.10	.05
221	Joe Niekro	.10	.05
222	Joe Pittman	.10	.05
223	Terry Puhl	.10	.05
224	Luis Pujols	.10	.05
225	Craig Reynolds	.10	.05
226	J.R. Richard	.12	.07
227	Dave Roberts	.10	.05
228	Vern Ruhle	.10	.05
229	Nolan Ryan	9.00	5.75
230	Joe Sambito	.10	.05
231	Tony Scott	.10	.05
232	Dave Smith	.10	.05
233	Harry Spilman	.10	.05
234	Don Sutton	.50	.30
235	Dickie Thon	.10	.05
236	Denny Walling	.10	.05
237	Gary Woods	.10	.05
238	Luis Aguayo (R)	.12	.07
239	Ramon Aviles	.10	.05
240	Bob Boone	.15	.10
241	Larry Bowa	.12	.07
242	Warren Brusstar	.10	.05
243	Steve Carlton	2.50	1.50
244	Larry Christenson	.10	.05
245	Dick Davis	.10	.05
246	Greg Gross	.10	.05
247	Sparky Lyle	.12	.07
248	Garry Maddox	.10	.05
249	Gary Matthews	.10	.05
250	Bake McBride	.10	.05
251	Tug McGraw	.15	.10
252	Keith Moreland	.10	.05
253	Dickie Noles	.10	.05
254	Mike Proly	.10	.05
255	Ron Reed	.10	.05
256	Pete Rose	3.00	1.75
257	Dick Ruthven	.10	.05
258	Mike Schmidt	3.50	2.50
259	Lonnie Smith	.15	.10
260	Manny Trillo	.10	.05
261	Del Unser	.10	.05
262	George Vukovich	.10	.05
263	Tom Brookens	.10	.05
264	George Cappuzzello	.10	.05
265	Marty Castillo	.10	.05
266	Al Cowens	.10	.05
267	Kirk Gibson	1.00	.70
268	Richie Hebner	.10	.05
269	Ron Jackson	.10	.05
270	Lynn Jones	.10	.05
271	Steve Kemp	.10	.05
272	Rick Leach (R)	.12	.07
273	Aurelio Lopez	.10	.05
274	Jack Morris	.80	.50
275	Kevin Saucier	.10	.05
276	Lance Parrish	.15	.10
277	Rick Peters	.10	.05
278	Dan Petry	.12	.07
279	Davis Rozema	.10	.05

280 Stan Papi	.10	.05
281 Dan Schatzeder	.10	.05
282 Champ Summers	.10	.05
283 Alan Trammell	1.00	.70
284 Lou Whitaker	.75	.45
285 Milt Wilcox	.10	.05
286 John Wockenfuss	.10	.05
287 Gary Allenson	.10	.05
288 Tom Burgmeier	.10	.05
289 Bill Campbell	.10	.05
290 Mark Clear	.10	.05
291 Steve Crawford	.10	.05
292 Dennis Eckersley	1.50	.90
293 Dwight Evans	.25	.15
294 Rich Gedman (R)	.12	.07
295 Garry Hancock	.10	.05
296 Glenn Hoffman	.10	.05
297 Bruce Hurst (R)	.60	.35
298 Carney Lansford	.12	.07
299 Rick Miller	.10	.05
300 Reid Nichols	.10	.05
301 Bob Ojeda (R)	.35	.20
302 Tony Perez	.50	.30
303 Chuck Rainey	.10	.05
304 Jerry Remy	.10	.05
305 Jim Rice	.25	.15
306 Joe Rudi	.12	.07
307 Bob Stanley	.10	.05
308 Dave Stapleton	.10	.05
309 Frank Tanana	.12	.07
310 Mike Torrez	.10	.05
311 John Tudor (R)	.15	.10
312 Carl Yastrzemski	1.75	1.00
313 Buddy Bell	.10	.05
314 Steve Comer	.10	.05
315 Danny Darwin	.10	.05
316 John Ellis	.10	.05
317 John Grubb	.10	.05
318 Rick Honeycutt	.10	.05
319 Charlie Hough	.12	.07
320 Ferguson Jenkins	.70	.40
321 John Henry Johnson	.10	.05
322 Jim Kern	.10	.05
323 Jon Matlack	.10	.05
324 Doc Medich	.10	.05
325 Mario Mendoza	.10	.05
326 Al Oliver	.15	.10
327 Pat Putnam	.10	.05
328 Mickey Rivers	.10	.05
329 Leon Roberts	.10	.05
330 Billy Sample	.10	.05
331 Bill Stein	.10	.05
332 Jim Sundberg	.10	.05
333 Mark Wagner	.10	.05
334 Bump Wills	.10	.05
335 Bill Almon	.10	.05
336 Harold Baines	.80	.50

337 Ross Baumgarten	.10	.05
338 Tony Bernazard	.10	.05
339 Britt Burns	.10	.05
340 Richard Dotson	.10	.05
341 Jim Essian	.10	.05
342 Ed Farmer	.10	.05
343 Carlton Fisk	1.75	1.00
344 Kevin Hickey	.10	.05
345 LaMarr Hoyt	.10	.05
346 Lamar Johnson	.10	.05
347 Jerry Koosman	.12	.07
348 Rusty Kuntz	.10	.05
349 Dennis Lamp	.10	.05
350 Ron LeFlore	.10	.05
351 Chet Lemon	.10	.05
352 Greg Luzinski	.12	.07
353 Bob Molinaro	.10	.05
354 Jim Morrison	.10	.05
355 Wayne Nordhagen	.10	.05
356 Greg Pryor	.10	.05
357 Mike Squires	.10	.05
358 Steve Trout	.10	.05
359 Alan Bannister	.10	.05
360 Len Barker	.10	.05
361 Bert Blyleven	.40	.25
362 Joe Charboneau	.10	.05
363 John Denny	.10	.05
364 Bo Diaz	.10	.05
365 Miguel Dilone	.10	.05
366 Jerry Dybzinski	.10	.05
367 Wayne Garland	.10	.05
368 Mike Hargrove	.10	.05
369 Toby Harrah	.10	.05
370 Ron Hassey	.10	.05
371 Von Hayes (R)	.25	.15
372 Pat Kelly	.10	.05
373 Duane Kuiper	.10	.05
374 Rick Manning	.10	.05
375 Sid Monge	.10	.05
376 Jorge Orta	.10	.05
377 Dave Rosello	.10	.05
378 Dan Spillner	.10	.05
379 Mike Stanton	.10	.05
380 Andre Thornton	.12	.07
381 Tom Veryzer	.10	.05
382 Rick Waits	.10	.05
383 Doyle Alexander	.10	.05
384 Vida Blue	.15	.10
385 Fred Breining	.10	.05
386 Enos Cabell	.10	.05
387 Jack Clark	.15	.10
388 Darrell Evans	.12	.07
389 Tom Griffin	.10	.05
390 Larry Herndon	.10	.05
391 Al Holland	.10	.05
392 Gary Lavelle	.10	.05
393 Johnnie LeMaster	.10	.05

394	Jerry Martin	.10	.05
395	Milt May	.10	.05
396	Greg Minton	.10	.05
397	Joe Morgan	.80	.50
398	Joe Pettini	.10	.05
399	Alan Ripley	.10	.05
400	Billy Smith	.10	.05
401	Rennie Stennett	.10	.05
402	Ed Whitson	.10	.05
403	Jim Wohlford	.10	.05
404	Willie Aikens	.10	.05
405	George Brett	3.50	2.50
406	Ken Brett	.10	.05
407	Dave Chalk	.10	.05
408	Rich Gale	.10	.05
409	Cesar Geronimo	.10	.05
410	Larry Gura	.10	.05
411	Clint Hurdle	.10	.05
412	Mike Jones	.10	.05
413	Dennis Leonard	.10	.05
414	Renie Martin	.10	.05
415	Lee May	.10	.05
416	Hal McRae	.12	.07
417	Darryl Motley	.10	.05
418	Rance Mulliniks	.10	.05
419	Amos Otis	.12	.07
420	Ken Phelps (R)	.15	.10
421	Jamie Quirk	.10	.05
422	Dan Quisenberry	.12	.07
423	Paul Splittorff	.12	.07
424	U.L. Washington	.10	.05
425	John Wathan	.10	.05
426	Frank White	.15	.10
427	Willie Wilson	.15	.10
428	Brian Asselstine	.10	.05
429	Bruce Benedict	.10	.05
430	Tom Boggs	.10	.05
431	Larry Bradford	.10	.05
432	Rick Camp	.10	.05
433	Chris Chambliss	.12	.07
434	Gene Garber	.10	.05
435	Preston Hanna	.10	.05
436	Bob Horner	.12	.07
437	Glenn Hubbard	.10	.05
438a	Al Hrabosky (5'1")	18.00	12.00
438b	Al Hrabosky (5'10")	1.00	.70
439	Rufino Linares	.10	.05
440	Rick Mahler (R)	.12	.07
441	Ed Miller	.10	.05
442	John Montefusco	.10	.05
443	Dale Murphy	1.00	.70
444	Phil Niekro	.75	.45
445	Gaylord Perry	.75	.45
446	Biff Pocoroba	.10	.05
447	Rafael Ramirez	.10	.05
448	Jerry Royster	.10	.05
449	Claudell Washington	.10	.05
450	Don Aase	.10	.05
451	Don Baylor	.20	.12
452	Juan Beniquez	.10	.05
453	Rick Burleson	.10	.05
454	Bert Campaneris	.12	.07
455	Rod Carew	1.75	1.00
456	Bob Clark	.10	.05
457	Brian Downing	.12	.07
458	Dan Ford	.10	.05
459	Ken Forsch	.10	.05
460	Dave Frost	.10	.05
461	Bobby Grich	.12	.07
462	Larry Harlow	.10	.05
463	John Harris	.10	.05
464	Andy Hassler	.10	.05
465	Butch Hobson	.12	.07
466	Jesse Jefferson	.10	.05
467	Bruce Kison	.10	.05
468	Fred Lynn	.20	.12
469	Angel Moreno	.10	.05
470	Ed Ott	.10	.05
471	Fred Patek	.10	.05
472	Steve Renko	.10	.05
473	Mike Witt (R)	.20	.12
474	Geoff Zahn	.10	.05
475	Gary Alexander	.10	.05
476	Dale Berra	.10	.05
477	Kurt Bevacqua	.10	.05
478	Jim Bibby	.10	.05
479	John Candelaria	.10	.05
480	Victor Cruz	.10	.05
481	Mike Easler	.10	.05
482	Tim Foli	.10	.05
483	Lee Lacy	.10	.05
484	Vance Law (R)	.12	.07
485	Bill Madlock	.15	.10
486	Willie Montanez	.10	.05
487	Omar Moreno	.10	.05
488	Steve Nicosia	.10	.05
489	Dave Parker	.30	.18
490	Tony Pena (R)	.25	.15
491	Pascual Perez (R)	.15	.10
492	Johnny Ray (R)	.12	.07
493	Rick Rhoden	.10	.05
494	Bill Robinson	.12	.07
495	Don Robinson	.10	.05
496	Enrique Romo	.10	.05
497	Rod Scurry	.10	.05
498	Eddie Solomon	.10	.05
499	Willie Stargell	.80	.50
500	Kent Tekulve	.10	.05
501	Jason Thompson	.10	.05
502	Glenn Abbott	.10	.05
503	Jim Anderson	.10	.05
504	Floyd Bannister	.10	.05
505	Bruce Bochte	.10	.05
506	Jeff Burroughs	.10	.05

507 Bryan Clark	.10	.05	
508 Ken Clay	.10	.05	
509 Julio Cruz	.10	.05	
510 Dick Drago	.10	.05	
511 Gary Gray	.10	.05	
512 Dan Meyer	.10	.05	
513 Jerry Narron	.10	.05	
514 Tom Paciorek	.10	.05	
515 Casey Parsons	.10	.05	
516 Lenny Randle	.10	.05	
517 Shane Rawley	.10	.05	
518 Joe Simpson	.10	.05	
519 Richie Zisk	.10	.05	
520 Neil Allen	.10	.05	
521 Bob Bailor	.10	.05	
522 Hubie Brooks (R)	.35	.20	
523 Mike Cubbage	.10	.05	
524 Pete Falcone	.10	.05	
525 Doug Flynn	.10	.05	
526 Tom Hausman	.10	.05	
527 Ron Hodges	.10	.05	
528 Randy Jones	.12	.07	
529 Mike Jorgensen	.10	.05	
530 Dave Kingman	.15	.10	
531 Ed Lynch	.10	.05	
532 Mike Marshall	.12	.07	
533 Lee Mazzilli	.10	.05	
534 Dyar Miller	.10	.05	
535 Mike Scott (R)	.25	.15	
536 Rusty Staub	.20	.12	
537 John Stearns	.10	.05	
538 Craig Swan	.10	.05	
539 Frank Taveras	.10	.05	
540 Alex Trevino	.10	.05	
541 Ellis Valentine	.10	.05	
542 Mookie Wilson (R)	.15	.10	
543 Joel Youngblood	.10	.05	
544 Pat Zachry	.10	.05	
545 Glenn Adams	.10	.05	
546 Fernando Arroyo	.10	.05	
547 John Verhoeven	.10	.05	
548 Sal Butera	.10	.05	
549 John Castino	.10	.05	
550 Don Cooper	.10	.05	
551 Doug Corbett	.10	.05	
552 Dave Engle	.10	.05	
553 Roger Erickson	.10	.05	
554 Danny Goodwin	.10	.05	
555a Darrell Jackson (Red cap)	.10	.05	
555b Darrell Jackson (Red cap, no logo)	2.50	1.50	
555c Darrell Jackson (Black Cap)	.35	.20	
556 Pete Mackanin	.10	.05	
557 Jack O'Connor	.10	.05	
558 Hosken Powell	.10	.05	
559 Pete Redfern	.10	.05	
560 Roy Smalley	.10	.05	
561 Chuck Baker	.10	.05	
562 Gary Ward	.10	.05	
563 Rob Wilfong	.10	.05	
564 Al Williams	.10	.05	
565 Butch Wynegar	.10	.05	
566 Randy Bass	.10	.05	
567 Juan Bonilla	.10	.05	
568 Danny Boone	.10	.05	
569 John Curtis	.10	.05	
570 Juan Eichelberger	.10	.05	
571 Barry Evans	.10	.05	
572 Tim Flannery	.10	.05	
573 Ruppert Jones	.10	.05	
574 Terry Kennedy	.10	.05	
575 Joe Lefebvre	.10	.05	
576a John Littlefield (Throwing Left-handed)	275.00	135.00	
576b John Littlefield (Throwing Right-handed)	.10	.05	
577 Gary Lucas	.10	.05	
578 Steve Mura	.10	.05	
579 Broderick Perkins	.10	.05	
580 Gene Richards	.10	.05	
581 Luis Salazar	.10	.05	
582 Ozzie Smith	2.50	1.50	
583 John Urrea	.10	.05	
584 Chris Welsh	.10	.05	
585 Rick Wise	.10	.05	
586 Doug Bird	.10	.05	
587 Tim Blackwell	.10	.05	
588 Bobby Bonds	.15	.10	
589 Bill Buckner	.12	.07	
590 Bill Caudill	.10	.05	
591 Hector Cruz	.10	.05	
592 Jody Davis (R)	.15	.10	
593 Ivan DeJesus	.10	.05	
594 Steve Dillard	.10	.05	
595 Leon Durham	.12	.07	
596 Rawly Eastwick	.10	.05	
597 Steve Henderson	.10	.05	
598 Mike Krukow	.10	.05	
599 Mike Lum	.10	.05	
600 Randy Martz	.10	.05	
601 Jerry Morales	.10	.05	
602 Ken Reitz	.10	.05	
603 Lee Smith (R)	9.00	5.75	
604 Dick Tidrow	.10	.05	
605 Jim Tracy	.10	.05	
606 Mike Tyson	.10	.05	
607 Ty Waller	.10	.05	
608 Danny Ainge	1.25	.80	
609 Jorge Bell (R)	4.00	2.50	
610 Mark Bomback	.10	.05	

611	Barry Bonnell	.10	.05
612	Jim Clancy	.10	.05
613	Damaso Garcia	.10	.05
614	Jerry Garvin	.10	.05
615	Alfredo Griffin	.10	.05
616	Garth Iorg	.10	.05
617	Luis Leal	.10	.05
618	Ken Macha	.10	.05
619	John Mayberry	.12	.07
620	Joey McLaughlin	.10	.05
621	Lloyd Moseby	.10	.05
622	Dave Stieb	.25	.15
623	Jackson Todd	.10	.05
624	Willie Upshaw (R)	.15	.10
625	Otto Velez	.10	.05
626	Ernie Whitt	.10	.05
627	Al Woods	.10	.05
628	1981 All-Star Game	.10	.05
629	All-Star Infielders Bucky Dent, Frank White	.12	.07
630	Big Red Machine Dave Concepcion, Dan Driessen, George Foster	.12	.07
631	N.L. Relief Pitcher Bruce Sutter	.12	.07
632	Steve Carlton/Carlton Fisk	1.50	.90
633	Carl Yastrzemski (3,000th Game)	.75	.45
634	Johnny Bench/Tom Seaver	1.75	1.00
635	Gary Carter/Fernando Valenzuela	.25	.15
636	N.L. Strikeout King (Fernando Valenzuela)	.15	.08
637	1981 Home Run King (Mike Schmidt)	2.00	1.25
638	N.L. All-Stars(Gary Carter, Dave Parker)	.20	.12
639	Perfect Game (Len Barker, Bo Diaz)	.12	.07
640	Pete & Re-Pete(Pete Rose, Pete Rose, Jr.)	1.75	1.00
641	Phillies' Finest(Steve Carlton, Mike Schmidt, Lonnie Smith)	1.25	.80
642	Red Sox Reunion (Dwight Evans, Fred Lynn)	.15	.10
643	1981 Most Hits, Runs (Rickey Henderson)	2.00	1.25
644	Most Saves (Rollie Fingers)	.50	.30
645	Most Wins (Tom Seaver)	.80	.50

646	Yankee Powerhouse (Reggie Jackson, Dave Winfield)	3.00	1.75
647	Checklist (1-56)	.12	.05
648	Checklist (57-109)	.12	.05
649	Checklist (110-156)	.12	.05
650	Checklist (157-211)	.12	.05
651	Checklist (212-262)	.12	.05
652	Checklist (263-312)	.12	.05
653	Checklist (313-358)	.12	.05
654	Checklist (359-403)	.12	.05
655	Checklist (404-449)	.12	.05
656	Checklist (450-501)	.12	.05
657	Checklist (502-544)	.12	.05
658	Checklist (545-585)	.12	.05
659	Checklist (586-627)	.12	.05
660	Checklist (628-646)	.12	.05

1983 Fleer

Willie Stargell

This 660-card set features full color photos surrounded by a brown border. Team logos appear in a small sphere in the lower left corner. Player's names and positions are printed across the bottom of the card. The reverse side is vertical and includes a small black and white head shot of the player. Cards measure 2-1/2" by 3-1/2".

		MINT	NR/MT
Complete Set (660)		125.00	85.00
Commons		.10	.05
1	Joaquin Andujar	.10	.05
2	Doug Bair	.10	.05
3	Steve Braun	.10	.05
4	Glenn Brummer	.10	.05

5	Bob Forsch	.10	.05
6	David Green	.10	.05
7	George Hendrick	.12	.07
8	Keith Hernandez	.15	.10
9	Tom Herr	.10	.05
10	Dan Iorg	.10	.05
11	Jim Kaat	.15	.10
12	Jeff Lahti	.10	.05
13	Tito Landrum	.10	.05
14	Dave LaPoint (R)	.12	.07
15	Willie McGee (R)	3.50	2.50
16	Steve Mura	.10	.05
17	Ken Oberkfell	.10	.05
18	Darrell Porter	.10	.05
19	Mike Ramsey	.10	.05
20	Gene Roof	.10	.05
21	Lonnie Smith	.12	.07
22	Ozzie Smith	1.75	1.00
23	John Stuper	.10	.05
24	Bruce Sutter	.15	.10
25	Gene Tenace	.12	.07
26	Jerry Augustine	.10	.05
27	Dwight Bernard	.10	.05
28	Mark Brouhard	.10	.05
29	Mike Caldwell	.10	.05
30	Cecil Cooper	.12	.07
31	Jamie Easterly	.10	.05
32	Marshall Edwards	.10	.05
33	Rollie Fingers	.75	.45
34	Jim Gantner	.10	.05
35	Moose Haas	.10	.05
36	Roy Howell	.10	.05
37	Peter Ladd	.10	.05
38	Bob McClure	.10	.05
39	Doc Medich	.10	.05
40	Paul Molitor	2.50	1.50
41	Don Money	.10	.05
42	Charlie Moore	.10	.05
43	Ben Oglivie	.10	.05
44	Ed Romero	.10	.05
45	Ted Simmons	.12	.07
46	Jim Slaton	.10	.05
47	Don Sutton	.50	.30
48	Gorman Thomas	.12	.07
49	Pete Vuckovich	.12	.07
50	Ned Yost	.10	.05
51	Robin Yount	2.75	1.75
52	Benny Ayala	.10	.05
53	Bob Bonner	.10	.05
54	Al Bumbry	.10	.05
55	Terry Crowley	.10	.05
56	Storm Davis (R)	.15	.10
57	Rich Dauer	.10	.05
58	Rick Dempsey	.10	.05
59	Jim Dwyer	.10	.05
60	Mike Flanagan	.15	.10
61	Dan Ford	.10	.05
62	Glenn Gulliver	.10	.05
63	John Lowenstein	.10	.05
64	Dennis Martinez	.20	.12
65	Tippy Martinez	.10	.05
66	Scott McGregor	.10	.05
67	Eddie Murray	1.75	1.00
68	Joe Nolan	.10	.05
69	Jim Palmer	1.00	.70
70	Cal Ripken, Jr.	18.00	12.00
71	Gary Roenicke	.10	.05
72	Lenn Sakata	.10	.05
73	Ken Singleton	.10	.05
74	Sammy Stewart	.10	.05
75	Tim Stoddard	.10	.05
76	Don Aase	.10	.05
77	Don Baylor	.12	.07
78	Juan Beniquez	.10	.05
79	Bob Boone	.15	.10
80	Rick Burleson	.10	.05
81	Rod Carew	1.25	.80
82	Bobby Clark	.10	.05
83	Doug Corbett	.10	.05
84	John Curtis	.10	.05
85	Doug DeCinces	.10	.05
86	Brian Downing	.12	.07
87	Joe Ferguson	.10	.05
88	Tim Foli	.10	.05
89	Ken Forsch	.10	.05
90	Dave Goltz	.10	.05
91	Bobby Grich	.12	.07
92	Andy Hassler	.10	.05
93	Reggie Jackson	2.50	1.50
94	Ron Jackson	.10	.05
95	Tommy John	.15	.10
96	Bruce Kison	.10	.05
97	Fred Lynn	.12	.07
98	Ed Ott	.10	.05
99	Steve Renko	.10	.05
100	Luis Sanchez	.10	.05
101	Rob Wilfong	.10	.05
102	Mike Witt	.12	.07
103	Geoff Zahn	.10	.05
104	Willie Aikens	.10	.05
105	Mike Armstrong	.10	.05
106	Vida Blue	.12	.07
107	Bud Black (R)	.40	.25
108	George Brett	3.00	1.75
109	Bill Castro	.10	.05
110	Onix Concepcion	.10	.05
111	Dave Frost	.10	.05
112	Cesar Geronimo	.10	.05
113	Larry Gura	.10	.05
114	Steve Hammond	.10	.05
115	Don Hood	.10	.05
116	Dennis Leonard	.10	.05
117	Jerry Martin	.10	.05
118	Lee May	.10	.05

119	Hal McRae	.12	.07	176	George Vukovich	.10	.05
120	Amos Otis	.12	.07	177	Gary Allenson	.10	.05
121	Greg Pryor	.10	.05	178	Luis Aponte	.10	.05
122	Dan Quisenberry	.12	.07	179	Wade Boggs (R)	25.00	15.00
123	Don Slaught (R)	.80	.50	180	Tom Burgmeier	.10	.05
124	Paul Splittorff	.10	.05	181	Mark Clear	.10	.05
125	U.L. Washington	.10	.05	182	Dennis Eckersley	1.00	.70
126	John Wathan	.10	.05	183	Dwight Evans	.25	.15
127	Frank White	.12	.07	184	Rich Gedman	.10	.05
128	Willie Wilson	.12	.07	185	Glenn Hoffman	.10	.05
129	Steve Bedrosian (R)	.25	.15	186	Bruce Hurst	.25	.15
130	Bruce Benedict	.10	.05	187	Carney Lansford	.15	.10
131	Tommy Boggs	.10	.05	188	Rick Miller	.10	.05
132	Brett Butler (R)	1.00	.70	189	Reid Nichols	.10	.05
133	Rick Camp	.10	.05	190	Bob Ojeda	.12	.07
134	Chris Chambliss	.12	.07	191	Tony Perez	.50	.30
135	Ken Dayley (R)	.12	.07	192	Chuck Rainey	.10	.05
136	Gene Garber	.10	.05	193	Jerry Remy	.10	.05
137	Terry Harper	.10	.05	194	Jim Rice	.15	.10
138	Bob Horner	.12	.07	195	Bob Stanley	.10	.05
139	Glenn Hubbard	.10	.05	196	Dave Stapleton	.10	.05
140	Rufino Linares	.10	.05	197	Mike Torrez	.10	.05
141	Rick Mahler	.10	.05	198	John Tudor	.12	.07
142	Dale Murphy	.90	.60	199	Julio Valdez	.10	.05
143	Phil Niekro	.75	.45	200	Carl Yastrzemski	1.50	.90
144	Pascual Perez	.12	.07	201	Dusty Baker	.12	.07
145	Biff Pocoroba	.10	.05	202	Joe Beckwith	.10	.05
146	Rafael Ramirez	.10	.05	203	Greg Brock (R)	.12	.07
147	Jerry Royster	.10	.05	204	Ron Cey	.12	.07
148	Ken Smith	.10	.05	205	Terry Forster	.10	.05
149	Bob Walk	.12	.07	206	Steve Garvey	.50	.30
150	Claudell Washington	.10	.05	207	Pedro Guerrero	.20	.12
151	Bob Watson	.12	.07	208	Burt Hooton	.10	.05
152	Larry Whisenton	.10	.05	209	Steve Howe	.12	.07
153	Porfirio Altamirano	.10	.05	210	Ken Landreaux	.10	.05
154	Marty Bystrom	.10	.05	211	Mike Marshall	.10	.05
155	Steve Carlton	2.00	1.25	212	Candy Maldonado(R)	.60	.35
156	Larry Christenson	.10	.05	213	Rick Monday	.12	.07
157	Ivan DeJesus	.10	.05	214	Tom Niedenfuer	.10	.05
158	John Denny	.10	.05	215	Jorge Orta	.10	.05
159	Bob Dernier (R)	.12	.07	216	Jerry Reuss	.12	.07
160	Bo Diaz	.10	.05	217	Ron Roenicke	.10	.05
161	Ed Farmer	.10	.05	218	Vicente Romo	.10	.05
162	Greg Gross	.10	.05	219	Bill Russell	.12	.07
163	Mike Krukow	.10	.05	220	Steve Sax	.50	.30
164	Garry Maddox	.10	.05	221	Mike Scioscia	.12	.07
165	Gary Matthews	.10	.05	222	Dave Stewart	.80	.50
166	Tug McGraw	.12	.07	223	Derrel Thomas	.10	.05
167	Bob Molinaro	.10	.05	224	Fernando Valenzuela	.15	.10
168	Sid Monge	.10	.05	225	Bob Welch	.20	.12
169	Ron Reed	.10	.05	226	Ricky Wright	.10	.05
170	Bill Robinson	.12	.07	227	Steve Yeager	.10	.05
171	Pete Rose	1.75	1.00	228	Bill Almon	.10	.05
172	Dick Ruthven	.10	.05	229	Harold Baines	.50	.30
173	Mike Schmidt	3.00	2.00	230	Salome Barojas	.10	.05
174	Manny Trillo	.10	.05	231	Tony Bernazard	.10	.05
175	Ozzie Virgil (R)	.12	.07	232	Britt Burns	.10	.05

233	Richard Dotson	.10	.05	290	Al Oliver	.12	.07
234	Ernesto Escarrega	.10	.05	291	David Palmer	.10	.05
235	Carlton Fisk	1.50	.90	292	Tim Raines	.70	.40
236	Jerry Hairston	.10	.05	293	Jeff Reardon	1.00	.70
237	Kevin Hickey	.10	.05	294	Steve Rogers	.10	.05
238	LaMarr Hoyt	.10	.05	295	Scott Sanderson	.12	.07
239	Steve Kemp	.10	.05	296	Dan Schatzeder	.10	.05
240	Jim Kern	.10	.05	297	Bryn Smith	.12	.07
241	Ron Kittle (R)	.20	.12	298	Chris Speier	.10	.05
242	Jerry Koosman	.12	.07	299	Tim Wallach	.20	.12
243	Dennis Lamp	.10	.05	300	Jerry White	.10	.05
244	Rudy Law	.10	.05	301	Joel Youngblood	.10	.05
245	Vance Law	.10	.05	302	Ross Baumgarten	.10	.05
246	Ron LeFlore	.12	.07	303	Dale Berra	.10	.05
247	Greg Luzinski	.12	.07	304	John Candelaria	.10	.05
248	Tom Paciorek	.10	.05	305	Dick Davis	.10	.05
249	Aurelio Rodriguez	.10	.05	306	Mike Easler	.10	.05
250	Mike Squires	.10	.05	307	Richie Hebner	.10	.05
251	Steve Trout	.10	.05	308	Lee Lacy	.10	.05
252	Jim Barr	.10	.05	309	Bill Madlock	.15	.10
253	Dave Bergman	.10	.05	310	Larry McWilliams	.10	.05
254	Fred Breining	.10	.05	311	John Milner	.10	.05
255	Bob Brenly (R)	.12	.07	312	Omar Moreno	.10	.05
256	Jack Clark	.15	.10	313	Jim Morrison	.10	.05
257	Chili Davis (R)	.80	.50	314	Steve Nicosia	.10	.05
258	Darrell Evans	.12	.07	315	Dave Parker	.30	.18
259	Alan Fowlkes	.10	.05	316	Tony Pena	.12	.07
260	Rich Gale	.10	.05	317	Johnny Ray	.10	.05
261	Atlee Hammaker (R)	.12	.07	318	Rick Rhoden	.10	.05
262	Al Holland	.10	.05	319	Don Robinson	.10	.05
263	Duane Kuiper	.10	.05	320	Enrique Romo	.10	.05
264	Bill Laskey	.10	.05	321	Manny Sarmiento	.10	.05
265	Gary Lavelle	.10	.05	322	Rod Scurry	.10	.05
266	Johnnie LeMaster	.10	.05	323	Jim Smith	.10	.05
267	Renie Martin	.10	.05	324	Willie Stargell	.75	.45
268	Milt May	.10	.05	326	Kent Tekulve	.10	.05
269	Greg Minton	.10	.05	327	Tom Brookens	.10	.05
270	Joe Morgan	.75	.45	328	Enos Cabell	.10	.05
271	Tom O'Malley	.10	.05	329	Kirk Gibson	.40	.25
272	Reggie Smith	.10	.05	330	Larry Herndon	.10	.05
273	Guy Sularz	.10	.05	331	Mike Ivie	.10	.05
274	Champ Summers	.10	.05	332	Howard Johnson(R)	3.50	2.00
275	Max Venable	.10	.05	333	Lynn Jones	.10	.05
276	Jim Wohlford	.10	.05	334	Rick Leach	.10	.05
277	Ray Burris	.10	.05	335	Chet Lemon	.10	.05
278	Gary Carter	.75	.45	336	Jack Morris	.80	.50
279	Warren Cromartie	.10	.05	337	Lance Parrish	.12	.07
280	Andre Dawson	2.00	1.25	338	Larry Pashnick	.10	.05
281	Terry Francona	.10	.05	339	Dan Petry	.10	.05
282	Doug Flynn	.10	.05	340	Dave Rozema	.10	.05
283	Woody Fryman	.10	.05	341	Dave Rucker	.10	.05
284	Bill Gullickson	.15	.10	342	Elias Sosa	.10	.05
285	Wallace Johnson	.10	.05	344	Alan Trammell	.90	.60
286	Charlie Lea	.10	.05	345	Jerry Turner	.10	.05
287	Randy Lerch	.10	.05	346	Jerry Ujdur	.10	.05
288	Brad Mills	.10	.05	347	Pat Underwood	.10	.05
289	Dan Norman	.10	.05	348	Lou Whitaker	.50	.30

349	Milt Wilcox	.10	.05
350	Glenn Wilson (R)	.15	.10
351	John Wockenfuss	.10	.05
352	Kurt Bevacqua	.10	.05
353	Juan Bonilla	.10	.05
354	Floyd Chiffer	.10	.05
355	Luis DeLeon	.10	.05
356	Dave Dravecky (R)	.50	.30
357	Dave Edwards	.10	.05
358	Juan Eichelberger	.10	.05
359	Tim Flannery	.10	.05
360	Tony Gwynn (R)	26.00	16.00
361	Ruppert Jones	.10	.05
362	Terry Kennedy	.10	.05
363	Joe Lefebvre	.10	.05
364	Sixto Lezcano	.10	.05
365	Tim Lollar	.10	.05
366	Gary Lucas	.10	.05
367	John Montefusco	.10	.05
368	Broderick Perkins	.10	.05
369	Joe Pittman	.10	.05
370	Gene Richards	.10	.05
371	Luis Salazar	.10	.05
372	Eric Show (R)	.15	.10
373	Garry Templeton	.12	.07
374	Chris Welsh	.10	.05
375	Alan Wiggins	.10	.05
276	Rick Cerone	.10	.05
377	Dave Collins	.10	.05
378	Roger Erickson	.10	.05
379	George Frazier	.10	.05
380	Oscar Gamble	.12	.07
381	Goose Gossage	.25	.15
382	Ken Griffey	.15	.10
383	Ron Guidry	.20	.12
384	Dave LaRoche	.10	.05
385	Rudy May	.10	.05
386	John Mayberry	.12	.07
387	Lee Mazzilli	.10	.05
388	Mike Morgan (R)	.35	.20
389	Jerry Mumphrey	.10	.05
390	Bobby Murcer	.12	.07
391	Graig Nettles	.12	.07
392	Lou Piniella	.12	.07
393	Willie Randolph	.12	.07
394	Shane Rawley	.10	.05
395	Dave Righetti	.12	.07
396	Andre Robertson	.10	.05
397	Roy Smalley	.10	.05
398	Dave Winfield	3.00	1.75
399	Butch Wynegar	.10	.05
400	Chris Bando	.10	.05
401	Alan Bannister	.10	.05
402	Len Barker	.10	.05
403	Tom Brennan	.10	.05
404	Carmelo Castillo (R)	.10	.05
405	Miguel Dilone	.10	.05
406	Jerry Dybzinski	.10	.05
407	Mike Fischlin	.10	.05
408	Ed Glynn (Wrong Photo)	.10	.05
409	Mike Hargrove	.10	.05
410	Toby Harrah	.10	.05
411	Ron Hassey	.10	.05
412	Von Hayes	.12	.07
413	Rick Manning	.10	.05
414	Bake McBride	.10	.05
415	Larry Milbourne	.10	.05
416	Bill Nahorodny	.10	.05
417	Jack Perconte	.10	.05
418	Lary Sorensen	.10	.05
419	Dan Spillner	.10	.05
420	Rick Sutcliffe	.25	.15
421	Andre Thornton	.12	.07
422	Rick Waits	.10	.05
423	Eddie Whitson	.10	.05
424	Jesse Barfield (R)	.25	.15
425	Barry Bonnell	.10	.05
426	Jim Clancy	.10	.05
427	Damaso Garcia	.10	.05
428	Jerry Garvin	.10	.05
429	Alfredo Griffin	.10	.05
430	Garth Iorg	.10	.05
431	Roy Lee Jackson	.10	.05
432	Luis Leal	.10	.05
433	Buck Martinez	.10	.05
434	Joey McLaughlin	.10	.05
435	Lloyd Moseby	.10	.05
436	Rance Mulliniks	.10	.05
437	Dale Murray	.10	.05
438	Wayne Nordhagen	.10	.05
439	Gene Petralli (R)	.15	.10
440	Hosken Powell	.10	.05
441	Dave Stieb	.15	.10
442	Willie Upshaw	.10	.05
443	Ernie Whitt	.10	.05
444	Al Woods	.10	.05
445	Alan Ashby	.10	.05
446	Jose Cruz	.12	.07
447	Kiko Garcia	.10	.05
448	Phil Garner	.12	.07
449	Danny Heep	.10	.05
450	Art Howe	.10	.05
451	Bob Knepper	.10	.05
452	Alan Knicely	.10	.05
453	Ray Knight	.12	.07
454	Frank LaCorte	.10	.05
455	Mike LaCoss	.10	.05
456	Randy Moffitt	.10	.05
457	Joe Niekro	.10	.05
458	Terry Puhl	.10	.05
459	Luis Pujols	.10	.05
460	Craig Reynolds	.10	.05
461	Bert Roberge	.10	.05

462	Vern Ruhle	.10	.05
463	Nolan Ryan	9.00	5.75
464	Joe Sambito	.10	.05
465	Tony Scott	.10	.05
466	Dave Smith	.10	.05
467	Harry Spilman	.10	.05
468	Dickie Thon	.10	.05
469	Denny Walling	.10	.05
470	Larry Andersen	.10	.05
471	Floyd Bannister	.10	.05
472	Jim Beattie	.10	.05
473	Bruce Bochte	.10	.05
474	Manny Castillo	.10	.05
475	Bill Caudill	.10	.05
476	Bryan Clark	.10	.05
477	Al Cowens	.10	.05
478	Julio Cruz	.10	.05
479	Todd Cruz	.10	.05
480	Gary Gray	.10	.05
481	Dave Henderson (R)	.30	.18
482	Mike Moore (R)	.75	.45
483	Gaylord Perry	.50	.30
484	Dave Revering	.10	.05
485	Joe Simpson	.10	.05
486	Mike Stanton	.10	.05
487	Rick Sweet	.10	.05
488	Ed Vande Berg (R)	.10	.05
489	Richie Zisk	.10	.05
490	Doug Bird	.10	.05
491	Larry Bowa	.12	.07
492	Bill Buckner	.12	.07
493	Bill Campbell	.10	.05
494	Jody Davis	.10	.05
495	Leon Durham	.10	.05
496	Steve Henderson	.10	.05
497	Willie Hernandez	.12	.07
498	Ferguson Jenkins	.50	.30
499	Jay Johnstone	.12	.07
500	Junior Kennedy	.10	.05
501	Randy Martz	.10	.05
502	Jerry Morales	.10	.05
503	Keith Moreland	.10	.05
504	Dickie Noles	.10	.05
505	Mike Proly	.10	.05
506	Allen Ripley	.10	.05
507	Ryne Sandberg (R)	40.00	25.00
508	Lee Smith	2.50	1.50
509	Pat Tabler (R)	.12	.07
510	Dick Tidrow	.10	.05
511	Bump Wills	.10	.05
512	Gary Woods	.10	.05
513	Tony Armas	.10	.05
514	Dave Beard	.10	.05
515	Jeff Burroughs	.10	.05
516	John D'Acquisto	.10	.05
517	Wayne Gross	.10	.05
518	Mike Heath	.10	.05
519	Rickey Henderson	4.00	2..50
520	Cliff Johnson	.10	.05
521	Matt Keough	.10	.05
522	Brian Kingman	.10	.05
523	Rick Langford	.10	.05
524	Davey Lopes	.12	.07
525	Steve McCatty	.10	.05
526	Dave McKay	.10	.05
527	Dan Meyer	.10	.05
528	Dwayne Murphy	.10	.05
529	Jeff Newman	.10	.05
530	Mike Norris	.10	.05
531	Bob Owchinko	.10	.05
532	Joe Rudi	.12	.07
533	Jimmy Sexton	.10	.05
534	Fred Stanley	.10	.05
535	Tom Underwood	.10	.05
536	Neil Allen	.10	.05
537	Wally Backman	.10	.05
538	Bob Bailor	.10	.05
539	Hubie Brooks	.15	.10
540	Carlos Diaz	.10	.05
541	Pete Falcone	.10	.05
542	George Foster	.12	.07
543	Ron Gardenhire	.10	.05
544	Brian Giles	.10	.05
545	Ron Hodges	.10	.05
546	Randy Jones	.10	.05
547	Mike Jorgensen	.10	.05
548	Dave Kingman	.15	.10
549	Ed Lynch	.10	.05
550	Jesse Orosco (R)	.12	.07
551	Rick Ownbey	.10	.05
552	Charlie Puleo	.10	.05
553	Gary Rajsich	.10	.05
554	Mike Scott	.15	.10
555	Rusty Staub	.12	.07
556	John Stearns	.10	.05
557	Craig Swan	.10	.05
558	Ellis Valentine	.10	.05
559	Tom Veryzer	.10	.05
560	Mookie Wilson	.12	.07
561	Pat Zachry	.10	.05
562	Buddy Bell	.10	.05
563	John Butcher	.10	.05
564	Steve Comer	.10	.05
565	Danny Darwin	.10	.05
566	Bucky Dent	.12	.07
567	John Grubb	.10	.05
568	Rick Honeycutt	.10	.05
569	Dave Hostetler	.10	.05
570	Charlie Hough	.12	.07
571	Lamar Johnson	.10	.05
572	Jon Matlack	.12	.07
573	Paul Mirabella	.10	.05
574	Larry Parrish	.10	.05
575	Mike Richardt	.10	.05

576	Mickey Rivers	.10	.05
577	Billy Sample	.10	.05
578	Dave Schmidt (R)	.10	.05
579	Bill Stein	.10	.05
580	Jim Sundberg	.10	.05
581	Frank Tanana	.12	.07
582	Mark Wagner	.10	.05
583	George Wright	.10	.05
584	Johnny Bench	1.50	.90
585	Bruce Berenyi	.10	.05
586	Larry Biittner	.10	.05
587	Cesar Cedeno	.12	.07
588	Dave Concepcion	.15	.10
589	Dan Driessen	.10	.05
590	Greg Harris	.10	.05
591	Ben Hayes	.10	.05
592	Paul Householder	.10	.05
593	Tom Hume	.10	.05
594	Wayne Krenchicki	.10	.05
595	Rafael Landestoy	.10	.05
596	Charlie Leibrandt	.10	.05
597	Eddie Milner (R)	.12	.07
598	Ron Oester	.10	.05
599	Frank Pastore	.10	.05
600	Joe Price	.10	.05
601	Tom Seaver	1.75	1.00
602	Bob Shirley	.10	.05
603	Mario Soto	.10	.05
604	Alex Trevino	.10	.05
605	Mike Vail	.10	.05
606	Duane Walker	.10	.05
607	Tom Brunansky (R)	.35	.20
608	Bobby Castillo	.10	.05
609	John Castino	.10	.05
610	Ron Davis	.10	.05
611	Lenny Faedo	.10	.05
612	Terry Felton	.10	.05
613	Gary Gaetti (R)	.40	.25
614	Mickey Hatcher	.10	.05
615	Brad Havens	.10	.05
616	Kent Hrbek (R)	.70	.40
617	Randy Johnson	.10	.05
618	Tim Laudner (R)	.12	.07
619	Jeff Little	.10	.05
620	Bob Mitchell	.10	.05
621	Jack O'Connor	.10	.05
622	John Pacella	.10	.05
623	Pete Redfern	.10	.05
624	Jesus Vega	.10	.05
625	Frank Viola (R)	3.50	2.50
626	Ron Washington	.10	.05
627	Gary Ward	.10	.05
628	Al Williams	.10	.05
629	Red Sox All-Stars(Mark Clear, Dennis Eckersley, Carl Yastrzemski)	.75	.45
630	300 Wins(Terry Bulling, Gaylord Perry)	.25	.15
631	Pride of Venezuela (Dave Concepcion, Manny Trillo)	.10	.06
632	All-Star Infielders (Buddy Bell, Robin Yount)	.75	.45
633	Mr. Vet & Mr. Rookie (Kent Hrbek, Dave Winfield)	1.00	.70
634	Fountain of Youth (Pete Rose, Willie Stargell)	.80	.50
635	Big Chiefs (Toby Harrah, Andre Thornton)	.10	.05
636	Smith Bros. (Lonnie Smith, Ozzie Smith)	.50	.30
637	Base Stealers' Threat (Gary Carter, Bo Diaz)	.12	.07
638	All-Star Catchers (Gary Carter, Carlton Fisk)	.40	.25
639	The Silver Shoe (Rickey Henderson)	2.00	1.25
640	Home Run Threats (Reggie Jackson, Ben Oglivie)	.75	.45
641	Two Teams-Same Day (Joel Youngblood)	.10	.05
642	Last Perfect Game (Len Barker, Ron Hassey)	.10	.05
643	Black & Blue (Vida Blue)	.12	.07
644	Black & Blue (Bud Black)	.10	.06
645	Reggie Jackson (Power)	1.50	.90
646	Rickey Henderson (Speed)	1.75	1.00
647	Checklist (1-51)	.12	.05
648	Checklist (52-103)	.12	.05
649	Checklist (104-152)	.12	.05
650	Checklist (153-200)	.12	.05
651	Checklist (201-251)	.12	.05
652	Checklist (252-301)	.12	.05
653	Checklist (302-351)	.12	.05
654	Checklist (352-399)	.12	.05
655	Checklist (400-444)	.12	.05
656	Checklist (445-489)	.12	.05
657	Checklist (490-535)	.12	.05
658	Checklist (536-583)	.12	.05
659	Checklist (584-628)	.12	.05
660	Checklist (629-646)	.12	.05

1984 Fleer

Gaylord Perry

This 660-card set features full color photos on the fronts framed by white borders on all sides and blue stripes at the top and bottom. A full color team logo is printed in the right corner of the card front. Card backs are vertical and printed in blue and white. All cards measure 2-1/2" by 3-1/2".

		MINT	NR/MT
Complete Set (660)		200.00	125.00
Commons		.10	.06
1	Mike Boddicker	.25	.15
2	Al Bumbry	.10	.06
3	Todd Cruz	.10	.06
4	Rich Dauer	.10	.06
5	Storm Davis	.12	.07
6	Rick Dempsey	.10	.06
7	Jim Dwyer	.10	.06
8	Mike Flanagan	.15	.10
9	Dan Ford	.10	.06
10	John Lowenstein	.10	.06
11	Dennis Martinez	.20	.12
12	Tippy Martinez	.10	.06
13	Scott McGregor	.10	.06
14	Eddie Murray	4.50	3.00
15	Joe Nolan	.10	.06
16	Jim Palmer	3.00	2.00
17	Cal Ripken, Jr.	24.00	14.00
18	Gary Roenicke	.10	.06
19	Lenn Sakata	.10	.06
20	John Shelby (R)	.15	.10
21	Ken Singleton	.10	.06
22	Sammy Stewart	.10	.06
23	Tim Stoddard	.10	.06
24	Marty Bystrom	.10	.06
25	Steve Carlton	4.00	2.75
26	Ivan DeJesus	.10	.06
27	John Denny	.10	.06
28	Bob Dernier	.10	.06
29	Bo Diaz	.10	.06
30	Kiko Garcia	.10	.06
31	Greg Gross	.10	.06
32	Kevin Gross (R)	.30	.18
33	Von Hayes	.12	.07
34	Willie Hernandez	.15	.10
35	Al Holland	.10	.06
36	Charles Hudson (R)	.12	.07
37	Joe Lefebvre	.10	.06
38	Sixto Lezcano	.10	.06
39	Garry Maddox	.10	.06
40	Gary Matthews	.10	.06
41	Len Matuszek	.10	.06
42	Tug McGraw	.15	.10
43	Joe Morgan	1.00	.70
44	Tony Perez	.90	.60
45	Ron Reed	.10	.06
46	Pete Rose	4.00	2.75
47	Juan Samuel (R)	1.00	.70
48	Mike Schmidt	10.00	7.00
49	Ozzie Virgil	.10	.06
50	Juan Agosto (R)	.12	.07
51	Harold Baines	.70	.40
52	Floyd Bannister	.10	.06
53	Salome Barojas	.10	.06
54	Britt Burns	.10	.06
55	Julio Cruz	.10	.06
56	Richard Dotson	.10	.06
57	Jerry Dybzinski	.10	.06
58	Carlton Fisk	3.50	2.50
59	Scott Fletcher (R)	.15	.10
60	Jerry Hairston	.10	.06
61	Kevin Hickey	.10	.06
62	Marc Hill	.10	.06
63	LaMarr Hoyt	.10	.06
64	Ron Kittle	.15	.10
65	Jerry Koosman	.15	.10
66	Dennis Lamp	.10	.06
67	Rudy Law	.10	.06
68	Vance law	.10	.06
69	Greg Luzinski	.12	.07
70	Tom Paciorek	.10	.06
71	Mike Squires	.10	.06
72	Dick Tidrow	.10	.06
73	Greg Walker (R)	.12	.07
74	Glenn Abbott	.10	.06
75	Howard Bailey	.10	.06
76	Doug Bair	.10	.06
77	Juan Berenguer	.10	.06
78	Tom Brookens	.10	.06
79	Enos Cabell	.10	.06
80	Kirk Gibson	.75	.45
81	John Grubb	.10	.06
82	Larry Herndon	.10	.06
83	Wayne Krenchicki	.10	.06
84	Rick Leach	.10	.06
85	Chet Lemon	.10	.06
86	Aurelio Lopez	.10	.06

87	Jack Morris	1.50	.90	144	Butch Wynegar	.10	.06
88	Lance Parrish	.20	.12	145	Jim Acker (R)	.12	.07
89	Dan Petry	.10	.06	146	Doyle Alexander	.10	.06
90	Dave Rozema	.10	.06	147	Jesse Barfield	.25	.15
91	Alan Trammell	1.50	.90	148	Jorge Bell	1.50	.90
92	Lou Whitaker	1.00	.70	149	Barry Bonnell	.10	.06
93	Milt Wilcox	.10	.06	150	Jim Clancy	.10	.06
94	Glenn Wilson	.10	.06	151	Dave Collins	.10	.06
95	John Wockenfuss	.10	.06	152	Tony Fernandez (R)	3.50	2.50
96	Dusty Baker	.12	.07	153	Damaso Garcia	.10	.06
97	Joe Beckwith	.10	.06	154	Dave Geisel	.10	.06
98	Greg Brock	.10	.06	155	Jim Gott (R)	.25	.15
99	Jack Fimple	.10	.06	156	Alfredo Griffin	.10	.06
100	Pedro Guerrero	.15	.10	157	Garth Iorg	.10	.06
101	Rick Honeycutt	.10	.06	158	Roy Lee Jackson	.10	.06
102	Burt Hooton	.10	.06	159	Cliff Johnson	.10	.06
103	Steve Howe	.10	.06	160	Luis Leal	.10	.06
104	Ken Landreaux	.10	.06	161	Buck Martinez	.10	.06
105	Mike Marshall	.10	.06	162	Joey McLaughlin	.10	.06
106	Rick Monday	.12	.07	163	Randy Moffitt	.10	.06
107	Jose Morales	.10	.06	164	Lloyd Moseby	.10	.06
108	Tom Niedenfuer	.10	.06	165	Rance Mulliniks	.10	.06
109	Alejandro Pena (R)	.50	.30	166	Jorge Orta	.10	.06
110	Jerry Reuss	.12	.07	167	Dave Stieb	.25	.15
111	Bill Russell	.12	.07	168	Willie Upshaw	.10	.06
112	Steve Sax	.50	.30	169	Ernie Whitt	.10	.06
113	Mike Scioscia	.12	.07	170	Len Barker	.10	.06
114	Derrel Thomas	.10	.06	171	Steve Bedrosian	.15	.10
115	Fernando Valenzuela	.20	.12	172	Bruce Benedict	.10	.06
116	Bob Welch	.20	.12	173	Brett Butler	.70	.40
117	Steve Yeager	.10	.06	174	Rick Camp	.10	.06
118	Pat Zachry	.10	.06	175	Chris Chambliss	.15	.10
119	Don Baylor	.15	.10	176	Ken Dayley	.10	.06
120	Bert Campaneris	.15	.10	177	Pete Falcone	.10	.06
121	Rick Cerone	.10	.06	178	Terry Forster	.10	.06
122	Ray Fontenot	.10	.06	179	Gene Garber	.10	.06
123	George Frazier	.10	.06	180	Terry Harper	.10	.06
124	Oscar Gamble	.12	.07	181	Bob Horner	.12	.07
125	Goose Gossage	.30	.18	182	Glenn Hubbard	.10	.06
126	Ken Griffey	.20	.12	183	Randy Johnson	.10	.06
127	Ron Guidry	.25	.15	184	Craig McMurtry	.10	.06
128	Jay Howell (R)	.15	.10	185	Donnie Moore	.10	.06
129	Steve Kemp	.10	.06	186	Dale Murphy	1.75	1.00
130	Matt Keough	.10	.06	187	Phil Niekro	1.00	.70
131	Don Mattingly (R)	32.00	20.00	188	Pasqual Perez	.15	.10
132	John Montefusco	.10	.06	189	Biff Pocoroba	.10	.06
133	Omar Moreno	.10	.06	190	Rafael Ramirez	.10	.06
134	Dale Murray	.10	.06	191	Jerry Royster	.10	.06
135	Graig Nettles	.20	.12	192	Claudell Washington	.10	.06
136	Lou Piniella	.15	.10	193	Bob Watson	.15	.10
137	Willie Randolph	.15	.10	194	Jerry Augustine	.10	.06
138	Shane Rawley	.10	.06	195	Mark Brouhard	.10	.06
139	Dave Righetti	.15	.10	196	Mike Caldwell	.10	.06
140	Andre Robertson	.10	.06	197	Tom Candiotti (R)	.80	.50
141	Bob Shirley	.10	.06	198	Cecil Cooper	.15	.10
142	Roy Smalley	.10	.06	199	Rollie Fingers	1.25	.80
143	Dave Winfield	8.00	5.00	200	Jim Gantner	.10	.06

201	Bob Gibson	.10	.06
202	Moose Haas	.10	.06
203	Roy Howell	.10	.06
204	Pete Ladd	.10	.06
205	Rick Manning	.10	.06
206	Bob McClure	.10	.06
207	Paul Molitor	4.00	2.50
208	Don Money	.10	.06
209	Charlie Moore	.10	.06
210	Ben Oglivie	.10	.06
211	Chuck Porter	.10	.06
212	Ed Romero	.10	.06
213	Ted Simmons	.15	.10
214	Jim Slaton	.10	.06
215	Don Sutton	.80	.50
216	Tom Tellmann	.10	.06
217	Pete Vuckovich	.12	.07
218	Ned Yost	.10	.06
219	Robin Yount	6.50	3.75
220	Alan Ashby	.10	.06
221	Kevin Bass (R)	.20	.12
222	Jose Cruz	.15	.10
223	Bill Dawley	.10	.06
224	Frank DiPino	.10	.06
225	Bill Doran (R)	.40	.25
226	Phil Garner	.12	.07
227	Art Howe	.10	.06
228	Bob Knepper	.10	.06
229	Ray Knight	.12	.07
230	Frank LaCorte	.10	.06
231	Mike LaCoss	.10	.06
232	Mike Madden	.10	.06
233	Jerry Mumphrey	.10	.06
235	Terry Puhl	.10	.06
236	Luis Pujols	.10	.06
237	Craig Reynolds	.10	.06
238	Vern Ruhle	.10	.06
239	Nolan Ryan	22.00	13.50
240	Mike Scott	.15	.10
241	Tony Scott	.10	.06
242	Dave Smith	.10	.06
243	Dickie Thon	.10	.06
244	Denny Walling	.10	.06
245	Dale Berra	.10	.06
246	Jim Bibby	.10	.06
247	John Candelaria	.10	.06
248	Jose DeLeon (R)	.15	.10
249	Mike Easler	.10	.06
250	Cecilio Guante (R)	.10	.06
251	Richie Hebner	.10	.06
252	Lee Lacy	.10	.06
253	Bill Madlock	.20	.12
254	Milt May	.10	.06
255	Lee Mazzilli	.10	.06
256	Larry McWilliams	.10	.06
257	Jim Morrison	.10	.06
258	Dave Parker	.45	.28
259	Tony Pena	.12	.07
260	Johnny Ray	.10	.06
261	Rick Rhoden	.10	.06
262	Don Robinson	.10	.06
263	Manny Sarmiento	.10	.06
264	Rod Scurry	.10	.06
265	Kent Tekulve	.10	.06
266	Gene Tenace	.12	.07
267	Jason Thompson	.10	.06
268	Lee Tunnell	.10	.06
269	Marvell Wynne (R)	.12	.07
270	Ray Burris	.10	.06
271	Gary Carter	1.00	.70
272	Warren Cromartie	.10	.06
273	Andre Dawson	4.50	2.75
274	Doug Flynn	.10	.06
275	Terry Francona	.10	.06
276	Bill Gullickson	.12	.07
277	Bob James	.10	.06
278	Charlie Lea	.10	.06
279	Bryan Little	.10	.06
280	Al Oliver	.20	.12
281	Tim Raines	.75	.45
282	Bobby Ramos	.10	.06
283	Jeff Reardon	1.25	.80
284	Steve Rogers	.10	.06
285	Scott Sanderson	.12	.07
286	Dan Schatzeder	.10	.06
287	Bryn Smith	.12	.07
288	Chris Speier	.10	.06
289	Manny Trillo	.10	.06
290	Mike Vail	.10	.06
291	Tim Wallach	.25	.15
292	Chris Welsh	.10	.06
293	Jim Wohlford	.10	.06
294	Kurt Bevacqua	.10	.06
295	Juan Bonilla	.10	.06
296	Bobby Brown	.10	.06
297	Luis DeLeon	.10	.06
298	Dave Dravecky	.15	.10
299	Tim Flannery	.10	.06
300	Steve Garvey	.80	.50
301	Tony Gwynn	12.50	7.50
302	Andy Hawkins (R)	.15	.10
303	Ruppert Jones	.10	.06
304	Terry Kennedy	.10	.06
305	Tim Lollar	.10	.06
306	Gary Lucas	.10	.06
307	Kevin McReynolds (R)	1.50	.90
308	Sid Monge	.10	.06
309	Mario Ramirez	.10	.06
310	Gene Richards	.10	.06
311	Luis Salazar	.10	.06
312	Eric Show	.10	.06
313	Elias Sosa	.10	.06
314	Garry Templeton	.12	.07
315	Mark Thurmond (R)	.12	.07

316	Ed Whitson	.10	.06
317	Alan Wiggins	.10	.06
318	Neil Allen	.10	.06
319	Joaquin Andujar	.12	.07
320	Steve Braun	.10	.06
321	Glenn Brummer	.10	.06
322	Bob Forsch	.10	.06
323	David Green	.10	.06
324	George Hendrick	.12	.07
325	Tom Herr	.10	.06
326	Dane Iorg	.10	.06
327	Jeff Lahti	.10	.06
328	Dave LaPoint	.10	.06
329	Willie McGee	.75	.45
330	Ken Oberkfell	.10	.06
331	Darrell Porter	.10	.06
332	Jamie Quirk	.10	.06
333	Mike Ramsey	.10	.06
334	Floyd Rayford	.10	.06
335	Lonnie Smith	.12	.07
336	Ozzie Smith	4.00	2.75
337	John Stuper	.10	.06
338	Bruce Sutter	.20	.12
339	Andy Van Slyke (R)	7.50	4.50
340	Dave Von Ohlen	.10	.06
341	Willie Aikens	.10	.06
342	Mike Armstrong	.10	.06
343	Bud Black	.12	.07
344	George Brett	7.00	4.00
345	Onix Concepcion	.10	.06
346	Keith Creel	.10	.06
347	Larry Gura	.10	.06
348	Don Hood	.10	.06
349	Dennis Leonard	.10	.06
350	Hal McRae	.15	.10
351	Amos Otis	.12	.07
352	Gaylord Perry	.80	.50
353	Greg Pryor	.10	.06
354	Dan Quisenberry	.15	.10
355	Steve Renko	.10	.06
356	Leon Roberts	.10	.06
357	Pat Sheridan (R)	.12	.07
358	Joe Simpson	.10	.06
359	Don Slaught	.20	.12
360	Paul Splittorff	.10	.06
361	U.L. Washington	.10	.06
362	John Wathan	.10	.06
363	Frank White	.12	.07
364	Willie Wilson	.12	.07
365	Jim Barr	.10	.06
366	Dave Bergman	.10	.06
367	Fred Breining	.10	.06
368	Bob Brenly	.10	.06
369	Jack Clark	.15	.10
370	Chili Davis	.25	.15
371	Mark Davis (R)	.15	.10
372	Darrell Evans	.15	.10
373	Atlee Hammaker	.10	.06
374	Mike Krukow	.10	.06
375	Duane Kuiper	.10	.06
376	Bill Laskey	.10	.06
377	Gary Lavelle	.10	.06
378	Johnnie LeMaster	.10	.06
379	Jeff Leonard	.12	.07
380	Randy Lerch	.10	.06
381	Renie Martin	.10	.06
382	Andy McGaffigan	.10	.06
383	Greg Minton	.10	.06
384	Tom O'Malley	.10	.06
385	Max Venable	.10	.06
386	Brad Wellman	.10	.06
387	Joel Youngblood	.10	.06
388	Gary Allenson	.10	.06
389	Luis Aponte	.10	.06
390	Tony Armas	.10	.06
391	Doug Bird	.10	.06
392	Wade Boggs	11.00	6.75
393	Dennis Boyd (R)	.15	.10
394	Mike Brown	.10	.06
395	Mark Clear	.10	.06
396	Dennis Eckersley	2.50	1.50
397	Dwight Evans	.25	.15
298	Rich Gedman	.10	.06
399	Glenn Hoffman	.10	.06
400	Bruce Hurst	.20	.12
401	John Henry Johnson	.10	.06
402	Ed Jurak	.10	.06
403	Rick Miller	.10	.06
404	Jeff Newman	.10	.06
405	Reid Nichols	.10	.06
406	Bob Ojeda	.15	.10
407	Jerry Remy	.10	.06
408	Jim Rice	.25	.15
409	Bob Stanley	.10	.06
410	Dave Stapleton	.10	.06
411	John Tudor	.12	.07
412	Carl Yastrzemski	3.50	2.00
413	Buddy Bell	.10	.06
414	Larry Biittner	.10	.06
415	John Butcher	.10	.06
416	Danny Darwin	.10	.06
417	Bucky Dent	.12	.07
418	Dave Hostetler	.10	.06
419	Charlie Hough	.12	.07
420	Bobby Johnson	.10	.06
421	Odell Jones	.10	.06
422	Jon Matlack	.10	.06
423	Pete O'Brien (R)	.40	.25
424	Larry Parrish	.10	.06
425	Mickey Rivers	.10	.06
426	Billy Sample	.10	.06
427	Dave Schmidt	.10	.06
428	Mike Smithson	.10	.06
429	Bill Stein	.10	.06

430	Dave Stewart	1.25	.80
431	Jim Sundberg	.10	.06
432	Frank Tanana	.12	.07
433	Dave Tobik	.10	.06
434	Wayne Tolleson (R)	.10	.06
435	George Wright	.10	.06
436	Bill Almon	.10	.06
437	Keith Atherton (R)	.10	.06
438	Dave Beard	.10	.06
439	Tom Burgmeier	.10	.06
440	Jeff Burroughs	.10	.06
441	Chris Codiroli (R)	.10	.06
442	Tim Conroy	.10	.06
443	Mike Davis	.10	.06
444	Wayne Gross	.10	.06
445	Garry Hancock	.10	.06
446	Mike Heath	.10	.06
447	Rickey Henderson	7.50	4.50
448	Don Hill (R)	.10	.06
449	Bob Kearney	.10	.06
450	Bill Krueger	.30	.18
451	Rick Langford	.10	.06
452	Carney Lansford	.20	.12
453	Davey Lopes	.12	.07
454	Steve McCatty	.10	.06
455	Dan Meyer	.10	.06
456	Dwayne Murphy	.10	.06
457	Mike Norris	.10	.06
458	Ricky Peters	.10	.06
459	Tony Phillips (R)	3.00	1.75
460	Tom Underwood	.10	.06
461	Mike Warren	.10	.06
462	Johnny Bench	3.50	2.50
463	Bruce Berenyi	.10	.06
464	Dann Bilardello	.10	.06
465	Cesar Cedeno	.12	.07
466	Dave Concepcion	.25	.15
467	Dan Driessen	.10	.06
468	Nick Esasky (R)	.15	.10
469	Rich Gale	.10	.06
470	Ben Hayes	.10	.06
471	Paul Householder	.10	.06
472	Tom Hume	.10	.06
473	Alan Knicely	.10	.06
474	Eddie Milner	.10	.06
474	Ron Oester	.10	.06
476	Kelly Paris	.10	.06
477	Frank Pastore	.10	.06
478	Ted Power	.10	.06
479	Joe Price	.10	.06
480	Charlie Puleo	.10	.06
481	Gary Redus(FC)	.25	.15
482	Bill Scherrer	.10	.06
483	Mario Soto	.10	.06
484	Alex Trevino	.10	.06
485	Duane Walker	.10	.06
486	Larry Bowa	.15	.10
487	Warren Brusstar	.10	.06
488	Bill Buckner	.15	.10
489	Bill Campbell	.10	.06
490	Ron Cey	.12	.07
491	Jody Davis	.10	.06
492	Leon Durham	.10	.06
493	Mel Hall (R)	.75	.45
494	Ferguson Jenkins	.80	.50
495	Jay Johnstone	.12	.07
496	Craig Lefferts (R)	.40	.25
497	Carmelo Martinez(R)	.15	.10
498	Jerry Morales	.10	.06
499	Keith Moreland	.10	.06
500	Dickie Noles	.10	.06
501	Mike Proly	.10	.06
502	Chuck Rainey	.10	.06
503	Dick Ruthven	.10	.06
504	Ryne Sandberg	24.00	18.00
505	Lee Smith	2.00	1.25
506	Steve Trout	.10	.06
507	Gary Woods	.10	.06
508	Juan Beniquez	.10	.06
509	Bob Boone	.20	.12
510	Rick Burleson	.10	.06
511	Rod Carew	3.00	1.75
512	Bobby Clark	.10	.06
513	John Curtis	.10	.06
514	Doug DeCinces	.10	.06
515	Brian Downing	.12	.07
516	Tim Foli	.10	.06
517	Ken Forsch	.10	.06
518	Bobby Grich	.12	.07
519	Andy Hassler	.10	.06
520	Reggie Jackson	4.50	2.75
521	Ron Jackson	.10	.06
522	Tommy Jonn	.20	.12
523	Bruce Kison	.10	.06
524	Steve Lubratich	.10	.06
525	Fred Lynn	.15	.10
526	Gary Pettis (R)	.25	.15
527	Luis Sanchez	.10	.06
528	Daryl Sconiers	.10	.06
529	Ellis Valentine	.10	.06
530	Rob Wilfong	.10	.06
531	Mike Witt	.10	.06
532	Geoff Zahn	.10	.06
533	Bud Anderson	.10	.06
534	Chris Bando	.10	.06
535	Alan Bannister	.10	.06
536	Bert Blyleven	.70	.40
537	Tom Brennan	.10	.06
538	Jamie Easterly	.10	.06
539	Juan Eichelberger	.10	.06
540	Jim Essian	.10	.06
541	Mike Fischlin	.10	.06
542	Julio Franco (R)	2.50	1.50
543	Mike Hargrove	.10	.06

544	Toby Harrah	.10	.06
545	Ron Hassey	.10	.06
546	Neal Heaton (R)	.15	.10
547	Bake McBride	.10	.06
548	Broderick Perkins	.10	.06
549	Lary Sorensen	.10	.06
550	Dan Spillner	.10	.06
551	Rick Sutcliffe	.20	.12
552	Pat Tabler	.10	.06
553	Gorman Thomas	.15	.10
554	Andre Thornton	.15	.10
555	George Vukovich	.12	.07
556	Darrell Brown	.10	.06
557	Tom Brunansky	.20	.12
558	Randy Bush (R)	.15	.10
559	Bobby Castillo	.10	.06
560	John Castino	.10	.06
561	Ron Davis	.10	.06
562	Dave Engle	.10	.06
563	Lenny Faedo	.10	.06
564	Pete Filson	.10	.06
565	Gary Gaetti	.15	.10
566	Mickey Hatcher	.10	.06
567	Kent Hrbek	.50	.30
568	Rusty Kuntz	.10	.06
569	Tim Laudner	.10	.06
570	Rick Lysander	.10	.06
571	Bobby Mitchell	.10	.06
572	Ken Schrom	.10	.06
573	Ray Smith	.10	.06
574	Tim Teufel (R)	.25	.15
575	Frank Viola	1.00	.70
576	Gary Ward	.10	.06
577	Ron Washington	.10	.06
578	Len Whitehouse	.10	.06
579	Al Williams	.10	.06
580	Bob Bailor	.10	.06
581	Mark Bradley	.10	.06
582	Hubie Brooks	.20	.12
583	Carlos Diaz	.10	.06
584	George Foster	.15	.10
585	Brian Giles	.10	.06
586	Danny Heep	.10	.06
587	Keith Hernandez	.20	.12
588	Ron Hodges	.10	.06
589	Scott Holman	.10	.06
590	Dave Kingman	.15	.10
591	Ed Lynch	.10	.06
592	Jose Oquendo (R)	.20	.12
593	Jesse Orosco	.10	.06
594	Junior Ortiz (R)	.12	.07
595	Tom Seaver	4.50	2.75
596	Doug Sisk (R)	.10	.06
597	Rusty Staub	.15	.10
598	John Stearns	.10	.06
599	Darryl Strawberry(R)	18.00	11.00
600	Craig Swan	.10	.06
601	Walt Terrell (R)	.15	.10
602	Mike Torrez	.10	.06
603	Mookie Wilson	.15	.10
604	Jamie Allen	.10	.06
605	Jim Beattie	.10	.06
606	Tony Bernazard	.10	.06
607	Manny Castillo	.10	.06
608	Bill Caudill	.10	.06
609	Bryan Clark	.10	.06
610	Al Cowens	.10	.06
611	Dave Henderson	.25	.15
612	Steve Henderson	.10	.06
613	Orlando Mercado	.10	.06
614	Mike Moore	.10	.06
615	Ricky Nelson	.25	.15
616	Spike Owen (R)	.35	.20
617	Pat Putnam	.10	.06
618	Ron Roenicke	.10	.06
619	Mike Stanton	.10	.06
620	Bob Stoddard	.10	.06
621	Rick Sweet	.10	.06
622	Roy Thomas	.10	.06
623	Ed Vande Berg	.10	.06
624	Matt Young	.20	.12
625	Richie Zisk	.10	.06
626	Fred Lynn (AS)(RB)	.15	.10
627	Manny Trillo (AS)(RB)	.10	.06
628	Steve Garvey (Iron Man)	.30	.18
629	Rod Carew (AL Batting Runner Up)	.50	.30
630	Wade Boggs (AL Batting Champ)	2.75	1.65
631	Tim Raines (Letting Go)	.50	.30
632	Al Oliver (Double Trouble)	.15	.10
633	All-Star Second Base (Steve Sax)	.15	.10
634	All-Star Shortstop (Dickie Thon)	.12	.07
635	Ace Firemen (Tippy Martinez, Dan Quisenberry)	.12	.07
636	Reds Reunited (Joe Morgan, Tony Perez, Pete Rose)	1.25	.80
637	Backstop Stars (Bob Boone, Lance Parrish)	.15	.10
638	The Pine Tar Incident George Brett, Gaylord Perry	1.50	.90
639	1983 No-Hitters (Bob Forsch, Dave Righetti, Mike Warren)	.15	.10
640	Retiring Superstars Johnny Bench, Carl Yastrzemski	3.50	2.50
641	Going Out In Style	.30	.18

		MINT	NR/MT
Complete Set (132)		1,100.00	700.00
Commons		.80	.50

	(Gaylord Perry)		
642	300 Club & Strikout Record(Steve Carlton)	.90	.60
643	The Managers (Joe Altobelli, Paul Owens)	.10	.06
644	World Series MVP (Rick Dempsey)	.10	.06
645	Rookie Winner (Mike Boddicker)	.12	.07
646	The Clincher (Scott McGregor)	.10	.06
647	Checklist	.12	.05
648	Checklist	.12	.05
649	Checklist	.12	.05
650	Checklist	.12	.05
651	Checklist	.12	.05
652	Checklist	.12	.05
653	Checklist	.12	.05
654	Checklist	.12	.05
655	Checklist	.12	.05
656	Checklist	.12	.05
657	Checklist	.12	.05
658	Checklist	.12	.05
659	Checklist	.12	.05
660	Checklist	.12	.05

1984 Fleer Update

This 132-card set marks the first post-season set issued by Fleer. Like the Topps Traded Set, this set updates players who were traded during the year and introduces some promising rookies. Cards measure 2-1/2" by 3-1/2" and card numbers are preceded by the letter "U" on the card backs to signify the Update Set. Due to a limited print run this set is considered scarce.

1	Willie Aikens	.80	.50
2	Luis Aponte	.80	.50
3	Mark Bailey (R)	.80	.50
4	Bob Bailor	.80	.50
5	Dusty Baker	1.25	.80
6	Steve Balboni (R)	.90	.60
7	Alan Bannister	.80	.50
8	Marty Barrett (R)	1.25	.80
9	Dave Beard	.80	.50
10	Joe Beckwith	.80	.50
11	Dave Bergman	.80	.50
12	Tony Bernazard	.80	.50
13	Bruce Bochte	.80	.50
14	Barry Bonnell	.80	.50
15	Phil Bradley (R)	1.25	.80
16	Fred Breining	.80	.50
17	Mike Brown	.80	.50
18	Bill Buckner	.90	.60
19	Ray Burris	.80	.50
20	John Butcher	.80	.50
21	Brett Butler	4.50	2.75
22	Enos Cabell	.80	.50
23	Bill Campbell	.80	.50
24	Bill Caudill	.80	.50
25	Bobby Clark	.80	.50
26	Bryan Clark	.80	.50
27	Roger Clemens (R)	425.00	350.00
28	Jaime Cocanower	.80	.50
29	Ron Darling (R)	6.00	3.75
30	Alvin Davis (R)	1.50	.90
31	Bob Dernier	.80	.50
32	Carlos Diaz	.80	.50
33	Mike Easler	.80	.50
34	Dennis Eckersley	24.00	14.00
35	Jim Essian	.80	.50
36	Darrell Evans	1.25	.80
37	Mike Fitgerald (R)	.80	.50
38	Tim Foli	.80	.50
39	John Franco (R)	6.00	3.75
40	George Frazier	.80	.50
41	Rich Gale	.80	.50
42	Barbaro Garbey	.80	.50
43	Dwight Gooden (R)	75.00	45.00
44	Goose Gossage	1.50	.90
45	Wayne Gross	.80	.50
46	Mark Gubicza (R)	3.50	2.00
47	Jackie Gutierrez	.80	.50
48	Toby Harrah	.80	.50
49	Ron Hassey	.80	.50
50	Richie Hebner	.80	.50
51	Willie Hernandez	.90	.60
52	Ed Hodge	.80	.50

53	Ricky Horton (R)	.80	.50
54	Art Howe	.80	.50
55	Dane Iorg	.80	.50
56	Brook Jacoby (R)	1.25	.80
57	Dion James (R)	1.50	.90
58	Mike Jeffcoat (R)	.80	.50
59	Ruppert Jones	.80	.90
60	Bob Kearney	.80	.50
61	Jimmy Key (R)	32.00	20.00
62	Dave Kingman	1.00	.70
63	Brad Komminsk (R)	.80	.50
64	Jerry Koosman	1.00	.70
65	Wayne Krenchicki	.80	.50
66	Rusty Kuntz	.80	.50
67	Frank LaCorte	.80	.50
68	Dennis Lamp	.80	.50
69	Tito Landrum	.80	.50
70	Mark Langston (R)	35.00	22.00
71	Rick Leach	.80	.50
72	Craig Lefferts	1.00	.70
73	Gary Lucas	.80	.50
74	Jerry Martin	.80	.50
75	Carmelo Martinez	.80	.50
76	Mike Mason (R)	.80	.50
77	Gary Matthews	.80	.50
78	Andy McGaffigan	.80	.50
79	Joey McLaughlin	.80	.50
80	Joe Morgan	12.00	7.50
81	Darryl Motley	.80	.50
82	Graig Nettles	.90	.60
83	Phil Niekro	8.50	5.50
84	Ken Oberkfell	.80	.50
85	Al Oliver	.90	.60
86	Jorge Orta	.80	.50
87	Amos Otis	.90	.60
88	Bob Owchinko	.80	.50
89	Dave Parker	4.50	2.75
90	Jack Perconte	.80	.50
91	Tony Perez	8.50	5.50
92	Gerald Perry (R)	1.00	.70
93	Kirby Puckett (R)	475.00	290.00
94	Shane Rawley	.80	.50
95	Floyd Rayford	.80	.50
96	Ron Reed	.80	.50
97	R.J. Reynolds (R)	.80	.50
98	Gene Richards	.80	.50
99	Jose Rijo (R)	30.00	18.00
100	Jeff Robinson	.80	.50
101	Ron Romanick	.80	.50
102	Pete Rose	35.00	20.00
103	Bret Saberhagen (R)	25.00	15.00
104	Scott Sanderson	.90	.60
105	Dick Schofield (R)	1.00	.70
106	Tom Seaver	28.00	20.00
107	Jim Slaton	.80	.50
108	Mike Smithson	.80	.50
109	Lary Sorensen	.80	.50

110	Tim Stoddard	.80	.50
111	Jeff Stone (R)	.80	.50
112	Champ Summers	.80	.50
113	Jim Sundberg	.80	.50
114	Rick Sutcliffe	1.25	.80
115	Craig Swan	.80	.50
116	Derrel Thomas	.80	.50
117	Gorman Thomas	.90	.60
118	Alex Trevino	.80	.50
119	Manny Trillo	.80	.50
120	John Tudor	.90	.60
121	Tom Underwood	.80	.50
122	Mike Vail	.80	.50
123	Tom Waddell (R)	.80	.50
124	Gary Ward	.80	.50
125	Terry Whitfield	.80	.50
126	Curtis Wilkerson	.80	.50
127	Frank Williams (R)	.80	.50
128	Glenn Wilson	.80	.50
129	John Wockenfuss	.80	.50
130	Ned Yost	.80	.50
131	Mike Young	.90	.60
132	Checklist 1-132	1.00	.30

1985 Fleer

This 660-card set features full color photos on the card fronts with various border colors that correspond to the player's team colors. Cards measure 2-1/2" by 3-1/2". Card backs are vertical and printed in red, light red and black on a white stock. Fleer introduced a new 10-card subset, called Major League Prospects, which features two players on one card.

	MINT	NR/MT
Complete Set (660)	200.00	125.00
Commons	.10	.06

1	Doug Bair	.10	.06
2	Juan Berenguer	.10	.06
3	Dave Bergman	.10	.06
4	Tom Brookens	.10	.06
5	Marty Castillo	.10	.06
6	Darrell Evans	.12	.07
7	Barbaro Garbey	.10	.06
8	Kirk Gibson	.30	.18
9	John Grubb	.10	.06
10	Willie Hernandez	.12	.07
11	Larry Herndon	.10	.06
12	Howard Johnson	1.25	.80
13	Ruppert Jones	.10	.06
14	Rusty Kuntz	.10	.06
15	Chet Lemon	.10	.06
16	Aurelio Lopez	.10	.06
17	Sid Monge	.10	.06
18	Jack Morris	.90	.60
19	Lance Parrish	.12	.07
20	Dan Petry	.10	.06
21	Dave Rozema	.10	.06
22	Bill Scherrer	.10	.06
23	Alan Trammell	.80	.50
24	Lou Whitaker	.70	.40
25	Milt Wilcox	.10	.06
26	Kurt Bevacqua	.10	.06
27	Greg Booker (R)	.10	.06
28	Bobby Brown	.10	.06
29	Luis DeLeon	.10	.06
30	Dave Dravecky	.12	.07
31	Tim Flannery	.10	.06
32	Steve Garvey	.50	.30
33	Goose Gossage	.15	.10
34	Tony Gwynn	7.00	4.00
35	Greg Harris	.10	.06
36	Andy Hawkins	.10	.06
37	Terry Kennedy	.10	.06
38	Craig Lefferts	.10	.06
39	Tim Lollar	.10	.06
40	Carmelo Martinez	.10	.06
41	Kevin McReynolds	.30	.18
42	Graig Nettles	.15	.10
43	Luis Salazar	.10	.06
44	Eric Show	.10	.06
45	Garry Templeton	.10	.06
46	Mark Thurmond	.10	.06
47	Ed Whitson	.10	.06
48	Alan Wiggins	.10	.06
49	Rich Bordi	.10	.06
50	Larry Bowa	.10	.06
51	Warren Brusstar	.10	.06
52	Ron Cey	.12	.07
53	Henry Cotto (R)	.12	.07
54	Jody Davis	.10	.06
55	Bob Dernier	.10	.06
56	Leon Durham	.10	.06
57	Dennis Eckersley	1.25	.80
58	George Frazier	.10	.06
59	Richie Hebner	.10	.06
60	Dave Lopes	.12	.07
61	Gary Matthews	.10	.06
62	Keith Moreland	.10	.06
63	Rick Reuschel	.10	.06
64	Dick Ruthven	.10	.06
65	Ryne Sandberg	12.00	7.00
66	Scott Sanderson	.12	.07
67	Lee Smith	1.25	.80
68	Tim Stoddard	.10	.06
69	Rick Sutcliffe	.15	.10
70	Steve Trout	.10	.06
71	Gary Woods	.10	.06
72	Wally Backman	.10	.06
73	Bruce Berenyi	.10	.06
74	Hubie Brooks	.12	.07
75	Kelvin Chapman	.10	.06
76	Ron Darling	.30	.18
77	Sid Fernandez (R)	.50	.30
78	Mike Fitgerald	.10	.06
79	George Foster	.12	.07
80	Brent Gaff	.10	.06
81	Ron Gardenhire	.10	.06
82	Dwight Gooden	8.50	5.00
83	Tom Gorman	.10	.06
84	Danny Heep	.10	.06
85	Keith Hernandez	.15	.10
86	Ray Knight	.12	.07
87	Ed Lynch	.10	.06
88	Jose Oquendo	.10	.06
89	Jesse Orosco	.10	.06
90	Rafael Santana (R)	.12	.07
91	Doug Sisk	.10	.06
92	Rusty Staub	.12	.07
93	Darryl Strawberry	4.00	2.50
94	Walt Terrell	.10	.06
95	Mookie Wilson	.10	.06
96	Jim Acker	.10	.06
97	Willie Aikens	.10	.06
98	Doyle Alexander	.10	.06
99	Jesse Barfield	.15	.10
100	George Bell	.70	.40
101	Jim Clancy	.10	.06
102	Dave Collins	.10	.06
103	Tony Fernandez	.80	.50
104	Damaso Garcia	.10	.06
105	Jim Gott	.10	.06
106	Alfredo Griffin	.10	.06
107	Garth Iorg	.10	.06
108	Roy Lee Jackson	.10	.06
109	Cliff Johnson	.10	.06
110	Jimmy Key	4.00	2.50
111	Dennis Lamp	.10	.06
112	Rick Leach	.10	.06
113	Luis Leal	.10	.06
114	Buck Martinez	.10	.06

115	Lloyd Moseby	.10	.06
116	Rance Mulliniks	.10	.06
117	Dave Stieb	.20	.15
118	Willie Upshaw	.10	.06
119	Ernie Whitt	.10	.06
120	Mike Armstrong	.10	.06
121	Don Baylor	.15	.10
122	Marty Bystrom	.10	.06
123	Rick Cerone	.10	.06
124	Joe Cowley	.10	.06
125	Brian Dayett	.10	.06
126	Tim Foli	.10	.06
127	Ray Fontenot	.10	.06
128	Ken Griffey	.15	.10
129	Ron Guidry	.20	.12
130	Toby Harrah	.10	.06
131	Jay Howell	.10	.06
132	Steve Kemp	.10	.06
133	Don Mattingly	8.50	5.00
134	Bobby Meacham	.10	.06
135	John Montefusco	.10	.06
136	Omar Moreno	.10	.06
137	Dale Murray	.10	.06
138	Phil Niekro	.75	.45
139	Mike Pagliarulo (R)	.25	.15
140	Willie Randolph	.15	.10
141	Dennis Rasmussen	.10	.06
142	Dave Righetti	.12	.07
143	Jose Rijo	4.50	3.00
144	Andre Robertson	.10	.06
145	Bob Shirley	.10	.06
146	Dave Winfield	5.00	3.00
147	Butch Wynegar	.10	.06
148	Gary Allenson	.10	.06
149	Tony Armas	.10	.06
150	Marty Barrett	.12	.07
151	Wade Boggs	6.50	3.75
152	Dennis Boyd	.10	.06
153	Bill Buckner	.12	.07
154	Mark Clear	.10	.06
155	Roger Clemens	60.00	38.00
156	Steve Crawford	.10	.06
157	Mike Easler	.10	.06
158	Dwight Evans	.25	.15
159	Rich Gedman	.10	.06
160	Jackie Gutierrez	.10	.06
161	Bruce Hurst	.15	.10
162	John Henry Johnson	.10	.06
163	Rick Miller	.10	.06
164	Reid Nichols	.10	.06
165	Al Nipper (R)	.12	.07
166	Bob Ojeda	.10	.06
167	Jerry Remy	.10	.06
168	Jim Rice	.20	.12
169	Bob Stanley	.10	.06
170	Mike Boddicker	.10	.06
171	Al Bumbry	.10	.06
172	Todd Cruz	.10	.06
173	Rich Dauer	.10	.06
174	Storm Davis	.10	.06
175	Rick Dempsey	.10	.06
176	Jim Dwyer	.10	.06
177	Mike Flanagan	.12	.07
178	Dan Ford	.10	.06
179	Wayne Gross	.10	.06
180	John Lowenstein	.10	.06
181	Dennis Martinez	.20	.12
182	Tippy Martinez	.10	.06
183	Scott McGregor	.10	.06
184	Eddie Murray	3.00	2.00
185	Joe Nolan	.10	.06
186	Floyd Rayford	.10	.06
187	Cal Ripken, Jr.	12.50	7.50
188	Gary Roenicke	.10	.06
189	Lenn Sakata	.10	.06
190	John Shelby	.10	.06
191	Ken Singleton	.10	.06
192	Sammy Stewart	.10	.06
193	Bill Swaggerty	.10	.06
194	Tom Underwood	.10	.06
195	Mike Young	.10	.06
196	Steve Balboni	.10	.06
197	Joe Beckwith	.10	.06
198	Bud Black	.10	.06
199	George Brett	4.50	3.00
200	Onix Concepcion	.10	.06
201	Mark Gubicza	.60	.35
202	Larry Gura	.10	.06
203	Mark Huismann	.10	.06
204	Dane Iorg	.10	.06
205	Danny Jackson	.25	.15
206	Charlie Leibrandt	.10	.06
207	Hal McRae	.15	.10
208	Darryl Motley	.10	.06
209	Jorge Orta	.10	.06
210	Greg Pryor	.10	.06
211	Dan Quisenberry	.10	.06
212	Bret Saberhagen	3.50	2.00
213	Pat Sheridan	.10	.06
214	Don Slaught	.10	.06
215	U.L. Washington	.10	.06
216	John Wathan	.10	.06
217	Frank White	.12	.07
218	Willie Wilson	.12	.07
219	Neil Allen	.10	.06
220	Joaquin Andujar	.10	.06
221	Steve Braun	.10	.06
222	Danny Cox	.10	.06
223	Bob Forsch	.10	.06
224	David Green	.10	.06
225	George Hendrick	.12	.07
226	Tom Herr	.10	.06
227	Ricky Horton	.10	.06
228	Art Howe	.10	.06

229	Mike Jorgensen	.10	.06	286	Kirby Puckett	65.00	50.00
230	Kurt Kepshire	.10	.06	287	Pat Putnam	.10	.06
231	Jeff Lahti	.10	.06	288	Ken Schrom	.10	.06
232	Tito Landrum	.10	.06	289	Mike Smithson	.10	.06
233	Dave LaPoint	.10	.06	290	Tim Teufel	.10	.06
234	Willie McGee	.50	.30	291	Frank Viola	.50	.30
235	Tom Nieto (R)	.10	.06	292	Ron Washington	.10	.06
236	Terry Pendleton (R)	8.00	4.75	293	Don Aase	.10	.06
237	Darrell Porter	.10	.06	294	Juan Beniquez	.10	.06
238	Dave Rucker	.10	.06	295	Bob Boone	.15	.10
239	Lonnie Smith	.12	.07	296	Mike Brown	.10	.06
240	Ozzie Smith	2.75	1.75	297	Rod Carew	2.00	1.25
241	Bruce Sutter	.15	.10	298	Doug Corbett	.10	.06
242	Andy Van Slyke	2.75	1.75	299	Doug DeCinces	.10	.06
243	Dave Von Ohlen	.10	.06	300	Brian Downing	.12	.07
244	Larry Andersen	.10	.06	301	Ken Forsch	.10	.06
245	Bill Campbell	.10	.06	302	Bobby Grich	.12	.07
246	Steve Carlton	2.50	1.50	303	Reggie Jackson	3.50	2.50
247	Tim Corcoran	.10	.06	304	Tommy John	.15	.10
248	Ivan DeJesus	.10	.06	305	Curt Kaufman	.10	.06
249	John Denny	.10	.06	306	Bruce Kison	.10	.06
250	Bo Diaz	.10	.06	307	Fred Lynn	.15	.10
251	Greg Gross	.10	.06	308	Gary Pettis	.10	.06
252	Kevin Gross	.10	.06	309	Ron Romanick	.10	.06
253	Von Hayes	.10	.06	310	Luis Sanchez	.10	.06
254	Al Holland	.10	.06	311	Dick Schofield	.10	.06
255	Charles Hudson	.10	.06	312	Daryl Sconiers	.10	.06
256	Jerry Koosman	.12	.07	313	Jim Slaton	.10	.06
257	Joe Lefebvre	.10	.06	314	Derrel Thomas	.10	.06
258	Sixto Lezcano	.10	.06	315	Rob Wilfong	.10	.06
259	Garry Maddox	.10	.06	316	Mike Witt	.10	.06
260	Len Matuszek	.10	.06	317	Geoff Zahn	.10	.06
261	Tug McGraw	.12	.07	318	Len Barker	.10	.06
262	Al Oliver	.12	.07	319	Steve Bedrosian	.12	.07
263	Shane Rawley	.10	.06	320	Bruce Benedict	.10	.06
264	Juan Samuel	.15	.10	321	Rick Camp	.10	.06
265	Mike Schmidt	6.50	4.50	322	Chris Chambliss	.12	.07
266	Jeff Stone	.10	.06	323	Jeff Dedmon (R)	.10	.06
267	Ozzie Virgil	.10	.06	324	Terry Forster	.10	.06
268	Glenn Wilson	.10	.06	325	Gene Garber	.10	.06
269	John Wockenfuss	.10	.06	326	Albert Hall (R)	.12	.07
270	Darrell Brown	.10	.06	327	Terry Harper	.10	.06
271	Tom Brunansky	.12	.07	328	Bob Horner	.12	.07
272	Randy Bush	.10	.06	329	Glenn Hubbard	.10	.06
273	John Butcher	.10	.06	330	Randy Johnson	.10	.06
274	Bobby Castillo	.10	.06	331	Brad Komminsk	.10	.06
275	Ron Davis	.10	.06	332	Rick Mahler	.10	.06
276	Dave Engle	.10	.06	333	Craig McMurtry	.10	.06
277	Pete Filson	.10	.06	334	Donnie Moore	.10	.06
278	Gary Gaetti	.10	.06	335	Dale Murphy	.90	.60
279	Mickey Hatcher	.10	.06	336	Ken Oberkfell	.10	.06
280	Ed Hodge	.10	.06	337	Pascual Perez	.10	.06
281	Kent Hrbek	.30	.18	338	Gerald Perry	.10	.06
282	Houston Jimenez	.10	.06	339	Rafael Ramirez	.10	.06
283	Tim Laudner	.10	.06	340	Jerry Royster	.10	.06
284	Rick Lysander	.10	.06	341	Alex Trevino	.10	.06
285	Dave Meier	.10	.06	342	Claudell Washington	.10	.06

343	Alan Ashby	.10	.06
344	Mark Bailey	.10	.06
345	Kevin Bass	.12	.07
346	Enos Cabell	.10	.06
347	Jose Cruz	.12	.07
348	Bill Dawley	.10	.06
349	Frank DePino	.10	.06
350	Bill Doran	.10	.06
351	Phil Garner	.12	.07
352	Bob Knepper	.10	.06
353	Mike LaCoss	.10	.06
354	Jerry Mumphrey	.10	.06
355	Joe Niekro	.10	.06
356	Terry Puhl	.10	.06
357	Craig Reynolds	.10	.06
358	Vern Ruhle	.10	.06
359	Nolan Ryan	12.50	7.50
360	Joe Sambito	.10	.06
361	Mike Scott	.12	.07
362	Dave Smith	.10	.06
363	Julio Solano (R)	.10	.06
364	Dickie Thon	.10	.06
365	Denny Walling	.10	.06
366	Dave Anderson	.10	.06
367	Bob Bailor	.10	.06
368	Greg Brock	.10	.06
369	Carlos Diaz	.10	.06
370	Pedro Guerrero	.15	.10
371	Orel Hershiser (R)	3.50	2.00
372	Rick Honeycutt	.10	.06
373	Burt Hooton	.10	.06
374	Ken Howell (R)	.10	.06
375	Ken Landreaux	.10	.06
376	Candy Maldonado	.10	.06
377	Mike Marshall	.10	.06
378	Tom Niedenfuer	.10	.06
379	Alejandro Pena	.12	.07
380	Jerry Reuss	.12	.07
381	R.J. Reynolds	.10	.06
382	German Rivera	.10	.06
383	Bill Russell	.12	.07
384	Steve Sax	.40	.25
385	Mike Scioscia	.10	.06
386	Franklin Stubbs (R)	.20	.12
387	Fernando Valenzuela	.15	.10
388	Bob Welch	.15	.10
389	Terry Whitfield	.10	.06
390	Steve Yeager	.10	.06
391	Pat Zachry	.10	.06
392	Fred Breining	.10	.06
393	Gary Carter	.60	.35
394	Andre Dawson	3.00	1.75
395	Miguel Dilone	.10	.06
396	Dan Driessen	.10	.06
397	Doug Flynn	.10	.06
398	Terry Francona	.10	.06
399	Bill Gullickson	.12	.07
400	Bob James	.10	.06
401	Charlie Lea	.10	.06
402	Bryan Little	.10	.06
403	Gary Lucas	.10	.06
404	David Palmer	.10	.06
405	Tim Raines	.40	.25
406	Mike Ramsey	.10	.00
407	Jeff Reardon	.80	.50
408	Steve Rogers	.10	.06
409	Dan Schatzeder	.10	.06
410	Bryn Smith	.10	.06
411	Mike Stenhouse	.10	.06
412	Tim Wallach	.20	.12
413	Jim Wohlford	.10	.06
414	Bill Almon	.10	.06
415	Keith Atherton	.10	.06
416	Bruce Bochte	.10	.06
417	Tom Burgmeier	.10	.06
418	Ray Burris	.10	.06
419	Bill Caudill	.10	.06
420	Chris Codiroli	.10	.06
421	Tim Conroy	.10	.06
422	Mike Davis	.10	.06
423	Jim Essian	.10	.06
424	Mike Heath	.10	.06
425	Rickey Henderson	4.00	2.50
426	Donnie Hill	.10	.06
427	Dave Kingman	.12	.07
428	Bill Krueger	.10	.06
429	Carney Lansford	.12	.07
430	Steve McCatty	.10	.06
431	Joe Morgan	.75	.45
432	Dwayne Murphy	.10	.06
433	Tony Phillips	.50	.30
434	Lary Sorensen	.10	.06
435	Mike Warren	.10	.06
436	Curt Young (R)	.20	.12
437	Luis Aponte	.10	.06
438	Chris Bando	.10	.06
439	Tony Bernazard	.10	.06
440	Bert Blyleven	.40	.25
441	Brett Butler	.40	.25
442	Ernie Camacho	.10	.06
443	Joe Carter (R)	14.00	8.50
444	Carmelo Castillo	.10	.06
445	Jamie Easterly	.10	.06
446	Steve Farr (R)	.50	.30
447	Mike Fischlin	.10	.06
448	Julio Franco	.75	.45
449	Mel Hall	.12	.07
450	Mike Hargrove	.10	.06
451	Neal Heaton	.10	.06
452	Brook Jacoby	.10	.06
453	Mike Jeffcoat	.10	.06
454	Don Schulze (R)	.10	.06
455	Roy Smith	.10	.06
456	Pat Tabler	.10	.06

457	Andre Thornton	.12	.07
458	George Vukovich	.10	.06
459	Tom Waddoll	.10	.06
460	Jerry Willard	.10	.06
461	Dale Berra	.10	.06
462	John Candelaria	.10	.06
463	Jose DeLeon	.10	.06
464	Doug Frobel	.10	.06
465	Cecilio Guante	.10	.06
466	Brian Harper	.15	.10
467	Lee Lacy	.10	.06
468	Bill Madlock	.15	.10
469	Lee Mazzilli	.10	.06
470	Larry McWilliams	.10	.06
471	Jim Morrison	.10	.06
472	Tony Pena	.12	.07
473	Johnny Ray	.10	.06
474	Rick Rhoden	.10	.06
475	Don Robinson	.10	.06
476	Rod Scurry	.10	.06
477	Kent Tekulve	.10	.06
478	Jason Thompson	.10	.06
479	John Tudor	.10	.06
480	Lee Tunnell	.10	.06
481	Marvell Wynne	.10	.06
482	Salome Barojas	.10	.06
483	Dave Beard	.10	.06
484	Jim Beattie	.10	.06
485	Barry Bonnell	.10	.06
486	Phil Bradley	.12	.07
487	Al Cowens	.10	.06
488	Alvin Davis	.25	.15
489	Dave Henderson	.15	.10
490	Steve Henderson	.10	.06
491	Bob Kearney	.10	.06
492	Mark Langston	4.00	2.50
493	Larry Milbourne	.10	.06
494	Paul Mirabella	.10	.06
495	Mike Moore	.10	.06
496	Edwin Nunez	.10	.06
497	Spike Owen	.10	.06
498	Jack Perconte	.10	.06
499	Ken Phelps	.10	.06
500	Jim Presley (R)	.10	.06
501	Mike Stanton	.10	.06
502	Bob Stoddard	.10	.06
503	Gorman Thomas	.12	.07
504	Ed Vande Berg	.10	.06
505	Matt Young	.10	.06
506	Juan Agosto	.10	.06
507	Harold Baines	.30	.18
508	Floyd Bannister	.10	.06
509	Britt Burns	.10	.06
510	Julio Cruz	.10	.06
511	Richard Dotson	.10	.06
512	Jerry Dybzinski	.10	.06
513	Carlton Fisk	2.25	1.40
514	Scott Fletcher	.10	.06
515	Jerry Hairston	.10	.06
516	Marc Hill	.10	.00
517	LaMarr Hoyt	.10	.06
518	Ron Kittle	.10	.06
519	Rudy Law	.10	.06
520	Vance Law	.10	.06
521	Greg Luzinski	.12	.07
522	Gene Nelson	.10	.06
523	Tom Paciorek	.10	.06
524	Ron Reed	.10	.06
525	Bert Roberge	.10	.06
526	Tom Seaver	2.50	1.50
527	Roy Smalley	.10	.06
528	Dan Spillner	.10	.06
529	Mike Squires	.10	.06
530	Greg Walker	.10	.06
531	Cesar Cedeno	.12	.07
532	Dave Concepcion	.20	.12
533	Eric Davis (R)	7.00	4.00
534	Nick Esasky	.10	.06
535	Tom Foley	.10	.06
536	John Franco	1.00	.70
537	Brad Gulden	.10	.06
538	Tom Hume	.10	.06
539	Wayne Krenchicki	.10	.06
540	Andy McGaffigan	.10	.06
541	Eddie Milner	.10	.06
542	Ron Oester	.10	.06
543	Bob Owchinko	.10	.06
544	Dave Parker	.30	.18
545	Frank Pastore	.10	.06
546	Tony Perez	.60	.35
547	Ted Power	.10	.06
548	Joe Price	.10	.06
549	Gary Redus	.10	.06
550	Pete Rose	2.75	1.60
551	Jeff Russell	.20	.12
552	Mario Soto	.12	.07
553	Jay Tibbs (R)	.10	.06
554	Duane Walker	.10	.06
555	Alan Bannister	.10	.06
556	Buddy Bell	.10	.06
557	Danny Darwin	.10	.06
558	Charlie Hough	.12	.07
559	Bobby Jones	.10	.06
560	Odell Jones	.10	.06
561	Jeff Kunkel (R)	.10	.06
562	Mike Mason	.10	.06
563	Pete O'Brien	.12	.07
564	Larry Parrish	.10	.06
565	Mickey Rivers	.10	.06
566	Billy Sample	.10	.06
567	Dave Schmidt	.10	.06
568	Donnie Scott	.10	.06
569	Dave Stewart	.50	.30
570	Frank Tanana	.12	.07

571	Wayne Tolleson	.10	.06
572	Gary Ward	.10	.06
573	Curtis Wilkerson	.10	.06
574	George Wright	.10	.06
575	Ned Yost	.10	.06
576	Mark Brouhard	.10	.06
577	Mike Caldwell	.10	.06
578	Bobby Clark	.10	.06
579	Jaime Cocanower	.10	.06
580	Cecil Cooper	.12	.07
581	Rollie Fingers	.75	.45
582	Jim Gantner	.10	.06
583	Moose Haas	.10	.06
584	Dion James	.10	.06
585	Pete Ladd	.10	.06
586	Rick Manning	.10	.06
587	Bob McClure	.10	.06
588	Paul Molitor	2.75	1.60
589	Charlie Moore	.10	.06
590	Ben Oglivie	.10	.06
591	Chuck Porter	.10	.06
592	Randy Ready (R)	.12	.07
593	Ed Romero	.10	.06
594	Bill Schroeder	.10	.06
595	Ray Searage	.10	.06
596	Ted Simmons	.12	.07
597	Jim Sundberg	.10	.06
598	Don Sutton	.60	.35
599	Tom Tellmann	.10	.06
600	Rick Waits	.10	.06
601	Robin Yount	4.50	3.00
602	Dusty Baker	.12	.07
603	Bob Brenly	.10	.06
604	Jack Clark	.12	.07
605	Chili Davis	.15	.10
606	Mark Davis	.10	.06
607	Dan Gladden (R)	.40	.25
608	Atlee Hammaker	.10	.06
609	Mike Krukow	.10	.06
610	Duane Kuiper	.10	.06
611	Bob Lacey	.10	.06
612	Bill Laskey	.10	.06
613	Gary Lavelle	.10	.06
614	Johnnie LeMaster	.10	.06
615	Jeff Leonard	.10	.06
616	Randy Lerch	.10	.06
617	Greg Minton	.10	.06
618	Steve Nicosia	.10	.06
619	Gene Richards	.10	.06
620	Jeff Robinson	.10	.06
621	Scot Thompson	.10	.06
622	Manny Trillo	.10	.06
623	Brad Wellman	.10	.06
624	Frank Williams	.10	.06
625	Joel Youngblood	.10	.06
626	Cal Ripken (IA)	5.00	3.00
627	Mike Schmidt (IA)	3.00	1.75

628	Sparky Anderson (Giving Signs)	.12	.07
629	Pitcher's Nightmare (Rickey Henderson, Dave Winfield)	2.50	1.50
630	Pitcher's Nightmare (Ryne Sandberg, Mike Schmidt)	2.50	1.50
631	N.L. All-Stars (Gary Carter, Steve Garvey, Ozzie Smith, Darryl Strawberry)	1.00	.70
632	All-Star Game Winning Battery (Gary Carter, Charlie Lea)	.10	.06
633	N.L. Pennant Clinchers (Steve Garvey, Goose Gossage)	.15	.10
634	N.L. Rookie Phenoms (Dwight Gooden, Juan Samuel)	.40	.25
635	Toronto's Big Guns (Willie Upshaw)	.10 .10	.06 .06
636	Toronto's Big Guns (Lloyd Moseby)	.10 .10	.06 .06
637	Holland (Al Holland)	.10	.06
638	Tunnell (Lee Tunnell)	.10	.06
639	Reggie Jackson(500th)	1.75	1.00
640	Pete Rose (4000th)	1.50	.90
641	The Ripkens Sr. & Jr.	4.50	2.75
642	Cubs Team	.10	.06
643	1984's Two Perfect Games & One No-Hitter (Jack Morris, David Palmer, Mike Witt)	.10	.06
644	Major League Prospect Willie Lozado (R) Vic Mata (R)	.10	.06
645	Major League Prospect Kelly Gruber (R) Randy O'Neal (R)	1.75	1.00
646	Major League Prospect Jose Roman (R) Joel Skinner (R)	.10	.06
647	Major League Prospect Steve Kiefer (R) Danny Tartabull (R)	6.00	3.50
648	Major League Prospect Rob Deer (R) Alejandro Sanchez (R)	1.25	.80
649	Major League Prospect Shawon Dunston (R) Bill Hatcher (R)	1.75	1.00
650	Major League Prospect Mike Bielecki (R) Ron Robinson (R)	.25	.15
651	Major League Prospect	.40	.25

	Zane Smith (R)		
	Paul Zuvella (R)		
652	Major League Prospect	1.25	.80
	Glenn Davis (R)		
	Joe Hesketh (R)		
653	Major League Prospect	.10	.06
	Steve Jeltz (R)		
	John Russell (R)		
654	Checklist (1-95)	.12	.05
655	Checklist (96-195)	.12	.05
656	Checklist (196-292)	.12	.05
657	Checklist (293-391)	.12	.05
658	Checklist (392-481)	.12	.05
659	Checklist (482-575)	.12	.05
660	Checklist (576-660)	.12	.05

1985 Fleer Update

This 132-card update set is identical to Fleer's 1985 regular edition and features player's who changed teams during the year and a number of rookie prospects. Card backs contain the letter "U" before the card number. Cards measure 2-1/2" by 3-1/2".

		MINT	NR/MT
	Complete Set (132)	38.00	28.00
	Commons	.10	.06

1	Don Aase	.12	.07
2	Bill Almon	.10	.06
3	Dusty Baker	.12	.07
4	Dale Berra	.10	.06
5	Karl Best (R)	.10	.06
6	Tim Birtsas (R)	.12	.07
7	Vida Blue	.20	.12
8	Rich Bordi	.10	.06
9	Daryl Boston (R)	.40	.25
10	Hubie Brooks	.20	.12

11	Chris Brown (R)	.10	.06
12	Tom Browning (R)	1.00	.70
13	Al Bumbry	.10	.06
14	Tim Burke (R)	.20	.12
15	Ray Burris	.10	.06
16	Jeff Burroughs	.10	.06
17	Ivan Calderon (R)	1.00	.70
18	Jeff Calhoun	.10	.06
19	Bill Campbell	.10	.06
20	Don Carman (R)	.15	.10
21	Gary Carter	1.00	.70
22	Bobby Castillo	.10	.06
23	Bill Caudill	.10	.06
24	Rick Cerone	.10	.06
25	Jack Clark	.25	.15
26	Pat Clements (R)	.15	.10
27	Stewart Cliburn (R)	.12	.07
28	Vince Coleman (R)	1.75	1.00
29	Dave Collins	.10	.06
30	Fritz Connally	.10	.06
31	Henry Cotto	.10	.06
32	Danny Darwin	.10	.06
33	Darren Daulton (R)	22.00	14.00
34	Jerry Davis	.10	.06
35	Brian Dayett	.10	.06
36	Ken Dixon	.10	.06
37	Tommy Dunbar	.10	.06
38	Mariano Duncan (R)	1.00	.70
39	Bob Fallon	.10	.06
40	Brian Fisher (R)	.12	.07
41	Mike Fitzgerald	.10	.06
42	Ray Fontenot	.10	.06
43	Greg Gagne	.35	.20
44	Oscar Gamble	.12	.07
45	Jim Gott	.12	.07
46	David Green	.10	.06
47	Alfredo Griffin	.10	.06
48	Ozzie Guillen (R)	2.50	1.50
49	Toby Harrah	.10	.06
50	Ron Hassey	.10	.06
51	Rickey Henderson	4.50	3.00
52	Steve Henderson	.10	.06
53	George Hendrick	.12	.07
54	Teddy Higuera (R)	.35	.20
55	Al Holland	.10	.06
56	Burt Hooton	.10	.06
57	Jay Howell	.12	.07
58	LaMarr Hoyt	.12	.07
59	Tim Hulett (R)	.15	.10
60	Bob James	.10	.06
61	Cliff Johnson	.10	.06
62	Howard Johnson	1.50	.90
63	Ruppert Jones	.10	.06
64	Steve Kemp	.10	.06
65	Bruce Kison	.10	.06
66	Mike LaCoss	.10	.06
67	Lee Lacy	.10	.06

· 68	Dave LaPoint	.10	.06
69	Gary Lavelle	.10	.06
70	Vance Law	.10	.06
71	Manny Lee (R) –	.30	.18
72	Sixto Lezcano	.10	.06
73	Tim Lollar	.10	.06
74	Urbano Lugo (R)	.10	.06
75	Fred Lynn	.25	.15
76	Steve Lyons (R)	.15	.10
77	Mickey Mahler	.10	.06
78	Ron Mathis	.10	.06
79	Len Matuszek	.10	.06
80	Oddibe McDowell (R)	.15	.10
81	Roger McDowell (R)	.30	.18
82	Donnie Moore	.10	.06
83	Ron Musselman	.10	.06
84	Al Oliver	.25	.15
85	Joe Orsulak (R)	.60	.35
86	Dan Pasqua	.30	.18
87	Chris Pittaro	.10	.06
88	Rick Reuschel	.15	.10
89	Earnie Riles (R)	.15	.10
90	Jerry Royster	.10	.06
91	Dave Rozema	.10	.06
92	Dave Rucker	.10	.06
93	Vern Ruhle	.10	.06
94	Mark Salas (R)	.12	.07
95	Luis Salazar	.10	.06
96	Joe Sambito	.10	.06
97	Billy Sample	.10	.06
98	Alex Sanchez	.10	.06
99	Calvin Schiraldi (R)	.15	.10
100	Rick Schu (R)	.15	.10
101	Larry Sheets (R)	.12	.07
102	Ron Shepherd	.10	.06
103	Nelson Simmons (R)	.12	.07
104	Don Slaught	.20	.12
105	Roy Smalley	.10	.06
106	Lonnie Smith	.20	.12
107	Nate Snell (R)	.10	.06
108	Lary Sorensen	.10	.06
109	Chris Speier	.10	.06
110	Mike Stenhouse	.10	.06
111	Tim Stoddard	.10	.06
112	John Stuper	.10	.06
113	Jim Sundberg	.10	.06
114	Bruce Sutter	.25	.15
115	Don Sutton	.80	.50
116	Bruce Tanner (R)	.10	.06
117	Kent Tekulve	.10	.06
118	Walt Terrell	.10	.06
119	Mickey Tettleton (R)	8.50	5.00
120	Rich Thompson	.10	.06
121	Louis Thornton (R)	.10	.06
122	Alex Trevino	.10	.06
123	John Tudor	.15	.10
124	Jose Uribe (R)	.20	.12

125	Dave Valle (R)	.25	.15
126	Dave Von Ohlen	.10	.06
127	Curt Wardle	.10	.06
128	U.L. Washington	.10	.06
129	Ed Whitson	.10	.06
130	Herm Winningham (R)	.20	.12
131	Rich Yett	.10	.06
132	Checklist	.12	.05

1986 Fleer

The 1986 Fleer set contains 660-cards, each measuring 2-1/2" by 3-1/2". Card fronts feature full color photos framed by dark blue borders. Card backs are vertical with statistics and bio's printed in black and yellow on a white paper stock. The only subset of note is the 10-card Major League Prospects subset (644-653).

		MINT	NR/MT
Complete Set (660)		135.00	85.00
Commons		.08	.05

1	Steve Balboni	.10	.06
2	Joe Beckwith	.08	.05
3	Buddy Biancalana	.08	.05
4	Bud Black	.10	.06
5	George Brett	2.50	1.50
6	Onix Concepcion	.08	.05
7	Steve Farr	.08	.05
8	Mark Gubicza	.20	.12
9	Dane Iorg	.08	.05
10	Danny Jackson	.10	.06
11	Lynn Jones	.08	.05
12	Mike Jones	.08	.05
13	Charlie Leibrandt	.08	.05
14	Hal McRae	.12	.07

#	Player			#	Player		
15	Omar Moreno	.08	.05	72	Willie Upshaw	.08	.05
16	Darryl Motley	.08	.05	73	Ernie Whitt	.08	.05
17	Jorge Orta	.08	.05	74	Rick Aguilera (Π)	1.50	.90
18	Dan Quisenberry	.10	.06	75	Wally Backman	.08	.05
19	Bret Saberhagen	.60	.35	76	Gary Carter	.40	.25
20	Pat Sheridan	.08	.05	77	Ron Darling	.15	.10
21	Lonnie Smith	.10	.06	78	Len Dykstra (R)	6.50	3.75
22	Jim Sundberg	.08	.05	79	Sid Fernandez	.25	.15
23	John Wathan	.08	.05	80	George Foster	.10	.06
24	Frank White	.10	.06	81	Dwight Gooden	1.25	.80
25	Willie Wilson	.10	.06	82	Tom Gorman	.08	.05
26	Joaquin Andujar	.10	.06	83	Danny Heep	.08	.05
27	Steve Braun	.08	.05	84	Keith Hernandez	.15	.10
28	Bill Campbell	.08	.05	85	Howard Johnson	.60	.35
29	Cesar Cedeno	.10	.06	86	Ray Knight	.10	.06
30	Jack Clark	.12	.07	87	Terry Leach	.08	.05
31	Vince Coleman	.60	.35	88	Ed Lynch	.08	.05
32	Danny Cox	.08	.05	89	Roger McDowell	.20	.12
33	Ken Dayley	.08	.05	90	Jesse Orosco	.08	.05
34	Ivan DeJesus	.08	.05	91	Tom Paciorek	.08	.05
35	Bob Forsch	.08	.05	92	Ronn Reynolds	.08	.05
36	Brian Harper	.15	.10	93	Rafael Santana	.08	.05
37	Tom Herr	.08	.05	94	Doug Sisk	.08	.05
38	Ricky Horton	.08	.05	95	Rusty Staub	.12	.07
39	Kurt Kepshire	.08	.05	96	Darryl Strawberry	2.00	1.25
40	Jeff Lahti	.08	.05	97	Mookie Wilson	.10	.06
41	Tito Landrum	.08	.05	98	Neil Allen	.08	.05
42	Willie McGee	.30	.18	99	Don Baylor	.12	.07
43	Tom Nieto	.08	.05	100	Dale Berra	.08	.05
44	Terry Pendleton	1.75	1.00	101	Rich Bordi	.08	.05
45	Darrell Porter	.08	.05	102	Marty Bystrom	.08	.05
46	Ozzie Smith	1.25	.80	103	Joe Cowley	.08	.05
47	John Tudor	.08	.05	104	Brian Fisher	.08	.05
48	Andy Van Slyke	.90	.60	105	Ken Griffey	.12	.07
49	Todd Worrell (R)	.25	.15	106	Ron Guidry	.20	.12
50	Jim Acker	.08	.05	107	Ron Hassey	.08	.05
51	Doyle Alexander	.08	.05	108	Rickey Henderson	2.50	1.50
52	Jesse Barfield	.12	.07	109	Don Mattingly	2.75	1.75
53	George Bell	.40	.25	110	Bobby Meacham	.08	.05
54	Jeff Burroughs	.08	.05	111	John Montefusco	.08	.05
55	Bill Caudill	.08	.05	112	Phil Niekro	.50	.30
56	Jim Clancy	.08	.05	113	Mike Pagliarulo	.08	.05
57	Tony Fernandez	.25	.15	114	Dan Pasqua	.10	.06
58	Tom Filer	.08	.05	115	Willie Randolph	.10	.06
59	Damaso Garcia	.08	.05	116	Dave Righetti	.10	.06
60	Tom Henke	.30	.18	117	Andre Robertson	.08	.05
61	Garth Iorg	.08	.05	118	Billy Sample	.08	.05
62	Cliff Johnson	.08	.05	119	Bob Shirley	.08	.05
63	Jimmy Key	.80	.50	120	Ed Whitson	.08	.05
64	Dennis Lamp	.08	.05	121	Dave Winfield	1.75	1.00
65	Gary Lavelle	.08	.05	122	Butch Wynegar	.08	.05
66	Buck Martinez	.08	.05	123	Dave Anderson	.08	.05
67	Lloyd Moseby	.08	.05	124	Bob Bailor	.08	.05
68	Rance Mulliniks	.08	.05	125	Greg Brock	.08	.05
69	Al Oliver	.15	.10	126	Enos Cabell	.08	.05
70	Dave Stieb	.20	.12	127	Bobby Castillo	.08	.05
71	Louis Thornton	.08	.05	128	Carlos Diaz	.08	.05

129	Mariano Duncan	.25	.15		186	Tony Perez	.40	.25
130	Pedro Guerrero	.10	.06		187	Ted Power	.08	.05
131	Orel Hershiser	.50	.30		188	Joe Price	.08	.05
132	Rick Honeycutt	.08	.05		189	Gary Redus	.08	.05
133	Ken Howell	.08	.05		190	Ron Robinson	.08	.05
134	Ken Landreaux	.08	.05		191	Pete Rose	1.50	.90
135	Bill Madlock	.12	.07		192	Mario Soto	.08	.05
136	Candy Maldonado	.12	.07		193	John Stuper	.08	.05
137	Mike Marshall	.08	.05		194	Jay Tibbs	.08	.05
138	Len Matuszek	.08	.05		195	Dave Van Gorder	.08	.05
139	Tom Niedenfuer	.08	.05		196	Max Venable	.08	.05
140	Alejandro Pena	.12	.07		197	Juan Agosto	.08	.05
141	Jerry Reuss	.10	.06		198	Harold Baines	.20	.12
142	Bill Russell	.10	.06		199	Floyd Bannister	.08	.05
143	Steve Sax	.25	.15		200	Britt Burns	.08	.05
144	Mike Scioscia	.12	.07		201	Julio Cruz	.08	.05
145	Fernando Valenzuela	.15	.10		202	Joel Davis (R)	.08	.05
146	Bob Welch	.12	.07		203	Richard Dotson	.08	.05
147	Terry Whitfield	.08	.05		204	Carlton Fisk	1.00	.70
148	Juan Beniquez	.08	.05		205	Scott Fletcher	.08	.05
149	Bob Boone	.15	.10		206	Ozzie Guillen	.50	.30
150	John Candelaria	.08	.05		207	Jerry Hairston	.08	.05
151	Rod Carew	1.00	.70		208	Tim Hulett	.08	.05
152	Stewart Cliburn	.08	.05		209	Bob James	.08	.05
153	Doug DeCinces	.08	.05		210	Ron Kittle	.08	.05
154	Brian Downing	.10	.06		211	Rudy Law	.08	.05
155	Ken Forsch	.08	.05		212	Bryan Little	.08	.05
156	Craig Gerber	.08	.05		213	Gene Nelson	.08	.05
157	Bobby Grich	.10	.06		214	Reid Nichols	.08	.05
158	George Hendrick	.10	.06		215	Luis Salazar	.08	.05
159	Al Holland	.08	.05		216	Tom Seaver	1.25	.80
160	Reggie Jackson	1.75	1.00		217	Dan Spillner	.08	.05
161	Ruppert Jones	.08	.05		218	Bruce Tanner	.08	.05
162	Urbano Lugo	.08	.05		219	Greg Walker	.08	.05
163	Kirk McCaskill (R)	.25	.15		220	Dave Wehrmeister	.08	.05
164	Donnie Moore	.08	.05		221	Juan Berenguer	.08	.05
165	Gary Pettis	.08	.05		222	Dave Bergman	.08	.05
166	Ron Romanick	.08	.05		223	Tom Brookens	.08	.05
167	Dick Schofield	.08	.05		224	Darrell Evans	.12	.07
168	Daryl Sconiers	.08	.05		225	Barbaro Garbey	.08	.05
169	Jim Slaton	.08	.05		226	Kirk Gibson	.15	.10
170	Don Sutton	.35	.20		227	John Grubb	.08	.05
171	Mike Witt	.08	.05		228	Willie Hernandez	.10	.06
172	Buddy Bell	.08	.05		229	Larry Herndon	.08	.05
173	Tom Browning	.25	.15		230	Chet Lemon	.08	.05
174	Dave Concepcion	.15	.10		231	Aurelio Lopez	.08	.05
175	Eric Davis	1.00	.70		232	Jack Morris	.60	.35
176	Bo Diaz	.08	.05		233	Randy O'Neal	.08	.05
177	Nick Esasky	.08	.05		234	Lance Parrish	.12	.07
178	John Franco	.15	.10		235	Dan Petry	.08	.05
179	Tom Hume	.08	.05		236	Alex Sanchez	.08	.05
180	Wayne Krenchicki	.08	.05		237	Bill Scherrer	.08	.05
181	Andy McGaffigan	.08	.05		238	Nelson Simmons	.08	.05
182	Eddie Milner	.08	.05		239	Frank Tanana	.10	.06
183	Ron Oester	.08	.05		240	Walt Terrell	.08	.05
184	Dave Parker	.20	.12		241	Alan Trammell	.40	.25
185	Frank Pastore	.08	.05		242	Lou Whitaker	.30	.18

No.	Player	Price	Price
243	Milt Wilcox	.08	.05
244	Hubie Brooks	.12	.07
245	Tim Burke	.10	.00
246	Andre Dawson	1.25	.80
247	Mike Fitzgerald	.08	.05
248	Terry Francona	.08	.05
249	Bill Gullickson	.10	.06
250	Joe Hesketh	.08	.05
251	Bill Laskey	.08	.05
252	Vance Law	.08	.05
253	Charlie Lea	.08	.05
254	Gary Lucas	.08	.05
255	David Palmer	.08	.05
256	Tim Raines	.25	.15
257	Jeff Reardon	.50	.30
258	Bert Roberge	.08	.05
259	Dan Schatzeder	.08	.05
260	Bryn Smith	.10	.06
261	Randy St. Claire	.08	.05
262	Scot Thompson	.08	.05
263	Tim Wallach	.15	.10
264	U.L. Washington	.08	.05
265	Mitch Webster (R)	.20	.12
266	Herm Winningham	.15	.10
267	Floyd Youmans (R)	.08	.05
268	Don Aase	.08	.05
269	Mike Boddicker	.08	.05
270	Rich Dauer	.08	.05
271	Storm Davis	.08	.05
272	Rick Dempsey	.08	.05
273	Ken Dixon	.08	.05
274	Jim Dwyer	.08	.05
275	Mike Flanagan	.12	.07
276	Wayne Gross	.08	.05
277	Lee Lacy	.08	.05
278	Fred Lynn	.15	.10
279	Tippy Martinez	.08	.05
280	Dennis Martinez	.25	.15
281	Scott McGregor	.08	.05
282	Eddie Murray	1.25	.80
283	Floyd Rayford	.08	.05
284	Cal Ripken, Jr.	6.00	4.00
285	Gary Roenicke	.08	.05
286	Larry Sheets	.08	.05
287	John Shelby	.08	.05
288	Nate Snell	.08	.05
289	Sammy Stewart	.08	.05
290	Alan Wiggins	.08	.05
291	Mike Young	.08	.05
292	Alan Ashby	.08	.05
293	Mark Bailey	.08	.05
294	Kevin Bass	.10	.06
295	Jeff Calhoun	.08	.05
296	Jose Cruz	.12	.07
297	Glenn Davis	.20	.12
298	Bill Dawley	.08	.05
299	Frank DiPino	.08	.05
300	Bill Doran	.10	.06
301	Phil Garner	.10	.06
002	Jeff Heathcock (R)	.08	.05
303	Charlie Kerfeld (R)	.08	.05
304	Bob Knepper	.08	.05
305	Ron Mathis	.08	.05
306	Jerry Mumphrey	.08	.05
307	Jim Pankovits	.08	.05
308	Terry Puhl	.08	.05
309	Craig Reynolds	.08	.05
310	Nolan Ryan	7.00	4.00
311	Mike Scott	.12	.07
312	Dave Smith	.08	.05
313	Dickie Thon	.08	.05
314	Denny Walling	.08	.05
315	Kurt Bevacqua	.08	.05
316	Al Bumbry	.08	.05
317	Jerry Davis	.08	.05
318	Luis Deleon	.08	.05
319	Dave Dravecky	.10	.06
320	Tim Flannery	.08	.05
321	Steve Garvey	.45	.28
322	Goose Gossage	.20	.12
323	Tony Gwynn	3.50	2.50
324	Andy Hawkins	.08	.05
325	LaMarr Hoyt	.08	.05
326	Roy Lee Jackson	.08	.05
327	Terry Kennedy	.08	.05
328	Craig Lefferts	.12	.07
329	Carmelo Martinez	.08	.05
330	Lance McCullers (R)	.12	.07
331	Kevin McReynolds	.20	.12
332	Graig Nettles	.12	.07
333	Jerry Royster	.08	.05
334	Eric Show	.08	.05
335	Tim Stoddard	.08	.05
336	Garry Templeton	.10	.06
337	Mark Thurmond	.08	.05
338	Ed Wojna	.08	.05
339	Tony Armas	.08	.05
340	Marty Barrett	.08	.05
341	Wade Boggs	3.00	1.75
342	Dennis Boyd	.08	.05
343	Bill Buckner	.10	.06
344	Mark Clear	.08	.05
345	Roger Clemens	12.50	7.50
346	Steve Crawford	.08	.05
347	Mike Easler	.08	.05
348	Dwight Evans	.20	.12
349	Rich Gedman	.08	.05
350	Jackie Gutierrez	.08	.05
351	Glenn Hoffman	.08	.05
352	Bruce Hurst	.12	.07
353	Bruce Kison	.08	.05
354	Tim Lollar	.08	.05
355	Steve Lyons	.08	.05
356	Al Nipper	.08	.05

357	Bob Ojeda	.10	.06
358	Jim Rice	.20	.12
359	Bob Stanley	.08	.05
360	Mike Trujillo	.08	.05
361	Thad Bosley	.08	.05
362	Warren Brusstar	.08	.05
363	Ron Cey	.10	.06
364	Jody Davis	.08	.05
365	Bob Dernier	.08	.05
366	Shawon Dunston	.25	.15
367	Leon Durham	.08	.05
368	Dennis Eckersley	.75	.45
369	Ray Fontenot	.08	.05
370	George Frazier	.08	.05
371	Bill Hatcher	.10	.06
372	Dave Lopes	.10	.06
373	Gary Matthews	.08	.05
374	Ron Meredith	.08	.05
375	Keith Moreland	.08	.05
376	Reggie Patterson	.08	.05
377	Dick Ruthven	.08	.05
378	Ryne Sandberg	6.00	4.00
379	Scott Sanderson	.10	.06
380	Lee Smith	.80	.50
381	Lary Sorensen	.08	.05
382	Chris Speier	.08	.05
383	Rick Sutcliffe	.15	.10
384	Steve Trout	.08	.05
385	Gary Woods	.08	.05
386	Bert Blyleven	.25	.15
387	Tom Brunansky	.12	.07
388	Randy Bush	.08	.05
389	John Butcher	.08	.05
390	Ron Davis	.08	.05
391	Dave Engle	.08	.05
392	Frank Eufemia	.08	.05
393	Pete Filson	.08	.05
394	Gary Gaetti	.08	.05
395	Greg Gagne	.12	.07
396	Mickey Hatcher	.08	.05
397	Kent Hrbek	.20	.12
398	Tim Laudner	.08	.05
399	Rick Lysander	.08	.05
400	Dave Meier	.08	.05
401	Kirby Puckett	12.50	7.50
402	Mark Salas	.08	.05
403	Ken Schrom	.08	.05
404	Roy Smalley	.08	.05
405	Mike Smithson	.08	.05
406	Mike Stenhouse	.08	.05
407	Tim Teufel	.08	.05
408	Frank Viola	.30	.18
409	Ron Washington	.08	.05
410	Keith Atherton	.08	.05
411	Dusty Baker	.10	.06
412	Tim Birtsas	.08	.05
413	Bruce Bochte	.08	.05
414	Chris Codiroli	.08	.05
415	Dave Collins	.08	.05
416	Mike Davis	.08	.05
417	Alfredo Griffin	.08	.05
418	Mike Heath	.08	.05
419	Steve Henderson	.08	.05
420	Donnie Hill	.08	.05
421	Jay Howell	.08	.05
422	Tommy John	.15	.10
423	Dave Kingman	.12	.07
424	Bill Krueger	.08	.05
425	Rick Langford	.08	.05
426	Carney Lansford	.10	.06
427	Steve McCatty	.08	.05
428	Dwayne Murphy	.08	.05
429	Steve Ontiveros (R)	.10	.06
430	Tony Phillips	.30	.18
431	Jose Rijo	.60	.35
432	Mickey Tettleton	3.00	1.75
433	Luis Aguayo	.08	.05
434	Larry Andersen	.08	.05
435	Steve Carlton	1.50	.90
436	Don Carman	.08	.05
437	Tim Corcoran	.08	.05
438	Darren Daulton	5.00	3.00
439	John Denny	.08	.05
440	Tom Foley	.08	.05
441	Greg Gross	.08	.05
442	Kevin Gross	.08	.05
443	Von Hayes	.10	.06
444	Charles Hudson	.08	.05
445	Garry Maddox	.08	.05
446	Shane Rawley	.08	.05
447	Dave Rucker	.08	.05
448	John Russell	.08	.05
449	Juan Samuel	.12	.07
450	Mike Schmidt	3.50	2.50
451	Rick Schu	.08	.05
452	Dave Shipanoff	.08	.05
453	Dave Stewart	.25	.15
454	Jeff Stone	.08	.05
455	Kent Tekulve	.08	.05
456	Ozzie Virgil	.08	.05
457	Glenn Wilson	.08	.05
458	Jim Beattie	.08	.05
459	Karl Best	.08	.05
460	Barry Bonnell	.08	.05
461	Phil Bradley	.10	.06
462	Ivan Calderon	.40	.25
463	Al Cowens	.08	.05
464	Alvin Davis	.12	.07
465	Dave Henderson	.12	.07
466	Bob Kearney	.08	.05
467	Mark Langston	.60	.35
468	Bob Long	.08	.05
469	Mike Moore	.10	.06
470	Edwin Nunez	.08	.05

No.	Player			No.	Player		
471	Spike Owen	.08	.05	528	Zane Smith	.20	.12
472	Jack Perconte	.08	.05	529	Bruce Sutter	.15	.10
473	Jim Presley	.08	.05	530	Milt Thompson (R)	.20	.12
474	Donnie Scott	.08	.05	531	Claudell Washington	.08	.05
475	Bill Swift (R)	1.25	.80	532	Paul Zuvella	.08	.05
476	Danny Tartabull	1.75	1.00	533	Vida Blue	.12	.07
477	Gorman Thomas	.10	.06	534	Bob Brenly	.08	.05
478	Roy Thomas	.08	.05	535	Chris Brown	.08	.05
479	Ed Vande Berg	.08	.05	536	Chili Davis	.15	.10
480	Frank Wills	.08	.05	537	Mark Davis	.08	.05
481	Matt Young	.08	.05	538	Rob Deer	.20	.12
482	Ray Burris	.08	.05	539	Dan Driessen	.08	.05
483	Jaime Cocanower	.08	.05	540	Scott Garrelts	.08	.05
484	Cecil Cooper	.10	.06	541	Dan Gladden	.08	.05
485	Danny Darwin	.08	.05	542	Jim Gott	.08	.05
486	Rollie Fingers	.60	.35	543	David Green	.08	.05
487	Jim Gantner	.08	.05	544	Atlee Hammaker	.08	.05
488	Bob Gibson	.08	.05	545	Mike Jeffcoat	.08	.05
489	Moose Haas	.08	.05	546	Mike Krukow	.08	.05
490	Teddy Higuera	.20	.12	547	Dave LaPoint	.08	.05
491	Paul Householder	.08	.05	548	Jeff Leonard	.08	.05
492	Pete Ladd	.08	.05	549	Greg Minton	.08	.05
493	Rick Manning	.08	.05	550	Alex Trevino	.08	.05
494	Bob McClure	.08	.05	551	Manny Trillo	.08	.05
495	Paul Molitor	1.50	.90	552	Jose Uribe	.12	.07
496	Charlie Moore	.08	.05	553	Brad Wellman	.08	.05
497	Ben Oglivie	.08	.05	554	Frank Williams	.08	.05
498	Randy Ready	.08	.05	555	Joel Youngblood	.08	.05
499	Ernie Riles	.08	.05	556	Alan Bannister	.08	.05
500	Ed Romero	.08	.05	557	Glenn Brummer	.08	.05
501	Bill Schroeder	.08	.05	558	Steve Buechele (R)	.75	.45
502	Ray Searage	.08	.05	559	Jose Guzman (R)	.80	.50
503	Ted Simmons	.15	.10	560	Toby Harrah	.08	.05
504	Pete Vuckovich	.10	.06	561	Greg Harris	.08	.05
505	Rick Waits	.08	.05	562	Dwayne Henry (R)	.12	.07
506	Robin Yount	2.50	1.50	563	Burt Hooton	.08	.05
507	Len Barker	.08	.05	564	Charlie Hough	.10	.06
508	Steve Bedrosian	.10	.06	565	Mike Mason	.08	.05
509	Bruce Benedict	.08	.05	566	Oddibe McDowell	.08	.05
510	Rick Camp	.08	.05	567	Dickie Noles	.08	.05
511	Rick Cerone	.08	.05	568	Pete O'Brien	.08	.05
512	Chris Chambliss	.10	.06	569	Larry Parrish	.08	.05
513	Jeff Dedmon	.08	.05	570	Dave Rozema	.08	.05
514	Terry Forster	.08	.05	571	Dave Schmidt	.08	.05
515	Gene Garber	.08	.05	572	Don Slaught	.10	.06
516	Terry Harper	.08	.05	573	Wayne Tolleson	.08	.05
517	Bob Horner	.10	.06	574	Duane Walker	.08	.05
518	Glenn Hubbard	.08	.05	575	Gary Ward	.08	.05
519	Joe Johnson	.08	.05	576	Chris Welsh	.08	.05
520	Brad Komminsk	.08	.05	577	Curtis Wilkerson	.08	.05
521	Rick Mahler	.08	.05	578	George Wright	.08	.05
522	Dale Murphy	.60	.35	579	Chris Bando	.08	.05
523	Ken Oberkfell	.08	.05	580	Tony Bernazard	.08	.05
524	Pascual Perez	.10	.06	581	Brett Butler	.25	.15
525	Gerald Perry	.08	.05	582	Ernie Camacho	.08	.05
526	Rafael Ramirez	.08	.05	583	Joe Carter	5.00	3.00
527	Steve Shields (R)	.10	.06	584	Carmelo Castillo	.08	.05

585	Jamie Easterly	.08	.05
586	Julio Franco	.40	.25
587	Mel Hall	.10	.06
588	Mike Hargrove	.08	.05
589	Neal Heaton	.08	.05
590	Brook Jacoby	.08	.05
591	Otis Nixon (R)	1.00	.70
592	Jerry Reed	.08	.05
593	Vern Ruhle	.08	.05
594	Pat Tabler	.08	.05
595	Rich Thompson	.08	.05
596	Andre Thornton	.10	.06
597	Dave Von Ohlen	.08	.05
598	George Vukovich	.08	.05
599	Tom Waddell	.08	.05
600	Curt Wardle	.08	.05
601	Jerry Willard	.08	.05
602	Bill Almon	.08	.05
603	Mike Bielecki	.08	.05
604	Sid Bream	.08	.05
605	Mike Brown	.08	.05
606	Pat Clements	.08	.05
607	Jose DeLeon	.08	.05
608	Denny Gonzalez	.08	.05
609	Cecilio Guante	.08	.05
610	Steve Kemp	.08	.05
611	Sam Khalifa	.08	.05
612	Lee Mazzilli	.08	.05
613	Larry McWilliams	.08	.05
614	Jim Morrison	.08	.05
615	Joe Orsulak	.25	.15
616	Tony Pena	.10	.06
617	Johnny Ray	.08	.05
618	Rick Reuschel	.08	.05
619	R.J. Reynolds	.08	.05
620	Rick Rhoden	.08	.05
621	Don Robinson	.08	.05
622	Jason Thompson	.08	.05
623	Lee Tunnell	.08	.05
624	Jim Winn	.08	.05
625	Marvell Wynne	.08	.05
626	Dwight Gooden (IA)	.35	.20
627	Don Mattingly (IA)	1.00	.70
628	Pete Rose (4,192)	.80	.50
629	Rod Carew (3,000 Hits)	.50	.30
630	Phil Niekro/Tom Seaver (300 Wins)	.75	.45
631	Don Baylor (Ouch!)	.12	.07
632	Tim Raines/Darryl Strawberry	.50	.30
633	Cal Ripken Jr./Alan Trammell)	1.75	1.00
634	Wade Boggs/George Brett	1.50	.90
635	Bob Horner/Dale Murphy	.12	.07
636	Vince Coleman/Willie McGee	.12	.07
637	Vince Coleman (Terror)	.12	.07
638	Dwight Gooden/Pete Rose	.80	.50
639	Wade Boggs/Don Mattingly	1.25	.80
640	N.L. West Sluggers (Steve Garvey, Dale Murphy, Dave Parker)	.25	.15
641	Staff Aces(Doc Gooden Fernando Valenzuela)	.15	.10
642	Jimmy Key/Dave Stieb	.15	.10
643	Carlton Fisk/Rich Gedman	.25	.15
644	Major League Prospect Benito Santiago (R) Gene Walter (R)	2.50	1.50
645	Major League Prospect Colin Ward (R) Mike Woodard (R)	.08	.05
646	Major League Prospect Kal Daniels (R) Paul O'Neill (R)	3.00	2.00
647	Major League Prospect Andres Galarraga (R) Fred Toliver (R)	5.00	3.00
648	Major League Prospect Curt Ford (R) Bob Kipper (R)	.10	.06
649	Major League Prospects Jose Canseco (R) Eric Plunk (R)	24.00	15.00
650	Major League Prospect Mark McLemore (R) Gus Polidor (R)	.25	.15
651	Major League Prospect Mickey Brantley (R) Rob Woodward (R)	.10	.06
652	Major League Prospect Mark Funderburk (R) Billy Joe Robidoux (R)	.08	.05
653	Major League Prospects Cecil Fielder (R) Cory Snyder (R)	22.00	13.50
654	Checklist (1-97)	.10	.04
655	Checklist (98-196)	.10	.04
656	Checklist (197-291)	.10	.04
657	Checklist (292-385)	.10	.04
658	Checklist (386-482)	.10	.04
659	Checklist (483-578)	.10	.04
660	Checklist (579-660)	.10	.04

1986 Fleer Update

ANDRES GALARRAGA
FIRST BASE

This 132-card update set mirrors the design of Fleer's regular edition. Cards measure 2-1/2" by 3-1/2" and the numbers on the card backs are preceeded by the letter "U". The set contains players who were traded during the season and a number of key rookie cards.

		MINT	NR/MT
Complete Set (132)		34.00	20.00
Commons		.07	.04

1	Mike Aldrete (R)	.12	.07
2	Andy Allanson(FC)	.10	.06
3	Neil Allen	.07	.04
4	Joaquin Andujar	.08	.05
5	Paul Assenmacher (R)	.15	.10
6	Scott Bailes (R)	.10	.06
7	Jay Baller (R)	.10	.06
8	Scott Bankhead (R)	.12	.07
9	Bill Bathe (R)	.10	.06
10	Don Baylor	.12	.07
11	Billy Beane (R)	.10	.06
12	Steve Bedrosian	.10	.06
13	Juan Beniquez	.07	.04
14	Barry Bonds (R)	18.00	12.00
15	Bobby Bonilla (R)	3.50	2.00
16	Rich Bordi	.07	.04
17	Bill Campbell	.07	.04
18	Tom Candiotti	.15	.10
19	John Cangelosi (R)	.12	.07
20	Jose Canseco	5.00	3.00
21	Chuck Cary (R)	.12	.07
22	Juan Castillo (R)	.10	.06
23	Rick Cerone	.08	.05
24	John Cerutti (R)	.15	.10
25	Will Clark (R)	10.00	6.50
26	Mark Clear	.07	.04
27	Darnell Coles (R)	.12	.07
28	Dave Collins	.08	.05
29	Tim Conroy	.07	.04
30	Ed Correa (R)	.08	.05
31	Joe Cowley	.07	.04
32	Bill Dawley	.07	.04
33	Rob Deer	.25	.15
34	John Denny	.08	.05
35	Jim Deshaies (R)	.20	.12
36	Doug Drabek (R)	1.75	1.00
37	Mike Easler	.08	.05
38	Mark Eichhorn (R)	.12	.07
39	Dave Engle	.07	.04
40	Mike Fischlin	.07	.04
41	Scott Fletcher	.08	.05
42	Terry Forster	.07	.04
43	Terry Francona	.07	.04
44	Andres Galarraga	3.00	1.75
45	Lee Guetterman (R)	.12	.07
46	Bill Gullickson	.10	.06
47	Jackie Gutierrez	.07	.04
48	Moose Haas	.07	.04
49	Billy Hatcher	.10	.06
50	Mike Heath	.07	.04
51	Guy Hoffman (R)	.08	.05
52	Tom Hume	.08	.05
53	Pete Incaviglia (R)	1.00	.60
54	Dane Iorg	.07	.04
55	Chris James (R)	.15	.10
56	Stan Javier (R)	.12	.07
57	Tommy John	.15	.10
58	Tracy Jones (R)	.10	.06
59	Wally Joyner (R)	1.50	.90
60	Wayne Krenchicki	.07	.04
61	John Kruk (R)	4.00	2.50
62	Mike LaCoss	.07	.04
63	Pete Ladd	.07	.04
64	Dave LaPoint	.07	.04
65	Mike LaValliere (R)	.25	.15
66	Rudy Law	.07	.04
67	Dennis Leonard	.08	.05
68	Steve Lombardozzi (R)	.12	.07
69	Aurelio Lopez	.08	.05
70	Mickey Mahler	.07	.04
71	Candy Maldonado	.15	.10
72	Roger Mason (R)	.12	.07
73	Greg Mathews (R)	.10	.06
74	Andy McGaffigan	.07	.04
75	Joel McKeon (R)	.08	.05
76	Kevin Mitchell (R)	2.00	1.25
77	Bill Mooneyham (R)	.08	.05
78	Omar Moreno	.07	.04
79	Jerry Mumphrey	.07	.04
80	Al Newman (R)	.10	.06
81	Phil Niekro	.40	.25
82	Randy Niemann	.07	.04
83	Juan Nieves (R)	.10	.06
84	Bob Ojeda	.10	.06
85	Rick Ownbey	.07	.04
86	Tom Paciorek	.07	.04
87	David Palmer	.07	.04

88	Jeff Parrett (R)	.15	.10
89	Pat Perry (R)	.10	.06
90	Dan Plesac (R)	.15	.10
91	Darrell Porter	.08	.05
92	Luis Quinones (R)	.10	.06
93	Rey Quinonez (R)	.10	.06
94	Gary Redus	.10	.06
95	Jeff Reed (R)	.10	.06
96	Bip Roberts (R)	.75	.45
97	Billy Joe Robidoux	.07	.04
98	Gary Roenicke	.07	.04
99	Ron Roenicke	.07	.04
100	Angel Salazar	.07	.04
101	Joe Sambito	.07	.04
102	Billy Sample	.08	.05
103	Dave Schmidt	.07	.04
104	Ken Schrom	.07	.04
105	Ruben Sierra (R)	6.50	3.75
106	Ted Simmons	.15	.10
107	Sammy Stewart	.07	.04
108	Kurt Stillwell (R)	.15	.10
109	Dale Sveum (R)	.15	.10
110	Tim Teufel	.08	.05
111	Bob Tewksbury (R)	.80	.50
112	Andres Thomas (R)	.10	.06
113	Jason Thompson	.07	.04
114	Milt Thompson	.10	.06
115	Robby Thompson (R)	1.25	.80
116	Jay Tibbs	.07	.04
117	Fred Toliver	.07	.04
118	Wayne Tolleson	.07	.04
119	Alex Trevino	.07	.04
120	Manny Trillo	.08	.05
121	Ed Vande Berg	.07	.04
122	Ozzie Virgil	.08	.05
123	Tony Walker (R)	.08	.05
124	Gene Walter	.07	.04
125	Duane Ward (R)	.80	.50
126	Jerry Willard	.07	.04
127	Mitch Williams (R)	.50	.30
128	Reggie Williams (R)	.08	.05
129	Bobby Witt (R)	.50	.30
130	Marvell Wynne	.07	.04
131	Steve Yeager	.07	.04
132	Checklist	.07	.03

1987 Fleer

This 660-card set features full color player photos framed by a blue and white border. The vertical card backs are red, white and blue and includes a unique "scouting report" graphic that addresses the hitter's or pitcher's strengths. Cards measure 2-1/2" by 3-1/2".

		MINT	NR/MT
Complete Set (660)		100.00	70.00
Commons		.07	.04

1	Rick Aguilera	.30	.18
2	Richard Anderson	.07	.04
3	Wally Backman	.07	.04
4	Gary Carter	.30	.18
5	Ron Darling	.12	.07
6	Len Dykstra	.90	.60
7	Kevin Elster (R)	.15	.10
8	Sid Fernandez	.15	.10
9	Dwight Gooden	.60	.35
10	Ed Hearn (R)	.07	.04
11	Danny Heep	.07	.04
12	Keith Hernandez	.12	.07
13	Howard Johnson	.25	.15
14	Ray Knight	.10	.06
15	Lee Mazzilli	.07	.04
16	Roger McDowell	.07	.04
17	Kevin Mitchell	2.50	1.50
18	Randy Niemann	.07	.04
19	Bob Ojeda	.08	.05
20	Jesse Orosco	.07	.04
21	Rafael Santana	.07	.04
22	Doug Sisk	.07	.04
23	Darryl Strawberry	.75	.45
24	Tim Teufel	.07	.04
25	Mookie Wilson	.10	.06
26	Tony Armas	.07	.04
27	Marty Barrett	.07	.04
29	Wade Boggs	1.75	1.00
30	Oil Can Boyd	.07	.04
31	Bill Buckner	.10	.06

32	Roger Clemens	4.00	2.50
33	Steve Crawford	.07	.04
34	Dwight Evans	.20	.12
36	Dave Henderson	.12	.07
37	Bruce Hurst	.15	.10
38	Tim Lollar	.07	.04
39	Al Nipper	.07	.04
40	Spike Owen	.07	.04
41	Jim Rice	.15	.10
42	Ed Romero	.07	.04
43	Joe Sambito	.07	.04
44	Calvin Schiraldi	.07	.04
45	Tom Seaver	1.00	.70
46	Jeff Sellers (R)	.08	.05
47	Bob Stanley	.07	.04
48	Sammy Stewart	.07	.04
49	Larry Andersen	.07	.04
50	Alan Ashby	.07	.04
51	Kevin Bass	.08	.05
52	Jeff Calhoun	.07	.04
53	Jose Cruz	.12	.07
54	Danny Darwin	.07	.04
55	Glenn Davis	.15	.10
56	Jim Deshaies	.12	.07
57	Bill Doran	.08	.05
58	Phil Garner	.08	.05
59	Billy Hatcher	.10	.06
60	Charlie Kerfeld	.07	.04
61	Bob Knepper	.07	.04
62	Dave Lopes	.10	.06
63	Aurelio Lopez	.07	.04
64	Jim Pankovits	.07	.04
65	Terry Puhl	.07	.04
66	Craig Reynolds	.07	.04
67	Nolan Ryan	4.50	2.75
68	Mike Scott	.12	.07
69	Dave Smith	.07	.04
70	Dickie Thon	.07	.04
71	Tony Walker	.07	.04
72	Denny Walling	.07	.04
73	Bob Boone	.12	.07
74	Rick Burleson	.07	.04
75	John Candelaria	.07	.04
76	Doug Corbett	.07	.04
77	Doug DeCinces	.07	.04
78	Brian Downing	.10	.06
79	Chuck Finley (R)	1.50	.90
80	Terry Forster	.07	.04
81	Bobby Grich	.10	.06
82	George Hendrick	.08	.05
83	Jack Howell (R)	.10	.06
84	Reggie Jackson	1.50	.90
85	Ruppert Jones	.07	.04
86	Wally Joyner	2.50	1.50
87	Gary Lucas	.07	.04
88	Kirk McCaskill	.07	.04
89	Donnie Moore	.07	.04
90	Gary Pettis	.07	.04
91	Vern Ruhle	.07	.04
92	Dick Scholfield	.07	.04
93	Don Sutton	.35	.20
94	Rob Wilfong	.07	.04
95	Mike Witt	.07	.04
96	Doug Drabek	2.50	1.50
97	Mike Easler	.07	.04
98	Mike Fischlin	.07	.04
99	Brian Fisher	.07	.04
100	Ron Guidry	.15	.10
101	Rickey Henderson	2.00	1.25
102	Tommy John	.12	.07
103	Ron Kittle	.08	.05
104	Don Mattingly	1.75	1.00
105	Bobby Meacham	.07	.04
106	Joe Niekro	.07	.04
107	Mike Pagliarulo	.07	.04
108	Dan Pasqua	.08	.05
109	Willie Randolph	.12	.07
110	Dennis Rasmussen	.07	.04
111	Dave Righetti	.12	.07
112	Gary Roenicke	.07	.04
113	Rod Scurry	.07	.04
114	Bob Shirley	.07	.04
115	Joel Skinner	.07	.04
116	Tim Stoddard	.07	.04
117	Bob Tewksbury	.75	.45
118	Wayne Tolleson	.07	.04
119	Claudell Washington	.07	.04
120	Dave Winfield	1.50	.90
121	Steve Buechele	.10	.06
122	Ed Correa	.07	.04
123	Scott Fletcher	.07	.04
124	Jose Guzman	.08	.05
125	Toby Harrah	.07	.04
126	Greg Harris	.07	.04
127	Charlie Hough	.10	.06
128	Pete Incaviglia	1.00	.70
129	Mike Mason	.07	.04
130	Oddibe McDowell	.07	.04
131	Dale Mohorcic (R)	.08	.05
132	Pete O'Brien	.07	.04
133	Tom Paciorek	.07	.04
134	Larry Parrish	.07	.04
135	Geno Petralli	.07	.04
136	Darrell Porter	.07	.04
137	Jeff Russell	.10	.06
138	Ruben Sierra	10.00	6.50
139	Don Slaught	.10	.06
140	Gary Ward	.07	.04
141	Curtis Wilkerson	.07	.04
142	Mitch Williams	.40	.25
143	Bobby Witt	.60	.35
144	Dave Bergman	.07	.04
145	Tom Brookens	.07	.04
146	Bill Campbell	.07	.04

147	Chuck Cary	.07	.04
148	Darnell Coles	.07	.04
149	Dave Collins	.07	.04
150	Darrell Evans	.12	.07
151	Kirk Gibson	.12	.07
152	John Grubb	.07	.04
153	Willie Hernandez	.08	.05
154	Larry Herndon	.07	.04
155	Eric King	.07	.04
156	Chet Lemon	.07	.04
157	Dwight Lowry	.07	.04
158	Jack Morris	.60	.35
159	Randy O'Neal	.07	.04
160	Lance Parrish	.10	.06
161	Dan Petry	.07	.04
162	Pat Sheridan	.07	.04
163	Jim Slaton	.07	.04
164	Frank Tanana	.08	.05
165	Walt Terrell	.07	.04
166	Mark Thurmond	.07	.04
167	Alan Trammell	.40	.25
168	Lou Whitaker	.25	.15
169	Luis Aguayo	.07	.04
170	Steve Bedrosian	.08	.05
171	Don Carman	.07	.04
172	Darren Daulton	1.25	.80
173	Greg Gross	.07	.04
174	Kevin Gross	.07	.04
175	Von Hayes	.07	.04
176	Charles Hudson	.07	.04
177	Tom Hume	.07	.04
178	Steve Jeltz	.07	.04
179	Mike Maddux (R)	.08	.05
180	Shane Rawley	.07	.04
181	Gary Redus	.07	.04
182	Ron Roenicke	.07	.04
183	Bruce Ruffin (R)	.10	.06
184	John Russell	.07	.04
185	Juan Samuel	.10	.06
186	Dan Schatzeder	.07	.04
187	Mike Schmidt	2.50	1.50
188	Rick Schu	.07	.04
189	Jeff Stone	.07	.04
190	Kent Tekulve	.07	.04
191	Milt Thompson	.08	.05
192	Glenn Wilson	.07	.04
193	Buddy Bell	.07	.04
194	Tom Browning	.15	.10
195	Sal Butera	.07	.04
196	Dave Concepcion	.15	.10
197	Kal Daniels	.12	.07
198	Eric Davis	.60	.35
199	John Denny	.07	.04
200	Bo Diaz	.07	.04
201	Nick Esasky	.07	.04
202	John Franco	.15	.10
203	Bill Gullickson	.08	.05
204	Barry Larkin (R)	7.50	4.50
205	Eddie Milner	.07	.04
206	Rob Murphy (R)	.08	.05
207	Ron Oester	.07	.04
208	Dave Parker	.15	.10
209	Tony Perez	.30	.18
210	Ted Power	.07	.04
211	Joe Price	.07	.04
212	Ron Robinson	.07	.04
213	Pete Rose	1.00	.60
214	Mario Soto	.07	.04
215	Kirt Stillwell	.20	.12
216	Max Venable	.07	.04
217	Chris Welsh	.07	.04
218	Carl Willis (R)	.10	.06
219	Jesse Barfield	.12	.07
220	George Bell	.35	.20
221	Bill Caudill	.07	.04
222	John Cerutti	.07	.04
223	Jim Clancy	.07	.04
224	Mark Eichhorn	.07	.04
225	Tony Fernandez	.25	.15
226	Damaso Garcia	.07	.04
227	Kelly Gruber	.30	.18
228	Tom Henke	.12	.07
229	Garth Iorg	.07	.04
230	Cliff Johnson	.07	.04
231	Joe Johnson	.07	.04
232	Jimmy Key	.35	.20
233	Dennis Lamp	.07	.04
234	Rick Leach	.07	.04
235	Buck Martinez	.07	.04
236	Lloyd Moseby	.07	.04
237	Rancy Mulliniks	.07	.04
238	Dave Stieb	.15	.10
239	Willie Upshaw	.07	.04
240	Ernie Whitt	.07	.04
241	Andy Allanson	.07	.04
242	Scott Bailes	.07	.04
243	Chris Bando	.07	.04
244	Tony Bernazard	.07	.04
245	John Butcher	.07	.04
246	Brett Butler	.25	.15
247	Ernie Camacho	.07	.04
248	Tom Candiotti	.10	.06
249	Joe Carter	2.00	1.25
240	Carmen Castillo	.07	.04
251	Julio Franco	.35	.20
252	Mel Hall	.10	.06
253	Brook Jacoby	.07	.04
254	Phil Niekro	.35	.20
255	Otis Nixon	.40	.25
256	Dickie Noles	.07	.04
257	Bryan Oelkers	.07	.04
258	Ken Schrom	.07	.04
259	Don Schulze	.07	.04
260	Cory Snyder	.12	.07

261	Pat Tabler	.07	.04
262	Andre Thornton	.08	.05
263	Rich Yett	.07	.04
264	Mike Aldrete	.08	.05
265	Juan Berenguer	.07	.04
266	Vida Blue	.12	.07
267	Bob Brenly	.07	.04
268	Chris Brown	.07	.04
269	Will Clark	22.00	14.00
270	Chili Davis	.10	.06
271	Mark Davis	.08	.05
272	Kelly Downs (R)	.15	.10
273	Scott Garrelts	.07	.04
274	Dan Gladden	.07	.04
275	Mike Krukow	.07	.04
276	Randy Kutcher	.07	.04
277	Mike LaCoss	.07	.04
278	Jeff Leonard	.07	.04
279	Candy Maldonado	.10	.06
280	Roger Mason	.07	.04
ä281	Bob Melvin (R)	.10	.06
282	Greg Minton	.07	.04
283	Jeff Robinson	.07	.04
284	Harry Spilman	.07	.04
285	Robby Thompson	1.75	1.00
286	Jose Uribe	.08	.05
287	Frank Williams	.07	.04
288	Joel Youngblood	.07	.04
289	Jack Clark	.15	.10
290	Vince Coleman	.20	.12
291	Tim Conroy	.07	.04
292	Danny Cox	.07	.04
293	Ken Dayley	.07	.04
294	Curt Ford	.07	.04
295	Bob Forsch	.07	.04
296	Tom Herr	.07	.04
297	Ricky Horton	.07	.04
298	Clint Hurdle	.07	.04
299	Jeff Lahti	.07	.04
300	Steve Lake	.07	.04
301	Tito Landrum	.07	.04
302	Mike LaValliere	.15	.10
303	Greg Mathews	.07	.04
304	Willie McGee	.25	.15
305	Jose Oquendo	.07	.04
306	Terry Pendleton	1.00	.70
307	Pat Perry	.07	.04
308	Ozzie Smith	1.00	.70
209	Ray Soff	.07	.04
310	John Tudor	.08	.05
311	Andy Van Slyke	.75	.45
312	Todd Worrell	.10	.06
313	Dann Bilardello	.07	.04
314	Hubie Brooks	.10	.06
315	Tim Burke	.08	.05
316	Andre Dawson	1.00	.70
317	Mike Fitzgerald	.07	.04
318	Tom Foley	.07	.04
319	Andres Galarraga	1.00	.60
320	Joe Hesketh	.07	.04
321	Wallace Johnson	.07	.04
322	Wayne Krenchicki	.07	.04
323	Vance Law	.07	.04
324	Dennis Martinez	.20	.12
325	Bob McClure	.07	.04
326	Andy McGaffigan	.07	.04
327	Al Newman	.07	.04
328	Tim Raines	.25	.15
329	Jeff Reardon	.40	.25
330	Luis Rivera (R)	.07	.04
331	Bob Sebra (R)	.08	.05
332	Bryn Smith	.08	.05
333	Jay Tibbs	.07	.04
334	Tim Wallach	.15	.10
335	Mitch Webster	.07	.04
336	Jim Wohlford	.07	.04
337	Floyd Youmans	.07	.04
338	Chris Bosio (R)	.50	.30
339	Glenn Braggs (R)	.25	.15
340	Rick Cerone	.07	.04
341	Mark Clear	.07	.04
342	Bryan Clutterbuck	.07	.04
343	Cecil Cooper	.10	.06
344	Rob Deer	.15	.10
345	Jim Gantner	.07	.04
346	Ted Higuera	.08	.05
347	John Henry Johnson	.07	.04
348	Tim Leary (R)	.15	.10
349	Rick Manning	.07	.04
350	Paul Molitor	.75	.45
351	Charlie Moore	.07	.04
352	Juan Nieves	.07	.04
353	Ben Oglivie	.07	.04
354	Dan Plesac	.15	.10
355	Ernest Riles	.07	.04
356	Billy Joe Robidoux	.07	.04
357	Bill Schroeder	.07	.04
358	Dale Sveum	.10	.06
359	Gorman Thomas	.10	.06
360	Bill Wegman (R)	.15	.10
361	Robin Yount	1.75	1.00
362	Steve Balboni	.07	.04
363	Scott Bankhead	.10	.06
364	Buddy Biancalana	.07	.04
365	Bud Black	.08	.05
366	George Brett	2.00	1.25
367	Steve Farr	.07	.04
368	Mark Gubicza	.20	.12
369	Bo Jackson	8.00	5.00
370	Danny Jackson	.08	.05
371	Mike Kingery	.07	.04
372	Rudy Law	.07	.04
373	Charlie Leibrandt	.08	.05
374	Dennis Leonard	.07	.04

375 Hal McRae	.12	.07
376 Jorge Orta	.07	.04
377 Jamie Quirk	.07	.04
378 Dan Quisenberry	.08	.05
379 Bret Saberhagen	.30	.18
380 Angel Salazar	.07	.04
381 Lonnie Smith	.10	.06
382 Jim Sundberg	.07	.04
383 Frank White	.08	.05
384 Willie Wilson	.10	.06
385 Joaquin Andujar	.08	.05
386 Doug Bair	.07	.04
387 Dusty Baker	.08	.05
388 Bruce Bochte	.07	.04
389 Jose Canseco	7.00	4.00
390 Chris Codiroli	.07	.04
391 Mike Davis	.07	.04
392 Alfredo Griffin	.07	.04
393 Moose Haas	.07	.04
394 Donnie Hill	.07	.04
395 Jay Howell	.08	.05
396 Dave Kingman	.12	.07
397 Carney Lansford	.08	.05
398 David Leiper	.08	.05
399 Bill Mooneyham	.07	.04
400 Dwayne Murphy	.07	.04
401 Steve Ontiveros	.07	.04
402 Tony Phillips	.15	.10
403 Eric Plunk	.07	.04
404 Jose Rijo	.40	.25
405 Terry Steinbach (R)	.70	.40
406 Dave Steward	.40	.25
407 Mickey Tettleton	.35	.20
408 Dave Von Ohlen	.07	.04
409 Jerry Willard	.07	.04
410 Curt Young	.07	.04
411 Bruce Bochy	.07	.04
412 Dave Dravecky	.10	.06
413 Tim Flannery	.07	.04
414 Steve Garvey	.40	.25
415 Goose Gossage	.20	.12
416 Tony Gwynn	2.00	1.25
417 Andy Hawkins	.07	.04
418 LaMarr Hoyt	.07	.04
419 Terry Kennedy	.07	.04
420 John Kruk	5.00	3.00
421 Dave LaPoint	.07	.04
422 Craig Lefferts	.08	.05
423 Carmelo Martinez	.07	.04
424 Lance McCullers	.07	.04
425 Kevin McReynolds	.15	.10
426 Graig Nettles	.10	.06
427 Bip Roberts	.60	.35
428 Jerry Royster	.07	.04
429 Benito Santiago	.45	.28
430 Eric Show	.07	.04
431 Bob Stoddard	.07	.04

432 Garry Templeton	.08	.05
433 Gene Walter	.07	.04
434 Ed Whitson	.07	.04
435 Marvell Wynne	.07	.04
436 Dave Anderson	.07	.04
437 Greg Brock	.07	.04
438 Enos Cabell	.07	.04
439 Mariano Duncan	.10	.06
440 Pedro Guerrero	.10	.06
441 Orel Hershiser	.30	.18
442 Rick Honeycutt	.07	.04
443 Ken Howell	.07	.04
444 Ken Landreaux	.07	.04
445 Bill Madlock	.12	.07
446 Mike Marshall	.07	.04
447 Len Matuszek	.07	.04
448 Tom Niedenfuer	.07	.04
449 Alejandro Pena	.07	.04
450 Dennis Powell	.08	.05
451 Jerry Reuss	.10	.06
452 Bill Russell	.08	.05
453 Steve Sax	.20	.12
454 Mike Scioscia	.08	.05
455 Franklin Stubbs	.08	.05
456 Alex Trevino	.07	.04
457 Fernando Valenzuela	.20	.12
458 Ed Vande Berg	.07	.04
459 Bob Welch	.12	.07
460 Reggie Williams	.07	.04
461 Don Aase	.07	.04
462 Juan Beniquez	.07	.04
463 Mike Boddicker	.07	.04
464 Juan Bonilla	.07	.04
465 Rich Bordi	.07	.04
466 Storm Davis	.07	.04
467 Rick Dempsey	.07	.04
468 Ken Dixon	.07	.04
469 Jim Dwyer	.07	.04
470 Mike Flanagan	.12	.07
471 Jackie Gutierrez	.07	.04
472 Brad Havens	.07	.04
473 Lee Lacy	.07	.04
474 Fred Lynn	.15	.10
475 Scott McGregor	.07	.04
476 Eddie Murray	1.00	.70
477 Tom O'Malley	.07	.04
478 Cal Ripken, Jr.	4.00	2.50
479 Larry Sheets	.07	.04
480 John Shelby	.07	.04
481 Nate Snell	.07	.04
482 Jim Traber (R)	.07	.04
483 Mike Young	.07	.04
484 Neil Allen	.07	.04
485 Harold Baines	.20	.12
486 Floyd Bannister	.07	.04
487 Daryl Boston	.07	.04
488 Ivan Calderon	.20	.12

489	John Cangelosi	.07	.04	547	Steve Lombardozzi	.07	.04
490	Steve Carlton	1.25	.80	548	Mark Portugal (R)	.75	.45
491	Joe Cowloy	.07	.04	549	Kirby Puckell	4.50	2.75
492	Julio Cruz	.07	.04	550	Jeff Reed	.07	.04
493	Bill Dawley	.07	.04	551	Mark Salas	.07	.04
494	Jose DeLeon	.07	.04	552	Roy Smalley	.07	.04
495	Richard Dotson	.07	.04	553	Mike Smithson	.07	.04
496	Carlton Fisk	1.00	.70	554	Frank Viola	.25	.15
497	Ozzie Guillen	.15	.10	555	Thad Bosley	.07	.04
498	Jerry Hairston	.07	.04	556	Ron Cey	.08	.05
499	Ron Hassey	.07	.04	557	Jody Davis	.07	.04
500	Tim Hulett	.07	.04	558	Ron Davis	.07	.04
501	Bob James	.07	.04	559	Bob Dernier	.07	.04
502	Steve Lyons	.07	.04	560	Frank DiPino	.07	.04
503	Joel McKeon	.07	.04	561	Shawon Dunston	.20	.12
504	Gene Nelson	.07	.04	562	Leon Durham	.07	.04
505	Dave Schmidt	.07	.04	563	Dennis Eckersley	.70	.40
506	Ray Searage	.07	.04	564	Terry Francona	.07	.04
507	Bobby Thigpen (R)	.35	.20	565	Dave Gumpert	.07	.04
508	Greg Walker	.07	.04	566	Guy Hoffman	.07	.04
509	Jim Acker	.07	.04	567	Ed Lynch	.07	.04
510	Doyle Alexander	.07	.04	568	Gary Matthews	.07	.04
511	Paul Assenmacher	.07	.04	569	Keith Moreland	.07	.04
512	Bruce Benedict	.07	.04	570	Jamie Moyer	.20	.12
513	Chris Chambliss	.10	.06	571	Jerry Mumphrey	.07	.04
514	Jeff Dedmon	.07	.04	572	Ryne Sandberg	3.50	2.50
515	Gene Garber	.07	.04	573	Scott Sanderson	.07	.04
516	Ken Griffey	.12	.07	574	Lee Smith	.50	.30
517	Terry Harper	.07	.04	575	Chris Speier	.07	.04
518	Bob Horner	.10	.06	576	Rick Sutcliffe	.12	.07
520	Rick Mahler	.07	.04	577	Manny Trillo	.07	.04
521	Omar Moreno	.07	.04	578	Steve Trout	.07	.04
522	Dale Murphy	.40	.25	579	Karl Best	.07	.04
523	Ken Oberkfell	.07	.04	580	Scott Bradley	.07	.04
524	Ed Olwine	.07	.04	581	Phil Bradley	.07	.04
525	David Palmer	.07	.04	582	Mickey Brantley	.07	.04
526	Rafael Ramirez	.07	.04	583	Mike Brown	.07	.04
527	Billy Sample	.07	.04	584	Alvin Davis	.10	.06
528	Ted Simmons	.10	.06	585	Lee Guetterman (R)	.12	.07
529	Zane Smith	.12	.07	586	Mark Huismann	.07	.04
530	Bruce Sutter	.15	.10	587	Bob Kearney	.07	.04
531	Andres Thomas	.07	.04	588	Pete Ladd	.07	.04
532	Ozzie Virgil	.07	.04	589	Mark Langston	.40	.25
533	Allan Anderson (R)	.15	.10	590	Mike Moore	.10	.06
534	Keith Atherton	.07	.04	591	Mike Morgan	.10	.06
535	Billy Beane	.07	.04	592	John Moses	.07	.04
536	Bert Blyleven	.30	.18	593	Ken Phelps	.07	.04
537	Tom Brunansky	.15	.10	594	Jim Presley	.07	.04
538	Randy Bush	.07	.04	595	Rey Quinones	.07	.04
539	George Frazier	.07	.04	596	Harold Reynolds	.15	.10
540	Gary Gaetti	.07	.04	597	Billy Swift	.40	.25
541	Greg Gagne	.08	.05	598	Danny Tartabull	.50	.30
542	Mickey Hatcher	.07	.04	599	Steve Yeager	.07	.04
543	Neal Heaton	.07	.04	600	Matt Young	.07	.04
544	Kent Hrbek	.20	.12	601	Bill Almon	.07	.04
545	Roy Lee Jackson	.07	.04	602	Rafael Belliard (R)	.20	.12
546	Tim Laudner	.07	.04	603	Mike Bielecki	.07	.04

604	Barry Bonds	45.00	30.00
605	Bobby Bonilla	4.00	2.50
606	Sid Bream	.07	.04
607	Mike Brown	.07	.04
608	Pat Clements	.07	.04
609	Mike Diaz	.07	.04
610	Cecilio Guante	.07	.04
611	Barry Jones (R)	.10	.06
612	Bob Kipper	.07	.04
613	Larry McWilliams	.07	.04
614	Jim Morrison	.07	.04
615	Joe Orsulak	.12	.07
616	Junior Ortiz	.07	.04
617	Tony Pena	.10	.06
618	Johnny Ray	.07	.04
619	Rick Reuschel	.07	.04
620	R.J. Reynolds	.07	.04
621	Rick Rhoden	.07	.04
622	Don Robinson	.07	.04
623	Bob Walk	.07	.04
624	Jim Winn	.07	.04
625	Jose Canseco/Pete Incaviglia	.80	.50
626	Phil Niekro/Don Sutton	.25	.15
627	Don Aase/Dave Righetti	.08	.05
628	Jose Canseco/Wally Joyner	1.25	.80
629	Magic Mets(Gary Carter, Sid Fernandez, Dwight Gooden, Keith Hernandez, Darryl Strawberry)	.25	.15
630	Mike Krukow/Mike Scott	.10	.06
631	John Franco/Fernando Valenzuela)	.10 .07	.06 .04
632	Bob Horner(Count 'em)	.08	.05
633	Pitcher's Nightmare (Jose Canseco, Kirby Puckett, Jim Rice)	1.50	.90
634	Gary Carter/Roger Clemens	.80	.50
635	Steve Carlton (4,000)	.40	.25
636	Glenn Davis/Eddie Murray	.20	.12
637	Wade Boggs/Keith Hernandez	.20	.12
638	Don Mattingly/Darryl Strawberry	.75	.45
639	Dave Parker/Ryne Sandberg	.25	.15
640	Roger Clemens/Dwight Gooden	1.00	.70
641	Charlie Hough/Mike Witt	.07	.04
642	Tim Raines/Juan Samuel	.10	.06

643	Harold Baines/Jesse Barfield	.12	.07
644	Major League Prospects Dave Clark (R) Greg Swindell (R)	.80	.50
645	Major League Prospects Ron Karkovice (R) Russ Morman (R)	.08	.05
646	Major League Prospects Willie Fraser (R) Devon White (R)	2.00	1.25
647	Major League Prospects Jerry Browne (R) Mike Stanley (R)	1.00	.70
648	Major League Prospects Phil Lombardi (R) Dave Magadan (R)	.35	.20
649	Major League Prospects Ralph Bryant (R) Jose Gonzalez (R)	.10	.06
650	Major League Prospects Randy Asadoor (R) Jimmy Jones (R)	.20	.12
651	Major League Prospects Marvin Freeman (R) Tracy Jones (R)	.12	.07
652	Major League Prospects Kevin Seitzer (R) John Stefero (R)	.40	.25
653	Major League Prospects Steve Fireovid (R) Rob Nelson (R)	.08	.05
654	Checklist (1-95)	.08	.03
655	Checklist (96-192)	.08	.03
656	Checklist (193-288)	.08	.03
657	Checklist (289-384)	.08	.03
658	Checklist (385-483)	.08	.03
659	Checklist (484-578)	.08	.03
660	Checklist (579-660)	.08	.03

1987 Fleer Update

This 132-card update set is identical to Fleer's regular issue. The 2-1/2" by 3-1/2" cards features players traded during the season and promising rookies. Card numbers carry the "U" prefix on the card backs.

		MINT	NR/MT
Complete Set (132)		16.00	10.00
Commons		.05	.03
1	Scott Bankhead	.08	.05
2	Eric Bell (R)	.08	.05
3	Juan Beniquez	.05	.03
4	Juan Berenguer	.05	.03
5	Mike Birkbeck (R)	.08	.05
6	Randy Bockus (R)	.10	.06
7	Rod Booker (R)	.07	.04
8	Thad Bosley	.05	.03
9	Greg Brock	.05	.03
10	Bob Brower (R)	.07	.04
11	Chris Brown	.05	.03
12	Jerry Browne	.10	.06
13	Ralph Bryant	.07	.04
14	DeWayne Buice (R)	.07	.04
15	Ellis Burks (R)	.80	.50
16	Casey Candaele (R)	.10	.06
17	Steve Carlton	.75	.45
18	Juan Castillo	.05	.03
19	Chuck Crim (R)	.10	.06
20	Mark Davidson (R)	.10	.06
21	Mark Davis	.08	.05
22	Storm Davis	.05	.03
23	Bill Dawley	.05	.03
24	Andre Dawson	.60	.35
25	Brian Dayett	.05	.03
26	Rick Dempsey	.05	.03
27	Ken Dowell	.05	.03
28	Dave Dravecky	.10	.06
29	Mike Dunne (R)	.10	.06
30	Dennis Eckersley	.50	.30
31	Cecil Fielder	2.00	1.25
32	Brian Fisher	.05	.03
33	Willie Fraser	.05	.03
34	Ken Gerhart (R)	.05	.03
35	Jim Gott	.05	.03
36	Dan Gladden	.05	.03
37	Mike Greenwell (R)	.80	.50
38	Cecilio Guante	.05	.03
39	Albert Hall	.05	.03
40	Atlee Hammaker	.05	.03
41	Mickey Hatcher	.05	.03
42	Mike Heath	.05	.03
43	Neal Heaton	.05	.03
44	Mike Henneman (R)	.30	.18
45	Guy Hoffman	.05	.03
46	Charles Hudson	.05	.03
47	Chuck Jackson (R)	.10	.06
48	Mike Jackson (R)	.20	.12
49	Reggie Jackson	.90	.60
50	Chris James	.05	.03
51	Dion James	.05	.03
52	Stan Javier	.05	.03
53	Stan Jefferson (R)	.08	.05
54	Jimmy Jones	.08	.05
55	Tracy Jones	.05	.03
56	Terry Kennedy	.05	.03
57	Mike Kingery	.05	.03
58	Ray Knight	.10	.06
59	Gene Larkin (R)	.20	.12
60	Mike LaValliere	.08	.05
61	Jack Lazorko	.05	.03
62	Terry Leach	.05	.03
63	Rick Leach	.05	.03
64	Craig Lefferts	.05	.03
65	Jim Lindeman (R)	.12	.07
66	Bill Long (R)	.12	.07
67	Mike Loynd (R)	.08	.05
68	Greg Maddux (R)	6.00	3.75
69	Bill Madlock	.10	.06
70	Dave Magadan	.15	.10
71	Joe Magrane (R)	.15	.10
72	Fred Manrique (R)	.08	.05
73	Mike Mason	.05	.03
74	Lloyd McClendon (R)	.15	.10
75	Fred McGriff (R)	5.00	3.50
76	Mark McGwire (R)	3.00	1.75
77	Mark McLemore	.05	.03
78	Kevin McReynolds	.15	.10
79	Dave Meads	.07	.04
80	Greg Minton	.05	.03
81	John Mitchell (R)	.08	.05
82	Kevin Mitchell	.50	.30
83	John Morris	.05	.03
84	Jeff Musselman (R)	.10	.06
85	Randy Myers (R)	.80	.50
86	Gene Nelson	.05	.03
87	Joe Niekro	.05	.03
88	Tom Nieto	.05	.03

89	Reid Nichols	.05	.03
90	Matt Nokes (R)	.30	.18
91	Dickie Noles	.05	.03
92	Edwin Nunez	.05	.03
93	Jose Nunez (R)	.08	.05
94	Paul O'Neill	.40	.25
95	Jim Paciorek (R)	.08	.05
96	Lance Parrish	.10	.06
97	Bill Pecota (R)	.12	.07
98	Tony Pena	.10	.06
99	Luis Polonia (R)	.40	.25
100	Randy Ready	.05	.03
101	Jeff Reardon	.25	.15
102	Gary Redus	.05	.03
103	Rick Rhoden	.05	.03
104	Wally Ritchie (R)	.08	.05
105	Jeff Robinson (R)	.10	.06
106	Mark Salas	.05	.03
107	Dave Schmidt	.05	.03
108	Kevin Seitzer	.15	.10
109	John Shelby	.05	.03
110	John Smiley (R)	.75	.45
111	Lary Sorensen	.05	.03
112	Chris Speier	.05	.03
113	Randy St. Claire	.05	.03
114	Jim Sundberg	.05	.03
115	B.J. Surhoff (R)	.25	.15
116	Greg Swindell	.50	.30
117	Danny Tartabull	.40	.25
118	Dorn Taylor (R)	.08	.05
119	Lee Tunnell	.05	.03
120	Ed Vande Berg	.05	.03
121	Andy Van Slyke	.30	.18
122	Gary Ward	.05	.03
123	Devon White	.70	.40
124	Alan Wiggins	.05	.03
125	Bill Wilkinson	.05	.03
126	Jim Winn	.05	.03
127	Frank Williams	.05	.03
128	Ken Williams (R)	.08	.05
129	Matt Williams (R)	5.00	3.00
130	Herm Winningham	.05	.03
131	Matt Young	.05	.03
132	Checklist (1-132)	.05	.03

1988 Fleer

This set consists of 660-cards which measure 2-1/2" by 3-1/2". Card fronts feature full color player photos surrounded by a white frame with diagonal red and blue border stripes. Card backs are red and gray and printed vertically. A new feature at the bottom of the card backs, called "At Their Best", breaks down the player's statistics for home and road games as well as day and night games.

		MINT	NR/MT
Complete Set (660)		34.00	20.00
Commons		.05	.03

1	Keith Atherton	.05	.03
2	Don Baylor	.10	.06
3	Juan Berenguer	.05	.03
4	Bert Blyleven	.15	.10
5	Tom Brunansky	.08	.05
6	Randy Bush	.05	.03
7	Steve Carlton	.60	.35
8	Mark Davidson (R)	.07	.04
9	George Frazier	.05	.03
10	Gary Gaetti	.05	.03
11	Greg Gagne	.07	.04
12	Dan Gladden	.05	.03
13	Kent Hrbek	.12	.07
14	Gene Larkin	.10	.06
15	Tim Laudner	.05	.03
16	Steve Lombardozzi	.05	.03
17	Al Newman	.05	.03
18	Joe Niekro	.05	.03
19	Kirby Puckett	1.25	.80
20	Jeff Reardon	.20	.12
21	Dan Schatzader	.05	.03
22	Roy Smalley	.05	.03
23	Mike Smithson	.05	.03
24	Les Straker (R)	.07	.04
25	Frank Viola	.15	.10
26	Jack Clark	.10	.06

27	Vince Coleman	.12	.07
28	Danny Cox	.05	.03
29	Bill Dawley	.05	.03
30	Ken Dayley	.05	.03
31	Doug DeCinces	.05	.03
32	Curt Ford	.05	.03
33	Bob Forsch	.05	.03
34	David Green	.05	.03
35	Tom Herr	.05	.03
36	Ricky Horton	.05	.03
37	Lance Johnson (R)	.70	.40
38	Steve Lake	.05	.03
39	Jim Lindeman	.05	.03
40	Joe Magrane	.12	.07
41	Greg Mathews	.05	.03
42	Willie McGee	.12	.07
43	John Morris	.05	.03
44	Jose Oquendo	.05	.03
45	Tony Pena	.07	.04
46	Terry Pendleton	.35	.20
47	Ozzie Smith	.50	.30
48	John Tudor	.08	.05
49	Lee Tunnell	.05	.03
50	Todd Worrell	.08	.05
51	Doyle Alexander	.05	.03
52	Dave Bergman	.05	.03
53	Tom Brookens	.05	.03
54	Darrell Evans	.08	.05
55	Kirk Gibson	.12	.07
56	Mike Heath	.05	.03
57	Mike Henneman	.15	.10
58	Willie Hernandez	.07	.04
59	Larry Herndon	.05	.03
60	Eric King	.05	.03
61	Chet Lemon	.05	.03
62	Scott Lusader (R)	.08	.05
63	Bill Madlock	.10	.06
64	Jack Morris	.25	.15
65	Jim Morrison	.05	.03
66	Matt Nokes	.25	.15
67	Dan Petry	.05	.03
68	Jeff Robinson	.08	.05
69	Pat Sheridan	.05	.03
70	Nate Snell	.05	.03
71	Frank Tanana	.08	.05
72	Walt Terrell	.05	.03
73	Mark Thurmond	.05	.03
74	Alan Trammell	.25	.15
75	Lou Whitaker	.15	.10
76	Mike Aldrete	.05	.03
77	Bob Brenly	.05	.03
78	Will Clark	1.75	1.00
79	Chili Davis	.10	.06
80	Kelly Downs	.08	.05
81	Dave Dravecky	.08	.05
82	Scott Garrelts	.05	.03
83	Atlee Hammaker	.05	.03
84	Dave Henderson	.10	.06
85	Mike Krukow	.05	.03
86	Mike LaCoss	.05	.03
87	Craig Lefferts	.05	.03
88	Jeff Leonard	.05	.03
89	Candy Maldonado	.08	.05
90	Ed Milner	.05	.03
91	Bob Melvin	.05	.03
92	Kevin Mitchell	.30	.18
93	Jon Perlman	.05	.03
94	Rick Reuschel	.05	.03
95	Don Robinson	.05	.03
96	Chris Speier	.05	.03
97	Harry Spilman	.05	.03
98	Robbie Thompson	.25	.15
99	Jose Uribe	.05	.03
100	Mark Wasinger (R)	.05	.03
101	Matt Williams	5.00	3.00
102	Jesse Barfield	.08	.05
103	George Bell	.12	.07
104	Juan Beniquez	.05	.03
105	John Cerutti	.05	.03
106	Jim Clancy	.05	.03
107	Rob Ducey (R)	.10	.06
108	Mark Eichhorn	.05	.03
109	Tony Fernandez	.12	.07
110	Cecil Fielder	.75	.45
111	Kelly Gruber	.15	.10
112	Tom Henke	.08	.05
113	Garth Iorg	.05	.03
114	Jimmy Key	.15	.10
115	Rick Leach	.05	.03
116	Manny Lee	.05	.03
117	Nelson Liriano (R)	.10	.06
118	Fred McGriff	3.00	1.75
119	Lloyd Moseby	.05	.03
120	Rance Mulliniks	.05	.03
121	Jeff Musselman	.05	.03
122	Jose Nunez	.05	.03
123	Dave Stieb	.10	.06
124	Willie Upshaw	.05	.03
125	Duane Ward(R)	.35	.20
126	Ernie Whitt	.05	.03
127	Rick Aguilera	.08	.05
128	Wally Backman	.05	.03
129	Mark Carreon (R)	.20	.12
130	Gary Carter	.15	.10
131	David Cone (R)	1.50	.90
132	Ron Darling	.08	.05
133	Len Dykstra	.30	.18
134	Sid Fernandez	.08	.05
135	Dwight Gooden	.20	.12
136	Keith Hernandez	.08	.05
137	Gregg Jefferies (R)	4.50	2.75
138	Howard Johnson	.20	.12
139	Terry Leach	.05	.03
140	Barry Lyons (R)	.08	.05

141 Dave Magadan	.12	.07
142 Roger McDowell	.05	.03
143 Kevin McReynolds	.10	.06
144 Keith Miller (R)	.25	.15
145 John Mitchell (R)	.07	.04
146 Randy Myers	.25	.15
147 Bob Ojeda	.07	.04
148 Jesse Orosco	.05	.03
149 Rafael Santana	.05	.03
150 Doug Sisk	.05	.03
151 Darryl Strawberry	.50	.30
152 Tim Teufel	.05	.03
153 Gene Walter	.05	.03
154 Mookie Wilson	.07	.04
155 Jay Aldrich	.05	.03
156 Chris Bosio	.08	.05
157 Glenn Braggs	.05	.03
158 Greg Brock	.05	.03
159 Juan Castillo	.05	.03
160 Mark Clear	.05	.03
161 Cecil Cooper	.08	.05
162 Chuck Crim	.05	.03
163 Rob Deer	.07	.04
164 Mike Felder	.05	.03
165 Jim Gantner	.05	.03
166 Ted Higuera	.07	.04
167 Steve Kiefer	.05	.03
168 Rick Manning	.05	.03
169 Paul Molitor	.50	.30
170 Juan Nieves	.05	.03
171 Dan Plesac	.07	.04
172 Earnest Riles	.05	.03
173 Bill Schroeder	.05	.03
174 Steve Stanicek (R)	.05	.03
175 B.J. Surhoff	.08	.05
176 Dale Sveum	.05	.03
177 Bill Wegman	.05	.03
178 Robin Yount	.75	.45
179 Hubie Brooks	.08	.05
180 Tim Burke	.05	.03
181 Casey Candaele	.05	.03
182 Mike Fitgerald	.05	.03
183 Tom Foley	.05	.03
184 Andres Galarraga	.25	.15
185 Neal Heaton	.05	.03
186 Wallace Johnson	.05	.03
187 Vance Law	.05	.03
188 Dennis Martinez	.15	.10
189 Bob McClure	.05	.03
190 Andy McGaffigan	.05	.03
191 Reid Nichols	.05	.03
192 Pascual Perez	.07	.04
193 Tim Raines	.10	.06
194 Jeff Reed	.05	.03
195 Bob Sebra	.05	.03
196 Bryn Smith	.05	.03
197 Randy St. Claire	.05	.03
198 Tim Wallach	.10	.06
199 Mitch Webster	.05	.03
200 Herm Winningham	.05	.03
201 Floyd Youmans	.05	.03
202 Brad Arnsberg (R)	.08	.05
203 Rick Cerone	.05	.03
204 Pat Clements	.05	.03
205 Henry Cotto	.05	.03
206 Mike Easler	.05	.03
207 Ron Guidry	.10	.06
208 Bill Gullickson	.07	.04
209 Rickey Henderson	.75	.45
210 Charles Hudson	.05	.03
211 Tommy John	.10	.06
212 Roberto Kelly (R)	1.50	.90
213 Ron Kittle	.07	.04
214 Don Mattingly	.70	.40
215 Bobby Meacham	.05	.03
216 Mike Pagliarulo	.05	.03
217 Dan Pasqua	.05	.03
218 Willie Randolph	.08	.05
219 Rick Rhoden	.05	.03
220 Dave Righetti	.08	.05
221 Jerry Royster	.05	.03
222 Tim Stoddard	.05	.03
223 Wayne Tolleson	.05	.03
224 Gary Ward	.05	.03
225 Claudell Washington	.05	.03
226 Dave Winfield	.75	.45
227 Buddy Bell	.05	.03
228 Tom Browning	.08	.05
229 Dave Concepcion	.12	.07
230 Kal Daniels	.10	.06
231 Eric Davis	.20	.12
232 Bob Diaz	.05	.03
233 Nick Esasky	.05	.03
234 John Franco	.07	.04
235 Guy Hoffman	.05	.03
236 Tom Hume	.05	.03
237 Tracy Jones	.05	.03
238 Bill Landrum (R)	.10	.06
239 Barry Larkin	.40	.25
240 Terry McGriff (R)	.05	.03
241 Rob Murphy	.05	.03
242 Ron Oester	.05	.03
243 Dave Parker	.12	.07
244 Pat Perry	.05	.03
245 Ted Power	.05	.03
246 Dennis Rasmussen	.05	.03
248 Kurt Stillwell	.07	.04
249 Jeff Treadway (R)	.15	.10
250 Frank Williams	.05	.03
251 Steve Balboni	.05	.03
252 Bud Black	.07	.04
253 Thad Bosley	.05	.03
254 George Brett	.80	.50
255 John Davis (R)	.05	.03

256	Steve Farr	.05	.03
257	Gene Garber	.05	.03
258	Jerry Gleaton	.05	.03
259	Mark Gubicza	.10	.06
260	Bo Jackson	.75	.45
261	Danny Jackson	.07	.04
262	Ross Jones	.05	.03
263	Charlie Leibrandt	.05	.03
264	Bill Pecota	.08	.05
265	Melido Perez (R)	.60	.35
266	Jamie Quirk	.05	.03
267	Dan Quisenberry	.07	.04
268	Bret Saberhagen	.20	.12
269	Angel Salazar	.05	.03
270	Kevin Seitzer	.10	.06
271	Danny Tartabull	.25	.15
272	Gary Thurman (R)	.10	.06
273	Frank White	.05	.03
274	Willie Wilson	.07	.04
275	Tony Bernazard	.05	.03
276	Jose Canseco	1.50	.90
277	Mike Davis	.05	.03
278	Storm Davis	.05	.03
279	Dennis Eckersley	.30	.18
280	Alfredo Griffin	.05	.03
281	Rick Honeycutt	.05	.03
282	Jay Howell	.05	.03
283	Reggie Jackson	.80	.50
284	Dennis Lamp	.05	.03
285	Carney Lansford	.07	.04
286	Mark McGwire	1.75	1.00
287	Dwayne Murphy	.05	.03
288	Gene Nelson	.05	.03
289	Steve Ontiveros	.05	.03
290	Tony Phillips	.15	.10
291	Eric Plunk	.05	.03
292	Luis Polonia	.50	.30
293	Rick Rodriguez (R)	.08	.05
294	Terry Steinbach	.12	.07
295	Dave Stewart	.20	.12
296	Curt Young	.05	.03
297	Luis Aguayo	.05	.03
298	Steve Bedrosian	.05	.03
299	Jeff Calhoun	.05	.03
300	Don Carman	.05	.03
301	Todd Frohwirth (R)	.07	.04
302	Greg Gross	.05	.03
303	Kevin Gross	.05	.03
304	Von Hayes	.05	.03
305	Keith Hughes (R)	.07	.04
306	Mike Jackson	.12	.07
307	Chris James	.05	.03
308	Steve Jeltz	.05	.03
309	Mike Maddux	.05	.03
310	Lance Parrish	.08	.05
311	Shane Rawley	.05	.03
312	Wally Ritchie	.05	.03
313	Bruce Ruffin	.05	.03
314	Juan Samuel	.07	.04
315	Mike Schmidt	1.25	.00
316	Rick Schu	.05	.03
317	Jeff Stone	.05	.03
318	Kent Tekulve	.05	.03
319	Milt Thompson	.05	.03
320	Glenn Wilson	.05	.03
321	Rafael Belliard	.05	.03
322	Barry Bonds	3.75	2.25
323	Bobby Bonilla	.50	.30
324	Sid Bream	.05	.03
325	John Cangelosi	.05	.03
326	Mike Diaz	.05	.03
327	Doug Drabek	.25	.15
328	Mike Dunne	.05	.03
329	Brian Fisher	.05	.03
330	Brett Gideon (R)	.05	.03
331	Terry Harper	.05	.03
332	Bob Kipper	.05	.03
333	Mike LaValliere	.05	.03
334	Jose Lind (R)	.25	.15
335	Junior Ortiz	.05	.03
336	Vicente Palacios (R)	.12	.07
338	Al Pedrique (R)	.05	.03
339	R.J. Reynolds	.05	.03
340	John Smiley	.75	.45
341	Andy Van Slyke	.25	.15
342	Bob Walk	.05	.03
343	Marty Barrett	.05	.03
344	Todd Benzinger (R)	.15	.10
345	Wade Boggs	.60	.35
346	Tom Bolton (R)	.15	.10
347	Oil Can Boyd	.05	.03
348	Ellis Burks	1.00	.70
349	Roger Clemens	1.50	.90
350	Steve Crawford	.05	.03
351	Dwight Evans	.12	.07
352	Wes Gardner (R)	.08	.05
353	Rich Gedman	.05	.03
354	Mike Greenwell	.40	.25
355	Sam Horn (R)	.15	.10
356	Bruce Hurst	.10	.06
357	John Marzano (R)	.08	.05
358	Al Nipper	.05	.03
359	Spike Owen	.05	.03
360	Jody Reed (R)	.45	.28
361	Jim Rice	.12	.07
362	Ed Romero	.05	.03
363	Kevin Romine (R)	.07	.04
364	Joe Sambito	.05	.03
365	Calvin Schiraldi	.05	.03
366	Jeff Sellers	.05	.03
367	Bob Stanley	.05	.03
368	Scott Bankhead	.05	.03
369	Phil Bradley	.05	.03
370	Scott Bradley	.05	.03

371	Mickey Brantley	.05	.03
372	Mike Campbell (R)	.05	.03
373	Alvin Davis	.08	.05
374	Lee Guetterman	.05	.03
375	Dave Hengel (R)	.05	.03
376	Mike Kingery	.05	.03
377	Mark Langston	.20	.12
378	Edgar Martinez (R)	1.25	.80
379	Mike Moore	.05	.03
380	Mike Morgan	.07	.04
381	John Moses	.05	.03
382	Donnell Nixon (R)	.08	.05
383	Edwin Nunez	.05	.03
384	Ken Phelps	.05	.03
385	Jim Presley	.05	.03
386	Rey Quinones	.05	.03
387	Jerry Reed	.05	.03
388	Harold Reynolds	.08	.05
389	Dave Valle	.05	.03
390	Bill Wilkinson	.05	.03
391	Harold Baines	.10	.06
392	Floyd Bannister	.05	.03
393	Daryl Boston	.05	.03
394	Ivan Calderon	.10	.06
395	Jose DeLeon	.05	.03
396	Richard Dotson	.05	.03
397	Carlton Fisk	.50	.30
398	Ozzie Guillen	.10	.06
399	Ron Hassey	.05	.03
400	Donnie Hill	.05	.03
401	Bob James	.05	.03
402	Dave LaPoint	.05	.03
403	Bill Lindsey	.05	.03
404	Bill Long (R)	.07	.04
405	Steve Lyons	.05	.03
406	Fred Manrique	.05	.03
407	Jack McDowell (R)	5.00	3.00
408	Gary Redus	.05	.03
409	Ray Searage	.05	.03
410	Bobby Thigpen	.15	.10
411	Greg Walker	.05	.03
412	Kenny Williams	.05	.03
413	Jim Winn	.05	.03
414	Jody Davis	.05	.03
415	Andre Dawson	.60	.35
416	Brian Dayett	.05	.03
417	Bob Dernier	.05	.03
418	Frank DiPino	.05	.03
419	Shawon Dunston	.15	.10
420	Leon Durham	.05	.03
421	Les Lancaster (R)	.15	.10
422	Ed Lynch	.05	.03
423	Greg Maddux	1.75	1.00
424	Dave Martinez (R)	.12	.07
425a	Keith Moreland (Wrong Photo) (Bunting)	2.50	1.50

425b	Keith Moreland (Cor)	.10	.06
426	Jamie Moyer	.05	.03
427	Jerry Mumphrey	.05	.03
428	Paul Noce (R)	.07	.04
429	Rafael Palmeiro (R)	2.00	1.25
430	Wade Rowdon (R)	.05	.03
431	Ryne Sandberg	1.25	.80
432	Scott Sanderson	.07	.04
433	Lee Smith	.30	.18
434	Jim Sundberg	.05	.03
435	Rick Sutcliffe	.08	.05
436	Manny Trillo	.05	.03
437	Juan Agosto	.05	.03
438	Larry Andersen	.05	.03
439	Alan Ashby	.05	.03
440	Kevin Bass	.07	.04
441	Ken Caminiti (R)	.50	.30
442	Rocky Childress (R)	.05	.03
443	Jose Cruz	.08	.05
444	Danny Darwin	.05	.03
445	Glenn Davis	.08	.05
446	Jim Deshaies	.05	.03
447	Bill Doran	.07	.04
448	Ty Gainey	.05	.03
449	Billy Hatcher	.07	.04
450	Jeff Heathcock	.05	.03
451	Bob Knepper	.05	.03
452	Rob Mallicoat (R)	.07	.04
453	Dave Meads	.05	.03
454	Craig Reynolds	.05	.03
455	Nolan Ryan	2.00	1.25
456	Mike Scott	.10	.06
457	Dave Smith	.05	.03
458	Denny Walling	.05	.03
459	Robbie Wine (R)	.05	.03
460	Gerald Young (R)	.12	.07
461	Bob Brower	.05	.03
462a	Jerry Browne (Wrong Photo)	2.50	1.50
462b	Jerry Browne	.10	.06
463	Steve Buechele	.08	.05
464	Edwin Correa	.05	.03
465	Cecil Espy (R)	.15	.10
466	Scott Fletcher	.05	.03
467	Jose Guzman	.07	.04
468	Greg Harris	.05	.03
469	Charlie Hough	.07	.04
470	Pete Incaviglia	.15	.10
471	Paul Kilgus (R)	.07	.04
472	Mike Loynd	.05	.03
473	Oddibe McDowell	.05	.03
474	Dale Mohorcic	.05	.03
475	Pete O'Brien	.05	.03
476	Larry Parrish	.05	.03
477	Geno Petralli	.05	.03
478	Jeff Russell	.07	.04
479	Ruben Sierra	1.00	.70

480	Mike Stanley	.05	.03
481	Curtis Wilkerson	.05	.03
482	Mitch Williams	.07	.04
483	Bobby Witt	.12	.07
484	Tony Armas	.05	.03
485	Bob Boone	.10	.06
486	Bill Buckner	.08	.05
487	DeWayne Buice	.05	.03
488	Brian Downing	.07	.04
489	Chuck Finley	.20	.12
490	Willie Fraser	.05	.03
491	Jack Howell	.05	.03
492	Ruppert Jones	.05	.03
493	Wally Joyner	.20	.12
494	Jack Lazorko	.05	.03
495	Gary Lucas	.05	.03
496	Kirk McCaskill	.05	.03
497	Mark McLemore	.05	.03
498	Darrell Miller	.05	.03
499	Greg Minton	.05	.03
500	Donnie Moore	.05	.03
501	Gus Polidor	.05	.03
502	Johnny Ray	.05	.03
503	Mark Ryal (R)	.05	.03
504	Dick Schofield	.05	.03
505	Don Sutton	.20	.12
506	Devon White	.20	.12
507	Mike Witt	.05	.03
508	Dave Anderson	.05	.03
509	Tim Belcher	.25	.15
510	Ralph Bryant	.05	.03
511	Tim Crews (R)	.12	.07
512	Mike Devereaux (R)	1.50	.90
513	Mariano Duncan	.07	.04
514	Pedro Guerrero	.08	.05
515	Jeff Hamilton (R)	.08	.05
516	Mickey Hatcher	.05	.03
517	Brad Havens	.05	.03
518	Orel Hershiser	.15	.10
519	Shawn Hillegas (R)	.12	.07
520	Ken Howell	.05	.03
521	Tim Leary	.05	.03
522	Mike Marshall	.08	.05
523	Steve Sax	.15	.10
524	Mike Scioscia	.07	.04
525	Mike Sharperson (R)	.10	.06
526	John Shelby	.05	.03
527	Franklin Stubbs	.05	.03
528	Fernando Valenzuela	.12	.07
529	Bob Welch	.08	.05
530	Matt Young	.05	.03
531	Jim Acker	.05	.03
532	Paul Assenmacher	.05	.03
533	Jeff Blauser (R)	1.25	.80
534	Joe Boever (R)	.08	.05
535	Martin Clary	.05	.03
536	Kevin Coffman	.05	.03

537	Jeff Dedmon	.05	.03
538	Ron Gant (R)	6.50	3.75
539	Tom Glavine (R)	10.00	7.50
540	Ken Griffey	.08	.05
541	Albert Hall	.05	.03
542	Glenn Hubbard	.05	.03
543	Dion James	.05	.03
544	Dale Murphy	.20	.12
545	Ken Oberkfell	.05	.03
546	David Palmer	.05	.03
547	Gerald Perry	.05	.03
548	Charlie Puleo	.05	.03
549	Ted Simmons	.08	.05
550	Zane Smith	.10	.06
551	Andres Thomas	.05	.03
552	Ozzie Virgil	.05	.03
553	Don Aase	.05	.03
554	Jeff Ballard (R)	.10	.06
555	Eric Bell	.05	.03
556	Mike Boddicker	.05	.03
557	Ken Dixon	.05	.03
558	Jim Dwyer	.05	.03
559	Ken Gerhart	.05	.03
560	Rene Gonzales (R)	.15	.10
561	Mike Griffin	.05	.03
562	John Habyan	.07	.04
563	Terry Kennedy	.05	.03
564	Ray Knight	.08	.05
565	Lee Lacy	.05	.03
566	Fred Lynn	.15	.10
567	Eddie Murray	.50	.30
568	Tom Niedenfuer	.05	.03
569	Bill Ripken (R)	.15	.10
570	Cal Ripken, Jr.	1.50	.90
571	Dave Schmidt	.05	.03
572	Larry Sheets	.05	.03
573	Pete Stanicek	.05	.03
574	Mark Williamson (R)	.08	.05
575	Mike Young	.05	.03
576	Shawn Abner (R)	.07	.04
577	Greg Booker	.05	.03
578	Chris Brown	.05	.03
579	Keith Comstock	.07	.04
580	Joey Cora (R)	.20	.12
581	Mark Davis	.07	.04
582	Tim Flannery	.05	.03
583	Goose Gossage	.12	.07
584	Mark Grant	.05	.03
585	Tony Gwynn	.75	.45
586	Andy Hawkins	.05	.03
587	Stan Jefferson	.05	.03
588	Jimmy Jones	.05	.03
589	John Kruk	.40	.25
590	Shane Mack (R)	.75	.45
591	Carmelo Martinez	.05	.03
592	Lance McCullers	.05	.03
593	Eric Nolte (R)	.07	.04

594	Randy Ready	.05	.03
595	Luis Salazar	.05	.03
596	Benito Santiago	.15	.10
597	Eric Show	.05	.03
598	Garry Templeton	.07	.04
599	Ed Whitson	.05	.03
600	Scott Bailes	.05	.03
601	Chris Bando	.05	.03
602	Jay Bell (R)	1.75	1.00
603	Brett Butler	.15	.10
604	Tom Candiotti	.07	.04
605	Joe Carter	.75	.45
606	Carmen Castillo	.05	.03
607	Brian Dorsett (R)	.07	.04
608	John Farrell (R)	.08	.05
609	Julio Franco	.15	.10
610	Mel Hall	.08	.05
611	Tommy Hinzo	.05	.03
612	Brook Jacoby	.05	.03
613	Doug Jones (R)	.40	.25
614	Ken Schrom	.05	.03
615	Cory Snyder	.07	.04
616	Sammy Stewart	.05	.03
617	Greg Swindell	.15	.10
618	Pat Tabler	.05	.03
619	Ed Vande Berg	.05	.03
620	Eddie Williams	.05	.03
621	Rich Yett	.05	.03
622	Wally Joyner/Cory Snyder	.12	.07
623	George Bell/Pedro Guerrero	.10	.06
624	Jose Canseco/Mark McGwire	.75	.45
625	Dan Plesac/Dave Righetti	.08	.05
626	Jack Morris/Bret Saberhagen/Mike Witt	.12	.07
627	Steve Bedrosian/John Franco	.08	.05
628	Ryne Sandberg/Ozzie Smith	.60	.35
629	Mark McGwire (RB)	.60	.35
630	Todd Benzinger/Ellis Burks/Mike Greenwell	.20	.12
631	N.L. Batting Champs (Tony Gwynn, Tim Raines)	.25	.15
632	Orel Hershiser/Mike Scott	.12	.07
633	Mark McGwire/Pat Tabler	.30	.18
634	Vince Coleman/Tony Gwynn	.20	.12
635	Tony Fernandez/Cal Ripken, Jr./Alan Trammell	.50	.30
636	Gary Carter/Mike Schmidt	.50	.30
637	Eric Davis/Darryl Strawberry	.25	.15
638	A.L. All Stars(Matt Nokes, Kirby Puckett)	.30	.18
639	N.L. All Stars(Keith Hernandez, Dale Murphy)	.20	.12
640	Bill & Cal Ripken	.60	.35
641	Major League Prospects Mark Grace (R) Darrin Jackson (R)	4.50	3.50
642	Major League Prospects Damon Berryhill (R) Jeff Montgomery (R)	1.25	.80
643	Major League Prospects Felix Fermin (R) Jessie Reid (R)	.05	.03
644	Major League Propects Greg Myers (R) Greg Tabor (R)	.10	.06
645	Major League Prospects Jim Eppard (R) Joey Meyer (R)	.05	.03
646	Major League Prospects Adam Peterson (R) Randy Velarde (R)	.07	.04
647	Major League Prospects Chris Gwynn (R) Pete Smith (R)	.40	.25
648	Major League Prospects Greg Jelks (R) Tom Newell (R)	.05	.03
649	Major League Prospects Mario Diaz (R) Clay Parker (R)	.08	.05
650	Major League Prospects Jack Savage (R) Todd Simmons (R)	.05	.03
651	Major League Prospects John Burkett (R) Kirt Manwaring (R)	2.00	1.25
652	Major League Prospects Dave Otto (R) Walt Weiss (R)	.30	.18
653	Major League Prospects Randall Byers (R) Jeff King (R)	1.00	.70
654	Checklist (1-101)	.05	.02
655	Checklist (102-201)	.05	.02
656	Checklist (202-296)	.05	.02
657	Checklist (297-390)	.05	.02
658	Checklist (391-483)	.05	.02
659	Checklist (484-575)	.05	.02
660	Checklist (576-660)	.05	.02

1988 Fleer Update

As in previous years, this 132-card update set features players traded during the season and promising rookies. Cards are identical to the 1988 Fleer regular issue and the numbers on the card backs carry the prefix "U" for Update set. All cards measure 2-1/2" by 3-1/2".

		MINT	NR/MT
Complete Set (132)		17.00	12.00
Commons		.05	.03
1	Jose Bautista (R)	.07	.04
2	Joe Orsulak	.12	.07
3	Doug Sisk	.05	.03
4	Craig Worthington (R)	.07	.04
5	Mike Boddicker	.05	.03
6	Rick Cerone	.05	.03
7	Larry Parrish	.05	.03
8	Lee Smith	.30	.18
9	Mike Smithson	.05	.03
10	John Trautwein (R)	.05	.03
11	Sherman Corbett (R)	.07	.04
12	Chili Davis	.10	.06
13	Jim Eppard	.05	.03
14	Bryan Harvey (R)	2.00	1.25
15	John Davis	.05	.03
16	Dave Gallagher (R)	.10	.06
17	Ricky Horton	.05	.03
18	Dan Pasqua	.08	.05
19	Melido Perez	.30	.18
20	Jose Segura (R)	.10	.06
21	Andy Allanson	.05	.03
22	Jon Perlman	.05	.03
23	Domingo Ramos	.05	.03
24	Rick Rodriquez	.05	.03
25	Willie Upshaw	.05	.03
26	Paul Gibson (R)	.10	.06
27	Don Heinkel	.05	.03
28	Ray Knight	.08	.05
29	Gary Pettis	.05	.03
30	Luis Salazar	.05	.03
31	Mike Macfarlane	.35	.20
32	Jeff Montgomery	.40	.25
33	Ted Power	.05	.03
34	Israel Sanchez (R)	.05	.03
35	Kurt Stillwell	.08	.05
36	Pat Tabler	.05	.03
37	Don August (R)	.12	.07
38	Darryl Hamilton (R)	.60	.35
39	Jeff Leonard	.08	.05
40	Joey Meyer	.07	.04
41	Allan Anderson	.07	.04
42	Brian Harper	.08	.05
43	Tom Herr	.05	.03
44	Charlie Lea	.05	.03
45	John Moses	.05	.03
46	John Candelaria	.05	.03
47	Jack Clark	.08	.05
48	Richard Dotson	.05	.03
49	Al Leiter (R)	.12	.07
50	Rafael Santana	.05	.03
51	Don Slaught	.07	.04
52	Todd Burns (R)	.12	.07
53	Dave Henderson	.12	.07
54	Doug Jennings (R)	.10	.06
55	Dave Parker	.12	.07
56	Walt Weiss	.20	.12
57	Bob Welch	.10	.06
58	Henry Cotto	.05	.03
59	Mario Diaz	.07	.04
60	Mike Jackson	.12	.07
61	Bill Swift	.25	.15
62	Jose Cecena (R)	.08	.05
63	Ray Hayward (R)	.07	.04
64	Jim Steels (R)	.05	.03
65	Pat Borders (R)	.50	.30
66	Sil Campusano (R)	.10	.06
67	Mike Flanagan	.10	.06
68	Todd Stottlemyre (R)	.40	.25
69	David Wells (R)	.35	.20
70	Jose Alvarez (R)	.08	.05
71	Paul Runge	.05	.03
72	Cesar Jimenez (German) (R)	.05	.03
73	Pete Smith	.30	.18
74	John Smoltz (R)	5.00	3.50
75	Damon Berryhill	.10	.06
76	Goose Gossage	.10	.06
77	Mark Grace	3.00	1.75
78	Darrin Jackson	.12	.07
79	Vance Law	.05	.03
80	Jeff Pico	.10	.06
81	Gary Varsho (R)	.12	.07
82	Tim Birtsas	.05	.03
83	Rob Dibble (R)	.50	.30
84	Danny Jackson	.07	.04
85	Paul O'Neill	.15	.10
86	Jose Rijo	.15	.10

87	Chris Sabo (R)	.80	.50
88	John Fishel (R)	.05	.03
89	Craig Biggio (R)	1.50	.90
90	Terry Puhl	.05	.03
91	Rafael Ramirez	.05	.03
92	Louie Meadows (R)	.05	.03
93	Kirk Gibson	.10	.00
94	Alfredo Griffin	.05	.03
95	Jay Howell	.08	.05
96	Jesse Orosco	.05	.03
97	Alejandro Pena	.08	.05
98	Tracy Woodson	.08	.05
99	John Dopson	.10	.06
100	Brian Holman (R)	.20	.12
101	Rex Hudler (R)	.12	.07
102	Jeff Parrett	.08	.05
103	Nelson Santovenia (R)	.08	.05
104	Kevin Elster	.10	.06
105	Jeff Innis (R)	.10	.06
106	Mackey Sasser (R)	.10	.06
107	Phil Bradley	.08	.05
108	Danny Clay (R)	.05	.03
109	Greg Harris	.05	.03
110	Ricky Jordan (R)	.15	.10
111	David Palmer	.05	.03
112	Jim Gott	.05	.03
113	Tommy Gregg (Wrong Photo)	.08	.05
114	Barry Jones	.08	.05
115	Randy Milligan	.30	.18
116	Luis Alicea (R)	.12	.07
117	Tom Brunansky	.08	.05
118	John Costello (R)	.08	.05
119	Jose DeLeon	.05	.03
120	Bob Horner	.08	.05
121	Scott Terry (R)	.08	.05
122	Roberto Alomar (R)	12.00	9.00
123	Dave Leiper	.05	.03
124	Keith Moreland	.05	.03
125	Mark Parent (R)	.08	.05
126	Dennis Rasmussen	.05	.03
127	Randy Bockus	.05	.03
128	Brett Butler	.15	.10
129	Donell Nixon	.05	.03
130	Earnest Riles	.05	.03
131	Roger Samuels	.05	.03
132	Checklist	.05	.02

1989 Fleer

This 660-card set features full color photos on the card fronts against a gray and white pinstripe background and yellow borders. The vertical card backs are black, yellow and gray on a white background. All cards measure 2-1/2" by 3-1/2". 12 Bonus All-Star cards were packed randomly in Fleer's wax packs. Those cards are listed at the end of this checklist and numbered B1-B12.

		MINT	NR/MT
Complete Set (660)		20.00	12.00
Commons		.05	.03

1	Don Baylor	.10	.06
2	Lance Blankenship(R)	.12	.07
3	Todd Burns	.07	.04
4	Greg Cadaret (R)	.10	.06
5	Jose Canseco	.50	.30
6	Storm Davis	.05	.03
7	Dennis Eckersley	.15	.10
8	Mike Gallego(FC)	.10	.06
9	Ron Hassey	.05	.03
10	Dave Henderson	.08	.05
11	Rick Honeycutt	.05	.03
12	Glenn Hubbard	.05	.03
13	Stan Javier	.05	.03
14	Doug Jennings	.05	.03
15	Felix Jose (R)	.40	.25
16	Carney Lansford	.08	.05
17	Mark McGwire	.45	.28
18	Gene Nelson	.05	.03
19	Dave Parker	.08	.05
20	Eric Plunk	.05	.03
21	Luis Polonia	.08	.05
22	Terry Steinbach	.08	.05
23	Dave Stewart	.15	.10
24	Walt Weiss	.08	.05
25	Bob Welch	.08	.05
26	Curt Young	.05	.03
27	Rick Aguilera	.07	.04

28	Wally Backman	.05	.03
29	Mark Carreon	.08	.05
30	Gary Carter	.10	.06
31	David Cone	.20	.12
32	Ron Darling	.07	.04
33	Len Dykstra	.15	.10
34	Kevin Elster	.05	.03
35	Sid Fernandez	.08	.05
36	Dwight Gooden	.20	.12
37	Keith Hernandez	.08	.05
38	Gregg Jefferies	.30	.18
39	Howard Johnson	.12	.07
40	Terry Leach	.05	.03
41	Dave Magadan	.10	.06
42	Bob McClure	.05	.03
43	Roger McDowell	.05	.03
44	Kevin McReynolds	.08	.05
45	Keith Miller	.05	.03
46	Randy Myers	.08	.05
47	Bob Ojeda	.07	.04
48	Mackey Sasser	.05	.03
49	Darryl Strawberry	.25	.15
50	Tim Teufel	.05	.03
51	Dave West (R)	.15	.10
52	Mookie Wilson	.05	.03
53	Dave Anderson	.05	.03
54	Tim Belcher	.10	.06
55	Mike Davis	.05	.03
56	Mike Devereaux	.15	.10
57	Kirk Gibson	.08	.05
58	Alfredo Griffin	.05	.03
59	Chris Gwynn	.05	.03
60	Jeff Hamilton	.05	.03
61	Danny Heep	.07	.04
62	Orel Hershiser	.12	.07
63	Brian Holton	.05	.03
64	Jay Howell	.05	.03
65	Tim Leary	.05	.03
66	Mike Marshall	.05	.03
67	Ramon Martinez (R)	.50	.30
68	Jesse Orosco	.05	.03
69	Alejandro Pena	.05	.03
70	Steve Sax	.10	.06
71	Mike Scioscia	.07	.04
72	Mike Sharperson	.05	.03
73	John Shelby	.05	.03
74	Franklin Stubbs	.05	.03
75	John Tudor	.05	.03
76	Fernando Valenzuela	.10	.06
77	Tracy Woodson	.05	.03
78	Marty Barrett	.05	.03
79	Todd Benzinger	.05	.03
80	Mike Boddicker	.05	.03
81	Wade Boggs	.25	.15
82	Oil Can Boyd	.05	.03
83	Ellis Burks	.10	.06
84	Rick Cerone	.05	.03
85	Roger Clemens	.60	.35
86	Steve Curry (R)	.05	.03
87	Dwight Evans	.12	.07
88	Wes Gardner	.05	.03
89	Rich Gedman	.05	.03
90	Mike Greenwell	.10	.06
91	Bruce Hurst	.07	.04
92	Dennis Lamp	.05	.03
93	Spike Owen	.05	.03
94	Larry Parrish	.05	.03
95	Carlos Quintana (R)	.15	.10
96	Jody Reed	.05	.03
97	Jim Rice	.12	.07
98	Kevin Romine (Wrong Photo)	.08	.05
99	Lee Smith	.15	.10
100	Mike Smithson	.05	.03
101	Bob Stanley	.05	.03
102	Allan Anderson	.05	.03
103	Keith Atherton	.05	.03
104	Juan Berenguer	.05	.03
105	Bert Blyleven	.15	.10
106	Eric Bullock (R)	.07	.04
107	Randy Bush	.05	.03
108	John Christensen (R)	.05	.03
109	Mark Davidson	.05	.03
110	Gary Gaetti	.05	.03
111	Greg Gagne	.07	.04
112	Dan Gladden	.05	.03
113	German Gonzalez	.05	.03
114	Brian Harper	.07	.04
115	Tom Herr	.05	.03
116	Kent Hrbek	.10	.06
117	Gene Larkin	.05	.03
118	Tim Laudner	.05	.03
119	Charlie Lea	.05	.03
120	Steve Lombardozzi	.05	.03
121	John Moses	.05	.03
122	Al Newman	.05	.03
123	Mark Portugal	.08	.05
124	Kirby Puckett	.40	.25
125	Jeff Reardon	.15	.10
126	Fred Toliver	.05	.03
127	Frank Viola	.12	.07
128	Doyle Alexander	.05	.03
129	Dave Bergman	.05	.03
130a	Tom Brookens (Wrong Stats On Back)	.50	.30
130b	Tom Brookens(Cor)	.05	.03
131	Paul Gibson	.05	.03
132a	Mike Heath (Wrong Stats On Back)	.30	.18
132b	Mike Heath (Cor)	.05	.03
133	Don Heinkel	.05	.03
134	Mike Henneman	.05	.03
135	Guillermo Hernandez	.05	.03
136	Eric King	.05	.03

137	Chet Lemon	.05	.03
138	Fred Lynn	.12	.07
139	Jack Morris	.15	.10
140	Matt Nokes	.07	.04
141	Gary Pettis	.05	.03
142	Ted Power	.05	.03
143	Jeff Robinson	.05	.03
144	Luis Salazar	.05	.03
145	Steve Searcy	.07	.04
146	Pat Sheridan	.05	.03
147	Frank Tanana	.07	.04
148	Alan Trammell	.20	.12
149	Walt Terrell	.05	.03
150	Jim Walewander (R)	.07	.04
151	Lou Whitaker	.12	.07
152	Tim Birtsas	.05	.03
153	Tom Browning	.08	.05
154	Keith Brown (R)	.05	.03
155	Norm Charlton (R)	.20	.12
156	Dave Concepcion	.12	.07
157	Kal Daniels	.07	.04
158	Eric Davis	.12	.07
159	Bo Diaz	.05	.03
160	Rob Dibble	.20	.12
161	Nick Esasky	.05	.03
162	John Franco	.05	.03
163	Danny Jackson	.05	.03
164	Barry Larkin	.20	.12
165	Rob Murphy	.05	.03
166	Paul O'Neill	.12	.07
167	Jeff Reed	.05	.03
168	Jose Rijo	.12	.07
169	Ron Robinson	.05	.03
170	Chris Sabo	.25	.15
171	Candy Sierra (R)	.05	.03
172	Van Snider (R)	.08	.05
173	Jeff Treadway	.07	.04
174	Frank Williams	.05	.03
175	Herm Winningham	.05	.03
176	Jim Adduci (R)	.05	.03
177	Don August	.05	.03
178	Mike Birkbeck	.05	.03
179	Chris Bosio	.08	.05
180	Glenn Braggs	.05	.03
181	Greg Brock	.05	.03
182	Mark Clear	.05	.03
183	Chuck Crim	.05	.03
184	Rob Deer	.07	.04
185	Tom Filer	.05	.03
186	Jim Gantner	.05	.03
187	Darryl Hamilton	.25	.15
188	Ted Higuera	.07	.04
189	Odell Jones	.05	.03
190	Jeffrey Leonard	.05	.03
191	Joey Meyer	.05	.03
192	Paul Mirabella	.05	.03
193	Paul Molitor	.20	.12
194	Charlie O'Brien (R)	.08	.05
195	Dan Plesac	.05	.03
196	Gary Sheffield (R)	2.50	1.50
197	B.J. Surhoff	.05	.03
198	Dale Sveum	.05	.03
199	Bill Wegman	.05	.03
200	Robin Yount	.25	.15
201	Rafael Belliard	.05	.03
202	Barry Bonds	.75	.45
203	Bobby Bonilla	.15	.10
204	Sid Bream	.05	.03
205	Benny Distefano (R)	.05	.03
206	Doug Drabek	.15	.10
207	Mike Dunne	.05	.03
208	Felix Ferman	.05	.03
209	Brian Fisher	.05	.03
210	Jim Gott	.05	.03
211	Bob Kipper	.05	.03
212	Dave LaPoint	.05	.03
213	Mike LaValliere	.05	.03
214	Jose Lind	.05	.03
215	Junior Ortiz	.05	.03
216	Vicente Palacios	.07	.04
217	Tom Prince (R)	.08	.05
218	Gary Redus	.05	.03
219	R.J. Reynolds	.05	.03
220	Jeff Robinson	.05	.03
221	John Smiley	.15	.10
222	Andy Van Slyke	.15	.10
223	Bob Walk	.05	.03
224	Glenn Wilson	.05	.03
225	Jesse Barfield	.07	.04
226	George Bell	.12	.07
227	Pat Borders	.15	.10
228	John Cerutti	.05	.03
229	Jim Clancy	.05	.03
230	Mark Eichhorn	.05	.03
231	Tony Fernandez	.10	.06
232	Cecil Fielder	.35	.20
233	Mike Flanagan	.05	.03
234	Kelly Gruber	.12	.07
235	Tom Henke	.07	.04
236	Jimmy Key	.10	.06
237	Rick Leach	.05	.03
238	Manny Lee	.05	.03
239	Nelson Liriano	.05	.03
240	Fred McGriff	.35	.20
241	Lloyd Moseby	.05	.03
242	Rance Mulliniks	.05	.03
243	Jeff Musselman	.05	.03
244	Dave Stieb	.10	.06
245	Todd Stottlemyre	.12	.07
246	Duane Ward	.08	.05
247	David Wells	.15	.10
248	Ernie Whitt	.05	.03
249	Luis Aguayo	.05	.03
250	Neil Allen	.05	.03

251	John Candelaria	.05	.03
252	Jack Clark	.08	.05
253	Richard Dotson	.05	.03
254	Rickey Henderson	.30	.18
255	Tommy John	.08	.05
256	Roberto Kelly	.20	.12
257	Al Leiter	.05	.03
258	Don Mattingly	.25	.15
259	Dale Mohorcic	.05	.03
260	Hal Morris (R)	.50	.30
261	Scott Nielsen (R)	.05	.03
262	Mike Pagliarulo	.05	.03
263	Hipolito Pena (R)	.07	.04
264	Ken Phelps	.05	.03
265	Willie Randolph	.07	.04
266	Rick Rhoden	.05	.03
267	Dave Righetti	.07	.04
268	Rafael Santana	.05	.03
269	Steve Shields	.05	.03
270	Joel Skinner	.05	.03
271	Don Slaught	.05	.03
272	Claudell Washington	.05	.03
273	Gary Ward	.05	.03
274	Dave Winfield	.30	.18
275	Luis Aquino (R)	.07	.04
276	Floyd Bannister	.05	.03
277	George Brett	.30	.18
278	Bill Buckner	.08	.05
279	Nick Capra (R)	.05	.03
280	Jose DeJesus (R)	.08	.05
281	Steve Farr	.05	.03
282	Jerry Gleaton	.05	.03
283	Mark Gubicza	.10	.06
284	Tom Gordon (R)	.15	.10
285	Bo Jackson	.20	.12
286	Charlie Leibrandt	.05	.03
287	Mike Macfarlane	.10	.06
288	Jeff Montgomery	.08	.05
289	Bill Pecota	.05	.03
290	Jamie Quirk	.05	.03
291	Bret Saberhagen	.12	.07
292	Kevin Seitzer	.08	.05
293	Kurt Stillwell	.05	.03
294	Pat Tabler	.05	.03
295	Danny Tartabull	.15	.10
296	Gary Thurman	.05	.03
297	Frank White	.05	.03
298	Willie Wilson	.05	.03
299	Roberto Alomar	1.25	.80
300	Sandy Alomar Jr (R)	.25	.15
301	Chris Brown	.05	.03
302	Mike Brumley (R)	.07	.04
303	Mark Davis	.07	.04
304	Mark Grant	.05	.03
305	Tony Gwynn	.30	.18
306	Greg Harris(FC)	.12	.07
307	Andy Hawkins	.05	.03
308	Jimmy Jones	.05	.03
309	John Kruk	.15	.10
310	Dave Leiper	.05	.03
311	Carmelo Martinez	.05	.03
312	Lance McCullers	.05	.03
313	Keith Moreland	.05	.03
314	Dennis Rasmussen	.05	.03
315	Randy Ready	.05	.03
316	Benito Santiago	.12	.07
317	Eric Show	.05	.03
318	Todd Simmons	.05	.03
319	Garry Templeton	.07	.04
320	Dickie Thon	.05	.03
321	Ed Whitson	.05	.03
322	Marvell Wynne	.05	.03
323	Mike Aldrete	.05	.03
324	Brett Butler	.12	.07
325	Will Clark	.50	.30
327	Dave Dravecky	.07	.04
328	Scott Garrelts	.05	.03
329	Atlee Hammaker	.05	.03
330	Charlie Hayes (R)	.40	.25
331	Mike Krukow	.05	.03
332	Craig Lefferts	.05	.03
333	Candy Maldonado	.07	.04
334	Kirt Manwaring	.05	.03
335	Bob Melvin	.05	.03
336	Kevin Mitchell	.12	.07
337	Donell Nixon	.05	.03
338	Tony Perezchica (R)	.07	.04
339	Joe Price	.05	.03
340	Rick Reuschel	.05	.03
341	Earnest Riles	.05	.03
342	Don Robinson	.05	.03
343	Chris Speier	.05	.03
344	Robby Thompson	.10	.06
345	Jose Uribe	.05	.03
346	Matt Williams	.30	.18
347	Trevor Wilson (R)	.15	.10
348	Juan Agosto	.05	.03
349	Larry Andersen	.05	.03
350	Alan Ashby	.05	.03
351	Kevin Bass	.05	.03
352	Buddy Bell	.05	.03
353	Craig Biggio	.35	.20
354	Danny Darwin	.05	.03
355	Glenn Davis	.07	.04
356	Jim Deshaies	.05	.03
357	Bill Doran	.05	.03
358	John Fishel	.05	.03
359	Billy Hatcher	.05	.03
360	Bob Knepper	.05	.03
361	Louie Meadows	.05	.03
362	Dave Meads	.05	.03
363	Jim Pankovits	.05	.03
364	Terry Puhl	.05	.03
365	Rafael Ramirez	.05	.03

366 Craig Reynolds	.05	.03
367 Mike Scott	.08	.05
368 Nolan Ryan	.90	.60
369 Dave Smith	.05	.03
370 Gerald Young	.05	.03
371 Hubie Brooks	.07	.05
372 Tim Burke	.05	.03
373 John Dopson	.05	.03
374 Mike Fitzgerald	.05	.03
375 Tom Foley	.05	.03
376 Andres Galarraga	.15	.10
377 Neal Heaton	.05	.03
378 Joe Hesketh	.05	.03
379 Brian Holman	.10	.06
380 Rex Hudler	.05	.03
381 Randy Johnson (R)	.80	.50
382 Wallace Johnson	.05	.03
383 Tracy Jones	.05	.03
384 Dave Martinez	.05	.03
385 Dennis Martinez	.12	.07
386 Andy McGaffigan	.05	.03
387 Otis Nixon	.08	.05
388 Johnny Paredes (R)	.05	.03
389 Jeff Parrett	.05	.03
390 Pascual Perez	.05	.03
391 Tim Raines	.08	.05
392 Luis Rivera	.05	.03
393 Nelson Santovenia	.05	.03
394 Bryn Smith	.05	.03
395 Tim Wallach	.08	.05
396 Andy Allanson	.05	.03
397 Rod Allen	.05	.03
398 Scott Bailes	.05	.03
399 Tom Candiotti	.07	.04
400 Joe Carter	.30	.18
401 Carmen Castillo	.05	.03
402 Dave Clark	.05	.03
403 John Farrell	.05	.03
404 Julio Franco	.12	.07
405 Don Gordon	.05	.03
406 Mel Hall	.07	.04
407 Brad Havens	.05	.03
408 Brook Jacoby	.05	.03
409 Doug Jones	.05	.03
410 Jeff Kaiser (R)	.07	.04
411 Luis Medina (R)	.08	.05
412 Cory Snyder	.07	.04
413 Greg Swindell	.10	.06
414 Ron Tingley (R)	.08	.05
415 Willie Upshaw	.05	.03
416 Ron Washington	.05	.03
417 Rich Yett	.05	.03
418 Damon Berryhill	.05	.03
419 Mike Bielecki	.05	.03
420 Doug Dascenzo (R)	.12	.07
421 Jody Davis	.05	.03
422 Andre Dawson	.20	.12

423 Frank DiPino	.05	.03
424 Shawon Dunston	.10	.06
425 Goose Gossage	.08	.05
426 Mark Grace	.35	.20
427 Mike Harkey (R)	.20	.12
428 Darrin Jackson	.08	.05
429 Les Lancaster	.07	.04
430 Vance Law	.05	.03
431 Greg Maddux	.35	.20
432 Jamie Moyer	.05	.03
433 Al Nipper	.05	.03
434 Rafael Palmeiro	.30	.18
435 Pat Perry	.05	.03
436 Jeff Pico	.05	.03
437 Ryne Sandberg	.50	.30
438 Calvin Schiraldi	.05	.03
439 Rick Sutcliffe	.08	.05
440 Manny Trillo	.05	.03
441 Gary Varsho	.05	.03
442 Mitch Webster	.05	.03
443 Luis Alicea	.10	.06
444 Tom Brunansky	.08	.05
445 Vince Coleman	.07	.04
446 John Costello	.05	.03
447 Danny Cox	.05	.03
448 Ken Dayley	.05	.03
449 Jose DeLeon	.05	.03
450 Curt Ford	.05	.03
451 Pedro Guerrero	.08	.05
452 Bob Horner	.08	.05
453 Tim Jones (R)	.08	.05
454 Steve Lake	.05	.03
455 Joe Magrane	.08	.05
456 Greg Mathews	.05	.03
457 Willie McGee	.10	.06
458 Larry McWilliams	.05	.03
459 Jose Oquendo	.05	.03
460 Tony Pena	.07	.04
461 Terry Pendleton	.20	.12
462 Steve Peters (R)	.08	.05
463 Ozzie Smith	.20	.12
464 Scott Terry	.05	.03
465 Denny Walling	.05	.03
466 Todd Worrell	.07	.04
467 Tony Armas	.05	.03
468 Dante Bichette (R)	.35	.20
469 Bob Boone	.10	.06
470 Terry Clark (R)	.08	.05
471 Stew Cliburn	.05	.03
472 Mike Cook	.05	.03
473 Sherman Corbett	.05	.03
474 Chili Davis	.08	.05
475 Brian Downing	.07	.04
476 Jim Eppard	.05	.03
477 Chuck Finley	.15	.10
478 Willie Fraser	.05	.03
479 Bryan Harvey	.50	.30

480	Jack Howell	.05	.03	537	Bobby Witt	.10	.06
481	Wally Joyner	.12	.07	538	Steve Balboni	.05	.03
482	Jack Lazorko	.05	.03	539	Scott Bankhead	.05	.03
483	Kirk McCaskill	.05	.03	540	Scott Bradley	.05	.03
484	Mark McLemore	.05	.03	541	Mickey Brantley	.05	.03
485	Greg Minton	.05	.03	542	Jay Buhner (R)	.20	.12
486	Dan Petry	.05	.03	543	Mike Campbell	.05	.03
487	Johnny Ray	.05	.03	544	Darnell Coles	.05	.03
488	Dick Schofield	.05	.03	545	Henry Cotto	.05	.03
489	Devon White	.12	.07	546	Alvin Davis	.05	.03
490	Mike Witt	.05	.03	547	Mario Diaz	.05	.03
491	Harold Baines	.08	.05	548	Ken Griffey, Jr. (R)	8.50	5.00
492	Daryl Boston	.05	.03	549	Erik Hanson (R)	.25	.15
493	Ivan Calderon	.08	.05	550	Mike Jackson	.05	.03
494	Mike Diaz	.05	.03	551	Mark Langston	.15	.10
495	Carlton Fisk	.20	.12	552	Edgar Martinez	.30	.18
496	Dave Gallagher	.05	.03	553	Bill McGuire	.05	.03
497	Ozzie Guillen	.08	.05	554	Mike Moore	.05	.03
498	Shawn Hillegas	.05	.03	555	Jim Presley	.05	.03
499	Lance Johnson	.05	.03	556	Rey Quinones	.05	.03
500	Barry Jones	.05	.03	557	Jerry Reed	.05	.03
501	Bill Long	.05	.03	558	Harold Reynolds	.07	.04
502	Steve Lyons	.05	.03	559	Mike Schooler	.10	.06
503	Fred Manrique	.05	.03	560	Bill Swift	.15	.10
504	Jack McDowell	.50	.30	561	Dave Valle	.05	.03
505	Donn Pall	.05	.03	562	Steve Bedrosian	.05	.03
506	Kelly Paris	.05	.03	563	Phil Bradley	.05	.03
507	Dan Pasqua	.05	.03	564	Don Carman	.05	.03
508	Ken Patterson	.05	.03	565	Bob Dernier	.05	.03
509	Melido Perez	.08	.05	566	Marvin Freeman	.05	.03
510	Jerry Reuss	.05	.03	567	Todd Frohwirth	.05	.03
511	Mark Salas	.05	.03	568	Greg Gross	.05	.03
512	Bobby Thigpen	.10	.06	569	Kevin Gross	.05	.03
513	Mike Woodard	.05	.03	570	Greg Harris	.05	.03
514	Bob Brower	.05	.03	571	Von Hayes	.05	.03
515	Steve Buechele	.07	.04	572	Chris James	.05	.03
516	Jose Cecena	.05	.03	573	Steve Jeltz	.05	.03
517	Cecil Espy	.05	.03	574	Ron Jones (R)	.08	.05
518	Scott Fletcher	.05	.03	575	Ricky Jordan	.10	.06
519	Cecilio Guante	.05	.03	576	Mike Maddux	.05	.03
520	Jose Guzman	.07	.04	577	David Palmer	.05	.03
521	Ray Hayward	.05	.03	578	Lance Parrish	.07	.04
522	Charlie Hough	.07	.04	579	Shane Rawley	.05	.03
523	Pete Incaviglia	.08	.05	580	Bruce Ruffin	.05	.03
524	Mike Jeffcoat	.05	.03	581	Juan Samuel	.05	.03
525	Paul Kilgus	.05	.03	582	Mike Schmidt	.60	.35
526	Chad Kreuter	.20	.12	583	Kent Tekulve	.05	.03
527	Jeff Kunkel	.05	.03	584	Milt Thompson	.05	.03
528	Oddibe McDowell	.05	.03	585	Jose Alvarez	.05	.03
529	Pete O'Brien	.05	.03	586	Paul Assenmacher	.05	.03
530	Geno Petralli	.05	.03	587	Bruce Benedict	.05	.03
531	Jeff Russell	.07	.04	588	Jeff Blauser	.10	.06
532	Ruben Sierra	.30	.18	589	Terry Blocker (R)	.05	.03
533	Mike Stanley	.08	.05	590	Ron Gant	.40	.25
534	Ed Vande Berg	.05	.03	591	Tom Glavine	.70	.40
535	Curtis Wilkerson	.05	.03	592	Tommy Gregg	.05	.03
536	Mitch Williams	.07	.04	593	Albert Hall	.05	.03

594 Dion James		.05	.03
595 Rick Mahler		.05	.03
596 Dale Murphy		.12	.07
597 Gerald Perry		.05	.03
598 Charlie Puleo		.05	.03
599 Ted Simmons		.05	.03
600 Pete Smith		.10	.06
601 Zane Smith		.07	.04
602 John Smoltz		.90	.60
603 Bruce Sutter		.10	.06
604 Andres Thomas		.05	.03
605 Ozzie Virgil		.05	.03
606 Brady Anderson (R)		.60	.35
607 Jeff Ballard		.05	.03
608 Jose Bautista		.05	.03
609 Ken Gerhart		.05	.03
610 Terry Kennedy		.05	.03
611 Eddie Murray		.20	.12
612 Carl Nichols (R)		.05	.03
613 Tom Niedenfuer		.05	.03
614 Joe Orsulak		.08	.05
615 Oswald Peraza (R)		.07	.04
616a Bill Ripken (Er) (Obscenity on bat)		12.00	6.00
616b Bill Ripken (Er) (Scratched out)		10.00	5.00
616c Bill Ripken (Er) (Blacked out)		.50	.30
616d Bill Ripken (Er) (Whiteout)		30.00	20.00
617 Cal Ripken, Jr.		.75	.45
618 Dave Schmidt		.05	.03
619 Rick Schu		.05	.03
620 Larry Sheets		.05	.03
621 Doug Sisk		.05	.03
622 Pete Stanicek		.05	.03
623 Mickey Tettleton		.08	.05
624 Jay Tibbs		.05	.03
625 Jim Traber		.05	.03
626 Mark Williamson		.05	.03
627 Craig Worthington		.05	.03
628 Speed and Power(Jose Canseco)		.25	.15
629 Pitcher Perfect(Tom Browning)		.05	.03
		.10	.06
630 Roberto & Sandy Alomar Jr.		.50	.30
631 N.L. All-Stars (Will Clark, Rafael Palmeiro)		.25	.15
632 Will Clark/Darryl Strawberry		.25	.15
633 Wade Boggs/Carney Lansford		.12	.07
634 Jose Canseco/Mark McGwire/Terry Steinbach		.30	.18
635 Mark Davis/Dwight Gooden		.10	.06
636 David Cone/Danny Jackson		.08	.05
637 Bobby Bonilla/Chris Sabo		.08	.05
638 Andres Galaragga/ Gerald Perry		.08	.05
639 Eric Davis/Kirby Puckett		.15	.10
640 Major League Prospects Cameron Drew (R) Steve Wilson (R)		.08	.05
641 Major League Prospects Kevin Brown (R) Kevin Reimer (R)		.80	.50
642 Major League Prospects Jerald Clark (R) Brad Pounders (R)		.15	.10
643 Major League Propects Mike Capel (R) Drew Hall (R)		.08	.05
644 Major League Prospects Joe Girardi (R) Rolando Roomes (R)		.12	.07
645 Major League Prospects Marty Brown (R) Lenny Harris (R)		.12	.07
646 Major League Prospects Luis de los Santos (R) Jim Campbell (R)		.07	.04
647 Major League Prospects Miguel Garcia (R) Randy Kramer		.08	.05
648 Major League Prospects Torey Lovullo (R) Robert Palacios (R)		.08	.05
649 Major League Prospects Jim Corsi Bob Milacki (R)		.12	.07
650 Major League Prospects Grady Hall (R) Mike Rochford (R)		.07	.04
651 Major League Prospects Vance Lovelace (R) Terry Taylor (R)		.07	.04
652 Major League Prospects Dennis Cook (R) Ken Hill (R)		.50	.30
653 Major League Prospects Scott Service (R) Shane Turner (R)		.08	.05
654 Checklist (1-101)		.05	.02
655 Checklist (102-200)		.05	.02
656 Checklist (201-298)		.05	.02
657 Checklist (299-395)		.05	.02
658 Checklist (396-490)		.05	.02

		MINT	NR/MT
659	Checklist (491-584)	.05	.02
660	Checklist (585-660)	.05	.02
B1	Bobby Bonilla (AS)	.40	.25
B2	Jose Canseco (AS)	1.50	.90
B3	Will Clark (AS)	1.50	.90
B4	Dennis Eckersley (AS)	.75	.45
B5	Julio Franco (AS)	.25	.15
B6	Mike Greenwell (AS)	.25	.15
B7	Orel Hershiser (AS)	.30	.18
B8	Paul Molitor (AS)	.80	.50
B9	Mike Scioscia (AS)	.20	.12
B10	Darryl Strawberry(AS)	.75	.45
B11	Alan Trammell (AS)	.30	.18
B12	Frank Viola (AS)	.25	.15

1989 Fleer Update

This 132-card set updates players who were traded during the year and features a number of promising newcomers. The cards measure 2-1/2" by 3-1/2" and are identical to the design of Fleer's regular 1989 edition. Card backs are numbered with the letter "U" to distinguish the set from the regular issue.

		MINT	NR/MT
Complete Set (132)		12.50	7.50
Commons		.05	.03
1	Phil Bradley	.07	.04
2	Mike Devereaux	.20	.12
3	Steve Finley (R)	.25	.15
4	Kevin Hickey	.05	.03
5	Brian Holton	.07	.04
6	Bob Milacki	.10	.06
7	Randy Milligan	.10	.06
8	John Dopson	.07	.04
9	Nick Esasky	.05	.03
10	Rob Murphy	.05	.03

		MINT	NR/MT
11	Jim Abbott (R)	2.00	1.25
12	Bert Blyleven	.15	.10
13	Jeff Manto (R)	.10	.06
14	Bob McClure	.05	.03
15	Lance Parrish	.07	.04
16	Lee Stevens (R)	.10	.06
17	Claudell Washington	.05	.03
18	Mark Davis	.07	.04
19	Eric King	.05	.03
20	Ron Kittle	.05	.03
21	Matt Merullo (R)	.10	.06
22	Steve Rosenberg (R)	.07	.04
23	Robin Ventura (R)	3.00	2.00
24	Keith Atherton	.05	.03
25	Albert Belle (R)	5.00	3.00
26	Jerry Browne	.05	.03
27	Felix Fermin	.05	.03
28	Brad Komminsk	.05	.03
29	Pete O'Brien	.05	.03
30	Mike Brumley	.05	.03
31	Tracy Jones	.05	.03
32	Mike Schwabe (R)	.07	.04
33	Gary Ward	.05	.03
34	Frank Williams	.05	.03
35	Kevin Appier (R)	1.75	1.00
36	Bob Boone	.12	.07
37	Luis de los Santos	.07	.04
38	Jim Eisenreich (R)	.12	.07
39	Jaime Navarro (R)	.40	.25
40	Bill Spiers (R)	.12	.07
41	Greg Vaughn (R)	2.00	1.25
42	Randy Veres (R)	.07	.04
43	Wally Backman	.05	.03
44	Shane Rawley	.05	.03
45	Steve Balboni	.05	.03
46	Jesse Barfield	.08	.05
47	Alvaro Espinoza (R)	.10	.06
48	Bob Geren (R)	.10	.06
49	Mel Hall	.08	.05
50	Andy Hawkins	.05	.03
51	Hensley Meulens (R)	.12	.07
52	Steve Sax	.12	.07
53	Deion Sanders (R)	2.50	1.50
54	Rickey Henderson	.35	.20
55	Mike Moore	.08	.05
56	Tony Phillips	.10	.06
57	Greg Briley	.08	.05
58	Gene Harris (R)	.12	.07
59	Randy Johnson	.75	.45
60	Jeffrey Leonard	.05	.03
61	Dennis Powell	.05	.03
62	Omar Vizquel (R)	.20	.12
63	Kevin Brown	.35	.20
64	Julio Franco	.12	.07
65	Jamie Moyer	.05	.03
66	Rafael Palmeiro	.25	.15
67	Nolan Ryan	2.00	1.25

68	Francisco Cabrera (R)	.20	.12
69	Junior Felix (R)	.15	.10
70	Al Leiter	.07	.04
71	Alex Sanchez (R)	.07	.04
72	Geronimo Berroa	.05	.03
73	Derek Lilliquist (R)	.08	.05
74	Lonnie Smith	.10	.06
75	Jeff Treadway	.08	.05
76	Paul Kilgus	.05	.03
77	Lloyd McClendon	.05	.03
78	Scott Sanderson	.07	.04
79	Dwight Smith (R)	.20	.12
80	Jerome Walton (R)	.10	.06
81	Mitch Williams	.08	.05
82	Steve Wilson	.07	.04
83	Todd Benzinger	.08	.05
84	Ken Griffey	.12	.07
85	Rick Mahler	.05	.03
86	Rolando Roomes	.05	.03
87	Scott Scudder (R)	.15	.10
88	Jim Clancy	.05	.03
89	Rick Rhoden	.05	.03
90	Dan Schatzeder	.05	.03
91	Mike Morgan	.07	.04
92	Eddie Murray	.20	.12
93	Willie Randolph	.07	.04
94	Ray Searage	.05	.03
95	Mike Aldrete	.05	.03
96	Kevin Gross	.07	.04
97	Mark Langston	.12	.07
98	Spike Owen	.05	.03
99	Zane Smith	.08	.05
100	Don Aase	.05	.03
101	Barry Lyons	.05	.03
102	Juan Samuel	.05	.03
103	Wally Whitehurst (R)	.12	.07
104	Dennis Cook	.05	.03
105	Lenny Dykstra	.15	.10
106	Charlie Hayes	.25	.15
107	Tommy Herr	.05	.03
108	Ken Howell	.05	.03
109	John Kruk	.15	.10
110	Roger McDowell	.05	.03
111	Terry Mulholland	.20	.12
112	Jeff Parrett	.05	.03
113	Neal Heaton	.05	.03
114	Jeff King	.12	.07
115	Randy Kramer	.05	.03
116	Bill Landrum	.05	.03
117	Cris Carpenter (R)	.12	.07
118	Frank DiPino	.05	.03
119	Ken Hill	.40	.25
120	Dan Quisenberry	.07	.04
121	Milt Thompson	.05	.03
122	Todd Zeile (R)	.70	.40
123	Jack Clark	.08	.05
124	Bruce Hurst	.07	.04
125	Mark Parent	.05	.03
126	Bip Roberts	.15	.10
127	Jeff Brantley (R)	.15	.10
128	Terry Kennedy	.05	.03
129	Mike LaCoss	.05	.03
130	Greg Litton (R)	.10	.06
131	Mike Schmidt	.80	.50
132	Checklist	.05	.02

1990 Fleer

1990 marks the tenth straight year that Fleer produced a baseball set, and like the others, it consists of 660-cards measuring 2-1/2" by 3-12/" each. Card fronts feature full color action shots with an outer white border and a thin line around the photos that varies in color with each team assigned a different color. Card backs are vertical and printed in red, white and blue.

		MINT	NR/MT
Complete Set (660)		16.00	10.00
Commons		.05	.03

1	Lance Blankenship	.05	.03
2	Todd Burns	.05	.03
3	Jose Canseco	.40	.25
4	Jim Corsi	.05	.03
5	Storm Davis	.05	.03
6	Dennis Eckersley	.15	.10
7	Mike Gallego	.05	.03
8	Ron Hassey	.05	.03
9	Dave Henderson	.08	.05
10	Rickey Henderson	.25	.15
11	Rick Honeycutt	.05	.03
12	Stan Javier	.05	.03
13	Felix Jose	.15	.10
14	Carney Lansford	.07	.04

15 Mark McGwire	.30	.18
16 Mike Moore	.05	.03
17 Gene Nelson	.05	.03
18 Dave Parker	.08	.05
19 Tony Phillips	.08	.05
20 Terry Steinbach	.08	.05
21 Dave Stewart	.12	.07
22 Walt Weiss	.08	.05
23 Bob Welch	.05	.03
24 Curt Young	.05	.03
25 Paul Assenmacher	.05	.03
26 Damon Berryhill	.05	.03
27 Mike Bielecki	.05	.03
28 Kevin Blankenship	.05	.03
29 Andre Dawson	.15	.10
30 Shawon Dunston	.10	.06
31 Joe Girardi	.05	.03
32 Mark Grace	.20	.12
33 Mike Harkey	.10	.06
34 Paul Kilgus	.05	.03
35 Les Lancaster	.05	.03
36 Vance Law	.05	.03
37 Greg Maddux	.20	.12
38 Lloyd McClendon	.05	.03
39 Jeff Pico	.05	.03
40 Ryne Sandberg	.35	.20
41 Scott Sanderson	.05	.03
42 Dwight Smith	.08	.05
43 Rick Sutcliffe	.07	.04
44 Jerome Walton	.08	.05
45 Mitch Webster	.05	.03
46 Curt Wilkeron	.05	.03
47 Dean Wilkins (R)	.08	.05
48 Mitch Williams	.07	.04
49 Steve Wilson	.05	.03
50 Steve Bedrosian	.05	.03
51 Mike Benjamin (R)	.12	.07
52 Jeff Brantley	.08	.05
53 Brett Butler	.10	.06
54 Will Clark	.35	.20
55 Kelly Downs	.07	.04
56 Scott Garrelts	.05	.03
57 Atlee Hammaker	.05	.03
58 Terry Kennedy	.05	.03
59 Mike LaCoss	.05	.03
60 Craig Lefferts	.05	.03
61 Greg Litton	.05	.03
62 Candy Maldonado	.07	.04
63 Kirt Manwaring	.05	.03
64 Randy McCament (R)	.08	.05
65 Kevin Mitchell	.12	.07
66 Donell Nixon	.05	.03
ä67 Ken Oberkfell	.05	.03
68 Rick Reuschel	.05	.03
69 Ernest Riles	.05	.03
70 Don Robinson	.05	.03
71 Pat Sheridan	.05	.03
72 Chris Speier	.05	.03
73 Robby Thompson	.10	.06
74 Jose Uribe	.05	.03
75 Matt Williams	.20	.12
76 George Bell	.10	.06
77 Pat Borders	.05	.03
78 John Cerutti	.05	.03
79 Junior Felix	.07	.04
80 Tony Fernandez	.10	.06
81 Mike Flanagan	.05	.03
82 Mauro Gozzo (R)	.08	.05
83 Kelly Gruber	.10	.06
84 Tom Henke	.07	.04
85 Jimmy Key	.08	.05
86 Manny Lee	.05	.03
87 Nelson Liriano	.05	.03
88 Lee Mazzilli	.05	.03
89 Fred McGriff	.30	.18
90 Lloyd Moseby	.05	.03
91 Rance Mulliniks	.05	.03
92 Alex Sanchez	.05	.03
93 Dave Steib	.08	.05
94 Todd Stottlemyre	.07	.04
95 Duane Ward	.07	.04
96 David Wells	.07	.04
97 Ernie Whitt	.05	.03
98 Frank Wills	.05	.03
99 Mookie Wilson	.05	.03
100 Kevin Appier	.40	.25
101 Luis Aquino	.05	.03
102 Bob Boone	.08	.05
103 George Brett	.25	.15
104 Jose DeJesus	.05	.03
105 Luis de los Santos	.05	.03
106 Jim Eisenreich	.07	.04
107 Steve Farr	.05	.03
108 Tom Gordon	.10	.06
109 Mark Gubicza	.10	.06
110 Bo Jackson	.20	.12
111 Terry Leach	.05	.03
112 Charlie Leibrandt	.05	.03
113 Rick Luecken (R)	.08	.05
114 Mike Macfarlane	.08	.05
115 Jeff Montgomery	.07	.04
116 Bret Saberhagen	.10	.06
117 Kevin Seitzer	.07	.04
118 Kurt Stillwell	.05	.03
119 Pat Tabler	.05	.03
120 Danny Tartabull	.12	.07
121 Gary Thurman	.05	.03
122 Frank White	.07	.04
123 Willie Wilson	.05	.03
124 Matt Winters (R)	.08	.05
125 Jim Abbott	.25	.15
126 Tony Armas	.05	.03
127 Dante Bichette	.12	.07
128 Bert Blyleven	.10	.06

129	Chili Davis	.07	.04
130	Brian Downing	.05	.03
131	Mike Fetters (R)	.08	.05
132	Chuck Finley	.10	.06
133	Willie Fraser	.05	.03
134	Bryan Harvey	.10	.06
135	Jack Howell	.05	.03
136	Wally Joyner	.10	.06
137	Jeff Manto	.05	.03
138	Kirk McCaskill	.05	.03
139	Bob McClure	.05	.03
140	Greg Minton	.05	.03
141	Lance Parrish	.07	.04
142	Dan Petry	.05	.03
143	Johnny Ray	.05	.03
144	Dick Schofield	.05	.03
145	Lee Stevens	.07	.04
146	Claudell Washington	.05	.03
147	Devon White	.10	.06
148	Roberto Alomar	.60	.35
150	Sandy Alomar, Jr.	.10	.06
151	Andy Benes (R)	.30	.18
152	Jack Clark	.08	.05
153	Pat Clements	.05	.03
154	Joey Cora	.05	.03
155	Mark Davis	.05	.03
156	Mark Grant	.05	.03
157	Tony Gwynn	.25	.15
158	Greg Harris	.05	.03
159	Bruce Hurst	.07	.04
160	Darrin Jackson	.05	.03
161	Chris James	.05	.03
162	Carmelo Martinez	.05	.03
163	Mike Pagliarulo	.05	.03
164	Mark Parent	.05	.03
165	Dennis Rasmussen	.05	.03
166	Bip Roberts	.07	.04
167	Benito Santiago	.08	.05
168	Calvin Schiraldi	.05	.03
169	Eric Show	.05	.03
170	Garry Templeton	.05	.03
171	Ed Whitson	.05	.03
172	Brady Anderson	.15	.10
173	Jeff Ballard	.05	.03
174	Phil Bradley	.05	.03
175	Mike Devereaux	.08	.05
176	Steve Finley	.08	.05
177	Pete Harnisch (R)	.25	.15
178	Kevin Hickey	.05	.03
179	Brian Holton	.05	.03
180	Ben McDonald (R)	.45	.28
181	Bob Melvin	.05	.03
182	Bob Milacki	.05	.03
183	Randy Milligan	.08	.05
184	Gregg Olson (R)	.12	.07
185	Joe Orsulak	.07	.04
186	Bill Ripken	.05	.03
187	Cal Ripken, Jr.	.50	.30
188	Dave Schmidt	.05	.03
189	Larry Sheets	.05	.03
190	Mickey Tettleton	.08	.05
191	Mark Thurmond	.05	.03
192	Jay Tibbs	.05	.03
193	Jim Traber	.05	.03
194	Mark Williamson	.05	.03
195	Craig Worthington	.05	.03
196	Don Aase	.05	.03
197	Blaine Beatty (R)	.10	.06
198	Mark Carreon	.05	.03
199	Gary Carter	.10	.06
200	David Cone	.15	.10
201	Ron Darling	.07	.04
202	Kevin Elster	.05	.03
203	Sid Fernandez	.07	.04
204	Dwight Gooden	.12	.07
205	Keith Hernandez	.07	.04
206	Jeff Innis	.05	.03
207	Gregg Jefferies	.20	.12
208	Howard Johnson	.12	.07
209	Barry Lyons	.05	.03
210	Dave Magadan	.07	.04
211	Kevin McReynolds	.07	.04
212	Jeff Musselman	.05	.03
213	Randy Myers	.05	.03
214	Bob Ojeda	.05	.03
215	Juan Samuel	.05	.03
216	Mackey Sasser	.05	.03
217	Darryl Strawberry	.25	.15
218	Tim Teufel	.05	.03
219	Frank Viola	.08	.05
220	Juan Agosto	.05	.03
221	Larry Anderson	.05	.03
222	Eric Anthony (R)	.40	.25
223	Kevin Bass	.05	.03
224	Craig Biggio	.10	.06
225	Ken Caminiti	.07	.04
226	Jim Clancy	.05	.03
227	Danny Darwin	.05	.03
228	Glenn Davis	.07	.04
229	Jim Deshaies	.05	.03
230	Bill Doran	.05	.03
231	Bob Forsch	.05	.03
233	Terry Puhl	.05	.03
234	Rafael Ramirez	.05	.03
235	Rick Rhoden	.05	.03
236	Dan Schatzeder	.05	.03
237	Mike Scott	.07	.04
238	Dave Smith	.05	.03
239	Alex Trevino	.05	.03
240	Glenn Wilson	.05	.03
241	Gerald Young	.05	.03
242	Tom Brunansky	.07	.04
243	Cris Carpenter	.05	.03
244	Alex Cole (R)	.20	.12

245 Vince Coleman	.07	.04
246 John Costello	.05	.03
247 Ken Dayloy	.05	.00
248 Jose DeLeon	.05	.03
249 Frank DiPino	.05	.03
250 Pedro Guerrero	.08	.05
251 Ken Hill	.15	.10
252 Joe Magrane	.07	.04
253 Willie McGee	.08	.05
254 John Morris	.05	.03
255 Jose Oquendo	.05	.03
256 Tony Pena	.05	.03
257 Terry Pendelton	.15	.10
258 Ted Power	.05	.03
259 Dan Quisenberry	.05	.03
260 Ozzie Smith	.15	.10
261 Scott Terry	.05	.03
262 Milt Thompson	.05	.03
263 Denny Walling	.05	.03
264 Todd Worrell	.05	.03
265 Todd Zeile	.15	.10
266 Marty Barrett	.05	.03
267 Mike Boddicker	.05	.03
268 Wade Boggs	.20	.12
269 Ellis Burks	.08	.05
270 Rick Cerone	.05	.03
271 Roger Clemens	.45	.28
272 John Dopson	.05	.03
273 Nick Esasky	.05	.03
274 Dwight Evans	.08	.05
275 Wes Gardner	.05	.03
276 Rich Gedman	.05	.03
277 Mike Greenwell	.08	.05
278 Danny Heep	.05	.03
279 Eric Hetzel	.05	.03
280 Dennis Lamp	.05	.03
281 Rob Murphy	.05	.03
292 Joe Price	.05	.03
283 Carlos Quintana	.08	.05
284 Jody Reed	.05	.03
285 Luis Rivera	.05	.03
286 Kevin Romine	.05	.03
287 Lee Smith	.12	.07
288 Mike Smithson	.05	.03
289 Bob Stanley	.05	.03
290 Harold Baines	.07	.04
291 Kevin Brown	.12	.07
292 Steve Buechele	.07	.04
293 Scott Coolbaugh (R)	.07	.04
294 Jack Daugherty (R)	.10	.06
295 Cecil Espy	.05	.03
296 Julio Franco	.10	.06
297 Juan Gonzalez (R)	3.00	1.75
298 Cecilio Guante	.05	.03
299 Drew Hall	.05	.03
300 Charlie Hough	.05	.03
301 Pete Incaviglia	.07	.04

302 Mike Jeffcoat	.05	.03
303 Chad Kreuter	.07	.04
304 Jeff Kunkel	.05	.03
305 Rick Leach	.05	.03
306 Fred Manrique	.05	.03
307 Jamie Moyer	.05	.03
308 Rafael Palmeiro	.15	.10
309 Geno Petralli	.05	.03
310 Kevin Reimer	.05	.03
311 Kenny Rogers	.05	.03
312 Jeff Russell	.05	.03
313 Nolan Ryan	.70	.40
314 Ruben Sierra	.20	.12
315 Bobby Witt	.08	.05
316 Chris Bosio	.07	.04
317 Glenn Braggs	.05	.03
318 Greg Brock	.05	.03
319 Chuck Crim	.05	.03
320 Rob Deer	.07	.04
321 Mike Felder	.05	.03
322 Tom Filer	.05	.03
323 Tony Fossas (R)	.08	.05
324 Jim Gantner	.05	.03
325 Darryl Hamilton	.10	.06
326 Ted Higuera	.05	.03
327 Mark Knudson	.05	.03
328 Bill Krueger	.05	.03
329 Tim McIntosh (R)	.15	.10
330 Paul Molitor	.20	.12
331 Jaime Navarro	.10	.06
332 Charlie O'Brien	.05	.03
333 Jeff Peterek (R)	.08	.05
334 Dan Plesac	.05	.03
335 Jerry Reuss	.05	.03
336 Gary Sheffield	.60	.35
337 Bill Spiers	.05	.03
338 B.J. Surhoff	.05	.03
339 Greg Vaughn	.25	.15
340 Robin Yount	.20	.12
341 Hubie Brooks	.05	.03
342 Tim Burke	.05	.03
343 Mike Fitzgerald	.05	.03
344 Tom Foley	.05	.03
345 Andres Galarraga	.15	.10
346 Damaso Garcia	.05	.03
347 Marquis Grissom (R)	.75	.45
348 Kevin Gross	.05	.03
349 Joe Hesketh	.05	.03
350 Jeff Huson (R)	.10	.06
351 Wallace Johnson	.05	.03
352 Mark Langston	.10	.06
353 Dave Martinez	.05	.03
354 Dennis Martinez	.10	.06
355 Andy McGaffigan	.05	.03
356 Otis Nixon	.08	.05
357 Spike Owen	.05	.03
358 Pascual Perez	.05	.03

359	Tim Raines	.08	.05
360	Nelson Santovenia	.05	.03
361	Bryn Smith	.05	.03
362	Zane Smith	.05	.03
363	Larry Walker (R)	.90	.60
364	Tim Wallach	.08	.05
365	Rick Aguilera	.05	.03
366	Allan Anderson	.05	.03
367	Wally Backman	.05	.03
368	Doug Baker	.05	.03
369	Juan Berenguer	.05	.03
370	Randy Bush	.05	.03
371	Carmen Castillo	.05	.03
372	Mike Dyer (R)	.08	.05
373	Gary Gaetti	.05	.03
374	Greg Gagne	.07	.04
375	Dan Gladden	.05	.03
376	German Gonzalez	.05	.03
377	Brian Harper	.07	.04
378	Kent Hrbek	.10	.06
379	Gene Larkin	.05	.03
380	Tim Laudner	.05	.03
381	John Moses	.05	.03
382	Al Newman	.05	.03
383	Kirby Puckett	.30	.18
384	Shane Rawley	.05	.03
385	Jeff Reardon	.10	.06
386	Roy Smith	.05	.03
387	Gary Wayne (R)	.08	.05
388	Dave West	.05	.03
389	Tim Belcher	.08	.05
390	Tim Crews	.05	.03
391	Mike Davis	.05	.03
392	Rick Dempsey	.05	.03
393	Kirk Gibson	.07	.04
394	Jose Gonzalez	.05	.03
395	Alfredo Griffin	.05	.03
396	Jeff Hamilton	.05	.03
397	Lenny Harris	.05	.03
398	Mickey Hatcher	.05	.03
399	Orel Hershiser	.10	.06
400	Jay Howell	.05	.03
401	Mike Marshall	.05	.03
402	Ramon Martinez	.20	.12
403	Mike Morgan	.05	.03
404	Eddie Murray	.15	.10
405	Alejandro Pena	.05	.03
406	Willie Randolph	.07	.04
407	Mike Scioscia	.05	.03
408	Ray Searage	.05	.03
409	Fernando Valenzuela	.10	.06
410	Jose Vizcaino (R)	.10	.06
411	John Wetteland (R)	.20	.12
412	Jack Armstrong	.08	.05
413	Todd Benzinger	.07	.04
414	Tim Birtsas	.05	.03
415	Tom Browning	.07	.04
416	Norm Charlton	.08	.05
417	Eric Davis	.12	.07
418	Rob Dibble	.10	.06
419	John Franco	.05	.03
420	Ken Griffey, Sr.	.08	.05
421	Chris Hammond (R)	.20	.12
422	Danny Jackson	.05	.03
423	Barry Larkin	.15	.10
424	Tim Leary	.05	.03
425	Rick Mahler	.05	.03
426	Joe Oliver (R)	.12	.07
427	Paul O'Neill	.12	.07
428	Luis Quinones	.05	.03
429	Jeff Reed	.05	.03
430	Jose Rijo	.10	.06
431	Ron Robinson	.05	.03
432	Rolando Roomes	.05	.03
433	Chris Sabo	.10	.06
434	Scott Scudder	.08	.05
435	Herm Winningham	.05	.03
436	Steve Balboni	.05	.03
437	Jesse Barfield	.07	.04
438	Mike Blowers (R)	.10	.06
439	Tom Brookens	.05	.03
440	Greg Cadaret	.05	.03
441	Alvaro Espinoza	.05	.03
442	Bob Geren	.05	.03
443	Lee Guetterman	.05	.03
444	Mel Hall	.07	.04
445	Andy Hawkins	.05	.03
446	Roberto Kelly	.15	.10
447	Don Mattingly	.20	.12
448	Lance McCullers	.05	.03
449	Hensley Meulens	.08	.05
450	Dale Mohorcic	.05	.03
451	Clay Parker	.05	.03
452	Eric Plunk	.05	.03
453	Dave Righetti	.05	.03
454	Deion Sanders	.50	.30
455	Steve Sax	.08	.05
456	Don Slaught	.05	.03
457	Walt Terrell	.05	.03
458	Dave Winfield	.25	.15
459	Jay Bell	.10	.06
460	Rafael Belliard	.05	.03
461	Barry Bonds	.60	.35
462	Bobby Bonilla	.12	.07
463	Sid Bream	.05	.03
464	Benny Distefano	.05	.03
465	Doug Drabek	.10	.06
466	Jim Gott	.05	.03
467	Billy Hatcher	.05	.03
468	Neal Heaton	.05	.03
469	Jeff King	.08	.05
470	Bob Kipper	.05	.03
471	Randy Kramer	.05	.03
472	Bill Landrum	.05	.03

473	Mike LaValliere	.05	.03	530	Carlton Fisk	.12	.07
474	Jose Lind	.05	.03	531	Scott Fletcher	.05	.03
475	Junior Ortiz	.05	.03	532	Dave Gallagher	.05	.03
476	Gary Redus	.05	.03	533	Ozzie Guillen	.07	.04
477	Rick Reed (R)	.08	.05	534	Greg Hibbard (R)	.12	.07
478	R.J. Reynolds	.05	.03	535	Shawn Hillegas	.05	.03
479	Jeff Robinson	.05	.03	536	Lance Johnson	.07	.04
480	John Smiley	.10	.06	537	Eric King	.05	.03
481	Andy Van Slyke	.15	.10	538	Ron Kittle	.05	.03
482	Bob Walk	.05	.03	539	Steve Lyons	.05	.03
483	Andy Allanson	.05	.03	540	Carlos Martinez	.05	.03
484	Scott Bailes	.05	.03	541	Tom McCarthy (R)	.07	.04
485	Albert Belle	1.50	.90	542	Matt Merullo	.07	.04
486	Bud Black	.05	.03	543	Donn Pall	.05	.03
487	Jerry Browne	.05	.03	544	Dan Pasqua	.05	.03
488	Tom Candiotti	.05	.03	545	Ken Patterson	.05	.03
489	Joe Carter	.25	.15	546	Melido Perez	.08	.05
490	David Clark	.05	.03	547	Steve Rosenberg	.05	.03
491	John Farrell	.05	.03	548	Sammy Sosa (R)	.75	.45
492	Felix Fermin	.05	.03	549	Bobby Thigpen	.08	.05
493	Brook Jacoby	.05	.03	550	Robin Ventura	.70	.40
494	Dion James	.05	.03	551	Greg Walker	.05	.03
495	Doug Jones	.07	.04	552	Don Carman	.05	.03
496	Brad Komminsk	.05	.03	553	Pat Combs (R)	.10	.06
497	Rod Nichols	.05	.03	554	Dennis Cook	.05	.03
498	Pete O'Brien	.05	.03	555	Darren Daulton	.15	.10
499	Steve Olin (R)	.15	.10	556	Lenny Dykstra	.15	.10
500	Jesse Orosco	.05	.03	557	Curt Ford	.05	.03
501	Joel Skinner	.05	.03	558	Charlie Hayes	.07	.04
502	Cory Snyder	.07	.04	559	Von Hayes	.05	.03
503	Greg Swindell	.08	.05	560	Tom Herr	.05	.03
504	Rich Yett	.05	.03	561	Ken Howell	.05	.03
505	Scott Bankhead	.05	.03	562	Steve Jeltz	.05	.03
506	Scott Bradley	.05	.03	563	Ron Jones	.05	.03
507	Greg Briley	.05	.03	564	Ricky Jones	.05	.03
508	Jay Buhner	.12	.07	564	Ricky Jordan	.08	.05
509	Darnell Coles	.05	.03	565	John Kruk	.12	.07
510	Keith Comstock	.05	.03	566	Steve Lake	.05	.03
511	Henry Cotto	.05	.03	567	Roger McDowell	.05	.03
512	Alvin Davis	.07	.04	568	Terry Mulholland	.08	.05
513	Ken Griffey, Jr.	1.75	1.00	569	Dwayne Murphy	.05	.03
514	Erik Hanson	.08	.05	570	Jeff Parrett	.05	.03
515	Gene Harris	.05	.03	571	Randy Ready	.05	.03
516	Brian Holman	.08	.05	572	Bruce Ruffin	.05	.03
517	Mike Jackson	.05	.03	573	Dickie Thon	.05	.03
518	Randy Johnson	.20	.12	574	Jose Alvarez	.05	.03
519	Jeffrey Leonard	.05	.03	575	Geronimo Berroa	.05	.03
520	Edgar Martinez	.15	.10	576	Jeff Blauser	.05	.03
521	Dennis Powell	.05	.03	577	Joe Boever	.05	.03
522	Jim Presley	.05	.03	578	Marty Clary	.05	.03
523	Jerry Reed	.05	.03	579	Jody Davis	.05	.03
524	Harold Reynolds	.07	.04	580	Mark Eichhorn	.05	.03
525	Mike Schooler	.07	.04	581	Darrell Evans	.07	.04
526	Bill Swift	.10	.06	582	Ron Gant	.25	.15
527	David Valle	.05	.03	583	Tom Glavine	.30	.18
528	Omar Vizquel	.05	.03	584	Tommy Greene (R)	.60	.35
529	Ivan Calderon	.08	.05	585	Tommy Gregg	.05	.03

586	David Justice (R)	1.75	1.00
587	Mark Lemke (R)	.08	.05
588	Derek Lilliquist	.05	.03
589	Oddibe McDowell	.05	.03
590	Kent Mercker (R)	.12	.07
591	Dale Murphy	.12	.07
592	Gerald Perry	.05	.03
593	Lonnie Smith	.08	.05
594	Pete Smith	.08	.05
595	John Smoltz	.35	.20
596	Mike Stanton (R)	.15	.10
597	Andres Thomas	.05	.03
598	Jeff Treadway	.05	.03
599	Doyle Alexander	.05	.03
600	Dave Bergman	.05	.03
601	Brian Dubois (R)	.08	.05
602	Paul Gibson	.05	.03
603	Mike Heath	.05	.03
604	Mike Henneman	.05	.03
605	Guillermo Hernandez	.05	.03
606	Shawn Holman (R)	.07	.04
607	Tracy Jones	.05	.03
608	Chet Lemon	.05	.03
609	Fred Lynn	.10	.06
610	Jack Morris	.12	.07
611	Matt Nokes	.05	.03
612	Gary Pettis	.05	.03
613	Kevin Ritz (R)	.10	.06
614	Jeff Robinson	.05	.03
615	Steve Searcy	.05	.03
616	Frank Tanana	.05	.03
617	Alan Trammell	.15	.10
618	Gary Ward	.05	.03
619	Lou Whitaker	.08	.05
620	Frank Williams	.05	.03
621a	Players of the Decade George Brett (1980) Ten .390 seasons)(Er)	2.00	1.25
621b	Players of the Decade George Brett (1980) (Cor)	.25	.15
622	Players of the Decade- Fernando Valenzuela (1981)	.10	.06
623	Players of the Decade Dale Murphy (1982)	.10	.06
624a	Players of the Decade Cal Ripken (1983) (Name misspelled on back)	3.50	2.50
624b	Players of the Decade Cal Ripken (1983) (Cor)	.30	.18
625	Players of the Decade Ryne Sandberg (1984)	.15	.10
626	Players of the Decade Don Mattingly (1985)	.12	.07
627	Players of the Decade Roger Clemens (1986)	.20	.12
628	Players of the Decade George Bell (1987)	.10	.06
629	Players of the Decade Jose Canseco (1988)	.20	.12
000a	Players of the Decade Will Clark (1989) (Total bases 32)	1.50	.90
630b	Players of the Decade Will Clark (1989) (Total bases 321)	.15	.10
631	Mark Davis/Mitch Williams	.08	.05
632	Wade Boggs/Mike Greenwell	.15	.10
633	Mark Gubicza/Jeff Russell	.08	.05
634	Tony Fernandez/Cal Ripken Jr.	.20	.12
635	Bo Jackson/Kirby Puckett	.20	.12
636	Nolan Ryan/Mike Scott	.25	.15
637	Will Clark/Kevin Mitchell	.15	.10
638	Don Mattingly/Mark McGwire	.20	.12
639	Howard Johnson/Ryne Sandberg	.15	.10
640	Major League Prospects Rudy Seanez (R) Colin Charland (R)	.15	.10
641	Major League Prospects George Canale (R) Kevin Maas (R)	.15	.10
642	Major League Prospects Kelly Mann (R) Dave Hansen (R)	.15	.10
643	Major League Prospects Greg Smith (R) Stu Tate (R)	.10	.06
644	Major League Prospects Tom Drees (R) Dan Howitt (R)	.12	.07
645	Major League Prospects Mike Roesler (R) Derrick May (R)	.50	.30
646	Major League Prospects Scott Hemond (R) Mark Gardner (R)	.20	.12
647	Major League Prospects John Orton (R) Scott Leuis (R)	.20	.12
648	Major League Prospects Rich Monteleone (R) Dana Williams (R)	.08	.05

		MINT	NR/MT
649	Major League Prospects .08		.05
	Mike Huff (R)		
	Steve Frey (R)		
650	Major League Prospects .70		.40
	Chuck McElroy (R)		
	Moises Alou (R)		
651	Major League Prospects .10		.06
	Bobby Rose (R)		
	Mike Hartley (R)		
652	Major League Prospects .08		.05
	Matt Kinzer (R)		
	Wayne Edwards (R)		
653	Major League Prospects .75		.45
	Delino DeShields (R)		
	Jason Grimsley (R)		
654	Team Checklists	.05	.02
655	Team Checklists	.05	.02
656	Team Checklists	.05	.03
657	Team Checklists	.05	.03
658	Team Checklists	.05	.03
659	Team Checklists	.05	.03
660	Team Checklists	.05	.03

1990 Fleer Update

This 132-card update set is identical in design to Fleer's 1990 regular edition. The set consists of cards of players traded to new teams since the beginning of the year and a number of promising rookies. Cards measure 2-1/2' by 3-1/2' and the set includes a special Nolan Ryan commemorative card.

	MINT	NR/MT
Complete Set (132)	7.50	4.50
Commons	.05	.03

		MINT	NR/MT
1	Steve Avery (R)	.80	.50
2	Francisco Cabrera	.07	.04
3	Nick Esasky	.05	.03
4	Jim Kremers (R)	.08	.05
5	Greg Olson (R)	.10	.06
6	Jim Presley	.05	.03
7	Shawn Boskie (R)	.12	.07
8	Joe Kraemer (R)	.10	.06
9	Luis Salazar	.05	.03
10	Hector Villanueva (R)	.10	.06
11	Glenn Braggs	.05	.03
12	Mariano Duncan	.05	.03
13	Billy Hatcher	.07	.04
14	Tim Layana (R)	.12	.07
15	Hal Morris	.15	.10
16	Javier Ortiz	.12	.07
17	Dave Rohde (R)	.12	.07
18	Eric Yelding (R)	.12	.07
19	Hubie Brooks	.08	.05
20	Kal Daniels	.08	.05
21	Dave Hansen	.12	.07
22	Mike Hartley	.07	.04
23	Stan Javier	.05	.03
24	Jose Offerman (R)	.25	.15
25	Juan Samuel	.05	.03
26	Dennis Boyd	.05	.03
27	Delino DeShields	.70	.40
28	Steve Frey	.05	.03
29	Mark Gardner	.10	.06
30	Chris Nabholz (R)	.25	.15
31	Bill Sampen (R)	.10	.06
32	Dave Schmidt	.05	.03
33	Daryl Boston	.05	.03
34	Chuck Carr (R)	.50	.30
35	John Franco	.05	.03
36	Todd Hundley (R)	.15	.10
37	Julio Machado (R)	.10	.06
38	Alejandro Pena	.05	.03
39	Darren Reed (R)	.10	.06
40	Kelvin Torve (R)	.07	.04
41	Darrell Akerfelds (R)	.07	.04
42	Jose DeJesus	.05	.03
43	Dave Hollins (R)	1.25	.80
44	Carmelo Martinez	.05	.03
45	Brad Moore (R)	.08	.05
46	Dale Murphy	.12	.07
47	Wally Backman	.05	.03
48	Stan Belinda (R)	.12	.07
49	Bob Patterson	.05	.03
50	Ted Power	.05	.03
51	Don Slaught	.05	.03
52	Geronimo Pena (R)	.25	.15
53	Lee Smith	.15	.10
54	John Tudor	.07	.04
55	Joe Carter	.20	.12
56	Tom Howard	.15	.10
57	Craig Lefferts	.05	.03
58	Rafael Valdez (R)	.10	.06
59	Dave Anderson	.05	.03

60	Kevin Bass	.05	.03
61	John Burkett	.35	.20
62	Gary Carter	.10	.06
63	Rick Parker (R)	.07	.04
64	Trevor Wilson	.10	.06
65	Chris Hoiles (R)	.35	.20
66	Tim Hulett	.05	.03
67	Dave Johnson (R)	.10	.06
68	Curt Schilling (R)	.40	.25
69	David Segui (R)	.15	.10
70	Tom Brunansky	.07	.04
71	Greg Harris	.05	.03
72	Dana Kiecker (R)	.10	.06
73	Tim Naehring (R)	.12	.07
74	Tony Pena	.07	.04
75	Jeff Reardon	.10	.06
76	Jerry Reed	.05	.03
77	Mark Eichhorn	.05	.03
78	Mark Langston	.10	.06
79	John Orton	.10	.06
80	Luis Polonia	.08	.05
81	Dave Winfield	.25	.15
82	Cliff Young (R)	.10	.06
83	Wayne Edwards	.07	.04
84	Alex Fernandez (R)	1.25	.80
85	Craig Grebeck (R)	.12	.07
86	Scott Radinsky (R)	.20	.12
87	Frank Thomas (R)	4.00	2.75
88	Beau Allred (R)	.12	.07
89	Sandy Alomar, Jr.	.10	.06
90	Carlos Baerga (R)	1.75	1.00
91	Kevin Bearse (R)	.08	.05
92	Chris James	.05	.03
93	Candy Maldonado	.08	.05
94	Jeff Manto	.08	.05
95	Cecil Fielder	.25	.15
96	Travis Fryman (R)	1.50	.90
97	Lloyd Moseby	.05	.03
98	Edwin Nunez	.05	.03
99	Tony Phillips	.05	.03
100	Larry Sheets	.05	.03
101	Mark Davis	.07	.04
102	Strom Davis	.05	.03
103	Gerald Perry	.05	.03
104	Terry Shumpert (R)	.10	.06
105	Edgar Diaz (R)	.08	.05
106	Dave Parker	.08	.05
107	Tim Drummond (R)	.08	.05
108	Junior Ortiz	.05	.03
109	Park Pittman (R)	.08	.05
110	Kevin Tapani (R)	.20	.12
111	Oscar Azocar (R)	.10	.06
112	Jim Leyritz (R)	.15	.10
113	Kevin Maas	.12	.07
114	Alan Mills (R)	.12	.07
115	Matt Nokes	.07	.04
116	Pascual Perez	.07	.04
117	Ozzie Canseco (R)	.08	.05
118	Scott Sanderson	.07	.04
119	Tino Martinez (R)	.25	.15
120	Jeff Schaefer (R)	.08	.05
121	Matt Young	.05	.03
122	Brian Bohanon (R)	.10	.06
123	Jeff Huson	.08	.05
124	Ramon Manon (R)	.08	.05
125	Gary Mielke (R)	.08	.05
126	Willie Blair (R)	.15	.10
127	Glenallen Hill (R)	.15	.10
128	John Olerud (R)	2.00	1.25
129	Luis Sojo (R)	.10	.06
130	Mark Whiten (R)	.80	.50
131	Three Decades of No. Hitters(Nolan Ryan)	.75	.45
132	Checklist	.05	.02

1991 Fleer

For the first time since Fleer re-entered the baseball card market they increased the size of their set to 720-cards. The fronts feature bright yellow borders with black type at the top and bottom. A thin black line frames full color action photos. Card backs are vertical and include a small head shot of the player in a circle at the top. Cards measure 2-1/2" by 3-1/2"

		MINT	NR/MT
Complete Set (720)		16.00	10.00
Commons		.04	.02
1	Troy Afenir (R)	.10	.06
2	Harold Baines	.07	.04
3	Lance Blankenship	.04	.02
4	Todd Burns	.04	.02
5	Jose Canseco	.25	.15

6	Dennis Eckersley	.15	.10
7	Mike Gallego	.04	.02
8	Ron Hassey	.04	.02
9	Dave Henderson	.07	.04
10	Rickey Henderson	.15	.10
11	Rick Honeycutt	.04	.02
12	Doug Jennings	.04	.02
13	Joe Klink (R)	.08	.05
14	Carney Lansford	.08	.05
15	Darren Lewis (R)	.15	.10
16	Willie McGee	.08	.05
17	Mark McGwire	.20	.12
18	Mike Moore	.04	.02
19	Gene Nelson	.04	.02
20	Dave Otto	.04	.02
21	Jamie Quirk	.04	.02
22	Willie Randolph	.07	.04
23	Scott Sanderson	.04	.02
24	Terry Steinbach	.07	.04
25	Dave Stewart	.10	.06
26	Walt Weiss	.04	.02
27	Bob Welch	.07	.04
28	Curt Young	.04	.02
29	Wally Backman	.04	.02
30	Stan Belinda	.04	.02
31	Jay Bell	.04	.02
32	Rafael Belliard	.04	.02
33	Barry Bonds	.35	.20
34	Bobby Bonilla	.10	.06
35	Sid Bream	.04	.02
36	Doug Drabek	.10	.06
37	Carlos Garcia (R)	.70	.40
38	Neal Heaton	.04	.02
39	Jeff King	.07	.04
40	Bob Kipper	.04	.02
41	Bill Landrum	.04	.02
42	Mike LaValliere	.04	.02
43	Jose Lind	.04	.02
44	Carmelo Martinez	.04	.02
45	Bob Patterson	.04	.02
46	Ted Power	.04	.02
48	R.J. Reynolds	.04	.02
49	Don Slaught	.04	.02
50	John Smiley	.10	.06
51	Zane Smith	.04	.02
52	Randy Tomlin (R)	.12	.07
53	Andy Van Slyke	.12	.07
54	Bob Walk	.04	.02
55	Jack Armstrog	.04	.02
56	Todd Benzinger	.04	.02
57	Glenn Braggs	.04	.02
58	Keith Brown	.04	.02
59	Tom Browning	.07	.04
60	Norm Charlton	.07	.04
61	Eric Davis	.10	.06
62	Rob Dibble	.07	.04
63	Bill Doran	.04	.02
64	Mariano Duncan	.04	.02
65	Chris Hammond	.10	.06
66	Billy Hatcher	.04	.02
67	Danny Jackson	.04	.02
68	Barry Larkin	.12	.07
69	Tim Layana	.04	.02
70	Terry Lee (R)	.10	.06
71	Rick Mahler	.04	.02
72	Hal Morris	.12	.07
73	Randy Myers	.04	.02
74	Ron Oester	.04	.02
75	Joe Oliver	.07	.04
76	Paul O'Neill	.10	.06
77	Luis Quinones	.04	.02
78	Jeff Reed	.04	.02
79	Jose Rojo	.10	.06
80	Chris Sabo	.08	.05
81	Scott Scudder	.08	.05
82	Herm Winningham	.04	.02
83	Larry Anderson	.04	.02
84	Marty Barrett	.04	.02
85	Mike Boddicker	.04	.02
86	Wade Boggs	.15	.10
87	Tom Bolton	.04	.02
88	Tom Brunansky	.07	.04
89	Ellis Burks	.08	.05
90	Roger Clemens	.25	.15
91	Scott Cooper (R)	.20	.12
92	John Dopson	.04	.02
93	Dwight Evans	.08	.05
94	Wes Gardner	.04	.02
95	Jeff Gray (R)	.10	.06
96	Mike Greenwell	.08	.05
97	Greg Harris	.04	.02
98	Daryl Irvine (R)	.08	.05
99	Dana Kiecker	.04	.02
100	Randy Kutcher	.04	.02
101	Dennis Lamp	.04	.02
102	Mike Marshall	.04	.02
103	John Marzano	.04	.02
104	Rob Murphy	.04	.02
105	Tim Naehring	.07	.04
106	Tony Pena	.04	.02
107	Phil Plantier (R)	.75	.45
108	Carlos Quintana	.08	.05
109	Jeff Reardon	.08	.05
110	Jerry Reed	.04	.02
111	Jody Reed	.04	.02
112	Luis Rivera	.04	.02
113	Kevin Romine	.04	.02
114	Phil Bradley	.04	.02
115	Ivan Calderon	.08	.05
116	Wayne Edwards	.04	.02
117	Alex Fernandez	.35	.20
118	Carlton Fisk	.15	.10
119	Scott Fletcher	.04	.02
120	Craig Grebeck	.04	.02

121	Ozzie Guillen	.07	.04
122	Greg Hibbard	.04	.02
123	Lance Johnson	.04	.02
124	Barry Jones	.04	.02
125	Ron Karkovice	.04	.02
126	Eric King	.04	.02
127	Steve Lyons	.04	.02
128	Carlos Martinez	.04	.02
129	Jack McDowell	.20	.12
130	Donn Pall	.04	.02
131	Dan Pasqua	.04	.02
132	Ken Patterson	.04	.02
133	Melido Perez	.07	.04
134	Adam Peterson	.04	.02
135	Scott Radinsky	.07	.04
136	Sammy Sosa	.08	.05
137	Bobby Thigpen	.07	.04
138	Frank Thomas	1.50	.90
139	Robin Ventura	.25	.15
140	Daryl Boston	.04	.02
141	Chuck Carr	.04	.02
142	Mark Carreon	.04	.02
143	David Cone	.12	.07
144	Ron Darling	.07	.04
145	Kevin Elster	.04	.02
146	Sid Fernandez	.07	.04
147	John Franco	.04	.02
148	Dwight Gooden	.10	.06
149	Tom Herr	.04	.02
150	Todd Hundley	.08	.05
151	Gregg Jefferies	.15	.10
152	Howard Johnson	.10	.06
153	Dave Magadan	.07	.04
154	Kevin McReynolds	.07	.04
155	Keith Miller	.04	.02
156	Bob Ojeda	.04	.02
157	Tom O'Malley	.04	.02
158	Alejandro Pena	.04	.02
159	Darren Reed	.04	.02
160	Mackey Sasser	.04	.02
161	Darryl Strawberry	.15	.10
162	Tim Teufel	.04	.02
163	Kelvin Torve	.04	.02
164	Julio Valera	.08	.05
165	Frank Viola	.08	.05
166	Wally Whitehurst	.04	.02
167	Jim Acker	.04	.02
168	Derek Bell (R)	.35	.20
169	George Bell	.10	.06
170	Willie Blair	.08	.05
171	Pat Borders	.04	.02
172	John Cerutti	.04	.02
173	Junior Felix	.04	.02
174	Tony Fernandez	.08	.05
175	Kelly Gruber	.07	.04
176	Tom Henke	.04	.02
177	Glenallen Hill	.10	.06
178	Jimmy Key	.08	.05
179	Manny Lee	.04	.02
180	Fred McGriff	.20	.12
181	Rance Mulliniks	.04	.02
182	Greg Myers	.04	.02
183	John Olerud	.30	.18
184	Luis Sojo	.04	.02
185	Dave Steib	.08	.05
186	Todd Stottlemyre	.07	.04
187	Duane Ward	.04	.02
188	David Wells	.04	.02
189	Mark Whiten	.30	.18
190	Ken Williams	.04	.02
191	Frank Wills	.04	.02
192	Mookie Wilson	.04	.02
193	Don Aase	.04	.02
194	Tim Belcher	.07	.04
195	Hubie Brooks	.07	.04
196	Dennis Cook	.04	.02
197	Tim Crews	.04	.02
198	Kal Daniels	.04	.02
199	Kirk Gibson	.07	.04
200	Jim Gott	.04	.02
201	Alfredo Griffin	.04	.02
202	Chris Gwynn	.04	.02
203	Dave Hansen	.08	.05
204	Lenny Harris	.04	.02
205	Mike Hartley	.04	.02
206	Mickey Hatcher	.04	.02
207	Carlos Hernandez (R)	.12	.07
208	Orel Hershiser	.08	.05
209	Jay Howell	.04	.02
210	Mike Huff	.04	.02
211	Stan Javier	.04	.02
212	Ramon Martinez	.12	.07
213	Mike Morgan	.04	.02
214	Eddie Murray	.15	.10
215	Jim Neidlinger	.04	.02
216	Jose Offerman	.12	.07
217	Jim Poole (R)	.08	.05
218	Juan Samuel	.04	.02
219	Mike Scioscia	.04	.02
220	Ray Searage	.04	.02
221	Mike Sharperson	.04	.02
222	Fernando Valenzuela	.08	.05
223	Jose Vizcaino	.04	.02
224	Mike Aldrete	.04	.02
225	Scott Anderson (R)	.08	.05
226	Dennis Boyd	.04	.02
227	Tim Burke	.04	.02
228	Delino DeShields	.15	.10
229	Mike Fitzgerald	.04	.02
230	Tom Foley	.04	.02
231	Steve Frey	.04	.02
232	Andres Galarraga	.15	.10
233	Mark Gardner	.08	.05
234	Marquis Grissom	.15	.10

235	Kevin Gross	.04	.02	292	Jeff Kunkel	.04	.02
236	Drew Hall	.04	.02	293	Gary Mielke	.04	.02
237	Dave Martinez	.04	.02	294	Jamie Moyer	.04	.02
238	Dennis Martinez	.08	.05	295	Rafael Palmeiro	.15	.10
239	Dale Mohorcic	.04	.02	296	Geno Petralli	.04	.02
240	Chris Nabholz	.10	.06	297	Gary Pettis	.04	.02
241	Otis Nixon	.07	.04	298	Kevin Reimer	.04	.02
242	Junior Noboa	.04	.02	299	Kenny Rogers	.04	.02
243	Spike Owen	.04	.02	300	Jeff Russell	.04	.02
244	Tim Raines	.07	.04	301	John Russell	.04	.02
245	Mel Rojas (R)	.10	.06	302	Nolan Ryan	.60	.35
246	Scott Ruskin (R)	.10	.06	303	Ruben Sierra	.15	.10
247	Bill Sampen	.04	.02	304	Bobby Witt	.07	.04
248	Nelson Santovenia	.04	.02	305	Jim Abbott	.12	.07
249	Dave Schmidt	.04	.02	306	Kent Anderson (R)	.08	.05
250	Larry Walker	.20	.12	307	Dante Bichette	.08	.05
251	Tim Wallach	.08	.05	308	Bert Blyleven	.08	.05
252	Dave Anderson	.04	.02	309	Chili Davis	.07	.04
253	Kevin Bass	.04	.02	310	Brian Downing	.04	.02
254	Steve Bedrosian	.04	.02	311	Mark Eichhorn	.04	.02
255	Jeff Brantley	.07	.04	312	Mike Fetters	.04	.02
256	John Burkett	.07	.04	313	Chuck Finley	.08	.05
257	Brett Butler	.08	.05	314	Willie Fraser	.04	.02
258	Gary Carter	.08	.05	315	Bryan Harvey	.08	.05
259	Will Clark	.20	.12	316	Donnie Hill	.04	.02
260	Steve Decker (R)	.10	.06	317	Wally Joyner	.10	.06
261	Kelly Downs	.04	.02	318	Mark Langston	.08	.05
262	Scott Garrelts	.04	.02	319	Kirk McCaskill	.04	.02
263	Terry Kennedy	.04	.02	320	John Orton	.07	.04
264	Mike LaCoss	.04	.02	321	Lance Parrish	.04	.02
265	Mark Leonard (R)	.08	.05	322	Luis Polonia	.07	.04
266	Greg Litton	.04	.02	323	Johnny Ray	.04	.02
267	Kevin Mitchell	.08	.05	324	Bobby Rose	.04	.02
268	Randy O'Neal (R)	.08	.05	325	Dick Schofield	.04	.02
269	Rick Parker	.04	.02	326	Rick Schu	.04	.02
270	Rick Reuschel	.04	.02	327	Lee Stevens	.04	.02
271	Ernest Riles	.04	.02	328	Devon White	.08	.05
272	Don Robinson	.04	.02	329	Dave Winfield	.20	.12
273	Robby Thompson	.08	.05	330	Cliff Young	.04	.02
274	Mark Thurmond	.04	.02	331	Dave Bergman	.04	.02
275	Jose Uribe	.04	.02	332	Phil Clark (R)	.15	.10
276	Matt Williams	.15	.10	333	Darnell Coles	.04	.02
277	Trevor Wilson	.07	.04	334	Milt Cuyler (R)	.15	.10
278	Gerald Alexander (R)	.08	.05	335	Cecil Fielder	.20	.12
279	Brad Arnsberg	.04	.02	336	Travis Fryman	.60	.35
280	Kevin Belcher (R)	.08	.05	337	Paul Gibson	.04	.02
281	Joe Bitker	.04	.02	338	Jerry Don Gleaton	.04	.02
282	Kevin Brown	.08	.05	339	Mike Heath	.04	.02
283	Steve Buechele	.04	.02	340	Mike Henneman	.04	.02
284	Jack Daugherty	.04	.02	341	Chet Lemon	.04	.02
285	Julio Franco	.08	.05	342	Lance McCullers	.04	.02
286	Juan Gonzalez	.70	.40	343	Jack Morris	.12	.07
287	Bill Haselman (R)	.07	.04	344	Lloyd Moseby	.04	.02
288	Charlie Hough	.04	.02	345	Edwin Nunez	.04	.02
289	Jeff Huson	.04	.02	346	Clay Parker	.04	.02
290	Pete Incaviglia	.04	.02	347	Dan Petry	.04	.02
291	Mike Jeffcoat	.04	.02	348	Tony Phillips	.07	.04

349 Jeff Robinson	.04	.02
350 Mark Salas	.04	.02
351 Mike Schwabe	.04	.02
352 Larry Sheets	.04	.02
353 John Shelby	.04	.02
354 Frank Tanana	.04	.02
355 Alan Trammell	.10	.06
356 Gary Ward	.04	.02
357 Lou Whitaker	.07	.04
358 Beau Allred	.07	.04
359 Sandy Alomar, Jr.	.08	.05
360 Carlos Baerga	.35	.20
361 Kevin Bearse	.04	.02
362 Tom Brookens	.04	.02
363 Jerry Browne	.04	.02
364 Tom Candiotti	.04	.02
365 Alex Cole	.07	.04
366 John Farrell	.04	.02
367 Felix Fermin	.04	.02
368 Keith Hernandez	.07	.04
369 Brook Jacoby	.04	.02
370 Chris James	.04	.02
371 Dion James	.04	.02
372 Doug Jones	.04	.02
373 Candy Maldonado	.04	.02
374 Steve Olin	.07	.04
375 Jesse Orosco	.04	.02
376 Rudy Seanez	.08	.05
377 Joel Skinner	.04	.02
378 Cory Snyder	.04	.02
379 Greg Swindell	.08	.05
380 Sergio Valdez	.07	.04
381 Mike Walker (R)	.08	.05
382 Colby Ward (R)	.08	.05
383 Turner Ward (R)	.10	.06
384 Mitch Webster	.04	.02
385 Kevin Wickander	.07	.04
386 Darrel Akerfelds	.04	.02
387 Joe Boever	.04	.02
388 Rod Booker	.04	.02
389 Sil Campusano	.04	.02
390 Don Carman	.04	.02
391 Wes Chamberlain (R)	.15	.10
392 Pat Combs	.07	.04
393 Darren Daulton	.15	.10
394 Jose DeJesus	.04	.02
395 Len Dykstra	.15	.10
396 Jason Grimsley	.04	.02
397 Charlie Hayes	.04	.02
398 Von Hayes	.04	.02
399 David Hollins	.20	.12
400 Ken Howell	.04	.02
401 Ricky Jordan	.04	.02
402 John Kruk	.10	.06
403 Steve Lake	.04	.02
404 Chuck Malone (R)	.10	.06
405 Roger McDowell	.04	.02

406 Chuck McElroy	.04	.02
407 Mickey Morandini (R)	.15	.10
408 Terry Mulholland	.07	.04
409 Dale Murphy	.08	.05
410 Randy Ready	.04	.02
411 Bruce Ruffin	.04	.02
412 Dickie Thon	.04	.02
413 Paul Assenmacher	.04	.02
414 Damon Berryhill	.04	.02
415 Mike Bielecki	.04	.02
416 Shawn Boskie	.04	.02
417 Dave Clark	.04	.02
418 Doug Dascenzo	.04	.02
419 Andre Dawson	.15	.10
420 Shawon Dunston	.08	.05
421 Joe Girardi	.04	.02
422 Mark Grace	.12	.07
423 Mike Harkey	.08	.05
424 Les Lancaster	.04	.02
425 Bill Long	.04	.02
426 Greg Maddux	.15	.10
427 Derrick May	.20	.12
428 Jeff Pico	.04	.02
429 Domingo Ramos	.04	.02
430 Luis Salazar	.04	.02
431 Ryne Sandberg	.25	.15
432 Dwight Smith	.07	.04
433 Greg Smith	.08	.05
434 Rick Sutcliffe	.07	.04
435 Gary Varsho	.04	.02
436 Hector Vallanueva	.07	.04
437 Jerome Walton	.07	.04
438 Curtis Wilkerson	.04	.02
439 Mitch Williams	.04	.02
440 Steve Wilson	.04	.02
441 Marvell Wynne	.04	.02
442 Scott Bankhead	.04	.02
443 Scott Bradley	.04	.02
444 Greg Briley	.04	.02
445 Mike Brumley	.04	.02
446 Jay Buhner	.08	.05
447 Dave Burba (R)	.10	.06
448 Henry Cotto	.04	.02
449 Alvin Davis	.04	.02
450 Ken Griffey, Jr.	1.00	.70
451 Erik Hanson	.07	.04
452 Gene Harris	.04	.02
453 Brian Holman	.07	.04
454 Mike Jackson	.07	.04
455 Randy Johnson	.20	.12
456 Jeffrey Leonard	.04	.02
457 Edgar Martinez	.15	.10
458 Tino Martinez	.10	.06
459 Pete O'Brien	.04	.02
460 Harold Reynolds	.07	.04
461 Mike Schooler	.04	.02
462 Bill Swift	.10	.06

463 David Valle	.04	.02	
464 Omar Vizquel	.04	.02	
465 Matt Young	.04	.02	
466 Brady Anderson	.10	.06	
467 Jeff Ballard	.04	.02	
468 Juan Bell (R)	.08	.05	
469 Mike Devereaux	.08	.05	
470 Steve Finley	.04	.02	
471 Dave Gallagher	.04	.02	
472 Leo Gomez (R)	.15	.10	
473 Rene Gonzales	.07	.04	
474 Pete Harnisch	.07	.04	
475 Kevin Hickey	.04	.02	
476 Chris Hoiles	.12	.07	
477 Sam Horn	.07	.04	
478 Tim Hulett	.04	.02	
479 Dave Johnson	.04	.02	
480 Ron Kittle	.04	.02	
481 Ben McDonald	.15	.10	
482 Bob Melvin	.04	.02	
483 Bob Milacki	.04	.02	
484 Randy Milligan	.07	.04	
485 John Mitchell (R)	.08	.05	
486 Gregg Olson	.07	.04	
487 Joe Orsulak	.07	.04	
488 Joe Price	.04	.02	
489 Bill Ripken	.04	.02	
490 Cal Ripken, Jr.	.35	.20	
491 Curt Schilling	.08	.05	
492 David Segui	.07	.04	
493 Anthony Telford (R)	.12	.07	
494 Mickey Tettleton	.07	.04	
495 Mark Williamson	.04	.02	
496 Craig Worthington	.04	.02	
497 Juan Agosto	.04	.02	
498 Eric Anthony	.12	.07	
499 Craig Biggio	.08	.05	
500 Ken Caminiti	.07	.04	
501 Casey Candaele	.04	.02	
502 Andujar Cedeno (R)	.15	.10	
503 Danny Darwin	.04	.02	
504 Mark Davidson	.04	.02	
505 Glenn Davis	.07	.04	
506 Jim Deshaies	.04	.02	
507 Luis Gonzalez (R)	.20	.12	
508 Bill Gullickson	.04	.02	
509 Xavier Hernandez	.07	.04	
510 Brian Meyer	.04	.02	
511 Ken Oberkfell	.04	.02	
512 Mark Portugal	.04	.02	
513 Rafael Ramirez	.04	.02	
514 Karl Rhodes (R)	.07	.04	
515 Mike Scott	.07	.04	
516 Mike Simms (R)	.07	.04	
517 Dave Smith	.04	.02	
518 Franklin Stubbs	.04	.02	
519 Glenn Wilson	.04	.02	
520 Eric Yelding	.04	.02	
521 Gerald Young	.04	.02	
522 Shawn Abner	.04	.02	
523 Roberto Alomar	.30	.18	
524 Andy Benes	.12	.07	
525 Joe Carter	.15	.10	
526 Jack Clark	.07	.04	
527 Joey Cora	.04	.02	
528 Paul Faries (R)	.07	.04	
529 Tony Gwynn	.15	.10	
530 Atlee Hammaker	.04	.02	
531 Greg Harris	.04	.02	
532 Thomas Howard	.07	.04	
533 Bruce Hurst	.07	.04	
534 Craig Lefferts	.04	.02	
535 Derek Lilliquist	.04	.02	
536 Fred Lynn	.08	.05	
537 Mike Pagliarulo	.04	.02	
538 Mark Parent	.04	.02	
539 Dennis Rasmussen	.04	.02	
540 Bip Roberts	.07	.04	
541 Richard Rodriguez (R)	.10	.06	
542 Benito Santiago	.08	.05	
543 Calvin Schiraldi	.04	.02	
544 Eric Show	.04	.02	
545 Phil Stephenson	.04	.02	
546 Garry Templeton	.04	.02	
547 Ed Whitson	.04	.02	
548 Eddie Williams	.04	.02	
549 Kevin Appier	.12	.07	
550 Luis Aquino	.04	.02	
551 Bob Boone	.08	.05	
552 George Brett	.20	.12	
553 Jeff Conine (R)	.50	.30	
554 Steve Crawford	.04	.02	
555 Mark Davis	.04	.02	
556 Storm Davis	.04	.02	
557 Jim Eisenreich	.04	.02	
558 Steve Farr	.04	.02	
559 Tom Gordon	.07	.04	
560 Mark Gubicza	.08	.05	
561 Bo Jackson	.15	.10	
562 Mike Macfarlane	.04	.02	
563 Brian McRae (R)	.25	.15	
564 Jeff Montgomery	.07	.04	
565 Bill Pecota	.04	.02	
566 Gerald Perry	.04	.02	
567 Bret Saberhagen	.08	.05	
568 Jeff Schulz (R)	.08	.05	
569 Kevin Seitzer	.07	.04	
570 Terry Shumpert	.04	.02	
571 Kurt Stillwell	.04	.02	
572 Danny Tartabull	.10	.06	
573 Gary Thurman	.04	.02	
574 Frank White	.04	.02	
575 Willie Wilson	.04	.02	
576 Chris Bosio	.04	.02	

577	Greg Brock	.04	.02
578	George Canale	.04	.02
579	Chuck Crim	.04	.02
580	Rob Deer	.07	.04
581	Edgar Diaz	.04	.02
582	Tom Edens (R)	.08	.05
583	Mike Felder	.04	.02
584	Jim Gantner	.04	.02
585	Darryl Hamilton	.04	.02
586	Ted Higuera	.04	.02
587	Mark Knudson	.04	.02
588	Bill Krueger	.04	.02
589	Tim McIntosh	.10	.06
590	Pal Mirabella	.04	.02
591	Paul Molitor	.20	.12
592	Jaime Navarro	.10	.06
593	Dave Parker	.07	.04
594	Dan Plesac	.04	.02
595	Ron Robinson	.04	.02
596	Gary Sheffield	.30	.18
597	Bill Spiers	.04	.02
598	B.J. Surhoff	.04	.02
599	Greg Vaughn	.12	.07
600	Randy Veres	.04	.02
601	Robin Yount	.15	.10
602	Rick Aguilera	.04	.02
603	Allan Anderson	.04	.02
604	Juan Berenguer	.04	.02
605	Randy Bush	.04	.02
606	Carmen Castillo	.04	.02
607	Tim Drummond	.04	.02
608	Scott Erickson (R)	.20	.12
609	Gary Gaetti	.04	.02
610	Greg Gagne	.04	.02
611	Dan Gladden	.04	.02
612	Mark Guthrie (R)	.08	.05
613	Brian Harper	.07	.04
614	Kent Hrbek	.08	.05
615	Gene Larkin	.04	.02
616	Terry Leach	.04	.02
617	Nelson Liriano	.04	.02
618	Shane Mack	.10	.06
619	John Moses	.04	.02
620	Pedro Munoz (R)	.20	.12
621	Al Newman	.04	.02
622	Junior Ortiz	.04	.02
623	Kirby Puckett	.20	.12
624	Roy Smith	.04	.02
625	Kevin Tapani	.08	.05
626	Gary Wayne	.04	.02
627	David West	.04	.02
628	Cris Carpenter	.04	.02
629	Vince Coleman	.07	.04
630	Ken Dayley	.04	.02
631	Jose DeLeon	.04	.02
632	Frank DePino	.04	.02
633	Bernard Gilkey (R)	.20	.12
634	Pedro Guerrero	.07	.04
635	Ken Hill	.10	.06
636	Felix Jose	.10	.06
637	Ray Lankford (R)	.35	.20
638	Joe Magrane	.04	.02
639	Tom Niedenfuer	.04	.02
640	Jose Oquendo	.04	.02
641	Tom Pagnozzi	.08	.05
642	Terry Pendleton	.12	.07
643	Mike Perez (R)	.12	.07
644	Bryn Smith	.04	.02
645	Lee Smith	.12	.07
646	Ozzie Smith	.15	.10
647	Scott Terry	.04	.02
648	Bob Tewksbury	.04	.02
649	Milt Thompson	.04	.02
650	John Tudor	.04	.02
651	Denny Walling	.04	.02
652	Craig Wilson (R)	.12	.07
653	Todd Worrell	.07	.04
654	Todd Zeile	.08	.05
655	Oscar Azocar	.04	.02
656	Steve Balboni	.04	.02
657	Jesse Barfield	.07	.04
658	Greg Cadaret	.04	.02
659	Chuck Cary	.04	.02
660	Rick Cerone	.04	.02
661	Dave Eiland	.07	.04
662	Alvaro Espinoza	.04	.02
663	Bob Geren	.04	.02
664	Lee Guetterman	.04	.02
665	Mel Hall	.07	.04
666	Andy Hawkins	.04	.02
667	Jimmy Jones	.04	.02
668	Roberto Kelly	.12	.07
669	Dave LaPoint	.04	.02
670	Tim Leary	.04	.02
671	Jim Leyritz	.04	.02
672	Kevin Maas	.08	.05
673	Don Mattingly	.15	.10
674	Matt Nokes	.04	.02
675	Pascual Perez	.04	.02
676	Eric Plunk	.04	.02
677	Dave Righetti	.04	.02
678	Jeff Robinson	.04	.02
679	Steve Sax	.08	.05
680	Mike Witt	.04	.02
681	Steve Avery	.25	.15
682	Mike Bell	.04	.02
683	Jeff Blauser	.07	.04
684	Francisco Cabrera	.04	.02
685	Tony Castillo	.07	.04
686	Marty Clary	.04	.02
687	Nick Esasky	.04	.02
688	Ron Gant	.12	.07
689	Tom Glavine	.25	.15
690	Mark Grant	.04	.02

691	Tommy Gregg	.04	.02
692	Dwayne Henry	.04	.02
693	Dave Justice	.35	.20
694	Jimmy Kremers	.04	.02
695	Charlie Leibrandt	.04	.02
696	Mark Lemke	.04	.02
697	Oddibe McDowell	.04	.02
698	Greg Olson	.07	.04
699	Jeff Parrett	.04	.02
700	Jim Presley	.04	.02
701	Victor Rosario (R)	.08	.05
702	Lonnie Smith	.07	.04
703	Pete Smith	.08	.05
704	John Smoltz	.15	.10
705	Mike Stanton	.04	.02
706	Andres Thomas	.04	.02
707	Jeff Treadway	.04	.02
708	Jim Vatcher (R)	.08	.05
709	Ryne Sandberg/Cecil Fielder	.15	.10
710	Barry Bonds/Ken Griffey, Jr.	.50	.30
711	Bobby Bonilla/Barry Larkin	.08	.05
712	Bobby Thigpen/John Franco	.07	.04
713	Andre Dawson/Ryne Sandberg	.15	.10
714	Team Checklists	.04	.01
715	Team Checklists	.04	.01
716	Team Checklists	.04	.01
717	Team Checklists	.04	.01
718	Team Checklists	.04	.01
719	Team Checklists	.04	.01
720	Team Checklists	.04	.01

1991 Fleer Update

The cards in this update set are identical to Fleer's regular 1991 edition and include players traded during the year and a number of up and coming rookie prospects. Cards measure 2-1/2" by 3-1/2" and the set contains 132-cards.

		MINT	NR/MT
Complete Set (132)		7.00	4.00
Commons		.05	.03

1	Glenn Davis	.08	.05
2	Dwight Evans	.08	.05
3	Jose Mesa (R)	.08	.05
4	Jack Clark	.07	.04
5	Danny Darwin	.05	.03
6	Steve Lyons	.05	.03
7	Mo Vaughn (R)	.50	.30
8	Floyd Bannister	.05	.03
9	Gary Gaetti	.05	.03
10	Dave Parker	.08	.05
11	Joey Cora	.05	.03
12	Charlie Hough	.05	.03
13	Matt Merullo	.07	.04
14	Warren Newson (R)	.12	.07
15	Tim Raines	.08	.05
16	Albert Belle	.40	.25
17	Glenallen Hill	.08	.05
18	Shawn Hillegas	.05	.03
19	Mark Lewis (R)	.10	.06
20	Charles Nagy (R)	.50	.30
21	Mark Whiten	.25	.15
22	John Cerutti	.05	.03
23	Rob Deer	.07	.04
24	Mickey Tettleton	.08	.05
25	Warren Cromartie	.05	.03
26	Kirk Gibson	.08	.05
27	David Howard (R)	.08	.05
28	Brent Mayne (R)	.10	.06
29	Dante Bichette	.05	.03
30	Mark Lee (R)	.08	.05
31	Julio Machado	.05	.03
32	Edwin Nunez	.05	.03
33	Willie Randolph	.07	.04
34	Franklin Stubbs	.05	.03
35	Bill Wegman	.05	.03
36	Chili Davis	.08	.05
37	Chuck Knoblauch (R)	.30	.18
38	Scott Leius	.05	.03
39	Jack Morris	.10	.06
40	Mike Pagliarulo	.05	.03
41	Lenny Webster (R)	.10	.06
42	John Habyan	.05	.03
43	Steve Howe	.05	.03
44	Jeff Johnson (R)	.10	.06
45	Scott Kamieniecki (R)	.12	.07
46	Pet Kelly (R)	.15	.10
47	Hensley Meulens	.07	.04
48	Wade Taylor (R)	.12	.07

49	Bernie Williams (R)	.20	.12	106	Wally Backman	.05	.03
50	Kirk Dressendorfer (R)	.15	.10	107	Darrin Fletcher (R)	.10	.06
51	Ernest Riles	.05	.03	108	Tommy Greene	.12	.07
52	Rich DeLucia (R)	.08	.05	109	John Morris	.05	.03
53	Tracy Jones	.05	.03	110	Mitch Williams	.08	.05
54	Bill Krueger	.05	.03	111	Lloyd McClendon	.05	.03
55	Alonzo Powell	.08	.05	112	Orlando Merced (R)	.25	.16
56	Jeff Schaefer	.05	.03	113	Vicente Palacios	.05	.03
57	Russ Swan (R)	.08	.05	114	Gary Varsho	.05	.03
58	John Barfield (R)	.08	.05	115	John Wehner (R)	.08	.05
59	Rich Gossage	.08	.05	116	Rex Hudler	.05	.03
60	Jose Guzman	.07	.04	117	Tim Jones	.05	.03
61	Dean Palmer (R)	.35	.20	118	Geronimo Pena	.05	.03
62	Ivan Rodriguez (R)	1.00	.70	119	Gerald Perry	.05	.03
63	Roberto Alomar	.30	.18	120	Larry Andersen	.05	.03
64	Tom Candiotti	.07	.04	121	Jerald Clark	.08	.05
65	Joe Carter	.20	.12	122	Scott Coolbaugh	.05	.03
66	Ed Sprague	.12	.07	123	Tony Fernandez	.08	.05
67	Pat Tabler	.05	.03	124	Darrin Jackson	.07	.04
68	Mike Timlin (R)	.10	.06	125	Fred McGriff	.20	.12
69	Devon White	.08	.05	126	Jose Mota (R)	.10	.06
70	Rafael Belliard	.05	.03	127	Tim Teufel	.05	.03
71	Juan Berenguer	.05	.03	128	Bud Black	.07	.04
72	Sid Bream	.05	.03	129	Mike Felder	.05	.03
73	Marvin Freeman	.05	.03	130	Willie McGee	.08	.05
74	Kent Mercker	.08	.05	131	Dave Righetti	.07	.04
75	Otis Nixon	.07	.04	132	Checklist	.05	.02
76	Terry Pendleton	.12	.07				
77	George Bell	.10	.06				
78	Danny Jackson	.07	.04				
79	Chuck McElroy	.07	.04				
80	Gary Scott (R)	.10	.06				
81	Heathcliff Slocumb (R)	.12	.07				
82	Dave Smith	.05	.03				
83	Rick Wilkins (R)	.40	.25				
84	Freddie Benavides (R)	.10	.06				
85	Ted Power	.05	.03				
86	Mo Sanford (R)	.10	.06				
87	Jeff Bagwell (R)	1.50	.90				
88	Steve Finley	.05	.03				
89	Pete Harnisch	.07	.04				
90	Darryl Kile (R)	.35	.20				
91	Brett Butler	.10	.06				
92	John Candelaria	.05	.03				
93	Gary Carter	.10	.06				
94	Kevin Gross	.05	.03				
95	Bob Ojeda	.05	.03				
96	Darryl Strawberry	.15	.10				
97	Ivan Calderon	.08	.05				
98	Ron Hassey	.05	.03				
99	Gilberto Reyes	.05	.03				
100	Hubie Brooks	.08	.05				
101	Rick Cerone	.05	.03				
102	Vince Coleman	.07	.04				
103	Jeff Innis	.05	.03				
104	Pete Schourek (R)	.12	.07				
105	Andy Ashby (R)	.12	.07				

1991 Fleer Ultra

This 400-card set marks Fleer's first venture into the upscale premium baseball card market. Cards measure 2-1/2" by 3-1/2" and feature full color photos on the card fronts with gray borders at the top and bottom. Card backs are vertical and consist of three photos and a box with 1990 and career statistics. Special subsets include "Elite Performers" (EP) (391-396) and Major League Prospects (373-390). A special limited edition 10-card Ultra Gold

insert set was produced featuring cards
with a gold background and three photos
on the card fronts. Card backs contained
highlights from the player's career in
paragraph form. The Ultra Gold Inserts are
listed at the end of the checklist below but
are not included in the complete set price.

		MINT	NR/MT
	Complete Set(400)	26.00	16.00
	Commons	.07	.04
1	Steve Avery	1.25	.80
2	Jeff Blauser	.12	.07
3	Francisco Cabrera	.07	.04
4	Ron Gant	.35	.20
5	Tom Glavine	.50	.30
6	Tommy Gregg	.07	.04
7	Dave Justice	1.50	.90
8	Oddibe McDowell	.07	.04
9	Greg Olson	.08	.05
10	Terry Pendleton	.15	.10
11	Lonnie Smith	.08	.05
12	John Smoltz	.30	.18
13	Jeff Treadway	.07	.04
14	Glenn Davis	.08	.05
15	Mike Devereaux	.15	.10
16	Leo Gomez	.25	.15
17	Chris Hoiles	.25	.15
18	Dave Johnson	.07	.04
19	Ben McDonald	.30	.18
20	Randy Milligan	.10	.06
21	Gregg Olson	.12	.07
22	Joe Orsulak	.08	.05
23	Bill Ripken	.07	.04
24	Cal Ripken, Jr.	.80	.50
25	David Segui	.12	.07
26	Craig Worthington	.07	.04
27	Wade Boggs	.35	.20
28	Tom Bolton	.07	.04
29	Tom Brunansky	.10	.06
30	Ellis Burks	.12	.07
31	Roger Clemens	.80	.50
32	Mike Greenwell	.12	.07
33	Greg Harris	.07	.04
34	Daryl Irvine	.07	.04
35	Mike Marshall	.07	.04
36	Tim Naehring	.10	.06
37	Tony Pena	.07	.04
38	Phil Plantier (R)	1.50	.90
39	Carlos Quintana	.12	.07
40	Jeff Reardon	.15	.10
41	Jody Reed	.07	.04
42	Luis Rivera	.07	.04
43	Jim Abbott	.25	.15
44	Chuck Finley	.12	.07
45	Bryan Harvey	.10	.06
46	Donnie Hill	.07	.04
47	Jack Howell	.07	.04
48	Wally Joyner	.12	.07
49	Mark Langston	.12	.07
50	Kirk McCaskill	.07	.04
51	Lance Parrish	.10	.06
52	Dick Schofield	.07	.04
53	Lee Stevens	.08	.05
54	Dave Winfield	.30	.18
55	George Bell	.12	.07
56	Damon Berryhill	.07	.04
57	Mike Bielecki	.07	.04
58	Andre Dawson	.25	.15
59	Shawon Dunston	.10	.06
60	Joe Girardi	.07	.04
61	Mark Grace	.25	.15
62	Mike Harkey	.10	.06
63	Les Lancaster	.07	.04
64	Greg Maddux	.30	.18
65	Derrick May	.50	.30
66	Ryne Sandberg	.75	.45
67	Luis Salazar	.07	.04
68	Dwight Smith	.10	.06
69	Hector Villanueva	.10	.06
70	Jerome Walton	.08	.05
71	Mitch Williams	.07	.04
72	Carlton Fisk	.20	.12
73	Scott Fletcher	.07	.04
74	Ozzie Guillen	.07	.04
75	Greg Hibbard	.07	.04
76	Lance Johnson	.07	.04
77	Steve Lyons	.07	.04
78	Jack McDowell	.35	.20
79	Dan Pasqua	.07	.04
80	Melido Perez	.10	.06
81	Tim Raines	.10	.06
82	Sammy Sosa	.60	.35
83	Cory Snyder	.07	.04
84	Bobby Thigpen	.10	.06
85	Frank Thomas	5.00	3.50
86	Robin Ventura	.80	.50
87	Todd Benzinger	.07	.04
88	Glenn Braggs	.07	.04
89	Tom Browning	.10	.06
90	Norm Charlton	.10	.06
91	Eric Davis	.12	.07
92	Rob Dibble	.10	.06
93	Bill Doran	.07	.04
94	Mariano Duncan	.07	.04
95	Billy Hatcher	.07	.04
96	Barry Larkin	.15	.10
97	Randy Myers	.07	.04
98	Hal Morris	.15	.10
99	Joe Oliver	.10	.06
100	Paul O'Neill	.12	.07
101	Jeff Reed	.07	.04

102 Jose Rijo	.12	.07	
103 Chris Sabo	.10	.07	
104 Beau Allred	.12	.07	
105 Sandy Alomar, Jr.	.12	.07	
106 Carlos Baerga	1.25	.80	
107 Albert Belle	1.00	.70	
108 Jerry Browne	.07	.04	
109 Tom Candiotti	.07	.04	
110 Alex Cole	.07	.04	
111 John Farrell	.07	.04	
112 Felix Fermin	.07	.04	
113 Brook Jacoby	.07	.04	
114 Chris James	.07	.04	
115 Doug Jones	.07	.04	
116 Steve Olin	.10	.06	
117 Greg Swindell	.10	.06	
118 Turner Warner	.10	.06	
119 Mitch Webster	.07	.04	
120 Dave Bergman	.07	.04	
121 Cecil Fielder	.40	.25	
122 Travis Fryman	2.50	1.50	
123 Mike Henneman	.07	.04	
124 Lloyd Moseby	.07	.04	
125 Dan Petry	.07	.04	
126 Tony Phillips	.08	.05	
127 Mark Salas	.07	.04	
128 Frank Tanana	.07	.04	
129 Alan Trammell	.15	.10	
130 Lou Whitaker	.10	.06	
131 Eric Anthony	.25	.15	
132 Craig Biggio	.15	.10	
133 Ken Caminiti	.10	.06	
134 Casey Candaele	.07	.04	
135 Andujar Cedeno	.30	.18	
136 Mark Davidson	.07	.04	
137 Jim Deshaies	.07	.04	
138 Mark Portugal	.08	.05	
139 Rafael Ramirez	.07	.04	
140 Mike Scott	.10	.06	
141 Eric Yelding	.07	.04	
142 Gerald Young	.07	.04	
143 Kevin Appier	.12	.07	
144 George Brett	.30	.18	
145 Jeff Conine (R)	.70	.40	
146 Jim Eisenreich	.07	.04	
147 Tom Gordon	.10	.06	
148 Mark Gubicza	.10	.06	
149 Bo Jackson	.20	.12	
150 Brent Mayne	.10	.06	
151 Mike Macfarlane	.07	.04	
152 Brian McRae (R)	.70	.40	
153 Jeff Montgomery	.07	.04	
154 Bret Saberhagen	.15	.10	
155 Kevin Seitzer	.07	.04	
156 Terry Shumpert	.07	.04	
157 Kurt Stillwell	.07	.04	
158 Danny Tartabull	.15	.10	
159 Tim Belcher	.07	.04
160 Kal Daniels	.07	.04
161 Alfredo Griffin	.07	.04
162 Lenny Harris	.07	.04
163 Jay Howell	.07	.04
164 Ramon Martinez	.15	.10
165 Mike Morgan	.07	.04
166 Eddie Murray	.20	.12
167 Jose Offerman	.12	.07
168 Juan Samuel	.07	.04
169 Mike Scioscia	.07	.04
170 Mike Sharperson	.07	.04
171 Darryl Strwberry	.25	.15
172 Greg Brock	.07	.04
173 Chuck Crim	.07	.04
174 Jim Gantner	.07	.04
175 Ted Higuera	.07	.04
176 Mark Knudson	.07	.04
177 Tim McIntosh	.12	.07
178 Paul Molitor	.30	.18
179 Dan Plesac	.07	.04
180 Gary Sheffield	.90	.60
181 Bill Spiers	.07	.04
182 B.J. Surhoff	.07	.04
183 Greg Vaughn	.20	.12
184 Robin Yount	.30	.18
185 Rick Aguilera	.07	.04
186 Greg Gagne	.07	.04
187 Dan Gladden	.07	.04
188 Brian Harper	.07	.04
189 Kent Hrbek	.10	.06
190 Gene Larkin	.07	.04
191 Shane Mack	.12	.07
192 Pedro Munoz (R)	.35	.20
193 Al Newman	.07	.04
194 Junior Ortiz	.07	.04
195 Kirby Puckett	.75	.45
196 Kevin Tapani	.10	.06
197 Dennis Boyd	.07	.04
198 Tim Burke	.07	.04
199 Ivan Calderon	.10	.06
200 Delino DeShields	.50	.30
201 Mike Fitzgerald	.07	.04
202 Steve Frey	.07	.04
203 Andres Galarraga	.20	.12
204 Marquis Grissom	.50	.30
205 Dave Martinez	.07	.04
206 Dennis Martinez	.12	.07
207 Junior Noboa	.07	.04
208 Spike Owen	.07	.04
209 Scott Ruskin (R)	.10	.06
210 Tim Wallach	.10	.06
211 Daryl Boston	.07	.04
212 Vince Coleman	.08	.05
213 David Cone	.15	.10
214 Ron Darling	.07	.04
215 Kevin Elster	.07	.04

216	Sid Fernandez	.10	.06
217	John Franco	.07	.04
218	Dwight Gooden	.20	.12
219	Tom Herr	.07	.04
220	Todd Hundley	.10	.06
221	Gregg Jefferies	.30	.18
222	Howard Johnson	.12	.07
223	Dave Magadan	.10	.06
224	Kevin McReynolds	.10	.06
225	Keith Miller	.07	.04
226	Mackey Sasser	.07	.04
227	Frank Viola	.10	.06
228	Jesse Barfield	.10	.06
229	Greg Cadaret	.07	.04
230	Alvaro Espinoza (R)	.07	.04
231	Bob Geren	.07	.04
232	Lee Guetterman	.07	.04
233	Mel Hall	.10	.06
234	Andy Hawkins	.07	.04
235	Roberto Kelly	.15	.10
236	Tim Leary	.07	.04
237	Jim Leyritz	.07	.04
238	Kevin Maas	.12	.07
239	Don Mattingly	.30	.18
240	Hensley Meulens	.10	.06
241	Eric Plunk	.07	.04
242	Steve Sax	.10	.06
243	Todd Burns	.07	.04
244	Jose Canseco	.70	.40
245	Dennis Eckersley	.15	.10
246	Mike Gallego	.07	.04
247	Dave Henderson	.07	.04
248	Rickey Henderson	.35	.20
249	Rick Honeycutt	.07	.04
250	Carney Lansford	.08	.05
251	Mark McGwire	.50	.30
252	Mike Moore	.07	.04
253	Terry Steinbach	.10	.06
254	Dave Stewart	.12	.07
255	Walt Weiss	.07	.04
256	Bob Welch	.07	.04
257	Curt Young	.07	.04
258	Wes Chamberlain (R)	.35	.20
259	Pat Combs	.07	.04
260	Darren Daulton	.25	.15
261	Jose DeJesus	.07	.04
262	Len Dykstra	.25	.15
263	Charlie Hayes	.08	.05
264	Von Hayes	.07	.04
265	Ken Howell	.07	.04
266	John Kruk	.15	.10
267	Roger McDowell	.07	.04
268	Mickey Morandini (R)	.15	.10
269	Terry Mulholland	.07	.04
270	Dale Murphy	.15	.10
271	Randy Ready	.07	.04
272	Dickie Thon	.07	.04
273	Stan Belinda	.07	.04
274	Jay Bell	.15	.10
275	Barry Bonds	1.00	.70
276	Bobby Bonilla	.20	.12
277	Doug Drabek	.15	.10
278	Carlos Garcia (R)	.80	.50
279	Neal Heaton	.07	.04
280	Jeff King	.10	.06
281	Bill Landrum	.07	.04
282	Mike LaValliere	.07	.04
283	Jose Lind	.07	.04
284	Orlando Merced (R)	.70	.40
285	Gary Redus	.07	.04
286	Don Slaught	.07	.04
287	Andy Van Slyke	.15	.10
288	Jose DeLeon	.07	.04
289	Pedro Guerrero	.10	.06
290	Ray Lankford	.60	.35
291	Joe Magrane	.07	.04
292	Jose Oquendo	.07	.04
293	Tom Pagnozzi	.07	.04
294	Bryn Smith	.07	.04
295	Lee Smith	.12	.07
296	Ozzie Smith	.25	.15
297	Milt Thompson	.07	.04
298	Craig Wilson (R)	.12	.07
299	Todd Zeile	.12	.07
300	Shawn Abner	.07	.04
301	Andy Benes	.20	.12
302	Paul Faries (R)	.07	.04
303	Tony Gwynn	.35	.20
304	Greg Harris	.07	.04
305	Thomas Howard	.10	.06
306	Bruce Hurst	.10	.06
307	Craig Lefferts	.07	.04
308	Fred McGriff	.45	.28
309	Dennis Rasmussen	.07	.04
310	Bip Roberts	.10	.06
311	Benito Santiago	.12	.07
312	Garry Templeton	.07	.04
313	Ed Whitson	.07	.04
314	Dave Anderson	.07	.04
315	Kevin Bass	.07	.04
316	Jeff Brantley	.07	.04
317	John Burkett	.07	.04
318	Will Clark	.60	.35
319	Steve Decker (R)	.12	.07
320	Scott Garrelts	.07	.04
321	Terry Kennedy	.07	.04
322	Mark Leonard (R)	.10	.06
323	Darren Lewis	.20	.12
324	Greg Litton	.07	.04
325	Willie McGee	.10	.06
326	Kevin Mitchell	.12	.07
327	Don Robinson	.07	.04
328	Andres Santana (R)	.12	.07
329	Robby Thompson	.07	.04

330	Jose Uribe	.07	.04
331	Matt Williams	.35	.20
332	Scott Bradley	.07	.04
334	Alvin Davis	.07	.04
335	Ken Griffey, Sr.	.10	.06
336	Ken Griffey, Jr.	3.00	1.75
337	Erik Hanson	.10	.06
338	Brian Holman	.10	.06
339	Randy Johnson	.35	.20
340	Edgar Martinez	.20	.12
341	Tino Martinez	.12	.07
342	Pete O'Brien	.07	.04
343	Harold Reynolds	.08	.05
344	David Valle	.07	.04
345	Omar Vizquel	.07	.04
346	Brad Arnsberg	.07	.04
347	Kevin Brown	.12	.07
348	Julio Franco	.12	.07
349	Jeff Huson	.07	.04
350	Rafael Palmeiro	.35	.20
351	Geno Petralli	.07	.04
352	Gary Pettis	.07	.04
353	Kenny Rogers	.07	.04
354	Jeff Russell	.07	.04
355	Nolan Ryan	1.50	.90
356	Ruben Sierra	.35	.20
357	Bobby Witt	.10	.06
358	Roberto Alomar	1.00	.70
359	Pat Borders	.07	.04
360	Joe Carter	.50	.30
361	Kelly Gruber	.10	.06
362	Tom Henke	.07	.04
363	Glenallen Hill	.10	.06
364	Jimmy Key	.10	.06
365	Manny Lee	.07	.04
366	Rance Mulliniks	.07	.04
367	John Olerud	1.50	.90
368	Dave Stieb	.10	.06
369	Duane Ward	.07	.04
370	David Wells	.07	.04
371	Mark Whiten	.50	.30
372	Mookie Wilson	.07	.04
373	Willie Banks (R)	.25	.15
374	Steve Carter (R)	.10	.06
375	Scott Chiamparino (R)	.12	.07
376	Steve Chitren (R)	.12	.07
377	Darrin Fletcher (R)	.10	.06
378	Rich Garces (R)	.15	.10
379	Reggie Jefferson (R)	.30	.18
380	Eric Karros (R)	2.00	1.25
381	Pat Kelly (R)	.30	.18
382	Chuck Knoblauch (R)	.50	.30
383	Denny Neagle (R)	.15	.10
384	Dan Opperman (R)	.12	.07
385	John Ramos (R)	.12	.07
386	Henry Rodriguez (R)	.35	.20
387	Maurice Vaughn (R)	1.25	.80

388	Gerald Williams (R)	.50	.30
389	Mike York (R)	.10	.06
390	Eddie Zosky (R)	.12	.07
391	Barry Bonds (EP)	.30	.18
392	Cecil Fielder (EP)	.20	.12
393	Rickey Henderson (EP)	.20	.12
394	Dave Justice (EP)	.25	.15
395	Nolan Ryan (EP)	.60	.35
396	Bobby Thigpen (EP)	.08	.05
397	Checklist	.07	.02
398	Checklist	.07	.02
399	Checklist	.07	.02
400	Checklist	.07	.02
G1	Barry Bonds (Gold)	2.00	1.25
G2	Will Clark (Gold)	1.25	.80
G3	Doug Drabek (Gold)	.75	.45
G4	Ken Griffey Jr. (Gold)	3.50	2.00
G5	Rickey Henderson (Gold)	1.25	.80
G6	Bo Jackson (Gold)	.80	.50
G7	Ramon Martinez (Gold)	.50	.30
G8	Kirby Puckett (Gold)	1.75	1.00
G9	Chris Sabo (Gold)	.40	.25
G10	Ryne Sandberg (Gold)	1.50	.90

1991 Fleer Ultra Update

PETE HARNISCH

This 120-card update set is an extension of the Ultra set. Card fronts are identical to the regular edtion witha large action shot on the front and three small photos on the card backs. Cards measure 2-1/2" by 3-1/2" and the set features players who were traded during the year and a number of promising rookies.

		MINT	NR/MT
	Complete Set (120)	70.00	42.00
	Commons	.10	.06
1	Dwight Evans	.12	.07
2	Chito Martinez (R)	.25	.15
3	Bob Melvin	.10	.06
4	Mike Mussina (R)	12.00	7.50
5	Jack Clark	.12	.07
6	Dana Kiecker	.10	.06
7	Steve Lyons	.10	.06
8	Gary Gaetti	.10	.06
9	Dave Gallagher	.10	.06
10	Dave Parker	.12	.07
11	Luis Polonia	.10	.06
12	Luis Sojo	.10	.06
13	Wilson Alverez	2.50	1.50
14	Alex Fernandez	6.00	3.50
15	Craig Grebeck	.10	.06
16	Ron Karkovice	.10	.06
17	Warren Newson (R)	.20	.12
18	Scott Radinsky	.10	.06
19	Glenallen Hill	.10	.06
20	Charles Nagy	1.00	.70
21	Mark Whiten	1.75	1.00
22	Milt Cuyler (R)	.25	.15
23	Paul Gibson	.10	.06
24	Mickey Tettleton	.20	.12
25	Todd Benzinger	.10	.06
26	Storm Davis	.10	.06
27	Kirk Gibson	.12	.07
28	Bill Pecota	.10	.06
30	Darryl Hamilton	.60	.35
31	Jaime Navarro	.30	.18
32	Willie Randolph	.10	.06
33	Bill Wegman	.10	.06
34	Randy Bush	.10	.06
35	Chili Davis	.12	.07
36	Scott Erickson	.60	.35
37	Chuck Knoblauch	2.50	1.50
38	Scott Leius	.15	.10
39	Jack Morris	.35	.20
40	John Habyan	.10	.06
41	Pat Kelly	.35	.20
42	Matt Nokes	.10	.06
43	Scott Sanderson	.10	.06
44	Bernie Williams	1.25	.80
45	Harold Baines	.12	.07
46	Brook Jacoby	.10	.06
47	Ernest Riles	.10	.06
48	Willie Wilson	.10	.06
49	Jay Buhner	.40	.25
50	Rich DeLucia (R)	.15	.10
51	Mike Jackson	.12	.07
52	Bill Krueger	.10	.06
53	Bill Swift	.60	.35
54	Brian Downing	.10	.06
55	Juan Gonzalez	40.00	28.00
56	Dean Palmer	5.00	3.00
57	Kevin Reimer	.25	.15
58	Ivan Rodriguez	5.00	3.00
59	Tom Candiotti	.10	.06
60	Juan Guzman (R)	8.50	5.50
61	Bob MacDonald (R)	.15	.10
62	Greg Myers	.10	.06
63	Ed Sprague	.35	.20
64	Devon White	.20	.12
65	Rafael Belliard	.10	.06
66	Juan Berenguer	.10	.06
67	Brian Hunter (R)	.40	.25
68	Kent Mercker	.15	.10
69	Otis Nixon	.12	.07
70	Danny Jackson	.12	.07
71	Chuck McElroy	.10	.06
72	Gary Scott (R)	.20	.12
73	Heathcliff Slocumb	.12	.07
74	Chico Walker	.10	.06
75	Rick Wilkins (R)	4.50	2.75
76	Chris Hammond	.35	.20
77	Luis Quinones	.10	.06
78	Herm Winningham	.10	.06
79	Jeff Bagwell (R)	10.00	6.50
80	Jim Corsi	.10	.06
81	Steve Finley	.10	.06
82	Luis Gonzalez (R)	1.75	1.00
83	Pete Harnisch	.20	.12
84	Darryl Kile (R)	4.00	2.50
85	Brett Butler	.15	.10
86	Gary Carter	.12	.07
87	Tim Crews	.10	.06
88	Orel Hershiser	.12	.07
89	Bob Ojeda	.10	.06
90	Bret Barberie	.40	.25
91	Barry Jones	.10	.06
92	Gilberto Reyes	.10	.06
93	Larry Walker	3.00	1.75
94	Hubie Brooks	.12	.07
95	Tim Burke	.10	.06
96	Rick Cerone	.10	.06
97	Jeff Innis	.10	.06
98	Wally Backman	.10	.06
99	Tommy Greene	1.75	1.00
100	Ricky Jordan	.10	.06
101	Mitch Williams	.10	.06
102	John Smiley	.15	.10
103	Randy Tomlin (R)	.40	.25
104	Gary Varsho	.10	.06
105	Cris Carpenter	.10	.06
106	Ken Hill	.60	.35
107	Felix Jose	.25	.15
108	Omar Oliveras (R)	.25	.15
109	Gerald Perry	.10	.06
110	Jerald Clark	.12	.07

111	Tony Fernandez	.12	.07
112	Darrin Jackson	.12	.07
113	Mike Maddux	.10	.06
114	Tim Teufel	.10	.06
115	Bud Black	.10	.06
116	Kelly Downs	.10	.06
117	Mike Felder	.10	.06
118	Willie McGee	.15	.10
119	Trevor Wilson	.12	.07
120	Checklist	.10	.03

1992 Fleer

This 720-card set features full color action photos framed by a blue border on the card fronts. The player's name, position and team are located in the wide border to the right of the photo. The top half of the card backs contain a full color action shot with statistics and bio's below the picture. Key subsets include Record Setters (RS)(681-687), League Leaders (LL)(688-697) and Pro Vision Art cards (PV)(708-713). Twelve special limited edition Roger Clemens cards were randomly inserted into Fleer wax packs. Three additonal Clemens cards were available through the mail. These 15-cards are listed at the end of this checklist but are not included in the complete set price. All cards measure 2-1/2" by 3-1/2".

		MINT	NR/MT
Complete Set (720)		16.50	9.00
Commons		.04	.02

1	Brady Anderson	.12	.07
2	Jose Bautista	.04	.02
3	Juan Bell	.04	.02
4	Glenn Davis	.07	.04

5	Mike Devereaux	.08	.05
6	Dwight Evans	.08	.05
7	Mike Flanagan	.04	.02
8	Leo Gomez	.10	.06
9	Chris Hoiles	.10	.06
10	Sam Horn	.07	.04
11	Tim Hulett	.04	.02
12	Dave Johnson	.04	.02
13	Chito Martinez	.15	.10
14	Ben McDonald	.12	.07
15	Bob Melvin	.04	.02
16	Luis Mercedes	.15	.10
17	Jose Mesa	.04	.02
18	Bob Milacki	.04	.02
19	Randy Milligan	.07	.04
20	Mike Mussina	.60	.35
21	Gregg Olson	.07	.04
22	Joe Orsulak	.04	.02
23	Jim Poole	.04	.02
24	Arthur Rhodes	.15	.10
25	Billy Ripken	.04	.02
26	Cal Ripken, Jr.	.35	.20
27	David Segui	.07	.04
28	Roy Smith	.04	.02
29	Anthony Telford	.07	.04
30	Mark Williamson	.04	.02
31	Craig Worthington	.04	.02
32	Wade Boggs	.12	.07
33	Tom Bolton	.04	.02
34	Tom Brunansky	.07	.04
35	Ellis Burks	.08	.05
36	Jack Clark	.07	.04
37	Roger Clemens	.25	.15
38	Danny Darwin	.04	.02
39	Mike Greenwell	.08	.05
40	Joe Hesketh	.04	.02
41	Daryl Irvine	.04	.02
42	Dennis Lamp	.04	.02
43	Tony Pena	.04	.02
44	Phil Plantier	.15	.10
45	Carlos Quintana	.07	.04
46	Jeff Reardon	.08	.05
47	Jody Reed	.04	.02
48	Luis Rivera	.04	.02
49	Mo Vaughn	.25	.15
50	Jim Abbott	.12	.07
51	Kyle Abbott	.07	.04
52	Ruben Amaro	.10	.06
53	Scott Bailes	.04	.02
54	Chris Beasley (R)	.08	.05
55	Mark Eichhorn	.04	.02
56	Mike Fetters	.04	.02
57	Chuck Finley	.08	.05
58	Gary Gaetti	.04	.02
59	Dave Gallagher	.04	.02
60	Donnie Hill	.04	.02
61	Bryan Harvey	.07	.04

62	Wally Joyner	.08	.05
63	Mark Langston	.08	.05
64	Kirk McCaskill	.04	.02
65	John Orton	.04	.02
66	Lance Parrish	.04	.02
67	Luis Polonia	.07	.04
68	Bobby Rose	.04	.02
69	Dick Schofield	.04	.02
70	Luis Sojo	.04	.02
71	Lee Stevens	.04	.02
72	Dave Winfield	.20	.12
73	Cliff Young	.04	.02
74	Wilson Alvarez	.12	.07
75	Esteban Beltre (R)	.12	.07
76	Joey Cora	.04	.02
77	Brian Drahman	.08	.05
78	Alex Fernandez	.20	.12
79	Carlton Fisk	.12	.07
80	Scott Fletcher	.04	.02
81	Craig Grebeck	.04	.02
82	Ozzie Guillen	.04	.02
83	Greg Hibbard	.04	.02
84	Charlie Hough	.04	.02
85	Mike Huff	.04	.02
86	Bo Jackson	.12	.07
87	Lance Johnson	.04	.02
88	Ron Karkovice	.04	.02
89	Jack McDowell	.15	.10
90	Matt Merullo	.04	.02
91	Warren Newson	.07	.04
92	Donn Pall	.04	.02
93	Dan Pasqua	.04	.02
94	Ken Patterson	.04	.02
95	Melido Perez	.07	.04
96	Scott Radinsky	.04	.02
97	Tim Raines	.07	.04
98	Sammy Sosa	.12	.07
99	Bobby Thigpen	.07	.04
100	Frank Thomas	1.25	.80
101	Robin Ventura	.20	.12
102	Mike Aldrete	.04	.02
103	Sandy Alomar, Jr.	.08	.05
104	Carlos Baerga	.25	.15
105	Albert Belle	.20	.12
106	Willie Blair	.08	.05
107	Jerry Browne	.04	.02
108	Alex Cole	.04	.02
109	Felix Fermin	.04	.02
110	Glenallen Hill	.07	.04
111	Shawn Hillegas	.04	.02
112	Chris James	.04	.02
113	Reggie Jefferson	.12	.07
114	Doug Jones	.04	.02
115	Eric King	.04	.02
116	Mark Lewis	.08	.05
117	Carlos Martinez	.04	.02
118	Charles Nagy	.15	.10
119	Rod Nichols	.04	.02
120	Steve Olin	.04	.02
121	Jesse Orosco	.04	.02
122	Rudy Seanez	.08	.05
123	Joel Skinner	.04	.02
124	Greg Swindell	.08	.05
125	Jim Thome (R)	.20	.12
126	Mark Whiten	.08	.05
127	Scott Aldred	.04	.02
128	Andy Allanson	.04	.02
129	John Cerutti	.04	.02
130	Milt Cuyler	.08	.05
131	Mike Dalton (R)	.08	.05
132	Rob Deer	.07	.04
133	Cecil Fielder	.15	.10
134	Travis Fryman	.25	.15
135	Dan Gakeler (R)	.08	.05
136	Paul Gibson	.04	.02
137	Bill Gullickson	.04	.02
138	Mike Henneman	.04	.02
139	Pete Incaviglia	.04	.02
140	Mark Leiter	.07	.04
141	Scott Livingstone (R)	.15	.10
142	Lloyd Moseby	.04	.02
143	Tony Phillips	.07	.04
144	Mark Salas	.04	.02
145	Frank Tanana	.04	.02
146	Walt Terrell	.04	.02
147	Mickey Tettleton	.08	.05
148	Alan Trammell	.10	.06
149	Lou Whitaker	.07	.04
150	Kevin Appier	.08	.05
151	Luis Aquino	.04	.02
152	Todd Benzinger	.04	.02
153	Mike Boddicker	.04	.02
154	George Brett	.25	.15
155	Storm Davis	.04	.02
156	Jim Eisenreich	.04	.02
157	Kirk Gibson	.07	.04
158	Tom Gordon	.07	.04
159	Mark Gubicza	.07	.04
160	David Howard	.07	.04
161	Mike Macfarlane	.04	.02
162	Brent Mayne	.07	.04
163	Brian McRae	.12	.07
164	Jeff Montgomery	.07	.04
165	Bill Pecota	.04	.02
166	Harvey Pulliam (R)	.15	.10
167	Bret Saberhagen	.08	.05
168	Kevin Seitzer	.07	.04
169	Terry Shumpert	.04	.02
170	Kurt Stillwell	.04	.02
171	Danny Tartabull	.10	.06
172	Gary Thurman	.04	.02
173	Dante Bichette	.08	.05
174	Kevin Brown	.07	.04
175	Chuck Crim	.04	.02

176	Jim Gantner	.04	.02	233	Pat Kelly	.10	.06
177	Darryl Hamilton	.12	.07	234	Roberto Kelly	.12	.07
178	Ted Higuera	.04	.02	235	Tim Leary	.04	.02
179	Darren Holmes	.04	.02	236	Kevin Maas	.10	.06
180	Mark Lee	.04	.02	237	Don Mattingly	.20	.12
181	Julio Machado	.04	.02	238	Hensley Meulens	.07	.04
182	Paul Molitor	.20	.12	239	Matt Nokes	.04	.02
183	Jaime Navarro	.10	.06	240	Pascual Perez	.04	.02
184	Edwin Nunez	.04	.02	241	Eric Plunk	.04	.02
185	Dan Plesac	.04	.02	242	John Ramos	.12	.07
186	Willie Randolph	.04	.02	243	Scott Sanderson	.04	.02
187	Ron Robinson	.04	.02	244	Steve Sax	.08	.05
188	Gary Sheffield	.20	.12	245	Wade Taylor	.04	.02
189	Bill Spiers	.04	.02	246	Randy Velarde	.04	.02
190	B.J. Surhoff	.04	.02	247	Bernie Williams	.12	.07
191	Dale Sveum	.04	.02	248	Troy Afenir	.04	.02
192	Greg Vaughn	.10	.06	249	Harold Baines	.07	.04
193	Bill Wegman	.04	.02	250	Lance Blankenship	.04	.02
194	Robin Yount	.20	.12	251	Mike Bordick (R)	.12	.07
195	Rick Aguilera	.04	.02	252	Jose Canseco	.20	.12
196	Allan Anderson	.04	.02	253	Steve Chitren	.04	.02
197	Steve Bedrosian	.04	.02	254	Ron Darling	.04	.02
198	Randy Bush	.04	.02	255	Dennis Eckersley	.10	.06
199	Larry Casian (R)	.08	.05	256	Mike Gallego	.04	.02
200	Chili Davis	.07	.04	257	Dave Henderson	.04	.02
201	Scott Erickson	.12	.07	258	Rickey Henderson	.15	.10
202	Greg Gagne	.04	.02	259	Rick Honeycutt	.04	.02
203	Dan Gladden	.04	.02	260	Brook Jacoby	.04	.02
204	Brian Harper	.04	.02	261	Carney Lansford	.07	.04
205	Kent Hrbek	.07	.04	262	Mark McGwire	.20	.12
206	Chuck Knoblauch	.20	.12	263	Mike Moore	.04	.02
207	Gene Larkin	.04	.02	264	Gene Nelson	.04	.02
208	Terry Leach	.04	.02	265	Jamie Quirk	.04	.02
209	Scott Leius	.07	.04	266	Joe Slusarski (R)	.12	.07
210	Shane Mack	.10	.06	267	Terry Steinbach	.04	.02
211	Jack Morris	.10	.06	268	Dave Stewart	.08	.05
212	Pedro Munoz	.10	.06	269	Todd Van Poppel	.25	.15
213	Denny Neagle	.10	.06	270	Walt Weiss	.04	.02
214	Al Newman	.04	.02	271	Bob Welch	.07	.04
215	Junior Ortiz	.04	.02	272	Curt Young	.04	.02
216	Mike Pagliarulo	.04	.02	273	Scott Bradley	.04	.02
217	Kirby Puckett	.25	.15	274	Greg Briley	.04	.02
218	Paul Sorrento	.08	.05	275	Jay Buhner	.07	.04
219	Kevin Tapani	.07	.04	276	Henry Cotto	.04	.02
220	Lenny Webster	.04	.02	277	Alvin Davis	.04	.02
221	Jesse Barfield	.07	.04	278	Rich DeLucia	.04	.02
222	Greg Cadaret	.04	.02	279	Ken Griffey, Jr.	1.00	.70
223	Dave Eiland	.04	.02	280	Erik Hanson	.07	.04
224	Alvaro Espinoza	.04	.02	281	Brian Holman	.07	.04
225	Steve Farr	.04	.02	282	Mike Jackson	.04	.02
226	Bob Geren	.04	.02	283	Randy Johnson	.20	.12
227	Lee Guetterman	.04	.02	284	Tracy Jones	.04	.02
228	John Habyan	.04	.02	285	Bill Krueger	.04	.02
229	Mel Hall	.07	.04	286	Edgar Martinez	.12	.07
230	Steve Howe	.04	.02	287	Tino Martinez	.08	.05
231	Mike Humphreys (R)	.08	.05	288	Rob Murphy	.04	.02
232	Scott Kamieniecki	.08	.05	289	Pete O'Brien	.04	.02

290	Alonzo Powell	.04	.02	349	Steve Avery	.20	.12
291	Harold Reynolds	.04	.02	350	Mike Bell	.08	.05
292	Mike Schooler	.04	.02	351	Rafael Belliard	.04	.02
293	Russ Swan	.04	.02	353	Jeff Blauser	.08	.05
294	Bill Swift	.10	.06	354	Sid Bream	.04	.02
295	Dave Valle	.04	.02	355	Francisco Cabrera	.04	.02
296	Omar Vizquel	.04	.02	356	Marvin Freeman	.04	.02
297	Gerald Alexander	.04	.02	357	Ron Gant	.15	.10
298	Brad Arnsberg	.04	.02	358	Tom Glavine	.20	.12
299	Kevin Brown	.08	.05	359	Brian Hunter	.10	.06
300	Jack Daugherty	.04	.02	360	Dave Justice	.25	.15
301	Mario Diaz	.04	.02	361	Charlie Leibrandt	.04	.02
302	Brian Downing	.04	.02	362	Mark Lemke	.04	.02
303	Julio Franco	.08	.05	363	Kent Mercker	.07	.04
304	Juan Gonzalez	.80	.50	364	Keith Mitchell (R)	.10	.06
305	Rich Gossage	.07	.04	365	Greg Olson	.04	.02
306	Jose Guzman	.04	.02	366	Terry Pendleton	.15	.10
307	Jose Hernandez (R)	.08	.05	367	Armando Reynoso (R)	.10	.06
308	Jeff Huson	.04	.02	368	Deion Sanders	.15	.10
309	Mike Jeffcoat	.04	.02	369	Lonnie Smith	.07	.04
310	Terry Mathews (R)	.08	.05	370	Pete Smith	.08	.05
311	Rafael Palmeiro	.15	.10	371	John Smoltz	.15	.10
312	Dean Palmer	.20	.12	372	Mike Stanton	.04	.02
313	Geno Petralli	.04	.02	373	Jeff Treadway	.04	.02
314	Gary Pettis	.04	.02	374	Mark Wohlers (R)	.15	.10
315	Kevin Reimer	.07	.04	375	Paul Assenmacher	.04	.02
316	Ivan Rodriguez	.25	.15	376	George Bell	.10	.06
317	Kenny Rogers	.04	.02	377	Shawn Boskie	.04	.02
318	Wayne Rosenthal (R)	.08	.05	378	Frank Castillo	.04	.02
319	Jeff Russell	.04	.02	379	Andre Dawson	.15	.10
320	Nolan Ryan	.80	.50	380	Shawon Dunston	.08	.05
321	Ruben Sierra	.15	.10	381	Mark Grace	.15	.10
322	Jim Acker	.04	.02	382	Mike Harkey	.07	.04
323	Roberto Alomar	.30	.18	383	Danny Jackson	.04	.02
324	Derek Bell	.20	.12	384	Les Lancaster	.04	.02
325	Pat Borders	.04	.02	385	Cedric Landrum (R)	.08	.05
327	Joe Carter	.20	.12	386	Greg Maddux	.20	.12
328	Rob Ducey	.04	.02	387	Derrick May	.08	.05
329	Kelly Gruber	.07	.04	388	Chuck McElroy	.04	.02
330	Juan Guzman	.30	.18	389	Ryne Sanberg	.25	.15
331	Tom Henke	.04	.02	390	Heathcliff Slocumb	.07	.04
332	Jimmy Key	.08	.05	391	Dave Smith	.04	.02
333	Manny Lee	.04	.02	392	Dwight Smith	.07	.04
334	Al Leiter	.04	.02	393	Rick Sutcliffe	.07	.04
335	Bob MacDonald	.07	.04	394	Hector Villanueva	.04	.02
336	Candy Maldonado	.04	.02	395	Chico Walker	.04	.02
337	Rance Mulliniks	.04	.02	396	Jerome Walton	.07	.04
338	Greg Myers	.04	.02	397	Rick Wilkins	.40	.25
339	John Olerud	.30	.18	398	Jack Armstrong	.07	.04
340	Ed Sprague	.10	.06	399	Freddie Benavides	.04	.02
341	Dave Stieb	.07	.04	400	Glenn Braggs	.04	.02
342	Todd Stottlemyre	.07	.04	401	Tom Browning	.07	.04
343	Mike Timlin	.08	.05	402	Norm Charlton	.07	.04
344	Duane Ward	.04	.02	403	Eric Davis	.08	.05
345	David Wells	.04	.02	404	Rob Dibble	.07	.04
347	Mookie Wilson	.04	.02	405	Bill Doran	.04	.02
348	Eddie Zosky	.12	.07	406	Mariano Duncan	.04	.02

407 Kip Gross (R)	.08	.05
408 Chris Hammond	.08	.05
409 Billy Hatcher	.04	.02
410 Chris Jones (R)	.08	.05
411 Barry Larkin	.12	.07
412 Hal Morris	.10	.06
413 Randy Myers	.04	.02
414 Joe Oliver	.04	.02
415 Paul O'Neill	.08	.05
416 Ted Power	.04	.02
417 Luis Quinones	.04	.02
418 Jeff Reed	.04	.02
419 Jose Rijo	.08	.05
420 Chris Sabo	.07	.04
421 Reggie Sanders	.25	.15
422 Scott Scudder	.08	.05
423 Glenn Sutko	.04	.02
424 Eric Anthony	.12	.07
425 Jeff Bagwell	.35	.20
426 Craig Biggio	.08	.05
427 Ken Caminiti	.04	.02
428 Casey Candaele	.04	.02
429 Mike Capel	.04	.02
430 Andujar Cedeno	.10	.06
431 Jim Corsi	.04	.02
432 Mark Davidson	.04	.02
433 Steve Finley	.04	.02
434 Luis Gonzalez	.15	.10
435 Pete Harnisch	.07	.04
436 Dwayne Henry	.04	.02
437 Xavier Hernandez	.04	.02
438 Jimmy Jones	.04	.02
439 Darryl Kile	.12	.07
440 Rob Mallicoat	.04	.02
441 Andy Mota	.08	.05
442 Al Osuna	.04	.02
443 Mark Portugal	.07	.04
444 Scott Servais	.07	.04
445 Mike Simms	.04	.02
446 Gerald Young	.04	.02
447 Tim Belcher	.07	.04
448 Brett Butler	.08	.05
449 John Candelaria	.04	.02
450 Gary Carter	.08	.05
451 Dennis Cook	.04	.02
452 Tim Crews	.04	.02
453 Kal Daniels	.04	.02
454 Jim Gott	.04	.02
455 Alfredo Griffin	.04	.02
456 Kevin Gross	.04	.02
457 Chris Gwynn	.04	.02
458 Lenny Harris	.04	.02
459 Orel Hershiser	.08	.05
460 Jay Howell	.04	.02
461 Stan Javier	.04	.02
462 Eric Karros	.40	.25
463 Ramon Martinez	.10	.06

464 Roger McDowell	.04	.02
465 Mike Morgan	.04	.02
466 Eddie Murray	.15	.10
467 Jose Offerman	.08	.05
468 Bob Ojeda	.04	.02
469 Juan Samuel	.04	.02
470 Mike Scioscia	.04	.02
471 Darryl Strawberry	.15	.10
472 Bret Barberie	.12	.07
473 Brian Barnes	.08	.05
474 Eric Bullock	.04	.02
475 Ivan Calderon	.07	.04
476 Delino DeShields	.15	.10
477 Jeff Fassero	.08	.05
478 Mike Fitzgerald	.04	.02
479 Steve Frey	.04	.02
480 Andres Galarraga	.12	.07
481 Mark Gardner	.08	.05
482 Marquis Grissom	.15	.10
483 Chris Haney (R)	.12	.07
484 Barry Jones	.04	.02
485 Dave Martinez	.04	.02
486 Dennis Martinez	.08	.05
487 Chris Nabholz	.08	.05
488 Spike Owen	.04	.02
489 Gilberto Reyes	.04	.02
490 Mel Rojas	.07	.04
491 Scott Ruskin	.04	.02
492 Bill Sampen	.04	.02
493 Larry Walker	.15	.10
494 Tim Wallach	.07	.04
495 Daryl Boston	.04	.02
496 Hubie Brooks	.07	.04
497 Tim Burke	.04	.02
498 Mark Carreon	.04	.02
499 Tony Castillo	.04	.02
500 Vince Coleman	.07	.04
501 David Cone	.10	.06
502 Kevin Elster	.04	.02
503 Sid Fernandez	.07	.04
504 John Franco	.04	.02
505 Dwight Gooden	.12	.07
506 Todd Hundley	.08	.05
507 Jeff Innis	.04	.02
508 Gregg Jefferies	.12	.07
509 Howard Johnson	.10	.06
510 Dave Magadan	.07	.04
511 Terry McDaniel (R)	.10	.06
512 Kevin McReynolds	.07	.04
513 Keith Miller	.04	.02
514 Charlie O'Brien	.04	.02
515 Mackey Sasser	.04	.02
516 Pete Schourek	.07	.04
517 Julio Valera	.04	.02
518 Frank Viola	.08	.05
519 Wally Whitehurst	.04	.02
520 Anthony Young (R)	.20	.12

521	Andy Ashby	.04	.02	578	Bernard Gilkey	.10	.06
522	Kim Batiste	.10	.06	579	Pedro Guerero	.07	.04
523	Joe Boever	.04	.02	580	Ken Hill	.08	.05
524	Wes Chamberlain	.10	.06	581	Rex Hudler	.04	.02
525	Pat Combs	.07	.04	582	Felix Jose	.10	.06
526	Danny Cox	.04	.02	583	Ray Lankford	.15	.10
527	Darren Daulton	.12	.07	584	Omar Olivares	.08	.05
528	Jose DeJesus	.04	.02	585	Jose Oquendo	.04	.02
529	Lenny Dykstra	.12	.07	586	Tom Pagnozzi	.07	.04
530	Darrin Fletcher	.04	.02	587	Geronimo Pena	.04	.02
531	Tommy Greene	.10	.06	588	Mike Perez	.04	.02
532	Jason Grimsley	.04	.02	589	Gerald Perry	.04	.02
533	Charlie Hayes	.04	.02	590	Bryn Smith	.04	.02
534	Von Hayes	.04	.02	591	Lee Smith	.08	.05
535	Dave Hollins	.20	.12	592	Ozzie Smith	.15	.10
536	Ricky Jordan	.07	.04	593	Scott Terry	.04	.02
537	John Kruk	.10	.06	594	Bob Tewksbury	.04	.02
538	Jim Lindeman	.04	.02	595	Milt Thompson	.04	.02
539	Mickey Morandini	.08	.05	596	Todd Zeile	.08	.05
540	Terry Mulholland	.04	.02	597	Larry Andersen	.04	.02
541	Dale Murphy	.10	.06	598	Oscar Azocar	.04	.02
542	Randy Ready	.04	.02	599	Andy Benes	.12	.07
543	Wally Ritchie	.04	.02	600	Ricky Bones (R)	.10	.06
544	Bruce Ruffin	.04	.02	601	Jerald Clark	.04	.02
545	Steve Searcy	.04	.02	602	Pat Clements	.04	.02
546	Dickie Thon	.04	.02	603	Paul Faries	.04	.02
547	Mitch Williams	.04	.02	604	Tony Fernandez	.07	.04
548	Stan Belinda	.04	.02	605	Tony Gwynn	.15	.10
549	Jay Bell	.10	.06	606	Greg Harris	.04	.02
550	Barry Bonds	.50	.30	607	Thomas Howard	.04	.02
551	Bobby Bonilla	.10	.06	608	Bruce Hurst	.07	.04
552	Steve Buechele	.04	.02	609	Darrin Jackson	.04	.02
553	Doug Drabek	.10	.06	610	Tom Lampkin	.04	.02
554	Neal Heaton	.04	.02	611	Craig Lefferts	.04	.02
555	Jeff King	.07	.04	612	Jim Lewis (R)	.08	.05
556	Bob Kipper	.04	.02	613	Mike Maddux	.04	.02
557	Bill Landrum	.04	.02	614	Fred McGriff	.20	.12
558	Mike LaValliere	.04	.02	615	Jose Melendez (R)	.08	.05
559	Jose Lind	.04	.02	616	Jose Mota	.04	.02
560	Lloyd McClendon	.04	.02	617	Dennis Rasmussen	.04	.02
561	Orlando Merced	.12	.07	618	Bip Roberts	.04	.02
562	Bob Patterson	.04	.02	619	Rich Rodriguez	.04	.02
563	Joe Redfield (R)	.08	.05	620	Benito Santiago	.08	.05
564	Gary Redus	.04	.02	621	Craig Shipley (R)	.08	.05
565	Rosario Rodriguez	.04	.02	622	Tim Teufel	.04	.02
566	Don Slaught	.04	.02	623	Kevin Ward (R)	.08	.05
567	John Smiley	.08	.05	624	Ed Whitson	.04	.02
568	Zane Smith	.04	.02	625	Dave Anderson	.04	.02
569	Randy Tomlin	.08	.05	626	Kevin Bass	.04	.02
570	Andy Van Slyke	.12	.07	627	Rod Beck (R)	.20	.12
571	Gary Varsho	.04	.02	628	Bud Black	.04	.02
572	Bob Walk	.04	.02	629	Jeff Brantley	.04	.02
573	John Wehner	.07	.04	630	John Burkett	.08	.05
574	Juan Agosto	.04	.02	631	Will Clark	.20	.12
575	Cris Carpenter	.04	.02	632	Royce Clayton	.15	.10
576	Jose DeLeon	.04	.02	633	Steve Decker	.07	.04
577	Rich Gedman	.04	.02	634	Kelly Downs	.04	.02

635	Mike Felder	.04	.02
636	Scott Garrelts	.04	.02
637	Eric Gunderson	.04	.02
638	Bryan Hickerson (R)	.10	.06
639	Darren Lewis	.08	.05
640	Greg Litton	.04	.02
641	Kirt Manwaring	.04	.02
642	Paul McClellan (R)	.07	.04
643	Willie McGee	.08	.05
644	Kevin Mitchell	.08	.05
645	Francisco Olivares	.04	.02
646	Mike Remlinger (R)	.08	.05
647	Dave Righetti	.04	.02
648	Robby Thompson	.08	.05
649	Jose Uribe	.04	.02
650	Matt Williams	.15	.10
651	Trevor Wilson	.04	.02
652	Tom Goodwin	.12	.07
653	Terry Bross	.08	.05
654	Mike Christopher (R)	.08	.05
655	Kenny Lofton (R)	.40	.25
656	Chris Cron (R)	.08	.05
657	Willie Banks	.12	.07
658	Pat Rice (R)	.08	.05
659	Rob Maurer (R)	.20	.12
660	Don Harris	.10	.06
661	Henry Rodriguez	.10	.06
662	Cliff Brantley (R)	.10	.06
663	Mike Linskey (R)	.07	.04
664	Gary Disarcina	.10	.06
665	Gil Heredia (R)	.10	.06
666	Vinny Castilla (R)	.10	.06
667	Paul Abbott	.10	.06
668	Monty Fariss	.08	.05
669	Jarvis Brown (R)	.10	.06
670	Wayne Kirby (R)	.15	.10
671	Scott Brosius (R)	.10	.06
672	Bob Hamelin	.10	.06
673	Joel Johnston (R)	.10	.06
674	Tim Spehr (R)	.08	.05
675	Jeff Gardner (R)	.08	.05
676	Rico Rossy (R)	.08	.05
677	Roberto Hernandez (R)	.08	.05
678	Ted Wood	.10	.06
679	Cal Eldred	.30	.18
680	Sean Berry	.08	.05
681	Rickey Henderson(RS)	.12	.07
682	Nolan Ryan(RS)	.35	.20
683	Dennis Martinez(RS)	.08	.05
684	Wilson Alvarez(RS)	.08	.05
685	Joe Carter(RS)	.12	.07
686	Dave Winfield(RS)	.15	.10
687	David Cone(RS)	.08	.05
688	Jose Canseco(LL)	.15	.10
689	Howard Johnson(LL)	.07	.04
690	Julio Franco(LL)	.07	.04
691	Terry Pendleton(LL)	.08	.05

692	Cecil Fielder(LL)	.10	.06
693	Scott Erickson(LL)	.08	.05
694	Tom Glavine(LL)	.12	.07
695	Dennis Martinez(LL)	.07	.04
696	Bryan Harvey(LL)	.07	.04
697	Lee Smith(LL)	.08	.05
698	Super Siblings(Roberto & Sandy Alomar)	.15	.10
699	The Indispensables (B. Bonilla & W. Clark)	.10	.06
700	Teamwork(Wohlers, Mercker & Pena)	.08	.05
701	Tiger Tandems S. Jones, B. Jackson, G. Olson, F. Thomas)	.30	.18
702	The Ignitors(P. Molitor B. Butler)	.10	.06
703	The Indespensables II (C. Ripken, Jr., J. Carter)	.15	.10
704	Power Packs(B. Larkin, K. Puckett)	.12	.07
705	Today & Tomorrow (M. Vaughn, C. Fielder)	.15	.10
706	Teenage Sensations (R. Martinez, O. Guillen)	.10	.06
707	Designated Hitters (H. Baines, W. Boggs)	.10	.06
708	Robin Yount(PV)	.25	.15
709	Ken Griffey, Jr.(PV)	1.00	.70
710	Nolan Ryan(PV)	.90	.60
711	Cal Ripken, Jr.(PV)	.50	.30
712	Frank Thomas(PV)	1.25	.80
713	Dave Justice(PV)	.35	.20
714	Checklist	.04	.01
715	Checklist	.04	.01
716	Checklist	.04	.01
717	Checklist	.04	.01
718	Checklist	.04	.01
719	Checklist	.04	.01
720	Checklist	.04	.01
BC1-	Roger Clemens	1.25ea.	.80ea.
BC15	(Bonus Inserts.)		

1992 Fleer Update

This 132-card update set contains mostly rookies and players traded during the 1992 season. The card design is nearly identical to the regular Fleer edition except for the card numbers which carry the "U" designation. Factory sets contain 4 Bonus Cards called Headliners (H). Those cards are included at the end of this checklist but not in the complete set price below. All cards measure 2-1/2" by 3-1/2".

		MINT	NR/MT
Complete Set (132)		160.00	95.00
Commons		.25	.15

		MINT	NR/MT
1	Todd Frohwirth	.25	.15
2	Alan Mills	.30	.18
3	Rick Sutcliffe	.30	.18
4	John Valentin (R)	2.50	1.50
5	Frank Viola	.30	.18
6	Bob Zupcic (R)	1.25	.80
7	Mike Butcher (R)	.35	.20
8	Chad Curtis (R)	7.00	4.00
9	Damion Easley (R)	2.00	1.25
10	Tim Salmon	38.00	25.00
11	Julio Valera	.25	.15
12	George Bell	.35	.20
13	Roberto Hernandez	1.50	.90
14	Shawn Jeter (R)	.35	.20
15	Thomas Howard	.25	.15
16	Jesse Levis (R)	.35	.20
17	Kenny Lofton	10.00	6.50
18	Paul Sorrento	.50	.30
19	Rico Brogna	.60	.35
20	John Doherty (R)	1.25	.80
21	Dan Gladden	.25	.15
22	Buddy Groom (R)	.30	.18
23	Shawn Hare (R)	.40	.25
24	John Kiely (R)	.35	.20
25	Kurt Knudsen (R)	.40	.25
26	Gregg Jefferies	2.50	1.50
27	Wally Joyner	.35	.20
28	Kevin Koslofski (R)	.35	.20
29	Kevin McReynolds	.30	.18
30	Rusty Meacham	.25	.15
31	Keith Miller	.25	.15
32	Hipolito Pichardo (R)	.80	.50
33	James Austin (R)	.35	.20
34	Scott Fletcher	.25	.15
35	John Jaha (R)	2.50	1.50
36	Pat Listach (R)	2.00	1.25
37	Dave Nilsson	.60	.35
38	Kevin Seitzer	.25	.15
39	Tom Edens	.30	.18
40	Pat Mahomes (R)	1.75	1.00
41	John Smiley	.35	.20
42	Charlie Hayes	.50	.30
43	Sam Militello	1.00	.70
44	Andy Stankiewicz (R)	.40	.25
45	Danny Tartabull	.35	.20
46	Bob Wickman	3.50	2.00
47	Jerry Browne	.25	.15
48	Kevin Campbell (R)	.35	.20
49	Vince Horsman (R)	.40	.25
50	Troy Neel (R)	3.00	1.75
51	Ruben Sierra	1.25	.80
52	Bruce Walton	.25	.15
53	Willie Wilson	.25	.15
54	Bret Boone (R)	3.50	2.00
55	Dave Fleming	4.50	2.75
56	Kevin Mitchell	.35	.20
57	Jeff Nelson (R)	.35	.20
58	Shane Turner	.25	.15
59	Jose Ccanseco	1.75	1.00
60	Jeff Frye (R)	.40	.25
61	Danilo Leon (R)	.30	.18
62	Roger Pavlik (R)	2.00	1.25
63	David Cone	.35	.20
64	Pat Hentgen	6.50	3.75
65	Randy Knorr (R)	.40	.25
66	Jack Morris	.40	.25
67	Dave Winfield	4.00	2.50
68	David Nied (R)	7.00	4.00
69	Otis Nixon	.30	.18
70	Alejandro Pena	.25	.15
71	Jeff Reardon	.35	.20
72	Alex Arias (R)	.60	.35
73	Jim Bullinger	.25	.15
74	Mike Morgan	.25	.15
75	Rey Sanchez (R)	.80	.50
76	Bob Scanlan	.25	.15
77	Sammy Sosa	2.50	1.50
78	Scott Bankhead	.25	.15
79	Tim Belcher	.25	.15
80	Steve Foster (R)	.40	.25
81	Willie Greene	1.75	1.00
82	Bip Roberts	.25	.15
83	Scott Ruskin	.25	.15

84	Greg Swindell	.30	.18
85	Juan Guerrero (R)	.35	.20
86	Butch Henry (R)	.60	.35
87	Doug Jones	.25	.15
88	Brian Williams (R)	.80	.50
89	Tom Candiotti	.25	.15
90	Eric Davis	.35	.20
91	Carlos Hernandez	.30	.18
92	Mike Piazza (R)	70.00	40.00
93	Mike Sharperson	.25	.15
94	Eric Young (R)	2.00	1.25
95	Moises Alou	2.50	1.50
96	Greg Colbrunn	.80	.50
97	Wil Cordero	3.50	2.00
98	Ken Hill	.70	.40
99	John Vander Wal (R)	.60	.35
100	John Wetteland	.50	.30
101	Bobby Bonilla	.80	.50
102	Eric Hillman (R)	.60	.35
103	Pat Howell (R)	.35	.20
104	Jeff Kent (R)	3.00	1.75
105	Dick Schofield	.25	.15
106	Ryan Thompson (R)	1.75	1.00
107	Chico Walker	.25	.15
108	Juan Bell	.25	.15
109	Mariano Duncan	.25	.15
110	Jeff Grotewold (R)	.35	.20
111	Ben Rivers	.80	.50
112	Curt Schilling	1.25	.80
113	Victor Cole (R)	.40	.25
114	Albert Martin (R)	4.50	2.75
115	Roger Mason	.25	.15
116	Blas Minor (R)	.35	.20
117	Tim Wakefield (R)	1.25	.80
118	Mark Clark (R)	1.50	.90
119	Rheal Cormier	.40	.25
120	Donovan Osborne	3.00	1.75
121	Todd Worrell	.25	.15
122	Jeremy Hernandez (R)	.50	.30
123	Randy Myers	.30	.18
124	Frank Seminara (R)	.35	.20
125	Gary Sheffield	2.50	1.50
126	Dan Walters (R)	.75	.45
127	Steve Hosey	2.00	1.25
128	Mike Jackson	.30	.18
129	Jim Pena (R)	.35	.20
130	Cory Snyder	.25	.15
131	Bill Swift	.60	.35
132	Checklist	.25	.10
H1	Ken Griffey Jr.	45.00	30.00
H2	Robin Yount	7.50	4.50
H3	Jeff Reardon	1.00	.70
H4	Cecil Fielder	7.50	4.50

1992 Fleer Ultra

For the second straight year Fleer produced a premium, upscale baseball card set. The 1992 edition contains 600 cards, each measuring 2-1/2" by 3-1/2". Card fronts feature full color action photos with marble-looking borders and a box at the bottom that holds the player's name, team and position. The horizontal card backs feature two photos and, through computer enhancement, the cards have a three-dimensional look. The set was issued in two series and includes a number of limited insert cards which were randomly issued in the foil packs. Those inserts consist of a 12-card Tony Gwynn set which includes two Gwynn cards available only by mail, a 20-card Ultra All-Stars Insert set, a 10-card All-Rookie Team Insert Set and a 25-card Ultra Award Winners Insert Set. Those insert cards are listed at the end of this checklist but are not included in the complete set price.

		MINT	NR/MT
Complete Set (600)		62.00	45.00
Commons		.10	.06

1	Glenn Davis	.12	.07
2	Mike Devereaux	.12	.07
3	Dwight Evans	.12	.07
4	Leo Gomez	.20	.12
5	Chris Hoiles	.15	.10
6	Sam Horn	.10	.06
7	Chito Martinez	.15	.10
8	Randy Milligan	.10	.06
9	Mike Mussina	2.00	1.25
10	Billy Ripken	.10	.06
11	Cal Ripken, Jr.	1.50	.90
12	Tom Brunansky	.10	.06
13	Ellis Burks	.12	.07
14	Jack Clark	.12	.07

15	Roger Clemens	1.50	.90	72	Joel Johnston	.15	.10
16	Mike Greenwell	.12	.07	73	Mike Macfarlane	.10	.06
17	Joe Hesketh	.10	.06	74	Brent Mayne	.12	.07
18	Tony Pena	.10	.06	75	Brian McRae	.15	.10
19	Carlos Quintana	.12	.07	76	Jeff Montgomery	.12	.07
20	Jeff Reardon	.15	.10	77	Danny Tartabull	.20	.12
21	Jody Reed	.10	.06	78	Don August	.10	.06
22	Luis Rivera	.10	.06	79	Dante Bichette	.15	.10
23	Mo Vaughn	1.00	.70	80	Ted Higuera	.10	.06
24	Gary DiSarcina	.15	.10	81	Paul Molitor	.30	.18
25	Chuck Finley	.12	.07	82	Jamie Navarro	.15	.10
26	Gary Gaetti	.10	.06	83	Gary Sheffield	.70	.40
27	Bryan Harvey	.12	.07	84	Bill Spiers	.10	.06
28	Lance Parrish	.10	.06	85	B.J. Surhoff	.10	.06
29	Luis Polonia	.12	.07	86	Greg Vaughn	.15	.10
30	Dick Schofield	.10	.06	87	Robin Yount	.80	.50
31	Luis Sojo	.10	.06	88	Rick Aguilera	.10	.06
32	Wilson Alvarez	.30	.18	89	Chili Davis	.12	.07
33	Carlton Fisk	.30	.18	90	Scott Erickson	.25	.15
34	Craig Grebeck	.10	.06	91	Brian Harper	.10	.06
35	Ozzie Guillen	.12	.07	92	Ken Hrbek	.12	.07
36	Greg Hibbard	.10	.06	93	Chuck Knoblauch	.30	.18
37	Charlie Hough	.10	.06	94	Scott Leius	.15	.10
38	Lance Johnson	.10	.06	95	Shane Mack	.20	.12
39	Ron Karkovice	.10	.06	96	Mike Pagliarulo	.10	.06
40	Jack McDowell	.60	.35	97	Kirby Puckett	1.00	.70
41	Donn Pall	.10	.06	98	Kevin Tapani	.12	.07
42	Melido Perez	.12	.07	99	Jesse Barfield	.12	.07
43	Tim Raines	.15	.10	100	Alvaro Espinoza	.10	.06
44	Frank Thomas	5.00	3.00	101	Mel Hall	.12	.07
45	Sandy Alomar, Jr.	.12	.07	102	Pat Kelly	.15	.10
46	Carlos Baerga	1.00	.70	103	Roberto Kelly	.25	.15
47	Albert Belle	.90	.60	104	Kevin Maas	.12	.07
48	Jerry Browne	.10	.06	105	Don Mattingly	.60	.35
49	Felix Fermin	.10	.06	106	Hensley Meullens	.12	.07
50	Reggie Jefferson	.15	.10	107	Matt Nokes	.10	.06
51	Mark Lewis	.12	.07	108	Steve Sax	.15	.10
52	Carlos Martinez	.10	.06	109	Harold Baines	.12	.07
53	Steve Olin	.10	.06	110	Jose Canseco	.70	.40
54	Jim Thome	.60	.35	111	Ron Darling	.10	.06
55	Mark Whiten	.30	.18	112	Mike Gallego	.10	.06
56	Dave Bergman	.10	.06	113	Dave Henderson	.12	.07
57	Milt Culyer	.12	.07	114	Rickey Henderson	.50	.30
58	Rob Deer	.12	.07	115	Mark McGwire	.60	.35
59	Cecil Fielder	.60	.35	116	Terry Steinbach	.10	.06
60	Travis Fryman	1.25	.80	117	Dave Stewart	.12	.07
61	Scott Livingston	.20	.12	118	Todd Van Poppel	.80	.50
62	Tony Phillips	.12	.07	119	Bob Welch	.12	.07
63	Mickey Tettleton	.12	.07	120	Greg Briley	.10	.06
64	Alan Trammell	.20	.12	121	Jay Buhner	.12	.07
65	Lou Whitaker	.12	.07	122	Rich DeLucia	.12	.07
66	Kevin Appier	.15	.10	123	Ken Griffey, Jr.	4.00	3.00
67	Mike Boddicker	.10	.06	124	Erik Hanson	.15	.10
68	Geroge Brett	.80	.50	125	Randy Johnson	.35	.20
69	Jim Eisenreich	.10	.06	126	Edgar Martinez	.25	.15
70	Mark Gubicza	.12	.07	127	Tino Martinez	.12	.07
71	Dave Howard	.12	.07	128	Pete O'Brien	.10	.06

129	Harold Reynolds	.10	.06
130	Dave Valle	.10	.06
131	Julio Franco	.15	.10
132	Juan Gonzalez	3.00	2.00
133	Jeff Huson	.12	.07
134	Mike Jeffcoat	.10	.06
135	Terry Matthews	.10	.06
136	Rafael Palmeiro	.25	.15
137	Dean Palmer	.80	.50
138	Geno Petralli	.10	.06
139	Ivan Rodriquez	.90	.60
140	Jeff Russell	.10	.06
141	Nolan Ryan	3.50	2.50
142	Ruben Sierra	.30	.18
143	Roberto Alomar	1.50	.90
144	Pat Borders	.10	.06
145	Joe Carter	.75	.45
146	Kelly Gruber	.12	.07
147	Jimmy Key	.15	.10
148	Manny Lee	.10	.06
149	Rance Mulliniks	.10	.06
150	Greg Myers	.10	.06
151	John Olerud	1.25	.80
152	Dave Stieb	.12	.07
153	Todd Stottlemyre	.12	.07
154	Duane Ward	.10	.06
155	Devon White	.15	.10
156	Eddie Zosky	.20	.12
157	Steve Avery	1.00	.70
158	Rafael Belliard	.10	.06
159	Jeff Blauser	.15	.10
160	Sid Bream	.10	.06
161	Ron Gant	.40	.25
162	Tom Glavine	.70	.40
163	Brian Hunter	.25	.15
164	Dave Justice	1.25	.80
165	Mark Lemke	.10	.06
166	Greg Olson	.10	.06
167	Terry Pendleton	.30	.18
168	Lonnie Smith	.10	.06
169	John Smoltz	.30	.18
170	Mike Stanton	.12	.07
171	Jeff Treadway	.10	.06
172	Paul Assenmacher	.10	.06
173	George Bell	.20	.12
174	Shawon Dunston	.12	.07
175	Mark Grace	.25	.15
176	Danny Jackson	.10	.06
177	Les Lancaster	.10	.06
178	Greg Maddux	.35	.20
179	Luis Salazar	.10	.06
180	Rey Sanchez (R)	.25	.15
181	Ryne Sandberg	1.00	.70
182	Jose Viscaino	.10	.06
183	Chico Walker	.10	.06
184	Jerome Walton	.12	.07
185	Glenn Braggs	.10	.06
186	Tom Browning	.12	.07
187	Rob Dibble	.12	.07
188	Bill Doran	.10	.06
189	Chris Hammond	.20	.12
190	Billy Hatcher	.10	.06
191	Barry Larkin	.30	.18
192	Hal Morris	.15	.10
193	Joe Oliver	.10	.06
194	Paul O'Neill	.12	.07
195	Jeff Reed	.10	.06
196	Jose Rijo	.15	.10
197	Chris Sabo	.12	.07
198	Jeff Bagwell	1.50	.90
199	Craig Biggio	.15	.10
200	Ken Caminiti	.12	.07
201	Andujar Cedeno	.20	.12
202	Steve Finley	.10	.06
203	Luis Gonzalez	.20	.12
204	Pete Harnisch	.12	.07
205	Xavier Hernandez	.15	.10
206	Darryl Kile	.70	.40
207	Al Osuna	.10	.06
208	Curt Schilling	.15	.10
209	Brett Butler	.15	.10
210	Kal Daniels	.10	.06
211	Lenny Harris	.10	.06
212	Stan Javier	.10	.06
213	Ramon Martinez	.20	.12
214	Roger McDowell	.10	.06
215	Jose Offerman	.15	.10
216	Juan Samuel	.10	.06
217	Mike Scioscia	.10	.06
218	Mike Sharperson	.10	.06
219	Darryl Strawberry	.25	.15
220	Delino DeShields	.30	.18
221	Tom Foley	.10	.06
222	Steve Frey	.10	.06
223	Dennis Martinez	.15	.10
224	Spike Owen	.10	.06
225	Gilbert Reyes	.10	.06
226	Tim Wallach	.12	.07
227	Daryl Boston	.10	.06
228	Tim Burke	.10	.06
229	Vince Coleman	.12	.07
230	David Cone	.20	.12
231	Kevin Elster	.10	.06
232	Dwight Gooden	.25	.15
233	Todd Hundley	.12	.07
234	Jeff Innis	.10	.06
235	Howard Johnson	.15	.10
236	Dave Magadan	.12	.07
237	Mackey Sasser	.10	.06
238	Anthony Young	.20	.12
239	Wes Chamberlain	.20	.12
240	Darren Daulton	.30	.18
241	Lenny Dykstra	.30	.18
242	Tommy Greene	.20	.12

243	Charlie Hayes	.10	.06
244	Dave Hollins	.70	.40
245	Ricky Jordan	.12	.07
246	John Kruk	.25	.15
247	Mickey Morandini	.15	.10
248	Terry Mulholland	.10	.06
249	Dale Murphy	.15	.10
250	Jay Bell	.20	.12
251	Barry Bonds	1.75	1.00
252	Steve Buechele	.12	.07
253	Doug Drabek	.25	.15
254	Mike LaValliere	.10	.06
255	Jose Lind	.10	.06
256	Lloyd McClendon	.10	.06
257	Orlando Merced	.30	.18
258	Don Slaught	.10	.06
259	John Smiley	.15	.10
260	Zane Smith	.12	.07
261	Randy Tomlin	.15	.10
262	Andy Van Slyke	.25	.10
263	Pedro Guerrero	.12	.07
264	Felix Jose	.20	.12
265	Ray Lankford	.30	.18
266	Omar Olivares	.15	.10
267	Jose Oquendo	.10	.06
268	Tom Pagnozzi	.12	.07
269	Bryn Smith	.10	.06
270	Lee Smith	.15	.10
271	Ozzie Smith	.40	.25
272	Milt Thompson	.10	.06
273	Todd Zeile	.15	.10
274	Andy Benes	.25	.15
275	Jerald Clark	.12	.07
276	Tony Fernandez	.12	.07
277	Tony Gwynn	.40	.25
278	Gregg Harris	.12	.07
279	Thomas Howard	.12	.07
280	Bruce Hurst	.12	.07
281	Mike Maddux	.10	.06
282	Fred McGriff	.80	.50
283	Benito Santiago	.15	.10
284	Kevin Bass	.10	.06
285	Jeff Brantley	.10	.06
286	John Burkett	.20	.12
287	Will Clark	.75	.45
288	Royce Clayton	.50	.30
289	Steve Decker	.12	.07
290	Kelly Downs	.10	.06
291	Mike Felder	.10	.06
292	Darren Lewis	.15	.10
293	Kirt Manwaring	.10	.06
294	Willie McGee	.15	.10
295	Robby Thompson	.15	.10
296	Matt Williams	.35	.20
297	Trevor Wilson	.10	.06
298	Checklist	.10	.04
299	Checklist	.10	.04
300	Checklist	.10	.04
301	Brady Anderson	.20	.12
302	Todd Frohwirth	.10	.06
303	Ben McDonald	.30	.18
304	Mark McLemore	.10	.06
305	Jose Mesa	.10	.06
306	Bob Milacki	.10	.06
307	Gregg Olson	.15	.10
308	David Segui	.12	.07
309	Rick Sutcliffe	.12	.07
310	Jeff Tackett	.12	.07
311	Wade Boggs	.40	.25
312	Scott Cooper	.35	.20
313	John Flaherty (R)	.15	.10
314	Wayne Housie (R)	.15	.10
315	Peter Hoy (R)	.15	.10
316	John Marzano	.10	.06
317	Tim Naehring	.15	.10
318	Phil Plantier	.70	.40
319	Frank Viola	.15	.10
320	Matt Young	.10	.06
321	Jim Abbott	.35	.20
322	Hubie Brooks	.12	.07
323	Chad Curtis (R)	1.25	.80
324	Alvin Davis	.10	.06
325	Junior Felix	.10	.06
326	Von Hayes	.10	.06
327	Mark Langston	.20	.12
328	Scott Lewis	.12	.07
329	Don Robinson	.10	.06
330	Bobby Rose	.10	.06
331	Lee Stevens	.10	.06
332	George Bell	.15	.10
333	Esteban Beltre (R)	.20	.12
334	Joey Cora	.10	.06
335	Alex Fernandez	.75	.45
336	Roberto Hernandez	.25	.15
337	Mike Huff	.10	.06
338	Kirk McCaskill	.10	.06
339	Dan Pasqua	.10	.06
340	Scott Radinsky	.12	.07
341	Steve Sax	.12	.07
342	Bobby Thigpen	.12	.07
343	Robin Ventura	.70	.40
344	Jack Armstrong	.12	.07
345	Alex Cole	.10	.06
346	Dennis Cook	.10	.06
347	Glenallen Hill	.12	.07
348	Thomas Howard	.12	.07
349	Brook Jacoby	.10	.06
350	Kenny Lofton	1.50	.90
351	Charles Nagy	.50	.30
352	Rod Nichols	.10	.06
353	Junior Ortiz	.10	.06
354	Dave Otto	.10	.06
355	Tony Perezchica	.10	.06
356	Scott Scudder	.12	.07

357	Paul Sorrento	.15	.10
358	Skeeter Barnes	.10	.06
359	Mark Carreon	.10	.06
360	John Doherty (R)	.20	.12
361	Dan Gladden	.10	.06
362	Bill Gullickson	.10	.06
363	Shawn Hare (R)	.20	.12
364	Mike Henneman	.10	.06
365	Chad Kreuter	.12	.07
366	Mark Leiter	.10	.06
367	Mike Munoz	.10	.06
368	Kevin Ritz	.12	.07
369	Mark Davis	.10	.06
370	Tom Gordon	.12	.07
371	Chris Gwynn	.10	.06
372	Gregg Jefferies	.30	.18
373	Wally Joyner	.20	.12
374	Kevin McReynolds	.12	.07
375	Keith Miller	.10	.06
376	Rico Rossy (R)	.20	.12
377	Curtis Wilkerson	.10	.06
378	Ricky Bones	.20	.12
379	Chris Bosio	.10	.06
380	Cal Eldred	1.00	.70
381	Scott Fletcher	.10	.06
382	Jim Gantner	.10	.06
383	Darryl Hamilton	.20	.12
384	Doug Henry (R)	.35	.20
385	Pat Listach (R)	.90	.60
386	Tim McIntosh	.25	.15
387	Edwin Nunez	.10	.06
388	Dan Plesac	.10	.06
389	Kevin Seitzer	.12	.07
390	Franklin Stubbs	.10	.06
391	William Suero	.15	.10
392	Bill Wegman	.10	.06
393	Willie Banks	.25	.15
394	Jarvis Brown (R)	.20	.12
395	Greg Gagne	.10	.06
396	Mark Guthrie (R)	.20	.12
397	Bill Krueger	.12	.07
398	Pat Mahomes (R)	.75	.45
399	Pedro Munoz	.30	.18
400	John Smiley	.15	.10
401	Gary Wayne (R)	.15	.10
402	Lenny Webster	.10	.06
403	Carl Willis	.10	.06
404	Greg Cadaret	.10	.06
405	Steve Farr	.10	.06
406	Mike Gallego	.10	.06
407	Charlie Hayes	.10	.06
408	Steve Howe	.10	.06
409	Dion James	.10	.06
410	Jeff Johnson	.10	.06
411	Tim Leary	.10	.06
412	Jim Leyritz	.10	.06
413	Melido Perez	.12	.07
414	Scott Sanderson	.10	.06
415	Andy Stankiewicz (R)	.20	.12
416	Mike Stanley	.15	.10
417	Danny Tartabull	.20	.12
418	Lance Blankenship	.10	.06
419	Mike Bordick	.25	.15
420	Scott Brosius (R)	.20	.10
421	Dennis Eckersley	.30	.18
422	Scott Hemond (R)	.15	.10
423	Carney Lansford	.12	.07
424	Henry Mercedes (R)	.20	.12
425	Mike Moore	.10	.06
426	Gene Nelson	.10	.06
427	Randy Ready	.10	.06
428	Bruce Wilson (R)	.15	.10
429	Willie Wilson	.10	.06
430	Rich Amaral (R)	.20	.12
431	Dave Cochrane (R)	.15	.10
432	Henry Cotto	.10	.06
433	Calvin Jones (R)	.20	.12
434	Kevin Mitchell	.25	.15
435	Clay Parker	.10	.06
436	Omar Vizquel	.10	.06
437	Floyd Bannister	.10	.06
438	Kevin Brown	.15	.10
439	John Cangelosi	.10	.06
440	Brian Downing	.12	.07
441	Monty Fariss	.20	.12
442	Jose Guzman	.10	.06
443	Donald Harris	.15	.10
444	Kevin Reimer	.12	.07
445	Kenny Rogers	.10	.06
446	Wayne Rosenthal (R)	.12	.07
447	Dickie Thon	.10	.06
448	Derek Bell	.70	.40
449	Juan Guzman	1.25	.80
450	Tom Henke	.10	.06
451	Candy Maldonado	.10	.06
452	Jack Morris	.25	.15
453	David Wells	.10	.06
454	Dave Winfield	.75	.45
455	Juan Berenguer	.10	.06
456	Damon Berryhill	.10	.06
457	Mike Bielecki	.10	.06
458	Marvin Freeman	.10	.06
459	Charlie Leibrandt	.10	.06
460	Kent Mercker	.15	.10
461	Otis Nixon	.12	.07
462	Alejandro Pena	.10	.06
463	Ben Rivera	.15	.10
464	Deion Sanders	.40	.25
465	Mark Wohlers	.30	.18
466	Shawn Boskie	.12	.07
467	Frank Castillo	.10	.06
468	Andre Dawson	.35	.20
469	Joe Girardi	.10	.06
470	Chuck McElroy	.10	.06

471	Mike Morgan	.12	.07
472	Ken Patterson	.10	.06
473	Bob Scanlan	.10	.06
474	Gary Scott	.12	.07
475	Dave Smith	.10	.06
476	Sammy Sosa	.60	.35
477	Hector Villanueva	.10	.06
478	Scott Bankhead	.10	.06
479	Tim Belcher	.12	.07
480	Freddie Benavides	.10	.06
481	Jacob Brumfield (R)	.15	.10
482	Norm Charlton	.12	.07
483	Dwayne Henry	.12	.07
484	Dave Martinez	.10	.06
485	Bip Roberts	.12	.07
486	Reggie Sanders	.80	.50
487	Greg Swindell	.15	.10
488	Ryan Bowen	.15	.10
489	Casey Candaele	.10	.06
490	Juan Guerrero (R)	.15	.10
491	Pete Incaviglia	.10	.06
492	Jeff Juden	.30	.18
493	Rob Murphy	.10	.06
494	Mark Portugal	.12	.07
495	Rafael Ramirez	.10	.06
496	Scott Servais	.12	.07
497	Ed Taubensee (R)	.20	.12
498	Brian Williams (R)	.25	.15
499	Todd Benzinger	.10	.06
500	John Candelaria	.10	.06
501	Tom Candiotti	.10	.06
502	Tim Crews	.10	.06
503	Eric Davis	.20	.12
504	Jim Gott	.10	.06
505	Dave Hansen	.12	.07
506	Carlos Hernandez	.15	.10
507	Orel Hershiser	.20	.12
508	Eric Karros	1.50	.90
509	Bob Ojeda	.10	.06
510	Steve Wilson	.10	.06
511	Moises Alou	.50	.30
512	Bret Barberie	.15	.10
513	Ivan Calderon	.12	.07
514	Gary Carter	.20	.12
515	Archi Cianfrocco (R)	.30	.18
516	Jeff Fassero	.15	.10
517	Darrin Fletcher	.15	.10
518	Marquis Grissom	.50	.30
519	Chris Haney	.25	.15
520	Ken Hill	.20	.12
521	Chris Nabholz	.20	.12
522	Bill Sampen	.10	.06
523	John Vander Wal (R)	.20	.12
524	Dave Wainhouse (R)	.15	.10
525	Larry Walker	.40	.25
526	John Wetteland	.20	.12
527	Bobby Bonilla	.25	.15
528	Sid Fernandez	.12	.07
529	John Franco	.10	.06
530	Dave Gallagher	.10	.06
531	Paul Gibson	.10	.06
532	Eddie Murray	.35	.20
533	Junior Noboa	.10	.06
534	Charlie O'Brien	.10	.06
535	Bill Pecota	.10	.06
536	Willie Randolph	.12	.07
537	Bret Saberhagen	.20	.12
538	Dick Schofield	.10	.06
539	Pete Schourek	.15	.10
540	Ruben Amaro	.12	.07
541	Andy Ashby	.12	.07
542	Kim Batiste	.20	.12
543	Cliff Brantley	.12	.07
544	Mariano Duncan	.10	.06
545	Jeff Grotewold (R)	.15	.10
546	Barry Jones	.10	.06
547	Julio Peguero (R)	.20	.12
548	Curt Schilling	.20	.12
549	Mitch Williams	.12	.07
550	Stan Belinda	.10	.06
551	Scott Bullett (R)	.25	.15
552	Cecil Espy	.10	.06
553	Jeff King	.15	.10
554	Roger Mason	.10	.06
555	Paul Miller (R)	.25	.15
556	Denny Neagle	.15	.10
557	Victor Palacios (R)	.15	.10
558	Bob Patterson	.10	.06
559	Tom Prince (R)	.12	.07
560	Gary Redus	.10	.06
561	Gary Varsho	.10	.06
562	Juan Agosto	.10	.06
563	Cris Carpenter	.12	.07
564	Mark Clark (R)	.25	.15
565	Jose DeLeon	.10	.06
566	Rich Gedman	.10	.06
567	Bernard Gilkey	.20	.12
568	Rex Hudler	.10	.06
569	Tim Jones	.12	.07
570	Donovan Osborne	.50	.30
571	Mike Perez	.10	.06
572	Gerald Perry	.10	.06
573	Bob Tewksbury	.10	.06
574	Todd Worrell	.12	.07
575	Dave Eiland	.10	.06
576	Jeremy Hernandez (R)	.20	.12
577	Craig Lefferts	.10	.06
578	Jose Melendez	.12	.07
579	Randy Myers	.10	.06
580	Gary Pettis	.10	.06
581	Rich Rodriquez	.12	.07
582	Gary Sheffield	.70	.40
583	Craig Shipley	.10	.06
584	Kurt Stillwell	.10	.06

585	Tim Teufel	.10	.06
586	Rod Beck (R)	.75	.45
587	Dave Burba (R)	.15	.10
588	Craig Colbert (R)	.15	.10
589	Bryan Hickerson (R)	.20	.12
590	Mike Jackson (R)	.15	.10
591	Mark Leonard (R)	.20	.12
592	Jim McNamara (R)	.15	.10
593	John Patterson (R)	.15	.10
594	Dave Righetti	.10	.06
595	Cory Snyder	.12	.07
596	Bill Swift	.25	.15
597	Ted Wood (R)	.20	.12
598	Checklist	.10	.04
599	Checklist	.10	.04
600	Checklist	.10	.04
BC1-	Tony Gwynn (Bonus	1.25	.80ea
BC10	Inserts Cards)		
BC11	Tony Gwynn (Mail-in	1.50	.90
	Bonus Card)		
BC12	Tony Gwynn(Mail-in	1.50	.90
	Bonus Card)		
___	Tony Gwynn Signed	125.00	65.00

1992 Fleer Ultra Award Winners

		MINT	NR/MT
Complete Set (25)		55.00	32.00
Commons		.75	.45
1	Jack Morris	1.00	.70
2	Chuck Knoblauch	1.75	1.00
3	Jeff Bagwell	5.00	3.00
4	Terry Pendleton	1.00	.70
5	Cal Ripken Jr.	6.00	3.50
6	Roger Clemens	5.00	3.00
7	Tom Glavine	3.50	2.00
8	Tom Pagnozzi	.75	.45
9	Ozzie Smith	2.50	1.50
10	Andy Van Slyke	1.50	.90
11	Barry Bonds	8.00	5.00
12	Tony Gwynn	3.00	1.75
13	Matt Williams	2.50	1.50
14	Will Clark	3.50	2.00
15	Robin Ventura	2.50	1.50
16	Mark Langston	1.00	.70
17	Tony Pena	.75	.45
18	Devon White	1.00	.70

19	Don Mattingly	3.00	1.75
20	Roberto Alomar	6.00	3.50
21	Cal Ripken Jr	6.00	3.50
22	Ken Griffey Jr.	12.00	7.00
23	Kirby Puckett	5.00	3.00
24	Greg Maddux	2.50	1.50
25	Ryne Sandberg	5.00	3.00

1992 Fleer Ultra All-Stars

		MINT	NR/MT
Complete Set (20)		32.00	20.00
Commons		.60	.35
1	Mark McGwire	1.75	1.00
2	Roberto Alomar	4.00	2.50
3	Cal Ripken Jr.	5.00	3.00
4	Wade Boggs	1.25	.80
5	Mickey Tettleton	.60	.35
6	Ken Griffey Jr.	10.00	6.50
7	Roberto Kelly	1.25	.80
8	Kirby Puckett	3.50	2.00
9	Frank Thomas	12.00	7.50
10	Jack McDowell	2.50	1.50
11	Will Clark	3.00	1.75
12	Ryne Sandberg	4.00	2.50
13	Barry Larkin	1.25	.80
14	Gary Sheffield	2.50	1.50
15	Tom Pagnozzi	.60	.35
16	Barry Bonds	5.00	3.00
17	Deion Sanders	1.50	.90
18	Darryl Strawberry	1.25	.80
19	David Cone	.75	.45
20	Tom Glavine	2.50	1.50

1992 Fleer Ultra All-Rookies

		MINT	NR/MT
Complete Set (10)		22.00	13.00
Commons		.60	.35

1	Eric Karros	4.00	2.50
2	Andy Stankiewicz	.60	.25
3	Gary DiSarcina	.75	.45
4	Archi Cianfroco	1.00	.70
5	Jim McNamara	.60	.35
6	Chad Curtis	4.00	2.50
7	Kenny Lofton	7.50	4.50
8	Reggie Sanders	3.00	1.75
9	Pat Mahomes	1.50	.90
10	Donovan Osborne	2.00	1.25

1993 Fleer

This set was issued in two series. The card fronts feature full color action photos framed by a silver border. The player's name, team and position are printed vertically along the border. Card backs include another action shot set against a silver background with the player's last name headlined across the top. Subsets include League Leaders (LL) and Round Trippers (RT). A 12-card limited Tom Glavine Signature Series set is also included at the end of the checklist below but not included in the complete set price. All cards measure 2-1/2" by 3-1/2".

	MINT	NR/MT
Complete Set (360)	35.00	22.00
Commons	.05	.02

1	Steve Avery	.20	.12
2	Sid Bream	.05	.02
3	Ron Gant	.12	.07
4	Tom Glavine	.15	.10
5	Brian Hunter	.10	.06
6	Ryan Klesko (R)	.60	.35
7	Charlie Leibrandt	.05	.02
8	Kent Mercker	.05	.02
9	David Nied	.50	.30
10	Otis Nixon	.08	.05
11	Greg Olson	.05	.02
12	Terry Pendleton	.12	.07
13	Deion Sanders	.12	.07
14	John Smoltz	.10	.06
15	Mike Stanton	.05	.02
16	Mark Wohlers	.08	.05
17	Paul Assenmacher	.05	.02
18	Steve Buechele	.05	.02
19	Shawon Dunston	.08	.05
20	Mark Grace	.10	.06
21	Derrick May	.10	.06
22	Chuck McElroy	.05	.02
23	Mike Morgan	.05	.02
24	Rey Sanchez	.08	.05
25	Ryne Sandberg	.25	.15
26	Bob Scanlan	.05	.02
27	Sammy Sosa	.25	.15
28	Rick Wilkins	.10	.06
29	Bobby Ayala (R)	.10	.06
30	Tim Belcher	.08	.05
31	Jeff Branson	.05	.02
32	Norm Charlton	.05	.02
33	Steve Foster	.20	.12
34	Willie Greene	.15	.10
35	Chris Hammond	.05	.02
36	Milt Hill	.05	.02
37	Hal Morris	.08	.05
38	Joe Oliver	.05	.02
39	Paul O'Neill	.08	.05
40	Tim Pugh (R)	.12	.07
41	Jose Rijo	.07	.04
42	Bip Roberts	.05	.02
43	Chris Sabo	.07	.04
44	Reggie Sanders	.12	.07
45	Eric Anthony	.10	.06
46	Jeff Bagwell	.20	.12
47	Craig Biggio	.08	.05
48	Joe Boever	.05	.02
49	Casey Candaele	.05	.02
50	Steve Finley	.05	.02
51	Luis Gonzalez	.12	.07
52	Pete Harnisch	.10	.06
53	Xavier Hernandez	.05	.02
54	Doug Jones	.05	.02
55	Eddie Taubensee	.08	.05
56	Brian Williams	.10	.06
57	Pedro Astacio (R)	.20	.12
58	Todd Benzinger	.05	.02
59	Brett Butler	.08	.05
60	Tom Candiotti	.05	.02
61	Lenny Harris	.05	.02
62	Carlos Hernandez	.08	.05
63	Orel Hershiser	.10	.06
64	Eric Karros	.20	.12
65	Ramon Martinez	.10	.06
66	Jose Offerman	.08	.05
67	Mike Scioscia	.05	.02
68	Mike Sharperson	.05	.02

69	Eric Young	.15	.10
70	Moises Alou	.12	.07
71	Ivan Calderon	.07	.04
72	Archi Cianfrocco	.10	.06
73	Wil Cordero	.15	.10
74	Delino DeShields	.10	.06
75	Mark Gardner	.05	.02
76	Ken Hill	.08	.05
77	Tim Laker (R)	.10	.06
78	Chris Nabholz	.08	.05
79	Mel Rojas	.05	.02
80	John Vander Wal	.08	.05
81	Larry Walker	.12	.07
82	Tim Wallach	.07	.04
83	John Wetteland	.08	.05
84	Bobby Bonilla	.10	.06
85	Daryl Boston	.05	.02
86	Sid Fernandez	.07	.04
87	Eric Hillman	.05	.02
88	Todd Hundley	.07	.04
89	Howard Johnson	.08	.05
90	Jeff Kent	.15	.10
91	Eddie Murray	.12	.07
92	Bill Pecota	.05	.02
93	Bret Saberhagen	.10	.06
94	Dick Schofield	.05	.02
95	Pete Schourek	.05	.02
96	Anthony Young	.08	.05
97	Ruben Amaro, Jr.	.07	.04
98	Juan Bell	.05	.02
99	Wes Chanberlain	.10	.06
100	Darren Daulton	.12	.07
101	Mariano Duncan	.05	.02
102	Mike Hartley	.05	.02
103	Ricky Jordan	.05	.02
104	John Kruk	.10	.06
105	Mickey Morandini	.08	.05
106	Terry Mulholland	.05	.02
107	Ben Rivera	.05	.02
108	Curt Schilling	.08	.05
109	Keith Shepherd (R)	.12	.07
110	Stan Belinda	.05	.02
111	Jay Bell	.08	.05
112	Barry Bonds	.40	.25
113	Jeff King	.08	.05
114	Mike LaValliere	.05	.02
115	Jose Lind	.05	.02
116	Roger Mason	.05	.02
117	Orlando Merced	.08	.05
118	Bob Patterson	.05	.02
119	Don Slaught	.05	.02
120	Zane Smith	.05	.02
121	Randy Tomlin	.07	.04
122	Andy Van Slyke	.12	.07
123	Tim Wakefield	.15	.10
124	Rheal Cormier	.05	.02
125	Bernard Gilkey	.08	.05
126	Felix Jose	.07	.04
127	Ray Lankford	.10	.06
128	Bob McClure	.05	.02
129	Donovan Osborne	.15	.10
130	Tom Pagnozzi	.07	.04
131	Geronimo Pena	.05	.02
132	Mike Perez	.08	.05
133	Lee Smith	.10	.06
134	Bob Tewksbury	.05	.02
135	Todd Worrell	.05	.02
136	Todd Zeile	.08	.05
137	Jerald Clark	.05	.02
138	Tony Gwynn	.15	.10
139	Greg Harris	.05	.02
140	Jeremy Hernandez	.08	.05
141	Darrin Jackson	.05	.02
142	Mike Maddux	.05	.02
143	Fred McGriff	.15	.10
144	Jose Melendez	.05	.02
145	Rich Rodriguez	.05	.02
146	Frank Seminara	.08	.05
147	Gary Sheffield	.15	.10
148	Kurt Stillwell	.05	.02
149	Dan Walters	.08	.05
150	Rod Beck	.10	.06
151	Bud Black	.05	.02
152	Jeff Brantley	.05	.02
153	John Burkett	.08	.05
154	Will Clark	.15	.10
155	Royce Clayton	.12	.07
156	Mike Jackson	.05	.02
157	Darren Lewis	.08	.05
158	Kirt Manwaring	.05	.02
159	Willie McGee	.08	.05
160	Cory Snyder	.05	.02
161	Bill Swift	.12	.07
162	Trevor Wilson	.05	.02
163	Brady Anderson	.08	.05
164	Glenn Davis	.07	.04
165	Mike Devereaux	.07	.04
166	Todd Frohwirth	.05	.02
167	Leo Gomez	.08	.05
168	Chris Hoiles	.08	.05
169	Ben McDonald	.10	.06
170	Randy Milligan	.05	.02
171	Alan Mills	.05	.02
172	Mike Mussina	.25	.15
173	Gregg Olson	.07	.04
174	Arthur Rhodes	.08	.05
175	David Segui	.08	.05
176	Ellis Burks	.07	.04
177	Roger Clemens	.25	.15
178	Scott Cooper	.10	.06
179	Danny Darwin	.05	.02
180	Tony Fossas	.05	.02
181	Paul Quantrill (R)	.10	.06
182	Jody Reed	.05	.02

183	John Valentin	.12	.07
184	Mo Vaughn	.12	.07
185	Frank Viola	.08	.05
186	Bob Zupcic	.12	.07
187	Jim Abbott	.12	.07
188	Gary DiSarcina	.08	.05
189	Damion Easley	.12	.07
190	Junior Felix	.05	.02
191	Chuck Finley	.08	.05
192	Joe Grahe	.05	.02
193	Bryan Harvey	.08	.05
194	Mark Langston	.10	.06
195	John Orton	.08	.05
196	Luis Polonia	.07	.04
197	Tim Salmon	1.50	.90
198	Luis Sojo	.05	.02
199	Wilson Alvarez	.08	.05
200	George Bell	.08	.05
201	Alex Fernandez	.12	.07
202	Craig Grebeck	.05	.02
203	Ozzie Guillen	.05	.02
204	Lance Johnson	.05	.02
205	Ron Karkovice	.05	.02
206	Kirk McCaskill	.05	.02
207	Jack McDowell	.15	.10
208	Scott Radinsky	.05	.02
209	Tim Raines	.07	.04
210	Frank Thomas	1.50	.90
211	Robin Ventura	.15	.10
212	Sandy Alomar, Jr.	.08	.05
213	Carlos Baerga	.25	.15
214	Dennis Cook	.05	.02
215	Thomas Howard	.07	.04
216	Mark Lewis	.07	.04
217	Derek Lilliquist	.05	.02
218	Kenny Lofton	.20	.12
219	Charles Nagy	.10	.06
220	Steve Olin	.05	.02
221	Paul Sorrento	.08	.05
222	Jim Thome	.10	.06
223	Mark Whiten	.12	.07
224	Milt Cuyler	.08	.05
225	Rob Deer	.07	.04
226	John Doherty	.08	.05
227	Cecil Fielder	.15	.10
228	Travis Fryman	.20	.12
229	Mike Henneman	.05	.02
230	John Kiely	.08	.05
231	Kurt Knudsen	.08	.05
232	Scott Livingstone	.07	.04
233	Tony Phillips	.07	.04
234	Mickey Tettleton	.07	.04
235	Kevin Appier	.08	.05
236	George Brett	.20	.12
237	Tom Gordon	.07	.04
238	Gregg Jefferies	.12	.07
239	Wally Joyner	.08	.05
240	Kevin Koslofski	.08	.05
241	Mike Macfarlane	.05	.02
242	Brian McRae	.08	.05
243	Rusty Meacham (R)	.15	.10
244	Keith Miller	.05	.02
245	Jeff Montgomery	.05	.02
246	Hipolito Pichardo	.07	.04
247	Ricky Bones	.08	.05
248	Cal Eldred	.10	.06
249	Mike Fetters	.05	.02
250	Darryl Hamilton	.08	.05
251	Doug Henry	.05	.02
252	John Jaha	.15	.10
253	Pat Listach	.12	.07
254	Paul Molitor	.15	.10
255	Jaime Navarro	.07	.04
256	Kevin Seitzer	.05	.02
257	B.J. Surhoff	.05	.02
258	Greg Vaughn	.08	.05
259	Bill Wegman	.05	.02
260	Robin Yount	.15	.10
261	Rick Aguilera	.05	.02
262	Chili Davis	.07	.04
263	Scott Erickson	.08	.05
264	Greg Gagne	.05	.02
265	Mark Guthrie	.05	.02
266	Brian Harper	.05	.02
267	Kent Hrbek	.07	.04
268	Terry Jorgensen	.05	.02
269	Gene Larkin	.05	.02
270	Scott Leius	.05	.02
271	Pat Mahomes	.10	.06
272	Pedro Munoz	.08	.05
273	Kirby Puckett	.25	.15
274	Kevin Tapani	.07	.04
275	Carl Willis	.05	.02
276	Steve Farr	.05	.02
277	John Habyan	.05	.02
278	Mel Hall	.05	.02
279	Charlie Hayes	.05	.02
280	Pat Kelly	.08	.05
281	Don Mattingly	.20	.12
282	Sam Militello	.10	.06
283	Matt Nokes	.05	.02
284	Melido Perez	.05	.02
285	Andy Stankiewicz	.07	.04
286	Danny Tartabull	.10	.06
287	Randy Velarde	.05	.02
288	Bob Wickman	.12	.07
289	Bernie Williams	.10	.06
290	Lance Blankenship	.05	.02
291	Mike Bordick	.08	.05
292	Jerry Browne	.05	.02
293	Dennis Eckersley	.10	.06
294	Rickey Henderson	.15	.10
295	Vince Horsman	.08	.05
296	Mark McGwire	.15	.10

297	Jeff Parrett	.05	.02
298	Ruben Sierra	.12	.07
299	Terry Steinbach	.05	.02
300	Walt Weiss	.05	.02
301	Bob Welch	.05	.02
302	Willie Wilson	.05	.02
000	Bobby Witt	.05	.02
304	Bret Boone	.15	.10
305	Jay Buhner	.07	.04
306	Dave Fleming	.15	.10
307	Ken Griffey, Jr.	1.00	.70
308	Erik Hanson	.05	.02
309	Edgar Martinez	.08	.05
310	Tino Martinez	.07	.04
311	Jeff Nelson	.08	.05
312	Dennis Powell	.05	.02
313	Mike Schooler	.05	.02
314	Russ Swan	.05	.02
315	Dave Valle	.05	.02
316	Omar Vizquel	.05	.02
317	Kevin Brown	.08	.05
318	Todd Burns	.05	.02
319	Jose Canseco	.20	.12
320	Julio Franco	.07	.04
321	Jeff Frye	.08	.05
322	Juan Gonzalez	.70	.40
323	Jose Guzman	.05	.02
324	Jeff Huson	.05	.02
325	Dean Palmer	.10	.06
326	Kevin Reimer	.05	.02
327	Ivan Rodriquez	.20	.12
328	Kenny Rogers	.05	.02
329	Dan Smith (R)	.15	.10
330	Roberto Alomar	.30	.18
351	Derek Bell	.10	.06
332	Pat Borders	.05	.02
333	Joe Carter	.20	.12
334	Kelly Gruber	.07	.04
335	Tom Henke	.05	.02
336	Jimmy Key	.08	.05
337	Manuel Lee	.05	.02
338	Candy Maldonado	.05	.02
339	John Olerud	.25	.15
340	Todd Stottlemyre	.05	.02
341	Duane Ward	.05	.02
342	Devon White	.07	.04
343	Dave Winfield	.20	.12
344	Edgar Martinez (LL)	.07	.04
345	Ceci Fielder (LL)	.10	.06
346	Kenny Lofton (LL)	.10	.06
347	Jack Morris (LL)	.07	.04
348	Roger Clemens (LL)	.10	.06
349	Fred McGriff (RT)	.12	.07
350	Barry Bonds (RT)	.25	.15
351	Gary Sheffield (RT)	.10	.06
352	Darren Daulton (RT)	.10	.06
353	Dave Hollins (RT)	.10	.06

354	Pedro Martinez Ramon Martinez	.10	.06
355	Ivan Rodriguez Kirby Puckett	.15	.10
356	Ryne Sandberg Gary Sheffield	.15	.10
357	Roberto Alomar Chuck Knoblauch Carlos Baerga	.20	.12
358	Checklist	.05	.02
359	Checklist	.05	.02
360	Checklist	.05	.02
361	Rafael Belliard	.05	.02
362	Damon Berryhill	.05	.02
363	Mike Bielecki	.05	.02
364	Jeff Blauser	.08	.05
365	Francisco Cabrera	.05	.02
366	Marvin Freeman	.05	.02
367	David Justice	.25	.15
368	Mark Lemke	.50	.02
369	Alejandro Pena	.05	.02
370	Jeff Reardon	.07	.04
371	Lonnie Smith	.07	.04
372	Pete Smith	.07	.04
373	Shawn Boskie	.05	.02
374	Jim Bullinger	.05	.02
375	Frank Castillo	.05	.02
376	Doug Dascenzo	.05	.02
377	Andre Dawson	.12	.07
378	Mike Harkey	.07	.04
379	Greg Hibbard	.05	.02
380	Greg Maddux	.15	.10
381	Ken Patterson	.05	.02
382	Jeff Robinson	.05	.02
383	Luis Salazar	.05	.02
384	Dwight Smith	.07	.04
385	Jose Vizcaino	.05	.02
386	Scott Bankhead	.05	.02
387	Tom Browning	.07	.04
388	Darnell Coles	.05	.02
389	Rob Dibble	.07	.04
390	Bill Doran	.05	.02
391	Dwayne Henry	.05	.02
392	Cesar Hernandez	.05	.02
393	Roberto Kelly	.12	.07
394	Barry Larkin	.12	.07
395	Dave Martinez	.05	.02
396	Kevin Mitchell	.08	.05
397	Jeff Reed	.05	.02
398	Scott Ruskin	.07	.04
399	Greg Swindell	.08	.05
400	Dan Wilson	.10	.06
401	Andy Ashby	.05	.02
402	Freddie Benavides	.05	.02
403	Dante Bichette	.08	.05
404	Willie Blair	.08	.05
405	Denis Boucher	.05	.02

406	Vinny Castilla	.05	.02	464	Matt Stairs	.07	.04
407	Braulio Castillo	.05	.02	465	Sergio Valdez	.08	.05
408	Alex Cole	.07	.04	466	Kevin Bass	.05	.02
409	Andres Galarraga	.15	.10	467	Vince Coleman	.07	.04
410	Joe Girardi	.05	.02	468	Mark Dewey	.07	.04
411	Butch Henry	.05	.02	469	Kevin Elster	.05	.02
412	Darren Holmes	.07	.04	470	Tony Fernandez	.07	.04
413	Calvin Jones	.07	.04	471	John Franco	.07	.04
414	Steve Reed (R)	.10	.06	472	Dave Gallagher	.05	.02
415	Kevin Ritz	.07	.04	473	Paul Gibson	.05	.02
416	Jim Tatum (R)	.10	.06	474	Dwight Gooden	.10	.06
417	Jack Armstrong	.05	.02	475	Lee Guetterman	.05	.02
418	Bret Barberie	.05	.02	476	Jeff Innis	.05	.02
420	Ryan Bowen	.08	.05	477	Dave Magadan	.05	.02
421	Cris Carpenter	.05	.02	478	Charlie O'Brien	.05	.02
421	Chuck Carr	.12	.07	479	Willie Randolph	.05	.02
422	Scott Chiamparino	.05	.02	480	Mackey Sasser	.05	.02
423	Jeff Conine	.12	.07	481	Ryan Thompson	.12	.07
424	Jim Corsi	.05	.02	482	Chico Walker	.05	.02
425	Steve Decker	.07	.04	483	Kyle Abbott	.07	.04
426	Chris Donnels	.05	.02	484	Bob Ayrault	.05	.02
427	Monty Fariss	.05	.02	485	Kim Batiste	.07	.04
428	Bob Natal	.05	.02	486	Cliff Brantley	.08	.05
429	Pat Rapp	.12	.07	487	Jose DeLeon	.05	.02
430	Dave Weathers	.08	.05	488	Lenny Dykstra	.15	.10
431	Nigel Wilson	.50	.30	489	Tommy Greene	.15	.10
432	Ken Caminiti	.05	.02	490	Jeff Grotewold	.05	.02
433	Andujar Cedeno	.08	.05	491	Dave Hollins	.20	.12
434	Tom Edens	.05	.02	492	Danny Jackson	.05	.02
435	Juan Guerrero	.07	.04	493	Stan Javier	.05	.02
436	Pete Incaviglia	.07	.04	494	Tom Marsh	.07	.04
437	Jimmy Jones	.05	.02	495	Greg Mathews	.07	.04
438	Darryl Kile	.20	.12	496	Dale Murphy	.10	.06
439	Rob Murphy	.05	.02	497	Todd Pratt (R)	.08	.05
440	Al Osuna	.05	.02	498	Mitch Williams	.05	.02
441	Mark Portugal	.07	.04	499	Danny Cox	.05	.02
442	Scott Servais	.05	.02	500	Doug Drabek	.08	.05
443	John Candelaria	.05	.02	501	Carlos Garcia	.15	.10
444	Tim Crews	.05	.02	502	Lloyd McClendon	.05	.02
445	Eric Davis	.08	.05	503	Denny Neagle	.05	.02
446	Tom Goodwin	.08	.05	504	Gary Redus	.05	.02
447	Jim Gott	.05	.02	505	Bob Walk	.05	.02
448	Kevin Gross	.05	.02	506	John Wehner	.05	.02
449	Dave Hansen	.05	.02	507	Luis Alicea	.05	.02
450	Jay Howell	.05	.02	508	Mark Clark	.10	.06
451	Roger McDowell	.05	.02	509	Pedro Geurrero	.07	.04
452	Bob Ojeda	.05	.02	510	Rex Hudler	.05	.02
453	Henry Rodriquez	.08	.05	511	Brian Jordan	.12	.07
454	Darryl Strawberry	.12	.07	512	Omar Olivares	.05	.02
455	Mitch Webster	.05	.02	513	Jose Oquendo	.05	.02
456	Steve Wilson	.05	.02	514	Gerald Perry	.05	.02
457	Brian Barnes	.08	.05	515	Bryn Smith	.05	.02
458	Jeff Fassero	.07	.04	516	Craig Wilson	.07	.04
460	Darrin Fletcher	.07	.04	517	Tracy Woodson	.05	.02
461	Marquis Grissom	.12	.07	518	Larry Andersen	.05	.02
462	Dennis Martinez	.08	.05	519	Andy Benes	.10	.06
463	Spike Owen	.05	.02	520	Jim Deshaies	.05	.02

521	Bruce Hurst	.07	.04
522	Randy Myers	.07	.04
523	Benito Santiago	.08	.05
524	Tim Scott	.07	.04
525	Tim Teufel	.05	.02
526	Mike Benjamin	.05	.02
527	Dave Burba	.05	.02
528	Craig Colbert	.05	.02
529	Mike Felder	.05	.02
530	Bryan Hickerson	.07	.04
531	Chris James	.05	.02
532	Mark Leonard	.05	.02
533	Greg Litton	.05	.02
534	Francisco Oliveras	.05	.02
535	John Patterson	.05	.02
536	Jim Pena	.05	.02
537	Dave Righetti	.05	.02
538	Robby Thompson	.10	.06
539	Jose Uribe	.05	.02
540	Matt Williams	.15	.10
541	Storm Davis	.05	.02
542	Sam Horn	.05	.02
543	Tim Hulett	.05	.02
544	Craig Lefferts	.05	.02
545	Chito Martinez	.07	.04
546	Mark McLemore	.05	.02
547	Luis Mercedes	.08	.05
548	Bob Milacki	.05	.02
549	Joe Orsulak	.05	.02
550	Billy Ripken	.05	.02
551	Cal Ripken Jr.	.30	.18
552	Rick Sutcliffe	.05	.02
553	Jeff Tackett	.05	.02
554	Wade Boggs	.15	.10
555	Tom Brunansky	.07	.04
556	Jack Clark	.07	.04
557	John Dopson	.05	.02
558	Mike Gardiner	.07	.04
559	Mike Greenwell	.08	.05
560	Greg Harris	.05	.02
561	Billy Hatcher	.05	.02
562	Joe Hesketh	.05	.02
563	Tony Pena	.05	.02
564	Phil Plantier	.15	.10
565	Luis Riveria	.05	.02
566	Herm Winningham	.05	.02
567	Matt Young	.05	.02
568	Bert Blyleven	.08	.05
569	Mike Butcher	.05	.02
570	Chuck Crim	.05	.02
571	Chad Curtis	.15	.10
572	Tim Fortugno	.07	.04
573	Steve Frey	.05	.02
574	Gary Gaetti	.05	.02
575	Scott Lewis	.07	.04
576	Lee Stevens	.05	.02
577	Ron Tingley	.05	.02
578	Julio Valera	.05	.02
579	Shawn Abner	.05	.02
580	Joey Cora	.05	.02
581	Chris Cron	.05	.02
582	Carlton Fisk	.10	.06
583	Roberto Hernandez	.08	.05
584	Charlie Hough	.05	.02
585	Terry Leach	.05	.02
586	Donn Pall	.05	.02
587	Dan Pasqua	.05	.02
588	Steve Sax	.07	.04
589	Bobby Thigpen	.05	.02
590	Albert Belle	.25	.15
591	Felix Fermin	.05	.02
592	Glenallen Hill	.08	.05
593	Brook Jacoby	.05	.02
594	Reggie Jefferson	.08	.05
595	Carlos Martinez	.05	.02
596	Jose Mesa	.07	.04
597	Rod Nichols	.05	.02
598	Junior Ortiz	.05	.02
599	Eric Plunk	.05	.02
600	Ted Power	.05	.02
601	Scott Scudder	.05	.02
602	Kevin Wickander	.05	.02
603	Skeeter Barnes	.05	.02
604	Mark Carreon	.05	.02
605	Dan Gladden	.05	.02
606	Bill Gullickson	.05	.02
607	Chad Kreuter	.07	.04
608	Mark Leiter	.05	.02
609	Mike Munoz	.05	.02
610	Rich Rowland	.08	.05
611	Frank Tanana	.05	.02
612	Walt Terrell	.05	.02
613	Alan Trammell	.10	.06
614	Lou Whitaker	.07	.04
615	Luis Aquino	.05	.02
616	Mike Boddicker	.05	.02
617	Jim Eisenreich	.05	.02
618	Mark Gubicza	.07	.04
619	David Howard	.05	.02
620	Mike Magnante	.05	.02
621	Brent Mayne	.07	.04
622	Kevin McReynolds	.07	.04
623	Ed Pierce (R)	.15	.10
624	Bill Sampen	.05	.02
625	Steve Shifflett	.07	.04
626	Gary Thurman	.07	.04
627	Curtis Wilkerson	.05	.02
628	Chris Bosio	.07	.04
629	Scott Fletcher	.05	.02
630	Jim Gantner	.05	.02
631	Dave Nilsson	.08	.05
632	Jesse Orosco	.05	.02
633	Dan Plesac	.05	.02
634	Ron Robinson	.05	.02

635	Bill Spiers	.05	.02	692	Alfredo Griffin	.05	.02
636	Franklin Stubbs	.05	.02	683	Juan Guzman	.12	.07
637	Willie Banks	.08	.05	684	Pat Hentgen	.10	.06
638	Randy Bush	.05	.02	695	Randy Knorr	.07	.04
639	Chuck Knoblauch	.10	.06	696	Bob MacDonald	.07	.04
640	Shane Mack	.10	.06	697	Jack Morris	.10	.06
641	Mike Pagliarulo	.05	.02	698	Ed Sprague	.07	.04
642	Jeff Reboulet	.05	.02	699	Dave Stieb	.07	.04
643	John Smiley	.08	.05	700	Pat Tabler	.05	.02
644	Mike Trombley	.05	.02	701	Mike Timlin	.05	.02
645	Gary Wayne	.05	.02	702	David Wells	.05	.02
646	Lenny Webster	.05	.02	703	Eddie Zosky	.07	.04
647	Tim Burke	.05	.02	704	Gary Sheffield (LL)	.10	.06
648	Mike Gallego	.05	.02	705	Darren Daulton (LL)	.08	.05
649	Dion James	.05	.02	706	Marquis Grissom (LL)	.08	.05
650	Jeff Johnson	.08	.05	707	Greg Maddux (LL)	.08	.05
651	Scott Kamieniecki	.07	.04	708	Bill Swift (LL)	.08	.05
652	Kevin Maas	.08	.05	709	Juan Gonzalez (RT)	.35	.20
653	Rich Monteleone	.05	.02	710	Mark McGwire (RT)	.10	.06
654	Jerry Nielsen	.07	.04	711	Cecil Fielder (RT)	.10	.06
655	Scott Sanderson	.05	.02	712	Albert Belle (RT)	.15	.10
656	Mike Stanley	.10	.06	713	Joe Carter (RT)	.10	.06
657	Gerald Williams	.10	.06	714	Power Brokers	.40	.25
658	Curt Young	.05	.02		Frank Thomas		
659	Harold Baines	.07	.04		Cecil Fielder		
660	Kevin Campbell	.05	.02	715	Unsung Heroes	.10	.06
661	Ron Darling	.05	.02		Darren Daulton		
662	Kelly Downs	.05	.02		Larry Walker		
663	Eric Fox	.07	.04	716	Hot Corner	.10	.06
664	Dave Henderson	.05	.02		Edgar Martinez		
665	Rick Honeycutt	.05	.02		Robin Ventura		
666	Mike Moore	.05	.02	717	Start To Finish	.15	.10
667	Jamie Quirk	.05	.02		Roger Clemens		
668	Jeff Russell	.05	.02		Dennis Eckersley		
669	Dave Stewart	.10	.06	718	Checklist	.05	.02
670	Greg Briley	.05	.02	719	Checklist	.05	.02
671	Dave Cochrane	.07	.04	720	Checklist	.05	.02
672	Henry Cotto	.05	.02	___	Tom Glavine Inserts ea.	1.00	.70
673	Rich DeLucia	.07	.04	___	Tom Glavine Signed	125.00	65.00
674	Brian Fisher	.05	.02				
675	Mark Grant	.05	.02				
676	Randy Johnson	.15	.10				
677	Tim Leary	.05	.02				
678	Pete O'Brien	.05	.02				
679	Larry Parrish	.05	.02				
680	Harold Reynolds	.05	.02				
681	Shane Turner	.08	.05				
682	Jack Daugherty	.05	.02				
683	David Hulse (R)	.15	.10				
684	Terry Mathews	.07	.04				
685	Al Newman	.05	.02				
686	Edwin Nunez	.05	.02				
687	Rafael Palmeiro	.12	.07				
688	Roger Pavlik	.15	.10				
689	Geno Petralli	.05	.02				
690	Nolan Ryan	.80	.50				
691	David Cone	.08	.05				

1993 Fleer Team Leaders

These limited inserts were distributed randomly in Fleer Series rack packs with American League players (A) in Series I and National League players (N) in Series II. Card fronts feature full color player photos with the player's

name and Team Leader printed vertically
along the border. All cards measure 2-1/2"
by 3-1/2".

		MINT	NR/MT
Complete Set (20)		30.00	18.00
Commons		75	45
1A	Kirby Puckett	2.50	1.50
2A	Mark McGwire	1.75	1.00
3A	Pat Listach	1.00	.70
4A	Roger Clemens	2.50	1.50
5A	Frank Thomas	8.50	5.00
6A	Carlos Baerga	2.50	1.50
7A	Brady Anderson	.75	.45
8A	Juan Gonzalez	6.00	4.00
9A	Roberto Alomar	3.50	2.00
10A	Ken Griffey, Jr.	7.50	4.50
1N	Will Clark	2.50	1.50
3N	Ray Lankford	1.00	.70
4N	Eric Karros	1.75	1.00
5N	Gary Sheffield	1.75	1.00
6N	Ryne Sandberg	3.00	1.75
7N	Marquis Grissom	1.25	.80
9N	Jeff Bagwell	2.00	1.25

1993 Fleer I
Rookie Sensations

		MINT	NR/MT
Complete Set (10)		28.00	18.00
Commons		1.25	.80
1	Kenny Lofton	8.50	5.00
2	Cal Eldred	6.00	3.75
3	Pat Listach	2.50	1.50
4	Roberto Hernandez	1.25	.80
5	Dave Fleming	5.00	3.00
6	Eric Karros	5.00	3.00
7	Reggie Sanders	4.00	2.50
8	Derrick May	4.00	2.50
9	Mike Perez	1.25	.80
10	Donovan Osborne	4.50	2.75

1993 Fleer II
Rookie Sensations

		MINT	NR/MT
Complete Set (20)		20.00	12.50
Commons		1.00	.60
1	Moises Alou	3.00	1.75
2	Pedro Astacio	3.00	1.75
4	Chad Curtis	7.00	4.00
6	Eric Karros	2.00	1.25
7	Sam Militello	1.50	.90
8	Arthur Rhodes	1.25	.80
9	Tim Wakefield	1.25	.80
10	Bob Zupcic	1.25	.80

1993 Fleer
AL All-Stars

The cards in this insert set were
distributed randomly in Fleer Series II
packs. The cards feature American
League All-Stars and are printed in a
horizontal format with two images on the
card fronts, a head shot and an action
shot along with the words All-Stars
printed across the bottom. Cards
measure 3-1/2" by 2-1/2".

		MINT	NR/MT
Complete Set (12)		32.00	22.00
Commons		.75	.45
1	Frank Thomas	10.00	6.50
2	Roberto Alomar	4.00	2.75
3	Edgar Martinez	.75	.45
4	Pat Listach	1.00	.70
5	Cecil Fielder	2.00	1.25
6	Juan Gonzalez	6.50	3.75
7	Ken Griffey Jr.	8.50	5.00
8	Joe Carter	2.50	1.50
9	Kirby Puckett	3.00	1.75
10	Brian Harper	.75	.45
11	Dave Fleming	1.50	.90
12	Jack McDowell	2.50	1.50

1993 Fleer
NL All-Stars

The cards in this limited set feature National League stars and were randomly issued in Fleer Series I packs. The horizontal fronts feature two full-color images, a head shot and an action shot. Cards measure 3-1/2" by 2-1/2".

		MINT	NR/MT
Complete Set (12)		16.00	9.00
Commons		.75	.45

1	Fred McGriff	2.50	1.50
2	Delino DeShields	1.25	.80
3	Gary Sheffield	2.00	1.25
4	Barry Larkin	1.25	.80
5	Felix Jose	.75	.45
6	Larry Walker	1.25	.80
7	Barry Bonds	5.00	3.00
8	Andy Van Slyke	1.00	.70
9	Darren Daulton	1.25	.80
10	Greg Maddux	1.75	1.00
11	Tom Glavine	2.00	1.25
12	Lee Smith	1.00	.70

1993 Fleer I
ML Prospects

These limited insert cards were issued randomly in Fleer Series I packs. The full-color fronts feature an action shot with a Major Leagues Prospects logo in a triangle centered at the bottom. All cards measure 2-1/2" by 3-1/2".

		MINT	NR/MT
Complete Set (18)		28.00	18.00
Commons		.75	.45

1	Melvin Nieves	3.50	2.00
2	Sterling Hitchcock	1.75	1.00

3	Tim Costo	1.00	.70
4	Manny Alexander	.75	.45
5	Alan Embree	1.00	.70
6	Kevin Young	2.50	1.50
7	J.T. Snow	3.00	1.75
8	Russ Springer	.75	.45
9	Billy Ashley	3.50	2.00
10	Kevin Rogers	.75	.45
11	Steve Hosey	1.75	1.00
12	Eric Wedge	.75	.45
13	Mike Piazza	18.50	12.50
14	Jesse Levis	.75	.45
15	Rico Brogna	1.00	.70
16	Alex Arias	.75	.45
17	Rod Brewer	.75	.45
18	Troy Neel	1.75	1.00

1993 Fleer II
ML Prospects

These limited insert cards were randomly packed into Fleer Series II packs. The design is identical to Series I. All cards measure 2-1/2" by 3-1/2".

		MINT	NR/MT
Complete Set (18)		15.00	9.00
Commons		.75	.45

1	Scooter Tucker	.75	.45
2	Kerry Woodson	.75	.45
3	Greg Colbrunn	.90	.60
4	Pedro Martinez	1.25	.80
5	Dave Silvestri	.75	.45
6	Ken Bottenfield	.75	.45
7	Rafael Bournigal	.90	.60
8	J.T.Bruett	.75	.45
9	Dave Mlicki	.90	.60
10	Paul Wagner	1.00	.70
11	Mike Williams	.75	.45
12	Henry Mercedes	.75	.45
13	Scott Taylor	.75	.45
14	Dennis Moeller	.75	.45
15	Javier Lopez	5.00	3.00
16	Steve Cooke	1.50	.90
17	Peter Young	.75	.45
18	Ken Ryan	1.50	.90

1993 Fleer
Golden Moments

These limited inserts were found in Fleer wax packs, the first three in Series I and the last three in Series II. The fronts feature full color action photos with the player's name appearing in a pennant-type design under his photo. All cards measure 2-1/2" by 3-1/2"

		MINT	NR/MT
Complete Set (6)		12.00	7.00
Commons		.75	.45
1a	George Brett	3.50	2.00
2a	Mickey Morandini	.75	.45
3a	Dave Winfield	3.00	1.75
1b	Dennis Eckersley	.90	.60
2b	Bip Roberts	.75	.45
3b	Juan Gonzalez	6.00	3.75
	Frank Thomas		

1993 Fleer
Pro Visions

These colorful art cards were randomly distributed in Fleer wax packs, the first three in Series I and the last three in Series II. Cards measure 2-1/2" by 3-1/2".

		MINT	NR/MT
Complete Set (6)		10.00	6.50
Commons		.75	.45
1a	Roberto Alomar	3.50	2.00
2a	Dennis Eckersley	.75	.45
3a	Gary Sheffield	1.75	1.00
1b	Andy Van Slyke	.75	.45
2b	Tom Glavine	2.00	1.25
3b	Cecil Fielder	2.00	1.25

1993 Fleer
Final Edition

This 300-card set marks the largest post-season update set ever issued. The card design is nearly identical to the regular Fleer issue. Card backs contain the prefix "F" next to the card numbers. A 10-card insert set called Diamond Tribute was included in the Final Edition sets. Those cards are listed at the end of this checklist but are not included in the complete set price below. All cards measure 2-1/2" by 3-1/2".

		MINT	NR/MT
Complete Set (300)		12.50	7.50
Commons		.05	.02
1	Steve Bedrosian	.05	.02
2	Jay Howell	.05	.02
3	Greg Maddux	.20	.12
4	Greg McMichael (R)	.20	.12
5	Tony Tarasco (R)	.30	.18
6	Jose Bautista	.05	.02
7	Jose Guzman	.08	.05
8	Greg Hibbard	.05	.02
9	Camdy Maldonado	.05	.02
10	Randy Myers	.08	.05
11	Matt Walbeck (R)	.10	.06
12	Turk Wendell	.10	.06
13	Willie Wilson	.05	.02
14	Greg Cadaret	.05	.02
15	Roberto Kelly	.12	.07
16	Randy Milligan	.05	.02
17	Kevin Mitchell	.08	.05
18	Jeff Reardon	.07	.04
19	John Roper	.08	.05
20	John Smiley	.08	.05
21	Andy Ashby	.05	.02
22	Dante Bichette	.15	.10
23	Willie Blair	.08	.05
24	Pedro Castellano	.08	.05
25	Vinny Castilla	.05	.02
26	Jerald Clark	.05	.02
27	Alex Cole	.07	.04
28	Scott Fredrickson (R)	.15	.10
29	Jay Gainer (R)	.15	.10
30	Andres Galarraga	.12	.07
31	Joe Girardi	.05	.02
32	Ryan Hawblitzel	.10	.06
33	Charlie Hayes	.07	.04
34	Darren Holmes	.05	.02

35	Chris Jones	.05	.02	92	Cliff Floyd	1.75	1.00
36	David Nied	.50	.30	93	Lou Frazier (R)	.12	.07
37	J. Owens (R)	.15	.10	94	Mike Gardiner	.05	.02
38	Lance Painter (R)	.12	.07	95	Mike Lansing (R)	.20	.12
39	Jeff Parrett	.05	.02	96	Bill Risley (R)	.08	.05
40	Steve Reed	.08	.05	97	Jeff Shaw	.05	.02
41	Armondo Reynoso	.05	.02	98	Kevin Baez	.05	.02
42	Bruce Ruffin	.05	.02	99	Tim Bogar (R)	.10	.06
43	Danny Sheaffer (R)	.10	.06	100	Jeromy Burnitz	.20	.12
44	Keith Shepherd	.08	.05	101	Mike Draper (R)	.12	.07
45	Jim Tatum	.08	.05	102	Darrin Jackson	.05	.02
46	Gary Wayne	.05	.02	103	Mike Maddux	.05	.02
47	Eric Young	.10	.06	104	Joe Orsulak	.05	.02
48	Luis Aquino	.05	.02	105	Doug Saunders (R)	.10	.06
49	Alex Arias	.05	.02	106	Frank Tanana	.05	.02
50	Jack Armstrong	.05	.02	107	Dave Teigheder (R)	.10	.06
51	Bret Barberie	.05	.02	108	Larry Andersen	.05	.02
52	Geronimo Pena	.05	.02	109	Jim Eisenreich	.05	.02
53	Ryan Bowen	.08	.05	110	Pete Incaviglia	.05	.02
54	Greg Briley	.05	.02	111	Danny Jackson	.05	.02
55	Cris Carpenter	.05	.02	112	David West	.05	.02
56	Chuck Carr	.12	.07	113	Al Martin	.20	.12
57	Jeff Conine	.12	.07	114	Blas Minor	.05	.02
58	Jim Corsi	.05	.02	115	Dennis Moeller	.05	.02
59	Orestes Destrade	.05	.02	116	Will Pennyfeather	.08	.05
60	Junior Felix	.05	.02	117	Rich Robertson (R)	.10	.06
61	Chris Hammond	.05	.02	118	Ben Shelton	.07	.04
62	Bryan Harvey	.08	.05	119	Lonnie Smith	.05	.02
63	Charlie Hough	.05	.02	120	Freddie Toliver	.05	.02
64	Joe Klink	.05	.02	121	Paul Wagner	.15	.10
65	Richie Lewis (R)	.12	.07	122	Kevin Young	.20	.12
66	Mitch Lyden (R)	.10	.06	123	Rene Arocha (R)	.20	.12
67	Bob Natal	.07	.04	124	Gregg Jefferies	.10	.06
68	Scott Pose (R)	.12	.07	125	Paul Kilgus	.05	.02
69	Rich Renteria	.05	.02	126	Les Lancaster	.05	.02
70	Benito Santiago	.08	.05	127	Joe Magrane	.05	.02
71	Gary Sheffield	.15	.10	128	Rob Murphy	.05	.02
72	Matt Turner (R)	.10	.06	129	Erik Pappas	.08	.05
73	Walt Weiss	.05	.02	130	Stan Royer	.05	.02
74	Darrell Whitmore (R)	.30	.18	131	Ozzie Smith	.15	.10
75	Nigel Wilson	.75	.45	132	Tom Urbani (R)	.12	.07
76	Kevin Bass	.05	.02	133	Mark Whiten	.15	.10
77	Doug Drabek	.08	.05	134	Derek Bell	.10	.06
78	Tom Edens	.07	.04	135	Doug Brocail	.05	.02
79	Chris James	.05	.02	136	Phil Clark	.08	.05
80	Greg Swindell	.07	.04	137	Mark Ettles (R)	.10	.06
81	Omar Daal (R)	.15	.10	138	Jeff Gardner	.05	.02
82	Raul Mondesi	.20	.12	139	Pat Gomez (R)	.12	.07
83	Jody Reed	.05	.02	140	Ricky Gutierrez	.10	.06
84	Cory Snyder	.07	.04	141	Gene Harris	.05	.02
85	Rick Trlicck	.07	.04	142	Kevin Higgins (R)	.10	.06
86	Tim Wallach	.05	.02	143	Trevor Hoffman	.10	.06
87	Todd Worrell	.05	.02	144	Phil Plantier	.20	.12
88	Tavo Alvarez	.08	.05	145	Kerry Taylor (R)	.12	.07
89	Frank Bolick	.05	.02	146	Guillermo Velasquez	.05	.02
90	Kent Bottenfield	.05	.02	147	Wally Whitehurst	.05	.02
91	Greg Colbrunn	.08	.05	148	Tim Worrell (R)	.12	.07

149	Todd Benzinger	.05	.02	206	Bill Wertz (R)	.08	.05
150	Barry Bonds	.50	.30	207	Cliff Young	.05	.02
151	Greg Brummett (R)	.10	.06	208	Matt Young	.05	.02
152	Mark Carreon	.05	.02	209	Kirk Gibson	.07	.04
153	Dave Martinez	.05	.02	210	Greg Gohr	.08	.05
154	Jeff Reed	.05	.02	211	Bill Krueger	.07	.04
155	Kevin Rogers	.07	.04	212	Bob MacDonald	.07	.04
156	Harold Baines	.07	.04	213	Mike Moore	.05	.02
157	Damon Buford	.08	.05	214	David Wells	.05	.02
158	Paul Carey (R)	.20	.12	215	Billy Brewer (R)	.12	.07
159	Jeffery Hammond	.60	.35	216	David Cone	.08	.05
160	Jamie Moyer	.05	.02	217	Greg Gagne	.05	.02
161	Sherman Obando (R)	.12	.07	218	Mark Gardner	.05	.02
162	John O'Donoghue (R)	.12	.07	219	Chris Haney	.05	.02
163	Brad Pennington	.05	.02	220	Phil Hiatt	.15	.10
164	Jim Poole	.05	.02	221	Jose Lind	.05	.02
165	Harold Reynolds	.05	.02	222	Juan Bell	.05	.02
166	Fernando Valenzuela	.05	.02	223	Tom Brunansky	.07	.04
167	Jack Voigt (R)	.12	.07	224	Mike Ignasiak	.07	.04
168	Mark Williamson	.05	.02	225	Joe Kmak	.07	.04
169	Scott Bankhead	.05	.02	226	Tom Lampkin	.05	.02
170	Greg Blosser	.20	.12	227	Graeme Lloyd (R)	.12	.07
171	Jim Byrd (R)	.08	.05	228	Carlos Maldonado	.08	.05
172	Ivan Calderon	.05	.02	229	Matt Mieske	.08	.05
173	Andre Dawson	.10	.06	230	Angel Miranda	.07	.04
174	Scott Fletcher	.05	.02	231	Troy O'Leary (R)	.15	.10
175	Jose Melendez	.05	.02	232	Kevin Reimer	.05	.02
176	Carlos Quintana	.05	.02	233	Larry Casian	.05	.02
177	Jeff Russell	.05	.02	234	Jim Deshaies	.05	.02
178	Aaron Sele	1.50	.90	235	Eddie Guardado (R)	.12	.07
179	Rod Correia (R)	.10	.06	236	Chip Hale	.05	.02
180	Chili Davis	.05	.02	237	Mike Maksudian (R)	.10	.06
181	Jim Edmonds (R)	.20	.12	238	David McCarty	.30	.18
182	Rene Gonzalez	.05	.02	239	Pat Meares (R)	.12	.07
183	Hilly Hathaway (R)	.15	.10	240	George Tsamis (R)	.10	.06
184	Torey Lovullo	.05	.02	241	Dave Winfield	.20	.12
185	Greg Myers	.05	.02	242	Jim Abbott	.12	.07
186	Gene Nelson	.05	.02	243	Wade Boggs	.15	.10
187	Troy Percival	.08	.05	244	Andy Cook (R)	.15	.10
188	Scott Sanderson	.05	.02	245	Russ Davis (R)	.60	.35
189	Darryl Scott (R)	.10	.06	246	Mike Humphreys	.05	.02
190	J.T. Snow (R)	.75	.45	247	Jimmy Key	.08	.05
191	Russ Springer	.07	.04	248	Jim Leyritz	.05	.02
192	Jason Bere	.75	.45	249	Bobby Munoz	.08	.05
193	Rodney Bolton	.05	.02	250	Paul O'Neill	.08	.05
194	Ellis Burks	.07	.04	251	Spike Owen	.05	.02
195	Bo Jackson	.10	.06	252	Dave Silvestri	.05	.02
196	Mike LaValliere	.05	.02	253	Marcos Armas (R)	.20	.12
197	Scott Ruffcorn	.25	.15	254	Brent Gates	.20	.12
198	Jeff Schwartz (R)	.10	.06	255	Goose Gossage	.07	.04
199	Jerry DiPoto	.05	.02	256	Scott Lydy (R)	.20	.12
200	Alvaro Espinoza	.05	.02	257	Henry Mercedes	.08	.05
201	Wayne Kirby	.05	.02	258	Mike Mohler (R)	.10	.06
202	Tom Kramer (R)	.12	.07	259	Troy Neel	.15	.10
203	Jesse Levis	.05	.02	260	Edwin Nunez	.05	.02
204	Manny Ramirez	1.25	.80	261	Craig Paquette	.08	.05
205	Jeff Treadway	.05	.02	262	Kevin Seitzer	.05	.02

263	Rich Amaral	.08	.05
264	Mike Blowers	.05	.02
265	Chris Bosio	.07	.04
266	Norm Charlton	.05	.02
267	Jim Converse (R)	.12	.07
268	John Cummings (R)	.20	.12
269	Mike Felder	.05	.02
270	Mike Hampton	.07	.04
271	Bill Haselman	.05	.02
272	Dwayne Henry	.05	.02
273	Greg Litton	.05	.02
274	Mackey Sasser	.05	.02
275	Lee Tinsley	.07	.04
276	David Wainhouse	.05	.02
277	Jeff Bronkey (R)	.10	.06
278	Benji Gil	.15	.10
279	Tom Henke	.05	.02
280	Charlie Leibrandt	.05	.02
281	Robb Nen	.10	.06
282	Bill Ripken	.05	.02
283	Jon Shave (R)	.10	.06
284	Doug Strange	.05	.02
285	Matt Whiteside (R)	.12	.07
286	Scott Brow (R)	.12	.07
287	Willie Canate (R)	.12	.07
288	Tony Castillo	.05	.02
289	Domingo Cedeno (R)	.12	.07
290	Darnell Coles	.05	.02
291	Danny Cox	.05	.02
292	Mark Eichhorn	.05	.02
293	Tony Fernandez	.05	.02
294	Al Leiter	.05	.02
295	Paul Molitor	.20	.12
296	Dave Stewart	.10	.06
297	Woody Williams (R)	.12	.07
298	Checklist	.05	.02
299	Checklist	.05	.02
300	Checklist	.05	.02
DT1	Wade Boggs	.75	.45
DT2	George Brett	2.00	1.25
DT3	Andre Dawson	.60	.35
DT4	Carlton Fisk	.60	.35
DT5	Paul Molitor	1.00	.70
DT6	Nolan Ryan	5.00	3.00
DT7	Lee Smith	.50	.30
DT8	Ozzie Smith	1.25	.80
DT9	Dave Winfield	2.00	1.25
DT10	Robin Yount	2.00	1.25

1993 Fleer Ultra

The cards in this set feature full-color, full-bleed action photographs on the card fronts with the player's name printed in gold inside a horizontal color stripe under his photo. A Fleer Ultra logo with a small baseball appears in the upper corner. The horizontal crd backs contain two color images, a large head shot and a smaller action shot superimposed over a baseball diamond. The set includes random limited insert cards of Dennis Eckersley. Those cards are listed at the end of this checklist but not included in the complete set price below. Cards measure 2-1/2" by 3-1/2".

		MINT	NR/MT
Complete Set (650)		42.00	26.00
Commons		.08	.05
1	Steve Avery	.35	.20
2	Rafael Belliard	.08	.05
3	Damon Berryhill	.08	.05
4	Sid Bream	.08	.05
5	Ron Gant	.15	.10
6	Tom Glavine	.40	.25
7	Ryan Klesko	.60	.35
8	Mark Lemke	.08	.05
9	Javier Lopez	1.25	.80
10	Greg Olson	.08	.05
11	Terry Pendleton	.12	.07
12	Deion Sanders	.20	.12
13	Mike Stanton	.08	.05
14	Paul Assenmacher	.08	.05
15	Steve Buechele	.08	.05
16	Frank Castillo	.08	.05
17	Shawon Dunston	.10	.06
18	Mark Grace	.15	.10
19	Derrick May	.15	.10
20	Chuck McElroy	.08	.05
21	Mike Morgan	.08	.05

22	Bob Scanlan	.08	.05
23	Dwight Smith	.10	.06
24	Sammy Sosa	.25	.15
25	Rick Wilkins	.15	.10
26	Tim Belcher	.08	.05
27	Jeff Branson	.08	.05
28	Bill Doran	.08	.05
29	Chris Hammond	.08	.05
30	Barry Larkin	.12	.07
31	Hal Morris	.10	.06
32	Joe Oliver	.08	.05
33	Jose Rijo	.10	.06
34	Bip Roberts	.08	.05
35	Chris Sabo	.10	.06
36	Reggie Sanders	.20	.12
37	Craig Biggio	.10	.06
38	Ken Caminiti	.08	.05
39	Steve Finley	.08	.05
40	Luis Gonzalez	.10	.06
41	Juan Guerrero	.10	.06
42	Pete Harnisch	.10	.06
43	Xavier Hernandez	.10	.06
44	Doug Jones	.08	.05
45	Al Osuna	.08	.05
46	Eddie Taubensee	.08	.05
47	Scooter Tucker	.08	.05
48	Brian Williams	.10	.06
49	Pedro Astacio	.25	.15
50	Rafael Bournigal (R)	.15	.10
51	Brett Butler	.10	.06
52	Tom Candiotti	.08	.05
53	Eric Davis	.12	.07
54	Lenny Harris	.08	.05
55	Orel Hershiser	.12	.07
56	Eric Karros	.35	.20
57	Pedro Martinez	.25	.15
58	Roger McDowell	.08	.05
59	Jose Offerman	.10	.06
60	Mike Piazza	6.00	3.50
61	Moises Alou	.15	.10
62	Kent Bottenfield	.08	.05
63	Archi Cianfrocco	.10	.06
64	Greg Colbrunn	.10	.06
65	Wil Cordero	.25	.15
66	Delino DeShields	.15	.10
67	Darrin Fletcher	.08	.05
68	Ken Hill	.10	.06
69	Chris Nabholz	.08	.05
70	Mel Rojas	.08	.05
71	Larry Walker	.20	.12
72	Sid Fernandez	.10	.06
73	John Franco	.08	.05
74	Dave Gallagher	.08	.05
75	Todd Hundley	.08	.05
76	Howard Johnson	.10	.06
77	Jeff Kent	.15	.10
78	Eddie Murray	.12	.07
79	Bret Saberhagen	.12	.07
80	Chico Walker	.08	.05
81	Anthony Young	.08	.05
82	Kyle Abbott	.08	.05
83	Ruben Amaro Jr.	.10	.06
84	Juan Bell	.08	.05
85	Wes Chamberlain	.12	.07
86	Darren Daulton	.25	.15
87	Mariano Duncan	.08	.05
88	Dave Hollins	.25	.15
89	Ricky Jordan	.08	.05
90	John Kruk	.12	.07
91	Mickey Morandini	.10	.06
92	Terry Mullholland	.08	.05
93	Ben Rivera	.08	.05
94	Mike Williams	.08	.05
95	Stan Belinda	.08	.05
96	Jay Bell	.15	.10
97	Jeff King	.10	.06
98	Mike LaValliere	.08	.05
99	Lloyd McClendon	.08	.05
100	Orlando Merced	.15	.10
101	Zane Smith	.08	.05
102	Randy Tomlin	.10	.06
103	Andy Van Slyke	.15	.10
104	Tim Wakefield	.20	.12
105	John Wehner	.08	.05
106	Bernard Gilkey	.15	.10
107	Brian Jordan	.20	.12
108	Ray Lankford	.15	.10
109	Donovan Osborne	.20	.12
110	Tom Pagnozzi	.08	.05
111	Mike Perez	.12	.07
112	Lee Smith	.12	.07
113	Ozzie Smith	.20	.12
114	Bob Tewksbury	.08	.05
115	Todd Zeile	.10	.06
116	Andy Benes	.12	.07
117	Greg Harris	.08	.05
118	Darrin Jackson	.08	.05
119	Fred McGriff	.50	.30
120	Rich Rodriquez	.08	.05
121	Frank Seminara	.10	.06
122	Gary Sheffield	.35	.20
123	Craig Shipley	.08	.05
124	Kurt Stillwell	.08	.05
125	Dan Walters	.10	.06
126	Rod Beck	.10	.06
127	Mike Benjamin	.08	.05
128	Jeff Brantley	.08	.05
129	John Burkett	.12	.07
130	Will Clark	.35	.20
131	Royce Clayton	.15	.10
132	Steve Hosey	.20	.12
133	Mike Jackson	.10	.06
134	Darren Lewis	.10	.06
135	Kirt Manwaring	.08	.05

136	Bill Swift	.15	.10	193	Mark Whiten	.25	.15
137	Robby Thompson	.15	.10	194	Milt Cuyler	.10	.06
138	Brady Anderson	.12	.07	195	Rob Deer	.10	.06
139	Glenn Davis	.08	.05	196	John Doherty	.10	.06
140	Leo Gomez	.10	.06	197	Travis Fryman	.70	.40
141	Chito Martinez	.10	.06	198	Dan Gladden	.08	.05
142	Ben McDonald	.15	.10	199	Mike Henneman	.08	.05
143	Alan Mills	.10	.06	200	John Kiely	.08	.05
144	Mike Mussina	.50	.30	201	Chad Kreuter	.10	.06
145	Gregg Olson	.10	.06	202	Scott Livingstone	.08	.05
146	David Segui	.10	.06	203	Tony Phillips	.10	.06
147	Jeff Tackett	.08	.05	204	Alan Trammell	.15	.10
148	Jack Clark	.10	.06	205	Mike Boddicker	.08	.05
149	Scott Cooper	.10	.06	206	George Brett	.50	.30
150	Danny Darwin	.08	.05	207	Tom Gordon	.10	.06
151	John Dopson	.08	.05	208	Mark Gubicza	.10	.06
152	Mike Greenwell	.12	.07	209	Gregg Jefferies	.20	.12
153	Tim Naehring	.10	.06	210	Wally Joyner	.10	.06
154	Tony Pena	.08	.05	211	Kevin Koslofski	.10	.06
155	Paul Quantrill	.08	.05	212	Brent Mayne	.08	.05
156	Mo Vaughn	.35	.20	213	Brian McRae	.15	.10
157	Frank Viola	.10	.06	214	Kevin McReynolds	.10	.06
158	Bob Zupcic	.10	.06	215	Rusty Meacham	.12	.07
159	Chad Curtis	.30	.18	216	Steve Shifflett	.10	.06
160	Gary Discarcina	.08	.05	217	James Austin	.10	.06
161	Damion Easley	.20	.12	218	Cal Eldred	.25	.15
162	Chuck Finley	.12	.07	219	Darryl Hamilton	.15	.10
163	Tim Fortugno	.08	.05	220	Doug Henry	.08	.05
164	Rene Gonzales	.08	.05	221	John Jaha	.20	.12
165	Joe Grahe	.10	.06	222	Dave Nilsson	.12	.07
166	Mark Langston	.12	.07	223	Jesse Orosco	.08	.05
167	John Orton	.10	.06	224	B.J. Surhoff	.08	.05
168	Luis Polonia	.08	.05	225	Greg Vaughn	.15	.10
169	Julio Valera	.08	.05	226	Bill Wegman	.08	.05
170	Wilson Alvarez	.15	.10	227	Robin Yount	.40	.25
171	George Bell	.12	.07	228	Rick Aguilera	.08	.05
172	Joey Cora	.08	.05	229	J.T. Bruett	.12	.07
173	Alex Fernandez	.25	.15	230	Scott Erickson	.12	.07
174	Lance Johnson	.08	.05	231	Kent Hrbek	.08	.05
175	Ron Karkovice	.08	.05	232	Terry Jorgensen	.10	.06
176	Jack McDowell	.30	.18	233	Scott Leius	.08	.05
177	Scott Radinsky	.08	.05	234	Pat Mahomes	.15	.10
178	Tim Raines	.10	.06	235	Pedro Munoz	.12	.07
179	Steve Sax	.10	.06	236	Kirby Puckett	.70	.40
180	Bobby Thigpen	.08	.05	237	Kevin Tapani	.10	.06
181	Frank Thomas	3.50	2.00	238	Lenny Webster	.08	.05
182	Sandy Alomar Jr.	.10	.06	239	Carl Willis	.08	.05
183	Carlos Baerga	.60	.35	240	Mike Gallego	.08	.05
184	Felix Fermin	.08	.05	241	John Habyan	.08	.05
185	Thomas Howard	.08	.05	242	Pat Kelly	.10	.06
186	Mark Lewis	.10	.06	243	Kevin Maas	.10	.06
187	Derek Lilliquist	.08	.05	244	Don Mattingly	.50	.30
188	Carlos Martinez	.08	.05	245	Hensley Meulens	.10	.06
189	Charles Nagy	.12	.07	246	Sam Militello	.20	.12
190	Scott Scudder	.08	.05	247	Matt Nokes	.08	.05
191	Paul Sorrento	.10	.06	248	Melido Perez	.08	.05
192	Jim Thome	.15	.10	249	Andy Stankiewicz	.10	.06

250	Randy Velarde	.08	.05
251	Bob Wickman	.50	.30
252	Bernie Williams	.15	.10
253	Lance Blankenship	.08	.05
254	Mike Bordick	.12	.07
255	Jerry Browne	.08	.05
256	Ron Darling	.00	.05
257	Dennis Eckersley	.20	.12
258	Rickey Henderson	.40	.25
259	Vince Horsman	.12	.07
260	Troy Neel	.35	.20
261	Jeff Parrett	.08	.05
262	Terry Steinbach	.08	.05
263	Bob Welch	.08	.05
264	Bobby Witt	.10	.06
265	Rich Amaral	.12	.07
266	Bret Boone	.25	.15
267	Jay Buhner	.10	.06
268	Dave Fleming	.30	.18
269	Randy Johnson	.35	.20
270	Edgar Martinez	.15	.10
271	Mike Schooler	.08	.05
272	Russ Swan	.08	.05
273	Dave Valle	.08	.05
274	Omar Vizquel	.08	.05
275	Kerry Woodson	.10	.06
276	Kevin Brown	.12	.07
277	Julio Franco	.12	.07
278	Jeff Frye	.10	.06
279	Juan Gonzalez	1.25	.80
280	Jeff Huson	.08	.05
281	Rafael Palmeiro	.30	.18
282	Dean Palmer	.25	.15
283	Roger Pavlik	.20	.12
284	Ivan Rodriquez	.30	.18
285	Kenny Rogers	.08	.05
286	Derek Bell	.20	.12
287	Pat Borders	.08	.05
288	Joe Carter	.50	.30
289	Bob MacDonald	.12	.07
290	Jack Morris	.12	.07
291	John Olerud	1.00	.70
292	Ed Sprague	.10	.06
293	Todd Stottlemyre	.08	.05
294	Mike Timlin	.08	.05
295	Duane Ward	.10	.06
296	David Wells	.10	.06
297	Devon White	.15	.10
298	Checklist	.08	.03
299	Checklist	.08	.03
300	Checklist	.08	.03
301	Steve Bedrosian	.08	.05
302	Jeff Blauser	.12	.07
303	Francisco Cabrera	.08	.05
304	Marvin Freeman	.08	.05
305	Brian Hunter	.12	.07
306	David Justice	.70	.40
307	Greg Maddux	.35	.20
308	Greg McMichael (R)	.40	.25
309	Kent Mercker	.08	.05
310	Otis Nixon	.10	.06
311	Pete Smith	.12	.07
312	John Smoltz	.25	.15
313	Jose Guzman	.10	.06
314	Mike Harkey	.10	.06
315	Greg Hibbard	.08	.05
316	Candy Maldonado	.08	.05
317	Randy Myers	.10	.06
318	Dan Plesac	.08	.05
319	Rey Sanchez	.12	.07
320	Ryne Sandberg	.70	.40
321	Tommy Shields (R)	.20	.12
322	Jose Vizcaino	.08	.05
323	Matt Walbeck (R)	.15	.10
324	Willie Wilson	.08	.05
325	Tom Browning	.10	.06
326	Tim Costo	.12	.07
327	Rob Dibble	.10	.06
328	Steve Foster	.12	.07
329	Roberto Kelly	.20	.12
330	Randy Milligan	.08	.05
331	Kevin Mitchell	.12	.07
332	Tim Pugh (R)	.25	.15
333	Jeff Reardon	.12	.07
334	John Roper	.12	.07
335	Juan Samuel	.08	.05
336	John Smiley	.12	.07
337	Dan Wilson	.20	.12
338	Scott Aldred	.10	.06
339	Andy Ashby	.08	.05
340	Freddie Benavides	.08	.05
341	Dante Bichette	.15	.10
342	Willie Blair	.12	.07
343	Daryl Boston	.08	.05
344	Vinny Castilla	.10	.06
345	Jerald Clark	.08	.05
346	Alex Cole	.08	.05
347	Andres Galarraga	.20	.12
348	Joe Girardi	.08	.05
349	Ryan Hawblitzel	.15	.10
350	Charlie Hayes	.10	.06
351	Butch Henry	.08	.05
352	Darren Holmes	.10	.06
353	Dale Murphy	.12	.07
354	David Nied	1.00	.70
355	Jeff Parrett	.08	.05
356	Steve Reed (R)	.15	.10
357	Bruce Ruffin	.08	.05
358	Danny Sheaffer (R)	.12	.07
359	Bryn Smith	.08	.05
360	Jim Tatum (R)	.20	.12
361	Eric Young	.20	.12
362	Gerald Young	.08	.05
363	Luis Aquino	.08	.05

364 Alex Arias	.08	.05
365 Jack Armstrong	.08	.05
366 Brot Barberie	.08	.05
367 Ryan Bowen	.12	.07
368 Greg Briley	.08	.05
369 Cris Carpenter	.08	.05
370 Chuck Carr	.20	.12
371 Jeff Conine	.25	.15
372 Steve Decker	.10	.06
373 Orestes Destrade	.08	.05
374 Monty Fariss	.08	.05
375 Junior Felix	.08	.05
376 Chris Hammond	.08	.05
377 Bryan Harvey	.12	.07
378 Trevor Hoffman	.20	.12
379 Charlie Hough	.08	.05
380 Joe Klink	.08	.05
381 Richie Lewis (R)	.15	.10
382 Dave Magadan	.08	.05
383 Bob McClure	.08	.05
384 Scott Pose (R)	.20	.12
385 Rich Renteria	.12	.07
386 Benito Santiago	.12	.07
387 Walt Weiss	.08	.05
388 Nigel Wilson	1.50	.90
389 Eric Anthony	.15	.10
390 Jeff Bagwell	.50	.30
391 Andujar Cedeno	.12	.07
392 Doug Drabek	.12	.07
393 Darryl Kile	.25	.15
394 Mark Portugal	.10	.06
395 Karl Rhodes	.10	.06
396 Scott Servais	.08	.05
397 Greg Swindell	.10	.06
398 Tom Goodwin	.12	.07
399 Kevin Gross	.08	.05
400 Carlos Hernandez	.08	.05
401 Ramon Martinez	.15	.10
402 Raul Mondesi	.30	.18
403 Jody Reed	.08	.05
404 Mike Sharperson	.08	.05
405 Cory Snyder	.10	.06
406 Darryl Strawberry	.20	.12
407 Rick Trlicek	.12	.07
408 Tim Wallach	.10	.06
409 Todd Worrell	.08	.05
410 Tavo Alvarez	.15	.10
411 Sean Berry	.15	.10
412 Frank Bolick	.12	.07
413 Cliff Floyd	3.50	2.00
414 Mike Gardiner	.08	.05
415 Marquis Grissom	.20	.12
416 Tim Laker (R)	.20	.12
417 Mike Lansing (R)	.40	.25
418 Dennis Martinez	.12	.07
419 John Vander Wal	.08	.05
420 John Wetteland	.10	.06
421 Rondell White	.75	.45
422 Bobby Bonilla	.15	.10
423 Jeromy Burnitz	.40	.25
424 Vince Coleman	.10	.06
425 Mike Draper	.15	.10
426 Tony Fernandez	.10	.06
427 Dwight Gooden	.15	.10
428 Jeff Innis	.08	.05
429 Bobby Jones	.50	.30
430 Mike Maddux	.08	.05
431 Charlie O'Brien	.08	.05
432 Joe Orsulak	.08	.05
433 Pete Schourek	.10	.06
434 Frank Tanana	.08	.05
435 Ryan Thompson	.35	.20
436 Kim Batiste	.08	.05
437 Mark Davis	.08	.05
438 Jose DeLeon	.08	.05
439 Lenny Dykstra	.30	.18
440 Jim Eisenreich	.08	.05
441 Tommy Greene	.20	.12
442 Pete Incaviglia	.10	.06
443 Danny Jackson	.10	.06
444 Todd Pratt (R)	.25	.15
445 Curt Schilling	.15	.10
446 Milt Thompson	.08	.05
447 David West	.08	.05
448 Mitch Williams	.08	.05
449 Steve Cooke	.40	.25
450 Carlos Garcia	.25	.15
451 Al Martin	.40	.25
452 Blas Minor	.12	.07
453 Dennis Moeller	.15	.10
454 Denny Neagle	.10	.06
455 Don Slaught	.08	.05
456 Lonnie Smith	.10	.06
457 Paul Wagner	.40	.25
458 Bob Walk	.08	.05
459 Kevin Young	.40	.25
460 Rene Arocha (R)	.50	.30
461 Brian Barber	.40	.25
462 Rheal Cormier	.12	.07
463 Gregg Jefferies	.20	.12
464 Joe Magrane	.08	.05
465 Omar Olivares	.08	.05
466 Geronimo Pena	.08	.05
467 Allen Watson	.75	.45
468 Mark Whiten	.25	.15
469 Derek Bell	.20	.12
470 Phil Clark	.12	.07
471 Pat Gomez (R)	.20	.12
472 Tony Gwynn	.40	.25
473 Jeremy Hernandez	.08	.05
474 Bruce Hurst	.10	.06
475 Phil Plantier	.40	.25
476 Scott Sanders (R)	.15	.10
477 Tim Scott	.10	.06

478 Darrell Sherman (R)	.35	.20
479 Guillermo Velasquez	.12	.07
480 Tim Worrell (R)	.20	.12
481 Todd Benzinger	.08	.05
482 Bud Black	.08	.05
483 Barry Bonds	1.25	.80
484 Dave Burba	.10	.06
485 Bryan Hickerson	.12	.07
486 Dave Martinez	.08	.05
487 Willie McGee	.12	.07
488 Jeff Reed	.08	.05
489 Kevin Rogers	.15	.10
490 Matt Williams	.35	.20
491 Trevor Wilson	.08	.05
492 Harold Baines	.12	.07
493 Mike Devereaux	.10	.06
494 Todd Frohwirth	.08	.05
495 Chris Hoiles	.12	.07
496 Luis Mercedes	.10	.06
497 Sherman Obando (R)	.25	.15
498 Brad Pennington	.12	.07
499 Harold Reynolds	.08	.05
500 Arthur Rhodes	.12	.07
501 Cal Ripken Jr.	.70	.40
502 Rick Sutcliffe	.10	.06
503 Fernando Valenzuela	.10	.06
504 Mark Williamson	.08	.05
505 Scott Bankhead	.08	.05
506 Greg Blosser	.35	.20
507 Ivan Calderon	.08	.05
508 Roger Clemens	.50	.30
509 Andre Dawson	.20	.12
510 Scott Fletcher	.08	.05
511 Greg Harris	.08	.05
512 Billy Hatcher	.08	.05
513 Bob McIvin	.12	.07
514 Carlos Quintana	.08	.05
515 Luis Rivera	.08	.05
516 Jeff Russell	.08	.05
517 Ken Ryan (R)	.35	.20
518 Chili Davis	.12	.07
519 Jim Edmonds (R)	.30	.18
520 Gary Gaetti	.08	.05
521 Torey Lovullo	.10	.06
522 Troy Percival	.12	.07
523 Tim Salmon	3.00	1.75
524 Scott Sanderson	.08	.05
525 J.T. Snow (R)	1.00	.70
526 Jerome Walton	.08	.05
527 Jason Bere	1.75	1.00
528 Rod Bolton	.12	.07
529 Ellis Burks	.12	.07
530 Carlton Fisk	.15	.10
531 Craig Grebeck	.08	.05
532 Ozzie Guillen	.10	.06
533 Roberto Hernandez	.15	.10
534 Bo Jackson	.25	.15

535 Kirk McCaskill	.08	.05
536 Dave Stieb	.10	.06
537 Robin Ventura	.30	.18
538 Albert Belle	.70	.40
539 Mike Bielecki	.08	.05
540 Glenallen Hill	.12	.07
541 Reggie Jefferson	.12	.07
542 Kenny Lofton	.40	.25
543 Jeff Mutis	.12	.07
544 Junior Ortiz	.08	.05
545 Manny Ramirez	1.50	.90
546 Jeff Treadway	.08	.05
547 Kevin Wickander	.08	.05
548 Cecil Fielder	.35	.20
549 Kirk Gibson	.12	.07
550 Greg Gohr	.15	.10
551 David Haas	.10	.06
552 Bill Kreuger	.10	.06
553 Mike Moore	.08	.05
554 Mickey Tettleton	.15	.10
555 Lou Whitaker	.12	.07
556 Kevin Appier	.20	.12
557 Billy Brewer (R)	.15	.10
558 David Cone	.12	.07
559 Greg Gagne	.08	.05
560 Mark Gardner	.08	.05
561 Phil Hiatt	.60	.35
562 Felix Jose	.10	.06
563 Jose Lind	.08	.05
564 Mike Macfarlane	.08	.05
565 Keith Miller	.08	.05
566 Jeff Montgomery	.10	.06
567 Hipolito Pichardo	.10	.06
568 Ricky Bones	.10	.06
569 Tom Brunansky	.10	.06
570 Joe Kmak	.10	.06
571 Pat Listach	.15	.10
572 Graeme Lloyd (R)	.15	.10
573 Carlos Maldonado	.15	.10
574 Josias Manzanillo (R)	.12	.07
575 Matt Mieske	.15	.10
576 Kevin Reimer	.08	.05
577 Bill Spiers	.08	.05
578 Dickie Thon	.08	.05
579 Willie Banks	.12	.07
580 Jim Deshaies	.08	.05
581 Mark Guthrie	.10	.06
582 Brian Harper	.10	.06
583 Chuck Knoblauch	.15	.10
584 Gene Larkin	.08	.05
585 Shane Mack	.15	.10
586 David McCarty	.75	.45
587 Mike Pagliarulo	.08	.05
588 Mike Trombley	.12	.07
589 Dave Winfield	.40	.25
590 Jim Abbott	.20	.12
591 Wade Boggs	.40	.25

592	Russ Davis (R)	.80	.50
593	Steve Farr	.08	.05
594	Steve Howe	.08	.05
595	Mike Humphreys	.12	.07
596	Jimmy Key	.12	.07
597	Jim Leyritz	.08	.05
598	Bobby Munoz	.12	.07
599	Paul O'Neill	.15	.10
600	Spike Owen	.08	.05
601	Mike Stanley	.12	.07
602	Danny Tartabull	.15	.10
603	Scott Brosius	.08	.05
604	Storm Davis	.08	.05
605	Eric Fox	.12	.07
606	Goose Gossage	.10	.06
607	Scott Hemond	.08	.05
608	Dave Henderson	.08	.05
609	Mark McGwire	.35	.20
610	Mike Mohler (R)	.15	.10
611	Edwin Nunez	.08	.05
612	Kevin Seitzer	.08	.05
613	Ruben Sierra	.20	.12
614	Chris Bosio	.10	.06
615	Norm Charlton	.08	.05
616	Jim Converse (R)	.15	.10
617	John Cummings (R)	.40	.25
618	Mike Felder	.08	.05
619	Ken Griffey Jr.	3.00	1.75
620	Mike Hampton	.12	.07
621	Erik Hanson	.08	.05
622	Bill Haselman	.08	.05
623	Tino Martinez	.12	.07
624	Lee Tinsley	.12	.07
625	Fernando Vina (R)	.12	.07
626	David Wainhouse	.10	.06
627	Jose Canseco	.35	.20
628	Benji Gil	.50	.30
629	Tom Henke	.08	.05
630	David Hulse (R)	.30	.18
631	Manuel Lee	.08	.05
632	Craig Lefferts	.08	.05
633	Robb Nen	.20	.12
634	Gary Redus	.08	.05
635	Bill Ripken	.08	.05
636	Nolan Ryan	2.50	1.50
637	Dan Smith	.15	.10
638	Matt Whiteside (R)	.20	.12
639	Roberto Alomar	.70	.40
640	Juan Guzman	.35	.20
641	Pat Hentgen	.40	.25
642	Darrin Jackson	.08	.05
643	Randy Knorr	.10	.06
644	Domingo Martinez (R)	.50	.30
645	Paul Molitor	.25	.15
646	Dick Schofield	.08	.05
647	Dave Stewart	.15	.10
648	Checklist	.08	.05
649	Checklist	.08	.05
650	Checklist	.08	.05
___	Dennis Eckersley Ea	1.25	.80
___	Dennis Eckersley (Autographed)	125.00	65.00

1993 Fleer Ultra All-Stars

The cards in this limited insert set were issued randomly in Ultra Series II Packs. The full-color fronts featuring action photos that appear to be carved out of stone. The words "Ultra All-Star" and the player's name are centered under the photograph. All cards measure 2-1/2" by 3-1/2".

	MINT	NR/MT
Complete Set (20)	60.00	38.00
Commons	1.00	.65

1	Darren Daulton	2.50	1.50
2	Will Clark	3.50	2.00
3	Ryne Sandberg	6.00	3.50
4	Barry Larkin	1.25	.75
5	Gary Sheffield	2.50	1.50
6	Barry Bonds	7.50	4.50
7	Ray Lankford	1.25	.75
8	Larry Walker	1.25	.75
9	Greg Maddux	2.00	1.25
10	Lee Smith	1.00	.65
11	Ivan Rodriquez	2.50	1.50
12	Mark McGwire	3.50	1.75
13	Carlos Baerga	5.00	3.00
14	Cal Ripken Jr.	6.50	3.75
15	Edgar Martinez	1.00	.65
16	Juan Gonzalez	10.00	6.50

		MINT	NR/MT
17	Ken Griffey Jr.	12.00	7.50
18	Kirby Puckett	6.00	3.50
19	Frank Thomas	15.00	10.00
20	Mike Mussina	6.00	3.50

1993 Fleer Ultra Award Winners

These limited insert cards were distributed randomly in Ultra Series I packs. Card fronts are horizontal and contain two photo images on a marble-type background. The player's name appears in script in the lower corner just above his achievement. All cards measure 2-1/2" by 3-1/2".

		MINT	NR/MT
	Complete Set (25)	50.00	30.00
	Commons	.75	.45
1	Greg Maddux	2.50	1.50
2	Tom Pagnozzi	.75	.45
3	Mark Grace	1.75	1.00
4	Jose Lind	.75	.45
5	Terry Pendleton	1.00	.65
6	Ozzie Smith	2.50	1.50
7	Barry Bonds	7.50	4.50
8	Andy Van Slyke	1.00	.65
9	Larry Walker	1.25	.75
10	Mark Langston	.80	.50
11	Ivan Rodriquez	2.50	1.50
12	Don Mattingly	4.00	2.50
13	Roberto Alomar	6.50	3.75
14	Robin Ventura	3.50	2.00
15	Cal Ripken Jr.	6.50	3.75
16	Ken Griffey Jr.	12.00	7.50
17	Kirby Puckett	6.00	3.50
18	Devon White	.75	.45
19	Pat Listach	1.25	.75
20	Eric Karros	3.00	1.75
21	Pat Borders	.75	.45
22	Greg Maddux	2.50	1.50
23	Dennis Eckersley	1.25	.75
24	Barry Bonds	7.50	4.50
25	Gary Sheffield	2.50	1.50

1993 Fleer Ultra All-Rookies

The Ultra All-Rookie Team inserts were issued randomly in Series Ii packs. The card fronts feature a full color ation shot superimposed over a lettered background that includes the player's team name and also says "All-Rookie" in block letters. All cards measure 2-1/2" by 3-1/2".

		MINT	NR/MT
	Complete Set (10)	40.00	28.00
	Commons	2.00	1.25
1	Rene Arocha	2.00	1.25
2	Jeff Conine	2.00	1.25
3	Phil Hiatt	2.50	1.50
4	Mike Lansing	2.00	1.25
5	Al Martin	3.00	1.75
6	David Nied	5.00	3.00
7	Mike Piazza	24.00	14.00
8	Tim Salmon	12.00	7.50
9	J.T. Snow	5.00	3.00
10	Kevin Young	3.00	1.75

1993 Fleer Ultra Home Run Kings

This 10-card insert set features full color action photos on the card fronts. The pictures are superimposed over a large baseball floating in an outer space background. The player's name is printed in script in the lower corner. The cards were distributed randomly in all Ultra packs and measure 2-1/2" by 3-1/2".

		MINT	NR/MT
Complete Set (10)		36.00	24.00
Commons		2.50	1.50
1	Juan Gonzalez	8.50	5.00
2	Mark McGwire	3.00	1.75
3	Cecil Fielder	3.00	1.75
4	Fred McGriff	4.00	2.50
5	Albert Belle	5.00	3.00
6	Barry Bonds	7.50	4.50
7	Joe Carter	3.50	12.00
8	Gary Sheffield	3.00	1.75
9	Darren Daulton	2.50	1.50
10	Dave Hollins	2.50	1.50

1993 Fleer Ultra Strikeout Kings

The five cards in this limited insert set were issued randomly in Ultra Series II packs. The fronts feature a full-color action shot superimposed over a large baseball floating in outer space. The player's name is printed under his photo. All cards measure 2-1/2" by 3-1/2".

		MINT	NR/MT
Complete Set (5)		20.00	12.50
Commons		2.00	1.25
1	Roger Clemens	5.00	3.00
2	Juan Guzman	2.00	1.25
3	Randy Johnson	2.50	1.50

4	Nolan Ryan	10.00	6.50
5	John Smoltz	2.00	1.25

1993 Fleer Ultra Performers

The cards in this set were only available through the mail. The card fronts include five different photographs, a larger full color action shot of the player superimposed over four smaller photos. All cards measure 2-1/2" by 3-1/2".

		MINT	NR/MT
Complete Set (10)		24.00	14.00
Commons		.75	.45
1	Barry Bonds	4.00	2.50
2	Juan Gonzalez	5.00	3.00
3	Ken Griffey jr.	6.50	3.75
4	Eric Karros	1.50	.90
5	Pat Listach	.75	.45
6	Greg Maddux	1.50	.90
7	David Nied	2.00	1.25
8	Gary Sheffield	1.50	.90
9	J.T. Snow	2.00	1.25
10	Frank Thomas	7.50	4.50

1993 Fleer Flair

This 300-card set marks Fleer's first Super-Premium baseball card set. The card fronts feature a full-bleed design with two full-color action shots of the player printed on a thick glossy card stock. The player's name is printed in the lower corner in gold type while the Flair logo is printed in the upper corner. Card backs contain another full color action shot with the player's stats superimposed over the lower portion of his photograph. All cards measure 2-1/2" by 3-1/2".

		MINT	NR/MT
Complete Set (300)		105.00	70.00
Commons		.20	.12
1	Steve Avery	.70	.40
2	Jeff Blauser	.25	.15
3	Ron Gant	.50	.30
4	Tom Glavine	.80	.50
5	David Justice	1.25	.80
6	Mark Lemke	.20	.12
7	Greg Maddux	.70	.40
8	Fred McGriff	1.00	.70
9	Terry Pendleton	.30	.18
10	Deion Sanders	.50	.30
11	John Smoltz	.30	.18
12	Mike Stanton	.20	.12
13	Steve Buechele	.20	.12
14	Mark Grace	.50	.30
15	Greg Larkin	.20	.12
16	Derrick May	.40	.25
17	Chuck McElroy	.20	.12
18	Mike Morgan	.20	.12
19	Randy Myers	.25	.15
20	Ryne Sandberg	1.25	.80
21	Dwight Smith	.25	.15
22	Sammy Sosa	.50	.30
23	Jose Vizcaino	.20	.12
24	Tim Belcher	.20	.12
25	Rob Dibble	.25	.15
26	Roberto Kelly	.30	.18
27	Barry Larkin	.30	.18
28	Kevin Mitchell	.25	.15
29	Hal Morris	.25	.15
30	Joe Oliver	.20	.12
31	Jose Rijo	.25	.15
32	Bip Roberts	.20	.12
33	Chris Sabo	.25	.15
34	Reggie Sanders	.60	.35
35	Dante Bichette	.30	.18
36	Willie Blair	.25	.15
37	Jerald Clark	.20	.12
38	Alex Cole	.20	.12
39	Andres Galarraga	.50	.30
40	Joe Girardi	.20	.12
41	Charlie Hayes	.25	.15
42	Chris Jones	.20	.12
43	David Nied	1.00	.70
44	Eric Young	.50	.30
45	Alex Arias	.20	.12
46	Jack Armstrong	.20	.12
47	Bret Barberie	.20	.12
48	Chuck Carr	.35	.20
49	Jeff Conine	.35	.20
50	Orestes Destrade	.20	.12
51	Chris Hammond	.20	.12
52	Bryan Harvey	.25	.15
53	Benito Santiago	.25	.15
54	Gary Sheffield	.60	.35
55	Walt Weiss	.20	.12
56	Eric Anthony	.30	.18
57	Jeff Bagwell	1.00	.70
58	Craig Biggio	.25	.15
59	Ken Caminiti	.20	.12
60	Andujar Cedeno	.25	.15
61	Doug Drabek	.25	.15
62	Steve Finley	.20	.12
63	Luis Gonzalez	.25	.15
64	Pete Harnisch	.25	.15
65	Doug Jones	.20	.12
66	Darryl Kile	.50	.30
67	Greg Swindell	.25	.15
68	Brett Butler	.25	.15
69	Jim Gott	.20	.12
70	Orel Hershiser	.25	.15
71	Eric Karros	.70	.40
72	Pedro Martinez	.40	.25
73	Ramon Martinez	.30	.18
74	Roger McDowell	.20	.12
75	Mike Piazza	12.50	8.50
76	Jody Reed	.20	.12
77	Tim Wallach	.25	.15
78	Moises Alou	.35	.20
79	Greg Colbrunn	.25	.15
80	Wil Cordero	.60	.35
81	Delino DeShields	.35	.20
82	Jeff Fassero	.20	.12
83	Marquis Grissom	.40	.25
84	Ken Hill	.25	.15
85	Mike Lansing (R)	.80	.50
86	Dennis Martinez	.25	.15
87	Larry Walker	.50	.30
88	John Wetteland	.25	.15
89	Bobby Bonilla	.30	.18
90	Vince Coleman	.25	.15
91	Dwight Gooden	.30	.18
92	Todd Hundley	.20	.12
93	Howard Johnson	.25	.15
94	Eddie Murray	.40	.25
95	Joe Orsulak	.20	.12
96	Bret Saberhagen	.25	.15
97	Darren Daulton	.40	.25
98	Mariano Duncan	.20	.12
99	Lenny Dykstra	.40	.25

#	Player			#	Player		
100	Jim Eisenreich	.20	.12	157	Cal Ripken Jr.	2.00	1.25
101	Tommy Greene	.35	.20	158	Rick Sutcliffe	.25	.15
102	Dave Hollins	.75	.45	159	Fernando Valenzuela	.25	.15
103	Pete Incaviglia	.25	.15	160	Roger Clemens	1.25	.00
104	Danny Jackson	.20	.12	161	Scott Cooper	.25	.15
105	John Kruk	.40	.25	162	Andre Dawson	.40	.25
106	Terry Mulholland	.20	.12	163	Scott Fletcher	.20	.12
107	Curt Schilling	.30	.18	164	Mike Greenwell	.25	.15
108	Mitch Williams	.20	.12	165	Greg Harris	.20	.12
109	Stan Belinda	.20	.12	166	Billy Hatcher	.20	.12
110	Jay Bell	.35	.20	167	Jeff Russell	.20	.12
111	Steve Cooke	.75	.45	168	Mo Vaughn	.70	.40
112	Carlos Garcia	.60	.35	169	Frank Viola	.25	.15
113	Jeff King	.25	.15	170	Chad Curtis	.80	.50
114	Al Martin	.80	.50	171	Chili Davis	.25	.15
115	Orlando Merced	.40	.25	172	Gary DiSarcina	.20	.12
116	Don Slaught	.20	.12	173	Damion Easley	.50	.30
117	Andy Van Slyke	.30	.18	174	Chuck Finley	.25	.15
118	Tim Wakefield	.35	.20	175	Mark Langston	.25	.15
119	Rene Arocha (R)	1.00	.70	176	Luis Polonia	.20	.12
120	Bernard Gilkey	.30	.18	177	Tim Salmon	8.50	5.00
121	Gregg Jefferies	.40	.25	178	Scott Sanderson	.20	.12
122	Ray Lankford	.40	.25	179	J.T. Snow	1.50	.90
123	Donovan Osborne	.40	.25	180	Wilson Alvarez	.50	.30
124	Tom Pagnozzi	.25	.15	181	Ellis Burks	.25	.15
125	Erik Pappas	.25	.15	182	Joey Cora	.20	.12
126	Geronimo Pena	.20	.12	183	Alex Fernandez	.60	.35
127	Lee Smith	.25	.15	184	Ozzie Guillen	.25	.15
128	Ozzie Smith	.70	.40	185	Roberto Hernandez	.25	.15
129	Bob Tewksbury	.20	.12	186	Bo Jackson	.50	.30
130	Mark Whiten	.50	.30	187	Lance Johnson	.20	.12
131	Derek Bell	.40	.25	188	Jack McDowell	.80	.50
132	Andy Benes	.30	.18	189	Frank Thomas	10.00	6.50
133	Tony Gwynn	.75	.45	190	Robin Ventura	1.00	.70
134	Gene Harris	.20	.12	191	Carlos Baerga	1.50	.90
135	Trevor Hoffman	.35	.20	192	Albert Belle	1.25	.80
136	Phil Plantier	.75	.45	193	Wayne Kirby	.30	.18
137	Rod Beck	.25	.15	194	Derek Lilliquist	.20	.12
138	Barry Bonds	3.00	1.75	195	Kenny Lofton	1.25	.80
139	John Burkett	.50	.30	196	Carlos Martinez	.25	.15
140	Will Clark	1.00	.70	197	Jose Mesa	.25	.15
141	Royce Clayton	.40	.25	198	Eric Plunk	.20	.12
142	Mike Jackson	.25	.15	199	Paul Sorrento	.30	.18
143	Darren Lewis	.25	.15	200	John Doherty	.40	.25
144	Kirt Manwaring	.20	.12	201	Cecil Fielder	.75	.45
145	Willie McGee	.25	.15	202	Travis Fryman	1.00	.70
146	Bill Swift	.35	.20	203	Kirk Gibson	.25	.15
147	Robby Thompson	.30	.18	204	Mike Henneman	.20	.12
148	Matt Williams	.60	.35	205	Chad Kreuter	.25	.15
149	Brady Anderson	.30	.18	206	Scott Livingstone	.20	.12
150	Mike Devereaux	.25	.15	207	Tony Phillips	.25	.15
151	Chris Hoiles	.25	.15	208	Mickey Tettleton	.25	.15
152	Ben McDonald	.30	.18	209	Alan Trammell	.40	.25
153	Mark McLemore	.20	.12	210	David Wells	.20	.12
154	Mike Mussina	1.25	.80	211	Lou Whitaker	.25	.15
155	Gregg Olson	.25	.15	212	Kevin Appier	.50	.30
156	Harold Reynolds	.20	.12	213	George Brett	1.00	.70

214	David Cone	.30	.18
215	Tom Gordon	.25	.15
216	Phil Hiatt	.80	.50
217	Felix Jose	.25	.15
218	Wally Joyner	.30	.18
219	Jose Lind	.20	.12
220	Mike Macfarlane	.20	.12
221	Brian McRae	.35	.20
222	Jeff Montgomery	.25	.15
223	Cal Eldred	.50	.30
224	Darryl Hamilton	.30	.18
225	John Jaha	.40	.25
226	Pat Listach	.35	.20
227	Graeme Lloyd (R)	.35	.20
228	Kevin Reimer	.20	.12
229	Bill Spiers	.20	.12
230	B.J. Surhoff	.20	.12
231	Greg Vaughn	.50	.30
232	Robin Yount	1.00	.70
233	Rick Aguilera	.25	.15
234	Jim Deshaies	.20	.12
235	Brian Harper	.25	.15
236	Kent Hrbek	.20	.12
237	Chuck Knoblauch	.30	.18
238	Shane Mack	.30	.18
239	David McCarty	1.25	.80
240	Pedro Munoz	.30	.18
241	Mike Pagliarulo	.20	.12
242	Kirby Puckett	1.50	.90
243	Dave Winfield	1.25	.80
244	Jim Abbott	.50	.30
245	Wade Boggs	.75	.45
246	Pat Kelly	.25	.15
247	Jimmy Key	.30	.18
248	Jim Leyritz	.20	.12
249	Don Mattingley	1.00	.70
250	Matt Nokes	.20	.12
251	Paul O'Neill	.35	.20
252	Mike Stanley	.25	.15
253	Danny Tartabull	.30	.18
254	Bob Wickman	.80	.50
255	Bernie Williams	.35	.20
256	Mike Bordick	.25	.15
257	Dennis Eckersley	.35	.20
258	Brent Gates	1.00	.70
259	Goose Gossage	.25	.15
260	Rickey Henderson	.70	.40
261	Mark McGwire	.60	.35
262	Ruben Sierra	.40	.25
263	Terry Steinbach	.25	.15
264	Bob Welch	.20	.12
265	Bobby Witt	.25	.15
266	Rich Amaral	.30	.18
267	Chris Bosio	.25	.15
268	Jay Buhner	.25	.15
269	Norm Charlton	.20	.12

270	Ken Griffey Jr.	8.50	5.00
271	Erik Hanson	.20	.12
272	Randy Johnson	.50	.30
273	Edgar Martinez	.30	.18
274	Tino Martinez	.25	.15
275	Dave Valle	.20	.12
276	Omar Vizquel	.20	.12
277	Kevin Brown	.30	.18
278	Jose Canseco	.60	.35
279	Julio Franco	.25	.15
280	Juan Gonzalez	6.00	3.50
281	Tom Henke	.20	.12
282	David Hulse	.75	.45
283	Rafael Palmeiro	.70	.40
284	Dean Palmer	.60	.35
285	Ivan Rodriquez	.75	.45
286	Nolan Ryan	5.00	3.00
287	Roberto Alomar	1.75	1.00
288	Pat Borders	.20	.12
289	Joe Carter	.80	.50
290	Juan Guzman	.75	.45
291	Pat Hentgen	.80	.50
292	Paul Molitor	.75	.45
293	John Olerud	1.75	1.00
294	Ed Sprague	.25	.15
295	Dave Stewart	.35	.20
296	Duane Ward	.25	.15
297	Devon White	.30	.18
298	Checklist	.20	.08
299	Checklist	.20	.08
300	Checklist	.20	.08

1993 Fleer Flair
Wave Of The Future

The 20-cards in this insert set were randomly issued in Flair packs. The card fronts depict full color action shots of the player's superimposed over a swirl of colors. The player's name is centered at the bottom of the card just under a Wave of the Future headline. All cards measure 2-1/2" by 3-1/2".

	MINT	NR/MT
Complete Set (20)	120.00	75.00
Commons	3.00	1.75

1	Jason Bere	10.00	6.50
2	Jeromy Burnitz	5.00	3.00
3	Russ Davis	8.00	5.00
4	Jim Edmonds	3.50	2.00
5	Cliff Floyd	20.00	12.50
6	Jeffrey Hammonds	12.00	7.50
7	Trevor Hoffman	3.50	2.00
8	Domingo Jean	3.50	2.00
9	David McCarty	5.00	3.00
10	Bobby Munoz	3.00	1.75
11	Brad Pennington	3.00	1.75
12	Mike Piazza	25.00	15.00
13	Manny Ramirez	6.50	3.75
14	John Roper	3.00	1.75
15	Tim Salmon	15.00	10.00
16	Aaron Sele	10.00	6.50
17	Allen Watson	5.00	3.00
18	Rondell White	6.00	3.50
19	Darrell Whitmore	4.50	2.75
20	Nigel Wilson	6.50	3.75

LEAF

1948 Leaf

MARTIN MARION

This 98-card set is skip-numbered through card number 168 and is very difficult to complete. Half of the cards in the set are short printed and considered scarce. Cards were the first post World War II set issued in color and measure 2-3/8" by 2-7/8".

		NR MT	EX
Complete Set (98)		32,000.00	16,500.00
Commons		28.00	12.00
Commons (Scarce)		325.00	150.00

1	Joe DiMaggio	2,200.00	1,000.00
3	Babe Ruth	2,500.00	1,200.00
4	Stan Musial (R)	875.00	375.00
5	Virgil Trucks	400.00	175.00
8	Satchel Paige (R)	2,200.00	1,000.00
10	Paul "Dizzy" Trout	28.00	12.00
11	Phil Rizzuto	250.00	100.00
13	Casimer Michaels	325.00	150.00
14	Billy Johnson	28.00	12.00
17	Frank Overmire	28.00	12.00
19	Johnny Wyrostek	325.00	150.00
20	Hank Sauer	450.00	200.00
22	Al Evans	28.00	12.00
26	Sam Chapman	28.00	12.00
27	Mickey Harris	28.00	12.00
28	Jim Hegan	35.00	15.00
29	Elmer Valo	30.00	12.50
30	Billy Goodman	375.00	160.00
31	Lou Brissie	28.00	12.00
32	Warren Spahn	280.00	125.00
33	Peanuts Lowrey	350.00	155.00
36	Al Zarilla	325.00	150.00
38	Ted Kluszewski	120.00	50.00
39	Ewell Blackwell	60.00	25.00
42	Kent Peterson	28.00	12.00
43	Ed Stevens	325.00	150.00
45	Ken Keltner	325.00	150.00
46	Johnny Mize	100.00	45.00
47	George Vico	28.00	12.00
48	Johnny Schmitz	325.00	150.00
49	Del Ennis	40.00	18.00
50	Dick Wakefield	28.00	12.00
51	Al Dark	425.00	190.00
53	Johnny VanderMeer	50.00	22.00
54	Bobby Adams	325.00	150.00
55	Tommy Henrich	450.00	200.00
56	Larry Jansen	30.00	12.50
57	Bob McCall	28.00	12.00
59	Luke Appling	100.00	45.00
61	Jake Early	28.00	12.00
62	Eddie Joost	325.00	150.00
63	Barney McCosky	325.00	150.00
65	Bob Elliot (ER)	35.00	15.00
66	Orval Grove	325.00	150.00
68	Eddie Miller	325.00	150.00
70	Honus Wagner	300.00	125.00
72	Hank Edwards	28.00	12.00
73	Pat Seerey	28.00	12.00
75	Dom DiMaggio	550.00	250.00
76	Ted Williams	850.00	400.00
77	Roy Smalley	28.00	12.00
78	Hoot Evers	325.00	150.00
79	Jackie Robinson (R)	950.00	450.00
81	Whitey Kurowski	325.00	150.00
82	Johnny Lindell	28.00	12.00
83	Bobby Doerr	150.00	60.00
84	Sid Hudson	28.00	12.00

85	Dave Philley	350.00	160.00
86	Ralph Weigel	28.00	12.00
88	Frank Gustine	325.00	150.00
91	Ralph Kiner	200.00	95.00
93	Bob Feller	1,500.00	650.00
95	George Stirnweiss	28.00	12.00
97	Marty Marion	66.00	26.00
98	Hal Newhouser	650.00	300.00
102a	Gene Hermansk (Er)	325.00	150.00
102b	Gene Hermanski	28.00	12.00
104	Edward Stewart	325.00	150.00
106	Lou Boudreau	100.00	45.00
108	Matt Batts	325.00	150.00
111	Jerry Priddy	28.00	12.00
113	Dutch Leonard	350.00	160.00
117	Joe Gordon	40.00	18.00
120	George Kell	600.00	275.00
121	Johnny Pesky	450.00	200.00
123	Cliff Fannin	325.00	150.00
125	Andy Pafko	30.00	12.50
127	Enos Slaughter	750.00	350.00
128	Buddy Rosar	28.00	12.00
129	Kirby Higbe	325.00	150.00
131	Sid Gordon	325.00	150.00
133	Tommy Holmes	400.00	175.00
136a	Cliff Aberson (Full Sleeve)	28.00	12.00
136b	Cliff Aberson (Short Sleeve)	250.00	100.00
137	Harry Walker	400.00	175.00
138	Larry Doby	600.00	275.00
139	Johnny Hopp	28.00	12.00
142	Danny Murtaugh	400.00	175.00
143	Dick Sisler	400.00	175.00
144	Bob Dillinger	325.00	150.00
146	Pete Reiser	500.00	225.00
149	Hank Majeski	325.00	150.00
153	Floyd Baker	325.00	150.00
158	Harry Brecheen	400.00	175.00
159	Mizell Platt	28.00	12.00
160	Bob Scheffing	325.00	150.00
161	Vern Stephens	400.00	175.00
163	Fred Hutchinson	425.00	200.00
165	Dale Mitchell	400.00	1750.00
168	Phil Cavarretta	500.00	225.00

1960 Leaf

HOYT WILHELM

This 144-card set was produced by Leaf for Sports Novelties, Inc. of Chicago. The cards were sold in wax packs with a marble instead of bubble gum. Cards feature black and white photos on the front and cards 73-144 are considered scarce.

		NR MT	EX
Complete Set(144)		1,500.00	700.00
Commons (1-72)		3.00	1.25
Commons (73-144)		15.00	7.00

1	Luis Aparicio	24.00	10.00
2	Woody Held	3.00	1.25
3	Frank Lary	3.50	1.50
4	Camilo Pascual	3.50	1.50
5	Frank Herrera	3.00	1.25
6	Felipe Alou	4.00	1.75
7	Ben Daniels	3.00	1.25
8	Roger Craig	4.00	1.75
9	Eddie Kasko	3.00	1.25
10	Bob Grim	3.00	1.25
11	Jim Busby	3.00	1.25
12	Ken Boyer	5.00	2.25
13	Bob Boyd	3.00	1.25
14	Sam Jones	3.00	1.25
15	Larry Jackson	3.00	1.25
16	Roy Face	4.00	1.75
17	Walt Moryn	3.00	1.25
18	Jim Gilliam	4.00	1.75
19	Don Newcombe	4.00	1.75
20	Glen Hobbie	3.00	1.25
21	Pedro Ramos	3.00	1.25
22	Ryne Duran	3.50	1.50
23	Joey Jay	3.00	1.25
24	Lou Berberet	3.00	1.25
25a	Jim Grant (White Cap, Wrong Photo)	15.00	7.00
25b	Jim Grant (Cor)	30.00	12.50
26	Tom Borland	3.00	1.25
27	Brooks Robinson	40.00	18.00

28	Jerry Adair	3.00	1.25
29	Ron Jackson	3.00	1.25
30	George Strickland	3.00	1.25
31	Rocky Bridges	3.50	1.50
32	Bill Tuttle	3.00	1.25
33	Ken Hunt	3.00	1.25
34	Hal Griggs	3.00	1.25
35	Jim Coates	3.00	1.25
36	Brooks Lawrence	3.00	1.25
37	Duke Snider	60.00	28.00
38	Al Spangler	3.00	1.25
39	Jim Owens	3.00	1.25
40	Bill Virdon	3.50	1.50
41	Ernie Broglio	3.50	1.50
42	Andre Rodgers	3.00	1.25
43	Julio Becquer	3.00	1.25
44	Tony Taylor	3.50	1.50
45	Jerry Lynch	3.50	1.50
46	Clete Boyer	4.50	2.00
47	Jerry Lumpe	3.00	1.25
48	Charlie Maxwell	3.00	1.25
49	Jim Perry	3.50	1.50
50	Danny McDevitt	3.00	1.25
51	Juan Pizarro	3.00	1.25
52	Dallas Green	7.50	3.50
53	Bob Friend	3.50	1.50
54	Jack Sanford	3.50	1.50
55	Jim Rivera	3.00	1.25
56	Ted Wills	3.00	1.25
57	Milt Pappas	3.50	1.50
58	Hal Smith	3.00	1.25
59	Bobby Avila	3.00	1.25
60	Clem Labine	3.50	1.50
61	Vic Rehm	3.00	1.25
62	John Gabler	3.00	1.25
63	John Tsitouris	3.00	1.25
64	Dave Sisler	3.00	1.25
65	Vic Power	3.50	1.50
66	Earl Battey	3.50	1.50
67	Bob Purkey	3.50	1.50
68	Moe Drabowsky	3.00	1.25
69	Hoyt Wilhelm	15.00	6.75
70	Humberto Robinson	3.00	1.25
71	Whitey Herzog	7.50	3.50
72	Dick Donovan	3.00	1.25
73	Gordon Jones	15.00	7.00
74	Joe Hicks	15.00	7.00
75	Ray Culp	16.50	7.50
76	Dick Drott	15.00	7.00
77	Bob Duliba	15.00	7.00
78	Art Ditmar	15.00	7.00
79	Steve Korcheck	15.00	7.00
80	Henry Mason	15.00	7.00
81	Harry Simpson	15.00	7.00
82	Gene Green	15.00	7.00
83	Bob Shaw	15.00	7.00
84	Howard Reed	15.00	7.00
85	Dick Stigman	15.00	7.00
86	Rip Repulski	15.00	7.00
87	Seth Morehead	15.00	7.00
88	Camilo Carreon	15.00	7.00
89	John Blanchard	20.00	8.50
90	Billy Hoeft	15.00	7.00
91	Fred Hopke	15.00	7.00
92	Joe Martin	15.00	7.00
93	Wally Shannon	15.00	7.00
94	Hal R. Smith/ Hal W. Smith	20.00	8.50
95	Al Schroll	15.00	7.00
96	John Kucks	15.00	7.00
97	Tom Morgan	15.00	7.00
98	Willie Jones	15.00	7.00
99	Marshall Renfroe	15.00	7.00
100	Willie Tasby	15.00	7.00
101	Irv Noren	15.00	7.00
102	Russ Snyder	15.00	7.00
103	Bob Turley	20.00	8.50
104	Jim Woods	15.00	7.00
105	Ronnie Kline	15.00	7.00
106	Steve Bilko	15.00	7.00
107	Elmer Valo	15.00	7.00
108	Tom McAvoy	15.00	7.00
109	Stan Williams	15.00	7.00
110	Earl Averill	15.00	7.00
111	Lee Walls	15.00	7.00
112	Paul Richards	16.50	8.50
113	Ed Sadowski	15.00	7.00
114	Stover McIlwain	15.00	7.00
115	Chuck Tanner (Wrong Photo)	18.00	8.00
116	Lou Klimchock	15.00	7.00
117	Neil Chrisley	15.00	7.00
118	John Callison	18.00	8.00
119	Hal Smith	15.00	7.00
120	Carl Sawatski	15.00	7.00
121	Frank Leja	15.00	7.00
122	Earl Torgeson	16.50	7.50
123	Art Schult	15.00	7.00
124	Jim Brosnan	16.50	7.50
125	George Anderson	50.00	22.00
126	Joe Pignatano	15.00	7.00
127	Rocky Nelson	15.00	7.00
128	Orlando Cepeda	60.00	28.00
129	Daryl Spencer	15.00	7.00
130	Ralph Lumenti	15.00	7.00
131	Sam Taylor	15.00	7.00
132	Harry Brecheen	16.50	7.50
133	Johnny Groth	15.00	7.00
134	Wayne Terwilliger	15.00	7.00
135	Kent Hadley	15.00	7.00
136	Faye Throneberry	15.00	7.00
137	Jack Meyer	15.00	7.00
138	Chuck Cottier	15.00	7.00
139	Joe DeMaestri	15.00	7.00

		MINT	NR MT
140	Gene Freese	15.00	7.00
141	Curt Flood	35.00	15.00
142	Gino Cimoli	15.00	7.00
143	Clay Dalrymple	15.00	7.00
144	Jim Bunning	60.00	25.00

1990 Leaf

GREG MADDUX

This was the first premium set produced by Donruss. The cards are printed on a glossy high quality paper stock and feature full color photos on both the fron and back. The set was released in two 264-card series. All cards measure 2-1/2" by 3-1/2".

		MINT	NR MT
Complete Set (528)		265.00	145.00
Commons		.25	.15
1.	Introductory Card	.25	.15
2	Mike Henneman	.25	.15
3	Steve Bedrosian	.25	.15
4	Mike Scott	.25	.15
5	Allan Anderson	.25	.15
6	Rick Sutcliffe	.25	.15
7	Gregg Olson	1.00	.70
8	Kevin Elster	.25	.15
9	Pete O'Brien	.25	.15
10	Carlton Fisk	1.00	.70
11	Joe Magrane	.25	.15
12	Roger Clemens	3.50	2.00
13	Tom Glavine	7.00	4.00
14	Tom Gordon	.30	.18
15	Todd Benzinger	.25	.15
16	Hubie Brooks	.30	.18
17	Roberto Kelly	.75	.45
18	Barry Larkin	.75	.45
19	Mike Boddicker	.25	.15
20	Roger McDowell	.25	.15

21	Nolan Ryan	7.50	4.50
22	John Farrell	.25	.15
23	Bruce Hurst	.25	.15
24	Wally Joyner	.35	.20
25	Greg Maddux	5.00	3.00
26	Chris Bosio	.25	.15
27	John Cerutti	.25	.15
28	Tim Burke	.25	.15
29	Dennis Eckersley	.75	.45
30	Glenn Davis	.25	.15
31	Jim Abbott	4.00	2.50
32	Mike LaValliere	.25	.15
33	Andres Thomas	.25	.15
34	Lou Whitaker	.30	.18
35	Alvin Davis	.25	.15
36	Melido Perez	.25	.15
37	Craig Biggio	.35	.20
38	Rick Aguilera	.25	.15
39	Pete Harnisch	.40	.25
40	David Cone	.50	.30
41	Scott Garrelts	.25	.15
42	Jay Howell	.25	.15
43	Eric King	.25	.15
44	Pedro Guerrero	.25	.15
45	Mike Bielecki	.25	.15
46	Bob Boone	.30	.18
47	Kevin Brown	.80	.50
48	Jerry Browne	.25	.15
49	Mike Scioscia	.25	.15
50	Chuck Cary	.25	.15
51	Wade Boggs	2.50	1.50
52	Von Hayes	.25	.15
53	Tony Fernandez	.25	.15
54	Dennis Martinez	.30	.18
55	Tom Candiotti	.25	.15
56	Andy Benes	3.00	1.75
57	Rob Dibble	.30	.18
58	Chuck Crim	.25	.15
59	John Smoltz	4.50	2.75
60	Mike Heath	.25	.15
61	Kevin Gross	.25	.15
62	Mark McGwire	3.00	1.75
63	Bert Blyleven	.30	.18
64	Bob Walk	.25	.15
65	Mickey Tettleton	.40	.25
66	Sid Fernandez	.25	.15
67	Terry Kennedy	.25	.15
68	Fernando Valenzuela	.25	.15
69	Don Mattingly	2.50	1.50
70	Paul O'Neill	.35	.20
71	Robin Yount	2.50	1.50
72	Bret Saberhagen	.35	.20
73	Geno Petralli	.25	.15
74	Brook Jacoby	.25	.15
75	Roberto Alomar	8.00	5.00
76	Devon White	.40	.25
77	Jose Lind	.25	.15

No.	Player			No.	Player		
78	Pat Combs	.25	.15	135	Rafael Ramirez	.25	.15
79	Dave Steib	.30	.18	136	Shane Mack	.40	.25
80	Tim Wallach	.25	.15	137	Mark Grace	2.00	1.25
81	Dave Stewart	.50	.30	138	Phil Bradley	.25	.15
82	Eric Anthony (R)	3.00	1.75	139	Dwight Gooden	.60	.35
83	Randy Bush	.25	.15	140	Harold Reynolds	.25	.15
84	Checklist	.30	.10	141	Scott Fletcher	.25	.15
85	Jaime Navarro	.75	.45	142	Ozzie Smith	1.00	.70
86	Tommy Gregg	.25	.15	143	Mike Greenwell	.35	.20
87	Frank Tanana	.25	.15	144	Pete Smith	.30	.18
88	Omar Vizquel	.30	.18	145	Mark Gubicza	.25	.15
89	Ivan Calderon	.25	.15	146	Chris Sabo	.30	.18
90	Vince Coleman	.25	.15	147	Ramon Martinez	1.75	1.00
91	Barry Bonds	7.00	4.00	148	Tim Leary	.25	.15
92	Randy Milligan	.25	.15	149	Randy Myers	.30	.18
93	Frank Viola	.30	.18	150	Jody Reed	.25	.15
94	Matt Williams	3.50	2.00	151	Bruce Ruffin	.25	.15
95	Alfredo Griffin	.25	.15	152	Jeff Russell	.30	.18
96	Steve Sax	.35	.20	153	Doug Jones	.30	.18
97	Gary Gaetti	.25	.15	154	Tony Gwynn	2.75	1.60
98	Ryne Sandberg	4.50	2.50	155	Mark Langston	.30	.18
99	Danny Tartabull	.75	.45	156	Mitch Williams	.25	.15
100	Rafael Palmeiro	1.75	1.00	157	Gary Sheffield	10.00	6.00
101	Jesse Orosco	.25	.15	158	Tom Henke	.25	.15
102	Garry Templeton	.25	.15	159	Oil Can Boyd	.25	.15
103	Frank DiPino	.25	.15	160	Rickey Henderson	2.00	1.25
104	Tony Pena	.25	.15	161	Bill Doran	.25	.15
105	Dickie Thon	.25	.15	162	Chuck Finley	.30	.18
106	Kelly Gruber	.25	.15	163	Jeff King	.30	.18
107	Marquis Grisson (R)	5.00	3.00	164	Nick Esasky	.25	.15
108	Jose Canseco	2.75	1.60	165	Cecil Fielder	2.50	1.50
109	Mike Blowers	.25	.15	166	Dave Valle	.25	.15
110	Tom Browning	.25	.15	167	Robin Ventura	8.50	5.00
111	Greg Vaughn	3.50	2.00	168	Jim DeShaies	.25	.15
112	Oddibe McDowell	.25	.15	169	Juan Berenguer	.25	.15
113	Gary Ward	.25	.15	170	Craig Worthington	.25	.15
114	Jay Buhner	.75	.45	171	Gregg Jefferies	4.00	2.50
115	Eric Show	.25	.15	172	Will Clark	3.50	2.00
116	Bryan Harvey	.75	.45	173	Kirk Gibson	.30	.18
117	Andy Van Slyke	.75	.45	174	Checklist	.30	.10
118	Jeff Ballard	.25	.15	175	Bobby Thigpen	.25	.15
119	Barry Lyons	.25	.15	176	John Tudor	.25	.15
120	Kevin Mitchell	.40	.25	177	Andre Dawson	1.00	.70
121	Mike Gallego	.25	.15	178	George Brett	2.50	1.50
122	Dave Smith	.25	.15	179	Steve Buechele	.25	.15
123	Kirby Puckett	4.50	2.50	180	Albert Belle	18.00	12.00
124	Jerome Walton	.25	.15	181	Eddie Murray	1.00	.70
125	Bo Jackson	2.00	1.25	182	Bob Geren	.25	.15
126	Harold Baines	.30	.18	183	Rob Murphy	.25	.15
127	Scott Bankhead	.25	.15	184	Tom Herr	.25	.15
128	Ozzie Guillen	.25	.15	185	George Bell	.35	.20
129	Jose Oquendo	.25	.15	186	Spike Owen	.25	.15
130	John Dopson	.25	.15	187	Cory Snyder	.30	.18
131	Charlie Hayes	.50	.30	188	Fred Lynn	.30	.18
132	Fred McGriff	3.50	2.00	189	Eric Davis	.70	.40
133	Chet Lemon	.25	.15	190	Dave Parker	.30	.18
134	Gary Carter	.35	.20	191	Jeff Blauser	.40	.25

192	Matt Nokes	.25	.15	249	Ben McDonald (R)	1.75	1.00
193	Delino DeShields (R)	5.00	3.00	250	Darryl Strawberry	.90	.60
194	Scott Sanderson	.25	.15	251	Bret Butler	.30	.18
195	Lance Parrish	.25	.15	252	Terry Steinbach	.25	.15
196	Bobby Bonilla	.80	.50	253	Ken Caminiti	.25	.15
197	Cal Ripken	5.00	3.00	254	Dan Gladden	.25	.15
198	Kevin McReynolds	.30	.18	255	Dwight Smith	.30	.18
199	Robby Thompson	.50	.30	256	Kurt Stillwell	.25	.15
200	Tim Belcher	.25	.15	257	Ruben Sierra	2.00	1.25
201	Jesse Barfield	.25	.15	258	Mike Schooler	.25	.15
202	Mariano Duncan	.25	.15	259	Lance Johnson	.30	.18
203	Bill Spiers	.25	.15	260	Terry Pendleton	.80	.50
204	Frank White	.30	.18	261	Ellis Burks	.30	.18
205	Julio Franco	.35	.20	262	Len Dykstra	1.25	.80
206	Greg Swindell	.30	.18	263	Mookie Wilson	.25	.15
207	Benito Santiago	.30	.18	264	Checklist (Ryan)	.50	.30
208	Johnny Ray	.25	.15	265	No Hit king (Nolan Ryan)	6.00	3.50
209	Gary Redus	.25	.15				
210	Jeff Parrett	.25	.15	266	Brian DuBois	.25	.15
211	Jimmy Key	.35	.20	267	Don Robinson	.25	.15
212	Tim Raines	.35	.20	268	Glenn Wilson	.25	.15
213	Carney Lansford	.25	.15	269	Kevin Tapani (R)	.80	.50
214	Gerald Young	.25	.15	270	Marvell Wynn	.25	.15
215	Gene Larkin	.25	.15	271	Billy Ripken	.25	.15
216	Dan Plesac	.25	.15	272	Howard Johnson	.40	.25
217	Lonnie Smith	.25	.15	273	Brian Holman	.25	.15
218	Alan Trammell	.50	.30	274	Dan Pasqua	.25	.15
219	Jeffrey Leonard	.25	.15	275	Ken Dayley	.25	.15
220	Sammy Sosa (R)	6.50	3.75	276	Jeff Reardon	.40	.25
221	Todd Zeile	1.00	.70	277	Jim Presley	.25	.15
222	Bill Landrum	.25	.15	278	Jim Eisenreich	.25	.15
223	Mike Devereaux	.40	.25	279	Danny Jackson	.25	.15
224	Mike Marshall	.25	.15	280	Orel Hershiser	.30	.18
225	Jose Uribe	.25	.15	281	Andy Hawkins	.25	.15
226	Juan Samuel	.25	.15	282	Jose Rijo	.30	.18
227	Mel Hall	.30	.18	283	Luis Rivera	.25	.15
228	Kent Hrbek	.25	.15	284	John Kruk	1.25	.80
229	Shawon Dunston	.35	.20	285	Jeff Huson (R)	.30	.18
230	Kevin Seitzer	.25	.15	286	Joel Skinner	.25	.15
231	Pete Incaviglia	.25	.15	287	Jack Clark	.30	.18
232	Sandy Alomar	.35	.20	288	Chili Davis	.30	.18
233	Bip Roberts	.25	.15	289	Joe Girardi	.25	.15
234	Scott Terry	.25	.15	290	B.J. Surhoff	.25	.15
235	Dwight Evans	.30	.18	291	Luis Sojo (R)	.30	.18
236	Ricky Jordan	.25	.15	292	Tim Foley	.25	.15
237	John Olerud (R)	24.00	14.00	293	Mike Moore	.25	.15
238	Zane Smith	.25	.15	294	Ken Oberkfell	.25	.15
239	Walt Weiss	.25	.15	295	Luis Polonia	.25	.15
240	Alvaro Espinoza	.25	.15	296	Doug Drabek	.35	.20
241	Billy Hatcher	.25	.15	297	Dave Justice (R)	18.00	12.00
242	Paul Molitor	1.50	.90	298	Paul Gibson	.25	.15
243	Dale Murphy	.50	.30	299	Edgar Martinez	.80	.50
244	Dave Bergman	.25	.15	300	Frank Thomas	65.00	38.00
245	Ken Griffey Jr.	25.00	15.00	301	Eric Yelding	.30	.18
246	Ed Whitson	.25	.15	302	Greg Gagne	.25	.15
247	Kirk McCaskill	.25	.15	303	Brad Komminsk	.25	.15
248	Jay Bell	.50	.30	304	Ron Darling	.25	.15

305	Kevin Bass	.25	.15
306	Jeff Hamilton	.25	.15
307	Ron Karkovice	.25	.15
308	Milt Thompson	.30	.18
309	Mike Harkey	.35	.20
310	Mel Stottlemyre Jr.	.30	.18
311	Kenny Rogers	.25	.15
312	Mitch Webster	.25	.15
313	Kal Daniels	.25	.15
314	Matt Nokes	.25	.15
315	Dennis Lamp	.25	.15
316	Ken Howell	.25	.15
317	Glenallen Hill	.30	.18
318	Dave Martinez	.25	.15
319	Chris James	.25	.15
320	Mike Pagliarulo	.25	.15
321	Hal Morris	1.00	.70
322	Rob Deer	.30	.18
323	Greg Olson (R)	.35	.20
324	Tony Phillips	.35	.20
325	Larry Walker (R)	8.50	5.00
326	Ron Hassey	.25	.15
327	Jack Howell	.25	.15
328	John Smiley	.30	.18
329	Steve Finley	.30	.18
330	Dave Magadan	.25	.15
331	Greg Litton	.25	.15
332	Mickey Hatcher	.25	.15
333	Lee Guetterman	.25	.15
334	Norm Charlton	.30	.18
335	Edgar Diaz	.25	.15
336	Willie Wilson	.25	.15
337	Bobby Witt	.30	.18
338	Candy Maldonado	.25	.15
339	Craig Lefferts	.25	.15
340	Dante Bichette	1.00	.70
341	Wally Backman	.25	.15
342	Dennis Cook	.25	.15
343	Pat Borders	.30	.18
344	Wallace Johnson	.25	.15
345	Willie Randolph	.25	.15
346	Danny Darwin	.25	.15
347	Al Newman	.25	.15
348	Mark Knudson	.25	.15
349	Joe Boever	.25	.15
350	Larry Sheets	.25	.15
351	Mike Jackson	.30	.18
352	Wayne Edwards	.25	.15
353	Bernard Gilkey (R)	2.50	1.50
354	Don Slaught	.25	.15
355	Joe Orsulak	.30	.18
356	John Franco	.25	.15
357	Jeff Brantley	.25	.15
358	Mike Morgan	.25	.15
359	Deion Sanders	7.50	4.50
360	Terry Leach	.25	.15
361	Les Lancaster	.25	.15
362	Storm Davis	.25	.15
363	Scott Coolbaugh	.25	.15
364	Checklist	.30	.10
365	Cecilio Guante	.25	.15
366	Joey Cora	.25	.15
367	Willie McGee	.30	.18
368	Jerry Reed	.25	.15
369	Darren Daulton	1.50	.90
370	Manny Lee	.25	.15
371	Mark Gardner (R)	.60	.35
372	Rick Honeycutt	.25	.15
373	Steve Balboni	.25	.15
374	Jack Armstrong	.25	.15
375	Charlie O'Brien	.25	.15
376	Ron Gant	3.00	1.75
377	Lloyd Moseby	.25	.15
378	Gene Harris	.25	.15
379	Joe Carter	3.50	2.00
380	Scott Bailes	.25	.15
381	R.J. Reynolds	.25	.15
382	Bob Melvin	.25	.15
383	Tim Teufel	.25	.15
384	John Burkett	2.50	1.50
385	Felix Jose	.80	.50
386	Larry Anderson	.25	.15
387	David West	.25	.15
388	Luis Salazar	.25	.15
389	Mike MacFarlane	.35	.20
390	Charlie Hough	.25	.15
391	Greg Briley	.25	.15
392	Donn Pall	.25	.15
393	Bryn Smith	.25	.15
394	Carlos Quintana	.30	.18
395	Steve Lake	.25	.15
396	Mark Whiten (R)	4.50	2.75
397	Edwin Nunez	.25	.15
398	Rick Parker	.25	.15
399	Mark Portugal	.30	.18
400	Roy Smith	.25	.15
401	Hector Villanueva (R)	.30	.18
402	Bob Milacki	.25	.15
403	Alejandro Pena	.25	.15
404	Scott Bradley	.25	.15
405	Ron Kittle	.25	.15
406	Bob Tewksbury	.25	.15
407	Wes Gardner	.25	.15
408	Ernie Whitt	.25	.15
409	Terry Shumpert (R)	.25	.15
410	Tim Layana (R)	.25	.15
411	Chris Gwynn (R)	.30	.18
412	Jeff Robinson	.25	.15
413	Scott Scudder	.30	.18
414	Kevin Romine	.25	.15
415	Jose DeJesus	.25	.15
416	Mike Jeffcoat	.25	.15
417	Rudy Seanez (R)	.40	.25
418	Mike Dunne	.25	.15

419	Dick Schofield	.25	.15
420	Steve Wilson	.25	.15
421	Bill Krueger	.25	.15
422	Junior Felix	.30	.18
423	Drew Hall	.25	.15
424	Curt Young	.25	.15
425	Franklin Stubbs	.25	.15
426	Dave Winfield	2.50	1.50
427	Rick Reed (R)	.25	.15
428	Charlie Leibrandt	.25	.15
429	Jeff Robinson	.25	.15
430	Erik Hanson	.50	.30
431	Barry Jones	.25	.15
432	Alex Trevino	.25	.15
433	John Moses	.25	.15
434	Dave Johnson	.25	.15
435	Mackey Sasser	.25	.15
436	Rick Leach	.25	.15
437	Lenny Harris	.25	.15
438	Carlos Martinez	.25	.15
439	Rex Hudler	.25	.15
440	Domingo Ramos	.25	.15
441	Gerald Perry	.25	.15
442	John Russell	.25	.15
443	Carlos Baerga	20.00	13.00
444	Checklist (Will Clark)	.35	.18
445	Stan Javier	.25	.15
446	Kevin Maas (R)	.40	.25
447	Tom Brunansky	.30	.18
448	Carmelo Martinez	.25	.15
449	Willie Blair (R)	.40	.25
450	Andres Galarraga	1.25	.80
451	Bud Black	.25	.15
452	Greg Harris	.30	.18
453	Joe Oliver	.30	.18
454	Greg Brock	.25	.15
455	Jeff Treadway	.25	.15
456	Lance McCullers	.25	.15
457	Dave Schmidt	.25	.15
458	Todd Burns	.25	.15
459	Max Venable	.25	.15
460	Neal Heaton	.25	.15
461	Mark Williamson	.25	.15
462	Keith Miller	.25	.15
463	Mike LaCoss	.25	.15
464	Jose Offerman (R)	1.00	.70
465	Jim Leyritz (R)	.80	.50
466	Glenn Braggs	.25	.15
467	Ron Robinson	.25	.15
468	Mark Davis	.25	.15
469	Gary Pettis	.25	.15
470	Keith Hernandez	.30	.18
471	Dennis Rasmussen	.25	.15
472	Mark Eichhorn	.25	.15
473	Ted Power	.25	.15
474	Terry Mulholland	.30	.18
475	Todd Stottlemyre	.35	.20
476	Jerry Goff	.25	.15
477	Gene Nelson	.25	.15
478	Rich Gedman	.25	.15
479	Brian Harper	.30	.18
480	Mike Felder	.30	.18
481	Steve Avery	12.50	7.50
482	Jack Morris	.60	.35
483	Randy Johnson	3.00	1.75
484	Scott Radinsky (R)	.40	.25
485	Jose DeLeon	.25	.15
486	Stan Belinda (R)	.35	.20
487	Brian Holton	.30	.18
488	Mark Carreon	.25	.15
489	Trevor Wilson	.25	.15
490	Mike Sharperson	.25	.15
491	Alan Mills (R)	.50	.30
492	John Candelaria	.25	.15
493	Paul Assenmacher	.25	.15
494	Steve Crawford	.25	.15
495	Brad Arnsberg	.25	.15
496	Sergio Valdez	.30	.18
497	Mark Parent	.25	.15
498	Tom Pagnozzi	.30	.18
499	Greg Harris	.25	.15
500	Randy Ready	.25	.15
501	Duane Ward	.25	.15
502	Nelson Santovenia	.25	.15
503	Joe Klink	.25	.15
504	Eric Plunk	.25	.15
505	Jeff Reed	.25	.15
506	Ted Higuera	.25	.15
507	Joe Hesketh	.25	.15
508	Dan Petry	.25	.15
509	Matt Young	.25	.15
510	Jerald Clark (R)	.30	.18
511	John Orton (R)	.30	.18
512	Scott Ruskin (R)	.35	.20
513	Chris Hoiles (R)	2.50	1.50
514	Daryl Boston	.25	.15
515	Francisco Oliveras	.25	.15
516	Ozzie Canseco (R)	.30	.18
517	Xavier Hernandez (R)	.35	.20
518	Fred Manrique	.25	.15
519	Shawn Boskie (R)	.40	.25
520	Jeff Montgomery (R)	.50	.30
521	Jack Daugherty (R)	.25	.15
522	Keith Comstock	.25	.15
523	Greg Hibbard (R)	.50	.30
524	Lee Smith	.50	.30
525	Dana Kiecker	.25	.15
526	Darrel Akerfelds	.25	.15
527	Greg Myers	.25	.15
528	Checklist (Sandberg)	.35	.18

1991 Leaf

This 528-card set was released in two 264-card series and features silver borders around four-color action photos. Numbered card backs consist of a small photo, stat box and background information. Cards measure 2-1/2" by 3-1/2".

		MINT	NR MT
Complete Set (528)		32.00	20.00
Commons		.07	.03
1	Leaf Card	.10	.06
2	Kurt Stillwell	.07	.03
3	Bobby Witt	.10	.06
4	Tony Phillips	.12	.07
5	Scott Garrelts	.07	.03
6	Greg Swindell	.12	.07
7	Billy Ripken	.07	.03
8	Dave Martinez	.07	.03
9	Kelly Gruber	.12	.07
10	Juan Samuel	.07	.03
11	Brian Holman	.10	.06
12	Craig Biggio	.25	.15
13	Lonnie Smith	.07	.03
14	Ron Robinson	.07	.03
15	Mike LaValliere	.07	.03
16	Mark Davis	.07	.03
17	Jack Daugherty	.07	.03
18	Mike Henneman	.07	.03
19	Mike Greenwell	.25	.15
20	Dave Magadan	.10	.06
21	Mark Williamson	.07	.03
22	Marquis Grissom	.60	.35
23	Pat Borders	.07	.03
24	Mike Scioscia	.07	.03
25	Shawon Dunston	.12	.07
26	Randy Bush	.07	.03
27	John Smoltz	.50	.30
28	Chuck Crim	.07	.03
29	Don Slaught	.07	.03
30	Mike Macfarlane	.10	.06
31	Wally Joyner	.15	.10
32	Pat Combs	.10	.06
33	Tony Pena	.10	.06
34	Howard Johnson	.20	.12
35	Leo Gomez (H)	.35	.20
36	Spike Owen	.07	.03
37	Eric Davis	.20	.12
38	Roberto Kelly	.25	.15
39	Jerome Walton	.05	.02
40	Shane Mack	.20	.12
41	Kent Mercker	.12	.07
42	B.J. Surhoff	.07	.03
43	Jerry Browne	.07	.03
44	Lee Smith	.25	.15
45	Chuck Finley	.15	.10
46	Terry Mulholland	.10	.06
47	Tom Bolton	.07	.03
48	Tom Herr	.07	.03
49	Jim Deshaies	.07	.03
50	Walt Weiss	.10	.06
51	Hal Morris	.25	.15
52	Lee Guetterman	.07	.03
53	Paul Assenmacher	.07	.03
54	Brian Harper	.10	.06
55	Paul Gibson	.07	.03
56	John Burkett	.20	.12
57	Doug Jones	.12	.07
58	Jose Oquendo	.10	.06
59	Dick Schofield	.07	.03
60	Dickie Thon	.07	.03
61	Ramon Martinez	.25	.15
62	Jay Buhner	.15	.10
63	Mark Portugal	.08	.05
64	Bob Welch	.10	.06
65	Chris Sabo	.10	.06
66	Chuck Cary	.07	.03
67	Mark Langston	.15	.10
68	Joe Boever	.07	.03
69	Jody Reed	.10	.06
70	Alejandro Pena	.10	.06
71	Jeff King	.10	.06
72	Tom Pagnozzi	.15	.10
73	Joe Oliver	.10	.06
74	Mike Witt	.07	.03
75	Hector Villanueva	.10	.06
76	Dan Gladden	.07	.03
77	Dave Justice	1.50	.90
78	Mike Gallego	.07	.03
79	Tom Candiotti	.10	.06
80	Ozzie Smith	.25	.15
81	Luis Polonia	.10	.06
82	Randy Ready	.07	.03
83	Greg Harris	.10	.06
84	Checklist (Justice)	.20	.10
85	Kevin Mitchell	.12	.07
86	Mark McLemore	.07	.03
87	Terry Steinbach	.10	.06
88	Tom Browning	.10	.06

No.	Player			No.	Player		
89	Matt Nokes	.10	.06	146	Jose Lind	.07	.03
90	Mike Harkey	.15	.10	147	Danny Tartabull	.25	.15
91	Omar Vizquel	.07	.03	148	Geno Petralli	.07	.03
92	Dave Bergman	.07	.03	149	Travis Fryman (R)	3.00	1.75
93	Matt Williams	.35	.20	150	Tim Naehring (R)	.15	.10
94	Steve Olin	.07	.03	151	Kevin McReynolds	.12	.07
95	Craig Wilson	.15	.10	152	Joe Orsulak	.10	.06
96	Dave Stieb	.10	.06	153	Steve Frey	.07	.03
97	Ruben Sierra	.40	.25	154	Duane Ward	.07	.03
98	Jay Howell	.05	.02	155	Stan Javier	.07	.03
99	Scott Bradley	.05	.02	156	Damon Berryhill	.07	.03
100	Eric Yelding	.07	.03	157	Gene Larkin	.07	.03
101	Rickey Henderson	.50	.30	158	Greg Olson	.10	.06
102	Jeff Reed	.07	.03	159	Mark Knudson	.07	.03
103	Jimmy Key	.15	.10	160	Carmelo Martinez	.07	.03
104	Terry Shumpert	.15	.10	161	Storm Davis	.07	.03
105	Kenny Rogers	.07	.03	162	Jim Abbott	.30	.18
106	Cecil Fielder	.50	.30	163	Len Dykstra	.20	.12
107	Robby Thompson	.12	.07	164	Tom Brunansky	.10	.06
108	Alex Cole	.20	.12	165	Dwight Gooden	.25	.15
109	Randy Milligan	.10	.06	166	Jose Mesa	.07	.03
110	Andres Galarraga	.15	.10	167	Oil Can Boyd	.07	.03
111	Bill Spiers	.07	.03	168	Barry Larkin	.25	.15
112	Kal Daniels	.10	.06	169	Scott Sanderson	.10	.06
113	Henry Cotto	.07	.03	170	Mark Grace	.25	.15
114	Casey Candaele	.07	.03	171	Mark Guthrie	.12	.07
115	Jeff Blauser	.10	.06	172	Tom Glavine	.80	.50
116	Robin Yount	.50	.30	173	Gary Sheffield	1.00	.70
117	Ben McDonald	.30	.18	174	Checklist (Clemens)	.20	.12
118	Bret Saberhagen	.15	.10	175	Chris James	.07	.03
119	Juan Gonzalez (R)	6.00	3.50	176	Milt Thompson	.07	.03
120	Lou Whitaker	.10	.06	177	Donnie Hill	.07	.03
121	Ellis Burks	.15	.10	178	Wes Chamberlain (R)	.50	.30
122	Charlie O'Brien	.07	.03	179	John Marzano	.07	.03
123	John Smiley	.15	.10	180	Frank Viola	.12	.07
124	Tim Burke	.07	.03	181	Eric Anthony	.35	.20
125	John Olerud	1.75	1.00	182	Jose Canseco	.75	.45
126	Eddie Murray	.25	.15	183	Scott Scudder	.10	.06
127	Greg Maddux	.35	.20	184	Dave Eiland	.07	.03
128	Kevin Tapani	.12	.07	185	Luis Salazar	.07	.03
129	Ron Gant	.50	.30	186	Pedro Munoz (R)	.35	.20
130	Jay Bell	.15	.10	187	Steve Searcy	.07	.03
131	Chris Hoiles	.30	.18	188	Don Robinson	.07	.03
132	Tom Gordon	.10	.06	189	Sandy Alomar Jr.	.15	.10
133	Kevin Seitzer	.10	.06	190	Jose DeLeon	.07	.03
134	Jeff Huson	.07	.03	191	John Orton	.10	.06
135	Jerry Don Gleaton	.07	.03	192	Darren Daulton	.25	.15
136	Jeff Brantley	.07	.03	193	Mike Morgan	.10	.06
137	Felix Fermin	.07	.03	194	Greg Briley	.07	.03
138	Mike Deavereaux	.15	.10	195	Karl Rhodes (R)	.20	.12
139	Delino DeShields	.50	.30	196	Harold Baines	.10	.06
140	David Wells	.07	.03	197	Bill Doran	.07	.03
141	Tim Crews	.07	.03	198	Alvaro Espinoza	.07	.03
142	Erik Hanson	.15	.10	199	Kirk McCaskill	.07	.03
143	Mark Davidson	.07	.03	200	Jose DeJesus	.07	.03
144	Tommy Gregg	.07	.03	201	Jack Clark	.10	.06
145	Jim Gantner	.07	.03	202	Daryl Boston	.07	.03

203 Randy Tomlin (R)	.20	.12
204 Pedro Guerrero	.10	.06
205 Billy Hatcher	.07	.03
206 Tim Leary	.07	.03
207 Ryne Sandberg	.80	.50
208 Kirby Puckett	.75	.45
209 Charlie Leibrandt	.10	.06
210 Rick Honeycutt	.07	.03
211 Joel Skinner	.07	.03
212 Rex Hudler	.07	.03
213 Bryan Harvey	.12	.07
214 Charlie Hayes	.10	.06
215 Matt Young	.07	.03
216 Terry Kennedy	.07	.03
217 Carl Nichols	.07	.03
218 Mike Moore	.10	.06
219 Paul O'Neill	.20	.12
220 Steve Sax	.10	.06
221 Shawn Boskie	.10	.06
222 Rich DeLucia (R)	.15	.10
223 Lloyd Moseby	.07	.03
224 Mike Kingery	.07	.03
225 Carlos Baerga	1.50	.90
226 Bryn Smith	.07	.03
227 Todd Stottlemyre	.10	.06
228 Julio Franco	.25	.15
229 Jim Gott	.07	.03
230 Mike Schooler	.07	.03
231 Steve Finley	.15	.10
232 Dave Henderson	.10	.06
233 Luis Quinones	.07	.03
234 Mark Whiten	.60	.35
235 Brian McRae (R)	.75	.45
236 Rich Gossage	.10	.06
237 Rob Deer	.07	.03
238 Will Clark	.75	.45
239 Albert Belle	1.00	.70
240 Bob Melvin	.07	.03
241 Larry Walker	.60	.35
242 Dante Bichette	.15	.10
243 Orel Hershiser	.15	.10
244 Pete O'Brien	.07	.03
245 Pete Harnisch	.12	.07
246 Jeff Treadway	.07	.03
247 Julio Machado	.07	.03
248 Dave Johnson	.07	.03
249 Kirk Gibson	.10	.06
250 Kevin Brown	.15	.10
251 Milt Cuyler (R)	.20	.12
252 Jeff Reardon	.15	.10
253 David Cone	.15	.10
254 Gary Redus	.07	.03
255 Junior Noboa	.07	.03
256 Greg Myers	.07	.03
257 Dennis Cook	.07	.03
258 Joe Girardi	.10	.06
259 Allan Anderson	.07	.03
260 Paul Marak (R)	.12	.07
261 Barry Bonds	1.00	.70
262 Juan Bell	.10	.06
263 Russ Morman	.07	.03
264 Checklist (Brett)	.20	.12
265 Jerald Clark	.12	.05
266 Dwight Evans	.10	.06
267 Roberto Alomar	1.50	.90
268 Danny Jackson	.10	.06
269 Brian Downing	.07	.03
270 John Cerutti	.07	.03
271 Robin Ventura	.80	.50
272 Gerald Perry	.07	.03
273 Wade Boggs	.50	.30
274 Dennis Martinez	.15	.10
275 Andy Benes	.30	.18
276 Tony Fossas	.07	.03
277 Franklin Stubbs	.07	.03
278 John Kruk	.15	.10
279 Kevin Gross	.07	.03
280 Von Hayes	.07	.03
281 Frank Thomas	6.00	3.75
282 Rob Dibble	.12	.07
283 Mel Hall	.10	.06
284 Rick Mahler	.07	.03
285 Dennis Eckersley	.35	.20
286 Bernard Gilkey	.30	.18
287 Dan Plesac	.07	.03
288 Jason Grimsley (R)	.15	.10
289 Mark Lewis (R)	.20	.12
290 Tony Gwynn	.50	.30
291 Jeff Russell	.07	.03
292 Curt Schilling	.15	.10
293 Pascual Perez	.10	.06
294 Jack Morris	.20	.12
295 Hubie Brooks	.10	.06
296 Alex Fernandez (R)	.80	.50
297 Harold Reynolds	.10	.06
298 Craig Worthington	.07	.03
299 Willie Wilson	.07	.03
300 Mike Maddux	.07	.03
301 Dave Righetti	.10	.06
302 Paul Molitor	.35	.20
303 Gary Gaetti	.10	.06
304 Terry Pendleton	.15	.10
305 Kevin Elster	.07	.03
306 Scott Fletcher	.07	.03
307 Jeff Robinson	.07	.03
308 Jesse Barfield	.10	.06
309 Mike LaCoss	.07	.03
310 Andy Van Slyke	.20	.12
311 Glenallen Hill	.15	.10
312 Bud Black	.10	.06
313 Kent Hrbek	.10	.06
314 Tim Teufel	.07	.03
315 Tony Fernandez	.10	.06
316 Beau Allred	.15	.10

#	Player			#	Player		
317	Curtis Wilkerson	.07	.03	374	Chili Davis	.10	.06
318	Bill Sampen	.10	.06	375	Joey Cora	.07	.03
319	Randy Johnson	.25	.15	376	Ken Hill	.15	.10
320	Mike Heath	.07	.03	377	Darryl Strawberry	.35	.20
321	Sammy Sosa	.50	.30	378	Ron Darling	.10	.06
322	Mickey Tettleton	.10	.06	379	Sid Bream	.07	.03
323	Jose Vizcaino	.12	.07	380	Bill Swift	.25	.16
324	John Candelaria	.07	.03	381	Shawn Abner	.07	.03
325	Dave Howard (R)	.15	.10	382	Eric King	.07	.03
326	Jose Rijo	.12	.07	383	Mickey Morandini	.20	.12
327	Todd Zeile	.15	.10	384	Carlton Fisk	.35	.20
328	Gene Nelson	.07	.03	385	Steve Lake	.07	.03
329	Dwayne Henry	.07	.03	386	Mike Jeffcoat	.07	.03
330	Mike Boddicker	.07	.03	387	Darren Holmes (R)	.15	.10
331	Ozzie Guillen	.10	.06	388	Tim Wallach	.12	.07
332	Sam Horn	.10	.06	389	George Bell	.15	.10
333	Wally Whitehurst	.07	.03	390	Craig Lefferts	.07	.03
334	Dave Parker	.12	.07	391	Ernie Whitt	.07	.03
335	George Brett	.40	.25	392	Felix Jose	.15	.10
336	Bobby Thigpen	.10	.06	393	Kevin Maas	.15	.10
337	Ed Whitson	.07	.03	394	Devon White	.15	.10
338	Ivan Calderon	.10	.06	395	Otis Nixon	.10	.06
339	Mike Pagliarulo	.07	.03	396	Chuck Knoblauch (R)	.70	.40
340	Jack McDowell	.50	.30	397	Scott Coolbaugh	.07	.03
341	Dana Kiecker	.07	.03	398	Glenn Davis	.08	.05
342	Fred McGriff	.60	.35	399	Manny Lee	.07	.03
343	Mark Lee (R)	.15	.10	400	Andre Dawson	.35	.20
344	Alfredo Griffin	.07	.03	401	Scott Chiamparino	.10	.06
345	Scott Bankhead	.07	.03	402	Bill Gullickson	.10	.06
346	Darrin Jackson	.10	.06	403	Lance Johnson	.10	.06
347	Rafael Palmeiro	.35	.20	404	Juan Agosto	.07	.03
348	Steve Farr	.07	.03	405	Danny Darwin	.07	.03
349	Hensley Meulens	.10	.06	406	Barry Jones	.07	.03
350	Danny Cox	.07	.03	407	Larry Andersen	.07	.03
351	Alan Trammell	.20	.12	408	Luis Rivera	.07	.03
352	Edwin Nunez	.07	.03	409	Jaime Navarro	.15	.10
353	Joe Carter	.50	.30	410	Roger McDowell	.07	.03
354	Eric Show	.07	.03	411	Brett Butler	.15	.10
355	Vance Law	.07	.03	412	Dale Murphy	.25	.15
356	Jeff Gray (R)	.12	.07	413	Tim Raines	.10	.06
357	Bobby Bonilla	.25	.15	414	Norm Charlton	.15	.10
358	Ernest Riles	.07	.03	415	Greg Cadaret	.07	.03
359	Ron Hassey	.07	.03	416	Chris Nabholtz (R)	.15	.10
360	Willie McGee	.10	.06	417	Dave Stewart	.15	.10
361	Mackey Sasser	.07	.03	418	Rich Gedman	.07	.03
362	Glenn Braggs	.07	.03	419	Willie Randolph	.10	.06
363	Mario Diaz	.07	.03	420	Mitch Williams	.10	.06
364	Checklist (Bonds)	.20	.12	421	Brook Jacoby	.07	.03
365	Kevin Bass	.07	.03	422	Greg Harris	.10	.06
366	Pete Incaviglia	.07	.03	423	Nolan Ryan	2.00	1.25
367	Luis Sojo	.10	.06	424	Dave Rhode	.12	.07
368	Lance Parrish	.10	.06	425	Don Mattingly	.50	.30
369	Mark Leonard (R)	.15	.10	426	Greg Gagne	.07	.03
370	Heathcliff Slocumb (R)	.15	.10	427	Vince Coleman	.10	.06
371	Jimmy Jones	.07	.03	428	Dan Pasqua	.07	.03
372	Ken Griffey Jr.	3.50	2.00	429	Alvin Davis	.07	.03
373	Chris Hammond (R)	.25	.15	430	Cal Ripken	1.00	.70

431 Jamie Quirk	.07	.03
432 Benito Santiago	.12	.07
433 Jose Uribe	.07	.03
434 Candy Maldonado	.07	.03
435 Junior Felix	.10	.06
436 Deion Sanders	.70	.40
437 John Franco	.07	.03
438 Greg Hibbard	.07	.03
439 Floyd Bannister	.07	.03
440 Steve Howe	.07	.03
441 Steve Decker (R)	.15	.10
442 Vicente Palacious	.07	.03
443 Pat Tabler	.07	.03
444 Checklist (Strawberry)	.10	.05
445 Mike Felder	.07	.03
446 Al Newman	.07	.03
447 Chris Donnels (R)	.15	.10
448 Rich Rodriquez (R)	.15	.10
449 Turner Ward (R)	.15	.10
450 Bob Walk	.07	.03
451 Gilberto Reyes	.07	.03
452 Mike Jackson	.12	.07
453 Rafael Belliard	.07	.03
454 Wayne Edwards	.07	.03
455 Andy Allanson	.07	.03
456 Dave Smith	.07	.03
457 Gary Carter	.15	.10
458 Warren Cromartie	.07	.03
459 Jack Armstrong	.10	.06
460 Bob Tewksbury	.12	.07
461 Joe Klink	.07	.03
462 Xavier Hernandez	.07	.03
463 Scott Radinsky	.15	.10
464 Jeff Robinson	.07	.03
465 Gregg Jefferies	.30	.18
466 Denny Neagle (R)	.20	.12
467 Carmelo Martinez	.07	.03
468 Donn Paul	.07	.03
469 Bruce Hurst	.10	.06
470 Eric Bullock	.07	.03
471 Rick Aguilera	.10	.06
472 Charlie Hough	.07	.03
473 Carlos Quintana	.10	.06
474 Marty Barrett	.07	.03
475 Kevin Brown	.10	.06
476 Bobby Ojeda	.07	.03
477 Edgar Martinez	.25	.15
478 Bip Roberts	.07	.03
479 Mike Flanagan	.07	.03
480 John Habyan	.07	.03
481 Larry Casian (R)	.12	.07
482 Wally Backman	.07	.03
483 Doug Dascenzo	.07	.03
484 Rick Dempsey	.07	.03
485 Ed Sprague	.25	.15
486 Steve Chitren (R)	.15	.10
487 Mark McGwire	.50	.30

488 Roger Clemens	.75	.45
489 Orlando Merced (R)	1.25	.80
490 Rene Gonzalez	.08	.05
491 Mike Stanton	.10	.06
492 Al Osuna (R)	.10	.06
493 Rick Cerone	.07	.03
494 Mariano Duncun	.07	.03
495 Zane Smith	.08	.05
496 John Morris	.07	.03
497 Frank Tanana	.10	.06
498 Junior Ortiz	.07	.03
499 Dave Winfield	.35	.20
500 Gary Varsho	.07	.03
501 Chico Walker	.07	.03
502 Ken Caminiti	.10	.06
503 Ken Griffey Sr.	.10	.06
504 Randy Myers	.10	.06
505 Steve Bedrosian	.07	.03
506 Cory Snyder	.10	.06
507 Cris Carpenter	.10	.06
508 Tim Belcher	.10	.06
509 Jeff Hamilton	.07	.03
510 Steve Avery	1.25	.80
511 Dave Valle	.07	.03
512 Tom Lampkin	.07	.03
513 Shawn Hillegas	.07	.03
514 Reggie Jefferson (R)	.50	.30
515 Ron Karkovice	.07	.03
516 Doug Drabek	.15	.10
517 Tom Henke	.07	.03
518 Chris Bosio	.08	.05
519 Gregg Olson	.12	.07
520 Bob Scanlan (R)	.15	.10
521 Alonzo Powell (R)	.15	.10
522 Jeff Ballard	.07	.03
523 Ray Lankford (R)	1.25	.80
524 Tommy Greene	.25	.15
525 Mike Timlin (R)	.15	.10
526 Juan Berenguer	.07	.03
527 Scott Erickson (R)	.40	.25
528 Checklist(S. Alomar)	.10	05

1991 Leaf Gold Rookies

These bonus cards were randomly inserted into packs of 1991 Leaf cards and featured some of the hottest prospects in baseball. Though the card numbers carry the BC designation, some variations numbered 265-276 have surfaced. All cards measure 2-1/2" by 3-1/2".

		MINT	NR/MT
Complete Set (26)		48.00	30.00
Commons		1.00	.70
1	Scott Leius	1.00	.70
2	Luis Gonzalez	2.50	1.50
3	Wilfredo Cordero	4.50	2.75
4	Gary Scott	1.00	.70
5	Willie Banks	2.50	1.50
6	Arthur Rhodes	1.50	.90
7	Mo Vaughn	5.00	3.00
8	Henry Rodriquez	1.50	.90
9	Todd Van Poppel	5.00	3.00
10	Reggie Sanders	5.00	3.00
11	Rico Brogna	1.25	.80
12	Mike Mussina	12.00	7.00
13	Kirk Dressendorfer	1.25	.80
14	Jeff Bagwell	10.00	6.00
15	Pete Schourek	1.25	.80
16	Wade Taylor	1.00	.70
17	Pat Kelly	1.50	.90
18	Tim Costo	1.75	1.00
19	Roger Salkeld	2.50	1.50
20	Andujar Cedeno	2.50	1.50
21	Ryan Klesko	7.50	4.50
22	Mike Huff	1.00	.70
23	Anthony Young	1.00	.70
24	Eddie Zosky	1.25	.80
25	Nolan Ryan (7th No-Hitter)	4.00	2.50
26	Rickey Henderson (Steals)	1.75	1.00

1991 Leaf Studio

This 264-card set is the first black and white set issued since 1960 and features close-up portrait photos framed by a maroon border on the card fronts. The set was issued with a Rod Carew puzzle. All cards measure 2-1/2" by 3-1/2".

		MINT	NR/MT
Complete Set (264)		24.00	14.00
Commons		.05	.02
1	Glenn Davis	.05	.02
2	Dwight Evans	.10	.06
3	Leo Gomez	15	.10
4	Chris Hoiles	.25	.15
5	Sam Horn	.05	.02
6	Ben McDonald	.25	.15
7	Randy Milligan	.05	.02
8	Gregg Olson	.05	.02
9	Cal Ripken Jr.	1.00	.70
10	David Segui	.10	.06
11	Wade Boggs	.30	.18
12	Ellis Burks	.10	.06
13	Jack Clark	.05	.02
14	Roger Clemens	.75	.45
15	Mike Greenwell	.10	.06
16	Tim Naehring	.08	.05
17	Tony Pena	.05	.02
18	Phil Plantier	.50	.30
19	Jeff Reardon	.12	.07
20	Mo Vaughn	.75	.45
21	Jimmy Reese	.05	.02
22	Jim Abbott	.20	.12
23	Bert Blyleven	.10	.06
24	Chuck Finley	.12	.07
25	Gary Gaetti	.05	.02
26	Wally Joyner	.12	.07
27	Mark Langston	.12	.07
28	Kirk McCaskill	.05	.02
29	Lance Parrish	.05	.02
30	Dave Winfield	.35	.20
31	Alex Fernandez	.40	.25

32	Carlton Fisk	.15	.10
33	Scott Fletcher	.05	.02
34	Greg Hibbard	.05	.02
35	Charlie Hough	.05	.02
36	Jack McDowell	.50	.30
37	Tim Raines	.10	.06
38	Sammy Sosa	.20	.12
39	Bobby Thigpen	.05	.02
40	Frank Thomas	5.00	3.00
41	Sandy Alomar	.10	.06
42	John Farrell	.05	.02
43	Glenallen Hill	.10	.06
44	Brook Jacoby	.05	.02
45	Chris James	.05	.02
46	Doug Jones	.08	.05
47	Eric King	.05	.02
48	Mark Lewis	.15	.10
49	Greg Swindell	.10	.06
50	Mark Whiten	.40	.25
51	Milt Cuyler	.20	.12
52	Rob Deer	.08	.05
53	Cecil Fielder	.40	.25
54	Travis Fryman	1.75	1.00
55	Bill Gullickson	.05	.02
56	Lloyd Moseby	.05	.02
57	Frank Tanana	.05	.02
58	Mickey Tettleton	.10	.06
59	Alan Trammell	.20	.12
60	Lou Whitaker	.10	.07
61	Mike Boddicker	.05	.02
62	George Brett	.40	.25
63	Jeff Conine (R)	.40	.25
64	Warren Cromartie	.05	.02
65	Storm Davis	.05	.02
66	Kirk Gibson	.10	.06
67	Mark Gubicza	.08	.05
68	Brian McRae	.60	.35
69	Bret Saberhagen	.12	.07
70	Kurt Stillwell	.05	.02
71	Tim McIntosh	.10	.06
72	Candy Maldonado	.05	.02
73	Paul Molitor	.25	.15
74	Willie Randolph	.05	.02
75	Ron Robinson	.05	.02
76	Gary Sheffield	.60	.35
77	Franklin Stubbs	.05	.02
78	B.J. Surhoff	.05	.02
79	Greg Vaughn	.35	.20
80	Robin Yount	.40	.25
81	Rick Aguilera	.08	.05
82	Steve Bedrosian	.05	.02
83	Scott Erickson	.30	.18
84	Greg Gagne	.05	.02
85	Dan Gladden	.05	.02
86	Brian Harper	.05	.02
87	Kent Hrbek	.05	.02
88	Shane Mack	.10	.06
89	Jack Morris	.15	.10
90	Kirby Puckett	.60	.35
91	Jesse Barfield	.05	.02
92	Steve Farr	.05	.02
93	Steve Howe	.05	.02
94	Roberto Kelly	.25	.15
95	Tim Leary	.05	.02
96	Kevin Maas	.12	.07
97	Don Mattingly	.50	.30
98	Hensley Meulens	.08	.05
99	Scott Sanderson	.05	.02
100	Steve Sax	.08	.05
101	Jose Canseco	.50	.30
102	Dennis Eckersley	.20	.12
103	Dave Henderson	.05	.02
104	Rickey Henderson	.50	.30
105	Rick Honeycutt	.05	.02
106	Mark McGwire	.50	.30
107	Dave Stewart	.15	.10
108	Eric Show	.05	.02
109	Todd Van Poppel	1.25	.80
110	Bob Welch	.05	.02
111	Alvin Davis	.05	.02
112	Ken Griffey Jr.	3.50	2.00
113	Ken Griffey Sr.	.10	.06
114	Eric Hanson	.15	.10
115	Brian Holman	.10	.06
116	Randy Johnson	.25	.15
117	Edgar Martinez	.20	.12
118	Tino Martinez	.15	.10
119	Harold Reynolds	.05	.02
120	David Valle	.05	.02
121	Kevin Belcher (R)	.10	.06
122	Scott Chiamparino	.08	.05
123	Julio Franco	.12	.07
124	Juan Gonzalez	3.00	1.75
125	Rich Gossage	.08	.05
126	Jeff Kunkel	.05	.02
127	Rafael Palmeiro	.30	.18
128	Nolan Ryan	2.50	1.50
129	Ruben Sierra	.40	.25
130	Bobby Witt	.10	.06
131	Roberto Alomar	1.50	.90
132	Tom Candiotti	.05	.02
133	Joe Carter	.40	.25
134	Ken Dayley	.05	.02
135	Kelly Gruber	.08	.05
136	John Olerud	1.25	.80
137	Dave Stieb	.08	.05
138	Turner Ward (R)	.10	.06
139	Devon White	.12	.07
140	Mookie Wilson	.05	.02
141	Steve Avery	1.00	.70
142	Sid Bream	.05	.02
143	Nick Esasky	.05	.02
144	Ron Gant	.40	.25
145	Tom Glavine	.75	.45

146	David Justice	1.00	.70	203	John Franco	.05	.02
147	Kelly Mann	.05	.02	204	Dwight Gooden	.20	.12
148	Terry Pendleton	.15	.10	205	Tom Herr	.05	.02
149	John Smoltz	.30	.18	206	Gregg Jefferies	.30	.18
150	Jeff Treadway	.05	.02	207	Howard Johnson	.12	.07
151	George Bell	.12	.07	208	Dave Magadan	.08	.05
152	Shawn Boskie	.08	.05	209	Kevin McReynolds	.05	.02
153	Andre Dawson	.35	.20	210	Frank Viola	.08	.05
154	Lance Dickson (R)	.30	.18	211	Wes Chamberlain	.40	.25
155	Shawon Dunston	.10	.06	212	Darren Daulton	.25	.15
156	Joe Girardi	.05	.02	213	Lenny Dykstra	.25	.15
157	Mark Grace	.25	.15	214	Charlie Hayes	.05	.02
158	Ryne Sandberg	1.00	.70	215	Ricky Jordan	.05	.02
159	Gary Scott (R)	.15	.10	216	Steve Lake	.05	.02
160	Dave Smith	.05	.02	217	Roger McDowell	.05	.02
161	Tom Browning	.08	.05	218	Mickey Morandini	.15	.10
162	Eric Davis	.15	.10	219	Terry Mulholland	.08	.05
163	Rob Dibble	.08	.05	220	Dale Murphy	.20	.12
164	Mariano Duncan	.05	.02	221	Jay Bell	.12	.07
165	Chris Hammond	.10	.06	222	Barry Bonds	1.25	.80
166	Billy Hatcher	.05	.02	223	Bobby Bonilla	.20	.12
167	Barry Larkin	.20	.12	224	Doug Drabek	.12	.07
168	Hal Morris	.20	.12	225	Bill Landrum	.05	.02
169	Paul O'Neill	.20	.12	226	Mike LaValliere	.05	.02
170	Chris Sabo	.10	.06	227	Jose Lind	.05	.02
171	Eric Anthony	.20	.12	228	Don Slaught	.05	.02
172	Jeff Bagwell (R)	2.50	1.50	229	John Smiley	.10	.06
173	Craig Biggio	.10	.06	230	Andy Van Slyke	.20	.12
174	Ken Caminiti	.05	.02	231	Bernard Gilkey	.20	.12
175	Jim Deshaies	.05	.02	232	Pedro Guerrero	.08	.05
176	Steve Finley	.08	.05	233	Rex Hudler	.05	.02
177	Pete Harnisch	.12	.07	234	Ray Lankford	.40	.25
178	Darryl Kile	.40	.25	235	Joe Magrane	.05	.02
179	Curt Schilling	.10	.06	236	Jose Oquendo	.05	.02
180	Mike Scott	.05	.02	237	Lee Smith	.20	.12
181	Brett Butler	.10	.06	238	Ozzie Smith	.35	.20
182	Gary Carter	.12	.07	239	Milt Thompson	.05	.02
183	Orel Hershiser	.12	.07	240	Todd Zeile	.15	.10
184	Ramon Martinez	.20	.12	241	Larry Andersen	.05	.02
185	Eddie Murray	.35	.20	242	Andy Benes	.15	.10
186	Jose Offerman	.15	.10	243	Paul Faries (R)	.05	.02
187	Bob Ojeda	.05	.02	244	Tony Fernandez	.05	.02
188	Juan Samuel	.05	.02	245	Tony Gwynn	.40	.25
189	Mike Scioscia	.05	.02	246	Atlee Hammaker	.05	.02
190	Darryl Strawberry	.30	.18	247	Fred McGriff	.50	.30
191	Moises Alou	.25	.15	248	Bip Roberts	.05	.02
192	Brian Barnes (R)	.25	.15	249	Benito Santiago	.10	.06
193	Oil Can Boyd	.05	.02	250	Ed Whitson	.05	.02
194	Ivan Calderon	.05	.02	251	Dave Anderson	.05	.02
195	Delino DeShields	.40	.25	252	Mike Benjamin	.05	.02
196	Mike Fitzgerald	.05	.02	253	John Burkett	.10	.06
197	Andres Galarraga	.15	.10	254	Will Clark	.80	.50
198	Marquis Grissom	.50	.30	255	Scott Garrelts	.05	.02
199	Bill Sampen	.05	.02	256	Willie McGee	.08	.05
200	Tim Wallach	.05	.02	257	Kevin Mitchell	.08	.05
201	Daryl Boston	.05	.02	258	Dave Righetti	.05	.02
202	Vince Coleman	.05	.02	259	Matt Williams	.25	.15

		MINT	NR/MT
260	Black & Decker (Bud Black, Steve Decker)	.08	.05
261	Checklist	.08	.03
262	Checklist	.08	.03
263	Checklist	.08	.03
	Cover Card	.10	.06

1992 Leaf

For the third straight year Donruss has produced a premium baseball set under the Leaf name. The cards feature full color player photos framed in silver borders. A gold bordered edition was also produced and currently books for eight to ten times the value of the silver set. All cards measure 2-1/2" by 3-1/2".

	MINT	NR/MT
Complete Set (528)	32.00	20.00
Commons	.05	.02
Complete Set (Gold)	285.00	160.00
Commons (Gold)	.25	.15

		MINT	NR/MT
1	Jim Abbott	.20	.12
2	Cal Eldred	.50	.30
3	Bud Black	.05	.02
4	Dave Howard	.05	.02
5	Luis Sojo	.05	.02
6	Gary Scott	.08	.05
7	Joe Oliver	.08	.05
8	Chris Gardner (R)	.15	.10
9	Sandy Alomar	.10	.06
10	Greg Harris	.05	.02
11	Doug Drabek	.10	.06
12	Darryl Hamilton	.15	.10
13	Mike Mussina	1.25	.80
14	Kevin Tapani	.08	.05
15	Ron Gant	.25	.15
16	Mark McGwire	.35	.20
17	Robin Ventura	.40	.25
18	Pedro Guerrero	.05	.02
19	Roger Clemens	.75	.45
20	Steve Farr	.05	.02
21	Frank Tanana	.05	.02
22	Joe Hesketh	.05	.02
23	Erik Hanson	.10	.06
24	Greg Cadaret	.05	.02
25	Rex Hudler	.05	.02
26	Mark Grace	.15	.10
27	Kelly Gruber	.07	.04
28	Jeff Bagwell	.70	.40
29	Darryl Strawberry	.20	.12
30	Dave Smith	.05	.02
31	Kevin Appier	.10	.06
32	Steve Chitren	.10	.06
33	Kevin Gross	.05	.02
34	Rick Aguilera	.08	.05
35	Juan Guzman	.50	.30
36	Joe Orsulak	.07	.04
37	Tim Raines	.10	.06
38	Harold Reynolds	.05	.02
39	Charlie Hough	.05	.02
40	Tony Phillips	.08	.05
41	Nolan Ryan	1.75	1.00
42	Vince Coleman	.08	.05
43	Andy Van Slyke	.15	.10
44	Tim Burke	.05	.02
45	Luis Polonia	.07	.04
46	Tom Browning	.08	.05
47	Willie McGee	.08	.05
48	Gary DiSarcina	.08	.05
49	Mark Lewis	.08	.05
50	Phil Plantier	.40	.25
51	Doug Dascenzo	.05	.02
52	Cal Ripken	.75	.45
53	Pedro Munoz	.20	.12
54	Carlos Hernandez	.05	.02
55	Jerald Clark	.07	.04
56	Jeff Brantley	.08	.05
57	Don Mattingly	.35	.20
58	Roger McDowell	.05	.02
59	Steve Avery	.50	.30
60	John Olerud	.75	.45
61	Bill Gullickson	.05	.02
62	Juan Gonzalez	2.00	1.25
63	Felix Jose	.08	.05
64	Robin Yount	.40	.25
65	Greg Briley	.05	.02
66	Steve Finley	.05	.02
67	Checklist	.10	.03
68	Tom Gordon	.10	.06
69	Rob Dibble	.08	.05
70	Glenallen Hill	.08	.05
71	Calvin Jones (R)	.20	.12
72	Joe Girardi	.05	.02
73	Barry Larkin	.15	.10

74	Andy Benes	.15	.10
75	Milt Cuyler	.10	.06
76	Kevin Bass	.05	.02
77	Pete Harnisch	.08	.05
78	Wilson Alvarez	.10	.06
79	Mike Devereaux	.10	.06
80	Doug Henry (R)	.20	.12
81	Orel Hershiser	.10	.06
82	Shane Mack	.10	.06
83	Mike Macfarlane	.05	.02
84	Thomas Howard	.08	.05
85	Alex Fernandez	.50	.30
86	Reggie Jefferson	.12	.07
87	Leo Gomez	.10	.06
88	Mel Hall	.07	.04
89	Mike Greenwell	.10	.06
90	Jeff Russell	.08	.05
91	Steve Buechele	.10	.06
92	David Cone	.12	.07
93	Kevin Reimer	.08	.05
94	Mark Lemke	.05	.02
95	Bob Tewksbury	.08	.05
96	Zane Smith	.07	.04
97	Mark Eichhorn	.05	.02
98	Kirby Puckett	.60	.35
99	Paul O'Neill	.10	.06
100	Dennis Eckersley	.15	.10
101	Duane Ward	.10	.06
102	Matt Nokes	.05	.02
103	Mo Vaughn	.50	.30
104	Pat Kelly	.10	.06
105	Ron Karkovice	.05	.02
106	Bill Spiers	.05	.02
107	Gary Gaetti	.05	.02
108	Mackey Sasser	.05	.02
109	Robby Thompson	.10	.06
110	Marvin Freeman	.05	.02
111	Jimmy Key	.08	.05
112	Dwight Gooden	.12	.07
113	Charlie Leibrandt	.05	.02
114	Devon White	.10	.06
115	Charles Nagy	.35	.20
116	Rickey Henderson	.30	.18
117	Paul Assenmacher	.05	.02
118	Junior Felix	.05	.02
119	Julio Franco	.08	.05
120	Norm Charlton	.08	.05
121	Scott Servais	.08	.05
122	Gerald Perry	.05	.02
123	Brian McRae	.15	.10
124	Don Slaught	.05	.02
125	Juan Samuel	.05	.02
126	Harold Baines	.10	.06
127	Scott Livingstone	.10	.06
128	Jay Buhner	.12	.07
129	Darrin Jackson	.08	.05
130	Luis Mercedes	.12	.07
131	Brian Harper	.10	.06
132	Howard Johnson	.10	.06
133	Checklist	.10	.03
134	Dante Bichette	.10	.06
135	Dave Righetti	.05	.02
136	Jeff Montgomery	.05	.02
137	Joe Grahe	.05	.02
138	Delino DeShields	.25	.15
139	Jose Rijo	.10	.06
140	Ken Caminiti	.08	.05
141	Steve Olin	.05	.02
142	Kurt Stillwell	.05	.02
143	Jay Bell	.10	.06
144	Jaime Navarro	.15	.10
145	Ben McDonald	.20	.12
146	Greg Gagne	.07	.04
147	Jeff Blauser	.08	.05
148	Carney Lansford	.07	.04
149	Ozzie Guillen	.08	.05
150	Milt Thompson	.05	.02
151	Jeff Reardon	.10	.06
152	Scott Sanderson	.05	.02
153	Cecil Fielder	.35	.20
154	Greg Harris	.07	.04
155	Rich DeLucia	.05	.02
156	Roberto Kelly	.15	.10
157	Bryn Smith	.05	.02
158	Chuck McElroy	.05	.02
159	Tom Henke	.05	.02
160	Luis Gonzalez	.15	.10
161	Steve Wilson	.05	.02
162	Shawn Boskie	.08	.05
163	Mark Davis	.05	.02
164	Mike Moore	.05	.02
165	Mike Scioscia	.05	.02
166	Scott Erickson	.15	.10
167	Todd Stottlemyre	.05	.02
168	Alvin Davis	.05	.02
169	Greg Hibbard	.05	.02
170	David Valle	.05	.02
171	Dave Winfield	.30	.18
172	Alan Trammell	.10	.06
173	Kenny Rogers	.10	.06
174	John Franco	.07	.04
175	Jose Lind	.05	.02
176	Pete Schourek	.10	.06
177	Von Hayes	.05	.02
178	Chris Hammond	.10	.06
179	John Burkett	.10	.06
180	Dickie Thon	.05	.02
181	Joel Skinner	.05	.02
182	Scott Cooper	.15	.10
183	Andre Dawson	.20	.12
184	Billy Ripken	.05	.02
185	Kevin Mitchell	.08	.05
186	Brett Butler	.10	.06
187	Tony Fernandez	.05	.02

#	Player			#	Player		
188	Cory Snyder	.05	.02	245	Terry Pendleton	.10	.06
189	John Habyan	.05	.02	246	Randy Ready	.05	.02
190	Dennis Martinez	.10	.06	247	Jack Armstrong	.05	.02
191	John Smoltz	.20	.12	248	Todd Van Poppel	.60	.35
192	Greg Myers	.05	.02	249	Shawon Dunston	.10	.06
193	Rob Deer	.05	.02	250	Bobby Rose	.10	.06
194	Ivan Rodriguez	.60	.35	251	Jeff Huson	.05	.02
195	Ray Lankford	.20	.12	252	Bip Roberts	.05	.02
196	Bill Wegman	.05	.02	253	Doug Jones	.07	.04
197	Edgar Martinez	.15	.10	254	Lee Smith	.15	.10
198	Darryl Kile	.25	.15	255	George Brett	.40	.25
199	Checklist	.10	.03	256	Randy Tomlin	.08	.05
200	Brent Mayne	.05	.02	257	Todd Benzinger	.05	.02
201	Larry Walker	.20	.12	258	Dave Stewart	.10	.06
202	Carlos Baerga	.70	.40	259	Mark Carreon	.05	.02
203	Russ Swan	.05	.02	260	Pete O'Brien	.05	.02
204	Mike Morgan	.05	.02	261	Tim Teufel	.05	.02
205	Hal Morris	.12	.07	262	Bob Milacki	.05	.02
206	Tony Gwynn	.30	.18	263	Mark Guthrie	.05	.02
207	Mark Leiter	.05	.02	264	Darrin Fletcher	.05	.02
208	Kirt Manwaring	.05	.02	265	Omar Vizquel	.05	.02
209	Al Osuna	.05	.02	266	Chris Bosio	.08	.05
210	Bobby Thigpen	.05	.02	267	Jose Canseco	.35	.20
211	Chris Hoiles	.15	.10	268	Mike Boddicker	.05	.02
212	B.J. Surhoff	.05	.02	269	Lance Parrish	.05	.02
213	Lenny Harris	.05	.02	270	Jose Vizcaino	.05	.02
214	Scott Leius	.08	.05	271	Chris Sabo	.08	.05
215	Gregg Jefferies	.20	.12	272	Royce Clayton	.25	.15
216	Bruce Hurst	.08	.05	273	Marquis Grissom	.25	.15
217	Steve Sax	.08	.05	274	Fred McGriff	.40	.25
218	Dave Otto	.05	.02	275	Barry Bonds	1.00	.70
219	Sam Horn	.05	.02	276	Greg Vaughn	.15	.10
220	Charlie Hayes	.08	.05	277	Gregg Olson	.08	.05
221	Frank Viola	.08	.05	278	Dave Hollins	.35	.20
222	Jose Guzman	.10	.06	279	Tom Glavine	.35	.20
223	Gary Redus	.05	.02	280	Bryan Hickerson	.07	.04
224	Dave Gallagher	.05	.02	281	Scott Radinsky	.08	.05
225	Dean Palmer	.50	.30	282	Omar Olivares	.05	.02
226	Greg Olson	.10	.06	283	Ivan Calderon	.07	.04
227	Jose DeLeon	.05	.02	284	Kevin Maas	.10	.06
228	Mike LaValliere	.05	.02	285	Mickey Tettleton	.08	.05
229	Mark Langston	.10	.06	286	Wade Boggs	.35	.20
230	Chuck Knoblauch	.20	.12	287	Stan Belinda	.05	.02
231	Bill Doran	.05	.02	288	Bret Barberie	.10	.06
232	Dave Henderson	.05	.02	289	Jose Oquendo	.05	.02
233	Roberto Alomar	.80	.50	290	Frank Castillo	.10	.06
234	Scott Fletcher	.05	.02	291	Dave Stieb	.08	.05
235	Tim Naehring	.08	.05	292	Tommy Greene	.20	.12
236	Mike Gallego	.05	.02	293	Eric Karros	.60	.35
237	Lance Johnson	.08	.05	294	Greg Maddux	.25	.15
238	Paul Molitor	.25	.15	295	Jim Eisenreich	.05	.02
239	Dan Gladden	.05	.02	296	Rafael Palmeiro	.20	.12
240	Willie Randolph	.05	.02	297	Ramon Martinez	.15	.08
241	Will Clark	.40	.25	298	Tim Wallach	.08	.05
242	Sid Bream	.05	.02	299	Jim Thome	.40	.25
243	Derek Bell	.35	.20	300	Chito Martinez	.10	.06
244	Bill Pecota	.05	.02	301	Mitch Williams	.05	.02

302	Randy Johnson	.20	.12
303	Carlton Fisk	.15	.10
304	Travis Fryman	.50	.30
305	Bobby Witt	.10	.06
306	Dave Magadan	.05	.02
307	Alex Cole	.08	.05
308	Bobby Bonilla	.15	.10
309	Bryan Harvey	.08	.05
310	Rafael Belliard	.05	.02
311	Mariano Duncan	.05	.02
312	Chuck Crim	.05	.02
313	John Kruk	.15	.10
314	Ellis Burks	.10	.06
315	Craig Biggio	.08	.05
316	Glenn Davis	.05	.02
317	Ryne Sandberg	.60	.35
318	Mike Sharperson	.05	.02
319	Rich Rodriquez	.10	.06
320	Lee Guetterman	.05	.02
321	Benito Santiago	.10	.06
322	Jose Offerman	.10	.06
323	Tony Pena	.05	.02
324	Pat Borders	.05	.02
325	Mike Henneman	.05	.02
326	Kevin Brown	.12	.07
327	Chris Nabholtz	.12	.07
328	Franklin Stubbs	.05	.02
329	Tino Martinez	.12	.07
330	Mickey Morandini	.10	.06
331	Checklist	.10	.03
332	Mark Gubicza	.08	.05
333	Bill Landrum	.05	.02
334	Mark Whiten	.25	.15
335	Darren Daulton	.25	.15
336	Rick Wilkins	.12	.07
337	Brian Jordan	.50	.30
338	Kevin Ward	.10	.06
339	Ruben Amaro	.10	.06
340	Trevor Wilson	.08	.05
341	Andujar Cedeno	.15	.08
342	Michael Huff	.08	.05
343	Brady Anderson	.15	.10
344	Craig Grebeck	.05	.02
345	Bobby Ojeda	.05	.02
346	Mike Pagliarulo	.05	.02
347	Terry Shumpert	.05	.02
348	Dann Bilardello	.05	.02
349	Frank Thomas	3.50	2.50
350	Albert Belle	.50	.30
351	Jose Mesa	.05	.02
352	Rich Monteleone	.05	.02
353	Bob Walk	.05	.02
354	Monty Fariss	.05	.02
355	Luis Rivera	.05	.02
356	Anthony Young	.08	.05
357	Geno Petralli	.05	.02
358	Otis Nixon	.08	.05
359	Tom Pagnozzi	.08	.05
360	Reggie Sanders	.50	.30
361	Lee Stevens	.07	.04
362	Kent Hrbek	.08	.05
363	Orlando Merced	.15	.08
364	Mike Bordick	.15	.08
365	Dion James	.05	.02
366	Jack Clark	.08	.05
367	Mike Stanley	.08	.05
368	Randy Velarde	.05	.02
369	Dan Pasqua	.05	.02
370	Pat Listach (R)	.35	.20
371	Mike Fitzgerald	.05	.02
372	Tom Foley	.05	.02
373	Matt Williams	.25	.15
374	Brian Hunter	.12	.07
375	Joe Carter	.30	.18
376	Bret Saberhagen	.10	.06
377	Mike Stanton	.05	.02
378	Hubie Brooks	.08	.05
379	Eric Bell	.05	.02
380	Walt Weiss	.05	.02
381	Danny Jackson	.08	.05
382	Manuel Lee	.05	.02
383	Ruben Sierra	.20	.12
384	Greg Swindell	.08	.05
385	Ryan Bowen	.12	.07
386	Kevin Ritz	.08	.05
387	Curtis Wilkerson	.05	.02
388	Gary Varsho	.05	.02
389	Dave Hansen	.10	.06
390	Bob Welch	.08	.05
391	Lou Whitaker	.10	.06
392	Ken Griffey Jr.	2.50	1.50
393	Mike Maddux	.05	.02
394	Arthur Rhodes	.15	.10
395	Chili Davis	.08	.05
396	Eddie Murray	.25	.15
397	Checklist	.10	.03
398	Dave Cochrane	.08	.05
399	Kevin Seitzer	.08	.05
400	Ozzie Smith	.20	.12
401	Paul Sorrento	.15	.10
402	Les Lancaster	.05	.02
403	Junior Noboa	.05	.02
404	David Justice	.50	.30
405	Andy Ashby	.10	.06
406	Danny Tartabull	.12	.07
407	Bill Swift	.10	.06
408	Craig Lefferts	.05	.02
409	Tom Candiotti	.05	.02
410	Lance Blankenship	.05	.02
411	Jeff Tackett	.05	.02
412	Sammy Sosa	.25	.15
413	Jody Reed	.05	.02
414	Bruce Ruffin	.05	.02
415	Gene Larkin	.05	.02

416	John Vanderwal	.10	.06
417	Tim Belcher	.07	.04
418	Steve Frey	.05	.02
419	Dick Schofield	.05	.02
420	Jeff King	.08	.05
421	Kim Batiste	.08	.05
422	Jack McDowell	.30	.18
423	Damon Berryhill	.05	.02
424	Gary Wayne	.10	.06
425	Jack Morris	.15	.08
426	Moises Alou	.20	.12
427	Mark McLemore	.05	.02
428	Juan Guerrero (R)	.15	.10
429	Scott Scudder	.05	.02
430	Eric Davis	.10	.06
431	Joe Slusarski	.08	.05
432	Todd Zeile	.10	.06
433	Dwayne Henry	.08	.05
434	Cliff Brantley (R)	.12	.07
435	Butch Henry (R)	.10	.06
436	Todd Worrell	.08	.05
437	Bob Scanlan	.08	.05
438	Wally Joyner	.10	.06
439	John Flaherty (R)	.10	.06
440	Brian Downing	.05	.02
441	Darren Lewis	.10	.06
442	Gary Carter	.10	.06
443	Wally Ritchie	.05	.02
444	Chris Jones	.08	.05
445	Jeff Kent (R)	.35	.20
446	Gary Sheffield	.30	.18
447	Ron Darling	.05	.02
448	Deion Sanders	.20	.12
449	Andres Galarraga	.15	.10
450	Chuck Finley	.10	.06
451	Derek Lilliquist	.05	.02
452	Carl Willis	.05	.02
453	Wes Chamberlain	.15	.08
454	Roger Mason	.05	.02
455	Spike Owen	.05	.02
456	Thomas Howard	.07	.04
457	Dave Martinez	.05	.02
458	Pete Incaviglia	.05	.02
459	Keith Miller	.05	.02
460	Mike Fetters	.05	.02
461	Paul Gibson	.05	.02
462	George Bell	.12	.07
463	Checklist	.10	.03
464	Terry Mulholland	.05	.02
465	Storm Davis	.05	.02
466	Gary Pettis	.05	.02
467	Randy Bush	.05	.02
468	Ken Hill	.10	.06
469	Rheal Cormier	.12	.07
470	Andy Stankiewicz (R)	.12	.07
471	Dave Burba	.05	.02
472	Henry Cotto	.05	.02
473	Dale Sveum	.05	.02
474	Rich Gossage	.07	.04
475	William Suero	.08	.05
476	Doug Strange	.05	.02
477	Bill Krueger	.05	.02
478	John Wetteland	.10	.06
479	Melido Perez	.08	.05
480	Lonnie Smith	.05	.02
481	Mike Jackson	.07	.04
482	Mike Gardiner	.12	.07
483	David Wells	.05	.02
484	Barry Jones	.05	.02
485	Scott Bankhead	.05	.02
486	Terry Leach	.05	.02
487	Vince Horsman (R)	.12	.07
488	Dave Eiland	.05	.02
489	Alejandro Pena	.05	.02
490	Julio Valera	.05	.02
491	Joe Boever	.05	.02
492	Paul Miller (R)	.15	.08
493	Archi Cianfrocco (R)	.20	.12
494	Dave Fleming	.50	.30
495	Kyle Abbott	.10	.06
496	Chad Kreuter	.08	.05
497	Chris James	.05	.02
498	Donnie Hill	.05	.02
499	Jacob Brumfield (R)	.12	.07
500	Ricky Bones	.10	.06
501	Terry Steinbach	.08	.05
502	Bernard Gilkey	.15	.08
503	Dennis Cook	.05	.02
504	Lenny Dykstra	.25	.15
505	Mike Bielecki	.05	.02
506	Bob Kipper	.05	.02
507	Jose Melendez	.08	.05
508	Rick Sutcliffe	.08	.05
509	Ken Patterson	.05	.02
510	Andy Allanson	.05	.02
511	Al Newman	.05	.02
512	Mark Gardner	.08	.05
513	Jeff Schaefer	.08	.05
514	Jim McNamara (R)	.12	.07
515	Peter Hoy (R)	.12	.07
516	Curt Schilling	.10	.06
517	Kirk McCaskill	.05	.02
518	Chris Gwynn	.05	.02
519	Sid Fernandez	.08	.05
520	Jeff Parrett	.05	.02
521	Scott Ruskin	.05	.02
522	Kevin McReynolds	.08	.05
523	Rick Cerone	.05	.02
524	Jesse Orosco	.05	.02
525	Troy Afenir	.10	.06
526	John Smiley	.10	.06
527	Dale Murphy	.12	.08
528	Leaf Cover Card	.15	.08

1992 Leaf Gold Rookies

The cards in this limited insert set were randomly distributed in Leaf packs. The card fronts feature full color action photos accented in gold. All cards measure 2-1/2" by 3-1/2".

		MINT	NR/MT
	Complete Set (24)	38.00	22.00
	Commons	.75	.45
1	Chad Curtis	3.50	2.00
2	Brent Gates	3.00	1.75
3	Pedro Martinez	1.75	1.00
4	Kenny Lofton	4.50	2.75
5	Turk Wendell	1.00	.70
6	Mark Hutton	1.50	.90
7	Todd Hundley	2.00	1.40
8	Matt Stairs	.75	.45
9	Eddie Taubensee	.90	.60
10	David Nied	3.50	2.00
11	Salomon Torres	4.00	2.50
12	Bret Boone	2.00	1.25
13	Johnny Ruffin	1.00	.70
14	Ed Martel	.75	.45
15	Rick Tricek	.75	.45
16	Raul Mondesi	2.50	1.50
17	Pat Mahomes	1.50	.90
18	Dan Wilson	1.25	.80
19	Donovan Osborne	2.00	1.25
20	Dave Silvestri	.75	.45
21	Gary DiSarcina	1.00	.70
22	Denny Neagle	.75	.45
23	Steve Hosey	2.00	1.25
24	John Doherty	.75	.45

1992 Leaf Studio

This 264-card set combines dramatic black and white action photos with small four-color portrait shots on the card fronts. Special limited bonus cards called "The Heritage Series" were randomly inserted into packs. The bonus cards feature portraits of current players wearing historic uniforms. Those cards are listed at the end of this checklist but are not included in the complete set price below. All cards measure 2-1/2" by 3-1/2".

		MINT	NR/MT
	Complete Set (264)	20.00	12.50
	Commons	.05	.02
1	Steve Avery	.35	.20
2	Sid Bream	.05	.02
3	Ron Gant	.20	.12
4	Tom Glavine	.40	.25
5	David Justice	.60	.35
6	Mark Lemke	.05	.02
7	Greg Olson	.05	.02
8	Terry Pendleton	.12	.07
9	Deion Sanders	.25	.15
10	John Smoltz	.15	.10
11	Doug Dascenzo	.05	.02
12	Andre Dawson	.20	.12
13	Joe Girardi	.05	.02
14	Mark Grace	.20	.12
15	Greg Maddux	.25	.15
16	Chuck McElroy	.05	.02
17	Mike Morgan	.05	.02
18	Ryne Sandberg	.50	.30
19	Gary Scott	.07	.04
20	Sammy Sosa	.20	.12
21	Norm Charlton	.05	.02
22	Rob Dibble	.08	.05
23	Barry Larkin	.15	.10
24	Hal Morris	.12	.07
25	Paul O'Neill	.12	.07
26	Jose Rijo	.10	.06

27	Bip Roberts	.05	.02
28	Chris Sabo	.08	.05
29	Reggie Sanders	.50	.30
30	Greg Swindell	.08	.05
31	Jeff Bagwell	.60	.35
32	Craig Biggio	.08	.05
33	Ken Caminiti	.05	.02
34	Andujar Cedeno	.20	.12
35	Steve Finley	.05	.02
36	Pete Harnisch	.08	.05
37	Butch Henry	.05	.02
38	Doug Jones	.05	.02
39	Darryl Kile	.20	.12
40	Eddie Taubensee	.08	.05
41	Brett Butler	.10	.06
42	Tom Candiotti	.05	.02
43	Eric Davis	.12	.07
44	Orel Hershiser	.12	.07
45	Eric Karros	.75	.45
46	Ramon Martinez	.15	.08
47	Jose Offerman	.12	.07
48	Mike Scioscia	.05	.02
49	Mike Sharperson	.05	.02
50	Darryl Strawberry	.20	.12
51	Bret Barberie	.10	.06
52	Ivan Calderon	.07	.04
53	Gary Carter	.12	.07
54	Delino DeShields	.20	.12
55	Marquis Grissom	.25	.15
56	Ken Hill	.10	.06
57	Dennis Martinez	.10	.06
58	Spike Owen	.05	.02
59	Larry Walker	.35	.20
60	Tim Wallach	.07	.04
61	Bobby Bonilla	.15	.10
62	Tim Burke	.05	.02
63	Vince Coleman	.07	.04
64	John Franco	.05	.02
65	Dwight Gooden	.15	.08
66	Todd Hundley	.08	.05
67	Howard Johnson	.10	.06
68	Eddie Murray	.20	.12
69	Bret Saberhagen	.12	.08
70	Anthony Young	.08	.05
71	Kim Batiste	.08	.05
72	Wes Chamberlain	.20	.12
73	Darren Daulton	.20	.12
74	Mariano Duncan	.05	.02
75	Lenny Dykstra	.20	.12
76	John Kruk	.15	.10
77	Mickey Morandini	.10	.06
78	Terry Mulholland	.05	.02
79	Dale Murphy	.15	.08
80	Mitch Williams	.05	.02
81	Jay Bell	.12	.07
82	Barry Bonds	.75	.45
83	Steve Buechele	.05	.02
84	Doug Drabek	.12	.07
85	Mike LaValliere	.05	.02
86	Jose Lind	.05	.02
87	Denny Neagle	.08	.05
88	Randy Tomlin	.08	.05
89	Andy Van Slyke	.12	.07
90	Gary Varsho	.05	.02
91	Pedro Guerrero	.05	.02
92	Rex Hudler	.05	.02
93	Brian Jordan	.35	.20
94	Felix Jose	.08	.05
95	Donovan Osborne	.35	.20
96	Tom Pagnozzi	.07	.04
97	Lee Smith	.12	.07
98	Ozzie Smith	.15	.10
99	Todd Worrell	.07	.04
100	Todd Zeile	.10	.06
101	Andy Benes	.12	.07
102	Jerald Clark	.05	.02
103	Tony Fernandez	.05	.02
104	Tony Gwynn	.30	.18
105	Greg Harris	.05	.02
106	Fred McGriff	.30	.18
107	Benito Santiago	.10	.06
108	Gary Sheffield	.50	.30
109	Kurt Stillwell	.05	.02
110	Tim Teufel	.05	.02
111	Kevin Bass	.05	.02
112	Jeff Brantley	.08	.05
113	John Burkett	.10	.06
114	Will Clark	.50	.30
115	Royce Clayton	.25	.15
116	Mike Jackson	.05	.02
117	Darren Lewis	.10	.06
118	Bill Swift	.10	.06
119	Robby Thompson	.10	.06
120	Matt Williams	.15	.08
121	Brady Anderson	.15	.10
122	Glenn Davis	.07	.04
123	Mike Devereaux	.10	.06
124	Chris Hoiles	.15	.10
125	Sam Horn	.07	.04
126	Ben McDonald	.15	.10
127	Mike Mussina	.80	.50
128	Gregg Olson	.08	.05
129	Cal Ripken Jr.	.80	.50
130	Rick Sutcliffe	.07	.04
131	Wade Boggs	.30	.18
132	Roger Clemens	.50	.30
133	Greg Harris	.05	.02
134	Tim Naehring	.08	.05
135	Tony Pena	.05	.02
136	Phil Plantier	.40	.25
137	Jeff Reardon	.10	.06
138	Jody Reed	.05	.02
139	Mo Vaughn	.25	.15
140	Frank Viola	.08	.05

141	Jim Abbott	.15	.10
142	Hubie Brooks	.05	.02
143	Chad Curtis	.50	.30
144	Gary DiSarcina	.10	.06
145	Chuck Finley	.12	.07
146	Bryan Harvey	.10	.06
147	Von Hayes	.05	.02
148	Mark Langston	.12	.07
149	Lance Parrish	.05	.02
150	Lee Stevens	.05	.02
151	George Bell	.12	.07
152	Alex Fernandez	.40	.25
153	Greg Hibbard	.05	.02
154	Lance Johnson	.07	.04
155	Kirk McCaskill	.05	.02
156	Tim Raines	.10	.06
157	Steve Sax	.08	.05
158	Bobby Thigpen	.07	.04
159	Frank Thomas	3.00	2.00
160	Robin Ventura	.50	.30
161	Sandy Alomar Jr.	.10	.06
162	Jack Armstrong	.05	.02
163	Carlos Baerga	.75	.45
164	Albert Belle	.60	.35
165	Alex Cole	.08	.05
166	Glenallen Hill	.10	.06
167	Mark Lewis	.08	.05
168	Kenny Lofton	.70	.40
169	Paul Sorrento	.15	.10
170	Mark Whiten	.20	.12
171	Milt Cuyler	.10	.06
172	Rob Deer	.08	.05
173	Cecil Fielder	.30	.18
174	Travis Fryman	.60	.35
175	Mike Henneman	.05	.02
176	Tony Phillips	.08	.05
177	Frank Tanana	.05	.02
178	Mickey Tettleton	.10	.06
179	Alan Trammell	.15	.08
180	Lou Whitaker	.10	.06
181	George Brett	.35	.20
182	Tom Gordon	.08	.05
183	Mark Gubicza	.07	.04
184	Gregg Jefferies	.20	.12
185	Wally Joyner	.10	.06
186	Brent Mayne	.10	.06
187	Brian McRae	.12	.07
188	Kevin McReynolds	.08	.05
189	Keith Miller	.05	.02
190	Jeff Montgomery	.05	.02
191	Dante Bichette	.10	.06
192	Ricky Bones	.10	.06
193	Scott Fletcher	.05	.02
194	Paul Molitor	.20	.12
195	Jaime Navarro	.12	.07
196	Franklin Stubbs	.05	.02
197	B.J. Surhoff	.05	.02
198	Greg Vaughn	.15	.08
199	Bill Wegman	.05	.02
200	Robin Yount	.35	.20
201	Rick Aguilera	.05	.02
202	Scott Erickson	.20	.12
203	Greg Gagne	.05	.02
204	Brian Harper	.05	.02
205	Kent Hrbek	.07	.04
206	Scott Leius	.05	.02
207	Shane Mack	.10	.06
208	Pat Mahomes	.30	.18
209	Kirby Puckett	.60	.35
210	John Smiley	.10	.06
211	Mike Gallego	.05	.02
212	Charlie Hayes	.07	.04
213	Pat Kelly	.10	.06
214	Roberto Kelly	.20	.12
215	Kevin Maas	.10	.06
216	Don Mattingly	.30	.18
217	Matt Nokes	.05	.02
218	Melido Perez	.05	.02
219	Scott Sanderson	.05	.02
220	Danny Tartabull	.12	.07
221	Harold Baines	.08	.05
222	Jose Canseco	.50	.30
223	Dennis Eckersley	.20	.12
224	Dave Henderson	.05	.02
225	Carney Lansford	.05	.02
226	Mark McGwire	.60	.35
227	Mike Moore	.05	.02
228	Randy Ready	.05	.02
229	Terry Steinbach	.08	.05
230	Dave Stewart	.15	.10
231	Jay Buhner	.10	.06
232	Ken Griffey Jr.	1.25	.80
233	Erik Hanson	.08	.05
234	Randy Johnson	.20	.12
235	Edgar Martinez	.15	.10
236	Tino Martinez	.10	.06
237	Kevin Mitchell	.08	.05
238	Pete O'Brien	.05	.02
239	Harold Reynolds	.05	.02
240	David Valle	.05	.02
241	Julio Franco	.10	.06
242	Juan Gonzalez	1.75	1.00
243	Jose Guzman	.05	.02
244	Rafael Palmeiro	.20	.12
245	Dean Palmer	.30	.18
246	Ivan Rodriquez	.50	.30
247	Jeff Russell	.05	.02
248	Nolan Ryan	1.75	1.00
249	Ruben Sierra	.20	.12
250	Dickie Thon	.05	.02
251	Roberto Alomar	.70	.40
252	Derek Bell	.25	.15
253	Pat Borders	.05	.02
254	Joe Carter	.30	.18

255	Kelly Gruber	.07	.04
256	Juan Guzman	.50	.30
257	Jack Morris	.15	.10
258	John Olerud	.75	.45
259	Devon White	.10	.06
260	Dave Winfield	.30	.18
261	Checklist	.05	.02
262	Checklist	.05	.02
263	Checklist	.05	.02
264	History Card	.20	.12
BC1	Ryne Sandberg	4.50	2.75
BC2	Carlton Fisk	1.00	.70
BC3	Wade Boggs	1.50	.90
BC4	Jose Canseco	2.50	1.50
BC5	Don Mattingly	3.50	2.00
BC6	Darryl Strawberry	1.50	.90
BC7	Cal Ripken Jr	5.00	3.50
BC8	Will Clark	2.50	1.50
BC9	Andre Dawson	1.50	.90
BC10	Andy Van Slyke	1.00	.70
BC11	Paul Molitor	2.50	1.50
BC12	Jeff Bagwell	3.50	2.00
BC13	Darren Daulton	1.75	1.00
BC14	Kirby Puckett	4.00	2.50

1993 Leaf

The cards in this set consist of full-color action photos on full-bleed card fronts. A gold Leaf logo appears in the lower right corner while the player's name and team name are printed diagonally next to the Leaf logo. Card backs contain another full-color action shot superimposed over a scene from the player's home team city. All cards measure 2-1/2" by 3-1/2".

	MINT	NR/MT
Complete Set (550)	65.00	45.00
Commons	.08	.05

1	Ben McDonald	.15	.10
2	Sid Fernandez	.08	.05
3	Juan Guzman	.35	.20
4	Curt Schilling	.12	.07
5	Ivan Rodriguez	.30	.18
6	Don Slaught	.08	.05
7	Terry Steinbach	.08	.05
8	Todd Zeile	.10	.06
9	Andy Stankiewicz	.08	.05
10	Tim Teufel	.08	.05
11	Marvin Freeman	.08	.05
12	Jim Austin	.12	.07
13	Bob Scanlan	.08	.05
14	Rusty Meacham	.12	.07
15	Casey Candaele	.08	.05
16	Travis Fryman	.60	.35
17	Jose Offerman	.12	.07
18	Albert Belle	.70	.40
19	John Vander Wal	.08	.05
20	Dan Pasqua	.08	.05
21	Frank Viola	.10	.06
22	Terry Mulholland	.08	.05
23	Gregg Olson	.10	.06
24	Randy Tomlin	.10	.06
25	Todd Stottlemyre	.08	.05
26	Jose Oquendo	.08	.05
27	Julio Franco	.12	.07
28	Tony Gwynn	.25	.15
29	Ruben Sierra	.20	.12
30	Bobby Thigpen	.08	.05
31	Jim Bullinger	.08	.05
32	Rick Aguilera	.08	.05
33	Scott Servais	.08	.05
34	Cal Eldred	.20	.12
35	Mike Piazza	6.00	3.50
36	Brent Mayne	.08	.05
37	Wil Cordero	.25	.15
38	Milt Cuyler	.10	.06
39	Howard Johnson	.10	.06
40	Kenny Lofton	.60	.35
41	Alex Fernandez	.35	.20
42	Denny Neagle	.10	.06
43	Tony Pena	.08	.05
44	Bob Tewksbury	.10	.06
45	Glenn Davis	.08	.05
46	Fred McGriff	.60	.35
47	John Olerud	1.00	.70
48	Steve Hosey	.35	.20
49	Rafael Palmeiro	.30	.18
50	David Justice	.70	.40
51	Pete Harnisch	.10	.06
52	Sam Militello	.20	.12
53	Orel Hershiser	.12	.07
54	Pat Mahomes	.15	.10
55	Greg Colbrunn	.12	.07
56	Greg Vaughn	.15	.10
57	Vince Coleman	.10	.06

58	Brian McRae	.12	.07
59	Lenny Dykstra	.20	.12
60	Dan Gladden	.08	.05
61	Ted Power	.08	.05
62	Donovan Osborne	.20	.12
63	Ron Karkovice	.08	.05
64	Frank Seminara	.08	.05
65	Bob Zupcic	.12	.07
66	Kirt Manwaring	.08	.05
67	Mike Devereaux	.10	.06
68	Mark Lemke	.08	.05
69	Devon White	.12	.07
70	Sammy Sosa	.25	.15
71	Pedro Astacio	.30	.18
72	Dennis Eckersley	.12	.07
73	Chris Nabholz	.10	.06
74	Melido Perez	.08	.05
75	Todd Hundley	.08	.05
76	Kent Hrbek	.10	.06
77	Mickey Morandini	.10	.06
78	Tim McIntosh	.10	.06
79	Andy Van Slyke	.15	.10
80	Kevin McReynolds	.10	.06
81	Mike Henneman	.08	.05
82	Greg Harris	.08	.05
83	Sandy Alomar Jr.	.10	.06
84	Mike Jackson	.10	.06
85	Ozzie Guillen	.08	.05
86	Jeff Blauser	.12	.07
87	John Valentin	.20	.12
88	Rey Sanchez	.10	.06
89	Rick Sutcliffe	.08	.05
90	Luis Gonzalez	.12	.07
91	Jeff Fassero	.08	.05
92	Kenny Rogers	.08	.05
93	Bret Saberhagen	.12	.07
94	Bob Welch	.08	.05
95	Darren Daulton	.20	.12
96	Mike Gallego	.08	.05
97	Orlando Merced	.12	.07
98	Chuck Knoblauch	.15	.10
99	Bernard Gilkey	.15	.10
100	Billy Ahsley	.75	.45
101	Kevin Appier	.15	.10
102	Jeff Brantley	.08	.05
103	Bill Gullickson	.08	.05
104	John Smoltz	.12	.07
105	Paul Sorrento	.10	.06
106	Steve Buechele	.08	.05
107	Steve Sax	.10	.06
108	Andujar Cedeno	.12	.07
109	Billy Hatcher	.08	.05
110	Checklist	.10	.03
111	Alan Mills	.08	.05
112	John Franco	.08	.05
113	Jack Morris	.12	.07
114	Mitch Williams	.08	.05
115	Nolan Ryan	1.75	1.00
116	Jay Bell	.12	.07
117	Mike Bordick	.10	.06
118	Geronimo Pena	.08	.05
119	Danny Tartabull	.12	.07
120	Checklist	.10	.03
121	Steve Avery	.30	.18
122	Ricky Bones	.10	.06
123	Mike Morgan	.08	.05
124	Jeff Montgomery	.08	.05
125	Jeff Bagwell	.60	.35
126	Tony Phillips	.12	.07
127	Lenny Harris	.08	.05
128	Glenallen Hill	.12	.07
129	Marquis Grissom	.20	.12
130	Bernie Williams	.12	.07
131	Greg Harris	.08	.05
132	Tommy Greene	.12	.07
133	Chris Hoiles	.12	.07
134	Bob Walk	.08	.05
135	Duane Ward	.10	.06
136	Tom Pagnozzi	.10	.06
137	Jeff Huson	.08	.05
138	Kurt Stillwell	.08	.05
139	Dave Henderson	.08	.05
140	Darrin Jackson	.10	.06
141	Frank Castillo	.08	.05
142	Scott Erickson	.12	.07
143	Darryl Kile	.20	.12
144	Bill Wegman	.08	.05
145	Steve Wilson	.10	.06
146	George Brett	.50	.30
147	Moises Alou	.15	.10
148	Lou Whitaker	.10	.06
149	Chico Walker	.08	.05
150	Jerry Browne	.08	.05
151	Kirk McCaskill	.08	.05
152	Zane Smith	.08	.05
153	Matt Young	.08	.05
154	Lee Smith	.12	.07
155	Leo Gomez	.12	.07
156	Dan Walters	.12	.07
157	Pat Borders	.08	.05
158	Matt Williams	.20	.12
159	Dean Palmer	.35	.20
160	John Patterson	.08	.05
161	Doug Jones	.08	.05
162	John Habyan	.08	.05
163	Pedro Martinez	.30	.18
164	Carl Willis	.08	.05
165	Darrin Fletcher	.08	.05
166	B.J. Surhoff	.08	.05
167	Eddie Murray	.15	.10
168	Keith Miller	.08	.05
169	Ricky Jordan	.08	.05
170	Juan Gonzalez	2.00	1.25
171	Charles Nagy	.15	.10

172	Mark Clark	.12	.07
173	Bobby Thigpen	.08	.05
174	Tim Scott	.08	.05
175	Scott Cooper	.12	.07
176	Royce Clayton	.15	.10
177	Brady Anderson	.12	.07
178	Sid Bream	.08	.05
179	Derek Bell	.20	.12
180	Otis Nixon	.10	.06
181	Kevin Gross	.08	.05
182	Ron Darling	.08	.05
183	John Wetteland	.10	.06
184	Mike Stanley	.12	.07
185	Jeff Kent	.15	.10
186	Brian Harper	.10	.06
187	Mariano Duncan	.08	.05
188	Robin Yount	.40	.25
189	Al Martin	.40	.25
190	Eddie Zosky	.10	.06
191	Mike Munoz	.10	.06
192	Andy Benes	.12	.07
193	Dennis Cook	.08	.05
194	Bill Swift	.12	.07
195	Frank Thomas	3.50	2.00
196	Damon Berryhill	.08	.05
197	Mike Greenwell	.10	.06
198	Mark Grace	.15	.10
199	Darryl Hamilton	.12	.07
200	Derrick May	.15	.10
201	Ken Hill	.10	.06
202	Kevin Brown	.10	.06
203	Dwight Gooden	.12	.07
204	Bobby Witt	.10	.06
205	Juan Bell	.08	.05
206	Kevin Maas	.10	.06
207	Jeff King	.10	.06
208	Scott Leius	.08	.05
209	Rheal Cormier	.10	.06
210	Darryl Strawberry	.15	.10
211	Tom Gordon	.10	.06
212	Bud Black	.08	.05
213	Mickey Tettleton	.10	.06
214	Pete Smith	.10	.06
215	Felix Fermin	.08	.05
216	Rick Wilkins	.15	.10
217	George Bell	.12	.07
218	Eric Anthony	.12	.07
219	Pedro Munoz	.10	.06
220	Checklist	.10	.03
221	Lance Blankenship	.08	.05
222	Deion Sanders	.20	.12
223	Craig Biggio	.10	.06
224	Ryne Sandberg	.70	.40
225	Ron Gant	.15	.10
226	Tom Brunansky	.10	.06
227	Chad Curtis	.40	.25
228	Joe Carter	.50	.30
229	Brian Jordan	.25	.15
230	Brett Butler	.12	.07
231	Frank Bolick	.10	.06
232	Hod Beck	.10	.06
233	Carlos Baerga	.60	.35
234	Eric Karros	.35	.20
235	Jack Armstrong	.08	.05
236	Bobby Bonilla	.12	.07
237	Don Mattingly	.50	.30
238	Jeff Gardner	.08	.05
239	Dave Hollins	.25	.15
240	Steve Cooke	.30	.18
241	Jose Canseco	.30	.18
242	Ivan Calderon	.08	.05
243	Tim Belcher	.08	.05
244	Freddie Benavides	.08	.05
245	Roberto Alomar	.75	.45
246	Rob Deer	.10	.06
247	Will Clark	.50	.30
248	Mike Felder	.08	.05
249	Harold Baines	.10	.06
250	David Cone	.12	.07
251	Mark Guthrie	.10	.06
252	Ellis Burks	.10	.06
253	Jim Abbott	.20	.12
254	Chili Davis	.10	.06
255	Chris Bosio	.10	.06
256	Bret Barberie	.10	.06
257	Hal Morris	.12	.07
258	Dante Bichette	.15	.10
259	Storm Davis	.08	.05
260	Gary DiSarcina	.12	.07
261	Ken Caminiti	.08	.05
262	Paul Molitor	.25	.15
263	Joe Oliver	.08	.05
264	Pat Listach	.20	.12
265	Gregg Jefferies	.20	.12
266	Jose Guzman	.10	.06
267	Eric Davis	.12	.07
268	Delino DeShields	.15	.10
269	Barry Bonds	1.25	.80
270	Mike Bielecki	.08	.05
271	Jay Buhner	.10	.06
272	Scott Pose (R)	.20	.12
273	Tony Fernandez	.10	.06
274	Chito Martinez	.10	.06
275	Phil Plantier	.50	.30
276	Pete Incaviglia	.08	.05
277	Carlos Garcia	.25	.15
278	Tom Henke	.08	.05
279	Roger Clemens	.50	.30
280	Rob Dibble	.10	.06
281	Daryl Boston	.08	.05
282	Greg Gagne	.08	.05
283	Cecil Fielder	.30	.18
284	Carlton Fisk	.12	.07
285	Wade Boggs	.25	.15

286	Damion Easley	.12	.07
287	Norm Charlton	.08	.05
288	Jeff Conine	.25	.15
289	Roberto Kelly	.15	.10
290	Jerald Clark	.08	.05
291	Rickey Henderson	.30	.18
292	Chuck Finley	.12	.07
293	Doug Drabek	.12	.07
294	Dave Stewart	.15	.10
295	Tom Glavine	.40	.25
296	Jaime Navarro	.10	.06
297	Ray Lankford	.20	.12
298	Greg Hibbard	.08	.05
299	Jody Reed	.08	.05
300	Dennis Martinez	.10	.06
301	Dave Martinez	.08	.05
302	Reggie Jefferson	.12	.07
303	John Cummings (R)	.30	.18
304	Orestes Destrade	.12	.07
305	Mike Maddux	.08	.05
306	David Segui	.10	.06
307	Gary Sheffield	.35	.20
308	Danny Jackson	.10	.06
309	Craig Lefferts	.08	.05
310	Andre Dawson	.15	.10
311	Barry Larkin	.12	.07
312	Alex Cole	.08	.05
313	Mark Gardner	.08	.05
314	Kirk Gibson	.10	.06
315	Shane Mack	.10	.06
316	Bo Jackson	.20	.12
317	Jimmy Key	.12	.07
318	Greg Myers	.08	.05
319	Ken Griffey Jr.	3.00	1.75
320	Monty Fariss	.08	.05
321	Kevin Mitchell	.10	.06
322	Andres Galarraga	.15	.10
323	Mark McGwire	.30	.18
324	Mark Langston	.12	.07
325	Steve Finley	.08	.05
326	Greg Maddux	.30	.18
327	Dave Nilsson	.10	.06
328	Ozzie Smith	.15	.10
329	Candy Maldonado	.08	.05
330	Checklist	.10	.03
331	Tim Pugh (R)	.25	.15
332	Joe Girardi	.08	.05
333	Junior Felix	.08	.05
334	Greg Swindell	.10	.06
335	Ramon Martinez	.12	.07
336	Sean Berry	.12	.07
337	Joe Orsulak	.08	.05
338	Wes Chamberlain	.12	.07
339	Stan Belinda	.08	.05
340	Checklist	.10	.03
341	Bruce Hurst	.10	.06
342	John Burkett	.12	.07
343	Mike Mussina	.75	.45
344	Scott Fletcher	.08	.05
345	Rene Gonzalez	.08	.05
346	Roberto Hernandez	.10	.06
347	Carlos Martinez	.08	.05
348	Bill Krueger	.12	.07
349	Felix Jose	.10	.00
350	John Jaha	.20	.12
351	Willie Banks	.12	.07
352	Matt Nokes	.08	.05
353	Kevin Seitzer	.08	.05
354	Erik Hanson	.10	.06
355	David Hulse (R)	.30	.18
356	Domingo Martinez (R)	.40	.25
357	Greg Olson	.08	.05
358	Randy Myers	.10	.06
359	Tom Browning	.10	.06
360	Charlie Hayes	.12	.07
361	Bryan Harvey	.12	.07
362	Eddie Taubensee	.10	.06
363	Tim Wallach	.10	.06
364	Mel Rojas	.10	.06
365	Frank Tanana	.08	.05
366	John Kruk	.20	.12
367	Tim Laker (R)	.20	.12
368	Rich Rodriquez	.08	.05
369	Darren Lewis	.12	.07
370	Harold Reynolds	.08	.05
371	Jose Melendez	.08	.05
372	Joe Grahe	.10	.06
373	Lance Johnson	.10	.06
374	Jose Mesa	.10	.06
375	Scott Livingstone	.08	.05
376	Wally Joyner	.12	.07
377	Kevin Reimer	.08	.05
378	Kirby Puckett	.70	.40
379	Paul O'Neill	.12	.07
380	Randy Johnson	.25	.15
381	Manuel Lee	.08	.05
382	Dick Schofield	.08	.05
383	Darren Holmes	.10	.06
384	Charlie Hough	.08	.05
385	John Orton	.10	.06
386	Edgar Martinez	.15	.10
387	Terry Pendleton	.15	.10
388	Dan Plesac	.08	.05
389	Jeff Reardon	.10	.06
390	David Nied	.80	.50
391	Dave Magadan	.08	.05
392	Larry Walker	.25	.15
393	Ben Rivera	.10	.06
394	Lonnie Smith	.10	.06
395	Craig Shipley	.08	.05
396	Willie McGee	.12	.07
397	Arthur Rhodes	.10	.06
398	Mike Stanton	.10	.06
399	Luis Polonia	.10	.06

400	Jack McDowell	.30	.18
401	Mike Moore	.08	.05
402	Jose Lind	.08	.05
403	Bill Spiers	.08	.05
404	Kevin Tapani	.10	.06
405	Spike Owen	.08	.05
406	Tino Martinez	.12	.07
407	Charlie Leibrandt	.08	.05
408	Ed Sprague	.12	.07
409	Bryn Smith	.08	.05
410	Benito Santiago	.12	.07
411	Jose Rijo	.12	.07
412	Pete O'Brien	.08	.05
413	Willie Wilson	.08	.05
414	Bip Roberts	.10	.06
415	Eric Young	.20	.12
416	Walt Weiss	.08	.05
417	Milt Thompson	.08	.05
418	Chris Sabo	.10	.06
419	Scott Sanderson	.08	.05
420	Tim Raines	.12	.07
421	Alan Trammell	.20	.12
422	Mike Macfarlane	.08	.05
423	Dave Winfield	.50	.30
424	Bob Wickman	.40	.25
425	Dave Valle	.08	.05
426	Gary Redus	.08	.05
427	Turner Ward	.10	.06
428	Reggie Sanders	.25	.15
429	Todd Worrell	.08	.05
430	Julio Velera	.08	.05
431	Cal Ripken Jr.	.75	.45
432	Mo Vaughn	.30	.18
433	John Smiley	.10	.06
434	Omar Vizquel	.08	.05
435	Billy Ripken	.08	.05
436	Corey Snyder	.10	.06
437	Carlos Quintana	.08	.05
438	Omar Olivares	.08	.05
439	Robin Ventura	.30	.18
440	Checklist	.10	.03
441	Kevin Higgins (R)	.20	.12
442	Carlos Hernandez	.10	.06
443	Dan Peltier	.12	.07
444	Derek Lilliquist	.08	.05
445	Tim Salmon	4.00	2.50
446	Sherman Obando (R)	.30	.18
447	Pat Kelly	.10	.06
448	Todd Van Poppel	.40	.25
449	Mark Whiten	.35	.20
450	Checklist	.10	.03
451	Pat Meares (R)	.30	.18
452	Tony Tarasco (R)	.75	.45
453	Chris Gwynn	.10	.06
454	Armando Reynoso	.08	.05
455	Danny Darwin	.08	.05
456	Willie Greene	.25	.15
457	Mike Blowers	.08	.05
458	Kevin Roberson (R)	.50	.30
459	Graeme Lloyd (R)	.20	.12
460	David West	.08	.05
461	Joey Cora	.08	.05
462	Alex Arias	.08	.05
463	Chad Kreuter	.15	.10
464	Mike Lansing (R)	.40	.25
465	Mike Timlin	.15	.10
466	Paul Wagner	.30	.18
467	Mark Portugal	.10	.06
468	Jim Leyritz	.10	.06
469	Ryan Klesko	.80	.50
470	Mario Diaz	.08	.05
471	Guillermo Velasquez	.10	.06
472	Fernando Valenzuela	.10	.06
473	Raul Mondesi	.30	.18
474	Mike Pagliarulo	.08	.05
475	Chris Hammond	.08	.05
476	Torey Lovullo	.10	.06
477	Trevor Wilson	.08	.05
478	Marcos Armas (R)	.50	.30
479	Dave Gallagher	.08	.05
480	Jeff Treadway	.08	.05
481	Jeff Branson	.08	.05
482	Dickie Thon	.08	.05
483	Eduardo Perez	1.75	1.00
484	David Wells	.08	.05
485	Brian Williams	.12	.07
486	Domingo Cedeno (R)	.25	.15
487	Tom Candiotti	.08	.05
488	Steve Frey	.08	.05
489	Greg McMichael (R)	.40	.25
490	Marc Newfield	.75	.45
491	Larry Andersen	.08	.05
492	Damon Buford	.15	.10
493	Ricky Gutierrez	.15	.10
494	Jeff Russell	.08	.05
495	Vinny Castilla	.12	.07
496	Wilson Alvarez	.20	.12
497	Scott Bullett	.12	.07
498	Larry Casian	.12	.07
499	Jose Vizcaino	.08	.05
500	J.T. Snow (R)	1.50	.90
501	Bryan Hickerson	.12	.07
502	Jeremy Hernandez	.10	.06
503	Jeromy Burnitz	.40	.25
504	Steve Farr	.10	.06
505	J. Owens (R)	.40	.25
506	Craig Paquette	.15	.10
507	Jim Eisenreich	.08	.05
508	Matt Whiteside (R)	.20	.12
509	Luis Aquino	.08	.05
510	Mike LaValliere	.08	.05
511	Jim Gott	.08	.05
512	Mark McLemore	.08	.05
513	Randy Milligan	.10	.06

514	Gary Gaetti	.08	.05
515	Lou Frazier (R)	.25	.15
516	Rich Amaral	.12	.07
517	Gene Harris	.08	.05
518	Aaron Sele	3.00	1.75
519	Mark Wohlers	.12	.07
520	Scott Kamieniecki	.10	.06
521	Kent Mercker	.10	.06
522	Jim Deshaies	.08	.05
523	Kevin Stocker	1.50	.90
524	Jason Bere	2.50	1.50
525	Tim Bogar (R)	.25	.15
526	Brad Pennington	.12	.07
527	Curt Leskanic (R)	.15	.10
528	Wayne Kirby	.12	.07
529	Tim Costo	.12	.07
530	Doug Henry	.12	.07
531	Trevor Hoffman	.20	.12
532	Kelly Gruber	.10	.06
533	Mike Harkey	.10	.06
534	John Doherty	.20	.12
535	Erik Pappas	.12	.07
536	Brent Gates	.60	.35
537	Roger McDowell	.08	.05
538	Chris Haney	.10	.06
539	Blas Minor	.10	.06
540	Pat Hentgen	.60	.35
541	Chuck Carr	.15	.10
542	Doug Strange	.10	.06
543	Xavier Hernandez	.10	.06
544	Paul Quantrill	.10	.06
545	Anthony Young	.08	.05
546	Bret Boone	.20	.12
547	Dwight Smith	.10	.06
548	Bobby Munoz	.10	.06
549	Russ Springer	.12	.07
550	Roger Pavlik	.20	.12
___	Dave Winfield (3,000)	7.50	4.50
___	Frank Thomas Ea.	4.00	2.75
___	Frank Thomas (Autographed)	400.00	250.00

1993 Leaf
Gold Rookies

The cards in this limited insert set were distributed randomly in Leaf Foil hobby packs. The card fronts feature a full-color action shots with the Leaf logo in the top corner and the player's name superimposed over the words "Gold Rookies" in a box under his picture. All cards measure 2-1/2" by 3-1/2".

	MINT	NR/MT
Complete Set (20)	55.00	34.00
Commons	1.25	.80

1	Kevin Young	2.50	1.50
2	Wil Cordero	2.50	1.50
3	Mark Kiefer	1.25	.80
4	Gerald Williams	1.50	.90
5	Brandon Wilson	1.25	.80
6	Greg Gohr	1.25	.80
7	Ryan Thompson	2.00	1.25
8	Tim Wakefield	1.50	.90
9	Troy Neel	2.50	1.50
10	Tim Salmon	15.00	10.00
11	Kevin Rogers	1.25	.80
12	Rod Bolton	1.25	.80
13	Ken Ryan	2.00	1.25
14	Phil Hiatt	2.50	1.50
15	Rene Arocha	2.00	1.25
16	Nigel Wilson	6.00	3.50
17	J.T. Snow	5.00	3.00
18	Benji Gil	2.50	1.50
19	Chipper Jones	6.00	3.50
20	Darrell Sherman	1.50	.90

1993 Leaf
Gold All-Stars

The cards in this insert set were issued randomly in Leaf jumbo packs. The cards depict one All-Star on each side and consist of full-bleed, full-color action shots with an All-Stars logo in a diagonal stripe in the lower right corner just above the player's name. All cards measure 2-1/2" by 3-1/2".

	MINT	NR/MT
Complete Set (20)	32.00	20.00
Commons	.75	.45

1	D. Daulton/I. Rodriguez	1.50	.90
2	D. Mattingly/F. McGriff	3.00	1.75
3	J. Bagwell/C. Fielder	2.50	1.50

4	C. Baerga/R. Sandberg	3.50	2.00
5	D. DeShields/C. Knoblauch	1.00	.70
6	T. Pendleton/R. Ventura	1.75	1.00
7	K. Griffey Jr./A. Van Slyke	5.00	3.00
8	J. Carter/D. Justice	2.50	1.50
9	J. Canseco/T. Gwynn	2.00	1.25
10	R. Dibble/D. Eckersley	.75	.45
11	W. Clark/M. McGwire	2.50	1.50
12	M. Grace/F. Thomas	7.50	4.50
13	R. Alomar/C. Biggio	3.00	1.75
14	B. Larkin/C. Ripken Jr.	3.00	1.75
15	E. Martinez/G. Sheffield	1.25	.80
16	B. Bonds/J. Gonzalez	8.00	5.00
17	M. Grissom/K. Puckett	2.50	1.50
18	J. Abbott/T. Glavine	2.00	1.25
19	G. Maddux/N. Ryan	6.00	3.50
20	R. Clemens/D. Drabek	2.50	1.50

1993 Leaf Fastrack

These random inserts were issued randomly in Leaf foil packs. The card fronts feature full color action shots with the headline "Fasttrack" printed in a diagonal stripe in the lower right corner of the card just above the player's name. All cards measure 2-1/2" by 3-1/2".

		MINT	NR/MT
Complete Set (20)		85.00	50.00
Commons		1.25	.80
1	Frank Thomas	18.00	12.00
2	Tim Wakefield	1.25	.80
3	Kenny Lofton	5.00	3.00
4	Mike Mussina	7.00	4.00
5	Juan Gonzalez	14.00	9.00
6	Chuck Knoblauch	1.50	.90
7	Eric Karros	4.00	2.75
8	Ray Lankford	2.00	1.25
9	Juan Guzman	4.00	2.50
10	Pat Listach	1.75	1.00
11	Carlos Baerga	6.50	3.75
13	Steve Avery	4.50	2.75
14	Robin Ventura	4.00	2.50

15	Ivan Rodriguez	4.00	2.50
16	Cal Eldred	2.50	1.50
17	Jeff Bagwell	5.00	3.00
18	David Justice	6.50	3.75
19	Travis Fryman	5.00	3.00
20	Marquis Grissom	3.00	1.75

1993 Leaf Heading For The Hall

The cards in this limited insert set were distributed randomly in all Leaf foil packs. The full-bleed design features full-color action shots on the card fronts with a Heading for The Hall logo centered under the player's picture. All cards measure 2-1/2" by 3-1/2".

		MINT	NR/MT
Complete Set (10)		60.00	38.00
Commons		2.00	1.25
1	Nolan Ryan	18.00	12.00
2	Tony Gwynn	3.50	2.00
3	Robin Yount	4.00	2.50
4	Eddie Murray	2.00	1.25
5	Cal Ripken	7.50	4.50
6	Roger Clemens	5.00	3.00
7	George Brett	6.00	3.50
8	Ryne Sandberg	7.00	4.00
9	Kirby Puckett	6.00	3.50
10	Ozzie Smith	3.50	2.00

1993 Leaf Update Gold Rookies

These five insert cards were issued randomly in Leaf Update packs. The card design is identical to the regular Gold Rookies inserts. All cards measure 2-1/2" by 3-1/2".

		MINT	NR/MT
Complete Set (5)		35.00	22.00
Commons		3.00	1.75
1	Allen Watson	5.00	3.00
2	Jeffrey Hammonds	7.00	4.00
3	David McCarty	4.50	2.75
4	Mike Piazza	25.00	15.00
5	Roberta Mejia	3.00	1.75

1993 Leaf Update Gold All-Stars

The cards in this 10-card insert set were randomly distributed in Leaf Update foil packs and are identical to the regular Gold All-Stars inserts and feature different All-Stars on each side of the card.. All cards measure 2-1/2" by 3-1/2".

		MINT	NR/MT
Complete Set (10)		18.50	12.50
Commons		.75	.45
1	M. Langston/ T. Mulholland	.75	.45
2	D. Daulton/I. Rodriguez	1.50	.90
3	J. Kruk/J. Olerud	3.00	1.75
4	R. Alomar/R. Sandberg	4.50	2.75
5	W. Boggs/G. Sheffield	1.50	.90
6	B. Larkin/C. Ripken	3.00	1.75
7	B. Bonds/K. Puckett	6.50	3.75
8	K. Griffey Jr./ M. Grissom	6.00	3.50
9	J. Carter/D. Justice	2.50	1.50
10	M. Grace/P. Molitor	2.00	1.25

1993 Leaf Studio

The cards in this set feature close-up full color portrait shots of the player's posing in front of a large team logo. The card backs consist of another large close up head shot along with a personal profile of each player. Limited Frank Thomas insert cards were randomly issued in Leaf Studio packs. Those cards are listed at the end of this checklist but not included in the complete set price below. All cards measure 2-1/2" by 3-1/2".

		MINT	NR/MT
Complete Set (220)		18.00	12.00
Commons		.05	.02
1	Dennis Eckersley	.12	.07
2	Chad Curtis	.20	.12
3	Eric Anthony	.12	.07
4	Roberto Alomar	.40	.25
5	Steve Avery	.25	.15
6	Cal Eldred	.15	.10
7	Bernard Gilkey	.12	.07
8	Steve Buechele	.05	.02
9	Brett Butler	.08	.05
10	Terry Mulholland	.05	.02
11	Moises Alou	.12	.07
12	Barry Bonds	.75	.45
13	Sandy Alomar Jr.	.08	.05
14	Chris Bosio	.05	.02
15	Scott Sanderson	.05	.02
16	Bobby Bonilla	.12	.07
17	Brady Anderson	.10	.06
18	Derek Bell	.15	.10
19	Wes Chamberlain	.10	.06
20	Jay Bell	.10	.06
21	Kevin Brown	.08	.05
22	Roger Clemens	.40	.25
23	Roberto Kelly	.12	.07
24	Dante Bichette	.10	.06
25	George Brett	.40	.25
26	Rob Deer	.07	.04
27	Brian Harper	.05	.02
28	George Bell	.08	.05
29	Jim Abbott	.15	.10
30	Dave Henderson	.05	.02
31	Wade Boggs	.20	.12
32	Chili Davis	.05	.02
33	Ellis Burks	.07	.04
34	Jeff Bagwell	.25	.15
35	Kent Hrbek	.05	.02
36	Pat Borders	.05	.02
37	Cecil Fielder	.25	.15
38	Sid Bream	.05	.02
39	Greg Gagne	.05	.02
40	Darryl Hamilton	.10	.06
41	Jerald Clark	.05	.02
42	Mark Grace	.15	.10

#	Player			#	Player		
43	Barry Larkin	.12	.07	100	Tony Gwynn	.25	.15
44	John Burkett	.10	.06	101	Lenny Dykstra	.20	.12
45	Scott Cooper	.10	.06	102	Jeff King	.07	.04
46	Mike Lansing	.20	.12	103	Julio Franco	.08	.05
47	Jose Canseco	.25	.15	104	Andre Dawson	.15	.10
48	Will Clark	.25	.15	105	Randy Milligan	.05	.02
49	Carlos Garcia	.20	.12	106	Alex Cole	.05	.02
50	Carlos Baerga	.50	.30	107	Phil Hiatt	.25	.15
51	Darren Daulton	.12	.07	108	Travis Fryman	.40	.25
52	Jay Buhner	.07	.04	109	Chuck Knoblauch	.12	.07
53	Andy Benes	.10	.06	110	Bo Jackson	.20	.12
54	Jeff Conine	.12	.07	111	Pat Kelly	.08	.05
55	Mike Devereaux	.07	.04	112	Bret Saberhagen	.08	.05
56	Vince Coleman	.05	.02	113	Ruben Sierra	.12	.07
57	Terry Steinbach	.05	.02	114	Tim Salmon	2.50	1.50
58	J.T. Snow	.60	.35	115	Doug Jones	.05	.02
59	Greg Swindell	.07	.04	116	Ed Sprague	.07	.04
60	Devon White	.08	.05	117	Terry Pendleton	.10	.06
61	John Smoltz	.10	.06	118	Robin Yount	.30	.18
62	Todd Zeile	.08	.05	119	Mark Whiten	.20	.12
63	Rick Wilkins	.08	.05	120	Checklist	.07	.02
64	Tim Wallach	.05	.02	121	Sammy Sosa	.20	.12
65	John Wetteland	.07	.04	122	Darryl Strawberry	.15	.10
66	Matt Williams	.20	.12	123	Larry Walker	.15	.10
67	Paul Sorrento	.10	.06	124	Robby Thompson	.10	.06
68	David Valle	.05	.02	125	Carlos Martinez	.05	.02
69	Walt Weiss	.05	.02	126	Edgar Martinez	.12	.07
70	John Franco	.05	.02	127	Benito Santiago	.08	.05
71	Nolan Ryan	2.50	1.50	128	Howard Johnson	.08	.05
72	Frank Viola	.07	.04	129	Harold Reynolds	.05	.02
73	Chris Sabo	.07	.04	130	Craig Shipley	.05	.02
74	David Nied	.75	.45	131	Curt Schilling	.08	.05
75	Kevin McReynolds	.07	.04	132	Andy Van Slyke	.12	.07
76	Lou Whitaker	.08	.05	133	Ivan Rodriquez	.25	.15
77	Dave Winfield	.25	.15	134	Mo Vaughn	.25	.15
78	Robin Ventura	.25	.15	135	Bip Roberts	.05	.02
79	Spike Owen	.05	.02	136	Charlie Hayes	.07	.04
80	Cal Ripken Jr.	.60	.35	137	Brian McRae	.10	.06
81	Dan Walters	.12	.07	138	Mickey Tettleton	.07	.04
82	Mitch Williams	.05	.02	139	Frank Thomas	3.50	2.00
83	Tim Wakefield	.15	.10	140	Pau O'Neill	.10	.06
84	Rickey Henderson	.25	.15	141	Mark McGwire	.25	.15
85	Gary DiSarcina	.07	.04	142	Damion Easley	.08	.05
86	Craig Biggio	.07	.04	143	Ken Caminiti	.05	.02
87	Joe Carter	.30	.18	144	Juan Guzman	.20	.12
88	Ron Gant	.12	.07	145	Tom Glavine	.30	.18
89	John Jaha	.15	.10	146	Pat Listach	.15	.10
90	Gregg Jefferies	.20	.12	147	Lee Smith	.08	.05
91	Jose Guzman	.05	.02	148	Derrick May	.15	.10
92	Eric Karros	.25	.15	149	Ramon Martinez	.10	.06
93	Wil Cordero	.20	.12	150	Delino DeShields	.12	.07
94	Royce Clayton	.12	.07	151	Kirt Manwaring	.05	.02
95	Albert Belle	.60	.35	152	Reggie Jefferson	.10	.06
96	Ken Griffey Jr.	2.75	1.60	153	Randy Johnson	.25	.15
97	Orestes Destrade	.08	.05	154	Dave Magadan	.05	.02
98	Tony Fernandez	.05	.02	155	Dwight Gooden	.12	.07
99	Leo Gomez	.08	.05	156	Chris Hoiles	.10	.06

157	Fred McGriff	.35	.20
158	Dave Hollins	.20	.12
159	Al Martin	.30	.18
160	Juan Gonzalez	2.00	1.25
161	Mike Greenwell	.08	.05
162	Kevin Mitchell	.08	.05
163	Andres Galarraga	.12	.07
164	Wally Joyner	.08	.05
165	Kirk Gibson	.07	.04
166	Pedro Munoz	.08	.05
167	Ozzie Guillen	.05	.02
168	Jimmy Key	.08	.05
169	Kevin Seitzer	.05	.02
170	Luis Polonia	.05	.02
171	Luis Gonzalez	.08	.05
172	Paul Molitor	.25	.15
173	David Justice	.50	.30
174	B.J. Surhoff	.05	.02
175	Ray Lankford	.15	.10
176	Ryne Sandberg	.50	.30
177	Jody Reed	.05	.02
178	Marquis Grissom	.15	.10
179	Willie McGee	.07	.04
180	Kenny Lofton	.30	.18
181	Junior Felix	.05	.02
182	Jose Offerman	.08	.05
183	John Kruk	.12	.07
184	Orlando Merced	.10	.06
185	Rafael Palmeiro	.15	.10
186	Billy Hatcher	.05	.02
187	Joe Oliver	.05	.02
188	Joe Girardi	.05	.02
189	Jose Lind	.05	.02
190	Harold Baines	.07	.04
191	Mike Pagliarulo	.05	.02
192	Lance Johnson	.07	.04
193	Don Mattingly	.30	.18
194	Doug Drabek	.10	.06
195	John Olerud	.75	.45
196	Greg Maddux	.25	.15
197	Greg Vaughn	.10	.06
198	Tom Pagnozzi	.05	.02
199	Willie Wilson	.05	.02
200	Jack McDowell	.25	.15
201	Mike Piazza	6.00	3.50
202	Mike Mussina	.35	.20
203	Charles Nagy	.15	.10
204	Tino Martinez	.08	.05
205	Charlie Hough	.05	.02
206	Todd Hundley	.05	.02
207	Gary Sheffield	.25	.15
208	Mickey Morandini	.07	.04
209	Don Slaught	.05	.02
210	Dean Palmer	.20	.12
211	Jose Rijo	.08	.05
212	Vinny Castilla	.08	.05
213	Tony Phillips	.08	.05

214	Kirby Puckett	.50	.30
215	Tim Raines	.08	.05
216	Otis Nixon	.05	.02
217	Ozzie Smith	.20	.12
218	Jose Vizcaino	.05	.02
220	Checklist	.07	.02
___	Frank Thomas	4.50	2.75
	Inserts (Ea.)		

1993 Leaf Studio Heritage

The cards in this limited insert set were distributed randomly if Leaf Studio packs. The card fronts are designed to replicate the lok of old-time baseball cards. The player's name is centered along the bottom border under his photograph. All cards measure 2-1/2" by 3-1/2".

		MINT	NR/MT
Complete Set (12)		32.00	20.00
Commons		1.50	.90
1	George Brett	4.50	2.75
2	Juan Gonzalez	7.50	4.50
3	Roger Clemens	4.00	2.50
4	Mark McGwire	2.50	1.50
5	Mark Grace	1.50	.90
6	Ozzie Smith	2.00	1.25
7	Barry Larkin	1.50	.90
8	Frank Thomas	10.00	6.50
9	Carlos Baerga	5.00	3.00
10	Eric Karros	2.00	1.25
11	J.T. Snow	1.50	.90
12	John Kruk	1.75	1.00

		MINT	NR/MT
6	J.T. Snow	2.50	1.50
7	John Kruk	1.75	1.00
8	Jeff Blauser	1.00	.70
9	Mike Piazza	10.00	6.50
10	Nolan Ryan	8.00	5.00

1993 Leaf Studio Superstars On Canvas

These random inserts were issued in Leaf Studio packs and feature posed art portrait shots of the player on the card front with a Superstars on Canvas logo centered under his picture just below the player's name which appears in a horizontal bar. All cards measure 2-1/2" by 3-1/2".

		MINT	NR/MT
Complete Set (10)		35.00	22.00
Commons		1.50	.90
1	Ken Griffey Jr.	10.00	6.50
2	Jose Canseco	2.00	1.25
3	Mark McGwire	2.00	1.25
4	Mike Mussina	4.00	2.50
5	Joe Carter	3.50	2.00
6	Frank Thomas	12.00	7.50
7	Darren Daulton	1.75	1.00
8	Mark Grace	1.50	.90
9	Andres Galarraga	1.50	.90
10	Barry Bonds	7.50	4.50

1993 Leaf Studio Silhouettes

These cards appeared as random inserts in Leaf Studio jumbo packs. The card fronts contain a close-up portrait shot of the player against an action silhouette in the background. All cards measure 2-1/2" by 3-1/2".

		MINT	NR/MT
Complete Set (10)		36.00	22.50
Commons		1.00	.70
1	Frank Thomas	8.50	5.50
2	Barry Bonds	6.00	3.50
3	Jeff Bagwell	3.50	2.00
4	Juan Gonzalez	7.00	4.00
5	Travis Fryman	3.00	1.75

O-PEE-CHEE

1991 O-Pee-Chee Premier

This 132-card set is the first premium issue from Canadian based O-Pee-Chee. Card fronts feature four-color action photos framed in white with multi-colored border stripes. Horizontal card backs are numbered and include small head shots, player stats and bio's. All cards measure 2-1/2" by 3-1/2".

		MINT	NR/MT
Complete Set (132)		15.00	10.00
Commons		.05	.02
1	Roberto Alomar	.60	.35
2	Sandy Alomar	.10	.06
3	Moises Alou	.40	.25
4	Brian Barnes (R)	.20	.12
5	Steve Bedrosian	.05	.02
6	George Bell	.10	.06
7	Juan Bell	.08	.05
8	Albert Belle	.60	.35
9	Bud Black	.05	.02
10	Mike Boddicker	.05	.02
11	Wade Boggs	.25	.15

12	Barry Bonds	.75	.45
13	Denis Boucher	.20	.12
14	George Brett	.25	.15
15	Hubie Brooks	.05	.02
16	Brett Butler	.10	.06
17	Ivan Calderon	.05	.02
18	Jose Canseco	.35	.20
19	Gary Carter	.12	.07
20	Joe Carter	.25	.15
21	Jack Clark	.07	.04
22	Will Clark	.30	.18
23	Roger Clemens	.50	.30
24	Alex Cole	.07	.04
25	Vince Coleman	.07	.04
26	Jeff Conine (R)	.50	.30
27	Milt Cuyler	.10	.06
28	Danny Darwin	.05	.02
29	Eric Davis	.12	.07
30	Glenn Davis	.07	.04
31	Andre Dawson	.20	.12
32	Ken Dayley	.05	.02
33	Steve Decker (R)	.20	.12
34	Delino DeShields	.20	.12
35	Lance Dickson (R)	.25	.15
36	Kirk Dressendorfer (R)	.15	.10
37	Shawon Dunston	.10	.06
38	Dennis Eckersley	.12	.07
39	Dwight Evans	.10	.06
40	Howard Farmer	.08	.05
41	Junior Felix	.08	.05
42	Alex Fernandez	.40	.25
43	Tony Fernandez	.07	.04
44	Cecil Fielder	.25	.15
45	Carlton Fisk	.15	.10
46	Willie Fraser	.05	.02
47	Gary Gaetti	.07	.04
48	Andres Galarraga	.15	.10
49	Ron Gant	.20	.12
50	Kirk Gibson	.08	.05
51	Bernard Gilkey	.25	.15
52	Leo Gomez	.15	.10
53	Rene Gonzalez	.05	.02
54	Juan Gonzalez	2.50	1.50
55	Dwight Gooden	.20	.12
56	Ken Griffey Jr.	2.00	1.25
57	Kelly Gruber	.08	.05
58	Pedro Guerrero	.08	.05
59	Tony Gwynn	.25	.15
60	Chris Hammond	.15	.10
61	Ron Hassey	.05	.02
62	Rickey Henderson	.25	.15
63	Tom Henke	.08	.05
64	Orel Hershiser	.12	.07
65	Chris Hoiles	.25	.15
66	Todd Hundley	.25	.15
67	Pete Incaviglia	.10	.06
68	Danny Jackson	.07	.04
69	Barry Jones	.05	.02
70	David Justice	.50	.30
71	Jimmy Key	.10	.06
72	Ray Lankford	.35	.20
73	Darren Lewis	.20	.12
74	Kevin Maas	.12	.07
75	Denny Martinez	.12	.07
76	Tino Martinez	.12	.07
77	Don Mattingly	.30	.18
78	Willie McGee	.10	.06
79	Fred McGriff	.35	.20
80	Hensley Meulens	.08	.05
81	Kevin Mitchell	.10	.06
82	Paul Molitor	.25	.15
83	Mickey Morandini	.12	.07
84	Jack Morris	.12	.07
85	Dale Murphy	.12	.07
86	Eddie Murray	.20	.12
87	Chris Nabholz	.12	.07
88	Tim Naehring	.12	.07
89	Otis Nixon	.10	.06
90	Jose Offerman	.15	.10
91	Bob Ojeda	.05	.02
92	John Olerud	.80	.50
93	Gregg Olson	.10	.06
94	Dave Parker	.10	.06
95	Terry Pendleton	.15	.10
96	Kirby Puckett	.60	.35
97	Tim Raines	.12	.07
98	Jeff Reardon	.10	.06
99	Dave Righetti	.05	.02
100	Cal Ripken	.75	.45
101	Mel Rojas	.12	.07
102	Nolan Ryan	1.75	1.00
103	Ryne Sandberg	.60	.35
104	Scott Sanderson	.05	.02
105	Benito Santiago	.12	.07
106	Pete Schourek (R)	.25	.15
107	Gary Scott (R)	.15	.10
108	Terry Shumpert	.07	.04
109	Ruben Sierra	.20	.12
110	Doug Simons	.15	.10
111	Dave Smith	.05	.02
112	Ozzie Smith	.20	.12
113	Cory Snyder	.08	.05
114	Luis Sojo	.07	.04
115	Dave Stewart	.15	.10
116	Dave Stieb	.10	.06
117	Darryl Strawberry	.20	.12
118	Pat Tabler	.05	.02
119	Wade Taylor	.10	.06
120	Bobby Thigpen	.07	.04
121	Frank Thomas	5.00	3.00
122	Mike Timlin (R)	.20	.12
123	Alan Trammell	.20	.12
124	Mo Vaughn	.60	.35
125	Tim Wallach	.08	.05

		MINT	NR/MT
126	Devon White	.10	.06
127	Mark Whiten	.40	.25
128	Bernie Williams	.35	.20
129	Willie Wilson	.08	.05
130	Dave Winfield	.25	.15
131	Robin Yount	.25	.15
132	Checklist	.05	.02

1992 O-Pee-Chee Premier

BOBBY BONILLA

This second year premium set from O-Pee-Chee of Canada is similar to their 1991 set but larger with 198-cards compared to 132-cards in 1991. The cards feature four-color action shots on the fronts with a small head shot on the back along with career statistics. All cards measure 2-1/2" by 3-1/2".

		MINT	NR/MT
Complete Set (198)		12.50	7.50
Commons		.05	.02
1	Wade Boggs	.20	.12
2	John Smiley	.10	.06
3	Checklist	.05	.02
4	Ron Gant	.15	.10
5	Mike Bordick	.15	.10
6	Charlie Hayes	.08	.05
7	Kevin Morton	.05	.02
8	Checklist	.05	.02
9	Chris Gwynn	.05	.02
10	Melido Perez	.10	.06
11	Dan Gladden	.05	.02
12	Brian McRae	.15	.10
13	Denny Martinez	.10	.06
14	Bob Scanlan	.10	.06
15	Julio Franco	.12	.07
16	Ruben Amaro (R)	.20	.12
17	Mo Sanford	.10	.06
18	Scott Bankhead	.05	.02
19	Dickie Thon	.05	.03
20	Chris James	.05	.02
21	Mike Huff (R)	.12	.07
22	Orlando Merced	.15	.10
23	Chris Sabo	.10	.06
24	Jose Canseco	.25	.15
25	Reggie Sanders (R)	.50	.30
26	Chris Nabholz	.10	.06
27	Kevin Seitzer	.05	.02
28	Ryan Bowen	.12	.07
29	Gary Carter	.10	.06
30	Wayne Rosenthal	.10	.06
31	Alan Trammell	.15	.10
32	Doug Drabek	.12	.07
33	Craig Shipley	.05	.02
34	Ryne Sandberg	.40	.25
35	Chuck Knoblauch	.20	.12
36	Bret Barberie	.12	.07
37	Tim Naehring	.10	.06
38	Omar Oliveres	.08	.05
39	Royce Clayton	.20	.12
40	Brent Mayne	.05	.02
41	Darrin Fletcher	.12	.07
42	Howard Johnson	.10	.06
43	Steve Sax	.08	.05
44	Greg Swindell	.07	.04
45	Andre Dawson	.15	.10
46	Kent Hrbek	.07	.03
47	Dwight Gooden	.10	.06
48	Mark Leiter	.08	.05
49	Tom Glavine	.25	.15
50	Mo Vaughn	.25	.15
51	Doug Jones	.05	.02
52	Brian Barnes	.10	.06
53	Rob Dibble	.07	.04
54	Kevin McReynolds	.05	.03
55	Ivan Rodriquez	.20	.12
56	Scott Livingstone	.10	.06
57	Mike Magnante	.10	.06
58	Pete Schourek	.10	.06
59	Frank Thomas	1.50	.90
60	Kirk McCaskill	.05	.02
61	Wally Joyner	.10	.06
62	Rick Aguilera	.07	.04
63	Eric Karros	.30	.18
64	Tino Martinez	.10	.06
65	Bryan Hickerson	.12	.07
66	Ruben Sierra	.20	.12
67	Willie Randolph	.05	.02
68	Bill Landrum	.05	.02
69	Bip Roberts	.07	.03
70	Cecil Fielder	.25	.15
71	Pat Kelly	.10	.06

72	Kenny Lofton	.40	.25
73	John Franco	.07	.03
74	Phil Plantier	.35	.20
75	Dave Martinez	.05	.02
76	Warren Newson	.10	.06
77	Chito Martinez	.10	.06
78	Brian Hunter	.20	.12
79	Jack Morris	.10	.06
80	Eric King	.07	.03
81	Nolan Ryan	1.00	.70
82	Bret Saberhagen	.10	.06
83	Roberto Kelly	.20	.12
84	Ozzie Smith	.20	.12
85	Chuck McElroy	.08	.05
86	Carlton Fisk	.12	.07
87	Mike Mussina	.40	.25
88	Mark Carreon	.05	.02
89	Ken Hill	.10	.06
90	Rick Cerone	.07	.03
91	Deion Sanders	.20	.12
92	Don Mattingly	.25	.15
93	Danny Tartabull	.12	.07
94	Keith Miller	.05	.02
95	Gregg Jefferies	.15	.10
96	Barry Larkin	.12	.07
97	Kevin Mitchell	.10	.06
98	Rick Sutcliffe	.07	.03
99	Mark McGwire	.25	.15
100	Albert Belle	.30	.18
101	Gregg Olson	.07	.04
102	Kirby Puckett	.35	.20
103	Luis Gonzalez	.12	.07
104	Randy Myers	.07	.04
105	Roger Clemens	.35	.20
106	Tony Gwynn	.20	.12
107	Jeff Bagwell	.35	.20
108	John Wetteland	.10	.06
109	Bernie Williams	.12	.07
110	Scott Kamieniecki	.08	.05
111	Robin Yount	.25	.15
112	Dean Palmer	.25	.15
113	Tim Belcher	.05	.02
114	George Brett	.30	.18
115	Frank Viola	.08	.05
116	Kelly Gruber	.07	.03
117	David Justice	.30	.18
118	Scott Leius	.08	.05
119	Jeff Fassero	.08	.05
120	Sammy Sosa	.20	.12
121	Al Osuna	.07	.03
122	Wilson Alvarez	.15	.10
123	Jose Offerman	.12	.07
124	Mel Rojas	.07	.04
125	Shawon Dunston	.08	.05
126	Pete Incaviglia	.07	.03
127	Von Hayes	.05	.02
128	Dave Gallagher	.05	.02
129	Eric Davis	.12	.07
130	Roberto Alomar	.40	.25
131	Mike Gallego	.05	.02
132	Robin Ventura	.20	.12
133	Bill Swift	.15	.10
134	John Kruk	.15	.10
135	Craig Biggio	.08	.05
136	Eddie Taubensee	.08	.05
137	Cal Ripken	.35	.20
138	Charles Nagy	.20	.12
139	Jose Melendez	.10	.06
140	Jim Abbott	.15	.10
141	Paul Molitor	.20	.12
142	Tom Candiotti	.05	.02
143	Bobby Bonilla	.12	.07
144	Matt Williams	.20	.12
145	Brett Butler	.08	.05
146	Will Clark	.25	.15
147	Rickey Henderson	.25	.15
148	Ray Lankford	.15	.10
149	Bill Pecota	.05	.02
150	Dave Winfield	.20	.12
151	Darren Lewis	.07	.03
152	Bob MacDonald	.10	.06
153	David Segui	.10	.06
154	Benito Santiago	.07	.03
155	Chuck Finley	.10	.06
156	Andujar Cedeno	.15	.10
157	Barry Bonds	.50	.30
158	Joe Grahe	.07	.03
159	Frank Castillo	.05	.02
160	Dave Burba	.07	.03
161	Leo Gomez	.12	.07
162	Orel Hershiser	.10	.06
163	Delino DeShields	.15	.10
164	Sandy Alomar	.08	.05
165	Denny Neagle	.08	.05
166	Fred McGriff	.25	.15
167	Ken Griffey Jr.	1.25	.80
168	Juan Guzman	.35	.20
169	Bobby Rose	.12	.07
170	Steve Avery	.25	.15
171	Rich DeLucia	.07	.03
172	Mike Timlin	.07	.03
173	Randy Johnson	.20	.12
174	Paul Gibson	.07	.03
175	David Cone	.10	.06
176	Marquis Grissom	.15	.10
177	Kurt Stillwell	.05	.02
178	Mark Whiten	.20	.12
179	Darryl Strawberry	.20	.12
180	Mike Morgan	.05	.02
181	Scott Scudder	.07	.04
182	George Bell	.07	.03
183	Alvin Davis	.05	.02
184	Len Dykstra	.15	.10
185	Kyle Abbott	.08	.05

186	Chris Haney	.10	.06	1	Barry Bonds	1.00	.70
187	Junior Naboa	.05	.02	2	Chad Curtis	.50	.30
188	Dennis Eckersley	.12	.07	3	Chris Bosio	.07	.03
189	Derek Bell	.20	.12	4	Cal Eldred	.25	.15
190	Lee Smith	.10	.06	5	Dan Walters	.12	.07
191	Andres Galarraga	.15	.10	6	Rene Arocha (R)	.40	.25
192	Jack Armstrong	.07	.03	7	Delino DeShields	.15	.10
193	Eddie Murray	.20	.12	8	Spike Owen	.07	.03
194	Joe Carter	.25	.15	9	Jeff Russell	.07	.03
195	Terry Pendleton	.12	.07	10	Phil Plantier	.40	.25
196	Darryl Kile	.25	.15	11	Mike Christopher	.08	.05
197	Rod Beck (R)	.25	.15	12	Darren Daulton	.20	.12
198	Hubie Brooks	.05	.02	13	Scott Cooper	.10	.06
				14	Paul O'Neill	.12	.07
				15	Jimmy Key	.10	.06
				16	Dickie Thon	.07	.03
				17	Greg Gohr	.15	.10

1993 O-Pee-Chee Premier

TIM SALMON • CF

The cards in this premium set include both full-color action shots and some posed photos framed by a white border on the card fronts. The player's name and position appear in the lower left corner opposite an O-Pee-Chee Premier logo. The flip side contains another full-color head shot over a sky blue background along with a box containing player stats. The set includes a Star Performers limited insert set and four limited Draft Picks cards. Those inserts are printed at the end of this checklist but are not included in the complete set price below. All cards measure 2-1/2" by 3-1/2".

	MINT	NR/MT
Complete Set (132)	15.00	10.00
Commons	.07	.03

18	Andre Dawson	.15	.10
19	Steve Cooke	.40	.25
20	Tony Fernandez	.07	.03
21	Mark Gardner	.07	.03
22	Dave Martinez	.07	.03
23	Jose Guzman	.07	.03
24	Chili Davis	.08	.05
25	Randy Knorr	.10	.06
26	Mike Piazza	5.00	3.00
27	Benji Gil	.35	.20
28	Dave Winfield	.30	.18
29	Wil Cordero	.25	.15
30	Butch Henry	.10	.06
31	Eric Young	.15	.10
32	Orestes Destrade	.08	.05
33	Randy Myers	.08	.05
34	Tom Brunansky	.08	.05
35	Dan Wilson	.12	.07
36	Juan Guzman	.40	.25
37	Tim Salmon	3.50	2.00
38	Bill Krueger	.07	.03
39	Larry Walker	.25	.15
40	David Hulse (R)	.30	.18
41	Ken Ryan (R)	.50	.30
42	Jose Lind	.07	.03
43	Benito Santiago	.10	.06
44	Ray Lankford	.15	.10
45	Dave Stewart	.12	.07
46	Don Mattingly	.35	.20
47	Fernando Valenzuela	.07	.03
48	Scott Fletcher	.07	.03
49	Wade Boggs	.25	.15
50	Norm Charlton	.07	.03
51	Carlos Baerga	.75	.45
52	John Olerud	1.00	.70
53	Willie Wilson	.07	.03
54	Dennis Moeller	.10	.06
55	Joe Orsulak	.07	.03
56	John Smiley	.10	.06
57	Al Martin	.30	.18

58	Andres Galarraga	.15	.10
59	Billy Ripken	.07	.03
60	Dave Stieb	.08	.05
61	Dave Magadan	.07	.03
62	Todd Worrell	.07	.03
63	Sherman Obando (R)	.25	.15
64	Kent Bottenfield	.10	.06
65	Vinny Castilla	.08	.05
66	Charlie Hayes	.08	.05
67	Mike Hartley	.08	.05
68	Harold Baines	.08	.05
69	John Cummings (R)	.35	.20
70	J.T. Snow (R)	1.00	.70
71	Graeme Lloyd (R)	.20	.12
72	Frank Bolick	.10	.06
73	Doug Drabek	.12	.07
74	Milt Thompson	.07	.03
75	Tim Pugh (R)	.25	.15
76	John Kruk	.12	.07
77	Tom Henke	.07	.03
78	Kevin Young	.35	.20
79	Ryan Thompson	.25	.15
80	Mike Hampton	.10	.06
81	Jose Canseco	.25	.15
82	Mike Lansing (R)	.40	.25
83	Candy Maldonado	.07	.03
84	Alex Arias	.07	.03
85	Troy Neel	.35	.20
86	Greg Swindell	.08	.05
87	Tim Wallach	.08	.05
88	Andy Van Slyke	.12	.07
89	Harold Reynolds	.07	.03
90	Bryan Harvey	.10	.06
91	Jerald Clark	.07	.03
92	David Cone	.10	.06
93	Ellis Burks	.08	.05
94	Scott Bankhead	.07	.03
95	Pete Incaviglia	.07	.03
96	Cecil Fielder	.30	.18
97	Sean Berry	.12	.07
98	Gregg Jefferies	.20	.12
99	Billy Brewer (R)	.15	.10
100	Scott Sanderson	.07	.03
101	Walt Weiss	.07	.03
102	Travis Fryman	.60	.35
103	Barry Larkin	.12	.07
104	Darren Holmes	.12	.07
105	Ivan Calderon	.07	.03
106	Terry Jorgensen	.10	.06
107	David Nied	.80	.50
108	Tim Bogar (R)	.20	.12
109	Roberto Kelly	.15	.10
110	Mike Moore	.07	.03
111	Carlos Garcia	.25	.15
112	Mike Bielecki	.07	.03
113	Trevor Hoffman	.25	.15
114	Rich Amaral	.10	.06

115	Jody Reed	.07	.03
116	Charlie Liebrandt	.07	.03
117	Greg Gagne	.07	.03
118	Darrell Sherman (R)	.30	.18
119	Jeff Conine	.15	.10
120	Tim Laker (R)	.20	.12
121	Kevin Seitzer	.07	.03
122	Jeff Mutis	.07	.03
123	Rico Rossy	.12	.07
124	Paul Molitor	.25	.15
125	Cal Ripken Jr.	.80	.50
126	Greg Maddux	.30	.18
127	Greg McMichael (R)	.40	.25
128	Felix Jose	.08	.05
129	Dick Schofield	.07	.03
130	Jim Abbott	.20	.12
131	Kevin Reimer	.07	.03
132	Checklist	.08	.03
DP1	B.J. Wallace	7.00	4.00
DP2	Shannon Stewart	3.50	2.00
DP3	Rod Henderson	5.00	3.00
DP4	Todd Steverson	4.00	2.50

1993 O-Pee-Chee Premier Star Performers

The cards in this limited insert set were issued one per pack in Premier foil packs. The cards feature full-color action photos on the fronts framed by a gold colored border. The words "Star Performer" are printed above the photograph while the player's name and position are printed across the bottom. A very limited foil version of each card was also issued randomly. The foil cards are valued at 15 X the regular inserts. All cards measure 2-1/2" by 3-1/2".

		MINT	NR/MT
Complete Set (22)		15.00	10.00
Commons		.20	.12
Complete Set (Foil)		200.00	125.00
Commons (Foil)		2.00	1.25

1	Frank Thomas	3.00	1.75
2	Fred McGriff	.60	.35
3	Roberto Alomar	1.00	.70
4	Ryne Sandberg	.75	.45
5	Edgar Martinez	.20	.12
6	Gary Sheffield	.35	.20
7	Juan Gonzalez	2.00	1.25
8	Eric Karros	.35	.20
9	Ken Griffey Jr.	2.50	1.50
10	Deion Sanders	.25	.15
11	Kirby Puckett	.75	.45
12	Will Clark	.50	.30
13	Joe Carter	.50	.30
14	Barry Bonds	1.25	.80
15	Pat Listach	.25	.15
16	Mark McGwire	.35	.20
17	Kenny Lofton	.60	.35
18	Roger Clemens	.75	.45
19	Greg Maddux	.35	.20
20	Nolan Ryan	2.00	1.25
21	Tom Glavine	.40	.25
22	Dennis Eckersley	.25	.15

SCORE

1988 Score

The premier set from Score featured four-color fronts and backs. The cards, measuring 2-1/2" by 3-1/2", used six different border colors to frame game-action photos on the fronts while the card backs contained a small head shot of each player. Reggie Jackson is featured in a special 5-card subset.

		MINT	NR/MT
Complete Set (660)		18.00	12.00
Commons		.05	.02

1	Don Mattingly	.25	.15
2	Wade Boggs	.20	.12
3	Tim Raines	.07	.04
4	Andre Dawson	.20	.12
5	Mark McGwire	.50	.30
6	Kevin Seitzer	.07	.04
7	Wally Joyner	.15	.08
8	Jesse Barfield	.07	.04
9	Pedro Guerrero	.07	.04
10	Eric Davis	.10	.06
11	George Brett	.35	.20
12	Ozzie Smith	.20	.12
13	Rickey Henderson	.30	.18
14	Jim Rice	.07	.04
15	Matt Nokes (R)	.12	.07
16	Mike Schmidt	.50	.30
17	Dave Parker	.10	.06
18	Eddie Murray	.20	.12
19	Andres Galarraga	.07	.04
20	Tony Fernandez	.07	.04
21	Kevin McReynolds	.07	.04
22	B.J. Surhoff	.05	.02
23	Pat Tabler	.05	.02
24	Kirby Puckett	.50	.30
25	Benny Santiago	.15	.08
26	Ryne Sandberg	.50	.30
27	Kelly Downs	.07	.04
28	Jose Cruz	.07	.04
29	Pete O'Brien	.05	.02
30	Mark Langston	.10	.06
31	Lee Smith	.15	.08
32	Juan Samuel	.05	.02
33	Kevin Bass	.05	.02
34	R.J. Reynolds	.05	.02
35	Steve Sax	.10	.06
36	John Kruk	.15	.08
37	Alan Trammell	.15	.08
38	Chris Bosio	.08	.05
39	Brook Jacoby	.05	.02
40	Willie McGee	.10	.06
41	Dave Magadan	.05	.02
42	Fred Lynn	.08	.05
43	Kent Hrbek	.08	.05
44	Brian Downing	.05	.02
45	Jose Canseco	.40	.25
46	Jim Presley	.05	.02
47	Mike Stanley	.05	.02

48	Tony Pena	.05	.02	105	Don Sutton	.12	.07
49	David Cone	.35	.20	106	Danny Tartabull	.15	.08
50	Rick Sutcliffe	.07	.04	107	Fred McGriff	.60	.35
51	Doug Drabek	.15	.08	108	Les Straker (R)	.05	.02
52	Bill Doran	.05	.02	109	Lloyd Moseby	.05	.02
53	Mike Scioscia	.05	.02	110	Roger Clemens	.60	.35
54	Candy Maldonado	.05	.02	111	Glenn Hubbard	.05	.02
55	Dave Winfield	.20	.12	112	Ken Williams (R)	.05	.02
56	Lou Whitaker	.07	.04	113	Ruben Sierra	.40	.25
57	Tom Henke	.05	.02	114	Stan Jefferson	.05	.02
58	Ken Gerhart	.05	.02	115	Milt Thompson	.05	.02
59	Glenn Braggs	.05	.02	116	Bobby Bonilla	.20	.12
60	Julio Franco	.12	.07	117	Wayne Tolleson	.05	.02
61	Charlie Leibrandt	.05	.02	118	Matt Williams (R)	1.50	.90
62	Gary Gaetti	.05	.02	119	Chet Lemon	.05	.02
63	Bob Boone	.08	.05	120	Dale Sveum	.05	.02
64	Louis Polonia (R)	.12	.07	121	Dennis Boyd	.05	.02
65	Dwight Evans	.08	.05	122	Brett Butler	.08	.05
66	Phil Bradley	.05	.02	123	Terry Kennedy	.05	.02
67	Mike Boddicker	.05	.02	124	Jack Howell	.05	.02
68	Vince Coleman	.08	.05	125	Curt Young	.05	.02
69	Howard Johnson	.15	.08	126a	Dale Valle (Er)	.10	.06
70	Tim Wallach	.10	.06	126b	Dave Valle (Correct)	.05	.02
71	Keith Moreland	.05	.02	127	Curt Wilkerson	.05	.02
72	Barry Larkin	.20	.12	128	Tim Teufel	.05	.02
73	Alan Ashby	.05	.02	129	Ozzie Virgil	.05	.02
74	Rick Rhoden	.05	.02	130	Brian Fisher	.05	.02
75	Darrell Evans	.07	.04	131	Lance Parrish	.07	.04
76	Dave Stieb	.07	.04	132	Tom Browning	.07	.04
77	Dan Plesac	.05	.02	133a	Larry Anderson (Er)	.10	.06
78	Will Clark	.60	.35	133b	Larry Andersen (Cor)	.05	.02
79	Frank White	.05	.02	134a	Bob Brenley (Er)	.10	.06
80	Joe Carter	.30	.18	134b	Bob Brenly (Cor)	.05	.02
81	Mike Witt	.05	.02	135	Mike Marshall	.05	.02
82	Terry Steinbach	.05	.02	136	Gerald Perry	.05	.02
83	Alvin Davis	.05	.02	137	Bobby Meacham	.05	.02
84	Tom Herr	.05	.02	138	Larry Herndon	.05	.02
85	Vance Law	.05	.02	139	Fred Manrique (R)	.05	.02
86	Kal Daniels	.05	.02	140	Charlie Hough	.05	.02
87	Rick Honeycutt	.05	.02	141	Ron Darling	.07	.04
88	Alfredo Griffin	.05	.02	142	Herm Winningham	.05	.02
89	Bret Saberhagen	.12	.07	143	Mike Diaz	.05	.02
90	Bert Blyleven	.12	.07	144	Mike Jackson (R)	.12	.07
91	Jeff Reardon	.15	.10	145	Denny Walling	.05	.02
92	Cory Snyder	.05	.02	146	Rob Thompson	.05	.02
93	Greg Walker	.05	.02	147	Franklin Stubbs	.05	.02
94	Joe Magrane (R)	.10	.06	148	Albert Hall	.05	.02
95	Rob Deer	.05	.02	149	Bobby Witt	.10	.06
96	Ray Knight	.05	.02	150	Lance McCullers	.05	.02
97	Casey Candaele	.05	.02	151	Scott Bradley	.05	.02
98	John Cerutti	.05	.02	152	Mark McLemore	.05	.02
99	Buddy Bell	.05	.02	153	Tim Laudner	.05	.02
100	Jack Clark	.07	.04	154	Greg Swindell	.08	.05
101	Eric Bell	.05	.02	155	Marty Barrett	.05	.02
102	Willie Wilson	.05	.02	156	Mike Heath	.05	.02
103	Dave Schmidt	.05	.02	157	Gary Ward	.05	.02
104	Dennis Eckersley	.20	.12	158a	Lee Mazilli (Er)	.10	.06

158bLee Mazzilli (Cor)	.05	.02
159 Tom Foley	.05	.02
160 Robin Yount	.35	.20
161 Steve Bedrosian	.05	.02
162 Bob Walk	.05	.02
163 Nick Esasky	.05	.02
164 Ken Caminiti (R)	.25	.12
165 Jose Uribe	.05	.02
166 Dave Anderson	.05	.02
167 Ed Whitson	.05	.02
168 Ernie Whitt	.05	.02
169 Cecil Cooper	.05	.02
170 Mike Pagliarulo	.05	.02
171 Pat Sheridan	.05	.02
172 Chris Bando	.05	.02
173 Lee Lacy	.05	.02
174 Steve Lonbardozzi	.05	.02
175 Mike Greenwell	.10	.06
176 Greg Minton	.05	.02
177 Moose Haas	.05	.02
178 Mike Kingery	.05	.02
179 Greg Harris	.05	.02
180 Bo Jackson	.35	.20
181 Carmelo Martinez	.05	.02
182 Alex Trevino	.05	.02
183 Ron Oester	.05	.02
184 Danny Darwin	.05	.02
185 Mike Krukow	.05	.02
186 Rafael Palmeiro	.35	.20
187 Tim Burke	.05	.02
188 Roger McDowell	.05	.02
189 Garry Templeton	.05	.02
190 Terry Pendleton	.20	.12
191 Larry Parrish	.05	.02
192 Rey Quinones	.05	.02
193 Joaqin Andujar	.05	.02
194 Tom Brunansky	.07	.04
195 Donnie Moore	.05	.02
196 Dan Pasqua	.05	.02
197 Jim Gantner	.05	.02
198 Mark Eichhorn	.05	.02
199 John Grubb	.05	.02
200 Bill Ripken (R)	.10	.06
201 Sam Horn (R)	.15	.08
202 Todd Worrell	.05	.02
203 Terry Leach	.05	.02
204 Garth Iorg	.05	.02
205 Brian Dayett	.05	.02
206 Bo Diaz	.05	.02
207 Craig Reynolds	.05	.02
208 Brian Holton	.07	.04
209 Marvelle Wynne (Er)	.05	.02
210 Dave Concepcion	.10	.06
211 Mike Davis	.05	.02
212 Devon White	.12	.07
213 Mickey Brantley	.05	.02
214 Greg Gagne	.05	.02

215 Oddibe McDowell	.05	.02
216 Jimmy Key	.08	.05
217 Dave Bergman	.05	.02
218 Calvin Schiraldi	.05	.02
219 Larry Sheets	.05	.02
220 Mike Easler	.05	.02
221 Kurt Stillwell	.05	.02
222 Chuck Jackson	.05	.02
223 Dave Martinez	.05	.02
224 Tim Leary	.05	.02
225 Steve Garvey	.15	.08
226 Greg Mathews	.05	.02
227 Doug Sisk	.05	.02
228 Dave Henderson	.05	.02
229 Jimmy Dwyer	.05	.02
230 Larry Owen	.05	.02
231 Andre Thornton	.05	.02
232 Mark Salas	.05	.02
233 Tom Brookens	.05	.02
234 Greg Brock	.05	.02
235 Rance Mulliniks	.05	.02
236 Bob Brower	.05	.02
237 Joe Niekro	.05	.02
238 Scott Bankhead	.05	.02
239 Doug DeCinces	.05	.02
240 Tommy John	.07	.04
241 Rich Gedman	.05	.02
242 Ted Power	.05	.02
243 Dave Meads (R)	.05	.02
244 Jim Sundberg	.05	.02
245 Ken Oberkfell	.05	.02
246 Jimmy Jones	.05	.02
247 Ken Landreaux	.05	.02
248 Jose Oquendo	.05	.02
249 John Mitchell	.05	.02
250 Don Baylor	.07	.04
251 Scott Fletcher	.05	.02
252 Al Newman (R)	.05	.02
253 Carney Lansford	.07	.04
254 Johnny Ray	.05	.02
255 Gary Pettis	.05	.02
256 Ken Phelps	.05	.02
257 Rick Leach	.05	.02
258 Tim Stoddard	.05	.02
259 Ed Romero	.05	.02
260 Sid Bream	.05	.02
261aTom Neidenfuer (Er)	.10	.06
261bTom Niedenfuer (Cor)	.05	.02
262 Rick Dempsey	.05	.02
263 Lonnie Smith	.05	.02
264 Bob Forsch	.05	.02
265 Barry Bonds	.75	.45
266 Willie Randolph	.05	.02
267 Mike Ramsey	.05	.02
268 Don Slaught	.05	.02
269 Mickey Tettleton	.08	.05
270 Jerry Reuss	.05	.02

271	Marc Sullivan	.05	.02	327	Floyd Youmans	.05	.02
272	Jim Morrison	.05	.02	328	Bill Dawley	.05	.02
273	Steve Balboni	.05	.02	329	Paul Noce (R)	.05	.02
274	Dick Schofield	.05	.02	330	Angel Salazar	.05	.02
275	John Tudor	.05	.02	331	Goose Gossage	.07	.04
276	Gene Larkin (R)	.10	.06	332	George Frazier	.05	.02
277	Harold Reynolds	.07	.04	333	Ruppert Jones	.05	.02
278	Jerry Browne	.05	.02	334	Billy Jo Robidoux	.05	.02
279	Willie Upshaw	.05	.02	335	Mike Scott	.05	.02
280	Ted Higuera	.05	.02	336	Randy Myers	.05	.02
281	Terry McGriff	.05	.02	337	Bob Sebra	.05	.02
282	Terry Puhl	.05	.02	338	Eric Show	.05	.02
283	Mark Wasinger	.05	.02	339	Mitch Williams	.05	.02
284	Luis Salazar	.05	.02	340	Paul Molitor	.25	.15
285	Ted Simmons	.07	.04	341	Gus Polidor	.05	.02
286	John Shelby	.05	.02	342	Steve Trout	.05	.02
287	John Smiley (R)	.30	.18	343	Jerry Don Gleaton	.05	.02
288	Curt Ford	.05	.02	344	Bob Knepper	.05	.02
289	Steve Crawford	.05	.02	345	Mitch Webster	.05	.02
290	Dan Quisenberry	.05	.02	346	John Morris	.05	.02
291	Alan Wiggins	.05	.02	347	Andy Hawkins	.05	.02
292	Randy Bush	.05	.02	348	Dave Leiper	.05	.02
293	John Candelaria	.05	.02	349	Ernest Riles	.05	.02
294	Tony Phillips	.07	.04	350	Dwight Gooden	.12	.07
295	Mike Morgan	.05	.02	351	Dave Righetti	.05	.02
296	Bill Wegman	.05	.02	352	Pat Dodson	.05	.02
297a	Terry Franconia (Er)	.10	.06	353	John Habyan	.05	.02
297b	Terry Francona (Cor)	.05	.02	354	Jim Deshaies	.05	.02
298	Mickey Hatcher	.05	.02	355	Butch Wynegar	.05	.02
299	Andres Thomas	.05	.02	356	Bryn Smith	.05	.02
300	Bob Stanley	.05	.02	357	Matt Young	.05	.02
301	Al Pedrique (R)	.05	.02	358	Tom Pagnozzi (R)	.20	.12
302	Jim Lindeman	.05	.02	359	Floyd Rayford	.05	.02
303	Wally Backman	.05	.02	360	Darryl Strawberry	.25	.15
304	Paul O'Neill	.10	.06	361	Sal Butera	.05	.02
305	Hubie Brooks	.08	.05	362	Domingo Ramos	.05	.02
306	Steve Buechele	.07	.04	363	Chris Brown	.05	.02
307	Bobby Thigpen	.08	.05	364	Jose Gonzalez	.05	.02
308	George Hendrick	.05	.02	365	Dave Smith	.05	.02
309	John Moses	.05	.02	366	Andy McGaffigan	.05	.02
310	Ron Guidry	.10	.06	367	Stan Javier	.05	.02
311	Bill Schroeder	.05	.02	368	Henry Cotto	.05	.02
312	Jose Nunez (R)	.08	.05	369	Mike Birkbeck	.05	.02
313	Bud Black	.07	.04	370	Len Dykstra	.20	.12
314	Joe Sambito	.05	.02	371	Dave Collins	.05	.02
315	Scott McGregor	.05	.02	372	Spike Owen	.05	.02
316	Rafael Santana	.05	.02	373	Geno Petralli	.05	.02
317	Frank Williams	.05	.02	374	Ron Karkovice	.05	.02
318	Mike Fitzgerald	.05	.02	375	Shane Rawley	.05	.02
319	Rick Mahler	.05	.02	376	DeWayne Buice (R)	.05	.02
320	Jim Gott	.05	.02	377	Bill Pecota (R)	.08	.05
321	Mariano Duncan	.05	.02	378	Leon Durham	.05	.02
322	Jose Guzman	.05	.02	379	Ed Olwine	.05	.02
323	Lee Guetterman	.05	.02	380	Bruce Hurst	.07	.04
324	Dan Gladden	.05	.02	381	Bob McClure	.05	.02
325	Gary Carter	.10	.06	382	Mark Thurmond	.05	.02
326	Tracy Jones	.05	.02	383	Buddy Biancalana	.05	.02

384	Tim Conroy	.05	.02
385	Tony Gwynn	.30	.18
386	Greg Gross	.05	.02
387	Barry Lyons (R)	.05	.02
388	Mike Felder	.05	.02
389	Pat Clements	.05	.02
390	Ken Griffey	.08	.05
391	Mark Davis	.05	.02
392	Jose Rijo	.08	.05
393	Mike Young	.05	.02
394	Willie Fraser	.05	.02
395	Dion James	.05	.02
396	Steve Shields (R)	.05	.02
397	Randy St. Claire	.05	.02
398	Danny Jackson	.07	.04
399	Cecil Fielder	.35	.20
400	Keith Hernandez	.07	.04
401	Don Carman	.05	.02
402	Chuck Crim (R)	.07	.04
403	Rob Woodward	.05	.02
404	Junior Ortiz	.05	.02
405	Glenn Wilson	.05	.02
406	Ken Howell	.05	.02
407	Jeff Kunkel	.05	.02
408	Jeff Reed	.05	.02
409	Chris James	.05	.02
410	Zane Smith	.07	.04
411	Ken Dixon	.05	.02
412	Ricky Horton	.05	.02
413	Frank DiPino	.05	.02
414	Shane Mack (R)	.25	.15
415	Danny Cox	.05	.02
416	Andy Van Slyke	.15	.08
417	Danny Heep	.05	.02
418	John Cangelosi	.05	.02
419a	John Christiansen (Er)	.10	.06
419b	John Christensen (Cor)	.05	.02
420	Joey Cora	.05	.02
421	Mike LaValliere	.05	.02
422	Kelly Gruber	.08	.05
423	Bruce Benedict	.05	.02
424	Len Matuszek	.05	.02
425	Kent Tekulve	.05	.02
426	Rafael Ramirez	.05	.02
427	Mike Flanagan	.05	.02
428	Mike Gallego	.05	.02
429	Juan Castillo	.05	.02
430	Neal Heaton	.05	.02
431	Phil Garner	.05	.02
432	Mike Dunne (R)	.05	.02
433	Wallace Johnson	.05	.02
434	Jack O'Connor	.05	.02
435	Steve Jeltz	.05	.02
436	Donnell Nixon (R)	.07	.04
437	Jack Lazorko	.05	.02
438	Keith Comstock (R)	.05	.02
439	Jeff Robinson	.05	.02
440	Graig Nettles	.07	.04
441	Mel Hall	.07	.04
442	Gerald Young (R)	.08	.05
443	Gary Redux	.05	.02
444	Charlie Moore	.05	.02
445	Bill Madlock	.07	.04
446	Mark Clear	.05	.02
447	Greg Booker	.05	.02
448	Rick Schu	.05	.02
449	Ron Kittle	.05	.02
450	Dale Murphy	.15	.08
451	Bob Dernier	.05	.02
452	Dale Mohorcic	.05	.02
453	Rafael Belliard	.05	.02
454	Charlie Puleo	.05	.02
455	Dwayne Murphy	.05	.02
456	Jim Eisenreich	.05	.02
457	David Palmer	.05	.02
458	Dave Stewart	.15	.10
459	Pascual Perez	.05	.02
460	Glenn Davis	.05	.02
461	Dan Petry	.05	.02
462	Jim Winn	.05	.02
463	Darrell Miller	.05	.02
464	Mike Moore	.05	.02
465	Mike LaCoss	.05	.02
466	Steve Farr	.05	.02
467	Jerry Mumphrey	.05	.02
468	Kevin Gross	.05	.02
469	Bruce Bochy	.05	.02
470	Orel Hershiser	.10	.06
471	Eric King	.05	.02
472	Ellis Burks (R)	.35	.20
473	Darren Daulton	.20	.12
474	Mookie Wilson	.05	.02
475	Frank Viola	.07	.04
476	Ron Robinson	.05	.02
477	Bob Melvin	.05	.02
478	Jeff Musselman	.05	.02
479	Charlie Kerfeld	.05	.02
480	Richard Dotson	.05	.02
481	Kevin Mitchell	.15	.10
482	Gary Roenicke	.05	.02
483	Tim Flannery	.05	.02
484	Rich Yett	.05	.02
485	Pete Incaviglia	.07	.04
486	Rick Cerone	.05	.02
487	Tony Armas	.05	.02
488	Jerry Reed	.05	.02
489	Davey Lopes	.07	.04
490	Frank Tanana	.07	.04
491	Mike Loynd	.05	.02
492	Bruce Ruffin	.05	.02
493	Chris Speier	.05	.02
490	Tom Hume	.05	.02
495	Jesse Orosco	.05	.02
496	Robby Wine, Jr. (R)	.05	.02

497	Jeff Mongomery (R)	.50	.30
498	Jeff Dedmon	.05	.02
499	Luis Aguayo	.05	.02
500	Reggie Jackson (A'S)	.25	.15
501	Reggie Jackson (O's)	.25	.15
502	Reggie Jackson (Yanks)	.25	.15
503	Reggie Jackson (Angels)	.25	.15
504	Reggie Jackson (A's)	.25	.15
505	Billy Hatcher	.05	.02
506	Ed Lynch	.05	.02
507	Willie Hernandez	.05	.02
508	Jose DeLeon	.05	.02
509	Joel Youngblood	.05	.02
510	Bob Welch	.07	.04
511	Steve Ontiveros	.05	.02
512	Randy Ready	.05	.02
513	Juan Nieves	.05	.02
514	Jeff Russell	.05	.02
515	Von Hayes	.05	.02
516	Mark Gubicza	.07	.04
517	Ken Dayley	.05	.02
518	Don Aase	.05	.02
519	Rick Reuschel	.05	.02
520	Mike Henneman (R)	.15	.10
512	Rick Aguilera	.05	.02
522	Jay Howell	.05	.02
523	Ed Correa	.05	.02
524	Manny Trillo	.05	.02
525	Kirk Gibson	.07	.04
526	Wally Ritchie (R)	.07	.04
527	Al Nipper	.05	.02
528	Atlee Hammaker	.05	.02
529	Shawon Dunston	.08	.05
530	Jim Clancy	.05	.02
531	Tom Paciorek	.05	.02
532	Joel Skinner	.05	.02
533	Scott Garrelts	.05	.02
534	Tom O'Malley	.05	.02
535	John Franco	.05	.02
536	Paul Kilgus (R)	.07	.04
537	Darrell Porter	.05	.02
538	Walt Terrell	.05	.02
539	Bill Long (R)	.05	.02
540	George Bell	.10	.06
541	Jeff Sellers	.05	.02
542	Joe Boever (R)	.05	.02
543	Steve Howe	.05	.02
544	Scott Sanderson	.05	.02
545	Jack Morris	.12	.07
546	Todd Benzinger (R)	.12	.07
547	Steve Henderson	.05	.02
548	Eddie Milner	.05	.02
549	Jeff Robinson (R)	.08	.05
550	Cal Ripkin, Jr.	.75	.45
551	Jody Davis	.05	.02
552	Kirk McCaskill	.05	.02
553	Craig Lefferts	.05	.02
554	Darnell Coles	.05	.02
555	Phil Niekro	.20	.12
556	Mike Aldrete	.05	.02
557	Pat Perry	.05	.02
558	Juan Agosto	.05	.02
559	Rob Murphy	.05	.02
560	Dennis Rasmussen	.05	.02
561	Manny Lee	.05	.02
562	Jeff Blauser (R)	.40	.25
563	Bob Ojeda	.05	.02
564	Dave Dravecky	.05	.02
565	Gene Garber	.05	.02
566	Ron Roenicke	.05	.02
567	Tommy Hinzo (R)	.08	.05
568	Eric Nolte (R)	.05	.02
569	Ed Hearn	.05	.02
570	Mark Davidson (R)	.07	.04
571	Jim Walewander (R)	.07	.04
572	Donnie Hill	.05	.02
573	Jamie Moyer	.05	.02
574	Ken Schrom	.05	.02
575	Nolan Ryan	.80	.50
576	Jim Acker	.05	.02
577	Jamie Quirk	.05	.02
578	Jay Aldrich (R)	.05	.02
579	Claudell Washington	.05	.02
580	Jeff Leonard	.05	.02
581	Carmen Castillo	.05	.02
582	Daryl Boston	.05	.02
583	Jeff DeWillis (R)	.07	.04
584	John Marzano (R)	.07	.04
585	Bill Gullickson	.05	.02
586	Andy Allanson	.05	.02
587	Lee Tunnell	.05	.02
588	Gene Nelson	.05	.02
589	Dave LaPoint	.05	.02
590	Harold Baines	.08	.05
591	Bill Buckner	.07	.04
592	Carlton Fisk	.20	.12
593	Rick Manning	.05	.02
594	Doug Jones (R)	.20	.12
595	Tom Candiotti	.07	.04
596	Steve Lake	.05	.02
597	Jose Lind (R)	.20	.12
598	Ross Jones (R)	.05	.02
599	Gary Matthews	.05	.02
600	Fernando Valezuela	.07	.04
601	Dennis Martinez	.10	.06
602	Les Lancaster (R)	.08	.05
603	Ozzie Guillen	.08	.05
604	Tony Bernazard	.05	.02
605	Chili Davis	.07	.04
606	Roy Smalley	.05	.02
607	Ivan Calderon	.07	.04
608	Jay Tibbs	.05	.02
609	Guy Hoffman	.05	.02
610	Doyle Alexander	.05	.02

611	Mike Bielecki	.05	.02
612	Shawn Hillegas (R)	.12	.07
613	Keith Atherton	.05	.02
614	Eric Plunk	.05	.02
615	Sid Fernandez	.07	.04
616	Dennis Lamp	.05	.02
617	Dave Engle	.05	.02
618	Harry Spillman	.05	.02
619	Don Robinson	.05	.02
620	John Farrell (R)	.07	.04
621	Nelson Liriano (R)	.10	.06
622	Floyd Bannister	.05	.02
623	Randy Milligan (R)	.25	.15
624	Kevin Elster (R)	.08	.05
625	Jody Reed (R)	.15	.08
626	Shawn Abner (R)	.07	.04
627	Kirt Manwaring (R)	.10	.06
628	Pete Stanicek (R)	.07	.04
629	Rob Ducey (R)	.07	.04
630	Steve Kiefer (R)	.07	.04
631	Gary Thurman (R)	.08	.05
632	Darrel Akerfelds (R)	.07	.04
633	Dave Clark (R)	.07	.04
634	Roberto Kelly (R)	.60	.35
635	Keith Hughes (R)	.05	.02
636	John Davis (R)	.05	.02
637	Mike Devereaux (R)	.60	.35
638	Tom Glavine (R)	2.50	1.50
639	Keith Miller (R)	.15	.08
640	Chris Gwynn (R)	.08	.05
641	Tim Crews (R)	.08	.05
642	Mackey Sasser (R)	.08	.05
643	Vicente Palacios (R)	.08	.05
644	Kevin Romine (R)	.07	.05
645	Gregg Jefferies (R)	1.75	1.00
646	Jeff Treadway (R)	.10	.06
647	Ron Gant (R)	2.00	1.25
648	M. McGwire, M. Nokes	.20	.12
649	Eric Davis, Tim Raines	.10	.06
650	J. Clark, D. Mattingly	.12	.07
651	T.Femandez, C.Ripken, A.Trammell)	.20	.12
652	Vince Coleman (HL)	.08	.05
653	Kirby Puckett (HL)	.25	.15
654	Benito Santiago (HL)	.07	.04
655	Juan Nieves (HL)	.07	.04
656	Steve Bedrosian (HL)	.07	.04
657	Mike Schmidt (HL)	.25	.15
658	Don Mattingly (HL)	.15	.08
659	Mark McGwire (HL)	.25	.15
660	Paul Molitor (HL)	.10	.06

1988 Score Traded

Score's first update set consists of 110-cards featuring rookie and traded players. The orange borders on the card fronts distinguish it from Score's regular edition. Card numbers contain the letter "T". The set was underproduced and is considered scarce. All cards measure 2-1/2" by 3-1/2".

	MINT	NR/MT
Complete Set (110)	95.00	62.50
Commons	.15	.08

1T	Jack Clark	.20	.12
2T	Danny Jackson	.15	.08
3T	Brett Butler	.30	.18
4T	Kurt Stillwell	.15	.08
5T	Tom Brunansky	.20	.12
6T	Dennis Lamp	.15	.08
7T	Jose DeLeon	.15	.08
8T	Tom Herr	.15	.08
9T	Keith Moreland	.15	.08
10T	Kirk Gibson	.20	.12
11T	Bud Black	.15	.08
12T	Rafael Ramirez	.15	.08
13T	Luis Salazar	.15	.08
14T	Goose Gossage	.20	.12
15T	Bob Welch	.20	.12
16T	Vance Law	.15	.08
17T	Ray Knight	.20	.12
18T	Dan Quisenberry	.15	.08
19T	Don Slaught	.15	.08
20T	Lee Smith	.80	.50
21T	Rick Cerone	.15	.08
22T	Pat Tabler	.15	.08
23T	Larry McWilliams	.15	.08
24T	Rick Horton	.15	.08
25T	Graig Nettles	.20	.12
26T	Dan Petry	.15	.08
27T	Jose Rijo	.60	.35
28T	Chili Davis	.20	.12

29T	Dickie Thon	.15	.08
30T	Mackey Sasser	.20	.12
31T	Mickey Tettleton	.60	.35
32T	Rick Dempsey	.15	.08
33T	Ron Hassey	.15	.08
34T	Phil Bradley	.15	.08
35T	Jay Howell	.15	.08
36T	Bill Buckner	.20	.12
37T	Alfredo Griffin	.15	.08
38T	Gary Pettis	.15	.08
39T	Calvin Schiraldi	.15	.08
40T	John Candelaria	.15	.08
41T	Joe Orsulak	.20	.12
42T	Willie Upshaw	.15	.08
43T	Herm Winningham	.15	.08
44T	Ron Kittle	.15	.08
45T	Bob Dernier	.15	.08
46T	Steve Balboni	.15	.08
47T	Steve Shields	.15	.08
48T	Henry Cotto	.15	.08
49T	Dave Henderson	.20	.12
50T	Dave Parker	.25	.15
51T	Mike Young	.15	.08
52T	Mark Salas	.15	.08
53T	Mike Davis	.15	.08
54T	Rafael Santana	.15	.08
55T	Don Baylor	.20	.12
56T	Dan Pasqua	.15	.08
57T	Ernest Riles	.15	.08
58T	Glenn Hubbard	.15	.08
59T	Mike Smithson	.15	.08
60T	Richard Dotson	.15	.08
61T	Jerry Reuss	.15	.08
62T	Mike Jackson	.15	.08
63T	Floyd Bannister	.15	.08
64T	Jesse Orosco	.15	.08
65T	Larry Parrish	.15	.08
66T	Jeff Bittiger	.15	.08
67T	Ray Hayward	.15	.08
68T	Ricky Jordan (R)	.35	.20
69T	Tommy Gregg (R)	.20	.12
70T	Brady Anderson (R)	3.50	2.00
71T	Jeff Montgomery	2.50	1.50
72T	Darryl Hamilton (R)	3.00	1.75
73T	Cecil Espy (R)	.20	.12
74T	Greg Briley (R)	.30	.18
75T	Joey Meyer (R)	.20	.12
76T	Mike Macfarlane (R)	1.75	1.00
77T	Oswald Peraza (R)	.20	.12
78T	Jack Armstrong (R)	.50	.30
79T	Don Heinkel (R)	.15	.08
80T	Mark Grace (R)	20.00	12.50
81T	Steve Curry (R)	.20	.12
82T	Damon Berryhill (R)	.30	.18
83T	Steve Ellsworth (R)	.15	.08
84T	Pete Smith (R)	1.00	.70
85T	Jack McDowell (R)	24.00	14.00

86T	Rob Dibble (R)	1.25	.80
87T	Brian Harvey (R)	5.00	3.00
88T	John Dopson (R)	.20	.12
89T	Dave Gallagher (R)	.20	.12
90T	Todd Stottlemyre (R)	2.00	1.25
91T	Mike Schooler (R)	.35	.20
92T	Don Gordon (R)	.15	.08
93T	Sil Campusano (R)	.25	.15
94T	Jeff Pico (R)	.15	.08
95T	Jay Buhner (R)	3.50	2.00
96T	Nelson Santovenia (R)	.20	.12
97T	Al Leiter (R)	.20	.12
98T	Luis Alicea (R)	.25	.15
99T	Pat Borders (R)	1.50	.90
100T	Chris Sabo (R)	3.50	2.00
101T	Tim Becher (R)	.40	.25
102T	Walt Weiss (R)	.50	.30
103T	Craig Biggio (R)	5.00	3.00
104T	Don August (R)	.15	.08
105T	Roberto Alomar (R)	65.00	40.00
106T	Todd Burns (R)	.40	.25
107T	John Costello (R)	.20	.12
108T	Melido Perez (R)	2.00	1.25
109T	Darrin Jackson (R)	1.25	.80
110T	Orestes Destrade (R)	2.00	1.25

1989 Score

Score's second set consists of 660-cards with six different border colors on the card fronts framed in white. Card backs contain full-color head shots of the players. The cards measure 2-1/2" by 3-1/2".

		MINT	NR/MT
Complete Set (660)		18.00	12.00
Commons		.05	.02
1	Jose Canseco	.35	.20
2	Andre Dawson	.15	.08

3	Mark McGwire	.30	.18
4	Benny Santiago	.07	.04
5	Rick Reuschel	.05	.02
6	Fred McGriff	.25	.15
7	Kal Daniels	.05	.02
8	Gary Gaetti	.05	.02
9	Ellis Burks	.08	.05
10	Darryl Strawberry	.25	.15
11	Julio Franco	.12	.07
12	Lloyd Moseby	.05	.02
13	Jeff Pico	.12	.07
14	Johnny Ray	.05	.02
15	Cal Ripken, Jr.	.50	.30
16	Dick Schofield	.05	.02
17	Mel Hall	.07	.04
18	Bill Ripken	.05	.02
19	Brook Jacoby	.05	.02
20	Kirby Puckett	.35	.20
21	Bill Doran	.05	.02
22	Pete O'Brien	.05	.02
23	Matt Nokes	.05	.02
24	Brian Fisher	.05	.02
25	Jack Clark	.07	.04
26	Gary Pettis	.05	.02
27	Dave Valle	.05	.02
28	Willie Wilson	.05	.02
29	Curt Young	.05	.02
30	Dale Murphy	.10	.06
31	Barry Larkin	.15	.08
32	Dave Stewart	.10	.06
33	Mike LaValliere	.05	.02
34	Glen Hubbard	.05	.02
35	Ryne Sandberg	.40	.25
36	Tony Pena	.05	.02
37	Greg Walker	.05	.02
38	Von Hayes	.05	.02
39	Kevin Mitchell	.10	.06
40	Tim Raines	.08	.05
41	Keith Hernandez	.05	.02
42	Keith Moreland	.05	.02
43	Ruben Sierra	.30	.18
44	Chet Lemon	.05	.02
45	Willie Randolph	.05	.02
46	Andy Allanson	.05	.02
47	Candy Maldonado	.05	.02
48	Sid Bream	.05	.02
49	Denny Walling	.05	.02
50	Dave Winfield	.25	.15
51	Alvin Davis	.05	.02
52	Cory Snyder	.05	.02
53	Hubie Brooks	.05	.02
54	Chili Davis	.05	.02
55	Kevin Seitzer	.07	.04
56	Jose Uribe	.05	.02
57	Tony Fernandez	.05	.02
58	Tim Teufel	.05	.02
59	Oddibe McDowell	.05	.02
60	Les Lancaster	.05	.02
61	Billy Hatcher	.05	.02
62	Dan Gladden	.05	.02
63	Marty Barrett	.05	.02
64	Nick Esasky	.05	.02
65	Wally Joyner	.10	.06
66	Mike Greenwell	.08	.05
67	Ken Williams	.05	.02
68	Bob Horner	.07	.04
69	Steve Sax	.08	.05
70	Rickey Henderson	.25	.12
71	Mitch Webster	.05	.02
72	Rob Deer	.05	.02
73	Jim Presley	.05	.02
74	Albert Hall	.05	.02
75a	George Brett (Er)	.80	.50
75b	George Brett (Cor)	.30	.18
76	Brian Downing	.05	.02
77	Dave Martinez	.05	.02
78	Scott Fletcher	.05	.02
79	Phil Bradley	.05	.02
80	Ozzie Smith	.15	.10
81	Larry Sheets	.05	.02
82	Mike Aldrete	.05	.02
83	Darnell Coles	.05	.02
84	Len Dykstra	.15	.10
85	Jim Rice	.07	.04
86	Jeff Treadway	.05	.02
87	Jose Lind	.05	.02
88	Willie McGee	.07	.04
89	Mickey Brantley	.05	.02
90	Tony Gwynn	.25	.15
91	R.J. Reynolds	.05	.02
92	Milt Thompson	.05	.02
93	Kevin McReynolds	.07	.04
94	Eddie Murray	.15	.08
95	Lance Parrish	.05	.02
96	Ron Kittle	.05	.02
97	Gerald Young	.05	.02
98	Ernie Whitt	.05	.02
99	Jeff Reed	.05	.02
100	Don Mattingly	.25	.15
101	Gerald Perry	.50	.02
102	Vance Law	.05	.02
103	John Shelby	.05	.02
104	Chris Sabo	.25	.15
105	Danny Tartabull	.15	.08
106	Glenn Wilson	.05	.02
107	Mark Davidson	.05	.02
108	Dave Parker	.07	.04
109	Eric Davis	.12	.07
110	Alan Trammell	.10	.06
111	Ozzie Virgil	.05	.02
112	Frank Tanana	.05	.02
113	Rafael Ramirez	.05	.02
114	Dennis Martinez	.08	.05
115	Jose DeLeon	.05	.02

116	Bob Ojeda	.05	.02	172	Robby Thompson	.08	.05
117	Doug Drabek	.10	.06	173	Jody Davis	.05	.02
118	Andy Hawkins	.05	.02	174	Andy Van Slyke	.12	.07
119	Greg Maddux (R)	.40	.25	175	Wade Boggs (Er)	.25	.15
120	Cecil Fielder (Er)	.30	.18	176	Garry Templeton	.05	.02
121	Mike Scioscia	.05	.02	177	Gary Redus	.05	.02
122	Dan Petry	.05	.02	178	Craig Lefferts	.05	.02
123	Terry Kennedy	.05	.02	179	Carney Lansford	.05	.02
124	Kelly Downs	.05	.02	180	Ron Darling	.05	.02
125	Greg Gross (Er)	.05	.02	181	Kirk McCaskill	.05	.02
126	Fred Lynn	.07	.04	182	Tony Armas	.05	.02
127	Barry Bonds	.60	.35	183	Steve Farr	.05	.02
128	Harold Baines	.07	.04	184	Tom Brunansky	.05	.02
129	Doyle Alexander	.05	.02	185	Bryan Harvey	.35	.20
130	Kevin Elster	.05	.02	186	Mike Marshall	.05	.02
131	Mike Heath	.05	.02	187	Bo Diaz	.05	.02
132	Teddy Higuera	.05	.02	188	Willie Upshaw	.05	.02
133	Charlie Leibrandt	.05	.02	189	Mike Pagliarulo	.05	.02
134	Tim Laudner	.05	.02	190	Mike Krukow	.05	.02
135a	Ray Knight (Er)	.35	.20	191	Tommy Herr	.05	.02
135b	Ray Knight (Cor)	.08	.05	192	Jim Pankovits	.05	.02
136	Howard Johnson	.10	.06	193	Dwight Evans	.05	.02
137	Terry Pendleton	.15	.08	194	Kelly Gruber	.07	.04
138	Andy McGaffigan	.05	.02	195	Bobby Bonilla	.15	.07
139	Ken Oberkfell	.05	.02	196	Wallace Johnson	.05	.02
140	Butch Wynegar	.05	.02	197	Dave Sieb	.05	.02
141	Rob Murphy	.05	.02	198	Pat Borders	.15	.10
142	Rich Renteria (R)	.07	.04	199	Rafael Palmeiro	.15	.07
143	Jose Guzman	.05	.02	200	Doc Gooden	.12	.07
144	Andres Galarraga	.15	.10	201	Pete Incaviglia	.05	.02
145	Rick Horton	.05	.02	202	Chris James	.05	.02
146	Frank DiPino	.05	.02	203	Marvell Wynne	.05	.02
147	Glenn Braggs	.05	.02	204	Pat Sheridan	.05	.02
148	John Kruk	.12	.07	205	Don Baylor	.05	.02
149	Mike Schmidt	.40	.25	206	Paul O'Neill	.08	.05
150	Lee Smith	.12	.07	207	Pete Smith	.10	.06
151	Robin Yount	.30	.18	208	Mark McLemore	.05	.02
152	Mark Eichhorn	.05	.02	209	Henry Cotto	.05	.02
153	DeWayne Buice	.05	.02	210	Kirk Gibson	.07	.04
154	B.J. Surhoff	.05	.02	211	Claudell Washington	.05	.02
155	Vince Coleman	.07	.04	212	Randy Bush	.05	.02
156	Tony Phillips	.07	.04	213	Joe Carter	.20	.12
157	Willie Fraser	.05	.02	214	Bill Buckner	.05	.02
158	Lance McCullers	.05	.02	215	Bert Blyleven	.08	.05
159	Greg Gagne	.05	.02	216	Brett Butler	.07	.04
160	Jesse Barfield	.05	.02	217	Lee Mazzilli	.05	.02
161	Mark Langston	.08	.05	218	Spike Owen	.05	.02
162	Kurt Sttillwell	.05	.02	219	Bill Swift	.10	.06
163	Dion James	.05	.02	220	Tim Wallach	.07	.04
164	Glenn Davis	.05	.02	221	David Cone	.12	.07
165	Walt Weiss	.07	.04	222	Don Carman	.05	.02
166	Dave Concepcion	.07	.04	223	Rich Gossage	.07	.04
167	Alfredo Griffin	.05	.02	224	Bob Walk	.05	.02
168	Don Heinkel	.05	.02	225	Dave Righetti	.05	.02
169	Luis Rivera (R)	.05	.02	226	Kevin Bass	.05	.02
170	Shane Rawley	.05	.02	227	Kevin Gross	.05	.02
171	Darrell Evans	.05	.02	228	Tim Burke	.05	.02

No.	Player	Price	Price
229	Rick Mahler	.05	.02
230	Lou Whitaker	.07	.04
231	Luis Alicea	.07	.04
232	Roberto Alomar	1.00	.70
233	Bob Boone	.07	.04
234	Dickie Thon	.05	.02
235	Shawon Dunston	.07	.04
236	Pete Stanicek	.05	.02
237	Craig Biggio	.30	.18
238	Dennis Boyd	.05	.02
239	Tom Candiotti	.05	.02
240	Gary Carter	.10	.06
241	Mike Stanley	.05	.02
242	Ken Phelps	.05	.02
243	Chris Bosio	.07	.04
244	Les Straker	.05	.02
245	Dave Smith	.05	.02
246	John Candelaria	.05	.02
247	Joe Orsulak	.05	.02
248	Storm Davis	.05	.02
249	Floyd Bannister	.05	.02
250	Jack Morris	.12	.07
251	Bret Saberhagen	.10	.06
252	Tom Niedenfuer	.05	.02
253	Neal Heaton	.05	.02
254	Eric Show	.05	.02
255	Juan Samuel	.05	.02
256	Dale Sveum	.05	.02
257	Jim Gott	.05	.02
258	Scott Garrelts	.05	.02
259	Larry McWilliams	.05	.02
260	Steve Bedrosian	.05	.02
261	Jack Howell	.05	.02
262	Jay Tibbs	.05	.02
263	Jamie Moyer	.05	.02
264	Doug Sisk	.05	.02
265	Todd Worrell	.07	.04
266	John Farrell	.05	.02
267	Dave Collins	.05	.02
268	Sid Fernandez	.05	.02
276	Dennis Eckersley	.12	.07
277	Graig Nettles	.05	.02
278	Rich Dotson	.05	.02
279	Larry Herndon	.05	.02
280	Gene Larkin	.05	.02
281	Roger McDowell	.05	.02
282	Greg Swindell	.07	.04
283	Juan Agosto	.05	.02
284	Jeff Robinson	.05	.02
285	Mike Dunne	.05	.02
286	Greg Mathews	.05	.02
287	Kent Tekulve	.05	.02
288	Jerry Mumphrey	.05	.02
289	Jack McDowell	.60	.35
290	Frank Viola	.08	.05
291	Mark Gubicza	.07	.04
292	Dave Schmidt	.05	.02
293	Mike Henneman	.05	.02
294	Jimmy Jones	.05	.02
295	Charlie Hough	.05	.02
296	Rafael Santana	.05	.02
297	Chris Speier	.05	.02
298	Mike Witt	.05	.02
299	Pascual Perez	.05	.02
300	Nolan Ryan	.75	.45
301	Mitch Williams	.05	.02
302	Mookie Wilson	.05	.02
303	Mackey Sasser	.05	.02
304	John Cerutti	.05	.02
305	Jeff Reardon	.10	.06
306	Randy Myers	.05	.02
308	Bob Welch	.07	.04
309	Jeff Robinson	.05	.02
310	Harold Reynolds	.05	.02
311	Jim Walewander	.05	.02
312	Dave Magadan	.05	.02
313	Jim Gantner	.05	.02
314	Walt Terrell	.05	.02
315	Wally Backman	.05	.02
316	Luis Salazar	.05	.02
317	Rick Rhoden	.05	.02
318	Tom Henke	.05	.02
319	Mike Macfarlane	.15	.08
320	Dan Plesac	.05	.02
321	Calvin Schiraldi	.05	.02
322	Stan Javier	.05	.02
323	Devon White	.08	.05
324	Scott Bradley	.05	.02
325	Bruce Hurst	.07	.04
326	Manny Lee	.05	.02
327	Rick Aguilera	.05	.02
328	Bruce Ruffin	.05	.02
329	Ed Whitson	.05	.02
330	Bo Jackson	.30	.18
331	Ivan Calderon	.05	.02
332	Mickey Hatcher	.05	.02
333	Barry Jones	.05	.02
334	Ron Hassey	.05	.02
335	Bill Wegman	.05	.02
336	Damon Berryhill	.05	.02
337	Steve Ontiveros	.05	.02
338	Dan Pasqua	.05	.02
339	Bill Pecota	.05	.02
340	Greg Cadaret	.05	.02
341	Scott Bankhead	.05	.02
342	Ron Guidry	.08	.05
343	Danny Heep	.05	.02
344	Bob Brower	.05	.02
345	Rich Gedman	.05	.02
346	Nelson Santovenia	.07	.04
347	George Bell	.10	.06
348	Ted Power	.05	.02
349	Mark Grant	.05	.02
350a	Roger Clemens (Er)	3.50	2.00

350b	Roger Clemens (Cor)	.50	.30
351	Bill Long	.05	.02
352	Jay Bell (R)	.25	.15
353	Steve Balboni	.05	.02
354	Bob Kipper	.05	.02
355	Steve Jeltz	.05	.02
356	Jesse Orosco	.05	.02
357	Bob Dernier	.05	.02
358	Mickey Tettleton	.08	.05
359	Duane Ward (R)	.10	.06
360	Darrin Jackson	.08	.05
361	Rey Quinones	.05	.02
362	Mark Grace	.50	.30
363	Steve Lake	.05	.05
364	Pat Perry	.05	.02
365	Terry Steinbach	.05	.02
366	Alan Ashby	.05	.02
367	Jeff Montgomery	.15	.10
368	Steve Buechele	.05	.02
369	Chris Brown	.05	.02
370	Orel Hershier	.08	.05
371	Todd Benzinger	.05	.02
372	Ron Gant	.50	.30
373	Paul Assenmacher (R)	.10	.06
374	Joey Meyer	.05	.02
375	Neil Allen	.05	.02
376	Mike Davis	.05	.02
377	Jeff Parrett (R)	.07	.04
378	Jay Howell	.05	.02
379	Rafael Belliard	.05	.02
380	Luis Polonia	.08	.05
381	Keith Atherton	.05	.02
382	Kent Hrbek	.07	.04
383	Bob Stanley	.05	.02
384	Dave LaPoint	.05	.02
385	Rance Mulliniks	.05	.02
386	Melido Perez	.10	.06
387	Doug Jones	.05	.02
388	Steve Lyons	.05	.02
389	Alejandro Pena	.05	.02
390	Frank White	.05	.02
391	Pat Tabier	.05	.02
392	Eric Plunk (R)	.08	.05
393	Mike Maddux (R)	.05	.02
394	Allan Anderson (R)	.07	.04
395	Bob Brenly	.05	.02
396	Rick Cerone	.05	.02
397	Scott Terry (R)	.07	.04
398	Mike Jackson	.05	.02
399	Bobby Thigpen	.05	.02
400	Don Sutton	.10	.06
401	Cecil Espey	.05	.02
402	Junio Ortiz	.05	.02
403	Mike Smithson	.05	.02
404	Bud Black	.05	.02
405	Tom Foley	.05	.02
406	Andres Thomas	.05	.02
407	Rick Sutcliffe	.05	.02
408	Brian Harper	.07	.04
409	John Smiley	.10	.06
410	Juan Nieves	.05	.02
411	Shawn Abner	.05	.02
412	Wes Gardner (R)	.08	.05
413	Darren Daulton	.15	.10
414	Juan Berenguer	.05	.02
415	Charles Hudson	.05	.02
416	Rick Honeycutt	.05	.02
417	Greg Booker	.05	.02
418	Tim Belcher	.07	.04
419	Don August	.05	.02
420	Dale Mohorcic	.05	.02
421	Steve Lombardozzi	.05	.02
422	Atlee Hammaker	.05	.02
423	Jerry Don Gleaton	.05	.02
424	Scott Bailes (R)	.10	.06
425	Bruce Sutter	.08	.05
426	Randy Ready	.05	.02
427	Gerry Reed	.05	.02
428	Bryn Smith	.05	.02
429	Tim Leary	.05	.02
430	Mark Clear	.05	.02
431	Terry Leach	.05	.02
432	John Moses	.05	.02
433	Ozzie Guillen	.07	.04
434	Gene Nelson	.05	.02
435	Gary Ward	.05	.02
436	Luis Aguayo	.05	.02
437	Fernando Valenzuela	.07	.04
438	Jeff Russell	.05	.02
439	Cecilio Guante	.05	.02
440	Don Robinson	.05	.02
441	Rick Anderson (R)	.07	.04
442	Tom Glavine	1.00	.70
443	Daryl Boston	.05	.02
444	Joe Price	.05	.02
445	Stewart Cliburn	.05	.02
446	Manny Trillo	.05	.02
447	Joel Skinner	.05	.02
448	Charlie Puleo	.05	.02
449	Carlton Fisk	.15	.08
450	Will Clark	.50	.30
451	Otis Nixon	.07	.04
452	Rick Schu	.05	.02
453	Todd Stottlemyre	.12	.07
454	Tim Birtsas	.05	.02
455	Dave Gallagher	.07	.04
456	Barry Lyons	.05	.02
457	Fred Manrique	.05	.02
458	Ernest Riles	.05	.02
459	Doug Jennings (R)	.08	.05
460	Joe Magrane	.07	.04
461	Jamie Quirk	.05	.02
462	Jack Armstrong	.10	.06
463	Bobby Witt	.07	.04

464 Keith Miller	.05	.02
465 Todd Burns	.05	.02
466 John Dopson (R)	.12	.07
467 Rich Yett	.05	.02
468 Craig Reynolds	.05	.02
469 Dave Bergman	.05	.02
470 Rex Hudler	.07	.04
471 Eric King	.05	.02
472 Joaquin Andujar	.05	.02
473 Sil Campusano	.08	.05
474 Terry Mulholland (R)	.15	.10
475 Mike Flanagan	.05	.02
476 Greg Harris	.05	.02
477 Tommy John	.07	.04
478 Dave Anderson	.05	.02
479 Fred Toliver	.05	.02
480 Jimmy Key	.08	.05
481 Donell Nixon	.05	.02
482 Mark Portugal (R)	.12	.07
483 Tom Pagnozzi	.08	.05
484 Jeff Kunkel	.05	.02
485 Frank Williams	.05	.02
486 Jody Reed	.07	.04
487 Roberto Kelly	.25	.15
488 Shawn Hillegas	.05	.02
489 Jerry Reuss	.05	.02
490 Mark Davis	.05	.02
491 Jeff Sellers	.05	.02
492 Zane Smith	.05	.02
493 Al Newman	.05	.02
494 Mike Young	.05	.02
495 Larry Parrish	.05	.02
496 Herm Winningham	.05	.02
497 Carmen Castillo	.05	.02
498 Joe Hesketh	.05	.02
499 Darrell Miller	.05	.02
500 Mike LaCoss	.05	.02
501 Charlie Lea	.05	.02
502 Bruce Benedict	.05	.02
503 Chuck Finley (R)	.25	.15
504 Brad Wellman (R)	.07	.04
505 Tim Crews	.05	.02
506 Ken Gerhart	.05	.02
507 Brian Holton (Er)	.07	.04
508 Dennis Lamp	.05	.02
509 Bobby Meacham (Er)	.07	.04
510 Tracy Jones	.05	.02
511 Mike Fitzgerald	.05	.02
512 Jeff Bittiger	.05	.02
513 Tim Flannery	.05	.02
514 Ray Hayward (R)	.07	.04
515 Dave Leiper	.05	.02
516 Rod Scurry	.05	.02
517 Carmelo Martinez	.05	.02
518 Curtis Wilkerson	.05	.02
519 Stan Jefferson	.05	.02
520 Dan Quisenberry	.05	.02

521 Lloyd McClendon (R)	.07	.04
522 Steve Trout	.05	.02
523 Larry Andersen	.05	.02
524 Don Aase	.05	.02
525 Bob Forsch	.05	.02
526 Geno Petralli	.05	.02
527 Angel Salazar	.05	.02
529 Jose Oquendo	.05	.02
530 Jay Buhner	.15	.08
531 Tom Bolton (R)	.08	.05
532 Al Nipper	.05	.02
533 Dave Henderson	.05	.02
534 John Costello (R)	.07	.04
535 Donnie Moore	.05	.02
536 Mike Laga	.05	.02
537 Mike Gallego	.05	.02
538 Jim Clancy	.05	.02
539 Joel Youngblood	.05	.02
540 Rick Leach	.05	.02
541 Kevin Romine	.05	.02
542 Mark Salas	.05	.02
543 Greg Minton	.05	.02
544 Dave Palmer	.05	.02
545 Dwayne Murphy	.05	.02
546 Jim Deshaies	.05	.02
547 Don Gordon	.05	.02
548 Ricky Jordan	.08	.05
549 Mike Boddicker	.05	.02
550 Mike Scott	.05	.02
551 Jeff Ballard	.07	.04
552a Jose Rijo (Uniform #27 on card back)	.40	.25
552b Jose Rijo (uniform #24 on card back)	.12	.07
553 Danny Darwin	.05	.02
554 Tom Browning	.07	.04
555 Danny Jackson	.07	.04
556 Rick Dempsey	.05	.02
557 Jeffrey Leonard	.05	.02
558 Jeff Musselman	.05	.02
559 Ron Robinson	.05	.02
560 John Tudor	.05	.02
561 Don Slaught	.05	.02
562 Dennis Rasmussen	.05	.02
563 Brady Anderson	.60	.35
564 Pedro Guerrero	.05	.02
565 Paul Molitor	.20	.12
566 Terry Clark	.07	.04
567 Terry Puhl	.05	.02
568 Mike Campbell	.05	.02
569 Paul Mirabella	.05	.02
570 Jeff Hamilton (R)	.07	.04
571 Oswald Peraza	.07	.04
572 Bob McClure	.05	.02
573 Jose Bautista (R)	.08	.05
574 Alex Trevino	.05	.02
575 John Franco	.05	.02

576	Mark Parent	.07	.04
577	Nelson Liriano	.05	.02
578	Steve Shields	.05	.02
579	Odell Jones	.05	.02
580	Al Leiter	.05	.02
581	Dave Stapleton (R)	.08	.05
582	1988 World Series (J. Canseco, O. Hershiser, K. Gibons. D. Stewart)	.12	.07
583	Donnie Hill	.05	.02
584	Chuck Jackson	.05	.02
585	Rene Gonzales	.05	.02
586	Tracy Woodson (R)	.07	.04
587	Jim Adduci (R)	.07	.04
588	Mario Soto	.05	.02
589	Jeff Blauser	.12	.07
590	Jim Traber	.05	.02
591	Jon Perlman (R)	.05	.02
592	Mark Williamson	.05	.02
593	Dave Meads	.05	.02
594	Jim Eisenreich	.05	.02
595	Paul Gibson	.05	.02
596	Mike Birkbeck	.05	.02
597	Terry Francona	.05	.02
598	Paul Zuvella (R)	.07	.04
599	Franklin Stubbs	.05	.02
600	Gregg Jefferies	.35	.20
601	John Cangelosi	.05	.02
602	Mike Sharperson (R)	.08	.05
603	Mike Diaz	.05	.02
604	Gary Varsho (R)	.07	.04
605	Terry Blocker (R)	.07	.04
606	Charlie O'Brien (R)	.07	.04
607	Jim Eppard (R)	.07	.04
608	John Davis	.05	.02
609	Ken Griffey, Sr.	.07	.04
610	Buddy Bell	.05	.02
611	Ted Simmons	.07	.04
612	Matt Williams	.40	.25
613	Danny Cox	.05	.02
614	Al Pedrique	.05	.02
615	Ron Oester	.05	.02
616	John Smoltz (R)	.75	.45
617	Bob Melvin	.05	.02
618	Rob Dibble	.20	.12
619	Kirt Manwaring	.05	.02
620	Felix Fermin (R)	.07	.04
621	Doug Descenzo (R)	.10	.06
622	Bill Brennan (R)	.07	.04
623	Carlos Quintana (R)	.15	.08
624	Mike Harkey (R)	.12	.07
625	Gary Sheffield (R)	2.00	1.25
626	Tom Prince (R)	.07	.04
627	Steve Searcy (R)	.07	.04
628	Charlie Hayes (R)	.40	.25
629	Felix Jose (R)	.30	.18
630	Sandy Alomar Jr. (R)	.25	.15

631	Derek Lilliquist (R)	.10	.06
632	Geronimo Berroa (R)	.07	.04
633	Luis Medina (R)	.07	.04
634	Tom Gordon (R)	.15	.08
635	Ramon Martinez (R)	.50	.30
636	Craig Worthington (R)	.07	.04
637	Edgar Martinez (H)	.35	.20
638	Chad Kreuter (R)	.20	.12
639	Ron Jones (R)	.07	.04
640	Van Snyder (R)	.07	.04
641	Lance Blankenship (R)	.10	.06
642	Dwight Smith (R)	.10	.06
643	Cameron Drew (R)	.07	.04
644	Jerald Clark (R)	.10	.06
645	Randy Johnson (R)	.80	.50
646	Norm Charlton (R)	.20	.12
647	Todd Frohwirth (R)	.10	.06
648	Luis de los Santos (R)	.07	.04
649	Tim Jones (R)	.07	.04
650	Dave West (R)	.12	.07
651	Bob Milacki (R)	.08	.05
652	Wrigley Field (Night)	.05	.02
653	Orel Hershiser (HL)	.08	.05
654a	Wade Boggs (HL) (Er)	2.50	1.50
654b	Wade Boggs (HL) (Cor)	.12	.07
655	Jose Canseco (HL)	.25	.15
656	Doug Jones (HL)	.05	.02
657	Rickey Henderson (HL)	.12	.07
658	Toom Browning (HL)	.07	.04
659	Mike Greenwell (HL)	.07	.04
660	Red Sox Steak (HL)	.07	.04

1989 Score Traded

Score's second straight update set is similar in design to their regular edition. Card fronts feature blue-green borders. Vertical card backs contain full-color head shots of the players. Cards measure 2-1/2" by 3-1/2" and the set includes rookies and players traded during the regular 1989 season.

	MINT	NR/MT
Complete Set (110)	12.00	8.00
Commons	.05	.02

		MINT	NR/MT
1T	Rafael Palmeiro	.20	.12
2T	Nolan Ryan	1.75	1.00
3T	Jack Clark	.07	.04
4T	Dave LaPoint	.05	.02
5T	Mike Moore	.05	.02
6T	Pete O'Brien	.05	.02
7T	Jeffrey Leonard	.05	.02
8T	Rob Murphy	.05	.02
9T	Tom Herr	.05	.02
10T	Claudell Washington	.05	.02
11T	Mike Pagliarulo	.05	.02
12T	Steve Lake	.05	.02
13T	Spike Owen	.05	.02
14T	Andy Hawkins	.05	.02
15T	Todd Benzinger	.05	.02
16T	Mookie Wilson	.05	.02
17T	Bert Blyleven	.12	.07
18T	Jeff Treadway	.05	.02
19T	Bruce Hurst	.10	.06
20T	Steve Sax	.10	.06
21T	Juan Samuel	.05	.02
22T	Jesse Barfield	.07	.04
23T	Carmelo Castillo	.05	.02
24T	Terry Leach	.05	.02
25T	Mark Langston	.12	.07
26T	Eric King	.07	.04
27T	Steve Balboni	.05	.02
28T	Len Dykstra	.15	.10
29T	Keith Moreland	.05	.02
30T	Terry Kennedy	.05	.02
31T	Eddie Murray	.15	.08
32T	Mitch Williams	.07	.04
33T	Jeff Parrett	.05	.02
34T	Wally Backman	.05	.02
35T	Julio Franco	.10	.06
36T	Lance Parrish	.07	.04
37T	Nick Esasky	.05	.02
38T	Luis Polonia	.07	.04
39T	Kevin Gross	.05	.02
40T	John Dopson	.05	.02
41T	Willie Randolph	.05	.02
42T	Jim Clancy	.05	.02
43T	Tracy Jones	.05	.02
44T	Phil Bradley	.05	.02
45T	Milt Thompson	.05	.02
46T	Chris James	.05	.02
47T	Scott Fletcher	.05	.02
48T	Kal Daniels	.07	.04
49T	Steve Bedrosian	.05	.02
50T	Rickey Henderson	.30	.18
51T	Dion James	.05	.02
52T	Tim Leary	.05	.02
53T	Roger McDowell	.05	.02
54T	Mel Hall	.08	.05
55T	Dickie Thon	.05	.02
56T	Zane Smith	.07	.04
57T	Danny Heep	.05	.02
58T	Bob McClure	.05	.02
59T	Brian Holton	.05	.02
60T	Randy Ready	.05	.02
61T	Bob Melvin	.05	.02
62T	Harold Baines	.08	.05
63T	Lance McCullers	.05	.02
64T	Jody Davis	.05	.02
65T	Darrell Evans	.07	.04
66T	Joel Youngblood	.05	.02
67T	Frank Viola	.08	.05
68T	Mike Aldrete	.05	.02
69T	Greg Cadaret	.07	.04
70T	John Kruk	.12	.07
71T	Pat Sheridan	.05	.02
72T	Oddibe McDowell	.05	.02
73T	Tom Brookens	.05	.02
74T	Bob Boone	.10	.06
75T	Walt Terrell	.05	.02
76T	Joel Skinner	.05	.02
77T	Randy Johnson	.75	.45
78T	Felix Fermin	.05	.02
79T	Rick Mahler	.05	.02
80T	Rich Dotson	.05	.02
81T	Cris Carpenter (R)	.15	.10
82T	Bill Spiers (R)	.10	.06
83T	Junior Felix (R)	.15	.10
84T	Joe Girardi (R)	.08	.05
85T	Jerome Walton (R)	.08	.05
86T	Greg Litton (R)	.08	.05
87T	Greg Harris (R)	.12	.07
88T	Jim Abbott (R)	1.50	.90
89T	Kevin Brown (R)	.30	.18
90T	John Wetteland (R)	.40	.25
91T	Gary Wayne (R)	.08	.05
92T	Rich Monteleone (R)	.07	.04
93T	Bob Geren (R)	.10	.06
94T	Clay Parker (R)	.08	.05
95T	Steve Finley (R)	.30	.18
96T	Gregg Olson (R)	.40	.25
97T	Ken Patterson (R)	.08	.05
98T	Ken Hill (R)	.50	.30
99T	Scott Scudder (R)	.15	.08
100T	Ken Griffey, Jr. (R)	6.50	3.75
101T	Jeff Brantley (R)	.10	.06
102T	Donn Pall (R)	.10	.06
103T	Carlos Martinez (R)	.12	.07
104T	Joe Oliver (R)	.12	.07
105T	Omar Vizquel (R)	.20	.12
106T	Albert Belle (R)	5.00	3.00
107T	Kenny Rogers (R)	.10	.06
108T	Mark Carreon (R)	.10	.06
109T	Rolando Roomes (R)	.08	.05
110T	Pete Harnsisch (R)	.30	.18

1990 Score

Score increased the size of their 1990 set to 704-cards and introduced several new subsets including First Round Draft Picks and the Dream Team (DT). Card fronts feature four different border colors, red, white, green and blue. The flip side contains a full-color head shot. Cards measure 2-1/2" by 3-1/2". 10 bonus Dream Team cards were inserted in Score's Factory Set. These cards carry the BC prefix at the end of the checklist.

		MINT	NR/MT
Complete Set (704)		22.00	15.00
Commons:		.05	.02
1	Don Mattingly	.20	.12
2	Cal Ripken, Jr.	.35	.20
3	Dwight Evans	.07	.04
4	Barry Bonds	.45	.28
5	Kevin McReynolds	.05	.02
6	Ozzie Guillen	.05	.02
7	Terry Kennedy	.05	.02
8	Bryan Harvey	.08	.05
9	Alan Trammell	.08	.05
10	Cory Snyder	.05	.02
11	Jody Reed	.05	.02
12	Roberto Alomar	.50	.30
13	Pedro Guerrero	.05	.02
14	Gary Redus	.05	.02
15	Marty Barrett	.05	.02
16	Ricky Jordan	.07	.04
17	Joe Magrane	.07	.04
18	Sid Fernandez	.05	.02
19	Rich Dotson	.05	.02
20	Jack Clark	.05	.02
21	Bob Walk	.05	.02
22	Ron Karkovice	.05	.02
23	Lenny Harris	.08	.05
24	Phil Bradley	.05	.02
25	Andres Galarraga	.15	.10
26	Brian Downing	.05	.02
27	Dave Martinez	.05	.02
28	Eric King	.05	.02
29	Barry Lyons	.05	.02
30	Dave Schmidt	.05	.02
31	Mike Boddicker	.05	.02
32	Tom Foley	.05	.02
33	Brady Anderson	.15	.07
34	Jim Presley	.05	.02
35	Lance Parrish	.05	.02
36	Von Hayes	.05	.02
37	Lee Smith	.08	.05
38	Herm Winningham	.05	.02
39	Alejandro Pena	.05	.02
40	Mike Scott	.05	.02
41	Joe Orsulak	.05	.02
42	Rafael Ramirez	.05	.02
43	Gerald Young	.05	.02
44	Dick Schofield	.05	.02
45	Dave Smith	.05	.02
46	Dave Magadan	.05	.02
47	Dennis Martinez	.07	.04
48	Greg Minton	.05	.02
49	Milt Thompson	.05	.02
50	Orel Hershiser	.07	.04
51	Bip Roberts	.10	.06
52	Jerry Browne	.05	.02
53	Bob Ojeda	.05	.02
54	Fernando Valenzuela	.07	.04
55	Matt Nokes	.05	.02
56	Brook Jacoby	.05	.02
57	Frank Tanana	.05	.02
58	Scott Fletcher	.05	.02
59	Ron Oester	.05	.02
60	Bob Boone	.07	.04
61	Dan Gladden	.05	.02
62	Darnell Coles	.05	.02
63	Gregg Olson	.10	.06
64	Todd Burns	.07	.04
65	Todd Benzinger	.05	.02
66	Dale Murphy	.10	.06
67	Mike Flanagan	.05	.02
68	Jose Oquendo	.05	.02
69	Cecil Espy	.05	.02
70	Chris Sabo	.08	.05
71	Shane Rawley	.05	.02
72	Tom Brunansky	.05	.02
73	Vance Law	.05	.02
74	B.J. Surhoff	.05	.02
75	Lou Whitaker	.07	.04
76	Ken Caminiti	.07	.04
77	Nelson Liriano	.05	.02
78	Tommy Gregg	.05	.02
79	Don Slaught	.05	.02
80	Eddie Murray	.10	.06
81	Joe Boever	.05	.02
82	Charlie Leibrandt	.05	.02
83	Jose Lind	.05	.02

84	Tony Phillips	.07	.04
85	Mitch Webster	.05	.02
86	Dan Plesac	.05	.02
87	Rick Mahler	.05	.02
88	Steve Lyons	.05	.02
89	Tony Fernandez	.05	.02
90	Ryne Sandberg	.35	.20
91	Nick Esasky	.05	.02
92	Luis Salazar	.05	.02
93	Pete Incaviglia	.05	.02
94	Ivan Calderon	.05	.02
95	Jeff Treadway	.05	.02
96	Kurt Stillwell	.05	.02
97	Gary Sheffield	.50	.30
98	Jeffrey Leonard	.05	.02
99	Andres Thomas	.05	.02
100	Roberto Kelly	.20	.12
101	Alvaro Espinoza (R)	.07	.04
102	Greg Gagne	.05	.02
103	John Farrell	.05	.02
104	Willie Wilson	.05	.02
105	Glenn Braggs	.05	.02
106	Chet Lemon	.05	.02
107	Jamie Moyer	.05	.02
108	Chuck Crim	.05	.02
109	Dave Valle	.05	.02
110	Walt Weiss	.07	.04
111	Larry Sheets	.05	.02
112	Don Robinson	.05	.02
113	Danny Heep	.05	.02
114	Carmelo Martinez	.05	.02
115	Dave Gallagher	.05	.02
116	Mike LaValliere	.05	.02
117	Bob McClure	.05	.02
118	Rene Gonzales	.05	.02
119	Mark Parent	.05	.02
120	Wally Joyner	.08	.05
121	Mark Gubicza	.05	.02
122	Tony Pena	.05	.02
123	Carmen Castillo	.05	.02
124	Howard Johnson	.08	.05
125	Steve Sax	.07	.04
126	Tim Belcher	.05	.02
127	Tim Burke	.05	.02
128	Al Newman	.05	.02
129	Dennis Rasmussen	.05	.02
130	Doug Jones	.05	.02
131	Fred Lynn	.07	.04
132	Jeff Hamilton	.05	.02
133	German Gonzalez	.05	.02
134	John Morris	.05	.02
135	Dave Parker	.07	.04
136	Gary Pettis	.05	.02
137	Dennis Boyd	.05	.02
138	Candy Maldonado	.05	.02
139	Rick Cerone	.05	.02
140	George Brett	.15	.08
141	Dave Clark	.05	.02
142	Dickie Thon	.05	.02
143	Junior Ortiz	.05	.02
144	Don August	.05	.02
145	Gary Gaetti	.05	.02
146	Kirt Manwaring	.05	.02
147	Jeff Reed	.05	.02
148	Jose Alvarez (R)	.07	.04
149	Mike Schooler	.05	.02
150	Mark Grace	.20	.12
151	Geronimo Berroa	.05	.02
152	Barry Jones	.05	.02
153	Geno Petralli	.05	.02
154	Jim Deshaies	.05	.02
155	Barry Larkin	.12	.07
156	Alredo Griffin	.05	.02
157	Tom Henke	.05	.02
158	Mike Jeffcoat (R)	.07	.04
159	Bob Welch	.05	.02
160	Julio Franco	.08	.05
161	Henry Cotto	.05	.02
162	Terry Steinbach	.05	.02
163	Damon Berryhill	.05	.02
164	Tim Crews	.05	.02
165	Tom Browning	.05	.02
166	Fred Manrique	.05	.02
167	Harold Reynolds	.05	.02
168	Ron Hassey	.05	.02
169	Shawon Dunston	.08	.05
170	Bobby Bonilla	.12	.07
171	Tom Herr	.05	.02
172	Mike Heath	.05	.02
173	Rich Gedman	.05	.02
174	Bill Ripken	.05	.02
175	Pete O'Brien	.05	.02
176a	Lloyd McClendon (Er)	.30	.18
176b	Lloyd McClendon (Cor)	.05	.02
177	Brian Holton	.07	.04
178	Jeff Blauser	.08	.05
179	Jim Eisenreich	.05	.02
180	Bert Blyleven	.07	.04
181	Rob Murphy	.05	.02
182	Bill Doran	.05	.02
183	Curt Ford	.05	.02
184	Mike Henneman	.05	.02
185	Eric Davis	.10	.06
186	Lance McCullers	.05	.02
187	Steve Davis (R)	.07	.04
188	Bill Wegman	.05	.02
189	Brian Harper	.07	.04
190	Mike Moore	.05	.02
191	Dale Mohorcic	.05	.02
192	Tim Wallach	.07	.04
193	Keith Hernandez	.07	.04
194	Dave Righetti	.05	.02
195a	Bret Saberhagen (Er)	.10	.06
195b	Bret Saberhagen (Cor)	.15	.10

196	Paul Kilgus	.05	.02
197	Bud Black	.05	.02
198	Juan Samuel	.05	.02
199	Kevin Seitzer	.05	.02
200	Darryl Strawberry	.20	.12
201	Dave Steib	.07	.04
202	Charlie Hough	.05	.02
203	Jack Morris	.10	.06
204	Rance Mulliniks	.05	.02
205	Alvin Davis	.05	.02
206	Jack Howell	.05	.02
207	Ken Patterson	.07	.04
208	Terry Pendleton	.12	.07
209	Craig Lefferts	.05	.02
210	Kevin Brown	.08	.05
211	Dan Petry	.05	.02
212	Dave Leiper	.05	.02
213	Daryl Boston	.05	.02
214	Kevin Hickey	.07	.04
215	Mike Krukow	.05	.02
216	Terry Francona	.05	.02
217	Kirk McCaskill	.05	.02
218	Scott Bailes	.05	.02
219	Bob Forsch	.05	.02
220	Mike Aldrete	.05	.02
221	Steve Buechele	.05	.02
222	Jesse Barfield	.05	.02
223	Juan Berenguer	.05	.02
224	Andy McGaffigan	.05	.02
225	Pete Smith	.05	.02
226	Mike Witt	.05	.02
227	Jay Howell	.05	.02
228	Scott Bradley	.05	.02
229	Jerome Walton	.07	.04
230	Greg Swindell	.07	.04
231	Atlee Hammaker	.05	.02
232	Mike Deveraux	.10	.06
233	Ken Hill	.30	.18
234	Craig Worthington	.05	.02
235	Scott Henry	.05	.02
236	Brett Butler	.07	.04
237	Doyle Alexander	.05	.02
238	Dave Anderson	.05	.02
239	Bob Milacki	.05	.02
240	Dwight Smith	.07	.04
241	Otis Nixon	.07	.04
242	Pat Tabler	.05	.02
243	Derek Lilliquist	.05	.02
244	Danny Tartabull	.10	.06
245	Wade Boggs	.20	.12
246	Scott Garrelts	.05	.02
247	Spike Owen	.05	.02
248	Norm Charlton	.05	.02
249	Gerald Perry	.05	.02
250	Nolan Ryan	.60	.35
251	Kevin Gross	.05	.02
252	Randy Milligan	.05	.02
253	Mike LaCoss	.05	.02
254	Dave Bergman	.05	.02
255	Tony Gwynn	.20	.12
256	Felix Fermin	.05	.02
257	Greg Harris	.05	.02
258	Junior Felix (R)	.08	.05
259	Mark Davis	.05	.02
260	Vince Coleman	.07	.04
261	Paul Gibson	.05	.02
262	Mitch Williams	.05	.02
263	Jeff Russell	.05	.02
264	Omar Vizquel (R)	.12	.07
265	Andre Dawson	.12	.07
266	Storm Davis	.05	.02
267	Guillermo Hernandez	.05	.02
268	Mike Felder	.05	.02
269	Tom Candiotti	.05	.02
270	Bruce Hurst	.06	.03
271	Fred McGriff	.25	.15
272	Glenn Davis	.05	.02
273	John Franco	.05	.02
274	Rich Yett	.05	.02
275	Craig Biggio	.08	.05
276	Gene Larkin	.05	.02
277	Rob Dibble	.07	.04
278	Randy Bush	.05	.02
279	Kevin Bass	.05	.02
280a	Bo Jackson (Er)	.20	.12
280b	Bo Jackson (Cor)	.60	.35
281	Wally Backman	.05	.02
282	Larry Andersen	.05	.02
283	Chris Bosio	.05	.02
284	Juan Agosto	.05	.02
285	Ozzie Smith	.12	.07
286	George Bell	.10	.06
287	Rex Hudler	.05	.02
288	Pat Borders	.05	.02
289	Danny Jackson	.05	.02
290	Carlton Fisk	.10	.06
291	Tracy Jones	.05	.02
292	Allan Anderson	.05	.02
293	Johnny Ray	.05	.02
294	Lee Guetterman	.05	.02
295	Paul O'Neill	.07	.04
296	Carney Lansford	.05	.02
297	Tom Brookens	.05	.02
298	Claudell Washington	.05	.02
299	Hubie Brooks	.05	.02
300	Will Clark	.35	.20
301	Kenny Rogers (R)	.05	.02
302	Darrell Evans	.05	.02
303	Greg Briley	.05	.02
304	Donn Pall	.05	.02
305	Teddy Higuera	.05	.02
306	Dan Pasqua	.05	.02
307	Dave Winfield	.20	.12
308	Dennis Powell	.05	.02

309	Jose DeLeon	.05	.02
310	Roger Clemens	.30	.18
311	Melido Perez	.05	.02
312	Devon White	.08	.05
313	Doc Gooden	.10	.06
314	Carlos Martinez (R)	.12	.08
315	Dennis Eckersley	.10	.06
316	Clay Parker	.05	.02
317	Rick Honeycutt	.05	.02
318	Tim Laudner	.05	.02
319	Joe Carter	.20	.12
320	Robin Yount	.20	.12
321	Felix Jose	.15	.08
322	Mickey Tettleton	.07	.04
323	Mike Gallego	.05	.02
324	Edgar Martinez	.20	.12
325	Dave Henderson	.05	.02
326	Chili Davis	.05	.02
327	Steve Balboni	.05	.02
328	Jody Davis	.05	.02
329	Shawn Hillegas	.05	.02
330	Jim Abbott	.20	.12
331	John Dopson	.05	.02
332	Mark Williamson	.05	.02
333	Jeff Robinson	.05	.02
334	John Smiley	.08	.05
335	Bobby Thigpen	.05	.02
336	Garry Templeton	.05	.02
337	Marvell Wynne	.05	.02
338a	Ken Griffey, Sr. (#25 uniform on back)	.08	.05
338b	Ken Griffey, Sr. (#30 uniform on back)	1.25	.80
339	Steve Finley (R)	.07	.04
340	Ellis Burks	.08	.05
341	Frank Williams	.05	.02
342	Mike Morgan	.05	.02
343	Kevin Mitchell	.08	.05
344	Joel Youngblood	.05	.02
345	Mike Greenwell	.08	.05
346	Glenn Wilson	.05	.02
347	John Costello	.05	.02
348	Wes Gardner	.05	.02
349	Jeff Ballard	.05	.02
350	Mark Thurmond	.05	.02
351	Randy Myers	.05	.02
352	Shawn Abner	.05	.02
353	Jesse Orosco	.05	.02
354	Greg Walker	.05	.02
355	Pete Harnisch	.08	.05
356	Steve Farr	.05	.02
357	Dave LaPoint	.05	.02
358	Willie Fraser	.05	.02
359	Mickey Hatcher	.05	.02
360	Rickey Henderson	.20	.12
361	Mike Fitzgerald	.05	.02
362	Bill Schroeder	.05	.02
363	Mark Carreon	.05	.02
364	Ron Jones	.05	.02
365	Jeff Montgomery	.08	.05
366	Bill Krueger	.05	.02
367	John Cangelosi	.05	.02
368	Jose Gonzalez	.05	.02
369	Greg Hibbard (R)	.20	.12
370	John Smoltz	.35	.20
371	Jeff Brantley (R)	.08	.05
372	Frank White	.05	.02
373	Ed Whitson	.05	.02
374	Willie McGee	.07	.04
375	Jose Canseco	.35	.20
376	Randy Ready	.05	.02
377	Don Aase	.05	.02
378	Tony Armas	.05	.02
379	Steve Bedrosian	.05	.02
380	Chuck Finley	.08	.05
381	Kent Hrbek	.07	.04
382	Jim Gantner	.05	.02
383	Mel Hall	.07	.04
384	Mike Marshall	.05	.02
385	Mark McGwire	.30	.18
386	Wayne Tolleson	.05	.02
387	Brian Holton	.08	.05
388	John Wetteland (R)	.40	.25
389	Darren Daulton	.15	.10
390	Rob Deer	.05	.02
391	John Moses	.05	.02
392	Todd Worrell	.05	.02
393	Chuck Cary	.07	.04
394	Stan Javier	.05	.02
395	Willie Randolph	.05	.02
396	Bill Buckner	.05	.02
397	Robby Thompson	.08	.05
398	Mike Scioscia	.05	.02
399	Lonnie Smith	.05	.02
400	Kirby Puckett	.30	.18
401	Mark Langston	.08	.05
402	Danny Darwin	.05	.02
403	Greg Maddux	.20	.12
404	Lloyd Moseby	.05	.02
405	Rafael Palmeiro	.15	.10
406	Chad Kreuter	.08	.05
407	Jimmy Key	.07	.04
408	Tim Birtsas	.05	.02
409	Tim Raines	.07	.04
410	Dave Stewart	.08	.05
411	Eric Yelding (R)	.12	.07
412	Kent Anderson (R)	.07	.04
413	Les Lancaster	.05	.02
414	Rick Dempsey	.05	.02
415	Randy Johnson	.20	.12
416	Gary Carter	.10	.06
417	Rolando Roomes	.05	.02
418	Dan Schatzeder	.05	.02
419	Bryn Smith	.05	.02

420	Ruben Sierra	.25	.15
421	Steve Jeltz	.05	.02
422	Ken Oberkfell	.05	.02
423	Sid Bream	.05	.02
424	Jim Clancy	.05	.02
425	Kelly Gruber	.08	.05
426	Rick Leach	.05	.02
427	Lenny Dykstra	.15	.10
428	Jeff Pico	.05	.02
429	John Cerutti	.05	.02
430	David Cone	.08	.05
431	Jeff Kunkel	.05	.02
432	Luis Aquino	.05	.02
433	Ernie Whitt	.05	.02
434	Bo Diaz	.05	.02
435	Steve Lake	.05	.02
436	Pat Perry	.05	.02
437	Mike Davis	.05	.02
438	Cecilio Guante	.05	.02
439	Duane Ward	.05	.02
440	Andy Van Slyke	.10	.06
441	Gene Nelson	.05	.02
442	Luis Polonia	.07	.04
443	Kevin Elster	.05	.02
444	Keith Moreland	.05	.02
445	Roger McDowell	.05	.02
446	Ron Darling	.05	.02
447	Ernest Riles	.05	.02
448	Mookie Wilson	.05	.02
449a	Bill Spiers (R) (Er)	.40	.25
449b	Bill Spiers (R) (Cor)	.15	.08
450	Rick Sutcliffe	.05	.02
451	Nelson Santovenia	.05	.02
452	Andy Allanson	.05	.02
453	Bob Melvin	.05	.02
454	Benny Santiago	.07	.04
455	Jose Uribe	.05	.02
456	Bill Landrum	.07	.04
457	Bobby Witt	.08	.05
458	Kevin Romine	.05	.02
459	Lee Mazzilli	.05	.02
460	Paul Molitor	.15	.10
461	Ramon Martinez	.20	.12
462	Frank DiPino	.05	.02
463	Walt Terrell	.05	.02
464	Bob Geren (R)	.12	.07
465	Rick Reuchel	.05	.02
466	Mark Grant	.05	.02
467	John Kruk	.10	.06
468	Gregg Jefferies	.20	.12
469	R.J. Reynolds	.05	.02
470	Harold Baines	.07	.04
471	Dennis Lamp	.05	.02
472	Tom Gordon	.07	.04
473	Terry Puhl	.05	.02
474	Curtis Wilkerson	.05	.02
475	Dan Quisenberry	.05	.02
476	Oddibe McDowell	.05	.02
477	Zane Smith	.05	.02
478	Franklin Stubbs	.05	.02
479	Wallace Johnson	.05	.02
480	Jay Tibbs	.05	.02
481	Tom Glavine	.50	.30
482	Manny Lee	.05	.02
483	Joe Hesketh	.05	.02
484	Mike Bielecki	.05	.02
485	Greg Brock	.05	.02
486	Pascual Perez	.05	.02
487	Kirk Gibson	.07	.04
488	Scott Sanderson	.05	.02
489	Domingo Ramos	.05	.02
490	Kal Daniels	.05	.02
491a	David Wells (Reverse negative on card back)	2.00	1.25
491b	David Wells (Cor)	.07	.04
492	Jerry Reed	.05	.02
493	Eric Show	.05	.02
494	Mike Pagliarulo	.05	.02
495	Ron Robinson	.05	.02
496	Brad Komminsk	.05	.02
497	Greg Litton (R)	.10	.06
498	Chris James	.05	.02
499	Luis Quinones (R)	.08	.05
500	Frank Viola	.07	.04
501	Tim Teufel	.05	.02
502	Terry Leach	.05	.02
503	Matt Williams	.15	.10
504	Tim Leary	.05	.02
505	Doug Drabek	.08	.05
506	Mariano Duncan	.05	.02
507	Charlie Hayes	.08	.05
508	Albert Belle (R)	1.25	.80
509	Pat Sheridan	.05	.02
510	Mackey Sasser	.05	.02
511	Jose Rijo	.08	.05
512	Mike Smithson	.05	.02
513	Gary Ward	.05	.02
514	Dion James	.05	.02
515	Jim Gott	.05	.02
516	Drew Hall (R)	.07	.04
517	Doug Bair	.05	.02
518	Scott Scudder (R)	.15	.08
519	Rick Aguilera	.05	.02
520	Rafael Belliard	.05	.02
521	Jay Buhner	.08	.05
522	Jeff Reardon	.08	.05
523	Steve Rosenberg (R)	.07	.04
524	Randy Velarde (R)	.08	.05
525	Jeff Musselman	.05	.02
526	Bill Long	.05	.02
527	Gary Wayne	.05	.02
528	Dave Johnson (R)	.07	.04
529	Ron Kittle	.05	.02
530	Erik Hanson (R)	.15	.07

531 Steve Wilson (R)	.07	.04
532 Joey Meyer	.05	.02
533 Curt Young	.05	.02
534 Kelly Downs	.05	.02
535 Joe Girardi	.05	.02
536 Lance Blankenship	.07	.04
537 Greg Mathews	.05	.02
538 Donell Nixon	.05	.02
539 Mark Knudson (R)	.08	.05
540 Jeff Wetherby (R)	.08	.05
541 Darrin Jackson	.07	.04
542 Terry Mulholland	.07	.04
543 Eric Hetzel (R)	.08	.05
544 Rick Reed (R)	.10	.06
545 Dennis Cook (R)	.07	.04
546 Mike Jackson	.05	.02
547 Brian Fisher	.05	.02
548 Gene Harris (R)	.07	.04
549 Jeff King (R)	.25	.15
550 Dave Dravecky (Salute)	.05	.02
551 Randy Kutcher (R)	.07	.04
552 Mark Portugal	.07	.04
553 Jim Corsi (R)	.07	.04
554 Todd Stottlemyre	.07	.04
555 Scott Bankhead	.05	.02
556 Ken Dayley	.05	.02
557 Rick Wrona (R)	.07	.04
558 Sammy Sosa (R)	.80	.50
559 Keith Miller	.05	.02
560 Ken Griffey, Jr.	1.50	.90
561a Ryne Sandberg (Er 3B)	10.00	7.00
561b Ryne Sandberg (Cor)	.25	.15
562 Billy Hatcher	.05	.02
563 Jay Bell	.10	.06
564 Jack Daugherty (R)	.08	.05
565 Rich Monteleone	.05	.02
566 Bo Jackson (AS- MVP)	.20	.12
567 Tony Fossas (R)	.10	.06
568 Roy Smith (R)	.07	.04
569 Jaime Navarro (R)	.20	.12
570 Lance Johnson (R)	.15	.10
571 Mike Dyer (R)	.07	.04
572 Kevin Ritz (R)	.08	.05
573 Dave West	.05	.02
574 Gary Mielke (R)	.08	.05
575 Scott Lusader (R)	.08	.05
576 Joe Oliver (R)	.15	.08
577 Sandy Alomar, Jr.	.10	.06
578 Andy Benes (R)	.30	.18
579 Tim Jones	.05	.02
580 Randy McCament (R)	.07	.04
581 Curt Schilling (R)	.20	.12
582 John Orton (R)	.12	.07
583a Milt Cuyler (R) (Er)	.80	.50
583b Milt Cuyler (R) (Cor)	.20	.12
584 Eric Anthony (R)	.40	.25
585 Greg Vaughn (R)	.40	.25

586 Deion Sanders (R)	.60	.35
587 Jose DeJesus (R)	.07	.04
588 Chip Hale (R)	.07	.04
589 John Olerud (R)	2.00	1.25
590 Steve Olin (R)	.12	.07
591 Marquis Grissom (R)	.75	.45
592 Moises Alou (R)	.60	.35
593 Mark Lemke (R)	.10	.06
594 Dean Palmer (R)	.75	.45
595 Robin Ventura (R)	.75	.45
596 Tino Martinez (R)	.25	.15
597 Mike Huff (R)	.10	.06
598 Scott Hemond (R)	.10	.06
599 Wally Whitehurst (R)	.10	.06
600 Todd Zeile (R)	.20	.12
601 Glenallen Hill (R)	.20	.12
602 Hal Morris (R)	.20	.12
603 Juan Bell (R)	.08	.05
604 Bobby Rose (R)	.12	.07
605 Matt Merullo (R)	.10	.06
606 Kevin Maas (R)	.15	.10
607 Randy Nosek (R)	.07	.04
608 Billy Bates (R)	.10	.06
609 Mike Stanton (R)	.20	.12
610 Mauro Gozzo (R)	.08	.05
611 Charles Nagy (R)	.30	.18
612 Scott Coolbaugh (R)	.07	.04
613 Jose Vizcaino (R)	.15	.08
614 Greg Smith (R)	.10	.06
615 Jeff Huson (R)	.10	.06
616 Mickey Weston (R)	.08	.05
617 John Pawlowski (R)	.08	.05
618a Joe Skalski (R) (#27 uniform on back)	.12	.07
618b Joe Skalski (R) (#67 uniform on back)	.40	.25
619 Bernie Williams (R)	.35	.20
620 Shawn Holman (R)	.08	.05
621 Gary Eave (R)	.10	.06
622 Darrin Fletcher (R)	.12	.07
623 Pat Combs (R)	.15	.07
624 Mike Blowers (R)	.10	.06
625 Kevin Appier (R)	.25	.15
626 Pat Austin (R)	.10	.06
627 Kelly Mann (R)	.08	.05
628 Matt Kinzer (R)	.08	.05
629 Chris Hammond (R)	.35	.20
630 Dean Wilkins (R)	.12	.07
631 Larry Walker (R)	.80	.50
632 Blaine Beatty (R)	.12	.07
633a Tom Barrett (R) (#29 uniform on back)	.08	.05
633b Tom Barrett (R) (#14 uniform on back)	.50	.30
634 Stan Belinda (R)	.12	.07
635 Tex Smith (R)	.10	.06
636 Hensley Meulens (R)	.10	.06

637	Juan Gonzalez (R)	2.50	1.50
638	Lenny Webster (R)	.10	.06
639	Mark Gardner (R)	.15	.08
640	Tommy Greene (R)	.50	.30
641	Mike Hartley (R)	.15	.08
642	Phil Stephenson (R)	.08	.05
040	Kevin Mmahat (R)	.15	.09
644	Ed Whited (R)	.10	.06
645	Delino DeShields (R)	.75	.45
646	Kevin Blankenship (R)	.08	.05
647	Paul Sorrento (R)	.25	.15
648	Mike Roesler (R)	.10	.06
649	Jason Grimsley (R)	.12	.07
650	Dave Justice (R)	1.75	1.00
651	Scott Cooper (R)	.50	.30
652	Dave Eiland (R)	.08	.05
653	Mike Munoz (R)	.10	.06
654	Jeff Fischer (R)	.08	.05
655	Terry Jorgenson (R)	.08	.05
656	George Canale (R)	.10	.06
657	Brian DuBois (R)	.12	.07
658	Carlos Quintana	.08	.05
659	Luis De los santos	.05	.02
660	Jerald Clark	.07	.04
661	Donald Harris (R)	.15	.08
662	Paul Coleman (R)	.15	.08
663	Frank Thomas (R)	7.00	4.00
664	Brent Mayne (R)	.15	.08
665	Eddie Zosky (R)	.15	.08
666	Steve Hosey (R)	.40	.25
667	Scott Bryant (R)	.15	.08
668	Tom Goodwin (R)	.20	.12
669	Cal Eldred (R)	.75	.45
670	Earl Cunningham (R)	.15	.10
671	Alan Zinter (R)	.15	.08
672	Chuck Knoblauch (R)	.50	.30
673	Kyle Abbott (R)	.20	.12
674	Roger Salkeld (R)	.30	.18
675	Mo Vaughn (R)	1.25	.80
676	Kiki Jones (R)	.15	.08
677	Tyler Houston (R)	.12	.07
678	Jeff Jackson (R)	.15	.08
679	Greg Gohr (R)	.15	.08
680	Ben McDonald (R)	.40	.25
681	Greg Blosser (R)	.25	.15
682	Willie Greene (R)	.30	.18
683	Wade Boggs (DT)	.10	.06
684	Will Clark (DT)	.20	.12
685	Tony Gwynn (DT)	.12	.07
686	Rickey Henderson (DT)		.15
.08			
687	Bo Jackson (DT)	.20	.12
688	Mark Langston (DT)	.08	.05
689	Barry Larkin (DT)	.10	.06
690	Kirby Puckett (DT)	.15	.08
691	Ryne Sandberg (DT)	.20	.12
692	Mike Scott (DT)	.07	.04

693	Terry Steinbach (DT)	.07	.04
694	Bobby Thigpen (DT)	.07	.04
695	Mitch Williams (DT)	.07	.04
696	Nolan Ryan (5,000 K)	.35	.20
697	Bo Jackson (BB/FB)	1.75	1.00
698	Rickey Henderson (HL)	.12	.07
699	Will Clark (Hl)	15	.08
700	World Series (1,2)	.08	.05
701	Candlestick Park	.12	.07
702	World Series (3)	.08	.05
703	World Series (Wrap up)	.08	.05
704	Wade Boggs (HL)	.12	.07
BC1	Bart Giamatti (DT)	1.25	.80
BC2	Pat Combs (DT)	.30	.18
BC3	Todd Zeile (DT)	1.00	.70
BC4	Luis de los Santos (DT)	.20	.12
BC5	Mark Lemke (DT)	.30	.18
BC6	Robin Ventura (DT)	6.00	4.00
BC7	Jeff Huson (DT)	.20	.12
BC8	Greg Vaughn (DT)	2.50	1.50
BC9	Marquis Grissom (DT)	3.50	2.00
BC10	Eric Anthony (DT)	1.50	.90

1990 Score Traded

Similar in design to Score's 1990 regular edition, this update set contains cards of rookies and players who changed teams during the regular season. The standard-size cards feature a yellow and orange border. Card backs contain a small head shot of the player. The set contains a card of hockey player Eric Lindros.

		MINT	NR/MT
Complete Set (110)		12.50	7.50
Commons		.05	.02
1T	Dave Winfield	.20	.12
2T	Kevin Bass	.05	.02
3T	Nick Esasky	.05	.02

4T	Mitch Webster	.05	.02	61T	Scott Sanderson	.05	.02
5T	Pascual Perez	.05	.02	62T	Bill Long	.05	.02
6T	Gary Pettis	.05	.02	63T	Rick Cerone	.05	.02
7T	Tony Pena	.05	.02	64T	Scott Bailes	.05	.02
8T	Candy Maldonado	.05	.02	65T	Larry Sheets	.05	.02
9T	Cecil Fielder	.20	.12	66T	Junior Ortiz	.05	.02
10T	Carmelo Martinez	.05	.02	67T	Francisco Cabrera (R)	.15	.08
11T	Mark Langston	.10	.06	68T	Gary DiSarcina (R)	.15	.08
12T	Dave Parker	.08	.05	69T	Greg Olson (R)	.12	.07
13T	Don Slaught	.05	.02	70T	Beau Allred (R)	.12	.07
14T	Tony Phillips	.07	.04	71T	Oscar Azocar (R)	.12	.07
15T	John Franco	.05	.02	72T	Kent Mercker (R)	.15	.07
16T	Randy Myers	.05	.02	73T	John Burkett (R)	.35	.20
17T	Jeff Reardon	.12	.07	74T	Carlos Baerga (R)	3.50	2.00
18T	Sandy Alomar, Jr.	.12	.07	75T	Dave Hollin (R)	1.25	.80
19T	Joe Carter	.20	.12	76T	Todd Hundley (R)	.15	.08
20T	Fred Lynn	.07	.04	77T	Rick Parker (R)	.10	.06
21T	Storm Davis	.05	.02	78T	Steve Cummings (R)	.10	.06
22T	Craig Lefferts	.05	.02	79T	Bill Sampen (R)	.15	.07
23T	Pete O'Brien	.05	.02	80T	Jerry Kutzier (R)	.08	.05
24T	Dennis Boyd	.05	.02	81T	Derek Bell (R)	1.25	.80
25T	Lloyd Moseby	.05	.02	82T	Kevin Tapani (R)	.25	.15
26T	Mark Davis	.05	.02	83T	Jim Leyritz (R)	.15	.10
27T	Tim Leary	.05	.02	84T	Ray Lankford (R)	.80	.50
28T	Gerald Perry	.05	.02	85T	Wayne Edwards (R)	.10	.06
29T	Don Aase	.05	.02	86T	Frank Thomas	7.00	4.00
30T	Ernie Whitt	.05	.02	87T	Tim Naehring (R)	.12	.07
31T	Dale Murphy	.12	.07	88T	Willie Blair (R)	.12	.07
32T	Alejandro Pena	.05	.02	89T	Alan Mills (R)	.10	.06
33T	Juan Samuel	.05	.02	90T	Scott Radinsky (R)	.15	.08
34T	Hubie Brooks	.05	.02	91T	Howard Farmer (R)	.10	.06
35T	Gary Carter	.10	.06	92T	Julio Machado (R)	.12	.07
36T	Jim Presley	.05	.02	93T	Rafael Valdez (R)	.10	.06
37T	Wally Backman	.05	.02	94T	Shawn Boskie (R)	.10	.06
38T	Matt Nokes	.05	.02	95T	David Segui (R)	.12	.07
39T	Dan Petry	.05	.02	96T	Chris Hoiles (R)	.40	.25
40T	Franklin Stubbs	.05	.02	97T	D.J. Dozier (R)	.15	.08
41T	Jeff Huson	.07	.04	98T	Hector Villanueva (R)	.12	.07
42T	Billy Hatcher	.05	.02	99T	Eric Gunderson (R)	.10	.06
43T	Terry Leach	.05	.02	100T	Eric Lindros (R)	6.50	3.75
44T	Phil Bradley	.05	.02	101T	Dave Otto (R)	.10	.06
45T	Claudell Washington	.05	.02	102T	Dana Kiecker (R)	.10	.06
46T	Luis Polonia	.05	.02	103T	Tim Drummond (R)	.08	.05
47T	Daryl Boston	.05	.02	104T	Mickey Pina (R)	.10	.06
48T	Lee Smith	.10	.06	105T	Craig Grebeck (R)	.12	.07
49T	Tom Brunansky	.07	.04	106T	Bernard Gilkey (R)	.60	.35
50T	Mike Witt	.05	.02	107T	Tim Layana (R)	.12	.07
51T	Willie Randolph	.05	.02	108T	Scott Chiamparino (R)	.12	.07
52T	Stan Javier	.05	.02	109T	Steve Avery (R)	1.50	.90
53T	Brad Komminsk	.05	.02	110T	Terry Shumpert (R)	.15	.08
54T	John Candelaria	.05	.02				
55T	Bryn Smith	.05	.02				
56T	Glenn Braggs	.05	.02				
57T	Keith Hernandez	.07	.04				
58T	Ken Oberkfell	.05	.02				
59T	Steve Jeltz	.05	.02				
60T	Chris James	.05	.02				

1991 Score

Score increased the size of their set in 1991 and, for the first time, issued cards in two series. Card fronts feature multiple solid color borders and game action photos. The flip side contains a close-up head shot of the player. In addition to the Dream Team, score introduced a number of new subsets including K-Men, Master Blasters, Riflemen, and Franchise. The Factory Set includes 7 bonus Cooperstown Cards. Those cards are listed at the end of this checklist. All cards measure 2-1/2" by 3-1/2".

		MINT	NR/MT
Complete Set (893)		21.00	13.00
Commons		.05	.02
1	Jose Canseco	.25	.15
2	Ken Griffey, Jr.	.50	.30
3	Ryne Sandberg	.20	.12
4	Nolan Ryan	.40	.25
5	Bo Jackson	.20	.12
6	Bret Saberhagen	.08	.05
7	Will Clark	.20	.12
8	Ellis Burks	.07	.04
9	Joe Carter	.15	.10
10	Rickey Henderson	.15	.10
11	Ozzie Guillen	.05	.02
12	Wade Boggs	.15	.10
13	Jerome Walton	.07	.04
14	John Franco	.05	.02
15	Ricky Jordan	.05	.02
16	Wally Backman	.05	.02
17	Rob Dibble	.07	.04
18	Glenn Braggs	.05	.02
19	Cory Snyder	.05	.02
20	Kal Daniels	.05	.02
21	Mark Langston	.08	.05
22	Kevin Gross	.05	.02
23	Don Mattingly	.15	.10
24	Dave Righetti	.05	.02
25	Roberto Alomar	.30	.18
26	Robby Thompson	.07	.04
27	Jack McDowell	.20	.12
28	Bip Roberts	.05	.02
29	Jay Howell	.05	.02
30	Dave Stieb	.05	.02
31	Johnny Ray	.05	.02
32	Steve Sax	.07	.04
33	Terry Mulholland	.07	.04
34	Lee Guetterman	.05	.02
35	Tim Raines	.07	.04
36	Scott Fletcher	.05	.02
37	Lance Parrish	.05	.02
38	Tony Phillips	.07	.04
39	Todd Stottlemyre	.07	.04
40	Alan Trammell	.08	.05
41	Todd Burns	.05	.02
42	Mookie Wilson	.05	.02
43	Chris Bosio	.05	.02
44	Jeffrey Leonard	.05	.02
45	Doug Jones	.05	.02
46	Mike Scott	.05	.02
47	Andy Hawkins	.05	.02
48	Harold Reynolds	.05	.02
49	Paul Molitor	.15	.10
50	John Farrell	.05	.02
51	Danny Darwin	.05	.02
52	Jeff Blauser	.08	.05
53	John Tudor	.05	.02
54	Milt Thompson	.05	.02
55	Dave Justice	.30	.18
56	Greg Olson	.06	.03
57	Willie Blair	.07	.04
58	Rick Parker	.05	.02
59	Shawn Boskie	.05	.02
60	Kevin Tapani	.07	.04
61	Dave Hollins	.25	.15
62	Scott Radinsky	.07	.04
63	Francisco Cabrera	.05	.02
64	Tim Layana	.05	.02
65	Jim Leyritz	.05	.02
66	Wayne Edwards	.05	.02
67	Lee Stevens	.07	.04
68	Bill Sampen	.05	.02
69	Craig Grebeck	.05	.02
70	John Burkett	.12	.07
71	Hector Villanueva	.05	.02
72	Oscar Azocar	.05	.02
73	Alan Mills	.05	.02
74	Carlos Baerga	.40	.25
75	Charles Nagy	.20	.12
76	Tim Drummond	.05	.02
77	Dana Kiecker	.05	.02
78	Tom Edens (R)	.08	.05
79	Kent Mercker	.07	.04
80	Steve Avery	.20	.12

81	Lee Smith	.10	.06	138 Phil Stephenson	.05	.02
82	Dave Martinez	.05	.02	139 Felix Fermin	.05	.02
83	Dave Winfield	.12	.07	140 Pedro Guerrero	.05	.02
84	Bill Spiers	.05	.02	141 Charlie Hough	.05	.02
85	Dan Pasqua	.05	.02	142 Mike Henneman	.05	.02
86	Randy Milligan	.05	.02	143 Jeff Montgomery	.07	.04
87	Tracy Jones	.05	.02	144 Lenny Harris	.05	.02
88	Greg Myers	.05	.02	145 Bruce Hurst	.07	.04
89	Keith Hernandez	.05	.02	146 Eric Anthony	.12	.07
90	Todd Benzinger	.05	.02	147 Paul Assenmacher	.05	.02
91	Mike Jackson	.05	.02	148 Jesse Barfield	.07	.04
92	Mike Stanley	.10	.06	149 Carlos Quintana	.07	.04
93	Candy Maldonado	.05	.02	150 Dave Stewart	.08	.05
94	John Kruk	.10	.06	151 Roy Smith	.05	.02
95	Cal Ripken, Jr.	.35	.20	152 Paul Gibson	.05	.02
96	Willie Fraser	.05	.02	153 Mickey Hatcher	.05	.02
97	Mike Felder	.05	.02	154 Jim Eisenreich	.05	.02
98	Bill Landrum	.05	.02	155 Kenny Rogers	.05	.02
99	Chuck Crim	.05	.02	156 Dave Schmidt	.05	.02
100	Chuck Finley	.07	.04	157 Lance Johnson	.07	.04
101	Kirt Manwaring	.05	.02	158 Dave West	.05	.02
102	Jaime Navarro	.07	.04	159 Steve Balboni	.05	.02
103	Dickie Thon	.05	.02	160 Jeff Brantley	.05	.02
104	Brian Downing	.05	.02	161 Craig Biggio	.07	.04
105	Jim Abbott	.12	.07	162 Brook Jacoby	.05	.02
106	Tom Brookens	.05	.02	163 Dan Gladden	.05	.02
107	Darryl Hamilton	.10	.06	164 Jeff Reardon	.08	.05
108	Bryan Harvey	.08	.05	165 Mark Carreon	.05	.02
109	Greg Harris	.05	.02	166 Mel Hall	.05	.02
110	Greg Swindell	.07	.04	167 Gary Mielke	.05	.02
111	Juan Berenguer	.05	.02	168 Cecil Fielder	.15	.08
112	Mike Heath	.05	.02	169 Darrin Jackson	.05	.02
113	Scott Bradley	.05	.02	170 Rick Aguilera	.05	.02
114	Jack Morris	.08	.05	171 Walt Weiss	.05	.02
115	Barry Jones	.05	.02	172 Steve Farr	.05	.02
116	Kevin Romine	.05	.02	173 Jody Reed	.05	.02
117	Gary Templeton	.05	.02	174 Mike Jeffcoat	.05	.02
118	Scott Sanderson	.05	.02	175 Mark Grace	.10	.06
119	Roberto Kelly	.10	.06	176 Larry Sheets	.05	.02
120	George Brett	.15	.08	177 Bill Gullickson	.05	.02
121	Oddibe McDowell	.05	.02	178 Chris Gwynn	.05	.02
122	Jim Acker	.05	.02	179 Melido Perez	.05	.02
123	Bill Swift	.10	.06	180 Sid Fernandez	.05	.02
124	Eric King	.05	.02	181 Tim Burke	.05	.02
125	Jay Buhner	.07	.04	182 Gary Pettis	.05	.02
126	Matt Young	.05	.02	183 Rob Murphy	.05	.02
127	Alvaro Espinoza	.05	.02	184 Craig Lefferts	.05	.02
128	Greg Hibbard	.05	.02	185 Howard Johnson	.08	.05
129	Jeff Robinson	.05	.02	186 Ken Caminiti	.07	.04
130	Mike Greenwell	.08	.05	187 Tim Belcher	.07	.04
131	Dion James	.05	.02	188 Greg Cadaret	.05	.02
132	Donn Pall	.05	.02	189 Matt Williams	.15	.10
133	Lloyd Moseby	.05	.02	190 Dave Magadan	.05	.02
134	Randy Velarde	.05	.02	191 Geno Petralli	.05	.02
135	Allan Anderson	.05	.02	192 Jeff Robinson	.05	.02
136	Mark Davis	.05	.02	193 Jim Deshaies	.05	.02
137	Eric Davis	.08	.05	194 Willie Randolph	.05	.02

195	George Bell	.08	.05	252	Mike Hartley	.05	.02
196	Hubie Brooks	.05	.02	253	Joey Cora	.05	.02
197	Tom Gordon	.07	.04	254	Ivan Calderon	.05	.02
198	Mike Fitzgerald	.05	.02	255	Ted Power	.05	.02
199	Mike Pagliarulo	.05	.02	256	Sammy Sosa	.12	.07
200	Kirby Puckett	.20	.12	257	Steve Buechele	.05	.02
201	Shawon Dunston	.07	.04	258	Mike Devereaux	.08	.05
202	Dennis Boyd	.05	.02	259	Brad Komminsk	.05	.02
203	Junior Felix	.05	.02	260	Teddy Higuera	.05	.02
204	Alejandro Pena	.05	.02	261	Shawn Abner	.05	.02
205	Pete Smith	.10	.06	262	Dave Valle	.05	.02
206	Tom Glavine	.20	.12	263	Jeff Huson	.05	.02
207	Luis Salazar	.05	.02	264	Edgar Martinez	.10	.06
208	John Smoltz	.15	.10	265	Carlton Fisk	.10	.06
209	Doug Dascenzo	.05	.02	266	Steve Finley	.07	.04
210	Tim Wallach	.07	.04	267	John Wetteland	.10	.06
211	Greg Gagne	.05	.02	268	Kevin Appier	.08	.05
212	Mark Gubicza	.05	.02	269	Steve Lyons	.05	.02
213	Mark Parent	.05	.02	270	Mickey Tettleton	.07	.04
214	Ken Oberkfell	.05	.02	271	Luis Rivera	.05	.02
215	Gary Carter	.08	.05	272	Steve Jeltz	.05	.02
216	Rafael Palmeiro	.15	.10	273	R.J. Reynolds	.05	.02
217	Tom Niedenfuer	.05	.02	274	Carlos Martinez	.05	.02
218	Dave LaPoint	.05	.02	275	Dan Plesac	.05	.02
219	Jeff Treadway	.05	.02	276	Mike Morgan	.05	.02
220	Mitch Williams	.05	.02	277	Jeff Russell	.05	.02
221	Jose DeLeon	.05	.02	278	Pete Incaviglia	.05	.02
222	Mike LaValliere	.05	.02	279	Kevin Seitzer	.05	.02
223	Darrel Akerfelds	.05	.02	280	Bobby Thigpen	.05	.02
224	Kent Anderson	.05	.02	281	Stan Javier	.05	.02
225	Dwight Evans	.07	.04	282	Henry Cotto	.05	.02
226	Gary Redus	.05	.02	283	Gary Wayne	.05	.02
227	Paul O'Neill	.07	.04	284	Shane Mack	.07	.04
228	Marty Barrett	.05	.02	285	Brian Holman	.07	.04
229	Tom Browning	.07	.04	286	Gerald Perry	.05	.02
230	Terry Pendleton	.10	.06	287	Steve Crawford	.05	.02
231	Jack Armstrong	.05	.02	288	Nelson Liriano	.05	.02
232	Mike Boddicker	.05	.02	289	Don Aase	.05	.02
233	Neal Heaton	.05	.02	290	Randy Johnson	.15	.10
234	Marquis Grissom	.20	.12	291	Harold Baines	.07	.04
235	Bert Blyleven	.08	.05	292	Kent Hrbek	.07	.04
236	Curt Young	.05	.02	293	Les Lancaster	.05	.02
237	Don Carman	.05	.02	294	Jeff Musselman	.05	.02
238	Charlie Hayes	.07	.04	295	Kurt Stillwell	.05	.02
239	Mark Knudson	.05	.02	296	Stan Belinda	.05	.02
240	Todd Zeile	.10	.06	297	Lou Whitaker	.07	.04
241	Larry Walker	.20	.12	298	Glenn Wilson	.05	.02
242	Jerald Clark	.05	.02	299	Omar Vizquel	.08	.05
243	Jeff Ballard	.05	.02	300	Ramon Martinez	.12	.07
244	Jeff King	.07	.04	301	Dwight Smith	.07	.04
245	Tom Brunansky	.05	.02	302	Tim Crews	.05	.02
246	Darren Daulton	.15	.10	303	Lance Blankenship	.05	.02
247	Scott Terry	.05	.02	304	Sid Bream	.05	.02
248	Rob Deer	.05	.02	305	Rafael Ramirez	.05	.02
249	Brady Anderson	.12	.07	306	Steve Wilson	.05	.02
250	Lenny Dykstra	.15	.10	307	Mackey Sasser	.05	.02
251	Greg Harris	.05	.02	308	Franklin Stubbs	.05	.02

309	Jack Daugherty	.05	.02	366	Rafael Novoa (R)	.10	.06
310	Eddie Murray	.10	.06	367	Joe Grahe (R)	.12	.07
311	Bob Woloh	.07	.04	368	Darron Rood	.10	.06
312	Brian Harper	.05	.02	369	Jeff McKnight	.10	.06
313	Lance McCullers	.05	.02	370	Scott Leius	.10	.06
314	Dave Smith	.05	.02	371	Mark Dewey (R)	.10	.06
315	Bobby Bonilla	.10	.06	372	Mark Lee (R)	.10	.06
316	Jerry Don Gleaton	.05	.02	373	Rosario Rodriguez (R)	.10	.06
317	Greg Maddux	.15	.10	374	Chuck McElroy	.07	.04
318	Keith Miller	.05	.02	375	Mike Bell (R)	.08	.05
319	Mark Portugal	.05	.02	376	Mickey Morandini	.12	.07
320	Robin Ventura	.25	.15	377	Bill Haselman	.08	.05
321	Bob Ojeda	.05	.02	378	Dave Pavlas	.08	.05
322	Mike Harkey	.08	.05	379	Derrick May	.25	.15
323	Jay Bell	.08	.05	380	Jeromy Burnitz (R)	.50	.30
324	Mark McGwire	.20	.12	381	Donald Peters (R)	.15	.08
325	Gary Gaetti	.05	.02	382	Alex Fernandez	.30	.18
326	Jeff Pico	.05	.02	383	Mike Mussina (R)	1.25	.80
327	Kevin McReynolds	.05	.02	384	Daniel Smith (R)	.12	.07
328	Frank Tanana	.05	.02	385	Lance Dickson (R)	.15	.08
329	Eric Yelding	.05	.02	386	Carl Everett (R)	.25	.15
330	Barry Bonds	.35	.20	387	Thomas Nevers (R)	.15	.08
331	Brian McRae (R)	.25	.15	388	Adam Hyzdu (R)	.20	.12
332	Pedro Munoz (R)	.20	.12	389	Todd Van Poppel (R)	.75	.45
333	Daryl Irvine (R)	.08	.05	390	Rondell White (R)	.80	.50
334	Chris Hoiles	.15	.08	391	Marc Newfield (R)	.60	.35
335	Thomas Howard	.10	.06	392	Julio Franco (AS)	.05	.02
336	Jeff Schultz	.08	.05	393	Wade Boggs (AS)	.10	.06
337	Jeff Manto (R)	.10	.06	394	Ozzie Guillen (AS)	.05	.02
338	Beau Allred	.08	.05	395	Cecil Fielder (AS)	.10	.06
339	Mike Bordick (R)	.25	.15	396	Ken Griffey, Jr. (AS)	.25	.15
340	Todd Hundley	.08	.05	397	Rickey Henderson (AS)	.15	.08
341	Jim Vatcher (R)	.10	.06	398	Jose Canseco (AS)	.20	.12
342	Luis Sojo	.10	.06	399	Roger Clemens (AS)	.15	.08
343	Jose Offerman	.15	.07	400	Sandy Alomar, Jr. (AS)	.07	.04
344	Pete Coachman (R)	.08	.05	401	Bobby Thigpen (AS)	.05	.02
345	Mike Benjamin	.07	.04	402	Bobby Bonilla (MB)	.08	.05
346	Ozzie Canseco (R)	.10	.06	403	Eric Davis (MB)	.07	.04
347	Tim McIntosh	.10	.06	404	Fred McGriff (MB)	.12	.07
348	Phil Plantier (R)	.75	.45	405	Glenn Davis (MB)	.05	.02
349	Terry Shumpert	.07	.04	406	Kevin Mitchell (MB)	.08	.05
350	Darren Lewis	.15	.10	407	Rob Dibble (KM)	.05	.02
351	David Walsh (R)	.10	.06	408	Ramon Martinez (KM)	.08	.05
352	Scott Chiamparino	.10	.06	409	David Cone (KM)	.08	.05
353	Julio Valera	.07	.04	410	Bobby Witt (KM)	.05	.02
354	Anthony Telford (R)	.20	.12	411	Mark Langston (KM)	.08	.05
355	Kevin Wickander	.08	.05	412	Bo Jackson (Rifle)	.15	.08
356	Tim Naehring	.10	.06	413	Shawon Dunston (Rifle)	.05	.02
357	Jim Poole (R)	.10	.06	414	Jesse Barfield (Rifle)	.05	.02
358	Mark Whiten(R)	.30	.18	415	Ken Caminiti (Rifle)	.05	.02
359	Terry Wells (R)	.10	.06	416	Benito Santiago (Rifle)	.07	.04
360	Rafael Valdez	.07	.04	417	Nolan Ryan (HL)	.30	.18
361	Mel Stottlemyre	.07	.04	418	Bobby Thigpen (HL)	.05	.02
362	David Segui	.07	.04	419	Ramon Martinez (HL)	.07	.04
363	Paul Abbott (R)	.10	.06	420	Bo Jackson (HL)	.15	.08
364	Steve Howard	.08	.05	421	Carlton Fisk (HL)	.10	.06
365	Karl Rhodes	.10	.06	422	Jimmy Key	.05	.02

423	Junior Noboa (R)	.05	.02
424	Al Newman	.05	.02
425	Pat Borders	.05	.02
426	Von Hayes	.05	.02
427	Tim Teufel	.05	.02
428	Eric Plunk	.05	.02
429	John Moses	.05	.02
430	Mike Witt	.05	.02
431	Otis Nixon	.07	.04
432	Tony Fernandez	.05	.02
433	Rance Mulliniks	.05	.02
434	Dan Petry	.05	.02
435	Bob Geren	.05	.02
436	Steve Frey	.07	.04
437	Jamie Moyer	.05	.02
438	Junio Ortiz	.05	.02
439	Tom O'Malley	.05	.02
440	Pat Combs	.07	.04
441	Jose Canseco (DT)	1.00	.70
442	Alfredo Griffin	.05	.02
443	Andres Galarraga	.12	.07
444	Bryn Smith	.05	.02
445	Andre Dawson	.10	.06
446	Juan Samuel	.05	.02
447	Mike Aldrete	.05	.02
448	Ron Gant	.15	.08
449	Fernando Valenzuela	.05	.02
450	Vince Coleman	.05	.02
451	Kevin Mitchell	.08	.05
452	Spike Owen	.05	.02
453	Mike Bielecki	.05	.02
454	Dennis Martinez	.08	.05
455	Brett Butler	.07	.04
456	Ron Darling	.05	.02
457	Dennis Rasmussen	.05	.02
458	Ken Howell	.05	.02
459	Steve Bedrosian	.05	.02
460	Frank Viola	.07	.04
461	Jose Lind	.05	.02
462	Chris Sabo	.07	.04
463	Dante Bichette	.05	.02
464	Rick Mahler	.05	.02
465	John Smiley	.08	.05
466	Devon White	.08	.05
467	John Orton	.05	.02
468	Mike Stanton	.05	.02
469	Billy Hatcher	.05	.02
470	Wally Joyner	.08	.05
471	Gene Larkin	.05	.02
472	Doug Drabek	.08	.05
473	Gary Sheffield	.25	.15
474	David Wells	.05	.02
475	Andy Van Slyke	.08	.05
476	Mike Gallego	.05	.02
477	B.J. Surhoff	.05	.02
478	Gene Nelson	.05	.02
479	Mariano Duncan	.05	.02
480	Fred McGriff	.20	.12
481	Jerry Browne	.05	.02
482	Alvin Davis	.05	.02
483	Bill Wegman	.05	.02
484	Dave Parker	.07	.04
485	Dennis Eckersley	.10	.06
486	Erik Hanson	.08	.05
487	Bill Ripken	.05	.02
488	Tom Candiotti	.05	.02
489	Mike Schooler	.05	.02
490	Gregg Olson	.05	.02
491	Chris James	.05	.02
492	Pete Harnisch	.08	.05
493	Julio Franco	.07	.04
494	Greg Briley	.05	.02
495	Ruben Sierra	.15	.08
496	Steve Olin	.05	.02
497	Mike Fetters	.05	.02
498	Mark Williamson	.05	.02
499	Bob Tewksbury	.05	.02
500	Tony Gwynn	.15	.10
501	Randy Myers	.05	.02
502	Keith Comstock	.05	.02
503	Craig Worthington	.05	.02
504	Mark Eichhorn	.05	.02
505	Barry Larkin	.08	.05
506	Dave Johnson	.05	.02
507	Bobby Witt	.07	.04
508	Joe Orsulak	.05	.02
509	Pete O'Brien	.05	.02
510	Brad Arnsberg	.05	.02
511	Storm Davis	.05	.02
512	Bob Milacki	.05	.02
513	Bill Pecota	.05	.02
514	Glenallen Hill	.08	.05
515	Danny Tartabull	.10	.06
516	Mike Moore	.05	.02
517	Ron Robinson	.05	.02
518	Mark Gardner	.07	.04
519	Rick Wrona	.05	.02
520	Mike Scioscia	.05	.02
521	Frank Willis	.05	.02
522	Greg Brock	.05	.02
523	Jack Clark	.05	.02
524	Bruce Ruffin	.05	.02
525	Robin Yount	.15	.10
526	Tom Foley	.05	.02
527	Pat Perry	.05	.02
528	Greg Vaughn	.10	.06
529	Wally Whitehurst	.05	.02
530	Norm Charlton	.05	.02
531	Marvell Wynne	.05	.02
532	Jim Gantner	.05	.02
533	Greg Litton	.05	.02
534	Manny Lee	.05	.02
535	Scott Bailes	.05	.02
536	Charlie Leibrandt	.05	.02

537	Roger McDowell	.05	.02
538	Andy Benes	.12	.07
539	Rick Honeycutt	.05	.02
540	Doc Gooden	.10	.06
541	Scott Garrelts	.05	.02
542	Dave Clark	.05	.02
543	Lonnie Smith	.05	.02
544	Rick Rueschel	.05	.02
545	Delino DeShields	.15	.08
546	Mike Sharperson	.05	.02
547	Mike Kingery	.05	.02
548	Terry Kennedy	.05	.02
549	David Cone	.10	.06
550	Orel Hershiser	.08	.05
551	Matt Nokes	.05	.02
552	Eddie Williams	.05	.02
553	Frank DiPino	.05	.02
554	Fred Lynn	.07	.04
555	Alex Cole	.12	.07
556	Terry Leach	.05	.02
557	Chet Lemon	.05	.02
558	Paul Mirabella	.05	.02
559	Bill Long	.05	.02
560	Phil Bradley	.05	.02
561	Duane Ward	.05	.02
562	Dave Bergman	.05	.02
563	Eric Show	.05	.02
564	Xavier Hernandez	.08	.05
565	Jeff Parrett	.05	.02
566	Chuck Cary	.05	.02
567	Ken Hill	.08	.05
568	Bob Welch	.07	.04
569	John Mitchell	.05	.02
570	Travis Fryman (R)	.60	.35
571	Derek Lilliquist	.05	.02
572	Steve Lake	.05	.02
573	John Barfield (R)	.10	.06
574	Randy Bush	.05	.02
575	Joe Magrane	.05	.02
576	Edgar Diaz	.05	.02
577	Casy Candaele	.05	.02
578	Jesse Orosco	.05	.02
579	Tom Henke	.05	.02
580	Rick Cerone	.05	.02
581	Drew Hall	.05	.02
582	Tony Castillo	.05	.02
583	Jimmy Jones	.05	.02
584	Rick Reed	.05	.02
585	Joe Girardi	.05	.02
586	Jeff Gray (R)	.12	.07
587	Luis Polonia	.05	.02
588	Joe Klink	.07	.04
589	Rex Hudler	.05	.02
590	Kirk McCaskill	.05	.02
591	Juan Agosto	.05	.02
592	Wes Gardner	.05	.02
593	Rich Rodriguez (R)	.12	.07

594	Mitch Webster	.05	.02
595	Kelly Gruber	.07	.04
606	Dalo Mohoroio	.05	.02
597	Willie McGee	.07	.04
598	Bill Krueger	.05	.02
599	Bob Walk	.05	.02
600	Kevin Mass	.08	.05
601	Danny Jackson	.05	.02
602	Craig McMurtry	.05	.02
603	Curtis Wilkerson	.05	.02
604	Adam Peterson	.05	.02
605	Sam Horn	.05	.02
606	Tommy Gregg	.05	.02
607	Ken Dayley	.05	.02
608	Carmelo Castillo	.05	.02
609	John Shelby	.05	.02
610	Don Slaught	.05	.02
611	Calvin Schiraldi	.05	.02
612	Dennis Lamp	.05	.02
613	Andres Thomas	.05	.02
614	Jose Gonzalez	.05	.02
615	Randy Ready	.05	.02
616	Kevin Bass	.05	.02
617	Mike Marshall	.05	.02
618	Daryl Boston	.05	.02
619	Andy McGaffigan	.05	.02
620	Joe Oliver	.07	.04
621	Jim Gott	.05	.02
622	Jose Oquendo	.05	.02
623	Jose DeJesus	.05	.02
624	Mike Brumley	.05	.02
625	John Olerud	.40	.25
626	Ernest Riles	.05	.02
627	Gene Harris	.05	.02
628	Jose Uribe	.05	.02
629	Darnell Coles	.05	.02
630	Carney Lansford	.05	.02
631	Tim Leary	.05	.02
632	Tim Hulett	.05	.02
633	Kevin Elster	.05	.02
634	Tony Fossas	.05	.02
635	Francisco Oliveras	.05	.02
636	Bob Patterson	.05	.02
637	Gary Ward	.05	.02
638	Rene Gonzales	.05	.02
639	Don Robinson	.05	.02
640	Darryl Strawberry	.15	.08
641	Dave Anderson	.05	.02
642	Scott Scudder	.05	.02
643	Reggie Harris (R)	.10	.06
644	Dave Henderson	.05	.02
645	Ben McDonald	.15	.08
646	Bob Kipper	.05	.02
647	Hal Morris	.10	.06
648	Tim Birtsas	.05	.02
649	Steve Searcy	.05	.02
650	Dale Murphy	.10	.06

651	Ron Oester	.05	.02
652	Mike LaCoss	.05	.02
653	Ron Jones	.05	.02
654	Kelly Downs	.05	.02
655	Roger Clemens	.25	.15
656	Herm Winningham	.05	.02
657	Trevor Wilson	.05	.02
658	Jose Rijo	.07	.04
659	Dann Bilardello	.05	.02
660	Gregg Jefferies	.12	.07
661	Doug Drabek (AS)	.08	.05
662	Randy Myers (AS)	.05	.02
663	Benito Santiago (AS)	.07	.04
664	Will Clark (AS)	.12	.07
665	Ryne Sandberg (AS)	.12	.07
666	Barry Larkin (AS)	.08	.05
667	Matt Williams (AS)	.08	.05
668	Barry Bonds (AS)	.15	.10
669	Eric Davis (AS)	.07	.04
670	Bobby Bonilla (AS)	.08	.05
671	Chipper Jones (R)	1.25	.80
672	Eric Christopherson (R)	.10	.06
673	Robbie Beckett (R)	.12	.07
674	Shane Andrews (R)	.20	.12
675	Steve Karsay (R)	.60	.35
676	Aaron Holbert (R)	.15	.10
677	Donovan Osborne (R)	.50	.30
678	Todd Ritchie (R)	.15	.08
679	Ron Walden (R)	.10	.06
680	Tim Costo (R)	.25	.15
681	Dan Wilson (R)	.15	.08
682	Kurt Miller (R)	.25	.15
683	Mike Lieberthal (R)	.25	.15
684	Roger Clemens (KM)	.15	.08
685	Doc Gooden (KM)	.10	.06
686	Nolan Ryan (KM)	.30	.18
687	Frank Viola (KM)	.07	.04
688	Erik Hanson (KM)	.07	.04
689	Matt Williams (MB)	.08	.05
690	Jose Canseco (MB)	.15	.08
691	Darryl Strawberry (MB)	.10	.06
692	Bo Jackson (MB)	.12	.07
693	Cecil Fielder (MB)	.12	.07
694	Sandy Alomar, Jr.(Rifle)	.07	.04
695	Cory Snyder (Rifle)	.05	.02
696	Eric Davis (Rifle)	.08	.05
697	Ken Griffey, Jr. (Rifle)	.25	.15
698	Andy Van Slyke (Rifle)	.07	.04
699	Langston/Witt (No-Hit)	.08	.05
700	Randy Johnson (No-Hit)	.10	.06
701	Nola Ryan (No-Hit)	.30	.18
702	Dave Stewart (No-Hit)	.08	.05
703	Fernando Valenzuela (No-Hit)	.07	.04
704	Andy Hawkins (No-Hit)	.05	.02
705	Melido Perez (No-Hit)	.05	.02
706	Terry Mulholland (NH)	.05	.02
707	Dave Stieb (No-Hit)	.07	.04
708	Brian Barnes (R)	.15	.08
709	Bernard Gilkey (R)	.15	.08
710	Steve Decker (R)	.10	.06
711	Paul Faries (R)	.07	.04
712	Paul Marak (R)	.08	.05
713	Wes Chamberlain (H)	.25	.15
714	Kevin Belcher (R)	.10	.06
715	Dan Boone (R)	.08	.05
716	Steve Adkins (R)	.10	.06
717	Geronimo Pena (R)	.10	.06
718	Howard Farmer (R)	.07	.04
719	Mark Leonard (R)	.10	.06
720	Tom Lampkin	.05	.02
721	Mike Gardiner (R)	.15	.08
722	Jeff Conine (R)	.35	.20
723	Efrain Valdez (R)	.08	.05
724	Chuck Malone	.07	.04
725	Leo Gomez (R)	.15	.10
726	Paul McClellan (R)	.08	.05
727	Mark Leiter (R)	.10	.06
728	Rich DeLucia (R)	.10	.06
729	Mel Rojas (R)	.10	.06
730	Hector Wagner (R)	.10	.06
731	Ray Lankford	.30	.18
732	Turner Ward (R)	.12	.07
733	Gerald Alexander (R)	.08	.05
734	Scott Anderson (R)	.08	.05
735	Tony Perezchica	.07	.04
736	Jimmy Kremers	.07	.04
737	American Flag	.25	.15
738	Mike York (R)	.07	.04
739	Mike Rochford	.07	.04
740	Scott Aldred	.10	.06
741	Rico Brogna (R)	.15	.10
742	Dave Burba (R)	.12	.07
743	Ray Stephens (R)	.08	.05
744	Eric Gunderson	.07	.04
745	Troy Afenir (R)	.12	.07
746	Jeff Shaw (R)	.08	.05
747	Orlando Merced (R)	.25	.15
748	Omar Oliveras (R)	.12	.07
749	Jerry Kutzler	.07	.04
750	Mo Vaughn	.35	.20
751	Matt Stark (R)	.12	.07
752	Randy Hennis (R)	.08	.05
753	Andujar Cedeno (R)	.20	.12
754	Kevin Torve	.08	.05
755	Joe Kraemer	.08	.05
756	Phil Clark (R)	.15	.10
757	Ed Vosberg (R)	.10	.06
758	Mike Perez (R)	.15	.10
759	Scott Lewis (R)	.10	.06
760	Steve Chitren (R)	.12	.07
761	Ray Young (R)	.08	.05
762	Andres Santana	.10	.06
763	Rodney McCray (R)	.08	.05

#	Name			#	Name		
764	Sean Berry (R)	.15	.10	820	Tom Herr	.05	.02
765	Brent Mayne	.07	.04	821	Rob Ducey	.05	.02
766	Mike Simms (R)	.08	.05	822	Luis Quinones	.05	.02
767	Glenn Sutko (R)	.08	.05	823	Greg Minton	.05	.02
768	Gary Disarcina	.07	.04	824	Mark Grant	.05	.02
769	George Brett (HL)	.10	.06	825	Ozzie Smith	.10	.06
770	Cecil Fielder (HL)	.10	.06	826	Dave Eiland	.05	.02
771	Jim Presley	.05	.02	827	Danny Heep	.05	.02
772	John Dopson	.05	.02	828	Hensley Meulens	.07	.04
773	Bo Jackson (Breaker)	.20	.12	829	Charlie O'Brien	.05	.02
774	Brent Knackert	.07	.04	830	Glenn Davis	.05	.02
775	Bill Doran	.05	.02	831	John Marzano	.05	.02
776	Dick Schofield	.05	.02	832	Steve Ontiveros	.05	.02
777	Nelson Santovenia	.05	.02	833	Ron Karkovice	.05	.02
778	Mark Guthrie	.07	.04	834	Jerry Goff	.07	.04
779	Mark Lemke	.05	.02	835	Ken Griffey, Sr.	.05	.02
780	Terry Steinbach	.05	.02	836	Kevin Reimer	.08	.05
781	Tom Bolton	.05	.02	837	Randy Kutcher	.05	.02
782	Randy Tomlin (R)	.15	.10	838	Mike Blowers	.05	.02
783	Jeff Kunkel	.05	.02	839	Mike McFarlane	.05	.02
784	Felix Jose	.08	.05	840	Frank Thomas	1.50	.90
785	Rick Sutcliffe	.05	.02	841	Ken Griffey, Jr. & Sr.	.50	.30
786	John Cerutti	.05	.02	842	Jack Howell	.05	.02
787	Jose Vizcaino	.05	.02	843	Mauro Gozzo	.07	.04
788	Curt Schilling	.08	.05	844	Gerald Young	.05	.02
789	Ed Whitson	.05	.02	845	Zane Smith	.05	.02
790	Tony Pena	.05	.02	846	Kevin Brown	.10	.06
791	John Candelaria	.05	.02	847	Sil Campusano	.05	.02
792	Carmelo Martinez	.05	.02	848	Larry Andersen	.05	.02
793	Sandy Alomar, Jr.	.07	.04	849	Cal Ripken, Jr. (Fran)	.20	.12
794	Jim Neidinger (R)	.08	.05	850	Roger Clemens (Fran)	.15	.10
795	Red's October	.07	.04	851	Sandy Alomar, Jr (Fr)	.07	.04
796	Paul Sorrento	.07	.04	852	Alan Trammell (Fran)	.08	.05
797	Tom Pagnozzi	.05	.02	853	George Brett (Fran)	.15	.10
798	Tino Martinez	.10	.06	854	Robin Yount (Fran)	.15	.10
799	Scott Ruskin (R)	.08	.05	855	Kirby Puckett (Fran)	.15	.10
800	Kirk Gibson	.05	.02	856	Don Mattingly (Fran)	.12	.07
801	Walt Terrell	.05	.02	857	Rickey Henderson (Fr)	.10	.06
802	John Russell	.05	.02	858	Ken Griffey, Jr. (Fran)	.25	.15
803	Chili Davis	.05	.02	859	Ruben Sierra (Fran)	.12	.07
804	Chris Nabholz	.10	.06	860	John Olerud (Fran)	.20	.12
805	Juan Gonzalez	.70	.40	861	Dave Justice (Fran)	.15	.10
806	Ron Hassey	.05	.02	862	Ryne Sandberg (Fran)	.15	.10
807	Todd Worrell	.05	.02	863	Eric Davis (Fran)	.08	.05
808	Tommy Greene	.08	.05	864	Darryl Strawberry (Fr)	.12	.07
809	Joel Skinner	.05	.02	865	Tim Wallach (Fran)	.08	.05
810	Benito Santiago	.07	.04	866	Doc Gooden (Fran)	.12	.07
811	Pat Tabler	.05	.02	867	Lenny Dykstra (Fran)	.10	.06
812	Scott Erickson (R)	.20	.12	868	Barry Bonds (Fran)	.20	.12
813	Moises Alou	.25	.15	869	Todd Zeile (Fran)	.07	.04
814	Dale Sveum	.05	.02	870	Benito Santiago (Fran)	.07	.04
815	Ryne Sandberg (Man of the year)	.20	.12	871	Will Clark (Fran)	.15	.08
816	Rick Dempsey	.05	.02	872	Craig Biggio (Fran)	.07	.04
817	Scott Bankhead	.05	.02	873	Wally Joyner (Fran)	.08	.05
818	Jason Grimsley	.05	.02	874	Frank Thomas (FR)	.75	.45
819	Doug Jennings	.05	.02	875	Rickey Henderson (MVP)	.10	.06

		MINT	NR/MT
876	Barry Bonds (MVP)	.15	.10
877	Bob Welch (Cy Young)	.07	.04
878	Doug Drabek (Cy Young)	.07	.04
879	Sandy Alomar, Jr (ROY)	.08	.05
880	Dave Justice (ROY)	.15	.10
881	Damon Berryhill	.05	.02
882	Frank Viola (DT)	.08	.05
883	Dave Stewart (DT)	.08	.05
884	Doug Jones (DT)	.07	.04
885	Randy Myers (DT)	.07	.04
886	Will Clark (DT)	.40	.25
887	Robert Alomar (DT)	.40	.25
888	Barry Larkin (DT)	.10	.06
889	Wade Boggs (DT)	.20	.12
890	Rickey Henderson (DT)	.30	.18
891	Kirby Puckett (DT)	.40	.25
892	Ken Griffey, Jr. (DT)	1.50	.90
893	Benito Santiago (DT)	.08	.05
BC1	Wade Boggs	.80	.50
BC2	Barry Larkin	.50	.30
BC3	Ken Griffey Jr.	3.50	2.00
BC4	Rickey Henderson	1.25	.80
BC5	George Brett	1.50	.90
BC6	Will Clark	1.25	.80
BC7	Nolan Ryan	3.00	1.75

1991 Score Traded

Score's 110-card update set is similar in design to their regular edition except for the purple and white border colors. The set features rookies and players who were traded during the regular season. All cards measure 2-1/2" by 3-1/2".

		MINT	NR/MT
Complete Set (110)		6.50	3.50
Commons		.05	.02
1	Bo Jackson	.25	.15
2	Mike Flanagan	.05	.02
3	Pete Incaviglia	.05	.02
4	Jack Clark	.05	.02
5	Hubie Brooks	.05	.02
6	Ivan Calderon	.05	.02
7	Glenn Davis	.05	.02
8	Wally Backman	.05	.02
9	Dave Smith	.05	.02
10	Tim Raines	.05	.02
11	Joe Carter	.12	.07
12	Sid Bream	.05	.02
13	George Bell	.08	.05
14	Steve Bedrosian	.05	.02
15	Willie Wilson	.05	.02
16	Darryl Strawberry	.15	.08
17	Danny Jackson	.05	.02
18	Kirk Gibson	.05	.02
19	Willie McGee	.07	.04
20	Junior Felix	.05	.02
21	Steve Farr	.05	.02
22	Pat Tabler	.05	.02
23	Brett Butler	.07	.04
24	Danny Darwin	.05	.02
25	Mikey Tettleton	.07	.04
26	Gary Carter	.08	.05
27	Mitch Williams	.05	.02
28	Candy Maldonado	.05	.02
29	Otis Nixon	.05	.02
30	Brian Downing	.05	.02
31	Tom Candiotti	.05	.02
32	John Candelaria	.05	.02
33	Rob Murphy	.05	.02
34	Deion Sanders	.25	.15
35	Willie Randolph	.05	.02
36	Pete Harnisch	.07	.04
37	Dante Bichette	.05	.02
38	Garry Templeton	.05	.02
39	Gary Gaetti	.05	.02
40	John Cerutti	.05	.02
41	Rick Cerone	.05	.02
42	Mike Pagliarulo	.05	.02
43	Ron Hassey	.05	.02
44	Roberto Alomar	.30	.18
45	Mike Boddicker	.05	.02
46	Bud Black	.05	.02
47	Rob Deer	.05	.02
48	Devon White	.08	.05
49	Luis Sojo	.05	.02
50	Terry Pendleton	.12	.07
51	Kevin Gross	.05	.02
52	Mike Huff	.05	.02
53	Dave Righetti	.05	.02
54	Matt Young	.05	.02
55	Ernest Riles	.05	.02
56	Bill Gullickson	.05	.02
57	Vince Coleman	.07	.04
58	Fred McGriff	.20	.12
59	Franklin Stubbs	.05	.02

1992 Score

For the second straight year Score issued their baseball card in two series which totaled 893-cards. The company redesigned the card fronts using thick border stripes on the left side with smaller borders at the top and bottom. Th ecards measure 2-1/2" by 3-1/2". The set is loaded with subsets plus a 5-card insert set honoring Joe DiMaggio. Those listings follow the checklist under the prefix BC. A special 4-card Franchise insert set featuring Musical, Mantle and Yastzremski are also listed at the end of this checklist under the prefix SP.

		MINT	NR/MT
Complete Set (893)		22.00	14.00
Commons		.05	.02

60	Eric King	.05	.02
61	Cory Snyder	.05	.02
62	Dwight Evans	07	04
63	Gerald Perry	.05	.02
64	Eric Show	.05	.02
65	Shawn Hillegas	.05	.02
66	Tony Fernandez	.05	.02
67	Tim Teufel	.05	.02
68	Mitch Webster	.05	.02
69	Mike Heath	.05	.02
70	Chili Davis	.05	.02
71	Larry Andersen	.05	.02
72	Gary Varsho	.05	.02
73	Juan Berenguer	.05	.02
74	Jack Morris	.10	.06
75	Barry Jones	.05	.02
76	Rafael Belliard	.05	.02
77	Steve Buechele	.05	.02
78	Scott Sanderson	.05	.02
79	Bob Ojeda	.05	.02
80	Curt Schilling	.08	.05
81	Brian Drahman (R)	.08	.05
82	Ivan Rodriguez (R)	1.25	.80
83	David Howard (R)	.10	.06
84	Healthcliff Slocumb (R)	.10	.06
85	Mike Timlin (R)	.10	.06
86	Darryl Kile (R)	.40	.25
87	Pete Schourek (R)	.10	.06
88	Bruce Walton (R)	.08	.05
89	Al Osuna (R)	.08	.05
90	Gary Scott (R)	.10	.06
91	Doug Simon	.07	.04
92	Chris Jones	.07	.04
93	Chuck Knoblauch	.20	.12
94	Dana Allison (R)	.08	.05
95	Erik Pappas (R)	.08	.05
96	Jeff Bagwell (R)	1.50	.90
97	Kirk Dressendorfer (R)	.12	.07
98	Freddie Benavides (R)	.08	.05
99	Luis Gonzalez (R)	.30	.18
100	Wade Taylor (R)	.15	.08
101	Ed Sprague	.12	.07
102	Bob Scanlan (R)	.10	.06
103	Rick Wilkins (R)	.35	.20
104	Chris Donnels (R)	.08	.05
105	Joe Slusarski (R)	.10	.06
106	Mark Lewis (R)	.15	.10
107	Pat Kelly (R)	.20	.12
108	John Briscoe (R)	.10	.06
109	Luis Lopez (R)	.10	.06
110	Jeff Johnson (R)	.12	.07
1	Ken Griffey, Jr.	1.00	.70
2	Nolan Ryan	.80	.50
3	Will Clark	.20	.12
4	Dave Justice	.20	.12
5	Dave Henderson	.05	.02
6	Bret Saberhagen	.07	.04
7	Fred McGriff	.15	.08
8	Erik Hanson	.08	.05
9	Darryl Strawberry	.15	.08
10	Doc Gooden	.10	.06
11	Juan Gonzalez	.80	.50
12	Mark Langston	.07	.04
13	Lonnie Smith	.05	.02
14	Jeff Montgomery	.08	.05
15	Robert Alomar	.25	.15
16	Delino DeShields	.15	.08
17	Steve Bedrosian	.05	.02
18	Terry Pendleton	.10	.06
19	Mark Carreon	.05	.02
20	Mark McGwire	.25	.15
21	Roger Clemens	.20	.12
22	Chuck Crim	.05	.02
23	Don Mattingly	.20	.12

24	Dickie Thon	.05	.02
25	Ron Gant	.15	.08
26	Milt Cuyler	.08	.05
27	Mike Macfarlane	.05	.02
28	Dan Gladden	.05	.02
29	Melido Perez	.05	.02
30	Willie Randolph	.05	.02
31	Albert Belle	.30	.18
32	Dave Winfield	.15	.10
33	Jimmy Jones	.05	.02
34	Kevin Gross	.05	.02
35	Andres Galarraga	.10	.06
36	Mike Deveraux	.05	.02
37	Chris Bosio	.05	.02
38	Mike LaValliere	.05	.02
39	Gary Gaetti	.05	.02
40	Felix Jose	.08	.05
41	Alvaro Espinoza	.05	.02
42	Rick Aguilera	.05	.02
43	Mike Gallego	.05	.02
44	Eric Davis	.07	.04
45	George Bell	.08	.05
46	Tom Brunansky	.05	.02
47	Steve Farr	.05	.02
48	Duane Ward	.05	.02
49	David Wells	.05	.02
50	Cecil Fielder	.15	.08
51	Walt Weiss	.05	.02
52	Todd Zeile	.08	.05
53	Doug Jones	.05	.02
54	Bob Walk	.05	.02
55	Rafael Palmeiro	.12	.07
56	Rob Deer	.05	.02
57	Paul O'Neill	.07	.04
58	Jeff Reardon	.08	.05
59	Randy Ready	.05	.02
60	Scott Erickson	.12	.07
61	Paul Molitor	.15	.08
62	Jack McDowell	.15	.08
63	Jim Acker	.05	.02
64	Jay Buhner	.07	.04
65	Travis Fryman	.25	.15
66	Marquis Grissom	.20	.12
67	Mike Harkey	.07	.04
68	Luis Polonia	.05	.02
69	Ken Caminiti	.07	.04
70	Chris Sabo	.08	.05
71	Gregg Olson	.07	.04
72	Carlton Fisk	.08	.05
73	Juan Samuel	.05	.02
74	Todd Stottlemyre	.07	.04
75	Andre Dawson	.10	.06
76	Alvin Davis	.05	.02
77	Bill Doran	.05	.02
78	B.J. Surhoff	.05	.02
79	Kirk McCaskill	.05	.02
80	Dale Murphy	.10	.06
81	Jose DeLeon	.05	.02
82	Alex Fernandez	.20	.12
83	Ivan Calderon	.05	.02
84	Brent Mayne	.05	.02
85	Jody Reed	.05	.02
86	Randy Tomlin	.08	.05
87	Randy Milligan	.05	.02
88	Pascual Perez	.05	.02
89	Hensley Meulens	.05	.02
90	Joe Carter	.20	.12
91	Mike Moore	.05	.02
92	Ozzie Guillen	.05	.02
93	Shawn Hillegas	.05	.02
94	Chili Davis	.05	.02
95	Vince Coleman	.07	.04
96	Jimmy Key	.07	.04
97	Billy Ripken	.05	.02
98	Dave Smith	.05	.02
99	Tom Bolton	.05	.02
100	Barry Larkin	.08	.05
101	Kenny Rogers	.05	.02
102	Mike Boddicker	.05	.02
103	Kevin Elster	.05	.02
104	Ken Hill	.07	.04
105	Charlie Leibrandt	.05	.02
106	Pat Combs	.05	.02
107	Hubie Brooks	.05	.02
108	Julio Franco	.08	.05
109	Vicente Palacios	.05	.02
110	Kal Daniels	.05	.02
111	Bruce Hurst	.07	.04
112	Willie McGee	.07	.04
113	Ted Power	.05	.02
114	Milt Thompson	.05	.02
115	Doug Drabek	.08	.05
116	Rafael Belliard	.05	.02
117	Scott Garrelts	.05	.02
118	Terry Mulholland	.05	.02
119	Jay Howell	.05	.02
120	Danny Jackson	.05	.02
121	Scott Ruskin	.05	.02
122	Robin Ventura	.20	.12
123	Bip Roberts	.05	.02
124	Jeff Russell	.05	.02
125	Hal Morris	.10	.06
126	Teddy Higuera	.05	.02
127	Luis Sojo	.05	.02
128	Carlos Baerga	.30	.18
129	Jeff Ballard	.05	.02
130	Tom Gordon	.05	.02
131	Sid Bream	.05	.02
132	Rance Mulliniks	.05	.02
133	Andy Benes	.10	.06
134	Mickey Tettleton	.05	.02
135	Rich DeLucia	.05	.02
136	Tom Pagnozzi	.05	.02
137	Harold Baines	.05	.02

138 Danny Darwin	.05	.02
139 Kevin Bass	.05	.02
140 Chris Nabholtz	.07	.04
141 Pete O'Brien	.05	.02
142 Jeff Treadway	.05	.02
143 Mickey Morandini	.07	.04
144 Eric King	.05	.02
145 Danny Tartabull	.10	.06
146 Lance Johnson	.05	.02
147 Casey Candaele	.05	.02
148 Felix Fermin	.05	.02
149 Rich Rodriguez	.05	.02
150 Dwight Evans	.07	.04
151 Joe Klink	.05	.02
152 Kevin Reimer	.07	.04
153 Orlando Merced	.10	.06
154 Mel Hall	.07	.04
155 Randy Myers	.05	.02
156 Greg Harris	.05	.02
157 Jeff Brantley	.05	.02
158 Jim Eisenreich	.05	.02
159 Luis Rivera	.05	.02
160 Cris Carpenter	.05	.02
161 Bruce Ruffin	.05	.02
162 Omar Vizquel	.07	.04
163 Gerald Alexander	.05	.02
164 Mark Guthrie	.05	.02
165 Scott Lewis	.05	.02
166 Bill Sampen	.05	.02
167 Dave Anderson	.05	.02
168 Kevin McReynolds	.05	.02
169 Jose Vizcaino	.05	.02
170 Bob Geren	.05	.02
171 Mike Morgan	.05	.02
172 Jim Gott	.05	.02
173 Mike Pagliarulo	.05	.02
174 Mike Jeffcoat	.05	.02
175 Craig Lefferts	.05	.02
176 Steve Finley	.05	.02
177 Wally Backman	.05	.02
178 Kent Mercker	.05	.02
179 John Cerutti	.05	.02
180 Jay Bell	.08	.05
181 Dale Sveum	.05	.02
182 Greg Gagne	.05	.02
183 Donnie Hill	.05	.02
184 Rex Hudler	.05	.02
185 Pat Kelly	.10	.06
186 Jeff Robinson	.05	.02
187 Jeff Gray	.05	.02
188 Jerry Willard	.05	.02
189 Carlos Quintana	.07	.04
190 Dennis Eckersley	.10	.06
191 Kelly Downs	.05	.02
192 Gregg Jefferies	.10	.06
193 Darrin Fletcher	.05	.02
194 Mike Jackson	.05	.02

195 Eddie Murray	.10	.06
196 Billy Landrum	.05	.02
197 Eric Yelding	.05	.02
198 Devon White	.07	.04
199 Larry Walker	.12	.07
200 Ryne Sandberg	.25	.15
201 Dave Magadan	.05	.02
202 Steve Chitren	.05	.02
203 Scott Fletcher	.05	.02
204 Dwayne Henry	.05	.02
205 Scott Coolbaugh	.05	.02
206 Tracy Jones	.05	.02
207 Von Hayes	.05	.02
208 Bob Melvin	.05	.02
209 Scott Scudder	.05	.02
210 Luis Gonzalez	.12	.07
211 Scott Sanderson	.05	.02
212 Chris Donnels	.08	.05
213 Heathcliff Slocumb	.07	.04
214 Mike Timlin	.07	.04
215 Brian Harper	.05	.02
216 Juan Berenguer	.05	.02
217 Mike Henneman	.05	.02
218 Bill Spiers	.05	.02
219 Scott Terry	.05	.02
220 Frank Viola	.07	.04
221 Mark Eichhorn	.05	.02
222 Ernest Riles	.05	.02
223 Ray Lankford	.20	.12
224 Pete Harnisch	.07	.04
225 Bobby Bonilla	.10	.06
226 Mike Scioscia	.05	.02
227 Joel Skinner	.05	.02
228 Brian Holman	.05	.02
229 Gilberto Reyes	.07	.04
230 Matt Williams	.12	.07
231 Jaime Navarro	.08	.05
232 Jose Rijo	.08	.05
233 Atlee Hammaker	.05	.02
234 Tim Teufel	.05	.02
235 John Kruk	.08	.05
236 Kurt Stillwell	.05	.02
237 Dan Pasqua	.05	.02
238 Tim Crews	.05	.02
239 Dave Gallagher	.05	.02
240 Leo Gomez	.12	.07
241 Steve Avery	.20	.12
242 Bill Gullickson	.05	.02
243 Mark Portugal	.07	.04
244 Lee Guetterman	.05	.02
245 Benny Santiago	.07	.04
246 Jim Gantner	.05	.02
247 Robby Thompson	.07	.04
248 Terry Shumpert	.05	.02
249 Mike Bell (R)	.10	.06
250 Harold Reynolds	.05	.02
251 Mike Felder	.05	.02

252 Bill Pecota	.05	.02
253 Bill Krueger	.05	.02
254 Alfredo Griffin	.05	.02
255 Lou Whitaker	.07	.04
256 Roy Smith	.05	.02
257 Jerald Clark	.05	.02
258 Cammy Cooa	.16	.09
259 Tim Naehring	.07	.04
260 Dave Righetti	.05	.02
261 Paul Gibson	.05	.02
262 Chris James	.05	.02
263 Larry Andersen	.05	.02
264 Storm Davis	.05	.02
265 Jose Lind	.05	.02
266 Greg Hibbard	.05	.02
267 Norm Charlton	.05	.02
268 Paul Kilgus	.05	.02
269 Greg Maddux	.15	.08
270 Ellis Burks	.07	.04
271 Frank Tanana	.05	.02
272 Gene Larkin	.05	.02
273 Ron Hassey	.05	.02
274 Jeff Robinson	.05	.02
275 Steve Howe	.05	.02
276 Daryl Boston	.05	.02
277 Mark Lee	.05	.02
278 Jose Segura (R)	.10	.06
279 Lance Blankenship	.05	.02
280 Don Slaught	.05	.02
281 Russ Swan	.05	.02
282 Bob Tewksbury	.05	.02
283 Geno Petralli	.05	.02
284 Shane Mack	.08	.05
285 Bob Scanlan	.05	.02
286 Tim Leary	.05	.02
287 John Smoltz	.12	.07
288 Pat Borders	.05	.02
289 Mark Davidson	.05	.02
290 Sam Horn	.05	.02
291 Lenny Harris	.05	.02
292 Franklin Stubbs	.05	.02
293 Thomas Howard	.08	.05
294 Steve Lyons	.05	.02
295 Francisco Oliveras	.05	.02
296 Terry Leach	.05	.02
297 Barry Jones	.05	.02
298 Lance Parrish	.05	.02
299 Wally Whitehurst	.05	.02
300 Bob Welch	.07	.04
301 Charlie Hayes	.05	.02
302 Charlie Hough	.05	.02
303 Gary Redus	.05	.02
304 Scott Bradley	.05	.02
305 Jose Oquendo	.05	.02
306 Pete Incaviglia	.05	.02
307 Marvin Freeman	.05	.02
308 Gary Pettis	.05	.02

309 Joe Slusarski	.07	.04
310 Kevin Seitzer	.07	.04
311 Jeff Reed	.05	.02
312 Pat Tabler	.05	.02
313 Mike Maddux	.05	.02
314 Bob Milacki	.05	.02
315 Eric Anthony	.09	.06
316 Dante Bichette	.07	.04
317 Steve Decker	.08	.05
318 Jack Clark	.05	.02
319 Doug Dascenzo	.05	.02
320 Scott Leius	.05	.02
321 Jim Lindeman	.05	.02
322 Bryan Harvey	.07	.04
323 Spike Owen	.05	.02
324 Roberto Kelly	.10	.06
325 Stan Belinda	.05	.02
326 Joe Cora	.05	.02
327 Jeff Innis	.05	.02
328 Willie Wilson	.05	.02
329 Juan Agosto	.05	.02
330 Charles Nagy	.15	.08
331 Scott Bailes	.05	.02
332 Pete Schourek	.07	.04
333 Mike Flanagan	.05	.02
334 Omar Olivares	.05	.02
335 Dennis Lamp	.05	.02
336 Tommy Greene	.08	.05
337 Randy Velarde	.05	.02
338 Tom Lampkin	.05	.02
339 John Russell	.05	.02
340 Bob Kipper	.05	.02
341 Todd Burns	.05	.02
342 Ron Jones	.05	.02
343 Dave Valle	.05	.02
344 Mike Heath	.05	.02
345 John Olerud	.35	.20
346 Gerald Young	.05	.02
347 Ken Patterson	.05	.02
348 Les Lancaster	.05	.02
349 Steve Crawford	.05	.02
350 John Candelaria	.05	.02
351 Mike Aldrete	.05	.02
352 Mariano Duncan	.05	.02
353 Julio Machado	.05	.02
354 Ken Williams	.05	.02
355 Walt Terrell	.05	.02
356 Mitch Williams	.05	.02
357 Al Newman	.05	.02
358 Bud Black	.05	.02
359 Joe Hesketh	.05	.02
360 Paul Assenmacher	.05	.02
361 Bo Jackson	.15	.08
362 Jeff Blauser	.08	.05
363 Mike Brumley	.05	.02
364 Jim Deshaies	.05	.02
365 Brady Anderson	.10	.06

366	Chuck McElroy	.05	.02
367	Matt Merullo	.05	.02
368	Tim Belcher	.07	.04
369	Luis Aquino	.05	.02
370	Joe Oliver	.05	.02
371	Greg Swindell	.07	.04
372	Lee Stevens	.05	.02
373	Mark Knudson	.05	.02
374	Bill Wegman	.05	.02
375	Jerry Don Gleaton	.05	.02
376	Pedro Guerrero	.05	.02
377	Randy Bush	.05	.02
378	Greg Harris	.05	.02
379	Eric Plunk	.05	.02
380	Jose DeJesus	.05	.02
381	Bobby Witt	.07	.04
382	Curtis Wilkerson	.05	.02
383	Gene Nelson	.05	.02
384	Wes Chamberlain	.10	.06
385	Tom Henke	.05	.02
386	Mark Lemke	.05	.02
387	Greg Briley	.05	.02
388	Rafael Ramirez	.05	.02
389	Tony Fossas	.05	.02
390	Henry Cotto	.05	.02
391	Tim Hulett	.05	.02
392	Dean Palmer	.20	.12
393	Glen Braggs	.05	.02
394	Mark Salas	.05	.02
395	Rusty Meacham (R)	.10	.06
396	Andy Ashby (R)	.12	.07
397	Jose Melendez (R)	.12	.07
398	Warren Newson (R)	.10	.06
399	Frank Castillo (R)	.12	.07
400	Chito Martinez (R)	.12	.07
401	Bernie Williams	.12	.07
402	Derek Bell	.20	.12
403	Javier Ortiz (R)	.08	.05
404	Tim Sherrill (R)	.08	.05
405	Rob MacDonald (R)	.08	.05
406	Phil Plantier	.20	.12
407	Troy Afenir	.07	.04
408	Gino Minutelli (R)	.08	.05
409	Reggie Jefferson (R)	.20	.12
410	Mike Remlinger (R)	.07	.04
411	Carlos Rodriguez (R)	.07	.04
412	Joe Redfield (R)	.08	.05
413	Alfonzo Powell (R)	.12	.07
414	Scott Livingstone (R)	.12	.07
415	Scott Kamieniecki (R)	.08	.05
416	Tim Spehr (R)	.08	.05
417	Brian Hunter (R)	.12	.07
418	Ced Landrum (R)	.08	.05
419	Bret Barberie	.12	.07
420	Kevin Morton	.08	.05
421	Doug Henry (R)	.15	.08
422	Doug Piatt (R)	.08	.05
423	Pat Rice (R)	.08	.05
424	Juan Guzman (R)	.30	.18
425	Nolan Ryan (No-Hit)	.40	.25
426	Tommy Greene (No-Hit)	.08	.05
427	Milacki/Flanagan/ Williamson (No-Hit)	.07	.04
428	Wilson Alvarez (NH)	.08	.05
429	Otis Nixon (HL)	.05	.02
430	Rickey Henderson (HL)	.10	.06
431	Cecil Fielder (AS)	.10	.06
432	Julio Franco (AS)	.08	.05
433	Cal Ripken, Jr. (AS)	.15	.08
434	Wade Boggs (AS)	.08	.05
435	Joe Carter (AS)	.10	.06
436	Ken Griffey, Jr. (AS)	.40	.25
437	Ruben Sierra (AS)	.10	.06
438	Scott Erickson (AS)	.08	.05
439	Tom Henke (AS)	.05	.02
440	Terry Steinbach (AS)	.05	.02
441	Ricky Henderson (DT)	.15	.08
442	Ryne Sandberg (DT)	.50	.30
443	Otis Nixon	.05	.02
444	Scott Radinsky	.05	.02
445	Mark Grace	.10	.06
446	Tony Pena	.05	.02
447	Billy Hatcher	.05	.02
448	Glenallen Hill	.08	.05
449	Chris Gwynn	.05	.02
450	Tom Glavine	.20	.12
451	John Habyan	.05	.02
452	Al Osuna	.05	.02
453	Tony Phillips	.07	.04
454	Greg Cadaret	.05	.02
455	Rob Dibble	.07	.04
456	Rick Honeycutt	.05	.02
457	Jerome Walton	.07	.04
458	Mookie Wilson	.05	.02
459	Mark Gubicza	.05	.02
460	Craig Biggio	.07	.04
461	Dave Cochrane	.05	.02
462	Keith Miller	.05	.02
463	Alex Cole	.05	.02
464	Pete Smith	.07	.04
465	Brett Butler	.07	.04
466	Jeff Huson	.05	.02
467	Steve Lake	.05	.02
468	Lloyd Moseby	.05	.02
469	Tim McIntosh	.07	.04
470	Dennis Martinez	.08	.05
471	Greg Myers	.05	.02
472	Mackey Sasser	.05	.02
473	Junior Ortiz	.05	.02
474	Greg Olson	.05	.02
475	Steve Sax	.07	.04
476	Ricky Jordan	.05	.02
477	Max Venable	.05	.02
478	Brian McRae	.15	.08

479	Doug Simons	.05	.02	536	Dennis Rasmussen	.05	.02
480	Rickey Henderson	.15	.08	537	Andy Allanson	.05	.02
481	Gary Varsho	.05	.02	538	Goose Gossage	.05	.02
482	Carl Willis	.05	.02	539	John Marzano	.05	.02
483	Rick Wilkins	.15	.10	540	Cal Ripken	.35	.20
484	Donn Pall	.05	.02	541	Bill Swift	.08	.05
485	Edgar Martinez	.10	.00	542	Kevin Appier	.07	.04
486	Tom Foley	.05	.02	543	Dave Bergman	.05	.02
487	Mark Williamson	.05	.02	544	Bernard Gilkey	.12	.07
488	Jack Armstrong	.05	.02	545	Mike Greenwell	.08	.05
489	Gary Carter	.08	.05	546	Jose Uribe	.05	.02
490	Ruben Sierra	.15	.08	547	Jesse Orasco	.05	.02
491	Gerald Perry	.05	.02	548	Bob Patterson	.05	.02
492	Rob Murphy	.05	.02	549	Mike Stanley	.05	.02
493	Zane Smith	.05	.02	550	Howard Johnson	.08	.05
494	Darryl Kile	.12	.07	551	Joe Orsulak	.05	.02
495	Kelly Gruber	.07	.04	552	Dick Schofield	.05	.02
496	Jerry Browne	.05	.02	553	Dave Hollins	.20	.12
497	Darryl Hamilton	.08	.05	554	David Segui	.07	.04
498	Mike Stanton	.07	.04	555	Barry Bonds	.40	.25
499	Mark Leonard	.05	.02	556	Mo Vaughn	.25	.15
500	Jose Canseco	.20	.12	557	Craig Wilson	.10	.06
501	Dave Martinez	.05	.02	558	Bobby Rose	.07	.04
502	Jose Guzman	.05	.02	559	Rod Nichols	.05	.02
503	Terry Kennedy	.05	.02	560	Len Dykstra	.15	.08
504	Ed Sprague	.07	.04	561	Craig Grebeck	.05	.02
505	Frank Thomas	1.50	.90	562	Darren Lewis	.07	.04
506	Darren Daulton	.15	.10	563	Todd Benzinger	.05	.02
507	Kevin Tapani	.07	.04	564	Ed Whitson	.05	.02
508	Luis Salazar	.05	.02	565	Jesse Barfield	.05	.02
509	Paul Faries	.05	.02	566	Lloyd McClendon	.05	.02
510	Sandy Alomar Jr.	.08	.05	567	Dan Plesac	.05	.02
511	Jeff King	.07	.04	568	Danny Cox	.05	.02
512	Gary Thurman	.05	.02	569	Skeeter Barnes	.05	.02
513	Chris Hammond	.07	.04	570	Bobby Thigpen	.05	.02
514	Pedro Munoz	.08	.05	571	Deion Sanders	.15	.08
515	Alan Trammell	.08	.05	572	Chuck Knoblauch	.12	.07
516	Geronimo Pena	.05	.02	573	Matt Nokes	.05	.02
517	Rodney McCray	.05	.02	574	Herm Winningham	.05	.02
518	Manny Lee	.05	.02	575	Tom Candiotti	.05	.02
519	Junior Felix	.05	.02	576	Jeff Bagwell	.35	.20
520	Kirk Gibson	.05	.02	577	Brook Jacoby	.05	.02
521	Darrin Jackson	.05	.02	578	Chico Walker	.05	.02
522	John Burkett	.08	.05	579	Brian Downing	.05	.02
523	Jeff Johnson	.07	.04	580	Dave Stewart	.08	.05
524	Jim Corsi	.05	.02	581	Francisco Cabrera	.05	.02
525	Robin Yount	.20	.12	582	Rene Gonzales	.05	.02
526	Jamie Quirk	.05	.02	583	Stan Javier	.05	.02
527	Bob Ojeda	.05	.02	584	Randy Johnson	.12	.07
528	Mark Lewis	.10	.06	585	Chuck Finley	.07	.04
529	Bryn Smith	.05	.02	586	Mark Gardner	.05	.02
530	Kent Hrbek	.05	.02	587	Mark Whiten	.12	.07
531	Dennis Boyd	.05	.02	588	Garry Templeton	.05	.02
532	Ron Karkovice	.05	.02	589	Gary Sheffield	.20	.12
533	Don August	.05	.02	590	Ozzie Smith	.12	.07
534	Todd Frohwirth	.05	.02	591	Candy Maldonado	.05	.02
535	Wally Joyner	.08	.05	592	Mike Sharperson	.05	.02

593	Carlos Martinez	.05	.02
594	Scott Bankhead	.05	.02
595	Tim Walloch	.05	.02
596	Tino Martinez	.10	.06
597	Roger McDowell	.05	.02
598	Cory Snyder	.05	.02
599	Andujar Cedeno	.12	.07
600	Kirby Puckett	.30	.18
601	Rick Parker	.05	.02
602	Todd Hundley	.07	.04
603	Greg Litton	.05	.02
604	Dave Johnson	.05	.02
605	John Franco	.05	.02
606	Mike Fetters	.05	.02
607	Luis Alicea	.05	.02
608	Trevor Wilson	.05	.02
609	Rob Ducey	.05	.02
610	Ramon Martinez	.10	.06
611	Dave Burba	.07	.04
612	Dwight Smith	.07	.04
613	Kevin Maas	.08	.05
614	John Costello	.05	.02
615	Glenn Davis	.05	.02
616	Shawn Abner	.05	.02
617	Scott Hemond	.08	.05
618	Tom Prince	.07	.04
619	Wally Ritchie	.07	.04
620	Jim Abbott	.12	.07
621	Charlie O'Brien	.05	.02
622	Jack Daugherty	.05	.02
623	Tommy Gregg	.05	.02
624	Jeff Shaw	.05	.02
625	Tony Gwynn	.15	.08
626	Mark Leiter	.07	.04
627	Jim Clancy	.05	.02
628	Tim Layana	.05	.02
629	Jeff Shaefer	.05	.02
630	Lee Smith	.10	.06
631	Wade Taylor	.08	.05
632	Mike Simms	.07	.04
633	Terry Steinbach	.05	.02
634	Shawon Dunston	.07	.04
635	Tim Raines	.05	.02
636	Kirt Manwaring	.05	.02
637	Warren Cromartie	.05	.02
638	Luis Quinones	.05	.02
639	Greg Vaughn	.10	.06
640	Kevin Mitchell	.10	.06
641	Chris Hoiles	.10	.06
642	Tom Browning	.07	.04
643	Mitch Webster	.05	.02
644	Steve Olin	.05	.02
645	Tony Fernandez	.05	.02
646	Juan Bell	.05	.02
647	Joe Boever	.05	.02
648	Carney Lansford	.07	.04
649	Mike Benjamin	.05	.02
650	George Brett	.25	.15
651	Tim Burke	.05	.02
652	Jack Morris	.10	.06
653	Orel Hershiser	.08	.05
654	Mike Schooler	.05	.02
655	Andy Van Slyke	.08	.05
656	Dave Stieb	.07	.04
657	Dave Clark	.05	.02
658	Ben McDonald	.12	.07
659	John Smiley	.08	.05
660	Wade Boggs	.15	.08
661	Eric Bullock	.05	.02
662	Eric Show	.05	.02
663	Lenny Webster	.05	.02
664	Mike Huff	.05	.02
665	Rick Sutcliffe	.05	.02
666	Jeff Manto	.05	.02
667	Mike Fitzgerald	.05	.02
668	Matt Young	.05	.02
669	Dave West	.05	.02
670	Mike Hartley	.05	.02
671	Curt Schilling	.07	.04
672	Brian Bohanon	.05	.02
673	Cecil Espy	.05	.02
674	Joe Grahe	.05	.02
675	Sid Fernandez	.05	.02
676	Edwin Nunez	.05	.02
677	Hector Villanueva	.07	.04
678	Sean Berry	.08	.05
679	Dave Eiland	.05	.02
680	David Cone	.10	.06
681	Mike Bordick	.12	.07
682	Tony Castillo	.05	.02
683	John Barfield	.05	.02
684	Jeff Hamilton	.05	.02
685	Ken Dayley	.05	.02
686	Carmelo Martinez	.05	.02
687	Mike Capel	.05	.02
688	Scott Chiamparino	.07	.04
689	Rich Gedman	.05	.02
690	Rich Monteleone	.05	.02
691	Alejandro Pena	.05	.02
692	Oscar Azocar	.05	.02
693	Jim Poole	.08	.05
694	Mark Gardiner	.07	.04
695	Steve Buechele	.05	.02
696	Rudy Seanez	.10	.06
697	Paul Abbott	.05	.02
698	Steve Searcy	.05	.02
699	Jose Offerman	.08	.05
700	Ivan Rodriguez	.20	.12
701	Joe Girardi	.05	.02
702	Tony Perezchica	.05	.02
703	Paul McClellan	.05	.02
704	David Howard	.05	.02
705	Dan Petry	.05	.02
706	Jack Howell	.05	.02

707	Jose Mesa	.05	.02
708	Randy St. Claire	.05	.02
709	Kevin Brown	.07	.04
710	Ron Darling	.05	.02
711	Jason Grimsley	.05	.02
712	John Orton	.05	.02
713	Shawn Boskie	.05	.02
714	Pat Clements	.05	.02
715	Brian Barnes	.07	.04
716	Luis Lopez	.07	.04
717	Bob McClure	.05	.02
718	Mark Davis	.05	.02
719	Dann Bilardello	.05	.02
720	Tom Edens	.05	.02
721	Willie Fraser	.05	.02
722	Curt Young	.05	.02
723	Neal Heaton	.05	.02
724	Craig Worthington	.05	.02
725	Mel Rojas	.08	.05
726	Daryl Irvine	.05	.02
727	Roger Mason	.05	.02
728	Kirk Dressendorfer	.08	.05
729	Scott Aldred	.05	.02
730	Willie Blair	.05	.02
731	Allan Anderson	.05	.02
732	Dana Kiecker	.05	.02
733	Jose Gonzalez	.05	.02
734	Brian Drahman	.07	.04
735	Brad Komminsk	.05	.02
736	Arthur Rhodes	.15	.08
737	Terry Matthews (R)	.10	.06
738	Jeff Fassero (R)	.10	.06
739	Mike Magnante (R)	.10	.06
740	Kip Gross (R)	.10	.06
741	Jim Hunter (R)	.10	.06
742	Jose Mota (R)	.10	.06
743	Joe Bitker (R)	.08	.05
744	Tim Mauser (R)	.10	.06
745	Ramon Garcia (R)	.08	.05
746	Rod Beck (R)	.25	.15
747	Jim Austin (R)	.08	.05
748	Keith Mitchell	.10	.06
749	Wayne Rosenthal	.08	.05
750	Bryan Hickerson (R)	.15	.08
751	Bruce Egloff	.08	.05
752	John Wehner (R)	.10	.06
753	Darren Holmes (R)	.10	.06
754	Dave Hansen	.10	.06
755	Mike Mussina	.50	.30
756	Anthony Young	.10	.06
757	Ron Tingley	.07	.04
758	Ricky Bones	.08	.05
759	Mark Wohlers	.12	.07
760	Wilson Alvarez	.07	.04
761	Harvey Pulliam	.08	.05
762	Ryan Bowen	.10	.06
763	Terry Bross	.08	.05
764	Joel Johnston	.08	.05
765	Terry McDaniel (R)	.08	.05
766	Esteban Beltre (R)	.10	.06
767	Rob Maurer (R)	.15	.08
768	Ted Wood (R)	.15	.08
769	Mo Sanford	.10	.06
770	Jeff Carter	.08	.05
771	Gil Heredia (R)	.10	.06
772	Monty Fariss	.10	.06
773	Will Clark AS	.12	.07
774	Ryne Sandberg AS	.15	.08
775	Barry Larkin AS	.08	.05
776	Howard Johnson AS	.08	.05
777	Barry Bonds AS	.25	.15
778	Brett Butler AS	.07	.04
779	Tony Gwynn AS	.10	.06
780	Ramon Martinez AS	.08	.05
781	Lee Smith AS	.07	.04
782	Mike Scioscia AS	.05	.02
783	Dennis Martinez HL	.07	.04
784	Dennis Martinez (No-Hit)	.07	.04
785	Mark Gardner (No-Hit)	.08	.05
786	Bret Saberhagen (No-Hit)	.08	.05
787	Kent Mercker, Mark Wohlers, Alejandro Pena (No-Hit)	.08	.05
788	Cal Ripken (MVP)	.15	.08
789	Terry Pendleton (MVP)	.10	.06
790	Roger Clemens (CY)	.15	.08
791	Tom Glavine (CY)	.10	.06
792	Chuck Knoblauch (ROY)	.10	.06
793	Jeff Bagwell (ROY)	.25	.15
794	Cal Ripken (Man of the Year)	.15	.08
795	David Cone (HL)	.10	.06
796	Kirby Puckett (HL)	.12	.07
797	Steve Avery (HL)	.12	.07
798	Jack Morris (HL)	.10	.06
799	Allen Watson (R)	.35	.20
800	Manny Ramirez (R)	1.50	.90
801	Cliff Floyd (R)	2.50	1.50
802	Al Shirley (R)	.20	.12
803	Brian Barber (R)	.30	.18
804	Jon Farrell (R)	.10	.06
805	Brent Gates (R)	.40	.25
806	Scott Ruffcorn (R)	.35	.20
807	Tyrone Hill (R)	.25	.15
808	Benji Gil (R)	.35	.20
809	Aaron Sele (R)	2.00	1.25
810	Tyler Green (R)	.20	.12
811	Chris Jones	.07	.04
812	Steve Wilson	.07	.04
813	Freddie Benavides	.05	.02
814	Don Wakamatsu (R)	.08	.05
815	Mike Humphreys (R)	.08	.05

816	Scott Servais (R)	.10	.06
817	Rico Rossy (R)	.10	.06
818	John Ramos (R)	.08	.05
819	Rob Mallicoat (R)	.08	.05
820	Milt Hill (R)	.08	.05
821	Carlos Garcia (R)	.20	.12
822	Stan Royer (R)	.10	.06
823	Jeff Plympton (R)	.08	.05
824	Braulio Castillo (R)	.12	.07
825	David Haas (R)	.08	.05
826	Luis Mercedes	.12	.07
827	Eric Karros	.30	.18
828	Shawn Hare (R)	.10	.06
829	Reggie Sanders	.30	.18
830	Tom Goodwin	.10	.06
831	Dan Gakeler (R)	.08	.05
832	Stacy Jones (R)	.08	.05
833	Kim Batiste	.10	.06
834	Cal Eldred	.20	.12
835	Chris George	.08	.05
836	Wayne Housie (R)	.08	.05
837	Mike Ignasiak (R)	.08	.05
838	Jose Manzanillo (R)	.10	.06
839	Jim Olander (R)	.08	.05
840	Gary Cooper (R)	.08	.05
841	Royce Clayton	.15	.08
842	Hector Fajardo (R)	.15	.08
843	Blaine Beatty	.07	.04
844	Jorge Pedre (R)	.08	.05
845	Kenny Lofton	.35	.20
846	Scott Brosius (R)	.10	.06
847	Chris Cron (R)	.10	.06
848	Denis Boucher	.07	.04
849	Kyle Abbott	.12	.07
850	Robert Zupcic (R)	.20	.12
851	Rheal Cormier	.12	.07
852	Jim Lewis (R)	.08	.05
853	Anthony Telford	.08	.05
854	Cliff Brantley (R)	.08	.05
855	Kevin Campbell (R)	.08	.05
856	Craig Shipley (R)	.08	.05
857	Chuck Carr	.15	.08
858	Tony Eusebio (R)	.08	.05
859	Jim Thome	.20	.12
860	Vinny Castilla (R)	.08	.05
861	Dann Howitt	.08	.05
862	Kevin Ward (R)	.08	.05
863	Steve Wapnick (R)	.08	.05
864	Rod Brewer	.07	.04
865	Todd Van Poppel	.25	.15
866	Jose Hernandez (R)	.12	.07
867	Amalio Carreno (R)	.08	.05
868	Calvin Jones (R)	.10	.06
869	Jeff Gardner (R)	.08	.05
870	Jarvis Brown (R)	.10	.06
871	Eddie Taubensee (R)	.12	.07
872	Andy Mota	.10	.06

873	Chris Haney	.12	.07
874	Roberto Hernandez	.10	.06
875	Laddie Renfroe (R)	.08	.05
876	Scott Cooper	.15	.08
877	Armando Reynoso (R)	.12	.07
878	Ty Cobb	.25	.15
879	Babe Ruth	.50	.30
880	Honus Wagner	.25	.15
881	Lou Gehrig	.35	.20
882	Satchel Page	.25	.15
883	Will Clark DT	.25	.15
884	Cal Ripken DT	.35	.20
885	Wade Boggs DT	.15	.08
886	Tony Gwynn DT	.20	.12
887	Kirby Puckett DT	.25	.15
888	Craig Biggio DT	.10	.06
889	Scott Erikson DT	.10	.06
890	Tom Glavine DT	.20	.12
891	Rob Dibble DT	.08	.05
892	Mitch Williams DT	.08	.05
893	Frank Thomas DT	1.25	.80
BC1	Joe DiMaggio	35.00	20.00
BC2	Joe DiMaggio	35.00	20.00
BC3	Joe DiMaggio	35.00	20.00
BC4	Joe DiMaggio	35.00	20.00
BC5	Joe DiMaggio	35.00	20.00
SP1	Stan Musial	10.00	6.50
SP2	Mickey Mantle	20.00	12.50
SP3	Carl Yastzremski	10.00	6.50
SP4	S. Musial, M. Mantle, C. Yastzremski	12.50	7.50

1992 Score Impact

The cards in this 90-card set were available in Score cello packs and feature both superstars and prospects. Different photos and border colors were used to distinguish the set from Score's regular issue. Cards measure 2-1/2" by 3-1/2".

		MINT	NR/MT
	Complete Set (90)	20.00	14.00
	Commons	.08	.05
1	Chuck Knoblauch	.20	.12
2	Jeff Bagwell	.80	.50
3	Juan Guzman	.60	.35
4	Milt Cuyler	.12	.07
5	Ivan Rodriquez	.75	.45
6	Rich DeLucia	.10	.06
7	Orlando Merced	.20	.12
8	Ray Lankford	.25	.15
9	Brian Hunter	.12	.07
10	Roberto Alomar	.75	.45
11	Wes Chamberlain	.12	.07
12	Steve Avery	.40	.25
13	Scott Erickson	.20	.12
14	Jim Abbott	.25	.15
15	Mark Whiten	.25	.15
16	Leo Gomez	.15	.08
17	Doug Henry	.15	.08
18	Brent Mayne	.08	.05
19	Charles Nagy	.20	.12
20	Phil Plantier	.50	.30
21	Mo Vaughn	.60	.35
22	Craig Biggio	.08	.05
23	Derek Bell	.50	.30
24	Royce Clayton	.35	.20
25	Gary Cooper	.10	.06
26	Scott Cooper	.20	.12
27	Juan Gonzalez	2.00	1.25
28	Ken Griffey Jr.	3.00	1.75
29	Larry Walker	.25	.15
30	John Smoltz	.25	.15
31	Todd Hundley	.10	.06
32	Kenny Lofton	1.00	.70
33	Andy Mota	.08	.05
34	Todd Zeile	.10	.06
35	Arthur Rhodes	.20	.12
36	Jim Thome	.60	.35
37	Todd Van Poppel	.60	.35
38	Mark Wohlers	.15	.08
39	Anthony Young	.15	.08
40	Sandy Alomar Jr.	.10	.06
41	John Olerud	1.25	.80
42	Robin Ventura	.50	.30
43	Frank Thomas	4.50	2.75
44	Dave Justice	.75	.45
45	Hal Morris	.15	.08
46	Ruben Sierra	.25	.15
47	Travis Fryman	.80	.50
48	Mike Mussina	1.25	.80
49	Tom Glavine	.50	.30
50	Barry Larkin	.15	.08
51	Will Clark	.50	.30
52	Jose Canseco	.40	.25
53	Bo Jackson	.25	.15
54	Dwight Gooden	.15	.08
55	Barry Bonds	1.25	.80
56	Fred McGriff	.40	.25
57	Roger Clemens	.75	.45
58	Benito Santiago	.12	.07
59	Darryl Strawberry	.25	.15
60	Cecil Fielder	.35	.20
61	John Franco	.08	.05
62	Matt Williams	.25	.15
63	Marquis Grissom	.25	.15
64	Danny Tartabull	.15	.08
65	Ron Gant	.20	.12
66	Paul O'Neill	.12	.07
67	Devon White	.10	.06
68	Rafael Palmeiro	.20	.12
69	Tom Gordon	.08	.05
70	Shawon Dunston	.10	.06
71	Rob Dibble	.08	.05
72	Eddie Zosky	.12	.07
73	Jack McDowell	.35	.20
74	Lenny Dykstra	.08	.05
75	Ramon Martinez	.10	.06
76	Reggie Sanders	.60	.35
77	Greg Maddux	.25	.15
78	Ellis Burks	.10	.06
79	John Smiley	.10	.06
80	Roberto Kelly	.15	.08
81	Ben McDonald	.20	.12
82	Mark Lewis	.12	.07
83	Jose Rijo	.10	.06
84	Ozzie Guillen	.08	.05
85	Lance Dickson	.15	.08
86	Kim Batiste	.15	.08
87	Gregg Olson	.10	.06
88	Andy Benes	.12	.07
89	Cal Eldred	.40	.25
90	David Cone	.15	.08

1992 Score Pinnacle

Score entered the premium card market with their first upscale baseball set. The 620-card set was issued in two series and features a number of innovative subsets such as Idols, Sidelines, Technicians and Shades. Random insert subsets include the 12-card Team Pinnacle set and the 18-card Rookie Idols set. Cello packs contain a special 40-card insert set dubbed Team 2000 featuring projected stars in the year 2000. All cards measure 2-1/2" by 3-1/2".

		MINT	NR/MT
	Complete Set (620)	50.00	32.00
	Commons	.07	.04
1	Frank Thomas	4.50	2.75
2	Benito Santiago	.10	.06
3	Carlos Baerga	.80	.50
4	Cecil Fielder	.40	.25
5	Barry Larkin	.15	.08
6	Ozzie Smith	.20	.12
7	Willie McGee	.10	.06
8	Paul Molitor	.20	.12
9	Andy Van Slyke	.12	.07
10	Ryne Sandberg	.80	.50
11	Kevin Seitzer	.07	.04
12	Lenny Dykstra	.20	.12
13	Edgar Martinez	.15	.10
14	Ruben Sierra	.35	.20
15	Howard Johnson	.15	.08
16	Dave Henderson	.07	.04
17	Devon White	.08	.05
18	Terry Pendleton	.15	.08
19	Steve Finley	.08	.05
20	Kirby Puckett	.75	.45
21	Orel Hershiser	.12	.07
22	Hal Morris	.15	.08
23	Don Mattingly	.35	.20
24	Delino DeShields	.30	.18
25	Dennis Eckersley	.15	.08
26	Ellis Burks	.08	.05
27	Jay Buhner	.10	.06
28	Matt Williams	.25	.15
29	Lou Whitaker	.07	.04
30	Alex Fernandez	.40	.25
31	Albert Belle	.80	.50
32	Todd Zeile	.12	.07
33	Tony Pena	.07	.04
34	Jay Bell	.08	.05
35	Rafael Palmeiro	.20	.12
36	Wes Chamberlain	.12	.07
37	George Bell	.10	.06
38	Robin Yount	.40	.25
39	Vince Coleman	.08	.05
40	Bruce Hurst	.08	.05
41	Harold Baines	.08	.05
42	Chuck Finley	.08	.05
43	Ken Caminiti	.07	.04
44	Ben McDonald	.20	.15
45	Roberto Alomar	.00	.50
46	Chili Davis	.07	.04
47	Bill Doran	.07	.04
48	Jerald Clark	.08	.05
49	Jose Lind	.07	.04
50	Nolan Ryan	2.50	1.50
51	Phil Plantier	.50	.30
52	Gary DiSarcina	.08	.05
53	Kevin Bass	.07	.04
54	Pat Kelly	.10	.06
55	Mark Wohlers	.15	.10
56	Walt Weiss	.07	.04
57	Lenny Harris	.07	.04
58	Ivan Calderon	.07	.04
59	Harold Reynolds	.07	.04
60	George Brett	.50	.30
61	Gregg Olson	.08	.05
62	Orlando Merced	.20	.12
63	Steve Decker	.08	.05
64	John Franco	.07	.04
65	Greg Maddux	.30	.18
66	Alex Cole	.08	.05
67	Dave Hollins	.50	.30
68	Kent Hrbek	.07	.04
69	Tom Pagnozzi	.07	.04
70	Jeff Bagwell	.80	.50
71	Jim Gantner	.07	.04
72	Matt Nokes	.07	.04
73	Brian Harper	.07	.04
74	Andy Benes	.12	.07
75	Tom Glavine	.40	.25
76	Terry Steinbach	.07	.04
77	Dennis Martinez	.08	.05
78	John Olerud	1.25	.80
79	Ozzie Guillen	.07	.04
80	Darryl Strawberry	.20	.12
81	Gary Gaetti	.07	.04
82	Dave Righetti	.07	.04
83	Chris Hoiles	.12	.07
84	Andujar Cedeno	.15	.08
85	Jack Clark	.07	.04
86	David Howard	.07	.04
87	Bill Gullickson	.07	.04
88	Bernard Gilkey	.15	.08
89	Kevin Elster	.07	.04
90	Kevin Maas	.08	.05
91	Mark Lewis	.12	.07
92	Greg Vaughn	.15	.10
93	Bret Barberie	.08	.05
94	Dave Smith	.07	.04
95	Roger Clemens	.80	.50
96	Doug Drabek	.12	.07
97	Omar Vizquel	.07	.04
98	Jose Guzman	.07	.04
99	Juan Samuel	.07	.04

100	Dave Justice	.80	.50
101	Tom Browning	.07	.04
102	Mark Gubicza	.07	.04
103	Mickey Morandini	.08	.05
104	Ed Whitson	.07	.04
105	Lance Parrish	.07	.04
106	Scott Erickson	.12	.07
107	Jack McDowell	.35	.20
108	Dave Stieb	.08	.05
109	Mike Moore	.07	.04
110	Travis Fryman	.80	.50
111	Dwight Gooden	.12	.07
112	Fred McGriff	.40	.25
113	Alan Trammell	.08	.05
114	Roberto Kelly	.15	.08
115	Andre Dawson	.20	.12
116	Bill Landrum	.07	.04
117	Brian McRae	.12	.07
118	B.J. Surhoff	.07	.04
119	Chuck Knoblauch	.15	.10
120	Steve Olin	.07	.04
121	Robin Ventura	.50	.30
122	Will Clark	.50	.30
123	Tino Martinez	.15	.10
124	Dale Murphy	.12	.07
125	Pete O'Brien	.07	.04
126	Ray Lankford	.20	.12
127	Juan Gonzalez	2.50	1.50
128	Ron Gant	.20	.12
129	Marquis Grissom	.30	.18
130	Jose Canseco	.35	.20
131	Mike Greenwell	.12	.07
132	Mark Langston	.12	.07
133	Brett Butler	.10	.06
134	Kelly Gruber	.08	.05
135	Chris Sabo	.08	.05
136	Mark Grace	.15	.08
137	Tony Fernandez	.08	.05
138	Glenn Davis	.08	.05
139	Pedro Munoz	.10	.06
140	Craig Biggio	.10	.06
141	Pete Schourek	.10	.06
142	Mike Boddicker	.07	.04
143	Robby Thompson	.10	.06
144	Mel Hall	.08	.05
145	Bryan Harvey	.10	.06
146	Mike LaValliere	.07	.04
147	John Kruk	.12	.07
148	Joe Carter	.35	.20
149	Greg Olson	.08	.05
150	Julio Franco	.10	.06
151	Darryl Hamilton	.12	.07
152	Felix Fermin	.07	.04
153	Jose Offerman	.10	.06
154	Paul O'Neill	.10	.06
155	Tommy Greene	.12	.07
156	Ivan Rodriquez	.60	.35
157	Dave Stewart	.10	.06
158	Jeff Reardon	.10	.06
159	Felix Jose	.10	.06
160	Doug Dascenzo	.07	.04
161	Tim Wallach	.08	.05
162	Dan Plesac	.07	.04
163	Luis Gonzalez	.12	.07
164	Mike Henneman	.07	.05
165	Mike Devereaux	.10	.06
166	Luis Polonia	.07	.04
167	Mike Sharperson	.07	.04
168	Chris Donnels	.08	.05
169	Greg Harris	.07	.04
170	Deion Sanders	.25	.15
171	Mike Schooler	.07	.04
172	Jose DeJesus	.07	.04
173	Jeff Montgomery	.08	.05
174	Milt Cuyler	.10	.06
175	Wade Boggs	.25	.15
176	Kevin Tapani	.08	.05
177	Bill Spiers	.07	.04
178	Tim Raines	.08	.05
179	Randy Milligan	.07	.04
180	Rob Dibble	.08	.05
181	Kirt Manwaring	.07	.04
182	Pascual Perez	.07	.04
183	Juan Guzman	.60	.35
184	John Smiley	.10	.06
185	David Segui	.08	.05
186	Omar Oliveras	.07	.04
187	Joe Slusarski	.08	.05
188	Erik Hanson	.08	.05
189	Mark Portugal	.08	.05
190	Walt Terrell	.07	.04
191	John Smoltz	.25	.15
192	Wilson Alvarez	.10	.06
193	Jimmy Key	.08	.05
194	Larry Walker	.25	.15
195	Lee Smith	.12	.07
196	Pete Harnisch	.10	.06
197	Mike Harkey	.08	.05
198	Frank Tanana	.07	.04
199	Terry Mulholland	.07	.04
200	Cal Ripken Jr.	.90	.60
201	Dave Magadan	.08	.05
202	Bud Black	.07	.04
203	Terry Shumpert	.08	.05
204	Mike Mussina	1.75	1.00
205	Mo Vaughn	.40	.25
206	Steve Farr	.07	.04
207	Darrin Jackson	.07	.04
208	Jerry Browne	.07	.04
209	Jeff Russell	.07	.04
210	Mike Scioscia	.07	.04
211	Rick Aguilera	.07	.04
212	Jaime Navarro	.10	.06
213	Randy Tomlin	.10	.06

214	Bobby Thigpen	.08	.05
215	Mark Gardner	.08	.05
216	Norm Charlton	.07	.04
217	Mark McGwire	.35	.20
218	Skeeter Barnes	.07	.04
219	Bob Tewksbury	.07	.04
220	Junior Felix	.07	.04
221	Sam Horn	.07	.04
222	Jody Reed	.07	.04
223	Luis Sojo	.07	.04
224	Jerome Walton	.08	.05
225	Darryl Kile	.15	.10
226	Mickey Tettleton	.08	.05
227	Dan Pasqua	.07	.04
228	Jim Gott	.07	.04
229	Bernie Williams	.15	.08
230	Shane Mack	.12	.07
231	Steve Avery	.50	.30
232	Dave Valle	.07	.04
233	Mark Leonard	.07	.04
234	Spike Owen	.07	.04
235	Gary Sheffield	.40	.25
236	Steve Chitren	.08	.05
237	Zane Smith	.07	.04
238	Tom Gordon	.08	.05
239	Jose Oquendo	.07	.04
240	Todd Stottlemyre	.08	.05
241	Darren Daulton	.20	.12
242	Tim Naehring	.10	.06
243	Tony Phillips	.08	.05
244	Shawon Dunston	.10	.06
245	Manuel Lee	.07	.04
246	Mike Pagliarulo	.07	.04
247	Jim Thome	.75	.45
248	Luis Mercedes	.15	.08
249	Cal Eldred	.35	.20
250	Derek Bell	.40	.25
251	Arthur Rhodes	.12	.07
252	Scott Cooper	.25	.15
253	Roberto Hernandez	.15	.10
254	Mo Sanford	.10	.06
255	Scott Servais	.10	.06
256	Eric Karros	.75	.45
257	Andy Mota	.08	.05
258	Keith Mitchell	.08	.05
259	Joel Johnson	.10	.06
260	John Wehner	.08	.05
261	Gino Minutelli	.08	.05
262	Greg Gagne	.08	.05
263	Stan Royer	.08	.05
264	Carlos Garcia	.35	.20
265	Andy Ashby	.08	.05
266	Kim Batiste	.10	.06
267	Julio Velera	.08	.05
268	Royce Clayton	.35	.20
269	Gary Scott	.10	.06
270	Kirk Dressendorfer	.10	.06
271	Sean Berry	.12	.07
272	Lance Dickson	.12	.07
273	Rob Maurer (R)	.15	.10
274	Scott Brosius (R)	.10	.06
275	Dave Fleming	.60	.35
276	Lenny Webster	.07	.04
277	Mike Humphries	.08	.05
278	Fred Benavides	.07	.04
279	Harvey Pulliam	.10	.06
280	Joe Carter	.25	.15
281	Jim Abbott (ID)	.40	.25
282	Wade Boggs (ID)	.20	.12
283	Ken Griffey Jr. (ID)	.75	.45
284	Wally Joyner (ID)	.10	.06
285	Chuck Knoblauch (ID)	.15	.10
286	Robin Ventura (ID)	.35	.20
287	Robin Yount (SL)	.25	.15
288	Bob Tewksbury (SL)	.07	.04
289	Kirby Puckett (SL)	.35	.20
290	Kenny Lofton (SL)	.40	.25
291	Jack McDowell SL)	.20	.12
292	John Burkett (SL)	.08	.05
293	Dwight Smith (SL)	.07	.04
294	Nolan Ryan (SL)	.80	.50
295	Manny Ramirez (R)	2.50	1.50
296	Cliff Floyd (R)	4.50	2.75
297	Al Shirley (R)	.25	.15
298	Brian Barber (R)	.40	.25
299	Jon Farrell (R)	.25	.15
300	Scott Ruffcorn (R)	.80	.50
301	Tyrone Hill (R)	.50	.30
302	Benji Gil (R)	.60	.35
303	Tyler Green (R)	.30	.18
304	Allen Watson (R)	.75	.45
305	Jay Buhner	.10	.06
306	Roberto Alomar (SH)	.35	.20
307	Chuck Knoblauch (SH)	.12	.07
308	Darryl Strawberry (SH)	.12	.07
309	Danny Tartabull (SH)	.10	.06
310	Bobby Bonilla (SH)	.10	.06
311	Mike Felder	.08	.05
312	Storm Davis	.07	.04
313	Tim Teufel	.07	.04
314	Tom Brunansky	.07	.04
315	Rex Hudler	.07	.04
316	Dave Otto	.07	.04
317	Jeff King	.10	.06
318	Dan Gladden	.07	.04
319	Bill Pecota	.07	.04
320	Franklin Stubbs	.07	.04
321	Gary Carter	.12	.07
322	Melido Perez	.08	.05
323	Eric Davis	.12	.07
324	Greg Myers	.07	.04
325	Pete Incaviglia	.07	.04
326	Von Hayes	.07	.04
327	Greg Swindell	.08	.05

328	Steve Sax	.08	.05
329	Chuck McElroy	.08	.05
330	Gregg Jefferies	.30	.18
331	Joe Oliver	.08	.05
332	Paul Faries	.07	.04
333	David West	.07	.04
334	Craig Grebeck	.08	.05
335	Chris Hammond	.10	.06
336	Billy Ripken	.07	.04
337	Scott Sanderson	.07	.04
338	Dick Schofield	.07	.04
339	Bob Milacki	.07	.04
340	Kevin Reimer	.08	.05
341	Jose DeLeon	.07	.04
342	Henry Cotto	.07	.04
343	Daryl Boston	.07	.04
344	Kevin Gross	.07	.04
345	Milt Thompson	.07	.04
346	Luis Rivera	.07	.04
347	Al Osuna	.07	.04
348	Rob Deer	.07	.04
349	Tim Leary	.07	.04
350	Mike Stanton	.07	.04
351	Dean Palmer	.40	.25
352	Trevor Wilson	.08	.05
353	Mark Eichhorn	.07	.04
354	Scott Aldred	.10	.06
355	Mark Whiten	.25	.15
356	Leo Gomez	.10	.06
357	Rafael Belliard	.07	.04
358	Carlos Quintana	.08	.05
359	Mark Davis	.07	.04
360	Chris Nabholz	.10	.06
361	Carlton Fisk	.20	.12
362	Joe Orsulak	.08	.05
363	Eric Anthony	.25	.15
364	Greg Hibbard	.08	.05
365	Scott Leius	.07	.04
366	Hensley Meulens	.08	.05
367	Chris Bosio	.07	.04
368	Brian Downing	.07	.04
369	Sammy Sosa	.30	.18
370	Stan Belinda	.08	.05
371	Joe Grahe	.08	.05
372	Luis Salazar	.07	.04
373	Lance Johnson	.08	.05
374	Kal Daniels	.07	.04
375	Dave Winfield	.40	.25
376	Brook Jacoby	.07	.04
377	Mariano Duncan	.07	.04
378	Ron Darling	.07	.04
379	Randy Johnson	.25	.15
380	Chito Martinez	.12	.07
381	Andres Galarraga	.20	.12
382	Willie Randolph	.07	.04
383	Charles Nagy	.25	.15
384	Tim Belcher	.08	.05
385	Duane Ward	.07	.04
386	Vicente Palacios	.07	.04
387	Mike Gallego	.07	.04
388	Rich DeLucia	.08	.05
389	Scott Radinsky	.08	.05
390	Damon Berryhill	.07	.04
391	Kirk McCaskill	.07	.04
392	Pedro Guerrero	.08	.05
393	Kevin Mitchell	.12	.07
394	Dickie Thon	.07	.04
395	Bobby Bonilla	.15	.08
396	Bill Wegman	.07	.04
397	Dave Martinez	.07	.04
398	Rick Sutcliffe	.08	.05
399	Larry Anderson	.07	.04
400	Tony Gwynn	.30	.18
401	Rickey Henderson	.30	.18
402	Greg Cadaret	.07	.04
403	Keith Miller	.07	.04
404	Bip Roberts	.07	.04
405	Kevin Brown	.10	.06
406	Mitch Williams	.08	.05
407	Frank Viola	.10	.06
408	Darren Lewis	.12	.07
409	Bob Welch	.10	.06
410	Bob Walk	.07	.04
411	Todd Frohwirt	.10	.06
412	Brian Hunter	.12	.07
413	Ron Karkovice	.07	.04
414	Mike Morgan	.07	.04
415	Joe Hesketh	.07	.04
416	Don Slaught	.07	.04
417	Tom Henke	.07	.04
418	Kurt Stillwell	.07	.04
419	Hector Villanueva	.08	.05
420	Glenallen Hill	.10	.06
421	Pat Borders	.07	.04
422	Charlie Hough	.07	.04
423	Charlie Leibrandt	.07	.04
424	Eddie Murray	.20	.12
425	Jesse Barfield	.07	.04
426	Mark Lemke	.07	.04
427	Kevin McReynolds	.08	.05
428	Gilberto Reyes	.07	.04
429	Ramon Martinez	.15	.08
430	Steve Buechele	.07	.04
431	David Wells	.07	.04
432	Kyle Abbott	.12	.07
433	John Habyan	.07	.04
434	Kevin Appier	.12	.07
435	Gene Larkin	.07	.04
436	Sandy Alomar, Jr.	.12	.07
437	Mike Jackson	.08	.05
438	Todd Benzinger	.07	.04
439	Teddy Higuera	.07	.04
440	Reggie Sanders	.50	.30
441	Mark Carreon	.07	.04

442	Bret Saberhagen	.15	.08
443	Gene Nelson	.07	.04
444	Jay Howell	.07	.04
445	Roger McDowell	.07	.04
446	Sid Bream	.07	.04
447	Mackey Sasser	.07	.04
448	Bill Swift	.10	.06
449	Hubie Brooks	.08	.05
450	David Cone	.12	.07
451	Bobby Witt	.12	.07
452	Brady Anderson	.15	.10
453	Lee Stevens	.07	.04
454	Luis Aquino	.07	.04
455	Carney Lansford	.07	.04
456	Carlos Hernandez	.08	.05
457	Danny Jackson	.07	.04
458	Gerald Young	.08	.05
459	Tom Candiotti	.07	.04
460	Billy Hatcher	.07	.04
461	John Wetteland	.20	.12
462	Mike Bordick	.15	.08
463	Don Robinson	.07	.04
464	Jeff Johnson	.10	.06
465	Lonnie Smith	.08	.05
466	Paul Assenmacher	.07	.04
467	Alvin Davis	.07	.04
468	Jim Eisenreich	.07	.04
469	Brent Mayne	.08	.05
470	Jeff Brantley	.08	.05
471	Tim Burke	.07	.04
472	Pat Mahomes (R)	.25	.15
473	Ryan Bowen	.15	.08
474	Bryn Smith	.07	.04
475	Mike Flanagan	.07	.04
476	Reggie Jefferson	.12	.07
477	Jeff Blauser	.07	.04
478	Craig Lefferts	.07	.04
479	Todd Worrell	.08	.05
480	Scott Scudder	.08	.05
481	Kirk Gibson	.08	.05
482	Kenny Rogers	.07	.04
483	Jack Morris	.15	.08
484	Russ Swann	.07	.04
485	Mike Huff	.07	.04
486	Ken Hill	.12	.07
487	Geronimo Pena	.10	.06
488	Charlie O'Brien	.07	.04
489	Mike Maddux	.07	.04
490	Scott Livingstone	.10	.06
491	Carl Willis	.07	.04
492	Kelly Downs	.07	.04
493	Dennis Cook	.07	.04
494	Joe Magrane	.08	.05
495	Bob Kipper	.07	.04
496	Jose Mesa	.07	.04
497	Charlie Hayes	.08	.05
498	Joe Girardi	.07	.04
499	Doug Jones	.07	.04
500	Barry Bonds	1.25	.80
501	Bill Krueger	.07	.04
502	Glenn Braggs	.07	.04
503	Eric King	.07	.04
504	Frank Castillo	.08	.05
505	Mike Gardiner	.10	.06
506	Cory Snyder	.07	.04
507	Steve Howe	.07	.04
508	Jose Rijo	.10	.06
509	Sid Fernandez	.08	.05
510	Archi Cianfrocco (R)	.20	.12
511	Mark Guthrie	.08	.05
512	Bob Ojeda	.07	.04
513	John Doherty	.07	.04
514	Dante Bichette	.08	.05
515	Juan Berenguer	.07	.04
516	Jeff Robinson	.07	.04
517	Mike McFarlane	.08	.05
518	Matt Young	.07	.04
519	Otis Nixon	.08	.05
520	Brian Holman	.08	.05
521	Chris Haney	.12	.07
522	Jeff Kent (R)	.40	.25
523	Chad Curtis (R)	.60	.35
524	Vince Horsman (R)	.12	.07
525	Rod Nichols	.10	.06
526	Peter Hoy (R)	.10	.06
527	Shawn Boskie	.08	.05
528	Alejandro Pena	.07	.04
529	Dave Burba	.07	.04
530	Ricky Jordan	.07	.04
531	Dave Silvestri (R)	.12	.07
532	John Patterson (R)	.10	.06
533	Jeff Branson (R)	.10	.06
534	Derrick May (R)	.35	.20
535	Esteban Beltre (R)	.15	.08
536	Jose Melendez	.12	.07
537	Wally Joyner	.12	.07
538	Eddie Taubensee (R)	.12	.07
539	Jim Abbott	.20	.12
540	Brian Williams (R)	.20	.12
541	Donovan Osborne	.40	.25
542	Patrick Lennon	.15	.08
543	Mike Groppuso (R)	.12	.07
544	Jarvis Brown (R)	.15	.08
545	Shawn Livsey (R)	.20	.12
546	Jeff Ware	.15	.10
547	Danny Tartabull	.15	.08
548	Bobby Jones (R)	.80	.50
549	Ken Griffey Jr.	3.50	2.00
550	Rey Sanchez (R)	.20	.12
551	Eric Wedge (R)	.15	.10
552	Juan Guerrero (R)	.15	.10
553	Jacob Brumfield (R)	.12	.07
554	Ben Rivera	.10	.06
555	Brian Jordan (R)	.75	.45

556	Denny Neagle	.10	.06
557	Cliff Brantley	.10	.06
558	Anthony Young	.12	.07
559	John Vander Wal (R)	.15	.08
560	Monty Fariss	.12	.07
561	Russ Springer (R)	.15	.08
562	Pat Listach (R)	.30	.18
563	Pat Hentgen	.60	.35
564	Andy Stankiewicz (R)	.10	.06
565	Mike Perez	.12	.07
566	Mike Bielecki	.07	.04
567	Butch Henry (R)	.10	.06
568	Dave Nilsson (R)	.20	.12
569	Scott Hatteberg (R)	.25	.15
570	Ruben Amaro Jr.	.10	.06
571	Todd Hundley	.08	.05
572	Moises Alou	.20	.12
573	Hector Fajardo (R)	.20	.12
574	Todd Van Poppel	.60	.35
575	Willie Banks	.15	.08
576	Eddie Zosky (R)	.15	.10
577	J.J. Johnson (R)	.20	.12
578	John Burkett (R)	.75	.45
579	Trevor Miller (R)	.12	.07
580	Scott Bankhead	.07	.04
581	Rich Amaral (R)	.10	.06
582	Kenny Lofton	1.00	.60
583	Matt Stairs (R)	.12	.07
584	Don Mattingly (ID)	.20	.12
585	Steve Avery (ID)	.25	.15
586	Roberto Alomar (ID)	.30	.18
587	Scott Sanderson (ID)	.07	.04
588	Dave Justice (ID)	.25	.15
589	Rex Hudler (ID)	.15	.10
590	David Cone (ID)	.15	.08
591	Tony Gwynn (ID)	.15	.10
592	Orel Hershiser (SL)	.10	.06
593	John Wetteland (SL)	.10	.06
594	Tom Glavine (SL)	.20	.12
595	Randy Johnson (SL)	.15	.08
596	Jim Gott (SL)	.07	.04
597	Dave Weathers (R)	.25	.15
598	Shawn Hare (R)	.12	.07
599	Chris Gardner (R)	.20	.12
600	Rusty Meacham	.08	.05
601	Benito Santiago (SH)	.08	.05
602	Eric Davis (SH)	.10	.06
603	Jose Lind (SH)	.07	.04
604	Dave Justice (SH)	.35	.20
605	Tim Raines (SH)	.08	.05
606	Randy Tomlin (G)	.08	.05
607	Jack McDowell (G)	.15	.08
608	Greg Maddux (G)	.12	.07
609	Charles Nagy (G)	.08	.05
610	Tom Candiotti (G)	.07	.04
611	David Cone (G)	.08	.05
612	Steve Avery (G)	.12	.07

613	Rod Beck (R)	.60	.35
614	Rickey Henderson	.20	.12
615	Benito Santiago	.08	.05
616	Ruben Sierra	.12	.07
617	Ryne Sandberg	.35	.20
618	Nolan Ryan	.80	.50
619	Brett Butler	.08	.05
620	Dave Justice	.35	.20

1992 Score Team Pinnacle

These All-Star cards were randomly inserted into Pinnacle foil packs and consist of side-by-side drawings of two players on the card fronts. The cards feature the artwork of noted illustrator Chris Greco. All cards measure 2-1/2" by 3-1/2".

		MINT	NR/MT
Complete Set (12)		325.00	180.00
Commons		10.00	6.50
1B	Frank Thomas/Will Clark	80.00	55.00
2B	Roberto Alomar/Ryne Sandberg	60.00	40.00
3B	Robin Ventura/Matt Williams	30.00	20.00
SS	Cal Ripken/Barry Larkin	40.00	25.00
LF	Danny Tartabull/Barry Bonds	50.00	35.00
CF	Ken Griffey Jr./Brett Butler	60.00	40.00
RF	Ruben Sierra/Dave Justice	40.00	25.00
C	Ivan Rodriguez/	30.00	20.00

	Benito Santiago		
RP	Roger Clemens/ Ramon Martinez	50.00	35.00
LP	Jim Abbott/Steve Avery	30.00	20.00
RRP	Dennis Eckersley/ Rob Dibble	12.00	7.50
LRP	Scott Radinsky/ John Franco	10.00	6.50

1992 Score Pinnacle Rookies

This 30-card update set features some of baseball's top 1992 rookies. Card fronts include full-bleed, full color action photos with the player's name printed in gold in a color bar under the photo. His team logo appears opposite his name. The words "1992 Rookie" is located in a black border under his name. The horizontal card backs contain another full color action photo and a brief description of the player. All cards measure 2-1/2" by 3-1/2".

		MINT	NR/MT
Complete Set (30)		10.00	6.50
Commons		.08	.05
1	Luis Mercedes	.20	.12
2	Scott Cooper	.35	.20
3	Kenny Lofton	1.50	.90
4	John Doherty	.30	.18
5	Pat Listach	.35	.20
6	Andy Stankiewicz	.12	.07
7	Derek Bell	.80	.50
8	Gary DiSarcina	.08	.05
9	Roberto Hernandez	.20	.12
10	Joel Johnston	.08	.05
11	Pat Mahomes	.50	.30
12	Todd Van Poppel	.75	.45
13	Dave Fleming	.80	.50
14	Monty Fariss	.08	.05
15	Gary Scott	.10	.06
16	Moises Alou	.75	.45
17	Todd Hundley	.10	.06
18	Kim Batiste	.12	.07
19	Denny Neagle	.10	.06
20	Donovan Osborne	.60	.35
21	Mark Wohlers	.20	.12
22	Reggie Sanders	.80	.50
23	Brian Williams	.25	.15
24	Eric Karros	.80	.50
25	Frank Seminara	.20	.12
26	Royce Clayton	.40	.25
27	Dave Nilsson	.25	.15
28	Matt Stairs	.12	.07
29	Chad Curtis	.80	.50
30	Carlos Hernandez	.10	.06

1992 Score Pinnacle Rookie Idols

This 18-card insert set features dual pictures on the card fronts featuring rookies and their idols. The standard-size cards were randomly issued in Pinnacle foil packs.

		MINT	NR/MT
Complete Set (18)		160.00	90.00
Commons		4.00	2.75
1	Reggie Sanders/ Eric Davis	8.50	5.00
2	Hector Fajardo/ Jim Abbott	7.50	4.50
3	Gary Cooper/ George Brett	15.00	10.00
4	Mark Wohlers/ Roger Clemens	20.00	12.50
5	Luis Mercedes/ Julio Franco	4.00	2.75
6	Willie Banks/ Doc Gooden	5.00	3.00
7	Kenny Lofton/ Rickey Henderson	25.00	15.00
8	Keith Mitchell/ Dave Henderson	4.00	2.75
9	Kim Batiste/	5.00	3.00

Barry Larkin

		MINT	NR/MT
10	Todd Hundley/ Thurman Munson	4.50	3.00
11	Eddie Zosky/Cal Ripken Jr.	25.00	15.00
12	Todd Van Poppel/ Nolan Ryan	40.00	30.00
13	Jim Thome/Ryne Sandberg	25.00	15.00
14	Dave Fleming/ Bobby Murcer	7.00	4.00
15	Royce Clayton/ Ozzie Smith	15.00	10.00
16	Donald Harris/ Darryl Strawberry	7.00	4.00
17	Chad Curtis/ Alan Trammell	12.00	7.50
18	Derek Bell/Dave Winfield	25.00	15.00

1992 Score Traded

		MINT	NR/MT
	Complete Set (110)	60.00	38.00
	Commons	.20	.12
1	Gary Sheffield	1.50	.90
2	Kevin Seitzer	.20	.12
3	Danny Tartabull	.25	.15
4	Steve Sax	.20	.12
5	Bobby Bonilla	.60	.35
6	Frank Viola	.20	.12
7	Dave Winfield	2.50	1.50
8	Rick Sutcliffe	.20	.12
9	Jose Canseco	1.00	.70
10	Greg Swindell	.20	.12
11	Eddie Murray	.80	.50
12	Randy Myers	.20	.12
13	Wally Joyner	.20	.12
14	Kenny Lofton	7.50	4.50
15	Jack Morris	.25	.15
16	Charlie Hayes	.35	.20

17	Pete Incaviglia	.20	.12
18	Kevin Mitchell	.25	.15
19	Kurt Stillwell	.20	.12
20	Bret Saberhagen	.25	.15
21	Steve Buechele	.20	.12
22	John Smiley	.20	.12
23	Sammy Sosa	1.75	1.00
24	George Bell	.25	.15
25	Curt Schilling	.60	.35
26	Dick Schofield	.20	.12
27	David Cone	.25	.15
28	Dan Gladden	.20	.12
29	Kirk McCaskill	.20	.12
30	Mike Gallego	.20	.12
31	Kevin McReynolds	.20	.12
32	Bill Swift	.40	.25
33	Dave Martinez	.20	.12
34	Storm Davis	.20	.12
35	Willie Randolph	.20	.12
36	Melido Perez	.20	.12
37	Mark Carreon	.20	.12
38	Doug Jones	.20	.12
39	Gregg Jefferies	1.75	1.00
40	Mike Jackson	.20	.12
41	Dickie Thon	.20	.12
42	Eric King	.20	.12
43	Herm Winningham	.20	.12
44	Derek Lilliquist	.20	.12
45	Dave Anderson	.20	.12
46	Jeff Reardon	.25	.15
47	Scott Bankhead	.20	.12
48	Cory Snyder	.20	.12
49	Al Newman	.20	.12
50	Keith Miller	.20	.12
51	Dave Burba	.20	.12
52	Bill Pecota	.20	.12
53	Chuck Crim	.20	.12
54	Mariano Duncan	.20	.12
55	Dave Gallagher	.20	.12
56	Chris Gwynn	.20	.12
57	Scott Ruskin	.20	.12
58	Jack Armstrong	.20	.12
59	Gary Carter	.25	.15
60	Andres Galarraga	.80	.50
61	Ken Hill	.30	.18
62	Eric Davis	.25	.15
63	Ruben Sierra	.75	.45
64	Darrin Fletcher	.25	.15
65	Tim Belcher	.20	.12
66	Mike Morgan	.20	.12
67	Scott Scudder	.20	.12
68	Tom Candiotti	.20	.12
69	Hubie Brooks	.20	.12
70	Kal Daniels	.20	.12
71	Bruce Ruffin	.20	.12
72	Billy Hatcher	.20	.12
73	Bob Melvin	.20	.12

74	Lee Guetterman	.20	.12
75	Rene Gonzales	.25	.15
76	Kevin Bass	.20	.12
77	Tom Bolton	.20	.12
78	John Wetteland	.70	.40
79	Bip Roberts	.20	.12
80	Pat Listach (R)	1.25	.80
81	John Doherty (R)	.60	.35
82	Sam Militello	.40	.25
83	Brian Jordan (R)	1.50	.90
84	Jeff Kent (R)	2.00	1.25
85	Dave Fleming	2.50	1.50
86	Jeff Tackett	.20	.12
87	Chad Curtis (R)	6.50	3.75
88	Eric Fox (R)	.35	.20
89	Denny Neagle	.20	.12
90	Donovan Osborne	1.75	1.00
91	Carlos Hernandez	.25	.15
92	Tim Wakefield (R)	1.25	.80
93	Tim Salmon	28.00	18.00
94	Dave Nilsson	.50	.30
95	Mike Perez	.30	.18
96	Pat Hentgen	6.00	3.50
97	Frank Seminara (R)	.35	.20
98	Ruben Amaro, Jr.	.25	.15
99	Archi Cianfrocco (R)	.50	.30
100	Andy Stankiewicz (R)	.35	.20
101	Jim Bullinger'	.20	.12
102	Pat Mahomes (R)	1.25	.80
103	Hipolito Pichardo (R)	.60	.35
104	Bret Boone	2.50	1.50
105	John Vander Wal (R)	.40	.25
106	Vince Horsman (R)	.30	.18
107	James Austin (R)	.30	.18
108	Brian Williams (R)	.80	.50
109	Dan Walters (R)	.50	.30
110	Wil Cordero (R)	2.50	1.50

1993 Score Select

This 405-card set is the premier edition of Score's newest baseball set. Card fronts feature full color action photos on a green card stock. The player's name appears in yellow in the bottom corner of the card. A Score Select logo is located in a corner of the photograph. Card backs contain a full color photo, stats and a brief description of the player. All cards measure 2-1/2" by 3-1/2".

		MINT	NR/MT
Complete Set (405)		35.00	22.00
Commons		.06	.03
1	Barry Bonds	.75	.45
2	Ken Griffey, Jr.	1.75	1.00
3	Will Clark	.30	.18
4	Kirby Puckett	.35	.20
5	Tony Gwynn	.20	.12
6	Frank Thomas	2.50	1.50
7	Tom Glavine	.20	.12
8	Roberto Alomar	.40	.25
9	Andre Dawson	.15	.10
10	Ron Darling	.06	.03
11	Bobby Bonilla	.12	.07
12	Danny Tartabull	.12	.07
13	Darren Daulton	.20	.12
14	Roger Clemens	.40	.25
15	Ozzie Smith	.15	.10
16	Mark McGwire	.25	.15
17	Terry Pendleton	.15	.10
18	Cal Ripken, Jr.	.50	.30
19	Fred McGriff	.25	.15
20	Cecil Fielder	.25	.15
21	Darryl Strawberry	.20	.12
22	Robin Yount	.25	.15
23	Barry Larkin	.15	.10
24	Don Mattingly	.20	.12
25	Craig Biggio	.08	.05
26	Sandy Alomar, Jr.	.07	.04

27	Larry Walker	.15	.10
28	Junior Felix	.06	.03
29	Eddie Murray	.15	.10
30	Robin Ventura	.20	.12
31	Greg Maddux	.20	.12
32	Dave Winfield	.25	.15
33	John Kruk	.12	.07
34	Wally Joyner	.08	.05
35	Andy Van Slyke	.08	.05
36	Chuck Knoblauch	.20	.12
37	Tom Pagnozzi	.07	.04
38	Dennis Eckersley	.15	.10
39	Dave Justice	.40	.25
40	Juan Gonzalez	1.50	.90
41	Gary Sheffield	.30	.18
42	Paul Molitor	.20	.12
43	Delino DeShields	.12	.07
44	Travis Fryman	.35	.20
45	Hal Morris	.08	.05
46	Gregg Olson	.07	.04
47	Ken Caminiti	.06	.03
48	Wade Boggs	.20	.12
49	Orel Hershiser	.08	.05
50	Albert Belle	.50	.30
51	Bill Swift	.12	.07
52	Mark Langston	.10	.06
53	Joe Girardi	.06	.03
54	Keith Miller	.06	.03
55	Gary Carter	.12	.07
56	Brady Anderson	.15	.10
57	Doc Gooden	.15	.10
58	Julio Franco	.06	.03
59	Lenny Dykstra	.20	.12
60	Mickey Tettleton	.07	.04
61	Randy Tomlin	.06	.03
62	B.J. Surhoff	.06	.03
63	Todd Zeile	.08	.05
64	Roberto Kelly	.10	.06
65	Rob Dibble	.07	.04
66	Leo Gomez	.08	.05
67	Doug Jones	.06	.03
68	Ellis Burks	.08	.05
69	Mike Scioscia	.06	.03
70	Charles Nagy	.12	.07
71	Cory Snyder	.06	.03
72	Devon White	.10	.06
73	Mark Grace	.15	.10
74	Luis Polonia	.06	.03
75	John Smiley	.08	.05
76	Carlton Fisk	.15	.10
77	Luis Sojo	.06	.03
78	George Brett	.30	.18
79	Mitch Williams	.06	.03
80	Kent Hrbek	.06	.03
81	Jay Bell	.08	.05
82	Edgar Martinez	.12	.07
83	Lee Smith	.08	.05
84	Deion Sanders	.20	.12
85	Bill Gullickson	.06	.03
86	Paul O'Neill	.10	.06
87	Kevin Seitzer	.06	.03
88	Steve Finley	.06	.03
89	Mel Hall	.07	.04
90	Nolan Ryan	.00	.50
91	Eric Davis	.12	.07
92	Mike Mussina	.50	.30
93	Tony Fernandez	.08	.05
94	Frank Viola	.08	.05
95	Matt Williams	.20	.12
96	Joe Carter	.25	.15
97	Ryne Sandberg	.40	.25
98	Jim Abbott	.20	.12
99	Marquis Grissom	.15	.10
100	George Bell	.10	.06
101	Howard Johnson	.10	.06
102	Kevin Appier	.10	.06
103	Dale Murphy	.10	.06
104	Shane Mack	.08	.05
105	Jose Lind	.06	.03
106	Rickey Henderson	.25	.15
107	Bob Tewksbury	.06	.03
108	Kevin Mitchell	.10	.06
109	Steve Avery	.25	.15
110	Candy Maldonado	.06	.03
111	Bip Roberts	.06	.03
112	Lou Whitaker	.07	.04
113	Jeff Bagwell	.35	.20
114	Dante Bichette	.08	.05
115	Brett Butler	.08	.05
116	Melido Perez	.07	.04
117	Andy Benes	.12	.07
118	Randy Johnson	.20	.12
119	Willie McGee	.10	.06
120	Jody Reed	.06	.03
121	Shawon Dunston	.08	.05
122	Carlos Baerga	.40	.25
123	Bret Saberhagen	.12	.07
124	John Olerud	.50	.30
125	Ivan Calderon	.07	.04
126	Bryan Harvey	.08	.05
127	Terry Mulholland	.06	.03
128	Ozzie Guillen	.06	.03
129	Steve Buechele	.06	.03
130	Kevin Tapani	.07	.04
131	Felix Jose	.08	.05
132	Terry Steinbach	.08	.05
133	Ron Gant	.20	.12
134	Harold Reynolds	.06	.03
135	Chris Sabo	.07	.04
136	Ivan Rodriquez	.25	.15
137	Eric Anthony	.10	.06
138	Mike Henneman	.06	.03
139	Robby Thompson	.08	.05
140	Scott Fletcher	.06	.03

#	Player			#	Player		
141	Bruce Hurst	.08	.05	198	Chuck Finley	.08	.05
142	Kevin Maas	.10	.06	199	Darrin Jackson	.06	.03
143	Tom Candiotti	.06	.03	200	Kelly Gruber	.07	.04
144	Chris Hoiles	.08	.05	201	John Wetteland	.10	.06
145	Mike Morgan	.06	.03	202	Jay Buhner	.08	.05
146	Mark Whiten	.15	.10	203	Mike LaValliere	.06	.03
147	Dennis Martinez	.08	.05	204	Kevin Brown	.08	.05
148	Tony Pena	.06	.03	205	Luis Gonzalez	.10	.06
149	Dave Magadan	.06	.03	206	Rick Aguilera	.06	.03
150	Mark Lewis	.08	.05	207	Norm Charlton	.06	.03
151	Mariano Duncan	.06	.03	208	Mike Bordick	.08	.05
152	Gregg Jefferies	.20	.12	209	Charlie Leibrandt	.06	.03
153	Doug Drabek	.10	.06	210	Tom Brunansky	.07	.04
154	Brian Harper	.06	.03	211	Tom Henke	.06	.03
155	Ray Lankford	.15	.10	212	Randy Milligan	.06	.03
156	Carney Lansford	.06	.03	213	Ramon Martinez	.10	.06
157	Mike Sharperson	.06	.03	214	Mo Vaughn	.25	.15
158	Jack Morris	.15	.10	215	Randy Myers	.06	.03
159	Otis Nixon	.08	.05	216	Greg Hibbard	.06	.03
160	Steve Sax	.07	.04	217	Wes Chamberlain	.12	.07
161	Mark Lemke	.06	.03	218	Tony Phillips	.06	.03
162	Rafael Palmeiro	.15	.10	219	Pete Harnisch	.07	.04
163	Jose Rijo	.10	.06	220	Mike Gallego	.06	.03
164	Omar Visquel	.08	.05	221	Bud Black	.06	.03
165	Sammy Sosa	.20	.12	222	Greg Vaughn	.12	.07
166	Milt Cuyler	.08	.05	223	Milt Thompson	.06	.03
167	John Franco	.06	.03	224	Ben McDonald	.15	.10
168	Darryl Hamilton	.10	.06	225	Billy Hatcher	.06	.03
169	Ken Hill	.08	.05	226	Paul Sorrento	.10	.06
170	Mike Devereaux	.08	.05	227	Mark Gubicza	.07	.04
171	Don Slaught	.06	.03	228	Mike Greenwell	.10	.06
172	Steve Farr	.06	.03	229	Curt Schilling	.10	.06
173	Bernard Gilkey	.12	.07	230	Alan Trammell	.10	.06
174	Mike Fetters	.06	.03	231	Zane Smith	.06	.03
175	Vince Coleman	.07	.04	232	Bobby Thigpen	.07	.04
176	Kevin McReynolds	.07	.04	233	Greg Olson	.06	.03
177	John Smoltz	.20	.12	234	Joe Orsulak	.06	.03
178	Greg Gagne	.06	.03	235	Joe Oliver	.06	.03
179	Greg Swindell	.07	.04	236	Tim Raines	.08	.05
180	Juan Guzman	.30	.18	237	Juan Samuel	.06	.03
181	Kal Daniels	.06	.03	238	Chili Davis	.08	.05
182	Rick Sutcliffe	.06	.03	239	Spike Owen	.06	.03
183	Orlando Merced	.08	.05	240	Dave Stewart	.10	.06
184	Bill Wegman	.06	.03	241	Jim Eisenreich	.06	.03
185	Mark Gardner	.06	.03	242	Phil Plantier	.25	.15
186	Rob Deer	.08	.05	243	Sid Fernandez	.08	.05
187	Dave Hollins	.20	.12	244	Dan Gladden	.06	.03
188	Jack Clark	.08	.05	245	Mickey Morandini	.08	.05
189	Brian Hunter	.12	.07	246	Tino Martinez	.08	.05
190	Tim Wallach	.07	.04	247	Kirt Manwaring	.06	.03
191	Tim Belcher	.07	.04	248	Dean Palmer	.25	.15
192	Walt Weiss	.06	.03	249	Tom Browning	.07	.04
193	Kurt Stillwell	.06	.03	250	Brian McRae	.10	.06
194	Charlie Hayes	.15	.10	251	Scott Leius	.06	.03
195	Willie Randolph	.07	.04	252	Bert Blyleven	.10	.06
196	Jack McDowell	.20	.12	253	Scott Erickson	.15	.10
197	Jose Offerman	.10	.06	254	Bob Welch	.07	.04

255 Pat Kelly	.08	.05
256 Felix Fermin	.06	.03
257 Harold Baines	.07	.04
258 Duane Ward	.06	.03
259 Bill Spiers	.06	.03
260 Jamie Navarro	.10	.06
261 Scott Sanderson	.06	.03
262 Gary Gaetti	.06	.03
263 Bob Ojeda	.06	.03
264 Jeff Montgomery	.08	.05
265 Scott Bankhead	.06	.03
266 Lance Johnson	.07	.04
267 Rafael Belliard	.06	.03
268 Kevin Reimer	.08	.05
269 Benito Santiago	.10	.06
270 Mike Moore	.06	.03
271 Dave Fleming	.20	.12
272 Moises Alou	.12	.07
273 Pat Listach	.15	.10
274 Reggie Sanders	.20	.12
275 Kenny Lofton	.35	.20
276 Donovan Osborne	.15	.10
277 Rusty Meacham	.10	.06
278 Eric Karros	.30	.18
279 Andy Stankiewicz	.10	.06
280 Brian Jordan	.20	.12
281 Gary DiSarcina	.08	.05
282 Mark Wohlers	.08	.05
283 Dave Nilsson	.10	.06
284 Anthony Young	.08	.05
285 Jim Bullinger	.07	.04
286 Derek Bell	.20	.12
287 Brian Williams	.20	.12
288 Julio Valera	.06	.03
289 Dan Walters	.12	.07
290 Chad Curtis	.20	.12
291 Michael Tucker (R)	.70	.40
292 Bob Zupcic	.08	.05
293 Todd Hundley	.08	.05
294 Jeff Tackett	.10	.06
295 Greg Colbrunn	.10	.06
296 Cal Eldred	.20	.12
297 Chris Roberts (R)	.30	.18
298 John Doherty	.10	.06
299 Denny Neagle	.08	.05
300 Arthur Rhodes	.12	.07
301 Mark Clark	.10	.06
302 Scott Cooper	.12	.07
303 Jamie Arnold (R)	.25	.15
304 Jim Thome	.20	.12
305 Frank Seminara	.10	.06
306 Kurt Knudsen	.08	.05
307 Tim Wakefield (R)	.30	.18
308 John Jaha	.15	.10
309 Pat Hentgen	.08	.05
310 B.J. Wallace (R)	.50	.30
311 Roberto Hernandez	.08	.05

312 Hipolito Pachardo	.10	.06
313 Eric Fox	.10	.06
314 Willie Banks	.08	.05
315 Sam Militello	.25	.15
316 Vince Horsman	.12	.07
317 Carlos Hernandez	.07	.04
318 Jeff Kent	.20	.12
319 Mike Perez	.10	.06
320 Scott Livingstone	.07	.04
321 Jeff Conine	.15	.10
322 James Austin	.10	.06
323 John Vander Wal	.12	.07
324 Pat Mahomes	.25	.15
325 Pedro Astacio	.25	.15
326 Bret Boone	.20	.12
327 Matt Stairs	.10	.06
328 Damion Easley	.15	.10
329 Ben Rivera	.07	.04
330 Reggie Jefferson	.10	.06
331 Luis Mercedes	.10	.06
332 Kyle Abbott	.10	.06
333 Eddie Taubensee	.08	.05
334 Tim McIntosh	.10	.06
335 Phil Clark	.08	.05
336 Wil Cordero	.30	.18
337 Russ Springer	.12	.07
338 Craig Colbert	.08	.05
339 Tim Salmon	2.50	1.50
340 Braulio Castillo	.08	.05
341 Donald Harris	.10	.06
342 Eric Young	.15	.10
343 Bob Wickman	.20	.12
344 John Valentin	.15	.10
345 Dan Wilson	.12	.07
346 Steve Hosey	.20	.12
347 Mike Piazza	3.00	1.75
348 Willie Greene	.20	.12
349 Tom Goodwin	.12	.07
350 Eric Hillman	.12	.07
351 Steve Reed (R)	.15	.10
352 Dan Serafini (R)	.30	.18
353 Todd Steverson (R)	.35	.20
354 Benji Grigsby (R)	.25	.15
355 Shannon Stewart (R)	.30	.18
356 Sean Lowe (R)	.20	.12
357 Derek Wallace (R)	.25	.15
358 Rick Helling	.35	.20
359 Jason Kendall (R)	.30	.18
360 Derek Jeter (R)	.80	.50
361 David Cone	.12	.07
362 Jeff Reardon	.10	.06
363 Bobby Witt	.08	.05
364 Jose Canseco	.25	.15
365 Jeff Russell	.06	.03
366 Ruben Sierra	.25	.15
367 Alan Mills	.07	.04
368 Matt Nokes	.07	.04

369	Pat Borders	.07	.04
370	Pedro Munoz	.10	.06
071	Danny Jackson	.00	.03
372	Geronimo Pena	.06	.03
373	Craig Lefferts	.06	.03
374	Joe Grahe	.06	.03
375	Roger McDowell	.06	.03
376	Jimmy Key	.08	.05
377	Steve Olin	.07	.04
378	Glenn Davis	.06	.03
379	Rene Gonzales	.07	.04
380	Manuel Lee	.06	.03
381	Ron Karkovice	.06	.03
382	Sid Bream	.06	.03
383	Gerald Williams	.15	.10
384	Lenny Harris	.06	.03
385	J.T. Snow (R)	1.00	.60
386	Dave Steib	.10	.06
387	Kirk McCaskill	.06	.03
388	Lance Parrish	.07	.04
389	Craig Grebeck	.06	.03
390	Rick Wilkins	.12	.07
391	Manny Alexander	.08	.05
392	Mike Schooler	.06	.03
393	Bernie Williams	.12	.07
394	Kevin Koslofski (R)	.12	.07
395	Willie Wilson	.06	.03
396	Jeff Parrett	.06	.03
397	Mike Harkey	.08	.05
398	Frank Tanana	.06	.03
399	Doug Henry	.06	.03
400	Royce Clayton	.15	.10
401	Eric Wedge (R)	.15	.10
402	Derrick May	.15	.10
403	Carlos Garcia (R)	.25	.15
404	Henry Rodriquez	.12	.07
405	Ryan Klesko	.50	.30

1	Fred McGriff	7.50	4.50
2	Ryne Sandberg	15.00	10.00
3	Ozzie Smith	5.00	3.00
4	Gary Sheffield	6.00	3.50
5	Darren Daulton	5.00	3.00
6	Andy Van Slyke	2.50	1.50
7	Barry Bonds	18.00	12.00
8	Tony Gwynn	7.00	4.00
9	Greg Maddux	7.00	4.00
10	Tom Glavine	7.50	4.50
11	John Franco	2.50	1.50
12	Lee Smith	2.50	1.50
13	Cecil Fielder	7.50	4.50
14	Roberto Alomar	15.00	10.00
15	Cal Ripken, Jr.	16.00	11.00
16	Edgar Martinez	2.75	1.75
17	Ivan Rodriguez	6.00	3.50
18	Kirby Puckett	12.00	7.50
19	Ken Griffey, Jr.	24.00	14.00
20	Joe Carter	8.50	5.00
21	Roger Clemens	12.00	7.50
22	Dave Fleming	5.00	3.00
23	Paul Molitor	7.50	4.50
24	Dennis Eckersley	2.75	1.75

1993 Score Select Rookies

The cards in this limited edition 24-card set were available through the hobby trade and include some of the msot promising rookies in baseball plus three Triple Crown Winners, Mickey Mantle, Carl Yastzremski and Frank Robinson. Cards measure 2-1/2" by 3-1/2".

	MINT	NR/MT
Complete Set (24)	300.00	175.00
Commons	6.00	3.50

1	Pat Listach	6.50	3.75
2	Moises Alou	8.50	5.00
3	Reggie Sanders	15.00	10.00
4	Kenny Lofton	35.00	20.00
5	Eric Karros	28.00	18.00
6	Brian Williams	6.50	3.75
7	Donovan Osborne	12.00	7.50

1993 Score Select Stars

This 24-card limited edition set consists of bonus cards which were randomly distributed in Score Select foil packs. Cards measure 2-1/2" by 3-1/2".

	MINT	NR/MT
Complete Set (24)	125.00	80.00
Commons	2.50	1.50

		MINT	NR/MT
8	Sam Militello	7.00	4.00
9	Chad Curtis	28.00	18.00
10	Bob Zupcic	6.50	3.75
11	Tim Salmon	60.00	38.00
12	Jeff Conine	10.00	6.50
13	Pedro Astacio	12.00	7.50
14	Arthur Rhodes	6.50	3.75
15	Cal Eldred	15.00	10.00
16	Tim Wakefield	6.50	3.75
17	Andy Stankiewicz	6.00	3.50
18	Wil Cordero	12.00	6.50
19	Todd Hundley	6.50	3.75
20	Dave Fleming	18.00	12.00
21	Bret Boone	18.00	12.00
22	Mickey Mantle	20.00	14.00
23	Carl Yastrzemski	6.50	4.50
24	Frank Robinson	6.50	4.50

		MINT	NR/MT
17	John Smoltz	5.00	3.00
18	Greg Swindell	3.00	1.75
19	Bruce Hurst	3.00	1.75
20	Mike Mussina	10.00	6.50
21	Cal Eldred	5.00	3.00
22	Melido Perez	3.00	1.75
23	Dave Fleming	6.00	3.75
24	Kevin Tapani	3.00	1.75

1993 Score Select Diamond Aces

The cards in this limited edition 24-card set were only available in Score Select Cello packs. Cards measure 2-1/2" by 3-1/2" and feature some fo the top pitchers in the Majors.

		MINT	NR/MT
Complete Set (24)		75.00	45.00
Commons		3.00	1.75
1	Roger Clemens	12.00	7.50
2	Tom Glavine	8.00	4.75
3	Jack McDowell	8.50	5.00
4	Greg Maddux	8.00	4.75
5	Jack Morris	4.00	2.75
6	Dennis Martinez	3.00	1.75
7	Kevin Brown	3.00	1.75
8	Dwight Gooden	4.00	2.75
9	Kevin Appier	4.50	3.00
10	Mike Morgan	3.00	1.75
11	Juan Guzman	7.50	4.50
12	Charles Nagy	4.00	2.75
13	John Smiley	3.00	1.75
14	Ken Hill	3.50	2.00
15	Bob Tewksbury	3.00	1.75
16	Doug Drabek	4.00	2.75

1993 Score Select Rookie & Traded

The cards in this set feature mostly rookies and players who were traded during the 1993 season. The card design is similar to the regular Score Select edition. The set includes limited Rookie Of The Year insert cards of Mike Piazza and Tim Salmon along with a Nolan Ryan Tribute card. Those cards were distributed randomly in Score Select Rookie-Traded packs and are listed at the end of this checklist but not included in the complete set price below. All cards measure 2-1/2" by 3-1/2".

		MINT	NR/MT
Complete Set (150)		85.00	50.00
Commons		.20	.12
1	Rickey Henderson	.80	.50
2	Rob Deer	.20	.12
3	Tim Belcher	.20	.12
4	Gary Sheffield	.75	.45
5	Fred McGriff	1.75	1.00
6	Mark Whiten	.30	.18
7	Jeff Russell	.20	.12
8	Harold Baines	.25	.15
9	Dave Winfield	1.50	.90
10	Ellis Burks	.20	.12
11	Andre Dawson	.40	.25
12	Gregg Jefferies	.40	.25
13	Jimmy Key	.25	.15
14	Harold Reynolds	.20	.12
15	Tom Henke	.20	.12
16	Paul Molitor	1.25	.80
17	Wade Boggs	1.25	.80

18	David Cone	.25	.15
19	Tony Fernandez	.20	.12
20	Roberto Kelly	.30	.18
21	Paul O'Neil	.25	.15
22	Jose Lind	.20	.12
23	Barry Bonds	2.50	1.50
24	Dave Stewart	.25	.15
25	Randy Myers	.25	.15
26	Benito Santiago	.25	.15
27	Tim Wallach	.20	.12
28	Greg Gagne	.20	.12
29	Kevin Mitchell	.25	.15
30	Jim Abbott	.35	.20
31	Lee Smith	.25	.15
32	Bobby Munoz (R)	.50	.30
33	Mo Sanford	.25	.15
34	John Roper (R)	.35	.20
35	David Hulse (R)	.75	.45
36	Pedro Martinez	1.00	.79
37	Chuck Carr (R)	.75	.45
38	Armando Reynoso	.25	.15
39	Ryan Thompson	.60	.35
40	Carlos Garcia	.75	.45
41	Matt Whiteside	.50	.30
42	Benji Gil	1.50	.90
43	Rod Bolton	.30	.18
44	J.T. Snow	3.00	1.75
45	David McCarty	2.00	1.25
46	Paul Quantrill	.35	.20
47	Al Martin	1.00	.70
48	Lance Painter (R)	.60	.35
49	Lou Frazier (R)	.40	.25
50	Eduardo Perez	3.00	1.75
51	Kevin Young	1.00	.70
52	Mike Trombley	.30	.18
53	Sterling Hitchcock (R)	1.50	.90
54	Tim Bogar (R)	.40	.25
55	Hilly Hathaway (R)	.75	.45
56	Wayne Kirby	.35	.20
57	Craig Paquette	.35	.20
58	Bret Boone	.80	.50
59	Greg McMichael (R)	.90	.60
60	Mike Lansing (R)	1.00	.70
61	Brent Gates	1.50	.90
62	Rene Arocha (R)	1.50	.90
63	Ricky Gutierrez (R)	.60	.35
64	Kevin Rogers	.35	.20
65	Ken Ryan (R)	.60	.35
66	Phil Hiatt	1.25	.80
67	Pat Meares (R)	.50	.30
68	Troy Neel	1.25	.80
69	Steve Cooke	1.00	.70
70	Sherman Obando (R)	.75	.45
71	Blas Minor (R)	.30	.18
72	Angel Miranda	.25	.15
73	Tom Kramer (R)	.60	.35
74	Chip Hale	.25	.15
75	Brad Pennington	.30	.18
76	Graeme Lloyd (R)	.50	.30
77	Darrell Whitmore (R)	2.00	1.25
78	David Nied	1.50	.90
79	Todd Van Poppel	1.25	.80
80	Chris Gomez (R)	1.25	.80
81	Jason Bere	5.00	3.00
82	Jeffrey Hammonds	3.50	2.00
83	Brad Ausmus (R)	.25	.15
84	Kevin Stocker	4.00	2.50
85	Jeromy Burnitz	1.75	1.00
86	Aaron Sele	6.00	3.75
87	Roberto Mejia (R)	2.50	1.50
88	Kirk Rueter (R)	5.00	3.00
89	Kevin Roberson (R)	1.25	.80
90	Allen Watson	2.00	1.25
91	Charlie Leibrandt	.20	.12
92	Eric Davis	.25	.15
93	Jody Reed	.20	.12
94	Danny Jackson	.20	.12
95	Gary Gaetti	.20	.12
96	Norm Charlton	.20	.12
97	Doug Drabek	.25	.15
98	Scott Fletcher	.20	.12
99	Greg Swindell	.25	.15
100	John Smiley	.25	.15
101	Kevin Reimer	.20	.12
102	Andres Galarraga	.60	.35
103	Greg Hibbard	.20	.12
104	Chris Hammond	.20	.12
105	Darnell Coles	.20	.12
106	Mike Felder	.20	.12
107	Jose Guzman	.25	.15
108	Chris Bosio	.25	.15
109	Spike Owen	.20	.12
110	Felix Jose	.25	.15
111	Cory Snyder	.25	.15
112	Craig Lefferts	.20	.12
113	David Wells	.20	.12
114	Pete Incaviglia	.20	.12
115	Mike Pagliarulo	.20	.12
116	Dave Magadan	.20	.12
117	Charlie Hough	.20	.12
118	Ivan Calderon	.20	.12
119	Manuel Lee	.20	.12
120	Bob Patterson	.20	.12
121	Bob Ojeda	.20	.12
122	Scott Bankhead	.20	.12
123	Greg Maddux	.80	.50
124	Chili Davis	.25	.15
125	Milt Thompson	.20	.12
126	Dave Martinez	.20	.12
127	Frank Tanana	.20	.12
128	Phil Plantier	.75	.45
129	Juan Samuel	.20	.12
130	Eric Young	.60	.35
131	Joe Orsulak	.20	.12

132	Derek Bell	.75	.45
133	Darrin Jackson	.20	.12
134	Tom Brunansky	.20	.12
135	Jeff Reardon	.25	.15
136	Kevin Higgins (R)	.35	.20
137	Joel Johnston (R)	.25	.15
138	Rick Trlicek (R)	.25	.15
139	Richie Lewis (R)	.60	.35
140	Jeff Gardner (R)	.25	.15
141	Jack Voight (R)	.40	.25
142	Rod Correia (R)	.35	.20
143	Billy Brewer (R)	.40	.25
144	Terry Jorgensen (R)	.35	.20
145	Rich Amaral (R)	.60	.35
146	Sean Berry (R)	.60	.35
147	Dan Peltier	.30	.18
148	Paul Wagner (R)	.60	.35
149	Damon Buford	.30	.18
150	Wil Cordero (R)	.75	.45
___	Tim Salmon (ROY)	150.00	90.00
___	Mike Piazza (ROY)	250.00	140.00
___	Nolan Ryan Tribute	200.00	125.00

1993 Score Select
All-Star Rookies

The cards in this limited insert set were randomly issued in Score Select Rookie-Update packs. The full-color cards are designed using hi-tech FX technology and consist of the hottest rookies from the 1993 season. All cards measure 2-1/2" by 3-1/2".

		MINT	NR/MT
Complete Set (10)		400.00	250.00
Commons		20.00	12.50
1	Jeff Conine	30.00	18.00
2	Brent Gates	30.00	18.00
3	Mike Lansing	25.00	15.00
4	Kevin Stocker	40.00	25.00
5	Mike Piazza	150.00	90.00
6	Jeffrey Hammonds	50.00	30.00
7	David Hulse	25.00	15.00
8	Tim Salmon	80.00	50.00
9	Rene Arocha	20.00	12.50

10	Greg McMichael	20.00	12.50

1993 Score Select
Stat Leaders

The 90-cards in this limited insert set were not found in Score Select packs but distributed one per pack in Score's 1993 regular edition. The cards are identical to the 1993 Score Select Series and highlight the stat leaders from the 1992 season. All cards measure 2-1/2" by 3-1/2".

		MINT	NR/MT
Complete Set (90)		15.00	10.00
Commons		.08	.05
1	Edgar Martinez	.15	.10
2	Kirby Puckett	.50	.30
3	Frank Thomas	2.50	1.50
4	Gary Sheffield	.25	.15
5	Andy Van Slyke	.15	.10
6	John Kruk	.15	.10
7	Kirby Puckett	.50	.30
8	Carlos Baerga	.50	.30
9	Paul Molitor	.30	.18
10	Terry Pendleton	.25	.15
11	Ryne Sandberg	.50	.30
12	Mark Grace	.20	.12
13	Edgar Martinez Frank Thomas	.75	.45
14	Don Mattingly	.30	.18
15	Ken Griffey Jr.	1.75	1.00
16	Andy Van Slyke	.15	.10
17	Will Clark, Ray Lankford, Mariano Duncan	.20	.12
18	Marquis Grissom Terry Pendleton	.15	.10
19	Lance Johnson	.08	.05
20	Mike Devereaux	.08	.05
21	Brady Anderson	.15	.10
22	Deion Sanders	.25	.15
23	Steve Finley	.08	.05
24	Andy Van Slyke	.15	.10
25	Juan Gonzalez	1.50	.90

26	Mark McGwire	.25	.15
27	Cecil Fielder	.25	.15
28	Fred McGriff	.30	.18
29	Barry Bonds	.75	.45
30	Gary Sheffield	.25	.15
31	Cecil Fielder	.25	.15
32	Joe Carter	.30	.18
33	Frank Thomas	2.50	1.50
34	Darren Daulton	.30	.18
35	Terry Pendleton	.25	.15
36	Fred McGriff	.30	.18
37	Tony Phillips	.10	.06
38	Frank Thomas	2.50	1.50
39	Roberto Alomar	.60	.35
40	Barry Bonds	.75	.45
41	Dave Hollins	.25	.15
42	Andy Van Slyke	.15	.10
43	Mark McGwire	.25	.15
44	Edgar Matinez	.15	.10
45	Frank Thomas	2.50	1.50
46	Barry Bonds	.75	.45
47	Gary Sheffield	.25	.15
48	Fred McGriff	.30	.18
49	Frank Thomas	2.50	1.50
50	Danny Tartabull	.10	.06
51	Roberto Alomar	.60	.35
52	Barry Bonds	.75	.45
53	John Kruk	.15	.10
54	Brett Butler	.08	.05
55	Kenny Lofton	.30	.18
56	Pat Listach	.20	.12
57	Brady Anderson	.15	.10
58	Marquis Grissom	.20	.12
59	Delino DeShields	.20	.12
60	Steve Finley	.08	.05
61	Jack McDowell	.25	.15
62	Kevin Brown	.25	.15
	Roger Clemens		
63	Melido Perez	.08	.05
64	Terry Mulholland	.08	.05
65	Curt Schilling	.10	.06
66	Doug Drabek	.20	.12
	Greg Maddux		
	John Smoltz		
67	Dennis Eckersley	.20	.12
68	Rick Aguilera	.08	.05
69	Jeff Montgomery	.10	.06
70	Lee Smith	.10	.06
71	Randy Myers	.08	.05
72	John Wetteland	.10	.06
73	Randy Johnson	.25	.15
74	Melido Perez	.08	.05
75	Roger Clemens	.40	.25
76	John Smoltz	.10	.06
77	David Cone	.10	.06
78	Greg Maddux	.25	.15
79	Roger Clemens	.40	.25

80	Kevin Appier	.10	.06
81	Mike Mussina	.40	.25
82	Bill Swift	.10	.06
83	Bob Tewksbury	.08	.05
84	Greg Maddux	.25	.15
85	Kevin Brown	.10	.06
86	Jack McDowell	.25	.15
87	Roger Clemens	.40	.25
88	Tom Glavine	.30	.18
89	Ken Hill	.08	.05
	Bob Tewksbury		
90	Dennis Martinez	.08	.05
	Mike Morgan		

1993 Score

Score goes back to the basics with this single series 660-card set. White borders frame full color action shots on the card fronts. The backs contain a small color photo, the player's personal data and stats. Key subsets include Award Winners, Draft Picks, All-Stars, Highlights and Dream Team. All cards measure 2-1/2" by 3-1/2".

		MINT	NR/MT
Complete Set (660)		32.50	20.00
Commons		.05	.02

1	Ken Griffey, Jr.	1.00	.60
2	Gary Sheffield	.20	.12
3	Frank Thomas	1.25	.80
4	Ryne Sandberg	.25	.15
5	Larry Walker	.12	.07
6	Cal Ripken, Jr.	.25	.15
7	Roger Clemens	.25	.15
8	Bobby Bonilla	.12	.07
9	Carlos Baerga	.25	.15
10	Darren Daulton	.15	.10

11	Travis Fryman	.25	.15
12	Andy Van Slyke	.10	.06
13	Jose Canseco	.20	.12
14	Roberto Alomar	.25	.15
15	Tom Glavine	.15	.10
16	Barry Larkin	.10	.06
17	Gregg Jefferies	.12	.07
18	Craig Biggio	.07	.04
19	Shane Mack	.08	.05
20	Brett Butler	.08	.05
21	Dennis Eckersley	.12	.07
22	Will Clark	.20	.12
23	Don Mattingly	.20	.12
24	Tony Gwynn	.15	.10
25	Ivan Rodriquez	.20	.12
26	Shawon Dunston	.08	.05
27	Mike Mussina	.25	.15
28	Marquis Grissom	.15	.10
29	Charles Nagy	.12	.07
30	Lenny Dykstra	.15	.10
31	Cecil Fielder	.15	.10
32	Jay Bell	.08	.05
33	B.J. Surhoff	.05	.02
34	Bob Tewksbury	.05	.02
35	Danny Tartabull	.10	.06
36	Terry Pendleton	.12	.07
37	Jack Morris	.12	.07
38	Hal Morris	.08	.05
39	Luis Polonia	.07	.04
40	Ken Caminiti	.05	.02
41	Robin Ventura	.15	.10
42	Darryl Strawberry	.15	.10
43	Wally Joyner	.08	.05
44	Fred McGriff	.20	.12
45	Kevin Tapani	.07	.04
46	Matt Williams	.15	.10
47	Robin Yount	.20	.12
48	Ken Hill	.07	.04
49	Edgar Martinez	.10	.06
50	Mark Grace	.12	.07
51	Juan Gonzalez	1.00	.60
52	Curt Schilling	.07	.04
53	Dwight Gooden	.12	.07
54	Chris Hoiles	.08	.05
55	Frank Viola	.08	.05
56	Ray Lankford	.15	.10
57	George Brett	.25	.15
58	Kenny Lofton	.25	.15
59	Nolan Ryan	.80	.50
60	Mickey Tettleton	.07	.04
61	John Smoltz	.10	.06
62	Howard Johnson	.08	.05
63	Eric Karros	.20	.12
64	Rick Aguilera	.05	.02
65	Steve Finley	.05	.02
66	Mark Langston	.10	.06
67	Bill Swift	.08	.05
68	John Olerud	.30	.18
69	Kevin McReynolds	.07	.04
70	Jack McDowell	.15	.10
71	Rickey Henderson	.15	.10
72	Brian Harper	.05	.02
73	Mike Morgan	.05	.02
74	Rafael Palmeiro	.12	.07
75	Dennis Martinez	.08	.05
76	Tino Martinez	.08	.05
77	Eddie Murray	.12	.07
78	Ellis Burks	.08	.05
79	John Kruk	.10	.06
80	Gregg Olson	.07	.04
81	Bernard Gilkey	.10	.06
82	Milt Cuyler	.08	.05
83	Mike LaValliere	.05	.02
84	Albert Belle	.25	.15
85	Bip Roberts	.05	.02
86	Melido Perez	.07	.04
87	Otis Nixon	.08	.05
88	Bill Spiers	.05	.02
89	Jeff Bagwell	.20	.12
90	Orel Hershiser	.10	.06
91	Andy Benes	.10	.06
92	Devon White	.07	.04
93	Willie McGee	.08	.05
94	Ozzie Guillen	.05	.02
95	Ivan Calderon	.07	.04
96	Keith Miller	.05	.02
97	Steve Buechele	.05	.02
98	Kent Hrbek	.07	.04
99	Dave Hollins	.15	.10
100	Mike Bordick	.10	.06
101	Randy Tomlin	.08	.05
102	Omar Vizquel	.05	.02
103	Lee Smith	.10	.06
104	Leo Gomez	.08	.05
105	Jose Rijo	.08	.05
106	Mark Whiten	.15	.10
107	Dave Justice	.25	.15
108	Eddie Taubensee	.08	.05
109	Lance Johnson	.05	.02
110	Felix Jose	.08	.05
111	Mike Harkey	.07	.04
112	Randy Milligan	.05	.02
113	Anthony Young	.08	.05
114	Rico Brogna	.10	.06
115	Bret Saberhagen	.10	.06
116	Sandy Alomar, Jr.	.08	.05
117	Terry Mulholland	.05	.02
118	Darryl Hamilton	.10	.06
119	Todd Zeile	.08	.05
120	Bernie Williams	.10	.06
121	Zane Smith	.05	.02
122	Derek Bell	.20	.12
123	Deion Sanders	.15	.10
124	Luis Sojo	.05	.02

#	Name			#	Name		
125	Joe Oliver	.05	.02	182	Scott Radinsky	.05	.02
126	Craig Grebeck	.05	.02	183	Luis Alicea	.05	.02
127	Andujar Cedeno	.10	.06	184	Tom Gordon	.07	.04
128	Brian McRae	.08	.05	185	Rick Wilkins	.08	.05
129	Jose Offerman	.10	.06	186	Todd Stottlemyre	.07	.04
130	Pedro Munoz	.08	.05	187	Moises Alou	.15	.10
131	Bud Black	.05	.02	188	Joe Grahe	.05	.02
132	Mo Vaughn	.20	.12	189	Jeff Kent	.20	.12
133	Bruce Hurst	.08	.05	190	Bill Wegman	.05	.02
134	Dave Henderson	.08	.05	191	Kim Batiste	.07	.04
135	Tom Pagnozzi	.08	.05	192	Matt Nokes	.05	.02
136	Erik Hanson	.05	.02	193	Mark Wohlers	.08	.05
137	Orlando Merced	.08	.05	194	Paul Sorrento	.10	.06
138	Dean Palmer	.15	.10	195	Chris Hammond	.08	.05
139	John Franco	.07	.04	196	Scott Livingstone	.07	.04
140	Brady Anderson	.10	.06	197	Doug Jones	.05	.02
141	Ricky Jordan	.07	.04	198	Scott Cooper	.10	.06
142	Jeff Blauser	.07	.04	199	Ramon Martinez	.10	.06
143	Sammy Sosa	.12	.07	200	Dave Valle	.05	.02
144	Bob Walk	.05	.02	201	Mariano Duncan	.05	.02
145	Delino DeShields	.12	.07	202	Ben McDonald	.12	.07
146	Kevin Brown	.10	.06	203	Darren Lewis	.08	.05
147	Mark Lemke	.05	.02	204	Kenny Rogers	.05	.02
148	Chuck Knoblauch	.12	.07	205	Manuel Lee	.05	.02
149	Chris Sabo	.07	.04	206	Scott Erickson	.12	.07
150	Bobby Witt	.07	.04	207	Dan Gladden	.05	.02
151	Luis Gonzalez	.08	.05	208	Bob Welch	.07	.04
152	Ron Karkovice	.05	.02	209	Greg Olson	.05	.02
153	Jeff Brantley	.05	.02	210	Dan Pasqua	.05	.02
154	Kevin Appier	.08	.05	211	Tim Wallach	.08	.05
155	Darrin Jackson	.07	.04	212	Jeff Montgomery	.05	.02
156	Kelly Gruber	.07	.04	213	Derrick May	.10	.06
157	Royce Clayton	.15	.10	214	Ed Sprague	.08	.05
158	Chuck Finley	.08	.05	215	David Haas	.05	.02
159	Jeff King	.07	.04	216	Darrin Fletcher	.08	.05
160	Greg Vaughn	.12	.07	217	Brian Jordan	.10	.06
161	Geronimo Pena	.05	.02	218	Jaime Navarro	.10	.06
162	Steve Farr	.05	.02	219	Randy Velarde	.05	.02
163	Jose Oquendo	.05	.02	220	Ron Gant	.12	.07
164	Mark Lewis	.07	.04	221	Paul Quantrill (R)	.12	.07
165	John Wetteland	.07	.04	222	Damion Easley (R)	.15	.10
166	Mike Henneman	.05	.02	223	Charlie Hough	.05	.02
167	Todd Hundley	.08	.05	224	Brad Brink (R)	.12	.07
168	Wes Chamberlain	.10	.06	225	Barry Manuel (R)	.12	.07
169	Steve Avery	.15	.10	226	Kevin Koslofski (R)	.15	.10
170	Mike Devereaux	.08	.05	227	Ryan Thompson (R)	.20	.12
171	Reggie Sanders	.12	.07	228	Mike Munoz (R)	.15	.10
172	Jay Buhner	.07	.04	229	Dan Wilson	.12	.07
173	Eric Anthony	.10	.06	230	Peter Hoy (R)	.15	.10
174	John Burkett	.08	.05	231	Pedro Astacio (R)	.20	.12
175	Tom Candiotti	.05	.02	232	Matt Stairs (R)	.12	.07
176	Phil Plantier	.15	.10	233	Jeff Reboulet (R)	.15	.10
177	Doug Henry	.08	.05	234	Manny Alexander (R)	.12	.07
178	Scott Leius	.05	.02	235	Willie Banks	.15	.10
179	Kirt Manwaring	.05	.02	236	John Jaha	.20	.12
180	Jeff Parrett	.05	.02	237	Scooter Tucker (R)	.15	.10
181	Don Slaught	.05	.02	238	Russ Springer (R)	.15	.10

239	Paul Miller (R)	.20	.12
240	Dan Peltier (R)	.15	.10
241	Ozzie Canseco	.08	.05
242	Ben Rivera (R)	.12	.07
243	John Valentin (R)	.20	.12
244	Henry Rodriguez (R)	.20	.12
245	Derek Parks (R)	.15	.10
246	Carlos Garcia	.20	.12
247	Tim Pugh (R)	.15	.10
248	Melvin Nieves (R)	.40	.25
249	Rich Amaral (R)	.15	.10
250	Willie Greene	.15	.10
251	Tim Scott (R)	.15	.10
252	Dave Silvestri (R)	.12	.07
253	Rob Mallicoat (R)	.10	.06
254	Donald Harris	.10	.06
255	Craig Colbert (R)	.12	.07
256	Jose Guzman	.10	.06
257	Domingo Martinez (R)	.20	.12
258	William Suero (R)	.15	.10
259	Juan Guerrero (R)	.15	.10
260	J.T. Snow (R)	.60	.35
261	Tony Pena	.05	.02
262	Tim Fortugno (R)	.15	.10
263	Tom Marsh (R)	.15	.10
264	Kurt Knudsen (R)	.12	.07
265	Tim Costo	.15	.10
266	Steve Shifflett (R)	.15	.10
267	Billy Ashley (R)	.30	.18
268	Jerry Nielsen (R)	.12	.07
269	Pete Young (R)	.12	.07
270	Johnny Guzman (R)	.15	.10
271	Greg Colbrunn (R)	.15	.10
272	Jeff Nelson (R)	.15	.10
273	Kevin Young (R)	.20	.12
274	Jeff Frye (R)	.15	.10
275	J.T. Bruett (R)	.15	.10
276	Todd Pratt (R)	.15	.10
277	Mike Butcher (R)	.15	.10
278	John Flaherty (R)	.20	.12
279	John Patterson (R)	.12	.07
280	Eric Hillman (R)	.12	.07
281	Bien Figueroa (R)	.15	.10
282	Shane Reynolds (R)	.15	.10
283	Rich Rowland (R)	.12	.07
284	Steve Foster (R)	.15	.10
285	Dave Mlicki (R)	.12	.07
286	Mike Piazza (R)	2.50	1.50
287	Mike Trombley (R)	.15	.10
288	Jim Pena (R)	.12	.07
289	Bob Ayrault (R)	.12	.07
290	Henry Mercedes (R)	.15	.10
291	Bob Wickman (R)	.20	.12
292	Jacob Brumfield (R)	.20	.12
293	David Hulse (R)	.15	.10
294	Ryan Klesko (R)	.40	.25
295	Doug Linton (R)	.15	.10
296	Steve Cooke (R)	.20	.12
297	Eddie Zosky	.12	.07
298	Gerald Williams	.15	.10
299	Jonathan Hurst (R)	.12	.07
300	Larry Carter (R)	.15	.10
301	Wm. Pennyfeather (R)	.15	.10
302	Cesar Hernandez (R)	.10	.06
303	Steve Hosey	.15	.10
304	Blas Minor (R)	.10	.06
305	Jeff Grotewald (R)	.12	.07
306	Bernardo Brito (R)	.10	.06
307	Rafael Bournigal (R)	.12	.07
308	Jeff Branson (R)	.12	.07
309	Tom Quinlan (R)	.15	.10
310	Pat Gomez (R)	.12	.07
311	Sterling Hitchcock (R)	.35	.20
312	Kent Bottenfield (R)	.10	.06
313	Alan Trammell	.10	.06
314	Cris Colon (R)	.20	.12
315	Paul Wagner (R)	.20	.12
316	Matt Maysey (R)	.15	.10
317	Mike Stanton	.05	.02
318	Rick Trlicek (R)	.12	.07
319	Kevin Rogers (R)	.15	.10
320	Mark Clark (R)	.20	.12
321	Pedro Martinez (R)	.25	.15
322	Al Martin	.30	.18
323	Mike Macfarlane	.07	.04
324	Rey Sanchez	.15	.10
325	Roger Pavlik (R)	.15	.10
326	Troy Neel (R)	.15	.10
327	Kerry Woodson (R)	.15	.10
328	Wayne Kirby (R)	.15	.10
329	Ken Ryan (R)	.15	.10
330	Jesse Levis (R)	.15	.10
331	James Austin	.08	.05
332	Dan Walters	.08	.05
333	Brian Williams	.12	.07
334	Wil Cordero	.20	.12
335	Bret Boone	.15	.10
336	Hipolito Pichardo	.08	.05
337	Pat Mahomes	.15	.10
338	Andy Stankiewicz	.08	.05
339	Jim Bullinger	.08	.05
340	Archi Cianfrocco	.10	.06
341	Ruben Amaro Jr.	.08	.05
342	Frank Seminara	.08	.05
343	Pat Hentgen	.15	.10
344	Dave Nilsson	.12	.07
345	Mike Perez	.08	.05
346	Tim Salmon	1.50	.90
347	Tim Wakefield	.10	.06
348	Carlos Hernandez	.08	.05
349	Donovan Osborne	.12	.07
350	Denny Neagle	.08	.05
351	Sam Militello	.15	.10
352	Eric Fox	.08	.05

353	John Doherty	.08	.05
354	Chad Curtis	.20	.12
355	Jeff Tackett	.08	.05
356	Dave Fleming	.20	.12
357	Pat Listach	.15	.10
358	Kevin Wickander	.08	.05
359	John Vander Wal	.08	.05
360	Arthur Rhodes	.08	.05
361	Bob Scanlan	.08	.05
362	Bob Zupcic	.08	.05
363	Mel Rojas	.07	.04
364	Jim Thome	.12	.07
365	Bill Pecota	.05	.02
366	Mark Carreon	.05	.02
367	Mitch Williams	.05	.02
368	Cal Eldred	.15	.10
369	Stan Belinda	.05	.02
370	Pat Kelly	.08	.05
371	Rheal Cormier	.07	.04
372	Juan Guzman	.20	.12
373	Damon Berryhill	.05	.02
374	Gary DiSarcina	.08	.05
375	Norm Charlton	.05	.02
376	Roberto Hernandez	.07	.04
377	Scott Kamieniecki	.07	.04
378	Rusty Meacham	.08	.05
379	Kurt Stillwell	.05	.02
380	Lloyd McClendon	.05	.02
381	Mark Leonard	.05	.02
382	Jerry Browne	.05	.02
383	Glenn Davis	.05	.02
384	Randy Johnson	.15	.10
385	Mike Greenwell	.08	.05
386	Scott Chiamparino	.07	.04
387	George Bell	.08	.05
388	Steve Olin	.07	.04
389	Chuck McElroy	.05	.02
390	Mark Gardner	.07	.04
391	Rod Beck	.07	.04
392	Dennis Rasmussen	.05	.02
393	Charlie Leibrandt	.05	.02
394	Julio Franco	.08	.05
395	Pete Harnisch	.08	.05
396	Sid Bream	.05	.02
397	Milt Thompson	.05	.02
398	Glenallen Hill	.08	.05
399	Chico Walker	.05	.02
400	Alex Cole	.05	.02
401	Trevor Wilson	.05	.02
402	Jeff Conine	.12	.07
403	Kyle Abbott	.08	.05
404	Tom Browning	.07	.04
405	Jerald Clark	.07	.04
406	Vince Horsman	.08	.05
407	Kevin Mitchell	.10	.06
408	Pete Smith	.10	.06
409	Jeff Innis	.05	.02
410	Mike Timlin	.07	.04
411	Charlie Hayes	.08	.05
412	Alex Fernandez	.12	.07
413	Jeff Russell	.05	.02
414	Jody Reed	.05	.02
415	Mickey Morandini	.08	.05
416	Darnell Coles	.05	.02
417	Xavier Hernandez	.07	.04
418	Steve Sax	.07	.04
419	Joe Girardi	.05	.02
420	Mike Fetters	.05	.02
421	Danny Jackson	.07	.04
422	Jim Gott	.05	.02
423	Tim Belcher	.07	.04
424	Jose Mesa	.07	.04
425	Junior Felix	.05	.02
426	Thomas Howard	.07	.04
427	Julio Valerz	.05	.02
428	Dante Bichette	.08	.05
429	Mike Sharperson	.05	.02
430	Darryl Kile	.10	.06
431	Lonnie Smith	.07	.04
432	Monty Fariss	.07	.04
433	Reggie Jefferson	.10	.06
434	Bob McClure	.05	.02
435	Craig Lefferts	.05	.02
436	Duane Ward	.05	.02
437	Shawn Abner	.05	.02
438	Roberto Kelly	.10	.06
439	Paul O'Neill	.10	.06
440	Alan Mills	.07	.04
441	Roger Mason	.05	.02
442	Gary Pettis	.05	.02
443	Steve Lake	.05	.02
444	Gene Larkin	.05	.02
445	Larry Andersen	.05	.02
446	Doug Dascenzo	.05	.02
447	Daryl Boston	.05	.02
448	John Candelaria	.05	.02
449	Storm Davis	.05	.02
450	Tom Edens	.07	.04
451	Mike Maddux	.05	.02
452	Tim Naehring	.08	.05
453	John Orton	.07	.04
454	Joey Cora	.05	.02
455	Chuck Crim	.05	.02
456	Dan Plesac	.05	.02
457	Mike Bielecki	.05	.02
458	Terry Jorgensen (R)	.12	.07
459	John Habyan	.05	.02
460	Pete O'Brien	.05	.02
461	Jeff Treadway	.05	.02
462	Frank Castillo	.05	.02
463	Jimmy Jones	.05	.02
464	Tommy Greene	.10	.06
465	Tracy Woodson	.05	.02
466	Rich Rodriguez	.08	.05

467	Joe Hesketh	.05	.02
468	Greg Myers	.05	.02
469	Kirk McCaskill	.05	.02
470	Ricky Bones	.08	.05
471	Lenny Webster	.05	.02
472	Francisco Cabrera	.05	.02
473	Turner Ward	.05	.02
474	Dwayne Henry	.05	.02
475	Al Osuna	.05	.02
476	Craig Wilson	.05	.02
477	Chris Nabholz	.07	.04
478	Rafael Belliard	.05	.02
479	Terry Leach	.05	.02
480	Tim Teufel	.05	.02
481	Dennis Eckersley (MVP)	.08	.05
482	Barry Bonds (MVP)	.25	.15
483	Dennis Eckersley (CY)	.08	.05
484	Greg Maddux (CY)	.08	.05
485	Pat Listach (ROY)	.08	.05
486	Eric Karros (ROY)	.12	.07
487	Jamie Arnold (R)	.15	.10
488	B.J. Wallace (R)	.25	.15
489	Derek Jeter (R)	.40	.25
490	Jason Kendall (R)	.30	.18
491	Rick Helling (R)	.25	.15
492	Derek Wallace (R)	.20	.12
493	Sean Lowe (R)	.20	.12
494	Shannon Stewart (R)	.25	.15
495	Benji Grigsby (R)	.20	.12
496	Todd Steverson (R)	.20	.12
497	Dan Serafini (R)	.25	.15
498	Michael Tucker (R)	.40	.25
499	Chris Roberts (R)	.25	.15
500	Pete Janicki (R)	.10	.06
501	Jeff Schmidt (R)	.10	.06
502	Edgar Martinez (AS)	.08	.05
503	Omar Vizquel (AS)	.05	.02
504	Ken Griffey Jr. (AS)	.35	.20
505	Kirby Puckett (AS)	.15	.10
506	Joe Carter (AS)	.12	.07
507	Ivan Rodriguez (AS)	.10	.06
508	Jack Morris (AS)	.08	.05
509	Dennis Eckersley (AS)	.08	.05
510	Frank Thomas (AS)	.50	.30
511	Roberto Alomar (AS)	.15	.10
512	Mickey Morandini (HL)	.07	.04
513	Dennis Eckersley (HL)	.08	.05
514	Jeff Reardon (HL)	.07	.04
515	Danny Tartabull (HL)	.07	.04
516	Bip Roberts (HL)	.05	.02
517	George Brett (HL)	.12	.07
518	Robin Yount (HL)	.12	.07
519	Kevin Gross (HL)	.07	.04
520	Ed Sprague (HL)	.07	.04
521	Dave Winfield (HL)	.10	.06
522	Ozzie Smith (AS)	.08	.05
523	Barry Bonds (AS)	.25	.15
524	Andy Van Slyke (AS)	.07	.04
525	Tony Gwynn (AS)	.10	.06
526	Darren Daulton (AS)	.07	.04
527	Greg Maddux (AS)	.07	.04
528	Fred McGriff (AS)	.10	.06
529	Lee Smith (AS)	.05	.02
530	Ryne Sandberg (AS)	.12	.07
531	Gary Sheffield (AS)	.08	.05
532	Ozzie Smith (DT)	.12	.07
533	Kirby Puckett (DT)	.25	.15
534	Gary Sheffield (DT)	.15	.10
535	Andy Van Slyke (DT)	.10	.06
537	Ivan Rodriguez (DT)	.12	.07
539	Tom Glavine (DT)	.15	.10
540	Dennis Eckersley (DT)	.10	.06
541	Frank Thomas (DT)	.80	.50
542	Roberto Alomar (DT)	.20	.12
543	Sean Berry	.10	.06
544	Mike Schooler	.05	.02
545	Chuck Carr	.10	.06
546	Lenny Harris	.05	.02
547	Gary Scott	.08	.05
548	Derek Lilliquist	.05	.02
549	Brian Hunter	.10	.06
550	Kirby Puckett (Man Of The year)	.15	.10
551	Jim Eisenreich	.05	.02
552	Andre Dawson	.12	.07
553	David Nied	.60	.35
554	Spike Owen	.05	.02
555	Greg Gagne	.05	.02
556	Sid Fernandez	.07	.04
557	Mark McGwire	.15	.10
558	Bryan Harvey	.07	.04
559	Harold Reynolds	.05	.02
560	Barry Bonds	.40	.25
561	Eric Wedge (R)	.10	.06
562	Ozzie Smith	.12	.07
563	Rick Sutcliffe	.05	.02
564	Jeff Reardon	.08	.05
565	Alex Arias (R)	.10	.06
566	Greg Swindell	.07	.04
567	Brook Jacoby	.05	.02
568	Pete Incaviglia	.05	.02
569	Butch Henry (R)	.15	.10
570	Eric Davis	.08	.05
571	Kevin Seitzer	.05	.02
572	Tony Fernandez	.08	.05
573	Steve Reed (R)	.12	.07
574	Cory Snyder	.05	.02
575	Joe Carter	.20	.12
576	Greg Maddux	.15	.10
577	Bert Blyleven	.08	.05
578	Kevin Bass	.05	.02
579	Carlton Fisk	.12	.07
580	Doug Drabek	.10	.06
581	Mark Gubicza	.07	.04

582	Bobby Thigpen	.05	.02
583	Chili Davis	.07	.04
584	Scott Bankhead	.05	.02
585	Harold Baines	.07	.04
586	Eric Young (R)	.15	.10
587	Lance Parrish	.07	.04
588	Juan Bell	.05	.02
589	Bob Ojeda	.05	.02
590	Joe Orsulak	.05	.02
591	Benito Santiago	.08	.05
592	Wade Boggs	.12	.07
593	Robby Thompson	.07	.04
594	Eric Plunk	.05	.02
595	Hensley Meulens	.07	.04
596	Lou Whitaker	.07	.04
597	Dale Murphy	.10	.06
598	Paul Molitor	.20	.12
599	Greg W. Harris	.05	.02
600	Darren Holmes	.07	.04
601	Dave Martinez	.05	.02
602	Tom Henke	.05	.02
603	Mike Benjamin	.07	.04
604	Rene Gonzales	.08	.05
605	Roger McDowell	.05	.02
606	Kirby Puckett	.25	.15
607	Randy Myers	.05	.02
608	Ruben Sierra	.15	.10
609	Wilson Alvarez	.07	.04
610	David Segui	.07	.04
611	Juan Samuel	.05	.02
612	Tom Brunansky	.07	.04
613	Willie Randolph	.07	.04
614	Tony Phillips	.07	.04
615	Candy Maldonado	.05	.02
616	Chris Bosio	.07	.04
617	Bret Barberie	.10	.06
618	Scott Sanderson	.05	.02
619	Ron Darling	.07	.04
620	Dave Winfield	.20	.12
621	Mike Felder	.05	.02
622	Greg Hibbard	.07	.04
623	Mike Scioscia	.05	.02
624	John Smiley	.08	.05
625	Alejandro Pena	.05	.02
626	Terry Steinbach	.07	.04
627	Freddie Benavides	.05	.02
628	Kevin Reimer	.07	.04
629	Braulio Castillo	.08	.05
630	Dave Stieb	.07	.04
631	Dave Magadan	.07	.04
632	Scott Fletcher	.05	.02
633	Cris Carpenter	.07	.04
634	Kevin Maas	.08	.05
635	Todd Worrell	.05	.02
636	Rob Deer	.07	.04
637	Dwight Smith	.05	.02
638	Chito Martinez	.08	.05
639	Jimmy Key	.08	.05
640	Greg Harris	.05	.02
641	Mike Moore	.05	.02
642	Pat Borders	.07	.04
643	Bill Gullickson	.05	.02
644	Gary Gaetti	.05	.02
645	David Howard	.07	.04
646	Jim Abbott	.12	.07
647	Willie Wilson	.05	.02
648	David Wells	.05	.02
649	Andres Galarraga	.12	.07
650	Vince Coleman	.07	.04
651	Rob Dibble	.07	.04
652	Frank Tanana	.05	.02
653	Steve Decker	.08	.05
654	David Cone	.10	.06
655	Jack Armstrong	.07	.04
656	Dave Stewart	.10	.06
657	Billy Hatcher	.05	.02
658	Tim Raines	.07	.04
659	Walt Weiss	.05	.02
660	Jose Lind	.05	.02

1993 Score The Franchise

The cards in this limited insert set were distributed randomly in Score foil packs. The full-bleed, full-color card fronts consist of an action photo of the player with the word "Franchise" printed diagonally in the bottom corner of the card. The player's name appears in a color bar in the lower center of the card. All cards measure 2-1/2" by 3-1/2"

		MINT	NR/MT
Complete Set (28)		100.00	65.00
Commons		1.25	.70
1	Cal Ripken Jr.	8.50	5.00
2	Roger Clemens	6.00	3.75
3	Mark Langston	1.25	.70
4	Frank Thomas	22.00	14.00
5	Carlos Baerga	6.00	3.75
6	Cecil Fielder	4.00	2.50
7	Gregg Jefferies	2.00	1.25

		MINT	NR/MT
8	Robin Yount	6.00	3.75
9	Kirby Puckett	7.50	4.50
10	Don Mattingly	5.00	3.00
11	Dennis Eckersley	1.50	.90
12	Ken Griffey Jr.	18.50	12.50
13	Juan Gonzalez	15.00	10.00
14	Roberto Alomar	7.50	4.50
15	Terry Pendleton	1.25	.70
16	Ryne Sandberg	7.50	4.50
17	Barry Larkin	1.50	.90
18	Jeff Bagwell	4.50	2.75
19	Brett Butler	1.25	.70
20	Larry Walker	2.00	1.25
21	Bobby Bonilla	1.50	.90
22	Darren Daulton	2.50	1.50
23	Andy Van Slyke	1.25	.70
24	Ray Lankford	1.50	.90
25	Gary Sheffield	3.50	2.00
26	Will Clark	5.00	3.00
27	Bryan Harvey	1.25	.70
28	David Nied	3.50	2.00

1993 Score Pinnacle

John Burkett

For the second straight year Score issued a premium baseball card set under the Pinnacle name. The set was issued in two series. The cards feature full color photos on the front and back. Key subsets include Rookies (R), Now and Then (289-296, 470-476), Idols (ID) and Hometown Hero (HH). Two limited 5-card insert sets pay tribute to George Brett and Nolan Ryan. Those cards are listed at the end of this checklist but are not included in the complete set price below. All cards measure 2-1/2" by 3-1/2".

		MINT	NR/MT
Complete Set (620)		48.00	28.00
Commons		.08	.05

1	Gary Sheffield	.30	.18
2	Cal Eldred	.25	.15
3	Larry Walker	.25	.15
4	Deion Sanders	.30	.18
5	Dave Fleming	.30	.18
6	Carlos Baerga	.70	.40
7	Bernie Williams	.15	.10
8	John Kruk	.10	.06
9	Jimmy Key	.08	.05
10	Jeff Bagwell	.40	.25
11	Jim Abbott	.20	.12
12	Terry Steinbach	.10	.06
13	Bob Tewksbury	.08	.05
14	Eric Karros	.40	.25
15	Ryne Sandberg	.70	.40
16	Will Clark	.50	.30
17	Edgar Martinez	.15	.10
18	Eddie Murray	.20	.12
19	Andy Van Slyke	.12	.07
20	Cal Ripken Jr.	.75	.45
21	Ivan Rodriguez	.25	.15
22	Barry Larkin	.15	.10
23	Don Mattingly	.40	.25
24	Gregg Jefferies	.20	.12
25	Roger Clemens	.60	.35
26	Cecil Fielder	.30	.18
27	Kent Hrbek	.10	.06
28	Robin Ventura	.30	.18
29	Rickey Henderson	.25	.15
30	Roberto Alomar	.60	.35
31	Luis Polonia	.08	.05
32	Andujar Cedeno	.12	.07
33	Pat Listach	.15	.10
34	Mark Grace	.20	.12
35	Otis Nixon	.10	.06
36	Felix Jose	.10	.06
37	Mike Sharperson	.08	.05
38	Dennis Martinez	.10	.06
39	Willie McGee	.10	.06
40	Kenny Lofton	.40	.25
41	Randy Johnson	.20	.12
42	Andy Benes	.12	.07
43	Bobby Bonilla	.15	.10
44	Mike Mussina	.60	.35
45	Lenny Dykstra	.20	.12
46	Ellis Burks	.10	.06
47	Chris Sabo	.10	.06
48	Jay Bell	.10	.06
49	Jose Canseco	.30	.18
50	Craig Biggio	.10	.06
51	Wally Joyner	.12	.07
52	Mickey Tettleton	.10	.06
53	Tim Raines	.10	.06
54	Brian Harper	.08	.05
55	Rene Gonzales	.08	.05
56	Mark Langston	.15	.10
57	Jack Morris	.20	.12

58	Mark McGwire	.30	.18
59	Ken Caminiti	.08	.05
60	Terry Pendleton	.20	.12
61	Dave Nilsson	.15	.10
62	Tom Pagnozzi	.10	.06
63	Mike Morgan	.08	.05
64	Darryl Strawberry	.20	.12
65	Charles Nagy	.15	.10
66	Ken Hill	.10	.06
67	Matt Williams	.25	.15
68	Jay Buhner	.10	.06
69	Vince Coleman	.10	.06
70	Brady Anderson	.15	.10
71	Fred McGriff	.50	.30
72	Ben McDonald	.15	.10
73	Terry Mulholland	.08	.05
74	Randy Tomlin	.10	.06
75	Nolan Ryan	2.00	1.25
76	Frank Viola	.10	.06
77	Jose Rijo	.12	.07
78	Shane Mack	.10	.06
79	Travis Fryman	.60	.35
80	Jack McDowell	.35	.20
81	Mark Gubicza	.08	.05
82	Matt Nokes	.08	.05
83	Bert Blyleven	.10	.06
84	Eric Anthony	.12	.07
85	Mike Bordick	.10	.06
86	John Olerud	1.00	.60
87	B.J. Surhoff	.08	.05
88	Bernard Gilkey	.15	.10
89	Shawon Dunston	.10	.06
90	Tom Glavine	.35	.20
91	Brett Butler	.10	.06
92	Moises Alou	.20	.12
93	Albert Belle	.60	.35
94	Darren Lewis	.10	.06
95	Omar Vizquel	.08	.05
96	Doc Gooden	.20	.12
97	Gregg Olson	.10	.06
98	Tony Gwynn	.30	.18
99	Darren Daulton	.20	.12
100	Dennis Eckersley	.20	.12
101	Rob Dibble	.10	.06
102	Mike Greenwell	.10	.06
103	Jose Lind	.08	.05
104	Julio Franco	.10	.06
105	Tom Gordon	.10	.06
106	Scott Livingstone	.10	.06
107	Chuck Knoblauch	.15	.10
108	Frank Thomas	3.00	1.75
109	Melido Perez	.10	.06
110	Ken Griffey Jr.	2.50	1.50
111	Harold Baines	.10	.06
112	Gary Gaetti	.08	.05
113	Pete Harnisch	.10	.06
114	David Wells	.08	.05
115	Charlie Leibrandt	.08	.05
116	Ray Lankford	.25	.15
117	Kevin Seitzer	.08	.05
118	Robin Yount	.30	.18
119	Lenny Harris	.08	.05
120	Chris James	.08	.05
121	Delino DeShields	.20	.12
122	Kirt Manwaring	.08	.05
123	Glenallen Hill	.12	.07
124	Hensley Meulens	.10	.06
125	Darrin Jackson	.08	.05
126	Todd Hundley	.10	.06
127	Dave Hollins	.25	.15
128	Sam Horn	.08	.05
129	Roberto Hernandez	.10	.06
130	Vicente Palacios	.08	.05
131	George Brett	.50	.30
132	Dave Martinez	.08	.05
133	Kevin Appier	.10	.06
134	Pat Kelly	.10	.06
135	Pedro Munoz	.12	.07
136	Mark Carreon	.08	.05
137	Lance Johnson	.08	.05
138	Devon White	.10	.06
139	Julio Valera	.08	.05
140	Eddie Taubensee	.10	.06
141	Willie Wilson	.08	.05
142	Stan Belinda	.08	.05
143	John Smoltz	.20	.12
144	Darryl Hamilton	.12	.07
145	Sammy Sosa	.15	.10
146	Carlos Hernandez	.12	.07
147	Tom Candiotti	.08	.05
148	Mike Felder	.08	.05
149	Rusty Meacham	.10	.06
150	Ivan Calderon	.08	.05
151	Pete O'Brien	.08	.05
152	Erik Hanson	.08	.05
153	Billy Ripken	.08	.05
154	Kurt Stillwell	.08	.05
155	Jeff Kent	.15	.10
156	Mickey Morandini	.10	.06
157	Randy Milligan	.08	.05
158	Reggie Sanders	.25	.15
159	Luis Rivera	.10	.06
160	Orlando Merced	.10	.06
161	Dean Palmer	.15	.10
162	Mike Perez	.12	.07
163	Scott Erickson	.12	.07
164	Kevin McReynolds	.10	.06
165	Kevin Maas	.10	.06
166	Ozzie Guillen	.08	.05
167	Rob Deer	.10	.06
168	Danny Tartabull	.12	.07
169	Lee Stevens	.08	.05
170	Dave Henderson	.08	.05
171	Derek Bell	.25	.15

172	Steve Finley	.08	.05
173	Greg Olson	.08	.05
174	Geronimo Pena	.08	.05
175	Paul Quantrill	.15	.10
176	Steve Buechele	.08	.05
177	Kevin Gross	.08	.05
178	Tim Wallach	.00	.05
179	Dave Valle	.08	.05
180	Dave Silvestri	.12	.07
181	Bud Black	.08	.05
182	Henry Rodriguez	.15	.10
183	Tim Teufel	.08	.05
184	Mark McLemore	.08	.05
185	Bret Saberhagen	.12	.07
186	Chris Hoiles	.12	.07
187	Ricky Jordan	.08	.05
188	Don Slaught	.08	.05
189	Mo Vaughn	.25	.15
190	Joe Oliver	.08	.05
191	Juan Gonzalez	2.50	1.50
192	Scott Leius	.08	.05
193	Milt Cuyler	.10	.06
194	Chris Haney	.10	.06
195	Ron Karkovice	.08	.05
196	Steve Farr	.08	.05
197	John Orton	.10	.06
198	Kelly Gruber	.10	.06
199	Ron Darling	.10	.06
200	Ruben Sierra	.25	.15
201	Chuck Finley	.12	.07
202	Mike Moore	.08	.05
203	Pat Borders	.10	.06
204	Sid Bream	.08	.05
205	Todd Zeile	.12	.07
206	Rick Wilkins	.12	.07
207	Jim Gantner	.08	.05
208	Frank Castillo	.08	.05
209	Dave Hansen	.08	.05
210	Trevor Wilson	.08	.05
211	Sandy Alomar Jr.	.12	.07
212	Sean Berry	.15	.10
213	Tino Martinez	.12	.07
215	Dan Walters	.15	.10
216	John Franco	.08	.05
217	Glenn Davis	.08	.05
218	Mariano Duncan	.08	.05
219	Mike LaValliere	.08	.05
220	Rafael Palmeiro	.20	.12
221	Jack Clark	.10	.06
222	Hal Morris	.15	.10
223	Ed Sprague	.12	.07
224	John Valentin (R)	.25	.15
225	Sam Militello	.20	.12
226	Bob Wickman	.35	.20
227	Damion Easley	.20	.12
228	John Jaha	.20	.12
229	Bob Ayrault	.12	.07
230	Mo Sanford	.10	.06
231	Walt Weiss	.08	.05
232	Dante Bichette	.10	.06
233	Steve Decker	.10	.06
234	Jerald Clark	.10	.06
235	Bryan Harvey	.10	.06
236	Joe Girardi	.08	.05
237	Dave Magadan	.08	.05
238	David Nied (R)	.80	.50
239	Eric Wedge (R)	.20	.12
240	Rico Brogna	.15	.10
241	J.T. Bruett (R)	.20	.12
242	Jonathan Hurst (R)	.20	.12
243	Bret Boone	.30	.18
244	Manny Alexander	.15	.10
245	Scooter Tucker (R)	.20	.12
246	Troy Neel (R)	.40	.25
247	Eddie Zosky	.15	.10
248	Melvin Nieves (R)	.75	.45
249	Ryan Thompson	.25	.15
250	Shawn Barton (R)	.20	.12
251	Ryan Klesko	.80	.50
252	Mike Piazza	5.00	3.00
253	Steve Hosey	.30	.18
254	Shane Reynolds (R)	.25	.15
255	Dan Wilson	.25	.15
256	Tom Marsh	.15	.10
257	Barry Manuel	.15	.10
258	Paul Miller	.25	.15
259	Pedro Martinez	.40	.25
260	Steve Cooke (R)	.35	.20
261	Johnny Guzman	.15	.10
262	Mike Butcher (R)	.25	.15
263	Bien Figueroa	.15	.10
264	Rich Rowland	.12	.07
265	Shawn Jeter	.25	.15
266	Gerald Williams	.25	.15
267	Derek Parks	.15	.10
268	Henry Mercedes	.15	.10
269	David Hulse (R)	.25	.15
270	Tim Pugh (R)	.25	.15
271	Williams Suero (R)	.20	.12
272	Ozzie Canseco	.10	.06
273	Fernando Ramsey (R)	.20	.12
274	Bernardo Brito (R)	.15	.10
275	Dave Mlicki (R)	.20	.12
276	Tim Salmon	3.50	2.00
277	Mike Raczka (R)	.15	.10
278	Ken Ryan (R)	.25	.15
279	Rafael Bournigal (R)	.15	.10
280	Wil Cordero	.30	.18
281	Billy Ashley	.75	.45
282	Paul Wagner	.20	.12
283	Blas Minor	.10	.06
284	Rick Trlicek	.10	.06
285	Willie Greene	.30	.18
286	Ted Wood	.12	.07

287	Phil Clark	.15	.10
288	Jesse Levis (R)	.15	.10
289	Tony Gwynn	.15	.10
290	Nolan Ryan	.90	.60
291	Dennis Martinez	.10	.06
292	Eddie Murray	.20	.12
293	Robin Yount	.20	.12
294	George Brett	.25	.15
295	Dave Winfield	.20	.12
296	Bert Blyleven	.10	.06
297	Jeff Bagwell (ID)	.25	.15
298	John Smoltz (ID)	.10	.06
299	Larry Walker (ID)	.10	.06
300	Gary Sheffield (ID)	.15	.10
301	Ivan Rodriguez (ID)	.15	.10
302	Delino DeShields (ID)	.20	.12
303	Tim Salmon (ID)	.50	.30
304	Bernard Gilkey (HH)	.08	.05
305	Cal Ripken Jr. (HH)	.35	.20
306	Barry Larkin (HH)	.10	.06
307	Kent Hrbek (HH)	.08	.05
308	Rickey Henderson (HH)	.12	.07
309	Darryl Strawberry(HH)	.15	.10
310	John Franco (HH)	.08	.05
311	Todd Stottlemyre	.08	.05
312	Luis Gonzalez	.12	.07
313	Tommy Greene	.20	.12
314	Randy Velarde	.08	.05
315	Steve Avery	.35	.20
316	Jose Oquendo	.08	.05
317	Rey Sanchez	.08	.05
318	Greg Vaughn	.20	.12
319	Orel Hershiser	.12	.07
320	Paul Sorrento	.12	.07
321	Royce Clayton	.20	.12
322	John Vander Wal	.08	.05
323	Henry Cotto	.08	.05
324	Pete Schourek	.10	.06
325	David Segui	.10	.06
326	Arthur Rhodes	.12	.07
327	Bruce Hurst	.10	.06
328	Wes Chamberlain	.15	.10
329	Ozzie Smith	.30	.18
330	Scott Cooper	.15	.10
331	Felix Fermin	.08	.05
332	Mike Macfarlane	.08	.05
333	Dan Gladden	.08	.05
334	Kevin Tapani	.10	.06
335	Steve Sax	.10	.06
336	Jeff Montgomery	.08	.05
337	Gary DiSarcina	.10	.06
338	Lance Blankenship	.08	.05
339	Brian Williams	.12	.07
340	Duane Ward	.10	.06
341	Chuck McElroy	.08	.05
342	Joe Magrane	.08	.05
343	Jaime Navarro	.12	.07
344	David Justice	.75	.45
345	Jose Offerman	.12	.07
346	Marquis Grissom	.25	.15
347	Bill Swift	.15	.10
348	Jim Thome	.15	.10
349	Archi Cianfrocco	.12	.07
350	Anthony Young	.10	.06
351	Leo Gomez	.10	.06
352	Bill Gullickson	.08	.05
353	Alan Trammel	.20	.12
354	Dan Pasqua	.08	.05
355	Jeff King	.10	.06
356	Kevin Brown	.12	.07
357	Tim Belcher	.08	.05
358	Bip Roberts	.08	.05
359	Brent Mayne	.08	.05
360	Rheal Cormier	.10	.06
361	Mark Guthrie	.10	.06
362	Craig Grebeck	.08	.05
363	Andy Stankiewicz	.08	.05
364	Juan Guzman	.30	.18
365	Bobby Witt	.10	.06
366	Mark Portugal	.10	.06
367	Brian McRae	.12	.07
368	Mark Lemke	.08	.05
369	Bill Wegman	.08	.05
370	Donovan Osborne	.20	.12
371	Derrick May	.15	.10
372	Carl Willis	.08	.05
373	Chris Nabholz	.08	.05
374	Mark Lewis	.10	.06
375	John Burkett	.12	.07
376	Luis Mercedes	.12	.07
377	Ramon Martinez	.15	.10
378	Kyle Abbott	.12	.07
379	Mark Wohlers	.12	.07
380	Bob Walk	.08	.05
381	Kenny Rogers	.08	.05
382	Tim Naehring	.10	.06
383	Alex Fernandez	.30	.18
384	Keith Miller	.08	.05
385	Mike Henneman	.08	.05
386	Rick Aguilera	.08	.05
387	George Bell	.12	.07
388	Mike Gallego	.08	.05
389	Howard Johnson	.10	.06
390	Kim Batiste	.08	.05
391	Jerry Browne	.08	.05
392	Damon Berryhill	.08	.05
393	Ricky Bones	.10	.06
394	Omar Olivares	.08	.05
395	Mike Harkey	.10	.06
396	Pedro Astacio	.30	.18
397	John Wetteland	.10	.06
398	Rod Beck	.12	.07
399	Thomas Howard	.10	.06
400	Mike Devereaux	.12	.07

401	Tim Wakefield	.20	.12
402	Curt Schilling	.12	.07
403	Zane Smith	.08	.05
404	Bob Zupcic	.10	.06
405	Tom Browning	.10	.06
406	Tony Phillips	.10	.06
407	John Doherty	.15	.10
408	Pat Mahomes	.12	.07
409	John Habyan	.08	.05
410	Steve Olin	.08	.05
411	Chad Curtis	.35	.20
412	Joe Grahe	.10	.06
413	John Patterson	.08	.05
414	Brian Hunter	.12	.07
415	Doug Henry	.10	.06
416	Lee Smith	.12	.07
417	Bob Scanlan	.08	.05
418	Kent Mercker	.10	.06
419	Mel Rojas	.10	.06
420	Mark Whiten	.25	.15
421	Carlton Fisk	.15	.10
422	Candy Maldonado	.08	.05
423	Doug Drabek	.12	.07
424	Wade Boggs	.30	.18
425	Mark Davis	.08	.05
426	Kirby Puckett	.70	.40
427	Joe Carter	.50	.30
428	Paul Molitor	.35	.20
429	Eric Davis	.12	.07
430	Darryl Kile	.20	.12
431	Jeff Parrett	.08	.05
432	Jeff Blauser	.12	.07
433	Dan Plesac	.08	.05
434	Andres Galarraga	.20	.12
435	Jim Gott	.08	.05
436	Jose Mesa	.10	.06
437	Ben Rivera	.08	.05
438	Dave Winfield	.40	.25
439	Norm Charlton	.08	.05
440	Chris Bosio	.10	.06
441	Wilson Alvarez	.20	.12
442	Dave Stewart	.15	.10
443	Doug Jones	.08	.05
444	Jeff Russell	.08	.05
445	Ron Gant	.20	.12
446	Paul O'Neill	.15	.10
447	Charlie Hayes	.10	.06
448	Joe Hesketh	.08	.05
449	Chris Hammond	.08	.05
450	Hipolito Pichardo	.10	.06
451	Scott Radinsky	.08	.05
452	Bobby Thigpen	.08	.05
453	Xavier Hernandez	.10	.06
454	Lonnie Smith	.08	.05
455	Jamie Arnold (R)	.35	.20
456	B.J. Wallace	.50	.30
457	Derek Jeter (R)	.80	.50
458	Jason Kendall (R)	.50	.30
459	Rick Helling	.40	.25
460	Derek Wallace (R)	.30	.18
461	Sean Lowe (R)	.25	.15
462	Shannon Stewart (R)	.35	.20
463	Benji Grigsby (R)	.30	.18
464	Todd Steverson (R)	.60	.35
465	Dan Serafini (R)	.40	.25
466	Michael Tucker	1.50	.90
467	Chris Roberts	.40	.25
468	Pete Janicki (R)	.25	.15
469	Jeff Schmidt (R)	.20	.12
470	Don Mattingly (NT)	.30	.18
471	Cal Ripken Jr. (NT)	.50	.30
472	Jack Morris (NT)	.10	.06
473	Terry Pendleton (NT)	.10	.06
474	Dennis Eckersley (NT)	.12	.07
475	Carlton Fisk (NT)	.12	.07
476	Wade Boggs (NT)	.15	.10
477	Lenny Dykstra (ID)	.10	.06
478	Danny Tartabull (ID)	.10	.06
479	Jeff Conine (ID)	.12	.07
480	Gregg Jefferies (ID)	.12	.07
481	Paul Molitor (ID)	.12	.07
482	John Valentin (ID)	.10	.06
483	Alex Arias (ID)	.15	.10
484	Bary Bonds (HH)	.60	.35
485	Doug Drabek (HH)	.10	.06
486	Dave Winfield (HH)	.20	.12
487	Brett Butler (HH)	.10	.06
488	Harold Baines (HH)	.08	.05
489	David Cone (HH)	.10	.06
490	Willie McGee (HH)	.10	.06
491	Robby Thompson	.15	.10
492	Pete Incaviglia	.08	.05
493	Manuel Lee	.08	.05
494	Rafael Belliard	.08	.05
495	Scott Fletcher	.08	.05
496	Jeff Frye	.12	.07
497	Andre Dawson	.25	.15
498	Mike Scioscia	.08	.05
499	Spike Owen	.08	.05
500	Sid Fernandez	.10	.06
501	Joe Orsulak	.08	.05
502	Benito Santiago	.12	.07
503	Dale Murphy	.15	.10
504	Barry Bonds	1.25	.80
505	Jose Guzman	.08	.05
506	Tony Pena	.08	.05
507	Greg Swindell	.10	.06
508	Mike Pagliarulo	.08	.05
509	Lou Whitaker	.12	.07
510	Greg Gagne	.08	.05
511	Butch Henry	.08	.05
512	Jeff Brantley	.08	.05
513	Jack Armstrong	.08	.05
514	Danny Jackson	.10	.06

515 Junior Felix	.08	.05
516 Milt Thompson	.08	.05
517 Greg Maddux	.30	.18
518 Eric Young	.20	.12
519 Jody Reed	.08	.05
520 Roberto Kelly	.20	.12
521 Darren Holmes	.12	.07
522 Craig Lefferts	.08	.05
523 Charlie Hough	.08	.05
524 Bo Jackson	.25	.15
525 Bill Spiers	.08	.05
526 Orestes Destrade	.10	.06
527 Greg Hibbard	.08	.05
528 Roger McDowell	.08	.05
529 Cory Snyder	.10	.06
530 Harold Reynolds	.08	.05
531 Kevin Reimer	.08	.05
532 Rick Sutcliffe	.10	.06
533 Tony Fernandez	.10	.06
534 Tom Brunansky	.10	.06
535 Jeff Reardon	.12	.07
536 Chili Davis	.10	.06
537 Bob Ojeda	.08	.05
538 Greg Colbrunn	.12	.07
539 Phil Plantier	.35	.20
540 Brian Jordan	.25	.15
541 Pete Smith	.12	.07
542 Frank Tanana	.08	.05
543 John Smiley	.12	.07
544 David Cone	.12	.07
545 Daryl Boston	.08	.05
546 Tom Henke	.08	.05
547 Bill Krueger	.08	.05
548 Freddie Benavides	.08	.05
549 Randy Myers	.10	.06
550 Reggie Jefferson	.12	.07
551 Kevin Mitchell	.12	.07
552 Dave Stieb	.10	.06
553 Bret Barberie	.10	.06
554 Tim Crews	.08	.05
555 Doug Dascenzo	.08	.05
556 Alex Cole	.08	.05
557 Jeff Innis	.08	.05
558 Carlos Garcia	.30	.18
559 Steve Howell	.08	.05
560 Kirk McCaskill	.08	.05
561 Frank Seminara	.10	.06
562 Cris Carpenter	.08	.05
563 Mike Stanley	.12	.07
564 Carlos Quintana	.08	.05
565 Mitch Williams	.08	.05
566 Juan Bell	.10	.06
567 Eric Fox	.12	.07
568 Al Leiter	.08	.05
569 Mike Stanton	.10	.06
570 Scott Kamieniecki	.08	.05
571 Ryan Bowen	.12	.07

572 Andy Ashby	.10	.06
573 Bob Welch	.08	.05
574 Scott Sanderson	.08	.05
575 Joe Kmak (R)	.20	.12
576 Scott Pose (R)	.20	.12
577 Ricky Gutierrez	.20	.12
578 Mike Trombley	.12	.07
579 Sterling Hitchcock (R)	.60	.35
580 Rodney Bolton	.12	.07
581 Tyler Green	.20	.12
582 Tim Costo	.20	.12
583 Tim Laker (R)	.20	.12
584 Steve Reed (R)	.20	.12
585 Tom Kramer (R)	.25	.15
586 Robb Nen	.20	.12
587 Jim Tatum (R)	.20	.12
588 Frank Bolick	.12	.07
589 Kevin Young	.40	.25
590 Matt Whiteside (R)	.25	.15
591 Cesar Hernandez	.12	.07
592 Mike Mohler (R)	.20	.12
593 Alan Embree	.20	.12
594 Terry Jorgensen	.15	.10
595 John Cummings (R)	.35	.20
596 Domingo Martinez (R)	.40	.25
597 Benji Gil	.40	.25
598 Todd Pratt (R)	.25	.15
599 Rene Arocha (R)	.40	.25
600 Dennis Moeller (R)	.20	.12
601 Jeff Conine	.20	.12
602 Trevor Hoffman (R)	.30	.18
603 Daniel Smith (R)	.20	.12
604 Lee Tinsley	.15	.10
605 Dan Peltier	.12	.07
606 Billy Brewer	.15	.10
607 Matt Walbeck (R)	.30	.18
608 Richie Lewis (R)	.20	.12
609 J.T. Snow (R)	1.25	.80
610 Pat Gomez (R)	.15	.10
611 Phil Hiatt	.35	.20
612 Alex Arias	.12	.07
613 Kevin Rogers	.15	.10
614 Al Martin	.40	.25
615 Greg Gohr	.12	.07
616 Graeme Lloyd (R)	.15	.10
617 Kent Bottenfield	.12	.07
618 Chuck Carr	.25	.15
619 Darrell Sherman (R)	.25	.15
620 Mike Lansing (R)	.30	.18
___ George Brett (Ea)	5.00	3.00
___ Nolan Ryan Tribute	8.50	5.00

1993 Score Pinnacle Team Pinnacle

The cards in this limited insert set were issued randomly in Pinnacle Series I foil packs. The cards feature two player's, one per side, in full-color action shots with the headline "Team Pinnacle" printed across the top. The player's name and league is printed in a color bar under his photo. The cards are numbered on the front. Cards measure 2-1/2" by 3-1/2".

		MINT	NR/MT
Complete Set (10)		175.00	100.00
Commons		10.00	6.50

1	Maddux/Mussina	20.00	12.50
2	Glavine/Smiley	12.50	7.50
3	Daulton/Rodriquez	10.00	6.50
4	McGriff/Thomas	65.00	40.00
5	DeShields/Baerga	20.00	12.50
6	Sheffield/Martinez	12.50	7.50
7.	Smith/Listach	10.00	6.50
8.	Bonds/Gonzalez	55.00	35.00
9.	Puckett/Van Slyke	20.00	12.50
10.	Carter/Walker	20.00	12.50

1993 Score Pinnacle Rookie Team Pinnacle

These limited insert cards were distributed randomly in Pinnacle Series II foil packs. The full-color cards feature two players, one per side. All cards measure 2-1/2" by 3-1/2".

	MINT	NR/MT
Complete Set (10)	275.00	165.00
Commons	12.00	7.00

1	Martinez/Trombley	15.00	10.00
2	Hitchcock/Rogers	15.00	10.00
3	Levis/Piazza	100.00	65.00
4	Klesko/Snow	45.00	28.00
5	Boone/Patterson	15.00	10.00
6	Martinez/Young	20.00	12.50
7	Alexander/Cordero	18.00	11.00
8	Hosey/Salmon	70.00	40.00
9	Thompson/Williams	15.00	10.00
10	Hulse/Nieves	25.00	15.00

TOPPS

1951 Topps Blue Backs

This is the first card set to carry the Topps name. The 56-card set featured black and white photos on the card fronts surrounded by a red, green, yellow and white background. Card backs were printed in blue on a white background. The cards were used as a baseball card game and came packaged two to a pack with a piece of candy. Cards measured 2" by 2-5/8".

	NR/MT	EX
Complete Set (52)	2,200.00	1,000.00
Commons	35.00	20.00

1	Eddie Yost	65.00	35.00
2	Hank Majeski	35.00	20.00
3	Richie Ashburn	180.00	95.00
4	Del Ennis	40.00	22.00
5	Johnny Pesky	45.00	25.00
6	Red Schoendienst	125.00	65.00
7	Gerald Staley	35.00	20.00
8	Dick Sisler	40.00	22.00
9	Johnny Sain	50.00	28.00
10	Joe Page	40.00	22.00
11	Johnny Groth	35.00	20.00

12	Sam Jethroe	35.00	20.00
13	Mickey Vernon	40.00	22.00
14	George Munger	35.00	20.00
15	Eddie Joost	35.00	20.00
16	Murry Dickson	35.00	20.00
17	Roy Smalley	35.00	20.00
18	Ned Garver	35.00	20.00
19	Phil Masi	35.00	20.00
20	Ralph Branca	50.00	28.00
21	Billy Johnson	35.00	20.00
22	Bob Kuzava	35.00	20.00
23	Paul "Dizzy" Trout	35.00	20.00
24	Sherman Lollar	40.00	22.00
25	Sam Mele	35.00	20.00
26	Chico Carrasquel	35.00	20.00
27	Andy Pafko	40.00	22.00
28	Harry Brecheen	35.00	20.00
29	Granny Hamner	35.00	20.00
30	Enos Slaughter	135.00	70.00
31	Lou Brissie	35.00	20.00
32	Bob Elliott	35.00	20.00
33	Don Lenhardt	35.00	20.00
34	Earl Torgeson	35.00	20.00
35	Tommy Byrne	40.00	22.00
36	Cliff Fannin	35.00	20.00
37	Bobby Doerr	125.00	65.00
38	Irv Noren	40.00	22.00
39	Ed Lopat	45.00	25.00
40	Vic Wertz	40.00	22.00
41	Johnny Schmitz	35.00	20.00
42	Bruce Edwards	35.00	20.00
43	Willie Jones	35.00	20.00
44	Johnny Wyrostek	35.00	20.00
45	Bill Pierce	50.00	28.00
46	Gerry Priddy	35.00	20.00
47	Herman Wehmeier	35.00	20.00
48	Billy Cox	40.00	22.00
49	Hank Sauer	40.00	22.00
50	Johnny Mize	175.00	75.00
51	Eddie Waitkus	35.00	20.00
52	Sam Chapman	45.00	25.00

1951 Topps Red Backs

This 52-card set is identical to the Blue Backs except the black and white photos on the front are framed by blue, red, yellow and white backgrounds and the card backs feature red type on a white background. Cards measure 2" by 2-5/8".

		NR/MT	EX
Complete Set (52)		800.00	450.00
Commons		7.50	4.50
1	Yogi Berra	150.00	80.00
2	Sid Gordon	7.50	4.50
3	Ferris Fain	8.50	5.00
4	Vern Stephens	10.00	6.00
5	Phil Rizzuto	40.00	22.00
6	Allie Reynolds	15.00	8.00
7	Howie Pollet	7.50	4.50
8	Early Wynn	25.00	14.00
9	Roy Sievers	10.00	6.00
10	Mel Parnell	8.50	5.00
11	Gene Hermanski	7.50	4.50
12	Jim Hegan	8.50	5.00
13	Dale Mitchell	10.00	6.00
14	Wayne Terwilliger	7.50	4.50
15	Ralph Kiner	35.00	20.00
16	Preacher Roe	10.00	6.00
17	Gus Bell	12.00	7.00
18	Jerry Coleman	12.00	7.00
19	Dick Kokos	7.50	4.50
20	Dom DiMaggio	12.00	7.00
21	Larry Jansen	8.50	5.00
22	Bob Feller	60.00	35.00
23	Ray Boone	12.00	7.00
24	Hank Bauer	16.00	9.00
25	Cliff Chambers	7.50	4.50
26	Luke Easter	10.00	6.00
27	Wally Westlake	7.50	4.50
28	Elmer Valo	7.50	4.50
29	Bob Kennedy	7.50	4.50
30	Warren Spahn	60.00	35.00
31	Gil Hodges	40.00	22.00
32	Hank Thompson	10.00	6.00
33	William Werle	7.50	4.50
34	Grady Hatton	7.50	4.50
35	Al Rosen	15.00	8.00
36a	Gus Zernial (Chicago)	35.00	20.00
36b	Gus Zernial (Philly)	20.00	12.00
37	Wes Westrum	7.50	4.50
38	Duke Snider	90.00	55.00
39	Ted Kluszewski	20.00	12.00
40	Mike Garcia	10.00	6.00
41	Whitey Lockman	8.50	5.00
42	Ray Scarborough	7.50	4.50
43	Maurice McDermott	7.50	4.50
44	Sid Hudson	7.50	4.50
45	Andy Seminick	7.50	4.50

46	Billy Goodman	8.50	5.00
47	Tommy Glaviano	7.50	4.50
48	Eddie Stanky	12.00	7.00
49	Al Zarilla	7.50	4.50
50	Monte Irvin	48.00	28.00
51	Eddie Robinson	7.50	4.50
52a	Tommy Holmes (Boston)	40.00	25.00
52b	Tommy Holmes (Hartford)	20.00	12.00

1952 Topps

This 407-card set is considered the father of modern day card sets. Cards measure 2-5/8" by 3-3/4". Card fronts feature colorized black and white photos. The card backs were the first to utilize player stats. Card numbers 311 through 407 are considered scarce due to shorter print runs. The set contains the first ever Mickey Mantle Topps card and the set is considered the most sought after set in the hobby.

	NR/MT	EX
Complete Set (407)	75,000.00	35,000.00
Commons (1-80)	65.00	30.00
Commons (81-250)	28.00	12.00
Commons (251-280)	48.00	20.00
Commons (281-300)	55.00	25.00
Commons (301-310)	48.00	20.00
Commons (311-407)	225.00	100.00

1	Andy Pafko	1,250.00	400.00
2	Pete Runnels (R)	75.00	35.00
3	Hank Thompson	70.00	32.00
4	Don Lenhardt	65.00	30.00
5	Larry Jansen	65.00	30.00
6	Grady Hatton	65.00	30.00
7	Wayne Terwilliger	65.00	30.00
8	Fred Marsh	65.00	30.00
9	Bobby Hogue	65.00	30.00
10	Al Rosen	100.00	48.00

11	Phil Rizzuto	200.00	95.00
12	Monty Basgall	65.00	30.00
13	Johnny Wyrostek	65.00	30.00
14	Bob Elliott	65.00	30.00
15	Johnny Pesky	75.00	35.00
16	Gene Hermanski	65.00	30.00
17	Jim Hegan	65.00	30.00
18	Merrill Combs	65.00	30.00
19	Johnny Bucha	65.00	30.00
20	Bill Loes (R)	110.00	50.00
21	Ferris Fain	60.00	28.00
22	Dom DiMaggio	100.00	48.00
23	Billy Goodman	65.00	30.00
24	Luke Easter	65.00	30.00
25	Johnny Groth	65.00	30.00
26	Monty Irvin	125.00	60.00
27	Sam Jethroe	65.00	30.00
28	Jerry Priddy	65.00	30.00
29	Ted Kluszewski	110.00	50.00
30	Mel Parnell	70.00	32.00
31	Gus Zernial	70.00	32.00
32	Eddie Robinson	65.00	30.00
33	Warren Spahn	280.00	130.00
34	Elmer Valo	60.00	28.00
35	Hank Sauer	75.00	35.00
36	Gil Hodges	175.00	80.00
37	Duke Snider	340.00	160.00
38	Wally Westlake	65.00	30.00
39	"Dizzy" Trout	65.00	30.00
40	Irv Noren	65.00	30.00
41	Bob Wellman	65.00	30.00
42	Lou Kretlow	65.00	30.00
43	Ray Scarborough	65.00	30.00
44	Con Dempsey	65.00	30.00
45	Eddie Joost	65.00	30.00
46	Gordon Goldsberry	65.00	30.00
47	Willie Jones	65.00	30.00
48a	Joe Page (Er)	300.00	125.00
48b	Joe Page (Cor)	75.00	35.00
49a	Johnny Sain (Er)	325.00	140.00
49b	Johnny Sain (Cor)	90.00	42.00
50	Marv Rickert	65.00	30.00
51	Jim Russell	65.00	30.00
52	Don Mueller	65.00	30.00
53	Chris Van Cuyk	65.00	30.00
54	Leo Kiely	65.00	30.00
55	Ray Boone	70.00	32.00
56	Tommy Glaviano	65.00	30.00
57	Ed Lopat	110.00	50.00
58	Bob Mahoney	65.00	30.00
59	Robin Roberts	180.00	85.00
60	Sid Hudson	65.00	30.00
61	"Tookie" Gilbert	65.00	30.00
62	Chuck Stobbs	65.00	30.00
63	Howie Pollet	65.00	30.00
64	Roy Sievers	70.00	32.00
65	Enos Slaughter	150.00	65.00

66	"Preacher" Roe	110.00	50.00
67	Allie Reynolds	110.00	50.00
68	Cliff Chambers	65.00	30.00
69	Virgil Stallcup	65.00	30.00
70	Al Zarilla	65.00	30.00
71	Tom Upton	65.00	30.00
72	Karl Olson	65.00	30.00
73	William Werle	65.00	30.00
74	Andy Hansen	65.00	30.00
75	Wes Westrum	65.00	30.00
76	Eddie Stanky	75.00	35.00
77	Bob Kennedy	65.00	30.00
78	Ellis Kinder	65.00	30.00
79	Gerald Staley	65.00	30.00
80	Herman Wehmeier	65.00	30.00
81	Vernon Law	35.00	15.00
82	Duane Pillette	28.00	12.00
83	Billy Johnson	28.00	12.00
84	Vern Stephens	32.00	13.50
85	Bob Kuzava	28.00	12.00
86	Ted Gray	28.00	12.00
87	Dale Coogan	28.00	12.00
88	Bob Feller	175.00	80.00
89	Johnny Lipon	28.00	12.00
90	Mickey Grasso	28.00	12.00
91	Al Schoendienst	100.00	48.00
92	Dale Mitchell	32.00	13.50
93	Al Sima	28.00	12.00
94	Sam Mele	28.00	12.00
95	Ken Holcombe	28.00	12.00
96	Willard Marshall	28.00	12.00
97	Earl Torgeson	28.00	12.00
98	Bill Pierce	32.00	13.50
99	Gene Woodling (R)	65.00	30.00
100	Del Rice	28.00	12.00
101	Max Lanier	28.00	12.00
102	Bill Kennedy	28.00	12.00
103	Cliff Mapes	28.00	12.00
104	Don Kolloway	28.00	12.00
105	John Pramesa	28.00	12.00
106	Mickey Vernon	35.00	15.00
107	Connie Ryan	28.00	12.00
108	Jim Konstanty	35.00	15.00
109	Ted Wilks	28.00	12.00
110	Dutch Leonard	28.00	12.00
111	Harry Lowrey	28.00	12.00
112	Henry Majeski	28.00	12.00
113	Dick Sisler	32.00	13.50
114	Willard Ramsdell	28.00	12.00
115	George Munger	28.00	12.00
116	Carl Scheib	28.00	12.00
117	Sherman Lollar	32.00	13.50
118	Ken Raffensberger	28.00	12.00
119	Maurice McDermott	28.00	12.00
120	Bob Chakales	28.00	12.00
121	Gus Niarhos	28.00	12.00
122	Jackie Jensen (R)	80.00	38.00
123	Eddie Yost	32.00	13.50
124	Monte Kennedy	28.00	12.00
125	Bill Rigney	32.00	13.50
126	Fred Hutchinson	32.00	13.50
127	Paul Minner	28.00	12.00
128	Don Bollweg	28.00	12.00
129	Johnny Mize	100.00	48.00
130	Sheldon Jones	28.00	12.00
131	Morrie Martin	28.00	12.00
132	Clyde Kluttz	28.00	12.00
133	Al Widmar	28.00	12.00
134	Joe Tipton	28.00	12.00
135	Dixie Howell	28.00	12.00
136	Johnny Schmitz	28.00	12.00
137	Roy McMillan (R)	35.00	15.00
138	Bill MacDonald	28.00	12.00
139	Ken Wood	28.00	12.00
140	John Antonelli	32.00	13.50
141	Clint Hartung	28.00	12.00
142	Harry Perkowski	28.00	12.00
143	Les Moss	28.00	12.00
144	Ed Blake	28.00	12.00
145	Joe Haynes	28.00	12.00
146	Frank House	28.00	12.00
147	Bob Young	28.00	12.00
148	Johnny Klippstein	28.00	12.00
149	Dick Kryhoski	28.00	12.00
150	Ted Beard	28.00	12.00
151	Wally Post (R)	32.00	13.50
152	Al Evans	28.00	12.00
153	Bob Rush	28.00	12.00
154	Joe Muir	28.00	12.00
155	Frank Overmire	28.00	12.00
156	Frank Hiller	28.00	12.00
157	Bob Usher	28.00	12.00
158	Eddie Waitkus	28.00	12.00
159	Saul Rogovin	28.00	12.00
160	Owen Friend	28.00	12.00
161	Bud Byerly	28.00	12.00
162	Del Crandall	32.00	13.50
163	Stan Rojek	28.00	12.00
164	Walt Dubiel	28.00	12.00
165	Eddie Kazak	28.00	12.00
166	Paul LaPalme	28.00	12.00
167	Bill Howerton	28.00	12.00
168	Charlie Silvera	32.00	13.50
169	Howie Judson	28.00	12.00
170	Gus Bell	35.00	15.00
171	Ed Erautt	28.00	12.00
172	Eddie Miksis	28.00	12.00
173	Roy Smalley	28.00	12.00
174	Clarence Marshall	28.00	12.00
175	Billy Martin	350.00	165.00
176	Hank Edwards	28.00	12.00
177	Bill Wight	28.00	12.00
178	Cass Michaels	28.00	12.00
179	Frank Smith	28.00	12.00

180	Charley Maxwell (R)	32.00	13.50
181	Bob Swift	28.00	12.00
182	Billy Hitchcock	28.00	12.00
183	Erv Dusak	28.00	12.00
184	Bob Ramazzotti	28.00	12.00
185	Bill Nicholson	28.00	12.00
186	Walt Masterson	28.00	12.00
187	Bob Miller	28.00	12.00
188	Clarence Podbielan	28.00	12.00
189	Pete Reiser	35.00	15.00
190	Don Johnson	28.00	12.00
191	Yogi Berra	500.00	240.00
192	Myron Ginsberg	28.00	12.00
193	Harry Simpson	28.00	12.00
194	Joe Hatten	28.00	12.00
195	Minnie Minoso	150.00	70.00
196	Solly Hemus	32.00	13.50
197	George Strickland	32.00	13.50
198	Phil Haugstad	28.00	12.00
199	George Zuverink	28.00	12.00
200	Ralph Houk (R)	70.00	32.00
201	Alex Kellner	28.00	12.00
202	Joe Collins	35.00	15.00
203	Curt Simmons	32.00	13.50
204	Ron Northey	28.00	12.00
205	Clyde King	28.00	12.00
206	Joe Ostrowski	28.00	12.00
207	Mickey Harris	28.00	12.00
208	Marlin Stuart	28.00	12.00
209	Howie Fox	28.00	12.00
210	Dick Fowler	28.00	12.00
211	Ray Coleman	28.00	12.00
212	Ned Garver	28.00	12.00
213	Nippy Jones	28.00	12.00
214	Johnny Hopp	28.00	12.00
215	Hank Bauer	60.00	28.00
216	Richie Ashburn	125.00	60.00
217	George Stirnweiss	32.00	13.50
218	Clyde McCullough	28.00	12.00
219	Bobby Shantz	35.00	15.00
220	Joe Presko	28.00	12.00
221	Granny Hamner	28.00	12.00
222	"Hoot" Evers	28.00	12.00
223	Del Ennis	28.00	12.00
224	Bruce Edwards	28.00	12.00
225	Frank Baumholtz	28.00	12.00
226	Dave Philley	28.00	12.00
227	Joe Garagiola	125.00	60.00
228	Al Brazie	28.00	12.00
229	Gene Bearden	28.00	12.00
230	Matt Batts	28.00	12.00
231	Sam Zoldak	28.00	12.00
232	Billy Cox	35.00	15.00
233	Bob Friend (R)	40.00	18.50
234	Steve Souchock	28.00	12.00
235	Walt Dropo	35.00	13.50
236	Ed FitzGerald	28.00	12.00
237	Jerry Coleman	32.00	13.50
238	Art Houtteman	28.00	12.00
239	Rocky Bridges	28.00	12.00
240	Jack Phillips	28.00	12.00
241	Tommy Byrne	28.00	12.00
242	Tom Poholsky	28.00	12.00
243	Larry Doby	50.00	22.00
244	Vic Wertz	32.00	13.50
245	Sherry Robertson	28.00	12.00
246	George Kell	80.00	38.00
247	Randy Gumpert	28.00	12.00
248	Frank Shea	28.00	12.00
249	Bobby Adams	28.00	12.00
250	Carl Erskine	75.00	35.00
251	Chico Carrasquel	48.00	20.00
252	Vern Bickford	48.00	20.00
253	Johnny Berardino	55.00	25.00
254	Joe Dobson	48.00	20.00
255	Clyde Vollmer	48.00	20.00
256	Pete Suder	48.00	20.00
257	Bobby Avila	50.00	22.00
258	Steve Gromek	48.00	20.00
259	Bob Addis	48.00	20.00
260	Pete Castiglione	48.00	20.00
261	Willie Mays	3,200.00	1,450.00
262	Virgil Trucks	55.00	25.00
263	Harry Brecheen	50.00	22.00
264	Roy Hartsfield	48.00	20.00
265	Chuck Diering	48.00	20.00
266	Murry Dickson	48.00	20.00
267	Sid Gordon	48.00	20.00
268	Bob Lemon	180.00	80.00
269	Willard Nixon	48.00	20.00
270	Lou Brissie	48.00	20.00
271	Jim Delsing	48.00	20.00
272	Mike Garcia	55.00	25.00
273	Erv Palica	48.00	20.00
274	Ralph Branca	90.00	40.00
275	Pat Mullin	48.00	20.00
276	Jim Wilson	48.00	20.00
277	Early Wynn	200.00	95.00
278	Al Clark	48.00	20.00
279	Ed Stewart	48.00	20.00
280	Cloyd Boyer	48.00	20.00
281	Tommy Brown	55.00	25.00
282	Birdie Tebbetts	65.00	30.00
283	Phil Masi	55.00	25.00
284	Hank Arft	55.00	25.00
285	Cliff Fannin	55.00	25.00
286	Joe DeMaestri	55.00	25.00
287	Steve Bilko	55.00	25.00
288	Chet Nichols	55.00	25.00
289	Tommy Holmes	60.00	28.00
290	Joe Astroth	55.00	25.00
291	Gil Coan	55.00	25.00
292	Floyd Baker	55.00	25.00
293	Sibby Sisti	55.00	25.00

294	Walker Cooper	55.00	25.00
295	Phil Cavarretta	65.00	30.00
296	Red Rolfe	60.00	28.00
297	Andy Seminick	60.00	28.00
298	Bob Ross	55.00	25.00
299	Ray Murray	55.00	25.00
300	Barney McCosky	55.00	25.00
301	Bob Porterfield	48.00	20.00
302	Max Surkont	48.00	20.00
303	Harry Dorish	48.00	20.00
304	Sam Dente	48.00	20.00
305	Paul Richards	55.00	25.00
306	Lou Sleator	48.00	20.00
307	Frank Campos	48.00	20.00
308	Luis Aloma	48.00	20.00
309	Jim Busby	48.00	20.00
310	George Metkovich	48.00	20.00
311	Mickey Mantle	35,000.00	18000.00
312	Jackie Robinson	1,500.00	700.00
313	Bobby Thomson	275.00	130.00
314	Roy Campanella	2,250.00	975.00
315	Leo Durocher	375.00	175.00
316	Davey Williams	240.00	110.00
317	Connie Marrero	240.00	110.00
318	Hal Gregg	225.00	100.00
319	Al Walker	225.00	100.00
320	John Rutherford	240.00	110.00
321	Joe Black (R)	275.00	130.00
322	Randy Jackson	225.00	100.00
323	Bubba Church	225.00	100.00
324	Warren Hacker	225.00	100.00
325	Bill Serena	225.00	100.00
326	George Shuba	260.00	125.00
327	Archie Wilson	225.00	100.00
328	Bob Borkowski	225.00	100.00
329	Ivan Delock	225.00	100.00
330	Turk Lown	225.00	100.00
331	Tom Morgan	225.00	100.00
332	Tony Bartirome	225.00	100.00
333	Pee Wee Reese	1,300.00	600.00
334	Wilmer Mizell	275.00	130.00
335	Ted Lepcio	225.00	100.00
336	Dave Koslo	225.00	100.00
337	Jim Hearn	225.00	100.00
338	Sal Yvars	225.00	100.00
339	Russ Meyer	225.00	100.00
340	Bob Hooper	225.00	100.00
341	Hal Jeffcoat	225.00	100.00
342	Clem Labine (R)	275.00	130.00
343	Dick Gernert	225.00	100.00
344	Ewell Blackwell	275.00	130.00
345	Sam White	225.00	100.00
346	George Spencer	225.00	100.00
347	Joe Adcock	275.00	130.00
348	Bob Kelly	225.00	100.00
349	Bob Cain	225.00	100.00
350	Cal Abrams	225.00	100.00
351	Al Dark	250.00	115.00
352	Karl Drews	225.00	100.00
353	Bob Del Greco	225.00	100.00
354	Fred Hatfield	225.00	100.00
355	Bobby Morgan	225.00	100.00
356	Toby Atwell	225.00	100.00
357	Smoky Burgess	260.00	125.00
358	John Kucab	225.00	100.00
359	Dee Fondy	225.00	100.00
360	George Crowe	240.00	110.00
361	Bill Posedel	225.00	100.00
362	Ken Heintzelman	225.00	100.00
363	Dick Rozek	225.00	100.00
364	Clyde Sukeforth	225.00	100.00
365	Cookie Lavagetto	240.00	110.00
366	Dave Madison	225.00	100.00
367	Bob Thorpe	225.00	100.00
368	Ed Wright	225.00	100.00
369	Dick Groat (R)	375.00	175.00
370	Billy Hoeft	240.00	110.00
371	Bob Hofman	225.00	100.00
372	Gil McDougald (R)	375.00	175.00
373	Jim Turner	250.00	120.00
374	Al Benton	225.00	100.00
375	Jack Merson	225.00	100.00
376	Faye Throneberry	225.00	100.00
377	Chuck Dressen	240.00	110.00
378	Les Fusselman	225.00	100.00
379	Joe Rossi	225.00	100.00
380	Clem Koshorek	225.00	100.00
381	Milton Stock	225.00	100.00
382	Sam Jones	240.00	110.00
383	Del Wilber	225.00	100.00
384	Frank Crosetti	260.00	125.00
385	Herman Franks	230.00	105.00
386	Eddie Yuhas	225.00	100.00
387	Billy Meyer	225.00	100.00
388	Bob Chipman	225.00	100.00
389	Ben Wade	225.00	100.00
390	Glenn Nelson	225.00	100.00
391	Ben Chapman (Wrong Photo)	225.00	100.00
392	Hoyt Wilhelm	700.00	340.00
393	Ebba St. Claire	225.00	100.00
394	Billy Herman	280.00	130.00
395	Jake Pitler	225.00	100.00
396	Dick Williams (R)	250.00	120.00
397	Forrest Main	225.00	100.00
398	Hal Rice	225.00	100.00
399	Jim Fridley	225.00	100.00
400	Bill Dickey	750.00	350.00
401	Bob Schultz	225.00	100.00
402	Earl Harrist	225.00	100.00
403	Bill Miller	225.00	100.00
404	Dick Brodowski	225.00	100.00
405	Eddie Pellagrini	225.00	100.00
406	Joe Nuxhall (R)	275.00	130.00

407 Ed Mathews   3,150.00 1,475.00

1953 Topps

YOGI BERRA
NEW YORK YANKEES

The 1953 Topps set consists of 274-cards measuring 2-5/8" by 3-3/4". Card fronts feature colorful drawings of players. Although the checklist is numbered to 280, 6-cards are missing from the set. 253, 261, 267, 268, 271, and 275 were never issued. Short prints account for a scarcity of cards 221-280. Many high number cards were double printed. Those are marked with the symbol(DP).

	NR/MT	EX
Complete Set (274)	15,000.00	9,000.00
Commons (1-165)	25.00	12.00
Commons (166-220)	20.00	8.50
Commons (221-280)	95.00	45.00
Commons (DP)	50.00	22.00

1	Jackie Robinson	650.00	300.00
2	Luke Easter	25.00	12.00
3	George Crowe	25.00	12.00
4	Ben Wade	25.00	12.00
5	Joe Dobson	25.00	12.00
6	Sam Jones	25.00	12.00
7	Bob Borkowski	25.00	12.00
8	Clem Koshorek	25.00	12.00
9	Joe Collins	35.00	15.00
10	Smoky Burgess	60.00	25.00
11	Sal Yvars	25.00	12.00
12	Howie Judson	25.00	12.00
13	Connie Marrero	25.00	12.00
14	Clem Labine	25.00	12.00
15	Bobo Newsom	30.00	13.50
16	Harry Lowrey	25.00	12.00
17	Billy Hitchcock	25.00	12.00
18	Ted Lepcio	25.00	12.00
19	Mel Parnell	25.00	12.00
20	Hank Thompson	25.00	12.00
21	Billy Johnson	25.00	12.00
22	Howie Fox	25.00	12.00
23	Toby Atwell	25.00	12.00
24	Ferris Fain	25.00	12.00
25	Ray Boone	30.00	13.50
26	Dale Mitchell	25.00	12.00
27	Roy Campanella	240.00	115.00
28	Eddie Pellagrini	25.00	12.00
29	Hal Jeffcoat	25.00	12.00
30	Willard Nixon	25.00	12.00
31	Ewell Blackwell	45.00	20.00
32	Clyde Vollmer	25.00	12.00
33	Bob Kennedy	25.00	12.00
34	George Shuba	25.00	12.00
35	Irv Noren	25.00	12.00
36	Johnny Groth	25.00	12.00
37	Ed Mathews	125.00	60.00
38	Jim Hearn	25.00	12.00
39	Eddie Miksis	25.00	12.00
40	John Lipon	25.00	12.00
41	Enos Slaughter	100.00	48.00
42	Gus Zernial	25.00	12.00
43	Gil McDougald	50.00	22.00
44	Ellis Kinder	35.00	15.00
45	Grady Hatton	25.00	12.00
46	Johnny Klippstein	25.00	12.00
47	Bubba Church	25.00	12.00
48	Bob Del Greco	25.00	12.00
49	Faye Throneberry	25.00	12.00
50	Chuck Dressen	25.00	12.00
51	Frank Campos	25.00	12.00
52	Ted Gray	25.00	12.00
53	Sherman Lollar	25.00	12.00
54	Bob Feller	125.00	60.00
55	Maurice McDermott	25.00	12.00
56	Gerald Staley	25.00	12.00
57	Carl Scheib	25.00	12.00
58	George Metkovich	25.00	12.00
59	Karl Drews	25.00	12.00
60	Cloyd Boyer	25.00	12.00
61	Early Wynn	100.00	48.00
62	Monte Irvin	45.00	20.00
63	Gus Niarhos	25.00	12.00
64	Dave Philley	25.00	12.00
65	Earl Harrist	25.00	12.00
66	Orestes Minoso	50.00	22.00
67	Roy Sievers	25.00	12.00
68	Del Rice	25.00	12.00
69	Dick Brodowski	25.00	12.00
70	Ed Yuhas	25.00	12.00
71	Tony Baritrome	25.00	12.00
72	Fred Hutchinson	35.00	15.00
73	Eddie Robinson	25.00	12.00
74	Joe Rossi	25.00	12.00
75	Mike Garcia	30.00	13.50
76	Pee Wee Reese	180.00	85.00
77	John Mize	75.00	35.00
78	Red Schoendienst	75.00	35.00

79	Johnny Wyrostek	25.00	12.00
80	Jim Hegan	25.00	12.00
81	Joe Black	70.00	32.00
82	Mickey Mantle	4,200.00	2,000.00
83	Howie Pollet	25.00	12.00
84	Bob Hooper	25.00	12.00
85	Bobby Morgan	25.00	12.00
86	Billy Martin	160.00	75.00
87	Ed Lopat	45.00	20.00
88	Willie Jones	25.00	12.00
89	Chuck Stobbs	25.00	12.00
90	Hank Edwards	25.00	12.00
91	Ebba St. Claire	25.00	12.00
92	Paul Minner	25.00	12.00
93	Hal Rice	25.00	12.00
94	William Kennedy	25.00	12.00
95	Willard Marshall	25.00	12.00
96	Virgil Trucks	25.00	12.00
97	Don Kolloway	25.00	12.00
98	Cal Abrams	25.00	12.00
99	Dave Madison	25.00	12.00
100	Bill Miller	25.00	12.00
101	Ted Wilks	25.00	12.00
102	Connie Ryan	25.00	12.00
103	Joe Astroth	25.00	12.00
104	Yogi Berra	325.00	150.00
105	Joe Nuxhall	25.00	12.00
106	Johnny Antonelli	30.00	13.50
107	Danny O'Connell	25.00	12.00
108	Bob Porterfield	25.00	12.00
109	Alvin Dark	35.00	15.00
110	Herman Wehmeier	25.00	12.00
111	Hank Sauer	25.00	12.00
112	Ned Garver	25.00	12.00
113	Jerry Priddy	25.00	12.00
114	Phil Rizzuto	150.00	70.00
115	George Spencer	25.00	12.00
116	Frank Smith	25.00	12.00
117	Sid Gordon	25.00	12.00
118	Gus Bell	25.00	12.00
119	John Sain	50.00	22.00
120	Davey Williams	25.00	12.00
121	Walt Dropo	30.00	13.50
122	Elmer Valo	25.00	12.00
123	Tommy Byrne	25.00	12.00
124	Sibby Sisti	25.00	12.00
125	Dick Williams	25.00	12.00
126	Bill Connelly	25.00	12.00
127	Clint Courtney	25.00	12.00
128	Wilmer Mizell	25.00	12.00
129	Keith Thomas	25.00	12.00
130	Turk Lown	25.00	12.00
131	Harry Byrd	25.00	12.00
132	Tom Morgan	25.00	12.00
133	Gil Coan	25.00	12.00
134	Rube Walker	25.00	12.00
135	Al Rosen	35.00	15.00
136	Ken Heintzelman	25.00	12.00
137	John Rutherford	25.00	12.00
138	George Kell	60.00	28.00
139	Sammy White	25.00	12.00
140	Tommy Glaviano	25.00	12.00
141	Allie Reynolds	35.00	15.00
142	Vic Wertz	30.00	13.50
143	Billy Pierce	30.00	13.50
144	Bob Schultz	25.00	12.00
145	Harry Dorish	25.00	12.00
146	Granville Hamner	25.00	12.00
147	Warren Spahn	160.00	75.00
148	Mickey Grasso	25.00	12.00
149	Dom DiMaggio	35.00	15.00
150	Harry Simpson	25.00	12.00
151	Hoyt Wilhelm	75.00	35.00
152	Bob Adams	25.00	12.00
153	Andy Seminick	25.00	12.00
154	Dick Groat	45.00	20.00
155	Dutch Leonard	25.00	12.00
156	Jim Rivera	25.00	12.00
157	Bob Addis	25.00	12.00
158	John Logan (R)	35.00	15.00
159	Wayne Terwilliger	25.00	12.00
160	Bob Young	25.00	12.00
161	Vern Bickford	25.00	12.00
162	Ted Kluszewski	55.00	25.00
163	Fred Hatfield	25.00	12.00
164	Frank Shea	25.00	12.00
165	Billy Hoeft	30.00	13.50
166	Bill Hunter	20.00	8.50
167	Art Schult	20.00	8.50
168	Willard Schmidt	20.00	8.50
169	Dizzy Trout	20.00	8.50
170	Bill Werle	20.00	8.50
171	Bill Glynn	20.00	8.50
172	Rip Repulski	20.00	8.50
173	Preston Ward	20.00	8.50
174	Billy Loes	25.00	12.00
175	Ron Kline (R)	20.00	8.50
176	Don Hoak (R)	30.00	13.50
177	Jim Dyck	20.00	8.50
178	Jim Waugh	20.00	8.50
179	Gene Hermanski	20.00	8.50
180	Virgil Stallcup	20.00	8.50
181	Al Zarilla	20.00	8.50
182	Bob Hofman	20.00	8.50
183	Stu Miller (R)	25.00	12.00
184	Hal Brown (R)	20.00	8.50
185	Jim Pendleton	20.00	8.50
186	Charlie Bishop	20.00	8.50
187	Jim Fridley	20.00	8.50
188	Andy Carey (R)	35.00	15.00
189	Ray Jablonski	20.00	8.50
190	Dixie Walker	20.00	8.50
191	Ralph Kiner	75.00	35.00
192	Wally Westlake	20.00	8.50

193	Mike Clark	20.00	8.50
194	Eddie Kazak	20.00	8.50
195	Ed McGhee	20.00	8.50
196	Bob Keegan	20.00	8.50
197	Del Crandall	25.00	12.00
198	Forrest Main	20.00	8.50
100	Marrion Frioano	20.00	8.50
200	Gordon Goldsberry	20.00	8.50
201	Paul LaPalme	20.00	8.50
202	Carl Sawatski	20.00	8.50
203	Cliff Fannin	20.00	8.50
204	Dick Bokelmann	20.00	8.50
205	Vern Benson	20.00	8.50
206	Ed Bailey (R)	25.00	12.00
207	Whitey Ford	200.00	95.00
208	Jim Wilson	20.00	8.50
209	Jim Greengrass	20.00	8.50
210	Bob Cerv (R)	25.00	12.00
211	J.W. Porter	20.00	8.50
212	Jack Dittmer	20.00	8.50
213	Ray Scaborough	20.00	8.50
214	Bill Bruton (R)	25.00	12.00
215	Gene Conley (R)	30.00	13.50
216	Jim Hughes	20.00	8.50
217	Murray Wall	20.00	8.50
218	Les Fusselman	20.00	8.50
219	Pete Runnels (Er) (Wrong Photo)	25.00	12.00
220	Satchell Paige	500.00	240.00
221	Bob Milliken	95.00	45.00
222	Vic Janowicz(R)(DP)	60.00	28.00
223	John O'Brien (DP)	50.00	22.00
224	Lou Sleater (DP)	50.00	22.00
225	Bobby Shantz	100.00	48.00
226	Ed Erautt	95.00	45.00
227	Morris Martin	95.00	45.00
228	Hal Newhouser	160.00	75.00
229	Rocky Krsnich	95.00	45.00
230	Johnny Lindell (DP)	50.00	22.00
231	Solly Hemus(DP)	50.00	22.00
232	Dick Kokos	95.00	45.00
233	Al Aber	95.00	45.00
234	Ray Murray (DP)	50.00	22.00
235	John Hetki (DP)	50.00	22.00
236	Harry Perkowski (DP)	50.00	22.00
237	Clarence Podbielan (DP)	50.00	22.00
238	Cal Hogue (DP)	50.00	22.00
239	Jim Delsing	95.00	45.00
240	Freddie Marsh	95.00	45.00
241	Al Sima (DP)	50.00	22.00
242	Charlie Silvera	95.00	45.00
243	Carlos Bernier (DP)	50.00	22.00
244	Willie Mays	2,750.00	1,350.00
245	Bill Norman	95.00	45.00
246	Roy Face (R) (DP)	100.00	48.00
247	Mike Sandlock (DP)	50.00	22.00
248	Gene Stephens (DP)	50.00	22.00
249	Ed O'Brien (DP)	50.00	22.00
250	Bob Wilson	95.00	45.00
251	Sid Hudson	95.00	45.00
252	Henry Foiles	95.00	45.00
253	No Card	00.00	00.00
254	Preacher Roe (DP)	95.00	45.00
255	Dixie Howell	95.00	45.00
256	Les Peden	95.00	45.00
257	Bob Boyd	95.00	45.00
258	Jim Gilliam (R)	300.00	140.00
259	Roy McMillan (DP)	95.00	45.00
260	Sam Calderone	95.00	45.00
261	No Card	00.00	00.00
262	Bob Oldis	95.00	45.00
263	John Podres (R)	275.00	130.00
264	Gene Woodling (DP)	80.00	38.00
265	Jackie Jensen	125.00	55.00
266	Bob Cain	95.00	45.00
267	No Card	00.00	00.00
268	No Card	00.00	00.00
269	Duane Pillette	95.00	45.00
270	Vern Stephens	95.00	45.00
271	No Card	00.00	00.00
272	Bill Antonello	95.00	45.00
273	Harvey Haddix (R)	135.00	65.00
274	John Riddle	95.00	45.00
275	No Card	00.00	00.00
276	Ken Raffensberger	95.00	45.00
277	Don Lund	95.00	45.00
278	Willie Miranda	95.00	45.00
279	Joe Coleman (DP)	50.00	22.00
280	Milt Bolling	350.00	160.00

1954 Topps

This 250-card set measures 2-5/8" by 3-3/4" and remains one of Topps most popular issues. Card fronts were the first to use two player images, a small head and shoulder shot in color and a larger black and white action photo. Card backs contained a small cartoon, player stats and a brief biography.

		NR/MT	EX
	Complete Set (250)	8,500.00	4,200.00
	Commons (1-50)	15.00	9.00
	Commons (51-75)	30.00	14.00
	Commons (76-250)	15.00	9.00
1	Ted Williams	750.00	300.00
2	Gus Zernial	15.00	9.00
3	Monte Irvin	40.00	22.00
4	Hank Sauer	15.00	9.00
5	Ed Lopat	20.00	12.00
6	Pete Runnels	15.00	9.00
7	Ted Kluszewski	30.00	16.00
8	Bobby Young	15.00	9.00
9	Harvey Haddix	18.00	10.00
10	Jackie Robinson	300.00	155.00
11	Paul Smith	15.00	9.00
12	Del Crandall	15.00	9.00
13	Billy Martin	90.00	45.00
14	Preacher Roe	25.00	14.00
15	Al Rosen	25.00	14.00
16	Vic Janowicz	18.00	10.00
17	Phil Rizzuto	80.00	42.00
18	Walt Dropo	15.00	9.00
19	Johnny Lipon	15.00	9.00
20	Warren Spahn	100.00	55.00
21	Bobby Shantz	18.00	10.00
22	Jim Greengrass	15.00	9.00
23	Luke Easter	15.00	9.00
24	Granny Hamner	15.00	9.00
25	Harvey Kuenn (R)	40.00	22.00
26	Ray Jablonski	15.00	9.00
27	Ferris Fain	15.00	9.00
28	Paul Minner	15.00	9.00
29	Jim Hegan	15.00	9.00
30	Ed Mathews	110.00	60.00
31	Johnny Klippstein	15.00	9.00
32	Duke Snider	165.00	85.00
33	Johnny Schmitz	15.00	9.00
34	Jim Rivera	15.00	9.00
35	Junior Gilliam	30.00	16.00
36	Hoyt Wilhelm	50.00	27.00
37	Whitey Ford	110.00	60.00
38	Eddie Stanky	18.00	10.00
39	Sherm Lollar	15.00	9.00
40	Mel Parnell	15.00	9.00
41	Willie Jones	15.00	9.00
42	Don Mueller	15.00	9.00
43	Dick Groat	20.00	12.00
44	Ned Garver	15.00	9.00
45	Richie Ashburn	50.00	27.00
46	Ken Raffensberger	15.00	9.00
47	Ellis Kinder	15.00	9.00
48	Billy Hunter	15.00	9.00
49	Ray Murray	15.00	9.00
50	Yogi Berra	260.00	135.00
51	Johnny Lindell	30.00	14.00
52	Vic Power (R)	35.00	18.50
53	Jack Dittmer	30.00	14.00
54	Vern Stephens	32.00	17.00
55	Phil Cavarretta	35.00	18.50
56	Willie Miranda	30.00	14.00
57	Luis Aloma	30.00	14.00
58	Bob Wilson	30.00	14.00
59	Gene Conley	35.00	18.50
60	Frank Baumholtz	30.00	14.00
61	Bob Cain	30.00	14.00
62	Eddie Robinson	30.00	14.00
63	Johnny Pesky	35.00	18.50
64	Hank Thompson	32.00	17.00
65	Bob Swift	30.00	14.00
66	Ted Lepcio	30.00	14.00
67	Jim Willis	30.00	14.00
68	Sammy Calderone	30.00	14.00
69	Bud Podbielan	30.00	14.00
70	Larry Doby	75.00	38.00
71	Frank Smith	30.00	14.00
72	Preston Ward	30.00	14.00
73	Wayne Terwilliger	30.00	14.00
74	Bill Taylor	30.00	14.00
75	Fred Haney	30.00	14.00
76	Bob Scheffing	15.00	9.00
77	Ray Boone	18.00	10.00
78	Ted Kazanski	15.00	9.00
79	Andy Pafko	18.00	10.00
80	Jackie Jensen	25.00	14.00
81	Dave Hoskins	15.00	9.00
82	Milt Bolling	15.00	9.00
83	Joe Collins	18.00	10.00
84	Dick Cole	15.00	9.00
85	Bob Turley (R)	30.00	16.00
86	Billy Herman	25.00	14.00
87	Roy Face	18.00	10.00
88	Matt Batts	15.00	9.00
89	Howie Pollet	15.00	9.00
90	Willie Mays	575.00	290.00
91	Bob Oldis	15.00	9.00
92	Wally Westlake	15.00	9.00
93	Sid Hudson	15.00	9.00
94	Ernie Banks (R)	850.00	450.00
95	Hal Rice	15.00	9.00
96	Charlie Silvera	15.00	9.00
97	Jerry Lane	15.00	9.00
98	Joe Black	20.00	12.00
99	Bob Hofman	15.00	9.00
100	Bob Keegan	15.00	9.00
101	Gene Woodling	20.00	12.00
102	Gil Hodges	90.00	48.00
103	Jim Lemon (R)	20.00	12.00

104	Mike Sandlock	15.00	9.00
105	Andy Carey	18.00	10.00
106	Dick Kokos	15.00	9.00
107	Duane Pillette	15.00	9.00
108	Thornton Kipper	15.00	9.00
109	Bill Bruton	15.00	9.00
110	Harry Dorish	15.00	9.00
111	Jim Delsing	15.00	9.00
112	Bill Renna	15.00	9.00
113	Bob Boyd	15.00	9.00
114	Dean Stone	15.00	9.00
115	Rip Repulski	15.00	9.00
116	Steve Bilko	15.00	9.00
117	Solly Hemus	15.00	9.00
118	Carl Scheib	15.00	9.00
119	Johnny Antonelli	18.00	10.00
120	Roy McMillan	15.00	9.00
121	Clem Labine	18.00	10.00
122	Johnny Logan	18.00	10.00
123	Bobby Adams	15.00	9.00
124	Marion Fricano	15.00	9.00
125	Harry Perkowski	15.00	9.00
126	Ben Wade	15.00	9.00
127	Steve O'Neill	15.00	9.00
128	Henry Aaron (R)	2,275.00	1,150.00
129	Forrest Jacobs	15.00	9.00
130	Hank Bauer	30.00	16.00
131	Reno Bertoia	15.00	9.00
132	Tom Lasorda (R)	150.00	80.00
133	Del Baker	15.00	9.00
134	Cal Hogue	15.00	9.00
135	Joe Presko	15.00	9.00
136	Connie Ryan	15.00	9.00
137	Wally Moon (R)	30.00	16.00
138	Bob Borkowski	15.00	9.00
139	Ed & Johnny O'Brien	32.00	17.00
140	Tom Wright	15.00	9.00
141	Joe Jay (R)	18.00	10.00
142	Tom Poholski	15.00	9.00
143	Rollie Hemsley	15.00	9.00
144	Bill Werle	15.00	9.00
145	Elmer Valo	15.00	9.00
146	Don Johnson	15.00	9.00
147	John Riddle	15.00	9.00
148	Bob Trice	15.00	9.00
149	Jim Robertson	15.00	9.00
150	Dick Kryhoski	15.00	9.00
151	Alex Grammas	15.00	9.00
152	Mike Blyzka	15.00	9.00
153	Rube Walker	15.00	9.00
154	Mike Fornieles	15.00	9.00
155	Bob Kennedy	15.00	9.00
156	Joe Coleman	15.00	9.00
157	Don Lenhardt	15.00	9.00
158	Peanuts Lowrey	15.00	9.00
159	Dave Philley	15.00	9.00
160	Red Kress	15.00	9.00
161	John Hetki	15.00	9.00
162	Herman Wehmeier	15.00	9.00
163	Frank House	15.00	9.00
164	Stu Miller	18.00	10.00
165	Jim Pendleton	15.00	9.00
166	Johnny Podres	35.00	18.00
167	Don Lund	15.00	9.00
168	Morrie Martin	15.00	9.00
169	Jim Hughes	15.00	9.00
170	Dusty Rhodes (R)	20.00	12.00
171	Leo Kiely	15.00	9.00
172	Hal Brown	15.00	9.00
173	Jack Harshman	15.00	9.00
174	Tom Qualters	15.00	9.00
175	Frank Leja	15.00	9.00
176	Bob Keely	15.00	9.00
177	Bob Milliken	15.00	9.00
178	Bill Glynn	15.00	9.00
179	Gair Allie	15.00	9.00
180	Wes Westrum	15.00	9.00
181	Mel Roach	15.00	9.00
182	Chuck Harmon	15.00	9.00
183	Earle Combs	30.00	16.00
184	Ed Bailey	18.00	10.00
185	Chuck Stobbs	15.00	9.00
186	Karl Olson	15.00	9.00
187	Heinie Manush	30.00	16.00
188	Dave Jolly	15.00	9.00
189	Bob Ross	15.00	9.00
190	Ray Herbert	15.00	9.00
191	Dick Schofield (R)	20.00	12.00
192	Ellis Deal	15.00	9.00
193	Johnny Hopp	15.00	9.00
194	Bill Sarni	15.00	9.00
195	Bill Consolo	15.00	9.00
196	Stank Jok	15.00	9.00
197	Schoolboy Rowe	15.00	9.00
198	Carl Sawatski	15.00	9.00
199	Rocky Nelson	15.00	9.00
200	Larry Jansen	18.00	10.00
201	Al Kaline (R)	800.00	450.00
202	Bob Purkey (R)	18.00	10.00
203	Harry Brecheen	15.00	9.00
204	Angel Scull	15.00	9.00
205	Johnny Sain	30.00	16.00
206	Ray Crone	15.00	9.00
207	Tom Oliver	15.00	9.00
208	Grady Hatton	15.00	9.00
209	Charlie Thompson	15.00	9.00
210	Bob Buhl (R)	18.00	10.00
211	Don Hoak	18.00	10.00
212	Mickey Micelotta	15.00	9.00
213	John Fitzpatrick	15.00	9.00
214	Arnold Portocarrero	15.00	9.00
215	Ed McGhee	15.00	9.00
216	Al Sima	15.00	9.00
217	Paul Schreiber	15.00	9.00

218	Fred Marsh	15.00	9.00
219	Charlie Kress	15.00	9.00
220	Ruben Gomez	15.00	9.00
221	Dick Brodowski	15.00	9.00
222	Bill Wilson	15.00	9.00
223	Joe Haynes	15.00	9.00
224	Dick Weik	15.00	9.00
225	Don Liddle	15.00	9.00
226	Jehosie Heard	15.00	9.00
227	Buster Mills	15.00	9.00
228	Gene Hermanski	15.00	9.00
229	Bob Talbot	15.00	9.00
230	Bob Kuzava	15.00	9.00
231	Roy Smalley	15.00	9.00
232	Lou Limmer	15.00	9.00
233	Augie Galan	15.00	9.00
234	Jerry Lynch (R)	20.00	12.00
235	Vern Law	18.00	10.00
236	Paul Penson	15.00	9.00
237	Mike Ryba	15.00	9.00
238	Al Aber	15.00	9.00
239	Bill Skowron (R)	80.00	42.00
240	Sam Mele	15.00	9.00
241	Bob Miller	15.00	9.00
242	Curt Roberts	15.00	9.00
243	Ray Blades	15.00	9.00
244	Leroy Wheat	15.00	9.00
245	Roy Sievers	15.00	9.00
246	Howie Fox	15.00	9.00
247	Eddie Mayo	15.00	9.00
248	Al Smith (R)	18.00	10.00
249	Wilmer Mizell	15.00	9.00
250	Ted Williams	800.00	350.00

1955 Topps

ERNIE BANKS shortstop CHICAGO CUBS

For the first time, Topps introduced a horizontal format on the card fronts. The design is similar to the 1954 set with two photos on the front, a large head shot and a smaller action shot. The card fronts are in color and the card size is 3-3/4" by 2-5/8".

Although the checklist is numbered to 210, four cards were never issued, 175, 186, 203 and 209.

	NR/MT	EX
Complete Set (206)	7,850.00	3,850.00
Commons (1-150)	9.00	4.50
Commons (151-160)	18.00	9.00
Commons (161-210)	28.00	14.00

1	Dusty Rhodes	48.00	24.00
2	Ted Williams	500.00	250.00
3	Art Fowler	9.00	4.50
4	Al Kaline	250.00	125.00
5	Jim Gilliam	18.00	9.00
6	Stan Hack	12.00	6.00
7	Jim Hegan	9.00	4.50
8	Hal Smith	9.00	4.50
9	Bob Miller	9.00	4.50
10	Bob Keegan	9.00	4.50
11	Ferris Fain	9.00	4.50
12	Jake Thies	9.00	4.50
13	Fred Marsh	9.00	4.50
14	Jim Finigan	9.00	4.50
15	Jim Pendleton	9.00	4.50
16	Roy Sievers	12.00	6.00
17	Bobby Hofman	9.00	4.50
18	Russ Kemmerer	9.00	4.50
19	Billy Herman	12.00	6.00
20	Andy Carey	12.00	6.00
21	Alex Grammas	9.00	4.50
22	Bill Skowron	20.00	10.00
23	Jack Parks	9.00	4.50
24	Hal Newhouser	25.00	12.50
25	Johnny Podres	20.00	10.00
26	Dick Groat	12.00	6.00
27	Billy Gardner	9.00	4.50
28	Ernie Banks	240.00	120.00
29	Herman Wehmeier	9.00	4.50
30	Vic Power	10.00	5.00
31	Warren Spahn	90.00	45.00
32	Ed McGhee	9.00	4.50
33	Tom Qualters	9.00	4.50
34	Wayne Terwilliger	9.00	4.50
35	Dave Jolly	9.00	4.50
36	Leo Kiely	9.00	4.50
37	Joe Cunningham (R)	10.00	5.00
38	Bob Turley	15.00	7.50
39	Bill Glynn	9.00	4.50
40	Don Hoak	10.00	5.00
41	Chuck Stobbs	9.00	4.50
42	Windy McCall	9.00	4.50
43	Harvey Haddix	12.00	6.00
44	Corky Valentine	9.00	4.50
45	Hank Sauer	10.00	5.00

46	Ted Kazanski	9.00	4.50	103	Charlie White	9.00	4.50
47	Hank Aaron	525.00	275.00	104	Jack Harshman	9.00	4.50
48	Bob Kennedy	9.00	4.50	105	Chuck Diering	9.00	4.50
49	J.W. Porter	9.00	4.50	106	Frank Sullivan	9.00	4.50
50	Jackie Robinson	275.00	140.00	107	Curt Roberts	9.00	4.50
51	Jim Hughes	9.00	4.50	108	Rube Walker	9.00	4.50
52	Bill Tremel	9.00	4.50	109	Ed Lopat	15.00	7.50
53	Bill Taylor	9.00	4.50	110	Gus Zernial	10.00	5.00
54	Lou Limmer	9.00	4.50	111	Bob Milliken	9.00	4.50
55	"Rip" Repulski	9.00	4.50	112	Nelson King	9.00	4.50
56	Ray Jablonski	9.00	4.50	113	Harry Brecheen	9.00	4.50
57	Billy O'Dell	9.00	4.50	114	Lou Ortiz	9.00	4.50
58	Jim Rivera	9.00	4.50	115	Ellis Kinder	9.00	4.50
59	Gair Allie	9.00	4.50	116	Tom Hurd	9.00	4.50
60	Dean Stone	9.00	4.50	117	Mel Roach	9.00	4.50
61	Forrest Jacobs	9.00	4.50	118	Bob Purkey	9.00	4.50
62	Thornton Kipper	9.00	4.50	119	Bob Lennon	9.00	4.50
63	Joe Collins	12.00	6.00	120	Ted Kluszewski	30.00	15.00
64	Gus Triandos (R)	12.00	6.00	121	Bill Renna	9.00	4.50
65	Ray Boone	10.00	6.00	122	Carl Sawatski	9.00	4.50
66	Ron Jackson	9.00	4.50	123	Sandy Koufax (R)	1,300.00	650.00
67	Wally Moon	12.00	6.00	124	Harmon Killebrew (R)	400.00	200.00
68	Jim Davis	9.00	4.50				
69	Ed Bailey	9.00	4.50	125	Ken Boyer (R)	80.00	40.00
70	Al Rosen	12.00	6.00	126	Dick Hall	9.00	4.50
71	Ruben Gomez	9.00	4.50	127	Dale Long (R)	12.00	6.00
72	Karl Olson	9.00	4.50	128	Ted Lepcio	9.00	4.50
73	Jack Shepard	9.00	4.50	129	Elvin Tappe	9.00	4.50
74	Bob Borkowski	9.00	4.50	130	Mayo Smith	9.00	4.50
75	Sandy Amoros (R)	25.00	12.50	131	Grady Hatton	9.00	4.50
76	Howie Pollet	9.00	4.50	132	Bob Trice	9.00	4.50
77	Arnold Portcarrero	9.00	4.50	133	Dave Hoskins	9.00	4.50
78	Gordon Jones	9.00	4.50	134	Joe Jay	9.00	4.50
79	Danny Schell	9.00	4.50	135	Johnny O'Brien	9.00	4.50
80	Bob Grim (R)	15.00	7.50	136	Bunky Stewart	9.00	4.50
81	Gene Conley	12.00	6.00	137	Harry Elliott	9.00	4.50
82	Chuck Harmon	9.00	4.50	138	Ray Herbert	9.00	4.50
83	Tom Brewer	9.00	4.50	139	Steve Kraly	9.00	4.50
84	Camilo Pascual (R)	15.00	7.50	140	Mel Parnell	10.00	5.00
85	Don Mossi (R)	15.00	7.50	141	Tom Wright	9.00	4.50
86	Bill Wilson	9.00	4.50	142	Jerry Lynch	9.00	4.50
87	Frank House	9.00	4.50	143	Dick Schofield	9.00	4.50
88	Bob Skinner (R)	15.00	7.50	144	Joe Amalfitano (R)	12.00	6.00
89	Joe Frazier	9.00	4.50	145	Elmer Valo	9.00	4.50
90	Karl Spooner (R)	12.00	6.00	146	Dick Donovan (R)	10.00	5.00
91	Milt Bolling	9.00	4.50	147	Laurin Pepper	9.00	4.50
92	Don Zimmer (R)	35.00	18.00	148	Hal Brown	9.00	4.50
93	Steve Bilko	9.00	4.50	149	Ray Crone	9.00	4.50
94	Reno Bertoia	9.00	4.50	150	Mike Higgins	9.00	4.50
95	Preston Ward	9.00	4.50	151	Red Kress	18.00	9.00
96	Charlie Bishop	9.00	4.50	152	Harry Agganis (R)	80.00	40.00
97	Carlos Paula	9.00	4.50	153	Bud Podbielan	18.00	9.00
98	Johnny Riddle	9.00	4.50	154	Willie Miranda	18.00	9.00
99	Frank Leja	9.00	4.50	155	Ed Mathews	125.00	65.00
100	Monte Irvin	35.00	18.00	156	Joe Black	35.00	18.00
101	Johnny Gray	9.00	4.50	157	Bob Miller	18.00	9.00
102	Wally Westlake	9.00	4.50	158	Tom Carroll	18.00	9.00

159	Johnny Schmitz	18.00	9.00
160	Ray Narleski (R)	25.00	12.50
161	Chuck Tanner (R)	30.00	15.00
162	Joe Coleman	28.00	14.00
163	Faye Throneberry	28.00	14.00
164	Roberto Clemente (R)	2,400.00	1,200.00
165	Don Johnson	28.00	14.00
166	Hank Bauer	50.00	25.00
167	Tom Casagrande	28.00	14.00
168	Duane Pillette	28.00	14.00
169	Bob Oldis	28.00	14.00
170	Jim Pearce	28.00	14.00
171	Dick Brodowski	28.00	14.00
172	Frank Baumholtz	28.00	14.00
173	Bob Kline	28.00	14.00
174	Rudy Minarcin	28.00	14.00
175	Not issued	28.00	14.00
176	Norm Zauchin	28.00	14.00
177	Jim Robertson	28.00	14.00
178	Bobby Adams	28.00	14.00
179	Jim Bolger	28.00	14.00
180	Clem Labine	35.00	18.00
181	Roy McMillan	30.00	15.00
182	Humberto Robinson	28.00	14.00
183	Tony Jacobs	28.00	14.00
184	Harry Perkowski	28.00	14.00
185	Don Ferrarese	28.00	14.00
186	No Card	00.00	00.00
187	Gil Hodges	175.00	90.00
188	Charlie Silvera	28.00	14.00
189	Phil Rizzuto	175.00	90.00
190	Gene Woodling	35.00	18.00
191	Ed Stanky	30.00	15.00
192	Jim Delsing	28.00	14.00
193	Johnny Sain	48.00	24.00
194	Willie Mays	600.00	300.00
195	Ed Roebuck (R)	35.00	18.00
196	Gale Wade	28.00	14.00
197	Al Smith	28.00	14.00
198	Yogi Berra	275.00	140.00
199	Bert Hamric	28.00	14.00
200	Jack Jensen	50.00	25.00
201	Sherm Lollar	30.00	15.00
202	Jim Owens	28.00	14.00
203	No Card	00.00	00.00
204	Frank Smith	28.00	14.00
205	Gene Freese (R)	32.00	16.00
206	Pete Daley	28.00	14.00
207	Bill Consolo	28.00	14.00
208	Ray Moore	28.00	14.00
209	No Card	00.00	00.00
210	Duke Snider	600.00	275.00

1956 Topps

This 340-card set is similar to Topp's 1955 set with horizontal fronts with two player photos. Cards measure 2-5/8" by 3-3/4". Card backs contain a three panel cartoon. For the first time Topps created team cards and also included cards of the league presidents. Two unnumbered checklists were issued as part of the set. Though they are not included in the set price, the checklists are included at the end of this listing.

	NR/MT	EX
Complete Set (340)	7,700.00	3,850.00
Commons (1-100)	9.00	4.50
Commons (101-180)	10.00	5.00
Commons (181-260)	16.00	8.00
Commons (261-340)	12.00	6.00

1	William Harridge	110.00	40.00
2	Warren Giles	20.00	10.00
3	Elmer Valo	9.00	4.50
4	Carlos Paula	9.00	4.50
5	Ted Williams	365.00	185.00
6	Ray Boone	10.00	5.00
7	Ron Negray	9.00	4.50
8	Walter Alston	40.00	20.00
9	Ruben Gomez	9.00	4.50
10	Warren Spahn	90.00	45.00
11a	Cubs Team (Date)	55.00	25.00
11b	Cubs Team (No Date)	18.00	9.00
12	Andy Carey	10.00	5.00
13	Roy Face	12.00	6.00
14	Ken Boyer	18.00	9.00
15	Ernie Banks	100.00	50.00
16	Hector Lopez (R)	12.00	6.00
17	Gene Conley	10.00	5.00
18	Dick Donovan	9.00	4.50
19	Chuck Diering	9.00	4.50
20	Al Kaline	135.00	70.00

No.	Player	Price 1	Price 2
21	Joe Collins	9.00	4.50
22	Jim Finigan	9.00	4.50
23	Freddie Marsh	9.00	4.50
24	Dick Groat	12.00	5.00
25	Ted Kluszewski	28.00	14.00
26	Grady Hatton	9.00	4.50
27	Nelson Burbrink	9.00	4.50
28	Bobby Hofman	9.00	4.50
29	Jack Harshman	9.00	4.50
30	Jackie Robinson	185.00	95.00
31	Hank Aaron	300.00	150.00
32	Frank House	9.00	4.50
33	Roberto Clemente	450.00	225.00
34	Tom Brewer	9.00	4.50
35	Al Rosen	12.00	6.00
36	Rudy Minarcin	9.00	4.50
37	Alex Grammas	9.00	4.50
38	Bob Kennedy	9.00	4.50
39	Don Mossi	10.00	5.00
40	Bob Turley	12.00	6.00
41	Hank Sauer	12.00	6.00
42	Sandy Amoros	12.00	6.00
43	Ray Moore	9.00	4.50
44	Windy McCall	9.00	4.50
45	Gus Zernial	9.00	4.50
46	Gene Freese	9.00	4.50
47	Art Fowler	9.00	4.50
48	Jim Hegan	9.00	4.50
49	Pedro Ramos	9.00	4.50
50	Dusty Rhodes	10.00	5.00
51	Ernie Oravetz	9.00	4.50
52	Bob Grim	9.00	4.50
53	Arnold Portocarrero	9.00	4.50
54	Bob Keegan	9.00	4.50
55	Wally Moon	10.00	5.00
56	Dale Long	10.00	5.00
57	Duke Maas	9.00	4.50
58	Ed Roebuck	10.00	5.00
59	Jose Santiago	9.00	4.50
60	Mayo Smith	9.00	4.50
61	Bill Skowron	18.00	9.00
62	Hal Smith	9.00	4.50
63	Roger Craig (R)	30.00	15.00
64	Luis Arroyo (R)	10.00	5.00
65	Johnny O'Brien	9.00	4.50
66	Bob Speake	9.00	4.50
67	Vic Power	9.00	4.50
68	Chuck Stobbs	9.00	4.50
69	Chuck Tanner	12.00	6.00
70	Jim Rivera	9.00	4.50
71	Frank Sullivan	9.00	4.50
72a	Phillies Team (Date)	55.00	25.00
72b	Phillies Team (No Date)	18.00	9.00
73	Wayne Terwilliger	9.00	4.50
74	Jim King	9.00	4.50
75	Roy Sievers	9.00	4.50
76	Ray Crone	9.00	4.50
77	Harvey Haddix	9.00	4.50
78	Herman Wehmeier	9.00	4.50
79	Sandy Koufax	450.00	225.00
80	Gus Triandos	9.00	4.50
81	Wally Westlake	9.00	4.50
82	Bill Renna	9.00	4.50
83	Karl Spooner	9.00	4.50
84	"Babe" Birrer	9.00	4.50
85a	Indians Team (Date)	55.00	25.00
85b	Indians Team (No Date)	18.00	9.00
86	Ray Jablonski	9.00	4.50
87	Dean Stone	9.00	4.50
88	Johnny Kucks (R)	10.00	5.00
89	Norm Zauchin	9.00	4.50
90a	Reds Team (Date)	55.00	25.00
90b	Reds Team (No date)	18.00	9.00
91	Gail Harris	9.00	4.50
92	Red Wilson	9.00	4.50
93	George Susce, Jr.	9.00	4.50
94	Ronnie Kline	9.00	4.50
95a	Braves Team (Date)	70.00	30.00
95b	Braves Team (No Date)	20.00	10.00
96	Bill Tremel	9.00	4.50
97	Jerry Lynch	9.00	4.50
98	Camilo Pascual	9.00	4.50
99	Don Zimmer	15.00	7.50
100a	Orioles Team (Date)	70.00	30.00
100b	Orioles Team (No Date)	20.00	10.00
101	Roy Campanella	175.00	90.00
102	Jim Davis	10.00	5.00
103	Willie Miranda	10.00	5.00
104	Bob Lennon	10.00	5.00
105	Al Smith	10.00	5.00
106	Joe Astroth	10.00	5.00
107	Ed Mathews	70.00	35.00
108	Laurin Pepper	10.00	5.00
109	Enos Slaughter	35.00	18.00
110	Yogi Berra	160.00	80.00
111	Red Sox Team	25.00	12.50
112	Dee Fondy	10.00	5.00
113	Phil Rizzuto	70.00	35.00
114	Jim Owens	10.00	5.00
115	Jackie Jensen	15.00	7.50
116	Eddie O'Brien	10.00	5.00
117	Virgil Trucks	10.00	5.00
118	Nellie Fox	35.00	18.00
119	Larry Jackson (R)	15.00	7.50
120	Richie Ashburn	38.00	19.00
121	Pirates Team	25.00	12.50
122	Willard Nixon	10.00	5.00
123	Roy McMillan	10.00	5.00
124	Don Kaiser	10.00	5.00
125	Minnie Minoso	25.00	12.50

No.	Name	Price	Price
126	Jim Brady	10.00	5.00
127	Willie Jones	10.00	5.00
128	Eddie Yost	10.00	5.00
129	Jake Martin	10.00	5.00
130	Willie Mays	400.00	200.00
131	Bob Roselli	10.00	5.00
132	Bobby Avila	12.00	6.00
133	Ray Narleski	12.00	6.00
134	Cardinals Team	25.00	12.50
135	Mickey Mantle	1,400.00	700.00
136	Johnny Logan	12.00	6.00
137	Al Silvera	10.00	5.00
138	Johnny Antonelli	12.00	6.00
139	Tommy Carrol	10.00	5.00
140	Herb Score (R)	40.00	20.00
141	Joe Frazier	10.00	5.00
142	Gene Baker	10.00	5.00
143	Jim Piersall	15.00	7.50
144	Leroy Powell	10.00	5.00
145	Gil Hodges	60.00	30.00
146	Senators Team	25.00	12.50
147	Earl Torgeson	10.00	5.00
148	Alvin Dark	12.00	6.00
149	Dixie Howell	10.00	5.00
150	Duke Snider	160.00	80.00
151	Spook Jacobs	10.00	5.00
152	Billy Hoeft	10.00	5.00
153	Frank Thomas	12.00	6.00
154	Dave Pope	10.00	5.00
155	Harvey Kuenn	20.00	10.00
156	Wes Westrum	10.00	5.00
157	Dick Brodowski	10.00	5.00
158	Wally Post	12.00	6.00
159	Clint Courtney	12.00	6.00
160	Billy Pierce	12.00	6.00
161	Joe DeMaestri	10.00	5.00
162	Gus Bel	12.00	6.00
163	Gene Woodling	15.00	7.50
164	Harmon Killebrew	160.00	80.00
165	Red Schoendienst	35.00	18.00
166	Dodgers Team	180.00	90.00
167	Harry Dorish	10.00	5.00
168	Sammy White	10.00	5.00
169	Bob Nelson	10.00	5.00
170	Bill Virdon	12.00	6.00
171	Jim Wilson	10.00	5.00
172	Frank Torre (R)	15.00	7.50
173	Johnny Podres	18.00	9.00
174	Glen Gorbous	10.00	5.00
175	Del Crandall	12.00	6.00
176	Alex Kellner	10.00	5.00
177	Hank Bauer	18.00	9.00
178	Joe Black	15.00	7.50
179	Harry Chiti	10.00	5.00
180	Robin Roberts	45.00	22.50
181	Billy Martin	100.00	50.00
182	Paul Minner	16.00	8.00
183	Stan Lopata	16.00	8.00
184	Don Bessent	16.00	8.00
185	Bill Bruton	16.00	8.00
186	Ron Jackson	16.00	8.00
187	Early Wynn	45.00	22.50
188	White Sox Team	35.00	18.00
189	Ned Garver	16.00	8.00
190	Carl Furillo	30.00	15.00
191	Frank Lary (R)	20.00	10.00
192	Smoky Burgess	18.00	9.00
193	Wilmer Mizell	16.00	8.00
194	Monte Irvin	35.00	18.00
195	George Kell	35.00	18.00
196	Tom Poholsky	16.00	8.00
197	Granny Hamner	16.00	8.00
198	Ed Fitzgerald	16.00	8.00
199	Hank Thompson	18.00	9.00
200	Bob Feller	130.00	65.00
201	Rip Repulski	16.00	8.00
202	Jim Hearn	16.00	8.00
203	Bill Tuttle	16.00	8.00
204	Art Swanson	16.00	8.00
205	Whitey Lockman	18.00	9.00
206	Erv Palica	16.00	8.00
207	Jim Small	16.00	8.00
208	Elston Howard	60.00	30.00
209	Max Surkont	16.00	8.00
210	Mike Garcia	18.00	9.00
211	Murry Dickson	16.00	8.00
212	Johnny Temple	20.00	10.00
213	Tigers Team	50.00	25.00
214	Bob Rush	16.00	8.00
215	Tommy Byrne	16.00	8.00
216	Jerry Schoonmaker	16.00	8.00
217	Billy Klaus	16.00	8.00
218	Joe Nuxhall	20.00	10.00
219	Lew Burdette	25.00	12.50
220	Del Ennis	18.00	9.00
221	Bob Friend	18.00	9.00
222	Dave Philley	16.00	8.00
223	Randy Jackson	16.00	8.00
224	Bud Podbielan	16.00	8.00
225	Gil McDougald	30.00	15.00
226	Giants Team	70.00	35.00
227	Russ Meyer	16.00	8.00
228	Mickey Vernon	18.00	9.00
229	Harry Brecheen	16.00	8.00
230	Chico Carrasquel	16.00	8.00
231	Bob Hale	16.00	8.00
232	Toby Atwell	16.00	8.00
233	Carl Erskine	28.00	14.00
234	Pete Runnels	18.00	9.00
235	Don Newcombe	60.00	30.00
236	Athletics Team	30.00	15.00
237	Jose Valdivielso	16.00	8.00
238	Walt Dropo	18.00	9.00
239	Harry Simpson	16.00	8.00

240	Whitey Ford	150.00	75.00
241	Don Mueller	16.00	8.00
242	Hershell Freeman	16.00	8.00
243	Sherm Lollar	18.00	9.00
244	Bob Buhl	18.00	9.00
245	Billy Goodman	16.00	8.00
246	Tom Gorman	16.00	8.00
247	Bill Sarni	16.00	8.00
248	Bob Porterfield	16.00	8.00
249	Johnny Klippstein	16.00	8.00
250	Larry Doby	32.00	16.00
251	Yankees Team	250.00	125.00
252	Vernon Law	18.00	9.00
253	Irv Noren	18.00	9.00
254	George Crowe	16.00	8.00
255	Bob Lemon	40.00	20.00
256	Tom Hurd	16.00	8.00
257	Bobby Thomson	28.00	14.00
258	Art Ditmar	18.00	9.00
259	Sam Jones	16.00	8.00
260	Pee Wee Reese	150.00	75.00
261	Bobby Shantz	15.00	7.50
262	Howie Pollet	12.00	6.00
263	Bob Miller	12.00	6.00
264	Ray Monzant	12.00	6.00
265	Sandy Consuegra	12.00	6.00
266	Don Ferrarese	12.00	6.00
267	Bob Nieman	12.00	6.00
268	Dale Mitchell	16.00	8.00
269	Jack Meyer	12.00	6.00
270	Billy Loes	12.00	6.00
271	Foster Castleman	12.00	6.00
272	Danny O'Connell	12.00	6.00
273	Walker Cooper	12.00	6.00
274	Frank Baumholtz	12.00	6.00
275	Jim Greengrass	12.00	6.00
276	George Zuverink	12.00	6.00
277	Daryl Spencer	12.00	6.00
278	Chet Nichols	12.00	6.00
279	Johnny Groth	12.00	6.00
280	Jim Gilliam	20.00	10.00
281	Art Houtteman	12.00	6.00
282	Warren Hacker	12.00	6.00
283	Hal Smith (R)	14.00	7.00
284	Ike Delock	12.00	6.00
285	Eddie Miksis	12.00	6.00
286	Bill Wright	12.00	6.00
287	Bobby Adams	12.00	6.00
288	Bob Cerv	25.00	12.50
289	Hal Jeffcoat	12.00	6.00
290	Curt Simmons	15.00	7.50
291	Frank Kellert	12.00	6.00
292	Luis Aparicio (R)	160.00	80.00
293	Stu Miller	15.00	7.50
294	Ernie Johnson	12.00	6.00
295	Clem Labine	15.00	7.50
296	Andy Seminick	12.00	6.00
297	Bob Skinner	15.00	9.00
298	Johnny Schmitz	12.00	6.00
299	Charley Neal	28.00	14.00
300	Vic Wertz	15.00	7.50
301	Marv Grissom	12.00	6.00
302	Eddie Robinson	12.00	6.00
303	Jim Dyck	12.00	0.00
304	Frank Malzone	20.00	10.00
305	Brooks Lawrence	12.00	6.00
306	Curt Roberts	12.00	6.00
307	Hoyt Wilhelm	38.00	19.00
308	Chuck Harmon	12.00	6.00
309	Don Blasingame (R)	18.00	9.00
310	Steve Gromek	12.00	6.00
311	Hal Naragon	12.00	6.00
312	Andy Pafko	12.00	6.00
313	Gene Stephens	12.00	6.00
314	Hobie Landrith	12.00	6.00
315	Milt Bolling	12.00	6.00
316	Jerry Coleman	15.00	7.50
317	Al Aber	12.00	6.00
318	Fred Hatfield	12.00	6.00
319	Jack Crimian	12.00	6.00
320	Joe Adcock	15.00	7.50
321	Jim Konstanty	15.00	7.50
322	Karl Olson	12.00	6.00
323	Willard Schmidt	12.00	6.00
324	Rocky Bridges	12.00	6.00
325	Don Liddle	12.00	6.00
326	Connie Johnson	12.00	6.00
327	Bob Wiesler	12.00	6.00
328	Preston Ward	12.00	6.00
329	Lou Berberet	12.00	6.00
330	Jim Busby	12.00	6.00
331	Dick Hall	12.00	6.00
332	Don Larsen	50.00	25.00
333	Rube Walker	12.00	6.00
334	Bob Miller	12.00	6.00
335	Don Hoak	12.00	6.00
336	Ellis Kinder	12.00	6.00
337	Bobby Morgan	12.00	6.00
338	Jim Delsing	12.00	6.00
339	Rance Pless	12.00	6.00
340	Mickey McDermott	45.00	20.00
___	Checklist 1/3	250.00	110.00
___	Checklist 2/4	250.00	110.00

1957 Topps

Starting in 1957 Topps adopted a smaller card size, 2-1/2" by 3-1/2", a size that's become the standard in the hobby. Card fronts feature full color photos and, for the first time, Topps introduced muli-player card fronts. The 407-card set does not include four unnumbered checklists. Those values are listed at the end of this checklist.

	NR/MT	EX
Complete Set (407)	7,850.00	3,850.00
Commons (1-264)	8.00	4.00
Commons (265-352)	20.00	10.00
Commons (353-407)	6.50	3.25

1	Ted Williams	475.00	175.00
2	Yogi Berra	150.00	75.00
3	Dale Long	8.00	4.00
4	Johnny Logan	10.00	5.00
5	Sal Maglie	12.00	6.00
6	Hector Lopez	8.00	4.00
7	Luis Aparicio	48.00	24.00
8	Don Mossi	10.00	5.00
9	Johnny Temple	10.00	5.00
10	Willie Mays	275.00	140.00
11	George Zuverink	8.00	4.00
12	Dick Groat	12.00	6.00
13	Wally Burnette	8.00	4.00
14	Bob Nieman	8.00	4.00
15	Robin Roberts	30.00	15.00
16	Walt Moryn	8.00	4.00
17	Billy Gardner	8.00	4.00
18	Don Drysdale (R)	285.00	145.00
19	Bob Wilson	8.00	4.00
20	Hank Aaron (Photo Reversed)	275.00	140.00
21	Frank Sullivan	8.00	4.00
22	Jerry Snyder (Wrong Photo)	8.00	4.00
23	Sherm Lollar	8.00	4.00
24	Bill Mazeroski (R)	75.00	38.00
25	Whitey Ford	75.00	38.00
26	Bob Boyd	8.00	4.00
27	Ted Kazanskı	8.00	4.00
28	Gene Conley	8.00	4.00
29	Whitey Herzog (R)	32.00	16.00
30	Pee Wee Reese	75.00	38.00
31	Ron Northey	8.00	4.00
32	Hersh Freeman	8.00	4.00
33	Jim Small	8.00	4.00
34	Tom Sturdivant	8.00	4.00
35	Frank Robinson (R)	300.00	150.00
36	Bob Grim	10.00	5.00
37	Frank Torre	10.00	5.00
38	Nellie Fox	28.00	14.00
39	Al Worthington	8.00	4.00
40	Early Wynn	28.00	14.00
41	Hal Smith	8.00	4.00
42	Dee Fondy	8.00	4.00
43	Connie Johnson	8.00	4.00
44	Joe DeMaestri	8.00	4.00
45	Carl Furillo	18.00	9.00
46	Bob Miller	8.00	4.00
47	Don Blasingame	8.00	4.00
48	Bill Bruton	8.00	4.00
49	Daryl Spencer	8.00	4.00
50	Herb Score	20.00	10.00
51	Clint Courtney	8.00	4.00
52	Lee Walls	8.00	4.00
53	Clem Labine	12.00	6.00
54	Elmer Valo	8.00	4.00
55	Ernie Banks	140.00	70.00
56	Dave Sisler	8.00	4.00
57	Jim Lemon	8.00	4.00
58	Ruben Gomez	8.00	4.00
59	Dick Williams	8.00	4.00
60	Billy Hoeft	8.00	4.00
61	Dusty Rhodes	8.00	4.00
62	Billy Martin	50.00	25.00
63	Ike Delock	8.00	4.00
64	Pete Runnels	10.00	5.00
65	Wally Moon	10.00	5.00
66	Brooks Lawrence	8.00	4.00
67	Chico Carrasquel	8.00	4.00
68	Ray Crone	8.00	4.00
69	Roy McMillan	8.00	4.00
70	Richie Ashburn	28.00	14.00
71	Murry Dickson	8.00	4.00
72	Bill Tuttle	8.00	4.00
73	George Crowe	8.00	4.00
74	Vito Valentinetti	8.00	4.00
75	Jim Piersall	12.00	6.00
76	Roberto Clemente	275.00	140.00
77	Paul Foytack	8.00	4.00
78	Vic Wertz	10.00	5.00
79	Lindy McDaniel (R)	15.00	7.50
80	Gil Hodges	60.00	30.00

81	Herm Wehmeier	8.00	4.00
82	Elston Howard	25.00	12.50
83	Lou Skizas	8.00	4.00
84	Moe Drabowsky	8.00	4.00
85	Larry Doby	12.00	6.00
86	Bill Sarni	8.00	4.00
87	Tom Gorman	8.00	4.00
88	Harvey Kuenn	12.00	6.00
89	Roy Sievers	8.00	4.00
90	Warren Spahn	80.00	40.00
91	Mack Burk	8.00	4.00
92	Mickey Vernon	8.00	4.00
93	Hal Jeffcoat	8.00	4.00
94	Bobby Del Greco	8.00	4.00
95	Mickey Mantle	1,450.00	750.00
96	Hank Aguirre	8.00	4.00
97	Yankees Team	60.00	30.00
98	Al Dark	8.00	4.00
99	Bob Keegan	8.00	4.00
100	League Presidents (Giles/Harridge)	10.00	5.00
101	Chuck Stobbs	8.00	4.00
102	Ray Boone	8.00	4.00
103	Joe Nuxhall	8.00	4.00
104	Hank Foiles	8.00	4.00
105	Johnny Antonelli	8.00	4.00
106	Ray Moore	8.00	4.00
107	Jim Rivera	8.00	4.00
108	Tommy Byrne	8.00	4.00
109	Hank Thompson	8.00	4.00
110	Bill Virdon	10.00	5.00
111	Hal Smith	8.00	4.00
112	Tom Brewer	8.00	4.00
113	Wilmer Mizell	8.00	4.00
114	Braves Team	15.00	7.50
115	Jim Gilliam	15.00	7.50
116	Mike Fornieles	8.00	4.00
117	Joe Adcock	10.00	5.00
118	Bob Porterfield	8.00	4.00
119	Stan Lopata	8.00	4.00
120	Bob Lemon	28.00	14.00
121	Cletis Boyer (R)	30.00	15.00
122	Ken Boyer	18.00	9.00
123	Steve Ridzik	8.00	4.00
124	Dave Philley	8.00	4.00
125	Al Kaline	100.00	50.00
126	Bob Wiesler	8.00	4.00
127	Bob Buhl	8.00	4.00
128	Ed Bailey	8.00	4.00
129	Saul Rogovin	8.00	4.00
130	Don Newcombe	16.00	8.00
131	Milt Bolling	8.00	4.00
132	Art Ditmar	8.00	4.00
133	Del Crandall	8.00	4.00
134	Don Kaiser	8.00	4.00
135	Bill Skowron	18.00	9.00
136	Jim Hegan	8.00	4.00
137	Bob Rush	8.00	4.00
138	Minnie Minoso	18.00	9.00
139	Lou Kretlow	8.00	4.00
140	Frank Thomas	8.00	4.00
141	Al Aber	8.00	4.00
142	Charley Thompson	8.00	4.00
143	Andy Pafko	8.00	4.00
144	Ray Narleski	8.00	4.00
145	Al Smith	8.00	4.00
146	Don Ferrarese	8.00	4.00
147	Al Walker	8.00	4.00
148	Don Mueller	8.00	4.00
149	Bob Kennedy	8.00	4.00
150	Bob Friend	8.00	4.00
151	Willie Miranda	8.00	4.00
152	Jack Harshman	8.00	4.00
153	Karl Olson	8.00	4.00
154	Red Schoendienst	28.00	14.00
155	Jim Brosnan	8.00	4.00
156	Gus Triandos	8.00	4.00
157	Wally Post	8.00	4.00
158	Curt Simmons	8.00	4.00
159	Solly Drake	8.00	4.00
160	Billy Pierce	10.00	5.00
161	Pirates Team	15.00	7.50
162	Jack Meyer	8.00	4.00
163	Sammy White	8.00	4.00
164	Tommy Carroll	8.00	4.00
165	Ted Kluszewski	48.00	24.00
166	Roy Face	10.00	5.00
167	Vic Power	8.00	4.00
168	Frank Lary	8.00	4.00
169	Herb Plews	8.00	4.00
170	Duke Snider	125.00	65.00
171	Red Sox Team	15.00	7.50
172	Gene Woodling	10.00	5.00
173	Roger Craig	15.00	7.50
174	Willie Jones	8.00	4.00
175	Don Larsen	20.00	10.00
176	Gene Baker	8.00	4.00
177	Eddie Yost	8.00	4.00
178	Don Bessent	8.00	4.00
179	Ernie Oravetz	8.00	4.00
180	Gus Bell	8.00	4.00
181	Dick Donovan	8.00	4.00
182	Hobie Landrith	8.00	4.00
183	Cubs Team	15.00	7.50
184	Tito Francona (R)	8.00	4.00
185	Johnny Kucks	8.00	4.00
186	Jim King	8.00	4.00
187	Virgil Trucks	8.00	4.00
188	Felix Mantilla (R)	8.00	4.00
189	Willard Nixon	8.00	4.00
190	Randy Jackson	8.00	4.00
191	Joe Margoneri	8.00	4.00
192	Jerry Coleman	8.00	4.00
193	Del Rice	8.00	4.00

194	Hal Brown	8.00	4.00
195	Bobby Avila	8.00	4.00
196	Larry Jackson	8.00	4.00
197	Hank Sauer	8.00	4.00
198	Tigers Team	15.00	7.50
199	Vernon Law	8.00	4.00
200	Gil McDougald	18.00	9.00
201	Sandy Amoros	10.00	5.00
202	Dick Gernert	8.00	4.00
203	Hoyt Wilhelm	25.00	12.50
204	Athletics Team	15.00	7.50
205	Charley Maxwell	8.00	4.00
206	Willard Schmidt	8.00	4.00
207	Billy Hunter	8.00	4.00
208	Lew Burdette	12.00	6.00
209	Bob Skinner	8.00	4.00
210	Roy Campanella	140.00	70.00
211	Camilo Pascual	8.00	4.00
212	Rocky Colavito (R)	160.00	80.00
213	Les Moss	8.00	4.00
214	Phillies Team	15.00	7.50
215	Enos Slaughter	30.00	15.00
216	Marv Grissom	8.00	4.00
217	Gene Stephens	8.00	4.00
218	Ray Jablonski	8.00	4.00
219	Tom Acker	8.00	4.00
220	Jackie Jensen	12.00	6.00
221	Dixie Howell	8.00	4.00
222	Alex Grammas	8.00	4.00
223	Frank House	8.00	4.00
224	Marv Blaylock	8.00	4.00
225	Harry Simpson	8.00	4.00
226	Preston Ward	8.00	4.00
227	Jerry Staley	8.00	4.00
228	Smoky Burgess	8.00	4.00
229	George Susce	8.00	4.00
230	George Kell	20.00	10.00
231	Solly Hemus	8.00	4.00
232	Whitey Lockman	10.00	5.00
233	Art Fowler	8.00	4.00
234	Dick Cole	8.00	4.00
235	Tom Poholsky	8.00	4.00
236	Joe Ginsberg	8.00	4.00
237	Foster Castleman	8.00	4.00
238	Eddie Robinson	8.00	4.00
239	Tom Morgan	8.00	4.00
240	Hank Bauer	15.00	7.50
241	Joe Lonnett	8.00	4.00
242	Charley Neal	8.00	4.00
243	Cardinals Team	15.00	7.50
244	Billy Loes	8.00	4.00
245	Rip Repulski	8.00	4.00
246	Jose Valdivielso	8.00	4.00
247	Turk Lown	8.00	4.00
248	Jim Finigan	8.00	4.00
249	Dave Pope	8.00	4.00
250	Eddie Mathews	48.00	24.00
251	Orioles Team	15.00	7.50
252	Carl Erskine	12.00	6.00
253	Gus Zernial	8.00	4.00
254	Ron Negray	8.00	4.00
255	Charlie Silvera	8.00	4.00
256	Ronnie Kline	8.00	4.00
257	Walt Dropo	8.00	4.00
258	Steve Gromek	8.00	4.00
259	Eddie O'Brien	8.00	4.00
260	Del Ennis	8.00	4.00
261	Bob Chakales	8.00	4.00
262	Bobby Thomson	12.00	6.00
263	George Strickland	8.00	4.00
264	Bob Turley	14.00	7.00
265	Harvey Haddix	20.00	10.00
266	Ken Kuhn	20.00	10.00
267	Danny Kravitz	20.00	10.00
268	Jackie Collum	20.00	10.00
269	Bob Cerv	20.00	10.00
270	Senators Team	45.00	22.50
271	Danny O'Connell	20.00	10.00
272	Bobby Shantz	30.00	15.00
273	Jim Davis	20.00	10.00
274	Don Hoak	20.00	10.00
275	Indians Team	45.00	22.50
276	Jim Pyburn	20.00	10.00
277	Johnny Podres	50.00	25.00
278	Fred Hatfield	20.00	10.00
279	Bob Thurman	20.00	10.00
280	Alex Kellner	20.00	10.00
281	Gail Harris	20.00	10.00
282	Jack Dittmer	20.00	10.00
283	Wes Covington	20.00	10.00
284	Don Zimmer	30.00	15.00
285	Ned Garver	20.00	10.00
286	Bobby Richardson(R)	140.00	70.00
287	Sam Jones	20.00	10.00
288	Ted Lepcio	20.00	10.00
289	Jim Bolger	20.00	10.00
290	Andy Carey	20.00	10.00
291	Windy McCall	20.00	10.00
292	Billy Klaus	20.00	10.00
293	Ted Abernathy	20.00	10.00
294	Rocky Bridges	20.00	10.00
295	Joe Collins	20.00	10.00
296	Johnny Klippstein	20.00	10.00
297	Jack Crimian	20.00	10.00
298	Irv Noren	20.00	10.00
299	Chuck Harmon	20.00	10.00
300	Mike Garcia	20.00	10.00
301	Sam Esposito	20.00	10.00
302	Sandy Koufax	350.00	175.00
303	Billy Goodman	20.00	10.00
304	Joe Cunningham	20.00	10.00
305	Chico Fernandez	20.00	10.00
306	Darrell Johnson	20.00	10.00
307	Jack Phillips	20.00	10.00

308	Dick Hall	20.00	10.00
309	Jim Busby	20.00	10.00
310	Max Surkont	20.00	10.00
311	Al Pilarcik	20.00	10.00
312	Tony Kubek (R)	125.00	65.00
313	Mel Parnell	20.00	10.00
314	Ed Bouchee	20.00	10.00
315	Lou Berberet	20.00	10.00
316	Billy O'Dell	20.00	10.00
317	Giants Team	50.00	25.00
318	Mickey McDermott	20.00	10.00
319	Gino Cimoli (R)	22.00	11.00
320	Neil Chrisley	20.00	10.00
321	Red Murff	20.00	10.00
322	Redlegs Team	50.00	25.00
323	Wes Westrum	20.00	10.00
324	Dodgers Team	125.00	65.00
325	Frank Bolling	20.00	10.00
326	Pedro Ramos	20.00	10.00
327	Jim Pendleton	20.00	10.00
328	Brooks Robinson(R)	450.00	225.00
329	White Sox Team	50.00	25.00
330	Jim Wilson	20.00	10.00
331	Ray Katt	20.00	10.00
332	Bob Bowman	20.00	10.00
333	Ernie Johnson	20.00	10.00
334	Jerry Schoonmaker	20.00	10.00
335	Granny Hamner	20.00	10.00
336	Haywood Sullivan (R)	24.00	12.00
337	Rene Valdes	20.00	10.00
338	Jim Bunning (R)	165.00	85.00
339	Bob Speake	20.00	10.00
340	Bill Wight	20.00	10.00
341	Don Gross	20.00	10.00
342	Gene Mauch	25.00	12.50
343	Taylor Phillips	20.00	10.00
344	Paul LaPalme	20.00	10.00
345	Paul Smith	20.00	10.00
346	Dick Littlefield	20.00	10.00
347	Hal Naragon	20.00	10.00
348	Jim Hearn	20.00	10.00
349	Nelson King	20.00	10.00
350	Eddie Miksis	20.00	10.00
351	Dave Hillman	20.00	10.00
352	Ellis Kinder	20.00	10.00
353	Cal Neeman	6.50	3.25
354	Rip Coleman	6.50	3.25
355	Frank Malzone	6.50	3.25
356	Faye Throneberry	6.50	3.25
357	Earl Torgeson	6.50	3.25
358	Jerry Lynch	6.50	3.25
359	Tom Cheney (R)	7.00	3.50
360	Johnny Groth	6.50	3.25
361	Curt Barclay	6.50	3.25
362	Roman Mejias	6.50	3.25
363	Eddie Kasko	6.50	3.25
364	Cal McLish	6.50	3.25
365	Ossie Virgil	6.50	3.25
366	Ken Lehman	6.50	3.25
367	Ed FitzGerald	6.50	3.25
368	Bob Purkey	6.50	3.25
369	Milt Graff	6.50	3.25
370	Warren Hacker	6.50	3.25
371	Bob Lennon	6.50	3.25
372	Norm Zauchin	6.50	3.25
373	Pete Whisenant	6.50	3.25
374	Don Cardwell	6.50	3.25
375	Jim Landis	6.50	3.25
376	Don Elston	6.50	3.25
377	Andre Rodgers	6.50	3.25
378	Elmer Singleton	6.50	3.25
379	Don Lee	6.50	3.25
380	Walker Cooepr	6.50	3.25
381	Dean Stone	6.50	3.25
382	Jim Brideweser	6.50	3.25
383	Juan Pizarro	6.50	3.25
384	Bobby Gene Smith	6.50	3.25
385	Art Houtteman	6.50	3.25
386	Lyle Luttrell	6.50	3.25
387	Jack Sanford (R)	8.50	4.25
388	Pete Daley	6.50	3.25
389	Dave Jolly	6.50	3.25
390	Reno Bertoia	6.50	3.25
391	Ralph Terry	10.00	5.00
392	Chuck Tanner	8.50	4.25
393	Raul Sanchez	6.50	3.25
394	Luis Arroyo	6.50	3.25
395	Bubba Phillips	6.50	3.25
396	Casey Wise	6.50	3.25
397	Roy Smalley	6.50	3.25
398	Al Cicotte	6.50	3.25
399	Billy Consolo	6.50	3.25
400	Dodgers' Sluggers	260.00	130.00
	(Campanella, Furillo,		
	Hodges, Snider)		
401	Earl Battey (R)	8.50	4.25
402	Jim Pisoni	6.50	3.25
403	Dick Hyde	6.50	3.25
404	Harry Anderson	6.50	3.25
405	Duke Maas	6.50	3.25
406	Bob Hale	6.50	3.25
407	Yankee Power	485.00	250.00
	(Y. Berra, M. Mantle)		
___	Checklist 1-2	225.00	110.00
___	Checklist 2-3	375.00	150.00
___	Checklist 3-4	700.00	340.00
___	Checklist 4-5	850.00	400.00

1958 Topps

Sandy Koufax

L. A. DODGERS

Topps expanded their baseball set in 1958 to 494-cards. Although the checklist below is numbered to 495, card number 145 was never issued. The larger set contains Topps first All-Star subset (475-495). For the first time Topps began numbering their checklist cards whcih appear on the back of the team cards. Color variations exist on the lettering of some cards with yellow (Y) being the most scarce and white more common. Those variations are listed below.

		NR/MT	EX
Complete Set (494)		5,600.00	2,800.00
Commons (1-110)		8.00	4.00
Commons (111-495)		5.00	2.50
1	Ted Williams	425.00	140.00
2a	Bob Lemon (Y)	50.00	25.00
2b	Bob Lemon	24.00	12.00
3	Alex Kellner	8.00	4.00
4	Hank Foiles	8.00	4.00
5	Willie Mays	230.00	115.00
6	George Zuverink	8.00	4.00
7	Dale Long	8.00	4.00
8a	Eddie Kasko (Y)	25.00	12.50
8b	Eddie Kasko	8.00	4.00
9	Hank Bauer	12.00	6.00
10	Lou Burdette	10.00	5.00
11a	Jim Rivera (Y)	20.00	10.00
11b	Jim Rivera	8.00	4.00
12	George Crowe	8.00	4.00
13a	Billy Hoeft (Y)	24.00	12.00
13b	Billy Hoeft	8.00	4.00
14	Rip Repulski	8.00	4.00
15	Jim Lemon	8.00	4.00
16	Charley Neal	8.00	4.00
17	Felix Mantilla	8.00	4.00
18	Frank Sullivan	8.00	4.00
19	Giants Team	32.00	16.00
	(Checklist 1-88)		
20a	Gil McDougald (Y)	50.00	25.00
20b	Gil McDougald	18.00	9.00
21	Curt Barclay	8.00	4.00
22	Hal Naragon	8.00	4.00
23a	Bill Tuttle (Y)	24.00	12.00
23b	Bill Tuttle	8.00	4.00
24a	Hobie Landrith(Y)	24.00	12.00
24b	Hobie Landrith	8.00	4.00
25	Don Drysdale	90.00	45.00
26	Ron Jackson	8.00	4.00
27	Bud Freeman	8.00	4.00
28	Jim Busby	8.00	4.00
29	Ted Lepcio	8.00	4.00
30a	Hank Aaron (Y)	450.00	225.00
30b	Hank Aaron	200.00	100.00
31	Tex Clevenger	8.00	4.00
32a	J.W. Porter (Y)	24.00	12.00
32b	J.W. Porter	8.00	4.00
33a	Cal Neeman (Y)	20.00	10.00
33b	Cal Neeman	8.00	4.00
34	Bob Thurman	8.00	4.00
35a	Don Mossi (Y)	24.00	12.00
35b	Don Mossi	8.00	4.00
36	Ted Kazanski	8.00	4.00
37	Mike McCormick (R)	10.00	5.00
	(wrong Photo)		
38	Dick Gernert	8.00	4.00
39	Bob Martyn	8.00	4.00
40	George Kell	16.00	8.00
41	Dave Hillman	8.00	4.00
42	John Roseboro (R)	18.00	9.00
43	Sal Maglie	12.00	6.00
44	Senators Team	18.00	9.00
	(Checklist 1-88)	8.00	4.00
45	Dick Groat	10.00	5.00
46a	Lou Sleater (Y)	24.00	12.00
46b	Lou Sleater	8.00	4.00
47	Roger Marix	8.00	4.00
48	Chuck Harmon	8.00	4.00
49	Smoky Burgess	10.00	5.00
50a	Billy Pierce (Y)	40.00	20.00
50b	Billy Pierce	10.00	5.00
51	Del Rice	8.00	4.00
52a	Bob Clemente (Y)	450.00	225.00
52b	Bob Clemente	200.00	100.00
53a	Morrie Martin (Y)	24.00	12.00
53b	Morrie Martin	8.00	4.00
54	Norm Siebern (R)	10.00	5.00
55	Chico Carrasquel	8.00	4.00
56	Bill Fischer	8.00	4.00
57a	Tim Thompson (Y)	24.00	12.00
57b	Tim Thompson	8.00	4.00
58a	Art Schult (Y)	20.00	10.00
58b	Art Schult	8.00	4.00
59	Dave Sisler	8.00	4.00
60a	Del Ennis (Y)	8.00	4.00

60b	Del Ennis	8.00	4.00
61a	Darrell Johnson (Y)	24.00	12.00
61b	Darrell Johnson	8.00	4.50
62	Joe DeMaestri	8.00	4.00
63	Joe Nuxhall	8.00	4.00
64	Joe Lonnett	8.00	4.00
65a	Von McDaniel (T) (R)	40.00	20.00
65b	Von McDaniel(R)	10.00	5.00
66	Lee Walls	8.00	4.00
67	Joe Ginsberg	8.00	4.00
68	Daryl Spencer	8.00	4.00
69	Wally Burnette	8.00	4.00
70a	Al Kaline (Y)	185.00	95.00
70b	Al Kaline	90.00	45.00
71	Dodgers Team (Checklist 1-88)	50.00	25.00
72	Bud Byerly	8.00	4.00
73	Pete Daley	8.00	4.00
74	Roy Face	10.00	5.00
75	Gus Bell	8.00	4.00
76a	Dick Farrell (Y)	25.00	12.50
76b	Dick Farrell	8.00	4.00
77a	Don Zimmer (Y)	40.00	20.00
77b	Don Zimmer	12.00	6.00
78a	Ernie Johnson (Y)	24.00	12.00
78b	Ernie Johnson	8.00	4.00
79a	Dick Williams (Y)	40.00	20.00
79b	Dick Williams	10.00	5.00
80	Dick Drott	8.00	4.00
81a	Steve Boros (Y)	40.00	20.00
81b	Steve Boros	10.00	5.00
82	Ronnie Kline	8.00	4.00
83	Bob Hazle (R)	10.00	5.00
84	Billy O'Dell	8.00	4.00
85a	Luis Aparicio (Y)	60.00	30.00
85b	Luis Aparicio	28.00	14.00
86	Valmy Thomas	8.00	4.00
87	Johnny Kucks	8.00	4.00
88	Duke Snider	80.00	40.00
89	Billy Klaus	8.00	4.00
90	Robin Roberts	28.00	14.00
91	Chuck Tanner	8.00	4.00
92a	Clint Courtney (Y)	24.00	12.00
92b	Clint Courtney	8.00	4.00
93	Sandy Amoros	10.00	5.00
94	Bob Skinner	8.00	4.00
95	Frank Bolling	8.00	4.00
96	Joe Durham	8.00	4.00
97a	Larry Jackson (Y)	24.00	12.00
97b	Larry Jackson	8.00	4.00
98a	Billy Hunter (Y)	24.00	12.00
98b	Billy Hunter	8.00	4.00
99	Bobby Adams	8.00	4.00
100a	Early Wynn (Y)	55.00	28.00
100b	Early Wynn	24.00	12.00
101a	Bobby Richardson (Y)	55.00	28.00
101b	Bobby Richardson	20.00	10.00
102	George Strickland	8.00	4.00
103	Jerry Lynch	8.00	4.00
104	Jim Pendleton	8.00	4.00
105	Billy Gardner	8.00	4.00
106	Dick Schofield	8.00	4.00
107	Ossie Virgil	8.00	4.00
108a	Jim Landis (Y)	20.00	10.00
108b	Jim Landis	8.00	4.00
109	Herb Plews	8.00	4.00
110	Johnny Logan	8.00	4.00
111	Stu Miller	7.50	4.50
112	Gus Zernial	5.00	2.50
113	Jerry Walker	6.00	3.00
114	Irv Noren	5.00	2.50
115	Jim Bunning	28.00	14.00
116	Dave Philley	5.00	2.50
117	Frank Torre	5.00	2.50
118	Harvey Haddix	8.00	4.00
119	Harry Chiti	5.00	2.50
120	Johnny Podres	10.00	5.00
121	Eddie Miksis	5.00	2.50
122	Walt Moryn	5.00	2.50
123	Dick Tomanek	5.00	2.50
124	Bobby Usher	5.00	2.50
125	Al Dark	7.00	3.50
126	Stan Palys	5.00	2.50
127	Tom Sturdivant	5.00	2.50
128	Willie Kirkland	7.00	3.50
129	Jim Derrington	5.00	2.50
130	Jackie Jensen	12.00	6.00
131	Bob Henrich	5.00	2.50
132	Vernon Law	7.00	3.50
133	Russ Nixon (R)	7.50	4.50
134	Phillies Team (Checklist 89-176)	14.00	7.00
135	Moe Drabowsky	7.00	3.50
136	Jim Finnigan	5.00	2.50
137	Russ Kemmerer	5.00	2.50
138	Earl Torgeson	5.00	2.50
139	George Brunet	5.00	2.50
140	Wes Covington	7.00	3.50
141	Ken Lehman	5.00	2.50
142	Enos Slaughter	28.00	14.00
143	Billy Muffett	5.00	2.50
144	Bobby Morgan	5.00	2.50
145	No Card	5.00	2.50
146	Dick Gray	5.00	2.50
147	Don McMahon (R)	8.00	4.00
148	Billy Consolo	5.00	2.50
149	Tom Acker	5.00	2.50
150	Mickey Mantle	750.00	375.00
151	Buddy Pritchard	5.00	2.50
152	Johnny Antonelli	7.00	3.50
153	Les Moss	5.00	2.50
154	Harry Byrd	5.00	2.50
155	Hector Lopez	5.00	2.50
156	Dick Hyde	5.00	2.50

157 Dee Fondy	5.00	2.50
158 Indians Team	14.00	7.00
(Checklist 177-264)		
159 Taylor Phillips	5.00	2.50
160 Don Hoak	5.00	2.50
161 Don Larsen	12.00	6.00
162 Gil Hodges	30.00	15.00
163 Jim Wilson	5.00	2.50
164 Bob Taylor	5.00	2.50
165 Bob Nieman	5.00	2.50
166 Danny O'Connell	5.00	2.50
167 Frank Baumann	5.00	2.50
168 Joe Cunningham	5.00	2.50
169 Ralph Terry	7.00	3.50
170 Vic Wertz	5.00	2.50
171 Harry Anderson	5.00	2.50
172 Don Gross	5.00	2.50
173 Eddie Yost	5.00	2.50
174 A's Team	14.00	7.00
(Checklist 89-176)		
175 Marv Throneberry(R)	12.00	6.00
176 Bob Buhl	7.00	3.50
177 Al Smith	5.00	2.50
178 Ted Kluszewski	15.00	7.50
179 Willy Miranda	5.00	2.50
180 Lindy McDaniel	7.00	3.50
181 Willie Jones	5.00	2.50
182 Joe Cafie	5.00	2.50
183 Dave Jolly	5.00	2.50
184 Elvin Tappe	5.00	2.50
185 Ray Boone	5.00	2.50
186 Jack Meyer	5.00	2.50
187 Sandy Koufax	240.00	120.00
188 Milt Bolling	5.00	2.50
(Wrong Photo)		
189 George Susce	5.00	2.50
190 Red Schoendienst	25.00	12.50
191 Art Ceccarelli	5.00	2.50
192 Milt Graff	5.00	2.50
193 Jerry Lumpe (R)	6.00	3.00
194 Roger Craig	8.50	4.25
195 Whitey Lockman	6.00	3.00
196 Mike Garcia	6.00	3.00
197 Haywood Sullivan	5.00	2.50
198 Bill Virdon	7.00	3.50
199 Don Blasingame	5.00	2.50
200 Bob Keegan	5.00	2.50
201 Jim Bolger	5.00	2.50
202 Woody Held (R)	6.00	3.00
203 Al Walker	5.00	2.50
204 Leo Kiely	5.00	2.50
205 Johnny Temple	5.00	2.50
206 Bob Shaw	5.00	2.50
207 Solly Hemus	5.00	2.50
208 Cal McLish	5.00	2.50
209 Bob Anderson	5.00	2.50
210 Wally Moon	6.00	3.00
211 Pete Burnside	5.00	2.50
212 Bubba Phillips	5.00	2.50
213 Red Wilson	5.00	2.50
214 Willard Schmidt	5.00	2.50
215 Jim Gilliam	12.00	6.00
216 Cards Team	14.00	7.00
(Checklist 177-264)		
217 Jack Harshman	5.00	2.50
218 Dick Rand	5.00	2.50
219 Camilo Pascual	5.00	2.50
220 Tom Brewer	5.00	2.50
221 Jerry Kindall (R)	6.00	3.00
222 Bud Daley	5.00	2.50
223 Andy Pafko	6.00	3.00
224 Bob Grim	5.00	2.50
225 Billy Goodman	5.00	2.50
226 Bob Smith	5.00	2.50
227 Gene Stephens	5.00	2.50
228 Duke Maas	5.00	2.50
229 Frank Zupo	5.00	2.50
230 Richie Ashburn	22.00	11.00
231 Lloyd Merritt	5.00	2.50
232 Reno Bertoia	5.00	2.50
233 Mickey Vernon	6.00	3.00
234 Carl Sawatski	5.00	2.50
235 Tom Gorman	5.00	2.50
236 Ed FitzGerald	5.00	2.50
237 Bill Wight	5.00	2.50
238 Bill Mazeroski	18.00	9.00
239 Chuck Stobbs	5.00	2.50
240 Moose Skowron	15.00	7.50
241 Dick Littlefield	5.00	2.50
242 Johnny Klippstein	5.00	2.50
243 Larry Raines	5.00	2.50
244 Don Demeter (R)	5.00	2.50
245 Frank Lary	7.00	3.50
246 Yankess Team	60.00	30.00
(Checklist 177-264)		
247 Casey Wise	5.00	2.50
248 Herm Wehmeier	5.00	2.50
249 Ray Moore	5.00	2.50
250 Roy Sievers	6.00	3.00
251 Warren Hacker	5.00	2.50
252 Bob Trowbridge	5.00	2.50
253 Don Mueller	5.00	2.50
254 Alex Grammas	5.00	2.50
255 Bob Turley	10.00	5.00
256 White Sox Team	14.00	7.00
(Checklist 265-353)		
257 Hal Smith	5.00	2.50
258 Carl Erskine	10.00	5.00
259 Al Pilarcik	5.00	2.50
260 Frank Malzone	6.00	3.00
261 Turk Lown	5.00	2.50
262 Johnny Groth	5.00	2.50
263 Eddie Bressoud	5.00	2.50
264 Jack Sanford	5.00	2.50

265	Pete Runnels	7.00	3.50
266	Connie Johnson	5.00	2.50
267	Sherm Lollar	5.00	2.50
268	Granny Hamner	5.00	2.50
269	Paul Smith	5.00	2.50
270	Warren Spahn	65.00	35.00
271	Billy Martin	24.00	12.00
272	Ray Crone	5.00	2.50
273	Hal Smith	5.00	2.50
274	Rocky Bridges	5.00	2.50
275	Elston Howard	16.00	8.00
276	Bobby Avila	5.00	2.50
277	Virgil Trucks	5.00	2.50
278	Mack Burk	5.00	2.50
279	Bob Boyd	5.00	2.50
280	Jim Piersall	8.00	4.00
281	Sam Taylor	5.00	2.50
282	Paul Foytack	5.00	2.50
283	Ray Shearer	5.00	2.50
284	Ray Katt	5.00	2.50
285	Frank Robinson	110.00	55.00
286	Gino Cimoli	5.00	2.50
287	Sam Jones	5.00	2.50
288	Harmon Killebrew	100.00	50.00
289	Series Hurling Rivals (Burdette/Shantz)	6.00	3.00
290	Dick Donovan	5.00	2.50
291	Don Landrum	5.00	2.50
292	Ned Garver	5.00	2.50
293	Gene Freese	5.00	2.50
294	Hal Jeffcoat	5.00	2.50
295	Minnie Minoso	12.00	6.00
296	Ryne Duren (R)	15.00	7.50
297	Don Buddin	5.00	2.50
298	Jim Hearn	5.00	2.50
299	Harry Simpson	5.00	2.50
300	League Presidents (Giles/Harridge)	8.00	4.00
301	Randy Jackson	5.00	2.50
302	Mike Baxes	5.00	2.50
303	Neil Chrisley	5.00	2.50
304	Tigers' Big Bats (Kaline/Kuenn)	20.00	10.00
305	Clem Labine	6.00	3.00
306	Whammy Douglas	5.00	2.50
307	Brooks Robinson	125.00	65.00
308	Paul Giel	5.00	2.50
309	Gail Harris	5.00	2.50
310	Ernie Banks	100.00	50.00
311	Bob Purkey	5.00	2.50
312	Red Sox Team (Checklist 353-440)	14.00	7.00
313	Bob Rush	5.00	2.50
314	Dodgers' Boss&Power (Alston/Snider)	24.00	12.00
		5.00	2.50
315	Bob Friend	6.00	3.00
316	Tito Francona	5.00	2.50

317	Albie Pearson	5.00	2.50
318	Frank House	5.00	2.50
319	Lou Skizas	5.00	2.50
320	Whitey Ford	60.00	30.00
321	Sluggers Supreme (Kluszewski/Williams)	55.00	28.00
322	Harding Peterson	5.00	2.50
323	Elmer Valo	5.00	2.50
324	Hoyt Wilhelm	22.00	11.00
325	Joe Adcock	7.00	3.50
326	Bob Miller	5.00	2.50
327	Cubs Team (Checklist 265-352)	14.00	7.00
328	Ike Delock	5.00	2.50
329	Bob Cerv	5.00	2.50
330	Ed Bailey	5.00	2.50
331	Pedro Ramos	5.00	2.50
332	Jim King	5.00	2.50
333	Andy Carey	5.00	2.50
334	Mound Aces (Friend/ Pierce)	6.00	3.00
335	Ruben Gomez	5.00	2.50
336	Bert Hamric	5.00	2.50
337	Hank Aguirre	6.00	3.00
338	Walt Dropo	6.00	3.00
339	Fred Hatfield	5.00	2.50
340	Don Newcombe	12.00	6.00
341	Pirates Team (Checklist 265-352)	14.00	7.00
342	Jim Brosnan	6.00	3.00
343	Orlando Cepeda (R)	110.00	55.00
344	Bob Porterfield	5.00	2.50
345	Jim Hegan	5.00	2.50
346	Steve Bilko	5.00	2.50
347	Don Rudolph	5.00	2.50
348	Chico Fernandez	5.00	2.50
349	Murry Dickson	5.00	2.50
350	Ken Boyer	15.00	7.50
351	Braves' Fence Busters (Aaron/Crandall/ Adcock/Mathews)	40.00	20.00
352	Herb Score	12.00	6.00
353	Stan Lopata	5.00	2.50
354	Art Ditmar	5.00	2.50
355	Bill Bruton	5.00	2.50
356	Bob Malkmus	5.00	2.50
357	Danny McDevitt	5.00	2.50
358	Gene Baker	5.00	2.50
359	Billy Loes	5.00	2.50
360	Roy McMillan	5.00	2.50
361	Mike Fornieles	5.00	2.50
362	Ray Jablonski	5.00	2.50
363	Don Elston	5.00	2.50
364	Earl Battey	5.00	2.50
365	Tom Morgan	5.00	2.50
366	Gene Green	5.00	2.50
367	Jack Urban	5.00	2.50

368	Rocky Colavito	45.00	22.50
369	Ralph Lumenti	5.00	2.50
370	Yogi Berra	125.00	65.00
371	Marty Keough	5.00	2.50
372	Don Cardwell	5.00	2.50
373	Joe Pignatano	5.00	2.50
374	Brooks Lawrence	5.00	2.50
375	Pee Wee Reese	65.00	33.00
376	Charley Rabe	5.00	2.50
377a	Braves Team (Alphabetical Checklist)	14.00	7.00
377b	Braves Team (Numerical Checklist)	80.00	40.00
378	Hank Sauer	6.00	3.00
379	Ray Herbert	5.00	2.50
380	Charley Maxwell	5.00	2.50
381	Hal Brown	5.00	2.50
382	Al Cicotte	5.00	2.50
383	Lou Berberet	5.00	2.50
384	John Goryl	5.00	2.50
385	Wilmer Mizell	5.00	2.50
386	Birdie's Sluggers (Ed Bailey/Frank Robinson/Birdie Tebbetts)	12.00	6.00
387	Wally Post	6.00	3.00
388	Billy Moran	5.00	2.50
389	Bill Taylor	5.00	2.50
390	Del Crandall	7.00	3.50
391	Dave Melton	5.00	2.50
392	Bennie Daniels	5.00	2.50
393	Tony Kubek	24.00	12.00
394	Jim Grant (R)	7.00	3.50
395	Willard Nixon	5.00	2.50
396	Dutch Dotterer	5.00	2.50
397a	Tigers Team (Alphabetical Checklist)	14.00	7.00
397b	Tigers Team (Numerical Checklist)	80.00	40.00
398	Gene Woodling	6.00	3.00
399	Marv Grissom	5.00	2.50
400	Nellie Fox	18.00	9.00
401	Don Bessent	5.00	2.50
402	Bobby Gene Smith	5.00	2.50
403	Steve Korcheck	5.00	2.50
404	Curt Simmons	6.00	3.00
405	Ken Aspromonte	5.00	2.50
406	Vic Power	5.00	2.50
407	Carlton Willey	5.00	2.50
408a	Orioles Team (Alphabetical Checklist)	14.00	7.00
408b	Orioles Team (Numerical Checklist)	80.00	40.00
409	Frank Thomas	5.00	2.50
410	Murray Wall	5.00	2.50
411	Tony Taylor (R)	7.50	3.50
412	Jerry Staley	5.00	2.50
413	Jim Davenport (R)	7.50	3.50
414	Sammy White	5.00	2.50
415	Bob Bowman	5.00	2.50
416	Foster Castleman	5.00	2.50
417	Carl Furillo	10.00	5.00
418	World Series Foes (Aaron/Mantle)	240.00	120.00
419	Bobby Shantz	6.00	3.00
420	Vada Pinson (R)	32.00	16.00
421	Dixie Howell	5.00	2.50
422	Norm Zauchin	5.00	2.50
423	Phil Clark	5.00	2.50
424	Larry Doby	7.50	3.75
425	Sam Esposito	5.00	2.50
426	Johnny O'Brien	5.00	2.50
427	Al Worthington	5.00	2.50
428a	Redlegs Team (Alphabetical Checklist)	14.00	7.00
428b	Redlegs Team (Numerical Checklist)	80.00	40.00
429	Gus Triandos	5.00	2.50
430	Bobby Thomson	7.50	3.75
431	Gene Conley	5.00	2.50
432	John Powers	5.00	2.50
433	Pancho Herrera	5.00	2.50
434	Harvey Kuenn	7.00	3.50
435	Ed Roebuck	5.00	2.50
436	Rivals (Mays/Snider)	85.00	45.00
437	Bob Speake	5.00	2.50
438	Whitey Herzog	7.50	3.75
439	Ray Narleski	5.00	2.50
440	Ed Mathews	40.00	20.00
441	Jim Marshall	5.00	2.50
442	Phil Paine	5.00	2.50
443	Billy Harrell	5.00	2.50
444	Danny Kravitz	5.00	2.50
445	Bob Smith	5.00	2.50
446	Carroll Hardy	5.00	2.50
447	Ray Monzant	5.00	2.50
448	Charlie Lau (R)	7.50	3.75
449	Gene Fodge	5.00	2.50
450	Preston Ward	5.00	2.50
451	Joe Taylor	5.00	2.50
452	Roman Mejias	5.00	2.50
453	Tom Qualters	5.00	2.50
454	Harry Hanebrink	5.00	2.50
455	Hal Griggs	5.00	2.50
456	Dick Brown	5.00	2.50
457	Milt Pappas (R)	7.00	3.50
458	Julio Becquer	5.00	2.50
459	Ron Blackburn	5.00	2.50
460	Chuck Essegian	5.00	2.50
461	Ed Mayer	5.00	2.50
462	Gary Geiger	5.00	2.50
463	Vito Valentinetti	5.00	2.50
464	Curt Flood	28.00	14.00
465	Arnie Portocarrero	5.00	2.50
466	Pete Whisenant	5.00	2.50

467	Glen Hobbie	5.00	2.50
468	Bob Schmidt	5.00	2.50
469	Don Ferrarese	5.00	2.50
470	R.C. Stevens	5.00	2.50
471	Lenny Green	5.00	2.50
472	Joe Jay	5.00	2.50
470	Dill Nenna	5.00	2.50
474	Roman Semproch	5.00	2.50
475	All-Star Managers	20.00	10.00
	(Haney/Stengel)		
476	Stan Musial AS	45.00	22.50
477	Bill Skowron AS	7.50	3.75
478	Johnny Temple AS	5.00	2.50
479	Nellie Fox AS	8.00	4.00
480	Eddie Mathews AS	18.00	9.00
481	Frank Malzone AS	5.00	2.50
482	Ernie Banks AS	32.00	16.00
483	Luis Aparicio AS	18.00	9.00
484	Frank Robinson AS	30.00	15.00
485	Ted Williams AS	100.00	50.00
486	Willie Mays AS	65.00	38.00
487	Mickey Mantle AS	140.00	70.00
488	Hank Aaron AS	65.00	38.00
489	Jackie Jensen AS	6.00	3.00
490	Ed Bailey AS	5.00	2.50
491	Sherm Lollar AS	5.00	2.50
492	Bob Friend AS	5.00	2.50
493	Bob Turley AS	5.00	2.50
494	Warren Spahn AS	24.00	12.00
495	Herb Score AS	15.00	7.50
___	Contest Card	20.00	10.00

1959 Topps

gil hodges

LOS ANGELES DODGERS
FIRST BASE

This 572-card set is Topps largest to date. Card fronts feature player photos in a circle with a fascimile autograph across the front of the photograph. For the first time Topps included a Rookie Subset (116-146). Other Subsets include All-Stars (551-572) and Highlights (461-470). Cards measure 2-1/2" by 3-1/2".

		NR/MT	EX
Complete Set (572)		5,600.00	2,850.00
Commons (1-110)		6.00	3.00
Commons (111-506)		4.00	2.00
Commons (507-572)		16.00	8.00
1	Ford Frick	75.00	20.00
2	Eddie Yost	6.00	3.00
3	Don McMahon	6.00	3.00
4	Albie Pearson	6.00	3.00
5	Dick Donovan	6.00	3.00
6	Alex Grammas	6.00	3.00
7	Al Pilarcik	6.00	3.00
8	Phillies Team	45.00	22.50
	Checklist 1-88		
9	Paul Giel	6.00	3.00
10	Mickey Mantle	650.00	325.00
11	Billy Hunter	6.00	3.00
12	Vern Law	6.00	3.00
13	Dick Gernert	6.00	3.00
14	Pete Whisenant	6.00	3.00
15	Dick Drott	6.00	3.00
16	Joe Pignatano	6.00	3.00
17	Danny's All-Stars	7.00	3.50
	(Ted Kluszewski,		
	Danny Murtaugh,		
	Frank Thomas)		
18	Jack Urban	6.00	3.00
19	Ed Bressoud	6.00	3.00
20	Duke Snider	75.00	38.00
21	Connie Johnson	6.00	3.00
22	Al Smith	6.00	3.00
23	Murry Dickson	6.00	3.00
24	Red Wilson	6.00	3.00
25	Don Hoak	6.00	3.00
26	Chuck Stobbs	6.00	3.00
27	Andy Pafko	6.00	3.00
28	Red Worthington	6.00	3.00
29	Jim Bolger	6.00	3.00
30	Nellie Fox	16.00	8.00
31	Ken Lehman	6.00	3.00
32	Don Buddin	6.00	3.00
33	Ed Fitz Gerald	6.00	3.00
34	Al Kaline/Charlie	18.00	9.00
	Maxwell		
35	Ted Kluszewski	16.00	8.00
36	Hank Aguirre	6.00	3.00
37	Gene Green	6.00	3.00
38	Morrie Martin	6.00	3.00
39	Ed Bouchee	6.00	3.00
40	Warren Spahn	70.00	35.00
41	Bob Martyn	6.00	3.00
42	Murry Wall	6.00	3.00
43	Steve Bilko	6.00	3.00
44	Vito Valentinetti	6.00	3.00
45	Andy Carey	6.00	3.00

46	Bill Henry	6.00	3.00
47	Jim Finigan	6.00	3.00
48	Orioles Team Checklist 1-88	20.00	10.00
49	Bill Hall	6.00	3.00
50	Willie Mays	190.00	95.00
51	Rip Coleman	6.00	3.00
52	Coot Veal	6.00	3.00
53	Stan Williams (R)	8.00	4.00
54	Mel Roach	6.00	3.00
55	Tom Brewer	6.00	3.00
56	Carl Sawatski	6.00	3.00
57	Al Cicotte	6.00	3.00
58	Eddie Miksis	6.00	3.00
59	Irv Noren	6.00	3.00
60	Bob Turley	10.00	5.00
61	Dick Brown	6.00	3.00
62	Tony Taylor	6.00	3.00
63	Jim Hearn	6.00	3.00
64	Joe DeMaestri	6.00	3.00
65	Frank Torre	6.00	3.00
66	Joe Ginsberg	6.00	3.00
67	Brooks Lawrence	6.00	3.00
68	Dick Schofield	6.00	3.00
69	Giants Team Checklist 89-176	20.00	10.00
70	Harvey Kuenn	10.00	5.00
71	Don Bessent	6.00	3.00
72	Bill Renna	6.00	3.00
73	Ron Jackson	6.00	3.00
74	Directing the Power (Cookie Lavagetto, Jim Lemon, Roy Sievers)	7.00	3.50
75	Sam Jones	6.00	3.00
76	Bobby Richardson	18.00	9.00
77	John Goryl	6.00	3.00
78	Pedro Ramos	6.00	3.00
79	Harry Chiti	6.00	3.00
80	Minnie Minoso	12.00	6.00
81	Hal Jeffcoat	6.00	3.00
82	Bob Boyd	6.00	3.00
83	Bob Smith	6.00	3.00
84	Reno Bertoia	6.00	3.00
85	Harry Anderson	6.00	3.00
86	Bob Keegan	6.00	3.00
87	Danny O'Connell	6.00	3.00
88	Herb Score	10.00	5.00
89	Billy Gardner	6.00	3.00
90	Bill Skowron	16.00	8.00
91	Herb Moford	6.00	3.00
92	Dave Philley	6.00	3.00
93	Julio Becquer	6.00	3.00
94	White Sox Team Checklist 89-176	25.00	12.50
95	Carl Willey	6.00	3.00
96	Lou Berberet	6.00	3.00
97	Jerry Lynch	6.00	3.00
98	Arnie Portocarrero	6.00	3.00
99	Ted Kazanski	6.00	3.00
100	Bob Cerv	6.00	3.00
101	Alex Kellner	6.00	3.00
102	Felipe Alou (R)	28.00	14.00
103	Billy Goodman	6.00	3.00
104	Del Rice	6.00	3.00
105	Lee Walls	6.00	3.00
106	Hal Woodeshick	6.00	3.00
107	Norm Larker	6.00	3.00
108	Zack Monroe	6.00	3.00
109	Bob Schmidt	6.00	3.00
110	George Witt	6.00	3.00
111	Redlegs Team Checklist 89-176	12.00	6.00
112	Billy Consolo	4.00	2.00
113	Taylor Phillips	4.00	2.00
114	Earl Battey	4.00	2.00
115	Mickey Vernon	5.00	2.25
116	Bob Allison (R)	8.00	4.00
117	John Blanchard (R)	8.00	4.00
118	John Buzhardt (R)	4.00	2.00
119	John Callison (R)	12.00	6.00
120	Chuck Coles	4.00	2.00
121	Bob Conley	4.00	2.00
122	Bennie Daniels	4.00	2.00
123	Don Dillard	4.00	2.00
124	Dan Dobbek	4.00	2.00
125	Ron Fairly (R)	8.00	4.00
126	Eddie Haas	4.00	2.00
127	Kent Hadley	4.00	2.00
128	Bob Hartman	4.00	2.00
129	Frank Herrera	4.00	2.00
130	Lou Jackson	4.00	2.00
131	Deron Johnson (R)	8.00	4.00
132	Don Lee	4.00	2.00
133	Bob Lillis (R)	5.00	2.50
134	Jim McDaniel	4.00	2.00
135	Gene Oliver	4.00	2.00
136	Jim O'Toole (R)	6.00	3.00
137	Dick Ricketts	4.00	2.00
138	John Romano	4.00	2.00
139	Ed Sadowski	4.00	2.00
140	Charlie Secrest	4.00	2.00
141	Joe Shipley	4.00	2.00
142	Dick Stigman	4.00	2.00
143	Willie Tasby	4.00	2.00
144	Jerry Walker	4.00	2.00
145	Dom Zanni	4.00	2.00
146	Jerry Zimmerman	4.00	2.00
147	Cub's Clubbers (Ernie Banks, Dale Long, Walt Moryn)	18.00	9.00
		4.00	2.00
148	Mike McCormick	4.00	2.00
149	Jim Bunning	16.00	8.00
150	Stan Musial	190.00	95.00
151	Bob Malkmus	4.00	2.00

152	Johnny Klippstein	4.00	2.00
153	Jim Marshall	4.00	2.00
154	Ray Herbert	4.00	2.00
155	Enos Slaughter	20.00	10.00
156	Ace Hurlers (Billy Pierce, Robin Roberts)	8.00	4.00
157	Felix Mantilla	4.00	2.00
158	Walt Dropo	4.00	2.00
159	Bob Shaw	4.00	2.00
160	Dick Groat	6.00	3.00
161	Frank Baumann	4.00	2.00
162	Bobby G. Smith	4.00	2.00
163	Sandy Koufax	180.00	90.00
164	Johnny Groth	4.00	2.00
165	Bill Bruton	4.00	2.00
166	Destruction Crew (Rocky Colavito, Larry Doby, Minnie Minoso)	12.00	6.00
167	Duke Maas	4.00	2.00
168	Carroll Hardy	4.00	2.00
169	Ted Abernathy	4.00	2.00
170	Gene Woodling	5.00	2.50
171	Willard Schmidt	4.00	2.00
172	A's Team Checklist 177-242	12.00	6.00
173	Bill Monbouquette (R)	5.00	2.50
174	Jim Pendleton	4.00	2.00
175	Dick Farrell	4.00	2.00
176	Preston Ward	4.00	2.00
177	Johnny Briggs	4.00	2.00
178	Ruben Amaro (R)	5.00	2.50
179	Don Rudolph	4.00	2.00
180	Yogi Berra	110.00	55.00
181	Bob Porterfield	4.00	2.00
182	Milt Graff	4.00	2.00
183	Stu Miller	4.00	2.00
184	Harvey Haddix	5.00	2.50
185	Jim Busby	4.00	2.00
186	Mudcat Grant	4.00	2.00
187	Bubba Phillips	4.00	2.00
188	Juan Pizarro	4.00	2.00
189	Neil Chrisley	4.00	2.00
190	Bill Virdon	5.00	2.50
191	Russ Kemmerer	4.00	2.00
192	Charley Beamon	4.00	2.00
193	Sammy Taylor	4.00	2.00
194	Jim Brosnan	4.00	2.00
195	Rip Repulski	4.00	2.00
196	Billy Moran	4.00	2.00
197	Ray Semproch	4.00	2.00
198	Jim Davenport	4.00	2.00
199	Leo Kiely	4.00	2.00
200	Warren Giles	5.00	2.50
201	Tom Acker	4.00	2.00
202	Roger Maris	150.00	75.00
203	Ozzie Virgil	4.00	2.00
204	Casey Wise	4.00	2.00
205	Don Larsen	7.00	3.50
206	Carl Furillo	6.00	3.00
207	George Strickland	4.00	2.00
208	Willie Jones	4.00	2.00
209	Lenny Green	4.00	2.00
210	Ed Bailey	4.00	2.00
211	Bob Blaylock	4.00	2.00
212	Fence Busters (Aaron/Mathews)	65.00	32.50
213	Jim Rivera	4.00	2.00
214	Marcelino Solis	4.00	2.00
215	Jim Lemon	4.00	2.00
216	Andre Rodgers	4.00	2.00
217	Carl Erskine	5.00	2.50
218	Roman Mejiaas	4.00	2.00
219	George Zuverink	4.00	2.00
220	Frank Malzone	5.00	2.50
221	Bob Bowman	4.00	2.00
222	Bobby Shantz	6.00	3.00
223	Cards Team Checklist 265-352	12.00	6.00
224	Claude Osteen (R)	7.50	3.75
225	Johnny Logan	4.00	2.00
226	Art Ceccarelli	4.00	2.00
227	Hal Smith	4.00	2.00
228	Don Gross	4.00	2.00
229	Vic Power	4.00	2.00
230	Bill Fischer	4.00	2.00
231	Ellis Burton	4.00	2.00
232	Eddie Kasko	4.00	2.00
233	Paul Foytack	4.00	2.00
234	Chuck Tanner	4.00	2.00
235	Valmy Thomas	4.00	2.00
236	Ted Bowsfield	4.00	2.00
237	McDougald, Turley, Richardson	8.50	4.25
238	Gene Baker	4.00	2.00
239	Bob Trowbridge	4.00	2.00
240	Hank Bauer	6.00	3.00
241	Billy Muffett	4.00	2.00
242	Ron Samford	4.00	2.00
243	Marv Grissom	4.00	2.00
244	Dick Gray	4.00	2.00
245	Ned Garver	4.00	2.00
246	J.W. Porter	4.00	2.00
247	Don Ferrarese	4.00	2.00
248	Red Sox Team Checklist 177-264	12.00	6.00
249	Bobby Adams	4.00	2.00
250	Billy O'Dell	4.00	2.00
251	Cletis Boyer	5.00	2.50
252	Ray Boone	4.00	2.00
253	Seth Morehead	4.00	2.00
254	Zeke Bella	4.00	2.00
255	Del Ennis	4.00	2.00
256	Jerry Davie	4.00	2.00
257	Leon Wagner (R)	5.00	2.50

258	Fred Kipp	4.00	2.00
259	Jim Pisoni	4.00	2.00
260	Early Wynn	18.00	9.00
261	Gene Stephens	4.00	2.00
262	Hitters' Foes (Don Drysdale, Clem Labine, Johnny Podres)	12.00	6.00
263	Buddy Daley	4.00	2.00
264	Chico Carrasquel	4.00	2.00
265	Ron Kline	4.00	2.00
266	Woody Held	4.00	2.00
267	John Romonosky	4.00	2.00
268	Tito Francona	4.00	2.00
269	Jack Meyer	4.00	2.00
270	Gil Hodges	25.00	12.50
271	Orlando Pena (R)	4.00	2.00
272	Jerry Lumpe	4.00	2.00
273	Joe Jay	4.00	2.00
274	Jerry Kindall	4.00	2.00
275	Jack Sanford	4.00	2.00
276	Pete Daley	4.00	2.00
277	Turk Lown	4.00	2.00
278	Chuck Essegian	4.00	2.00
279	Ernie Johnson	4.00	2.00
280	Frank Bolling	4.00	2.00
281	Walt Craddock	4.00	2.00
282	R.C. Stevens	4.00	2.00
283	Russ Heman	4.00	2.00
284	Steve Korcheck	4.00	2.00
285	Joe Cunningham	4.00	2.00
286	Dean Stone	4.00	2.00
287	Don Zimmer	5.00	2.50
288	Dutch Dotterer	4.00	2.00
289	Johnny Kucks	4.00	2.00
290	Wes Covington	5.00	2.50
291	Pitching Partners (Camilo Pascual, Pedro Ramos)	4.50	2.25
292	Dick Williams	4.00	2.00
293	Ray Moore	4.00	2.00
294	Hank Foiles	4.00	2.00
295	Billy Martin	18.00	9.00
296	Ernie Broglio (R)	6.00	3.00
297	Jackie Brandt	4.00	2.00
298	Tex Clevenger	4.00	2.00
299	Billy Klaus	4.00	2.00
300	Richie Ashburn	16.00	8.00
301	Earl Averill	4.00	2.00
302	Don Mossi	4.00	2.00
303	Marty Keough	4.00	2.00
304	Cubs Team Checklist 265-352	12.00	6.00
305	Curt Raydon	4.00	2.00
306	Jim Gilliam	7.00	3.50
307	Curt Barclay	4.00	2.00
308	Norm Siebern	4.00	2.00
309	Sal Maglie	5.00	2.50
310	Luis Aparicio	24.00	12.00
311	Norm Zauchin	4.00	2.00
312	Don Newcombe	6.00	3.00
313	Frank House	4.00	2.00
314	Don Cardwell	4.00	2.00
315	Joe Adcock	5.00	2.50
316a	Ralph Lumenti (No Option)	90.00	45.00
316b	Ralph Lumenti (With Option	4.00	2.00
317	N.L. Hitting Kings (Ashburn/Mays)	45.00	22.50
318	Rocky Bridges	4.00	2.00
319	Dave Hillman	4.00	2.00
320	Bob Skinner	4.00	2.00
321a	Bob Giallombardo (No Option)	90.00	45.00
321b	Bob Giallombardo (With Option)	4.00	2.00
322a	Harry Hanebrink (No Trader Statement)	90.00	45.00
322b	Harry Hanebrink (With Trade)	4.00	2.00
323	Frank Sullivan	4.00	2.00
324	Don Demeter	4.00	2.00
325	Ken Boyer	10.00	5.00
326	Marv Throneberry	5.00	2.50
327	Gary Bell	4.00	2.00
328	Lou Skizas	4.00	2.00
329	Tigers Team Checklist 353-429	12.00	6.00
330	Gus Triandos	4.00	2.00
331	Steve Boros	4.00	2.00
332	Ray Monzant	4.00	2.00
333	Harry Simpson	4.00	2.00
334	Glen Hobbie	4.00	2.00
335	Johnny Temple	4.00	2.00
336a	Billy Loes (No Trade)	90.00	45.00
336b	Billy Loes (With trade)	4.00	2.00
337	George Crowe	4.00	2.00
338	Sparky Anderson	70.00	35.00
339	Roy Face	5.00	2.50
340	Roy Sievers	4.00	2.00
341	Tom Qualters	4.00	2.00
342	Roy Jablonski	4.00	2.00
343	Billy Hoeft	4.00	2.00
344	Russ Nixon	4.00	2.00
345	Gil McDougald	8.00	4.00
346	Batter Bafflers (Tom Brewer, Dave Sisler)	4.00	2.00
347	Bob Buhl	4.00	2.00
348	Ted Lepcio	4.00	2.00
349	Hoyt Wilhelm	20.00	10.00
350	Ernie Banks	85.00	42.50
351	Earl Torgeson	4.00	2.00
352	Robin Roberts	20.00	10.00
353	Curt Flood	6.00	3.00

354	Pete Burnside	4.00	2.00
355	Jim Piersall	5.00	2.50
356	Bob Mabe	4.00	2.00
357	Dick Stuart (R)	6.50	3.25
358	Ralph Terry	5.00	2.50
359	Bill White (R)	38.00	19.00
360	Al Kaline	75.00	38.00
361	Willard Nixon	4.00	2.00
362a	Dolan Nichols (No Option)	90.00	45.00
362b	Dolan Nichols (With Option)	4.00	2.00
363	Bobby Avila	4.00	2.00
364	Danny McDevitt	4.00	2.00
365	Gus Bell	4.00	2.00
366	Humberto Robinson	4.00	2.00
367	Cal Neeman	4.00	2.00
368	Don Mueller	4.00	2.00
369	Dick Tomanek	4.00	2.00
370	Pete Runnels	5.00	2.50
371	Dick Brodowski	4.00	2.00
372	Jim Hegan	4.00	2.00
373	Herb Plews	4.00	2.00
374	Art Ditmar	4.00	2.00
375	Bob Nieman	4.00	2.00
376	Hal Naragon	4.00	2.00
377	Johnny Antonelli	5.00	2.50
378	Gail Harris	4.00	2.00
379	Bob Miller	4.00	2.00
380	Hank Aaron	150.00	75.00
381	Mike Baxes	4.00	2.00
382	Curt Simmons	4.00	2.00
383	Words of Wisdom (Don Larsen, Casey Stengel)	10.00	5.00
384	Dave Sisler	4.00	2.00
385	Sherm Lollar	4.00	2.00
286	Jim Delsing	4.00	2.00
387	Don Drysdale	50.00	25.00
388	Bob Will	4.00	2.00
389	Joe Nuxhall	4.00	2.00
390	Orlando Cepeda	24.00	12.00
391	Milt Pappas	4.00	2.00
392	Whitey Herzog	6.00	3.00
393	Frank Lary	5.00	2.50
394	Randy Jackson	4.00	2.00
395	Elston Howard	10.00	5.00
396	Bob Rush	4.00	2.00
397	Senators Team Checklist 430-495	12.00	6.00
398	Wally Post	4.00	2.00
399	Larry Jackson	4.00	2.00
400	Jackie Jensen	5.00	2.50
401	Ron Blackburn	4.00	2.00
402	Hector Lopez	4.00	2.00
403	Clem Labine	5.00	2.50
404	Hank Sauer	4.00	2.00
405	Roy McMillan	4.00	2.00
406	Solly Drake	4.00	2.00
407	Moe Drabowsky	4.00	2.00
408	Keystone Combo (Luis Aparicio, Nellie Fox	12.00	6.00
409	Gus Zernial	4.00	2.00
410	Billy Pierce	5.00	2.50
411	Whitey Lockman	4.00	2.00
412	Stan Lopata	4.00	2.00
413	Camilo Pascual	4.00	2.00
414	Dale Long	4.00	2.00
415	Bill Mazeroski	8.00	4.00
416	Haywood Sullivan	4.00	2.00
417	Virgil Trucks	4.00	2.00
418	Gino Cimoli	4.00	2.00
419	Braves Team Checklist 353-429	12.00	6.00
420	Rocky Colavito	24.00	12.00
421	Herm Wehmeier	4.00	2.00
422	Hobie Landrith	4.00	2.00
423	Bob Grim	4.00	2.00
424	Ken Aspromonte	4.00	2.00
425	Del Crandall	4.00	2.00
426	Jerry Staley	4.00	2.00
427	Charlie Neal	4.00	2.00
428	Buc Hill Aces (Roy Face, Bob Friend, Ron Kline, Vern Law)	5.00	2.50
429	Bobby Thompson	5.00	2.50
430	Whitey Ford	50.00	25.00
431	Whammy Douglas	4.00	2.00
432	Smoky Burgess	5.00	2.50
433	Billy Harrell	4.00	2.00
434	Hal Griggs	4.00	2.00
435	Frank Robinson	60.00	30.00
436	Granny Hamner	4.00	2.00
437	Ike Delock	4.00	2.00
438	Sam Esposito	4.00	2.00
439	Brooks Robinson	65.00	38.00
440	Lou Burdette	7.00	3.50
441	John Roseboro	6.00	3.00
442	Ray Narleski	4.00	2.00
443	Daryl Spencer	4.00	2.00
444	Ronnie Hansen	4.50	2.25
445	Cal McLish	4.00	2.00
446	Rocky Nelson	4.00	2.00
447	Bob Anderson	4.00	2.00
448	Vada Pinson	8.50	4.25
449	Tom Gorman	4.00	2.00
450	Ed Mathews	30.00	15.00
451	Jimmy Constable	4.00	2.00
452	Chico Fernandez	4.00	2.00
453	Les Moss	4.00	2.00
454	Phil Clark	4.00	2.00
455	Larry Doby	7.00	3.50
456	Jerry Casale	4.00	2.00
457	Dodgers Team Checklist 430-495	25.00	12.50

458 Gordon Jones	4.00	2.00	
459 Bill Tuttle	4.00	2.00	
460 Bob Friend	4.00	2.00	
461 Mickey Mantle (HL)	75.00	38.00	
462 Rocky Colavito (HL)	12.00	6.00	
463 Al Kaline (HL)	18.00	9.00	
464 Willie Mays (HL)	38.00	19.00	
465 Roy Sievers (HL)	5.00	2.50	
466 Billy Pierce (HL)	5.00	2.50	
467 Hank Aaron (HL)	32.00	16.00	
468 Duke Snider (HL)	18.00	9.00	
469 Ernie Banks (HL)	18.00	9.00	
470 Stan Musial (HL)	25.00	12.50	
471 Tom Sturdivant	4.00	2.00	
472 Gene Freese	4.00	2.00	
473 Mike Fornieles	4.00	2.00	
474 Moe Thacker	4.00	2.00	
475 Jack Harshman	4.00	2.00	
476 Indians Team	12.00	6.00	
Checklist 496-572			
477 Barry Latman	4.00	2.00	
478 Bob Clemente	150.00	75.00	
479 Lindy McDaniel	4.00	2.00	
480 Red Schoendienst	16.00	8.00	
481 Charley Maxwell	4.00	2.00	
482 Russ Meyer	4.00	2.00	
483 Clint Courtney	4.00	2.00	
484 Willie Kirkland	4.00	2.00	
485 Ryne Duren	6.00	3.00	
486 Sammy White	4.00	2.00	
487 Hal Brown	4.00	2.00	
488 Walt Moryn	4.00	2.00	
489 John C. Powers	4.00	2.00	
490 Frank Thomas	4.00	2.00	
491 Don Blasingame	4.00	2.00	
492 Gene Conley	4.00	2.00	
493 Jim Landis	4.00	2.00	
494 Don Pavletich	4.00	2.00	
495 Johnny Podres	5.00	2.50	
496 Wayne Terwilliger	4.00	2.00	
497 Hal R. Smith	4.00	2.00	
498 Dick Hyde	4.00	2.00	
499 Johnny O'Brien	4.00	2.00	
500 Vic Wertz	5.00	2.50	
501 Bobby Tiefenauer	4.00	2.00	
502 Al Dark	5.00	2.50	
503 Jim Owens	4.00	2.00	
504 Ossie Alvarez	4.00	2.00	
505 Tony Kubek	15.00	7.50	
506 Bob Purkey	4.00	2.00	
507 Bob Hale	16.00	8.00	
508 Art Fowler	16.00	8.00	
509 Norm Cash (R)	75.00	38.00	
510 Yankees Team	90.00	45.00	
Checklist 496-572			
511 George Susce	16.00	8.00	
512 George Altman	16.00	8.00	
513 Tom Carroll	16.00	8.00	
514 Bob Gibson (R)	400.00	200.00	
515 Harmon Killebrew	160.00	80.00	
516 Mike Garcia	18.00	9.00	
517 Joe Koppe	16.00	8.00	
518 Mike Cuellar (R)	28.00	14.00	
519 Infield Power (Dick	18.00	9.00	
Gernert, Frank Malzone,			
Pete Runnells)			
520 Don Elston	16.00	8.00	
521 Gary Geiger	16.00	8.00	
522 Gene Snyder	16.00	8.00	
523 Harry Bright	16.00	8.00	
524 Larry Osborne	16.00	8.00	
525 Jim Coates	16.00	8.00	
526 Bob Speake	16.00	8.00	
527 Solly Hemus	16.00	8.00	
528 Pirates Team	50.00	25.00	
Checklist 496-572			
529 George Bamberger(R)	18.00	9.00	
530 Wally Moon	20.00	10.00	
531 Ray Webster	16.00	8.00	
532 Mark Freeman	16.00	8.00	
533 Darrel Johnson	16.00	8.00	
534 Fay Throneberry	16.00	8.00	
535 Ruben Gomez	16.00	8.00	
536 Dan Kravitz	16.00	8.00	
537 Rodolfo Arias	16.00	8.00	
538 Chick King	16.00	8.00	
539 Gary Blaylock	16.00	8.00	
540 Willy Miranda	16.00	8.00	
541 Bob Thurman	16.00	8.00	
542 Jim Perry (R)	25.00	12.50	
543 Corsair Outfield	80.00	40.00	
(Clemente, Skinner, Virdon)			
544 Lee Tate	16.00	8.00	
545 Tom Morgan	16.00	8.00	
546 Al Schroll	16.00	8.00	
547 Jim Baxes	16.00	8.00	
548 Elmer Singleton	16.00	8.00	
549 Howie Nunn	16.00	8.00	
550 Roy Campanella	190.00	95.00	
551 Fred Haney As	16.00	8.00	
552 Casey Stengel AS	36.00	18.00	
553 Orlando Cepeda AS	28.00	14.00	
554 Bill Skowron AS	28.00	14.00	
555 Bill Mazeroski AS	28.00	14.00	
556 Nellie Fox AS	30.00	15.00	
557 Ken Boyer AS	28.00	14.00	
558 Frank Malzone AS	18.00	9.00	
559 Ernie Banks AS	65.00	32.50	
560 Luis Aparicio AS	36.00	18.00	
561 Hank Aaron AS	145.00	75.00	
562 Al Kaline AS	65.00	32.50	
563 Willie Mays AS	145.00	75.00	
564 Mickey Mantle AS	340.00	175.00	
565 Wes Covington AS	18.00	9.00	

566	Roy Sievers As	18.00	9.00
567	Del Crandall AS	18.00	9.00
568	Gus Triandos AS	18.00	9.00
569	Bob Friend AS	18.00	9.00
570	Bob Turley AS	18.00	9.00
571	Warren Spahn AS	45.00	22.50
572	Billy Pierce AS	28.00	14.00

1960 Topps

Topps reverted to a horizontal format in 1960. Card fronts consist of a small color photo and a larger black and white action shot. Subsets include rookie prospects, managers, coaches, and, for the first time Topps included a World Series subset. The cards in this 572-card set are 2-1/2" by 3-1/2"

		NR/MT	EX
Complete Set (572)		4,200.00	2,100.00
Commons (1-440)		3.50	1.75
Commons (441-506)		5.00	2.50
Commons (507-572)		12.00	6.00

1	Early Wynn	38.00	15.00
2	Roman Mejias	3.50	1.75
3	Joe Adcock	5.00	2.50
4	Bob Purkey	3.50	1.75
5	Wally Moon	5.00	2.50
6	Lou Berberet	3.50	1.75
7	Master & Mentor (Willie Mays/ Bill Rigney)	25.00	12.50
8	Bud Daley	3.50	1.75
9	Faye Thronesberry	3.50	1.75
10	Ernie Banks	60.00	30.00
11	Norm Siebern	3.50	1.75
12	Milt Pappas	3.50	1.75
13	Wally Post	3.50	1.75
14	Jim Grant	3.50	1.75

15	Pete Runnels	5.00	2.50
16	Ernie Broglio	5.00	2.50
17	Johnny Callison	5.00	2.50
18	Dodgers Team Checklist 1-88	25.00	12.50
19	Felix Mantilla	3.50	1.75
20	Roy Face	5.00	2.50
21	Dutch Dotterer	3.50	1.75
22	Rocky Bridges	3.50	1.75
23	Eddie Fisher	3.50	1.75
24	Dick Gray	3.50	1.75
25	Roy Sievers	5.00	2.50
26	Wayne Terwilliger	3.50	1.75
27	Dick Drott	3.50	1.75
28	Brooks Robinson	60.00	30.00
29	Clem Labine	4.00	2.00
30	Tito Francona	3.50	1.75
31	Sammy Esposito	3.50	1.75
32	Sophomore Stalwarts (Jim O'Toole/ Vada Pinson)	4.00	2.00
33	Tom Morgan	3.50	1.75
34	George Anderson	16.00	8.00
35	Whitey Ford	48.00	24.00
36	Russ Nixon	3.50	1.75
37	Bill Bruton	3.50	1.75
38	Jerry Casale	3.50	1.75
39	Earl Averill	3.50	1.75
40	Joe Cunningham	3.50	1.75
41	Barry Latman	3.50	1.75
42	Hobie Landrith	3.50	1.75
43	Senators Team Checklist 1-88	7.50	3.75
44	Bobby Locke	3.50	1.75
45	Roy McMillan	3.50	1.75
46	Jack Fisher	3.50	1.75
47	Don Zimmer	5.00	2.50
48	Hal Smith	3.50	1.75
49	Curt Raydon	3.50	1.75
50	Al Kaline	60.00	30.00
51	Jim Coates	3.50	1.75
52	Dave Philley	3.50	1.75
53	Jackie Brandt	3.50	1.75
54	Mike Fornieles	3.50	1.75
55	Bill Mazeroski	8.00	4.00
56	Steve Korcheck	3.50	1.75
57	Win-Savers (Turk Lown/Jerry Staley)	3.50	1.75
58	Gino Cimoli	3.50	1.75
59	Juan Pizarro	3.50	1.75
60	Gus Triandos	3.50	1.75
61	Eddie Kasko	3.50	1.75
62	Roger Craig	5.00	2.50
63	George Strickland	3.50	1.75
64	Jack Meyer	3.50	1.75
65	Elston Howard	8.00	4.00
66	Bob Trowbridge	3.50	1.75

67	Jose Pagan (R)	4.00	2.00
68	Dave Hillman	3.50	1.75
69	Billy Goodman	3.50	1.75
70	Lou Burdette	6.50	3.25
71	Marty Keough	3.50	1.75
72	Tigers Team	7.50	3.75
	Checklist 89-176)		
73	Bob Gibson	70.00	35.00
74	Walt Moryn	3.50	1.75
75	Vic Power	3.50	1.75
76	Bill Bisher	3.50	1.75
77	Hank Foiles	3.50	1.75
78	Bob Grim	3.50	1.75
79	Walt Dropo	3.50	1.75
80	Johnny Antonelli	4.00	2.00
81	Russ Snyder	3.50	1.75
82	Ruben Gomez	3.50	1.75
83	Tony Kubek	8.50	4.25
84	Hal Smith	3.50	1.75
85	Frank Lary	4.00	2.00
86	Dick Gernert	3.50	1.75
87	John Romonosky	3.50	1.75
88	John Roseboro	5.00	2.50
89	Hal Brown	3.50	1.75
90	Bobby Avila	3.50	1.75
91	Bennie Daniels	3.50	1.75
92	Whitey Herzog	5.00	2.50
93	Art Schult	3.50	1.75
94	Leo Kiely	3.50	1.75
95	Frank Thomas	3.50	1.75
96	Ralph Terry	4.00	2.00
97	Ted Lepcio	3.50	1.75
98	Gordon Jones	3.50	1.75
99	Lenny Green	3.50	1.75
100	Nellie Fox	10.00	5.00
101	Bob Miller	3.50	1.75
102	Kent Hadley	3.50	1.75
103	Dick Farrell	3.50	1.75
104	Dick Schofield	3.50	1.75
105	Larry Sherry (R)	5.00	2.50
106	Billy Gardner	3.50	1.75
107	Carl Willey	3.50	1.75
108	Pete Daley	3.50	1.75
109	Cletis Boyer	6.00	3.00
110	Cal McLish	3.50	1.75
111	Vic Wertz	3.50	1.75
112	Jack Harshman	3.50	1.75
113	Bob Skinner	3.50	1.75
114	Ken Aspromonte	3.50	1.75
115	Fork & Knuckler (Roy	7.00	3.50
	Face, Hoyt Wilhelm)		
116	Jim Rivera	3.50	1.75
117	Tom Borland	3.50	1.75
118	Bob Bruce	3.50	1.75
119	Chico Cardenas	3.50	1.75
120	Duke Carmel	3.50	1.75
121	Camilo Carreon	3.50	1.75
122	Don Dillad	3.50	1.75
123	Dan Dobbek	3.50	1.75
124	Jim Donohue	3.50	1.75
125	Dick Ellsworth (R)	5.00	2.50
126	Chuck Estrada (R)	4.00	2.00
127	Ronnie Hansen	5.00	2.50
128	Bill Harris	3.50	1.75
129	Bob Hartman	3.50	1.75
130	Frank Herrera	3.50	1.75
131	Ed Hobaugh	3.50	1.75
132	Frank Howard (R)	20.00	10.00
133	Julian Javier (R)	5.00	2.50
134	Deron Johnson	3.50	1.75
135	Ken Johnson	3.50	1.75
136	Jim Kaat (R)	42.00	21.00
137	Lou Klimchock	3.50	1.75
138	Art Mahaffey (R)	3.50	1.75
139	Carl Mathias	3.50	1.75
140	Julio Navarro	3.50	1.75
141	Jim Proctor	3.50	1.75
142	Bill Short	3.50	1.75
143	Al Spangler	3.50	1.75
144	Al Stieglitz	3.50	1.75
145	Jim Umricht	3.50	1.75
146	Ted Wieand	3.50	1.75
147	Bob Will	3.50	1.75
148	Carl Yastrzemski(R)	300.00	150.00
149	Bob Nieman	3.50	1.75
150	Billy Pierce	3.50	1.75
151	Glants Team	10.00	5.00
	Checklist 177-264		
152	Gail Harris	3.50	1.75
153	Bobby Thompson	4.00	2.00
154	Jim Davenport	3.50	1.75
155	Charlie Neal	3.50	1.75
156	Art Ceccarelli	3.50	1.75
157	Rocky Nelson	3.50	1.75
158	Wes Covington	3.50	1.75
159	Jim Piersall	5.00	2.50
160	Rival All Stars (Ken	70.00	35.00
	Boyer/Mickey Mantle)		
161	Ray Narleski	3.50	1.75
162	Sammy Taylor	3.50	1.75
163	Hector Lopez	3.50	1.75
164	Reds Team	7.50	3.75
	Checklist 89-176		
165	Jack Sanford	3.50	1.75
166	Chuck Essegian	3.50	1.75
167	Valmy Thomas	3.50	1.75
168	Alex Grammas	3.50	1.75
169	Jake Striker	3.50	1.75
170	Del Crandall	3.50	1.75
171	Johnny Groth	3.50	1.75
172	Willie Kirkland	3.50	1.75
173	Billy Martin	12.00	6.00
174	Indians Team	7.50	3.75
	Checklist 89-176		

175	Pedro Ramos	3.50	1.75
176	Vada Pinson	7.00	3.50
177	Johnny Kucks	3.50	1.75
178	Woody Held	3.50	1.75
179	Rip Coleman	3.50	1.75
180	Harry Simpson	3.50	1.75
181	Billy Loes	3.50	1.75
182	Glen Hobbie	3.50	1.75
183	Eli Grba	3.50	1.75
184	Gary Geiger	3.50	1.75
185	Jim Owens	3.50	1.75
186	Dave Sisler	3.50	1.75
187	Jay Hook	3.50	1.75
188	Dick Williams	3.50	1.75
189	Don McMahon	3.50	1.75
190	Gene Woodling	4.00	2.00
191	Johnny Klippstein	3.50	1.75
192	Danny O'Connell	3.50	1.75
193	Dick Hyde	3.50	1.75
194	Bobby Gene Smith	3.50	1.75
195	Lindy McDaniel	3.50	1.75
196	Andy Carey	3.50	1.75
197	Ron Kline	3.50	1.75
198	Jerry Lynch	3.50	1.75
199	Dick Donovan	3.50	1.75
200	Willie Mays	125.00	65.00
201	Larry Osborne	3.50	1.75
202	Fred Kipp	3.50	1.75
203	Sammy White	3.50	1.75
204	Ryne Duren	5.00	2.50
205	Johnny Logan	3.50	1.75
206	Claude Osteen	4.00	2.00
207	Bob Boyd	3.50	1.75
208	White Sox Team	7.50	3.75
	Checklist 177-264		
209	Ron Blackburn	3.50	1.75
210	Harmon Killebrew	32.00	16.00
211	Taylor Phillips	3.50	1.75
212	Walt Alston	14.00	7.00
213	Chuck Dressen	3.50	1.75
214	Jimmie Dykes	3.50	1.75
215	Bob Elliott	3.50	1.75
216	Joe Gordon	3.50	1.75
217	Charley Grimm	3.50	1.75
218	Solly Hemus	3.50	1.75
219	Fred Hutchinson	3.50	1.75
220	Billy Jurges	3.50	1.75
221	Cookie Lavagetto	3.50	1.75
222	Al Lopez	5.00	2.50
223	Danny Murtaugh	5.00	2.50
224	Paul Richards	3.50	1.75
225	Bill Rigney	3.50	1.75
226	Eddie Sawyer	3.50	1.75
227	Casey Stengel	20.00	10.00
228	Ernie Johnson	3.50	1.75
229	Joe Morgan	3.50	1.75
230	Mound Magicians	9.00	4.50

	(Bob Buhl, Lou Burdette, Warren Spahn)		
231	Hal Naragon	3.50	1.75
232	Jim Busby	3.50	1.75
233	Don Elston	3.50	1.75
234	Don Demeter	3.50	1.75
235	Gus Bell	3.50	1.75
236	Dick Ricketts	3.50	1.75
237	Elmer Valo	3.50	1.75
238	Danny Kravitz	3.50	1.75
239	Joe Shipley	3.50	1.75
240	Luis Aparicio	16.00	8.00
241	Albie Pearson	3.50	1.75
242	Cards Team	7.50	3.75
	Checklist 265-352		
243	Bubba Phillips	3.50	1.75
244	Hal Griggs	3.50	1.75
245	Eddie Yost	3.50	1.75
246	Lee Maye	3.50	1.75
247	Gil McDougald	6.00	3.00
248	Del Rice	3.50	1.75
249	Earl Wilson (R)	4.00	2.00
250	Stan Musial	130.00	65.00
251	Bobby Malkmus	3.50	1.75
252	Ray Herbert	3.50	1.75
253	Eddie Bressoud	3.50	1.75
254	Arnie Portocarrero	3.50	1.75
255	Jim Gilliam	6.00	3.00
256	Dick Brown	3.50	1.75
257	Gordy Coleman (R)	4.00	2.00
258	Dick Groat	5.00	2.50
259	George Altman	3.50	1.75
260	Power Plus (Rocky	6.00	3.00
	Colavito/Tito Francona)		
261	Pete Burnside	3.50	1.75
262	Hank Bauer	4.00	2.00
263	Darrell Johnson	3.50	1.75
264	Robin Roberts	16.00	8.00
265	Rip Repulski	3.50	1.75
266	Joe Jay	3.50	1.75
267	Jim Marshall	3.50	1.75
268	Al Worthington	3.50	1.75
269	Gene Green	3.50	1.75
270	Bob Turley	4.00	2.00
271	Julio Becquer	3.50	1.75
272	Fred Green	3.50	1.75
273	Neil Chrisley	3.50	1.75
274	Tom Acker	3.50	1.75
275	Curt Flood	5.00	2.50
276	Ken McBride	3.50	1.75
277	Harry Bright	3.50	1.75
278	Stan Williams	3.50	1.75
279	Chuck Tanner	3.50	1.75
280	Frank Sullivan	3.50	1.75
281	Ray Boone	3.50	1.75
282	Joe Nuxhall	3.50	1.75

283	John Blanchard	4.00	2.00
284	Don Gross	3.50	1.75
285	Harry Anderson	3.50	1.75
286	Ray Semproch	3.50	1.75
287	Felipe Alou	7.00	3.50
288	Bob Mabe	3.50	1.75
289	Willie Jones	3.50	1.75
290	Jerry Lumpe	3.50	1.75
291	Bob Keegan	3.50	1.75
292	Dodger Backstops	4.00	2.00
	(Joe Pignatano,		
	John Roseboro)	3.50	1.75
293	Gene Conley	3.50	1.75
294	Tony Taylor	3.50	1.75
295	Gil Hodges	20.00	10.00
296	Nelson Chittum	3.50	1.75
297	Reno Bertoia	3.50	1.75
298	George Witt	3.50	1.75
299	Earl Torgeson	3.50	1.75
300	Hank Aaron	140.00	70.00
301	Jerry Davie	3.50	1.75
302	Phillies Team	7.50	3.75
	Checklist 353-429		
303	Billy O'Dell	3.50	1.75
304	Joe Ginsberg	3.50	1.75
305	Richie Ashburn	10.00	5.00
306	Frank Baumann	3.50	1.75
307	Gene Oliver	3.50	1.75
308	Dick Hall	3.50	1.75
309	Bob Hale	3.50	1.75
310	Frank Malzone	3.50	1.75
311	Raul Sanchez	3.50	1.75
312	Charlie Lau	3.50	1.75
313	Turk Lown	3.50	1.75
314	Chico Fernandez	3.50	1.75
315	Bobby Shantz	4.00	2.00
316	Willie McCovey (R)	240.00	120.00
317	Pumpsie Green	3.50	1.75
318	Jim Baxes	3.50	1.75
319	Joe Koppe	3.50	1.75
320	Bob Allison	6.00	3.00
321	Ron Fairly	5.00	2.50
322	Willie Tasby	3.50	1.75
323	Johnny Romano	3.50	1.75
324	Jim Perry	5.00	2.50
325	Jim O'Toole	4.00	2.00
326	Roberto Clemente	140.00	70.00
327	Ray Sadecki (R)	5.00	2.50
328	Earl Battey	3.50	1.75
329	Zack Monroe	3.50	1.75
330	Harvey Kuenn	5.00	2.50
331	Henry Mason	3.50	1.75
332	Yankees Team	38.00	19.00
	Checklist 265-352		
333	Danny McDevitt	3.50	1.75
334	Ted Abernathy	3.50	1.75
335	Red Schoendienst	12.00	6.00
336	Ike Delock	3.50	1.75
337	Cal Neeman	3.50	1.75
338	Ray Monzant	3.50	1.75
339	Harry Chitl	3.50	1.75
340	Harvey Haddix	4.00	2.00
341	Carroll Hardy	3.50	1.75
342	Casey Wise	3.50	1.75
343	Sandy Koufax	140.00	70.00
344	Clint Courtney	3.50	1.75
345	Don Newcombe	5.00	2.50
346	J.C. Martin (Wrong	3.50	1.75
	Photo)		
347	Ed Bouchee	3.50	1.75
348	Barry Shetrone	3.50	1.75
349	Moe Drabowsky	3.50	1.75
350	Micky Mantle	480.00	240.00
351	Don Nottebart	3.50	1.75
352	Cincy Clouters (Gus	8.50	4.25
	Bell, Jerry Lynch		
	Frank Robinson)		
353	Don Larsen	5.00	2.50
354	Bob Lillis	3.50	1.75
355	Bill White	7.00	3.50
356	Joe Amalfitano	3.50	1.75
357	Al Schroll	3.50	1.75
358	Joe DeMaestri	3.50	1.75
359	Buddy Gilbert	3.50	1.75
360	Herb Score	5.00	2.50
361	Bob Oldis	3.50	1.75
362	Russ Kemmerer	3.50	1.75
363	Gene Stephens	3.50	1.75
364	Paul Foytack	3.50	1.75
365	Minnie Minoso	7.00	3.50
366	Dallas Green (R)	8.50	4.25
367	Bill Tuttle	3.50	1.75
368	Daryl Spencer	3.50	1.75
369	Billy Hoeft	3.50	1.75
370	Bill Skowron	7.50	3.75
371	Bud Byerly	3.50	1.75
372	Frank House	3.50	1.75
373	Don Hoak	3.50	1.75
374	Bob Buhl	3.50	1.75
375	Dale Long	3.50	1.75
376	Johnny Briggs	3.50	1.75
377	Roger Maris	125.00	65.00
378	Stu Miller	3.50	1.75
379	Red Wilson	3.50	1.75
380	Bob Shaw	3.50	1.75
381	Braves Team	7.50	3.75
	Checklist 353-429		
382	Ted Bowsfield	3.50	1.75
383	Leon Wagner	3.50	1.75
384	Don Cardwell	3.50	1.75
385	World Series Game 1	6.00	3.00
386	World Series Game 2	6.00	3.00
387	World Series Game 3	6.00	3.00
388	World Series Game 4	10.00	5.00

389	World Series Game 5	9.00	4.50
390	World Series Game 6	6.00	3.00
391	World Series Summary	6.00	3.00
392	Tex Clevenger	3.50	1.75
393	Smoky Burgess	4.00	2.00
394	Norm Larker	3.50	1.75
395	Hoyt Wilhelm	14.00	7.00
396	Steve Bilko	3.50	1.75
397	Don Blasingame	3.50	1.75
398	Mike Cuellar	4.00	2.00
399	Young Hill Stars	3.50	1.75
	(Jack Fisher, Milt		
	Pappas, Jerry Walker)		
400	Rocky Colavito	14.00	7.00
401	Bob Duliba	5.00	2.50
402	Dick Stuart	5.00	2.50
403	Ed Sadowski	5.00	2.50
404	Bob Rush	5.00	2.50
405	Bobby Richardson	10.00	5.00
406	Billy Klaus	5.00	2.50
407	Gary Peters (R)	5.00	2.50
	(Wrong Photo)		
408	Carl Furillo	6.00	3.00
409	Ron Samford	5.00	2.50
410	Sam Jones	5.00	2.50
411	Ed Bailey	5.00	2.50
412	Bob Anderson	5.00	2.50
413	A's Team	7.50	3.75
	Checklist 430-495		
414	Don Williams	5.00	2.50
415	Bob Cerv	5.00	2.50
416	Humberto Robinso	5.00	2.50
417	Chuck Cottier (R)	6.00	3.00
418	Don Mossi	5.00	2.50
419	George Crowe	5.00	2.50
420	Ed Mathews	32.00	16.00
421	Duke Maas	5.00	2.50
422	Johnny Powers	5.00	2.50
423	Ed FitzGerald	5.00	2.50
424	Pete Whisenant	5.00	2.50
425	Johnny Podres	6.00	3.00
426	Ron Jackson	5.00	2.50
427	Al Grunwald	5.00	2.50
428	Al Smith	5.00	2.50
429	AL Kings (Nellie Fox,	7.00	3.50
	Harvey Kuenn)		
430	Art Ditmar	5.00	2.50
431	Andre Rodgers	5.00	2.50
432	Chuck Stobbs	5.00	2.50
433	Irv Noren	5.00	2.50
434	Brooks Lawrence	5.00	2.50
435	Gene Freese	5.00	2.50
436	Marv Throneberry	5.00	2.50
437	Bob Friend	5.00	2.50
438	Jim Coker	5.00	2.50
439	Tom Brewer	5.00	2.50
440	Jim Lemon	5.00	2.50
441	Gary Bell	5.00	2.50
442	Joe Pignatano	5.00	2.50
443	Charlie Maxwell	5.00	2.50
444	Jerry Kindall	5.00	2.50
445	Warren Spahn	50.00	25.00
446	Ellis Burton	5.00	2.50
447	Ray Moore	5.00	2.50
448	Jim Gentile (R)	14.00	7.00
449	Jim Brosnan	5.00	2.50
450	Orlando Cepeda	22.00	11.00
451	Curt Simmons	5.00	2.50
452	Ray Webster	5.00	2.50
453	Vern Law	6.50	3.25
454	Hal Woodeshick	5.00	2.50
455	Orioles Coaches	5.00	2.50
456	Red Sox Coaches	7.00	3.50
457	Cubs Coaches	5.00	2.50
458	White Sox Coaches	5.00	2.50
459	Reds Coaches	5.00	2.50
460	Indians Coaches	7.50	3.75
461	Tigers Coaches	7.50	3.75
462	A's Coaches	5.00	2.50
463	Dodgers Coaches	5.00	2.50
464	Braves Coaches	5.00	2.50
465	Yankees Coaches	14.00	7.00
466	Phillies Coaches	5.00	2.50
467	Pirates Coaches	5.00	2.50
468	Cardinals Coaches	5.00	2.50
469	Giants Coaches	5.00	2.50
470	Senators Coaches	5.00	2.50
471	Ned Garver	5.00	2.50
472	Al Dark	5.00	2.50
473	Al Cicotte	5.00	2.50
474	Haywood Sullivan	5.00	2.50
475	Don Drysdale	55.00	27.50
476	Lou Johnson	5.00	2.50
477	Don Ferrarese	5.00	2.50
478	Frank Torre	5.00	2.50
479	Georges Maranda	5.00	2.50
480	Yogi Berra	90.00	45.00
481	Wes Stock	5.00	2.50
482	Frank Bolling	5.00	2.50
483	Camilo Pascual	5.00	2.50
484	Pirates Team	35.00	17.50
	Checklist 430-495		
485	Ken Boyer	14.00	7.00
486	Bobby Del Greco	5.00	2.50
487	Tom Sturdivant	5.00	2.50
488	Norm Cash	16.00	8.00
489	Steve Ridzik	5.00	2.50
490	Frank Robinson	55.00	27.50
491	Mel Roach	5.00	2.50
492	Larry Jackson	5.00	2.50
493	Duke Snider	60.00	30.00
494	Orioles Team	15.00	7.50
	Checklist 496-572		
495	Sherm Lollar	5.00	2.50

496	Bill Virdon	7.00	3.50
497	John Tsitouris	5.00	2.50
498	Al Pilarcik	5.00	2.50
499	Johnny James	5.00	2.50
500	Johnny Temple	5.00	2.50
501	Bob Schmidt	5.00	2.50
502	Jim Bunning	15.00	7.50
503	Don Lee	5.00	2.50
504	Seth Morehead	5.00	2.50
505	Ted Kluszewski	15.00	7.50
506	Lee Walls	5.00	2.50
507	Dick Stigman	12.00	6.00
508	Billy Consolo	12.00	6.00
509	Tommy Davis (R)	28.00	14.00
510	Jerry Staley	12.00	6.00
511	Ken Walters	12.00	6.00
512	Joe Gibbon	12.00	6.00
513	Cubs Team Checklist 496-572	32.00	16.00
514	Steve Barber (R)	18.00	9.00
515	Stan Lopata	12.00	6.00
516	Marty Kutyna	12.00	6.00
517	Charley James	12.00	6.00
518	Tony Gonzalez (R)	14.00	7.00
519	Ed Roebuck	12.00	6.00
520	Don Buddin	12.00	6.00
521	Mike Lee	12.00	6.00
522	Ken Hunt	12.00	6.00
523	Clay Dalrymple (R)	12.00	6.00
524	Bill Henry	12.00	6.00
525	Marv Breeding	12.00	6.00
526	Paul Giel	12.00	6.00
527	Jose Valdivielso	12.00	6.00
528	Ben Johnson	12.00	6.00
529	Norm Sherry (R)	18.00	9.00
530	Mike McCormick	12.00	6.00
531	Sandy Amoros	12.00	6.00
532	Mike Garcia	12.00	6.00
533	Lu Clinton	12.00	6.00
534	Ken MacKenzie	12.00	6.00
535	Whitey Lockman	12.00	6.00
536	Wynn Hawkins	12.00	6.00
537	Red Sox Team Checklist 496-572	32.00	16.00
538	Frank Barnes	12.00	6.00
539	Gene Baker	12.00	6.00
540	Jerry Walker	12.00	6.00
541	Tony Curry	12.00	6.00
542	Ken Hamlin	12.00	6.00
543	Elio Chacon	12.00	6.00
544	Bill Monbouquette	12.00	6.00
545	Carl Sawatski	12.00	6.00
546	Hank Aguirre	12.00	6.00
547	Bob Aspromonte	12.00	6.00
548	Don Mincher	12.00	6.00
549	John Buzhardt	12.00	6.00
550	Jim Landis	12.00	6.00
551	Ed Rakow	12.00	6.00
552	Walt Bond	12.00	6.00
553	Bill Skowron AS	16.00	8.00
554	Willie McCovey AS	60.00	30.00
555	Nellie Fox AS	20.00	10.00
556	Charlie Neal AS	12.00	6.00
557	Frank Malzone AS	12.00	6.00
558	Eddie Mathews AS	35.00	18.00
559	Luis Aparicio AS	25.00	12.50
560	Ernie Banks AS	60.00	30.00
561	Al Kaline AS	60.00	30.00
562	Joe Cunningham AS	12.00	6.00
563	Mickey Mantle AS	325.00	165.00
564	Willie Mays AS	150.00	75.00
565	Roger Maris AS	125.00	60.00
566	Hank Aaron AS	150.00	75.00
567	Sherm Lollar AS	12.00	6.00
568	Del Crandall AS	12.00	6.00
569	Camilo Pascual AS	12.00	6.00
570	Don Drysdale AS	38.00	20.00
571	Billy Pierce AS	12.00	6.00
572	Johnny Antonelli AS	24.00	12.00

1961 Topps

For 1961 Topps returned to a vertical design on the card fronts which feature large color close up shots. Although the checklist is numbered through #589, only 587 cards were issued. Numbers 587 and 588 were never issued. For the first time Topps included a League Leaders subset (41-50). Cards measure 2-1/2" by 3-1/2".

	NR/MT	EX
Complete (Set 587)	5,800.00	2,900.00
Commons (1-370)	3.00	1.50
Commons (371-522)	4.50	2.25
Commons (523-589)	32.00	16.00

		NR/MT	EX
1	Dick Groat	20.00	8.50
2	Roger Maris	180.00	90.00
3	John Buzhardt	3.00	1.50
4	Lenny Green	3.00	1.50
5	Johnny Romano	3.00	1.50
6	Ed Roebuck	3.00	1.50
7	White Sox Team	7.00	3.50
8	Dick Williams	3.00	1.50
9	Bob Purkey	3.00	1.50
10	Brooks Robinson	40.00	20.00
11	Curt Simmons	3.00	1.50
12	Moe Thacker	3.00	1.50
13	Chuck Cottier	3.00	1.50
14	Don Mossi	3.00	1.50
15	Willie Kirkland	3.00	1.50
16	Billy Muffett	3.00	1.50
17	Checklist 1-88	10.00	3.00
18	Jim Grant	3.00	1.50
19	Cletis Boyer	3.00	1.50
20	Robin Roberts	14.00	7.00
21	Zoilo Versalles (R)	5.00	2.50
22	Clem Labine	3.00	1.50
23	Don Demeter	3.00	1.50
24	Ken Johnson	3.00	1.50
25	Red's Artillery (Gus	8.00	4.00
	Bell, Vada Pinson,		
	Frank Robinson)		
26	Wes Stock	3.00	1.50
27	Jerry Kindall	3.00	1.50
28	Hector Lopez	3.00	1.50
29	Don Nottebart	3.00	1.50
30	Nellie Fox	8.50	4.25
31	Bob Schmidt	3.00	1.50
32	Ray Sadecki	3.00	1.50
33	Gary Geiger	3.00	1.50
34	Wynn Hawkins	3.00	1.50
35	Ron Santo (R)	55.00	27.50
36	Jack Kralick	3.00	1.50
37	Charlie Maxwell	3.00	1.50
38	Bob Lillis	3.00	1.50
39	Leo Posada	3.00	1.50
40	Bob Turley	3.00	1.50
41	N.L. Batting Leaders	12.50	6.25
42	A.L. Batting Leaders	6.00	3.00
43	N.L. HR Leaders	16.00	8.00
44	A.L. HR Leaders	55.00	27.50
45	N.L. E.R.A. Leaders	7.50	3.75
46	A.L. E.R.A. Leaders	6.00	3.00
47	N.L. Pitching Leaders	7.50	3.75
48	A.L. Pitching Leaders	6.00	3.00
49	N.L. Strikeout Leaders	12.50	6.25
50	A.L. Strikeout Leaders	7.00	3.50
51	Tigers Team	7.00	3.50
52	George Crowe	3.00	1.50
53	Russ Nixon	3.00	1.50
54	Earl Francis	3.00	1.50
55	Jim Davenport	3.00	1.50
56	Russ Kemmerer	3.00	1.50
57	Marv Throneberry	3.50	1.75
58	Joe Schaffernoth	3.00	1.50
59	Jim Woods	3.00	1.50
60	Woodie Held	3.00	1.50
61	Ron Piche	3.00	1.50
62	Al Pilarcik	3.00	1.50
63	Jim Kaat	10.00	5.00
64	Alex Grammas	3.00	1.50
65	Ted Kluszewski	7.00	3.50
66	Bill Henry	3.00	1.50
67	Ossie Virgil	3.00	1.50
68	Deron Johnson	3.00	1.50
69	Earl Wilson	3.00	1.50
70	Bill Virdon	4.00	2.00
71	Jerry Adair	3.00	1.50
72	Stu Miller	3.00	1.50
73	Al Spangler	3.00	1.50
74	Joe Pignatano	3.00	1.50
75	Larry Jackson/Lindy	3.00	1.50
	McDaniel)		
76	Harry Anderson	3.00	1.50
77	Dick Stigman	3.00	1.50
78	Lee Walls	3.00	1.50
79	Joe Ginsberg	3.00	1.50

80	Harmon Killebrew	25.00	12.50
81	Tracy Stallard	3.00	1.50
82	Joe Christopher	3.00	1.50
83	Bob Bruce	3.00	1.50
84	Lee Maye	3.00	1.50
85	Jerry Walker	3.00	1.50
86	Dodgers Team	8.00	4.00
87	Joe Amalfitano	3.00	1.50
88	Richie Ashburn	8.50	4.25
89	Billy Martin	10.00	5.00
90	Jerry Staley	3.00	1.50
91	Walt Moryn	3.00	1.50
92	Hal Naragon	3.00	1.50
93	Tony Gonzalez	3.00	1.50
94	Johnny Kucks	3.00	1.50
95	Norm Cash	8.00	4.00
96	Billy O'Dell	3.00	1.50
97	Jerry Lynch	3.00	1.50
98	Checklist 89-176	10.00	3.00
99	Don Buddin	3.00	1.50
100	Harvey Haddix	5.00	2.50
101	Bubba Phillips	3.00	1.50
102	Gene Stephens	3.00	1.50
103	Ruben Amaro	3.00	1.50
104	John Blanchard	3.00	1.50
105	Carl Willey	3.00	1.50
106	Whitey Herzog	4.00	2.00
107	Seth Morehead	3.00	1.50
108	Dan Dobbek	3.00	1.50
109	Johnny Podres	4.00	2.00
110	Vada Pinson	6.00	3.00
111	Jack Meyer	3.00	1.50
112	Chico Fernandez	3.00	1.50
113	Mike Fornieles	3.00	1.50
114	Hobie Landrith	3.00	1.50
115	Johnny Antonelli	4.00	2.00
116	Joe DeMaestri	3.00	1.50
117	Dale Long	3.00	1.50
118	Chris Cannizzaro	3.00	1.50
119	A's Big Armor (Hank Bauer, Jerry Lumpe, Norm Siebern)	3.00	1.50
120	Ed Mathews	30.00	15.00
121	Eli Grba	3.00	1.50
122	Cubs Team	7.00	3.50
123	Billy Gardner	3.00	1.50
124	J.C. Martin	3.00	1.50
125	Steve Barber	3.50	1.75
126	Dick Stuart	3.00	1.50
127	Ron Kline	3.00	1.50
128	Rip Repulski	3.00	1.50
129	Ed Hobaugh	3.00	1.50
130	Norm Larker	3.00	1.50
131	Paul Richards	3.00	1.50
132	Al Lopez	4.00	2.00
133	Ralph Houk	4.00	2.00
134	Mickey Vernon	3.00	1.50
135	Fred Hutchinson	4.00	2.00
136	Walt Alston	5.00	2.50
137	Chuck Dressen	3.00	1.50
138	Danny Murtaugh	4.00	2.00
139	Solly Hemus	3.00	1.50
140	Gus Triandos	3.00	1.50
141	Billy Williams (R)	110.00	55.00
142	Luis Arroyo	3.00	1.50
143	Russ Snyder	3.00	1.50
144	Jim Coker	3.00	1.50
145	Bob Buhl	3.00	1.50
146	Marty Keough	3.00	1.50
147	Ed Rakow	3.00	1.50
148	Julian Javier	3.00	1.50
149	Bob Oldis	3.00	1.50
150	Willie Mays	140.00	70.00
151	Jim Donohue	3.00	1.50
152	Earl Torgeson	3.00	1.50
153	Don Lee	3.00	1.50
154	Bobby Del Greco	3.00	1.50
155	Johnny Temple	3.00	1.50
156	Ken Hunt	3.00	1.50
157	Cal McLish	3.00	1.50
158	Pete Daley	3.00	1.50
159	Orioles Team	7.00	3.50
160	Whitey Ford	42.00	21.00
161	Sherman Jones (Wrong Photo)	3.00	1.50
162	Jay Hook	3.00	1.50
163	Ed Sadowsi	3.00	1.50
164	Felix Mantilla	3.00	1.50
165	Gino Cimoli	3.00	1.50
166	Danny Kravitz	3.00	1.50
167	Giants Team	7.00	3.50
168	Tommy Davis	8.00	4.00
169	Don Elston	3.00	1.50
170	Al Smith	3.00	1.50
171	Paul Foytack	3.00	1.50
172	Don Dillard	3.00	1.50
173	Beantown Bombers (Jackie Jensen, Frank Malzone, Vic Wertz)	4.00	2.00
174	Ray Semproch	3.00	1.50
175	Gene Freese	3.00	1.50
176	Ken Aspromonte	3.00	1.50
177	Don Larsen	5.00	2.50
178	Bob Nieman	3.00	1.50
179	Joe Koppe	3.00	1.50
180	Bobby Richardson	10.00	5.00
181	Fred Green	3.00	1.50
182	Dave Nicholson	3.00	1.50
183	Andre Rodgers	3.00	1.50
184	Steve Bilko	3.00	1.50
185	Herb Score	5.00	2.50
186	Elmer Valo	3.00	1.50
187	Billy Klaus	3.00	1.50
188	Jim Marshall	3.00	1.50

189 Checklist 177-264	10.00	3.00
190 Stan Williams	3.00	1.50
191 Mike de la Hoz	3.00	1.50
192 Dick Brown	3.00	1.50
193 Gene Conley	3.00	1.50
194 Gordy Coleman	3.00	1.50
195 Jerry Casale	3.00	1.50
196 Ed Bouchee	3.00	1.50
197 Dick Hall	3.00	1.50
198 Carl Sawatski	3.00	1.50
199 Bob Boyd	3.00	1.50
200 Warren Spahn	38.00	20.00
201 Pete Whisenant	3.00	1.50
202 Al Neiger	3.00	1.50
203 Eddie Bressoud	3.00	1.50
204 Bob Skinner	3.00	1.50
205 Bill Pierce	3.00	1.50
206 Gene Green	3.00	1.50
207 Dodger Southpaws	28.00	14.00
(Sandy Koufax,		
Johnny Podres)		
208 Larry Osborne	3.00	1.50
209 Ken McBride	3.00	1.50
210 Pete Runnels	4.00	2.00
211 Bob Gibson	45.00	22.50
212 Haywood Sullivan	3.00	1.50
213 Bill Stafford	3.00	1.50
214 Danny Murphy	3.00	1.50
215 Gus Bell	3.00	1.50
216 Ted Bowsfield	3.00	1.50
217 Mel Roach	3.00	1.50
218 Hal Brown	3.00	1.50
219 Gene Mauch	4.00	2.00
220 Al Dark	3.00	1.50
221 Mike Higgins	3.00	1.50
222 Jimmie Dykes	4.00	2.00
223 Bob Scheffing	3.00	1.50
224 Joe Gordon	4.00	2.00
225 Bill Rigney	3.00	1.50
226 Harry Lavagetto	3.00	1.50
227 Juan Pizarro	3.00	1.50
228 Yankees Team	45.00	22.50
229 Rudy Hernandez	3.00	1.50
230 Don Hoak	3.00	1.50
231 Dick Drott	3.00	1.50
232 Bill White	6.00	3.00
233 Joe Jay	3.00	1.50
234 Ted Lepcio	3.00	1.50
235 Camilo Pascual	3.00	1.50
236 Don Gile	3.00	1.50
237 Billy Loes	3.00	1.50
238 Jim Gilliam	5.00	2.50
239 Dave Sisler	3.00	1.50
240 Ron Hansen	3.00	1.50
241 Al Cicotte	3.00	1.50
242 Hal W. Smith	3.00	1.50
243 Frank Lary	4.00	2.00

244 Chico Cardenas	3.00	1.50
245 Joe Adcock	4.00	2.00
246 Bob Davis	3.00	1.50
247 Billy Goodman	3.00	1.50
248 Ed Keegan	3.00	1.50
249 Reds Team	7.00	3.50
250 Buc Hill Aces (Roy	4.00	2.00
Face, Vern Law)		
251 Bill Bruton	3.00	1.50
252 Bill Short	3.00	1.50
253 Sammy Taylor	3.00	1.50
254 Ted Sadowski	3.00	1.50
255 Vic Power	3.00	1.50
256 Billy Hoeft	3.00	1.50
257 Carroll Hardy	3.00	1.50
258 Jack Sanford	3.00	1.50
259 John Schaive	3.00	1.50
260 Don Drysdale	35.00	17.50
261 Charlie Lau	3.00	1.50
262 Tony Curry	3.00	1.50
263 Ken Hamlin	3.00	1.50
264 Glen Hobbie	3.00	1.50
265 Tony Kubek	9.00	4.50
266 Lindy McDaniel	3.00	1.50
267 Norm Siebern	3.00	1.50
268 Ike Delock	3.00	1.50
269 Harry Chiti	3.00	1.50
270 Bob Friend	3.00	1.50
271 Jim Landis	3.00	1.50
272 Tom Morgan	3.00	1.50
273 Checklist 265-352	10.00	3.00
274 Gary Bell	3.00	1.50
275 Gene Woodling	3.50	1.75
276 Ray Rippelmeyer	3.00	1.50
277 Hank Foiles	3.00	1.50
278 Don McMahon	3.00	1.50
279 Jose Pagan	3.00	1.50
280 Frank Howard	7.00	3.50
281 Frank Sullivan	3.00	1.50
282 Faye Throneberry	3.00	1.50
283 Bob Anderson	3.00	1.50
284 Dick Gernert	3.00	1.50
285 Sherm Lollar	3.00	1.50
286 George Witt	3.00	1.50
287 Carl Yastrzemski	110.00	55.00
288 Albie Pearson	3.00	1.50
289 Ray Moore	3.00	1.50
290 Stan Musial	125.00	65.00
291 Tex Clevenger	3.00	1.50
292 Jim Baumer	3.00	1.50
293 Tom Sturdivant	3.00	1.50
294 Don Blasingame	3.00	1.50
295 Milt Pappas	3.00	1.50
296 Wes Covington	3.00	1.50
297 Athletics Team	7.00	3.50
298 Jim Golden	3.00	1.50
299 Clay Dalrymple	3.00	1.50

300	Mickey Mantle	480.00	240.00
301	Chet Nichols	3.00	1.50
302	Al Heist	3.00	1.50
303	Gary Peters	3.00	1.50
304	Rocky Nelson	3.00	1.50
305	Mike McCormick	3.00	1.50
306	World Series Game 1	7.50	3.75
307	World Series Game 2	50.00	25.00
308	World Series Game 3	7.50	3.75
309	World Series Game 4	7.50	3.75
310	World Series Game 5	7.50	3.75
311	World Series Game 6	12.00	6.00
312	World Series Game 7	12.00	6.00
313	WS Celebration	10.00	5.00
314	Bob Miller	3.00	1.50
315	Earl Battey	3.00	1.50
316	Bobby Gene Smith	3.00	1.50
317	Jim Brewer	3.00	1.50
318	Danny O'Connell	3.00	1.50
319	Valmy Thoms	3.00	1.50
320	Lou Burdette	4.00	2.00
321	Marv Breeding	3.00	1.50
322	Bill Kunkel	3.00	1.50
323	Sammy Esposito	3.00	1.50
324	Hank Aguirre	3.00	1.50
325	Wally Moon	3.50	1.75
326	Dave Hillman	3.00	1.50
327	Matty Alou (R)	7.50	3.75
328	Jim O'Toole	3.00	1.50
329	Julio Becquer	3.00	1.50
330	Rocky Colavito	16.00	8.00
331	Ned Garver	3.00	1.50
332	Dutch Dotterer	3.00	1.50
333	Fritz Brickell	3.00	1.50
334	Walt Bond	3.00	1.50
335	Frank Bolling	3.00	1.50
336	Don Mincher	3.00	1.50
337	Al's Aces (Al Lopez,	7.00	3.50
	Herb Score, Early Wynn)		
338	Don Landrum	3.00	1.50
339	Gene Baker	3.00	1.50
340	Vic Wertz	3.00	1.50
341	Jim Owens	3.00	1.50
342	Clint Courtney	3.00	1.50
343	Earl Robinson	3.00	1.50
344	Sandy Koufax	110.00	55.00
345	Jim Piersall	5.00	2.50
346	Howie Nunn	3.00	1.50
347	Cardinals Team	7.00	3.50
348	Steve Boros	3.00	1.50
349	Danny McDevitt	3.00	1.50
350	Ernie Banks	45.00	22.50
351	Jim King	3.00	1.50
352	Bob Shaw	3.00	1.50
353	Howie Bedell	3.00	1.50
354	Billy Harrell	3.00	1.50
355	Bob Allison	3.00	1.50
356	Ryne Duren	4.00	2.00
357	Daryl Spencer	3.00	1.50
358	Earl Averill	3.00	1.50
359	Dallas Green	4.00	2.00
360	Frank Robinson	48.00	24.00
361	Checklist 353-429	10.00	3.00
362	Frank Funk	3.00	1.50
363	John Roseboro	3.00	1.50
364	Moe Drabowsky	3.00	1.50
365	Jerry Lumpe	3.00	1.50
366	Eddie Fisher	3.00	1.50
367	Jim Rivera	3.00	1.50
368	Bennie Daniels	3.00	1.50
369	Dave Philley	3.00	1.50
370	Roy Face	4.00	2.00
371	Bill Skowron	42.00	21.00
372	Bob Hendley	4.50	2.25
373	Red Sox Team	7.00	3.50
374	Paul Giel	4.50	2.25
375	Ken Boyer	8.50	4.25
376	Mike Roarke	4.50	2.25
377	Ruben Gomez	4.50	2.25
378	Wally Post	4.50	2.25
379	Bobby Shantz	5.00	2.50
380	Minnie Minoso	7.00	3.50
381	Dave Wickersham	4.50	2.25
382	Frank Thomas	4.50	2.25
383	Frisco First Liners	5.00	2.50
	(Mike McCormick,		
	Billy O'Dell, Jack Sanford)		
384	Chuck Essegian	4.50	2.25
385	Jim Perry	5.00	2.50
386	Joe Hicks	4.50	2.25
387	Duke Maas	4.50	2.25
388	Bob Clemente	140.00	70.00
389	Ralph Terry	5.00	2.50
390	Del Crandall	4.50	2.25
391	Winston Brown	4.50	2.25
392	Reno Bertoia	4.50	2.25
393	Batter Bafflers (Don	4.50	2.25
	Cardwell, Glen Hobbie)		
394	Ken Walters	4.50	2.25
395	Chuck Estrada	4.50	2.25
396	Bob Aspromonte	4.50	2.25
397	Hal Woodeshick	4.50	2.25
398	Hank Bauer	5.00	2.50
399	Cliff Cook	4.50	2.25
400	Vern Law	4.50	2.25
401	Babe Ruth Hits 60th	36.00	18.00
402	Larsen' Perfect Game	20.00	10.00
403	26 Inning Tie	6.00	3.00
404	Hornsby Tops N.L.	10.00	5.00
405	Gehrig 2,130 Games	32.00	16.00
406	Mantle's 565' HR	60.00	30.00
407	Chesbro's 41st Win	6.00	3.00
408	Mathewson's K's	18.00	9.00
409	Johnson's Shutout's	10.00	5.00

410	Haddix 12 Perfect Innings	7.00	3.50
411	Tony Taylor	4.50	2.25
412	Larry Sherry	4.50	2.25
413	Eddie Yost	4.50	2.25
414	Dick Donovan	4.50	2.25
415	Hank Aaron	150.00	90.00
416	Dick Howser (R)	7.50	3.25
417	Juan Marichal (R)	140.00	70.00
418	Ed Bailey	4.50	2.25
419	Tom Borland	4.50	2.25
420	Ernie Broglio	4.50	2.25
421	Ty Cline	4.50	2.25
422	Bud Daley	4.50	2.25
423	Charlie Neal	4.50	2.25
424	Turk Lown	4.50	2.25
425	Yogi Berra	75.00	38.00
426	No Card	00.00	00.00
427	Dick Ellsworth	4.50	2.25
428	Ray Barker	4.50	2.25
429	Al Kaline	48.00	24.00
430	Bill Mazeroski	45.00	22.50
431	Chuck Stobbs	4.50	2.25
432	Coot Veal	4.50	2.25
433	Art Mahaffey	4.50	2.25
434	Tom Brewer	4.50	2.25
435	Orlando Cepeda	12.50	6.25
436	Jim Maloney (R)	12.00	6.00
437	Checklist 430-506	12.00	4.00
438	Curt Flood	6.00	3.00
439	Phil Regan (R)	5.00	2.50
440	Luis Aparicio	18.00	9.00
441	Dick Bertell	4.50	2.25
442	Gordon Jons	4.50	2.25
443	Duke Snider	48.00	24.00
444	Joe Nuxhall	4.50	2.25
445	Frank Malzone	4.50	2.25
446	Bob Taylor	4.50	2.25
447	Harry Bright	4.50	2.25
448	Del Rice	4.50	2.25
449	Bobby Bolin	4.50	2.25
450	Jim Lemon	4.50	2.25
451	Power For Ernie (Ernie Broglio, Daryl Spencer, Bill White)	5.00	2.50
452	Bob Allen	4.50	2.25
453	Dick Schofield	4.50	2.25
454	Pumpsie Green	4.50	2.25
455	Early Wynn	15.00	7.50
456	Hal Bevan	4.50	2.25
457	Johnny James	4.50	2.25
458	Willie Tasby	4.50	2.25
459	Terry Fox	4.50	2.25
460	Gil Hodges	18.00	9.00
461	Smoky Burgess	5.00	2.50
462	Lou Klimchock	4.50	2.25
463	Braves Team	8.00	4.00
463	Jack Fisher	4.50	2.25
464	Lee Thomas (R)	5.00	2.50
465	Roy McMillan	4.50	2.25
466	Ron Moeller	4.50	2.25
467	Indians Team	8.00	4.00
468	Johnny Callison	5.00	2.50
469	Ralph Lumenti	4.50	2.25
470	Roy Sievers	5.00	2.50
471	Phil Rizzuto MVP	18.00	9.00
472	Yogi Berra MVP	70.00	35.00
473	Bobby Shantz MVP	6.00	3.00
474	Al Rosen MVP	7.50	3.75
475	Mickey Mantle MVP	160.00	80.00
476	Jackie Jensen MVP	6.00	3.00
477	Nellie Fox MVP	8.00	4.00
478	Roger Maris MVP	50.00	25.00
479	Jim Konstanty MVP	6.00	3.00
480	Roy Campanella MVP	40.00	20.00
481	Hank Sauer MVP	5.00	2.50
482	Willie Mays MVP	50.00	25.00
483	Don Newcombe MVP	7.00	3.50
484	Hank Aaron MVP	50.00	25.00
485	Ernie Banks MVP	35.00	18.00
486	Dick Groat MVP	6.00	3.00
487	Gene Oliver	4.50	2.25
488	Joe McClain	4.50	2.25
489	Walt Dropo	4.50	2.25
490	Jim Bunning	12.00	6.00
491	Phillies Team	8.00	4.00
492	Ron Fairly	4.50	2.25
493	Don Zimmer	6.00	3.00
494	Tom Cheney	4.50	2.25
495	Elston Howard	10.00	5.00
496	Ken MacKenzie	4.50	2.25
497	Willie Jones	4.50	2.25
498	Ray Herbert	4.50	2.25
499	Chuck Schilling	4.50	2.25
500	Harvey Kuenn	7.00	3.50
501	John DeMerit	4.50	2.25
502	Clarence Coleman (R)	7.00	3.50
503	Tito Francona	4.50	2.25
504	Billy Consolo	4.50	2.25
505	Red Schoendienst	16.00	8.00
506	Willie Davis (R)	18.00	9.00
507	Pete Burnside	4.50	2.25
508	Rocky Bridges	4.50	2.25
509	Camilo Carreon	4.50	2.25
510	Art Ditmar	4.50	2.25
511	Joe Morgan	4.50	2.25
512	Bob Will	4.50	2.25
513	Jim Brosnan	4.50	2.25
514	Jake Wood	4.50	2.25
515	Jackie Brandt	4.50	2.25
516	Checklist 507-587	12.00	4.00
517	Willie McCovey	60.00	30.00
518	Andy Carey	4.50	2.25
519	Jim Pagliaroni	4.50	2.25

520	Joe Cunningham	4.50	2.25
521	Larry & Norm Sherry	5.00	2.50
522	Dick Farrell	4.50	2.25
523	Joe Gibbon	32.00	16.00
524	Johnny Logan	38.00	19.00
525	Ron Perranoski (R)	40.00	20.00
526	R.C. Stevens	32.00	16.00
527	Gene Leek	32.00	16.00
528	Pedro Ramos	32.00	16.00
529	Bob Roselli	32.00	16.00
530	Bobby Malkmus	32.00	16.00
531	Jim Coates	32.00	16.00
532	Bob Hale	32.00	16.00
533	Jack Curtis	32.00	16.00
534	Eddie Kasko	32.00	16.00
535	Larry Jackson	32.00	16.00
536	Bill Tuttle	32.00	16.00
537	Bobby Locke	32.00	16.00
538	Chuck Hiller	32.00	16.00
539	Johnny Klippstein	32.00	16.00
540	Jackie Jensen	38.00	20.00
541	Roland Sheldon	36.00	18.00
542	Twins Team	60.00	30.00
543	Roger Craig	36.00	18.00
544	George Thomas	32.00	16.00
545	Hoyt Wilhelm	70.00	35.00
546	Marty Kutyna	32.00	16.00
547	Leon Wagner	32.00	16.00
548	Ted Wills	32.00	16.00
549	Hal R. Smith	32.00	16.00
550	Frank Baumann	32.00	16.00
551	George Altman	32.00	16.00
552	Jim Archer	32.00	16.00
553	Bill Fischer	32.00	16.00
554	Pirates Team	60.00	30.00
555	Sam Jones	32.00	16.00
556	Ken R. Hunt	32.00	16.00
557	Jose Valdivielso	32.00	16.00
558	Don Ferrarese	32.00	16.00
559	Jim Gentile	38.00	19.00
560	Barry Latman	32.00	16.00
561	Charley James	32.00	16.00
562	Bill Monbouquette	32.00	16.00
563	Bob Cerv	40.00	20.00
564	Don Cardwell	32.00	16.00
565	Felipe Alou	48.00	24.00
566	Paul Richards AS	32.00	16.00
567	Danny Murtaugh AS	36.00	18.00
568	Bill Skowron AS	38.00	20.00
569	Frank Herrera AS	32.00	16.00
570	Nellie Fox As	42.00	21.00
571	Bill Mazeroski AS	40.00	20.00
572	Brooks Robinson AS	110.00	55.00
573	Ken Boyer AS	42.00	21.00
574	Luis Aparicio AS	50.00	25.00
575	Ernie Banks AS	110.00	55.00
576	Roger Maris AS	180.00	90.00
577	Hank Aaron AS	190.00	95.00
578	Mickey Mantle AS	525.00	265.00
579	Willie Mays AS	190.00	95.00
580	Al Kaline AS	110.00	55.00
581	Frank Robinson AS	110.00	55.00
582	Earl Battey AS	32.00	16.00
583	Del Crandall AS	32.00	16.00
584	Jim Perry AS	32.00	16.00
585	Bob Friend AS	32.00	16.00
586	Whitey Ford AS	100.00	50.00
587	No Card	00.00	00.00
588	No Card	00.00	00.00
589	Warren Spahn AS	140.00	70.00

1962 Topps

This 598-card set features a vertical format on the front with large color photos set against a wood grain background. Cards measure 2-1/2" by 3-1/2". The 1962 Topps set contains a special 10-card Babe Ruth subset, a new In-Action Subset (IA) plus League Leaders, World Series, All-Stars and Rookies. For the first time, Topps introduced multi-player rookie cards

	NR/MT	EX
Complete Set (598)	5,500.00	2,750.00
Commons (1-370)	2.50	1.25
Commons (371-522)	5.00	2.50
Commons (523-598)	15.00	7.50

1	Roger Maris	240.00	75.00
2	Jim Brosnan	2.50	1.25
3	Pete Runnels	2.50	1.25
4	John DeMerit	2.50	1.25
5	Sandy Koufax	130.00	65.00

6	Marv Breeding	2.50	1.25
7	Frank Thomas	2.50	1.25
8	Ray Herbert	2.50	1.25
9	Jim Davenport	2.50	1.25
10	Bob Clemente	130.00	65.00
11	Tom Morgan	2.50	1.25
12	Harry Craft	2.50	1.25
13	Dick Howser	3.00	1.50
14	Bill White	4.00	2.00
15	Dick Donovan	2.50	1.25
16	Darrell Johnson	2.50	1.25
17	Johnny Callison	2.50	1.25
18	Manager's Dream	175.00	90.00
	(Mantle/Mays)		
19	Ray Washburn (R)	2.50	1.25
20	Rocky Colavito	12.00	6.00
21	Jim Kaat	8.00	4.00
22a	Checklist 1-88	10.00	3.00
23	Norm Larker	2.50	1.25
24	Tigers Team	6.00	3.00
25	Ernie Banks	48.00	24.00
26	Chris Cannizzaro	2.50	1.25
27	Chuck Cottier	2.50	1.25
28	Minnie Minoso	6.00	3.00
29	Casey Stengel	20.00	10.00
30	Ed Mathews	24.00	12.00
31	Tom Tresh (R)	18.00	9.00
32	John Roseboro	2.50	1.25
33	Don Larsen	3.50	1.75
34	Johnny Temple	2.50	1.25
35	Don Schwall	2.50	1.25
36	Don Leppert	2.50	1.25
37	Tribe Hill Trio	2.50	1.25
	(Barry Latman, Jim		
	Perry, Dick Stigman)		
38	Gene Stephens	2.50	1.25
39	Joe Koppe	2.50	1.25
40	Orlando Cepeda	12.00	6.00
41	Cliff Cook	2.50	1.25
42	Jim King	2.50	1.25
43	Dodgers Team	6.00	3.00
44	Don Tausig	2.50	1.25
45	Brooks Robinson	40.00	20.00
46	Jack Baldschun	2.50	1.25
47	Bob Will	2.50	1.25
48	Ralph Terry	3.00	1.50
49	Hal Jones	2.50	1.25
50	Stan Musial	125.00	65.00
51	A.L. Batting Leaders	7.00	3.50
52	N.L. Batting Leaders	12.50	6.25
53	A.L. HR Leaders	65.00	32.50
54	N.L. HR Leaders	12.50	6.25
55	A.L. E.R.A. Leaders	5.00	2.50
56	N.L. E.R.A. Leaders	7.00	3.50
57	A.L. Win Leaders	7.00	3.50
58	N.L. Win Leaders	7.00	3.50
59	A.L. Strikeout Leaders	7.00	3.50
60	N.L. Strikeout Leaders	12.50	6.25
61	Cardinals Team	6.00	3.00
62	Steve Boros	2.50	1.25
63	Tony Cloninger (R)	4.00	2.00
64	Russ Snyder	2.50	1.25
65	Bobby Richardson	7.50	3.75
66	Curio Barragan	2.50	1.25
67	Harvey Haddix	3.00	1.50
68	Ken L. Hunt	2.50	1.25
69	Phil Ortega	2.50	1.25
70	Harmon Killebrew	24.00	12.00
71	Dick LeMay	2.50	1.25
72	Bob's Pupils (Steve	2.50	1.25
	Boros, Bob Scheffing,		
	Jake Wood)		
73	Nellie Fox	8.00	4.00
74	Bob Lillis	2.50	1.25
75	Milt Pappas	2.50	1.25
76	Howie Bedell	2.50	1.25
77	Tony Taylor	2.50	1.25
78	Gene Green	2.50	1.25
79	Ed Hobaugh	2.50	1.25
80	Vada Pinson	5.00	2.50
81	Jim Pagliaroni	2.50	1.25
82	Deron Johnson	2.50	1.25
83	Larry Jackson	2.50	1.25
84	Lenny Green	2.50	1.25
85	Gil Hodges	15.00	7.50
86	Donn Clendenon (R)	5.00	2.50
87	Mike Roarke	2.50	1.25
88	Ralph Houk	3.00	1.50
89	Barney Schultz	2.50	1.25
90	Jim Piersall	3.50	1.75
91	J.C. Martin	2.50	1.25
92	Sam Jones	2.50	1.25
93	John Blanchard	2.50	1.25
94	Jay Hook	2.50	1.25
95	Don Hoak	2.50	1.25
96	Eli Grba	2.50	1.25
97	Tito Francona	2.50	1.25
98	Checklist 89-176	10.00	3.00
99	Boog Powell (R)	25.00	12.50
100	Warren Spahn	32.00	16.00
101	Carroll Hardy	2.50	1.25
102	Al Schroll	2.50	1.25
103	Don Blasingame	2.50	1.25
104	Ted Savage	2.50	1.25
105	Don Mossi	2.50	1.25
106	Carl Sawatski	2.50	1.25
107	Mike McCormick	2.50	1.25
108	Willie Davis	4.00	2.00
109	Bob Shaw	2.50	1.25
110	Bill Skowron	5.00	2.50
111	Dallas Green	3.00	1.50
112	Hank Foiles	2.50	1.25
113	White Sox Team	6.00	3.00
114	Howie Koplitz	2.50	1.25

115	Bob Skinner	2.50	1.25
116	Herb Score	3.00	1.50
117	Gary Geiger	2.50	1.25
118	Julian Javier	2.50	1.25
119	Danny Murphy	2.50	1.25
120	Bob Purkey	2.50	1.25
121	Billy Hitchcock	2.50	1.25
122	Norm Bass	2.50	1.25
123	Mike de la Hoz	2.50	1.25
124	Bill Pleis	2.50	1.25
125	Gene Woodling	2.50	1.25
126	Al Cicotte	2.50	1.25
127	Pride of the A's (Hank Bauer, Jerry Lumpe, Norm Siebern)	3.00	1.50
128	Art Fowler	2.50	1.25
129a	Lee Walls (Left)	18.00	9.00
129b	Lee Walls (Right)	2.50	1.25
130	Frank Bolling	2.50	1.25
131	Pete Richert (R)	3.00	1.50
132a	Angels Team (With inset photos)	18.00	9.00
132b	Angels Team (W/O inset photos)	6.00	3.00
133	Felipe Alou	5.00	2.50
134a	Billy Hoeft (Green Sky)	18.00	9.00
134b	Billy Hoeft (Blue sky)	3.00	1.50
135	Babe as a Boy	10.00	5.00
136	Babe Joins Yanks	10.00	5.00
137	Babe and Huggins	10.00	5.00
138	The Famous Slugger	10.00	5.00
139a	Babe Hits 60	22.00	11.00
139b	Hal Reniff (Pitching)	50.00	25.00
139c	Hal Reniff (portrait)	12.00	6.00
140	Gehrig and Ruth	30.00	15.00
141	Babe Ruth (Twilight)	10.00	5.00
142	Babe Coaching Dodgers	10.00	5.00
143	Greatest Sports Hero	10.00	5.00
144	Babe's Farewell	10.00	5.00
145	Barry Latman	2.50	1.25
146	Don Demeter	2.50	1.25
147a	Bill Kunkel (Pitching)	18.00	9.00
147b	Bill Kunkel (Portrait)	2.50	1.25
148	Wally Post	2.50	1.25
149	Bob Duliba	2.50	1.25
150	Al Kaline	40.00	20.00
151	Johnny Klippstein	2.50	1.25
152	Mickey Vernon	2.50	1.25
153	Pumpsie Green	2.50	1.25
154	Lee Thomas	2.50	1.25
155	Stu Miller	2.50	1.25
156	Merritt Ranew	2.50	1.25
157	Wes Covington	2.50	1.25
158	Braves Team	6.00	3.00
159	Hal Reniff	3.00	1.50
160	Dick Stuart	2.50	1.25
161	Frank Baumann	2.50	1.25
162	Sammy Drake	2.50	1.25
163	Hot Corner (Cletis Boyer, Billy Gardner)	3.00	1.50
164	Hal Naragon	2.50	1.25
165	Jackie Brandt	2.50	1.25
166	Don Lee	2.50	1.25
167	Tim McCarver (R)	32.00	16.00
168	Leo Posada	2.50	1.25
169	Bob Cerv	2.50	1.25
170	Ron Santo	15.00	7.50
171	Dave Sisler	2.50	1.25
172	Fred Hutchinson	2.50	1.25
173	Chico Fernandez	2.50	1.25
174a	Carl Willey (Cap)	18.00	9.00
174b	Carl Willey (No cap)	2.50	1.25
175	Frank Howard	6.00	3.00
176a	Eddie Yost (Batting)	18.00	9.00
176b	Eddie Yost (Portrait)	2.50	1.25
177	Bobby Shantz	3.00	1.50
178	Camilo Carreon	2.50	1.25
179	Tom Sturdivant	2.50	1.25
180	Bob Allison	3.00	1.50
181	Paul Brown	2.50	1.25
182	Bob Nieman	2.50	1.25
183	Roger Craig	3.00	1.50
184	Haywood Sullivan	2.50	1.25
185	Roland Sheldon	2.50	1.25
186	Mack Jones	2.50	1.25
187	Gene Conley	2.50	1.25
188	Chuck Hiller	2.50	1.25
189	Dick Hall	2.50	1.25
190a	Wally Moon (Cap)	18.00	9.00
190b	Wally Moon (No Cap)	3.50	1.75
191	Jim Brewer	2.50	1.25
192	Checklist 177-264	10.00	3.00
193	Eddie Kasko	2.50	1.25
194	Dean Chance (R)	5.00	2.50
195	Joe Cunningham	2.50	1.25
196	Terry Fox	2.50	1.25
197	Daryl Spencer	2.50	1.25
198	Johnny Keane	2.50	1.25
199	Gaylord Perry (R)	125.00	65.00
200	Mickey Mantle	650.00	325.00
201	Ike Delock	2.50	1.25
202	Carl Warwick	2.50	1.25
203	Jack Fisher	2.50	1.25
204	Johnny Weekly	2.50	1.25
205	Gene Freese	2.50	1.25
206	Senators Team	6.00	3.00
207	Pete Burnside	2.50	1.25
208	Billy Martin	10.00	5.00
209	Jim Fregosi (R)	12.00	6.00
210	Roy Face	3.00	1.50
211	Midway Masters (Frank Bolling, Roy McMillan)	2.50	1.25

212	Jim Owens	2.50	1.25
213	Richie Ashburn	10.00	5.00
214	Dom Zanni	2.50	1.25
215	Woody Held	2.50	1.25
216	Ron Kline	2.50	1.25
217	Walt Alston	4.00	2.00
218	Joe Torre (R)	28.00	14.00
219	Al Downing	2.50	1.25
220	Roy Sievers	2.50	1.25
221	Bill Short	2.50	1.25
222	Jerry Zimmerman	2.50	1.25
223	Alex Grammas	2.50	1.25
224	Don Rudolph	2.50	1.25
225	Frank Malzone	3.50	1.75
226	Giants Team	6.00	3.00
227	Bobby Tiefenauer	2.50	1.25
228	Dale Long	2.50	1.25
229	Jesus McFarlane	2.50	1.25
230	Camilo Pascual	2.50	1.25
231	Ernie Bowman	2.50	1.25
232	World Series Game 1	5.00	2.50
233	World Series Game 2	5.00	2.50
234	World Series Game 3	18.00	9.00
235	World Series Game 4	10.00	5.00
236	World Series Game 5	5.00	2.50
237	WS (Yanks Celebrate)	5.00	2.50
238	Norm Sherry	2.50	1.25
239	Cecil Butler	2.50	1.25
240	George Altman	2.50	1.25
241	Johnny Kucks	2.50	1.25
242	Mel McGaha	2.50	1.25
243	Robin Roberts	15.00	7.50
244	Don Gile	2.50	1.25
245	Ron Hansen	2.50	1.25
246	Art Ditmar	2.50	1.25
247	Joe Pignatano	2.50	1.25
248	Bob Aspromonte	2.50	1.25
249	Ed Keegan	2.50	1.25
250	Norm Cash	8.00	4.00
251	Yankees Team	32.00	16.00
252	Earl Francis	2.50	1.25
253	Harry Chiti	2.50	1.25
254	Gordon Windhorn	2.50	1.25
255	Juan Pizarro	2.50	1.25
256	Elio Chacon	2.50	1.25
257	Jack Spring	2.50	1.25
258	Marty Keough	2.50	1.25
259	Lou Klimchock	2.50	1.25
260	Bill Piece	2.50	1.25
261	George Alusik	2.50	1.25
262	Bob Schmidt	2.50	1.25
263	The Right Pitch (Joe Jay, Bob Purkey, Jim Turner)	3.00	1.50
264	Dick Ellsworth	2.50	1.25
265	Joe Adcock	3.00	1.50
266	John Anderson	2.50	1.25
267	Dan Dobbek	2.50	1.25
268	Ken McBride	2.50	1.25
269	Bob Oldis	2.50	1.25
270	Dick Groat	3.00	1.50
271	Ray Rippelmeyer	2.50	1.25
272	Earl Robinson	2.50	1.25
273	Gary Bell	2.50	1.25
274	Sammy Taylor	2.50	1.25
275	Norm Siebern	2.50	1.25
276	Hal Kostad	2.50	1.25
277	Checklist 265-352	10.00	3.00
278	Ken Johnson	2.50	1.25
279	Hobie Landrith	2.50	1.25
280	Johnny Podres	3.00	1.50
281	Jake Gibbs (R)	3.00	1.50
282	Dave Hillman	2.50	1.25
283	Charlie Smith	2.50	1.25
284	Ruben Amaro	2.50	1.25
285	Curt Simmons	2.50	1.25
286	Al Lopez	4.00	2.00
287	George Witt	2.50	1.25
288	Billy Williams	38.00	19.00
289	Mike Krsnich	2.50	1.25
290	Jim Gentile	6.00	3.00
291	Hal Stowe	2.50	1.25
292	Jerry Kindall	2.50	1.25
293	Bob Miller	2.50	1.25
294	Phillies Team	6.00	3.00
295	Vern Law	3.00	1.50
296	Ken Hamlin	2.50	1.25
297	Ron Perranoski	4.00	2.00
298	Bill Tuttle	2.50	1.25
299	Don Wert	2.50	1.25
300	Willie Mays	160.00	80.00
301	Galen Cisco (R)	4.50	2.25
302	John Edwards (R)	3.50	1.75
303	Frank Torre	2.50	1.25
304	Dick Farrell	2.50	1.25
305	Jerry Lumpe	2.50	1.25
306	Redbird Rippers (Larry Jackson, Lindy McDaniel)	3.00	1.50
307	Jim Grant	3.00	1.50
308	Neil Chrisley	2.50	1.25
309	Moe Morhardt	2.50	1.25
310	Whitey Ford	42.00	21.00
311	Tony Kubek (IA)	7.00	3.50
312	Warren Spahn (IA)	12.00	6.00
313	Roger Maris (IA)	25.00	12.50
314	Rocky Colavito (IA)	8.00	4.00
315	Whitey Ford (IA)	12.00	6.00
316	Harmon Killebrew(IA)	10.00	5.00
317	Stan Musial (IA)	22.00	11.00
318	Mickey Mantle (IA)	90.00	45.00
319	Mike McCormick (IA)	4.00	2.00
320	Hank Aaron	175.00	90.00
321	Lee Stange	2.50	1.25

322	Al Dark	2.50	1.25	378	Bennie Daniels	5.00	2.50
323	Don Landrum	2.50	1.25	379	Chuck Essegian	5.00	2.50
324	Joe McClain	2.50	1.25	380	Lou Burdette	6.00	3.00
325	Luis Aparicio	16.00	8.00	381	Chico Cardenas	5.00	2.50
326	Tom Parsons	2.50	1.25	382	Dick Williams	5.00	2.50
327	Ozzie Virgil	2.50	1.25	383	Ray Sadecki	5.00	2.50
328	Ken Walters	2.50	1.25	384	Athletics Team	8.50	4.25
329	Bob Bolin	2.50	1.25	385	Early Wynn	20.00	10.00
330	Johnny Romano	2.50	1.25	386	Don Mincher	5.00	2.50
331	Moe Drabowsky	2.50	1.25	387	Lou Brock (R)	225.00	110.00
332	Don Buddin	2.50	1.25	388	Ryne Duren	6.00	3.00
333	Frank Cipriani	2.50	1.25	389	Smoky Burgess	6.00	3.00
334	Red Sox Team	6.00	3.00	390	Orlando Cepeda AS	8.50	4.25
335	Bill Bruton	2.50	1.25	391	Bill Mazeroski AS	8.00	4.00
336	Billy Muffett	2.50	1.25	392	Ken Boyer AS	8.00	4.00
337	Jim Marshall	2.50	1.25	393	Roy McMillan AS	5.00	2.50
338	Billy Gardner	2.50	1.25	394	Hank Aaron AS	55.00	27.50
339	Jose Valdivielso	2.50	1.25	395	Willie Mays AS	55.00	27.50
340	Don Drysdale	45.00	22.50	396	Frank Robinson AS	18.00	9.00
341	Mike Hershberger	2.50	1.25	397	John Roseboro AS	5.00	2.50
342	Ed Rakow	2.50	1.25	398	Don Drysdale AS	15.00	7.50
343	Albie Pearson	2.50	1.25	399	Warren Spahn AS	15.00	7.50
344	Ed Bauta	2.50	1.25	400	Elston Howard	10.00	5.00
345	Chuck Schilling	2.50	1.25	401	AL & NL HR Kings	55.00	27.50
346	Jack Kralick	2.50	1.25		(Orlando Cepeda,		
347	Chuck Hinton	2.50	1.25		Roger Maris)		
348	Larry Burright	2.50	1.25	402	Gino Cimoli	5.00	2.50
349	Paul Foytack	2.50	1.25	403	Chet Nichols	5.00	2.50
350	Frank Robinson	55.00	28.00	404	Tim Harkness	5.00	2.50
351	Braves' Backstops	4.50	2.25	405	Jim Perry	6.50	3.25
	Crandall/Torre)			406	Bob Taylor	5.00	2.50
352	Frank Sullivan	2.50	1.25	407	Hank Aguirre	5.00	2.50
353	Bill Mazeroski	8.00	4.00	408	Gus Bell	5.00	2.50
354	Roman Mejias	2.50	1.25	409	Pirates Team	8.50	4.25
355	Steve Barber	2.50	1.25	410	Al Smith	5.00	2.50
356	Tom Haller (R)	4.50	2.25	411	Danny O'Connell	5.00	2.50
357	Jerry Walker	2.50	1.25	412	Charlie James	5.00	2.50
358	Tommy Davis	8.00	4.00	413	Matty Alou	6.50	3.25
359	Bobby Locke	2.50	1.25	414	Joe Gaines	5.00	2.50
360	Yogi Berra	90.00	45.00	415	Bill Virdon	6.00	3.00
361	Bob Hendley	2.50	1.25	416	Bob Scheffing	5.00	2.50
362	Ty Cline	2.50	1.25	417	Joe Azcue	5.00	2.50
363	Bob Roselli	2.50	1.25	418	Andy Carey	5.00	2.50
364	Ken Hunt	2.50	1.25	419	Bob Bruce	5.00	2.50
365	Charley Neal	2.50	1.25	420	Gus Triandos	5.00	2.50
366	Phil Regan	2.50	1.25	421	Ken MacKenzie	5.00	2.50
367	Checklist 353-429	10.00	3.00	422	Steve Bilko	5.00	2.50
368	Bob Tillman	2.50	1.25	423	Rival Relief Aces	8.00	4.00
369	Ted Bowsfield	2.50	1.25		(Roy Face, Hoyt		
370	Ken Boyer	9.00	4.50		Wilhelm)		
371	Earl Battey	5.00	2.50	424	Al McBean	5.00	2.50
372	Jack Curtis	5.00	2.50	425	Carl Yastrzemski	180.00	90.00
373	Al Heist	5.00	2.50	426	Bob Farley	5.00	2.50
374	Gene Mauch	5.00	2.50	427	Jake Wood	5.00	2.50
375	Ron Fairly	5.00	2.50	428	Joe Hicks	5.00	2.50
376	Bud Daley	5.00	2.50	429	Bill O'Dell	5.00	2.50
377	Johnny Orsino	5.00	2.50	430	Tony Kubek	10.00	5.00

431	Bob Rodgers (R)	10.00	5.00
432	Jim Pendleton	5.00	2.50
433	Jim Archer	5.00	2.50
434	Clay Dalrymple	5.00	2.50
435	Larry Sherry	5.00	2.50
436	Felix Mantilla	5.00	2.50
437	Ray Moore	5.00	2.50
438	Dick Brown	5.00	2.50
439	Jerry Buchek	5.00	2.50
440	Joe Jay	5.00	2.50
441	Checklist 430-506	12.50	4.50
442	Wes Stock	5.00	2.50
443	Del Crandall	5.00	2.50
444	Ted Wills	5.00	2.50
445	Vic Power	5.00	2.50
446	Don Elston	5.00	2.50
447	Willie Kirkland	5.00	2.50
448	Joe Gibbon	5.00	2.50
449	Jerry Adair	5.00	2.50
450	Jim O'Toole	6.00	3.00
451	Jose Tartabull (R)	8.00	4.00
452	Earl Averill	5.00	2.50
453	Cal McLish	5.00	2.50
454	Floyd Robinsn	5.00	2.50
455	Luis Arroyo	5.00	2.50
456	Joe Amalfitano	5.00	2.50
457	Lou Clinton	5.00	2.50
458a	Bob Buhl ("M" on cap)	5.00	2.50
458b	Bob Buhl (No "M")	50.00	25.00
459	Ed Bailey	5.00	2.50
460	Jim Bunning	12.00	6.00
461	Ken Hubbs (R)	25.00	12.50
462a	Willie Tasby ("W" on cap)	5.00	2.50
462b	Willie Tasby(No "W")	50.00	25.00
463	Hank Bauer	6.00	3.00
464	Al Jackson (R)	8.00	4.00
465	Reds Team	12.00	6.00
466	Norm Cash AS	8.50	4.25
467	Chuck Schilling AS	6.00	3.00
468	Brooks Robinson AS	22.00	11.00
469	Luis Aparicio AS	12.00	6.00
470	Al Kaline AS	22.00	11.00
471	Mickey Mantle AS	185.00	95.00
472	Rocky Colavito AS	12.00	6.00
473	Elston Howard AS	10.00	5.00
474	Frank Lary AS	7.00	3.50
475	Whitey Ford AS	18.00	9.00
476	Orioles Team	12.00	6.00
477	Andre Rodgers	5.00	2.50
478	Don Zimmer	7.50	3.75
479	Joel Horlen	7.50	3.75
480	Harvey Kuenn	8.50	4.25
481	Vic Wertz	5.00	2.50
482	Sam Mele	5.00	2.50
483	Don McMahon	5.00	2.50
484	Dick Schofield	5.00	2.50
485	Pedro Ramos	5.00	2.50
486	Jim Gilliam	8.50	4.25
487	Jerry Lynch	5.00	2.50
488	Hal Brown	5.00	2.50
489	Julio Gotay	5.00	2.50
490	Clete Boyer	8.00	4.00
491	Leon Wagner	5.00	2.50
492	Hal Smith	5.00	2.50
493	Danny McDevitt	5.00	2.50
494	Sammy White	5.00	2.50
495	Don Cardwell	5.00	2.50
496	Wayne Causey	5.00	2.50
497	Ed Bouchee	5.00	2.50
498	Jim Donohue	5.00	2.50
499	Zoilo Versalles	5.00	2.50
500	Duke Snider	55.00	28.00
501	Claude Osteen	7.00	3.50
502	Hector Lopez	5.00	2.50
503	Danny Murtaugh	5.00	2.50
504	Eddie Bressoud	5.00	2.50
505	Juan Marichal	45.00	22.50
506	Charley Maxwell	5.00	2.50
507	Ernie Broglio	5.00	2.50
508	Gordy Coleman	5.00	2.50
509	Dave Giusti (R)	8.50	4.25
510	Jim Lemon	5.00	2.50
511	Bubba Phillips	5.00	2.50
512	Mike Fornieles	5.00	2.50
513	Whitey Herzog	7.50	3.75
514	Sherm Lollar	5.00	2.50
515	Stan Williams	5.00	2.50
516	Checklist 507-598	12.50	4.50
517	Dave Wickersham	5.00	2.50
518	Lee Maye	5.00	2.50
519	Bob Johnson	5.00	2.50
520	Bob Friend	5.00	2.50
521	Jacke Davis	5.00	2.50
522	Lindy McDaniel	5.00	2.50
523	Russ Nixon	15.00	7.50
524	Howie Nunn	15.00	7.50
525	George Thomas	15.00	7.50
526	Hal Woodeshick	15.00	7.50
527	Dick McAuliffe (R)	18.00	9.00
528	Turk Lown	15.00	7.50
529	John Schaive	15.00	7.50
530	Bob Gibson	175.00	90.00
531	Bobby G. Smith	15.00	7.50
532	Dick Stigman	15.00	7.50
533	Charley Lau	15.00	7.50
534	Tony Gonzalez	18.00	9.00
535	Ed Roebuck	15.00	7.50
536	Dick Gernert	15.00	7.50
537	Indians Team	35.00	17.50
538	Jack Sanford	15.00	7.50
539	Billy Moran	15.00	7.50
540	Jim Landis	15.00	7.50
541	Don Nottebart	15.00	7.50

542	Dave Philley	15.00	7.50
543	Bob Allen	15.00	7.50
544	Willie McCovey	150.00	75.00
545	Hoyt Wilhelm	50.00	25.00
546	Moe Thacker	15.00	7.50
547	Don Ferrarese	15.00	7.50
548	Bobby Del Greco	15.00	7.50
549	Bill Rigney	15.00	7.50
550	Art Mahaffey	15.00	7.50
551	Harry Bright	15.00	7.50
552	Cubs Team	40.00	20.00
553	Jim Coates	15.00	7.50
554	Bubba Morton	15.00	7.50
555	John Buzhardt	15.00	7.50
556	Al Spangler	15.00	7.50
557	Bob Anderson	15.00	7.50
558	John Goryl	15.00	7.50
559	Mike Higgins	15.00	7.50
560	Chuck Estrada	15.00	7.50
561	Gene Oliver	15.00	7.50
562	Bill Henry	15.00	7.50
563	Ken Aspromonte	15.00	7.50
564	Bob Grim	15.00	7.50
565	Jose Pagan	15.00	7.50
566	Marty Kutyna	15.00	7.50
567	Tracy Stallard	15.00	7.50
568	Jim Golden	15.00	7.50
569	Ed Sadowski	15.00	7.50
570	Bill Stafford	18.00	9.00
571	Billy Klaus	15.00	7.50
572	Bob Miller	20.00	10.00
573	Johnny Logan	15.00	7.50
574	Dean Stone	15.00	7.50
575	Red Schoendienst	45.00	22.50
576	Russ Kemmerer	15.00	7.50
577	Dave Nicholson	15.00	7.50
578	Jim Duffalo	15.00	7.50
579	Jim Schaffer	15.00	7.50
580	Bill Monbouquette	15.00	7.50
581	Mel Roach	15.00	7.50
582	Ron Piche	15.00	7.50
583	Larry Osborne	15.00	7.50
584	Twins Team	40.00	20.00
585	Glen Hobbie	15.00	7.50
586	Sammy Esposito	15.00	7.50
587	Frank Funk	15.00	7.50
588	Birdie Tebbetts	15.00	7.50
589	Bob Turley	18.00	9.00
590	Curt Flood	18.00	9.00
591	Rookie Pitchers	65.00	32.50
	Sam McDowell		
	Ron Taylor		
	Dick Radatz		
	Ron Nischwitz		
	Art Quirk		
592	Rookie Pitchers	75.00	38.00
	Bo Belinsky		
	Joe Bonikowski		
	Jim Bouton		
	Dan Pfister		
	Dave Stenhouse		
593	Rookie Pitchers	28.00	14.00
	Craig Anderson		
	Jack Hamilton		
	Jack Lamabe		
	Bob Moorhead		
	Bob Veale		
594	Rookie Catchers	90.00	45.00
	Doug Camilli		
	Doc Edwards		
	Don Pavletich		
	Ken Retzer		
	Bob Uecker		
595	Rookie Infielders	24.00	12.00
	Ed Charles		
	Marlin Coughtry		
	Bob Sadowski		
	Felix Torres		
596	Rookie Infielders	60.00	30.00
	Bernie Allen		
	Phil Linz		
	Joe Pepitone		
	Rich Rollins		
597	Rookie Infielders	35.00	17.50
	Rod Kanehl		
	Jim McKnight		
	Denis Menke		
	Amado Samuel		
598	Rookie Outfielders	70.00	35.00
	Howie Goss		
	Jim Hickman		
	Manny Jimenez		
	Al Luplow		
	Ed Olivares		

1963 Topps

GIBSON

The 1963 Topps set is one of Topp's most popular sets. There's a major improvement in the quality of the color reproduction over previous years. The 576-card set features two photos on the front, a large portrait shot and a smaller black and white photo in the bottom right corner. The set contains the popular League Leaders, World Series and Rookies subsets. Cards measure 2-1/2" by 3-1/2".

	NR/MT	EX
Complete Set (576)	5,300.00	2,650.00
Commons (1-283)	2.50	1.25
Commons (284-446)	3.50	1.75
Commons (447-522)	12.00	6.00
Commons (523-576)	9.00	4.50

		NR/MT	EX
1	N.L. Batting Leaders	40.00	15.00
2	A.L. Batting Leaders	28.00	14.00
3	N.L. HR Leaders	25.00	12.50
4	A.L. HR Leaders	10.00	5.00
5	N.L. E.R.A. Leaders	12.50	6.25
6	A.L. E.R.A. Leaders	7.00	3.50
7	N.L. Pitching Leaders	7.00	3.50
8	A.L. Pitching Leaders	4.00	2.00
9	N.L. Strikeout Leaders	12.50	6.25
10	A.L. Strikeout Leaders	3.50	1.75
11	Lee Walls	2.50	1.25
12	Steve Barber	2.50	1.25
13	Phillies Team	4.00	2.00
14	Pedro Ramos	2.50	1.25
15	Ken Hubbs	5.00	2.50
16	Al Smith	2.50	1.25
17	Ryne Duren	3.00	1.50
18	Buc Blasters	28.00	14.00
	(Smokey Burgess, Bob Clemente, Bob Skinner, Dick Stuart)		
19	Pete Burnside	2.50	1.25
20	Tony Kubek	5.00	2.50
21	Marty Keough	2.50	1.25
22	Curt Simmons	2.50	1.25
23	Ed Lopat	2.50	1.25
24	Bob Bruce	2.50	1.25
25	Al Kaline	38.00	19.00
26	Ray Moore	2.50	1.25
27	Choo Choo Coleman	2.50	1.25
28	Mike Fornieles	2.50	1.25
29a	1962 Rookie Stars	4.50	2.25
	(John Boozer, Ray Culp, Sammy Ellis, Jesse Gonder)		
29b	1963 Rookie Stars	3.00	1.50
	(John Boozer, Ray Culp, Sammy Ellis, Jesse Gonder)		
30	Harvey Kuenn	3.50	1.75
31	Cal Koonce	2.50	1.25
32	Tony Gonzalez	2.50	1.25
33	Bo Belinsky	2.50	1.25
34	Dick Schofield	2.50	1.25
35	John Buzhardt	2.50	1.25
36	Jerry Kindall	2.50	1.25
37	Jerry Lynch	2.50	1.25
38	Bud Daley	2.50	1.25
39	Angels Team	4.00	2.00
40	Vic Power	2.50	1.25
41	Charlie Lau	2.50	1.25
42	Stan Williams	2.50	1.25
43	Veteran Masters	4.00	2.00
	(Casey Stengel, Gene Woodling)		
44	Terry Fox	2.50	1.25
45	Bob Aspromonte	2.50	1.25
46	Tommie Aaron (R)	3.50	1.75
47	Don Lock	2.50	1.25
48	Birdie Tebbetts	2.50	1.25
49	Dal Maxvill (R)	4.00	2.00
50	Bill Pierce	2.50	1.25
51	George Alusik	2.50	1.25
52	Chuck Schilling	2.50	1.25
53	Joe Moeller	2.50	1.25
54a	1962 Rookie Stars	15.00	7.50
	(Jack Cullen, Dave DeBusschere, Harry Fanok, Nelson Mathews)		
54b	1963 Rookie Stars	5.00	2.50
	(Jack Cullen, Dave DeBusschere, Harry Fanok, Nelson Mathews)		
55	Bill Virdon	3.00	1.50
56	Dennis Bennett	2.50	1.25
57	Billy Moran	2.50	1.25
58	Bob Will	2.50	1.25
59	Craig Anderson	2.50	1.25
60	Elston Howard	7.00	3.50

61	Ernie Bowman	2.50	1.25
62	Bob Hendley	2.50	1.25
63	Reds Team	4.00	2.00
64	Dick McAuliffe	2.50	1.25
65	Jackie Brandt	2.50	1.25
66	Mike Joyce	2.50	1.25
67	Ed Charles	2.50	1.25
68	Friendly Foes (Gil	16.00	8.00
	Hodges, Duke Snider)		
69	Bud Zipfel	2.50	1.25
70	Jim O'Toole	2.50	1.25
71	Bobby Wine (R)	2.50	1.25
72	Johnny Romano	2.50	1.25
73	Bobby Bragan	3.50	1.75
74	Denny Lemaster (R)	2.50	1.25
75	Bob Allison	2.50	1.25
76	Earl Wilson	2.50	1.25
77	Al Spangler	2.50	1.25
78	Marv Throneberry	3.00	1.50
79	Checklist 1-88	8.00	3.00
80	Jim Gilliam	4.00	2.00
81	Jimmie Schaffer	2.50	1.25
82	Ed Rakow	2.50	1.25
83	Charley James	2.50	1.25
84	Ron Kline	2.50	1.25
85	Tom Haller	2.50	1.25
86	Charley Maxwell	2.50	1.25
87	Bob Veale	2.50	1.25
88	Ron Hansen	2.50	1.25
89	Dick Stigman	2.50	1.25
90	Gordy Coleman	2.50	1.25
91	Dallas Green	3.00	1.50
92	Hector Lopez	2.50	1.25
93	Galen Cisco	2.50	1.25
94	Bob Schmidt	2.50	1.25
95	Larry Jackson	2.50	1.25
96	Lou Clinton	2.50	1.25
97	Bob Duliba	2.50	1.25
98	George Thomas	2.50	1.25
99	Jim Umbricht	2.50	1.25
100	Joe Cunningham	2.50	1.25
101	Joe Gibbon	2.50	1.25
102	Checklist 89-176	8.00	3.00
103	Chuck Essegian	2.50	1.25
104	Lew Krausse	2.50	1.25
105	Ron Fairly	2.50	1.25
106	Bob Bolin	2.50	1.25
107	Jim Hickman	2.50	1.25
108	Hoyt Wilhelm	12.00	6.00
109	Lee Maye	2.50	1.25
110	Rich Rollins	2.50	1.25
111	Al Jackson	2.50	1.25
112	Dick Brown	2.50	1.25
113	Don Landrum	3.00	1.50
	(Wrong Photo)		
114	Dan Osinski	2.50	1.25
115	Carl Yastrzemski	70.00	35.00
116	Jim Brosnan	2.50	1.25
117	Jack Davis	2.50	1.25
118	Sherm Lollar	2.50	1.25
119	Bob Lillis	2.50	1.25
120	Roger Maris	70.00	35.00
121	Jim Hannan	2.50	1.25
122	Julio Gotay	2.50	1.25
123	Frank Howard	4.00	2.00
124	Dick Howser	3.00	1.50
125	Robin Roberts	12.00	6.00
126	Bob Uecker	20.00	10.00
127	Bill Tuttle	2.50	1.25
128	Matty Alou	3.00	1.50
129	Gary Bell	2.50	1.25
130	Dick Groat	3.00	1.50
131	Senators Team	4.00	2.00
132	Jack Hamilton	2.50	1.25
133	Gene Freese	2.50	1.25
134	Bob Scheffing	2.50	1.25
135	Richie Ashburn	10.00	5.00
136	Ike Delock	2.50	1.25
137	Mack Jones	2.50	1.25
138	Pride of N.L. (Willie	48.00	24.00
	Mays, Stan Musial)		
139	Earl Averill	2.50	1.25
140	Frank Lary	3.00	1.50
141	Manny Mota (R)	7.00	3.50
142	World Series Game 1	7.50	3.75
143	World Series Game 2	5.00	2.50
144	World Series Game 3	12.00	6.00
145	World Series Game 4	5.00	2.50
146	World Series Game 5	5.00	2.50
147	World Series Game 6	5.00	2.50
148	World Series Game 7	5.00	2.50
149	Marv Breeding	2.50	1.25
150	Johnny Podres	3.00	1.50
151	Pirates Team	4.00	2.00
152	Ron Nischwitz	2.50	1.25
153	Hal Smith	2.50	1.25
154	Walt Alston	3.50	1.75
155	Bill Stafford	2.50	1.25
156	Roy McMillan	2.50	1.25
157	Diego Segui (R)	3.50	1.75
158	1963 Rookie Stars	5.00	2.50
	Rogelio Alvarez		
	Tommy Harper		
	Dave Roberts		
	Bob Saverine		
159	Jim Pagliaroni	2.50	1.25
160	Juan Pizarro	2.50	1.25
161	Frank Torre	2.50	1.25
162	Twins Team	4.00	2.00
163	Don Larsen	4.00	2.00
164	Bubba Morton	2.50	1.25
165	Jim Kaat	5.00	2.50
166	Johnny Keane	2.50	1.25
167	Jim Fregosi	5.00	2.50

168	Russ Nixon	2.50	1.25
169	1963 Rookie Stars	32.00	16.00
	Dick Egan		
	Julio Navarro		
	Gaylord Perry		
	Tommy Sisk		
170	Joe Adcock	3.00	1.50
171	Steve Hamilton	2.50	1.25
172	Gene Oliver	2.50	1.25
173	Bomber's Best	90.00	45.00
	Mickey Mantle		
	Bobby Richardson		
	Tom Tresh)		
174	Larry Burright	2.50	1.25
175	Bob Buhl	2.50	1.25
176	Jim King	2.50	1.25
177	Bubba Phillips	2.50	1.25
178	Johnny Edwards	2.50	1.25
179	Ron Piche	2.50	1.25
180	Bill Skowron	4.00	2.00
181	Sammy Esposito	2.50	1.25
182	Albie Pearson	2.50	1.25
183	Joe Pepitone	3.50	1.75
184	Vern Law	3.00	1.50
185	Chuck Hiller	2.50	1.25
186	Jerry Zimmerman	2.50	1.25
187	Willie Kirkland	2.50	1.25
188	Eddie Bressoud	2.50	1.25
189	Dave Giusti	2.50	1.25
190	Minnie Minoso	5.00	2.50
191	Checklist 177-264	8.00	3.00
192	Clay Dalrymple	2.50	1.25
193	Andre Rodgers	2.50	1.25
194	Joe Nuxhall	2.50	1.25
195	Manny Jimenez	2.50	1.25
196	Doug Camilli	2.50	1.25
197	Roger Craig	3.50	1.75
198	Lenny Green	2.50	1.25
199	Joe Amalfitano	2.50	1.25
200	Mickey Mantle	575.00	290.00
201	Cecil Butler	2.50	1.25
202	Red Sox Team	5.00	2.00
203	Chico Cardenas	2.50	1.25
204	Don Nottebart	2.50	1.25
205	Luis Aparicio	16.00	8.00
206	Ray Washburn	2.50	1.25
207	Ken Hunt	2.50	1.25
208	1963 Rookie Stars	2.50	1.25
	Ron Herbel		
	John Miller		
	Ron Taylor		
	Wally Wolf		
209	Hobie Landrith	2.50	1.25
210	Sandy Koufax	175.00	90.00
211	Fred Whitfield	2.50	1.25
212	Glen Hobbie	2.50	1.25
213	Billy Hitchcock	2.50	1.25
214	Orlando Pena	2.50	1.25
215	Bob Skinner	2.50	1.25
216	Gene Conley	2.50	1.25
217	Joe Christopher	2.50	1.25
218	Tiger Twirlers (Jim	4.00	2.00
	Bunning, Frank Lary		
	Don Mossi)		
219	Chuck Cottier	2.50	1.25
220	Camilo Pascual	2.50	1.25
221	Cookie Rojas (R)	4.00	2.00
222	Cubs Team	5.00	2.50
223	Eddie Fisher	2.50	1.25
224	Mike Roarke	2.50	1.25
225	Joe Jay	2.50	1.25
226	Julian Javier	2.50	1.25
227	Jim Grant	3.00	1.50
228	1963 Rookie Stars	55.00	28.00
	Max Alvis		
	Bob Bailey		
	Ed Kranepool		
	Tony Oliva		
229	Willie Davis	3.00	1.50
230	Pete Runnels	3.00	1.50
231	Eli Grba (Wrong Photo)	2.50	1.25
232	Frank Malzone	3.00	1.50
233	Casey Stengel	15.00	7.50
234	Dave Nicholson	2.50	1.25
235	Billy O'Dell	2.50	1.25
236	Bill Bryan	2.50	1.25
237	Jim Coates	2.50	1.25
238	Lou Johnson	2.50	1.25
239	Harvey Haddix	3.00	1.50
240	Rocky Colavito	15.00	7.50
241	Billy Smith	2.50	1.25
242	Power Plus (Hank	50.00	25.00
	Aaron, Ernie Banks)		
243	Don Leppert	2.50	1.25
244	John Tsitouris	2.50	1.25
245	Gil Hodges	20.00	10.00
246	Lee Stange	2.50	1.25
247	Yankees Team	28.00	14.00
248	Tito Francona	2.50	1.25
249	Leo Burke	2.50	1.25
250	Stan Musial	110.00	55.00
251	Jack Lamabe	2.50	1.25
252	Ron Santo	8.50	4.25
253	1963 Rookie Stars	2.50	1.25
	Len Gabrielson		
	Pete Jerrigan		
	Deacon Jones		
	John Wojcik		
254	Mike Hershberger	2.50	1.25
255	Bob Shaw	2.50	1.25
256	Jerry Lumpe	2.50	1.25
257	Hank Aguirre	2.50	1.25
258	Alvin Dark	2.50	1.25
259	Johnny Logan	2.50	1.25

260	Jim Gentile	3.50	1.75
261	Bob Miller	2.50	1.25
262	Ellis Burton	2.50	1.25
263	Dave Stenhouse	2.50	1.25
264	Phil Linz	2.50	1.25
265	Vada Pinson	5.00	2.50
266	Bob Allen	2.50	1.25
267	Carl Sawatski	2.50	1.25
268	Don Demeter	2.50	1.25
269	Don Mincher	2.50	1.25
270	Felipe Alou	5.00	2.50
271	Dean Stone	2.50	1.25
272	Danny Murphy	2.50	1.25
273	Sammy Taylor	2.50	1.25
274	Checklist 265-352	8.00	3.00
275	Ed Mathews	24.00	12.00
276	Barry Shetrone	2.50	1.25
277	Dick Farrell	2.50	1.25
278	Chico Fernandez	2.50	1.25
279	Wally Moon	3.00	1.50
280	Bob Rodgers	5.00	2.50
281	Tom Sturdivant	2.50	1.25
282	Bob Del Greco	2.50	1.25
283	Roy Sievers	3.00	1.50
284	Dave Sisler	3.50	1.75
285	Dick Stuart	3.50	1.75
286	Stu Miller	3.50	1.75
287	Dick Bertell	3.50	1.75
288	White Sox Team	8.00	4.00
289	Hal Brown	3.50	1.75
290	Bill White	6.50	3.25
291	Don Rudolph	3.50	1.75
292	Pumpsie Green	3.50	1.75
293	Bill Pleis	3.50	1.75
294	Bill Rigney	3.50	1.75
295	Ed Roebuck	3.50	1.75
296	Doc Edwards	3.50	1.75
297	Jim Golden	3.50	1.75
298	Don Dillard	3.50	1.75
299	1963 Rookie Stars	3.50	1.75
	Tom Butters		
	Bob Dustal		
	Dave Morehead		
	Dan Schneider		
300	Willie Mays	190.00	95.00
301	Bill Fischer	3.50	1.75
302	Whitey Herzog	6.00	3.00
303	Earl Francis	3.50	1.75
304	Harry Bright	3.50	1.75
305	Don Hoak	3.50	1.75
306	Star Receivers (Earl	5.00	2.50
	Battey, Elston Howard)		
307	Chet Nichols	3.50	1.75
308	Camilo Carreon	3.50	1.75
309	Jim Brewer	3.50	1.75
310	Tommy Davis	6.00	3.00
311	Joe McClain	3.50	1.75
312	Colt .45s Team	15.00	7.50
313	Ernie Broglio	3.50	1.75
314	John Goryl	3.50	1.75
315	Ralph Terry	4.00	2.00
316	Norm Sherry	3.50	1.75
317	Sam McDowell	7.00	3.50
318	Gene Mauch	4.00	2.00
319	Joe Gaines	3.50	1.75
320	Warren Spahn	45.00	22.50
321	Gino Cimoli	3.50	1.75
322	Bob Turley	3.50	1.75
323	Bill Mazeroski	7.50	3.75
324	1963 Rookie Stars	6.00	3.00
	Vic Davalillo		
	Phil Roof		
	Pete Ward		
	George Williams		
325	Jack Sanford	3.50	1.75
326	Hank Foiles	3.50	1.75
327	Paul Foytack	3.50	1.75
328	Dick Williams	3.50	1.75
329	Lindy McDaniel	3.50	1.75
330	Chuck Hinton	3.50	1.75
331	Series Foes (Bill	4.00	2.00
	Pierce, Bill Stafford)		
332	Joel Horlen	3.50	1.75
333	Carl Warwick	3.50	1.75
334	Wynn Hawkins	3.50	1.75
335	Leon Wagner	3.50	1.75
336	Ed Bauta	3.50	1.75
337	Dodgers Team	15.00	7.50
338	Russ Kemmerer	3.50	1.75
339	Ted Bowsfield	3.50	1.75
340	Yogi Berra	80.00	40.00
341	Jack Baldschun	3.50	1.75
342	Gene Woodling	4.00	2.00
343	Johnny Pesky	3.50	1.75
344	Don Schwall	3.50	1.75
345	Brooks Robinson	70.00	35.00
346	Billy Hoeft	3.50	1.75
347	Joe Torre	8.50	4.25
348	Vic Wertz	3.50	1.75
349	Zoilo Versalles	4.00	2.00
350	Bob Purkey	3.50	1.75
351	Al Luplow	3.50	1.75
352	Ken Johnson	3.50	1.75
353	Billy Williams	28.00	14.00
354	Dom Zanni	3.50	1.75
355	Dean Chance	4.50	2.25
356	John Schaive	3.50	1.75
357	George Altman	3.50	1.75
358	Milt Pappas	3.50	1.75
359	Haywood Sullivan	3.50	1.75
360	Don Drysdale	55.00	27.50
361	Clete Boyer	6.50	3.25
362	Checklist 353-429	8.00	3.00
363	Dick Radatz	3.50	1.75

364	Howie Goss	3.50	1.75
365	Jim Bunning	12.00	6.00
366	Tony Taylor	3.50	1.75
367	Tony Cloninger	3.50	1.75
368	Ed Bailey	3.50	1.75
369	Jim Lemon	3.50	1.75
370	Dick Donovan	3.50	1.75
371	Rod Kanehl	3.50	1.75
372	Don Lee	3.50	1.75
373	Jim Campbell	3.50	1.75
374	Claude Osteen	4.00	2.00
375	Ken Boyer	8.00	4.00
376	Johnnie Wyatt	3.50	1.75
377	Orioles Team	8.00	4.00
378	Bill Henry	3.50	1.75
379	Bob Anderson	3.50	1.75
380	Ernie Banks	75.00	37.50
381	Frank Baumann	3.50	1.75
382	Ralph Houk	5.00	2.50
383	Pete Richert	3.50	1.75
384	Bob Tillman	3.50	1.75
385	Art Mahaffey	3.50	1.75
386	1963 Rookie Stars	4.00	2.00
	John Bateman		
	Larry Bearnarth		
	Ed Kirkpatrick		
	Garry Roggenburk		
387	Al McBean	3.50	1.75
388	Jim Davenport	3.50	1.75
389	Frank Sullivan	3.50	1.75
390	Hank Aaron	170.00	85.00
391	Bill Dailey	3.50	1.75
392	Tribe Thumpers	3.50	1.75
	Tito Francona, Johnny		
	Romano)		
393	Ken MacKenzie	3.50	1.75
394	Tim McCarver	14.00	7.00
395	Don McMahon	4.00	2.00
396	Joe Koppe	3.50	1.75
397	Athletics Team	8.00	4.00
398	Boog Powell	30.00	15.00
399	Dick Ellsworth	3.50	1.75
400	Frank Robinson	55.00	28.00
401	Jim Bouton	10.00	5.00
402	Mickey Vernon	3.50	1.75
403	Ron Perranoski	4.00	2.00
404	Bob Oldis	3.50	1.75
405	Floyd Robinson	3.50	1.75
406	Howie Koplitz	3.50	1.75
407	1963 Rookie Stars	3.50	1.75
	Larry Elliot		
	Frank Kostro		
	Chico Ruiz		
	Dick Simpson		
408	Billy Gardner	3.50	1.75
409	Roy Face	5.00	2.50
410	Earl Battey	4.00	2.00

411	Jim Constable	3.50	1.75
412	Dodgers' Big Three	45.00	22.50
	Don Drysdale, Sandy		
	Koufax, Johnny Podres		
413	Jerry Walker	3.50	1.75
414	Ty Cline	3.50	1.75
415	Bob Gibson	55.00	27.50
416	Alex Grammas	3.50	1.75
417	Giants team	8.00	4.00
418	Johnny Orsino	3.50	1.75
419	Tracy Stallard	3.50	1.75
420	Bobby Richardson	12.00	6.00
421	Tom Morgan	3.50	1.75
422	Fred Hutchinson	4.00	2.00
423	Ed Hobaugh	3.50	1.75
424	Charley Smith	3.50	1.75
425	Smoky Burgess	4.00	2.00
426	Barry Latman	3.50	1.75
427	Bernie Allen	3.50	1.75
428	Carl Boles	3.50	1.75
429	Lew Burdette	6.00	3.00
430	Norm Siebern	4.00	2.00
431	Checklist 430-506	10.00	4.00
432	Roman Mejias	3.50	1.75
433	Denis Menke	3.50	1.75
434	Johnny Callison	4.00	2.00
435	Woody Held	3.50	1.75
436	Tim Harkness	3.50	1.75
437	Bill Bruton	3.50	1.75
438	Wes Stock	3.50	1.75
439	Don Zimmer	5.00	2.50
440	Juan Marichal	32.00	16.00
441	Lee Thomas	3.50	1.75
442	J.C. Hartman	3.50	1.75
443	Jim Piersall	6.00	3.00
444	Jim Maloney	6.50	3.25
445	Norm Cash	7.50	3.75
446	Whitey Ford	42.00	21.00
447	Felix Mantilla	12.00	6.00
448	Jack Kralick	12.00	6.00
449	Jose Tartabull	12.00	6.00
450	Bob Friend	12.00	6.00
451	Indians Team	35.00	17.50
452	Barney Schultz	12.00	6.00
453	Jake Wood	12.00	6.00
454	Art Fowler	12.00	6.00
455	Ruben Amaro	12.00	6.00
456	Jim Coker	12.00	6.00
457	Tex Clevenger	12.00	6.00
458	Al Lopez	18.00	9.00
459	Dick LeMay	12.00	6.00
460	Del Crandall	14.00	7.00
461	Norm Bass	12.00	6.00
462	Wally Post	12.00	6.00
463	Joe Schaffernoth	12.00	6.00
464	Ken Aspromonte	12.00	6.00
465	Chuck Estrada	12.00	6.00

466	1963 Rookie Stars	60.00	30.00
	Bill Freehan		
	Tony Martinez		
	Nate Oliver		
	Jerry Robinson		
467	Phil Ortega	12.00	6.00
468	Carroll Hardy	15.00	7.50
469	Jay Hook	12.00	6.00
470	Tom Tresh	50.00	25.00
471	Ken Retzer	12.00	6.00
472	Lou Brock	140.00	70.00
473	Mets Team	125.00	60.00
474	Jack Fisher	12.00	6.00
475	Gus Triandos	12.00	6.00
476	Frank Funk	12.00	6.00
477	Donn Clendenon	12.00	6.00
478	Paul Brown	12.00	6.00
479	Ed Brinkman	12.00	6.00
480	Bill Monbouquette	12.00	6.00
481	Bob Taylor	12.00	6.00
482	Felix Torres	12.00	6.00
483	Jim Owens	12.00	6.00
484	Dale Long	12.00	6.00
385	Jim Landis	12.00	6.00
486	Ray Sadecki	12.00	6.00
487	John Roseboro	14.00	7.00
488	Jerry Adair	12.00	6.00
489	Paul Toth	12.00	6.00
490	Willie McCovey	135.00	65.00
491	Harry Craft	12.00	6.00
492	Dave Wickersham	12.00	6.00
493	Walt Bond	12.00	6.00
494	Phil Regan	12.00	6.00
495	Frank Thomas	15.00	7.50
496	1963 Rookie Stars	15.00	7.50
	Carl Bouldin		
	Steve Dalkowski		
	Fred Newman		
	Jack Smith		
497	Bennie Daniels	12.00	6.00
498	Eddie Kasko	12.00	6.00
499	J.C. Martin	12.00	6.00
500	Harmon Killebrew	150.00	75.00
501	Joe Azcue	12.00	6.00
502	Daryl Spencer	12.00	6.00
503	Braves Team	35.00	17.50
504	Bob Johnson	12.00	6.00
505	Curt Flood	18.00	12.00
506	Gene Green	12.00	6.00
507	Roland Sheldon	12.00	6.00
508	Ted Savage	12.00	6.00
509	Checklist 507-576	18.00	7.00
510	Ken McBride	12.00	6.00
511	Charlie Neal	12.00	6.00
512	Cal McLish	12.00	6.00
513	Gary Geiger	12.00	6.00
514	Larry Osborne	12.00	6.00
515	Don Elston	12.00	6.00
516	Purnell Goldy	12.00	6.00
517	Hal Woodeshick	12.00	6.00
518	Don Blasingame	12.00	6.00
519	Claude Raymond (R)	14.00	7.00
520	Orlando Cepeda	24.00	12.00
521	Dan Pfister	12.00	6.00
522	1963 Rookie Stars	12.00	6.00
	Mel Nelson		
	Gary Peters		
	Art Quirk		
	Jim Roland		
523	Bill Kunkel	9.00	4.50
524	Cardinals Team	24.00	12.00
525	Nellie Fox	22.00	11.00
526	Dick Hall	9.00	4.50
527	Ed Sadowski	9.00	4.50
528	Carl Willey	9.00	4.50
529	Wes Covington	10.00	5.00
530	Don Mossi	9.00	4.50
531	Sam Mele	9.00	4.50
532	Steve Boros	9.00	4.50
533	Bobby Shantz	12.00	6.00
534	Ken Walters	9.00	4.50
535	Jim Perry	10.00	5.00
536	Norm Larker	9.00	4.50
537	1963 Rookies	1,100.00	550.00
	Pedro Gonzalez		
	Ken McMullen		
	Pete Rose		
	Al Weis		
538	George Brunet	9.00	4.50
539	Wayne Causey	9.00	4.50
540	Bob Clemente	325.00	160.00
541	Ron Moeller	9.00	4.50
542	Lou Klimchock	9.00	4.50
543	Russ Snyder	9.00	4.50
544	1963 Rookie Stars	40.00	20.00
	Duke Carmel		
	Bill Haas		
	Dick Phillips		
	Rusty Staub		
545	Jose Pagan	9.00	4.50
546	Hal Reniff	9.00	4.50
547	Gus Bell	9.00	4.50
548	Tom Satriano	9.00	4.50
549	1963 Rookie Stars	9.00	4.50
	Marcelino Lopez		
	Pete Lovrich		
	Elmo Plaskett		
	Paul Ratliff	9.00	4.50
550	Duke Snider	80.00	40.00
551	Billy Klaus	9.00	4.50
552	Tigers Team	30.00	15.00
553	1963 Rookie Stars	225.00	115.00
	Brock Davis		
	Jim Gosger		

	John Herrnstein		
	Willie Stargell		
554	Hank Fischer	9.00	4.50
555	John Blanchard	9.00	4.50
556	Al Worthington	9.00	4.50
557	Cuno Barragan	9.00	4.50
558	1963 Rookie Stars	12.50	6.25
	Bill Faul		
	Ron Hunt		
	Bob Lipski		
	Al Moran		
559	Danny Murtaugh	9.00	4.50
560	Ray Herbert	9.00	4.50
561	Mike de la Hoz	9.00	4.50
562	1963 Rookie Stars	20.00	10.00
	Randy Cardinal		
	Dave McNally		
	Don Rowe		
	Ken Rowe		
563	Mike McCormick	9.00	4.50
564	George Banks	9.00	4.50
565	Larry Sherry	10.00	5.00
566	Cliff Cook	9.00	4.50
567	Jim Duffalo	9.00	4.50
568	Bob Sadowski	9.00	4.50
569	Luis Arroyo	10.00	5.00
570	Frank Bolling	9.00	4.50
571	Johnny Klippstein	9.00	4.50
572	Jack Spring	9.00	4.50
573	Coot Veal	9.00	4.50
574	Hal Kolstad	9.00	4.50
575	Don Cardwell	9.00	4.50
576	Johnny Temple	15.00	6.00

1964 Topps

This 587-card set features large color photos on the card fronts with a panel above the picture containing team names in large block letters. Cards measure 2-1/2" by 3-1/2". The orange colored card backs

contain a baseball trivia question in which the answer is revealed by scratching off a small white panel. Subsets include League Leaders, World Series Highlights and Rookie Prospects.

	NR/MT	EX
Complete Set (587)	3,450.00	1,725.00
Commons (1-370)	2.50	1.25
Commons (371-522)	4.00	2.00
Commons (523-587)	9.00	4.50

1	N.L. E.R.A. Leaders	20.00	10.00
2	A.L. E.R.A. Leaders	3.00	1.50
3	N.L. Pitching Leaders	14.00	7.00
4	A.L. Pitching Leaders	6.00	3.00
5	N.L. Strikeout Leaders	12.00	6.00
6	A.L. Strikeout Leaders	3.00	1.50
7	N.L. Batting Leaders	12.00	6.00
8	A.L. Batting Leaders	10.00	5.00
9	N.L. H.R. Leaders	25.00	12.50
10	A.L. H.R. Leaders	6.00	3.00
11	N.L. R.B.I. Leaders	10.00	5.00
12	A.L. R.B.I. Leaders	6.00	3.00
13	Hoyt Wilhelm	10.00	5.00
14	Dodgers Rookies	2.50	1.25
	Dick Nen (R)		
	Nick Willhite (R)		
15	Zoilo Versalles	2.50	1.25
16	John Boozer	2.50	1.25
17	Willie Kirkland	2.50	1.25
18	Billy O'Dell	2.50	1.25
19	Don Wert	2.50	1.25
20	Bob Friend	2.50	1.25
21	Yogi Berra	42.00	21.00
22	Jerry Adair	2.50	1.25
23	Chris Zachary	2.50	1.25
24	Carl Sawatski	2.50	1.25
25	Bill Monbouquette	2.50	1.25
26	Gino Cimoli	2.50	1.25
27	Mets Team	7.50	3.75
28	Claude Osteen	2.50	1.25
29	Lou Brock	40.00	20.00
30	Ron Perranoski	2.50	1.25
31	Dave Nicholson	2.50	1.25
32	Dean Chance	3.00	1.50
33	Reds Rookies	2.50	1.75
	Sammy Ellis (R)		
	Mel Queen (R)		
34	Jim Perry	3.00	1.50
35	Ed Mathews	18.00	9.00
36	Hal Reniff	2.50	1.25
37	Smoky Burgess	2.50	1.25
38	Jim Wynn (R)	8.00	4.00

39	Hank Aguirre	2.50	1.25
40	Dick Groat	2.50	1.25
41	Friendly Foes	7.00	3.50
	Willle McCovey		
	Leon Wagner		
42	Moe Drabowsky	2.50	1.25
43	Roy Sievers	3.00	1.50
44	Duke Carmel	2.50	1.25
45	Milt Pappas	2.50	1.25
46	Ed Brinkman	2.50	1.25
47	Giants Rookies	4.00	2.00
	Jesus Alou (R)		
	Ron Herbel (R)		
48	Bob Perry	2.50	1.25
49	Bill Henry	2.50	1.25
50	Mickey Mantle	325.00	165.00
51	Pete Richert	2.50	1.25
52	Chuck Hinton	2.50	1.25
53	Denis Menke	2.50	1.25
54	Sam Mele	2.50	1.25
55	Ernie Banks	32.00	16.00
56	Hal Brown	2.50	1.25
57	Tim Harkness	2.50	1.25
58	Don Demeter	2.50	1.25
59	Ernie Broglio	2.50	1.25
60	Frank Malzone	2.50	1.25
61	Angel Backstops	2.50	1.25
	Bob Rodgers		
	Ed Sadowski		
62	Ted Savage	2.50	1.25
63	Johnny Orsino	2.50	1.25
64	Ted Abernathy	2.50	1.25
65	Felipe Alou	4.00	2.00
66	Eddie Fisher	2.50	1.25
67	Tigers Team	4.50	2.25
68	Willie Davis	3.00	1.50
69	Clete Boyer	3.00	1.50
70	Joe Torre	4.50	2.25
71	Jack Spring	2.50	1.25
72	Chico Cardenas	2.50	1.25
73	Jimmie Hall	2.50	1.25
74	Pirates Rookies	2.50	1.25
	Tom Butlers (R)		
	Bob Priddy (R)		
75	Wayne Causey	2.50	1.25
76	Checklist 1-88	8.00	3.00
77	Jerry Walker	2.50	1.25
78	Merritt Ranew	2.50	1.25
79	Bob Heffner	2.50	1.25
80	Vada Pinson	4.00	2.00
81	All-Star Vets	8.50	4.25
	Nellie Fox		
	Harmon Killebrew		
82	Jim Davenport	2.50	1.25
83	Gus Triandos	2.50	1.25
84	Carl Willey	2.50	1.25
85	Pete Ward	2.50	1.25

86	Al Downing	3.00	1.50
87	Cardinals Team	4.50	2.25
88	John Roseboro	3.00	1.50
89	Boog Powell	7.00	3.50
90	Earl Battey	2.50	1.25
91	Bob Bailey	2.50	1.25
92	Steve Ridzik	2.50	1.25
93	Gary Geiger	2.50	1.25
94	Braves Rookies	2.50	1.25
	Jim Britton (R)		
	Larry Maxie (R)		
95	George Altman	2.50	1.25
96	Bob Buhl	2.50	1.25
97	Jim Fregosi	3.50	1.75
98	Bill Bruton	2.50	1.25
99	Al Stanek	2.50	1.25
100	Elston Howard	6.50	3.25
101	Walt Alston	3.50	1.75
102	Checklist 89-176	8.00	3.00
103	Curt Flood	3.00	1.50
104	Art Mahaffey	2.50	1.25
105	Woody Held	2.50	1.25
106	Joe Nuxhall	2.50	1.25
107	White Sox Rookies	2.50	1.25
	Bruce Howard (R)		
	Frank Kreutzer (R)		
108	John Wyatt	2.50	1.25
109	Rusty Staub	9.00	4.50
110	Albie Pearson	2.50	1.25
111	Don Elston	2.50	1.25
112	Bob Tillman	2.50	1.25
113	Grover Powell	2.50	1.25
114	Don Lock	2.50	1.25
115	Frank Bolling	2.50	1.25
116	Twins Rookies	18.00	9.00
	Tony Oliva		
	Jay Ward (R)		
117	Earl Francis	2.50	1.25
118	John Blanchard	2.50	1.25
119	Gary Kolb	2.50	1.25
120	Don Drysdale	25.00	12.50
121	Pete Runnels	3.00	1.50
122	Don McMahon	2.50	1.25
123	Jose Pagan	2.50	1.25
124	Orlando Pena	2.50	1.25
125	Pete Rose	180.00	90.00
126	Russ Snyder	2.50	1.25
127	Angels Rookies	2.50	1.25
	Aubrey Gatewood (R)		
	Dick Simpson (R)		
128	Mickey Lolich (R)	22.00	11.00
129	Amado Samuel	2.50	1.25
130	Gary Peters	2.50	1.25
131	Steve Boros	2.50	1.25
132	Braves Team	4.50	2.25
133	Jim Grant	2.50	1.25
134	Don Zimmer	3.00	1.50

135	Johnny Callison	3.00	1.50
136	World Series Game 1	18.00	9.00
137	World Series Game 2	4.00	2.00
138	World Series Game 3	4.00	2.00
139	World Series Game 4	4.00	2.00
140	WS Celebration	4.00	2.00
141	Danny Murtaugh	2.50	1.25
142	John Bateman	2.50	1.25
143	Bubba Phillips	2.50	1.25
144	Al Worthington	2.50	1.25
145	Norm Siebern	2.50	1.25
146	Indians Rookies	60.00	30.00
	Bob Chance (R)		
	Tommy John (R)		
147	Ray Sadecki	2.50	1.25
148	J.C. Martin	2.50	1.25
149	Paul Foytack	2.50	1.25
150	Willie Mays	125.00	65.00
151	Athletics Team	4.50	2.25
152	Denver Lemaster	2.50	1.25
153	Dick Williams	2.50	1.25
154	Dick Tracewski (R)	3.00	1.50
155	Duke Snider	30.00	15.00
156	Billy Dailey	2.50	1.25
157	Gene Mauch	3.00	1.50
158	Ken Johnson	2.50	1.25
159	Charlie Dees	2.50	1.25
160	Ken Boyer	6.00	3.00
161	Dave McNally	4.00	2.00
162	Hitting Area	3.00	1.50
	Vada Pinson		
	Dick Sisler		
163	Donn Clendenon	2.50	1.25
164	Bud Daley	2.50	1.25
165	Jerry Lumpe	2.50	1.25
166	Marty Keough	2.50	1.25
167	Senators Rookies	30.00	15.00
	Mike Brumley (R)		
	Lou Piniella (R)		
168	Al Weis	2.50	1.25
169	Del Crandall	2.50	1.25
170	Dick Radatz	2.50	1.25
171	Ty Cline	2.50	1.25
172	Indians Team	4.50	2.25
173	Ryne Duren	3.00	1.50
174	Doc Edwards	2.50	1.25
175	Billy Williams	16.00	8.00
176	Tracy Stallard	2.50	1.25
177	Harmon Killebrew	24.00	12.00
178	Hank Bauer	3.00	1.50
179	Carl Warwick	2.50	1.25
180	Tommy Davis	3.50	1.75
181	Dave Wickersham	2.50	1.25
182	Sox Sockers	15.00	7.50
	Chuck Schilling		
	Carl Yastrzemski		
183	Ron Taylor	2.50	1.25
184	Al Luplow	2.50	1.25
185	Jim O'Toole	2.50	1.25
186	Roman Mejias	2.50	1.25
187	Ed Roebuck	2.50	1.25
188	Checklist 177-264	8.00	3.00
189	Bob Hendley	2.50	1.25
190	Bobby Richardson	7.50	3.75
191	Clay Dalrymple	2.50	1.25
192	Cubs Rookies	2.50	1.25
	John Boccabella (R)		
	Billy Cowan (R)		
193	Jerry Lynch	2.50	1.25
194	John Goryl	2.50	1.25
195	Floyd Robinson	2.50	1.25
196	Jim Gentile	3.50	1.75
197	Frank Lary	3.00	1.50
198	Len Gabrielson	2.50	1.25
199	Joe Azcue	2.50	1.25
200	Sandy Koufax	125.00	65.00
201	Orioles Rookies	2.50	1.25
	Sam Bowens (R)		
	Wally Bunker (R)		
202	Galen Cisco	2.50	1.25
203	John Kennedy	2.50	1.25
204	Matty Alou	4.00	2.00
205	Nellie Fox	8.00	4.00
206	Steve Hamilton	2.50	1.25
207	Fred Hutchinson	2.50	1.25
208	Wes Covington	2.50	1.25
209	Bob Allen	2.50	1.25
210	Carl Yastrzemski	50.00	25.00
211	Jim Coker	2.50	1.25
212	Pete Lovrich	2.50	1.25
213	Angels Team	4.50	2.25
214	Ken McMullen	2.50	1.25
215	Ray Herbert	2.50	1.25
216	Mike de la Hoz	2.50	1.25
217	Jim King	2.50	1.25
218	Hank Fischer	2.50	1.25
219	Young Aces (Jim	4.00	2.00
	Bouton/Al Downing)		
220	Dick Ellsworth	2.50	1.25
221	Bob Saverine	2.50	1.25
222	Bill Pierce	2.50	1.25
223	George Banks	2.50	1.25
224	Tommie Sisk	2.50	1.25
225	Roger Maris	70.00	35.00
226	Colts Rookies	4.00	2.00
	Jerry Grote (R)		
	Larry Yellen (R)		
227	Barry Latman	2.50	1.25
228	Felix Mantilla	2.50	1.25
229	Charley Lau	2.50	1.25
230	Brooks Robinson	38.00	20.00
231	Dick Calmus	2.50	1.25
232	Al Lopez	4.00	2.00
233	Hal Smith	2.50	1.25

No.	Player	Price 1	Price 2
234	Gary Bell	2.50	1.25
235	Ron Hunt	2.50	1.25
236	Bill Faul	2.50	1.25
237	Cubs Team	4.50	2.25
238	Roy McMillan	2.50	1.25
239	Herm Starrette	2.50	1.25
240	Bill White	4.00	2.00
241	Jim Owens	2.50	1.25
242	Harvey Kuenn	3.50	1.75
243	Phillies Rookies	35.00	17.50
	Richie Allen (R)		
	John Hernstein (R)		
244	Tony LaRussa (R)	28.00	14.00
245	Dick Stigman	2.50	1.25
246	Manny Mota	4.00	2.00
247	Dave DeBusschere	4.00	2.00
248	Johnny Pesky	2.50	1.25
249	Doug Camilli	2.50	1.25
250	Al Kaline	38.00	19.00
251	Choo Choo Coleman	2.50	1.25
252	Ken Aspromonte	2.50	1.25
253	Wally Post	2.50	1.25
254	Don Hoak	2.50	1.25
255	Lee Thomas	2.50	1.25
256	Johnny Weekly	2.50	1.25
257	Giants Team	4.50	2.25
258	Garry Roggenburk	2.50	1.25
259	Harry Bright	2.50	1.25
260	Frank Robinson	32.00	16.00
261	Jim Hannan	2.50	1.25
262	Cardinals Rookie Stars	6.00	3.00
	Harry Fanok (R)		
	Mike Shannon (R)		
263	Chuck Estrada	2.50	1.25
264	Jim Landis	2.50	1.25
265	Jim Bunning	7.50	3.75
266	Gene Freese	2.50	1.25
267	Wilbur Wood (R)	6.00	3.00
268	Bill's Got It	3.00	1.50
	Danny Murtaugh		
	Bill Virdon		
269	Ellis Burton	2.50	1.25
270	Rich Rollins	2.50	1.25
271	Bob Sadowski	2.50	1.25
272	Jake Wood	2.50	1.25
273	Mel Nelson	2.50	1.25
274	Checklist 265-352	8.00	3.00
275	John Tsitouris	2.50	1.25
276	Jose Tartabull	2.50	1.25
277	Ken Retzer	2.50	1.25
278	Bobby Shantz	3.00	1.50
279	Joe Koppe	2.50	1.25
280	Juan Marichal	15.00	7.50
281	Yankees Rookies	2.50	1.25
	Jake Gibbs (R)		
	Tom Metcalf (R)		
282	Bob Bruce	2.50	1.25
283	Tommy McCraw	2.50	1.25
284	Dick Schofield	2.50	1.25
285	Robin Roberts	12.00	6.00
286	Don Landrum	2.50	1.25
287	Red Sox Rookies	40.00	20.00
	Tony Conigliaro (R)		
	Bill Spanswick (R)		
288	Al Moran	2.50	1.25
289	Frank Funk	2.50	1.25
290	Bob Allison	2.50	1.25
291	Phil Ortega	2.50	1.25
292	Mike Roarke	2.50	1.25
293	Phillies Team	4.50	2.25
294	Ken Hunt	2.50	1.25
295	Roger Craig	3.50	1.75
296	Ed Kirkpatrick	2.50	1.25
297	Ken MacKenzie	2.50	1.25
298	Harry Craft	2.50	1.25
299	Bill Stafford	2.50	1.25
300	Hank Aaron	140.00	70.00
301	Larry Brown	2.50	1.25
302	Dan Pfister	2.50	1.25
303	Jim Campbell	2.50	1.25
304	Bob Johnson	2.50	1.25
305	Jack Lamabe	2.50	1.25
306	Giant Gunners	35.00	17.50
	Orlando Cepeda		
	Willie Mays		
307	Joe Gibbon	2.50	1.25
308	Gene Stephens	2.50	1.25
309	Paul Toth	2.50	1.25
310	Jim Gilliam	5.00	2.50
311	Tom Brown	2.50	1.25
312	Tigers Rookies	2.50	1.25
	Fritz Fisher (R)		
	Fred Gladding (R)		
313	Chuck Hiller	2.50	1.25
314	Jerry Buchek	2.50	1.25
315	Bo Belinsky	4.00	2.00
316	Gene Oliver	2.50	1.25
317	Al Smith	2.50	1.25
318	Twins Team	4.50	2.25
319	Paul Brown	2.50	1.25
320	Rocky Colavito	10.00	5.00
321	Bob Lillis	2.50	1.25
322	George Brunet	2.50	1.25
323	John Buzhardt	2.50	1.25
324	Casey Stengel	16.00	8.00
325	Hector Lopez	2.50	1.25
326	Ron Brand	2.50	1.25
327	Don Blasingame	2.50	1.25
328	Bob Shaw	2.50	1.25
329	Russ Nixon	2.50	1.25
330	Tommy Harper	3.00	1.50
331	A.L. Bombers	175.00	90.00
	Norm Cash		
	Al Kaline		

Mickey Mantle		
Roger Maris		
332 Ray Washburn	2.50	1.25
333 Billy Moran	2.50	1.25
334 Lew Krausse	2.50	1.25
335 Don Mossi	2.50	1.25
336 Andre Rodgers	2.50	1.25
337 Dodgers Rookies	7.50	3.75
Al Ferrara (R)		
Jeff Torborg (R)		
338 Jack Kralick	2.50	1.25
339 Walt Bond	2.50	1.25
340 Joe Cunningham	2.50	1.25
341 Jim Roland	2.50	1.25
342 Willie Stargell	40.00	20.00
343 Senators Team	4.50	2.25
344 Phil Linz	2.50	1.25
345 Frank Thomas	2.50	1.25
346 Joe Jay	2.50	1.25
347 Bobby Wine	2.50	1.25
348 Ed Lopat	2.50	1.25
349 Art Fowler	2.50	1.25
350 Willie McCovey	26.00	13.00
351 Dan Schneider	2.50	1.25
352 Eddie Bressoud	2.50	1.25
353 Wally Moon	2.50	1.25
354 Dave Giusti	2.50	1.25
355 Vic Power	2.50	1.25
356 Reds Rookies	2.50	1.25
Bill McColl (R)		
Chico Ruiz (R)		
357 Charley James	2.50	1.25
358 Ron Kline	2.50	1.25
359 Jim Schaffer	2.50	1.25
360 Joe Pepitone	4.50	2.25
361 Jay Hook	2.50	1.25
362 Checklist 353-429	8.00	3.00
363 Dick McAuliffe	2.50	1.25
364 Joe Gaines	2.50	1.25
365 Cal McLish	2.50	1.25
366 Nelson Mathews	2.50	1.25
367 Fred Whitfield	2.50	1.25
368 White Sox Rookies	4.50	2.25
Fritz Ackley (R)		
Don Buford (R)		
369 Jerry Zimmerman	2.50	1.25
370 Hal Woodeshick	2.50	1.25
371 Frank Howard	7.00	3.50
372 Howie Koplitz	4.00	2.00
373 Pirates Team	10.00	5.00
374 Bobby Bolin	4.00	2.00
375 Ron Santo	7.50	3.75
376 Dave Morehead	4.00	2.00
377 Bob Skinner	4.00	2.00
378 Braves Rookies	6.00	3.00
Jack Smith (R)		
Woody Woodward (R)		
379 Tony Gonzalez	5.00	2.50
380 Whitey Ford	30.00	15.00
381 Bob Taylor	4.00	2.00
382 Wes Stock	4.00	2.00
383 Bill Rigney	4.00	2.00
384 Ron Hansen	4.00	2.00
385 Curt Simmons	4.00	2.00
386 Lenny Green	4.00	2.00
387 Terry Fox	4.00	2.00
388 Athletics Rookies	5.00	2.50
John O'Donoghue (R)		
George Williams (R)		
389 Jim Umbricht	4.00	2.00
390 Orlando Cepeda	10.00	5.00
391 Sam McDowell	5.00	2.50
392 Jim Pagliaroni	4.00	2.00
393 Casey Teaches	6.50	3.25
Ed Kranepool		
Casey Stengel		
394 Bob Miller	4.00	2.00
395 Tom Tresh	6.50	3.25
396 Dennis Bennett	4.00	2.00
397 Chuck Cottier	4.00	2.00
398 Mets Rookies	4.00	2.00
Bill Haas		
Dick Smith		
399 Jackie Brandt	4.00	2.00
400 Warren Spahn	40.00	20.00
401 Charlie Maxwell	4.00	2.00
402 Tom Sturdivant	4.00	2.00
403 Reds Team	10.00	5.00
404 Tony Martinez	4.00	2.00
405 Ken McBride	4.00	2.00
406 Al Spangler	4.00	2.00
407 Bill Freehan	8.00	4.00
408 Cubs Rookies	4.00	2.00
Fred Burdette (R)		
Jim Stewart (R)		
409 Bill Fischer	4.00	2.00
410 Dick Stuart	5.00	2.50
411 Lee Walls	4.00	2.00
412 Ray Culp	4.00	2.00
413 Johnny Keane	4.00	2.00
414 Jack Sanford	4.00	2.00
415 Tony Kubek	8.00	4.00
416 Lee Maye	4.00	2.00
417 Don Cardwell	4.00	2.00
418 Orioles Rookies	5.00	2.50
Darold Knowles (R)		
Les Narum (R)		
419 Ken Harrelson (R)	10.00	5.00
420 Jim Maloney	4.00	2.00
421 Camilo Carreon	4.00	2.00
422 Jack Fisher	4.00	2.00
423 Tops in NL	140.00	70.00
Hank Aaron		
Willie Mays		

424 Dick Bertell	4.00	2.00
425 Norm Cash	8.00	4.00
426 Bob Rodgers	4.00	2.00
427 Don Rudolph	4.00	2.00
428 Red Sox Rookies	4.00	2.00
Archie Skeen (R)		
Pete Smith (R)		
429 Tim McCarver	9.00	4.50
430 Juan Pizarro	4.00	2.00
431 George Alusik	4.00	2.00
432 Ruben Amaro	4.00	2.00
433 Yankees Team	22.00	11.00
434 Don Nottebart	4.00	2.00
435 Vic Davalillo	4.00	2.00
436 Charlie Neal	4.00	2.00
437 Ed Bailey	4.00	2.00
438 Checklist 430-506	12.00	5.00
439 Harvey Haddix	4.00	2.00
440 Roberto Clemente	190.00	95.00
441 Bob Duliba	4.00	2.00
442 Pumpsie Green	4.00	2.00
443 Chuck Dressen	4.00	2.00
444 Larry Jackson	4.00	2.00
445 Bill Skowron	6.00	3.00
446 Julian Javier	4.00	2.00
447 Ted Bowsfield	4.00	2.00
448 Cookie Rojas	5.00	2.50
449 Deron Johnson	5.00	2.50
450 Steve Barber	4.00	2.00
451 Joe Amalfitano	4.00	2.00
452 Giants Rookies	8.00	4.00
Gil Garrido (R)		
Jim Ray Hart (R)		
453 Frank Baumann	4.00	2.00
454 Tommie Aaron	4.00	2.00
455 Bernie Allen	4.00	2.00
456 Dodgers Rookies	7.00	3.50
Wes Parker (R)		
John Werhas (R)		
457 Jesse Gonder	4.00	2.00
458 Ralph Terry	5.00	2.50
459 Red Sox Rookies	4.00	2.00
Pete Charton (R)		
Dalton Jones (R)		
460 Bob Gibson	40.00	20.00
461 George Thomas	4.00	2.00
462 Birdie Tebbetts	4.00	2.00
463 Don Leppert	4.00	2.00
464 Dallas Green	5.00	2.50
465 Mike Hershberger	4.00	2.00
466 Athletics Rookies	4.00	2.00
Dick Green (R)		
Aurelio Monteagudo (R)		
467 Bob Aspromonte	4.00	2.00
468 Gaylord Perry	42.00	21.00
469 Cubs Rookies	4.00	2.00
Fred Norman (R)		
Sterling Slaughter (R)		
470 Jim Bouton	8.00	4.00
471 Gates Brown (R)	8.00	4.00
472 Vern Law	5.00	2.50
473 Orioles Team	10.00	5.00
474 Larry Sherry	4.00	2.00
475 Ed Charles	4.00	2.00
476 Braves Rookies	7.00	3.50
Rico Carty (R)		
Dick Kelley (R)		
477 Mike Joyce	4.00	2.00
478 Dick Howser	4.00	2.00
479 Cardinals Rookies	4.00	2.00
Dave Bakenhaster (R)		
Johnny Lewis (R)		
480 Bob Purkey	4.00	2.00
481 Chuck Schilling	4.00	2.00
482 Phillies Rookies	4.00	2.00
John Briggs (R)		
Danny Cater (R)		
483 Fred Valentine	4.00	2.00
484 Bill Pleis	4.00	2.00
485 Tom Haller	4.00	2.00
486 Bob Kennedy	4.00	2.00
487 Mike McCormick	4.00	2.00
488 Yankees Rookies	4.00	2.00
Bob Meyer (R)		
Pete Mikkelsen (R)		
489 Julio Navarro	4.00	2.00
490 Ron Fairly	4.00	2.00
491 Ed Rakow	4.00	2.00
492 Colts Rookies	4.50	2.25
Jim Beauchamp (R)		
Mike White (R)		
493 Don Lee	4.00	2.00
494 Al Jackson	4.00	2.00
495 Bill Virdon	5.00	2.50
496 White Sox Team	10.00	5.00
497 Jeoff Long	4.00	2.00
498 Dave Stenhouse	4.00	2.00
499 Indians Rookies	4.00	2.00
Chico Salmon (R)		
Gordon Seyfried (R)		
500 Camilo Pascual	4.00	2.00
501 Bob Veale	4.00	2.00
502 Angels Rookies	4.50	2.25
Bobby Knoop (R)		
Bob Lee (R)		
503 Earl Wilson	4.00	2.00
504 Claude Raymond	4.00	2.00
505 Stan Williams	4.00	2.00
506 Bobby Bragan	4.00	2.00
507 John Edwards	4.00	2.00
508 Diego Segui	4.00	2.00
509 Pirates Rookies	8.50	4.25
Gene Alley (R)		
Orlando McFarlane (R)		

510	Lindy McDaniel	4.00	2.00
511	Lou Jackson	4.00	2.00
512	Tigers Rookies	15.00	7.50
	Willie Horton (R)		
	Joe Sparma (R)		
513	Don Larsen	6.00	3.00
514	Jim Hickman	4.00	2.00
515	Johnny Romano	4.00	2.00
516	Twins Rookies	4.00	2.00
	Jerry Arrigo (R)		
	Dwight Siebler (R)		
517	Checklist 507-587	20.00	7.50
518	Carl Bouldin	4.00	2.00
519	Charlie Smith	4.00	2.00
520	Jack Baldschun	4.00	2.00
521	Tom Satriano	4.00	2.00
522	Bobby Tiefenauer	4.00	2.00
523	Lew Burdette	10.00	5.00
524	Reds Rookies	9.00	4.50
	Jim Dickson (R)		
	Bobby Klaus (R)		
525	Al McBean	9.00	4.50
526	Lou Clinton	9.00	4.50
527	Larry Bearnarth	9.00	4.50
528	Athletics Rookies	10.00	5.00
	Dave Duncan (R)		
	Tom Reynolds (R)		
529	Al Dark	9.00	4.50
530	Leon Wagner	9.00	4.50
531	Dodgers Team	28.00	14.00
532	Twins Rookies	9.00	4.50
	Bud Bloomfield (R)		
	Joe Nossek (R)		
533	Johnny Klippstein	9.00	4.50
534	Gus Bell	9.00	4.50
535	Phil Regan	9.00	4.50
536	Mets Rookies	9.00	4.50
	Larry Elliot (R)		
	John Stephenson (R)		
537	Dan Osinski	9.00	4.50
538	Minnie Minoso	14.00	7.00
539	Roy Face	10.00	5.00
540	Luis Aparicio	20.00	10.00
541	Braves Rookies	210.00	105.00
	Phil Niekro (R)		
	Phil Roof (R)		
542	Don Mincher	9.00	4.50
543	Bob Uecker	40.00	20.00
544	Colts Rookies	9.00	4.50
	Steve Hertz (R)		
	Joe Hoerner (R)		
545	Max Alvis	9.00	4.50
546	Joe Christopher	9.00	4.50
547	Gil Hodges	18.00	9.00
548	N.L. Rookies	9.00	4.50
	Wayne Schurr (R)		
	Paul Speckenbach (R)		
549	Joe Moeller	9.00	4.50
550	Ken Hubbs Memorial	28.00	14.00
551	Billy Hoeft	9.00	4.50
552	Indians Rookies	10.00	5.00
	Tom Kelley (R)		
	Sonny Siebert (R)		
553	Jim Drewer	9.00	4.50
554	Hank Foiles	9.00	4.50
555	Lee Stange	9.00	4.50
556	Mets Rookies	9.00	4.50
	Steve Dillon (R)		
	Ron Locke (R)		
557	Leo Burke	9.00	4.50
558	Don Schwall	9.00	4.50
559	Dick Phillips	9.00	4.50
560	Dick Farrell	9.00	4.50
561	Phillies Rookies	15.00	7.50
	Dave Bennett (R)		
	Rick Wise (R)		
562	Pedro Ramos	9.00	4.50
563	Dal Maxvill	9.00	4.50
564	A.L. Rookies	9.00	4.50
	Joe McCabe (R)		
	Jerry McNertney (R)		
565	Stu Miller	9.00	4.50
566	Ed Kranepool	15.00	7.50
567	Jim Kaat	16.00	8.00
568	N.L. Rookies	9.00	4.50
	Phil Gagliano (R)		
	Cap Peterson (R)		
569	Fred Newman	9.00	4.50
570	Bill Mazeroski	15.00	7.50
571	Gene Conley	9.00	4.50
572	A.L. Rookies	9.00	4.50
	Dick Egan (R)		
	Dave Gray (R)		
573	Jim Duffalo	9.00	4.50
574	Manny Jimenez	9.00	4.50
575	Tony Cloninger	9.00	4.50
576	Mets Rookies	9.00	4.50
	Jerry Hinsley (R)		
	Bill Wakefield (R)		
577	Gordy Coleman	9.00	4.50
578	Glen Hobbie	9.00	4.50
579	Red Sox Team	20.00	10.00
580	Johnny Podres	10.00	5.00
581	Yankees Rookies	9.00	4.50
	Pedro Gonzalez (R)		
	Archie Moore (R)		
582	Rod Kanehl	9.00	4.50
583	Tito Francona	9.00	4.50
584	Joel Horlen	9.00	4.50
585	Tony Taylor	9.00	4.50
586	Jim Piersall	15.00	7.50
587	Bennie Daniels	12.00	5.00

1965 Topps

WILLIE STARGELL

This 598-card set features large color photos on the card fronts with team names in a pennant-shaped design in the bottom corner. Player names are in a horizonal bar at the bottom of the card. Cards measure 2-1/2" by 3-1/2" and subsets include League Leaders, World Series Hightlights and Rookies.

		NR/MT	EX
Complete Set (598)		3,800.00	1,950.00
Commons (1-198)		1.50	.75
Commons (199-446)		3.50	1.75
Commons (447-522)		5.00	2.50
Commons (523-598)		6.00	3.00
1	A.L. Batting Leaders	20.00	10.00
2	N.L. Batting Leaders	14.00	7.00
3	A.L. HRLeaders	28.00	14.00
4	N.L. HR Leaders	10.00	5.00
5	A.L. RBI Leaders	28.00	14.00
6	N.L. RBI Leaders	7.00	3.50
7	A.L. ERA Leaders	3.50	1.75
8	N.L. ERA Leaders	16.00	8.00
9	A.L. Pitching Leaders	3.50	1.75
10	N.L. Pitching Leaders	3.50	1.75
11	A.L. Strikeout Leaders	3.50	1.75
12	N.L. Strikeout Leaders	7.00	3.50
13	Pedro Ramos	1.50	.75
14	Len Gabrielson	1.50	.75
15	Robin Roberts	10.00	5.00
16	Astros Rookies	125.00	65.00
	Sonny Jackson (R)		
	Joe Morgan (R)		
17	Johnny Romano	1.50	.75
18	Bill McCool	1.50	.75
19	Gates Brown	2.00	1.00
20	Jim Bunning	5.00	2.50
21	Don Blasingame	1.50	.75
22	Charlie Smith	1.50	.75
23	Bob Tiefenauer	1.50	.75
24	Twins Team	3.50	1.75
25	Al McBean	1.50	.75
26	Bobby Knoop	1.50	.75
27	Dick Bertell	1.50	.75
28	Barney Schultz	1.50	.75
29	Felix Mantilla	1.50	.75
30	Jim Bouton	4.00	2.00
31	Mike White	1.50	.75
32	Harman Franks	1.50	.75
33	Jackie Brandt	1.50	.75
34	Cal Koonce	1.50	.75
35	Ed Charles	1.50	.75
36	Bobby Wine	1.50	.75
37	Fred Gladding	1.50	.75
38	Jim King	1.50	.75
39	Gerry Arrigo	1.50	.75
40	Frank Howard	3.50	1.75
41	White Sox Rookies	1.50	.75
	Bruce Howard (R)		
	Marv Staehle (R)		
42	Earl Wilson	1.50	.75
43	Mike Shannon	1.50	.75
44	Wade Blasingame	1.50	.75
45	Roy McMillan	1.50	.75
46	Bob Lee	1.50	.75
47	Tommy Harper	2.00	1.00
48	Claude Raymond	1.50	.75
49	Orioles Rookies	2.50	1.25
	Curt Blefary (R)		
	John Miller (R)		
50	Juan Marichal	14.00	7.00
51	Billy Bryan	1.50	.75
52	Ed Roebuck	1.50	.75
53	Dick McAuliffe	1.50	.75
54	Joe Gibbon	1.50	.75
55	Tony Conigliaro	10.00	5.00
56	Ron Kline	1.50	.75
57	Cardinals Team	3.50	1.75
58	Fred Talbot	1.50	.75
59	Nate Oliver	1.50	.75
60	Jim O'Toole	1.50	.75
61	Chris Cannizzaro	1.50	.75
62	Jim Katt (Kaat)	6.00	3.00
63	Ty Cline	1.50	.75
64	Lou Burdette	2.50	1.25
65	Tony Kubek	4.00	2.00
66	Bill Rigney	1.50	.75
67	Harvey Haddix	1.50	.75
68	Del Crandall	1.50	.75
69	Bill Virdon	2.00	1.00
70	Bill Skowron	2.50	1.25
71	John O'Donoghue	1.50	.75
72	Tony Gonzalez	1.50	.75
73	Dennis Ribant	1.50	.75
74	Red Sox Rookies	8.00	4.00
	Rico Petrocelli (R)		
	Jerry Stephenson (R)		

75	Deron Johnson	2.00	1.00
76	Sam McDowell	2.50	1.25
77	Doug Camilli	1.50	.75
78	Dal Maxvill	1.50	.75
79	Checklist 1-88	8.00	3.00
80	Turk Farrell	1.50	.75
81	Don Buford	1.50	.75
82	Braves Rookies	4.50	2.25
	Sandy Alomar (R)		
	John Braun (R)		
83	George Thomas	1.50	.75
84	Ron Herbel	1.50	.75
85	Willie Smith	1.50	.75
86	Les Narum	1.50	.75
87	Nelson Mathews	1.50	.75
88	Jack Lamabe	1.50	.75
89	Mike Hershberger	1.50	.75
90	Rich Rollins	1.50	.75
91	Cubs Team	3.50	1.75
92	Dick Howser	1.50	.75
93	Jack Fisher	1.50	.75
94	Charlie Lau	1.50	.75
95	Bill Mazeroski	4.50	2.25
96	Sonny Siebert	1.50	.75
97	Pedro Gonzalez	1.50	.75
98	Bob Miller	1.50	.75
99	Gil Hodges	7.00	3.50
100	Ken Boyer	4.00	2.00
101	Fred Newman	1.50	.75
102	Steve Boros	1.50	.75
103	Harvey Kuenn	2.00	1.00
104	Checklist 89-176	8.00	3.00
105	Chico Salmon	1.50	.75
106	Gene Oliver	1.50	.75
107	Phillies Rookies	2.50	1.25
	Pat Corrales (R)		
	Costen Shockley (R)		
108	Don Mincher	1.50	.75
109	Walt Bond	1.50	.75
110	Ron Santo	4.00	2.00
111	Lee Thomas	1.50	.75
112	Derrell Griffith	1.50	.75
113	Steve Barber	1.50	.75
114	Jim Hickman	1.50	.75
115	Bobby Richardson	5.00	2.50
116	Cardinals Rookies	3.00	1.50
	Dave Dowling (R)		
	Bob Tolan (R)		
117	Wes Stock	1.50	.75
118	Hal Lanier (R)	2.50	1.25
119	John Kennedy	1.50	.75
120	Frank Robinson	30.00	15.00
121	Gene Alley	1.50	.75
122	Bill Pleis	1.50	.75
123	Frank Thomas	1.50	.75
124	Tom Satriano	1.50	.75
125	Juan Pizarro	1.50	.75
126	Dodgers Team	5.50	2.75
127	Frank Lary	2.00	1.00
128	Vic Davalillo	1.50	.75
129	Bennie Daniels	1.50	.75
130	Al Kaline	30.00	15.00
131	Johnny Keane	1.50	.75
132	World Series Game 1	4.00	2.00
133	World Series Game 2	4.00	2.00
134	World Series Game 3	60.00	30.00
135	World Series Game 4	4.00	2.00
136	World Series Game 5	4.00	2.00
137	World Series Game 6	4.00	2.00
138	World Series Game 7	10.00	5.00
139	WS Celebration	4.00	2.00
140	Dean Chance	1.75	.90
141	Charlie James	1.50	.75
142	Bill Monbouquette	1.50	.75
143	Pirates Rookies	1.50	.75
	John Gelnar (R)		
	Jerry May (R)		
144	Ed Kranepool	2.00	1.00
145	Luis Tiant (R)	18.00	9.00
146	Ron Hansen	1.50	.75
147	Dennis Bennett	1.50	.75
148	Willie Kirkland	1.50	.75
149	Wayne Schurr	1.50	.75
150	Brooks Robinson	34.00	17.00
151	Athletics Team	3.50	1.75
152	Phil Ortega	1.50	.75
153	Norm Cash	5.00	2.50
154	Bob Humphreys	1.50	.75
155	Roger Maris	65.00	32.50
156	Bob Sadowski	1.50	.75
157	Zoilo Versalles	2.50	1.25
158	Dick Sisler	1.50	.75
159	Jim Duffalo	1.50	.75
160	Roberto Clemente	85.00	42.50
161	Frank Baumann	1.50	.75
162	Russ Nixon	1.50	.75
163	John Briggs	1.50	.75
164	Al Spangler	1.50	.75
165	Dick Ellsworth	1.50	.75
166	Indians Rookies	3.50	1.75
	Tommie Agee (R)		
	George Culver (R)		
167	Bill Wakefield	1.50	.75
168	Dick Green	1.50	.75
169	Dave Vineyard	1.50	.75
170	Hank Aaron	110.00	55.00
171	Jim Roland	1.50	.75
172	Jim Piersall	2.00	1.00
173	Tigers Team	3.50	1.75
174	Joey Jay	1.50	.75
175	Bob Aspromonte	1.50	.75
176	Willie McCovey	20.00	10.00
177	Pete Mikkelsen	1.50	.75
178	Dalton Jones	1.50	.75

179	Hal Woodeshick	1.50	.75
180	Bob Allison	1.50	.75
181	Senators Rookies	1.50	.75
	Don Loun		
	Joe McCabe		
182	Mike de la Hoz	1.50	.75
183	Dave Nicholson	1.50	.75
184	John Boozer	1.50	.75
185	Max Alvis	1.50	.75
186	Billy Cowan	1.50	.75
187	Casey Stengel	15.00	7.50
188	Sam Bowens	1.50	.75
189	Checklist 177-264	8.00	3.00
190	Bill White	3.50	1.75
191	Phil Regan	1.50	.75
192	Jim Coker	1.50	.75
193	Gaylord Perry	20.00	10.00
194	Angels Rookies	2.00	1.00
	Bill Kelso (R)		
	Rick Reichardt (R)		
195	Bob Veale	1.50	.75
196	Ron Fairly	1.50	.75
197	Diego Segui	1.50	.75
198	Smoky Burgess	1.75	.90
199	Bob Heffner	3.50	1.75
200	Joe Torre	4.00	2.00
201	Twins Rookies	3.50	1.75
	Cesar Tovar (R)		
	Sandy Valdespino (R)		
202	Leo Burke	3.50	1.75
203	Dallas Green	3.50	1.75
204	Russ Snyder	3.50	1.75
205	Warren Spahn	32.00	16.00
206	Willie Horton	4.50	2.25
207	Pete Rose	175.00	90.00
208	Tommy John	12.00	6.00
209	Pirates Team	6.00	3.00
210	Jim Fregosi	4.00	2.00
211	Steve Ridzik	3.50	1.75
212	Ron Brand	3.50	1.75
213	Jim Davenport	3.50	1.75
214	Bob Purkey	3.50	1.75
215	Pete Ward	3.50	1.75
216	Al Worthington	3.50	1.75
217	Walt Alston	4.00	2.00
218	Dick Schofield	3.50	1.75
219	Bob Meyer	3.50	1.75
220	Billy Williams	14.00	7.00
221	John Tsitouris	3.50	1.75
222	Bob Tillman	3.50	1.75
223	Dan Osinski	3.50	1.75
224	Bob Chance	3.50	1.75
225	Bo Belinsky	3.50	1.75
226	Yankees Rookies	3.50	1.75
	Jake Gibbs		
	Elvio Jimenez (R)		
227	Bobby Klaus	3.50	1.75
228	Jack Sanford	3.50	1.75
229	Lou Clinton	3.50	1.75
230	Ray Sadecki	3.50	1.75
231	Jerry Adair	3.50	1.75
232	Steve Blass (R)	4.50	2.25
233	Don Zimmer	3.50	1.75
234	White Sox Team	6.00	3.00
235	Chuck Hinton	3.50	1.75
236	Dennis McLain (R)	32.00	16.00
237	Bernie Allen	3.50	1.75
238	Joe Moeller	3.50	1.75
239	Doc Edwards	3.50	1.75
240	Bob Bruce	3.50	1.75
241	Mack Jones	3.50	1.75
242	George Brunet	3.50	1.75
243	Reds Rookies	4.00	2.00
	Ted Davidson (R)		
	Tommy Helms (R)		
244	Lindy McDaniel	3.50	1.75
245	Joe Pepitone	4.00	2.00
246	Tom Butters	3.50	1.75
247	Wally Moon	3.50	1.75
248	Gus Triandos	3.50	1.75
249	Dave McNally	4.00	2.00
250	Willie Mays	110.00	55.00
251	Billy Herman	3.50	1.75
252	Pete Richert	3.50	1.75
253	Danny Carter	3.50	1.75
254	Roland Sheldon	3.50	1.75
255	Camilo Pascual	3.50	1.75
256	Tito Francona	3.50	1.75
257	Jim Wynn	4.00	2.00
258	Larry Bearnarth	3.50	1.75
259	Tigers Rookies	5.00	2.50
	Jim Northrup (R)		
	Ray Oyler (R)		
260	Don Drysdale	24.00	12.00
261	Duke Carmel	3.50	1.75
262	Bud Daley	3.50	1.75
263	Marty Keough	3.50	1.75
264	Bob Buhl	3.50	1.75
265	Jim Pagliaroni	3.50	1.75
266	Bert Campaneris (R)	10.00	5.00
267	Senators Team	6.00	3.00
268	Ken McBride	3.50	1.75
269	Frank Bolling	3.50	1.75
270	Milt Pappas	3.50	1.75
271	Don Wert	3.50	1.75
272	Chuck Schilling	3.50	1.75
273	Checklist 265-352	8.00	3.00
274	Lum Harris	3.50	1.75
275	Dick Groat	3.50	1.75
276	Hoyt Wilhelm	8.50	4.25
277	Johnny Lewis	3.50	1.75
278	Ken Retzer	3.50	1.75
279	Dick Tracewski	3.50	1.75
280	Dick Stuart	3.50	1.75

281	Bill Stafford	3.50	1.75
282	Giants Rookies	5.00	2.50
	Dick Estelle (R)		
	Masanori Murakami (R)		
283	Fred Whitfield	3.50	1.75
284	Nick Willhite	3.50	1.75
285	Ron Hunt	3.50	1.75
286	Athletics Rookies	3.50	1.75
	Jim Dickson (R)		
	Aurelio Monteagudo		
287	Gary Kolb	3.50	1.75
288	Jack Hamilton	3.50	1.75
289	Gordy Coleman	3.50	1.75
290	Wally Bunker	3.50	1.75
291	Jerry Lynch	3.50	1.75
292	Larry Yellen	3.50	1.75
293	Angels Team	6.00	3.00
294	Tim McCarver	6.00	3.00
295	Dick Radatz	3.50	1.75
296	Tony Taylor	3.50	1.75
297	Dave DeBusschere	4.00	2.00
298	Jim Stewart	3.50	1.75
299	Jerry Zimmerman	3.50	1.75
300	Sandy Koufax	140.00	70.00
301	Birdie Tebbetts	3.50	1.75
302	Al Stanek	3.50	1.75
303	Johnny Orsino	3.50	1.75
304	Dave Stenhouse	3.50	1.75
305	Rico Carty	4.50	2.25
306	Bubba Phillips	3.50	1.75
307	Barry Latman	3.50	1.75
308	Mets Rookies	8.50	4.25
	Cleon Jones (R)		
	Tom Parsons (R)		
309	Steve Hamilton	3.50	1.75
310	Johnny Callison	3.50	1.75
311	Orlanda Pena	3.50	1.75
312	Joe Nuxhall	3.50	1.75
313	Jimmie Schaffer	3.50	1.75
314	Sterling Slaughter	3.50	1.75
315	Frank Malzone	3.50	1.75
316	Reds Team	6.00	3.00
317	Don McMahon	3.50	1.75
318	Matty Alou	4.00	2.00
319	Ken McMullen	3.50	1.75
320	Bob Gibson	34.00	17.00
321	Rusty Staub	6.00	3.00
322	Rick Wise	3.50	1.75
323	Hank Bauer	3.50	1.75
324	Bobby Locke	3.50	1.75
325	Donn Clendenon	3.50	1.75
326	Dwight Siebler	3.50	1.75
327	Denis Menke	3.50	1.75
328	Eddie Fisher	3.50	1.75
329	Hawk Taylor	3.50	1.75
330	Whitey Ford	32.00	16.00
331	Dodgers Rookies	3.50	1.75
	Al Ferrara (R)		
	John Purdin (R)		
332	Ted Abernathy	3.50	1.75
333	Tommie Reynolds	3.50	1.75
334	Vic Roznovsky	3.50	1.75
335	Mickey Lolich	6.00	3.00
336	Woody Held	3.50	1.75
337	Mike Cuellar	4.00	2.00
338	Phillies Team	6.00	3.00
339	Ryne Duren	3.50	1.75
340	Tony Oliva	14.00	7.00
341	Bobby Bolin	3.50	1.75
342	Bob Rodgers	3.50	1.75
343	Mike McCormick	3.50	1.75
344	Wes Parker	3.50	1.75
345	Floyd Robinson	3.50	1.75
346	Bobby Bragan	3.50	1.75
347	Roy Face	4.00	2.00
348	George Banks	3.50	1.75
349	Larry Miller	3.50	1.75
350	Mickey Mantle	575.00	290.00
351	Jim Perry	3.50	1.75
352	Alex Johnson (R)	4.00	2.00
353	Jerry Lumpe	3.50	1.75
354	Cubs Rookies	3.50	1.75
	Billy Ott (R)		
	Jack Warner (R)		
355	Vada Pinson	4.00	2.00
356	Bill Spanswick	3.50	1.75
357	Carl Warwick	3.50	1.75
358	Albie Pearson	3.50	1.75
359	Ken Johnson	3.50	1.75
360	Orlando Cepeda	9.00	4.50
361	Checklist 353-429	8.00	3.00
362	Don Schwall	3.50	1.75
363	Bob Johnson	3.50	1.75
364	Galen Cisco	3.50	1.75
365	Jim Gentile	3.50	1.75
366	Dan Schneider	3.50	1.75
367	Leon Wagner	3.50	1.75
368	White Sox Rookies	3.50	1.75
	Ken Berry (R)		
	Joel Gibson (R)		
369	Phil Linz	3.50	1.75
370	Tommy Davis	4.50	2.25
371	Frank Kreutzer	3.50	1.75
372	Clay Dalrymple	3.50	1.75
373	Curt Simmons	3.50	1.75
374	Angels Rookies	6.50	3.25
	Jose Cardenal (R)		
	Dick Simpson (R)		
375	Dave Wickersham	3.50	1.75
376	Jim Landis	3.50	1.75
377	Willie Stargell	32.00	16.00
378	Chuck Estrada	3.50	1.75
379	Giants Team	8.00	4.00
380	Rocky Colavito	12.00	6.00

381	Al Jackson	3.50	1.75
382	J.C. Martin	3.50	1.75
383	Felipe Alou	6.50	3.25
384	Johnny Klippstein	3.50	1.75
385	Carl Yastrzemski	85.00	42.50
386	Cubs Rookies	3.50	1.75
	Paul Jaeckel (R)		
	Fred Norman		
387	Johnny Podres	5.00	2.50
388	John Blanchard	3.50	1.75
389	Don Larsen	5.00	2.50
390	Bill Freehan	6.50	3.25
391	Mel McGaha	3.50	1.75
392	Bob Friend	3.50	1.75
393	Ed Kirkpatrick	3.50	1.75
394	Jim Hannan	3.50	1.75
395	Jim Hart	4.50	2.25
396	Frank Bertaina	3.50	1.75
397	Jerry Buchek	3.50	1.75
398	Reds Rookies	5.00	2.50
	Dan Neville (R)		
	Art Shamsky (R)		
399	Ray Herbert	3.50	1.75
400	Harmon Killebrew	38.00	20.00
401	Carl Willey	3.50	1.75
402	Joe Amalfitano	3.50	1.75
403	Red Sox Team	8.00	4.00
404	Stan Williams	3.50	1.75
405	John Roseboro	4.00	2.00
406	Ralph Terry	4.00	2.00
407	Lee Maye	3.50	1.75
408	Larry Sherry	3.50	1.75
409	Astros Rookies	7.50	3.75
	Jim Beauchamp		
	Larry Dierker (R)		
410	Luis Aparicio	12.00	6.00
411	Roger Craig	4.50	2.25
412	Bob Bailey	3.50	1.75
413	Hal Reniff	3.50	1.75
414	Al Lopez	5.00	2.50
415	Curt Flood	6.00	3.00
416	Jim Brewer	3.50	1.75
417	Ed Brinkman	3.50	1.75
418	Johnny Edwards	3.50	1.75
419	Ruben Amaro	3.50	1.75
420	Larry Jackson	3.50	1.75
421	Twins Rookies	3.50	1.75
	Gary Dotter (R)		
	Jay Ward		
422	Aubrey Gatewood	3.50	1.75
423	Jesse Gonder	3.50	1.75
424	Gary Bell	3.50	1.75
425	Wayne Causey	3.50	1.75
426	Braves Team	8.00	4.00
427	Bob Saverine	3.50	1.75
428	Bob Shaw	3.50	1.75
429	Don Demeter	3.50	1.75
430	Gary Peters	3.50	1.75
431	Cardinals Rookies	6.50	3.25
	Nelson Briles (R)		
	Wayne Spiezio (R)		
432	Jim Grant	3.50	1.75
433	John Bateman	3.50	1.75
434	Dave Morehead	3.50	1.75
435	Willie Davis	4.00	2.00
436	Don Elston	3.50	1.75
437	Chico Cardenas	3.50	1.75
438	Harry Walker	3.50	1.75
439	Moe Drabowsky	3.50	1.75
440	Tom Tresh	6.50	3.25
441	Denver Lemaster	3.50	1.75
442	Vic Power	3.50	1.75
443	Checklist 430-506	10.00	4.00
444	Bob Hendley	3.50	1.75
445	Don Lock	3.50	1.75
446	Art Mahaffey	3.50	1.75
447	Julian Javier	5.00	2.50
448	Lee Stange	5.00	2.50
449	Mets Rookies	5.00	2.50
	Jerry Hinsley (R)		
	Gary Kroll (R)		
450	Elston Howard	8.50	4.25
451	Jim Owens	5.00	2.50
452	Gary Geiger	5.00	2.50
453	Dodgers Rookies	6.00	3.00
	Willie Crawford (R)		
	John Werhas		
454	Ed Rakow	5.00	2.50
455	Norm Siebern	5.00	2.50
456	Bill Henry	5.00	2.50
457	Bob Kennedy	5.00	2.50
458	John Buzhardt	5.00	2.50
459	Frank Kostro	5.00	2.50
460	Richie Allen	32.00	16.00
461	Braves Rookies	60.00	30.00
	Clay Carroll (R)		
	Phil Niekro		
462	Lew Krausse	5.00	2.50
463	Manny Mota	6.00	3.00
464	Ron Piche	5.00	2.50
465	Tom Haller	5.00	2.50
466	Senators Rookies	5.00	2.50
	Pete Craig (R)		
	Dick Nen		
467	Ray Washburn	5.00	2.50
468	Larry Brown	5.00	2.50
469	Don Nottebart	5.00	2.50
470	Yogi Berra	60.00	30.00
471	Billy Hoeft	5.00	2.50
472	Don Pavletich	5.00	2.50
473	Orioles Rookies	16.00	8.00
	Paul Blair (R)		
	Dave Johnson (R)		
474	Cookie Rojas	6.00	3.00

475	Clete Boyer	7.50	3.75
476	Billy O'Dell	5.00	2.50
477	Cardinals Rookies	525.00	265.00
	Fritz Ackley (R)		
	Steve Carlton (R)		
478	Wilbur Wood	6.00	3.00
479	Ken Harrelson	7.00	3.50
480	Joel Horlen	5.00	2.50
481	Indians Team	10.00	5.00
482	Bob Priddy	5.00	2.50
483	George Smith	5.00	2.50
484	Ron Perranoski	6.00	3.00
485	Nellie Fox	12.00	6.00
486	Angels Rookies	5.00	2.50
	Tom Egan (R)		
	Pat Rogan (R)		
487	Woody Woodward	5.00	2.50
488	Ted Wills	5.00	2.50
489	Gene Mauch	5.00	2.50
490	Earl Batte	5.00	2.50
491	Tracy Stallard	5.00	2.50
492	Gene Freese	5.00	2.50
493	Tigers Rookies	5.00	2.50
	Bruce Brubaker (R)		
	Bill Roman (R)		
494	Jay Ritchie	5.00	2.50
495	Joe Christopher	5.00	2.50
496	Joe Cunningham	5.00	2.50
497	Giants Rookies	5.00	2.50
	Ken Henderson (R)		
	Jack Hiatt (R)		
498	Gene Stephens	5.00	2.50
499	Stu Miller	5.00	2.50
500	Ed Mathews	38.00	20.00
501	Indians Rookies	5.00	2.50
	Ralph Gagliano (R)		
	Jim Rittwage (R)		
502	Don Cardwell	5.00	2.50
503	Phil Gagliano	5.00	2.50
504	Jerry Grote	6.00	3.00
505	Ray Culp	5.00	2.50
506	Sam Mele	5.00	2.50
507	Sammy Ellis	5.00	2.50
508	Checklist 507-598	10.00	5.00
509	Red Sox Rookies	5.00	2.50
	Bob Guindon (R)		
	Gerry Vezendy (R)		
510	Ernie Banks	80.00	40.00
511	Ron Lock	5.00	2.50
512	Cap Peterson	5.00	2.50
513	Yankees Team	25.00	12.50
514	Joe Azcue	5.00	2.50
515	Vern Law	5.00	2.50
516	Al Weis	5.00	2.50
517	Angels Rookies	5.00	2.50
	Paul Schaal (R)		
	Jack Warner (R)		

518	Ken Rowe	5.00	2.50
519	Bob Uecker	28.00	14.00
520	Tony Cloninger	5.00	2.50
521	Phillies Rookies	5.00	2.50
	Dave Bennett (R)		
	Morrie Stevens (R)		
522	Hank Aguirre	5.00	2.50
523	Mike Brumley	6.00	3.00
524	Dave Giusti	6.00	3.00
525	Eddie Ressoud	6.00	3.00
526	Athletics Rookies	140.00	70.00
	Catfish Hunter(R)		
	Rene Lachemann (R)		
	Skip Lockwood (R)		
	John Odom (R)		
527	Jeff Torborg	10.00	5.00
528	George Altman	6.00	3.00
529	Jerry Fosnow	6.00	3.00
530	Jim Maloney	6.00	3.00
531	Chuck Hiller	6.00	3.00
532	Hector Lopez	6.00	3.00
533	Mets Rookies	35.00	17.50
	Jim Bethke (R)		
	Tug McGraw (R)		
	Dan Napolean (R)		
	Ron Swoboda (R)		
534	John Herrnstein	6.00	3.00
535	Jack Kralick	6.00	3.00
536	Andre Rodgers	6.00	3.00
537	Angels Rookies	7.00	3.50
	Marcelino Lopez		
	Rudy May (R)		
	Phil Roof		
538	Chuck Dressen	6.00	3.00
539	Herm Starrette	6.00	3.00
540	Lou Brock	55.00	27.50
541	White Sox Rookies	6.00	3.00
	Greg Bollo		
	Bob Locker (R)		
542	Lou Klimchock	6.00	3.00
543	Ed Connolly	6.00	3.00
544	Howie Reed	6.00	3.00
545	Jesus Alou	7.00	3.50
546	Indians Rookies	6.00	3.00
	Ray Barker (R)		
	Bill Davis (R)		
	Mike Hedlund (R)		
	Floyd Weaver (R)		
547	Jake Wood	6.00	3.00
548	Dick Stigman	6.00	3.00
549	Cubs Rookies	18.00	9.00
	Glenn Beckert (R)		
	Roberto Pena (R)		
550	Mel Stottlemyre (R)	32.00	16.00
551	Mets Team	32.00	16.00
552	Julio Gotay	6.00	3.00
553	Astros Rookies	6.00	3.00

	Dan Coombs (R)		
	Jack McClure (R)		
	Gene Ratliff (R)		
554	Chico Ruiz	6.00	3.00
555	Jack Baldschun	6.00	3.00
556	Red Schoendienst	20.00	10.00
557	Jose Santiago	6.00	3.00
558	Tommie Sisk	6.00	3.00
559	Ed Bailey	6.00	3.00
560	Boog Powell	22.00	11.00
561	Dodgers Rookies	10.00	5.00
	Dennis Daboll (R)		
	Mike Kekich (R)		
	Jim Lefebvre (R)		
	Hector Valle (R)		
562	Billy Moran	6.00	3.00
563	Julio Navarro	6.00	3.00
564	Mel Nelson	6.00	3.00
565	Ernie Broglio	6.00	3.00
566	Yankees Rookies	6.00	3.00
	Gil Blanco (R)		
	ArtLopez (R)		
	Ross Moschitto (R)		
567	Tommie Aaron	6.00	3.00
568	Ron Taylor	6.00	3.00
569	Gino Cimoli	6.00	3.00
570	Claude Osteen	6.00	3.00
571	Ossie Virgil	6.00	3.00
572	Orioles Team	28.00	14.00
573	Red Sox Rookies	24.00	12.00
	Jim Lonborg (R)		
	Gerry Moses (R)		
	Mike Ryan (R)		
	Bill Schlesinger (R)		
574	Roy Sievers	6.00	3.00
575	Jose Pagan	6.00	3.00
576	Terry Fox	6.00	3.00
577	A.L. Rookies	8.00	4.00
	Jim Buschhorn (R)		
	Darold Knowles (R)		
	Richie Scheinblum (R)		
578	Camilo Carreon	6.00	3.00
579	Dick Smith	6.00	3.00
580	Jimmie Hall	6.00	3.00
581	N.L. Rookies	160.00	80.00
	Kevin Collins (R)		
	Tony Perez (R)		
	Dave Ricketts (R)		
582	Bob Schmidt	6.00	3.00
583	Wes Covington	6.00	3.00
584	Harry Bright	6.00	3.00
585	Hank Fischer	6.00	3.00
586	Tommy McCraw	6.00	3.00
587	Joe Sparma	6.00	3.00
588	Lenny Green	6.00	3.00
589	Giants Rookies	6.00	3.00
	Frank Linzy (R)		

	Bob Schroder (R)		
590	Johnnie Wyatt	6.00	3.00
591	Bob Skinner	6.00	3.00
592	Frank Bork	6.00	3.00
593	Tigers Rookies	9.00	4.50
	Jackie Moore (R)		
	John Sullivan (R)		
594	Joe Gaines	6.00	3.00
595	Don Lee	6.00	3.00
596	Don Landrum	6.00	3.00
597	Twins Rookies	6.00	3.00
	Joe Nossek		
	Dick Reese (R)		
	John Sevcik (R)		
598	Al Downing	16.00	6.00

1966 Topps

This 598-card set features color photos on the card fronts with team names appearing in a small diagonal stripe in the top left corner. Player's names and positions are printed across the bottom of the card fronts. Cards measure 2-1/2" by 3-1/2". Major subsets include League Leaders and Managers. Several variations exists in the set. Those cards are noted in the checklist below with the smaller valued card included in the complete set price.

	NR/MT	EX
Complete Set (598)	4,650.00	2,300.00
Commons (1-110)	1.50	.75
Commons (111-446)	2.50	1.25
Commons (447-522)	7.00	3.50
Commons (523-598)	15.00	7.50

1	Willie Mays	160.00	80.00
2	Ted Abernathy	1.50	.75

3	Sam Mele	1.50	.75
4	Ray Culp	1.50	.75
5	Jim Fregosi	2.00	1.00
6	Chuck Schilling	1.50	.75
7	Tracy Stallard	1.50	.75
8	Floyd Robinson	1.50	.75
9	Clete Boyer	2.50	1.25
10	Tony Cloninger	1.50	.75
11	Senators Rookies	1.50	.75
	Brant Alyea (R)		
	Pete Craig		
12	John Tsitouris	1.50	.75
13	Lou Johnson	1.50	.75
14	Norm Siebern	1.50	.75
15	Vern Law	1.50	.75
16	Larry Brown	1.50	.75
17	Johnny Stephenson	1.50	.75
18	Roland Sheldon	1.50	.75
19	Giants Team	3.50	1.75
20	Willie Horton	2.50	1.25
21	Don Nottebart	1.50	.75
22	Joe Nossek	1.50	.75
23	Jack Sanford	1.50	.75
24	Don Kessinger (R)	4.00	2.00
25	Pete Ward	1.50	.75
26	Ray Sadecki	1.50	.75
27	Orioles Rookies	1.50	.75
	Andy Etchebarren (R)		
	Darold Knowles		
28	Phil Niekro	22.00	11.00
29	Mike Brumley	1.50	.75
30	Pete Rose	48.00	24.00
31	Jack Cullen	1.50	.75
32	Adolfo Phillips	1.50	.75
33	Jim Pagliaroni	1.50	.75
34	Checklist 1-88	7.50	3.75
35	Ron Swoboda	2.50	1.25
36	Jim Hunter	28.00	14.00
37	Billy Herman	2.00	1.00
38	Ron Nischwitz	1.50	.75
39	Ken Henderson	1.50	.75
40	Jim Grant	1.50	.75
41	Don LeJohn	1.50	.75
42	Aubrey Gatewood	1.50	.75
43	Don Landrum	1.50	.75
44	Indians Rookies	1.50	.75
	Bill Davis (R)		
	Tom Kelley		
45	Jim Gentile	2.00	1.00
46	Howie Koplitz	1.50	.75
47	J.C. Martin	1.50	.75
48	Paul Blair	2.00	1.00
49	Woody Woodward	1.50	.75
50	Mickey Mantle	250.00	125.00
51	Gordon Richardson	1.50	.75
52	Power Plus	2.00	1.00
	Johnny Callison		

	Wes Covington		
53	Bob Duliba	1.50	.75
54	Jose Pagan	1.50	.75
55	Ken Harrelson	1.80	.90
56	Sandy Valdespino	1.50	.75
57	Jim Lefebvre	1.50	.75
58	Dave Wickersham	1.50	.75
59	Reds Team	3.50	1.75
60	Curt Flood	2.00	1.00
61	Bob Bolin	1.50	.75
62a	Merritt Ranew (no sold statement)	24.00	12.00
62b	Merritt Ranew (Sold Statement)	1.50	.75
63	Jim Stewart	1.50	.75
64	Bob Bruce	1.50	.75
65	Leon Wagner	1.50	.75
66	Al Weis	1.50	.75
67	Mets Rookies	2.50	1.25
	Cleon Jones		
	Dick Selma (R)		
68	Hal Reniff	1.50	.75
69	Ken Hamlin	1.50	.75
70	Carl Yastrzemski	40.00	20.00
71	Frank Carpin	1.50	.75
72	Tony Perez	35.00	17.50
73	Jerry Zimmerman	1.50	.75
74	Don Mossi	1.50	.75
75	Tommy Davis	3.00	1.50
76	Red Schoendienst	4.00	2.00
77	Johnny Orsino	1.50	.75
78	Frank Linzy	1.50	.75
79	Joe Pepitone	2.50	1.25
80	Richie Allen	5.00	2.50
81	Ray Oyler	1.50	.75
82	Bob Hendley	1.50	.75
83	Albie Pearson	1.50	.75
84	Braves Rookies	1.50	.75
	Jim Beauchamp		
	Dick Kelley (R)		
85	Eddie Fisher	1.50	.75
86	John Bateman	1.50	.75
87	Dan Napoleon	1.50	.75
88	Fred Whitfield	1.50	.75
89	Ted Davidson	1.50	.75
90	Luis Aparicio	8.00	4.00
91a	Bob Uecker (No trade statement)	40.00	20.00
91b	Bob Uecker (Trade statement)	15.00	7.50
92	Yankees Team	5.50	2.75
93	Jim Lonborg	2.50	1.25
94	Matty Alou	2.50	1.25
95	Pete Richert	1.50	.75
96	Felipe Alou	3.00	1.50
97	Jim Merritt	1.50	.75
98	Don Demeter	1.50	.75

99	Buc Belters	5.00	2.50
	Donn Clendenon		
	Willie Stargell		
100	Sandy Koufax	110.00	55.00
101a	Checklist 89-176	12.00	5.00
	(#115 is Spahn)		
101b	Checklist 89-176	8.50	3.50
	(#115 is Henry)		
102	Ed Kirkpatrick	1.50	.75
103a	Dick Groat (No trade	28.00	14.00
	statement)		
103b	Dick Groat (Trade	3.50	1.75
	statement)		
104a	Alex Johnson (No	24.00	12.00
	trade statement)		
104b	Alex Johnson (Trade	2.50	1.25
	statement)	1.50	.75
105	Milt Pappas	1.50	.75
106	Rusty Staub	4.00	2.00
107	Athletics Rookies	1.50	.75
	Larry Stahl (R)		
	Ron Tompkins (R)		
108	Bobby Klaus	1.50	.75
109	Ralph Terry	2.00	1.00
110	Ernie Banks	28.00	14.00
111	Gary Peters	2.50	1.25
112	Manny Mota	3.50	1.75
113	Hank Aguirre	2.50	1.25
114	Jim Gosger	2.50	1.25
115	Bill Henry	2.50	1.25
116	Walt Alston	3.50	1.75
117	Jake Gibbs	2.50	1.25
118	Mike McCormick	2.50	1.25
119	Art Shamsky	2.50	1.25
120	Harmon Killebrew	22.00	11.00
121	Ray Herbert	2.50	1.25
122	Joe Gaines	2.50	1.25
123	Pirates Rookies (R)	2.50	1.25
	Frank Bork		
	Jerry May		
124	Tug McGraw	6.00	3.00
125	Lou Brock	28.00	14.00
126	Jim Palmer (R)	200.00	100.00
127	Ken Berry	2.50	1.25
128	Jim Landis	2.50	1.25
129	Jack Kralick	2.50	1.25
130	Joe Torre	4.50	2.25
131	Angels Team	4.00	2.00
132	Orlando Cepeda	7.00	3.50
133	Don McMahon	2.50	1.25
134	Wes Parker	2.50	1.25
135	Dave Morehead	2.50	1.25
136	Woody Held	2.50	1.25
137	Pat Corrales	2.50	1.25
138	Roger Repoz	2.50	1.25
139	Cubs Rookies	2.50	1.25
	Byron Browne (R)		
	Don Young (R)		
140	Jim Maloney	2.50	1.25
141	Tom McCraw	2.50	1.25
142	Don Dennis	2.50	1.25
143	Jose Tartabull	2.50	1.25
144	Don Schwall	2.50	1.25
145	Bill Freehan	3.50	1.75
146	George Altman	2.50	1.25
147	Lum Harris	2.50	1.25
148	Bob Johnson	2.50	1.25
149	Dick Nen	2.50	1.25
150	Rocky Colavito	7.00	3.50
151	Gary Wagner	2.50	1.25
152	Frank Malzone	2.50	1.25
153	Rico Carty	3.00	1.50
154	Chuck Hiller	2.50	1.25
155	Marcelino Lopez	2.50	1.25
156	DP Combo (Hal Lanier	2.50	1.25
	Dick Schofield		
157	Rene Lachemann	2.50	1.25
158	Jim Brewer	2.50	1.25
159	Chico Ruiz	2.50	1.25
160	Whitey Ford	28.00	14.00
161	Jerry Lumpe	2.50	1.25
162	Lee Maye	2.50	1.25
163	Tito Francona	2.50	1.25
164	White Sox Rookies	3.00	1.50
	Tommie Agee (R)		
	Marv Staehle (R)		
165	Don Lock	2.50	1.25
166	Chris Krug	2.50	1.25
167	Boog Powell	6.00	3.00
168	Dan Osinski	2.50	1.25
169	Duke Sims	2.50	1.25
170	Cookie Rojas	3.00	1.50
171	Nick Willhite	2.50	1.25
172	Mets Team	4.00	2.00
173	Al Spangler	2.50	1.25
174	Ron Taylor	2.50	1.25
175	Bert Campaneris	3.50	1.75
176	Jim Davenport	2.50	1.25
177	Hector Lopez	2.50	1.25
178	Bob Tillman	2.50	1.25
179	Cardinals Rookies	3.00	1.50
	Dennis Aust (R)		
	Bob Tolan		
180	Vada Pinson	3.00	1.75
181	Al Worthington	2.50	1.25
182	Jerry Lynch	2.50	1.25
183	Checklist 177-264	7.50	3.00
184	Denis Menke	2.50	1.25
185	Bob Buhl	2.50	1.25
186	Ruben Amaro	2.50	1.25
187	Chuck Dressen	2.50	1.25
188	Al Luplow	2.50	1.25
189	John Roseboro	3.00	1.50
190	Jimmie Hall	2.50	1.25

191	Darrell Sutherland	2.50	1.25
192	Vic Power	2.50	1.25
193	Dave McNally	3.00	1.50
194	Senators Team	4.00	2.00
195	Joe Morgan	40.00	20.00
196	Don Pavletich	2.50	1.25
197	Sonny Siebert	2.50	1.25
198	Mickey Stanley (R)	4.00	2.00
199	Chisox Clubbers	2.50	1.25
	Floyd Robinson		
	Johnny Romano		
	Bill Skowron		
200	Ed Mathews	14.00	7.00
201	Jim Dickson	2.50	1.25
202	Clay Dalrymple	2.50	1.25
203	Jose Santiago	2.50	1.25
204	Cubs Team	4.00	2.00
205	Tom Tresh	3.50	1.75
206	Alvin Jackson	2.50	1.25
207	Frank Quilici	2.50	1.25
208	Bob Miller	2.50	1.25
209	Tigers Rookies	3.00	1.50
	Fritz Fisher (R)		
	John Hiller (R)		
210	Bill Mazeroski	4.50	2.25
211	Frank Kreutzer	2.50	1.25
212	Ed Kranepool	3.00	1.50
213	Fred Newman	2.50	1.25
214	Tommy Harper	3.00	1.50
215	N.L. Batting Leaders	40.00	20.00
216	A.L. Batting Leaders	7.00	3.50
217	N.L. HR Leaders	20.00	10.00
218	A.L. HR Leaders	5.00	2.50
219	N.L. RBI Leaders	8.50	4.25
220	A.L. RBI Leaders	5.00	2.50
221	N.L. ERA Leaders	10.00	5.00
222	A.L. ERA Leaders	4.50	2.25
223	N.L. Pitching Leaders	10.00	5.00
224	A.L. Pitching Leaders	4.50	2.25
225	N.L. Strikeout Leaders	10.00	5.00
226	A.L. Strikeout Leaders	4.50	2.25
	Siebert)		
227	Russ Nixon	2.50	1.25
228	Larry Dierker	3.00	1.75
229	Hank Bauer	3.00	1.75
230	Johnny Callison	3.00	1.75
231	Floyd Weaver	2.50	1.25
232	Glenn Beckert	2.50	1.25
233	Dom Zanni	2.50	1.25
234	Yankees Rookies	7.50	3.50
	Rich Beck		
	Roy White (R)		
235	Don Cardwell	2.50	1.25
236	Mike Hershberger	2.50	1.25
237	Billy O'Dell	2.50	1.25
238	Dodgers Team	4.50	2.25
239	Orlando Pena	2.50	1.25
240	Earl Battey	2.50	1.25
241	Dennis Ribant	2.50	1.25
242	Jesue Alou	2.50	1.25
243	Nelson Briles	2.50	1.25
244	Astros Rookies	2.50	1.25
	Chuck Harrison (R)		
	Sonny Jackson (R)		
245	John Buzhardt	2.50	1.25
246	Ed Bailey	2.50	1.25
247	Carl Warwick	2.50	1.25
248	Pete Mikkelsen	2.50	1.25
249	Bill Rigney	2.50	1.25
250	Sam Ellis	2.50	1.25
251	Ed Brinkman	2.50	1.25
252	Denver Lemaster	2.50	1.25
253	Don Wert	2.50	1.25
254	Phillies Rookies	125.00	65.00
	Ferguson Jenkins(R)		
	Bill Sorrell (R)		
255	Willie Stargell	25.00	12.50
256	Lew Krausse	2.50	1.25
257	Jeff Torborg	30.00	1.50
258	Dave Giusti	2.50	1.25
259	Red Sox Team	4.00	2.00
260	Bob Shaw	2.50	1.25
261	Ron Hansen	2.50	1.25
262	Jack Hamilton	2.50	1.25
263	Tom Egan	2.50	1.25
264	Twins Rookies	2.50	1.25
	Andy Kosco (R)		
	Ted Uhlaender (R)		
265	Stu Miller	2.50	1.25
266	Pedro Gonzalez	2.50	1.25
267	Joe Sparma	2.50	1.25
268	John Blanchard	2.50	1.25
269	Don Heffner	2.50	1.25
270	Claude Osteen	2.50	1.25
271	Hal Lanier	2.50	1.25
272	Jack Baldschun	2.50	1.25
273	Astros Aces (Bob	3.50	1.75
	Aspromonte, Rusty		
	Staub)		
274	Buster Narum	2.50	1.25
275	Tim McCarver	4.50	2.25
276	Jim Bouton	3.00	1.50
277	George Thomas	2.50	1.25
278	Calvin Koonce	2.50	1.25
279	Checklist 265-352	7.50	3.00
280	Bobby Knoop	2.50	1.25
281	Bruce Howard	2.50	1.25
282	Johnny Lewis	2.50	1.25
283	Jim Perry	2.50	1.25
284	Bobby Wine	2.50	1.25
285	Luis Tiant	5.00	2.50
286	Gary Geiger	2.50	1.25
287	Jack Aker	2.50	1.25
288	Dodgers Rookies	125.00	65.00

	Bill Singer (R)		
	Don Sutton (R)		
289	Larry Sherry	2.50	1.25
290	Ron Santo	5.50	2.75
291	Moe Drabowsky	2.50	1.25
292	Jim Coker	2.50	1.25
293	Mike Shannon	2.50	1.25
294	Steve Ridzik	2.50	1.25
295	Jim Hart	2.50	1.25
296	Johnny Keane	2.50	1.25
297	Jim Owens	2.50	1.25
298	Rico Petrocelli	3.50	1.75
299	Lou Burdette	3.50	1.75
300	Roberto Clemente	120.00	60.00
301	Greg Bollo	2.50	1.25
302	Ernie Bowman	2.50	1.25
303	Indians Team	4.50	2.25
304	John Herrnstein	2.50	1.25
305	Camilo Pascual	2.50	1.25
306	Ty Cline	2.50	1.25
307	Clay Carroll	2.50	1.25
308	Tom Haller	2.50	1.25
309	Diego Segui	2.50	1.25
310	Frank Robinson	40.00	20.00
311	Reds Rookies	3.50	1.75
	Tommy Helms (R)		
	Dick Simpson (R)		
312	Bob Saverine	2.50	1.25
313	Chris Zachary	2.50	1.25
314	Hector Valle	2.50	1.25
315	Norm Cash	4.50	2.25
316	Jack Fisher	2.50	1.25
317	Dalton Jones	2.50	1.25
318	Harry Walker	2.50	1.25
319	Gene Freese	2.50	1.25
320	Bob Gibson	30.00	15.00
321	Rick Reichardt	2.50	1.25
322	Bill Faul	2.50	1.25
323	Ray Barker	2.50	1.25
324	John Boozer	2.50	1.25
325	Vic Davalillo	3.00	1.75
326	Braves Team	4.50	2.25
327	Bernie Allen	2.50	1.25
328	Jerry Grote	2.50	1.25
329	Pete Charton	2.50	1.25
330	Ron Fairly	2.50	1.25
331	Ron Herbel	2.50	1.25
332	Billy Bryan	2.50	1.25
333	Senators Rookies	3.50	1.75
	Joe Coleman (R)		
	Jim French (R)		
334	Marty Keough	2.50	1.25
335	Juan Pizarro	2.50	1.25
336	Gene Alley	2.50	1.25
337	Fred Gladding	2.50	1.25
338	Dal Maxvill	2.50	1.25
339	Del Crandall	3.00	1.50
340	Dean Chance	2.50	1.25
341	Wes Westrum	2.50	1.25
342	Bob Humphreys	2.50	1.25
343	Joe Christopher	2.50	1.25
344	Steve Blass	3.00	1.50
345	Bob Allison	2.50	1.25
346	Mike de la Hoz	2.50	1.25
347	Phil Regan	3.00	1.50
348	Orioles Team	6.00	3.00
349	Cap Peterson	2.50	1.25
350	Mel Stottlemyre	4.00	2.00
351	Fred Valentine	2.50	1.25
352	Bob Aspromonte	2.50	1.25
353	Al McBean	2.50	1.25
354	Smoky Burgess	3.00	1.50
355	Wade Blasingame	2.50	1.25
356	Red Sox Rookies	2.50	1.25
	Owen Johnson (R)		
	Ken Sanders (R)		
357	Gerry Arrigo	2.50	1.25
358	Charlie Smith	2.50	1.25
359	Johnny Briggs	2.50	1.25
360	Ron Hunt	3.00	1.50
361	Tom Satriano	2.50	1.25
362	Gates Brown	2.50	1.25
363	Checklist 353-429	8.00	3.25
364	Nate Oliver	2.50	1.25
365	Roger Maris	60.00	30.00
366	Wayne Causey	2.50	1.25
367	Mel Nelson	2.50	1.25
368	Charlie Lau	2.50	1.25
369	Jim King	2.50	1.25
370	Chico Cardenas	2.50	1.25
371	Lee Stange	2.50	1.25
372	Harvey Kuenn	3.50	1.75
373	Giants Rookies	2.50	1.25
	Dick Estelle (R)		
	Jack Hiatt		
374	Bob Locker	2.50	1.25
375	Donn Clendenon	2.50	1.25
376	Paul Schaal	2.50	1.25
377	Turk Farrell	2.50	1.25
378	Dick Tracewski	2.50	1.25
379	Cardinals Team	8.00	4.00
380	Tony Conigliaro	9.00	4.50
381	Hank Fischer	2.50	1.25
382	Phil Roof	2.50	1.25
383	Jackie Brandt	2.50	1.25
384	Al Downing	2.50	1.25
385	Ken Boyer	5.00	2.50
386	Gil Hodges	8.00	4.00
387	Howie Reed	2.50	1.25
388	Don Mincher	2.50	1.25
389	Jim O'Toole	2.50	1.25
390	Brooks Robinson	38.00	19.00
391	Chuck Hinton	2.50	1.25
392	Cubs Rookies	6.00	3.00

	Bill Hands (R)		
	Randy Hundley (R)		
393	George Brunet	2.50	1.25
394	Ron Brand	2.50	1.25
395	Len Gabrielson	2.50	1.25
396	Jerry Stephenson	2.50	1.25
397	Bill White	4.50	2.25
398	Danny Cater	2.50	1.25
399	Ray Washburn	2.50	1.25
400	Zoilo Versalles	3.00	1.50
401	Ken McMullen	2.50	1.25
402	Jim Hickman	2.50	1.25
403	Fred Talbot	2.50	1.25
404	Pirates Team	8.00	4.00
405	Elston Howard	7.00	3.50
406	Joe Jay	2.50	1.25
407	John Kennedy	2.50	1.25
408	Lee Thomas	2.50	1.25
409	Billy Hoeft	2.50	1.25
410	Al Kaline	32.00	16.00
411	Gene Mauch	3.00	1.50
412	Sam Bowens	2.50	1.25
413	John Romano	2.50	1.25
414	Dan Coombs	2.50	1.25
415	Max Alvis	2.50	1.25
416	Phil Ortega	2.50	1.25
417	Angels Rookie	2.50	1.25
	Jim McGlothlin (R)		
	Ed Sukla (R)		
418	Phil Gagliano	2.50	1.25
419	Mike Ryan	2.50	1.25
420	Juan Marichal	14.00	7.00
421	Roy McMillan	2.50	1.25
422	Ed Charles	2.50	1.25
423	Ernie Broglio	2.50	1.25
424	Reds Rookies	8.00	4.00
	Lee May (R)		
	Darrell Osteen		
425	Bob Veale	2.50	1.25
426	White Sox Team	8.00	4.00
427	John Miller	2.50	1.25
428	Sandy Alomar	3.50	1.75
429	Bill Monbouquette	2.50	1.25
430	Don Drysdale	28.00	14.00
431	Walt Bond	2.50	1.25
432	Bob Heffner	2.50	1.25
433	Alvin Dark	2.50	1.25
434	Willie Kirkland	2.50	1.25
435	Jim Bunning	8.50	4.25
436	Julian Javier	2.50	1.25
437	Al Stanek	2.50	1.25
438	Willie Smith	2.50	1.25
439	Pedro Ramos	2.50	1.25
440	Deron Johnson	3.50	1.75
441	Tommie Sisk	2.50	1.25
442	Orioles Rookies	2.50	1.25
	Ed Barnowski (R)		

	Eddie Watt		
443	Bill Wakefield	2.50	1.25
444	Checklist 430-506	8.00	3.25
445	Jim Kaat	8.50	4.25
446	Mack Jones	2.50	1.25
447	Dick Ellsworth(Wrong	8.00	4.00
	Photo)		
448	Eddie Stanky	7.00	3.50
449	Joe Moeller	7.00	3.50
450	Tony Oliva	12.00	6.00
451	Barry Latman	7.00	3.50
452	Joe Azcue	7.00	3.50
453	Ron Kline	7.00	3.50
454	Jerry Buchek	7.00	3.50
455	Mickey Lolich	10.00	5.00
456	Red Sox Rookies	7.00	3.50
	Darrell Brandon (R)		
	Joe Foy (R)		
457	Joe Gibbon	7.00	3.50
458	Manny Jimenez	7.00	3.50
459	Bill McCool	7.00	3.50
460	Curt Blefary	7.00	3.50
461	Roy Face	7.00	3.50
462	Bob Rodgers	7.00	3.50
463	Phillies Team	12.00	6.00
464	Larry Bearnarth	7.00	3.50
465	Don Buford	7.00	3.50
466	Ken Johnson	7.00	3.50
467	Vic Roznovsky	7.00	3.50
468	Johnny Podres	8.00	4.00
469	Yankees Rookies	28.00	14.00
	Bobby Murcer (R)		
	Dooley Womack (R)		
470	Sam McDowell	8.00	4.00
471	Bob Skinner	7.00	3.50
472	Terry Fox	7.00	3.50
473	Rich Rollins	7.00	3.50
474	Dick Schofield	7.00	3.50
475	Dick Radatz	7.00	3.50
476	Bobby Bragan	7.00	3.50
477	Steve Barber	7.00	3.50
478	Tony Gonzalez	7.00	3.50
479	Jim Hannan	7.00	3.50
480	Dick Stuart	7.00	3.50
481	Bob Lee	7.00	3.50
482	Cubs Rookies	7.00	3.50
	John Boccabella (R)		
	Dave Dowling (R)		
483	Joe Nuxhall	7.00	3.50
484	Wes Covington	7.00	3.50
485	Bob Bailey	7.00	3.50
486	Tommy John	14.00	7.00
487	Al Ferrara	7.00	3.50
488	George Banks	7.00	3.50
489	Curt Simmons	7.00	3.50
490	Bobby Richardson	14.00	7.00
491	Dennis Bennett	7.00	3.50

492	Athletics Team	12.00	6.00
493	Johnny Klippstein	7.00	3.50
494	Gordon Coleman	7.00	3.50
495	Dick McAuliffe	7.00	3.50
496	Lindy McDaniel	7.00	3.50
497	Chris Cannizzaro	7.00	3.50
498	Pirates Rookies	7.00	3.50
	Woody Fryman (R)		
	Luke Walker (R)		
499	Wally Bunker	7.00	3.50
500	Hank Aaron	140.00	70.00
501	John O'Donoghue	7.00	3.50
502	Lenny Green	7.00	3.50
503	Steve Hamilton	7.00	3.50
504	Grady Hatton	7.00	3.50
505	Jose Cardenal	7.00	3.50
506	Bo Belinsky	7.00	3.50
507	John Edwards	7.00	3.50
508	Steve Hargan	7.00	3.50
509	Jake Wood	7.00	3.50
510	Hoyt Wilhelm	15.00	7.50
511	Giants Rookies	8.00	4.00
	Bob Barton (R)		
	Tito Fuentes (R)		
512	Dick Stigman	7.00	3.50
513	Camilo Carreon	7.00	3.50
514	Hal Woodeshick	7.00	3.50
515	Frank Howard	12.00	6.00
516	Eddie Bressoud	7.00	3.50
517	Checklist 507-598	12.50	5.00
518	Braves Rookies	7.00	3.50
	Herb Hippauf (R)		
	Arnie Umbach (R)		
519	Bob Friend	8.00	4.00
520	Jim Wynn	8.00	4.00
521	John Wyatt	7.00	3.50
522	Phil Linz	7.00	3.50
523	Bob Sadowski	15.00	7.50
524	Giants Rookies	15.00	7.50
	Ollie Brown (R)		
	Don Mason (R)		
525	Gary Bell	15.00	7.50
526	Twins Team	70.00	40.00
527	Julio Navarro	15.00	7.50
528	Jesse Gonder	15.00	7.50
529	White Sox Rookies	15.00	7.50
	Lee Elia (R)		
	Dennis Higgins (R)		
	Bill Voss (R)		
530	Robin Roberts	48.00	24.00
531	Joe Cunningham	15.00	7.50
532	Aurelio Monteagudo	15.00	7.50
533	Jerry Adair	15.00	7.50
534	Mets Rookies	15.00	7.50
	Dave Eilers (R)		
	Rob Gardner (R)		
535	Willie Davis	40.00	20.00
536	Dick Egan	15.00	7.50
537	Herman Franks	15.00	7.50
538	Bob Allen	15.00	7.50
539	Astros Rookies	15.00	7.50
	Bill Heath (R)		
	Carrol Sembera (R)		
540	Denny McLain	70.00	35.00
541	Gene Oliver	15.00	7.50
542	George Smith	15.00	7.50
543	Roger Craig	28.00	14.00
544	Cardinals Rookies	15.00	7.50
	Joe Hoerner (R)		
	George Kernek (R)		
	Jimmy Williams (R)		
545	Dick Green	15.00	7.50
546	Dwight Siebler	15.00	7.50
547	Horace Clarke	28.00	14.00
548	Gary Kroll	15.00	7.50
549	Senators Rookies	15.00	7.50
	Al Closter (R)		
	Casey Cox (R)		
550	Willie McCovey	125.00	65.00
551	Bob Purkey	15.00	7.50
552	Birdie Tebbets	15.00	7.50
553	M.L. Rookie Stars	15.00	7.50
	Pat Garrett (R)		
	Jackie Warner (R)		
554	Jim Northrup	15.00	7.50
555	Ron Perranoski	15.00	7.50
556	Mel Queen	15.00	7.50
557	Felix Mantilla	15.00	7.50
558	Red Sox Rookies	28.00	14.00
	Guido Grilli(R)		
	Pete Magrini (R)		
	George Scott (R)		
559	Roberto Pena	15.00	7.50
560	Joel Horlen	15.00	7.50
561	Choo Choo Coleman	28.00	14.00
562	Russ Snyder	15.00	7.50
563	Twins Rookies	15.00	7.50
	Pete Cimino (R)		
	Cesar Tovar		
564	Bob Chance	15.00	7.50
565	Jimmy Piersall	36.00	18.00
566	Mike Cuellar	28.00	14.00
567	Dick Howser	28.00	14.00
568	Athletics Rookies	15.00	7.50
	Paul Lindblad (R)		
	Ron Stone (R)		
569	Orlando McFarlane	15.00	7.50
570	Art Mahaffey	15.00	7.50
571	Dave Roberts	15.00	7.50
572	Bob Priddy	15.00	7.50
573	Derrell Griffith	15.00	7.50
574	Mets Rookies	15.00	7.50
	Bill Hepler (R)		
	Bill Murphy		

575	Earl Wilson	15.00	7.50
576	Dave Nicholson	15.00	7.50
577	Jack Lamabe	15.00	7.50
578	Chi Chi Olivo	15.00	7.50
579	Orioles Rookies	24.00	12.00
	Frank Bertaina (R)		
	Gene Brabender (R)		
	Dave Johnson (R)		
580	Billy Williams	100.00	50.00
581	Tony Martinez	15.00	7.50
582	Garry Roggenburk	15.00	7.50
583	Tigers Team	140.00	70.00
584	Yankees Rookies	15.00	7.50
	Frank Fernandez (R)		
	Fritz Peterson (R)		
585	Tony Taylor	15.00	7.50
586	Claude Raymond	15.00	7.50
587	Dick Bertell	15.00	7.50
588	Athletics Rookies	15.00	7.50
	Chuck Dobson (R)		
	Ken Suarez (R)		
589	Lou Klimchock	15.00	7.50
590	Bill Skowron	42.00	21.00
591	N.L. Rookies	38.00	19.00
	Grant Jackson (R)		
	Bart Shirley (R)		
592	Andre Rodgers	15.00	7.50
593	Doug Camilli	15.00	7.50
594	Chico Salmon	15.00	7.50
595	Larry Jackson	15.00	7.50
596	Astros Rookies	28.00	14.00
	Nate Colbert (R)		
	Greg Sims (R)		
597	John Sullivan	15.00	7.50
598	Gaylord Perry	275.00	125.00

1967 Topps

This 609-card set features large color photos on the card fronts framed by a white border. Fascimile autographs appear in the bottom right corner. This is the first Topps issue to sport vertical card backs. Cards measure 2-1/2" by 3-1/2" and the major subsets include League Leaders, World Series Highlights and Rookies.

		NR/MT	EX
Complete Set (609)		5,300.00	2,650.00
Commons (1-110)		1.25	.60
Commons (111-457)		2.50	1.25
Commons (458-533)		6.00	3.00
Commons (534-609)		15.00	7.50

1	The Champs	20.00	8.50
	(Hank Bauer		
	Brooks Robinson		
	Frank Robinson)		
2	Jack Hamilton	1.25	.60
3	Duke Sims	1.25	.60
4	Hal Lanier	1.25	.60
5	Whitey Ford	22.00	11.00
6	Dick Simpson	1.25	.60
7	Don McMahon	1.25	.60
8	Chuck Harrison	1.25	.60
9	Ron Hansen	1.25	.60
10	Matty Alou	2.00	1.00
11	Barry Moore	1.25	.60
12	Dodgers Rookies	2.00	1.25
	Jim Campanis (R)		
	Billy Singer (R)		
13	Joe Sparma	1.25	.60
14	Phil Linz	1.25	.60
15	Earl Battey	1.25	.60
16	Bill Hands	1.25	.60
17	Jim Gosger	1.25	.60
18	Gene Oliver	1.25	.60
19	Jim McGlothlin	1.25	.60
20	Orlando Cepeda	8.50	4.25
21	Dave Bristol	1.25	.60
22	Gene Brabender	1.25	.60
23	Larry Elliot	1.25	.60
24	Bob Allen	1.25	.60
25	Elston Howard	4.50	2.25
26a	Bob Priddy (No trade statement)	24.00	12.00
26b	Bob Priddy (Trade statement)	1.25	.60
27	Bob Saverine	1.25	.60
28	Barry Latman	1.25	.60
29	Tommy McCraw	1.25	.60
30	Al Kaline	20.00	10.00
31	Jim Brewer	1.25	.60
32	Bob Bailey	1.25	.60
33	Athletics Rookies	5.00	2.50

	Sal Bando (R)		
	Randy Schwartz (R)		
34	Pete Cimino	1.25	.60
35	Rico Carty	2.50	1.25
36	Bob Tillman	1.25	.60
37	Rick Wise	1.50	.75
38	Bob Johnson	1.25	.60
39	Curt Simmons	1.25	.60
40	Rick Reichardt	1.25	.60
41	Joe Hoerner	1.25	.60
42	Mets Team	6.50	3.75
43	Chico Salmon	1.25	.60
44	Joe Nuxhall	1.25	.60
45	Roger Maris	48.00	24.00
46	Lindy McDaniel	1.25	.60
47	Ken McMullen	1.25	.60
48	Bill Freehan	1.25	.60
49	Roy Face	1.25	.60
50	Tony Oliva	5.00	2.50
51	Astros Rookies	1.25	.60
	Dave Adlesh (R)		
	Wes Bales (R)		
52	Dennis Higgins	1.25	.60
53	Clay Dalrymple	1.25	.60
54	Dick Green	1.25	.60
55	Don Drysdale	18.00	9.00
56	Jose Tartabull	1.25	.60
57	Pat Jarvis	1.25	.60
58	Paul Schaal	1.25	.60
59	Ralph Terry	1.50	.75
60	Luis Aparicio	7.50	3.75
61	Gordy Coleman	1.25	.60
62	Checklist 1-109	7.00	3.50
63	Cards' Clubbers (Lou	8.50	4.25
	Brock/Curt Flood)		
64	Fred Valentine	1.25	.60
65	Tom Haller	1.25	.60
66	Manny Mota	1.50	.75
67	Ken Berry	1.25	.60
68	Bob Buhl	1.25	.60
69	Vic Davalillo	1.25	.60
70	Ron Santo	4.50	2.25
71	Camilo Pascual	1.25	.60
72	Tigers Rookies	1.25	.60
	George Korince (R)		
	John Matchick (R)		
73	Rusty Staub	4.00	2.00
74	Wes Stock	1.25	.60
75	George Scott	2.50	1.25
76	Jim Barbieri	1.25	.60
77	Dooley Womack	1.25	.60
78	Pat Corrales	1.50	.75
79	Bubba Morton	1.25	.60
80	Jim Maloney	1.25	.60
81	Eddie Stanky	1.25	.60
82	Steve Barber	1.25	.60
83	Ollie Brown	1.25	.60
84	Tommie Sisk	1.25	.60
85	Johnny Callison	1.50	.75
86a	Mike McCormick (No	20.00	10.00
	trade statement)		
86b	Mike McCormick	1.25	.60
	(Trade statement)		
87	George Altman	1.25	.60
88	Mickey Lolich	4.50	2.25
89	Felix Millan (R)	1.50	.75
90	Jim Nash	1.25	.60
91	Johnny Lewis	1.25	.60
92	Ray Washburn	1.25	.60
93	Yankees Rookies	4.00	2.00
	Stan Bahnsen (R)		
	Bobby Murcer		
94	Ron Fairly	1.25	.60
95	Sonny Siebert	1.25	.60
96	Art Shamsky	1.25	.60
97	Mike Cuellar	2.00	1.00
98	Rich Rollins	1.25	.60
99	Lee Stange	1.25	.60
100	Frank Robinson	20.00	10.00
101	Ken Johnson	1.25	.60
102	Phillies Team	3.00	1.50
103	Checklist 110-196	12.00	6.00
104	Minnie Rojas	1.25	.60
105	Ken Boyer	3.50	1.75
106	Randy Hundley	1.25	.60
107	Joel Horlen	1.25	.60
108	Alex Johnson	1.25	.60
109	Tribe Thumpers	2.50	1.25
	(Rocky Colavito,		
	Leon Wagner)		
110	Jack Aker	1.25	.60
111	John Kennedy	2.50	1.25
112	Dave Wickersham	2.50	1.25
113	Dave Nicholson	2.50	1.25
114	Jack Baldschun	2.50	1.25
115	Paul Casanova	2.50	1.25
116	Herman Franks	2.50	1.25
117	Darrell Brandon	2.50	1.25
118	Bernie Allen	2.50	1.25
119	Wade Blasingame	2.50	1.25
120	Floyd Robinson	2.50	1.25
121	Ed Bressoud	2.50	1.25
122	George Brunet	2.50	1.25
123	Pirates Rookies	1.25	.60
	Jim Price (R)		
	Luke Walker		
124	Jim Stewart	2.50	1.25
125	Moe Drabowsky	2.50	1.25
126	Tony Taylor	2.50	1.25
127	John O'Donoghue	2.50	1.25
128	Ed Spiezio	2.50	1.25
129	Phil Roof	2.50	1.25
130	Phil Regan	2.50	1.25
131	Yankees Team	6.50	3.25

132	Ozzie Virgil	2.50	1.25
133	Ron Kline	2.50	1.25
134	Gates Brown	2.50	1.25
135	Deron Johnson	2.50	1.25
136	Carroll Sembera	2.50	1.25
137	Twins Rookies Ron Clark (R) Jim Ollum (R)	2.50	1.25
138	Dick Kelley	2.50	1.25
139	Dalton Jones	2.50	1.25
140	Willie Stargell	22.00	11.00
141	John Miller	2.50	1.25
142	Jackie Brandt	2.50	1.25
143	Sox Sockers Don Buford Pete Ward	2.50	1.25
144	Bill Hepler	2.50	1.25
145	Larry Brown	2.50	1.25
146	Steve Carlton	130.00	65.00
147	Tom Egan	2.50	1.25
148	Adolfo Phillips	2.50	1.25
149	Joe Moeller	2.50	1.25
150	Mickey Mantle	300.00	150.00
151	World Series Game 1	4.00	2.00
152	World Series Game 2	7.50	3.75
153	World Series Game 3	4.00	2.00
154	World Series Game 4	4.00	2.00
155	WS (Celebration)	4.00	2.00
156	Ron Herbel	2.50	1.25
157	Danny Cater	2.50	1.25
158	Jimmy Coker	2.50	1.25
159	Bruce Howard	2.50	1.25
160	Willie Davis	2.50	1.25
161	Dick Williams	2.50	1.25
162	Billy O'Dell	2.50	1.25
163	Vic Roznovsky	2.50	1.25
164	Dwight Siebler	2.50	1.25
165	Cleon Jones	2.50	1.25
166	Eddie Mathews	15.00	7.50
167	Senators Rookies (Joe Coleman, Tim Cullen)	2.50	1.25
168	Ray Culp	2.50	1.25
169	Horace Clarke	2.50	1.25
170	Dick McAuliffe	2.50	1.25
171	Calvin Koonce	2.50	1.25
172	Bill Heath	2.50	1.25
173	Cardinals Team	3.50	1.75
174	Dick Radatz	2.50	1.25
175	Bobby Knoop	2.50	1.25
176	Sammy Ellis	2.50	1.25
177	Tito Fuentes	2.50	1.25
178	John Buzhardt	2.50	1.25
179	Braves Rookies Cecil Upshaw (R) Charles Vaugan (R)	2.50	1.25
180	Curt Blefary	2.50	1.25
181	Terry Fox	2.50	1.25
182	Ed Charles	2.50	1.25
183	Jim Pagliaroni	2.50	1.25
184	George Thomas	2.50	1.25
185	Ken Holtzman (R)	4.00	2.00
186	Mets Maulers (Ed Kranepool/Ron Swoboda)	3.00	1.50
187	Pedro Ramos	2.50	1.25
188	Ken Harrelson	3.00	1.50
189	Chuck Hinton	2.50	1.25
190	Turk Farrell	2.50	1.25
191	Checklist 197-283	12.00	5.00
192	Fred Gladding	2.50	1.25
193	Jose Cardenal	2.50	1.25
194	Bob Allison	2.50	1.25
195	Al Jackson	2.50	1.25
196	Johnny Romano	2.50	1.25
197	Ron Perranoski	2.50	1.25
198	Chuck Hiller	2.50	1.25
199	Billy Hitchcock	2.50	1.25
200	Willie Mays	110.00	55.00
201	Hal Reniff	2.50	1.25
202	Johnny Edwards	2.50	1.25
203	Al McBean	2.50	1.25
204	Orioles Rookies (Mike Epstein, Tom Phoebus)	2.50	1.25
205	Dick Groat	3.00	1.50
206	Dennis Bennett	2.50	1.25
207	John Orsino	2.50	1.25
208	Jack Lamabe	2.50	1.25
209	Joe Nossek	2.50	1.25
210	Bob Gibson	25.00	15.00
211	Twins Team	3.50	1.75
212	Chris Zachary	2.50	1.25
213	Jay Johnstone (R)	3.00	1.75
214	Tom Kelley	2.50	1.25
215	Ernie Banks	24.00	12.00
216	Bengal Belters (Norm Cash/Al Kaline)	9.00	4.50
217	Rob Gardner	2.50	1.25
218	Wes Parker	2.50	1.25
219	Clay Carroll	2.50	1.25
220	Jim Hart	2.50	1.25
221	Woody Fryman	2.50	1.25
222	Reds Rookies (Lee May, Darrell Osteen)	3.50	1.75
223	Mike Ryan	2.50	1.25
224	Walt Bond	2.50	1.25
225	Mel Stottlemyre	3.50	1.75
226	Julian Javier	2.50	1.25
227	Paul Lindblad	2.50	1.25
228	Gil Hodges	6.00	3.00
229	Larry Jackson	2.50	1.25
230	Boog Powell	4.50	2.25
231	John Bateman	2.50	1.25

232	Don Buford	2.50	1.25
233	A.L. ERA Leaders	4.00	2.00
234	N.L. ERA Leaders	11.00	5.50
235	A.L. Pitching Leaders	5.00	2.50
236	N.L. Pitching Leaders	20.00	10.00
237	A.L. Strikeout Leaders	4.00	2.00
238	N.L. Strikeout Leaders	10.00	5.00
239	A.L. Batting Leaders	8.00	4.00
240	N.L. Batting Leaders	4.00	2.00
241	A.L. RBI Leaders	8.00	4.00
242	N.L. RBI Leaders	15.00	7.50
243	A.L. HR Leaders	8.00	4.00
244	N.L. HR Leaders	14.00	7.00
245	Curt Flood	3.00	1.50
246	Jim Perry	2.50	1.25
247	Jerry Lumpe	2.50	1.25
248	Gene Mauch	2.50	1.25
249	Nick Willhite	2.50	1.25
250	Hank Aaron	110.00	55.00
251	Woody Held	2.50	1.25
252	Bob Bolin	2.50	1.25
253	Indians Rookies	2.50	1.25
	Bill Davis (R)		
	Gus Gil (R)		
254	Milt Pappas	2.50	1.25
255	Frank Howard	5.00	2.50
256	Bob Hendley	2.50	1.25
257	Charley Smith	2.50	1.25
258	Lee Maye	2.50	1.25
259	Don Dennis	2.50	1.25
260	Jim Lefebvre	2.50	1.25
261	John Wyatt	2.50	1.25
262	Athletics Team	3.50	1.75
263	Hank Aguirre	2.50	1.25
264	Ron Swoboda	2.50	1.25
265	Lou Burdette	3.00	1.50
266	Pitt Power (Donn	4.50	2.25
	Clendenon, Willie		
	Stargell)		
267	Don Schwall	2.50	1.25
268	John Briggs	2.50	1.25
269	Don Nottebart	2.50	1.25
270	Zoilo Versalles	3.00	1.50
271	Eddie Watt	2.50	1.25
272	Cubs Rookies	3.00	1.50
	Bill Connors (R)		
	Dave Dowling (R)		
273	Dick Lines	2.50	1.25
274	Bob Aspromonte	2.50	1.25
275	Fred Whitfield	2.50	1.25
276	Bruce Brubaker	2.50	1.25
277	Steve Whitaker	2.50	1.25
278	Checklist 284-370	7.00	3.00
279	Frank Linzy	2.50	1.25
280	Tony Conigliaro	8.50	4.25
281	Bob Rodgers	2.50	1.25
282	Johnny Odom	2.50	1.25
283	Gene Alley	2.50	1.25
284	Johnny Podres	3.00	1.50
285	Lou Brock	25.00	15.00
286	Wayne Causey	2.50	1.25
287	Mets Rookies	2.50	1.25
	Greg Gossen (R)		
	Bart Shirley		
288	Denver Lemaster	2.50	1.25
289	Tom Tresh	3.50	1.75
290	Bill White	3.50	1.75
291	Jim Hannan	2.50	1.25
292	Don Pavletich	2.50	1.25
293	Ed Kirkpatrick	2.50	1.25
294	Walt Alston	3.50	1.75
295	Sam McDowell	3.00	1.50
296	Glenn Beckert	3.00	1.50
297	Dave Morehead	2.50	1.25
298	Ron Davis	2.50	1.25
299	Norm Siebern	2.50	1.25
300	Jim Kaat	5.00	2.50
301	Jesse Gonder	2.50	1.25
302	Orioles Team	5.00	2.50
303	Gil Blanco	2.50	1.25
304	Phil Gagliano	2.50	1.25
305	Earl Wilson	2.50	1.25
306	Bub Harrelson (R)	4.00	2.00
307	Jim Beauchamp	2.50	1.25
308	Al Downing	2.50	1.25
309	Hurlers Beward	3.50	1.75
	(Richie Allen,		
	Johnny Callison)		
310	Gary Peters	2.50	1.25
311	Ed Brinkman	2.50	1.25
312	Don Mincher	2.50	1.25
313	Bob Lee	2.50	1.25
314	Red Sox Rookies	8.50	4.25
	Mike Andrews (R)		
	Reggie Smith (R)		
315	Billy Williams	14.00	7.00
316	Jack Kralick	2.50	1.25
317	Cesar Tovar	2.50	1.25
318	Dave Giusti	2.50	1.25
319	Paul Blair	3.00	1.50
320	Gaylord Perry	16.00	8.00
321	Mayo Smith	2.50	1.25
322	Jose Pagan	2.50	1.25
323	Mike Hershberger	2.50	1.25
324	Hal Woodeshick	2.50	1.25
325	Chico Cardenas	2.50	1.25
326	Bob Uecker	14.00	7.00
327	Angels Team	5.00	2.50
328	Clete Boyer	3.00	1.50
329	Charlie Lau	2.50	1.25
330	Claude Osteen	2.50	1.25
331	Joe Foy	2.50	1.25
332	Jesus Alou	2.50	1.25
333	Ferguson Jenkins	32.00	16.00

334	Twin Terrors (Bob Allison, Harmon Killebrew)	5.00	2.50
335	Bob Veale	2.50	1.25
336	Joe Azcue	2.50	1.25
337	Joe Morgan	24.00	12.00
338	Bob Locker	2.50	1.25
339	Chico Ruiz	2.50	1.25
340	Joe Pepitone	3.50	1.75
341	Giants Rookies Dick Dietz Bill Sorrell (R)	2.50	1.25
342	Hank Fischer	2.50	1.25
343	Tom Satriano	2.50	1.25
344	Ossie Chavarria	2.50	1.25
345	Stu Miller	2.50	1.25
346	Jim Hickman	2.50	1.25
347	Grady Hatton	2.50	1.25
348	Tug McGraw	4.50	2.25
349	Bob Chance	2.50	1.25
350	Joe Torre	4.50	2.25
351	Vern Law	2.50	1.25
352	Ray Oyler	2.50	1.25
353	Bill McCool	2.50	1.25
354	Cubs Team	3.50	1.75
355	Carl Yastrzemski	80.00	50.00
356	Larry Jaster	2.50	1.25
357	Bill Skowron	3.50	1.75
358	Ruben Amaro	2.50	1.25
359	Dick Ellsworth	2.50	1.25
360	Leon Wagner	2.50	1.25
361	Checklist 371-457	8.50	3.50
362	Darold Knowles	2.50	1.25
363	Dave Johnson	2.50	1.25
364	Claude Raymond	2.50	1.25
365	John Roseboro	2.50	1.25
366	Andy Kosco	2.50	1.25
367	Angels Rookies Bill Kelso (R) Don Wallace (R)	2.50	1.25
368	Jack Hiatt	2.50	1.25
369	Jim Hunter	20.00	10.00
370	Tommy Davis	3.50	1.75
371	Jim Lonborg	5.50	2.75
372	Mike de la Hoz	2.50	1.25
373	White Sox Rookies Duane Josephson (R) Fred Klages (R)	2.50	1.25
374	Mel Queen	2.50	1.25
375	Jake Gibbs	2.50	1.25
376	Don Lock	2.50	1.25
377	Luis Tiant	6.00	3.00
378	Tigers Team	6.00	3.00
379	Jerry May	2.50	1.25
380	Dean Chance	2.50	1.25
381	Dick Schofield	2.50	1.25
382	Dave McNally	3.50	1.75
383	Ken Henderson	2.50	1.25
384	Cardinals Rookies Jim Cosman (R) Dick Hughes	2.50	1.25
385	Jim Fregosi	3.00	1.50
386	Dick Selma	2.50	1.25
387	Cap Peterson	2.50	1.25
388	Arnold Earley	2.50	1.25
389	Al Dark	2.50	1.25
390	Jim Wynn	3.00	1.50
391	Wilbur Wood	3.00	1.50
392	Tommy Harper	3.00	1.50
393	Jim Bouton	4.00	2.00
394	Jake Wood	2.50	1.25
395	Chris Short	2.50	1.25
396	Atlanta Aces (Tony Cloninger, Denis Menke)	3.00	1.50
397	Willie Smith	2.50	1.25
398	Jeff Torborg	3.00	1.50
399	Al Worthington	2.50	1.25
400	Roberto Clemente	80.00	40.00
401	Jim Coates	2.50	1.25
402	Phillies Rookies Grant Jackson Billy Wilson (R)	2.50	1.25
403	Dick Nen	2.50	1.25
404	Nelson Briles	2.50	1.25
405	Russ Snyder	2.50	1.25
406	Lee Elia	2.50	1.25
407	Reds Team	6.00	3.00
408	Jim Northrup	2.50	1.25
409	Ray Sadecki	2.50	1.25
410	Lou Johnson	2.50	1.25
411	Dick Howser	2.50	1.25
412	Astros Rookies Norm Miller (R) Doug Rader (R)	4.00	2.00
413	Jerry Grote	2.50	1.25
414	Casey Cox	2.50	1.25
415	Sonny Jackson	2.50	1.25
416	Roger Repoz	2.50	1.25
417	Bob Bruce	2.50	1.25
418	Sam Mele	2.50	1.25
419	Don Kessinger	3.50	1.75
420	Denny McLain	8.00	4.00
421	Dal Maxvill	2.50	1.25
422	Hoyt Wilhelm	10.00	5.00
423	Fence Busters (Willie Mays/Willie McCovey)	28.00	14.00
424	Pedro Gonzalez	2.50	1.25
425	Pete Mikkelsen	2.50	1.25
426	Lou Clinton	2.50	1.25
427	Ruben Gomez	2.50	1.25
428	Dodgers Rookies Tom Hutton (R) Gene Michael (R)	4.00	2.00

No.	Player	Price 1	Price 2
429	Garry Roggenburk	2.50	1.25
430	Pete Rose	85.00	42.50
431	Ted Uhlaender	2.50	1.25
432	Jimmie Hall	2.50	1.25
433	AL Luplow	2.50	1.25
434	Eddie Fisher	2.50	1.25
435	Mack Jones	2.50	1.25
436	Pete Ward	2.50	1.25
437	Senators Team	6.00	3.00
438	Chuck Dobson	2.50	1.25
439	Byron Browne	2.50	1.25
440	Steve Hargan	2.50	1.25
441	Jim Davenport	2.50	1.25
442	Yankees Rookies	4.00	2.00
	Bill Robinson (R)		
	Joe Verbanic (R)		
443	Tito Francona	2.50	1.25
444	George Smith	2.50	1.25
445	Don Sutton	32.00	16.00
446	Russ Nixon	2.50	1.25
447	Bo Belinsky	2.50	1.25
448	Harry Walker	2.50	1.25
449	Orlando Pena	2.50	1.25
450	Richie Allen	7.50	3.75
451	Fred Newman	2.50	1.25
452	Ed Kranepool	3.00	1.50
453	Aurelio Monteagudo	2.50	1.25
454	Checklist 458-533	7.00	3.50
455	Tommie Agee	2.50	1.25
456	Phil Niekro	18.00	9.00
457	Andy Etchebarren	2.50	1.25
458	Lee Thomas	6.00	3.00
459	Senators Rookies	7.50	3.75
	Dick Bosman (R)		
	Pete Craig		
460	Harmon Killebrew	55.00	27.50
461	Bob Miller	6.00	3.00
462	Bob Barton	6.00	3.00
463	Tribe Hill Aces (Sam	7.00	3.50
	McDowell/Sonny		
	Siebert)		
464	Dan Coombs	6.00	3.00
465	Willie Horton	7.00	3.50
466	Bobby Wine	6.00	3.00
467	Jim O'Toole	6.00	3.00
468	Ralph Houk	6.00	3.00
469	Len Gabrielson	6.00	3.00
470	Bob Shaw	6.00	3.00
471	Rene Lachemann	6.00	3.00
472	Pirates Rookies	6.00	3.00
	John Gelnar (R)		
	George Spriggs (R)		
473	Jose Santiago	6.00	3.00
474	Bob Tolan	6.00	3.00
475	Jim Palmer	120.00	60.00
476	Tony Perez	80.00	40.00
477	Braves Team	12.00	6.00
478	Bob Humphreys	6.00	3.00
479	Gary Bell	6.00	3.00
480	Willie McCovey	40.00	20.00
481	Leo Durocher	12.00	6.00
482	Bill Monbouquette	6.00	3.00
483	Jim Landis	6.00	3.00
484	Jerry Adair	6.00	3.00
485	Tim McCarver	22.00	11.00
486	Twins Rookies	6.00	3.00
	Rich Reese (R)		
	Bill Whitby (R)		
487	Tom Reynolds	6.00	3.00
488	Gerry Arrigo	6.00	3.00
489	Doug Clemens	6.00	3.00
490	Tony Cloninger	6.00	3.00
491	Sam Bowens	6.00	3.00
492	Pirates Team	12.00	6.00
493	Phil Ortega	6.00	3.00
494	Bill Rigney	6.00	3.00
495	Fritz Peterson	6.00	3.00
496	Orlando McFarlane	6.00	3.00
497	Ron Campbell	6.00	3.00
498	Larry Dierker	6.50	3.25
499	Indians Rookies	6.00	3.00
	George Culver (R)		
	Jose Vidal (R)		
500	Juan Marichal	28.00	14.00
501	Jerry Zimmerman	6.00	3.00
502	Derrell Griffith	6.00	3.00
503	Dodgers Team	12.00	6.00
504	Orlando Martinez	6.00	3.00
505	Tommy Helms	7.00	3.50
506	Smoky Burgess	7.00	3.50
507	Orioles Rookies	6.50	3.25
	Ed Barnowski (R)		
	Larry Haney		
508	Dick Hall	6.00	3.00
509	Jim King	6.00	3.00
510	Bill Mazeroski	12.00	6.00
511	Don Wert	6.00	3.00
512	Red Schoendienst	12.00	6.00
513	Marcelino Lopez	6.00	3.00
514	John Werhas	6.00	3.00
515	Bert Campaneris	8.00	4.00
516	Giants Team	12.00	6.00
517	Fred Talbot	6.00	3.00
518	Denis Menke	6.00	3.00
519	Ted Davidson	6.00	3.00
520	Max Alvis	6.00	3.00
521	Bird Bombers (Curt	7.00	3.50
	Blefary/Boog Powell)		
522	John Stephenson	6.00	3.00
523	Jim Merritt	6.00	3.00
524	Felix Mantilla	6.00	3.00
525	Ron Hunt	6.00	3.00
526	Tigers Rookies	8.00	4.00
	Pat Dobson (R)		

George Korince (R)

527	Dennis Ribant	6.00	3.00
528	Rico Petrocelli	10.00	5.00
529	Gary Wagner	6.00	3.00
530	Felipe Alou	12.00	6.00
531	Checklist 534-609	12.00	6.00
532	Jim Hicks	6.00	3.00
533	Jack Fisher	6.00	3.00
534	Hank Bauer	15.00	7.50
535	Donn Clendenon	15.00	7.50
536	Cubs Rookies	35.00	17.50
	Joe Niekro (R)		
	Paul Popovich (R)		
537	Chuck Estrada	15.00	7.50
538	J.C. Martin	15.00	7.50
539	Dick Egan	15.00	7.50
540	Norm Cash	45.00	22.50
541	Joe Gibbon	15.00	7.50
542	Athletics Rookies	18.00	9.00
	Rick Monday (R)		
	Tony Pierce (R)		
543	Dan Schneider	15.00	7.50
544	Indians Team	15.00	7.50
545	Jim Grant	15.00	7.50
546	Woody Woodward	15.00	7.50
547	Red Sox Rookies	15.00	7.50
	Russ Gibson (R)		
	Bill Rohr (R)		
548	Tony Gonzalez	15.00	7.50
549	Jack Sanford	15.00	7.50
550	Vada Pinson	16.00	8.00
551	Doug Camilli	15.00	7.50
552	Ted Savage	15.00	7.50
553	Yankees Rookies	24.00	12.00
	Mike Hegan (R)		
	Thad Tillotson (R)		
554	Andre Rodgers	15.00	7.50
555	Don Cardwell	15.00	7.50
556	Al Weis	15.00	7.50
557	Al Ferrara	15.00	7.50
558	Orioles Rookies	60.00	30.00
	Mark Belanger (R)		
	Bill Dillman		
559	Dick Tracewski	15.00	7.50
560	Jim Bunning	50.00	25.00
561	Sandy Alomar	15.00	7.50
562	Steve Blass	15.00	7.50
563	Joe Adcock	22.00	11.00
564	Astros Rookies	15.00	7.50
	Alonzo Harris (R)		
	Aaron Pointer (R)		
565	Lew Krausse	15.00	7.50
566	Gary Geiger	15.00	7.50
567	Steve Hamilton	15.00	7.50
568	John Sullivan	15.00	7.50
569	A.L. Rookies	500.00	250.00
	Hank Allen (R)		

Rod Carew (R)

570	Maury Wills	90.00	45.00
571	Larry Sherry	15.00	7.50
572	Don Demeter	20.00	10.00
573	White Sox Team	15.00	7.50
574	Jerry Buchek	15.00	7.50
575	Dave Boswell	15.00	7.50
576	N.L. Rookies	18.00	9.00
	Norm Gigon (R)		
	Ramon Hernandez (R)		
577	Bill Short	15.00	7.50
578	John Boccabella	15.00	7.50
579	Bill Henry	15.00	7.50
580	Rocky Colavito	75.00	37.50
581	Mets Rookies	1,350.00	675.00
	Bill Denehy (R)		
	Tom Seaver (R)		
582	Jim Owens	15.00	7.50
583	Ray Barker	15.00	7.50
584	Jim Piersall	28.00	14.00
585	Wally Bunker	15.00	7.50
586	Manny Jimenez	15.00	7.50
587	N.L. Rookies	22.00	11.00
	Don Shaw (R)		
	Gary Sutherland (R)		
588	Johnny Klippstein	15.00	7.50
589	Dave Ricketts	15.00	7.50
590	Pete Richert	15.00	7.50
591	Ty Cline	15.00	7.50
592	N.L. Rookies	15.00	7.50
	Jim Shellenback (R)		
	Ron Willis (R)		
593	Wes Westrum	15.00	7.50
594	Dan Osinski	15.00	7.50
595	Cookie Rojas	15.00	7.50
596	Galen Cisco	15.00	7.50
597	Ted Abernathy	15.00	7.50
598	White Sox Rookies	15.00	7.50
	Ed Stroud (R)		
	Walt Williams (R)		
599	Bob Duliba	15.00	7.50
600	Brooks Robinson	265.00	135.00
601	Bill Bryan	15.00	7.50
602	Juan Pizarro	15.00	7.50
603	Athletics Rookies	15.00	7.50
	Tim Talton (R)		
	Ramon Webster (R)		
604	Red Sox Team	120.00	60.00
605	Mike Shannon	45.00	22.50
606	Ron Taylor	15.00	7.50
607	Mickey Stanley	32.00	16.00
608	Cubs Rookies		
	Rich Nye (R)		
	John Upham (R)		
609	Tommy John	120.00	50.00

1968 Topps

BROOKS
ROBINSON ORIOLES

This 598-card set features four-color photos on the front printed on a grainy background. Player's names appear below the pictures and team names are printed in a small circle in the lower right corner. Once again, the card backs are vertical with bio's, stats and a small cartoon. Cards measure 2-1/2" by 3-1/2" and subsets included League Leaders (1-12), World Series Highlights (151-158) and All-Stars (361-380).

		NR/MT	EX
Complete Set (598)		3,500.00	1,750.00
Commons (1-457)		1.25	.60
Commons (458-598)		3.50	1.75

		NR/MT	EX
1	N.L. Batting Leaders	20.00	10.00
2	A.L. Batting Leaders	12.00	6.00
3	N.L. RBI Leaders	10.00	5.00
4	A.L. RBI Leaders	10.00	5.00
5	N.L. HR Leaders	7.50	3.75
6	A.L. HR Leaders	8.00	4.00
7	N.L. ERA Leaders	3.00	1.50
8	A.L. ERA Leaders	3.00	1.50
9	N.L. Pitching Leaders	4.50	2.25
10	A.L. Pitching Leaders	4.50	2.25
11	N.L. Strikeout Leaders	5.00	2.50
12	A.L. Strikeout Leaders	3.00	1.50
13	Chuck Hartenstein	1.25	.60
14	Jerry McNertney	1.25	.60
15	Ron Hunt	1.25	.60
16	Indians Rookies	5.00	2.50
	Lou Piniella		
	Richie Scheinblum (R)		
17	Dick Hall	1.25	.60
18	Mike Hershberger	1.25	.60
19	Juan Pizarro	1.25	.60
20	Brooks Robinson	28.00	14.00
21	Ron Davis	1.25	.60
22	Pat Dobson	2.00	1.00
23	Chico Cardenas	1.25	.60
24	Bobby Locke	1.25	.60
25	Julian Javier	1.25	.60
26	Darrell Brandon	1.25	.60
27	Gil Hodges	8.00	4.00
28	Ted Uhlaender	1.25	.60
29	Joe Verbanic	1.25	.60
30	Joe Torre	3.50	1.75
31	Ed Stroud	1.25	.60
32	Joe Gibbon	1.25	.60
33	Pete Ward	1.25	.60
34	Al Ferrara	1.25	.60
35	Steve Hargan	1.25	.60
36	Pirates Rookies	1.50	.75
	Bob Moose (R)		
	Bob Robertson (R)		
37	Billy Williams	12.00	6.00
38	Tony Pierce	1.25	.60
39	Cookie Rojas	1.50	.75
40	Denny McLain	12.00	6.00
41	Julio Gotay	1.25	.60
42	Larry Haney	1.25	.60
43	Gary Bell	1.25	.60
44	Frank Kostro	1.25	.60
45	Tom Seaver	190.00	95.00
46	Dave Ricketts	1.25	.60
47	Ralph Houk	1.50	.75
48	Ted Davidson	1.25	.60
49a	Ed Brinkman (Yellow)	48.00	24.00
49b	Ed Brinkman (White)	1.25	.60
50	Willie Mays	85.00	42.50
51	Bob Locker	1.25	.60
52	Hawk Taylor	1.25	.60
53	Gene Alley	1.25	.60
54	Stan Williams	1.25	.60
55	Felipe Alou	2.00	1.00
56	Orioles Rookies	2.00	1.00
	Dave Leonhard (R)		
	Dave May (R)		
57	Dan Schneider	1.25	.60
58	Eddie Mathews	12.00	6.00
59	Don Lock	1.25	.60
60	Ken Holtzman	2.00	1.00
61	Reggie Smith	2.50	1.25
62	Chuck Dobson	1.25	.60
63	Dick Kenworthy	1.25	.60
64	Jim Merritt	1.25	.60
65	John Roseboro	1.25	.60
66a	Casey Cox (Yellow)	60.00	30.00
66b	Casey Cox (White)	1.25	.60
67	Checklist 1-109	5.00	2.00
68	Ron Willis	1.25	.60
69	Tom Tresh	1.50	.75
70	Bob Veale	1.25	.60
71	Vern Fuller	1.25	.60
72	Tommy John	5.00	2.50
73	Jim Hart	1.25	.60

74	Milt Pappas	1.25	.60
75	Don Mincher	1.25	.60
76	Braves Rookies	1.25	.60
	Jim Britton (R)		
	Ron Reed (R)		
77	Don Wilson	1.25	.60
78	Jim Northrup	1.50	75
79	Ted Kubiak	1.25	.60
80	Rod Carew	125.00	65.00
81	Larry Jackson	1.25	.60
82	Sam Bowens	1.25	.60
83	John Stephenson	1.25	.60
84	Bob Tolan	1.25	.60
85	Gaylord Perry	12.00	6.00
86	Willie Stargell	14.00	7.00
87	Dick Williams	1.25	.60
88	Phil Regan	1.25	.60
89	Jake Gibbs	1.25	.60
90	Vada Pinson	2.50	1.25
91	Jim Ollom	1.25	.60
92	Ed Kranepool	1.50	.75
93	Tony Cloninger	1.25	.60
94	Lee Maye	1.25	.60
95	Bob Aspromonte	1.25	.60
96	Senators Rookies	1.25	.60
	Frank Coggins (R)		
	Dick Nold (R)		
97	Tom Phoebus	1.25	.60
98	Gary Sutherland	1.25	.60
99	Rocky Colavito	4.50	2.25
100	Bob Gibson	25.00	12.50
101	Glenn Beckert	1.25	.60
102	Jose Cardenal	1.25	.60
103	Don Sutton	12.50	6.25
104	Dick Dietz	1.25	.60
105	Al Downing	1.25	.60
106	Dalton Jones	1.25	.60
107	Checklist 110-196	5.00	2.00
108	Don Pavletich	1.25	.60
109	Bert Campaneris	2.00	1.00
110	Hank Aaron	88.00	42.50
111	Rich Reese	1.25	.60
112	Woody Fryman	1.25	.60
113	Tigers Rookies	1.25	.60
	Tom Matchick (R)		
	Daryl Patterson (R)		
114	Ron Swoboda	1.50	.75
115	Sam McDowell	1.50	.75
116	Ken McMullen	1.25	.60
117	Larry Jaster	1.25	.60
118	Mark Belanger	1.50	.75
119	Ted Savage	1.25	.60
120	Mel Stotlemyre	2.50	1.25
121	Jimmie Hall	1.25	.60
122	Gene Mauch	1.25	.60
123	Jose Santiago	1.25	.60
124	Nate Oliver	1.25	.60

125	Joe Horlen	1.25	.60
126	Bobby Etheridge	1.25	.60
127	Paul Lindblad	1.25	.60
128	Astros Rookies	1.25	.60
	Tom Dukes (R)		
	Alonzo Harris (R)		
129	Mickey Stanley	2.50	1.25
130	Tony Perez	18.00	9.00
131	Frank Bertaina	1.25	.60
132	Bud Harrelson	2.50	1.25
133	Fred Whitfield	1.25	.60
134	Pat Jarvis	1.25	.60
135	Paul Blair	1.50	.75
136	Randy Hundley	1.25	.60
137	Twins Team	3.00	1.50
138	Ruben Amaro	1.25	.60
139	Chris Short	1.25	.60
140	Tony Conigliaro	5.00	2.50
141	Dal Maxvill	1.25	.60
142	White Sox Rookies	1.25	.60
	Buddy Bradford (R)		
	Bill Voss (R)		
143	Pete Cimino	1.25	.60
144	Joe Morgan	18.00	9.00
145	Don Drysdale	15.00	7.50
146	Sal Bando	2.50	1.25
147	Frank Linzy	1.25	.60
148	Dave Bristol	1.25	.60
149	Bob Saverine	1.25	.60
150	Roberto Clemente	60.00	30.00
151	World Series Game 1	8.00	4.00
152	World Series Game 2	10.00	5.00
153	World Series Game 3	3.50	1.75
154	World Series Game 4	8.00	4.00
155	World Series Game 5	3.50	1.75
156	World Series Game 6	3.50	1.75
157	World Series Game 7	4.50	2.25
158	WS (Celebration)	3.50	1.75
159	Don Kessinger	1.50	.75
160	Earl Wilson	1.25	.60
161	Norm Miller	1.25	.60
162	Cardinals Rookies	1.50	.75
	Hal Gilson (R)		
	Mike Torrez (R)		
163	Gene Brabender	1.25	.60
164	Ramon Webster	1.25	.60
165	Tony Oliva	5.00	2.50
166	Claude Raymond	1.25	.60
167	Elston Howard	4.00	2.00
168	Dodgers Team	4.00	2.00
169	Bob Bolin	1.25	.60
170	Jim Fregosi	1.50	.75
171	Don Nottebart	1.25	.60
172	Walt Williams	1.25	.60
173	John Boozer	1.25	.60
174	Bob Tillman	1.25	.60
175	Maury Wills	4.00	2.00

176	Bob Allen	1.25	.60
177	Mets Rookies	1,675.00	875.00
	Jerry Koosman(R)		
	Nolan Ryan (R)		
178	Don Wert	1.25	.60
179	Bill Stoneman	1.25	.60
180	Curt Flood	2.00	1.00
181	Jerry Zimmerman	1.25	.60
182	Dave Giusti	1.25	.60
183	Bob Kennedy	1.25	.60
184	Lou Johnson	1.25	.60
185	Tom Haller	1.25	.60
186	Eddie Watt	1.25	.60
187	Sonny Jackson	1.25	.60
188	Cap Peterson	1.25	.60
189	Bill Landis	1.25	.60
190	Bill White	2.00	1.00
191	Dan Frisella	1.25	.60
192	Checklist 197-283	6.00	2.00
193	Jack Hamilton	1.25	.60
194	Don Buford	1.25	.60
195	Joe Pepitone	1.50	.75
196	Gary Nolan	1.25	.60
197	Larry Brown	1.25	.60
198	Roy Face	1.25	.60
199	A's Rookies	1.25	.60
	Darrell Osteen		
	Roberto Rodriguez (R)		
200	Orlando Cepeda	5.00	2.50
201	Mike Marshall (R)	5.00	2.50
202	Adolfo Phillips	1.25	.60
203	Dick Kelley	1.25	.60
204	Andy Etchebarren	1.25	.60
205	Juan Marichal	12.00	6.00
206	Cal Ermer	1.25	.60
207	Carroll Sembera	1.25	.60
208	Willie Davis	1.50	.75
209	Tim Cullen	1.25	.60
210	Gary Peters	1.25	.60
211	J.C. Martin	1.25	.60
212	Dave Morehead	1.25	.60
213	Chico Ruiz	1.25	.60
214	Yankees Rookies	1.50	.75
	Stan Bahnsen (R)		
	Frank Fernandez (R)		
215	Jim Bunning	4.50	2.25
216	Bubba Morton	1.25	.60
217	Turk Farrell	1.25	.60
218	Ken Suarez	1.25	.60
219	Rob Gardner	1.25	.60
220	Harmon Killebrew	16.00	8.00
221	Braves Team	3.00	1.50
222	Jim Hardin	1.25	.60
223	Ollie Brown	1.25	.60
224	Jack Aker	1.25	.60
225	Richie Allen	4.00	2.00
226	Jimmie Price	1.25	.60
227	Joe Hoerner	1.25	.60
228	Dodgers Rookies	1.50	.75
	Jack Billingham (R)		
	Jim Falrey (R)		
229	Fred Klages	1.25	.60
230	Pete Rose	45.00	22.50
231	Dave Baldwin	1.25	.60
232	Denis Menke	1.25	.60
233	George Scott	2.00	1.00
234	Bill Monbouquette	1.25	.60
235	Ron Santo	4.00	2.00
236	Tug McGraw	3.00	1.50
237	Alvin Dark	1.25	.60
238	Tom Satriano	1.25	.60
239	Bill Henry	1.25	.60
240	Al Kaline	24.00	12.00
241	Felix Millan	1.25	.60
242	Moe Drabowsky	1.25	.60
243	Rich Rollins	1.25	.60
244	John Donaldson	1.25	.60
245	Tony Gonzalez	1.25	.60
246	Fritz Peterson	1.25	.60
247	Red Rookies	240.00	120.00
	Johnny Bench (R)		
	Ron Tompkins (R)		
248	Fred Valentine	1.25	.60
249	Bill Singer	1.25	.60
250	Carl Yastrzemski	40.00	20.00
251	Manny Sanguillen (R)	4.50	2.25
252	Angels Team	3.00	1.50
253	Dick Hughes	1.25	.60
254	Cleon Jones	1.25	.60
255	Dean Chance	1.25	.60
256	Norm Cash	5.00	2.50
257	Phil Niekro	8.50	4.25
258	Cubs Rookies	1.25	.60
	Jose Arcia (R)		
	Bill Schlesinger (R)		
259	Ken Boyer	2.50	1.25
260	Jim Wynn	1.50	.75
261	Dave Duncan	1.25	.60
262	Rick Wise	1.25	.60
263	Horace Clarke	1.25	.60
264	Ted Abernathy	1.25	.60
265	Tommy Davis	2.00	1.00
266	Paul Popovich	1.25	.60
267	Herman Franks	1.25	.60
268	Bob Humphreys	1.25	.60
269	Bob Tiefenauer	1.25	.60
270	Matty Alou	1.50	.75
271	Bobby Knoop	1.25	.60
272	Ray Culp	1.25	.60
273	Dave Johnson	1.25	.60
274	Mike Cuellar	1.50	.75
275	Tim McCarver	4.00	2.00
276	Jim Roland	1.25	.60
277	Jerry Buchek	1.25	.60

278	Checklist 284-370	5.00	2.00
279	Bill Hands	1.25	.60
280	Mickey Mantle	275.00	140.00
281	Jim Campanis	1.25	.60
282	Rick Monday	2.00	1.00
283	Mel Queen	1.25	.60
284	John Briggs	1.25	.60
285	Dick McAuliffe	2.00	1.00
286	Cecil Upshaw	1.25	.60
287	White Sox Rookies	1.25	.60
	Mickey Abarbanel (R)		
	Cisco Carlos (R)		
288	Dave Wickersham	1.25	.60
289	Woody Held	1.25	.60
290	Willie McCovey	14.00	7.00
291	Dick Lines	1.25	.60
292	Art Shamsky	1.25	.60
293	Bruce Howard	1.25	.60
294	Red Schoendienst	4.00	2.00
295	Sonny Siebert	1.25	.60
296	Byron Browne	1.25	.60
297	Russ Gibson	1.25	.60
298	Jim Brewer	1.25	.60
299	Gene Michael	1.50	.75
300	Rusty Staub	3.50	1.75
301	Twins Rookies	1.50	.75
	George Mitterwald(R)		
	Rick Renick (R)		
302	Gerry Arrigo	1.25	.60
303	Dick Green	1.25	.60
304	Sandy Valdespino	1.25	.60
305	Minnie Rojas	1.25	.60
306	Mike Ryan	1.25	.60
307	John Hiller	1.25	.60
308	Pirates Team	3.50	1.75
309	Ken Henderson	1.25	.60
310	Luis Aparicio	7.00	3.50
311	Jack Lamabe	1.25	.60
312	Curt Blefary	1.25	.60
313	Al Weis	1.25	.60
314	Red Sox Rookies	1.25	.60
	Bill Rohr (R)		
	George Spriggs (R)		
315	Zolio Versalles	1.50	.75
316	Steve Barber	1.25	.60
317	Ron Brand	1.25	.60
318	Chico Salmno	1.25	.60
319	George Culver	1.25	.60
320	Frank Howard	3.50	1.75
321	Leo Durocher	2.50	1.25
322	Dave Boswell	1.25	.60
323	Deron Johnson	1.50	.75
324	Jim Nash	1.25	.60
325	Manny Mota	1.50	.75
326	Dennis Ribant	1.25	.60
327	Tony Taylor	1.25	.60
328	Angels Rookies	1.25	.60

	Chuck Vinson (R)		
	Jim Weaver (R)		
329	Duane Josephson	1.25	.60
330	Roger Maris	40.00	20.00
331	Dan Osinski	1.25	.60
332	Doug Rader	1.50	.75
333	Ron Herbel	1.25	.60
334	Orioles Team	3.50	1.75
335	Bob Allison	1.25	.60
336	John Purdin	1.25	.60
337	Bill Robinson	1.50	.75
338	Bob Johnson	1.25	.60
339	Rich Nye	1.25	.60
340	Max Alvis	1.25	.60
341	Jim Lemon	1.25	.60
342	Ken Johnson	1.25	.60
343	Jim Gosger	1.25	.60
344	Donn Clendenon	1.50	.75
345	Bob Hendley	1.25	.60
346	Jerry Adair	1.25	.60
347	George Brunet	1.25	.60
348	Phillies Rookies	1.25	.60
	Larry Colton (R)		
	Dick Thoenen (R)		
349	Ed Spiezio	1.25	.60
350	Hoyt Wilhelm	7.00	3.50
351	Bob Barton	1.25	.60
352	Jackie Hernandez	1.25	.60
353	Mack Jones	1.25	.60
354	Pete Richert	1.25	.60
355	Ernie Banks	26.00	13.00
356	Checklist 371-457	5.00	2.00
357	Len Gabrielson	1.25	.60
358	Mike Epstein	1.25	.60
359	Joe Moeller	1.25	.60
360	Willie Horton	3.50	1.75
361	Harmon Killebrew AS	8.50	4.25
362	Orlando Cepeda AS	3.00	1.50
363	Rod Carew AS	12.00	6.00
364	Joe Morgan AS	10.00	5.00
365	Brooks Robinson AS	10.00	5.00
366	Ron Santo AS	3.00	1.50
367	Jim Fregosi AS	2.50	1.25
368	Gene Alley AS	2.50	1.25
369	Carl Yastrzemski AS	12.00	6.00
370	Hank Aaron AS	18.00	9.00
371	Tony Oliva AS	3.50	1.75
372	Lou Brock AS	12.00	6.00
373	Frank Robinson AS	12.00	6.00
374	Bob Clemente AS	22.00	11.00
375	Bill Freehan AS	2.50	1.25
376	Tim McCarver AS	3.00	1.50
377	Joe Horlen AS	2.00	1.00
378	Bob Gibson AS	10.00	5.00
379	Gary Peters AS	2.00	1.00
380	Ken Holtzman AS	2.50	1.25
381	Boog Powell	4.00	2.00

382	Ramon Hernandez	1.25	.60
383	Steve Whitaker	1.25	.60
384	Reds Rookies	12.50	6.25
	Bill Henry (R)		
	Hal McRae (R)		
385	Jim Hunter	15.00	7.50
386	Greg Goossen	1.25	.60
387	Joe Foy	1.25	.60
388	Ray Washburn	1.25	.60
389	Jay Johnstone	1.50	.75
390	Bill Mazeroski	3.00	1.50
391	Bob Priddy	1.25	.60
392	Grady Hatton	1.25	.60
393	Jim Perry	1.25	.60
394	Tommie Aaron	1.25	.60
395	Camilo Pascual	1.25	.60
396	Bobby Wine	1.25	.60
397	Vic Davalillo	1.25	.60
398	Jim Grant	1.25	.60
399	Ray Oyler	1.25	.60
400a	Mike McCormick	60.00	30.00
	(White)		
400b	Mike McCormick	1.50	.75
	(Yellow)		
401	Mets Team	3.50	1.75
402	Mike Hegan	1.25	.60
403	John Buzhardt	1.25	.60
404	Floyd Robinson	1.25	.60
405	Tommy Helms	1.25	.60
406	Dick Ellsworth	1.25	.60
407	Gary Kolb	1.25	.60
408	Steve Carlton	60.00	30.00
409	Orioles Rookies	1.25	.60
	Frank Peters (R)		
	Ron Stone (R)		
410	Ferguson Jenkins	20.00	10.00
411	Ron Hansen	1.25	.60
412	Clay Carroll	1.25	.60
413	Tommy McCraw	1.25	.60
414	Mickey Lolich	5.00	2.50
415	Johnny Callison	1.50	.75
416	Bill Rigney	1.25	.60
417	Willie Crawford	1.25	.60
418	Eddie Fisher	1.25	.60
419	Jack Hiatt	1.25	.60
420	Cesar Tovar	1.25	.60
421	Ron Taylor	1.25	.60
422	Rene Lachemann	1.25	.60
423	Fred Gladding	1.25	.60
424	White Sox Team	3.00	1.50
425	Jim Maloney	1.25	.60
426	Hank Allen	1.25	.60
427	Dick Calmus	1.25	.60
428	Vic Roznovsky	1.25	.60
429	Tommie Sisk	1.25	.60
430	Rico Petrocelli	2.00	1.00
431	Dooley Womack	1.25	.60
432	Indians Rookies	1.25	.60
	Bill Davis (R)		
	Jose Vidal (R)		
433	Bob Rodgers	1.25	.60
434	Ricardo Joseph	1.25	.60
435	Ron Perranoski	1.25	.60
436	Hal Lanier	1.25	.60
437	Don Cardwell	1.25	.60
438	Lee Thomas	1.25	.60
439	Luman Harris	1.25	.60
440	Claude Osteen	1.50	.75
441	Alex Johnson	1.50	.75
442	Dick Bosman	1.25	.60
443	Joe Azcue	1.25	.60
444	Jack Fisher	1.25	.60
445	Mike Shannon	1.50	.75
446	Ron Kline	1.25	.60
447	Tigers Rookies	1.25	.60
	George Korince (R)		
	Fred Lasher (R)		
448	Gary Wagner	1.25	.60
449	Gene Oliver	1.25	.60
450	Jim Kaat	5.00	2.50
451	Al Spangler	1.25	.60
452	Jesus Alou	1.25	.60
453	Sammy Ellis	1.25	.60
454	Checklist 458-533	6.00	2.50
455	Rico Carty	1.50	.75
456	John O'Donoghue	1.25	.60
457	Jim Lefebvre	1.50	.75
458	Lew Krausse	3.50	1.75
459	Dick Simpson	3.50	1.75
460	Jim Lonborg	4.50	2.25
461	Chuck Hiller	3.50	1.75
462	Barry Moore	3.50	1.75
463	Jimmie Schaffer	3.50	1.75
464	Don McMahon	3.50	1.75
465	Tommie Agee	3.50	1.75
466	Bill Dillman	3.50	1.75
467	Dick Howser	3.50	1.75
468	Larry Sherry	3.50	1.75
469	Ty Cline	3.50	1.75
470	Bill Freehan	5.00	2.50
471	Orlando Pena	3.50	1.75
472	Walt Alston	4.00	2.00
473	Al Worthington	3.50	1.75
474	Paul Schaal	3.50	1.75
475	Joe Niekro	4.00	2.00
476	Woody Woodward	3.50	1.75
477	Phillies Team	5.00	2.50
478	Dave McNally	4.50	2.25
479	Phil Gagliano	3.50	1.75
480	Manager's Dream	40.00	20.00
	(Chico Cardenas,		
	Bob Clemente,		
	Tony Oliva)		
481	John Wyatt	3.50	1.75

482	Jose Pagan	3.50	1.75
483	Darold Knowles	3.50	1.75
484	Phil Roof	3.50	1.75
485	Ken Berry	3.50	1.75
486	Cal Koonce	3.50	1.75
487	Lee May	4.50	2.25
488	Dick Tracowski	4.00	2.00
489	Wally Bunker	3.50	1.75
490	Super Stars	130.00	65.00
	(Harmon Killebrew,		
	Mickey Mantle,		
	Willie Mays)		
491	Denny Lemaster	3.50	1.75
492	Jeff Torborg	4.00	2.00
493	Jim McGlothlin	3.50	1.75
494	Ray Sadecki	3.50	1.75
495	Leon Wagner	3.50	1.75
496	Steve Hamilton	3.50	1.75
497	Cardinals Team	5.00	2.50
498	Bill Bryan	3.50	1.75
499	Steve Blass	3.50	1.75
500	Frank Robinson	30.00	15.00
501	John Odom	3.50	1.75
502	Mike Andrews	3.50	1.75
503	Al Jackson	3.50	1.75
504	Russ Snyder	3.50	1.75
505	Joe Sparma	4.50	2.25
506	Clarence Jones	4.00	2.00
507	Wade Blasingame	3.50	1.75
508	Duke Sims	3.50	1.75
509	Dennis Higgins	3.50	1.75
510	Ron Fairly	3.50	1.75
511	Bill Kelso	3.50	1.75
512	Grant Jackson	3.50	1.75
513	Hank Bauer	3.50	1.75
514	Al McBean	3.50	1.75
515	Russ Nixon	3.50	1.75
516	Pete Mikkelsen	3.50	1.75
517	Diego Segui	3.50	1.75
518	Checklist 534-598	10.00	4.00
519	Jerry Stephenson	3.50	1.75
520	Lou Brock	30.00	15.00
521	Don Shaw	3.50	1.75
522	Wayne Causey	3.50	1.75
523	John Tsitouris	3.50	1.75
524	Andy Kosco	3.50	1.75
525	Jim Davenport	3.50	1.75
526	Bill Denehy	3.50	1.75
527	Tito Francona	3.50	1.75
528	Tigers Team	75.00	37.50
529	Bruce Von Hoff	3.50	1.75
530	Bird Belters	20.00	10.00
	(Brooks Robinson,		
	Frank Robinson)		
531	Chuck Hinton	3.50	1.75
532	Luis Tiant	5.00	2.50
533	Wes Parker	3.50	1.75
534	Bob Miller	3.50	1.75
535	Danny Cater	3.50	1.75
536	Bill Short	3.50	1.75
537	Norm Siebern	3.50	1.75
538	Manny Jimenez	3.50	1.75
539	Major League Rookies	3.50	1.75
	Mike Ferraro (R)		
	Jim Ray (R)		
540	Nelson Briles	3.50	1.75
541	Sandy Alomar	3.50	1.75
542	John Boccabella	3.50	1.75
543	Bob Lee	3.50	1.75
544	Mayo Smith	4.50	2.25
545	Lindy McDaniel	3.50	1.75
546	Roy White	4.00	2.00
547	Dan Coombs	3.50	1.75
548	Bernie Allen	3.50	1.75
549	Orioles Rookies	3.50	1.75
	Curt Motton (R)		
	Roger Nelson (R)		
550	Clete Boyer	4.00	2.00
551	Darrell Sutherland	3.50	1.75
552	Ed Kirkpatrick	3.50	1.75
553	Hank Aguirre	3.50	1.75
554	A's Team	6.50	3.25
555	Jose Tartabull	3.50	1.75
556	Dick Selma	3.50	1.75
557	Frank Quilici	3.50	1.75
558	John Edwards	3.50	1.75
559	Pirates Rookies	3.50	1.75
	Carl Taylor (R)		
	Luke Walker		
560	Paul Casanova	3.50	1.75
561	Lee Elia	3.50	1.75
562	Jim Bouton	6.50	3.25
563	Ed Charles	3.50	1.75
564	Eddie Stanky	3.50	1.75
565	Larry Dierker	3.50	1.75
566	Ken Harrelson	4.00	2.00
567	Clay Dalrymple	3.50	1.75
569	Willie Smith	3.50	1.75
569	N.L. Rookies	3.50	1.75
	Ivan Murrell (R)		
	Les Rohr (R)		
570	Rick Reichardt	3.50	1.75
571	Tony LaRussa	7.50	3.75
572	Don Bosch	3.50	1.75
573	Joe Coleman	3.50	1.75
574	Reds Team	6.50	3.25
575	Jim Palmer	60.00	30.00
576	Dave Adlesh	3.50	1.75
577	Fred Talbot	3.50	1.75
578	Orlando Martinez	3.50	1.75
579	N.L. Rookies	6.50	3.25
	Larry Hisle (R)		
	Mike Lum (R)		
580	Bob Bailey	3.50	1.75

		NR/MT	EX
581	Garry Roggenburk	3.50	1.75
582	Jerry Grote	3.50	1.75
583	Gates Brown	5.00	2.50
584	Larry Shepard	3.50	1.75
585	Wilbur Wood	3.50	1.75
586	Jim Pagliaroni	3.50	1.75
587	Roger Repoz	3.50	1.75
588	Dick Schofield	3.50	1.75
589	Twins Rookies	3.50	1.75
	Ron Clark		
	Moe Ogier (R)		
590	Tommy Harper	3.50	1.75
591	Dick Nen	3.50	1.75
592	John Bateman	3.50	1.75
593	Lee Stange	3.50	1.75
594	Phil Linz	3.50	1.75
595	Phil Ortega	3.50	1.75
596	Charlie Smith	3.50	1.75
597	Bill McCool	3.50	1.75
598	Jerry May	4.00	1.75

1969 Topps

This 664-card set marks Topps largest
to date. Card fronts contain color player
photos with the player's name and
position in a circle. Card backs are
horizontal. Subsets include League
leaders, World Series Highlights, Rookies
and All-Stars. All cards measure 2-1/2"
by 3-1/2". Many variations exist in this
set. Those are pointed out in the checklist
below with the lower valued card included
in the complete set price.

	NR/MT	EX
Complete Set (664)	2,650.00	1,275.00
Commons (1-218)	1.25	.60
Commons (219-327)	2.25	1.10
Commons (328-512)	1.25	.60
Commons (513-664)	2.00	1.00

		NR/MT	EX
1	A.L. Batting Leaders	12.00	6.00
2	N.L. Batting Leaders	7.50	3.75
3	A.L. RBI Leaders	3.50	1.75
4	N.L. RBI Leaders	5.00	2.50
5	A.L. HR Leaders	3.50	1.75
6	N.L. HR Leaders	5.00	2.50
7	A.L. ERA Leaders	3.00	1.50
8	N.L. ERA Leaders	3.50	1.75
9	A.L. Pitching Leaders	3.00	1.50
10	N.L. Pitching Leaders	6.00	3.00
11	A.L. Strikeout Leaders	3.00	1.50
12	N.L. Strikeout Leaders	4.00	2.00
13	Mickey Stanley	1.50	.75
14	Al McBean	1.25	.60
15	Boog Powell	3.50	1.75
16	Giants Rookies	1.25	.60
	Cesar Gutierrez (R)	1.25	.60
	Rich Robinson (R)		
17	Mike Marshall	2.00	1.00
18	Dick Schofield	1.25	.60
19	Ken Suarez	1.25	.60
20	Ernie Banks	20.00	10.00
21	Jose Santiago	1.25	.60
22	Jesus Alou	1.25	.60
23	Lew Krausse	1.25	.60
24	Walt Alston	2.00	1.00
25	Roy White	1.50	.75
26	Clay Carroll	1.25	.60
27	Bernie Allen	1.25	.60
28	Mike Ryan	1.25	.60
29	Dave Morehead	1.25	.60
30	Bob Allison	1.25	.60
31	Mets Rookies	4.00	2.00
	Gary Gentry (R)		
	Amos Otis (R)		
32	Sammy Ellis	1.25	.60
33	Wayne Causey	1.25	.60
34	Gary Peters	1.25	.60
35	Joe Morgan	14.00	7.00
36	Luke Walker	1.25	.60
37	Curt Motton	1.25	.60
38	Zoilo Versalles	1.50	.75
39	Dick Hughes	1.25	.60
40	Mayo Smith	1.25	.60
41	Bob Barton	1.25	.60
42	Tommy Harper	1.25	.60
43	Joe Niekro	2.00	1.00
44	Danny Cater	1.25	.60
45	Maury Wills	2.50	1.25
46	Fritz Peterson	1.25	.60
47a	Paul Popovich (No	1.25	.60
	Helmet Logo)		
47b	Paul Popovich (Logo)	5.00	2.50
48	Brant Alyea	1.25	.60
49a	Royals Rookies	5.00	2.50
	Steve Jones (R)		
	Eliseo Rodriquez (Er)		

49b	Royals Rookies	1.25	.60
	Steve Jones (R)		
	Eliseo Rodriguez (R)		
50	Roberto Clemente	50.00	25.00
51	Woody Fryman	1.25	.60
52	Mike Andrews	1.25	.60
53	Sonny Jackson	1.25	.60
54	Cisco Carlos	1.25	.60
55	Jerry Grote	1.25	.60
56	Rich Reese	1.25	.60
57	Checklist 1-109	5.00	2.00
58	Fred Gladding	1.25	.60
59	Jay Johnstone	1.25	.60
60	Nelson Briles	1.25	.60
61	Jimmie Hall	1.25	.60
62	Chico Salmon	1.25	.60
63	Jim Hickman	1.25	.60
64	Bill Monbouquette	1.25	.60
65	Willie Davis	1.50	.75
66	Orioles Rookies	2.50	1.25
	Mike Adamson (R)		
	Merv Rettenmund (R)		
67	Bill Stoneman	1.25	.60
68	Dave Duncan	1.25	.60
69	Steve Hamilton	1.25	.60
70	Tommy Helms	1.25	.60
71	Steve Whitaker	1.25	.60
72	Ron Taylor	1.25	.60
73	Johnny Briggs	1.25	.60
74	Preston Gomez	1.25	.60
75	Luis Aparicio	6.00	3.00
76	Norm Miller	1.25	.60
77a	Ron Perranoski (No	1.25	.60
	Logo On Cap)		
77b	Ron Perranoski (Logo)	5.00	2.50
78	Tom Satriano	1.25	.60
79	Milt Pappas	1.25	.60
80	Norm Cash	3.00	1.50
81	Mel Queen	1.25	.60
82	Pirates Rookies	12.00	6.00
	Rich Hebner (R)		
	Al Oliver (R)		
83	Mike Ferraro	1.25	.60
84	Bob Humphreys	1.25	.60
85	Lou Brock	26.00	13.00
86	Pete Richert	1.25	.60
87	Horace Clarke	1.25	.60
88	Rich Nye	1.25	.60
89	Russ Gibson	1.25	.60
90	Jerry Koosman	5.00	2.50
91	Al Dark	1.25	.60
92	Jack Billigham	1.25	.60
93	Joe Foy	1.25	.60
94	Hank Aguirre	1.25	.60
95	Johnny Bench	110.00	55.00
96	Denver Lemaster	1.25	.60
97	Buddy Bradford	1.25	.60
98	Dave Giusti	1.25	.60
99a	Twins Rookies (Er)	25.00	12.00
	Danny Morris (R)		
	Graig Nettles (R)		
99b	Twins Rookies (Cor)	22.00	11.00
	Danny Morris (R)		
	Graig Nettles (R)		
100	Hank Aaron	65.00	32.50
101	Daryl Patterson	1.25	.60
102	Jim Davenport	1.25	.60
103	Roger Repoz	1.25	.60
104	Steve Blass	1.25	.60
105	Rick Monday	1.50	.75
106	Jim Hannan	1.25	.60
107	Checklist 110-218	5.00	2.00
108	Tony Taylor	1.25	.60
109	Jim Lonborg	2.00	1.00
110	Mike Shannon	1.25	.60
111	Johnny Morris	1.25	.60
112	J.C. Martin	1.25	.60
113	Dave May	1.25	.60
114	Yankees Rookies	1.25	.60
	Alan Closter (R)		
	John Cumberland (R)		
115	Bill Hands	1.25	.60
116	Chuck Harrison	1.25	.60
117	Jim Fairey	1.25	.60
118	Stan Williams	1.25	.60
119	Doug Rader	1.50	.75
120	Pete Rose	38.00	19.00
121	Joe Grzenda	1.25	.60
122	Ron Fairly	1.25	.60
123	Wilbur Wood	1.25	.60
124	Hank Bauer	1.25	.60
125	Ray Sadecki	1.25	.60
126	Dick Tracewski	1.25	.60
127	Kevin Collins	1.25	.60
128	Tommie Aaron	1.25	.60
129	Bill McCool	1.25	.60
130	Carl Yastrzemski	28.00	14.00
131	Chris Cannizzaro	1.25	.60
132	Dave Baldwin	1.25	.60
133	Johnny Callison	1.50	.75
134	Jim Weaver	1.25	.60
135	Tommy Davis	2.00	1.00
136	Cards Rookies	1.50	.75
	Steve Huntz (R)		
	Mike Torrez		
137	Wally Bunker	1.25	.60
138	John Bateman	1.25	.60
139	Andy Kosco	1.25	.60
140	Jim Lefebvre	1.50	.75
141	Bill Dillman	1.25	.60
142	Woody Woodward	1.25	.60
143	Joe Nossek	1.25	.60
144	Bob Hendley	1.25	.60
145	Max Alvis	1.25	.60

146	Jim Perry	1.25	.60
147	Leo Durocher	2.50	1.25
148	Lee Stange	1.25	.60
149	Ollie Brown	1.25	.60
150	Denny McLain	5.00	2.50
151a	Clay Dalrymple (Er) (Phillies)	10.00	5.00
151b	Clay Dalrymple (Cor) (Orioles)	1.25	.60
152	Tommie Sisk	1.25	.60
153	Ed Brinkman	1.25	.60
154	Jim Britton	1.25	.60
155	Pete Ward	1.25	.60
156	Astros Rookies Hal Gilson (R) Leon McFadden (R)	1.25	.60
157	Bob Rodgers	1.25	.60
158	Joe Gibbon	1.25	.60
159	Jerry Adair	1.25	.60
160	Vada Pinson	2.00	1.00
161	John Purdin	1.25	.60
162	World Series Game 1	7.00	3.50
163	World Series Game 2	4.00	2.00
164	World Series Game 3	7.00	3.50
165	World Series Game 4	7.00	3.50
166	World Series Game 5	7.00	3.50
167	World Series Game 6	4.00	2.00
168	World Series Game 7	7.00	3.50
169	WS (Celebration)	4.00	2.00
170	Frank Howard	3.00	1.50
171	Glenn Beckert	1.25	.60
172	Jerry Stephenson	1.25	.60
173	White Sox Rookies Bob Christian (R) Gerry Nyman (R)	1.25	.60
174	Grant Jackson	1.25	.60
175	Jim Bunning	4.00	2.00
176	Joe Azcue	1.25	.60
177	Ron Reed	1.25	.60
178	Ray Oyler	1.25	.60
179	Don Pavletich	1.25	.60
180	Willie Horton	1.50	.75
181	Mel Nelson	1.25	.60
182	Bill Rigney	1.25	.60
183	Don Shaw	1.25	.60
184	Roberto Pena	1.25	.60
185	Tom Phoebus	1.25	.60
186	John Edwards	1.25	.60
187	Leon Wagner	1.25	.60
188	Rick Wise	1.25	.60
189	Red Sox Rookies Joe Lahoud (R) John Thibodeau (R)	1.25	.60
190	Willie Mays	70.00	35.00
191	Lindy McDaniel	1.25	.60
192	Jose Pagan	1.25	.60
193	Don Cardwell	1.25	.60
194	Ted Uhlaender	1.25	.60
195	John Odom	1.25	.60
196	Lum Harris	1.25	.60
197	Dick Selma	1.25	.60
198	Willie Smith	1.25	.60
199	Jim French	1.25	.60
200	Bob Gibson	18.00	9.00
201	Russ Snyder	1.25	.60
202	Don Wilson	1.25	.60
203	Dave Johnson	1.25	.60
204	Jack Hiatt	1.25	.60
205	Rick Reichardt	1.25	.60
206	Phillies Rookies Larry Hisle Barry Lersch (R)	1.50	.75
207	Roy Face	1.25	.60
208a	Donn Clendenon (Er) (Expos)	10.00	5.00
208b	Donn CLendenon (Cor) (Houston)	1.50	.75
209	Larry Haney (Er)	1.25	.60
210	Felix Millan	1.25	.60
211	Galen Cisco	1.25	.60
212	Tom Tresh	1.50	.75
213	Gerry Arrigo	1.25	.60
214	Checklist 219-327	5.00	2.00
215	Rico Petrocelli	1.50	.75
216	Don Sutton	10.00	5.00
217	John Donaldson	1.25	.60
218	John Roseboro	1.25	.60
219	Freddie Patek (R)	4.00	2.00
220	Sam McDowell	2.50	1.25
221	Art Shamsky	2.25	1.10
222	Duane Josephson	2.25	1.10
223	Tom Dukes	2.25	1.10
224	Angels Rookies Bill Harrelson (R) Steve Kealey (R)	2.25	1.10
225	Don Kessinger	2.50	1.25
226	Bruce Howard	2.25	1.10
227	Frank Johnson	2.25	1.10
228	Dave Leonhard	2.25	1.10
229	Don Lock	2.25	1.10
230	Rusty Staub	4.00	2.00
231	Pat Dobson	2.50	1.25
232	Dave Ricketts	2.25	1.10
233	Steve Barber	2.25	1.10
234	Dave Bristol	2.25	1.10
235	Jim Hunter	15.00	7.50
236	Manny Mota	2.50	1.25
237	Bobby Cox (R)	7.00	3.50
238	Ken Johnson	2.25	1.10
239	Bob Taylor	2.25	1.10
240	Ken Harrelson	2.50	1.25
241	Jim Brewer	2.25	1.10
242	Frank Kostro	2.25	1.10
243	Ron Kline	2.25	1.10

244	Indians Rookies	3.50	1.75
	Ray Fosse (R)		
	George Woodson (R)		
245	Ed Charles	2.25	1.10
246	Joe Coleman	2.25	1.10
247	Gene Oliver	2.25	1.10
248	Bob Priddy	2.25	1.10
249	Ed Spiezio	2.25	1.10
250	Frank Robinson	32.00	16.00
251	Ron Herbel	2.25	1.10
252	Chuck Cottier	2.25	1.10
253	Jerry Johnson	2.25	1.10
254	Joe Schultz	2.25	1.10
255	Steve Carlton	60.00	30.00
256	Gates Brown	2.25	1.10
257	Jim Ray	2.25	1.10
258	Jackie Hernandez	2.25	1.10
259	Bill Short	2.25	1.10
260	Reggie Jackson (R)	650.00	325.00
261	Bob Johnson	2.25	1.10
262	Mike Kekich	2.25	1.10
263	Jerry May	2.25	1.10
264	Bill Landis	2.25	1.10
265	Chico Cardenas	2.25	1.10
266	Dodgers Rookies	2.25	1.10
	Alan Foster (R)		
	Tom Hutton (R)		
267	Vicente Romo	2.25	1.10
268	Al Spangler	2.25	1.10
269	Al Weis	2.25	1.10
270	Mickey Lolich	4.50	2.25
271	Larry Stahl	2.25	1.10
272	Ed Stroud	2.25	1.10
273	Ron Willis	2.25	1.10
274	Clyde King	2.25	1.10
275	Vic Davalillo	2.25	1.10
276	Gary Wagner	2.25	1.10
277	Elrod Hendricks (R)	4.00	2.00
278	Gary Geiger	2.25	1.10
279	Roger Nelson	2.25	1.10
280	Alex Johnson	2.50	1.25
281	Ted Kubiak	2.25	1.10
282	Pat Jarvis	2.25	1.10
283	Sandy Alomar	2.25	1.10
284	Expos Rookies	2.25	1.10
	Jerry Robertson		
	Mike Wegener (R)		
285	Don Mincher	2.25	1.10
286	Dock Ellis (R)	4.00	2.00
287	Jose Tartabull	2.25	1.10
288	Ken Holtzman	2.50	1.25
289	Bart Shirley	2.25	1.10
290	Jim Kaat	4.00	2.00
291	Vern Fuller	2.25	1.10
292	Al Downing	2.25	1.10
293	Dick Dietz	2.25	1.10
294	Jim Lemon	2.25	1.10
295	Tony Perez	15.00	7.50
296	Andy Messersmith (R)	4.00	2.00
297	Deron Johnson	2.50	1.25
298	Dave Nicholson	2.25	1.10
299	Mark Belanger	2.50	1.25
300	Felipe Alou	3.50	1.75
001	Darrell Brandon	2.25	1.10
302	Jim Pagliaroni	2.25	1.10
303	Cal Koonce	2.25	1.10
304	Padres Rookies	15.00	7.50
	Bill Davis (R)		
	Cito Gaston (R)		
305	Dick McAuliffe	2.25	1.10
306	Jim Grant	2.25	1.10
307	Gary Kolb	2.25	1.10
308	Wade Blasingame	2.25	1.10
309	Walt Williams	2.25	1.10
310	Tom Haller	2.25	1.10
311	Sparky Lyle (R)	16.00	8.00
312	Lee Elia	2.25	1.10
313	Bill Robinson	2.50	1.25
314	Checklist 328-425	5.00	2.00
315	Eddie Fisher	2.25	1.10
316	Hal Lanier	2.25	1.10
317	Bruce Look	2.25	1.10
318	Jack Fisher	2.25	1.10
319	Ken McMullen	2.25	1.10
320	Dal Maxvill	2.25	1.10
321	Jim McAndrew	2.25	1.10
322	Jose Vidal	2.25	1.10
323	Larry Miller	2.25	1.10
324	Tigers Rookies	2.25	1.10
	Les Cain (R)		
	Dave Campbell		
325	Jose Cardenal	2.25	1.10
326	Gary Sutherland	2.25	1.10
327	Willie Crawford	2.25	1.10
328	Joe Horlen	1.25	.60
329	Rick Joseph	1.25	.60
330	Tony Conigliaro	5.00	2.50
331	Braves Rookies	2.00	1.00
	Gil Garrido (R)	1.25	.60
	Tom House (R)		
332	Fred Talbot	1.25	.60
333	Ivan Murrell	1.25	.60
334	Phil Roof	1.25	.60
335	Bill Mazeroski	3.00	1.50
336	Jim Roland	1.25	.60
337	Marty Martinez	1.25	.60
338	Del Unser	1.25	.60
339	Reds Rookies	1.25	.60
	Steve Mingori (R)		
	Jose Pena		
340	Dave McNally	2.00	1.00
341	Dave Adlesh	1.25	.60
342	Bubba Morton	1.25	.60
343	Dan Frisella	1.25	.60

344	Tom Matchick	1.25	.60
345	Frank Linzy	1.25	.60
346	Wayne Comer	1.25	.60
347	Randy Hundley	1.25	.60
348	Steve Hargan	1.25	.60
349	Dick Williams	1.25	.60
350	Richie Allen	3.50	1.75
351	Carroll Sembera	1.25	.60
352	Paul Schaal	1.25	.60
353	Jeff Torborg	1.50	.75
354	Nate Oliver	1.25	.60
355	Phil Niekro	7.50	3.75
356	Frank Quilici	1.25	.60
357	Carl Taylor	1.25	.60
358	Athletics Rookies	1.25	.60
	George Lauzerique		
	Roberto Rodriquez (R)		
359	Dick Kelley	1.25	.60
360	Jim Wynn	1.50	.75
361	Gary Holman	1.25	.60
362	Jim Maloney	1.25	.60
363	Russ Nixon	1.25	.60
364	Tommie Agee	1.50	.75
365	Jim Fregosi	1.50	.75
366	Bo Belinsky	1.25	.60
367	Lou Johnson	1.25	.60
368	Vic Roznovsky	1.25	.60
369	Bob Skinner	1.25	.60
370	Juan Marichal	8.50	4.25
371	Sal Bando	1.50	.75
372	Adolfo Phillips	1.25	.60
373	Fred Lasher	1.25	.60
374	Bob Tillman	1.25	.60
375	Harmon Killebrew	20.00	10.00
376	Royals Rookies	2.50	1.50
	Mike Flore (R)		
	Jim Rooker (R)		
377	Gary Bell	1.25	.60
378	Jose Herrera	1.25	.60
379	Ken Boyer	2.50	1.25
380	Stan Bahnsen	1.25	.60
381	Ed Kranepool	2.00	1.00
382	Pat Corrales	1.50	.75
383	Casey Cox	1.25	.60
384	Larry Shepard	1.25	.60
385	Orlando Cepeda	3.50	1.75
386	Jim McGlothlin	1.25	.60
387	Bobby Klaus	1.25	.60
388	Tom McCraw	1.25	.60
389	Don Coombs	1.25	.60
390	Bill Freehan	2.50	1.25
391	Ray Culp	1.25	.60
392	Bob Burda	1.25	.60
393	Gene Brabender	1.25	.60
394	Pilots Rookies	4.50	2.25
	Lou Piniella		
	Marv Staehle (R)		
395	Chris Short	1.25	.60
396	Jim Campanis	1.25	.60
397	Chuck Dobson	1.25	.60
398	Tito Francona	1.25	.60
399	Bob Bailey	1.25	.60
400	Don Drysdale	16.00	8.00
401	Jake Gibbs	1.25	.60
402	Ken Boswell	1.25	.60
403	Bob Miller	1.25	.60
404	Cubs Rookies	1.25	.60
	Vic LaRose (R)		
	Gary Ross (R)		
405	Lee May	1.25	.60
406	Phil Ortega	1.25	.60
407	Tom Egan	1.25	.60
408	Nate Colbert	1.25	.60
409	Bob Moose	1.25	.60
410	Al Kaline	22.00	11.00
411	Larry Dierker	1.25	.60
412	Checklist 426-512	10.00	4.00
413	Roland Sheldon	1.25	.60
414	Duke Sims	1.25	.60
415	Ray Washburn	1.25	.60
416	Willie McCovey AS	7.00	3.50
417	Ken Harrelson AS	2.00	1.00
418	Tommy Helms AS	1.50	.75
419	Rod Carew AS	10.00	5.00
420	Ron Santo AS	2.50	1.25
421	Brooks Robinson AS	7.00	3.50
422	Don Kessinger AS	2.00	1.00
423	Bert Campaneris AS	2.00	1.00
424	Pete Rose AS	14.00	7.00
425	Carl Yastrzemski AS	10.00	5.00
426	Curt Flood AS	1.50	.75
427	Tony Oliva AS	2.50	1.25
428	Lou Brock AS	7.00	3.50
429	Willie Horton AS	2.00	1.00
430	Johnny Bench AS	12.50	6.25
431	Bill Freehan AS	1.50	.75
432	Bob Gibson AS	7.00	3.50
433	Denny McLain AS	4.00	2.00
434	Jerry Koosman AS	2.00	1.00
435	Sam McDowell AS	1.50	.75
436	Gene Alley	1.25	.60
437	Luis Alcaraz	1.25	.60
438	Gary Waslewski	1.25	.60
439	White Sox Rookies	1.25	.60
	Ed Herrmann (R)		
	Dan Lazar (R)		
440a	Willie McCovey	100.00	50.00
	(White Lettering)		
440b	Willie McCovey	18.00	9.00
	(Yellow Lettering)		
441a	Dennis Higgins	14.00	7.00
	(White Lettering)		
441b	Dennis Higgins	1.25	.60
	(Yellow Lettering)		

442	Ty Cline	1.25	.60
443	Don Wert	1.25	.60
444a	Joe Moeller (White Lettering)	8.00	4.00
444b	Joe Moeller (Yellow Lettering)	1.25	.60
445	Bobby Knoop	1.25	.60
446	Claude Raymond	1.25	.60
447a	Ralph Houk (White Lettering)	12.00	6.00
447b	Ralph Houk (Yellow Lettering)	1.50	.75
448	Bob Tolan	1.25	.60
449	Paul Lindblad	1.25	.60
450	Billy Williams	8.00	4.00
451a	Rich Rollins (White Lettering)	14.00	7.00
451b	Rich Rollins (Yellow Lettering)	1.25	.60
452a	Al Ferrara (White Lettering)	14.00	7.00
452b	Al Ferrara (Yellow Lettering)	1.25	.60
453	Mike Cuellar	2.00	1.00
454a	Phillies Rookies (White Lettering) Larry Colton (R) Don Money (R)	14.00	7.00
454b	Phillies Rookies (Yellow Lettering)	1.50	.75
455	Sonny Siebert	1.25	.60
456	Bud Harrelson	1.50	.75
457	Dalton Jones	1.25	.60
458	Curt Blefary	1.25	.60
459	Dave Boswell	1.25	.60
460	Joe Torre	3.00	1.50
461a	Mike Epstein (White Lettering)	12.00	6.00
461b	Mike Epstein (Yellow Lettering)	1.25	.60
462	Red Schoendienst	2.50	1.25
463	Dennis Ribant	1.25	.60
464a	Dave Marshall (White Lettering)	12.00	6.00
464b	Dave Marshall (Yellow Lettering)	1.25	.60
465	Tommy John	3.50	1.75
466	John Boccabella	1.25	.60
467	Tom Reynolds	1.25	.60
468a	Pirates Rookies (White Lettering) Bruce Dal Canton (R) Bob Robertson	14.00	7.00
468b	Pirates Rookies (Yellow Lettering)	1.50	.75
469	Chico Ruiz	1.25	.60
470a	Mel Stottlemyre (White Lettering)	24.00	12.00
470b	Mel Stottlemyre (Yellow Lettering)	2.50	1.25
471a	Ted Savage (White Lettering)	14.00	7.00
471b	Ted Savage (Yellow Lettering)	1.25	.60
472	Jim Price	1.25	.60
473a	Jose Arcia (White Lettering)	12.00	6.00
473b	Jose Arcia (Yellow Lettering)	1.25	.60
474	Tom Murphy	1.25	.60
475	Tim McCarver	2.50	1.25
476a	Red Sox Rookies (White Lettering) Ken Brett (R) Gerry Moses (R)	20.00	10.00
476b	Red Sox Rookies (Yellow Lettering)	2.50	1.25
477	Jeff James	1.25	.60
478	Don Buford	1.25	.60
479	Richie Scheinblum	1.25	.60
480	Tom Seaver	130.00	65.00
481	Bill Melton (R)	1.50	.75
482a	Jim Gosger (White Lettering)	14.00	7.00
482b	Jim Gosger (Yellow Lettering)	1.25	.60
483	Ted Abernathy	1.25	.60
484	Joe Gordon	1.25	.60
485a	Gaylord Perry (White Lettering)	80.00	40.00
485b	Gaylord Perry (Yellow Lettering)	12.00	6.00
486a	Paul Casanova (White Lettering)	12.00	6.00
486b	Paul Casanova (YELLOW Lettering)	1.25	.60
487	Denis Menke	1.25	.60
488	Joe Sparma	1.25	.60
489	Clete Boyer	1.50	.75
490	Matty Alou	1.50	.75
491a	Twins Rookies (White Lettering) Jerry Crider (R) George Mitterwald	14.00	7.00
491b	Twins Rookies (Yellow Lettering)	1.25	.60
492	Tony Cloninger	1.25	.60
493a	Wes Parker (White Lettering)	12.00	6.00
493b	Wes Parker (Yellow Lettering)	1.25	.60
494	Ken Berry	1.25	.60
495	Bert Campaneris	1.50	.75
496	Larry Jaster	1.25	.60

497	Julian Javier	1.25	.60
498	Juan Pizarro	1.25	.60
499	Astros Rookies	1.25	.60
	Don Bryant (R)		
	Steve Shea		
500a	Mickey Mantle	725.00	365.00
	(White Lettering)		
500b	Mickey Mantle	325.00	165.00
	(Yellow Lettering)		
501a	Tony Gonzalez	14.00	7.00
	(White Lettering)		
501b	Tony Gonzalez		
	(Yellow Lettering)		
502	Minnie Rojas	1.25	.60
503	Larry Brown	1.25	.60
504	Checklist 513-588	7.50	3.75
505a	Bobby Bolin (White	12.00	6.00
	Lettering)		
505b	Bobby Bolin (Yellow	1.25	.60
	Lettering)		
506	Paul Blair	1.50	.75
507	Cookie Rojas	1.25	.60
508	Moe Drabowsky	1.25	.60
509	Manny Sanguillen	2.00	1.00
510	Rod Carew	80.00	40.00
511a	Diego Segui (White	12.00	6.00
	Lettering)		
511b	Diego Segui (Yellow	1.25	.60
	Lettering)		
512	Cleon Jones	1.25	.60
513	Camilo Pascual	2.00	1.00
514	Mike Lum	2.00	1.00
515	Dick Green	2.00	1.00
516	Earl Weaver (R)	15.00	7.50
517	Mike McCormick	2.00	1.00
518	Fred Whittfield	2.00	1.00
519	Yankees Rookies	2.00	1.00
	Len Boehmer (R)		
	Gerry Kennedy		
520	Bob Veale	2.00	1.00
521	George Thomas	2.00	1.00
522	Joe Hoerner	2.00	1.00
523	Bob Chance	2.00	1.00
524	Expos Rookies	2.00	1.00
	Jose Laboy (R)		
	Floyd Wicker (R)		
525	Earl Wilson	2.00	1.00
526	Hector Torres	2.00	1.00
527	Al Lopez	2.50	1.25
528	Claude Osteen	2.00	1.00
529	Ed Kirkpatrick	2.00	1.00
530	Cesar Tovar	2.00	1.00
531	Dick Farrell	2.00	1.00
532	Bird Hill Aces (Mike	2.50	1.25
	Cuellar, Jim Hardin,		
	Dave McNally, Tom		
	Phoebus)		
533	Nolan Ryan	650.00	325.00
534	Jerry McNertney	2.00	1.00
535	Phil Regan	2.00	1.00
536	Padres Rookies	2.00	1.00
	Danny Breeden (R)		
	Dave Roberts (R)		
537	Mike Paul	2.00	1.00
538	Charlie Smith	2.00	1.00
539	Ted Shows How	8.00	4.00
	(Mike Epstein, Ted		
	Williams)		
540	Curt Flood	2.50	1.25
541	Joe Verbanic	2.00	1.00
542	Bob Aspromonte	2.00	1.00
543	Fred Newman	2.00	1.00
544	Tigers Rookies	2.00	1.00
	Mike Kilkenny (R)		
	Ron Woods (R)		
545	Willie Stargell	18.00	9.00
546	Jim Nash	2.00	1.00
547	Billy Martin	6.00	3.00
548	Bob Locker	2.00	1.00
549	Ron Brand	2.00	1.00
550	Brooks Robinson	24.00	12.00
551	Wayne Granger	2.00	1.00
552	Dodgers Rookies	3.50	1.75
	Ted Sizemore		
	Bill Sudakis (R)		
553	Ron Davis	2.00	1.00
554	Frank Bertaina	2.00	1.00
555	Jim Hart	2.00	1.00
556	A's Stars (Sal Bando,	2.50	1.25
	Bert Campaneris,		
	Danny Cater)		
557	Frank Fernandez	2.00	1.00
558	Tom Burgmeier	2.00	1.00
559	Cards Rookies	2.00	1.25
	Joe Hague (R)		
	Jim Hicks (R)		
560	Luis Tiant	3.50	1.75
561	Ron Clark	2.00	1.00
562	Bob Watson (R)	5.00	2.50
563	Marty Pattin	2.00	1.00
564	Gil Hodges	10.00	5.00
565	Hoyt Wilhelm	7.00	3.50
566	Ron Hansen	2.00	1.00
567	Pirates Rookies	2.00	1.25
	Elvio Jimenez (R)		
	Jim Shellenback		
568	Cecil Upshaw	2.00	1.00
569	Billy Harris	2.00	1.00
570	Ron Santo	6.00	3.00
571	Cap Peterson	2.00	1.00
572	Giants Heroes (Juan	18.00	9.00
	Marichal, Willie		
	McCovey)		
573	Jim Palmer	45.00	22.50

574	George Scott	2.00	1.00
575	Bill Singer	2.00	1.00
576	Phillies Rookies	2.00	1.25
	Ron Stone (R)		
	Bill Wilson (R)		
577	Mike Hegan	2.00	1.00
578	Don Bosch	2.00	1.00
579	Dave Nelson	2.00	1.00
580	Jim Northrup	2.50	1.25
581	Gary Nolan	2.00	1.00
582	Checklist 589-664	6.00	2.50
583	Clyde Wright	2.00	1.00
584	Don Mason	2.00	1.00
585	Ron Swoboda	2.50	1.25
586	Tim Cullen	2.00	1.00
587	Joe Rudi (R)	6.00	3.00
588	Bill White	2.50	1.25
589	Joe Pepitone	2.50	1.25
590	Rico Carty	2.50	1.25
591	Mike Hedlund	2.00	1.00
592	Padres Rookies	2.00	1.00
	Rafael Robles (R)		
	Al Santorini (R)		
593	Don Nottebart	2.00	1.00
594	Dooley Womack	2.00	1.00
595	Lee Maye	2.00	1.00
596	Chuck Hartenstein	2.00	1.00
597	A.L. Rookies	110.00	55.00
	Larry Burchart (R)		
	Rollie Fingers (R)		
	Bob Floyd (R)		
598	Ruben Amaro	2.00	1.00
599	John Boozer	2.00	1.00
600	Tony Oliva	7.00	3.50
601	Tug McGraw	5.00	2.50
602	Cubs Rookies	2.00	1.00
	Alec Distaco (R)		
	Jim Qualls (R)		
	Don Young (R)		
603	Joe Keough	2.00	1.00
604	Bobby Etheridge	2.00	1.00
605	Dick Ellsworth	2.00	1.00
606	Gene Mauch	2.00	1.00
607	Dick Bosman	2.00	1.00
608	Dick Simpson	2.00	1.00
609	Phil Gagliano	2.00	1.00
610	Jim Hardin	2.00	1.00
611	Braves Rookies	3.50	1.75
	Bob Didier (R)		
	Walt Hriniak (R)		
	Gary Neibauer (R)		
612	Jack Aker	2.00	1.00
613	Jim Beauchamp	2.00	1.00
614	Astros Rookies	2.00	1.00
	Tom Griffin (R)		
	Skip Guinn (R)		
615	Len Gabrielson	2.00	1.00

616	Don McMahon	2.00	1.00
617	Jesse Gonder	2.00	1.00
618	Ramon Webster	2.00	1.00
619	Royals Rookies	2.00	1.00
	Bill Butler (R)		
	Pat Kelly (R)		
	Juan Rios (R)		
620	Dean Chance	2.00	1.00
621	Bill Voss	2.00	1.00
622	Dan Osinski	2.00	1.00
623	Hank Allen	2.00	1.00
624	N.L. Rookies	3.50	1.75
	Darrel Chaney (R)		
	Duffy Dyer (R)		
	Terry Harmon (R)		
625	Mack Jones	2.00	1.00
626	Gene Michael	2.00	1.00
627	George Stone	2.00	1.00
628	Red Sox Rookies	4.50	2.25
	Bill Conigliaro (R)		
	Syd O'Brien (R)		
	Fred Wenz (R)		
629	Jack Hamilton	2.00	1.00
630	Bobby Bonds (R)	42.00	21.00
631	John Kennedy	2.00	1.00
632	Jon Warden	2.00	1.00
633	Harry Walker	2.00	1.00
634	Andy Etchebarren	2.00	1.00
635	George Culver	2.00	1.00
636	Woodie Held	2.00	1.00
637	Padres Rookies	2.00	1.00
	Jerry DaVanon (R)		
	Clay Kirby (R)		
	Frank Reberger (R)		
638	Ed Sprague	2.50	1.25
639	Barry Moore	2.00	1.00
640	Ferguson Jenkins	20.00	10.00
641	N.L. Rookies	2.00	1.00
	Bobby Darwin (R)		
	Tommy Dean (R)		
	John Miller (R)		
642	John Hiller	2.00	1.00
643	Billy Cowan	2.00	1.00
644	Chuck Hinton	2.00	1.00
645	George Brunet	2.00	1.00
646	Expos Rookies	2.50	1.25
	Dan McGinn (R)		
	Carl Morton (R)		
647	Dave Wickersham	2.00	1.00
648	Bobby Wine	2.00	1.00
649	Al Jackson	2.00	1.00
650	Ted Williams	15.00	7.50
651	Gus Gil	2.00	1.00
652	Eddie Watt	2.00	1.00
653	Aurelio Rodriguez	3.50	1.75
	(Wrong Photo)		
654	White Sox Rookies	4.00	2.00

		NR/MT	EX
	Carlos May (R)		
	Rich Morales (R)		
	Don Secrist		
655	Mike Hershberger	2.00	1.00
656	Dan Schneider	2.00	1.00
657	Bobby Murcer	5.00	2.50
658	A.L. Rookies	2.00	1.00
	Bill Burbach (R)		
	Tom Hall (R)		
	Jim Miles (R)		
659	Johnny Podres	2.50	1.25
660	Reggie Smith	5.00	2.50
661	Jim Merritt	2.00	1.00
662	Royals Rookies	2.50	1.25
	Dick Drago (R)		
	Bob Oliver (R)		
	George Spriggs (R)		
663	Dick Radatz	2.50	1.25
664	Ron Hunt	5.00	2.00

1970 Topps

This 720-card set features color photos on the card fronts framed by a thin white line and a gray border. Horizontal card backs are blue and yellow. Card measure 2-1/2" by 3-1/2". Major subsets include League Leaders, World Series and Playoff Highlights All-Stars and Rookies.

		NR/MT	EX
Complete Set (720)		2,350.00	1,175.00
Commons (1-459)		.90	.45
Commons (460-546)		1.50	.75
Commons (547-633)		3.50	1.75
Commons (634-720)		7.00	3.50
1	World Champion Mets	12.00	6.00
2	Diego Segui	.90	.45
3	Darrel Chaney	.90	.45
4	Tom Egan	.90	.45
5	Wes Parker	.90	.45
6	Grant Jackson	.90	.45
7	Indians Rookies	.90	.45
	Gary Boyd	.90	.45
	Russ Nagelson (R)	.90	.45
8	Jose Martinez	.90	.45
9	Checklist 1-132	4.00	2.00
10	Carl Yastrzemski	22.00	11.00
11	Nate Colbert	.90	.45
12	John Hiller	.90	.45
13	Jack Hiatt	.90	.45
14	Hank Allen	.90	.45
15	Larry Dierker	.90	.45
16	Charlie Metro	.90	.45
17	Hoyt Wilhelm	4.50	2.25
18	Carlos May	.90	.45
19	John Boccabella	.90	.45
20	Dave McNally	1.25	.60
21	Athletics Rookies	9.00	4.50
	Vida Blue (R)		
	Gene Tenace (R)		
22	Ray Washburn	.90	.45
23	Bill Robinson	1.00	.50
24	Dick Selma	.90	.45
25	Cesar Tovar	.90	.45
26	Tug McGraw	1.50	.75
27	Chuck Hinton	.90	.45
28	Billy Wilson	.90	.45
29	Sandy Alomar	.90	.45
30	Matty Alou	1.25	.60
31	Marty Pattin	.90	.45
32	Harry Walker	.90	.45
33	Don Wert	.90	.45
34	Willie Crawford	.90	.45
35	Joe Horlen	.90	.45
36	Reds Rookies	1.25	.60
	Danny Breeden (R)		
	Bernie Carbo (R)		
37	Dick Drago	.90	.45
38	Mack Jones	.90	.45
39	Mike Nagy	.90	.45
40	Dick Allen	2.50	1.25
41	George Lauzerique	.90	.45
42	Tito Fuentes	.90	.45
43	Jack Aker	.90	.45
44	Roberto Pena	.90	.45
45	Dave Johnson	.90	.45
46	Ken Rudolph	.90	.45
47	Bob Miller	.90	.45
48	Gil Carrido	.90	.45
49	Tim Cullen	.90	.45
50	Tommie Agee	.90	.45
51	Bob Christian	.90	.45
52	Bruce Dal Canton	.90	.45
53	John Kennedy	.90	.45
54	Jeff Torborg	1.00	.50

55	John Odom	.90	.45
56	Phillies Rookies	.90	.45
	Joe Lis (R)		
	Scott Reid (R)		
57	Pat Kelly	.90	.45
58	Dave Marshall	.90	.45
59	Dick Ellsworth	.50	.45
60	Jim Wynn	1.25	.60
61	N.L. Batting Leaders	7.00	3.50
62	A.L. Batting Leader	4.00	2.00
63	N.L. RBI Leaders	4.00	2.00
64	A.L. RBI Leaders	6.00	3.00
65	N.L. HR Leaders	6.00	3.00
66	A.L. HR Leaders	6.00	3.00
67	N.L. ERA Leaders	6.00	3.00
68	A.L. ERA Leaders	3.00	1.50
69	N.L. Pitching Leaders	7.00	3.50
70	A.L. Pitching Leaders	2.50	1.25
71	N.L. Strikeout Leaders	4.50	2.25
72	A.L. Strikeout Leaders	2.50	1.25
73	Wayne Granger	.90	.45
74	Angels Rookies	.90	.45
	Greg Washburn (R)		
	Wally Wolf (R)		
75	Jim Kaat	2.00	1.00
76	Carl Taylor	.90	.45
77	Frank Linzy	.90	.45
78	Joe Lahoud	.90	.45
79	Clay Kirby	.90	.45
80	Don Kessinger	1.25	.60
81	Dave May	.90	.45
82	Frank Fernandez	.90	.45
83	Don Cardwell	.90	.45
84	Paul Casanova	.90	.45
85	Max Alvis	.90	.45
86	Lum Harris	.90	.45
87	Steve Renko	.90	.45
88	Pilots Rookies	.90	.45
	Dick Baney (R)		
	Miguel Fuentes (R)		
89	Juan Rios	.90	.45
90	Tim McCarver	1.25	.60
91	Rich Morales	.90	.45
92	George Culver	.90	.45
93	Rick Renick	.90	.45
94	Fred Patek	.90	.45
95	Earl Wilson	.90	.45
96	Cards Rookies	3.50	1.75
	Leron Lee (R)		
	Jerry Reuss (R)		
97	Joe Moeller	.90	.45
98	Gates Brown	.90	.45
99	Bobby Pfeil	.90	.45
100	Mel Stottlemyre	1.50	.75
101	Bobby Floyd	.90	.45
102	Joe Rudi	1.25	.60
103	Frank Reberger	.90	.45
104	Gerry Moses	.90	.45
105	Tony Gonzalez	.90	.45
106	Darold Knowles	.90	.45
107	Bobby Etheridge	.90	.45
108	Tom Burgmeier	.90	.45
109	Expos Rookies	.90	.45
	Garry Jestadt (R)		
	Carl Morton		
110	Bob Moose	.90	.45
111	Mike Hegan	.90	.45
112	Dave Nelson	.90	.45
113	Jim Ray	.90	.45
114	Gene Michael	.90	.45
115	Alex Johnson	1.00	.50
116	Sparky Lyle	1.50	.75
117	Don Young	.90	.45
118	George Mitterwald	.90	.45
119	Chuck Taylor	.90	.45
120	Sal Bando	1.25	.60
121	Orioles Rookies	1.00	.50
	Fred Beene (R)		
	Terry Crowley (R)		
122	George Stone	.90	.45
123	Don Gutteridge	.90	.45
124	Larry Jaster	.90	.45
125	Deron Johnson	1.00	.50
126	Marty Martinez	.90	.45
127	Joe Coleman	.90	.45
128	Checklist 133-263	4.00	2.00
129	Jimmie Price	.90	.45
130	Ollie Brown	.90	.45
131	Dodgers Rookies	.90	.45
	Ray Lamb (R)		
	Bob Stinson (R)		
132	Jim McGlothlin	.90	.45
133	Clay Carroll	.90	.45
134	Danny Walton	.90	.45
135	Dick Dietz	.90	.45
136	Steve Hargan	.90	.45
137	Art Shamsky	.90	.45
138	Joe Foy	.90	.45
139	Rich Nye	.90	.45
140	Reggie Jackson	185.00	95.00
141	Pirates Rookies	1.25	.60
	Dave Cash (R)		
	Johnny Jeter (R)		
142	Fritz Peterson	.90	.45
143	Phil Gagliano	.90	.45
144	Ray Culp	.90	.45
145	Rico Carty	1.00	.50
146	Danny Murphy	.90	.45
147	Angel Hermoso	.90	.45
148	Earl Weaver	3.50	1.75
149	Billy Champion	.90	.45
150	Harmon Killebrew	10.00	5.00
151	Dave Roberts	.90	.45
152	Ike Brown	.90	.45

153	Gary Gentry	.90	.45
154	Senators Rookies	.90	.45
	Jan Dukes (R)		
	Jim Miles		
155	Denis Menke	.90	.45
156	Eddie Fisher	.90	.45
157	Manny Mota	1.00	.50
158	Jerry McNertney	.90	.45
159	Tommy Helms	.90	.45
160	Phil Niekro	6.00	3.00
161	Richie Scheinblum	.90	.45
162	Jerry Johnson	.90	.45
163	Syd O'Brien	.90	.45
164	Ty Cline	.90	.45
165	Ed Kirkpatrick	.90	.45
166	Al Oliver	2.50	1.25
167	Bill Burbach	.90	.45
168	Dave Watkins	.90	.45
169	Tom Hall	.90	.45
170	Billy Williams	8.00	4.00
171	Jim Nash	.90	.45
172	Braves Rookies	2.50	1.25
	Ralph Garr (R)		
	Garry Hill (R)		
173	Jim Hicks	.90	.45
174	Ted Sizemore	1.00	.50
175	Dick Bosman	.90	.45
176	Jim Hart	.90	.45
177	Jim Northrup	1.00	.50
178	Denny Lemaster	.90	.45
179	Ivan Murrell	.90	.45
180	Tommy John	2.50	1.25
181	Sparky Anderson	3.50	1.75
182	Dick Hall	.90	.45
183	Jerry Grote	.90	.45
184	Ray Fosse	.90	.45
185	Don Mincher	.90	.45
186	Rick Joseph	.90	.45
187	Mike Hedlund	.90	.45
188	Manny Sanguillen	1.00	.50
189	Yankees Rookies	90.00	45.00
	Dave McDonald (R)		
	Thurman Munson (R)		
190	Joe Torre	2.50	1.25
191	Vicente Romo	.90	.45
192	Jim Qualls	.90	.45
193	Mike Wegener	.90	.45
194	Chuck Manuel	.90	.45
195	N.L. Playoff Game 1	15.00	7.50
196	N.L. Playoff Game 2	2.00	1.00
197	N.L. Playoff Game 3	28.00	14.00
198	N.L. (Celebration)	15.00	7.50
199	A.L. Playoff Game 1	2.00	1.00
200	A.L. Playoff Game 2	2.00	1.00
201	A.L. Playoff Game 3	2.00	1.00
202	A.L. (Celebration)	2.00	1.00
203	Rudy May	.90	.45
204	Len Gabrielson	.90	.45
205	Bert Campaneris	1.25	.60
206	Clete Boyer	1.00	.50
207	Tigers Rookies	.90	.45
	Norman McRae (R)		
	Bob Reed (R)		
208	Fred Gladding	.90	.45
209	Ken Suarez	.90	.45
210	Juan Marichal	7.00	3.50
211	Ted Williams	12.00	6.00
212	Al Santorini	.90	.45
213	Andy Etchebarren	.90	.45
214	Ken Boswell	.90	.45
215	Reggie Smith	1.50	.75
216	Chuck Hartenstein	.90	.45
217	Ron Hansen	.90	.45
218	Ron Stone	.90	.45
219	Jerry Kenney	.90	.45
220	Steve Carlton	42.00	21.00
221	Ron Brand	.90	.45
222	Jim Rooker	.90	.45
223	Nate Oliver	.90	.45
224	Steve Barber	.90	.45
225	Lee May	.90	.45
226	Ron Perranoski	.90	.45
227	Astros Rookies	1.50	.75
	John Mayberry (R)		
	Bob Watkins		
228	Aurelio Rodriquez	.90	.45
229	Rich Robertson	.90	.45
230	Brooks Robinson	15.00	7.50
231	Luis Tiant	2.50	1.25
232	Bob Didier	.90	.45
233	Lew Krausse	.90	.45
234	Tommy Dean	.90	.45
235	Mike Epstein	.90	.45
236	Bob Veale	.90	.45
237	Russ Gibson	.90	.45
238	Jose Laboy	.90	.45
239	Ken Berry	.90	.45
240	Fergie Jenkins	10.00	5.00
241	Royals Rookies	.90	.45
	Al Fitzmorris		
	Scott Northey (R)		
242	Walter Alston	1.50	.75
243	Joe Sparma	.90	.45
244	Checklist 264-372	4.00	2.00
245	Leo Cardenas	.90	.45
246	Jim McAndrew	.90	.45
247	Lou Klimchock	.90	.45
248	Jesus Alou	.90	.45
249	Bob Locker	.90	.45
250	Willie McCovey	12.00	6.00
251	Dick Schofield	.90	.45
252	Lowell Palmer	.90	.45
253	Ron Woods	.90	.45
254	Camilo Pascual	.90	.45

255	Jim Spencer (R)	.90	.45
256	Vic Davalillo	.90	.45
257	Dennis Higgins	.90	.45
258	Paul Popovich	.90	.45
259	Tommie Reynolds	.90	.45
260	Claude Osteen	.90	.45
261	Curt Motton	.90	.45
262	Padres Rookies	1.25	.60
	Jerry Morales (R)		
	Jim Williams (R)		
263	Duane Josephson	.90	.45
264	Rich Hebner	1.00	.50
265	Randy Hundley	1.00	.50
266	Wally Bunker	.90	.45
267	Twins Rookies	.90	.45
	Herman Hill (R)		
	Paul Ratliff (R)		
268	Claude Raymond	.90	.45
269	Cesar Gutierrez	.90	.45
270	Chris Short	.90	.45
271	Greg Goossen	.90	.45
272	Hector Torres	.90	.45
273	Ralph Houk	1.00	.50
274	Gerry Arrigo	.90	.45
275	Duke Sims	.90	.45
276	Ron Hunt	.90	.45
277	Paul Doyle	.90	.45
278	Tommie Aaron	.90	.45
279	Bill Lee (R)	2.00	1.00
280	Donn Clendenon	.90	.45
281	Casey Cox	.90	.45
282	Steve Huntz	.90	.45
283	Angel Bravo	.90	.45
284	Jack Baldschun	.90	.45
285	Paul Blair	.90	.45
286	Dodgers Rookies	8.00	4.00
	Bill Buckner (R)		
	Jack Jenkins (R)		
287	Fred Talbot	.90	.45
288	Larry Hisle	1.25	.60
289	Gene Brabender	.90	.45
290	Rod Carew	45.00	22.50
291	Leo Durocher	1.50	.75
292	Eddie Leon	.90	.45
293	Bob Bailey	.90	.45
294	Jose Azcue	.90	.45
295	Cecil Upshaw	.90	.45
296	Woody Woodward	.90	.45
297	Curt Blefary	.90	.45
298	Ken Henderson	.90	.45
299	Buddy Bradford	.90	.45
300	Tom Seaver	90.00	45.00
301	Chico Salmon	.90	.45
302	Jeff James	.90	.45
303	Brant Alyea	.90	.45
304	Bill Russell (R)	4.50	2.25
305	World Series Game 1	3.50	1.75

306	World Series Game 2	3.50	1.75
307	World Series Game 3	3.50	1.75
308	World Series Game 4	3.50	1.75
309	World Series Game 5	3.50	1.75
310	WS (Celebration)	5.00	2.50
311	Dick Green	.90	.45
312	Mike Torrez	.90	.45
313	Mayo Smith	.90	.45
314	Bill McCool	.90	.45
315	Luis Aparicio	5.00	2.50
316	Skip Guinn	.90	.45
317	Red Sox Rookies	1.25	.60
	Luis Alvarado (R)		
	Billy Conigliaro		
318	Willie Smith	.90	.45
319	Clayton Dalrymple	.90	.45
320	Jim Maloney	.90	.45
321	Lou Piniella	2.50	1.25
322	Luke Walker	.90	.45
323	Wayne Comer	.90	.45
324	Tony Taylor	.90	.45
325	Dave Boswell	.90	.45
326	Bill Voss	.90	.45
327	Hal King	.90	.45
328	George Brunet	.90	.45
329	Chris Cannizzaro	.90	.45
330	Lou Brock	12.00	6.00
331	Chuck Dobson	.90	.45
332	Bobby Wine	.90	.45
333	Bobby Murcer	2.50	1.25
334	Phil Regan	.90	.45
335	Bill Freehan	1.25	.60
336	Del Unser	.90	.45
337	Mike McCormick	.90	.45
338	Paul Schaal	.90	.45
339	Johnny Edwards	.90	.45
340	Tony Conigliaro	3.00	1.50
341	Bill Sudakis	.90	.45
342	Wilbur Wood	.90	.45
343	Checklist 373-459	4.00	2.00
344	Marcelino Lopez	.90	.45
345	Al Ferrara	.90	.45
346	Red Schoendienst	2.00	1.25
347	Russ Snyder	.90	.45
348	Mets Rookies	1.25	.60
	Jesse Hudson (R)		
	Mike Jorgensen (R)		
349	Steve Hamilton	.90	.45
350	Roberto Clemente	55.00	27.50
351	Tom Murphy	.90	.45
352	Bob Barton	.90	.45
353	Stan Williams	.90	.45
354	Amos Otis	2.00	1.00
355	Doug Rader	1.00	.50
256	Fred Lasher	.90	.45
357	Bob Burda	.90	.45
358	Pedro Borbon (R)	1.50	.75

359	Phil Roof	.90	.45
360	Curt Flood	1.50	.75
361	Ray Jarvis	.90	.45
362	Joe Hague	.90	.45
363	Tom Shopay	.90	.45
364	Dan McGinn	.90	.45
365	Zoilo Versalles	1.00	.50
366	Barry Moore	.90	.45
367	Mike Lum	.90	.45
368	Ed Herrmann	.90	.45
369	Alan Foster	.90	.45
370	Tommy Harper	.90	.45
371	Rod Gaspar	.90	.45
372	Dave Giusti	.90	.45
373	Roy White	.90	.45
374	Tommie Sisk	.90	.45
375	Johnny Callison	.90	.45
376	Lefty Phillips	.90	.45
377	Bill Butler	.90	.45
378	Jim Davenport	.90	.45
379	Tom Tischinski	.90	.45
380	Tony Perez	10.00	5.00
381	Athletics Rookies	.90	.45
	Bobby Brooks (R)		
	Mike Olivo (R)		
382	Jack DiLauro	.90	.45
383	Mickey Stanley	1.00	.50
384	Gary Neibauer	.90	.45
385	George Scott	1.00	.50
386	Bill Dillman	.90	.45
387	Orioles Team	2.50	1.25
388	Byron Browne	.90	.45
389	Jim Shellenback	.90	.45
390	Willie Davis	.90	.45
391	Larry Brown	.90	.45
392	Walt Hriniak	.90	.45
393	John Gelnar	.90	.45
394	Gil Hodges	5.00	2.50
395	Walt Williams	.90	.45
396	Steve Blass	.90	.45
397	Roger Repoz	.90	.45
398	Bill Stoneman	.90	.45
399	Yankees Team	4.00	2.00
400	Denny McLain	2.50	1.25
401	Giants Rookie	.90	.45
	John Harrell (R)		
	Bernie Williams (R)		
402	Ellie Rodriguez	.90	.45
403	Jim Bunning	3.00	1.50
404	Rich Reese	.90	.45
405	Bill Hands	.90	.45
406	Mike Andrews	.90	.45
407	Bob Watson	2.00	1.00
408	Paul Lindblad	.90	.45
409	Bob Tolan	.90	.45
410	Boog Powell	4.00	2.00
411	Dodgers Team	2.50	1.25

412	Larry Burchart	.90	.45
413	Sonny Jackson	.90	.45
414	Paul Edmondson	.90	.45
415	Julian Javier	.90	.45
416	Joe Verbanic	.90	.45
417	John Bateman	.90	.45
418	John Donaldson	.90	.45
419	Ron Taylor	.90	.45
420	Ken McMullen	.90	.45
421	Pat Dobson	1.00	.50
422	Royals Team	2.50	1.25
423	Jerry May	.90	.45
424	Mike Kilkenny	.90	.45
425	Bobby Bonds	8.50	4.25
426	Bill Rigney	.90	.45
427	Fred Norman	.90	.45
428	Don Buford	.90	.45
429	Cubs Rookies	.90	.45
	Randy Bobb (R)		
	Jim Cosman		
430	Andy Messersmith	.90	.45
431	Ron Swoboda	1.25	.60
432	Checklist 460-546	4.00	2.00
433	Ron Bryant	.90	.45
434	Felipe Alou	2.50	1.25
435	Nelson Briles	.90	.45
436	Phillies Team	2.50	1.25
437	Danny Cater	.90	.45
438	Pat Jarvis	.90	.45
439	Lee Maye	.90	.45
440	Bill Mazeroski	2.50	1.25
441	John O'Donoghue	.90	.45
442	Gene Mauch	.90	.45
443	Al Jackson	.90	.45
444	White Sox Rookies	.90	.45
	Bill Farmer		
	John Matias (R)		
445	Vada Pinson	2.00	1.00
446	Billy Grabarkewitz (R)	.90	.45
447	Lee Stange	.90	.45
448	Astros Team	2.50	1.25
449	Jim Palmer	24.00	12.00
450	Willie McCovey AS	6.00	3.00
451	Boog Powell AS	2.00	1.00
452	Felix Millan AS	2.00	1.00
453	Rod Carew AS	8.00	4.00
454	Ron Santo AS	2.50	1.25
455	Brooks Robinson AS	7.00	3.50
456	Don Kessinger AS	2.00	1.00
457	Rico Petrocelli AS	2.00	1.00
458	Pete Rose AS	15.00	7.50
459	Reggie Jackson AS	25.00	12.50
460	Matty Alou AS	2.00	1.00
461	Carl Yastrzemski AS	10.00	5.00
462	Hank Aaron AS	15.00	7.50
463	Frank Robinson AS	7.00	3.50
464	Johnny Bench AS	14.00	7.00

465	Bill Freehan AS	2.00	1.00
466	Juan Marichal AS	5.00	2.50
467	Denny McLain AS	3.00	1.50
468	Jerry Koosman AS	2.00	1.00
469	Sam McDowell AS	2.00	1.00
470	Willie Stargell	12.00	6.00
471	Chris Zachary	1.50	.75
472	Braves Team	2.50	1.25
473	Don Bryant	1.50	.75
474	Dick Kelley	1.50	.75
475	Dick McAuliffe	1.50	.75
476	Don Shaw	1.50	.75
477	Orioles Rookies	1.50	.75
	Roger Freed (R)		
	Al Severinsen (R)		
478	Bob Heise	1.50	.75
479	Dick Woodson	1.50	.75
480	Glenn Beckert	1.50	.75
481	Jose Tartabull	1.50	.75
482	Tom Hilgendorf	1.50	.75
483	Gail Hopkins	1.50	.75
484	Gary Nolan	1.50	.75
485	Jay Johnstone	2.00	1.00
486	Terry Harmon	1.50	.75
487	Cisco Carlos	1.50	.75
488	J.C. Martin	1.50	.75
489	Eddie Kasko	1.50	.75
490	Bill Singer	1.50	.75
491	Graig Nettles	6.00	3.00
492	Astros Rookies	1.50	.75
	Keith Lampard (R)		
	Scipio Spinks (R)		
493	Lindy McDaniel	1.50	.75
494	Larry Stahl	1.50	.75
495	Dave Morehead	1.50	.75
496	Steve Whitaker	1.50	.75
497	Eddie Watt	1.50	.75
498	Al Weis	1.50	.75
499	Skip Lockwood	1.50	.75
500	Hank Aaron	60.00	30.00
501	White Sox Team	2.00	1.00
502	Rollie Fingers	30.00	15.00
503	Dal Maxvill	1.50	.75
504	Don Pavletich	1.50	.75
505	Ken Holtzman	2.00	1.00
506	Ed Stroud	1.50	.75
507	Pat Corrales	1.50	.75
508	Joe Niekro	2.00	1.00
509	Expos Team	2.50	1.25
510	Tony Oliva	3.50	1.75
511	Joe Hoerner	1.50	.75
512	Billy Harris	1.50	.75
513	Preston Gomez	1.50	.75
514	Steve Hovley	1.50	.75
515	Don Wilson	1.50	.75
516	Yankees Rookies	1.50	.75
	John Ellis (R)		
	Jim Lyttle (R)		
517	Joe Gibbon	1.50	.75
518	Bill Melton	1.50	.75
519	Don McMahon	1.50	.75
520	Willie Horton	2.00	1.00
521	Cal Koonce	1.50	.75
522	Angels Team	2.50	1.25
523	Jose Pena	1.50	.75
524	Alvin Dark	1.50	.75
525	Jerry Adair	1.50	.75
526	Ron Herbel	1.50	.75
527	Don Bosch	1.50	.75
528	Elrod Hendricks	2.00	1.00
529	Bob Aspromonte	1.50	.75
530	Bob Gibson	15.00	7.50
531	Ron Clark	1.50	.75
532	Danny Murtaugh	1.50	.75
533	Buzz Stephen	1.50	.75
534	Twins Team	2.50	1.25
535	Andy Kosco	1.50	.75
536	Mike Kekich	1.50	.75
537	Joe Morgan	15.00	7.50
538	Bob Humphreys	1.50	.75
539	Phillies Rookies	6.00	3.00
	Larry Bowa (R)		
	Dennis Doyle (R)		
540	Gary Peters	1.50	.75
541	Bill Heath	1.50	.75
542	Checklist 547-633	4.00	2.00
543	Clyde Wright	1.50	.75
544	Reds Team	2.50	1.25
545	Ken Harrelson	2.00	1.00
546	Ron Reed	1.50	.75
547	Rick Monday	4.00	2.00
548	Howie Reed	3.50	1.75
549	Cardinals Team	5.00	2.50
550	Frank Howard	6.00	3.00
551	Dock Ellis	3.50	1.75
552	Royals Rookies	2.50	1.25
	Don O'Riley (R)		
	Dennis Paepke (R)		
	Fred Rico (R)		
553	Jim Lefebvre	4.00	2.00
554	Tom Timmermann	3.50	1.75
555	Orlando Cepeda	6.00	3.00
556	Dave Bristol	3.50	1.75
557	Ed Kranepool	3.50	1.75
558	Vern Fuller	3.50	1.75
559	Tommy Davis	3.50	1.75
560	Gaylord Perry	14.00	7.00
561	Tom McCraw	3.50	1.75
562	Ted Abernathy	3.50	1.75
563	Red Sox Team	5.00	2.50
564	Johnny Briggs	3.50	1.75
565	Jim Hunter	15.00	7.50
566	Gene Alley	3.50	1.75
567	Bob Oliver	3.50	1.75

568 Stan Bahnsen	3.50	1.75
569 Cookie Rojas	3.50	1.75
570 Jim Fregosi	4.00	2.00
571 Jim Brewer	3.50	1.75
572 Frank Quilici	3.50	1.75
573 Padres Rookies	3.50	1.75
Mike Corkins (R)		
Rafael Robles (R)		
Ron Slocum (R)		
574 Bobby Bolin	3.50	1.75
575 Cleon Jones	3.50	1.75
576 Milt Pappas	3.50	1.75
577 Bernie Allen	3.50	1.75
578 Tom Griffin	3.50	1.75
579 Tigers Team	4.00	2.00
580 Pete Rose	75.00	37.50
581 Tom Satriano	3.50	1.75
582 Mike Paul	3.50	1.75
583 Hal Lanier	3.50	1.75
584 Al Downing	3.50	1.75
585 Rusty Staub	5.00	2.50
586 Rickey Clark	3.50	1.75
587 Jose Arcia	3.50	1.75
588a Checklist 634-720	7.00	3.00
(Er) (Aldolfo)		
588b Checklist 634-720	4.00	1.50
(Cor) (Adolpho)		
589 Joe Keough	3.50	1.75
590 Mike Cuellar	4.00	2.00
591 Mike Ryan	3.50	1.75
592 Daryl Patterson	3.50	1.75
593 Cubs Team	5.00	2.50
594 Jake Gibbs	3.50	1.75
595 Maury Wills	4.00	2.00
596 Mike Hershberger	3.50	1.75
597 Sonny Siebert	3.50	1.75
598 Joe Pepitone	4.00	2.00
599 Senators Rookies	3.50	1.75
Gene Martin (R)		
Dick Stelmaszek (R)		
Dick Such (R)		
600 Willie Mays	75.00	37.50
601 Pete Richert	3.50	1.75
602 Ted Savage	3.50	1.75
603 Ray Oyler	3.50	1.75
604 Cito Gaston	5.00	2.50
605 Rick Wise	4.00	2.00
606 Chico Ruiz	3.50	1.75
607 Gary Waslewski	3.50	1.75
608 Pirates Team	4.00	2.00
609 Buck Martinez (R)	4.00	2.00
610 Jerry Koosman	5.00	2.50
611 Norm Cash	5.00	2.50
612 Jim Hickman	3.50	1.75
613 Dave Baldwin	3.50	1.75
614 Mike Shannon	3.50	1.75
615 Mark Belanger	4.00	2.00

616 Jim Merritt	3.50	1.75
617 Jim French	3.50	1.75
618 Billy Wynne	3.50	1.75
619 Norm Miller	3.50	1.75
620 Jim Perry	5.00	2.50
621 Braves Rookies	20.00	10.00
Darrell Evans (R)		
Rick Kester (R)		
Mike McQueen		
622 Don Sutton	15.00	7.50
623 Horace Clarke	3.50	1.75
624 Clyde King	3.50	1.75
625 Dean Chance	3.50	1.75
626 Dave Ricketts	3.50	1.75
627 Gary Wagner	3.50	1.75
628 Wayne Garrett	3.50	1.75
629 Merv Rettenmund	3.50	1.75
630 Ernie Banks	48.00	24.00
631 Athletics Team	5.00	2.50
632 Gary Sutherland	3.50	1.75
633 Roger Nelson	3.50	1.75
634 Bud Harrelson	7.00	3.50
635 Bob Allison	7.00	3.50
636 Jim Stewart	7.00	3.50
637 Indians Team	10.00	5.00
638 Frank Bertaina	7.00	3.50
639 Dave Campbell	7.00	3.50
640 Al Kaline	48.00	24.00
641 Al McBean	7.00	3.50
642 Angels Rookies	7.00	3.50
Greg Garrett (R)		
Gordon Lund (R)		
Jarvis Tatum (R)		
643 Jose Pagan	7.00	3.50
644 Gerry Nyman	7.00	3.50
645 Don Money	7.00	3.50
646 Jim Britton	7.00	3.50
647 Tom Matchick	7.00	3.50
648 Larry Haney	7.00	3.50
649 Jimmie Hall	7.00	3.50
650 Sam McDowell	7.50	3.75
651 Jim Gosger	7.00	3.50
652 Rich Rollins	7.00	3.50
653 Moe Drabowsky	7.00	3.50
654 N.L. Rookies	7.50	3.75
Boots Day (R)		
Oscar Gamble (R)		
Angel Mangual (R)		
655 John Roseboro	7.00	3.50
656 Jim Hardin	7.00	3.50
657 Padres Team	10.00	5.00
658 Ken Tatum	7.00	3.50
659 Pete Ward	7.00	3.50
660 Johnny Bench	160.00	80.00
661 Jerry Robertson	7.00	3.50
662 Frank Lucchesi	7.00	3.50
663 Tito Francona	7.00	3.50

664	Bob Robertson	7.00	3.50
665	Jim Lonborg	7.50	3.75
666	Adolpho Phillips	7.00	3.50
667	Bob Meyer	7.00	3.50
668	Bob Tillman	7.00	3.50
669	White Sox Rookies	7.00	3.50
	Dan Johnson (R)		
	Dan Lazar (R)		
	Mickey Scott (R)		
670	Ron Santo	8.00	4.00
671	Jim Campanis	7.00	3.50
672	Leon McFadden	7.00	3.50
673	Ted Uhlaender	7.00	3.50
674	Dave Leonhard	7.00	3.50
675	Jose Cardenal	7.00	3.50
676	Senators Team	10.00	5.00
677	Woodie Fryman	7.00	3.50
678	Dave Duncan	7.00	3.50
679	Ray Sadecki	7.00	3.50
680	Rico Petrocelli	7.00	3.50
681	Bob Garibaldi	7.00	3.50
682	Dalton Jones	7.00	3.50
683	Reds Rookies	9.00	4.50
	Vern Geishert (R)		
	Hal McRae		
	Wayne Simpson (R)		
684	Jack Fisher	7.00	3.50
685	Tom Haller	7.00	3.50
686	Jackie Hernandez	7.00	3.50
687	Bob Priddy	7.00	3.50
688	Ted Kubiak	7.00	3.50
689	Frank Tepedino	7.00	3.50
690	Ron Fairly	7.00	3.50
691	Joe Grzenda	7.00	3.50
692	Duffy Dyer	7.00	3.50
693	Bob Johnson	7.00	3.50
694	Gary Ross	7.00	3.50
695	Bobby Knoop	7.00	3.50
696	Giants Team	10.00	5.00
697	Jim Hannan	7.00	3.50
698	Tom Tresh	7.50	3.75
699	Hank Aguirre	7.00	3.50
700	Frank Robinson	48.00	24.00
701	Jack Billingham	7.00	3.50
702	A.L. Rookies	7.00	3.50
	Bob Johnson (R)		
	Ron Klimkowski (R)		
	Bill Zepp (R)		
703	Lou Marone	7.00	3.50
704	Frank Baker	7.00	3.50
705	Tony Cloninger	7.00	3.50
706	John McNamara	7.00	3.50
707	Kevin Collins	7.00	3.50
708	Jose Santiago	7.00	3.50
709	Mike Fiore	7.00	3.50
710	Felix Millan	7.00	3.50
711	Ed Brinkman	7.00	3.50

712	Nolan Ryan	625.00	315.00
713	Seattle Pilots Team	20.00	10.00
714	Al Spangler	7.00	3.50
715	Mickey Lolich	8.00	4.00
716	Cards Rookies	7.00	3.50
	Sal Campisi (R)		
	Reggie Cleveland (R)		
	Santiago Guzman (R)		
717	Tom Phoebus	7.00	3.50
718	Ed Spiezio	7.00	3.50
719	Jim Roland	7.00	3.50
720	Rick Reichardt	7.50	3.75

1971 Topps

Topps increased the size of their set in 1971 to 752-cards. All cards measure 2-1/2" by 3-1/2". Card fronts feature large color photographs surrounded by a black border. Card backs are horizontal and include a black and white head shot of the player. Popular subsets include League Leaders, World Series and Playoff Highlights and rookies.

	NR/MT	EX
Complete Set (752)	2,400.00	1,200.00
Commons (1-393)	1.00	.50
Commons (394-523)	1.50	.75
Commons (524-643)	3.50	1.75
Commons (644-752)	6.00	3.00

1	Champions (Orioles)	12.00	6.00
2	Dock Ellis	1.00	.50
3	Dick McAuliffe	1.00	.50
4	Vic Davalillo	1.00	.50
5	Thurman Munson	38.00	19.00
6	Ed Spiezio	1.00	.50
7	Jim Holt	1.00	.50

8	Mike McQueen	1.00	.50
9	George Scott	1.25	.60
10	Claude Osteen	1.25	.60
11	Elliott Maddox (R)	1.00	.50
12	Johnny Callison	1.00	.50
13	White Sox Rookies	1.00	.50
	Charlie Brinkman (R)		
	Dick Moloney (R)		
14	Dave Concepcion (R)	25.00	12.50
15	Andy Messersmith	1.00	.50
16	Ken Singleton (R)	3.50	1.75
17	Billy Sorrell	1.00	.50
18	Norm Miller	1.00	.50
19	Skip Pitlock	1.00	.50
20	Reggie Jackson	125.00	60.00
21	Dan McGinn	1.00	.50
22	Phil Roof	1.00	.50
23	Oscar Gamble	1.25	.60
24	Rich Hand	1.00	.50
25	Clarence Gaston	2.50	1.25
26	Bert Blyleven (R)	40.00	20.00
27	Pirates Rookies	1.00	.50
	Fred Cambria (R)		
	Gene Clines (R)		
28	Ron Kimkowski	1.00	.50
29	Don Buford	1.00	.50
30	Phil Niekro	6.00	3.00
31	Eddie Kasko	1.00	.50
32	Jerry DaVanon	1.00	.50
33	Del Unser	1.00	.50
34	Sandy Vance	1.00	.50
35	Lou Piniella	2.00	1.00
36	Dean Chance	1.00	.50
37	Rich McKinney	1.00	.50
38	Jim Colborn	1.00	.50
39	Tigers Rookies	1.50	.75
	Gene Lamont (R)		
	Lerrin LaGrow (R)		
40	Lee May	1.00	.50
41	Rick Austin	1.00	.50
42	Boots Day	1.00	.50
43	Steve Kealey	1.00	.50
44	Johnny Edwards	1.00	.50
45	Jim Hunter	7.50	3.75
46	Dave Campbell	1.00	.50
47	Johnny Jeter	1.00	.50
48	Dave Baldwin	1.00	.50
49	Don Money	1.00	.50
50	Willie McCovey	12.00	6.00
51	Steve Kline	1.00	.50
52	Braves Rookies	1.25	.60
	Oscar Brown (R)		
	Earl Williams (R)		
53	Paul Blair	1.00	.50
54	Checklist 1-132	4.00	2.00
55	Steve Carlton	30.00	15.00
56	Duane Josephson	1.00	.50
57	Von Joshua	1.00	.50
58	Bill Lee	1.25	.60
59	Gene Mauch	1.00	.50
60	Dick Bosman	1.00	.50
61	A.L. Batting Leaders	4.00	2.00
62	N.L. Batting Leaders	2.00	1.00
63	A.L. RBI Leaders	2.00	1.00
64	N.L. RBI Leaders	5.00	2.50
65	A.L. HR Leaders	5.00	2.50
66	N.L. HR Leaders	6.00	3.00
67	A.L. ERA Leaders	3.50	1.75
68	N.L. ERA Leaders	4.00	2.00
69	A.L. Pitching Leaders	2.00	1.00
70	N.L. Pitching Leaders	6.00	3.00
71	A.L. Strikeout Leaders	2.00	1.00
72	N.L. Strikeout Leaders	6.00	3.00
73	George Brunet	1.00	.50
74	Twins Rookies	1.00	.50
	Pete Hamm (R)		
	Jim Nettles (R)		
75	Gary Nolan	1.00	.50
76	Ted Savage	1.00	.50
77	Mike Compton	1.00	.50
78	Jim Spencer	1.00	.50
79	Wade Blasingame	1.00	.50
80	Bill Melton	1.00	.50
81	Felix Millan	1.00	.50
82	Casey Cox	1.00	.50
83	Mets Rookies	1.50	.75
	Randy Bobb (R)		
	Tim Foli (R)		
84	Marcel Lachemann	1.25	.60
85	Billy Grabarkewitz	1.00	.50
86	Mike Kilkenny	1.00	.50
87	Jack Heidemann	1.00	.50
88	Hal King	1.00	.50
89	Ken Brett	1.00	.50
90	Joe Pepitone	1.25	.60
91	Bob Lemon	1.50	.75
92	Fred Wenz	1.00	.50
93	Senators Rookies	1.00	.50
	Norm McRae		
	Denny Riddleberger (R)		
94	Don Hahn	1.00	.50
95	Luis Tiant	2.50	1.25
96	Joe Hague	1.00	.50
97	Floyd Wicker	1.00	.50
98	Joe Decker	1.00	.50
99	Mark Belanger	1.25	.60
100	Pete Rose	48.00	24.00
101	Les Cain	1.00	.50
102	Astros Rookies	1.25	.60
	Ken Forsch (R)		
	Larry Howard (R)		
103	Rich Severson	1.00	.50
104	Dan Frisella	1.00	.50
105	Tony Conigliaro	2.50	1.25

106	Tom Dukes	1.00	.50
107	Roy Foster	1.00	.50
108	John Cumberland	1.00	.50
109	Steve Hovley	1.00	.50
110	Bill Mazeroski	2.00	1.00
111	Yankees Rookies	1.00	.50
	Loyd Colson (R)		
	Bobby Mitchell (R)		
112	Manny Mota	1.25	.60
113	Jerry Crider	1.00	.50
114	Billy Conigliaro	1.00	.50
115	Donn Clendenon	1.00	.50
116	Ken Sanders	1.00	.50
117	Ted Simmons (R)	24.00	12.00
118	Cookie Rojas	1.00	.50
119	Frank Lucchesi	1.00	.50
120	Willie Horton	1.25	.60
121	1971 Rookie Stars	1.00	.50
	Jim Dunegan (R)		
	Roe Skidmore (R)		
122	Eddie Watt	1.00	.50
123	Checklist 133-263	4.00	2.00
124	Don Gullett (R)	2.50	1.25
125	Ray Fosse	1.00	.50
126	Danny Coombs	1.00	.50
127	Danny Thompson (R)	1.00	.50
128	Frank Johnson	1.00	.50
129	Aurelio Monteagudo	1.00	.50
130	Denis Menke	1.00	.50
131	Curt Blefary	1.00	.50
132	Jose Laboy	1.00	.50
133	Mickey Lolich	2.50	1.25
134	Jose Arcia	1.00	.50
135	Rick Monday	1.25	.60
136	Duffy Dyer	1.00	.50
137	Marcelino Lopez	1.00	.50
138	Phillies Rookies	1.25	.60
	Joe Lis		
	Willie Montanez (R)		
139	Paul Casanova	1.00	.50
140	Gaylord Perry	10.00	5.00
141	Frank Quilici	1.00	.50
142	Mack Jones	1.00	.50
143	Steve Blass	1.00	.50
144	Jackie Hernandez	1.00	.50
145	Bill Singer	1.00	.50
146	Ralph Houk	1.25	.60
147	Bob Priddy	1.00	.50
148	John Mayberry	1.00	.50
149	Mike Hershberger	1.00	.50
150	Sam McDowell	1.25	.60
151	Tommy Davis	1.50	.75
152	Angels Rookies	1.00	.50
	Lloyd Allen (R)		
	Winston Llenas (R)		
153	Gary Ross	1.00	.50
154	Cesar Gutierrez	1.00	.50
155	Ken Henderson	1.00	.50
156	Bart Johnson	1.00	.50
157	Bob Bailey	1.00	.50
158	Jerry Reuss	2.00	1.00
159	Jarvis Tatum	1.00	.50
160	Tom Seaver	60.00	30.00
161	Coins Checklist	4.00	2.00
162	Jack Billingham	1.00	.50
163	Buck Martinez	1.00	.50
164	Reds Rookies	1.25	.60
	Frank Duffy (R)		
	Milt Wilcox (R)		
165	Cesar Tovar	1.00	.50
166	Joe Hoerner	1.00	.50
167	Tom Grieve (R)	1.50	.75
168	Bruce Dal Canton	1.00	.50
169	Ed Herrmann	1.00	.50
170	Mike Cuellar	1.50	.75
171	Bobby Wine	1.00	.50
172	Duke Sims	1.00	.50
173	Gil Garrido	1.00	.50
174	Dave LaRoche	1.00	.50
175	Jim Hickman	1.00	.50
176	Red Sox Rookies	1.00	.50
	Doug Griffin (R)		
	Bob Montgomery (R)		
177	Hal McRae	3.00	1.50
178	Dave Duncan	1.00	.50
179	Mike Corkins	1.00	.50
180	Al Kaline	22.00	11.00
181	Hal Lanier	1.00	.50
182	Al Downing	1.00	.50
183	Gil Hodges	6.00	3.00
184	Stan Bahnsen	1.00	.50
185	Julian Javier	1.00	.50
186	Bob Spence	1.00	.50
187	Ted Abernathy	1.00	.50
188	Dodgers Rookies	3.50	1.75
	Mike Strahler (R)		
	Bob Valentine (R)		
189	George Mitterwald	1.00	.50
190	Bob Tolan	1.00	.50
191	Mike Andrews	1.00	.50
192	Billy Wilson	1.00	.50
193	Bob Grich (R)	6.00	3.00
194	Mike Lum	1.00	.50
195	A.L. Playoff Game 1	2.50	1.25
196	A.L. Playoff Game 2	2.50	1.25
197	A.L. Playoff Game 3	4.50	2.25
198	A.L. (Celebration)	2.50	1.25
199	N.L. Playoff Game 1	2.50	1.25
200	N.L. Playoff Game 2	2.50	1.25
201	N.L. Playoff Game 3	2.50	1.25
202	N.L. (Celebration)	2.50	1.25
203	Larry Gura	1.00	.50
204	Brewers Rookies	1.00	.50
	George Kopacz (R)		

	Bernie Smith (R)		
205	Gerry Moses	1.00	.50
206	Checklist 264-393	4.00	2.00
207	Alan Foster	1.00	.50
208	Billy Martin	4.00	2.00
209	Steve Renko	1.00	.50
210	Rod Carew	42.00	21.00
211	Phil Hennigan	1.00	.50
212	Rich Hebner	1.00	.50
213	Frank Baker	1.00	.50
214	Al Ferrara	1.00	.50
215	Diego Segui	1.00	.50
216	Cards Rookies	1.00	.50
	Reggie Cleveland		
	Luis Melendez (R)		
217	Ed Stroud	1.00	.50
218	Tony Cloninger	1.00	.50
219	Elrod Hendricks	1.00	.50
220	Ron Santo	2.50	1.25
221	Dave Morehead	1.00	.50
222	Bob Watson	1.50	.75
223	Cecil Upshaw	1.00	.50
224	Alan Gallagher	1.00	.50
225	Gary Peters	1.00	.50
226	Bill Russell	2.50	1.25
227	Floyd Weaver	1.00	.50
228	Wayne Garrett	1.00	.50
229	Jim Hannan	1.00	.50
230	Willie Stargell	12.00	6.00
231	Indians Rookies	1.50	.75
	Vince Colbert (R)		
	John Lowenstein (R)		
232	John Strohmayer	1.00	.50
233	Larry Bowa	2.50	1.25
234	Jim Lyttle	1.00	.50
235	Nate Colbert	1.00	.50
236	Bob Humphreys	1.00	.50
237	Cesar Cedeno (R)	4.00	2.00
238	Chuck Dobson	1.00	.50
239	Red Schoendienst	2.00	1.00
240	Clyde Wright	1.00	.50
241	Dave Nelson	1.00	.50
242	Jim Ray	1.00	.50
243	Carlos May	1.00	.50
244	Bob Tillman	1.00	.50
245	Jim Kaat	3.50	1.75
246	Tony Taylor	1.00	.50
247	Royals Rookies	2.00	1.00
	Jerry Cram (R)		
	Paul Splittorff (R)		
248	Hoyt Wilhelm	4.50	2.25
249	Chico Salmon	1.00	.50
250	Johnny Bench	48.00	24.00
251	Frank Reberger	1.00	.50
252	Eddie Leon	1.00	.50
253	Bill Sudakis	1.00	.50
254	Cal Koonce	1.00	.50

255	Bob Robertson	1.00	.50
256	Tony Gonzalez	1.00	.50
257	Nelson Briles	1.00	.50
258	Dick Green	1.00	.50
259	Dave Marshall	1.00	.50
260	Tommy Harper	1.00	.50
261	Darold Knowles	1.00	.50
262	Padres Rookies	1.00	.50
	Dave Robinson (R)		
	Jim Williams (R)		
263	John Ellis	1.00	.50
264	Joe Morgan	12.00	6.00
265	Jim Northrup	1.00	.50
266	Bill Stoneman	1.00	.50
267	Rich Morales	1.00	.50
268	Phillies Team	2.00	1.00
269	Gail Hopkins	1.00	.50
270	Rico Carty	1.25	.60
271	Bill Zepp	1.00	.50
272	Tommy Helms	1.00	.50
273	Pete Richert	1.00	.50
274	Ron Slocum	1.00	.50
275	Vada Pinson	2.50	1.25
276	Giants Rookies	10.00	5.00
	Mike Davison (R)		
	George Foster (R)		
277	Gary Waslewski	1.00	.50
278	Jerry Grote	1.00	.50
279	Lefty Phillips	1.00	.50
280	Ferguson Jenkins	12.00	6.00
281	Danny Walton	1.00	.50
282	Jose Pagan	1.00	.50
283	Dick Such	1.00	.50
284	Jim Gosger	1.00	.50
285	Sal Bando	1.25	.60
286	Jerry McNertney	1.00	.50
287	Mike Fiore	1.00	.50
288	Joe Moeller	1.00	.50
289	White Sox Team	2.00	1.00
290	Tony Oliva	4.00	2.00
291	George Culver	1.00	.50
292	Jay Johnstone	1.25	.60
293	Pat Corrales	1.25	.60
294	Steve Dunning	1.00	.50
295	Bobby Bonds	5.00	2.50
296	Tom Timmermann	1.00	.50
297	Johnny Briggs	1.00	.50
298	Jim Nelson	1.00	.50
299	Ed Kirkpatrick	1.00	.50
300	Brooks Robinson	20.00	10.00
301	Earl Wilson	1.00	.50
302	Phil Gagliano	1.00	.50
303	Lindy McDaniel	1.00	.50
304	Ron Brand	1.00	.50
305	Reggie Smith	2.00	1.25
306	Jim Nash	1.00	.50
307	Don Wert	1.00	.50

308	Cardinals Team	2.00	1.00
309	Dick Ellsworth	1.00	.50
310	Tommie Agee	1.00	.50
311	Lee Stange	1.00	.50
312	Harry Walker	1.00	.50
313	Tom Hall	1.00	.50
314	Jeff Torborg	1.25	.00
315	Ron Fairly	1.00	.50
316	Fred Scherman	1.00	.50
317	Athletics Rookies	1.00	.50
	Jim Driscoll (R)		
	Angel Mangual		
318	Rudy May	1.00	.50
319	Ty Cline	1.00	.50
320	Dave McNally	1.25	.60
321	Tom Matchick	1.00	.50
322	Jim Beauchamp	1.00	.50
323	Billy Champion	1.00	.50
324	Graig Nettles	3.50	1.75
325	Juan Marichal	7.00	3.50
326	Richie Scheinblum	1.00	.50
327	World Series Game 1	2.50	1.25
328	World Series Game 2	2.50	1.25
329	World Series Game 3	4.50	2.25
330	World Series Game 4	2.50	1.25
331	World Series Game 5	5.50	2.75
332	WS (Celebration)	2.50	1.25
333	Clay Kirby	1.00	.50
334	Roberto Pena	1.00	.50
335	Jerry Koosman	3.00	1.50
336	Tigers Team	2.00	1.00
337	Jesus Alou	1.00	.50
338	Gene Tenace	2.00	1.00
339	Wayne Simpson	1.00	.50
340	Rico Petrocelli	1.25	.60
341	Steve Garvey (R)	65.00	32.50
342	Frank Tepedino	1.00	.50
343	Pirates Rookies	1.50	.75
	Ed Acosta (R)		
	Milt May (R)		
344	Ellie Rodriguez	1.00	.50
345	Joe Horlen	1.00	.50
346	Lum Harris	1.00	.50
347	Ted Uhlaender	1.00	.50
348	Fred Norman	1.00	.50
349	Rich Reese	1.00	.50
350	Billy Williams	7.00	3.50
351	Jim Shellenback	1.00	.50
352	Denny Doyle	1.00	.50
353	Carl Taylor	1.00	.50
354	Don McMahon	1.00	.50
355	Bud Harrelson	2.00	1.00
356	Bob Locker	1.00	.50
357	Reds Team	2.00	1.00
358	Danny Cater	1.00	.50
359	Ron Reed	1.00	.50
360	Jim Fregosi	1.25	.60
361	Don Sutton	8.50	4.25
362	Orioles Rookies	1.00	.50
	Mike Adamson (R)		
	Roger Freed		
363	Mike Nagy	1.00	.50
364	Tommy Dean	1.00	.50
365	Bob Johnson	1.00	.50
366	Ron Stone	1.00	.50
367	Dalton Jones	1.00	.50
368	Bob Veale	1.00	.50
369	Checklist 394-523	4.00	1.50
370	Joe Torre	4.00	2.00
371	Jack Hiatt	1.00	.50
372	Lew Krausse	1.00	.50
373	Tom McCraw	1.00	.50
374	Clete Boyer	1.25	.60
375	Steve Hargan	1.00	.50
376	Expos Rookies	1.00	.50
	Clyde Mashore (R)		
	Ernie McAnally (R)		
377	Greg Garrett	1.00	.50
378	Tito Fuentes	1.00	.50
379	Wayne Granger	1.00	.50
380	Ted Williams	10.00	5.00
381	Fred Gladding	1.00	.50
382	Jake Gibbs	1.00	.50
383	Rod Gaspar	1.00	.50
384	Rollie Fingers	14.00	7.00
385	Maury Wills	2.50	1.25
386	Red Sox Team	2.00	1.00
387	Ron Herbel	1.00	.50
388	Al Oliver	3.00	1.50
389	Ed Brinkman	1.00	.50
390	Glenn Beckert	1.00	.50
391	Twins Rookies	1.00	.60
	Steve Brye (R)		
	Cotton Nash (R)		
392	Grant Jackson	1.00	.50
393	Merv Rettenmund	1.00	.50
394	Clay Carroll	1.50	.75
395	Roy White	1.50	.75
396	Dick Schofield	1.50	.75
397	Alvin Dark	1.50	.75
398	Howie Reed	1.50	.75
399	Jim French	1.50	.75
400	Hank Aaron	60.00	30.00
401	Tom Murphy	1.50	.75
402	Dodgers Team	3.00	1.50
403	Joe Coleman	1.50	.75
404	Astros Rookies	2.00	1.00
	Buddy Harris		
	Roger Metzger (R)		
405	Leo Cardenas	1.50	.75
406	Ray Sadecki	1.50	.75
407	Joe Rudi	2.00	1.00
408	Rafael Robles	1.50	.75
409	Don Pavletich	1.50	.75

410	Ken Holtzman	1.50	.75
411	George Spriggs	1.50	.75
412	Jerry Johnson	1.50	.75
413	Pat Kelly	1.50	.75
414	Woodie Fryman	1.50	.75
415	Mike Hegan	1.50	.75
416	Gene Alley	1.50	.75
417	Dick Hall	1.50	.75
418	Adolfo Phillips	1.50	.75
419	Ron Hansen	1.50	.75
420	Jim Merritt	1.50	.75
421	John Stephenson	1.50	.75
422	Frank Bertaina	1.50	.75
423	Tigers Rookies	1.50	.75
	Tim Marting (R)		
	Dennis Saunders (R)		
424	Roberto Rodriquez	1.50	.75
425	Doug Rader	1.50	.75
426	Chris Canizzaro	1.50	.75
427	Bernie Allen	1.50	.75
428	Jim McAndrew	1.50	.75
429	Chuck Hinton	1.50	.75
430	Wes Parker	1.50	.75
431	Tom Burgmeier	1.50	.75
432	Bob Didier	1.50	.75
433	Skip Lockwood	1.50	.75
434	Gary Sutherland	1.50	.75
435	Jose Cardenal	1.50	.75
436	Wilbur Wood	1.50	.75
437	Danny Murtaugh	1.50	.75
438	Mike McCormick	1.50	.75
439	Phillies Rookies	6.50	3.25
	Greg Luzinski (R)		
	Scott Reid (R)		
440	Bert Campaneris	2.00	1.00
441	Milt Pappas	1.50	.75
442	Angels Team	3.50	1.75
443	Rich Robertson	1.50	.75
444	Jimmie Price	1.50	.75
445	Art Shamsky	1.50	.75
446	Bobby Bolin	1.50	.75
447	Cesar Geronimo (R)	2.00	1.00
448	Dave Roberts	1.50	.75
449	Brant Alyea	1.50	.75
450	Bob Gibson	18.00	9.00
451	Joe Keough	1.50	.75
452	John Boccabella	1.50	.75
453	Terry Crowley	1.50	.75
454	Mike Paul	1.50	.75
455	Don Kessinger	2.00	1.00
456	Bob Meyer	1.50	.75
457	Willie Smith	1.50	.75
458	White Sox Rookies (R)	1.50	.75
	Dave Lemond (R)		
	Ron Lolich (R)		
459	Jim Lefebvre	2.00	1.00
460	Fritz Peterson	1.50	.75
461	Jim Hart	1.50	.75
462	Senators Team	3.50	1.75
463	Tom Kelley	1.50	.75
464	Aurelio Rodriguez	1.50	.75
465	Tim McCarver	2.50	1.25
466	Ken Berry	1.50	.75
467	Al Santorini	1.50	.75
468	Frank Fernandez	1.50	.75
469	Bob Aspromonte	1.50	.75
470	Bob Oliver	1.50	.75
471	Tom Griffin	1.50	.75
472	Ken Rudolph	1.50	.75
473	Gary Wagner	1.50	.75
474	Jim Fairey	1.50	.75
475	Ron Perranoski	1.50	.75
476	Dal Maxvill	1.50	.75
477	Earl Weaver	3.50	1.75
478	Bernie Carbo	1.50	.75
479	Dennis Higgins	1.50	.75
480	Many Sanguillen	2.00	1.00
481	Daryl Patterson	1.50	.75
482	Padres Team	3.50	1.75
483	Gene Michael	1.50	.75
484	Don Wilson	1.50	.75
485	Ken McMullen	1.50	.75
486	Steve Huntz	1.50	.75
487	Paul Schaal	1.50	.75
488	Jerry Stephenson	1.50	.75
489	Luis Alvarado	1.50	.75
490	Deron Johnson	1.50	.75
491	Jim Hardin	1.50	.75
492	Ken Boswell	1.50	.75
493	Dave May	1.50	.75
494	Braves Rookies	2.50	1.25
	Ralph Garr		
	Rick Kester (R)		
495	Felipe Alou	2.50	1.25
496	Woody Woodward	1.50	.75
497	Horacio Pina	1.50	.75
498	John Kennedy	1.50	.75
499	Checklist 524-643	4.00	1.50
500	Jim Perry	1.50	.75
501	Andy Etchebarren	1.50	.75
502	Cubs Team	3.50	1.75
503	Gates Brown	1.50	.75
504	Ken Wright	1.50	.75
505	Ollie Brown	1.50	.75
506	Bobby Knoop	1.50	.75
507	George Stone	1.50	.75
508	Roger Repoz	1.50	.75
509	Jim Grant	1.50	.75
510	Ken Harrelson	2.00	1.00
511	Chris Short	2.50	1.25
512	Red Sox Rookies	1.50	.75
	Mike Garman (R)		
	Dick Mills (R)		
513	Nolan Ryan	290.00	145.00

514	Ron Woods	1.50	.75
515	Carl Morton	1.50	.75
516	Ted Kubiak	1.50	.75
517	Charlie Fox	1.50	.75
518	Joe Grzenda	1.50	.75
519	Willie Crawford	1.50	.75
520	Tommy John	4.50	2.25
521	Leron Lee	1.50	.75
522	Twins Team	3.00	1.50
523	John Odom	1.50	.75
524	Mickey Stanley	2.00	1.00
525	Ernie Banks	42.00	21.00
526	Ray Jarvis	3.50	1.75
527	Cleon Jones	3.50	1.75
528	Wally Bunker	3.50	1.75
529	N.L. Rookies	6.50	3.25
	Bill Buckner,		
	Enzo Hernandez		
	Marty Perez (R)		
530	Carl Yastrzemski	40.00	20.00
531	Mike Torrez	3.50	1.75
532	Bill Rigney	3.50	1.75
533	Mike Ryan	3.50	1.75
534	Luke Walker	3.50	1.75
535	Curt Flood	4.50	2.25
536	Claude Raymond	4.00	2.00
537	Tom Egan	3.50	1.75
538	Angel Bravo	3.50	1.75
539	Larry Brown	3.50	1.75
540	Larry Dierker	3.50	1.75
541	Bob Burda	3.50	1.75
542	Bob Miller	3.50	1.75
543	Yankees Team	5.50	2.75
544	Vida Blue	8.00	4.00
545	Dick Dietz	3.50	1.75
546	John Matias	3.50	1.75
547	Pat Dobson	3.50	1.75
548	Don Mason	3.50	1.75
549	Jim Brewer	4.00	2.00
550	Harmon Killebrew	25.00	12.50
551	Frank Linzy	3.50	1.75
552	Buddy Bradford	3.50	1.75
553	Kevin Collins	3.50	1.75
554	Lowell Palmer	3.50	1.75
555	Walt Williams	3.50	1.75
556	Jim McGlothlin	3.50	1.75
557	Tom Satriano	3.50	1.75
558	Hector Torres	3.50	1.75
559	A.L. Rookies	3.50	1.75
	Terry Cox		
	Bill Gogolewski		
	Gary Jones		
560	Rusty Staub	4.50	2.25
561	Syd O'Brien	3.50	1.75
562	Dave Giusti	3.50	1.75
563	Giants Team	7.00	3.50
564	Al Fitzmorris	3.50	1.75
565	Jim Wynn	4.50	2.25
566	Tim Cullen	3.50	1.75
567	Walt Alston	4.50	2.25
568	Sal Campisi	3.50	1.75
569	Ivan Murrell	3.50	1.75
570	Jim Palmer	45.00	22.50
571	Ted Sizemore	3.50	1.75
572	Jerry Kenney	3.50	1.75
573	Ed Kranepool	4.00	2.00
574	Jim Bunning	5.00	2.50
575	Bill Freehan	4.00	2.00
576	Cubs Rookies	3.50	1.75
	Brock Davis (R)		
	Adrian Garrett (R)		
	Garry Jestadt (R)		
577	Jim Lonborg	4.00	2.00
578	Ron Hunt	3.50	1.75
579	Marty Pattin	3.50	1.75
580	Tony Perez	18.00	9.00
581	Roger Nelson	3.50	1.75
582	Dave Cash	4.50	2.25
583	Ron Cook	3.50	1.75
584	Indians Team	7.00	3.50
585	Willie Davis	4.00	2.00
586	Dick Woodson	3.50	1.75
587	Sonny Jackson	3.50	1.75
588	Tom Bradley	3.50	1.75
589	Bob Barton	3.50	1.75
590	Alex Johnson	3.50	1.75
591	Jackie Brown	3.50	1.75
592	Randy Hundley	3.50	1.75
593	Jack Aker	3.50	1.75
594	Cards Rookies	6.00	3.00
	Bob Chlupsa (R)		
	Al Hrabosky (R)		
	Bob Stinson		
595	Dave Johnson	3.50	1.75
596	Mike Jorgensen	3.50	1.75
597	Ken Suarez	3.50	1.75
598	Rick Wise	3.50	1.75
599	Norm Cash	6.00	3.00
600	Willie Mays	100.00	50.00
601	Ken Tatum	3.50	1.75
602	Marty Martinez	3.50	1.75
603	Pirates Team	7.00	3.50
604	John Gelnar	3.50	1.75
605	Orlando Cepeda	6.00	3.00
606	Chuck Taylor	3.50	1.75
607	Paul Ratliff	3.50	1.75
608	Mike Wegener	3.50	1.75
609	Leo Durocher	4.50	2.25
610	Amos Otis	4.50	2.25
611	Tom Phoebus	3.50	1.75
612	Indians Rookies	3.50	1.75
	Lou Camilli (R)		
	Ted Ford (R)		
	Steve Mingori (R)		

613	Pedro Borbon	3.50	1.75
614	Billy Cowan	3.50	1.75
615	Mel Stottlemyre	5.00	2.50
616	Larry Hisle	3.50	1.75
617	Clay Dairymple	3.50	1.75
618	Tug McGraw	5.50	2.75
619	Checklist 644-752	8.50	3.50
620	Frank Howard	6.00	3.00
621	Ron Bryant	3.50	1.75
622	Joe Lahoud	3.50	1.75
623	Pat Jarvis	3.50	1.75
624	Athletics Team	7.00	3.50
625	Lou Brock	32.00	16.00
626	Freddie Patek	3.50	1.75
627	Steve Hamilton	3.50	1.75
628	John Bateman	3.50	1.75
629	John Hiller	3.50	1.75
630	Roberto Clemente	80.00	40.00
631	Eddie Fisher	3.50	1.75
632	Darrel Chaney	3.50	1.75
633	A.L. Rookies	3.50	1.75
	Bobby Brooks (R)		
	Pete Koegel		
	Scott Northey		
634	Phil Regan	3.50	1.75
635	Bobby Murcer	8.50	4.25
636	Denny Lemaster	3.50	1.75
637	Dave Bristol	3.50	1.75
638	Stan Williams	3.50	1.75
639	Tom Haller	3.50	1.75
640	Frank Robinson	42.00	21.00
641	Mets Team	12.00	6.00
642	Jim Roland	3.50	1.75
643	Rick Reichardt	3.50	1.75
644	Jim Stewart	6.00	3.00
645	Jim Maloney	6.00	3.00
646	Bobby Floyd	6.00	3.00
647	Juan Pizarro	6.00	3.00
648	Mets Rookies	14.00	7.00
	Rich Folkers (R)		
	Ted Martinez (R)		
	Jon Matlack (R)		
649	Sparky Lyle	12.50	7.50
650	Richie Allen	28.00	14.00
651	Jerry Robertson	6.00	3.00
652	Braves Team	10.00	5.00
653	Russ Snyder	6.00	3.00
654	Don Shaw	6.00	3.00
655	Mike Epstein	6.00	3.00
656	Gerry Nyman	6.00	3.00
657	Jose Azcue	6.00	3.00
658	Paul Lindblad	6.00	3.00
659	Byron Browne	6.00	3.00
660	Ray Culp	6.00	3.00
661	Chuck Tanner	6.00	3.00
662	Mike Hedlund	6.00	3.00
663	Marv Staehle	6.00	3.00
664	Major League Rookies	6.00	3.00
	Archie Reynolds (R)		
	Bob Reynolds (R)		
	Ken Reynolds (R)		
665	Ron Swoboda	10.00	5.00
666	Gene Brabender	6.00	3.00
667	Pete Ward	6.00	3.00
668	Gary Neibauer	6.00	3.00
669	Ike Brown	6.00	3.00
670	Bill Hands	6.00	3.00
671	Bill Voss	6.00	3.00
672	Ed Crosby	6.00	3.00
673	Gerry Janeski	6.00	3.00
674	Expos Team	10.00	5.00
675	Dave Boswell	6.00	3.00
676	Tommie Reynolds	6.00	3.00
677	Jack DiLauro	6.00	3.00
678	George Thomas	6.00	3.00
679	Don O'Riley	6.00	3.00
680	Don Mincher	6.00	3.00
681	Bill Butler	6.00	3.00
682	Terry Harmon	6.00	3.00
683	Bill Burbach	6.00	3.00
684	Curt Motton	6.00	3.00
685	Moe Drabowsky	6.00	3.00
686	Chico Ruiz	6.00	3.00
687	Ron Taylor	6.00	3.00
688	Sparky Anderson	25.00	12.50
689	Frank Baker	6.00	3.00
690	Bob Moose	6.00	3.00
691	Bob Heise	6.00	3.00
692	A.L. Rookies	6.00	3.00
	Hal Haydel (R)		
	Rogelio Moret (R)		
	Wayne Twitchel		
693	Jose Pena	6.00	3.00
694	Rick Renick	6.00	3.00
695	Joe Niekro	6.00	3.00
696	Jerry Morales	6.00	3.00
697	Rickey Clark	6.00	3.00
698	Brewers Team	15.00	7.50
699	Jim Britton	6.00	3.00
700	Boog Powell	24.00	12.00
701	Bob Garibaldi	6.00	3.00
702	Milt Ramirez	6.00	3.00
703	Mike Kekich	6.00	3.00
704	J.C. Martin	6.00	3.00
705	Dick Selma	6.00	3.00
706	Joe Foy	6.00	3.00
707	Fred Lasher	6.00	3.00
708	Russ Nagelson	6.00	3.00
709	Major League Rookies	80.00	40.00
	Dusty Baker (R)		
	Don Baylor (R)		
	Tom Paciorek (R)		
710	Sonny Siebert	6.00	3.00
711	Larry Stahl	6.00	3.00

712	Jose Martinez	6.00	3.00
713	Mike Marshall	6.00	3.00
714	Dick Williams	6.00	3.00
715	Horace Clarke	6.00	3.00
716	Dave Leonhard	6.00	3.00
717	Tommie Aaron	6.00	3.00
718	Billy Wynne	6.00	3.00
719	Jerry May	6.00	3.00
720	Matty Alou	6.00	3.00
721	John Morris	6.00	3.00
722	Astros Team	15.00	7.50
723	Vicente Romo	6.00	3.00
724	Tom Tischinski	6.00	3.00
725	Gary Gentry	6.00	3.00
726	Paul Popovich	6.00	3.00
727	Ray Lamb	6.00	3.00
728	N.L. Rookies	6.00	3.00
	Keith Lampard (R)		
	Wayne Redmond (R)		
	Bernie Williams		
729	Dick Billings	6.00	3.00
730	Jim Rooker	6.00	3.00
731	Jim Qualls	6.00	3.00
732	Bob Reed	6.00	3.00
733	Lee Maye	6.00	3.00
734	Rob Gardner	6.00	3.00
735	Mike Shannon	6.00	3.00
736	Mel Queen	6.00	3.00
737	Preston Gomez	6.00	3.00
738	Russ Gibson	6.00	3.00
739	Barry Lersch	6.00	3.00
740	Luis Aparicio	22.00	11.00
741	Skip Guinn	6.00	3.00
742	Royals Team	10.00	5.00
743	John O'Donoghue	6.00	3.00
744	Chuck Manuel	6.00	3.00
745	Sandy Alomar	6.00	3.00
746	Andy Kosco	6.00	3.00
747	N.L. Rookies	6.00	3.00
	Balor Moore (R)		
	Al Severinsen		
	Scipio Spinks		
748	John Purdin	6.00	3.00
749	Ken Szotkiewicz	6.00	3.00
750	Denny McLain	22.00	11.00
751	Al Weis	9.00	4.50
752	Dick Drago	8.00	3.50

1972 Topps

This 787-card set features several Topps innovations. Card fronts include large color photos wrapper in an arch-style frame. Team names appear in multi-colored letters at the top of the photo across the arch. Player's names are found at the bottom of the photograph. With this set Topps introduced their "In-Action" subset (IA), Traded cards (TR), Trophy cards and Childhood photos. Regular features include League Leaders, World Series and Playoff highlights. All cards measure 2-1/2" by 3-1/2".

		NR/MT	EX
Complete Set (787)		2,150.00	1,075.00
Commons (1-394)		.80	.40
Commons (395-525)		1.25	.60
Commons (526-656)		3.00	1.50
Commons (657-787)		7.00	3.50

1	Pirates (Champs)	7.00	3.50
2	Ray Culp	.80	.40
3	Bobby Tolan	.80	.40
4	Checklist 1-132	3.50	1.50
5	John Bateman	.80	.40
6	Fred Scherman	.80	.40
7	Enzo Hernandez	.80	.40
8	Ron Swoboda	1.00	.50
9	Stan Williams	.80	.40
10	Amos Otis	1.00	.50
11	Bobby Valentine	1.00	.50
12	Jose Cardenal	.80	.40
13	Joe Grzenda	.80	.40
14	Phillies Rookies	.80	.40
	Pete Koegel		
	Mike Anderson (R)		
	Wayne Twitchell		
15	Walt Williams	.80	.40
16	Mike Jorgensen	.80	.40
17	Dave Duncan	.80	.40

18a Juan Pizarro (Green Line Under C and S)	3.00	1.50	
18b Juan Pizarro (Yellow Line Under C and S)	.80	.40	
19 Billy Cowan	.80	.40	
20 Don Wilson	.80	.40	
21 Braves Team	1.50	.75	
22 Rob Gardner	.80	.40	
23 Ted Kubiak	.80	.40	
24 Ted Ford	.80	.40	
25 Bill Singer	.80	.40	
26 Andy Etchebarren	.80	.40	
27 Bob Johnson	.80	.40	
28 Twins Rookies	.80	.40	
Steve Brye (R)			
Bob Gebhard (R)			
Hal Haydel (R)			
29a Bill Bonham (Green Line)	3.00	1.50	
29b Bill Bonham (Yellow Line)	.80	.40	
30 Rico Petrocelli	.90	.45	
31 Cleon Jones	.80	.40	
32 Cleon Jones IA	.80	.40	
33 Billy Martin	4.00	2.00	
34 Billy Martin IA	1.50	.75	
35 Jerry Johnson	.80	.40	
36 Jerry Johnson IA	.80	.40	
37 Carl Yastrzemski	14.00	7.00	
38 Carl Yastrzemski IA	6.50	3.25	
39 Bob Barton	.80	.40	
40 Bob Barton IA	.80	.40	
41 Tommy Davis	1.25	.60	
42 Tommy Davis IA	1.00	.50	
43 Rick Wise	.80	.40	
44 Rick Wise IA	.80	.40	
45a Glenn Beckert (Green Line)	3.00	1.50	
45b Glenn Beckert (Yellow Line)	.80	.40	
46 Glenn Beckert IA	.80	.40	
47 John Ellis	.80	.40	
48 John Ellis IA	.80	.40	
49 Willie Mays	28.00	14.00	
50 Willie Mays IA	12.00	6.00	
51 Harmon Killebrew	7.00	3.50	
52 Harmon Killebrew IA	3.00	1.50	
53 Bud Harrelson	.90	.60	
54 Bud Harrelson IA	.80	.40	
55 Clyde Wright	.80	.40	
56 Rich Chiles	.80	.40	
57 Bob Oliver	.80	.40	
58 Ernie McAnally	.80	.40	
59 Fred Stanley	.80	.40	
60 Manny Sanguillen	1.00	.50	
61 Cubs Rookies	1.25	.60	
Gene Hiser			

Burt Hooton (R)			
Earl Stephenson (R)			
62 Angel Mangual	.80	.40	
63 Duke Sims	.80	.40	
64 Pete Broberg	.80	.40	
65 Cesar Cedeno	1.50	.75	
66 Ray Corbin	.80	.40	
67 Red Schoendienst	1.25	.65	
68 Jim York	.80	.40	
69 Roger Freed	.80	.40	
70 Mike Cuellar	1.00	.50	
71 Angels Team	1.50	.75	
72 Bruce Kison (R)	1.00	.50	
73 Steve Huntz	.80	.40	
74 Cecil Upshaw	.80	.40	
75 Bert Campaneris	1.25	.60	
76 Don Carrithers	.80	.40	
77 Ron Theobald	.80	.40	
78 Steve Arlin	.80	.40	
79 Red Sox Rookies	110.00	55.00	
Cecil Cooper (R)			
Carlton Fisk (R)			
Mike Garman (R)			
80 Tony Perez	6.00	3.00	
81 Mike Hedlund	.80	.40	
82 Ron Woods	.80	.40	
83 Dalton Jones	.80	.40	
84 Vince Colbert	.80	.40	
85 N.L. Batting Leaders	2.00	1.00	
86 A.L. Batting Leaders	2.00	1.00	
87 N.L. RBI Leaders	4.00	2.00	
88 A.L. RBI Leaders	4.00	2.00	
89 N.L. HR Leaders	4.00	2.00	
90 A.L. HR Leaders	5.00	2.50	
91 N.L. ERA Leaders	3.50	1.75	
92 A.L. ERA Leaders	3.50	1.75	
93 N.L. Pitching Leaders	4.00	2.00	
94 A.L. Pitching Leaders	3.50	1.75	
95 N.L. Strikeout Leaders	4.00	2.00	
96 A.L. Strikeout Leaders	3.50	1.75	
97 Tom Kelley	.80	.40	
98 Chuck Tanner	.80	.40	
99 Ross Grimsley	.80	.40	
100 Frank Robinson	7.00	3.50	
101 Astros Rookies	2.50	1.25	
Ray Busse (R)			
Bill Grief (R)			
J.R. Richard (R)			
102 Lloyd Allen	.80	.40	
103 Checklist 133-263	3.50	1.75	
104 Toby Harrah (R)	2.00	1.00	
105 Gary Gentry	.80	.40	
106 Brewers Team	1.50	.75	
107 Jose Cruz	2.50	1.25	
108 Gary Waslewski	.80	.40	
109 Jerry May	.80	.40	
110 Ron Hunt	.80	.40	

111	Jim Grant	.80	.40
112	Greg Luzinski	1.75	.90
113	Rogelio Moret	.80	.40
114	Bill Buckner	2.00	1.00
115	Jim Fregosi	1.00	.50
116	Ed Farmer (R)	.80	.40
117a	Cleo James (Green Line)	3.00	1.50
117b	Cleo James (Yellow Line)	.80	.50
118	Skip Lockwood	.80	.40
119	Marty Perez	.80	.40
120	Bill Freehan	1.00	.50
121	Ed Sprague	.80	.40
122	Larry Biittner	.80	.40
123	Ed Acosta	.80	.40
124	Yankees Rookies	.80	.50
	Alan Closter (R)		
	Roger Hambright (R)		
	Rusty Torres (R)		
125	Dave Cash	.80	.40
126	Bary Johnson	.80	.40
127	Duffy Dyer	.80	.40
128	Eddie Watt	.80	.40
129	Charlie Fox	.80	.40
130	Bob Gibson	7.50	3.25
131	Jim Nettles	.80	.40
132	Joe Morgan	7.50	3.25
133	Joe Keough	.80	.40
134	Carl Morton	.80	.40
135	Vada Pinson	1.25	.60
136	Darrel Chaney	.80	.40
137	Dick Williams	.80	.40
138	Mike Kekich	.80	.40
139	Tim McCarver	1.00	.50
140	Pat Dobson	.80	.40
141	Mets Rookies	1.25	.60
	Buzz Capra (R)		
	Jon Matlack		
	Leroy Stanton		
142	Chris Chambliss (R)	3.50	1.75
143	Garry Jestadt	.80	.40
144	Marty Pattin	.80	.40
145	Don Kessinger	1.00	.80
146	Steve Kealey	.80	.40
147	Dave Kingman (R)	6.00	3.00
148	Dick Billings	.80	.40
149	Gary Neibauer	.80	.40
150	Norm Cash	1.50	.75
151	Jim Brewer	.80	.40
152	Gene Clines	.80	.40
153	Rick Auerbach	.80	.40
154	Ted Simmons	3.00	1.50
155	Larry Dierker	.80	.40
156	Twins Team	1.50	.75
157	Don Gullett	1.00	.50
158	Jerry Kenney	.80	.40
159	John Boccabela	.80	.40
160	Andy Messersmith	.80	.40
161	Brock Davis	.80	.40
162	Brewers Rookies	1.25	.60
	Jerry Bell (R)		
	Darrell Porter (R)		
	Bob Reynolds (R)		
163	Tug McGraw	1.50	.75
164	Tug McGraw IA	1.00	.50
165	Chris Speier (R)	1.50	.75
166	Chris Speier IA	1.00	.50
167	Deron Johnson	.80	.40
168	Deron Johnson IA	.80	.40
169	Vida Blue	2.00	1.00
170	Vida Blue IA	1.25	.60
171	Darrell Evans	2.50	1.25
172	Darrell Evans IA	1.25	.60
173	Clay Kirby	.80	.40
174	Clay Kirby IA	.80	.40
175	Tom Haller	.80	.40
176	Tom Haller IA	.80	.40
177	Paul Schaal	.80	.40
178	Paul Schaal IA	.80	.40
179	Dock Ellis	.80	.40
180	Dock Ellis IA	.80	.40
181	Ed Kranepool	1.00	.50
182	Ed Kranepool IA	.80	.40
183	Bill Melton	.80	.40
184	Bill Melton IA	.80	.40
185	Ron Bryant	.80	.40
186	Ron Bryant IA	.80	.40
187	Gates Brown	.80	.40
188	Frank Lucchesi	.80	.40
189	Gene Tenace	1.00	.50
190	Dave Giusti	.80	.40
191	Jeff Burroughs (R)	1.50	.75
192	Cubs Team	1.50	.75
193	Kurt Bevacqua (R)	.80	.40
194	Fred Norman	.80	.40
195	Orlando Cepeda	3.00	1.50
196	Mel Queen	.80	.40
197	Johnny Briggs	.80	.40
198	Dodgers Rookies	7.00	3.50
	Charlie Hough (R)		
	Bob O'Brien (R)		
	Mike Strahler (R)		
199	Mike Fiore	.80	.40
200	Lou Brock	7.50	3.25
201	Phil Roof	.80	.40
202	Scipio Spinks	.80	.40
203	Ron Blomberg (R)	.80	.40
204	Tommy Helms	.80	.40
205	Dick Drago	.80	.40
206	Dal Maxvill	.80	.40
207	Tom Egan	.80	.40
208	Milt Pappas	.80	.40
209	Joe Rudi	1.00	.50

210	Denny McLain	1.50	.75
211	Gary Sutherland	.80	.40
212	Grant Jackson	.80	.40
213	Angels Rookies	.80	.50
	Art Kusnyer (R)		
	Billy Parker (R)		
	Tom Silverio (R)		
214	Mike McQueen	.80	.40
215	Alex Johnson	.80	.40
216	Joe Niekro	1.00	.50
217	Roger Metzger	.80	.40
218	Eddie Kasko	.80	.40
219	Rennie Stennett (R)	1.50	.75
220	Jim Perry	.80	.40
221	N.L. Playoffs (Bucs)	1.25	.60
222	A.L. Playoffs (Orioles)	2.50	1.25
223	World Series Game 1	1.25	.60
224	World Series Game 2	1.25	.60
225	World Series Game 3	1.25	.60
226	World Series Game 4	4.50	2.25
227	World Series Game 5	1.25	.60
228	World Series Game 6	1.25	.60
229	World Series Game 7	1.25	.60
230	WS (Celebration)	1.25	.60
231	Casey Cox	.80	.40
232	Giants Rookies	.80	.50
	Chris Arnold (R)		
	Jim Barr (R)		
	Dave Rader (R)		
233	Jay Johnstone	1.00	.50
234	Ron Taylor	.80	.40
235	Merv Rettenmund	.80	.40
236	Jim McGlothlin	.80	.40
237	Yankees Team	1.50	.75
238	Leron Lee	.80	.40
239	Tom Timmermann	.80	.40
240	Rich Allen	3.00	1.50
241	Rollie Fingers	8.00	4.00
242	Don Mincher	.80	.40
243	Frank Linzy	.80	.40
244	Steve Braun	.80	.40
245	Tommie Agee	.80	.40
246	Tom Burgmeier	.80	.40
247	Milt May	.80	.40
248	Tom Bradley	.80	.40
249	Harry Walker	.80	.40
250	Boog Powell	3.00	1.50
251	Checklist 264-394	3.50	1.50
252	Ken Reynolds	.80	.40
253	Sandy Alomar	.80	.40
254	Boots Day	.80	.40
255	Jim Lonborg	1.00	.50
256	George Foster	2.50	1.25
257	Tigers Rookies	.80	.40
	Jim Foor (R)		
	Tim Hosley (R)		
	Paul Jata (R)		
258	Randy Hundley	.80	.40
259	Sparky Lyle	1.50	.75
260	Ralph Garr	.80	.40
261	Steve Mingori	.80	.40
262	Padres Team	1.50	.75
263	Felipe Alou	1.50	.75
264	Tommy John	2.50	1.25
265	Wes Parker	.80	.40
266	Bobby Bolin	.80	.40
267	Dave Concepcion	4.00	2.00
268	A's Rookies	.80	.50
	Dwain Anderson (R)		
	Chris Floethe (R)		
269	Don Hahn	.80	.40
270	Jim Palmer	16.00	8.00
271	Ken Rudolph	.80	.40
272	Mickey Rivers (R)	2.00	1.00
273	Bobby Floyd	.80	.40
274	Al Severinsen	.80	.40
275	Cesar Tovar	.80	.40
276	Gene Mauch	.80	.40
277	Elliott Maddox	.80	.40
278	Dennis Higgins	.80	.40
279	Larry Brown	.80	.40
280	Willie McCovey	7.50	3.25
281	Bill Parsons	.80	.40
282	Astros Team	1.50	.75
283	Darrell Brandon	.80	.40
284	Ike Brown	.80	.40
285	Gaylord Perry	8.00	4.00
286	Gene Alley	.80	.40
287	Jim Hardin	.80	.40
288	Johnny Jeter	.80	.40
289	Syd O'Brien	.80	.40
290	Sonny Siebert	.80	.40
291	Hal McRae	2.50	1.25
292	Hal McRae IA	1.25	.65
293	Danny Frisella	.80	.40
294	Danny Frisella IA	.80	.40
295	Dick Dietz	.80	.40
296	Dick Dietz IA	.80	.40
297	Claude Osteen	1.00	.50
298	Claude Osteen IA	.80	.40
299	Hank Aaron	40.00	20.00
300	Hank Aaron IA	20.00	10.00
301	George Mitterwald	.80	.40
302	George Mitterwald IA	.80	.40
303	Joe Pepitone	1.00	.50
304	Joe Pepitone IA	.80	.40
305	Ken Boswell	.80	.40
306	Ken Boswell IA	.80	.40
307	Steve Renko	.80	.40
308	Steve Renko IA	.80	.40
309	Roberto Clemente	38.00	19.00
310	Roberto Clemente IA	18.00	9.00
311	Clay Carroll	.80	.40
312	Clay Carroll IA	.80	.40

313	Luis Aparicio	3.50	1.75
314	Luis Aparicio IA	1.50	.75
315	Paul Splittorff	.80	.40
316	Cardinals Rookies	1.25	.60
	Jim Bibby (R)		
	Santiago Guzman (R)		
	Jorge Roque (R)		
317	Rich Hand	.80	.40
318	Sonny Jackson	.80	.40
319	Aurelio Rodriguez	.80	.40
320	Steve Blass	.80	.40
321	Joe Lohoud	.80	.40
322	Jose Pena	.80	.40
323	Earl Weaver	1.50	.75
324	Mike Ryan	.80	.40
325	Mel Stottlemyre	1.00	.50
326	Pat Kelly	.80	.40
327	Steve Stone (R)	2.50	1.25
328	Red Sox Team	1.50	.75
329	Roy Foster	.80	.40
330	Jim Hunter	5.00	2.50
331	Stan Swanson	.80	.40
332	Buck Martinez	.80	.40
333	Steve Barber	.80	.40
334	Rangers Rookies	.80	.40
	Bill Fahey (R)		
	Jim Mason (R)		
	Tom Ragland (R)		
335	Bill Hands	.80	.40
336	Marty Martinez	.80	.40
337	Mike Kilkenny	.80	.40
338	Bob Grich	1.50	.75
339	Ron Cook	.80	.40
340	Roy White	.80	.40
341	Joe Torre (Child)	1.00	.50
342	Wilbur Wood (Child)	.80	.50
343	Willie Stargell (Child)	1.50	.75
344	Dave McNally (Child)	.80	.40
345	Rick Wise (Child)	.80	.40
346	Jim Fregosi (Child)	.80	.40
347	Tom Seaver (Child)	3.50	1.75
348	Sal Bando (Child)	.80	.50
349	Al Fitzmorris	.80	.40
350	Frank Howard	1.50	.75
351	Braves Rookies	1.00	.50
	Jimmy Britton (R)		
	Tom House		
	Rick Kester		
352	Dave LaRoche	.80	.40
353	Art Shamsky	.80	.40
354	Tom Murphy	.80	.40
355	Bob Watson	1.25	.60
356	Gerry Moses	.80	.40
357	Woodie Fryman	.80	.40
358	Sparky Anderson	2.50	1.25
359	Don Pavletich	.80	.40
360	Dave Roberts	.80	.40
361	Mike Andrews	.80	.40
362	Mets Team	1.50	.75
363	Ron Klimkowski	.80	.40
364	Johnny Callison	.80	.40
365	Dick Bosman	.80	.40
366	Jimmy Rosario	.80	.40
367	Ron Perranoski	.80	.40
368	Danny Thompson	.80	.40
369	Jim Lefebvre	1.00	.50
370	Don Buford	.80	.40
371	Denny Lemaster	.80	.40
372	Royals Rookies	.80	.40
	Lance Clemons (R)		
	Monty Montgomery		
373	John Mayberry	1.25	.60
374	Jack Heidemann	.80	.40
375	Reggie Cleveland	.80	.40
376	Andy Kosco	.80	.40
377	Terry Harmon	.80	.40
378	Checklist 395-525	3.50	1.50
379	Ken Berry	.80	.40
380	Earl Williams	.80	.40
381	White Sox Team	1.50	.75
382	Joe Gibbon	.80	.40
383	Brant Alyea	.80	.40
384	Dave Campbell	.80	.40
385	Mickey Stanley	1.00	.50
386	Jim Colborn	.80	.40
387	Horace Clarke	.80	.40
388	Charlie Williams	.80	.40
389	Bill Rigney	.80	.40
390	Willie Davis	1.00	.50
391	Ken Sanders	.80	.40
392	Pirates Rookies	1.25	.60
	Fred Cambria (R)		
	Richie Zisk (R)		
393	Curt Motton	.80	.40
394	Ken Forsch	.80	.40
395	Matty Alou	1.50	.75
396	Paul Lindblad	1.25	.60
397	Phillies Team	2.50	1.25
398	Larry Hisle	1.25	.60
399	Milt Wilcox	1.25	.60
400	Tony Oliva	2.50	1.25
401	Jim Nash	1.25	.60
402	Bobby Heise	1.25	.60
403	John Cumberland	1.25	.60
404	Jeff Torborg	1.50	.75
405	Ron Fairly	1.25	.60
406	George Hendrick (R)	2.00	1.00
407	Chuck Taylor	1.25	.60
408	Jim Northrup	1.25	.60
409	Frank Baker	1.25	.60
410	Ferguson Jenkins	8.00	4.00
411	Bob Montgomery	1.25	.60
412	Dick Kelley	1.25	.60
413	White Sox Rookies	1.25	.60

	Don Eddy (R)		
	Dave Lemonds (R)		
414	Bob Miller	1.25	.60
415	Cookie Rojas	1.25	.60
416	Johnny Edwards	1.25	.60
417	Tom Hall	1.25	.60
418	Tom Shopay	1.25	.60
419	Jim Spencer	1.25	.60
420	Steve Carlton	30.00	15.00
421	Ellie Rodriguez	1.25	.60
422	Ray Lamb	1.25	.60
423	Oscar Gamble	1.50	.75
424	Bill Gogolewski	1.25	.60
425	Ken Singleton	2.00	1.00
426	Ken Singleton IA	1.50	.75
427	Tito Fuentes	1.25	.60
428	Tito Fuentes IA	1.25	.60
429	Bob Robertson	1.25	.60
430	Bob Robertson IA	1.25	.60
431	Cito Gaston	3.00	1.50
432	Cito Gaston IA	1.50	.75
433	Johnny Bench	42.00	21.00
434	Johnny Bench IA	19.00	9.50
435	Reggie Jackson	55.00	27.50
436	Reggie Jackson IA	24.00	12.00
437	Maury Wills	2.50	1.25
438	Maury Wills IA	1.50	.75
439	Billy Williams	7.00	3.50
440	Billy Williams IA	2.50	1.25
441	Thurman Munson	18.00	9.00
442	Thurman Munson IA	8.50	4.25
443	Ken Henderson	1.25	.60
444	Ken Henderson IA	1.25	.60
445	Tom Seaver	45.00	22.50
446	Tom Seaver IA	20.00	10.00
447	Willie Stargell	7.50	3.25
448	Willie Stargell IA	3.00	1.50
449	Bob Lemon	1.50	.75
450	Mickey Lolich	2.50	1.25
451	Tony LaRussa	2.50	1.25
452	Ed Herrmann	1.25	.60
453	Barry Lersch	1.25	.60
454	A's Team	2.50	1.25
455	Tommy Harper	1.25	.60
456	Mark Belanger	1.50	.75
457	Padres Rookies	1.25	.60
	Darcy Fast (R)		
	Mike Ivie (R)		
	Derrell Thomas (R)		
458	Aurelio Monteagudo	1.25	.60
459	Rick Renick	1.25	.60
460	Al Downing	1.25	.60
461	Tim Cullen	1.25	.60
462	Rickey Clark	1.25	.60
463	Bernie Carbo	1.25	.60
464	Jim Roland	1.25	.60
465	Gil Hodges	5.00	2.50
466	Norm Miller	1.25	.60
467	Steve Kline	1.25	.60
468	Richie Scheinblum	1.25	.60
469	Ron Herbel	1.25	.60
470	Ray Fosse	1.25	.60
471	Luke Walker	1.25	.60
472	Phil Gagliano	1.25	.60
473	Dan McGinn	1.25	.60
474	Orioles Rookies	10.00	5.00
	Don Baylor		
	Roric Harrison (R)		
	Johnny Oates (R)		
475	Gary Nolan	1.25	.60
476	Lee Richard	1.25	.60
477	Tom Phoebus	1.25	.60
478	Checklist 526-656	3.50	1.50
479	Don Shaw	1.25	.60
480	Lee May	1.25	.60
481	Billy Conigliaro	1.25	.60
482	Joe Hoerner	1.25	.60
483	Ken Suarez	1.25	.60
484	Lum Harris	1.25	.60
485	Phil Regan	1.25	.60
486	John Lowenstein	1.25	.60
487	Tigers Team	2.50	1.25
488	Mike Nagy	1.25	.60
489	Expos Rookies	1.25	.60
	Terry Humphrey (R)		
	Keith Lampard		
490	Dave McNally	1.50	.75
491	Lou Piniella (Child)	2.00	1.00
492	Mel Stottlemyre(Child)	1.25	.60
493	Bob Bailey (Child)	1.25	.60
494	Willie Horton (Child)	1.25	.60
495	Bill Melton (Child)	1.25	.60
496	Bud Harrelson (Child)	1.25	.60
497	Jim Perry (Child)	1.25	.60
498	Brooks Robinson(Child)	2.50	1.25
499	Vicente Romo	1.25	.60
500	Joe Torre	2.00	1.00
501	Pete Hamm	1.25	.60
502	Jackie Hernandez	1.25	.60
503	Gary Peters	1.25	.60
504	Ed Spiezio	1.25	.60
505	Mike Marshall	1.50	.75
506	Indians Rookies	1.25	.60
	Terry Ley (R)		
	Jim Moyer (R)		
	Dick Tidrow (R)		
507	Fred Gladding	1.25	.60
508	Ellie Hendricks	1.25	.60
509	Don McMahon	1.25	.60
510	Ted Williams	8.50	4.25
511	Tony Taylor	1.25	.60
512	Paul Popovich	1.25	.60
513	Lindy McDaniel	1.25	.60
514	Ted Sizemore	1.25	.60

515	Bert Blyleven	10.00	5.00
516	Oscar Brown	1.25	.60
517	Ken Brett	1.25	.60
518	Wayne Garrett	1.25	.60
519	Ted Abernathy	1.25	.60
520	Larry Bowa	2.50	1.25
521	Alan Foster	1.25	.60
522	Dodgers Team	2.50	1.25
523	Chuck Dobson	1.25	.60
524	Reds Rookies	1.25	.60
	Ed Armbrister (R)		
	Mel Behney (R)		
525	Carlos May	1.25	.60
526	Bob Bailey	3.00	1.50
527	Dave Leonhard	3.00	1.50
528	Ron Stone	3.00	1.50
529	Dave Nelson	3.00	1.50
530	Don Sutton	7.50	3.25
531	Freddie Patek	3.00	1.50
532	Fred Kendall	3.00	1.50
533	Ralph Houk	4.00	2.00
534	Jim Hickman	3.00	1.50
535	Ed Brinkman	3.00	1.50
536	Doug Rader	3.00	1.50
537	Bob Locker	3.00	1.50
538	Charlie Sands	3.00	1.50
539	Terry Forster (R)	3.50	1.75
540	Felix Milan	3.00	1.50
541	Roger Repoz	3.00	1.50
542	Jack Billingham	3.00	1.50
543	Duane Josephson	3.00	1.50
544	Ted Martinez	3.00	1.50
545	Wayne Granger	3.00	1.50
546	Joe Hague	3.00	1.50
547	Indians Team	5.00	2.50
548	Frank Reberger	3.00	1.50
549	Dave May	3.00	1.50
550	Brooks Robinson	26.00	13.00
551	Ollie Brown	3.00	1.50
552	Ollie Brown IA	3.00	1.50
553	Wilbur Wood	3.00	1.50
554	Wilbur Wood IA	3.00	1.50
555	Ron Santo	5.00	2.50
556	Ron Santo IA	3.50	1.75
557	John Odom	3.00	1.50
558	John Odom IA	3.00	1.50
559	Pete Rose	50.00	25.00
560	Pete Rose IA	24.00	12.00
561	Leo Cardenas	3.00	1.50
562	Leo Cardenas IA	3.00	1.50
563	Ray Sadecki	3.00	1.50
564	Ray Sadecki IA	3.00	1.50
565	Reggie Smith	3.50	1.75
566	Reggie Smith IA	3.00	1.50
567	Juan Marichal	8.00	4.00
568	Juan Marichal IA	3.50	1.75
569	Ed Kirkpatrick	3.00	1.50
570	Ed Kirkpatrick IA	3.00	1.50
571	Nate Colbert	3.00	1.50
572	Nate Colbert IA	3.00	1.50
573	Fritz Peterson	3.00	1.50
574	Fritz Peterson IA	3.00	1.50
575	Al Oliver	4.00	2.00
576	Leo Durocher	3.50	1.75
577	Mike Paul	3.00	1.50
578	Billy Grabarkewitz	3.00	1.50
579	Doyle Alexander (R)	3.50	1.75
580	Lou Piniella	4.50	2.25
581	Wade Blasingame	3.00	1.50
582	Expos Team	5.00	2.50
583	Darold Knowles	3.00	1.50
584	Jerry McNertney	3.00	1.50
585	George Scott	3.50	1.75
586	Denis Menke	3.00	1.50
587	Billy Wilson	3.00	1.50
588	Jim Holt	3.00	1.50
589	Hal Lanier	3.00	1.50
590	Graig Nettles	6.00	3.00
591	Paul Casanova	3.00	1.50
592	Lew Krausse	3.00	1.50
593	Rich Morales	3.00	1.50
594	Jim Beauchamp	3.00	1.50
595	Nolan Ryan	275.00	140.00
596	Manny Mota	3.50	1.75
597	Jim Magnuson	3.00	1.50
598	Hal King	3.00	1.50
599	Billy Champion	3.00	1.50
600	Al Kaline	24.00	12.00
601	George Stone	3.00	1.50
602	Dave Bristol	3.00	1.50
603	Jim Ray	3.00	1.50
604	Checklist 657-787	8.00	3.00
605	Nelson Briles	3.00	1.50
606	Luis Melendez	3.00	1.50
607	Frank Duffy	3.00	1.50
608	Mike Corkins	3.00	1.50
609	Tom Grieve	3.00	1.50
610	Bill Stoneman	3.00	1.50
611	Rich Reese	3.00	1.50
612	Joe Decker	3.00	1.50
613	Mike Ferraro	3.00	1.50
614	Ted Uhlaender	3.00	1.50
615	Steve Hargan	3.00	1.50
616	Joe Ferguson (R)	4.00	2.00
617	Royals Team	5.00	2.50
618	Rich Robertson	3.00	1.50
619	Rich McKinney	3.00	1.50
620	Phil Niekro	8.00	4.00
621	Commissioners Award	4.00	2.00
622	MVP Award	4.00	2.00
623	Cy Young Award	4.00	2.00
624	Minor League Player	4.00	2.00
625	Rookie Of the Year	4.00	2.00
626	Babe Ruth Award	4.00	2.00

627	Moe Drabowsky	3.00	1.50
628	Terry Crowley	3.00	1.50
629	Paul Doyle	3.00	1.50
630	Rich Hebner	3.00	1.50
631	John Strohmayer	3.00	1.50
632	Mike Hegan	3.00	1.50
633	Jack Hiatt	3.00	1.50
634	Dick Woodson	3.00	1.50
635	Don Money	3.00	1.50
636	Bill Lee	3.50	1.75
637	Preston Gomez	3.00	1.50
638	Ken Wright	3.00	1.50
639	J.C. Martin	3.00	1.50
640	Joe Coleman	3.00	1.50
641	Mike Lum	3.00	1.50
642	Denny Riddleberger	3.00	1.50
643	Russ Gibson	3.00	1.50
644	Bernie Allen	3.00	1.50
645	Jim Maloney	3.00	1.50
646	Chico Salmon	3.00	1.50
647	Bob Moose	3.00	1.50
648	Jim Lyttle	3.00	1.50
649	Pete Richert	3.00	1.50
650	Sal Bando	3.50	1.75
651	Reds Team	5.00	2.50
652	Marcelino Lopez	3.00	1.50
653	Jim Fairey	3.00	1.50
654	Horacio Pina	3.00	1.50
655	Jerry Grote	3.00	1.50
656	Rudy May	3.00	1.50
657	Bobby Wine	7.50	3.75
658	Steve Dunning	7.50	3.75
659	Bob Aspromonte	7.50	3.75
660	Paul Blair	8.00	4.00
661	Bill Virdon	7.50	3.75
662	Stan Bahnsen	7.50	3.75
663	Fran Healy	7.50	3.75
664	Bobby Knoop	7.50	3.75
665	Chris Short	7.50	3.75
666	Hector Torres	7.50	3.75
667	Ray Newman	7.50	3.75
668	Rangers Team	14.00	7.00
669	Willie Crawford	7.50	3.75
670	Ken Holtzman	7.50	3.75
671	Donn Clendenon	7.50	3.75
672	Archie Reynolds	7.50	3.75
673	Dave Marshall	7.50	3.75
674	John Kennedy	7.50	3.75
675	Pat Jarvis	7.50	3.75
676	Danny Cater	7.50	3.75
677	Ivan Murrell	7.50	3.75
678	Steve Luebber	7.50	3.75
679	Astros Rookies	7.50	3.75
	Bob Fenwick (R)		
	Bob Stinson		
680	Dave Johnson	7.50	3.75
681	Bobby Pfeil	7.50	3.75
682	Mike McCormick	7.50	3.75
683	Steve Hovley	7.50	3.75
684	Hal Breeden	7.50	3.75
685	Joe Horlen	7.50	3.75
686	Steve Garvey	70.00	35.00
687	Del Unser	7.50	3.75
688	Cardinals Team	12.00	6.00
689	Eddie Fisher	7.50	3.75
690	Willie Montanez	7.50	3.75
691	Curt Blefary	7.50	3.75
692	Curt Blefary IA	7.50	3.75
693	Alan Gallagher	7.50	3.75
694	Alan Gallagher IA	7.50	3.75
695	Rod Carew	90.00	45.00
696	Rod Carew IA	45.00	22.50
697	Jerry Koosman	14.00	7.00
698	Jerry Koosman IA	8.50	4.25
699	Bobby Murcer	14.00	7.00
700	Bobby Murcer IA	8.50	4.25
701	Jose Pagan	7.50	3.75
702	Jose Pagan IA	7.50	3.75
703	Doug Griffin	7.50	3.75
704	Doug Griffin IA	7.50	3.75
705	Pat Corrales	7.50	3.75
706	Pat Corrales IA	7.50	3.75
707	Tim Foli	8.50	4.25
708	Tim Foli IA	7.50	3.75
709	Jim Kaat	14.00	7.00
710	Jim Kaat IA	8.50	4.25
711	Bobby Bonds	18.00	9.00
712	Bobby Bonds IA	12.00	6.00
713	Gene Michael	7.50	3.75
714	Gene Michael IA	7.50	3.75
715	Mike Epstein	7.50	3.75
716	Jesus Alou	7.50	3.75
717	Bruce Dal Canton	7.50	3.75
718	Del Rice	7.50	3.75
719	Cesar Geronimo	7.50	3.75
720	Sam McDowell	8.00	4.00
721	Eddie Leon	7.50	3.75
722	Bill Sudakis	7.50	3.75
723	Al Santorini	7.50	3.75
724	A.L. Rookies	8.50	4.25
	John Curtis (R)		
	Rich Hinton (R)		
	Mickey Scott (R)		
725	Dick McAuliffe	7.50	3.75
726	Dick Selma	7.50	3.75
727	Jose Laboy	7.50	3.75
728	Gail Hopkins	7.50	3.75
729	Bob Veale	7.50	3.75
730	Rick Monday	8.00	4.00
731	Orioles Team	12.00	6.00
732	George Culver	7.50	3.75
733	Jim Hart	7.50	3.75
734	Bob Burda	7.50	3.75
735	Diego Segui	7.50	3.75

736	Bill Russell	10.00	5.00
737	Lenny Randle (R)	7.50	3.75
738	Jim Merritt	7.50	3.75
739	Don Mason	7.50	3.75
740	Rico Carty	7.50	3.75
741	Major League Rookies	10.00	5.00
	Tom Hutton		
	Rick Miller (R)		
	John Milner (R)		
742	Jim Rooker	7.50	3.75
743	Cesar Gutierrez	7.50	3.75
744	Jim Slaton (R)	7.50	3.75
745	Julian Javier	7.50	3.75
746	Lowell Palmer	7.50	3.75
747	Jim Stewart	7.50	3.75
748	Phil Hennigan	7.50	3.75
749	Walter Alston	9.00	4.50
750	Willie Horton	8.00	4.00
751	Steve Carlton Traded	75.00	35.00
752	Joe Morgan Traded	55.00	27.50
753	Denny McLain Traded	15.00	7.50
754	Frank Robinson (TR)	40.00	20.00
755	Jim Fregosi Traded	10.00	5.00
756	Rick Wise Traded	7.50	3.75
757	Jose Cardenal Traded	9.00	4.50
758	Gil Garrido	7.50	3.75
759	Chris Cannizzaro	7.50	3.75
760	Bill Mazeroski	12.00	6.00
761	Major League Rookies	26.00	13.00
	Ron Cey (R)		
	Ben Oglivie (R)		
	Bernie Williams		
762	Wayne Simpson	7.50	3.75
763	Ron Hansen	7.50	3.75
764	Dusty Baker	15.00	7.50
765	Ken McMullen	7.50	3.75
766	Steve Hamilton	7.50	3.75
767	Tom McCraw	7.50	3.75
768	Denny Doyle	7.50	3.75
769	Jack Aker	7.50	3.75
770	Jim Wynn	8.00	4.00
771	Giants Team	12.00	6.00
772	Ken Tatum	7.50	3.75
773	Ron Brand	7.50	3.75
774	Luis Alvarado	7.50	3.75
775	Jerry Reuss	7.50	3.75
776	Bill Voss	7.50	3.75
777	Hoyt Wilhelm	20.00	10.00
778	Twins Rookies	14.00	7.00
	Vic Albury (R)		
	Rick Dempsey (R)		
	Jim Strickland (R)		
779	Tony Cloninger	7.50	3.75
780	Dick Green	7.50	3.75
781	Jim McAndrew	7.50	3.75
782	Larry Stahl	7.50	3.75
783	Les Cain	7.50	3.75

784	Ken Aspromonte	7.50	3.75
785	Vic Davalillo	7.50	3.75
786	Chuck Brinkman	7.50	3.75
787	Ron Reed	8.50	4.00

1973 Topps

Topps reduced the size of their set to 660-cards in 1973. The 2-1/2" by 3-1/2" cards feature color photos on the card fronts and vertical card backs. Topps introduced a new subset called All-Time Leaders. Other key subsets include League Leaders, World Series and Playoff Highlights, Childhood Cards and Rookies.

		NR/MT	EX
Complete Set (660)		1,250.00	625.00
Commons (1-396)		.50	.25
Commons (397-528)		1.10	.55
Commons (529-660)		2.50	1.25

1	All Time HR Leaders	40.00	20.00
	(Hank Aaron, Willie		
	Mays, Babe Ruth)		
2	Rich Hebner	.50	.25
3	Jim Lonborg	.75	.35
4	John Milner	.50	.25
5	Ed Brinkman	.50	.25
6	Mac Scarce	.50	.25
7	Rangers Team	.50	.25
8	Tom Hall	.50	.25
9	Johnny Oates	.75	.35
10	Don Sutton	3.50	1.75
11	Chris Chambliss	1.25	.65
12	Padres Mgr/Coaches	.75	.35
13	George Hendrick	.75	.35
14	Sonny Siebert	.50	.25

15	Ralph Garr	.60	.30
16	Steve Braun	.50	.25
17	Fred Gladding	.50	.25
18	Leroy Stanton	.50	.25
19	Tim Foli	.50	.25
20	Stan Bahnsen	.50	.25
21	Randy Hundley	.50	.25
22	Ted Abernathy	.50	.25
23	Dave Kingman	1.25	.60
24	Al Santorini	.50	.25
25	Roy White	.50	.25
26	Pirates Team	1.00	.50
27	Bill Gogolewski	.50	.25
28	Hal McRae	1.50	.75
29	Tony Taylor	.50	.25
30	Tug McGraw	1.25	.60
31	Buddy Bell (R)	3.00	1.50
32	Fred Norman	.50	.25
33	Jim Breazeale	.50	.25
34	Pat Dobson	.60	.30
35	Willie Davis	.60	.30
36	Steve Barber	.50	.25
37	Bill Robinson	.60	.30
38	Mike Epstein	.50	.25
39	Dave Roberts	.50	.25
40	Reggie Smith	.90	.45
41	Tom Walker	.50	.25
42	Mike Andrews	.50	.25
43	Randy Moffitt (R)	.50	.25
44	Rick Monday	.75	.35
45	Ellie Rodriguez (Wrong Photo)	.50	.25
46	Lindy McDaniel	.50	.25
47	Luis Melendez	.50	.25
48	Paul Splittorff	.50	.25
49a	Twins Mgr./Coaches	.75	.45
50	Roberto Clemente	40.00	20.00
51	Chuck Seelbach	.50	.25
52	Denis Menke	.50	.25
53	Steve Dunning	.50	.25
54	Checklist 1-132	2.50	1.00
55	Jon Matlack	.75	.35
56	Merv Rettenmund	.50	.25
57	Derrel Thomas	.50	.25
58	Mike Paul	.50	.25
59	Steve Yeager (R)	1.25	.60
60	Ken Holtzman	.50	.25
61	Batting Leaders	3.00	1.50
62	Home Run Leaders	3.00	1.50
63	RBI Leaders	3.00	1.50
64	Stolen Base Leaders	2.00	1.00
65	ERA Leaders	2.00	1.00
66	Victory Leaders	3.00	1.50
67	Strikeout Leaders (Ryan/Carlton)	24.00	12.00
68	Leading Firemen	1.50	.75
69	Phil Gagliano	.50	.25
70	Milt Pappas	.50	.25
71	Johnny Briggs	.50	.25
72	Ron Reed	.50	.25
73	Ed Herrmann	.50	.25
74	Billy Champion	.50	.25
75	Vada Pinson	1.00	.50
76	Doug Rader	.75	.35
77	Mike Torrez	.50	.25
78	Richie Scheinblum	.50	.25
79	Jim Willoughby	.50	.25
80	Tony Oliva	1.50	.75
81a	Cubs Mgr./Coaches	1.25	.60
82	Fritz Peterson	.50	.25
83	Leron Lee	.50	.25
84	Rollie Fingers	7.50	3.75
85	Ted Simmons	2.00	1.00
86	Tom McCraw	.50	.25
87	Ken Boswell	.50	.25
88	Mickey Stanley	.60	.30
89	Jack Billingham	.50	.25
90	Brooks Robinson	8.00	4.00
91	Dodgers Team	1.25	.65
92	Jerry Bell	.50	.25
93	Jesus Alou	.50	.25
94	Dick Billings	.50	.25
95	Steve Blass	.50	.25
96	Doug Griffin	.50	.25
97	Willie Montanez	.50	.25
98	Dick Woodson	.50	.25
99	Carl Taylor	.50	.25
100	Hank Aaron	30.00	15.00
101	Ken Henderson	.50	.25
102	Rudy May	.50	.25
103	Celerino Sanchez	.50	.25
104	Reggie Cleveland	.50	.25
105	Carlos May	.50	.25
106	Terry Humphrey	.50	.25
107	Phil Hennigan	.50	.25
108	Bill Russell	.80	.40
109	Doyle Alexander	.60	.30
110	Bob Watson	1.00	.50
111	Dave Nelson	.50	.25
112	Gary Ross	.50	.25
113	Jerry Grote	.50	.25
114	Lynn McGlothen	.50	.25
115	Ron Santo	1.25	.65
116	Yankees Mgr/Coaches	1.25	.65
117	Ramon Hernandez	.50	.25
118	John Mayberry	.75	.35
119	Larry Bowa	1.00	.50
120	Joe Coleman	.50	.25
121	Dave Rader	.50	.25
122	Jim Strickland	.50	.25
123	Sandy Alomar	.50	.25
124	Jim Hardin	.50	.25
125	Ron Fairly	.50	.25
126	Jim Brewer	.50	.25

No.	Player	Price 1	Price 2
127	Brewers Team	1.25	.60
128	Ted Sizemore	.60	.30
129	Terry Forster	.50	.25
130	Pete Rose	24.00	12.00
131	Red Sox Mgr/Coaches	.75	.35
132	Matty Alou	.90	.45
133	Dave Roberts	.50	.25
134	Milt Wilcox	.50	.25
135	Lee May	.50	.25
136	Orioles Mgr/Coaches	1.50	.75
137	Jim Beauchamp	.50	.25
138	Horacio Pina	.50	.25
139	Carmen Fanzone	.50	.25
140	Lou Piniella	1.25	.60
141	Bruce Kison	.50	.25
142	Thurman Munson	8.50	4.25
143	John Curtis	.50	.25
144	Marty Perez	.50	.25
145	Bobby Bonds	3.00	1.50
146	Woodie Fryman	.50	.25
147	Mike Anderson	.50	.25
148	Dave Goltz	.50	.25
149	Ron Hunt	.50	.25
150	Wilbur Wood	.50	.25
151	Wes Parker	.50	.25
152	Dave May	.50	.25
153	Al Hrabosky	.75	.35
154	Jeff Torborg	.75	.35
155	Sal Bando	.75	.35
156	Cesar Geronimo	.50	.25
157	Denny Riddleberger	.50	.25
158	Astros Team	1.25	.65
159	Cito Gaston	1.00	.50
160	Jim Palmer	12.00	6.00
161	Ted Martinez	.50	.25
162	Pete Broberg	.50	.25
163	Vic Davalillo	.50	.25
164	Monty Montgomery	.50	.25
165	Luis Aparicio	3.00	1.50
166	Terry Harmon	.50	.25
167	Steve Stone	.75	.45
168	Jim Northrup	.50	.25
169	Ron Schueler	.70	.35
170	Harmon Killebrew	6.50	3.25
171	Bernie Carbo	.50	.25
172	Steve Kline	.50	.25
173	Hal Breeden	.50	.25
174	Rich Gossage (R)	18.00	9.00
175	Frank Robinson	7.50	3.75
176	Chuck Taylor	.50	.25
177	Bill Plummer (R)	.75	.35
178	Don Rose	.50	.25
179	A's Mgr./Coaches	.75	.35
180	Fergie Jenkins	6.00	3.00
181	Jack Brohamer	.50	.25
182	Mike Caldwell	.50	.25
183	Don Buford	.50	.25
184	Jerry Koosman	1.00	.50
185	Jim Wynn	.75	.35
186	Bill Fahey	.50	.25
187	Luke Walker	.50	.25
188	Cookie Rojas	.50	.25
189	Greg Luzinski	1.25	.65
190	Bob Gibson	7.00	3.50
191	Tigers Team	1.25	.65
192	Pat Jarvis	.50	.25
193	Carlton Fisk	42.00	21.00
194	Jorge Orta	.50	.25
195	Clay Carroll	.50	.25
196	Ken McMullen	.50	.25
197	Ed Goodson	.50	.25
198	Horace Clarke	.50	.25
199	Bert Blyleven	5.00	2.50
200	Billy Williams	5.00	2.50
201	A.L. Playoffs	1.00	.50
202	N.L. Playoffs	1.00	.50
203	World Series Game 1	1.25	.60
204	World Series Game 2	1.25	.60
205	World Series Game 3	1.25	.60
206	World Series Game 4	1.25	.60
207	World Series Game 5	1.25	.60
208	World Series Game 6	1.25	.60
209	World Series Game 7	1.25	.60
210	WS Champions	1.25	.60
211	Balor Moore	.50	.25
212	Joe Lohoud	.50	.25
213	Steve Garvey	12.00	6.00
214	Dave Hamilton	.50	.25
215	Dusty Baker	2.00	1.00
216	Toby Harrah	.70	.35
217	Don Wilson	.50	.25
218	Aurelio Rodriguez	.50	.25
219	Cardinals Team	1.25	.65
220	Nolan Ryan	100.00	50.00
221	Fred Kendall	.50	.25
222	Rob Gardner	.50	.25
223	Bud Harrelson	.75	.35
224	Bill Lee	.60	.30
225	Al Oliver	1.50	.75
226	Ray Fosse	.50	.25
227	Wayne Twitchell	.50	.25
228	Bobby Darwin	.50	.25
229	Roric Harrison	.50	.25
230	Joe Morgan	7.00	3.50
231	Bill Parsons	.50	.25
232	Ken Singleton	.75	.35
233	Ed Kirkpatrick	.50	.25
234	Bill North (R)	.75	.45
235	Jim Hunter	5.00	2.50
236	Tito Fuentes	.50	.25
237	Braves Mgr/Coaches	1.50	.75
238	Tony Muser	.50	.25
239	Pete Richert	.50	.25
240	Bobby Murcer	.90	.45

241 Dwain Anderson	.50	.25
242 George Culver	.50	.25
243 Angels Team	1.25	.65
244 Ed Acosta	.50	.25
245 Carl Yastrzemski	15.00	7.50
246 Ken Sanders	.50	.25
247 Del Unser	.50	.25
248 Jerry Johnson	.50	.25
249 Larry Bittner	.50	.25
250 Manny Sanguillen	.75	.35
251 Roger Nelson	.50	.25
252 Giants Mgr/Coaches	.75	.35
253 Mark Belanger	.80	.40
254 Bill Stoneman	.50	.25
255 Reggie Jackson	38.00	19.00
256 Chris Zachary	.50	.25
257 Mets Mgr/Coaches	2.50	1.25
258 Tommy John	1.50	.75
259 Jim Holt	.50	.25
260 Gary Nolan	.50	.25
261 Pat Kelly	.50	.25
262 Jack Aker	.50	.25
263 George Scott	.60	.35
264 Checklist 133-264	2.50	1.00
265 Gene Michael	.50	.25
266 Mike Lum	.50	.25
267 Lloyd Allen	.50	.25
268 Jerry Morales	.50	.25
269 Tim McCarver	1.00	.50
270 Luis Tiant	1.25	.60
271 Tom Hutton	.50	.25
272 Ed Farmer	.50	.25
273 Chris Speier	.50	.25
274 Darold Knowles	.50	.25
275 Tony Perez	5.00	2.50
276 Joe Lovitto	.50	.25
277 Bob Miller	.50	.25
278 Orioles Team	1.25	.65
279 Mike Strahler	.50	.25
280 Al Kaline	7.00	3.50
281 Mike Jorgensen	.50	.25
282 Steve Hovley	.50	.25
283 Ray Sadecki	.50	.25
284 Glenn Borgmann	.50	.25
285 Don Kessinger	.75	.35
286 Frank Linzy	.50	.25
287 Eddie Leon	.50	.25
288 Gary Gentry	.50	.25
289 Bob Oliver	.50	.25
290 Cesar Cedeno	1.00	.50
291 Rogelio Moret	.50	.25
292 Jose Cruz	1.25	.60
293 Bernie Allen	.50	.25
294 Steve Arlin	.50	.25
295 Bert Campaneris	1.00	.50
296 Reds Mgr/Coaches	2.00	1.00
297 Walt Williams	.50	.25
298 Ron Bryant	.50	.25
299 Ted Ford	.50	.25
300 Steve Carlton	18.00	9.00
301 Billy Grabarkewitz	.50	.25
302 Terry Crowley	.50	.25
303 Nelson Briles	.50	.25
304 Duke Sims	.50	.25
305 Willie Mays	40.00	20.00
306 Tom Burgmeier	.50	.25
307 Boots Day	.50	.25
308 Skip Lockwood	.50	.25
309 Paul Popovich	.50	.25
310 Dick Allen	1.50	.75
311 Joe Decker	.50	.25
312 Oscar Brown	.50	.25
313 Jim Ray	.50	.25
314 Ron Swoboda	.75	.35
315 John Odom	.50	.25
316 Padres Team	1.25	.65
317 Danny Cater	.50	.25
318 Jim McGlothlin	.50	.25
319 Jim Spencer	.50	.25
320 Lou Brock	7.50	3.75
321 Rich Hinton	.50	.25
322 Garry Maddox (R)	1.50	.75
323 Tigers Mgr/Coaches	1.25	.65
324 Al Downing	.50	.25
325 Boog Powell	1.00	.50
326 Darrell Brandon	.50	.25
327 John Lowenstein	.50	.25
328 Bill Bonham	.50	.25
329 Ed Kranepool	1.00	.50
330 Rod Carew	14.00	7.00
331 Carl Morton	.50	.25
332 John Felski	.50	.25
333 Gene Clines	.50	.25
334 Freddie Patek	.50	.25
335 Bob Tolan	.50	.25
336 Tom Bradley	.50	.25
337 Dave Duncan	.50	.25
338 Checklist 265-396	2.50	1.00
339 Dick Tidrow	.50	.25
340 Nate Colbert	.50	.25
341 Jim Palmer (Child)	1.50	.75
342 Sam McDowell (Child)	.60	.30
343 Bobby Murcer (Child)	.75	.35
344 Jim Hunter (Child)	1.50	.75
345 Chris Speier (Child)	.60	.30
346 Gaylord Perry (Child)	1.50	.75
347 Royals Team	1.25	.65
348 Rennie Stennett	.90	.45
349 Dick McAuliffe	.50	.25
350 Tom Seaver	28.00	14.00
351 Jimmy Stewart	.50	.25
352 Don Stanhouse	.50	.25
353 Steve Brye	.50	.25
354 Billy Parker	.50	.25

#	Player	Price 1	Price 2
355	Mike Marshall	.60	.30
356	White Sox Mgr/Coaches	.75	.35
357	Ross Grimsley	.50	.25
358	Jim Nettles	.50	.25
359	Cecil Upshaw	.50	.25
360	Joe Rudi (Wrong Photo)	1.25	.60
361	Fran Healy	.50	.25
362	Eddie Watt	.50	.25
363	Jackie Hernandez	.50	.25
364	Rick Wise	.60	.30
365	Rico Petrocelli	.60	.30
366	Brock Davis	.50	.25
367	Burt Hooton	.60	.30
368	Bill Buckner	1.25	.60
369	Lerrin LaGrow	.50	.25
370	Willie Stargell	7.00	3.50
371	Mike Kekich	.50	.25
372	Oscar Gamble	.60	.30
373	Clyde Wright	.50	.25
374	Darrell Evans	1.25	.60
375	Larry Dierker	.50	.25
376	Frank Duffy	.50	.25
377	Expos Mgr/Coaches	.75	.35
378	Lenny Randle	.50	.25
379	Cy Acosta	.50	.25
380	Johnny Bench	20.00	10.00
381	Vincente Romo	.50	.25
382	Mike Hegan	.50	.25
383	Diego Segui	.50	.25
384	Don Baylor	2.50	1.25
385	Jim Perry	.75	.35
386	Don Money	.50	.25
387	Jim Barr	.50	.25
388	Ben Oglivie	.60	.30
389	Mets Team	3.50	1.75
390	Mickey Lolich	.70	.35
391	Lee Lacy (R)	.90	.45
392	Dick Drago	.50	.25
393	Jose Cardenal	.50	.25
394	Sparky Lyle	1.00	.50
395	Roger Metzger	.60	.30
396	Grant Jackson	.50	.25
397	Dave Cash	1.10	.55
398	Rich Hand	1.10	.55
399	George Foster	2.00	1.00
400	Gaylord Perry	6.00	3.00
401	Clyde Mashore	1.10	.55
402	Jack Hiatt	1.10	.55
403	Sonny Jackson	1.10	.55
404	Chuck Brinkman	1.10	.55
405	Cesar Tovar	1.10	.55
406	Paul Lindblad	1.10	.55
407	Felix Millan	1.10	.55
408	Jim Colborn	1.10	.55
409	Ivan Murrell	1.10	.55
410	Willie McCovey	7.00	3.50
411	Ray Corbin	1.10	.55
412	Manny Mota	1.50	.75
413	Tom Timmermann	1.10	.55
414	Ken Rudolph	1.10	.55
415	Marty Pattin	1.10	.55
416	Paul Schaal	1.10	.55
417	Scipio Spinks	1.10	.55
418	Bobby Grich	1.50	.75
419	Casey Cox	1.10	.55
420	Tommie Agee	1.10	.55
421	Angels Mgr/Coaches	1.50	.75
422	Bob Robertson	1.10	.55
423	Johnny Jeter	1.10	.55
424	Denny Doyle	1.10	.55
425	Alex Johnson	1.10	.55
426	Dave LaRoche	1.10	.55
427	Rick Auerbach	1.10	.55
428	Wayne Simpson	1.10	.55
429	Jim Fairey	1.10	.55
430	Vida Blue	2.00	1.00
431	Gerry Moses	1.10	.55
432	Dan Frisella	1.10	.55
433	Willie Horton	1.50	.75
434	Giants Team	2.00	1.00
435	Rico Carty	1.50	.75
436	Jim McAndrew	1.10	.55
437	John Kennedy	1.10	.55
438	Enzo Hernandez	1.10	.55
439	Eddie Fisher	1.10	.55
440	Glenn Beckert	1.10	.55
441	Gail Hopkins	1.10	.55
442	Dick Dietz	1.10	.55
443	Danny Thompson	1.10	.55
444	Ken Brett	1.10	.55
445	Ken Berry	1.10	.55
446	Jerry Reuss	1.50	.75
447	Joe Hague	1.10	.55
448	John Hiller	1.10	.55
449	Indians Mgr/Coaches	2.50	1.25
450	Joe Torre	1.50	.75
451	John Vukovich	1.10	.55
452	Paul Casanova	1.10	.55
453	Checklist 397-528	2.50	1.00
454	Tom Haller	1.10	.55
455	Bill Melton	1.10	.55
456	Dick Green	1.10	.55
457	John Strohmayer	1.10	.55
458	Jim Mason	1.10	.55
459	Jimmy Howarth	1.10	.55
460	Bill Freehan	1.50	.75
461	Mike Corkins	1.10	.55
462	Ron Blomberg	1.10	.55
463	Ken Tatum	1.10	.55
464	Cubs Team	2.00	1.00
465	Dave Giusti	1.10	.55
466	Jose Arcia	1.10	.55
467	Mike Ryan	1.10	.55
468	Tom Griffin	1.10	.55

469	Dan Monzon	1.10	.55
470	Mike Cuellar	1.50	.75
471	Hit Leader	6.00	3.00
	(Ty Cobb)		
472	Grand Slam Leader	8.00	4.00
	(Lou Gehrig)		
473	Total Base Leader	8.00	4.00
	(Hank Aaron)		
474	R.B.I. Leader	12.00	6.00
	(Babe Ruth)		
475	Batting Leader	6.00	3.00
	(Ty Cobb)		
476	Shutout Leader	3.50	1.75
	(Walter Johnson)		
477	Victory Leader	3.50	1.75
	(Cy Young)		
478	Strikeout Leader	3.50	1.75
	(Walter Johnson)		
479	Hal Lanier	1.10	.55
480	Juan Marichal	5.00	2.50
481	White Sox Team	2.00	1.00
482	Rick Reuschel (R)	3.00	1.50
483	Dal Maxvill	1.10	.55
484	Ernie McAnally	1.10	.55
485	Norm Cash	1.50	.75
486	Phillies Mgr/Coaches	1.50	.75
487	Bruce Dal Canton	1.10	.55
488	Dave Campbell	1.10	.55
489	Jeff Burroughs	1.50	.75
490	Claude Osteen	1.10	.55
491	Bob Montgomery	1.10	.55
492	Pedro Borbon	1.10	.55
493	Duffy Dyer	1.10	.55
494	Rich Morales	1.10	.55
495	Tommy Helms	1.10	.55
496	Ray Lamb	1.10	.55
497	Cardinals Mgr/Coaches	1.50	.75
498	Graig Nettles	3.00	1.50
499	Bob Moose	1.10	.55
500	A's Team	2.00	1.00
501	Larry Gura	1.10	.55
502	Bobby Valentine	1.50	.75
503	Phil Niekro	7.00	3.50
504	Earl Williams	1.10	.55
505	Bob Bailey	1.10	.55
506	Bart Johnson	1.10	.55
507	Darrel Chaney	1.10	.55
508	Gates Brown	1.10	.55
509	Jim Nash	1.10	.55
510	Amos Otis	1.50	.75
511	Sam McDowell	1.25	.60
512	Dalton Jones	1.10	.55
513	Dave Marshall	1.10	.55
514	Jerry Kenney	1.10	.55
515	Andy Messersmith	1.10	.55
516	Danny Walton	1.10	.55
517	Pirates Mgr/Coaches	1.50	.75
518	Bob Veale	1.10	.55
519	John Edwards	1.10	.55
520	Mel Stottlemyre	1.50	.75
521	Braves Team	2.00	1.00
522	Leo Cardenas	1.10	.55
523	Wayne Granger	1.10	.55
524	Gene Tenace	1.50	.75
525	Jim Fregosi	1.25	.60
526	Ollie Brown	1.10	.55
527	Dan McGinn	1.10	.55
528	Paul Blair	1.10	.55
529	Milt May	2.50	1.25
530	Jim Kaat	4.50	2.25
531	Ron Woods	2.50	1.25
532	Steve Mingori	2.50	1.25
533	Larry Stahl	2.50	1.25
534	Dave Lemonds	2.50	1.25
535	John Callison	2.50	1.25
536	Phillies Team	5.00	2.50
537	Bill Slayback	2.50	1.25
538	Jim Hart	2.50	1.25
539	Tom Murphy	2.50	1.25
540	Cleon Jones	2.50	1.25
541	Bob Bolin	2.50	1.25
542	Pat Corrales	2.50	1.25
543	Alan Foster	2.50	1.25
544	Von Joshua	2.50	1.25
545	Orlando Cepeda	5.00	2.50
546	Jim York	2.50	1.25
547	Bobby Heise	2.50	1.25
548	Don Durham	2.50	1.25
549	Rangers Mgr/Coaches	4.00	2.00
550	Dave Johnson	2.50	1.25
551	Mike Kilkenny	2.50	1.25
552	J.C. Martin	2.50	1.25
553	Mickey Scott	2.50	1.25
554	Dave Concepcion	5.00	2.50
555	Bill Hands	2.50	1.25
556	Yankees Team	8.00	4.00
557	Bernie Williams	2.50	1.25
558	Jerry May	2.50	1.25
559	Barry Lersch	2.50	1.25
560	Frank Howard	5.00	2.50
561	Jim Geddes	2.50	1.25
562	Wayne Garrett	2.50	1.25
563	Larry Haney	2.50	1.25
564	Mike Thompson	2.50	1.25
565	Jim Hickman	2.50	1.25
566	Lew Krause	2.50	1.25
567	Bob Fenwick	2.50	1.25
568	Ray Newman	2.50	1.25
569	Dodgers Mgr/Coaches	4.50	2.25
570	Bill Singer	2.50	1.25
571	Rusty Torres	2.50	1.25
572	Gary Sutherland	2.50	1.25
573	Fred Beene	2.50	1.25
574	Bob Didier	2.50	1.25

575	Dock Ellis	2.50	1.25
576	Expos Team	5.00	2.50
577	Eric Soderholm (R)	2.50	1.25
578	Ken Wright	2.50	1.25
579	Tom Grieve	2.50	1.25
580	Joe Pepitone	3.00	1.50
581	Steve Kealey	2.50	1.25
582	Darrell Porter	3.00	1.50
583	Bill Greif	2.50	1.25
584	Chris Arnold	2.50	1.25
585	Joe Niekro	2.50	1.25
586	Bill Sudakis	2.50	1.25
587	Rich McKinney	2.50	1.25
588	Checklist 529-660	8.50	3.50
589	Ken Forsch	2.50	1.25
590	Deron Johnson	2.50	1.25
591	Mike Hedlund	2.50	1.25
592	John Boccabella	2.50	1.25
593	Royals Mgr/Coaches	3.50	1.75
594	Vic Harris	2.50	1.25
595	Don Gullett	3.00	1.50
596	Red Sox Team	5.00	2.50
597	Mickey Rivers	3.50	1.75
598	Phil Roof	2.50	1.25
599	Ed Crosby	2.50	1.25
600	Dave McNally	3.00	1.50
601	Rookie Catchers	2.50	1.25
	George Pena (R)		
	Sergio Robles (R)		
	Rick Stelmaszek (R)		
602	Rookie Pitchers	2.50	1.25
	Mel Behney (R)		
	Ralph Garcia (R)		
	Doug Rau (R)		
603	Rookie Third Basemen	2.50	1.25
	Terry Hughes (R)		
	Bill McNulty (R)		
	Ken Reitz (R)		
604	Rookie Pitchers	2.50	1.25
	Jesse Jefferson (R)		
	Dennis O'Toole (R)		
	Bob Strampe (R)		
605	Rookie First Basemen	3.50	1.75
	Pat Bourque (R)		
	Enos Cabell (R)		
	Gonzalo Marquez (R)		
606	Rookie Outfielders	5.00	2.50
	Gary Matthews (R)		
	Tom Paciorek		
	Jorge Roque (R)		
607	Rookie Shortstops	2.50	1.25
	Ray Busse (R)		
	Pepe Frias (R)		
	Mario Guerrero (R)		
608	Rookie Pitchers	3.50	1.75
	Steve Busby (R)		
	Dick Colpaert (R)		

	George Medich (R)		
609	Rookie 2nd Basemen	5.50	2.75
	Larvell Blanks (R)		
	Pedro Garcia (R)		
	Davey Lopes (R)		
610	Rookie Pitchers	4.00	2.00
	Jimmy Freeman (R)		
	Charlie Hough		
	Hank Webb (R)		
611	Rookie Outfielders	3.00	1.50
	Rich Coggins (R)		
	Jim Wohlford (R)		
	Richie Zisk		
612	Rookie Pitchers	2.50	1.25
	Steve Lawson (R)		
	Bob Reynolds (R)		
	Brent Strom (R)		
613	Rookie Catchers	45.00	22.50
	Bob Boone (H)		
	Mike Ivie (R)		
	Skip Jutze (R)		
614	Rookie Outfielders	50.00	25.00
	Al Bumbry (R)		
	Dwight Evans (R)		
	Charlie Spikes (R)		
615	Rookie Third-Basemen	500.00	250.00
	Ron Cey		
	John Hilton (R)		
	Mike Schmidt (R)		
616	Rookie Pitchers	2.50	1.25
	Norm Angelini (R)		
	Steve Blateric (R)		
	Mike Garman (R)		
617	Rich Chiles	2.50	1.25
618	Andy Etchebarren	2.50	1.25
619	Billy Wilson	2.50	1.25
620	Tommy Harper	2.50	1.25
621	Joe Ferguson	3.00	1.50
622	Larry Hisle	2.50	1.25
623	Steve Renko	2.50	1.25
624	Astros Mgr/Coaches	4.00	2.00
625	Angel Mangual	2.50	1.25
626	Bob Barton	2.50	1.25
627	Luis Alvarado	2.50	1.25
628	Jim Slaton	2.50	1.25
629	Indians Team	5.00	2.50
630	Denny McLain	5.00	2.50
631	Tom Matchick	2.50	1.25
632	Dick Selma	2.50	1.25
633	Ike Brown	2.50	1.25
634	Alan Closter	2.50	1.25
635	Gene Alley	2.50	1.25
636	Rick Clark	2.50	1.25
637	Norm Miller	2.50	1.25
638	Ken Reynolds	2.50	1.25
639	Willie Crawford	2.50	1.25

640	Dick Bosman	2.50	1.25
641	Reds Team	5.00	2.50
642	Jose Laboy	2.50	1.25
643	Al Fitzmorris	2.50	1.25
644	Jack Heidemann	2.50	1.25
645	Bob Locker	2.50	1.25
646	Brewers Mgr/Coaches	4.50	2.25
647	George Stone	2.50	1.25
648	Tom Egan	2.50	1.25
649	Rich Folkers	2.50	1.25
650	Felipe Alou	4.50	2.25
651	Don Carrithers	2.50	1.25
652	Ted Kubiak	2.50	1.25
653	Joe Hoerner	2.50	1.25
654	Twins Team	5.00	2.50
655	Clay Kirby	2.50	1.25
656	John Ellis	2.50	1.25
657	Bob Johnson	2.50	1.25
658	Elliott Maddox	2.50	1.25
659	Jose Pagan	2.50	1.25
660	Fred Scherman	5.00	2.00

1974 Topps

This 660-card set marks the first time Topps released their cards all at once, rather than in series. Card fronts feature four-color photos framed by white borders. Card backs are horizontal. Cards measure 2-1/2" by 3-1/2". The set contains fifteen variations concerning the San Diego Padres who were on the verge of moving to Washington D.C. Cards with Washington printed on them are worth considerable more than those with San Diego. Those variations are noted in the checklist below but the higher valued cards are not included in the Complete Set price. The 1974 Topps set includes a 6-card tribute to Hank Aaron. Other notable subsets are

League Leaders, World Series and Playoff Highlights, All-Stars and Rookies.

		NR/MT	EX
Complete Set (660)		680.00	340.00
Commons (1-660)		.50	.25
1	Hank Aaron	38.00	18.00
2	Hank Aaron (1954-57)	6.00	3.00
3	Hank Aaron (1958-61)	6.00	3.00
4	Hank Aaron (1962-65)	6.00	3.00
5	Hank Aaron (1966-69)	6.00	3.00
6	Hank Aaron (1970-73)	6.00	3.00
7	Jim Hunter	5.00	2.50
8	George Theodore	.50	.25
9	Mickey Lolich	.80	.40
10	Johnny Bench	16.00	8.00
11	Jim Bibby	.50	.25
12	Dave May	.50	.25
13	Tom Hilgendorf	.50	.25
14	Paul Popovich	.50	.25
15	Joe Torre	1.25	.65
16	Orioles Team	1.00	.50
17	Doug Bird	.50	.25
18	Gary Thomasson	.50	.25
19	Gerry Moses	.50	.25
20	Nolan Ryan	95.00	48.00
21	Bob Gallagher	.50	.25
22	Cy Acosta	.50	.25
23	Craig Robinson	.50	.25
24	John Hiller	.50	.25
25	Ken Singleton	.75	.35
26	Bill Campbell (R)	.50	.25
27	George Scott	.60	.30
28	Manny Sanguillen	.60	.30
29	Phil Niekro	4.50	2.25
30	Bobby Bonds	2.00	1.00
31	Astros Mgr/Coaches	.60	.30
32a	John Grubb (Wash)	7.50	3.75
32b	John Grubb (SD)	.50	.25
33	Don Newhauser	.50	.25
34	Andy Kosco	.50	.25
35	Gaylord Perry	5.00	2.50
36	Cardinals Team	1.00	.50
37	Dave Sells	.50	.25
38	Don Kessinger	.60	.30
39	Ken Suarez	.50	.25
40	Jim Palmer	10.00	5.00
41	Bobby Floyd	.50	.25
42	Claude Osteen	.50	.25

43	Jim Wynn	.75	.35
44	Mel Stottlemyre	.60	.30
45	Dave Johnson	.50	.25
46	Pat Kelly	.50	.25
47	Dick Ruthven (R)	.50	.25
48	Dick Sharon	.50	.25
49	Steve Renko	.50	.25
50	Rod Carew	12.50	7.50
51	Bobby Heise	.50	.25
52	Al Oliver	1.00	.50
53a	Fred Kendall (Wash)	7.50	3.75
53b	Fred Kendall (SD)	.50	.25
54	Elias Sosa	.50	.25
55	Frank Robinson	7.00	3.50
56	Mets Team	1.00	.60
57	Darold Knowles	.50	.25
58	Charlie Spikes	.50	.25
59	Ross Grimsley	.50	.25
60	Lou Brock	7.00	3.50
61	Luis Aparicio	3.00	1.50
62	Bob Locker	.50	.25
63	Bill Sudakis	.50	.25
64	Doug Rau	.50	.25
65	Amos Otis	.60	.30
66	Sparky Lyle	.75	.35
67	Tommy Helms	.50	.25
68	Grant Jackson	.50	.25
69	Del Unser	.50	.25
70	Dick Allen	1.00	.50
71	Danny Frisella	.50	.25
72	Aurleio Rodriguez	.50	.25
73	Mike Marshall	.60	.30
74	Twins Team	1.00	.50
75	Jim Colburn	.50	.25
76	Mickey Rivers	.60	.30
77a	Rich Troedson (Wash)	7.50	3.75
77b	Rich Troedson (SD)	.50	.25
78	Giants Mgr/Coaches	.60	.30
79	Gene Tenace	.75	.35
80	Tom Seaver	20.00	10.00
81	Frank Duffy	.50	.25
82	Dave Giusti	.50	.25
83	Orlando Cepeda	1.25	.60
84	Rick Wise	.60	.30
85	Joe Morgan	7.00	3.50
86	Joe Ferguson	.60	.30
87	Ferguson Jenkins	6.00	3.00
88	Freddie Patek	.50	.25
89	Jackie Brown	.50	.25
90	Bobby Murcer	.75	.35
91	Ken Forsch	.50	.25
92	Paul Blair	.50	.25
93	Rod Gilbreath	.50	.25
94	Tigers Team	1.00	.50
95	Steve Carlton	15.00	7.50
96	Jerry Hairston (R)	.50	.25
97	Bob Bailey	.50	.25
98	Bert Blyleven	2.50	1.25
99	Brewers Mgr/Coaches	.60	.30
100	Willie Stargell	6.00	3.00
101	Bobby Valentine	.60	.30
102a	Bill Greif (Wash)	7.50	3.75
102b	Bill Greif (SD)	.50	.25
103	Sal Bando	.60	.30
104	Ron Bryant	.50	.25
105	Carlton Fisk	22.00	11.00
106	Harry Parker	.50	.25
107	Alex Johnson	.50	.25
108	Al Hrabosky	.60	.30
109	Bob Grich	.75	.35
110	Billy Williams	4.50	2.25
111	Clay Carroll	.50	.25
112	Dave Lopes	1.00	.50
113	Dick Drago	.50	.25
114	Angels Team	1.00	.50
115	Willie Horton	.60	.30
116	Jerry Reuss	.60	.30
117	Ron Blomberg	.50	.25
118	Bill Lee	.50	.25
119	Phillies Mgr/Coaches	.60	.30
120	Wilbur Wood	.50	.25
121	Larry Lintz	.50	.25
122	Jim Holt	.50	.25
123	Nelson Briles	.50	.25
124	Bob Coluccio	.50	.25
125a	Nate Colbert (Wash)	7.50	3.75
125b	Nate Colbert (SD)	.50	.25
126	Checklist 1-132	2.00	.80
127	Tom Paciorek	.50	.25
128	John Ellis	.50	.25
129	Chris Speier	.50	.25
130	Reggie Jackson	32.00	16.00
131	Bob Boone	4.00	2.00
132	Felix Milan	.50	.25
133	David Clyde (R)	.60	.30
134	Denis Menke	.50	.25
135	Roy White	.50	.25
136	Rick Reuschel	.80	.40
137	Al Bumbry	.60	.30
138	Ed Brinkman	.50	.25
139	Aurelio Monteagudo	.50	.25
140	Darrell Evans	.75	.35
141	Pat Bourque	.50	.25
142	Pedro Garcia	.50	.25
143	Dick Woodson	.50	.25
144	Dodgers Mgr/Coaches	1.25	.60
145	Dock Ellis	.50	.25
146	Ron Fairly	.50	.25
147	Bart Johnson	.50	.25
148a	Dave Hilton (Wash)	7.50	3.75
148b	Dave Hilton (SD)	.50	.25
149	Mac Scarce	.50	.25
150	John Mayberry	.60	.30
151	Diego Segui	.50	.25

152	Oscar Gamble	.60	.30
153	Jon Matlack	.75	.45
154	Astros Team	1.00	.50
155	Bert Campaneris	.75	.45
156	Randy Moffitt	.50	.25
157	Vic Harris	.50	.25
158	Jack Billingham	.50	.25
159	Jim Ray Hart	.50	.25
160	Brooks Robinson	8.00	4.00
161	Ray Burris (R)	.75	.45
162	Bill Freehan	.60	.30
163	Ken Berry	.50	.25
164	Tom House	.50	.25
165	Willie Davis	.60	.30
166	Royals Mgr/Coaches	.80	.40
167	Luis Tiant	.75	.35
168	Danny Thompson	.50	.25
169	Steve Rogers (R)	.75	.35
170	Bill Melton	.50	.25
171	Eduardo Rodriguez	.50	.25
172	Gene Clines	.50	.25
173a	Randy Jones (Wash)	10.00	5.00
173b	Randy Jones (SD)	1.00	.50
174	Bill Robinson	.60	.30
175	Reggie Cleveland	.50	.25
176	John Lowenstein	.50	.25
177	Dave Roberts	.50	.25
178	Garry Maddox	.60	.30
179	Mets Mgr/Coaches	2.00	1.00
180	Ken Holtzman	.50	.25
181	Cesar Geronimo	.50	.25
182	Lindy McDaniel	.50	.25
183	Johnny Oates	.60	.30
184	Rangers Team	1.00	.50
185	Jose Cardenal	.50	.25
186	Fred Scherman	.50	.25
187	Don Baylor	3.50	1.75
188	Rudy Meoli	.50	.25
189	Jim Brewer	.50	.25
190	Tony Oliva	1.50	.75
191	Al Fitzmorris	.50	.25
192	Mario Guerrero	.50	.25
193	Tom Walker	.50	.25
194	Darrell Porter	.50	.25
195	Carlos May	.50	.25
196	Jim Fregosi	.60	.30
197a	Vincente Romo (Wash)	7.50	3.75
197b	Vincente Romo (SD)	.50	.25
198	Dave Cash	.50	.25
199	Mike Kekich	.50	.25
200	Cesar Cedeno	.60	.30
201	Batting Leaders (Rod Carew, Pete Rose)	7.00	3.50
202	HR Leaders (Reggie Jackson, Willie Stargell)	7.50	3.25
203	RBI Leaders (Reggie Jackson, Willie Stargell)	7.50	3.25
204	Stolen Base Leaders (Lou Brock, Tommy Harper)	1.25	.60
205	Victory Leaders (Ron Bryant, Wilbur Wood)	1.25	.60
206	ERA Leaders (Jim Palmer, Tom Seaver)	6.00	3.00
207	Strikeout Leaders (Nolan Ryan, Tom Seaver)	20.00	10.00
208	Leading Firemen (John Hiller, Mike Marshall)	1.00	.50
209	Ted Sizemore	.50	.25
210	Bill Singer	.50	.25
211	Cubs Team	1.00	.50
212	Rollie Fingers	6.00	3.00
213	Dave Rader	.50	.25
214	Billy Grabarkewitz	.50	.25
215	Al Kaline	7.00	3.50
216	Ray Sadecki	.50	.25
217	Tim Foli	.50	.25
218	Johnny Briggs	.50	.25
219	Doug Griffin	.50	.25
220	Don Sutton	4.50	2.25
221	White Sox Mgr/Coaches	.80	.50
222	Ramon Hernandez	.50	.25
223	Jeff Burroughs	.60	.30
224	Roger Metzger	.50	.25
225	Paul Splittorff	.50	.25
226a	Washington Team	10.00	5.00
226b	Padres Team	1.50	.75
227	Mike Lum	.50	.25
228	Ted Kubiak	.50	.25
229	Fritz Peterson	.50	.25
230	Tony Perez	4.50	2.25
231	Dick Tidrow	.50	.25
232	Steve Brye	.50	.25
233	Jim Barr	.50	.25
234	John Milner	.50	.25
235	Dave McNally	.60	.30
236	Cardinals Mgr/Coaches (Barney Schultz)	.80	.40
237	Ken Brett	.50	.25
238	Fran Healy	.50	.25
239	Bill Russell	.75	.35
240	Joe Coleman	.50	.25
241a	Glenn Beckert (Wash)	7.50	3.75
241b	Glenn Beckert (SD)	.50	.25
242	Bill Gogolewski	.50	.25
243	Bob Oliver	.50	.25
244	Carl Morton	.50	.25
245	Cleon Jones	.50	.25
246	A's Team	1.25	.65
247	Rick Miller	.50	.25
248	Tom Hall	.50	.25
249	George Mitterwald	.50	.25

250a	Willie McCovey (Wash)	32.00	16.00
250b	Willie McCovey (SD)	7.00	3.50
251	Graig Nettles	2.00	1.00
252	Dave Parker (R)	25.00	12.50
253	John Boccabella	.50	.25
254	Stan Bahnsen	.50	.25
255	Larry Bowa	.80	.40
256	Tom Griffin	.50	.25
257	Buddy Bell	.60	.30
258	Jerry Morales	.50	.25
259	Bob Reynolds	.50	.25
260	Ted Simmons	2.00	1.00
261	Jerry Bell	.50	.25
262	Ed Kirkpatrick	.50	.25
263	Checklist 133-264	2.00	.80
264	Joe Rudi	.75	.35
265	Tug McGraw	1.25	.60
266	Jim Northrup	.50	.25
267	Andy Messersmith	.50	.25
268	Tom Grieve	.50	.25
269	Bob Johnson	.50	.25
270	Ron Santo	1.00	.50
271	Bill Hands	.50	.25
272	Paul Casanova	.50	.25
273	Checklist 265-396	2.00	.80
274	Fred Beene	.50	.25
275	Ron Hunt	.50	.25
276	Angels Mgr/Coaches	.60	.30
277	Gary Nolan	.50	.25
278	Cookie Rojas	.50	.25
279	Jim Crawford	.50	.25
280	Carl Yastrzemski	12.50	7.50
281	Giants Team	1.00	.50
282	Doyle Alexander	.50	.25
283	Mike Schmidt	100.00	50.00
284	Dave Duncan	.50	.25
285	Reggie Smith	.60	.30
286	Tony Muser	.50	.25
287	Clay Kirby	.50	.25
288	Gorman Thomas (R)	2.00	1.00
289	Rick Auerbach	.50	.25
290	Vida Blue	.80	.40
291	Don Hahn	.50	.25
292	Chuck Seelbach	.50	.25
293	Milt May	.50	.25
294	Rick Monday	.75	.45
296	Ray Corbin	.50	.25
297	Hal Breeden	.50	.25
298	Roric Harrison	.50	.25
299	Gene Michael	.50	.25
300	Pete Rose	15.00	7.50
301	Bob Montgomery	.50	.25
302	Rudy May	.50	.25
303	George Hendrick	.60	.30
304	Don Wilson	.50	.25
305	Tito Fuentes	.50	.25
306	Orioles Mgr/Coaches	.80	.40
307	Luis Melendez	.50	.25
308	Bruce Dal Canton	.50	.25
309a	Dave Roberts (Wash)	7.50	3.75
309b	Dave Roberts (SD)	.50	.25
310	Terry Forster	.50	.25
311	Jerry Grote	.50	.25
312	Deron Johnson	.50	.25
313	Barry Lersch	.50	.25
314	Brewers Team	.80	.40
315	Ron Cey	1.25	.65
316	Jim Perry	.60	.30
317	Richie Zisk	.50	.25
318	Jim Merritt	.50	.25
319	Randy Hundley	.50	.25
320	Dusty Baker	1.75	.90
321	Steve Braun	.50	.25
322	Ernie McAnally	.50	.25
323	Richie Scheinblum	.50	.25
324	Steve Kline	.50	.25
325	Tommy Harper	.50	.25
326	Reds Mgr/Coaches	2.00	1.00
327	Tom Timmermann	.50	.25
328	Skip Jutze	.50	.25
329	Mark Belanger	.75	.35
330	Juan Marichal	4.00	2.00
331	All Star Catchers (Johnny Bench, Carlton Fisk)	7.50	3.75
332	All Star First Base (Hank Aaron, Dick Allen)	5.00	2.50
333	All Star Second Base (Rod Carew, Joe Morgan)	4.00	2.00
334	All Star Third Base (Brooks Robinson, Ron Santo)	4.00	2.00
335	All Star Shortstops (Bert Campaneris, Chris Speier)	2.00	1.00
336	All Star Left Field (Bobby Murcer, Pete Rose)	4.00	2.00
337	All Star Center Field (Cesar Cedeno, Amos Otis)	2.00	1.00
338	All Star Right Field (Reggie Jackson, Billy Williams)	5.00	2.50
339	All Star Pitchers (Jim Hunter, Rick Wise)	2.00	1.00
340	Thurman Munson	8.00	4.00
341	Dan Driessen (R)	1.00	.50
342	Jim Lonborg	.60	.30
343	Royals Team	1.00	.50

344	Mike Caldwell	.50	.25
345	Bill North	.50	.25
346	Ron Reed	.50	.25
347	Sandy Alomar	.50	.25
348	Pete Richert	.50	.25
349	John Vukovich	.50	.25
350	Bob Gibson	7.00	3.50
351	Dwight Evans	6.00	3.00
352	Bill Stoneman	.50	.25
353	Rich Coggins	.50	.25
354	Cubs Mgr/Coaches	.60	.30
355	Dave Nelson	.50	.25
356	Jerry Koosman	.75	.35
357	Buddy Bradford	.50	.25
358	Dal Maxvill	.50	.25
359	Brent Strom	.50	.25
360	Greg Luzinski	1.00	.50
361	Don Carrithers	.50	.25
362	Hal King	.50	.25
363	Yankees Team	1.25	.65
364a	Cito Gaston (Wash)	12.00	6.00
364b	Cito Gaston (SD)	1.25	.65
365	Steve Busby	.50	.25
366	Larry Hisle	.50	.25
367	Norm Cash	.80	.40
368	Manny Mota	.75	.35
369	Paul Lindblad	.50	.25
370	Bob Watson	.75	.35
371	Jim Slaton	.50	.25
372	Ken Reitz	.50	.25
373	John Curtis	.50	.25
374	Marty Perez	.50	.25
375	Earl Williams	.50	.25
376	Jorge Orta	.50	.25
377	Ron Woods	.50	.25
378	Burt Hooton	.60	.30
379	Rangers Mgr/Coaches	1.00	.50
380	Bud Harrelson	.60	.30
381	Charlie Sands	.50	.25
382	Bob Moose	.50	.25
383	Phillies Team	1.00	.50
384	Chris Chambliss	.60	.30
385	Don Gullett	.60	.30
386	Gary Matthews	.60	.30
387a	Rich Morales (Wash)	7.50	3.75
387b	Rich Morales (SD)	.50	.25
388	Phil Roof	.50	.25
389	Gates Brown	.50	.25
390	Lou Piniella	1.25	.65
391	Billy Champion	.50	.25
392	Dick Green	.50	.25
393	Orlando Pena	.50	.25
394	Ken Henderson	.50	.25
395	Doug Rader	.50	.25
396	Tommy Davis	.80	.40
397	George Stone	.50	.25
398	Duke Sims	.50	.25
399	Mike Paul	.50	.25
400	Harmon Killebrew	6.00	3.00
401	Elliott Maddox	.50	.25
402	Jim Hooker	.50	.25
403	Red Sox Mgr/Coaches	.60	.30
404	Jim Howarth	.50	.25
405	Ellie Rodriguez	.50	.25
406	Steve Arlin	.50	.25
407	Jim Wohlford	.50	.25
408	Charlie Hough	.90	.45
409	Ike Brown	.50	.25
410	Pedro Borbon	.50	.25
411	Frank Baker	.50	.25
412	Chuck Taylor	.50	.25
413	Don Money	.50	.25
414	Checklist 397-528	2.00	.80
415	Gary Gentry	.50	.25
416	White Sox Team	1.00	.50
417	Rich Folkers	.50	.25
418	Walt Williams	.50	.25
419	Wayne Twitchell	.50	.25
420	Ray Fosse	.50	.25
421	Dan Fife	.50	.25
422	Gonzalo Marquez	.50	.25
423	Fred Stanley	.50	.25
424	Jim Beauchamp	.50	.25
425	Pete Broberg	.50	.25
426	Rennie Stennett	.60	.30
427	Bobby Bolin	.50	.25
428	Gary Sutherland	.50	.25
429	Dick Lange	.50	.25
430	Matty Alou	.60	.30
431	Gene Garber	.70	.40
432	Chris Arnold	.50	.25
433	Lerrin LaGrow	.50	.25
434	Ken McMullen	.50	.25
435	Dave Concepcion	3.00	1.50
436	Don Hood	.50	.25
437	Jim Lyttle	.50	.25
438	Ed Herrmann	.50	.25
439	Norm Miller	.50	.25
440	Jim Kaat	1.25	.65
441	Tom Ragland	.50	.25
442	Alan Foster	.50	.25
443	Tom Hutton	.50	.25
444	Vic Davalillo	.50	.25
445	George Medich	.50	.25
446	Len Randle	.50	.25
447	Twins Mgr/Coaches	.60	.30
448	Ron Hodges	.50	.25
449	Tom McCraw	.50	.25
450	Rich Hebner	.50	.25
451	Tommy John	1.50	.75
452	Gene Hiser	.50	.25
453	Balor Moore	.50	.25
454	Kurt Bevacqua	.50	.25
455	Tom Bradley	.50	.25

456	Dave Winfield (R)	260.00	130.00
457	Chuck Goggin	.50	.25
458	Jim Ray	.50	.25
459	Reds Team	.80	.40
460	Boog Powell	1.25	.65
461	John Odom	.50	.25
462	Luis Alvarado	.50	.25
463	Pat Dobson	.50	.25
464	Jose Cruz	.80	.40
465	Dick Bosman	.50	.25
466	Dick Billings	.50	.25
467	Winston Llenas	.50	.25
468	Pepe Frias	.50	.25
469	Joe Decker	.50	.25
470	A.L. Playoffs	7.00	3.50
471	N.L. Playoffs	1.25	.60
472	World Series Game 1	1.25	.60
473	World Series Game 2	6.00	3.00
474	World Series Game 3	1.25	.60
475	World Series Game 4	1.25	.60
476	World Series Game 5	1.25	.60
477	World Series Game 6	7.00	3.50
478	World Series Game 7	1.25	.60
479	WS (Celebration)	1.25	.60
480	Willie Crawford	.50	.25
481	Jerry Terrell	.50	.25
482	Bob Didier	.50	.25
483	Braves Team	1.00	.50
484	Carmen Fanzone	.50	.25
485	Felipe Alou	1.00	.50
486	Steve Stone	.60	.30
487	Ted Martinez	.50	.25
488	Andy Etchebarren	.50	.25
489	Pirates Mgr/Coaches	.75	.35
490	Vada Pinson	.80	.40
491	Roger Nelson	.50	.25
492	Mike Rogodzinski	.50	.25
493	Joe Hoerner	.50	.25
494	Ed Goodson	.50	.25
495	Dick McAuliffe	.50	.25
496	Tom Murphy	.50	.25
497	Bobby Mitchell	.50	.25
498	Pat Corrales	.50	.25
499	Rusty Torres	.50	.25
500	Lee May	.50	.25
501	Eddie Leon	.50	.25
502	Dave LaRoche	.50	.25
503	Eric Soderholm	.50	.25
504	Joe Niekro	.50	.25
505	Bill Buckner	1.00	.50
506	Ed Farmer	.50	.25
507	Larry Stahl	.50	.25
508	Expos Team	1.00	.50
509	Jesse Jefferson	.50	.25
510	Wayne Garrett	.50	.25
511	Toby Harrah	.50	.25
512	Joe Lahoud	.50	.25
513	Jim Campanis	.50	.25
514	Paul Schaal	.50	.25
515	Willie Montanez	.50	.25
516	Horacio Pina	.50	.25
517	Mike Hegan	.50	.25
518	Derrel Thomas	.50	.25
519	Bill Sharp	.50	.25
520	Tim McCarver	.80	.40
521	Indians Mgr/Coaches	.60	.30
522	J.R. Richard	.80	.40
523	Cecil Cooper	1.25	.65
524	Bill Plummer	.50	.25
525	Clyde Wright	.50	.25
526	Frank Tepedino	.50	.25
527	Bobby Darwin	.50	.25
528	Bill Bonham	.50	.25
529	Horace Clarke	.50	.25
530	Mickey Stanley	.50	.25
531	Expos Mgr/Coaches	.60	.30
532	Skip Lockwood	.50	.25
533	Mike Phillips	.50	.25
534	Eddie Watt	.50	.25
535	Bob Tolan	.50	.25
536	Duffy Dyer	.50	.25
537	Steve Mingori	.50	.25
538	Cesar Tovar	.50	.25
539	Lloyd Allen	.50	.25
540	Bob Robertson	.50	.25
541	Indians Team	1.00	.50
542	Rich Gossage	2.50	1.25
543	Danny Cater	.50	.25
544	Ron Schueler	.50	.25
545	Billy Conigliaro	.50	.25
546	Mike Corkins	.50	.25
547	Glenn Borgmann	.50	.25
548	Sonny Siebert	.50	.25
549	Mike Jorgensen	.50	.25
550	Sam McDowell	.60	.30
551	Von Joshua	.50	.25
552	Denny Doyle	.50	.25
553	Jim Willoughby	.50	.25
554	Tim Johnson	.50	.25
555	Woodie Fryman	.50	.25
556	Dave Campbell	.50	.25
557	Jim McGlothin	.50	.25
558	Bill Fahey	.50	.25
559	Darrel Chaney	.50	.25
560	Mike Cuellar	.60	.30
561	Ed Kranepool	.75	.35
562	Jack Aker	.50	.25
563	Hal McRae	1.25	.65
564	Mike Ryan	.50	.25
565	Milt Wilcox	.50	.25
566	Jackie Hernandez	.50	.25
567	Red Sox Team	1.00	.50
568	Mike Torrez	.50	.25
569	Rick Dempsey	.70	.40

570 Ralph Garr	.60	.30	Reggie Sanders (R)		
571 Rich Hand	.50	.25	601 Rookie Outfielders	5.00	2.50
572 Enzo Hernandez	.50	.25	Ed Armbrister		
573 Mike Adams	.50	.25	Rich Bladt (R)		
574 Bill Parsons	.50	.25	Brian Downing (R)		
575 Steve Garvey	10.00	5.00	Bake McBride (R)		
576 Scipio Spinks	.50	.25	602 Rookie Pitchers	.50	.25
577 Mike Sadek	.50	.25	Glenn Abbott (R)		
578 Ralph Houk	.60	.30	Rick Henninger (R)		
579 Cecil Upshaw	.50	.25	Craig Swan (R)		
580 Jim Spencer	.50	.25	Dan Vossler (R)		
581 Fred Norman	.50	.25	603 Rookie Catchers	.75	.35
582 Bucky Dent (R)	2.50	1.25	Barry Foote (R)		
583 Marty Pattin	.50	.25	Tom Lundstedt (R)		
584 Ken Rudolph	.50	.25	Charlie Moore (R)		
585 Merv Rettenmund	.50	.25	Sergio Robles (R)		
586 Jack Brohamer	.50	.25	604 Rookie Infielders	7.00	3.50
587 Larry Christenson	.50	.25	Terry Hughes (R)		
588 Hal Lanier	.50	.25	John Knox (R)		
589 Boots Day	.50	.25	Andy Thornton (R)		
590 Rogelio Moret	.50	.25	Frank White (R)		
591 Sonny Jackson	.50	.25	605 Rookie Pitchers	5.00	2.50
592 Ed Bane	.50	.25	Vic Albury (R)		
593 Steve Yeager	.60	.30	Ken Frailing (R)		
594 Leroy Stanton	.50	.25	Kevin Kobel (R)		
595 Steve Blass	.50	.25	Frank Tanana (R)		
596 Rookie Pitchers	.50	.25	606 Rookie Outfielders	.50	.25
Wayne Garland (R)			Jim Fuller (R)		
Fred Holdsworth (R)			Wilbur Howard (R)		
Mark Littell (R)			Tommy Smith (R)		
Dick Pole (R)			Otto Velez (R)		
597 Rookie Shortstops	.60	.30	607 Rookie Shortstops	.50	.25
Dave Chalk (R)			Leo Foster (R)		
John Gamble (R)			Tom Heintzelman (R)		
Pete Mackanin (R)			Dave Rosello (R)		
Manny Trillo (R)			Frank Taveras (R)		
598 Rookie Outfielders	20.00	10.00	608 Rookie Pitchers	.50	.25
Dave Augustine (R)			Bob Apodaco (R)		
Ken Griffey (R)			Dick Baney (R)		
Steve Ontiveros (R)			John D'Acquisto (R)		
Jim Tyrone (R)			Mike Wallace (R)		
599a Rookie Pitchers	7.50	3.75	609 Rico Petrocelli	.60	.30
Ron Diorio (R)			610 Dave Kingman	1.25	.60
Dave Freisleben (R)			611 Rick Stelmaszek	.50	.25
(Wash)			612 Luke Walker	.50	.25
Frank Riccelli (R)			613 Dan Monzon	.50	.25
Greg Shanahan (R)			614 Adrian Devine	.50	.25
599b Rookie Pitchers	.60	.30	615 Johnny Jeter	.50	.25
Ron Diorio (R)			616 Larry Gura	.50	.25
Dave Freisleben (R)			617 Ted Ford	.50	.25
(SD)			618 Jim Mason	.50	.25
Frank Riccelli (R)			619 Mike Anderson	.50	.25
Greg Shanahan (R)			620 Al Downing	.50	.25
600 Rookie Infielders	5.00	2.50	621 Bernie Carbo	.50	.25
Ron Cash (R)			622 Phil Gagliano	.50	.25
Jim Cox (R)			623 Celerino Sanchez	.50	.25
Bill Madlock (R)			624 Bob Miller	.50	.25

625	Ollie Brown	.50	.25
626	Pirates Team	1.00	.50
627	Carl Taylor	.50	.25
628	Ivan Murrell	.50	.25
629	Rusty Staub	1.00	.50
630	Tommie Agee	.50	.25
631	Steve Barber	.50	.25
632	George Culver	.50	.25
633	Dave Hamilton	.50	.25
634	Braves Mgr/Coaches	1.00	.50
635	John Edwards	.50	.25
636	Dave Goltz	.50	.25
637	Checklist 529-660	2.00	.80
638	Ken Sanders	.50	.25
639	Joe Lovitto	.50	.25
640	Milt Pappas	.50	.25
641	Chuck Brinkman	.50	.25
642	Terry Harmon	.50	.25
643	Dodgers team	1.00	.50
644	Wayne Granger	.50	.25
645	Ken Boswell	.50	.25
646	George Foster	1.50	.75
647	Juan Beniquez (R)	.60	.30
648	Terry Crowley	.50	.25
649	Fernando Gonzalez	.50	.25
650	Mike Epstein	.50	.25
651	Leron Lee	.50	.25
652	Gail Hopkins	.50	.25
653	Bob Stinson	.50	.25
654a	Jesus Alou (No Position Listed)	6.00	3.00
654b	Jesus Alou (Outfield)	.50	.25
655	Mike Tyson	.50	.25
656	Adrian Garrett	.50	.25
657	Jim Shellenback	.50	.25
658	Lee Lacy	.50	.25
659	Joe Lis	.50	.25
660	Larry Dierker	.80	.30

1974 Topps Traded

This 44-card set marks Topps first baseball update set and features players who changed uniforms during the season. The 2-1/2" by 3-1/2" cards feature color photos on the front with the word "Traded" printed in bold type below the photographs. Card backs resemble newspaper print. Card numbers are followed by the letter "T" and coincide with the numbers assigned to the traded players in Topps regular edition.

		NR/MT	EX
Complete Set (44)		12.50	6.25
Commons (23-649)		.30	.15
23T	Craig Robinson	.30	.15
42T	Claude Osteen	.30	.15
43T	Jim Wynn	.50	.25
51T	Bobby Heise	.30	.15
59T	Ross Grimsley	.30	.15
62T	Bob Locker	.30	.15
63T	Bill Sudakis	.30	.15
73T	Mike Marshall	.60	.30
123T	Nelson Briles	.30	.15
139T	Aurelio Monteagudo	.30	.15
151T	Diego Segui	.30	.15
165T	Willie Davis	.40	.20
175T	Reggie Cleveland	.30	.15
182T	Lindy McDaniel	.30	.15
186T	Fred Scherman	.30	.15
249T	George Mitterwald	.30	.15
262T	Ed Kirkpatrick	.30	.15
269T	Bob Johnson	.30	.15
270T	Ron Santo	.80	.40
313T	Barry Lersch	.30	.15
319T	Randy Hundley	.30	.15
330T	Juan Marichal	2.50	1.25
348T	Pete Richert	.30	.15
373T	John Curtis	.30	.15
390T	Lou Piniella	.75	.35

428T	Gary Sutherland	.30	.15
454T	Kurt Bevacqua	.30	.15
458T	Jim Ray	.30	.15
485T	Felipe Alou	.60	.30
486T	Steve Stone	.60	.30
496T	Tom Murphy	.30	.15
516T	Horacio Pina	.30	.15
534T	Eddie Watt	.30	.15
538T	Cesar Tovar	.30	.15
544T	Ron Schueler	.30	.15
579T	Cecil Upshaw	.30	.15
585T	Merv Rettenmund	.30	.15
612T	Luke Walker	.30	.15
616T	Larry Gura	.30	.15
618T	Jim Mason	.30	.15
530T	Tommie Agee	.30	.15
648T	Terry Crowley	.30	.15
649T	Fernando Gonzalez	.30	.15
___	Traded Checklist	.80	.30

1975 Topps

The cards in this 660-card set feature large color player photos with a fascimile autograph at the bottom of each picture. The photos are surrounded by two-color borders. Card backs are vertical and features red and green type on a gray paper stock. All cards measure 2-1/2" by 3-1/2". Subsets include Highlights (HL) (1-7), a 24-card MVP Series (189-212) that depicts MVP's from 1951 through 1974, League Leaders, World Series Highlights and Rookies. Topps also issued a Mini Set in 1975 which is valued at twice the price quoted for the regular editon below.

		NR/MT	EX
	Complete Set (660)	950.00	475.00
	Commons (1-660)	.50	.25
1	Hank Aaron (HL)	32.00	16.00
2	Lou Brock (HL)	3.00	1.50
3	Bob Gibson (HL)	3.50	1.75
4	Al Kaline (HL)	3.50	1.75
5	Nolan Ryan (HL)	32.00	16.00
6	Mike Marshall (HL)	.60	.30
7	Dick Bosman, Steve Busby, Nolan Ryan (HL)	12.50	7.50
8	Rogelio Moret	.50	.25
9	Frank Tepedino	.50	.25
10	Willie Davis	.60	.30
11	Bill Melton	.50	.25
12	David Clyde	.50	.25
13	Gene Locklear	.60	.30
14	Milt Wilcox	.50	.25
15	Jose Cardenal	.50	.25
16	Frank Tanana	2.00	1.00
17	Dave Concepcion	2.50	1.25
18	Tigers Team	2.00	1.00
19	Jerry Koosman	.75	.35
20	Thurman Munson	8.00	4.00
21	Rollie Fingers	5.00	2.50
22	Dave Cash	.50	.25
23	Bill Russell	.75	.35
24	Al Fitzmorris	.50	.25
25	Lee May	.50	.25
26	Dave McNally	.60	.30
27	Ken Reitz	.50	.25
28	Tom Murphy	.50	.25
29	Dave Parker	8.00	4.00
30	Bert Blyleven	2.50	1.25
31	Dave Rader	.50	.25
32	Reggie Cleveland	.50	.25
33	Dusty Baker	1.25	.65
34	Steve Renko	.50	.25
35	Ron Santo	1.00	.50
36	Joe Lovitto	.50	.25
37	Dave Freisleben	.50	.25
38	Buddy Bell	.60	.30
39	Andy Thornton	.50	.25
40	Bill Singer	.50	.25
41	Cesar Geronimo	.50	.25
42	Joe Coleman	.50	.25
43	Cleon Jones	.50	.25
44	Pat Dobson	.50	.25
45	Joe Rudi	.60	.30
46	Phillies Team	2.00	1.00
47	Tommy John	1.50	.75
48	Freddie Patek	.50	.25
49	Larry Dierker	.50	.25
50	Brooks Robinson	7.50	3.75
51	Bob Forsch (R)	.75	.35

No.	Player	Price 1	Price 2
52	Darrell Porter	.50	.25
53	Dave Giusti	.50	.25
54	Eric Soderholm	.50	.25
55	Bobby Bonds	2.00	1.00
56	Rick Wise	.60	.30
57	Dave Johnson	.50	.25
58	Chuck Taylor	.50	.25
59	Ken Henderson	.50	.25
60	Ferguson Jenkins	5.50	2.25
61	Dave Winfield	90.00	45.00
62	Fritz Peterson	.50	.25
63	Steve Swisher	.50	.25
64	Dave Chalk	.50	.25
65	Don Gullett	.60	.30
66	Willie Horton	.60	.30
67	Tug McGraw	1.25	.60
68	Ron Blomberg	.50	.25
69	John Odom	.50	.25
70	Mike Schmidt	80.00	40.00
71	Charlie Hough	.90	.45
72	Royals Team	2.00	1.00
73	J. R. Richard	.75	.35
74	Mark Belanger	.60	.30
75	Ted Simmons	1.50	.75
76	Ed Sprague	.50	.25
77	Richie Zisk	.50	.25
78	Ray Corbin	.50	.25
79	Gary Matthews	.60	.30
80	Carlton Fisk	20.00	10.00
81	Ron Reed	.50	.25
82	Pat Kelly	.50	.25
83	Jim Merritt	.50	.25
84	Enzo Hernandez	.50	.25
85	Bill Bonham	.50	.25
86	Joe Lis	.50	.25
87	George Foster	1.50	.75
88	Tom Egan	.50	.25
89	Jim Ray	.50	.25
90	Rusty Staub	1.25	.65
91	Dick Green	.50	.25
92	Cecil Upshaw	.50	.25
93	Dave Lopes	1.25	.65
94	Jim Lonborg	.60	.30
95	John Mayberry	.60	.30
96	Mike Cosgrove	.50	.25
97	Earl Williams	.50	.25
98	Rich Folkers	.50	.25
99	Mike Hegan	.50	.25
100	Willie Stargell	5.00	2.50
101	Expos Team	2.00	1.00
102	Joe Decker	.50	.25
103	Rick Miller	.50	.25
104	Bill Madlock	1.50	.75
105	Buzz Capra	.50	.25
106	Mike Hargrove (R)	1.00	.50
107	Jim Barr	.50	.25
108	Tom Hall	.50	.25
109	George Hendrick	.60	.30
110	Wilbur Wood	.50	.25
111	Wayne Garrett	.50	.25
112	Larry Hardy	.50	.25
113	Elliott Maddox	.50	.25
114	Dick Lange	.50	.25
115	Joe Ferguson	.00	.00
116	Lerrin LaGrow	.50	.25
117	Orioles Team	2.00	1.00
118	Mike Anderson	.50	.25
119	Tommy Helms	.50	.25
120	Steve Busby (Wrong Photo)	.50	.25
121	Bill North	.50	.25
122	Al Hrabosky	.60	.30
123	Johnny Briggs	.50	.25
124	Jerry Reuss	.75	.35
125	Ken Singleton	.60	.30
126	Checklist 1-132	2.00	.80
127	Glen Borgmann	.50	.25
128	Bill Lee	.50	.25
129	Rick Monday	.60	.30
130	Phil Niekro	4.50	2.25
131	Toby Harrah	.50	.25
132	Randy Moffitt	.50	.25
133	Dan Driessen	.75	.35
134	Ron Hodges	.50	.25
135	Charlie Spikes	.50	.25
136	Jim Mason	.50	.25
137	Terry Forster	.50	.25
138	Del Unser	.50	.25
139	Horacio Pina	.50	.25
140	Steve Garvey	8.50	4.25
141	Mickey Stanley	.60	.30
142	Bob Reynolds	.50	.25
143	Cliff Johnson (R)	.75	.35
144	Jim Wohlford	.50	.25
145	Ken Holtzman	.50	.25
146	Padres Team	2.00	1.00
147	Pedro Garcia	.50	.25
148	Jim Rooker	.50	.25
149	Tim Foli	.50	.25
150	Bob Gibson	6.50	3.25
151	Steve Brye	.50	.25
152	Mario Guerrero	.50	.25
153	Rick Reuschel	.75	.35
154	Mike Lum	.50	.25
155	Jim Bibby	.50	.25
156	Dave Kingman	1.00	.50
157	Pedro Borbon	.50	.25
158	Jerry Grote	.50	.25
159	Steve Arlin	.50	.25
160	Graig Nettles	1.50	.75
161	Stan Bahnsen	.50	.25
162	Willie Montanez	.50	.25
163	Jim Brewer	.50	.25
164	Mickey Rivers	.50	.25

165	Doug Rader	.50	.25
166	Woodie Fryman	.50	.25
167	Rich Coggins	.50	.25
168	Bill Greif	.50	.25
169	Cookie Rojas	.50	.25
170	Bert Campaneris	.75	.35
171	Ed Kirkpatrick	.50	.25
172	Red Sox Team	2.00	1.00
173	Steve Rogers	.60	.30
174	Bake McBride	.50	.25
175	Don Money	.50	.25
176	Burt Hooton	.50	.25
177	Vic Correll	.50	.25
178	Cesar Tovar	.50	.25
179	Tom Bradley	.50	.25
180	Joe Morgan	8.50	4.25
181	Fred Beene	.50	.25
182	Don Hahn	.50	.25
183	Mel Stottlemyre	.60	.30
184	Jorge Orta	.50	.25
185	Steve Carlton	15.00	7.50
186	Willie Crawford	.50	.25
187	Denny Doyle	.50	.25
188	Tom Griffin	.50	.25
189	1951 MVPs (Yogi Berra, Roy Campanella)	3.00	1.50
190	1952 MVPs (Hank Sauer, Bobby Shantz)	1.25	.60
191	1953 MVPs (Roy Campanella, Al Rosen)	1.50	.75
192	1954 MVPs (Yogi Berra, Willie Mays)	3.50	1.75
193	1955 MVPs (Yogi Berra, Roy Campanella)	3.00	1.50
194	1956 MVPs (Mickey Mantle, Don Newcombe)	8.50	4.25
195	1957 MVPs (Hank Aaron, Mickey Mantle)	12.50	6.25
196	1958 MVPs (Ernie Banks, Jackie Jensen)	2.50	1.25
197	1959 MVPs (Ernie Banks, Nellie Fox)	2.50	1.25
198	1960 MVPs (Dick Groat, Roger Maris)	2.00	1.00
199	1961 MVPs (Roger Maris, Frank Robinson)	3.00	1.50
200	1962 MVPs (Mickey Mantle, Maury Wills)	8.50	4.25
201	1963 MVPs (Elston Howard, Sandy Koufax)	2.50	1.25
202	1964 MVPs (Ken Boyer, Brooks Robinson)	2.00	1.00
203	1965 MVPs (Willie Mays, Zoilo Versalles)	2.50	1.25
204	1966 MVPs (Bob Clemente, Frank Robinson)	3.50	1.75
205	1967 MVPs (Orlando Cepeda, Carl Yastrzemski)	2.50	1.25
206	1968 MVPs (Bob Gibson, Denny McLain)	2.50	1.25
207	1969 MVPs (Harmon Killebrew, Willie McCovey)	3.00	1.50
208	1970 MVPs (Johnny Bench, Boog Powell)	2.50	1.25
209	1971 MVPs (Vida Blue, Joe Torre)	1.75	.90
210	1972 MVPs (Rich Allen, Johnny Bench)	2.00	1.00
211	1973 MVPs (Reggie Jackson, Pete Rose)	7.50	3.75
212	1974 MVPs (Jeff Burroughs, Steve Garvey)	1.50	.75
213	Oscar Gamble	.50	.25
214	Harry Parker	.50	.25
215	Bobby Valentine	.60	.30
216	Giants Team	2.00	1.00
217	Lou Piniella	1.00	.50
218	Jerry Johnson	.50	.25
219	Ed Herrmann	.50	.25
220	Don Sutton	4.50	2.25
221	Aurelio Rodriquez	.50	.25
222	Dan Spillner	.50	.25
223	Robin Yount (R)	210.00	105.00
224	Ramon Hernandez	.50	.30
225	Bob Grich	.60	.30
226	Bill Campbell	.50	.25
227	Bob Watson	.75	.35
228	George Brett (R)	240.00	120.00
229	Barry Foote	.50	.25
230	Jim Hunter	4.50	2.25
231	Mike Tyson	.50	.25
232	Diego Segui	.50	.25
233	Billy Grabarkewitz	.50	.25
234	Tom Grieve	.50	.25
235	Jack Billingham	.50	.25
236	Angels Team	2.00	1.00
237	Carl Morton	.50	.25
238	Dave Duncan	.50	.25
239	George Stone	.50	.25
240	Garry Maddox	.60	.30
241	Dick Tidrow	.50	.25
242	Jay Johnstone	.50	.25
243	Jim Kaat	1.25	.65
244	Bill Buckner	1.00	.50

245	Mickey Lolich	.80	.40
246	Cardinals Team	2.00	1.00
247	Enos Cabell	.50	.25
248	Randy Jones	.60	.30
249	Danny Thompson	.50	.25
250	Ken Brett	.50	.25
251	Fran Healy	.60	.05
252	Fred Scherman	.50	.25
253	Jesus Alou	.50	.25
254	Mike Torrez	.50	.25
255	Dwight Evans	4.00	2.00
256	Billy Champion	.50	.25
257	Checklist 133-264	2.00	.80
258	Dave LaRoche	.50	.25
259	Len Randle	.50	.25
260	Johnny Bench	18.00	9.00
261	Andy Hassler	.50	.25
262	Rowland Office	.50	.25
263	Jim Perry	.50	.25
264	John Milner	.50	.25
265	Ron Bryant	.50	.25
266	Sandy Alomar	.50	.25
267	Dick Ruthven	.50	.25
268	Hal McRae	1.25	.65
269	Doug Rau	.50	.25
270	Ron Fairly	.50	.25
271	Jerry Moses	.50	.25
272	Lynn McGlothen	.50	.25
273	Steve Braun	.50	.25
274	Vicente Romo	.50	.25
275	Paul Blair	.50	.25
276	White Sox Team	2.00	1.00
277	Frank Taveras	.50	.25
278	Paul Lindblad	.50	.25
279	Milt May	.50	.25
280	Carl Yastrzemski	10.00	5.00
281	Jim Slaton	.50	.25
282	Jerry Morales	.50	.25
283	Steve Foucault	.50	.25
284	Ken Griffey	4.00	2.00
285	Ellie Rodriguez	.50	.25
286	Mike Jorgensen	.50	.25
287	Roric Harrison	.50	.25
288	Bruce Ellingsen	.50	.25
289	Ken Rudolph	.50	.25
290	Jon Matlack	.60	.30
291	Bill Sudakis	.50	.25
292	Ron Schueler	.50	.25
293	Dick Sharon	.50	.25
294	Geoff Zahn (R)	.50	.25
295	Vada Pinson	.75	.35
296	Alan Foster	.50	.25
297	Craig Kusick	.50	.25
298	Johnny Grubb	.50	.25
299	Bucky Dent	.75	.35
300	Reggie Jackson	28.00	14.00
301	Dave Roberts	.50	.25
302	Rick Burleson (R)	.75	.35
303	Grant Jackson	.50	.25
304	Pirates Team	2.00	1.00
305	Jim Colborn	.50	.25
306	Batting Leaders (Rod Carew, Ralph Garr)	1.50	.75
007	HR Leaders (Dick Allen, Mike Schmidt)	4.00	2.00
308	RBI Leaders (Johnny Bench, Jeff Burroughs)	2.50	1.25
309	Stolen Base Leaders (Lou Brock, Bill North)	1.50	.75
310	Victory Leaders (Jim Hunter, Fergie Jenkins Andy Messersmith, Phil Niekro)	1.50	.75
311	ERA Leaders (Buzz Capra, Jim Hunter)	1.25	.60
312	Strikeout Leaders (Steve Carlton, Nolan Ryan)	22.00	11.00
313	Leading Firemen (Terry Forster, Mike Marshall)	1.00	.50
314	Buck Martinez	.50	.25
315	Don Kessinger	.60	.30
316	Jackie Brown	.50	.25
317	Joe Lahoud	.50	.25
318	Ernie McAnally	.50	.25
319	Johnny Oates	.50	.25
320	Pete Rose	24.00	12.00
321	Rudy May	.50	.25
322	Ed Goodson	.50	.25
323	Fred Holdsworth	.50	.25
324	Ed Kranepool	.75	.35
325	Tony Oliva	1.50	.75
326	Wayne Twitchell	.50	.25
327	Jerry Hairston	.50	.25
328	Sonny Siebert	.50	.25
329	Ted Kubiak	.50	.25
330	Mike Marshall	.60	.30
331	Indians Team	2.00	1.00
332	Fred Kendall	.50	.25
333	Dick Drago	.50	.25
334	Greg Gross (R)	.50	.25
335	Jim Palmer	10.00	5.00
336	Rennie Stennett	.50	.25
337	Kevin Kobel	.50	.25
338	Rick Stelmaszek	.50	.25
339	Jim Fregosi	.60	.30
340	Paul Splittorff	.50	.25
341	Hal Breeden	.50	.25
342	Leroy Stanton	.50	.25
343	Danny Frisella	.50	.25
344	Ben Oglivie	.50	.25
345	Clay Carroll	.50	.25

346	Bobby Darwin	.50	.25
347	Mike Caldwell	.50	.25
348	Tony Muser	.50	.25
349	Ray Sadecki	.50	.25
350	Bobby Murcer	.80	.40
351	Bob Boone	2.00	1.00
352	Darold Knowles	.50	.25
353	Luis Melendez	.50	.25
354	Dick Bosman	.50	.25
355	Chris Cannizzaro	.50	.25
356	Rico Petrocelli	.50	.25
357	Ken Forsch	.50	.25
358	Al Bumbry	.50	.25
359	Paul Popovich	.50	.25
360	George Scott	.60	.30
361	Dodgers Team	2.00	1.00
362	Steve Hargan	.50	.25
363	Carmen Fanzone	.50	.25
364	Doug Bird	.50	.25
365	Bob Bailey	.50	.25
366	Ken Sanders	.50	.25
367	Craig Robinson	.50	.25
368	Vic Albury	.50	.25
369	Merv Rettenmund	.50	.25
370	Tom Seaver	22.00	11.00
371	Gates Brown	.50	.25
372	John D'Acquisto	.50	.25
373	Bill Sharp	.50	.25
374	Eddie Watt	.50	.25
375	Roy White	.50	.25
376	Steve Yeager	.60	.30
377	Tom Hilgendorf	.50	.25
378	Derrel Thomas	.50	.25
379	Bernie Carbo	.50	.25
380	Sal Bando	.60	.30
381	John Curtis	.50	.25
382	Don Baylor	2.50	1.50
383	Jim York	.50	.25
384	Brewers Team	2.00	1.00
385	Dock Ellis	.50	.25
386	Checklist 265-396	2.00	.80
387	Jim Spencer	.50	.25
388	Steve Stone	.50	.25
389	Tony Spolaita	.50	.25
390	Ron Cey	1.00	.50
391	Don DeMola	.50	.25
392	Bruce Bochte	.50	.25
393	Gary Gentry	.50	.25
394	Larvell Blanks	.50	.25
395	Bud Harrelson	.60	.30
396	Fred Norman	.50	.25
397	Bill Freehan	.60	.30
398	Elias Sosa	.50	.25
399	Terry Harmon	.50	.25
400	Dick Allen	1.00	.50
401	Mike Wallace	.50	.25
402	Bob Tolan	.50	.25
403	Tom Buskey	.50	.25
404	Ted Sizemore	.50	.25
405	John Montague	.50	.25
406	Bob Gallagher	.50	.25
407	Herb Washington (R)	.50	.25
408	Clyde Wright	.50	.25
409	Bob Robertson	.50	.25
410	Mike Cuellar	.60	.30
411	George Mitterwald	.50	.25
412	Bill Hands	.50	.25
413	Marty Pattin	.50	.25
414	Manny Mota	.60	.30
415	John Hiller	.50	.25
416	Larry Lintz	.50	.25
417	Skip Lockwood	.50	.25
418	Leo Foster	.50	.25
419	Dave Goltz	.50	.25
420	Larry Bowa	.80	.40
421	Mets Team	2.00	1.00
422	Brian Downing	1.00	.50
423	Clay Kirby	.50	.25
424	John Lowenstein	.50	.25
425	Tito Fuentes	.50	.25
426	George Medich	.50	.25
427	Cito Gaston	.50	.25
428	Dave Hamilton	.50	.25
429	Jim Dwyer (R)	.50	.25
430	Luis Tiant	.80	.40
431	Rod Gilbreath	.50	.25
432	Ken Berry	.50	.25
433	Larry Demery	.50	.25
434	Bob Locker	.50	.25
435	Dave Nelson	.50	.25
436	Ken Frailing	.50	.25
437	Al Cowens	.50	.25
438	Don Carrithers	.50	.25
439	Ed Brinkman	.50	.25
440	Andy Messersmith	.50	.25
441	Bobby Heise	.50	.25
442	Maximino Leon	.50	.25
443	Twins Team	2.00	1.00
444	Gene Garber	.50	.25
445	Felix Millan	.50	.25
446	Bart Johnson	.50	.25
447	Terry Crowley	.50	.25
448	Frank Duffy	.50	.25
449	Charlie Williams	.50	.25
450	Willie McCovey	5.00	2.50
451	Rick Dempsey	.50	.25
452	Angel Mangual	.50	.25
453	Claude Osteen	.50	.25
454	Doug Griffin	.50	.25
455	Don Wilson	.50	.25
456	Bob Coluccio	.50	.25
457	Mario Mendoza	.50	.25
458	Ross Grimsley	.50	.25
459	A.L. Championships	1.25	.65

460	N.L. Championships	1.50	.75
461	World Series Game 1	5.00	2.50
462	World Series Game 2	1.25	.60
463	World Series Game 3	1.50	.75
464	World Series Game 4	1.25	.60
465	World Series Game 5	1.25	.60
466	WS (Celebration)	1.25	.65
467	Ed Halicki	.50	.25
468	Bobby Mitchell	.50	.25
469	Tom Dettore	.50	.25
470	Jeff Burroughs	.50	.25
471	Bob Stinson	.50	.25
472	Bruce Dal Canton	.50	.25
473	Ken McMullen	.50	.25
474	Luke Walker	.50	.25
475	Darrell Evans	.80	.40
476	Ed Figueroa (R)	.60	.30
477	Tom Hutton	.50	.25
478	Tom Burgmeier	.50	.25
479	Ken Boswell	.50	.25
480	Carlos May	.50	.25
481	Will McEnaney (R)	.50	.25
482	Tom McCraw	.50	.25
483	Steve Ontiveros	.50	.25
484	Glenn Beckert	.50	.25
485	Sparky Lyle	.60	.30
486	Ray Fosse	.50	.25
487	Astros Team	2.00	1.00
488	Bill Travers	.50	.25
489	Cecil Cooper	1.00	.50
490	Reggie Smith	.75	.35
491	Doyle Alexander	.50	.25
492	Rich Hebner	.50	.25
493	Don Stanhouse	.50	.25
494	Pete LaCock (R)	.50	.25
495	Nelson Briles	.50	.25
496	Pepe Frias	.50	.25
497	Jim Nettles	.50	.25
498	Al Downing	.50	.25
499	Marty Perez	.50	.25
500	Nolan Ryan	90.00	45.00
501	Bill Robinson	.60	.30
502	Pat Bourque	.50	.25
503	Fred Stanley	.50	.25
504	Buddy Bradford	.50	.25
505	Chris Speier	.50	.25
506	Leron Lee	.50	.25
507	Tom Carroll	.50	.25
508	Bob Hansen	.50	.25
509	Dave Hilton	.50	.25
510	Vida Blue	.75	.35
511	Rangers Team	2.00	1.00
512	Larry Milbourne	.50	.25
513	Dick Pole	.50	.25
514	Jose Cruz	.75	.35
515	Manny Sanguillen	.60	.30
516	Don Hood	.50	.25
517	Checklist 397-528	2.00	.80
518	Leo Cardenas	.50	.25
519	Jim Todd	.50	.25
520	Amos Otis	.60	.30
521	Dennis Blair	.50	.25
522	Gary Sutherland	.50	.25
523	Tom Paciorek	.50	.25
524	John Doherty	.50	.25
525	Tom House	.50	.25
526	Larry Hisle	.50	.25
527	Mac Scarce	.50	.25
528	Eddie Leon	.50	.25
529	Gary Thomasson	.50	.25
530	Gaylord Perry	5.00	2.50
531	Reds Team	2.50	1.25
532	Gorman Thomas	.60	.30
533	Rudy Meoli	.50	.25
534	Alex Johnson	.50	.25
535	Gene Tenace	.60	.30
536	Bob Moose	.50	.25
537	Tommy Harper	.50	.25
538	Duffy Dyer	.50	.25
539	Jesse Jefferson	.50	.25
540	Lou Brock	6.00	3.00
541	Roger Metzger	.50	.25
542	Pete Broberg	.50	.25
543	Larry Bittner	.50	.25
544	Steve Mingori	.50	.25
545	Billy Williams	4.50	2.25
546	John Knox	.50	.25
547	Von Joshua	.50	.25
548	Charlie Sands	.50	.25
549	Bill Butler	.50	.25
550	Ralph Garr	.60	.30
551	Larry Christenson	.50	.25
552	Jack Brohamer	.50	.25
553	John Boccabella	.50	.25
554	Rich Gossage	3.50	1.75
555	Al Oliver	1.00	.50
556	Tim Johnson	.50	.25
557	Larry Gura	.50	.25
558	Dave Roberts	.50	.25
559	Bob Montgomery	.50	.25
560	Tony Perez	4.50	2.25
561	A's Team	2.00	1.00
562	Gary Nolan	.50	.25
563	Wilbur Howard	.50	.25
564	Tommy Davis	.60	.30
565	Joe Torre	.80	.40
566	Ray Burris	.50	.25
567	Jim Sundberg (R)	1.00	.50
568	Dale Murray	.50	.25
569	Frank White	1.00	.50
570	Jim Wynn	.60	.30
571	Dave Lemanczyk	.50	.25
573	Orlando Pena	.50	.25
574	Tony Taylor	.50	.25

575	Gene Clines	.50	.25
576	Phil Roof	.50	.25
577	John Morris	.50	.25
578	Dave Tomlin	.50	.25
579	Skip Pitlock	.50	.25
580	Frank Robinson	6.50	3.25
581	Darrel Chaney	.50	.25
582	Eduardo Rodriguez	.50	.25
583	Andy Etchebarren	.50	.25
584	Mike Garman	.50	.25
585	Chris Chambliss	.60	.30
586	Tim McCarver	.75	.35
587	Chris Ward	.50	.25
588	Rick Auerbach	.50	.25
589	Braves Team	2.00	1.00
590	Cesar Cedeno	.60	.30
591	Glenn Abbott	.50	.25
592	Balor Moore	.50	.25
593	Gene Lamont	.50	.25
594	Jim Fuller	.50	.25
595	Joe Niekro	.50	.25
596	Ollie Brown	.50	.25
597	Winston Llenas	.50	.25
598	Bruch Kison	.50	.25
599	Nate Colbert	.50	.25
600	Rod Carew	10.00	5.00
601	Juan Beniquez	.50	.25
602	John Vukovich	.50	.25
603	Lew Krausse	.50	.25
604	Oscar Zamora	.50	.25
605	John Ellis	.50	.25
606	Bruce Miller	.50	.25
607	Jim Holt	.50	.25
608	Gene Michael	.50	.25
609	Ellie Hendricks	.50	.25
610	Ron Hunt	.50	.25
611	Yankees Team	2.00	1.00
612	Terry Hughes	.50	.25
613	Bill Parsons	.50	.25
614	Rookie Pitchers	.50	.25
	Jack Kucek (R)		
	Dyar Miller (R)		
	Vern Ruhle (R)		
	Paul Siebert (R)		
615	Rookie Pitchers	1.00	.50
	Pat Darcy (R)		
	Dennis Leonard (R)		
	Tom Underwood (R)		
	Hank Webb (R)		
616	Rookie Outfielders	22.00	11.00
	Dave Augustine (R)		
	Pepe Mangual (R)		
	Jim Rice (R)		
	John Scott (R)		
617	Rookie Infielders	2.00	1.00
	Mike Cubbage (R)		
	Doug DeCinces (R)		

	Reggie Sanders		
	Manny Trillo		
618	Rookie Pitchers	1.50	.75
	Jamie Easterly (R)		
	Tom Johnson (R)		
	Scott McGregor (R)		
	Rick Rhoden (R)		
619	Rookie Outfielders	.50	.25
	Benny Ayala (R)		
	Nyls Nyman (R)		
	Tommy Smith (R)		
	Jerry Turner (R)		
620	Rookie Catchers-OF	50.00	25.00
	Gary Carter (R)		
	Marc Hill (R)		
	Danny Meyer (R)		
	Leon Roberts (R)		
621	Rookie Pitchers	.80	.40
	John Denny (R)		
	Rawly Eastwick (R)		
	Jim Kern (R)		
	Juan Veintidos (R)		
622	Rookie Outfielders	12.00	6.00
	Ed Armbrister (R)		
	Fred Lynn (R)		
	Tom Poquette (R)		
	Terry Whitfield (R)		
623	Rookie Infielders	18.00	9.00
	Phil Garner (R)		
	Keith Hernandez (R)		
	Bob Sheldon (R)		
	Tom Veryzer (R)		
624	Rookie Pitchers	.50	.25
	Doug Konieczny (R)		
	Gary Lavelle (R)		
	Jim Otten (R)		
	Eddie Solomon (R)		
625	Boog Powell	1.25	.65
626	Larry Haney	.50	.25
627	Tom Walker	.50	.25
628	Ron LeFlore (R)	.80	.50
629	Joe Hoerner	.50	.25
630	Greg Luzinski	1.00	.50
631	Lee Lacy	.50	.25
632	Morris Nettles	.50	.25
633	Paul Casanova	.50	.25
634	Cy Acosta	.50	.25
635	Chuck Dobson	.50	.25
636	Charlie Moore	.50	.25
637	Ted Martinez	.50	.25
638	Cubs Team	2.00	1.00
639	Steve Kline	.50	.25
640	Harmon Killebrew	6.00	3.00
641	Jim Northrup	.50	.25
642	Mike Phillips	.50	.25
643	Brent Storm	.50	.25
644	Bill Fahey	.50	.25

645	Danny Cater	.50	.25
646	Checklist 529-660	2.00	.80
647	Claudell Washington(R)	1.00	.50
648	Dave Pagan	.50	.25
649	Jack Heidemann	.50	.25
650	Dave May	.50	.25
651	John Morlan	.50	.25
652	Lindy McDaniel	.50	.25
653	Lee Richards	.50	.25
654	Jerry Terrell	.50	.25
655	Rico Carty	.50	.25
656	Bill Plummer	.50	.25
657	Bob Oliver	.50	.25
658	Vic Harris	.50	.25
659	Bob Apodaca	.50	.25
660	Hank Aaron	30.00	15.00

1976 Topps

Topps improved the quality of their photographs with this 660-card set which features large color photos on the card fronts with a small drawing of a player in the bottom left corner. Cards measure 2-1/2" by 3-1/2". The major subsets include Record Breakers (RB)(1-6), a new Father and Sons subset (66-70) and an All Time All-Stars series (341-350). Also present are League Leaders, World Series and Playoff Highlights and Rookies.

		NR/MT	EX
Complete Set (660)		475.00	240.00
Commons (1-660)		.30	.15
1	Hank Aaron (RB)	16.00	8.00
2	Bobby Bonds (RB)	.80	.40
3	Mickey Lolich (RB)	.50	.25
4	Dave Lopes (RB)	.50	.25
5	Tom Seaver (RB)	5.00	2.50

6	Rennie Stennett (RB)	.50	.25
7	Jim Umbarger	.30	.15
8	Tito Fuentes	.30	.15
9	Paul Lindblad	.30	.15
10	Lou Brock	6.00	3.00
11	Jim Hughes	.30	.15
12	Richie Zisk	.30	.15
13	Johnny Wockenfuss	.30	.15
14	Gene Garber	.30	.15
15	George Scott	.40	.20
16	Bob Apodaca	.30	.15
17	Yankees Team	1.50	.75
18	Dale Murray	.30	.15
19	George Brett	75.00	37.50
20	Bob Watson	.60	.30
21	Dave LaRoche	.30	.15
22	Bill Russell	.40	.20
23	Brian Downing	.80	.40
24	Cesar Geronimo	.30	.15
25	Mike Torrez	.30	.15
26	Andy Thornton	.30	.15
27	Ed Figueroa	.30	.15
28	Dusty Baker	1.25	.65
29	Rick Burleson	.40	.20
30	John Montefusco (R)	.50	.25
31	Lenny Randle	.30	.15
32	Danny Frisella	.30	.15
33	Bill North	.30	.15
34	Mike Garman	.30	.15
35	Tony Oliva	1.25	.60
36	Frank Taveras	.30	.15
37	John Hiller	.30	.15
38	Garry Maddox	.40	.20
39	Pete Broberg	.30	.15
40	Dave Kingman	1.00	.50
41	Tippy Martinez (R)	.40	.20
42	Barry Foote	.30	.15
43	Paul Splittorff	.30	.15
44	Doug Rader	.30	.15
45	Boog Powell	.80	.50
46	Dodgers Team	1.50	.75
47	Jesse Jefferson	.30	.15
48	Dave Concepcion	1.50	.75
49	Dave Duncan	.30	.15
50	Fred Lynn	2.00	1.00
51	Ray Burris	.30	.15
52	Dave Chalk	.30	.15
53	Mike Beard	.30	.15
54	Dave Rader	.30	.15
55	Gaylord Perry	4.00	2.00
56	Bob Tolan	.30	.15
57	Phil Garner	.80	.40
58	Ron Reed	.30	.15
59	Larry Hisle	.30	.15
60	Jerry Reuss	.50	.25
61	Ron LeFlore	.50	.25
62	Johnny Oates	.30	.15

63	Bobby Darwin	.30	.15
64	Jerry Koosman	.50	.25
65	Chris Chambliss	.40	.20
66	Buddy & Gus Bell	.60	.30
67	Bob & Ray Boone	1.00	.50
68	Joe Coleman & Jr.	.50	.25
69	Jim & Mike Hegan	.50	.25
70	Roy Smalley & Jr.	.50	.25
71	Steve Rogers	.30	.15
72	Hal McRae	1.25	.65
73	Orioles Team	1.50	.75
74	Oscar Gamble	.30	.15
75	Larry Dierker	.30	.15
76	Willie Crawford	.30	.15
77	Pedro Borbon	.30	.15
78	Cecil Cooper	.70	.40
79	Jerry Morales	.30	.15
80	Jim Kaat	1.00	.50
81	Darrell Evans	.50	.25
82	Von Joshua	.30	.15
83	Jim Spencer	.30	.15
84	Brent Strom	.30	.15
85	Mickey Rivers	.30	.15
86	Mike Tyson	.30	.15
87	Tom Burgmeier	.30	.15
88	Duffy Dyer	.30	.15
89	Vern Ruhle	.30	.15
90	Sal Bando	.50	.25
91	Tom Hutton	.30	.15
92	Eduardo Rodriguez	.30	.15
93	Mike Phillips	.30	.15
94	Jim Dwyer	.30	.15
95	Brooks Robinson	6.50	3.25
96	Doug Bird	.30	.15
97	Wilbur Howard	.30	.15
98	Dennis Eckersley (R)	50.00	25.00
99	Lee Lacy	.30	.15
100	Jim Hunter	3.50	1.75
101	Pete LaCock	.30	.15
102	Jim Willoughby	.30	.15
103	Biff Pocoroba	.30	.15
104	Reds Team	2.00	1.00
105	Gary Lavelle	.30	.15
106	Tom Grieve	.30	.15
107	Dave Roberts	.30	.15
108	Don Kirkwood	.30	.15
109	Larry Lintz	.30	.15
110	Carlos May	.30	.15
111	Danny Thompson	.30	.15
112	Kent Tekulve (R)	1.25	.60
113	Gary Sutherland	.30	.15
114	Jay Johnstone	.40	.20
115	Ken Holtzman	.40	.20
116	Charlie Moore	.30	.15
117	Mike Jorgensen	.30	.15
118	Red Sox Team	1.50	.75
119	Checklist 1-132	1.50	.50
120	Rusty Staub	.75	.35
121	Tony Solaita	.30	.15
122	Mike Cosgrove	.30	.15
123	Walt Williams	.30	.15
124	Doug Rau	.30	.15
125	Don Baylor	1.75	.90
126	Tom Dettore	.30	.15
127	Larvell Blanks	.30	.15
128	Ken Griffey	2.50	1.25
129	Andy Etchebarren	.30	.15
130	Luis Tiant	.60	.30
131	Bill Stein	.30	.15
132	Don Hood	.30	.15
133	Gary Matthews	.40	.20
134	Mike Ivie	.30	.15
135	Bake McBride	.30	.15
136	Dave Goltz	.30	.15
137	Bill Robinson	.50	.25
138	Lerrin LaGrow	.30	.15
139	Gorman Thomas	.50	.25
140	Vida Blue	.60	.30
141	Larry Parrish (R)	1.25	.65
142	Dick Drago	.30	.15
143	Jerry Grote	.30	.15
144	Al Fitzmorris	.30	.15
145	Larry Bowa	.60	.30
146	George Medich	.30	.15
147	Astros Team	1.50	.75
148	Stan Thomas	.30	.15
149	Tommy Davis	.50	.25
150	Steve Garvey	7.00	3.50
151	Bill Bonham	.30	.15
152	Leroy Stanton	.30	.15
153	Buzz Capra	.30	.15
154	Bucky Dent	.60	.30
155	Jack Billingham	.30	.15
156	Rico Carty	.40	.20
157	Mike Caldwell	.30	.15
158	Ken Reitz	.30	.15
159	Jerry Terrell	.30	.15
160	Dave Winfield	48.00	24.00
161	Bruce Kison	.30	.15
162	Jack Pierce	.30	.15
163	Jim Slaton	.30	.15
164	Pepe Mangual	.30	.15
165	Gene Tenace	.40	.20
166	Skip Lockwood	.30	.15
167	Freddie Patek	.30	.15
168	Tom Hilgendorf	.30	.15
169	Graig Nettles	1.50	.75
170	Rick Wise	.40	.20
171	Greg Gross	.30	.15
172	Rangers Team	1.50	.75
173	Steve Swisher	.30	.15
174	Charlie Hough	.60	.30
175	Ken Singleton	.40	.20
176	Dick Lange	.30	.15

177 Marty Perez	.30	.15
178 Tom Buskey	.30	.15
179 George Foster	1.00	.50
180 Rich Gossage	2.50	1.25
181 Willie Montanez	.30	.15
182 Harry Rasmussen	.30	.15
183 Steve Braun	.00	.15
184 Bill Greif	.30	.15
185 Dave Parker	4.00	2.00
186 Tom Walker	.30	.15
187 Pedro Garcia	.30	.15
188 Fred Scherman	.30	.15
189 Claudell Washington	.40	.20
190 Jon Matlack	.50	.25
191 N.L. Batting Leaders	.80	.40
192 A.L. Batting Leaders	3.00	1.50
193 N.L. HR Leaders	3.00	1.50
194 A.L. HR Leaders	4.00	2.00
195 N.L. RBI Leaders	2.00	1.00
196 A.L. RBI Leaders	1.00	.50
197 N.L. Stolen Base Ldrs	2.00	1.00
198 A.L. Stolen Base Ldrs	.80	.50
199 N.L. Victory Leaders	2.00	1.00
200 A.L Victory Leaders	2.00	1.00
201 N.L. ERA Leaders	2.00	1.00
202 A.L. ERA Leaders	5.00	2.50
203 N.L. Strikeout Leaders	2.00	1.00
204 A.L. Strikeout Leaders	2.00	1.00
205 Major League Fireman	.80	.40
206 Manny Trillo	.30	.15
207 Andy Hassler	.30	.15
208 Mike Lum	.30	.15
209 Alan Ashby	.30	.15
210 Lee May	.30	.15
211 Clay Carroll	.30	.15
212 Pat Kelly	.30	.15
213 Dave Heaverlo	.30	.15
214 Eric Soderholm	.30	.15
215 Reggie Smith	.40	.20
216 Expos Team	1.50	.75
217 Dave Freisleben	.30	.15
218 John Knox	.30	.15
219 Tom Murphy	.30	.15
220 Manny Sanguillen	.50	.25
221 Jim Todd	.30	.15
222 Wayne Garrett	.30	.15
223 Ollie Brown	.30	.15
224 Jim York	.30	.15
225 Roy White	.30	.15
226 Jim Sundberg	.30	.15
227 Oscar Zamora	.30	.15
228 John Hale	.30	.15
229 Jerry Remy (R)	.40	.20
230 Carl Yastrzemski	8.50	4.25
231 Tom House	.30	.15
232 Frank Duffy	.30	.15
233 Grant Jackson	.30	.15
234 Mike Sadek	.30	.15
235 Bert Blyleven	2.50	1.25
236 Royals Team	1.50	.75
237 Dave Hamilton	.30	.15
238 Larry Biittner	.30	.15
239 John Curtis	.30	.15
240 Pete Rose	15.00	7.50
241 Hector Torres	.30	.15
242 Dan Meyer	.30	.15
243 Jim Rooker	.30	.15
244 Bill Sharp	.30	.15
245 Felix Millan	.30	.15
246 Cesar Tovar	.30	.15
247 Terry Harmon	.30	.15
248 Dick Tidrow	.30	.15
249 Cliff Johnson	.30	.15
250 Ferguson Jenkins	4.00	2.00
251 Rick Monday	.50	.25
252 Tim Nordbrook	.30	.15
253 Bill Buckner	.70	.40
254 Rudy Meoli	.30	.15
255 Fritz Peterson	.30	.15
256 Rowland Office	.30	.15
257 Ross Grimsley	.30	.15
258 Nyls Nyman	.30	.15
259 Darrel Chaney	.30	.15
260 Steve Busby	.30	.15
261 Gary Thomasson	.30	.15
262 Checklist 133-265	1.50	.50
263 Lyman Bostock (R)	.60	.30
264 Steve Renko	.30	.15
265 Willie Davis	.40	.20
266 Alan Foster	.30	.15
267 Aurelio Rodriguez	.30	.15
268 Del Unser	.30	.15
269 Rick Austin	.30	.15
270 Willie Stargell	4.00	2.00
271 Jim Lonborg	.50	.25
272 Rick Dempsey	.30	.15
273 Joe Niekro	.30	.15
274 Tommy Harper	.30	.15
275 Rick Manning (R)	.40	.20
276 Mickey Scott	.30	.15
277 Cubs Team	1.50	.75
278 Bernie Carbo	.30	.15
279 Roy Howell	.30	.15
280 Burt Hooton	.30	.15
281 Dave May	.30	.15
282 Dan Osborn	.30	.15
283 Merv Rettenmund	.30	.15
284 Steve Ontiveros	.30	.15
285 Mike Cuellar	.50	.25
286 Jim Wohlford	.30	.15
287 Pete Mackanin	.30	.15
288 Bill Campbell	.30	.15
289 Enzo Hernandez	.30	.15
290 Ted Simmons	1.00	.50

291	Ken Sanders	.30	.15
292	Leon Roberts	.30	.15
293	Bill Castro	.30	.15
294	Ed Kirkpatrick	.30	.15
295	Dave Cash	.30	.15
296	Pat Dobson	.30	.15
297	Roger Metzger	.30	.15
298	Dick Bosman	.30	.15
299	Champ Summers	.30	.15
300	Johnny Bench	12.50	6.25
301	Jackie Brown	.30	.15
302	Rick Miller	.30	.15
303	Steve Foucault	.30	.15
304	Angels Team	1.50	.75
305	Andy Messersmith	.30	.15
306	Rod Gilbreath	.30	.15
307	Al Bumbry	.30	.15
308	Jim Barr	.30	.15
309	Bill Melton	.30	.15
310	Randy Jones	.50	.25
311	Cookie Rojas	.30	.15
312	Don Carrithers	.30	.15
313	Dan Ford (R)	.30	.15
314	Ed Kranepool	.50	.25
315	Al Hrabosky	.30	.15
316	Robin Yount	70.00	35.00
317	John Candelaria (R)	2.50	1.25
318	Bob Boone	1.25	.60
319	Larry Gura	.30	.15
320	Willie Horton	.40	.20
321	Jose Cruz	.50	.25
322	Glenn Abbott	.30	.15
323	Rob Sperring	.30	.15
324	Jim Bibby	.30	.15
325	Tony Perez	3.00	1.50
326	Dick Pole	.30	.15
327	Dave Moates	.30	.15
328	Carl Morton	.30	.15
329	Joe Ferguson	.30	.15
330	Nolan Ryan	80.00	40.00
331	Padres Team	1.50	.75
332	Charlie Williams	.30	.15
333	Bob Coluccio	.30	.15
334	Dennis Leonard	.40	.20
335	Bob Grich	.50	.25
336	Vic Albury	.30	.15
337	Bud Harrelson	.50	.25
338	Bob Bailey	.30	.15
339	John Denny	.30	.15
340	Jim Rice	7.50	3.75
341	Lou Gehrig (AS)	7.50	3.75
342	Rogers Hornsby (AS)	3.50	1.75
343	Pie Traynor (AS)	1.50	.75
344	Honus Wagner (AS)	5.00	2.50
345	Babe Ruth (AS)	12.00	6.00
346	Ty Cobb (AS)	7.50	3.75
347	Ted Williams (AS)	8.50	4.25
348	Mickey Cochrane (AS)	1.50	.75
349	Walter Johnson	3.50	1.75
350	Lefty Grove (AS)	1.50	.75
351	Randy Hundley	.30	.15
352	Dave Giusti	.30	.15
353	Sixto Lezcano (R)	.40	.20
354	Ron Blomberg	.30	.15
355	Steve Carlton	10.00	5.00
356	Ted Martinez	.30	.15
357	Ken Forsch	.30	.15
358	Buddy Bell	.40	.20
359	Rick Reuschel	.50	.25
360	Jeff Burroughs	.40	.20
361	Tigers Team	1.50	.75
362	Will McEnaney	.30	.15
363	Dave Collins	.60	.30
364	Elias Sosa	.30	.15
365	Carlton Fisk	12.50	6.25
366	Bobby Valentine	.40	.20
367	Bruce Miller	.30	.15
368	Wilbur Wood	.30	.15
369	Frank White	.50	.25
370	Ron Cey	.75	.35
371	Ellie Hendricks	.30	.15
372	Rick Baldwin	.30	.15
373	Johnny Briggs	.30	.15
374	Dan Warthen	.30	.15
375	Ron Fairly	.30	.15
376	Rich Hebner	.30	.15
377	Mike Hegan	.30	.15
378	Steve Stone	.40	.20
379	Ken Boswell	.30	.15
380	Bobby Bonds	1.50	.75
381	Denny Doyle	.30	.15
382	Matt Alexander	.30	.15
383	John Ellis	.30	.15
384	Phillies Team	1.50	.75
385	Mickey Lolich	.50	.25
386	Ed Goodson	.30	.15
387	Mike Miley	.30	.15
388	Stan Perzanowski	.30	.15
389	Glenn Adams	.30	.15
390	Don Gullett	.40	.20
391	Jerry Hairston	.30	.15
392	Checklist 265-396	1.50	.50
393	Paul Mitchell	.30	.15
394	Fran Healy	.30	.15
395	Jim Wynn	.50	.25
396	Bill Lee	.30	.15
397	Tim Foli	.30	.15
398	Dave Tomlin	.30	.15
399	Luis Melendez	.30	.15
400	Rod Carew	10.00	5.00
401	Ken Brett	.30	.15
402	Don Money	.30	.15
403	Geoff Zahn	.30	.15
404	Enos Cabell	.30	.15

405	Rollie Fingers	4.50	2.25
406	Ed Herrmann	.30	.15
407	Tom Underwood	.30	.15
408	Charlie Spikes	.30	.15
409	Dave Lemancyzk	.30	.15
410	Ralph Garr	.40	.20
411	Bill Singer	.30	.15
412	Toby Harrah	.30	.15
413	Pete Varney	.30	.15
414	Wayne Garland	.30	.15
415	Vada Pinson	.60	.30
416	Tommy John	1.25	.60
417	Gene Clines	.30	.15
418	Jose Morales (R)	.50	.30
419	Reggie Cleveland	.30	.15
420	Joe Morgan	7.50	3.75
421	A's Team	1.50	.75
422	Johnny Grubb	.30	.15
423	Ed Halicki	.30	.15
424	Phil Roof	.30	.15
425	Rennie Stennett	.30	.15
426	Bob Forsch	.30	.15
427	Kurt Bevacqua	.30	.15
428	Jim Crawford	.30	.15
429	Fred Stanley	.30	.15
430	Jose Cardenal	.30	.15
431	Dick Ruthven	.30	.15
432	Tom Veryzer	.30	.15
433	Rick Waits	.30	.15
434	Morris Nettles	.30	.15
435	Phil Niekro	3.50	1.75
436	Bill Fahey	.30	.15
437	Terry Forster	.30	.15
438	Doug DeCinces	.60	.30
439	Rick Rhoden	.30	.15
440	John Mayberry	.40	.20
441	Gary Carter	12.00	6.00
442	Hank Webb	.30	.15
443	Giants Team	1.50	.75
444	Gary Nolan	.30	.15
445	Rico Petrocelli	.40	.20
446	Larry Haney	.30	.15
447	Gene Locklear	.30	.15
448	Tom Johnson	.30	.15
449	Bob Robertson	.30	.15
450	Jim Palmer	9.00	4.50
451	Buddy Bradford	.30	.15
452	Tom Hausman	.30	.15
453	Lou Piniella	.75	.35
454	Tom Griffin	.30	.15
455	Dick Allen	.75	.35
456	Joe Coleman	.30	.15
457	Ed Crosby	.30	.15
458	Earl Williams	.30	.15
459	Jim Brewer	.30	.15
460	Cesar Cedeno	.40	.20
461	NL & AL Championships	.75	.35
462	1975 World Series	.75	.35
463	Steve Hargan	.30	.15
464	Ken Henderson	.30	.15
465	Mike Marshall	.40	.20
466	Bob Stinson	.30	.15
467	Woodie Fryman	.30	.15
468	Jesus Alou	.30	.15
469	Rawly Eastwick	.30	.15
470	Bobby Murcer	.60	.30
471	Jim Burton	.30	.15
472	Bob Davis	.30	.15
473	Paul Blair	.30	.15
474	Ray Corbin	.30	.15
475	Joe Rudi	.50	.25
476	Bob Moose	.30	.15
477	Indians Team	1.50	.75
478	Lynn McGlothen	.30	.15
479	Bobby Mitchell	.30	.15
480	Mike Schmidt	40.00	20.00
481	Rudy May	.30	.15
482	Tim Hosley	.30	.15
483	Mickey Stanley	.30	.15
484	Eric Raich	.30	.15
485	Mike Hargrove	.30	.15
486	Bruce Dal Canton	.30	.15
487	Leron Lee	.30	.15
488	Claude Osteen	.40	.20
489	Skip Jutze	.30	.15
490	Frank Tanana	.90	.45
491	Terry Crowley	.30	.15
492	Marty Pattin	.30	.15
493	Derrel Thomas	.30	.15
494	Craig Swan	.30	.15
495	Nate Colbert	.30	.15
496	Juan Beniquez	.30	.15
497	Joe McIntosh	.30	.15
498	Glenn Borgmann	.30	.15
499	Mario Guerrero	.30	.15
500	Reggie Jackson	25.00	12.50
501	Billy Champion	.30	.15
502	Tim McCarver	.60	.30
503	Elliott Maddox	.30	.15
504	Pirates Team	1.50	.75
505	Mark Belanger	.50	.25
506	George Mitterwald	.30	.15
507	Ray Bare	.30	.15
508	Duane Kuiper (R)	.30	.15
509	Bill Hands	.30	.15
510	Amos Otis	.40	.20
511	Jamie Easterly	.30	.15
512	Ellie Rodriguez	.30	.15
513	Bart Johnson	.30	.15
514	Dan Driessen	.40	.20
515	Steve Yeager	.40	.20
516	Wayne Granger	.30	.15
517	John Milner	.30	.15
518	Doug Flynn (R)	.30	.15

519	Steve Brye	.30	.15
520	Willie McCovey	5.00	2.50
521	Jim Colborn	.30	.15
522	Ted Sizemore	.30	.15
523	Bob Montgomery	.30	.15
524	Pete Falcone	.30	.15
525	Billy Williams	4.50	2.25
526	Checklist 397-528	1.50	.50
527	Mike Anderson	.30	.15
528	Dock Ellis	.30	.15
529	Deron Johnson	.30	.15
530	Don Sutton	3.50	1.75
531	Mets Team	1.50	.75
532	Milt May	.30	.15
533	Lee Richard	.30	.15
534	Stan Bahnsen	.30	.15
535	Dave Nelson	.30	.15
536	Mike Thompson	.30	.15
537	Tony Muser	.30	.15
538	Pat Darcy	.30	.15
539	John Balaz	.30	.15
540	Bill Freehan	.40	.20
541	Steve Mingori	.30	.15
542	Keith Hernandez	3.00	1.50
543	Wayne Twitchell	.30	.15
544	Pepe Frias	.30	.15
545	Sparky Lyle	.50	.25
546	Dave Rosello	.30	.15
547	Roric Harrison	.30	.15
548	Manny Mota	.40	.20
549	Randy Tate	.30	.15
550	Hank Aaron	28.00	14.00
551	Jerry DaVanon	.30	.15
552	Terry Humphrey	.30	.15
553	Randy Moffitt	.30	.15
554	Ray Fosse	.30	.15
555	Dyar Miller	.30	.15
556	Twins Team	1.50	.75
557	Dan Spillner	.30	.15
558	Cito Gaston	.75	.35
660	Clyde Wright	.30	.15
560	Jorge Orta	.30	.15
561	Tom Carroll	.30	.15
562	Adrian Garrett	.30	.15
563	Larry Demery	.30	.15
564	Bubble Gum Champ (Kurt Bevacqua)	.50	.25
565	Tug McGraw	.75	.35
566	Ken McMullen	.30	.15
567	George Stone	.30	.15
568	Rob Andrews	.30	.15
569	Nelson Briles	.30	.15
570	George Hendrick	.40	.20
571	Don DeMola	.30	.15
572	Rich Coggins	.30	.15
573	Bill Travers	.30	.15
574	Don Kessinger	.30	.15

575	Dwight Evans	3.50	1.75
576	Maximino Leon	.30	.15
577	Marc Hill	.30	.15
578	Ted Kubiak	.30	.15
579	Clay Kirby	.30	.15
580	Bert Campaneris	.50	.25
581	Cardinals Team	1.50	.75
582	Mike Kekich	.30	.15
583	Tommy Helms	.30	.15
584	Stan Wall	.30	.15
585	Joe Torre	.60	.30
586	Ron Schueler	.30	.15
587	Leo Cardenas	.30	.15
588	Kevin Kobel	.30	.15
589	Rookie Pitchers	2.00	1.00
	Santo Alcala (R)		
	Mike Flanagan (R)		
	Joe Pactwa (R)		
	Pablo Torrealba (R)		
590	Rookie Outfielders	.80	.40
	Henry Cruz (R)		
	Chet Lemon (R)		
	Ellis Valentine (R)		
	Terry Whitfield		
591	Rookie Pitchers	.30	.15
	Steve Grilli (R)		
	Craig Mitchell (R)		
	Jose Sosa (R)		
	George Throop (R)		
592	Rookie Infielders	10.00	5.00
	Dave McKay (R)		
	Willie Randolph (R)		
	Jerry Royster (R)		
	Roy Staiger (R)		
593	Rookie Pitchers	.30	.15
	Larry Anderson (R)		
	Ken Crosby (R)		
	Mark Littell (R)		
	Butch Metzger (R)		
594	Rookie Catchers & OF	.40	.20
	Andy Merchant (R)		
	Ed Ott (R)		
	Royle Stillman (R)		
	Jerry White (R)		
595	Rookie Pitchers	.40	.20
	Steve Barr (R)		
	Art DeFilippi (R)		
	Randy Lerch (R)		
	Sid Monge (R)		
596	Rookie Infielders	.40	.20
	Lamar Johnson (R)		
	Johnny LeMaster (R)		
	Jerry Manuel (R)		
	Craig Reynolds (R)		
597	Rookie Pitchers	.40	.20
	Don Aase (R)		
	Jack Kucek (R)		

	Frank LaCorte (R)		
	Mike Pazik (R)		
598	Rookie Outfielders	.40	.20
	Hector Cruz (R)		
	Jamie Quirk (R)		
	Jerry Turner (R)		
	Joe Wallis (R)		
599	Rookie Pitchers	8.50	4.25
	Rob Dressler (R)		
	Ron Guidry (R)		
	Bob McClure (R)		
	Pat Zachry (R)		
600	Tom Seaver	18.00	9.00
601	Ken Rudolph	.30	.15
602	Doug Konieczny	.30	.15
603	Jim Holt	.30	.15
604	Joe Lovitto	.30	.15
605	Al Downing	.40	.20
606	Brewers Team	1.50	.75
607	Rich Hinton	.30	.15
608	Vic Correll	.30	.15
609	Fred Norman	.30	.15
610	Greg Luzinski	.70	.40
611	Rick Folkers	.30	.15
612	Joe Lahoud	.30	.15
613	Tim Johnson	.30	.15
614	Fernando Arroyo	.30	.15
615	Mike Cubbage	.30	.15
616	Buck Martinez	.30	.15
617	Darold Knowles	.30	.15
618	Jack Brohamer	.30	.15
619	Bill Butler	.30	.15
620	Al Oliver	.75	.35
621	Tom Hall	.30	.15
622	Rick Auerbach	.30	.15
623	Bob Allietta	.30	.15
624	Tony Taylor	.30	.15
625	J.R. Richard	.50	.25
626	Bob Sheldon	.30	.15
627	Bill Plummer	.30	.15
628	John D'Acquisto	.30	.15
629	Sandy Alomar	.30	.15
630	Chris Speier	.30	.15
631	Braves Team	1.50	.75
632	Rogelio Moret	.30	.15
633	John Stearns (R)	.40	.20
634	Larry Christenson	.30	.15
635	Jim Fregosi	.50	.30
636	Joe Decker	.30	.15
637	Bruce Bochte	.30	.15
638	Doyle Alexander	.30	.15
639	Fred Kendall	.30	.15
640	Bill Madlock	1.25	.60
641	Tom Paciorek	.30	.15
642	Dennis Blair	.30	.15
643	Checklist 529-660	1.50	.50
644	Tom Bradley	.30	.15

645	Darrell Porter	.30	.15
646	John Lowenstein	.30	.15
647	Ramon Hernandez	.30	.15
648	Al Cowens	.30	.15
649	Dave Roberts	.30	.15
650	Thurman Munson	6.50	3.25
651	John Odom	.30	.15
652	Ed Armbrister	.30	.15
653	Mike Norris	.30	.15
654	Doug Griffin	.30	.15
655	Mike Vail	.30	.15
656	White Sox Team	1.50	.75
657	Roy Smalley (R)	.40	.20
658	Jerry Johnson	.30	.15
659	Ben Oglivie	.30	.15
660	Dave Lopes	1.00	.50

1976 Topps Traded

This update set consistss of 44 cards including an unnumbered checklist. Cards measure 2-1/2" by 3-1/2". Card fronts feature color photos with a newspaper headline design. Card backs include a newspaper type graphic which contains biographical information about the player. Card numbers carry a "T" suffix and coincide with the players number in Topps 1976 regular edition.

	NR/MT	EX
Complete Set (44)	10.50	5.25
Commons	.30	.15
27T Ed Figueroa	.30	.15
28T Dusty Baker	.90	.45
44T Doug Rader	.30	.15
58T Ron Reed	.30	.15
74T Oscar Gamble	.70	.40

80T Jim Kaat	1.00	.50
83T Jim Spencer	.30	.15
85T Mickey Rivers	.30	.15
99T Lee Lacy	.30	.15
120T Rusty Staub	.60	.30
127T Larvell Blanks	.30	.15
146T George Medich	.30	.15
158T Ken Reitz	.30	.15
208T Mike Lum	.30	.15
211T Clay Carroll	.30	.15
231T Tom House	.30	.15
250T Ferguson Jenkins	3.00	1.50
259T Darrel Chaney	.30	.15
292T Leon Roberts	.30	.15
296T Pat Dobson	.30	.15
309T Bill Melton	.30	.15
338T Bob Bailey	.30	.15
380T Bobby Bonds	.90	.45
383T John Ellis	.30	.15
385T Mickey Lolich	.50	.25
401T Ken Brett	.30	.15
410T Ralph Garr	.30	.15
411T Bill Singer	.30	.15
428T Jim Crawford	.30	.15
434T Morris Nettles	.30	.15
464T Ken Henderson	.30	.15
497T Joe McIntosh	.30	.15
524T Pete Falcone	.30	.15
527T Mike Anderson	.30	.15
528T Dock Ellis	.30	.15
532T Milt May	.30	.15
554T Ray Fosse	.30	.15
579T Clay Kirby	.30	.15
583T Tommy Helms	.30	.15
592T Willie Randolph	4.50	2.25
618T Jack Brohamer	.30	.15
632T Rogelio Moret	.30	.15
649T Dave Roberts	.30	.15
___ Traded Checklist	.80	.30

1977 Topps

This 660-card set features full color photos on the card fronts with fascimile autographs. The player's name, team and position are printed above the photo. All cards measure 2-1/2" by 3-1/2". New subsets include "Turn Back The Clock" (433-437) and "Brothers" (631-634). Other subsets are League Leaders, Record Breakers, World Series and Playoff Highlights and Rookies.

		NR/MT	EX
Complete Set (660)		440.00	220.00
Commons		.25	.12
1	Batting Leaders (George Brett, Bill Madlock)	6.50	3.25
2	HR Leaders (Graig Nettles, Mike Schmidt)	2.50	1.25
3	RBI Leaders (George Foster, Lee May)	.50	.25
4	Stolen Base Leaders (Dave Lopes, Bill North)	.40	.20
5	Victory Leaders (Randy Jones, Jim Palmer)	.80	.50
6	Strikeout Leaders (Nolan Ryan, Tom Seaver)	18.00	9.00
7	ERA Leaders (John Denny, Mark Fidrych)	.50	.25
8	Leading Firemen (Bill Campbell, Rawly Eastwick)	.40	.20
9	Doug Rader	.25	.12
10	Reggie Jackson	18.00	9.00

11	Rob Dressler	.25	.12
12	Larry Haney	.25	.12
13	Luis Gomez	.25	.12
14	Tommy Smith	.25	.12
15	Don Gullett	.35	.18
16	Bob Jones	.25	.12
17	Steve Stone	.35	.18
18	Indians Team	1.25	.65
19	John D'Acquisto	.25	.12
20	Graig Nettles	1.25	.65
21	Ken Forsch	.25	.12
22	Bill Freehan	.35	.18
23	Dan Driessen	.30	.15
24	Carl Morton	.25	.12
25	Dwight Evans	2.50	1.25
26	Ray Sadecki	.25	.12
27	Bill Buckner	.40	.20
28	Woodie Fryman	.25	.12
29	Bucky Dent	.50	.25
30	Greg Luzinski	.45	.22
31	Jim Todd	.25	.12
32	Checklist 1-132	1.25	.50
33	Wayne Garland	.25	.12
34	Angels Team	1.25	.65
35	Rennie Stennett	.25	.12
36	John Ellis	.25	.12
37	Steve Hargan	.25	.12
38	Craig Kusick	.25	.12
39	Tom Griffin	.25	.12
40	Bobby Murcer	.40	.20
41	Jim Kern	.25	.12
42	Jose Cruz	.40	.20
43	Ray Bare	.25	.12
44	Bud Harrelson	.30	.15
45	Rawly Eastwick	.25	.12
46	Buck Martinez	.25	.12
47	Lynn McGlothen	.25	.12
48	Tom Paciorek	.25	.12
49	Grant Jackson	.25	.12
50	Ron Cey	.50	.25
51	Brewers Team	1.25	.65
52	Ellis Valentine	.25	.12
53	Paul Mitchell	.25	.12
54	Sandy Alomar	.25	.12
55	Jeff Burroughs	.30	.15
56	Rudy May	.25	.12
57	Marc Hill	.25	.12
58	Chet Lemon	.35	.18
59	Larry Christenson	.25	.12
60	Jim Rice	4.50	2.25
61	Manny Sanguillen	.40	.20
62	Eric Raich	.25	.12
63	Tito Fuentes	.25	.12
64	Larry Bittner	.25	.12
65	Skip Lockwood	.25	.12
66	Roy Smalley	.25	.12
67	Joaquin Andujar (R)	.75	.35
68	Bruce Bochte	.25	.12
69	Jim Crawford	.25	.12
70	Johnny Bench	10.00	5.00
71	Dock Ellis	.25	.12
72	Mike Anderson	.25	.12
73	Charlie Williams	.25	.12
74	A's Team	1.25	.65
75	Dennis Leonard	.35	.18
76	Tim Foli	.25	.12
77	Dyar Miller	.25	.12
78	Bob Davis	.25	.12
79	Don Money	.25	.12
80	Andy Messersmith	.25	.12
81	Juan Beniquez	.25	.12
82	Jim Rooker	.25	.12
83	Kevin Bell	.25	.12
84	Ollie Brown	.25	.12
85	Duane Kuiper	.25	.12
86	Pat Zachry	.25	.12
87	Glenn Borgmann	.25	.12
88	Stan Wall	.25	.12
89	Butch Hobson (R)	.90	.45
90	Cesar Cedeno	.35	.18
91	John Verhoeven	.25	.12
92	Dave Rosello	.25	.12
93	Tom Poquette	.25	.12
94	Craig Swan	.25	.12
95	Keith Hernandez	2.00	1.00
96	Lou Piniella	.60	.30
97	Dave Heaverlo	.25	.12
98	Milt May	.25	.12
99	Tom Hausman	.25	.12
100	Joe Morgan	5.00	2.50
101	Dick Bosman	.25	.12
102	Jose Morales	.25	.12
103	Mike Bacsik	.25	.12
104	Omar Moreno (R)	.25	.12
105	Steve Yeager	.30	.15
106	Mike Flanagan	.40	.20
107	Bill Melton	.25	.12
108	Alan Foster	.25	.12
109	Jorge Orta	.25	.12
110	Steve Carlton	9.00	4.50
111	Rico Petrocelli	.30	.18
112	Bill Greif	.25	.12
113	Blue Jays Mgr/Coaches	.75	.35
114	Bruce Dal Canton	.25	.12
115	Rick Manning	.25	.12
116	Joe Niekro	.30	.15
117	Frank White	.35	.18
118	Rick Jones	.25	.12
119	John Stearns	.25	.12
120	Rod Carew	8.00	4.00
121	Gary Nolan	.25	.12
122	Ben Oglivie	.35	.18
123	Fred Stanley	.25	.12
124	George Mitterwald	.25	.12

125	Bill Travers	.25	.12
126	Rod Gilbreath	.25	.12
127	Ron Fairly	.25	.12
128	Tommy John	1.00	.50
129	Mike Sadek	.25	.12
130	Al Oliver	.75	.35
131	Orlando Ramirez	.25	.12
132	Chip Lang	.25	.12
133	Ralph Garr	.25	.12
134	Padres Team	1.25	.65
135	Mark Belanger	.35	.18
136	Jerry Mumphrey (R)	.35	.18
137	Jeff Terpko	.25	.12
138	Bob Stinson	.25	.12
139	Fred Norman	.25	.12
140	Mike Schmidt	26.00	13.00
141	Mark Littell	.25	.12
142	Steve Dillard	.25	.12
143	Ed Herrmann	.25	.12
144	Bruce Sutter (R)	5.00	2.50
145	Tom Veryzer	.25	.12
146	Dusty Baker	.35	.18
147	Jackie Brown	.25	.12
148	Fran Healy	.25	.12
149	Mike Cubbage	.25	.12
150	Tom Seaver	12.00	6.00
151	Johnnie LeMaster	.25	.12
152	Gaylord Perry	3.00	1.50
153	Ron Jackson	.25	.12
154	Dave Giusti	.25	.12
155	Joe Rudi	.30	.15
156	Pete Mackanin	.25	.12
157	Ken Brett	.25	.12
158	Ted Kubiak	.25	.12
159	Bernie Carbo	.25	.12
160	Will McEnaney	.25	.12
161	Garry Templeton (R)	1.00	.50
162	Mike Cuellar	.30	.15
163	Dave Hilton	.25	.12
164	Tug McGraw	.50	.25
165	Jim Wynn	.35	.18
166	Bill Campbell	.25	.12
167	Rich Hebner	.25	.12
169	Charlie Spikes	.25	.12
170	Thurman Munson	5.00	2.50
171	Ken Sanders	.25	.12
172	John Milner	.25	.12
173	Chuck Scrivener	.25	.12
174	Nelson Briles	.25	.12
175	Butch Wynegar (R)	.35	.18
176	Bob Robertson	.25	.12
177	Bart Johnson	.25	.12
178	Bombo Rivera	.25	.12
179	Paul Hartzell	.25	.12
180	Dave Lopes	.35	.18
181	Ken McMullen	.25	.12
182	Dan Spillner	.25	.12
183	Cardinals Team	1.25	.65
184	Bo McLaughlin	.25	.12
185	Sixto Lezcano	.25	.12
186	Doug Flynn	.25	.12
187	Dick Pole	.25	.12
188	Bob Tolan	.25	.12
189	Rick Dempsey	.35	.18
190	Ray Burris	.25	.12
191	Doug Griffin	.25	.12
192	Cito Gaston	.25	.12
193	Larry Gura	.25	.12
194	Gary Matthews	.35	.18
195	Ed Figueroa	.25	.12
196	Len Randle	.25	.12
197	Ed Ott	.25	.12
198	Wilbur Wood	.25	.12
199	Pepe Frias	.25	.12
200	Frank Tanana	.80	.40
201	Ed Kranepool	.35	.18
202	Tom Johnson	.25	.12
203	Ed Armbrister	.25	.12
204	Jeff Newman	.25	.12
205	Pete Falcone	.25	.12
206	Boog Powell	.75	.35
207	Glenn Abbott	.25	.12
208	Checklist 133-264	1.25	.50
209	Rob Andrews	.25	.12
210	Fred Lynn	1.50	.75
211	Giants Team	1.25	.65
212	Jim Mason	.25	.12
213	Maximino Leon	.25	.12
214	Darrell Porter	.25	.12
215	Butch Metzger	.25	.12
216	Doug DeCinces	.30	.15
217	Tom Underwood	.25	.12
218	John Wathan (R)	.75	.35
219	Joe Coleman	.25	.12
220	Chris Chambliss	.40	.20
221	Bob Bailey	.25	.12
222	Francisco Barrios	.25	.12
223	Earl Williams	.25	.12
224	Rusty Torres	.25	.12
225	Bob Apodaca	.25	.12
226	Leroy Stanton	.25	.12
227	Joe Sambito (R)	.25	.12
228	Twins Team	1.25	.65
229	Don Kessinger	.35	.18
230	Vida Blue	.40	.20
231	George Brett (RB)	14.00	7.00
232	Minnie Minoso (RB)	.75	.35
233	Jose Morales (RB)	.35	.18
234	Nolan Ryan (RB)	20.00	10.00
235	Cecil Cooper	.50	.25
236	Tom Buskey	.25	.12
237	Gene Clines	.25	.12
238	Tippy Martinez	.25	.12
239	Bill Plummer	.25	.12

240	Ron LeFlore	.40	.20
241	Dave Tomlin	.25	.12
242	Ken Henderson	.25	.12
243	Ron Reed	.25	.12
244	John Mayberry	.30	.15
245	Rick Rhoden	.25	.12
246	Mike Vail	.25	.12
247	Chris Knapp	.25	.12
248	Wilbur Howard	.25	.12
249	Pete Redfern	.25	.12
250	Bill Madlock	.75	.35
251	Tony Muser	.25	.12
252	Dale Murray	.25	.12
253	John Hale	.25	.12
254	Doyle Alexander	.25	.12
255	George Scott	.30	.15
256	Joe Hoerner	.25	.12
257	Mike Miley	.25	.12
258	Luis Tiant	.60	.30
259	Mets Team	1.25	.65
260	J.R. Richard	.35	.18
261	Phil Garner	.50	.25
262	Al Cowens	.25	.12
263	Mike Marshall	.30	.18
264	Tom Hutton	.25	.12
265	Mark Fidrych (R)	2.50	1.25
266	Derrel Thomas	.25	.12
267	Ray Fosse	.25	.12
268	Rick Sawyer	.25	.12
269	Joe Lis	.25	.12
270	Dave Parker	4.00	2.00
271	Terry Forster	.25	.12
272	Lee Lacy	.25	.12
273	Eric Soderholm	.25	.12
274	Don Stanhouse	.25	.12
275	Mike Hargrove	.25	.12
276	A.L. Championship	.75	.35
277	N.L. Championship	2.50	1.25
278	Danny Frisella	.25	.12
279	Joe Wallis	.25	.12
280	Jim Hunter	3.00	1.50
281	Roy Staiger	.25	.12
282	Sid Monge	.25	.12
283	Jerry DaVanon	.25	.12
284	Mike Norris	.25	.12
285	Brooks Robinson	5.00	2.50
286	Johnny Grubb	.25	.12
287	Reds Team	1.25	.65
288	Bob Montgomery	.25	.12
289	Gene Garber	.25	.12
290	Amos Otis	.35	.18
291	Jason Thompson (R)	.40	.20
292	Rogelio Moret	.25	.12
293	Jack Brohamer	.25	.12
294	George Medich	.25	.12
295	Gary Carter	7.00	3.50
296	Don Hood	.25	.12
297	Ken Reitz	.25	.12
298	Charlie Hough	.40	.20
299	Otto Velez	.25	.12
300	Jerry Koosman	.45	.22
301	Toby Harrah	.25	.12
302	Mike Garman	.25	.12
303	Gene Tenace	.35	.18
304	Jim Hughes	.25	.12
305	Mickey Rivers	.30	.15
306	Rick Waits	.25	.12
307	Gary Sutherland	.25	.12
308	Gene Pentz	.25	.12
309	Red Sox Team	1.25	.65
310	Larry Bowa	.30	.15
311	Vern Ruhle	.25	.12
312	Rob Belloir	.25	.12
313	Paul Blair	.25	.12
314	Steve Mingori	.25	.12
315	Dave Chalk	.25	.12
316	Steve Rogers	.25	.12
317	Kurt Bevacqua	.25	.12
318	Duffy Dyer	.25	.12
319	Rich Gossage	1.50	.75
320	Ken Griffey	1.25	.60
321	Dave Goltz	.25	.12
322	Bill Russell	.35	.18
323	Larry Lintz	.25	.12
324	John Curtis	.25	.12
325	Mike Ivie	.25	.12
326	Jesse Jefferson	.25	.12
327	Astros Team	1.25	.65
328	Tommy Boggs	.25	.12
329	Ron Hodges	.25	.12
330	George Hendrick	.30	.15
331	Jim Colborn	.25	.12
332	Elliott Maddox	.25	.12
333	Paul Reuschel	.25	.12
334	Bill Stein	.25	.12
335	Bill Robinson	.30	.15
336	Denny Doyle	.25	.12
337	Ron Schueler	.25	.12
338	Dave Duncan	.25	.12
339	Adrian Devine	.25	.12
340	Hal McRae	.60	.30
341	Joe Kerrigan	.25	.12
342	Jerry Remy	.25	.12
343	Ed Halicki	.25	.12
344	Brian Downing	.50	.25
345	Reggie Smith	.30	.15
346	Bill Singer	.25	.12
347	George Foster	1.00	.50
348	Brent Strom	.25	.12
349	Jim Holt	.25	.12
350	Larry Dierker	.25	.12
351	Jim Sundberg	.30	.15
352	Mike Phillips	.25	.12
353	Stan Thomas	.25	.12

354	Pirates Team	1.25	.65
355	Lou Brock	5.00	2.50
356	Checklist 265-396	1.25	.50
357	Tim McCarver	.50	.30
358	Tom House	.25	.12
359	Willie Randolph	2.50	1.25
360	Rick Monday	.30	.15
361	Eduardo Rodriguez	.25	.12
362	Tommy Davis	.30	.15
363	Dave Roberts	.25	.12
364	Vic Correll	.25	.12
365	Mike Torrez	.25	.12
366	Ted Sizemore	.25	.12
367	Dave Hamilton	.25	.12
368	Mike Jorgensen	.25	.12
369	Terry Humphrey	.25	.12
370	John Montefusco	.25	.12
371	Royals Team	1.25	.65
372	Rich Folkers	.25	.12
373	Bert Campaneris	.35	.18
374	Kent Tekulve	.25	.12
375	Larry Hisle	.25	.12
376	Nino Espinosa	.25	.12
377	Dave McKay	.25	.12
378	Jim Umbarger	.25	.12
379	Larry Cox	.25	.12
380	Lee May	.25	.12
381	Bob Forsch	.25	.12
382	Charlie Moore	.25	.12
383	Stan Bahnsen	.25	.12
384	Darrel Chaney	.25	.12
385	Dave LaRoche	.25	.12
386	Manny Mota	.30	.15
387	Yankees Team	2.00	1.00
388	Terry Harmon	.25	.12
389	Ken Kravec	.25	.12
390	Dave Winfield	35.00	17.50
391	Don Warthen	.25	.12
392	Phil Roof	.25	.12
393	John Lowenstein	.25	.12
394	Bill Laxton	.25	.12
395	Manny Trillo	.25	.12
396	Tom Murphy	.25	.12
397	Larry Herndon (R)	.30	.15
398	Tom Burgmeier	.25	.12
399	Bruce Boisclair	.25	.12
400	Steve Garvey	4.50	2.25
401	Mickey Scott	.25	.12
402	Tommy Helms	.25	.12
403	Tom Grieve	.25	.12
404	Eric Rasmussen	.25	.12
405	Claudell Washington	.30	.15
406	Tim Johnson	.25	.12
407	Dave Freisleben	.25	.12
408	Cesar Tovar	.25	.12
409	Pete Broberg	.25	.12
410	Willie Montanez	.25	.12
411	WS Games 1 & 2	1.50	.75
412	WS Games 3 & 4	2.00	1.00
413	WS Summary	1.00	.50
414	Tommy Harper	.25	.12
415	Jay Johnstone	.30	.15
416	Chuck Hartenstein	.25	.12
417	Wayne Garrett	.25	.12
418	White Sox Team	1.25	.65
419	Steve Swisher	.25	.12
420	Rusty Staub	.40	.20
421	Doug Rau	.25	.12
422	Freddie Patek	.25	.12
423	Gary Lavelle	.25	.12
424	Steve Brye	.25	.12
425	Joe Torre	.50	.25
426	Dick Drago	.25	.12
427	Dave Rader	.25	.12
428	Rangers Team	1.25	.65
429	Ken Boswell	.25	.12
430	Ferguson Jenkins	3.00	1.50
431	Dave Collins	.25	.12
432	Buzz Capra	.25	.12
433	Nate Colbert (Clock)	.30	.15
434	Carl Yastrzemski (Clock)	1.50	.75
435	Maury Wills (Clock)	.50	.25
436	Bob Keegan (Clock)	.30	.15
437	Ralph Kiner (Clock)	.60	.30
438	Marty Perez	.25	.12
439	Gorman Thomas	.35	.18
440	Jon Matlack	.30	.15
441	Larvell Blanks	.25	.12
442	Braves Team	1.25	.65
443	Lamar Johnson	.25	.12
444	Wayne Twitchell	.25	.12
445	Ken Singleton	.30	.15
446	Bill Bonham	.25	.12
447	Jerry Turner	.25	.12
448	Ellie Rodriguez	.25	.12
449	Al Fitzmorris	.25	.12
450	Pete Rose	14.00	7.00
451	Checklist 397-528	1.25	.50
452	Mike Caldwell	.25	.12
453	Pedro Garcia	.25	.12
454	Andy Etchebarren	.25	.12
455	Rick Wise	.30	.15
456	Leon Roberts	.25	.12
457	Steve Luebber	.25	.12
458	Leo Foster	.25	.12
459	Steve Foucault	.25	.12
460	Willie Stargell	4.00	2.00
461	Dick Tidrow	.25	.12
462	Don Baylor	1.25	.65
463	Jamie Quirk	.25	.12
464	Randy Moffitt	.25	.12
465	Rico Carty	.30	.15
466	Fred Holdsworth	.25	.12

467	Phillies Team	1.25	.65
468	Ramon Hernandez	.25	.12
469	Pat Kelly	.25	.12
470	Ted Simmons	.75	.35
471	Del Unser	.25	.12
472	Rookie Pitchers	.30	.15
	Don Aase		
	Bob McClure		
	Gil Patterson (R)		
	Dave Wehrmeister (R)		
473	Rookie Outfielders	80.00	40.00
	Andre Dawson (R)		
	Gene Richards (R)		
	John Scott (R)		
	Denny Walling (R)		
474	Rookie Shortstops	.50	.25
	Bob Bailor		
	Kiko Garcia (R)		
	Craig Reynolds (R)		
	Alex Taveras		
475	Rookie Pitchers	.30	.15
	Chris Batton (R)		
	Rick Camp (R)		
	Scott McGregor		
	Manny Sarmiento (R)		
476	Rookie Catchers	30.00	15.00
	Gary Alexander		
	Rick Cerone (R)		
	Dale Murphy (R)		
	Kevin Pasley (R)		
477	Rookie Infielders	.30	.15
	Doug Ault (R)		
	Rich Dauer (R)		
	Orlando Gonzalez (R)		
	Phil Mankowski (R)		
478	Rookie Pitchers	.30	.15
	Jim Gideon (R)		
	Leon Hooten (R)		
	Dave Johnson (R)		
	Mark Lemongello (R)		
479	Rookie Outfielders	.30	.15
	Brian Asselstine (R)		
	Wayne Gross (R)		
	Sam Mejia (R)		
	Alvis Woods (R)		
480	Carl Yastrzemski	7.00	3.50
481	Roger Metzger	.25	.12
482	Tony Solaita	.25	.12
483	Richie Zisk	.25	.12
484	Burt Hooton	.25	.12
485	Roy White	.25	.12
486	Ed Bane	.25	.12
487	Rookie Pitchers	.25	.12
	Larry Anderson		
	Ed Glynn (R)		
	Joe Henderson (R)		
	Greg Terlecky (R)		
488	Rookie Outfielders	6.50	3.25
	Jack Clark (R)		
	Ruppert Jones (R)		
	Lee Mazzilli (R)		
	Dan Thomas (R)		
489	Rookie Pitchers (R)	.45	.22
	Lon Barkor (R)		
	Randy Lerch		
	Greg Minton (R)		
	Mike Overy (R)		
490	Rookie Shortstops	.30	.15
	Billy Almon (R)		
	Mickey Klutts (R)		
	Tommy McMillan (R)		
	Mark Wagner (R)		
491	Rookie Pitchers	8.00	4.00
	Mike Dupree (R)		
	Denny Martinez (R)		
	Craig Mitchell (R)		
	Bob Sykes (R)		
492	Rookie Outfielders	.75	.35
	Tony Armas (R)		
	Steve Kemp (R)		
	Carlos Lopez (R)		
	Gary Woods (R)		
493	Rookie Pitchers	.35	.18
	Mike Krukow (R)		
	Jim Otten		
	Gary Wheelock (R)		
	Mike Willis (R)		
494	Rookie Infielders	1.50	.75
	Juan Bernhardt (R)		
	Mike Champion		
	Jim Gantner (R)		
	Bump Wills (R)		
495	Al Hrabosky	.35	.18
496	Gary Thomasson	.25	.12
497	Clay Carroll	.25	.12
498	Sal Bando	.35	.18
499	Pablo Torrealba	.25	.12
500	Dave Kingman	.75	.35
501	Jim Bibby	.25	.12
502	Randy Hundley	.25	.12
503	Bill Lee	.25	.12
504	Dodgers Team	1.50	.75
505	Oscar Gamble	.35	.18
506	Steve Grilli	.25	.12
507	Mike Hegan	.25	.12
508	Dave Pagan	.25	.12
409	Cookie Rojas	.25	.12
510	John Candelaria	.50	.25
511	Bill Fahey	.25	.12
512	Jack Billingham	.25	.12
513	Jerry Terrell	.25	.12
514	Cliff Johnson	.25	.12
515	Chris Speier	.25	.12
516	Bake McBride	.25	.12

517	Pete Vuckovich (R)	.50	.25	574	Aurelio Rodriguez	.25	.12
518	Cubs Team	1.25	.65	575	Dick Ruthven	.25	.12
519	Don Kirkwood	.25	.12	576	Fred Kendall	.26	.12
520	Garry Maddox	.30	.15	577	Jerry Augustine	.25	.12
521	Bob Grich	.35	.18	578	Bob Randall	.25	.12
522	Enzo Hernandez	.25	.12	579	Don Carrithers	.25	.12
523	Rollie Fingers	3.50	1.75	580	George Brett	40.00	20.00
524	Rowland Office	.25	.12	581	Pedro Borbon	.25	.12
525	Dennis Eckersley	15.00	7.50	582	Ed Kirkpatrick	.25	.12
526	Larry Parrish	.30	.15	583	Paul Lindblad	.25	.12
527	Dan Meyer	.25	.12	584	Ed Goodson	.25	.12
528	Bill Castro	.25	.12	585	Rick Burleson	.30	.15
529	Jim Essian	.25	.12	586	Steve Renko	.25	.12
530	Rick Reuschel	.35	.18	587	Rick Baldwin	.25	.12
531	Lyman Bostock	.35	.18	588	Dave Moates	.25	.12
532	Jim Willoughby	.25	.12	589	Mike Cosgrove	.25	.12
533	Mickey Stanley	.25	.12	590	Buddy Bell	.30	.15
534	Paul Splittorff	.25	.12	591	Chris Arnold	.25	.12
535	Cesar Geronimo	.25	.12	592	Dan Briggs	.25	.12
536	Vic Albury	.25	.12	593	Dennis Blair	.25	.12
537	Dave Roberts	.25	.12	594	Biff Pocoroba	.25	.12
538	Frank Taveras	.25	.12	595	John Hiller	.25	.12
539	Mike Wallace	.25	.12	596	Jerry Martin (R)	.25	.12
540	Bob Watson	.40	.20	597	Mariners Mgr/Coaches	.60	.30
541	John Denny	.25	.12	598	Sparky Lyle	.60	.30
542	Frank Duffy	.25	.12	599	Mike Tyson	.25	.12
543	Ron Blomberg	.25	.12	600	Jim Palmer	7.00	3.50
544	Gary Ross	.25	.12	601	Mike Lum	.25	.12
545	Bob Boone	1.00	.50	602	Andy Hassler	.25	.12
546	Orioles Team	1.25	.65	603	Willie Davis	.30	.15
547	Willie McCovey	5.00	2.50	604	Jim Slaton	.25	.12
548	Joel Youngblood (R)	.30	.15	605	Felix Millan	.25	.12
549	Jerry Royster	.25	.12	606	Steve Braun	.25	.12
550	Randy Jones	.30	.15	607	Larry Demery	.25	.12
551	Bill North	.30	.15	608	Roy Howell	.25	.12
552	Pepe Mangual	.25	.12	609	Jim Barr	.25	.12
553	Jack Heidemann	.25	.12	610	Jose Cardenal	.25	.12
554	Bruce Kimm	.25	.12	611	Dave Lemanczyk	.25	.12
555	Dan Ford	.25	.12	612	Barry Foote	.25	.12
556	Doug Bird	.25	.12	613	Reggie Cleveland	.25	.12
557	Jerry White	.25	.12	614	Greg Gross	.25	.12
558	Elias Sosa	.25	.12	615	Phil Niekro	3.00	1.50
559	Alan Bannister	.25	.12	616	Tommy Sandt	.25	.12
560	Dave Concepcion	1.25	.60	617	Bobby Darwin	.25	.12
561	Pete LaCock	.25	.12	618	Pat Dobson	.30	.15
562	Checklist 529-660	1.25	.50	619	Johnny Oates	.30	.15
563	Bruce Kison	.25	.12	620	Don Sutton	3.00	1.75
564	Alan Ashby	.25	.12	621	Tigers Team	1.25	.65
565	Mickey Lolich	.45	.22	622	Jim Wohlford	.25	.12
566	Rick Miller	.25	.12	623	Jack Kucek	.25	.12
567	Enos Cabell	.25	.12	624	Hector Cruz	.25	.12
568	Carlos May	.25	.12	625	Ken Holtzman	.25	.12
569	Jim Lonborg	.30	.15	626	Al Bumbry	.25	.12
570	Bobby Bonds	1.25	.65	627	Bob Myrick	.25	.12
571	Darrell Evans	.45	.22	628	Mario Guerrero	.25	.12
572	Ross Grimsley	.25	.12	629	Bobby Valentine	.35	.18
573	Joe Ferguson	.25	.12	630	Bert Blyleven	2.00	1.00

631	George & Ken Brett	6.00	3.00
632	Bob & Ken Forsch	.35	.18
633	Carlos & Lee May	.35	.18
634	Paul & Rick Reuschel	.35	.18
635	Robin Yount	36.00	18.00
636	Santo Alcala	.25	.12
637	Alex Johnson	.25	.12
638	Jim Kaat	.80	.40
639	Jerry Morales	.25	.12
640	Carlton Fisk	9.00	4.50
641	Dan Larson	.25	.12
642	Willie Crawford	.25	.12
643	Mike Pazik	.25	.12
644	Matt Alexander	.25	.12
645	Jerry Reuss	.35	.18
646	Andres Mora	.25	.12
647	Expos Team	1.25	.65
648	Jim Spencer	.25	.12
649	Dave Cash	.25	.12
650	Nolan Ryan	55.00	27.50
651	Von Joshua	.30	.15
652	Tom Walker	.25	.12
653	Diego Segui	.25	.12
654	Ron Pruitt	.25	.12
655	Tony Perez	2.50	1.25
656	Ron Guidry	2.00	1.00
657	Mick Kelleher	.25	.12
658	Marty Pattin	.25	.12
659	Merv Rettenmund	.25	.12
660	Willie Horton	.60	.30

1978 Topps

REGGIE JACKSON

Topps increased the size of their set to 726-cards in 1978. Cards measure 2-1/2" by 3-1/2". Card fronts include large color photos with the player's name and team located in the border below the photo. The player's position is printed in a small baseball design at the top right corner. Key subsets include Record Breakers

((RB) (1-7), League Leaders, World Series and Playoff Hightlights, All-stars and Rookies.

		NR/MT	EX
	Complete Set (720)	000.00	105.00
	Commons (1-726)	.20	.10
1	Lou Brock (RB)	3.00	1.50
2	Sparky Lyle (RB)	.50	.25
3	Willie McCovey (RB)	1.50	.75
4	Brooks Robinson (RB)	2.00	1.00
5	Pete Rose (RB)	4.00	2.00
6	Nolan Ryan (RB)	16.00	8.00
7	Reggie Jackson (RB)	5.00	2.50
8	Mike Sadek	.20	.10
9	Doug DeCinces	.20	.10
10	Phil Niekro	2.50	1.25
11	Rick Manning	.20	.10
12	Don Aase	.20	.10
13	Art Howe (R)	.40	.20
14	Lerrin LaGrow	.20	.10
15	Tony Perez	1.00	.50
16	Roy White	.20	.10
17	Mike Krukow	.20	.10
18	Bob Grich	.25	.12
19	Darrell Porter	.20	.10
20	Pete Rose	6.00	3.00
21	Steve Kemp	.20	.10
22	Charlie Hough	.20	.10
23	Bump Wills	.20	.10
24	Don Money	.20	.10
25	Jon Matlack	.20	.10
26	Rich Hebner	.20	.10
27	Geoff Zahn	.20	.10
28	Ed Ott	.20	.10
29	Bob Lacey	.20	.10
30	George Hendrick	.20	.10
31	Glenn Abbott	.20	.10
32	Garry Templeton	.40	.20
33	Dave Lemanczyk	.20	.10
34	Willie McCovey	3.50	1.75
35	Sparky Lyle	.35	.18
36	Eddie Murray (R)	90.00	45.00
37	Rich Waits	.20	.10
38	Willie Montanez	.20	.10
39	Floyd Bannister (R)	.50	.25
40	Carl Yastrzemski	5.00	2.50
41	Burt Hooton	.20	.10
42	Jorge Orta	.20	.10
43	Bill Atkinson	.20	.10
44	Toby Harrah	.20	.10
45	Mark Fidrych	1.00	.50
46	Al Cowens	.20	.10
47	Jack Billingham	.20	.10

48	Don Baylor	1.00	.50	105	Reggie Cleveland	.20	.10
49	Ed Kranepool	.25	.12	106	Bill Plummer	.20	.10
50	Rick Reuschel	.25	.12	107	Ed Halicki	.20	.10
51	Charlie Moore	.20	.10	108	Von Joshua	.20	.10
52	Jim Lonborg	.25	.12	109	Joe Torre	.40	.20
53	Phil Garner	.25	.12	110	Richie Zisk	.20	.10
54	Tom Johnson	.20	.10	111	Mike Tyson	.20	.10
55	Mitchell Page	.20	.10	112	Astros Team	1.25	.65
56	Randy Jones	.25	.12	113	Don Carrithers	.20	.10
57	Dan Meyer	.20	.10	114	Paul Blair	.20	.10
58	Bob Forsch	.20	.10	115	Gary Nolan	.20	.10
59	Otto Velez	.20	.10	116	Tucker Ashford	.20	.10
60	Thurman Munson	4.00	2.00	117	John Montague	.20	.10
61	Larvell Blanks	.20	.10	118	Terry Harmon	.20	.10
62	Jim Barr	.20	.10	119	Denny Martinez	3.00	1.50
63	Don Zimmer	.20	.10	120	Gary Carter	4.50	2.25
64	Gene Pentz	.20	.10	121	Alvis Woods	.20	.10
65	Ken Singleton	.25	.12	122	Dennis Eckersley	8.50	4.25
66	White Sox Team	1.25	.65	123	Manny Trillo	.20	.10
67	Claudell Washington	.25	.12	124	Dave Rozema (R)	.20	.10
68	Steve Foucault	.20	.10	125	George Scott	.25	.12
69	Mike Vail	.20	.10	126	Paul Moskau	.20	.10
70	Rich Gossage	1.25	.60	127	Chet Lemon	.25	.12
71	Terry Humphrey	.20	.10	128	Bill Russell	.30	.15
72	Andre Dawson	22.00	11.00	129	Jim Colborn	.20	.10
73	Andy Hassler	.20	.10	130	Jeff Burroughs	.20	.10
74	Checklist 1-121	1.25	.50	131	Bert Blyleven	1.00	.50
75	Dick Ruthven	.20	.10	132	Enos Cabell	.20	.10
76	Steve Ontiveros	.20	.10	133	Jerry Augustine	.20	.10
77	Ed Kirkpatrick	.20	.10	134	Steve Henderson (R)	.20	.10
78	Pablo Torrealba	.20	.10	135	Ron Guidry	.80	.40
79	Darrell Johnson	.20	.10	136	Ted Sizemore	.20	.10
80	Ken Griffey	1.00	.50	137	Craig Kusick	.20	.10
81	Pete Redfern	.20	.10	138	Larry Demery	.20	.10
82	Giants Team	1.25	.65	139	Wayne Gross	.20	.10
83	Bob Montgomery	.20	.10	140	Rollie Fingers	3.50	1.75
84	Kent Tekulve	.20	.10	141	Rupert Jones	.20	.10
85	Ron Fairly	.20	.10	142	John Montefusco	.20	.10
86	Dave Tomlin	.20	.10	143	Keith Hernandez	1.50	.75
87	John Lowenstein	.20	.10	144	Jesse Jefferson	.20	.10
88	Mike Phillipsk	.20	.10	145	Rick Monday	.25	.12
89	Ken Clay	.20	.10	146	Doyle Alexander	.25	.12
90	Larry Bowa	.30	.15	147	Lee Mazzilli	.20	.10
91	Oscar Zamora	.20	.10	148	Andre Thornton	.25	.12
92	Adrian Devine	.20	.10	149	Dale Murray	.20	.10
93	Bobby Cox	.25	.12	150	Bobby Bonds	.60	.30
94	Chuck Scrivener	.20	.10	151	Milt Wilcox	.20	.10
95	Jamie Quirk	.20	.10	152	Ivan DeJesus (R)	.25	.12
96	Orioles Team	1.25	.65	153	Steve Stone	.30	.15
97	Stan Bahnsen	.20	.10	154	Cecil Cooper	.30	.15
98	Jim Essian	.20	.10	155	Butch Hopson	.25	.12
99	Willie Hernandez (R)	.50	.25	156	Andy Messersmith	.20	.10
100	George Brett	28.00	14.00	157	Pete LaCock	.20	.10
101	Sid Monge	.20	.10	158	Joaquin Andujar	.30	.18
102	Matt Alexander	.20	.10	159	Lou Piniella	.40	.20
103	Tom Murphy	.20	.10	160	Jim Palmer	6.00	3.00
104	Lee Lacy	.20	.10	161	Bob Boone	.80	.40

162	Paul Thormodsgard	.20	.10
163	Bill North	.20	.10
164	Bob Owchinko	.20	.10
165	Rennie Stennett	.20	.10
166	Carlos Lopez	.20	.10
167	Tim Foli	.20	.10
168	Reggie Smith	.30	.15
169	Jerry Johnson	.20	.10
170	Lou Brock	4.00	2.00
171	Pat Zachry	.20	.10
172	Mike Hargrove	.20	.10
173	Robin Yount	22.00	11.00
174	Wayne Garland	.20	.10
175	Jerry Morales	.25	.12
176	Milt May	.20	.10
177	Gene Garber	.20	.10
178	Dave Chalk	.20	.10
179	Dick Tidrow	.20	.10
180	Dave Concepcion	1.00	.50
181	Ken Forsch	.20	.10
182	Jim Spencer	.20	.10
183	Doug Bird	.20	.10
184	Checklist 122-242	1.25	.50
185	Ellis Valentine	.20	.10
186	Bob Stanley	.20	.10
187	Jerry Royster	.20	.10
188	Al Bumbry	.20	.10
189	Tom Lasorda	.40	.20
190	John Candelaria	.30	.15
191	Rodney Scott	.20	.10
192	Padres Team	1.25	.65
193	Rich Chiles	.20	.10
194	Derrel Thomas	.20	.10
195	Larry Dierker	.25	.12
196	Bob Bailor	.20	.10
197	Nino Espinosa	.20	.10
198	Ron Pruitt	.20	.10
199	Craig Reynolds	.20	.10
200	Reggie Jackson	14.00	7.00
201	Batting Leaders	1.25	.60
202	Home Run Leaders	.75	.35
203	RBI Leaders	.40	.20
204	Stolen Base Leaders	.30	.15
205	Victory Leaders	1.50	.75
206	Strikeout Leaders	5.00	2.50
207	ERA Leaders	.30	.15
208	Leading Firemen	1.00	.50
209	Dock Ellis	.20	.10
210	Jose Cardenal	.20	.10
211	Earl Weaver	.25	.12
212	Mike Caldwell	.20	.10
213	Alan Bannister	.20	.10
214	Angels Team	1.25	.65
215	Darrell Evans	.30	.15
216	Mike Paxton	.20	.10
217	Rod Gilbreath	.20	.10
218	Marty Pattin	.20	.10
219	Mike Cubbage	.20	.10
220	Pedro Borbon	.20	.10
221	Chris Speier	.20	.10
222	Jerry Martin	.20	.10
223	Bruce Kison	.20	.10
224	Jerry Tabb	.20	.10
225	Don Gullett	.25	.12
226	Joe Ferguson	.20	.10
227	Al Fitzmorris	.20	.10
228	Manny Mota	.20	.10
229	Leo Foster	.20	.10
230	Al Hrabosky	.20	.10
231	Wayne Nordhagen	.20	.10
232	Mickey Stanley	.20	.10
233	Dick Pole	.20	.10
234	Herman Franks	.20	.10
235	Tim McCarver	.25	.12
236	Terry Whitfield	.20	.10
237	Rich Dauer	.20	.10
238	Juan Beniquez	.20	.10
239	Dyar Miller	.20	.10
240	Gene Tenace	.25	.12
241	Pete Vuckovich	.25	.12
242	Barry Bonnell	.20	.10
243	Bob McClure	.20	.10
244	Expos Team	1.25	.65
245	Rick Burleson	.25	.12
246	Dan Driessen	.25	.12
247	Larry Christenson	.20	.10
248	Frank White	.25	.12
249	Dave Goltz	.20	.10
250	Graig Nettles	.50	.25
251	Don Kirkwood	.20	.10
252	Steve Swisher	.20	.10
253	Jim Kern	.20	.10
254	Dave Collins	.20	.10
255	Jerry Reuss	.25	.12
256	Joe Altobelli	.20	.10
257	Hector Cruz	.20	.10
258	John Hiller	.20	.10
259	Dodgers Team	1.25	.65
260	Bert Campaneris	.25	.12
261	Tim Hosley	.20	.10
262	Rudy May	.20	.10
263	Danny Walton	.20	.10
264	Jamie Easterly	.20	.10
265	Sal Bando	.25	.12
266	Bob Shirley	.20	.10
267	Doug Ault	.20	.10
268	Gil Flores	.20	.10
269	Wayne Twitchell	.20	.10
270	Carlton Fisk	7.50	3.75
271	Randy Lerch	.20	.10
272	Royle Stillman	.20	.10
273	Fred Norman	.20	.10
274	Freddie Patek	.20	.10
275	Dan Ford	.20	.10

276	Bill Bonham	.20	.10
277	Bruce Boisclair	.20	.10
278	Enrique Romo	.20	.10
279	Bill Virdon	.20	.10
280	Buddy Bell	.20	.10
281	Eric Rasmussen	.20	.10
282	Yankees Team	1.50	.75
283	Omar Moreno	.20	.10
284	Randy Moffitt	.20	.10
285	Steve Yeager	.20	.10
286	Ben Oglivie	.25	.12
287	Kiko Garcia	.20	.10
288	Dave Hamilton	.20	.10
289	Checklist 243-363	1.25	.50
290	Willie Horton	.25	.12
291	Gary Ross	.20	.10
292	Gene Richard	.20	.10
293	Mike Willis	.20	.10
294	Larry Parrish	.25	.12
295	Bill Lee	.20	.10
296	Biff Pocoroba	.20	.10
297	Warren Brusstar	.20	.10
298	Tony Armas	.25	.12
299	Whitey Herzog	.20	.10
300	Joe Morgan	4.00	2.00
301	Buddy Schultz	.20	.10
302	Cubs Team	1.25	.65
303	Sam Hinds	.20	.10
304	John Milner	.20	.10
305	Rico Carty	.20	.10
306	Joe Niekro	.20	.10
307	Glenn Borgmann	.20	.10
308	Jim Rooker	.20	.10
309	Cliff Johnson	.20	.10
310	Don Sutton	2.50	1.25
311	Jose Baez	.20	.10
312	Greg Minton	.20	.10
313	Andy Etchebarren	.20	.10
314	Paul Lindblad	.20	.10
315	Mark Belanger	.25	.12
316	Henry Cruz	.20	.10
317	Dave Johnson	.25	.12
318	Tom Griffin	.20	.10
319	Alan Ashby	.20	.10
320	Fred Lynn	1.25	.60
321	Santo Alcala	.20	.10
322	Tom Paciorek	.20	.10
323	Jim Fregosi	.25	.12
324	Vern Rapp	.20	.10
325	Bruce Sutter	1.25	.65
326	Mike Lum	.20	.10
327	Rick Langford	.20	.10
328	Brewers Team	1.25	.65
329	John Verhoeven	.20	.10
330	Bob Watson	.40	.20
331	Mark Littell	.20	.10
332	Duane Kuiper	.20	.10
333	Jim Todd	.20	.10
334	John Stearns	.20	.10
335	Bucky Dent	.50	.25
336	Steve Busby	.20	.10
337	Tom Grieve	.20	.10
338	Dave Heaverlo	.20	.10
339	Mario Guerrero	.20	.10
340	Bake McBride	.20	.10
341	Mike Flanagan	.30	.15
342	Aurelio Rodriguz	.20	.10
343	John Wathan	.20	.10
344	Sam Ewing	.20	.10
345	Luis Tiant	.40	.20
346	Larry Biittner	.20	.10
347	Terry Forster	.20	.10
348	Del Unser	.20	.10
349	Rick Camp	.20	.10
350	Steve Garvey	3.00	1.50
351	Jeff Torborg	.20	.10
352	Tony Scott	.20	.10
353	Doug Bair	.20	.10
354	Cesar Geronimo	.20	.10
355	Bill Travers	.20	.10
356	Mets Team	1.25	.65
357	Tom Poquette	.20	.10
358	Mark Lemongello	.20	.10
359	Marc Hill	.20	.10
360	Mike Schmidt	18.00	9.00
361	Chris Knapp	.20	.10
362	Dave May	.20	.10
363	Bob Randall	.20	.10
364	Jerry Turner	.20	.10
365	Ed Figueroa	.20	.10
366	Larry Milbourne	.20	.10
367	Rick Dempsey	.25	.12
368	Balor Moore	.20	.10
369	Tim Nordbrook	.20	.10
370	Rusty Staub	.40	.20
371	Ray Burris	.20	.10
372	Brian Asselstine	.20	.10
373	Jim Willoughby	.20	.10
374	Jose Morales	.20	.10
375	Tommy John	.80	.40
376	Jim Wohlford	.20	.10
377	Manny Sarmiento	.20	.10
378	Bobby Winkles	.20	.10
379	Skip Lockwood	.20	.10
380	Ted Simmons	.75	.35
381	Phillies Team	1.25	.65
382	Joe Lahoud	.20	.10
383	Mario Mendoza	.20	.10
384	Jack Clark	1.00	.50
385	Tito Fuentes	.20	.10
386	Bob Gorinski	.20	.10
387	Ken Holtzman	.20	.10
388	Bill Fahey	.20	.10
389	Julio Gonzalez	.20	.10

390	Oscar Gamble	.25	.12
391	Larry Haney	.20	.10
392	Billy Almon	.20	.10
393	Tippy Martinez	.20	.10
394	Roy Howell	.20	.10
395	Jim Hughes	.20	.10
396	Bob Stinson	.00	.10
397	Greg Gross	.20	.10
398	Don Hood	.20	.10
399	Pete Mackanin	.20	.10
400	Nolan Ryan	42.00	21.00
401	Sparky Anderson	.25	.12
402	Dave Campbell	.20	.10
403	Bud Harrelson	.25	.12
404	Tigers Team	1.25	.65
405	Rawly Eastwick	.20	.10
406	Mike Jorgensen	.20	.10
407	Odell Jones	.20	.10
408	Joe Zdeb	.20	.10
409	Ron Schueler	.20	.10
410	Bill Madlock	.75	.35
411	A.L. Championships	.75	.35
412	N.L. Championships	.60	.30
413	World Series	4.50	2.25
414	Darold Knowles	.20	.10
415	Ray Fosse	.20	.10
416	Jack Brohamer	.20	.10
417	Mike Garman	.20	.10
418	Tony Muser	.20	.10
419	Jerry Garvin	.20	.10
420	Greg Luzinski	.40	.20
421	Junior Moore	.20	.10
422	Steve Braun	.20	.10
423	Dave Rosello	.20	.10
424	Red Sox Team	1.25	.65
425	Steve Rogers	.20	.10
426	Fred Kendall	.20	.10
427	Mario Soto (R)	.50	.25
428	Joel Youngblood	.20	.10
429	Mike Barlow	.20	.10
430	Al Oliver	.50	.25
431	Butch Metzger	.20	.10
432	Terry Bulling	.20	.10
433	Fernando Gonzalez	.20	.10
434	Mike Norris	.20	.10
435	Checklist 364-484	1.25	.50
436	Vic Harris	.20	.10
437	Bo McLaughlin	.20	.10
438	John Ellis	.20	.10
439	Ken Kravec	.20	.10
440	Dave Lopes	.30	.15
441	Larry Gura	.20	.10
442	Elliott Maddox	.20	.10
443	Darrel Chaney	.20	.10
444	Roy Hartsfield	.20	.10
445	Mike Ivie	.20	.10
446	Tug McGraw	.40	.20
447	Leroy Stanton	.20	.10
448	Bill Castro	.20	.10
449	Tim Blackwell	.20	.10
450	Tom Seaver	8.50	4.25
451	Twins Team	1.25	.65
452	Jerry Mumphrey	.20	.10
453	Doug Flynn	.00	.10
454	Dave LaRoche	.20	.10
455	Bill Robinson	.25	.12
456	Vern Ruhle	.20	.10
457	Bob Bailey	.20	.10
458	Jeff Newman	.20	.10
459	Charlie Spikes	.20	.10
460	Jim Hunter	3.00	1.50
461	Rob Andrews	.20	.10
462	Rogelio Moret	.20	.10
463	Kevin Bell	.20	.10
464	Jerry Grote	.20	.10
465	Hal McRae	.40	.20
466	Dennis Blair	.20	.10
467	Alvin Dark	.20	.10
468	Warren Cromartie (R)	.35	.18
469	Rick Cerone	.25	.12
470	J.R. Richard	.30	.18
471	Roy Smalley	.20	.10
472	Ron Reed	.20	.10
473	Bill Buckner	.40	.20
474	Jim Slaton	.20	.10
475	Gary Matthews	.25	.12
476	Bill Stein	.20	.10
477	Doug Capilla	.20	.10
478	Jerry Remy	.20	.10
479	Cardinals Team	1.25	.65
480	Ron LeFlore	.25	.12
481	Jackson Todd	.20	.10
482	Rick Miller	.20	.10
483	Ken Macha	.20	.10
484	Jim Norris	.20	.10
485	Chris Chambliss	.25	.12
486	John Curtis	.20	.10
487	Jim Tyrone	.20	.10
488	Dan Spillner	.20	.10
489	Rudy Meoli	.20	.10
490	Amos Otis	.30	.15
491	Scott McGregor	.25	.15
492	Jim Sundberg	.20	.10
493	Steve Renko	.20	.10
494	Chuck Tanner	.20	.10
495	Dave Cash	.20	.10
496	Jim Clancy (R)	.25	.12
497	Glenn Adams	.20	.10
498	Joe Sambito	.20	.10
499	Mariners Team	1.25	.65
500	George Foster	.75	.35
501	Dave Roberts	.20	.10
502	Pat Rockett	.20	.10
503	Ike Hampton	.20	.10

504	Roger Freed	.20	.10
505	Felix Millan	.20	.10
506	Ron Blomberg	.20	.10
507	Willie Crawford	.20	.10
508	Johnny Oates	.25	.12
509	Brent Strom	.20	.10
510	Willie Stargell	3.50	1.75
511	Frank Duffy	.20	.10
512	Larry Herndon	.20	.10
513	Barry Foote	.20	.10
514	Rob Sperring	.20	.10
515	Tim Corcoran	.20	.10
516	Gary Beare	.20	.10
517	Andres Mora	.20	.10
518	Tommy Boggs	.20	.10
519	Brian Downing	.30	.15
520	Larry Hisle	.20	.10
521	Steve Staggs	.20	.10
522	Dick Williams	.20	.10
523	Donnie Moore (R)	.20	.10
524	Bernie Carbo	.20	.10
525	Jerry Terrell	.20	.10
526	Reds Team	1.25	.65
527	Vic Correll	.20	.10
528	Rob Picciolo	.20	.10
529	Paul Hartzell	.20	.10
530	Dave Winfield	28.00	14.00
531	Tom Underwood	.20	.10
532	Skip Jutze	.20	.10
533	Sandy Alomar	.20	.10
534	Wilbur Howard	.20	.10
535	Checklist 485-606	1.25	.50
536	Roric Harrison	.20	.10
537	Bruce Bochte	.20	.10
538	Johnnie LeMaster	.20	.10
539	Vic Davalillo	.20	.10
540	Steve Carlton	8.00	4.00
541	Larry Cox	.20	.10
542	Tim Johnson	.20	.10
543	Larry Harlow	.20	.10
544	Len Randle	.20	.10
545	Bill Campbell	.20	.10
546	Ted Martinez	.20	.10
547	John Scott	.20	.10
548	Billy Hunter	.20	.10
549	Joe Kerrigan	.20	.10
550	John Mayberry	.25	.12
551	Braves Team	1.25	.65
552	Francisco Barrios	.20	.10
553	Terry Puhl (R)	.35	.18
554	Joe Coleman	.20	.10
555	Butch Wynegar	.20	.10
556	Ed Armbrister	.20	.10
557	Tony Solaita	.20	.10
558	Paul Mitchell	.20	.10
559	Phil Mankowski	.20	.10
560	Dave Parker	2.50	1.25
561	Charlie Williams	.20	.10
562	Glenn Burke	.20	.10
563	Dave Rader	.20	.10
564	Mick Kelleher	.20	.10
565	Jerry Koosman	.40	.20
566	Merv Rettenmund	.20	.10
567	Dick Drago	.20	.10
568	Tom Hutton	.20	.10
569	Lary Sorensen (R)	.20	.10
570	Dave Kingman	.45	.22
571	Buck Martinez	.20	.10
572	Rick Wise	.20	.10
573	Luis Gomez	.20	.10
574	Bob Lemon	.30	.15
575	Pat Dobson	.20	.10
576	Sam Mejias	.20	.10
577	A's Team	1.25	.65
578	Buzz Capra	.20	.10
579	Rance Mulliniks (R)	.20	.10
580	Rod Carew	6.00	3.00
581	Lynn McGlothen	.20	.10
582	Fran Healy	.20	.10
583	George Medich	.20	.10
584	John Hale	.20	.10
585	Woodie Fryman	.20	.10
586	Ed Goodson	.20	.10
587	John Urrea	.20	.10
588	Jim Mason	.20	.10
589	Bob Knepper (R)	.35	.18
590	Bobby Murcer	.40	.20
591	George Zeber	.20	.10
592	Bob Apodaca	.20	.10
593	Dave Skaggs	.20	.10
594	Dave Freisleben	.20	.10
595	Sixto Lezcano	.20	.10
596	Gary Wheelock	.20	.10
597	Steve Dillard	.20	.10
598	Eddie Solomon	.20	.10
599	Gary Woods	.20	.10
600	Frank Tanana	.40	.20
601	Gene Mauch	.20	.10
602	Eric Soerholm	.20	.10
603	Will McEnaney	.20	.10
604	Earl Williams	.20	.10
605	Rick Rhoden	.20	.10
606	Pirates Team	1.25	.65
607	Fernando Arroyo	.20	.10
608	Johnny Grubb	.20	.10
609	John Denny	.20	.10
610	Garry Maddox	.25	.12
611	Pat Scanlon	.20	.10
612	Ken Henderson	.20	.10
613	Marty Perez	.20	.10
614	Joe Wallis	.20	.10
615	Clay Carroll	.20	.10
616	Pat Kelly	.20	.10
617	Joe Nolan	.20	.10

618	Tommy Helms	.20	.10
619	Thad Bosley (R)	.20	.10
620	Willie Randolph	1.25	.60
621	Craig Swan	.20	.10
622	Champ Summers	.20	.10
623	Eduardo Rodriguez	.20	.10
624	Gary Alexander	.20	.10
625	Jose Cruz	.30	.15
626	Blue Jays Team	1.25	.65
627	Dave Johnson	.20	.10
628	Ralph Garr	.20	.10
629	Don Stanhouse	.20	.10
630	Ron Cey	.35	.18
631	Danny Ozark	.20	.10
632	Rowland Office	.20	.10
633	Tom Veryzer	.20	.10
634	Len Barker	.20	.10
635	Joe Rudi	.25	.12
636	Jim Bibby	.20	.10
637	Duffy Dyer	.20	.10
638	Paul Splittorff	.20	.10
639	Gene Clines	.20	.10
640	Lee May	.20	.10
641	Doug Rau	.20	.10
642	Denny Doyle	.20	.10
643	Tom House	.20	.10
644	Jim Dwyer	.20	.10
645	Mike Torrez	.20	.10
646	Rick Auerbach	.20	.10
647	Steve Dunning	.20	.10
648	Gary Thomasson	.20	.10
649	Moose Haas (R)	.20	.10
650	Cesar Cedeno	.25	.12
651	Doug Rader	.20	.10
652	Checklist 606-726	1.25	.50
653	Ron Hodges	.20	.10
654	Pepe Frias	.20	.10
655	Lyman Bostock	.20	.10
656	Dave Garcia	.20	.10
657	Bombo Rivera	.20	.10
658	Manny Sanguillen	.25	.12
659	Rangers Team	1.25	.65
660	Jason Thompson	.20	.10
661	Grant Jackson	.20	.10
662	Paul Dade	.20	.10
663	Paul Reuschel	.20	.10
664	Fred Stanley	.20	.10
665	Dennis Leonard	.20	.10
666	Billy Smith	.20	.10
667	Jeff Byrd	.20	.10
668	Dusty Baker	.40	.20
669	Pete Falcone	.20	.10
670	Jim Rice	3.00	1.50
671	Gary Lavelle	.20	.10
672	Don Kessinger	.20	.10
673	Steve Brye	.20	.10
674	Ray Knight (R)	2.00	1.00

675	Jay Johnstone	.20	.10
676	Bob Myrick	.20	.10
677	Ed Herrmann	.20	.10
678	Tom Burgmeier	.20	.10
679	Wayne Garrett	.20	.10
680	Vida Blue	.40	.20
681	Rob Belloir	.20	.10
682	Ken Brett	.20	.10
683	Mike Champion	.20	.10
684	Ralph Houk	.25	.12
685	Frank Taveras	.20	.10
686	Gaylord Perry	3.00	1.50
687	Julio Cruz (R)	.20	.10
688	George Mitterwald	.20	.10
689	Indians Team	1.25	.65
690	Mickey Rivers	.20	.10
691	Ross Grimsley	.20	.10
692	Ken Reitz	.20	.10
693	Lamar Johnson	.20	.10
694	Elias Sosa	.20	.10
695	Dwight Evans	2.00	1.00
696	Steve Mingori	.20	.10
697	Roger Metzger	.20	.10
698	Juan Bernhardt	.20	.10
699	Jackie Brown	.20	.10
700	Johnny Bench	6.00	3.00
701	Rookie Pitchers	.20	.10
	Tom Hume (R)		
	Larry Landreth (R)		
	Steve McCatty (R)		
	Bruce Taylor (R)		
702	Rookie Catchers	.20	.10
	Bill Nahorodny (R)		
	Kevin Pasley		
	Rick Sweet (R)		
	Don Werner (R)		
703	Rookie Pitchers	12.00	6.00
	Larry Andersen (R)		
	Tim Jones (R)		
	Mickey Mahler (R)		
	Jack Morris (R)		
704	Rookie 2nd Basemen	24.00	12.00
	Garth Iorg (R)		
	Dave Oliver (R)		
	Sam Perlozzo (R)		
	Lou Whitaker (R)		
705	Rookie Outfielders	.50	.25
	Dave Bergman (R)		
	Miguel Dilone (R)		
	Clint Hurdle (R)		
	Willie Norwood (R)		
706	Rookie 1st Basemen	.20	.10
	Wayne Cage (R)		
	Ted Cox (R)		
	Pat Putnam (R)		
	Dave Revering (R)		
707	Rookie Shortstops	125.00	65.00

		NR/MT	EX
	Mickey Klutts		
	Paul Molitor (R)		
	Alan Trammell (R)		
	U.L. Washington (R)		
708	Rookie Catchers	14.00	7.00
	Bo Diaz (R)		
	Dale Murphy		
	Lance Parrish (R)		
	Ernie Whitt		
709	Rookie Pitchers	.25	.12
	Steve Burke (R)		
	Matt Keough		
	Lance Rautzhan (R)		
	Dan Schatzeder		
710	Rookie Outfielders	.50	.25
	Dell Alston		
	Rick Bosetti (R)		
	Mike Easler (R)		
	Keith Smith (R)		
711	Rookie Pitchers	.20	.10
	Cardell Camper		
	Dennis Lamp		
	Craig Mitchell (R)		
	Roy Thomas (R)		
712	Bobby Valentine	.20	.10
713	Bob Davis	.20	.10
714	Mike Anderson	.20	.10
715	Jim Kaat	.75	.35
716	Cito Gaston	.20	.10
717	Nelson Briles	.20	.10
718	Ron Jackson	.20	.10
719	Randy Elliott	.20	.10
720	Ferguson Jenkins	3.00	1.50
721	Billy Martin	.75	.35
722	Pete Broberg	.20	.10
723	Johnny Wockenfuss	.20	.10
724	Royals Team	1.25	.65
725	Kurt Bevacqua	.20	.10
726	Wilbur Wood	.25	.12

1979 Topps

The cards in this 726-card set are
similar in design to the 1978 Topps set.

Card fronts feature large color photos.
The Player's name and team are in
horizontal stripes below the photos. A
small baseball in the lower left corner
contains the player's position. Cards
measure 2-1/2" by 3-1/2". The set
contains League Leaders (1-8), 1978
Record Breakers, All-Time Record
Breakers and Rookie Prospects.

		NR/MT	EX
	Complete Set (726)	270.00	135.00
	Commons (1-726)	.15	.08
1	Batting Leaders	3.00	1.50
2	Home Run Leaders	.50	.25
3	RBI Leaders	.50	.25
4	Stolen Base Leaders	.20	.10
5	Victory Leaders	.50	.25
6	Strikeout Leaders	7.50	3.75
7	ERA Leaders	.30	.15
8	Leading Firemen	.50	.25
9	Dave Campbell	.15	.08
10	Lee May	.15	.08
11	Marc Hill	.15	.08
12	Dick Drago	.15	.08
13	Paul Dade	.15	.08
14	Rafael Landestoy	.15	.08
15	Ross Grimsley	.15	.08
16	Fred Stanley	.15	.08
17	Donnie Moore	.15	.08
18	Tony Solaita	.15	.08
19	Larry Gura	.15	.08
20	Joe Morgan	1.25	.65
21	Kevin Kobel	.15	.08
22	Mike Jorgensen	.15	.08
23	Terry Forster	.15	.08
24	Paul Molitor	38.00	19.00
25	Steve Carlton	6.00	3.00
26	Jamie Quirk	.15	.08
27	Dave Goltz	.15	.08
28	Steve Brye	.15	.08
29	Rick Langford	.15	.08
30	Dave Winfield	20.00	10.00
31	Tom House	.15	.08
32	Jerry Mumphrey	.15	.08
33	Dave Rozema	.15	.08
34	Rob Andrews	.15	.08
35	Ed Figueroa	.15	.08
36	Alan Ashby	.15	.08
37	Joe Kerrigan	.15	.08
38	Bernie Carbo	.15	.08
39	Dale Murphy	7.00	3.50
40	Dennis Eckersley	5.00	2.50
41	Twins Team	1.00	.50
42	Ron Blomberg	.15	.08
43	Wayne Twitchell	.15	.08

44	Kurt Bevacqua	.15	.08
45	Al Hrabosky	.20	.10
46	Ron Hodges	.15	.08
47	Fred Norman	.15	.08
48	Merv Rettenmund	.15	.08
49	Vern Ruhle	.15	.08
50	Steve Garvey	1.50	.75
51	Ray Fosse	.15	.08
52	Randy Lerch	.15	.08
53	Mick Kelleher	.15	.08
54	Dell Alston	.15	.08
55	Willie Stargell	3.00	1.50
56	John Hale	.15	.08
57	Eric Rasmussen	.15	.08
58	Bob Randall	.15	.08
59	John Denny	.15	.08
60	Mickey Rivers	.15	.08
61	Bo Diaz	.15	.08
62	Randy Moffitt	.15	.08
63	Jack Brohamer	.15	.08
64	Tom Underwood	.15	.08
65	Mark Balanger	.25	.12
66	Tigers Team	1.00	.50
67	Jim Mason	.15	.08
68	Joe Niekro	.20	.10
69	Elliott Maddox	.15	.08
70	John Candelaria	.25	.12
71	Brian Downing	.40	.20
72	Steve Mingori	.15	.08
73	Ken Henderson	.15	.08
74	Shane Rawley (R)	.30	.15
75	Steve Yeager	.15	.08
76	Warren Cromartie	.15	.08
77	Dan Briggs	.15	.08
78	Elias Sosa	.15	.08
79	Ted Cox	.15	.08
80	Jason Thompson	.15	.08
81	Roger Erickson	.15	.08
82	Mets Team	1.00	.50
83	Fred Kendall	.15	.08
84	Greg Minton	.15	.08
85	Gary Matthews	.20	.10
86	Rodney Scott	.15	.08
87	Pete Falcone	.15	.08
88	Bob Molinaro	.15	.08
89	Dick Tidrow	.15	.08
90	Bob Boone	.75	.35
91	Terry Crowley	.15	.08
92	Jim Bibby	.15	.08
93	Phil Mankowski	.15	.08
94	Len Barker	.15	.08
95	Robin Yount	15.00	7.50
96	Indians Team	1.00	.50
97	Sam Mejias	.15	.08
98	Ray Burris	.15	.08
99	John Wathan	.20	.10
100	Tom Seaver	4.50	2.25
101	Roy Howell	.15	.08
102	Mike Anderson	.15	.08
103	Jim Todd	.15	.08
104	Johnny Oates	.20	.10
105	Rick Camp	.15	.08
106	Frank Duffy	.15	.08
107	Jesus Alou	.15	.08
108	Eduardo Rodriguez	.15	.08
109	Joel Youngblood	.15	.08
110	Vida Blue	.25	.12
111	Roger Freed	.15	.08
112	Phillies Team	1.00	.50
113	Pete Redfern	.15	.08
114	Cliff Johnson	.15	.08
115	Nolan Ryan	32.00	16.00
116	Ozzie Smith (R)	100.00	50.00
117	Grant Jackson	.15	.08
118	Bud Harrelson	.20	.10
119	Don Stanhouse	.15	.08
120	Jim Sundberg	.15	.08
121	Checklist 1-121	.50	.20
122	Mike Paxton	.15	.08
123	Lou Whitaker	10.00	5.00
124	Dan Schatzeder	.15	.08
125	Rick Burleson	.20	.10
126	Doug Bair	.15	.08
127	Thad Bosley	.15	.08
128	Ted Martinez	.15	.08
129	Marty Pattin	.15	.08
130	Bob Watson	.30	.15
131	Jim Clancy	.15	.08
132	Rowland Office	.15	.08
133	Bill Castro	.15	.08
134	Alan Bannister	.15	.08
135	Bobby Murcer	.30	.15
136	Jim Kaat	.50	.25
137	Larry Wolfe	.15	.08
138	Mark Lee	.15	.08
139	Luis Pujols	.15	.08
140	Don Gullett	.20	.10
141	Tom Paciorek	.15	.08
142	Charlie Williams	.15	.08
143	Tony Scott	.15	.08
144	Sandy Alomar	.15	.08
145	Rick Rhoden	.15	.08
146	Duane Kuiper	.15	.08
147	Dave Hamilton	.15	.08
148	Bruce Boisclair	.15	.08
149	Manny Sarmiento	.15	.08
150	Wayne Cage	.15	.08
151	John Hiller	.15	.08
152	Rick Cerone	.25	.12
153	Dennis Lamp	.15	.08
154	Jim Gantner	.30	.15
155	Dwight Evans	1.25	.65
156	Buddy Solomon	.15	.08
157	U.L. Washington	.15	.08

158 Joe Sambito	.15	.08
159 Roy White	.15	.08
160 Mike Flanagan	.25	.12
161 Barry Foote	.15	.08
162 Tom Johnson	.15	.08
163 Glenn Burke	.15	.08
164 Mickey Lolich	.35	.18
165 Frank Taveras	.15	.08
166 Leon Roberts	.15	.08
167 Roger Metzger	.15	.08
168 Dave Freisleben	.15	.08
169 Bill Nahorodny	.15	.08
170 Don Sutton	2.00	1.00
171 Gene Clines	.15	.08
172 Mike Bruhert	.15	.08
173 John Lowenstein	.15	.08
174 Rick Auerbach	.15	.08
175 George Hendrick	.20	.10
176 Aurelio Rodriguez	.15	.08
177 Ron Reed	.15	.08
178 Alvis Woods	.15	.08
179 Jim Beattie	.15	.08
180 Larry Hisle	.15	.08
181 Mike Garman	.15	.08
182 Tim Johnson	.15	.08
183 Paul Splittorff	.20	.10
184 Darrel Chaney	.15	.08
185 Mike Torrez	.15	.08
186 Eric Soderholm	.15	.08
187 Mark Lemongello	.15	.08
188 Pat Kelly	.15	.08
189 Eddie Whitson (R)	.50	.25
190 Ron Cey	.35	.18
191 Mike Norris	.15	.08
192 Cardinals Team	1.00	.50
193 Glenn Adams	.15	.08
194 Randy Jones	.20	.10
195 Bill Madlock	.50	.25
196 Steve Kemp	.15	.08
197 Bob Apodaca	.15	.08
198 Johnny Grubb	.15	.08
199 Larry Milbourne	.15	.08
200 Johnny Bench	3.50	1.75
201 Mike Edwards (RB)	.15	.08
202 Ron Guidry (RB)	.25	.12
203 J.R. Richards (RB)	.20	.10
204 Pete Rose (RB)	3.00	1.50
205 John Stearns (RB)	.15	.08
206 Sammy Stewart (RB)	.15	.08
207 Dave Lemanczyk	.15	.08
208 Cito Gaston	.30	.15
209 Reggie Cleveland	.15	.08
210 Larry Bowa	.25	.12
211 Denny Martinez	2.00	1.00
212 Carney Lansford (R)	2.00	1.00
213 Bill Travers	.15	.08
214 Red Sox Team	1.00	.50

215 Willie McCovey	3.00	1.50
216 Wilbur Wood	.25	.12
217 Steve Dillard	.15	.08
218 Dennis Leonard	.15	.08
219 Roy Smalley	.15	.08
220 Cesar Geronimo	.15	.08
221 Jesse Jefferson	.15	.08
222 Bob Beall	.15	.08
223 Kent Tekulve	.20	.10
224 Dave Revering	.15	.08
225 Rich Gossage	1.00	.50
226 Ron Pruitt	.15	.08
227 Steve Stone	.25	.12
228 Vic Davalillo	.15	.08
229 Doug Flynn	.15	.08
230 Bob Forsch	.15	.08
231 Johnny Wockenfuss	.15	.08
232 Jimmy Sexton	.15	.08
233 Paul Mitchell	.15	.08
234 Toby Harrah	.15	.08
235 Steve Rogers	.20	.10
236 Jim Dwyer	.15	.08
237 Billy Smith	.15	.08
238 Balor Moore	.15	.08
239 Willie Horton	.25	.12
240 Rick Reuschel	.25	.12
241 Checklist 122-242	.50	.20
242 Pablo Torrealba	.15	.08
243 Buck Martinez	.15	.08
244 Pirates Team	1.00	.50
245 Jeff Burroughs	.20	.10
246 Darrell Jackson	.15	.08
247 Tucker Ashford	.15	.08
248 Pete LaCock	.15	.08
249 Paul Thormodsgard	.15	.08
250 Willie Randolph	.80	.40
251 Jack Morris	4.50	2.25
252 Bob Stinson	.15	.08
253 Rick Wise	.20	.12
254 Luis Gomez	.15	.08
255 Tommy John	.75	.35
256 Mike Sadek	.15	.08
257 Adrian Devine	.15	.08
258 Mike Phillips	.15	.08
259 Reds Team	1.00	.50
260 Richie Zisk	.15	.08
261 Mario Guerrero	.15	.08
262 Nelson Briles	.15	.08
263 Oscar Gamble	.20	.10
264 Don Robinson (R)	.40	.20
265 Don Money	.15	.08
266 Jim Willoughby	.15	.08
267 Joe Rudi	.20	.10
268 Julio Gonzalez	.15	.08
269 Woodie Fryman	.15	.08
270 Butch Hopson	.20	.10
271 Rawly Eastwick	.15	.08

272	Tim Corcoran	.15	.08
273	Jerry Terrell	.15	.08
274	Willie Norwood	.15	.08
275	Junior Moore	.15	.08
276	Jim Colburn	.15	.08
277	Tom Grieve	.15	.08
278	Andy Messersmith	.15	.08
279	Jerry Grote	.15	.08
280	Andre Thornton	.25	.12
281	Vic Correll	.15	.08
282	Blue Jays Team	1.00	.50
283	Ken Kravec	.15	.08
284	Johnnie LeMaster	.15	.08
285	Bobby Bonds	.50	.25
286	Duffy Dyer	.15	.08
287	Andres Mora	.15	.08
288	Milt Wilcox	.15	.08
289	Jose Cruz	.25	.12
290	Dave Lopes	.30	.15
291	Tom Griffin	.15	.08
292	Don Reynolds	.15	.08
293	Jerry Garvin	.15	.08
294	Pepe Frias	.15	.08
295	Mitchell Page	.15	.08
296	Preston Hanna	.15	.08
297	Ted Sizemore	.15	.08
298	Rich Gale	.15	.08
299	Steve Ontiveros	.15	.08
300	Rod Carew	4.50	2.25
301	Tom Hume	.15	.08
302	Braves Team	1.00	.50
303	Lary Sorensen	.15	.08
304	Steve Swisher	.15	.08
305	Willie Montanez	.15	.08
306	Floyd Bannister	.15	.08
307	Larvell Blanks	.15	.08
308	Bert Blyleven	.80	.40
309	Ralph Garr	.15	.08
310	Thurman Munson	3.00	1.50
311	Gary Lavelle	.15	.08
312	Bob Robertson	.15	.08
313	Dyar Miller	.15	.08
314	Larry Harlow	.15	.08
315	Jon Matlack	.20	.10
316	Milt May	.15	.08
317	Jose Cardenal	.15	.08
318	Bob Welch (R)	3.50	1.75
319	Wayne Garrett	.15	.08
320	Carl Yastrzemski	4.00	2.00
321	Gaylord Perry	2.50	1.25
322	Danny Goodwin	.15	.08
323	Lynn McGlothen	.15	.08
324	Mike Tyson	.15	.08
325	Cecil Cooper	.25	.12
326	Pedro Borbon	.15	.08
327	Art Howe	.20	.10
328	A's Team	1.00	.50
329	Joe Coleman	.15	.08
330	George Brett	22.00	11.00
331	Mickey Mahler	.15	.08
332	Gary Alexander	.15	.08
333	Chet Lemon	.20	.10
334	Craig Swan	.15	.08
335	Chris Chambliss	.25	.12
336	Bobby Thompson	.15	.08
337	John Montague	.15	.08
338	Vic Harris	.15	.08
339	Ron Jackson	.15	.08
340	Jim Palmer	4.00	2.00
341	Willie Upshaw (R)	.30	.15
342	Dave Roberts	.15	.08
343	Ed Glynn	.15	.08
344	Jerry Royster	.15	.08
345	Tug McGraw	.35	.18
346	Bill Buckner	.40	.20
347	Doug Rau	.15	.08
348	Andre Dawson	14.00	7.00
349	Jim Wright	.15	.08
350	Garry Templeton	.25	.12
351	Wayne Nordhagen	.15	.08
352	Steve Renko	.15	.08
353	Checklist 243-363	.80	.30
354	Bill Bonham	.15	.08
355	Lee Mazzilli	.15	.08
356	Giants Team	1.00	.50
357	Jerry Augustine	.15	.08
358	Alan Trammell	15.00	7.50
359	Dan Spilner	.15	.08
360	Amos Otis	.20	.10
361	Tom Dixon	.15	.08
362	Mike Cubbage	.15	.08
363	Craig Skok	.15	.08
364	Gene Richards	.15	.08
365	Sparky Lyle	.35	.18
366	Juan Bernhardt	.15	.08
367	Dave Skaggs	.15	.08
368	Daon Aase	.15	.08
369a	Bump Wills (Blue Jays)	2.00	1.00
369b	Bump Wills (Rangers)	3.00	1.50
370	Dave Kingman	.45	.22
371	Jeff Holly	.15	.08
372	Lamar Johnson	.15	.08
373	Lance Rautzhan	.15	.08
374	Ed Herrmann	.15	.08
375	Bill Campbell	.15	.08
376	Gorman Thomas	.25	.12
377	Paul Moskau	.15	.08
378	Rob Picciolo	.15	.08
379	Dale Murray	.15	.08
380	John Mayberry	.20	.10
381	Astros Team	1.00	.50
382	Jerry Martin	.15	.08
383	Phil Garner	.20	.10
384	Tommy Boggs	.15	.08

385	Dan Ford	.15	.08
386	Francisco Barrios	.15	.08
387	Gary Tomasson	.15	.08
388	Jack Billingham	.15	.08
389	Joe Zdeb	.15	.08
390	Rollie Fingers	2.00	1.00
391	Al Oliver	.45	.22
392	Doug Ault	.15	.08
393	Scott McGregor	.20	.10
394	Randy Stein	.15	.08
395	Dave Cash	.15	.08
396	Bill Plummer	.15	.08
397	Sergio Ferrer	.15	.08
398	Ivan DeJesus	.15	.08
399	David Clyde	.15	.08
400	Jim Rice	2.00	1.00
401	Ray Knight	.35	.18
402	Paul Hartzell	.15	.08
403	Tim Foli	.15	.08
404	White Sox Team	1.00	.50
405	Butch Wynegar	.15	.08
406	Joe Wallis	.15	.08
407	Pete Vuckovich	.20	.10
408	Charlie Moore	.15	.08
409	Willie Wilson (R)	2.50	1.25
410	Darrell Evans	.35	.18
411	Ty Cobb, George Sisler (Hits Record)	.60	.30
412	Hank Aaron, Hack Wilson (RBI Record)	1.00	.50
413	Hank Aaron, Roger Maris (HR Records)	1.50	.75
414	Ty Cobb, Roger Hornsby (Batting Avg Records)	.75	.35
415	Lou Brock (SB Record)	.60	.30
416	Jack Chesbro, Cy Young (Wins Record)	.40	.20
417	Walter Johnson, Nolan Ryan (Strikeout Records)	5.00	2.50
418	Walter Johnson, Dutch Leonard (ERA Records)	.40	.25
419	Dick Ruthven	.15	.08
420	Ken Griffey	.80	.40
421	Doug DeCinces	.20	.10
422	Ruppert Jones	.15	.08
423	Bob Montgomery	.15	.08
424	Angels Team	1.00	.50
425	Rick Manning	.15	.08
426	Chris Speier	.15	.08
427	Andy Replogle	.15	.08
428	Bobby Valentine	.20	.10
429	John Urrea	.15	.08
430	Dave Parker	2.00	1.00
431	Glenn Borgmann	.15	.08
432	Dave Heaverlo	.15	.08
433	Larry Bittner	.15	.08
434	Ken Clay	.15	.08
435	Gene Tenace	.25	.12
436	Hector Cruz	.15	.08
437	Rick Williams	.15	.08
438	Horace Speed	.15	.08
439	Frank White	.20	.10
440	Rusty Staub	.35	.18
441	Lee Lacy	.15	.08
442	Doyle Alexander	.15	.08
443	Bruce Bochte	.15	.08
444	Aurelio Lopez	.15	.08
445	Steve Henderson	.15	.08
446	Jim Lonborg	.20	.10
447	Manny Sanguillen	.20	.10
448	Moose Haas	.15	.08
449	Bombo Rivera	.15	.08
450	Dave Concepcion	.75	.35
451	Royals Team	1.00	.50
452	Jerry Morales	.15	.08
453	Chris Knapp	.15	.08
454	Len Randle	.15	.08
455	Bill Lee	.15	.08
456	Chuck Baker	.15	.08
457	Bruce Sutter	.80	.50
458	Jim Essian	.15	.08
459	Sid Monge	.15	.08
460	Graig Nettles	.50	.25
461	Jim Barr	.15	.08
462	Otto Velez	.15	.08
463	Steve Comer	.15	.08
464	Joe Nolan	.15	.08
465	Reggie Smith	.20	.10
466	Mark Littell	.15	.08
467	Don Kessinger	.15	.08
468	Stan Bahnsen	.15	.08
469	Lance Parrish	1.25	.65
470	Garry Maddox	.20	.10
471	Joaquin Andujar	.25	.12
472	Craig Kusick	.15	.08
473	Dave Roberts	.15	.08
474	Dick Davis	.15	.08
475	Dan Driessen	.20	.10
476	Tom Poquette	.15	.08
477	Bob Grich	.20	.10
478	Juan Beniquez	.15	.08
479	Padres Team	1.00	.50
480	Fred Lynn	.80	.40
481	Skip Lockwood	.15	.08
482	Craig Reynolds	.15	.08
483	Checklist 364-484	.50	.20
484	Rick Waits	.15	.08
485	Bucky Dent	.30	.15
486	Bob Knepper	.15	.08
487	Miguel Dilone	.15	.08
488	Bob Owchinko	.15	.08
489	Larry Cox (Wrong Photo)	.15	.08
490	Al Cowens	.15	.08

491	Tippy Martinez	.15	.08	548	Enrique Romo	.15	.08
492	Bob Bailor	.15	.08	549	Bob Bailey	.15	.08
493	Larry Christenson	.15	.08	550	Sal Bando	.20	.10
494	Jerry White	.15	.08	551	Cubs Team	1.00	.50
495	Tony Perez	1.25	.60	552	Jose Morales	.15	.08
496	Barry Bonnell	.15	.08	553	Denny Walling	.15	.08
497	Glenn Abbott	.15	.09	554	Matt Keough	.15	.00
498	Rich Chiles	.15	.08	555	Biff Pocoroba	.15	.08
499	Rangers Team	1.00	.50	556	Mike Lum	.15	.08
500	Ron Guidry	.60	.30	557	Ken Brett	.15	.08
501	Junior Kennedy	.15	.08	558	Jay Johnstone	.20	.10
502	Steve Braun	.15	.08	559	Greg Pryor	.15	.08
503	Terry Humphrey	.15	.08	560	John Montefusco	.15	.08
504	Larry McWilliams (R)	.20	.10	561	Ed Ott	.15	.08
505	Ed Kranepool	.20	.10	562	Dusty Baker	.25	.12
506	John D'Acquisto	.15	.08	563	Roy Thomas	.15	.08
507	Tony Armas	.20	.10	564	Jerry Turner	.15	.08
508	Charlie Hough	.15	.08	565	Rico Carty	.20	.10
509	Mario Mendoza	.15	.08	566	Nino Espinosa	.15	.08
510	Ted Simmons	.45	.22	567	Rich Hebner	.15	.08
511	Paul Reuschel	.15	.08	568	Carlos Lopez	.15	.08
512	Jack Clark	.75	.35	569	Bob Sykes	.15	.08
513	Dave Johnson	.20	.10	570	Cesar Cedeno	.20	.10
514	Mike Proly	.15	.08	571	Darrell Porter	.15	.08
515	Enos Cabell	.15	.08	572	Rod Gilbreath	.15	.08
516	Champ Summers	.15	.08	573	Jim Kern	.15	.08
517	Al Bumbry	.15	.08	574	Claudell Washington	.20	.10
518	Jim Umbarger	.15	.08	575	Luis Tiant	.40	.20
519	Ben Oglivie	.15	.08	576	Mike Parrott	.15	.08
520	Gary Carter	3.50	1.75	577	Brewers Team	.50	.25
521	Sam Ewing	.15	.08	578	Pete Broberg	.15	.08
522	Ken Holtzman	.20	.10	579	Greg Gross	.15	.08
523	John Milner	.15	.08	580	Ron Fairly	.15	.08
524	Tom Burgmeier	.15	.08	581	Darold Knowles	.15	.08
525	Freddie Patek	.15	.08	582	Paul Blair	.15	.08
526	Dodgers Team	1.25	.65	583	Julio Cruz	.15	.08
527	Lerrin LaGrow	.15	.08	584	Jim Rooker	.15	.08
528	Wayne Gross	.15	.08	585	Hal McRae	.35	.18
529	Brian Asselstine	.15	.08	586	Bob Horner (R)	1.25	.60
530	Frank Tanana	.30	.15	587	Ken Reitz	.15	.08
531	Fernando Gonzalez	.15	.08	588	Tom Murphy	.15	.08
532	Buddy Schultz	.15	.08	589	Terry Whitfield	.15	.08
533	Leroy Stanton	.15	.08	590	J.R. Richard	.25	.12
534	Ken Forsch	.15	.08	591	Mike Hargrove	.15	.08
535	Ellis Valentine	.15	.08	592	Mike Krukow	.15	.08
536	Jerry Reuss	.20	.10	593	Rick Dempsey	.20	.10
537	Tom Veryzer	.15	.08	594	Bob Shirley	.15	.08
538	Mike Ivie	.15	.08	595	Phil Niekro	2.00	1.00
539	John Ellis	.15	.08	596	Jim Wohlford	.15	.08
540	Greg Luzinski	.35	.18	597	Bob Stanley	.15	.08
541	Jim Slaton	.15	.08	598	Mark Wagner	.15	.08
542	Rick Bosetti	.15	.08	599	Jim Spencer	.15	.08
543	Kiko Garcia	.15	.08	600	George Foster	.50	.25
544	Ferguson Jenkins	2.00	1.00	601	Dave LaRoche	.15	.08
545	John Stearns	.15	.08	602	Checklist 485-605	.80	.30
546	Bill Russell	.25	.12	603	Rudy May	.15	.08
547	Clint Hurdle	.15	.08	604	Jeff Newman	.15	.08

605	Rick Monday	.20	.10
606	Expos Team	1.00	.50
607	Omar Moreno	.15	.08
608	Dave McKay	.15	.08
609	Silvio Martinez	.15	.08
610	Mike Schmidt	12.00	6.00
611	Jim Norris	.15	.08
612	Rick Honeycutt (R)	.40	.20
613	Mike Edwards	.15	.08
614	Willie Hernandez	.25	.12
615	Ken Singleton	.20	.10
616	Billy Almon	.15	.08
617	Terry Puhl	.15	.08
618	Jerry Remy	.15	.08
619	Ken Landreaux (R)	.25	.12
620	Bert Campaneris	.25	.12
621	Pat Zachry	.15	.08
622	Dave Collins	.15	.08
623	Bob McClure	.15	.08
624	Larry Herndon	.15	.08
625	Mark Fidrych	.40	.20
626	Yankees Team	1.25	.65
627	Gary Serum	.15	.08
628	Del Unser	.15	.08
629	Gene Garber	.15	.08
630	Bake McBride	.15	.08
631	Jorge Orta	.15	.08
632	Don Kirkwood	.15	.08
633	Rob Wilfong	.15	.08
634	Paul Lindblad	.15	.08
635	Don Baylor	.80	.40
636	Wayne Garland	.15	.08
637	Bill Robinson	.20	.10
638	Al Fitzmorris	.15	.08
639	Manny Trillo	.15	.08
640	Eddie Murray	26.00	13.00
641	Bobby Castillo (R)	.15	.08
642	Wilbur Howard	.15	.08
643	Tom Hausman	.15	.08
644	Manny Mota	.20	.10
645	George Scott	.15	.08
646	Rick Sweet	.15	.08
647	Bob Lacey	.15	.08
648	Lou Piniella	.35	.18
649	John Curtis	.15	.08
650	Pete Rose	6.50	3.25
651	Mike Caldwell	.15	.08
652	Stan Papi	.15	.08
653	Warren Brusstar	.15	.08
654	Rick Miller	.15	.08
655	Jerry Koosman	.35	.18
656	Hosken Powell	.15	.08
657	George Medich	.15	.08
658	Taylor Duncan	.15	.08
659	Mariners Team	1.00	.50
660	Ron LeFlore	.20	.10
661	Bruce Kison	.15	.08

662	Kevin Bell	.15	.08
663	Mike Vail	.15	.08
664	Doug Bird	.15	.08
665	Lou Brock	3.50	1.75
666	Rich Dauer	.15	.08
667	Ron Hood	.15	.08
668	Bill North	.15	.08
669	Checklist 606-726	.80	.30
670	Jim Hunter	.80	.40
671	Joe Ferguson	.15	.08
672	Ed Halicki	.15	.08
673	Tom Hutton	.15	.08
674	Dave Tomlin	.15	.08
675	Tim McCarver	.30	.15
676	Johnny Sutton	.15	.08
677	Larry Parrish	.20	.10
678	Geoff Zahn	.15	.08
679	Derrel Thomas	.15	.08
680	Carlton Fisk	6.50	3.25
681	John Henry Johnson	.15	.08
682	Dave Chalk	.15	.08
683	Dan Meyer	.15	.08
684	Jamie Easterly	.15	.08
685	Sixto Lezcano	.15	.08
686	Ron Schueler	.15	.08
687	Rennie Stennett	.15	.08
688	Mike Willis	.15	.08
689	Orioles Team	1.00	.50
690	Buddy Bell	.15	.08
691	Dock Ellis	.15	.08
692	Mickey Stanley	.15	.08
693	Dave Rader	.15	.08
694	Burt Hooton	.15	.08
695	Keith Hernandez	1.50	.75
696	Andy Hassler	.15	.08
697	Dave Bergman	.15	.08
698	Bill Stein	.15	.08
699	Hal Dues	.15	.08
700	Reggie Jackson	5.00	2.50
701	Orioles Prospects	.25	.12
	Mark Corey (R)		
	John Flinn (R)		
	Sammy Stewart (R)		
702	Red Sox Prospects	.15	.08
	Joel Finch (R)		
	Garry Hancock (R)		
	Allen Ripley (R)		
703	Angels Prospects	.15	.08
	Jim Anderson (R)		
	Dave Frost (R)		
	Bob Slater (R)		
704	White Sox Prospects	.15	.08
	Ross Baumgarten (R)		
	Mike Colbern (R)		
	Mike Squires (R)		
705	Indians Prospects	.50	.25
	Alfredo Griffin (R)		

Tim Norrid (R)
Dave Oliver (R)
706 Tigers Prospects .15 .08
Dave Stegman (R)
Dave Tobik (R)
Kip Young (R)
707 Royals Prospects .25 .12
Randy Bass (R)
Jim Gaudet (R)
Randy McGilberry (R)
708 Brewers Prospects .80 .40
Kevin Bass (R)
Eddie Romero (R)
Ned Yost (R)
709 Twins Prospects .15 .08
Sam Perlozzo,
Rick Sofield (R)
Kevin Stanfield (R)
710 Yankees Prospects .20 .10
Brian Doyle (R)
Mike Heath
Dave Rajsich (R)
711 A's Prospects .25 .12
Dwayne Murphy (R)
Bruce Robinson (R)
Alan Wirth
712 Mariners Prospects .15 .08
Bud Anderson (R)
Greg Biercevicz (R)
Byron McLaughlin (R)
713 Rangers Prospects .80 .40
Danny Darwin (R)
Pat Putnam (R)
Billy Sample (R)
714 Blue Jays Prospects .25 .12
Victor Cruz (R)
Pat Kelly
Ernie Whitt
715 Braves Prospects .25 .12
Bruce Benedict (R)
Glenn Hubbard (R)
Larry Whisenton (R)
716 Cubs Prospects .15 .08
Dave Geisel (R)
Karl Pagel (R)
Scot Thompson (R)
717 Reds Prospects .35 .18
Mike LaCoss (R)
Ron Oester (R)
Harry Spilman (R)
718 Astros Prospects .15 .08
Bruce Bochy (R)
Mike Fischlin (R)
Don Pisker (R)
719 Dodger Prospects 3.00 1.50
Pedro Guerrero (R)
Rudy Law (R)

Joe Simpson
720 Expos Prospects 1.25 .60
Jerry Fry (R)
Jerry Pirtle (R)
Scott Sanderson (R)
721 Mets Prospects .35 .18
Juan Berenguer (R)
Dwight Bernard (R)
Dan Norman (R)
722 Phillies Prospects 1.25 .60
Jim Morrison (R)
Lonnie Smith (R)
Jim Wright (R)
723 Pirates Prospects .25 .12
Dale Berra (R)
Eugenio Cotes (R)
Ben Wiltbank (R)
724 Cardinals Prospects .40 .20
Tom Bruno (R)
George Frazier (R)
Terry Kennedy (R)
725 Padres Prospects .15 .08
Jim Beswick (R)
Steve Mura (R)
Broderick Perkins
726 Giants Prospects .25 .12
Greg Johnston (R)
Joe Strain (R)
John Tamargo (R)

1980 Topps

This 726-card set marks another
design change for Topps. Card fronts
feature full color pictures with the player's
name above the photo. The player's
position appears in a pennant in the top
left corner while his team is listed in
another pennant at the lower right corner.
Cards measure 2-1/2" by 3-1/2". Subsets
include Hightlights (HL) (1-6), League

Leaders and Team Rookie cards.

	NR/MT	FX
Complete Set (726)	275.00	140.00
Commons (1-726)	.12	.06

#	Player	NR/MT	FX
1	Lou Brock, Carl Yastrzemski (HL)	3.00	1.50
2	Willie McCovey (HL)	1.25	.60
3	Manny Mota (HL)	.15	.08
4	Pete Rose (HL)	2.50	1.25
5	Garry Templeton (HL)	.15	.08
6	Del Unser (HL)	.15	.08
7	Mike Lum	.12	.06
8	Craig Swan	.12	.06
9	Steve Braun	.12	.06
10	Denny Martinez	.90	.45
11	Jimmy Sexton	.12	.06
12	John Curtis	.12	.06
13	Ron Pruitt	.12	.06
14	Dave Cash	.12	.06
15	Bill Campbell	.12	.06
16	Jerry Narron	.12	.06
17	Bruce Sutter	.75	.35
18	Ron Jackson	.12	.06
19	Balor Moore	.12	.06
20	Dan Ford	.12	.06
21	Manny Sarmiento	.12	.06
22	Pat Putnam	.12	.06
23	Derrel Thomas	.12	.06
24	Jim Slaton	.12	.06
25	Lee Mazzilli	.12	.06
26	Marty Pattin	.12	.06
27	Del Unser	.12	.06
28	Bruce Kison	.12	.06
29	Mark Wagner	.12	.06
30	Vida Blue	.25	.12
31	Jay Johnstone	.15	.08
32	Julio Cruz	.12	.06
33	Tony Scott	.12	.06
34	Jeff Newman	.12	.06
35	Luis Tiant	.30	.15
36	Rusty Torres	.12	.06
37	Kiko Garcia	.12	.06
38	Dan Spillner	.12	.06
39	Rowland Office	.12	.06
40	Carlton Fisk	5.50	2.75
41	Rangers Team	.50	.25
42	Dave Palmer	.12	.06
43	Bombo Rivera	.12	.06
44	Bill Fahey	.12	.06
45	Frank White	.20	.10
46	Rico Carty	.15	.08
47	Bill Bonham	.12	.06
48	Rick Miller	.12	.06
49	Mario Guerrero	.12	.06
50	J.R. Richard	.25	.12
51	Joe Ferguson	.12	.06
52	Warren Brusstar	.12	.06
53	Ben Oglivie	.12	.06
54	Dennis Lamp	.12	.06
55	Bill Madlock	.50	.25
56	Bobby Valentine	.15	.08
57	Pete Vuckovich	.12	.06
58	Doug Flynn	.12	.06
59	Eddy Putman	.12	.06
60	Bucky Dent	.20	.10
61	Gary Serum	.12	.06
62	Mike Ivie	.12	.06
63	Bob Stanley	.12	.06
64	Joe Nolan	.12	.06
65	Al Bumbry	.12	.06
66	Royals Team	.50	.25
67	Doyle Alexander	.12	.06
68	Larry Harlow	.12	.06
69	Rick Williams	.12	.06
70	Gary Carter	3.50	1.75
71	John Milner	.12	.06
72	Fred Howard	.12	.06
73	Dave Collins	.12	.06
74	Sid Monge	.12	.06
75	Bill Russell	.20	.10
76	John Stearns	.12	.06
77	Dave Stieb (R)	2.50	1.25
78	Ruppert Jones	.12	.06
79	Bob Owchinko	.12	.06
80	Ron LeFlore	.15	.08
81	Ted Sizemore	.12	.06
82	Astros Team	.50	.25
83	Steve Trout (R)	.20	.10
84	Gary Lavelle	.12	.06
85	Ted Simmons	.40	.20
86	Dave Hamilton	.12	.06
87	Pepe Frias	.12	.06
88	Ken Landreaux	.15	.08
89	Don Hood	.12	.06
90	Manny Trillo	.12	.06
91	Rick Dempsey	.15	.08
92	Rick Rhoden	.12	.06
93	Dave Roberts	.12	.06
94	Neil Allen (R)	.15	.08
95	Cecil Cooper	.15	.08
96	A's Team	.50	.25
97	Bill Lee	.12	.06
98	Jerry Terrell	.12	.06
99	Victor Cruz	.12	.06
100	Johnny Bench	5.00	2.50
101	Aurelio Lopez	.12	.06
102	Rich Dauer	.12	.06
103	Bill Caudill (R)	.15	.08
104	Manny Mota	.15	.08
105	Frank Tanana	.25	.12
106	Jeff Leonard (R)	.30	.15

107	Francisco Barrios	.12	.06
108	Bob Horner	.20	.10
109	Bill Travers	.12	.06
110	Fred Lynn	.30	.15
111	Bob Knepper	.12	.06
112	White Sox Team	.60	.30
113	Geoff Zahn	.12	.06
114	Juan Beniquez	.12	.06
115	Sparky Lyle	.15	.08
116	Larry Cox	.12	.06
117	Dock Ellis	.12	.06
118	Phil Garner	.15	.08
119	Sammy Stewart	.12	.06
120	Greg Luzinski	.25	.12
121	Checklist 1-121	.50	.20
122	Dave Rosello	.12	.06
123	Lynn Jones	.12	.06
124	Dave Lemanczyk	.12	.06
125	Tony Perez	1.50	.75
126	Dave Tomlin	.12	.06
127	Gary Thomasson	.12	.06
128	Tom Burgmeier	.12	.06
129	Craig Reynolds	.12	.06
130	Amos Otis	.15	.08
131	Paul Mitchell	.12	.06
132	Biff Pocoroba	.12	.06
133	Jerry Turner	.12	.06
134	Matt Keough	.12	.06
135	Bill Buckner	.25	.12
136	Dick Ruthven	.12	.06
137	John Castino (R)	.12	.06
138	Ross Baumgarten	.12	.06
139	Dane Iorg	.12	.06
140	Rich Gossage	.80	.40
141	Gary Alexander	.12	.06
142	Phil Huffman	.12	.06
143	Bruce Bochte	.12	.06
144	Steve Comer	.12	.06
145	Darrell Evans	.30	.15
146	Bob Welch	.60	.30
147	Terry Puhl	.12	.06
148	Manny Sanguillen	.15	.08
149	Tom Hume	.12	.06
150	Jason Thompson	.12	.06
151	Tom Hausman	.12	.06
152	John Fulgham	.12	.06
153	Tim Blackwell	.12	.06
154	Lary Sorensen	.12	.06
155	Jerry Remy	.12	.06
156	Tony Brizzolara	.12	.06
157	Willie Wilson	.30	.15
158	Rob Picciolo	.12	.06
159	Ken Clay	.12	.06
160	Eddie Murray	14.00	7.00
161	Larry Christenson	.12	.06
162	Bob Randall	.12	.06
163	Steve Swisher	.12	.06
164	Greg Pryor	.12	.06
165	Omar Moreno	.12	.06
166	Glenn Abbott	.12	.06
167	Jack Clark	.60	.30
168	Rick Waits	.12	.06
169	Luis Gomez	.12	.06
170	Burt Hooton	.12	.06
171	Fernando Gonzalez	.12	.06
172	Ron Hodges	.12	.06
173	John Henry Johnson	.12	.06
174	Ray Knight	.25	.12
175	Rick Reuschel	.15	.08
176	Champ Summers	.12	.06
177	Dave Heaverlo	.12	.06
178	Tim McCarver	.25	.12
179	Ron Davis (R)	.20	.10
180	Warren Cromartie	.12	.06
181	Moose Haas	.12	.06
182	Ken Reitz	.12	.06
183	Jim Anderson	.12	.06
184	Steve Renko	.12	.06
185	Hal McRae	.30	.15
186	Junior Moore	.12	.06
187	Alan Ashby	.12	.06
188	Terry Crowley	.12	.06
189	Kevin Kobel	.12	.06
190	Buddy Bell	.15	.08
191	Ted Martinez	.12	.06
192	Braves Team	.50	.25
193	Dave Goltz	.12	.06
194	Mike Easler	.12	.06
195	John Montefusco	.12	.06
196	Lance Parrish	.60	.30
197	Byron McLaughlin	.12	.06
198	Dell Alston	.12	.06
199	Mike LaCoss	.12	.06
200	Jim Rice	1.25	.60
201	Batting Leaders	.40	.20
202	Home Run Leaders	.40	.20
203	RBI Leaders	1.75	.90
204	Stolen Base Leaders	.25	.12
205	Victory Leaders	.40	.20
206	Strikeout Leaders	4.50	2.25
207	ERA Leaders	.40	.20
208	Wayne Cage	.12	.06
209	Von Joshua	.12	.06
210	Steve Carlton	6.00	3.00
211	Dave Skaggs	.12	.06
212	Dave Roberts	.12	.06
213	Mike Jorgensen	.12	.06
214	Angels Team	.50	.25
215	Sixto Lezcano	.12	.06
216	Phil Mankowski	.12	.06
217	Ed Halicki	.12	.06
218	Jose Morales	.12	.06
219	Steve Mingori	.12	.06
220	Dave Concepcion	.60	.30

221	Joe Cannon	.12	.06	278	Jim Spencer	.12	.06
222	Ron Hassey (R)	.40	.20	279	Rob Andrews	.12	.06
223	Bob Sykes	.12	.06	280	Gaylord Perry	2.00	1.00
224	Willie Montanez	.12	.06	281	Paul Blair	.12	.06
225	Lou Piniella	.25	.12	282	Mariners Team	.50	.25
226	Bill Stein	.12	.06	283	John Ellis	.12	.06
227	Len Barker	.12	.06	284	Larry Murray	.12	.06
228	Johnny Oates	.12	.06	285	Don Baylor	.60	.30
229	Jim Bibby	.12	.06	286	Darold Knowles	.12	.06
230	Dave Winfield	15.00	7.50	287	John Lowenstein	.12	.06
231	Steve McCatty	.12	.06	288	Dave Rozema	.12	.06
232	Alan Trammell	7.00	3.50	289	Bruce Bochy	.12	.06
233	LaRue Washington	.12	.06	290	Steve Garvey	1.50	.75
234	Vern Ruhle	.12	.06	291	Randy Scarbery	.12	.06
235	Andre Dawson	10.00	5.00	292	Dale Berra	.12	.06
236	Marc Hill	.12	.06	293	Elias Sosa	.12	.06
237	Scott McGregor	.12	.06	294	Charlie Spikes	.12	.06
238	Rob Wilfong	.12	.06	295	Larry Gura	.12	.06
239	Don Aase	.12	.06	296	Dave Rader	.12	.06
240	Dave Kingman	.30	.15	297	Tim Johnson	.12	.06
241	Checklist 122-242	.50	.20	298	Ken Holtzman	.12	.06
242	Lamar Johnson	.12	.06	299	Steve Henderson	.12	.06
243	Jerry Augustine	.12	.06	300	Ron Guidry	.75	.35
244	Cardinals Team	.50	.25	301	Mike Edwards	.12	.06
245	Phil Niekro	2.00	1.00	302	Dodgers Team	.70	.40
246	Tim Foli	.12	.06	303	Bill Castro	.12	.06
247	Frank Riccelli	.12	.06	304	Butch Wynegar	.12	.06
248	Jamie Quirk	.12	.06	305	Randy Jones	.15	.08
249	Jim Clancy	.12	.06	306	Denny Walling	.12	.06
250	Jim Kaat	.40	.20	307	Rick Honeycutt	.15	.08
251	Kip Young	.12	.06	308	Mike Hargrove	.12	.06
252	Ted Cox	.12	.06	309	Larry McWilliams	.12	.06
253	John Montague	.12	.06	310	Dave Parker	1.50	.75
254	Paul Dade	.12	.06	311	Roger Metzger	.12	.06
255	Dusty Baker	.25	.15	312	Mike Barlow	.12	.06
256	Roger Erickson	.12	.06	313	Johnny Grubb	.12	.06
257	Larry Herndon	.12	.06	314	Tim Stoddard (R)	.15	.08
258	Paul Moskau	.12	.06	315	Steve Kemp	.12	.06
259	Mets Team	.50	.25	316	Bob Lacey	.12	.06
260	Al Oliver	.40	.20	317	Mike Anderson	.12	.06
261	Dave Chalk	.12	.06	318	Jerry Reuss	.20	.10
262	Benny Ayala	.12	.06	319	Chris Speier	.12	.06
263	Dave LaRoche	.12	.06	320	Dennis Eckersley	2.50	1.25
264	Bill Robinson	.15	.08	321	Keith Hernandez	1.00	.50
265	Robin Yount	12.50	6.25	322	Claudell Washington	.15	.08
266	Bernie Carbo	.12	.06	323	Mick Kelleher	.12	.06
267	Dan Schatzeder	.12	.06	324	Tom Underwood	.12	.06
268	Rafael Landestoy	.12	.06	325	Dan Driessen	.15	.08
269	Dave Tobik	.12	.06	326	Bo McLaughlin	.12	.06
270	Mike Schmidt	6.00	3.00	327	Ray Fosse	.12	.06
271	Dick Drago	.12	.06	328	Twins Team	.50	.25
272	Ralph Garr	.12	.06	329	Bert Roberge	.12	.06
273	Eduardo Rodriguez	.12	.06	330	Al Cowens	.12	.06
274	Dale Murphy	4.00	2.00	331	Rich Hebner	.12	.06
275	Jerry Koosman	.25	.12	332	Enrique Romo	.12	.06
276	Tom Veryzer	.12	.06	333	Jim Norris	.12	.06
277	Rick Bosetti	.12	.06	334	Jim Beattie	.12	.06

335	Willie McCovey	3.00	1.50
336	George Medich	.12	.06
337	Carney Lansford	.50	.25
338	Johnny Wockenfuss	.12	.06
339	John D'Acquisto	.12	.06
340	Ken Singleton	.15	.08
341	Jim Essian	.12	.06
342	Odell Jone	.12	.06
343	Mike Vail	.12	.06
344	Randy Lerch	.12	.06
345	Larry Parrish	.15	.08
346	Buddy Solomon	.12	.06
347	Harry Chappas	.12	.06
348	Checklist 243-363	.50	.20
349	Jack Brohamer	.12	.06
350	George Hendrick	.15	.08
351	Bob Davis	.12	.06
352	Dan Briggs	.12	.06
353	Andy Hassler	.12	.06
354	Rick Auerbach	.12	.06
355	Gary Matthews	.15	.08
356	Padres Team	.50	.25
357	Bob McClure	.12	.06
358	Lou Whitaker	4.50	2.25
359	Randy Moffitt	.12	.06
360	Darrell Porter	.12	.06
361	Wayne Garland	.12	.06
362	Danny Goodwin	.12	.06
363	Wayne Gross	.12	.06
364	Ray Burris	.12	.06
365	Bobby Murcer	.25	.12
366	Rob Dressler	.12	.06
367	Billy Smith	.12	.06
368	Willie Aikens (R)	.20	.12
369	Jim Kern	.12	.06
370	Cesar Cedeno	.15	.08
371	Jack Morris	2.50	1.25
372	Joel Youngblood	.12	.06
373	Dan Petry (R)	.30	.15
374	Jim Gantner	.15	.08
375	Ross Grimsley	.12	.06
376	Gary Allenson	.12	.06
377	Junior Kennedy	.12	.06
378	Jerry Mumphrey	.12	.06
379	Kevin Bell	.12	.06
380	Garry Maddox	.15	.08
381	Cubs Team	.50	.25
382	Dave Freisleben	.12	.06
383	Ed Ott	.12	.06
384	Joey McLaughlin	.12	.06
385	Enos Cabell	.12	.06
386	Darrell Jackson	.12	.06
387a	Fred Stanley (Name in red)	.12	.06
387b	Fred Stanley (Name in yellow)	1.50	.75
388	Mike Paxton	.12	.06

389	Pete LaCock	.12	.06
390	Ferguson Jenkins	2.00	1.00
391	Tony Armas	.15	.08
392	Milt Wilcox	.12	.06
393	Ozzie Smith	22.00	11.00
394	Reggie Cleveland	.12	.06
395	Ellis Valentine	.12	.00
396	Dan Meyer	.12	.06
397	Roy Thomas	.12	.06
398	Barry Foote	.12	.06
399	Mike Proly	.12	.06
400	George Foster	.40	.20
401	Pete Falcone	.12	.06
402	Merv Rettenmund	.12	.06
403	Pete Redfern	.12	.06
404	Orioles Team	.60	.30
405	Dwight Evans	1.25	.65
406	Paul Molitor	18.00	9.00
407	Tony Solaita	.12	.06
408	Bill North	.12	.06
409	Paul Splittorff	.12	.06
410	Bobby Bonds	.40	.20
411	Frank LaCorte	.12	.06
412	Thad Bosley	.12	.06
413	Allen Ripley	.12	.06
414	George Scott	.15	.08
415	Bill Atkinson	.12	.06
416	Tom Brookens (R)	.15	.08
417	Craig Chamberlain	.12	.06
418	Roger Freed	.12	.06
419	Vic Correll	.12	.06
420	Butch Hobson	.15	.08
421	Doug Bird	.12	.06
422	Larry Milbourne	.12	.06
423	Dave Frost	.12	.06
424	Yankees Team	.50	.25
425	Mark Belanger	.20	.10
426	Grant Jackson	.12	.06
427	Tom Hutton	.12	.06
428	Pat Zachry	.12	.06
429	Duane Kuiper	.12	.06
430	Larry Hisle	.15	.08
431	Mike Krukow	.12	.06
432	Willie Norwood	.12	.06
433	Rich Gale	.12	.06
434	Johnnie LeMaster	.12	.06
435	Don Gullett	.15	.08
436	Billy Almon	.12	.06
437	Joe Niekro	.15	.08
438	Dave Revering	.12	.06
439	Mike Phillips	.12	.06
440	Don Sutton	1.50	.75
441	Eric Soderholm	.12	.06
442	Jorge Orta	.12	.06
443	Mike Parrott	.12	.06
444	Alvis Woods	.12	.06
445	Mark Fidrych	.25	.12

446 Duffy Dyer	.12	.06
447 Nino Espinosa	.12	.06
448 Jim Wohlford	.12	.06
449 Doug Bair	.12	.06
450 George Brett	18.00	9.00
451 Indians Team	.50	.25
452 Steve Dillard	.12	.06
453 Mike Bacsik	.12	.06
454 Tom Donohue	.12	.06
455 Mike Torrez	.12	.06
456 Frank Taveras	.12	.06
457 Bert Blyleven	.80	.40
458 Billy Sample	.12	.06
459 Mickey Lolich	.20	.10
460 Willie Randolph	.75	.35
461 Dwayne Murphy	.12	.06
462 Mike Sadek	.12	.06
463 Jerry Royster	.12	.06
464 John Denny	.12	.06
465 Rick Monday	.15	.08
466 Mike Squires	.12	.06
467 Jesse Jefferson	.12	.06
468 Aurelio Rodriguez	.12	.06
469 Randy Niemann	.12	.06
470 Bob Boone	.60	.30
471 Hosken Powell	.12	.06
472 Willie Hernandez	.20	.10
473 Bump Wills	.12	.06
474 Steve Busby	.12	.06
475 Cesar Geronimo	.12	.06
476 Bob Shirley	.12	.06
477 Buck Martinez	.12	.06
478 Gil Flores	.12	.06
479 Expos Team	.50	.25
480 Bob Watson	.30	.15
481 Tom Paciorek	.12	.06
482 Rickey Henderson(R)	110.00	55.00
483 Bo Diaz	.12	.06
484 Checklist 364-484	.50	.20
485 Mickey Rivers	.12	.06
486 Mike Tyson	.12	.06
487 Wayne Nordhagen	.12	.06
488 Roy Howell	.12	.06
489 Preston Hanna	.12	.06
490 Lee May	.12	.06
491 Steve Mura	.12	.06
492 Todd Cruz	.12	.06
493 Jerry Martin	.12	.06
494 Craig Minetto	.12	.06
495 Bake McBride	.12	.06
496 Silvio Martinez	.12	.06
497 Jim Mason	.12	.06
498 Danny Darwin	.20	.10
499 Giants Team	.50	.25
500 Tom Seaver	6.00	3.00
501 Rennis Stennett	.12	.06
502 Rich Wortham	.12	.06
503 Mike Cubbage	.12	.06
504 Gene Garber	.12	.06
505 Bert Campaneris	.20	.10
506 Tom Buskey	.12	.06
507 Leon Roberts	.12	.06
508 U.L. Washington	.12	.06
509 Ed Glynn	.12	.06
510 Ron Cey	.25	.12
511 Eric Wilkins	.12	.06
512 Jose Cardenal	.12	.06
513 Tom Dixon	.12	.06
514 Steve Ontiveros	.12	.06
515 Mike Caldwell	.12	.06
516 Hector Cruz	.12	.06
517 Don Stanhouse	.12	.06
518 Nelson Norman	.12	.06
519 Steve Nicosia	.12	.06
520 Steve Rogers	.15	.08
521 Ken Brett	.12	.06
522 Jim Morrison	.12	.06
523 Ken Henderson	.12	.06
524 Jim Wright	.12	.06
525 Clint Hurdle	.12	.06
526 Phillies Team	.50	.25
527 Doug Rau	.12	.06
528 Adrian Devine	.12	.06
529 Jim Barr	.12	.06
530 Jim Sundberg	.12	.06
531 Eric Rasmussen	.12	.06
532 Willie Horton	.15	.08
533 Checklist 485-605	.50	.20
534 Andre Thornton	.15	.08
535 Bob Forsch	.12	.06
536 Lee Lacy	.12	.06
537 Alex Trevino (R)	.15	.08
538 Joe Strain	.12	.06
539 Rudy May	.12	.06
540 Pete Rose	6.00	3.00
541 Miguel Dilone	.12	.06
542 Joe Coleman	.12	.06
543 Pat Kelly	.12	.06
544 Rick Sutcliffe (R)	3.50	1.75
545 Jeff Burroughs	.15	.08
546 Rick Langford	.12	.06
547 John Wathan	.12	.06
548 Dave Rajsich	.12	.06
549 Larry Wolfe	.12	.06
550 Ken Griffey	.50	.25
551 Pirates Team	.50	.25
552 Bill Nahorodny	.12	.06
553 Dick Davis	.12	.06
554 Art Howe	.12	.06
555 Ed Figueroa	.12	.06
556 Joe Rudi	.15	.08
557 Mark Lee	.12	.06
558 Alfredo Griffin	.20	.10
559 Dale Murray	.12	.06

560	Dave Lopes	.20	.10
561	Eddie Whitson	.15	.08
562	Joe Wallis	.12	.06
563	Will McEnaney	.12	.06
564	Rick Manning	.12	.06
565	Dennis Leonard	.12	.06
566	Bud Harrelson	.15	.00
567	Skip Lockwood	.12	.06
568	Gary Roenicke (R)	.12	.06
569	Terry Kennedy	.15	.08
570	Roy Smalley	.12	.06
571	Joe Sambito	.12	.06
572	Jerry Morales	.12	.06
573	Kent Tekulve	.12	.06
574	Scot Thompson	.12	.06
575	Ken Kravec	.12	.06
576	Jim Dwyer	.12	.06
577	Blue Jays Team	.50	.25
578	Scott Sanderson	.35	.18
579	Charlie Moore	.12	.06
580	Nolan Ryan	25.00	12.50
581	Bob Bailor	.12	.06
582	Brian Doyle	.12	.06
583	Bob Stinson	.12	.06
584	Kurt Bevacqua	.12	.06
585	Al Hrabosky	.15	.08
586	Mitchell Page	.12	.06
587	Gerry Templeton	.15	.08
588	Greg Minton	.12	.06
589	Chet Lemon	.12	.06
590	Jim Palmer	4.00	2.00
591	Rick Cerone	.15	.08
592	Jon Matlack	.12	.06
593	Jesus Alou	.12	.06
594	Dick Tidrow	.12	.06
595	Don Money	.12	.06
596	Rick Matula	.12	.06
597	Tom Poquette	.12	.06
598	Fred Kendall	.12	.06
599	Mike Norris	.12	.06
600	Reggie Jackson	8.50	4.25
601	Buddy Schultz	.12	.06
602	Brian Downing	.15	.08
603	Jack Billingham	.12	.06
604	Glenn Adams	.12	.06
605	Terry Forster	.12	.06
606	Reds Team	.50	.25
607	Woodie Fryman	.12	.06
608	Alan Bannister	.12	.06
609	Ron Reed	.12	.06
610	Willie Stargell	2.50	1.25
611	Jerry Garvin	.12	.06
612	Cliff Johnson	.12	.06
613	Randy Stein	.12	.06
614	John Hiller	.12	.06
615	Doug DeCinces	.15	.08
616	Gene Richards	.12	.06

617	Joaquin Andujar	.20	.10
618	Bob Montgomery	.12	.06
619	Sergio Ferrer	.12	.06
620	Richie Zisk	.12	.06
621	Bob Grich	.15	.08
622	Mario Soto	.15	.08
623	Gorman Thomas	.15	.00
624	Lerrin LaGrow	.12	.06
625	Chris Chambliss	.15	.08
626	Tigers Team	.60	.30
627	Pedro Borbon	.12	.06
628	Doug Capilla	.12	.06
629	Jim Todd	.12	.06
630	Larry Bowa	.15	.08
631	Mark Littell	.12	.06
632	Barry Bonnell	.12	.06
633	Bob Apodaca	.12	.06
634	Glenn Borgmann	.12	.06
635	John Candelaria	.25	.12
636	Toby Harrah	.12	.06
637	Joe Simpson	.12	.06
638	Mark Clear (R)	.15	.08
639	Larry Blittner	.12	.06
640	Mike Flanagan	.15	.08
641	Ed Kranepool	.20	.10
642	Ken Forsch	.12	.06
643	John Mayberry	.15	.08
644	Charlie Hough	.20	.10
645	Rick Burleson	.15	.08
646	Checklist 606-726	.50	.20
647	Milt May	.12	.06
648	Roy White	.12	.06
649	Tom Griffin	.12	.06
650	Joe Morgan	2.50	1.25
651	Rollie Fingers	2.00	1.00
652	Mario Mendoza	.12	.06
653	Stan Bahnsen	.12	.06
654	Bruce Boisclair	.12	.06
655	Tug McGraw	.35	.18
656	Larvell Blanks	.12	.06
657	Dave Edwards	.12	.06
658	Chris Knapp	.12	.06
659	Brewers Team	.50	.25
660	Rusty Staub	.35	.18
661	Orioles Future Star	.12	.06
	Mark Corey (R)		
	Dave Ford (R)		
	Wayne Krenchicki (R)		
662	Red Sox Future Stars	.12	.06
	Joel Finch (R)		
	Mike O'Berry (R)		
	Chuck Rainey (R)		
663	Angels Future Stars	.60	.30
	Ralph Botting (R)		
	Bob Clark (R)		
	Dickie Thon (R)		
664	White Sox Future Stars	.12	.06

Mike Colbern
Guy Hoffman (R)
Dewey Robinson (R)

665	Indians Future Stars	.20	.10

Larry Andersen
Bobby Cuellar (R)
Sandy Wihtol (R)

666	Tigers Future Stars	.12	.06

Mike Chris (R)
Al Greene (R)
Bruce Robbins (R)

667	Royals Future Stars	2.50	1.25

Renie Martin (R)
Bill Paschall (R)
Dan Quisenberry (R)

668	Brewers Future Stars	.12	.06

Danny Boitano
Willie Mueller (R)
Lenn Sakata (R)

669	Twins Future Stars	.15	.08

Dan Graham (R)
Rick Sofield (R)
Gary Ward

670	Yankees Future Stars	.15	.08

Bobby Brown (R)
Brad Gulden (R)
Darryl Jones (R)

671	A's Future Stars	2.00	1.00

Derek Bryant (R)
Brian Kingman (R)
Mike Morgan (R)

672	Mariners Future Stars	.12	.06

Charlie Beamon (R)
Rodney Craig
Rafael Vasquez (R)

673	Rangers Future Stars	.12	.06

Brian Allard (R)
Jerry Don Gleaton (R)
Greg Mahlberg (R)

674	Blue Jays Future Stars	.12	.06

Butch Edge (R)
Pat Kelly (R)
Ted Wilborn (R)

675	Braves Future Stars	.12	.06

Bruce Benedict
Larry Bradford (R)
Eddie Miller (R)

676	Cubs Future Stars	.12	.06

Dave Geisel
Steve Macko (R)
Karl Pagel

677	Reds Future Stars	.12	.06

Art DeFreites (R)
Frank Pastore (R)
Harry Spilman

678	Astros Future Stars	.12	.06

Reggie Baldwin (R)
Alan Knicely (R)
Pete Ladd

679	Dodgers Future Stars	.25	.12

Joe Beckwith
Mickey Hatcher (R)
Dave Patterson (R)

680	Expos Future Stars	.12	.06

Tony Bernazard (R)
Randy Miller (R)
John Tamargo (R)

681	Mets Future Stars	2.50	1.25

Dan Norman
Jesse Orosco (R)
Mike Scott (R)

682	Phillies Future Stars	.15	.08

Ramon Aviles
Dickie Noles
Kevin Saucier (R)

683	Pirates Future Stars	.12	.06

Dorian Boyland (R)
Alberto Lois (R)
Harry Saferight (R)

684	Cardinals Future Stars	.50	.25

George Frazier
Tom Herr (R)
Dan O'Brien (R)

685	Padres Future Stars	.12	.06

Tim Flannery (R)
Brian Greer (R)
Jim Wilhelm (R)

686	Giants Future Stars	.12	.06

Greg Johnston (R)
Dennis Littlejohn (R)
Phil Nastu (R)

687	Mike Heath	.12	.06
688	Steve Stone	.12	.06
689	Red Sox Team	.50	.25
690	Tommy John	.50	.25
691	Ivan DeJesus	.12	.06
692	Rawly Eastwick	.12	.06
693	Craig Kusick	.12	.06
694	Jim Rooker	.12	.06
695	Reggie Smith	.15	.08
696	Julio Gonzalez	.12	.06
697	David Clyde	.12	.06
698	Oscar Gamble	.15	.08
699	Floyd Bannister	.12	.06
700	Rod Carew	2.50	1.25
701	Ken Oberkfell (R)	.20	.10
702	Ed Farmer	.12	.06
703	Otto Velez	.12	.06
704	Gene Tenace	.15	.08
705	Freddie Patek	.12	.06
706	Tippy Martinez	.12	.06
707	Elliott Maddox	.12	.06
708	Bob Tolan	.12	.06
709	Pat Underwood	.12	.06

		NR/MT	EX
710	Graig Nettles	.25	.12
711	Bob Galasso	.12	.06
712	Rodney Scott	.12	.06
713	Terry Whitfield	.12	.06
714	Fred Norman	.12	.06
715	Sal Bando	.15	.08
716	Lynn McGlothen	.12	.06
717	Mickey Klutts	.12	.06
718	Greg Gross	.12	.06
719	Don Robinson	.15	.08
720	Carl Yastrzemski	2.00	1.00
721	Paul Hartzell	.12	.06
722	Jose Cruz	.20	.10
723	Shane Rawley	.12	.06
724	Jerry White	.12	.06
725	Rick Wise	.15	.08
726	Steve Yeager	.20	.10

1981 Topps

This 726-card set features full color photos on the card fronts with multi colored borders with each team assigned a different border color. The player's name appears below the photo with his position and team printed in a small baseball cap graphic in the lower left corner. Cards measure 2-1/2" by 3-1/2". Key subsets include League Leaders (1-8), Record Breakers, World Series and Playoff Highlights and Rookies.

		NR/MT	EX
Complete Set (726)		100.00	50.00
Commons (1-726)		.10	.05
1	Batting Leaders	2.50	1.25
2	Home Run Leaders	.75	.35
3	RBI Leaders	.75	.35

		NR/MT	EX
4	Stolen Base Leaders	2.00	1.00
5	Victory Leaders	.35	.18
6	Strikeout Leaders	.50	.25
7	ERA Leaders	.25	.12
8	Leading Firemen	.35	.18
9	Pete LaCock	.10	.05
10	Mike Flanagan	.15	.08
11	Jim Wohlford	.10	.05
12	Mark Clear	.10	.05
13	Joe Charboneau (R)	.15	.08
14	John Tudor (R)	.40	.20
15	Larry Parrish	.10	.05
16	Ron Davis	.10	.05
17	Cliff Johnson	.10	.05
18	Glenn Adams	.10	.05
19	Jim Clancy	.10	.05
20	Jeff Burroughs	.12	.06
21	Ron Oester	.10	.05
22	Danny Darwin	.12	.06
23	Alex Trevino	.10	.05
24	Don Stanhouse	.10	.05
25	Sixto Lezcano	.10	.05
26	U.L. Washington	.10	.05
27	Champ Summers	.10	.05
28	Enrique Romo	.10	.05
29	Gene Tenace	.12	.06
30	Jack Clark	.50	.25
31	Checklist 1-121	.12	.05
32	Ken Oberkfell	.10	.05
33	Rick Honeycutt	.12	.06
34	Aurelio Rodriguez	.10	.05
35	Mitchell Page	.10	.05
36	Ed Farmer	.10	.05
37	Gary Roenicke	.10	.05
38	Win Remmerswaal	.10	.05
39	Tom Veryzer	.10	.05
40	Tug McGraw	.25	.12
41	Rangers Future Stars	.10	.05
	Bob Babock (R)		
	John Butcher (R)		
	Jerry Don Gleaton		
42	Jerry White	.10	.05
43	Jose Morales	.10	.05
44	Larry McWilliams	.10	.05
45	Enos Cabell	.12	.06
46	Rick Bosetti	.10	.05
47	Ken Brett	.10	.05
48	Dave Skaggs	.10	.05
49	Bob Shirley	.10	.05
50	Dave Lopes	.20	.10
51	Bill Robinson	.12	.06
52	Hector Cruz	.10	.05
53	Kevin Saucier	.10	.05
54	Ivan DeJesus	.10	.05
55	Mike Norris	.10	.05
56	Buck Martinez	.10	.05
57	Dave Roberts	.10	.05

58	Joel Youngblood	.10	.05
59	Dan Petry	.15	.08
60	Willie Randolph	.40	.20
61	Butch Wynegar	.10	.05
62	Joe Pettini	.10	.05
63	Steve Renko	.10	.05
64	Brian Asselstine	.10	.05
65	Scott McGregor	.10	.05
66	Royals Future Stars	.12	.06
	Manny Castillo (R)		
	Tim Ireland (R)		
	Mike Jones (R)		
67	Ken Kravec	.10	.05
68	Matt Alexander	.10	.05
69	Ed Halicki	.10	.05
70	Al Oliver	.20	.10
71	Hal Dues	.10	.05
72	Barry Evans	.10	.05
73	Doug Bair	.10	.05
74	Mike Hargrove	.10	.05
75	Reggie Smith	.15	.08
76	Mario Mendoza	.10	.05
77	Mike Barlow	.10	.05
78	Steve Dillard	.10	.05
79	Bruce Robbins	.10	.05
80	Rusty Staub	.30	.15
81	Dave Stapleton	.10	.05
82	Astros Future Stars	.15	.08
	Danny Heep		
	Alan Knicely		
	Bobby Sprowl (R)		
83	Mike Proly	.10	.05
84	Johnnie LeMaster	.10	.05
85	Mike Caldwell	.10	.05
86	Wayne Gross	.10	.05
87	Rick Camp	.10	.05
88	Joe Lefebvre	.10	.05
89	Darrell Jackson	.10	.05
90	Bake McBride	.10	.05
91	Tim Stoddard	.10	.05
92	Mike Easler	.10	.05
93	Ed Glynn	.10	.05
94	Harry Spilman	.10	.05
95	Jim Sundberg	.10	.05
96	A's Future Stars	.15	.08
	Dave Beard		
	Ernie Camacho (R)		
	Pat Dempsey (R)		
97	Chris Speier	.10	.05
98	Clint Hurdle	.10	.05
99	Eric Wilkins	.10	.05
100	Rod Carew	3.50	1.75
101	Benny Ayala	.10	.05
102	Dave Tobik	.10	.05
103	Jerry Martin	.10	.05
104	Terry Forster	.10	.05
105	Jose Cruz	.15	.08

106	Don Money	.10	.05
107	Rich Wortham	.10	.05
108	Bruce Benedict	.10	.05
109	Mike Scott	.30	.15
110	Carl Yastrzemski	3.50	1.75
111	Greg Minton	.10	.05
112	White Sox Future Stars	.10	.05
	Rusty Kuntz		
	Fran Mullins (R)		
	Leo Sutherland (R)		
113	Mike Phillips	.10	.05
114	Tom Underwood	.10	.05
115	Roy Smalley	.10	.05
116	Joe Simpson	.10	.05
117	Pete Falcone	.10	.05
118	Kurt Bevacqua	.10	.05
119	Tippy Martinez	.10	.05
120	Larry Bowa	.15	.08
121	Larry Harlow	.10	.05
122	John Denny	.10	.05
123	Al Cowens	.10	.05
124	Jerry Garvin	.10	.05
125	Andre Dawson	4.50	2.25
126	Charlie Leibrandt (R)	1.00	.50
127	Rudy Law	.10	.05
128	Gary Allenson	.10	.05
129	Art Howe	.10	.05
130	Larry Gura	.10	.05
131	Keith Moreland (R)	.15	.08
132	Tommy Boggs	.10	.05
133	Jeff Cox	.10	.05
134	Steve Mura	.10	.05
135	Gorman Thomas	.12	.06
136	Doug Capilla	.10	.05
137	Hosken Powell	.10	.05
138	Rich Dotson (R)	.12	.06
139	Oscar Gamble	.12	.06
140	Bob Forsch	.10	.05
141	Miguel Dilone	.10	.05
142	Jackson Todd	.10	.05
143	Dan Meyer	.10	.05
144	Allen Ripley	.10	.05
145	Mickey Rivers	.10	.05
146	Bobby Castillo	.10	.05
147	Dale Berra	.10	.05
148	Randy Niemann	.10	.05
149	Joe Nolan	.10	.05
150	Mark Fidrych	.15	.08
151	Claudell Washington	.12	.06
152	John Urrea	.10	.05
153	Tom Poquette	.10	.05
154	Rick Langford	.10	.05
155	Chris Chambliss	.15	.08
156	Bob McClure	.10	.05
157	John Wathan	.10	.05
158	Ferguson Jenkins	1.25	.60
159	Brian Doyle	.10	.05

160	Garry Maddox	.12	.06
161	Dan Graham	.10	.05
162	Doug Corbett	.10	.05
163	Billy Almon	.10	.05
164	LaMarr Hoyt (R)	.20	.10
165	Tony Scott	.10	.05
100	Floyd Bannister	.10	.05
216	John Henry Johnson	.10	.05
167	Terry Whitfield	.10	.05
168	Don Robinson	.12	.06
169	John Mayberry	.12	.06
170	Ross Grimsley	.10	.05
171	Gene Richards	.10	.05
172	Gary Woods	.10	.05
173	Bump Wills	.10	.05
174	Doug Rau	.10	.05
175	Dave Collins	.10	.05
176	Mike Krukow	.10	.05
177	Rick Peters	.10	.05
178	Jim Essian	.10	.05
179	Rudy May	.10	.05
180	Pete Rose	5.00	2.50
181	Elias Sosa	.10	.05
182	Bob Grich	.15	.08
183	Dick Davis	.10	.05
184	Jim Dwyer	.10	.05
185	Dennis Leonard	.10	.05
186	Wayne Nordhagen	.10	.05
187	Mike Parrott	.10	.05
188	Doug DeCinces	.12	.06
189	Craig Swan	.10	.05
190	Cesar Cedeno	.15	.08
191	Rick Sutcliffe	.50	.25
192	Braves Future Stars	.20	.10
	Terry Harper (R)		
	Ed Miller		
	Rafael Ramirez (R)		
193	Pete Vuckovich	.12	.06
194	Rod Scurry (R)	.10	.05
195	Rich Murray	.10	.05
196	Duffy Dyer	.10	.05
197	Jim Kern	.10	.05
198	Jerry Dybzinski	.10	.05
199	Chuck Rainey	.10	.05
200	George Foster	.25	.12
201	Johnny Bench (RB)	1.00	.50
202	Steve Carlton (RB)	1.25	.65
203	Bill Gullickson (RB)	.25	.12
204	Ron LeFlore/Rodney Scott (RB)	.20	.10
205	Pete Rose (RB)	2.50	1.25
206	Mike Schmidt (RB)	2.50	1.25
207	Ozzie Smith (RB)	2.00	1.00
208	Willie Wilson (RB)	.20	.10
209	Dickie Thon	.10	.05
210	Jim Palmer	3.00	1.50
211	Derrel Thomas	.10	.05
212	Steve Nicosia	.10	.05

213	Al Holland (R)	.10	.05
214	Angels Future Stars	.10	.05
	Ralph Botting		
	Jim Dorsey (R)		
	John Harris (R)		
215	Larry Hisle	.10	.05
216	John Henry Johnson	.10	.05
217	Rich Hebner	.10	.05
218	Paul Splittorff	.12	.06
219	Ken Landreaux	.10	.05
220	Tom Seaver	4.00	2.00
221	Bob Davis	.10	.05
222	Jorge Orta	.10	.05
223	Roy Lee Jackson	.10	.05
224	Pat Zachry	.10	.05
225	Ruppert Jones	.10	.05
226	Manny Sanguillen	.15	.08
227	Fred Martinez	.10	.05
228	Tom Paciorek	.10	.05
229	Rollie Fingers	2.00	1.00
230	George Hendrick	.12	.06
231	Joe Beckwith	.10	.05
232	Mickey Klutts	.10	.05
233	Skip Lockwood	.10	.05
234	Lou Whitaker	1.50	.75
235	Scott Sanderson	.20	.10
236	Mike Ivie	.10	.05
237	Charlie Moore	.10	.05
238	Willie Hernandez	.15	.08
239	Rick Miller	.10	.05
240	Nolan Ryan	15.00	7.50
241	Checklist 122-242	.12	.05
242	Chet Lemon	.12	.06
243	Sal Butera	.10	.05
244	Cardinals Future Stars	.10	.05
	Tito Landrum (R)		
	Al Olmsted (R)		
	Andy Rincon		
245	Ed Figueroa	.10	.05
246	Ed Ott	.10	.05
247	Glenn Hubbard	.10	.05
248	Joey McLaughlin	.10	.05
249	Larry Cox	.10	.05
250	Ron Guidry	.50	.25
251	Tom Brookens	.10	.05
252	Victor Cruz	.10	.05
253	Dave Bergman	.10	.05
254	Ozzie Smith	6.50	3.25
255	Mark Littell	.10	.05
256	Bombo Rivera	.10	.05
257	Rennie Stennett	.10	.05
258	Joe Price (R)	.10	.05
259	Mets Future Stars	1.25	.65
	Juan Berenguer		
	Hubie Brooks (R)		
	Mookie Wilson (R)		
260	Ron Cey	.25	.12

261	Rickey Henderson	16.00	8.00
262	Sammy Stewart	.10	.05
263	Brian Downing	.10	.05
264	Jim Norris	.10	.05
265	John Candelaria	.15	.08
266	Tom Herr	.15	.08
267	Stan Bahnsen	.10	.05
268	Jerry Royster	.10	.05
269	Ken Forsch	.10	.05
270	Greg Luzinski	.25	.12
271	Bill Castro	.10	.05
272	Bruce Kimm	.10	.05
273	Stan Papi	.10	.05
274	Craig Chamberlain	.10	.05
275	Dwight Evans	.50	.25
276	Dan Spillner	.10	.05
277	Alfredo Griffin	.15	.08
278	Rick Sofield	.10	.05
279	Bob Knepper	.10	.05
280	Ken Griffey	.40	.20
281	Fred Stanley	.10	.05
282	Mariners Future Stars	.10	.05
	Rick Anderson		
	Greg Biercevicz		
	Rodney Craig		
283	Billy Sample	.10	.05
284	Brian Kingman	.10	.05
285	Jerry Turner	.10	.05
286	Dave Frost	.10	.05
287	Lenn Sakata	.10	.05
288	Bob Clark	.10	.05
289	Mickey Hatcher	.10	.05
290	Bob Boone	.25	.12
291	Aurelio Lopez	.10	.05
292	Mike Squiers	.10	.05
293	Charlie Lea (R)	.12	.06
294	Mike Tyson	.10	.05
295	Hal McRae	.30	.15
296	Bill Nahorodny	.10	.05
297	Bob Bailor	.10	.05
298	Buddy Solomon	.10	.05
299	Elliott Maddox	.10	.05
300	Paul Molitor	6.50	3.25
301	Matt Keough	.10	.05
302	Dodgers Future Stars	2.50	1.25
	Jack Perconte		
	Mike Scioscia(R)		
	Fernando Valenzuela (R)		
303	Johnny Oates	.12	.06
304	John Castino	.10	.05
305	Ken Clay	.10	.05
306	Juan Beniquez	.10	.05
307	Gene Garber	.10	.05
308	Rick Manning	.10	.05
309	Luis Salazar (R)	.15	.08
310	Vida Blue	.20	.10
311	Freddie Patek	.10	.05
312	Rick Rhoden	.10	.05
313	Luis Pujols	.10	.05
314	Rich Dauer	.10	.05
315	Kirk Gibson (R)	4.00	2.00
316	Criag Minetto	.10	.05
317	Lonnie Smith	.25	.12
318	Steve Yeager	.10	.05
319	Rowland Office	.10	.05
320	Tom Burgmeier	.10	.05
321	Leon Durham (R)	.15	.08
322	Neil Allen	.10	.05
323	Jim Morrison	.10	.05
324	Mike Willis	.10	.05
325	Ray Knight	.20	.10
326	Biff Pocoroba	.10	.05
327	Moose Haas	.10	.05
328	Twins Future Stars	.12	.06
	Dave Engle		
	Greg Johnston (R)		
	Gary Ward		
329	Joaquin Andujar	.15	.08
330	Frank White	.15	.08
331	Dennis Lamp	.10	.05
332	Lee Lacy	.10	.05
333	Sid Monge	.10	.05
334	Dane Jorg	.10	.05
335	Rick Cerone	.15	.08
336	Eddie Whitson	.12	.06
337	Lynn Jones	.10	.05
338	Checklist 243-363	.30	.12
339	John Ellis	.10	.05
340	Bruce Kison	.10	.05
341	Dwayne Murphy	.10	.05
342	Eric Rasmussen	.10	.05
343	Frank Taveras	.10	.05
344	Byron McLaughlin	.10	.05
345	Warren Cromartie	.10	.05
346	Larry Christenson	.10	.05
347	Harold Baines (R)	4.00	2.00
348	Bob Sykes	.10	.05
349	Glenn Hoffman	.10	.05
350	J.R. Richard	.20	.10
351	Otto Velez	.10	.05
352	Dick Tidrow	.10	.05
353	Terry Kennedy	.15	.08
354	Mario Soto	.15	.08
355	Bob Horner	.25	.12
356	Padres Future Stars	.10	.05
	George Stablein (R)		
	Craig Stimac (R)		
	Tom Tellmann (R)		
357	Jim Slaton	.10	.05
358	Mark Wagner	.10	.05
359	Tom Hausman	.10	.05
360	Willie Wilson	.25	.12
361	Joe Strain	.10	.05
362	Bo Diaz	.10	.05

363	Geoff Zahn	.10	.05
364	Mike Davis (R)	.12	.06
365	Graig Nettles	.20	.10
366	Mike Ramsey	.10	.05
367	Denny Martinez	.80	.40
368	Leon Roberts	.10	.05
369	Frank Tanana	.15	.08
370	Dave Winfield	6.50	3.25
371	Charlie Hough	.15	.08
372	Jay Johnstone	.12	.06
373	Pat Underwood	.10	.05
374	Tom Hutton	.10	.05
375	Dave Concepcion	.35	.18
376	Ron Reed	.10	.05
377	Jerry Morales	.10	.05
378	Dave Rader	.10	.05
379	Lary Sorensen	.10	.05
380	Willie Stargell	2.00	1.00
381	Cubs Future Stars	.10	.05
	Carlos Lezcano		
	Steve Macko		
	Randy Martz		
382	Paul Mirabella (R)	.10	.05
383	Eric Soderholm	.10	.05
384	Mike Sadek	.10	.05
385	Joe Sambito	.10	.05
386	Dave Edwards	.10	.05
387	Phil Niekro	1.25	.60
388	Andre Thornton	.15	.08
389	Marty Pattin	.10	.05
390	Cesar Geronimo	.10	.05
391	Dave Lemanczyk	.10	.05
392	Lance Parrish	.35	.18
393	Broderick Perkins	.10	.05
394	Woodie Fryman	.10	.05
395	Scot Thompson	.10	.05
396	Bill Campbell	.10	.05
397	Julio Cruz	.10	.05
398	Ross Baumgarten	.10	.05
399	Orioles Future Stars	.70	.40
	Mike Boddicker (R)		
	Mark Corey (R)		
	Floyd Rayford (R)		
400	Reggie Jackson	4.50	2.25
401	A.L. Championships	2.50	1.25
402	N.L. Championships	.25	.12
403	World Series	.25	.12
404	World Series Summary	.25	.12
405	Nino Espinosa	.10	.05
406	Dickie Noles	.10	.05
407	Ernie Whitt	.10	.05
408	Fernando Arroyo	.10	.05
409	Larry Herndon	.10	.05
410	Bert Campaneris	.15	.08
411	Terry Puhl	.10	.05
412	Britt Burns (R)	.12	.06
413	Tony Bernazard	.10	.05

414	John Pacella	.10	.05
415	Ben Oglivie	.10	.05
416	Gary Alexander	.10	.05
417	Dan Schatzeder	.10	.05
418	Bobby Brown	.10	.05
419	Tom Hume	.10	.05
420	Keith Hernandez	.40	.20
421	Bob Stanley	.10	.05
422	Dan Ford	.10	.05
423	Shane Rawley	.10	.05
424	Yankees Future Stars	.10	.05
	Tim Lollar (R)		
	Bruce Robinson (R)		
	Dennis Werth		
425	Al Bumbry	.10	.05
426	Warren Brusstar	.10	.05
427	John D'Acquisto	.10	.05
428	John Stearns	.10	.05
429	Mick Kelleher	.10	.05
430	Jim Bibby	.10	.05
431	Dave Roberts	.10	.05
432	Len Barker	.10	.05
433	Rance Mulliniks	.10	.05
434	Roger Erickson	.10	.05
435	Jim Spencer	.10	.05
436	Gary Lucas	.10	.05
437	Mike Heath	.10	.05
438	John Montefusco	.10	.05
439	Denny Walling	.10	.05
440	Jerry Reuss	.15	.08
441	Ken Reitz	.10	.05
442	Ron Pruitt	.10	.05
443	Jim Beattie	.10	.05
444	Garth Lorg	.10	.05
445	Ellis Valentine	.10	.05
446	Checklist 364-484	.30	.12
447	Junior Kennedy	.10	.05
448	Tim Corcoran	.10	.05
449	Paul Mitchell	.10	.05
450	Dave Kingman	.20	.10
451	Indians Future Stars	.10	.05
	Chris Bando (R)		
	Tom Brennan		
	Sandy Wihtol		
452	Renie Martin	.10	.05
453	Rob Wilfong	.10	.05
454	Andy Hassler	.10	.05
455	Rick Burleson	.12	.06
456	Jeff Reardon (R)	7.50	3.75
457	Mike Lum	.10	.05
458	Randy Jones	.12	.06
459	Greg Gross	.10	.05
460	Rich Gossage	.40	.20
461	Dave McKay	.10	.05
462	Jack Brohamer	.10	.05
463	Milt May	.10	.05
464	Adrian Devine	.10	.05

465 Bill Russell	.15	.08
466 Bob Molinaro	.10	.05
467 Dave Stieb	.60	.30
408 Johnny Wockenfuss	.10	.05
469 Jeff Leonard	.20	.10
470 Manny Trillo	.10	.05
471 Mike Vail	.10	.05
472 Dyar Miller	.10	.05
473 Jose Cardenal	.10	.05
474 Mike LaCoss	.10	.05
475 Buddy Bell	.12	.06
476 Jerry Koosman	.15	.08
477 Luis Gomez	.10	.05
478 Juan Eichelberger	.10	.05
479 Expos Future Stars	8.50	4.25
Bobby Pate (R)		
Tim Raines (R)		
Roberto Ramos		
480 Carlton Fisk	3.50	1.75
481 Bob Lacey	.10	.05
482 Jim Gantner	.10	.05
483 Mike Griffin	.10	.05
484 Max Venable	.10	.05
485 Garry Templeton	.15	.08
486 Marc Hill	.10	.05
487 Dewey Robinson	.10	.05
488 Damaso Garcia	.12	.06
489 John Littlefield	.10	.05
490 Eddie Murray	4.50	2.25
491 Gordy Pladson	.10	.05
492 Barry Foote	.10	.05
493 Dan Quisenberry	.35	.18
494 Bob Walk (R)	.40	.20
495 Dusty Baker	.20	.10
496 Paul Dade	.10	.05
497 Fred Norman	.10	.05
498 Pat Putnam	.10	.05
499 Frank Pastore	.10	.05
500 Jim Rice	.50	.25
501 Tim Foli	.10	.05
502 Giants Future Stars	.10	.05
Chris Bourjos		
Al Hargesheimer (R)		
Mike Rowland		
503 Steve McCatty	.10	.05
504 Dale Murphy	1.50	.75
505 Jason Thompson	.10	.05
506 Phil Huffman	.10	.05
507 Jamie Quirk	.10	.05
508 Rob Dressler	.10	.05
509 Pete Mackanin	.10	.05
510 Lee Mazzilli	.10	.05
511 Wayne Garland	.10	.05
512 Gary Thomasson	.10	.05
513 Frank LaCorte	.10	.05
514 George Riley	.10	.05
515 Robin Yount	6.00	3.00

516 Doug Bird	.10	.05
517 Richie Zisk	.10	.05
518 Grant Jackson	.10	.05
519 John Tamargo	.10	.05
520 Steve Stone	.15	.08
521 Sam Mejias	.10	.05
522 Mike Colbern	.10	.05
523 John Fulgham	.10	.05
524 Willie Aikens	.10	.05
525 Mike Torrez	.10	.05
526 Phillies Future Stars	.12	.06
Marty Bystrom		
Jay Loviglio (R)		
Jim Wright		
527 Danny Goodwin	.10	.05
528 Gary Matthews	.15	.08
529 Dave LaRoche	.10	.05
530 Steve Garvey	1.25	.60
531 John Curtis	.10	.05
532 Bill Stein	.10	.05
533 Jesus Figueroa	.10	.05
534 Dave Smith (R)	.25	.12
535 Omar Moreno	.10	.05
536 Bob Owchinko	.10	.05
537 Ron Hodges	.10	.05
538 Tom Griffin	.10	.05
539 Rodney Scott	.10	.05
540 Mike Schmidt	4.50	2.25
541 Steve Swisher	.10	.05
542 Larry Bradford	.10	.05
543 Terry Crowley	.10	.05
544 Rich Gale	.10	.05
545 Johnny Grubb	.10	.05
546 Paul Moskau	.10	.05
547 Mario Guerrero	.10	.05
548 Dave Goltz	.10	.05
549 Jerry Remy	.10	.05
550 Tommy John	.25	.12
551 Pirates Future Stars	1.00	.50
Vance Law (R)		
Tony Pena (R)		
Pascual Perez (R)		
552 Steve Trout	.10	.05
553 Tim Blackwell	.10	.05
554 Bert Blyleven	.70	.40
555 Cecil Cooper	.15	.08
556 Jerry Mumphrey	.10	.05
557 Chris Knapp	.10	.05
558 Barry Bonnell	.10	.05
559 Willie Montanez	.10	.05
560 Joe Morgan	2.00	1.00
561 Dennis Littlejohn	.10	.05
562 Checklist 485-605	.30	.12
563 Jim Kaat	.30	.15
564 Ron Hassey	.10	.05
565 Burt Hooton	.10	.05
566 Del Unser	.10	.05

567	Mark Bomback	.10	.05
568	Dave Revering	.10	.05
569	Al Williams	.10	.05
570	Ken Singleton	.12	.06
571	Todd Cruz	.10	.05
572	Jack Morris	1.75	.90
573	Phil Garner	.12	.06
574	Bill Caudill	.10	.05
575	Tony Perez	.75	.35
576	Reggie Cleveland	.10	.05
577	Blue Jays Future Stars	.12	.06
	Luis Leal (R)		
	Brian Milner		
	Ken Schrom		
578	Bill Gullickson (R)	1.00	.50
579	Tim Flannery	.10	.05
580	Don Baylor	.30	.15
581	Roy Howell	.10	.05
582	Gaylord Perry	1.25	.60
583	Larry Milbourne	.10	.05
584	Randy Lerch	.10	.05
585	Amos Otis	.12	.06
586	Silvio Martinez	.10	.05
587	Jeff Newman	.10	.05
588	Gary Lavelle	.10	.05
589	Lamar Johnson	.10	.05
590	Bruce Sutter	.25	.12
591	John Lowenstein	.10	.05
592	Steve Comer	.10	.05
593	Steve Kemp	.10	.05
594	Preston Hanna	.10	.05
595	Butch Hobson	.10	.05
596	Jerry Augustine	.10	.05
597	Rafael Landestoy	.10	.05
598	George Vukovich	.10	.05
599	Dennis Kinney	.10	.05
600	Johnny Bench	3.50	1.75
601	Don Aase	.10	.05
602	Bobby Murcer	.20	.10
603	John Verhoeven	.10	.05
604	Rob Picciolo	.10	.05
605	Don Sutton	1.00	.50
606	Reds Future Stars	.10	.05
	Bruce Berenyl (R)		
	Geoff Combe (R)		
	Paul Householder (R)		
607	Dave Palmer	.10	.05
608	Greg Pryor	.10	.05
609	Lynn McGlothen	.10	.05
610	Darrell Porter	.10	.05
611	Rick Matula	.10	.05
612	Duane Kuiper	.10	.05
613	Jim Anderson	.10	.05
614	Dave Rozema	.10	.05
615	Rick Dempsey	.12	.06
616	Rick Wise	.12	.06
617	Craig Reynolds	.10	.05
618	John Milner	.10	.05
619	Steve Henderson	.10	.05
620	Dennis Eckersley	2.50	1.25
621	Tom Donohue	.10	.05
622	Randy Moffitt	.10	.05
623	Sal Bando	.12	.06
624	Bob Welch	.40	.20
625	Bill Buckner	.20	.10
626	Tigers Future Stars	.10	.05
	Dave Steffen		
	Jerry Ujdur (R)		
	Roger Weaver (R)		
627	Luis Tiant	.25	.12
628	Vic Correll	.10	.05
629	Tony Armas	.12	.06
630	Steve Carlton	4.50	2.25
631	Ron Jackson	.10	.05
632	Alan Bannister	.10	.05
633	Bill Lee	.10	.05
634	Doug Flynn	.10	.05
635	Bobby Bonds	.25	.12
636	Al Hrabosky	.12	.06
637	Jerry Narron	.10	.05
638	Checklist 606-726	.30	.12
639	Carney Lansford	.35	.18
640	Dave Parker	.50	.25
641	Mark Belanger	.15	.08
642	Vern Ruhle	.10	.05
643	Lloyd Moseby (R)	.25	.12
644	Ramon Aviles	.10	.05
645	Rick Reuschel	.15	.08
646	Marvis Foley	.10	.05
647	Dick Drago	.10	.05
648	Darrell Evans	.25	.12
649	Many Sarmiento	.10	.05
650	Bucky Dent	.12	.06
651	Pedro Guerrero	.50	.25
652	John Montague	.10	.05
653	Bill Fahey	.10	.05
654	Ray Burris	.10	.05
655	Dan Driessen	.10	.05
656	Jon Matlack	.10	.05
657	Mike Cubbage	.10	.05
658	Milt Wilcox	.10	.05
659	Brewers Future Stars	.10	.05
	John Flinn (R)		
	Ed Romero		
	Ned Yost		
660	Gary Carter	1.50	.75
661	Orioles Team	.30	.15
662	Red Sox Team	.25	.12
663	Angels Team	.25	.12
664	White Sox Team	.30	.15
665	Indians Team	.25	.12
666	Tigers Team	.30	.15
667	Royals Team	.25	.12
668	Brewers Team	.25	.12

669	Twins Team	.25	.12
670	Yankees Team	.30	.15
671	A's Team	.35	.18
672	Mariners Team	.30	.15
673	Rangers Team	.25	.12
674	Blue Jays Team	.25	.12
675	Braves Team	.25	.12
676	Cubs Team	.25	.12
677	Reds Team	.25	.12
678	Astros Team	.25	.12
679	Dodgers Team	.30	.15
680	Expos Team	.25	.12
681	Mets Team	.30	.15
682	Phillies Team	.25	.12
683	Pirates Team	.25	.12
684	Cardinals Team	.30	.15
685	Padres Team	.25	.12
686	Giants Team	.25	.12
687	Jeff Jones	.10	.05
688	Kiko Garcia	.10	.05
689	Red Sox Future Stars	1.25	.65
	Bruce Hurst (R)		
	Keith MacWhorter (R)		
	Reid Nichols		
690	Bob Watson	.30	.15
691	Dick Ruthven	.10	.05
692	Lenny Randle	.10	.05
693	Steve Howe (R)	.15	.08
694	Bud Harrelson	.10	.05
695	Kent Tekulve	.10	.05
696	Alan Ashby	.10	.05
697	Rick Waits	.10	.05
698	Mike Jorgensen	.10	.05
699	Glenn Abbott	.10	.05
700	George Brett	7.50	3.75
701	Joe Rudi	.12	.06
702	George Medich	.10	.05
703	Alvis Woods	.10	.05
704	Bill Travers	.10	.05
705	Ted Simmons	.25	.12
706	Dave Ford	.10	.05
707	Dave Cash	.10	.05
708	Doyle Alexander	.10	.05
709	Alan Trammell	2.00	1.00
710	Ron LeFlore	.12	.06
711	Joe Ferguson	.10	.05
712	Bill Bonham	.10	.05
713	Bill North	.10	.05
714	Pete Redfern	.10	.05
715	Bill Madlock	.25	.12
716	Glenn Borgmann	.10	.05
717	Jim Barr	.10	.05
718	Larry Bittner	.10	.05
719	Sparky Lyle	.15	.08
720	Fred Lynn	.30	.15
721	Toby Harrah	.10	.05
722	Joe Niekro	.12	.06

723	Bruce Bochte	.10	.05
724	Lou Piniella	.20	.10
725	Steve Rogers	.12	.06
726	Rick Monday	.20	.10

1981 Topps Traded

This 132-card set marks Topps first update set since 1976. Card numbers pick up where the regular edition left off (727-858). The set features players who were traded during the season and rookies.

	MT	NR/MT
Complete Set (132)	48.00	24.00
Commons	.25	.12

727	Danny Ainge	7.00	3.50
728	Doyle Alexander	.25	.12
729	Gary Alexander	.25	.12
730	Bill Almon	.25	.12
731	Joaquin Andujar	.30	.15
732	Bob Bailor	.25	.12
733	Juan Beniquez	.25	.12
734	Dave Bergman	.25	.12
735	Tony Bernazard	.25	.12
736	Larry Biittner	.25	.12
737	Doug Bird	.25	.12
739	Bert Blyleven	1.50	.75
739	Mark Bomback	.25	.12
740	Bobby Bonds	.50	.25
741	Rick Bosetti	.25	.12
742	Hubie Brooks	.80	.40
743	Rick Burleson	.30	.15
744	Ray Burris	.25	.12
745	Jeff Burroughs	.25	.12
746	Enos Cabell	.25	.12
747	Ken Clay	.25	.12
748	Mark Clear	.25	.12

749 Larry Cox	.25	.12
750 Hector Cruz	.25	.12
751 Victor Cruz	.25	.12
752 Mike Cubbage	.25	.12
753 Dick Davis	.25	.12
754 Brian Doyle	.25	.12
755 Dick Drago	.25	.12
756 Leon Durham	.25	.12
757 Jim Dwyer	.25	.12
758 Dave Edwards	.25	.12
759 Jim Essian	.25	.12
760 Bill Fahey	.25	.12
761 Rollie Fingers	3.00	1.50
762 Carlton Fisk	7.50	3.75
763 Barry Foote	.25	.12
764 Ken Forsch	.25	.12
765 Kiko Garcia	.25	.12
766 Cesar Geronimo	.25	.12
767 Gary Gray	.25	.12
768 Mickey Hatcher	.25	.12
769 Steve Henderson	.25	.12
770 Marc Hill	.25	.12
771 Butch Hobson	.30	.15
772 Rick Honeycutt	.25	.12
773 Roy Howell	.25	.12
774 Mike Ivie	.25	.12
775 Roy Lee Jackson	.25	.12
776 Cliff Johnson	.25	.12
777 Randy Jones	.25	.12
778 Ruppert Jones	.25	.12
779 Mick Kelleher	.25	.12
780 Terry Kennedy	.25	.12
781 Dave Kingman	.40	.20
782 Bob Knepper	.25	.12
783 Ken Kravec	.25	.12
784 Bob Lacey	.25	.12
785 Dennis Lamp	.25	.12
786 Rafael Landestoy	.25	.12
787 Ken Landreaux	.25	.12
788 Carney Lansford	.60	.30
789 Dave LaRoche	.25	.12
790 Joe Lefebvre	.25	.12
791 Ron LeFlore	.30	.15
792 Randy Lerch	.25	.12
793 Sixto Lezcano	.25	.12
794 John Littlefield	.25	.12
795 Mike Lum	.25	.12
796 Greg Luzinski	.30	.15
797 Fred Lynn	.35	.18
798 Jerry Martin	.25	.12
799 Buck Martinez	.25	.12
800 Gary Matthews	.25	.12
801 Mario Mendoza	.25	.12
802 Larry Milbourne	.25	.12
803 Rick Miller	.25	.12
804 John Montefusco	.25	.12
805 Jerry Morales	.25	.12

806 Jose Morales	.25	.12
807 Joe Morgan	3.50	1.75
808 Jerry Mumphrey	.25	.12
809 Gene Nelson	.25	.12
810 Ed Ott	.25	.12
811 Bob Owchinko	.25	.12
812 Gaylord Perry	2.00	1.05
813 Mike Phillips	.25	.12
814 Darrell Porter	.25	.12
815 Mike Proly	.25	.12
816 Tim Raines	12.50	6.25
817 Lenny Randle	.25	.12
818 Doug Rau	.25	.12
819 Jeff Reardon	10.00	5.00
820 Ken Reitz	.25	.12
821 Steve Renko	.25	.12
822 Rick Reuschel	.25	.12
823 Dave Revering	.25	.12
824 Dave Roberts	.25	.12
825 Leon Roberts	.25	.12
826 Joe Rudi	.30	.15
827 Kevin Saucier	.25	.12
828 Tony Scott	.25	.12
829 Bob Shirley	.25	.12
830 Ted Simmons	.40	.20
831 Lary Sorensen	.25	.12
832 Jim Spencer	.25	.12
833 Harry Spilman	.25	.12
834 Fred Stanley	.25	.12
835 Rusty Staub	.25	.12
836 Bill Stein	.25	.12
837 Joe Strain	.25	.12
838 Bruce Sutter	.60	.30
839 Don Sutton	3.00	1.50
840 Steve Swisher	.25	.12
841 Frank Tanana	.25	.12
842 Gene Tenace	.30	.15
843 Jason Thompson	.25	.12
844 Dickie Thon	.25	.12
845 Bill Travers	.25	.12
846 Tom Underwood	.25	.12
847 John Urrea	.25	.12
848 Mike Vail	.25	.12
849 Ellis Valentine	.25	.12
850 Fernando Valenzuela	2.50	1.25
851 Pete Vuckovich	.30	.15
852 Mark Wagner	.25	.12
853 Bob Walk	.35	.18
854 Claudell Washington	.30	.15
855 Dave Winfield	18.00	9.00
856 Geoff Zahn	.25	.12
857 Richie Zisk	.25	.12
858 Checklist 727-858	.30	.12

1982 Topps

At 792-cards, this is the largest set Topps produced to this point. Cards measure 2-1/2" by 3-1/2" and feature large color photos on the fronts with a fascimile autograph beneath the picture. Subsets include Highlights (HL) (1-6), League Leaders, All-Stars, In-Action (IA), Future Stars (Rookies) and Team Leaders (TL).

		MINT	NR/MT
Complete Set (792)		155.00	110.00
Commons		.10	.06

1	Steve Carlton (HL)	1.50	.90
2	Ron Davis (HL)	.10	.06
3	Tim Raines (HL)	.60	.35
4	Pete Rose (HL)	1.50	.90
5	Nolan Ryan (HL)	5.00	3.00
6	Fernando Valenzuela (HL)	.20	.12
7	Scott Sanderson	.12	.07
8	Rich Dauer	.10	.06
9	Ron Guidry	.40	.25
10	Ron Guidry IA	.15	.10
11	Gary Alexander	.10	.06
12	Moose Haas	.10	.06
13	Lamar Johnson	.10	.06
14	Steve Howe	.10	.06
15	Ellis Valentine	.10	.06
16	Steve Comer	.10	.06
17	Darrell Evans	.15	.10
18	Fernando Arroyo	.10	.06
19	Ernie Whitt	.10	.06
20	Garry Maddox	.10	.06
21	Orioles Future Stars	75.00	40.00
	Bob Bonner (R)		
	Cal Ripken (R)		
	Jeff Schneider (R)		
22	Jim Beattie	.10	.06
23	Willie Hernandez	.15	.10
24	Dave Frost	.10	.06
25	Jerry Remy	.10	.06
26	Jorge Orta	.10	.06
27	Tom Herr	.12	.07
28	John Urrea	.10	.06
29	Dwayne Murphy	.10	.06
30	Tom Seaver	3.00	2.00
31	Tom Seaver (IA)	1.50	.90
32	Gene Garber	.10	.06
33	Jerry Morales	.10	.06
34	Joe Sambito	.10	.06
35	Willie Aikens	.10	.06
36	Rangers (TL)	.25	.15
	George Medich		
	Al Oliver		
37	Dan Graham	.10	.06
38	Charlie Lea	.10	.06
39	Lou Whitaker	1.00	.60
40	Dave Parker	.50	.35
41	Dave Parker IA	.25	.15
42	Rick Sofield	.10	.06
43	Mike Cubbage	.10	.06
44	Britt Burns	.10	.06
45	Rick Cerone	.12	.07
46	Jerry Augustine	.10	.06
47	Jeff Leonard	.12	.07
48	Bobby Castillo	.10	.06
49	Alvis Woods	.10	.06
50	Buddy Bell	.12	.07
51	Cubs Future Stars	.30	.18
	Jay Howell (R)		
	Carlos Lezcano		
	Ty Waller (R)		
52	Larry Andersen	.10	.06
53	Greg Gross	.10	.06
54	Ron Hassey	.12	.07
55	Rick Burleson	.12	.07
56	Mark Littell	.10	.06
57	Craig Reynolds	.10	.06
58	John D'Acquisto	.10	.06
59	Rich Gedman (R)	.15	.10
60	Tony Armas	.12	.07
61	Tommy Boggs	.10	.06
62	Mike Tyson	.10	.06
63	Mario Soto	.15	.10
64	Lynn Jones	.10	.06
65	Terry Kennedy	.12	.07
66	Astros (TL)(Art Howe	2.00	1.25
	Nolan Ryan)		
67	Rich Gale	.10	.06
68	Roy Howell	.10	.06
69	Al Williams	.10	.06
70	Tim Raines	2.50	1.40
71	Roy Lee Jackson	.10	.06
72	Rick Auerbach	.10	.06
73	Buddy Solomon	.10	.06
74	Bob Clark	.10	.06

75	Tommy John	.25	.15
76	Greg Pryor	.10	.06
77	Miguel Dilone	.10	.06
78	George Medich	.10	.06
79	Bob Bailor	.10	.06
80	Jim Palmer	2.00	1.25
81	Jim Palmer IA	1.00	.60
82	Bob Welch	.30	.20
83	Yankees Future Stars	.15	.10
	Steve Balboni (R)		
	Andy McGaffigan (R)		
	Andre Robertson		
84	Rennie Stennett	.10	.06
85	Lynn McGlothen	.10	.06
86	Dane Iorg	.10	.06
87	Matt Keough	.10	.06
88	Biff Pocoroba	.10	.06
89	Steve Henderson	.10	.06
90	Nolan Ryan	14.00	7.50
91	Carney Lansford	.20	.12
92	Brad Havens	.10	.06
93	Larry Hisle	.10	.06
94	Andy Hassler	.10	.06
95	Ozzie Smith	3.50	2.00
96	Royals (TL) (George	.75	.40
	Brett, Larry Gura)		
97	Paul Moskau	.10	.06
98	Terry Bulling	.10	.06
99	Bary Bonnell	.10	.06
100	Mike Schmidt	4.50	3.00
101	Mike Schmidt IA	2.00	1.25
102	Dan Briggs	.10	.06
103	Bob Lacey	.10	.06
104	Rance Mulliniks	.10	.06
105	Kirk Gibson	1.00	.60
106	Enrique Romo	.10	.06
107	Wayne Krenchicki	.10	.06
108	Bob Sykes	.10	.06
109	Dave Revering	.10	.06
110	Carlton Fisk	2.50	1.50
111	Carlton Fisk IA	1.50	.90
112	Billy Sample	.10	.06
113	Steve McCatty	.10	.06
114	Ken Landreaux	.10	.06
115	Gaylord Perry	.80	.50
116	Jim Wohlford	.10	.06
117	Rawly Eastwick	.10	.06
118	Expos Future Stars	.20	.12
	Terry Francona (R)		
	Brad Mills		
	Bryn Smith (R)		
119	Joe Pittman	.10	.06
120	Gary Lucas	.10	.06
121	Ed Lynch	.10	.06
122	Jamie Easterly	.10	.06
123	Danny Goodwin	.10	.06
124	Reid Nichols	.10	.06

125	Danny Ainge	2.50	1.40
126	Braves (TL)(Rick	.12	.07
	Mahler, Claudell		
	Washington)		
127	Lonnie Smith	.10	.06
128	Frank Pastore	.10	.06
129	Checklist 1-132	.15	.06
130	Julio Cruz	.10	.06
131	Stan Bahnsen	.10	.06
132	Lee May	.10	.06
133	Pat Underwood	.10	.06
134	Dan Ford	.10	.06
135	Andy Rincon	.10	.06
136	Lenn Sakata	.10	.06
137	George Cappuzzello	.10	.06
138	Tony Pena	.20	.12
139	Jeff Jones	.10	.06
140	Ron LeFlore	.12	.07
141	Indians Future Stars	.40	.25
	Chris Bando		
	Tom Brennan (R)		
	Von Hayes (R)		
142	Dave Laroche	.10	.06
143	Mookie Wilson	.15	.10
144	Fred Breining	.10	.06
145	Bob Horner	.15	.10
146	Mike Griffin	.10	.06
147	Denny Walling	.10	.06
148	Mickey Klutts	.10	.06
149	Pat Putnam	.10	.06
150	Ted Simmons	.20	.12
151	Dave Edwards	.10	.06
152	Ramon Aviles	.10	.06
153	Roger Erickson	.10	.06
154	Dennis Werth	.10	.06
155	Otto Velez	.10	.06
156	A's (TL) (Rickey	.80	.50
	Henderson, Steve		
	McCatty (R)		
157	Steve Crawford	.10	.06
158	Brian Downing	.12	.07
159	Larry Bittner	.10	.06
160	Luis Tiant	.20	.12
161	Batting Leaders	.25	.15
162	Home Run Leaders	.75	.40
163	Runs Batted In Leaders	1.25	.80
164	Stolen Base Leaders	1.50	.90
165	Victory Leaders	.80	.50
166	Strikeout Leaders	.20	.12
167	ERA Leaders	2.50	1.40
168	Leading Firemen	.35	.20
169	Charlie Leibrandt	.12	.07
170	Jim Bibby	.10	.06
171	Giants Future Stars	2.50	1.40
	Bob Brenly (R)		
	Chili Davis (R)		
	Bob Tufts (R)		

172 Bill Gullickson	.25	.12	
173 Jamie Quirk	.10	.06	
174 Dave Ford	.10	.06	
175 Jerry Mumphrey	.10	.06	
176 Dewey Robinson	.10	.06	
177 John Ellis	.10	.06	
178 Dyar Miller	.10	.06	
179 Steve Garvey	1.00	.60	
180 Steve Garvey IA	.50	.28	
181 Silvio Martinez	.10	.06	
182 Larry Herndon	.10	.06	
183 Mike Proly	.10	.06	
184 Mick Kelleher	.10	.06	
185 Phil Niekro	.80	.50	
186 Cardinals (TL)(Bob	.25	.15	
Forsch, Keith Hernandez)			
187 Jeff Newman	.10	.06	
188 Randy Martz	.10	.06	
189 Glenn Hoffman	.10	.06	
190 J.R. Richard	.20	.12	
191 Tim Wallach (R)	1.50	.90	
192 Broderick Perkins	.10	.06	
193 Darrell Jackson	.10	.06	
194 Mike Vail	.10	.06	
195 Paul Molitor	6.00	3.50	
196 Willie Upshaw	.10	.06	
197 Shane Rawley	.10	.06	
198 Chris Speier	.10	.06	
199 Don Aase	.10	.06	
200 George Brett	5.00	3.00	
201 George Brett IA	2.50	1.40	
202 Rick Maning	.10	.06	
203 Blue Jays Future Stars	.75	.40	
Jesse Barfield (R)			
Brian Milner			
Boomer Wells (R)			
204 Gary Roenicke	.10	.06	
205 Neil Allen	.10	.06	
206 Tony Bernazard	.10	.06	
207 Rod Scurry	.10	.06	
208 Bobby Murcer	.15	.10	
209 Gary Lavelle	.10	.06	
210 Keith Hernandez	.30	.20	
211 Dan Petry	.10	.06	
212 Mario Mendoza	.10	.06	
213 Dave Stewart (R)	6.00	3.50	
214 Brian Asselstine	.10	.06	
215 Mike Krukow	.10	.06	
216 White Sox (TL)	.15	.10	
(Dennis Lamp,			
Chet Lemon)			
217 Bo McLaughlin	.10	.06	
218 Dave Roberts	.10	.06	
219 John Curtis	.10	.06	
220 Manny Trillo	.10	.06	
221 Jim Slaton	.10	.06	
222 Butch Wynegar	.10	.06	
223 Lloyd Moseby	.10	.06	
224 Bruce Bochte	.15	.10	
225 Mike Torrez	.10	.06	
226 Checklist 133-264	.15	.06	
227 Ray Burris	.10	.06	
228 Sam Mejias	.10	.06	
229 Geoff Zahn	.10	.06	
230 Willie Wilson	.15	.10	
231 Phillies Future Stars	.25	.15	
Mark Davis (R)			
Bob Dernier			
Ozzie Virgil (R)			
232 Terry Crowley	.10	.06	
233 Duane Kuiper	.10	.06	
234 Ron Hodges	.10	.06	
235 Mike Easler	.10	.06	
236 John Martin	.10	.06	
237 Rusty Kuntz	.10	.06	
238 Kevin Saucier	.10	.06	
239 Jon Matlack	.12	.07	
240 Bucky Dent	.15	.10	
241 Bucky Dent IA	.10	.06	
242 Milt May	.10	.06	
243 Bob Owchinko	.10	.06	
244 Rufino Linares	.10	.06	
245 Ken Reitz	.10	.06	
246 Mets (TL)(Hubie	.25	.15	
Brooks, Mike Scott)			
247 Pedro Guerrero	.35	.20	
248 Frank LaCorte	.10	.06	
249 Tim Flannery	.10	.06	
250 Tug McGraw	.20	.12	
251 Fred Lynn	.30	.20	
252 Fred Lynn IA	.15	.10	
253 Chuck Baker	.10	.06	
254 Jorge Bell (R)	5.00	3.00	
255 Tony Perez	.80	.50	
256 Tony Perez IA	.40	.25	
257 Larry Harlow	.10	.06	
258 Bo Diaz	.10	.06	
259 Rodney Scott	.10	.06	
260 Bruce Sutter	.20	.12	
261 Tigers Future Stars	.12	.07	
Howard Bailey			
Marty Castillo			
Dave Rucker (R)			
262 Doug Bair	.10	.06	
263 Victor Cruz	.10	.06	
264 Dan Quisenberry	.20	.12	
265 Al Bumbry	.10	.06	
266 Rick Leach	.10	.06	
267 Kurt Bevacqua	.10	.06	
268 Rickey Keeton	.10	.06	
269 Jim Esian	.10	.06	
270 Rusty Staub	.25	.15	
271 Larry Bradford	.10	.06	
272 Bump Wills	.10	.06	

273	Doug Bird	.10	.06
274	Bob Ojeda (R)	.60	.35
275	Bob Watson	.25	.15
276	Angels (TL)(Rod Carew, Ken Forsch)	.40	.25
277	Terry Puhl	.10	.06
278	John Littlefield	.10	.06
279	Bill Russell	.15	.10
280	Ben Oglivie	.10	.06
281	John Verhoeven	.10	.06
282	Ken Macha	.10	.06
283	Brian Allard	.10	.06
284	Bob Grich	.15	.10
285	Sparky Lyle	.15	.10
286	Bill Fahey	.10	.06
287	Alan Bannister	.10	.06
288	Garry Templeton	.12	.07
289	Bob Stanley	.10	.06
290	Ken Singleton	.12	.07
291	Pirates Future Stars Vance Law Bob Long (R) Johnny Ray (R)	.25	.15
292	Dave Palmer	.10	.06
293	Rob Picciolo	.10	.06
294	Mike LaCoss	.10	.06
295	Jason Thompson	.10	.06
296	Bob Walk	.10	.06
297	Clint Hurdle	.10	.06
298	Danny Darwin	.12	.07
299	Steve Trout	.10	.06
300	Reggie Jackson	3.50	2.50
301	Reggie Jackson IA	2.00	1.25
302	Doug Flynn	.10	.06
303	Bill Caudill	.10	.06
304	Johnnie LeMaster	.10	.06
305	Don Sutton	.80	.50
306	Don Sutton IA	.40	.25
307	Randy Bass	.10	.06
308	Charlie Moore	.10	.06
309	Pete Redfern	.10	.06
310	Mike Hargrove	.10	.06
311	Dodgers (TL)(Dusty Baker, Burt Hooton)	.25	.15
312	Lenny Randle	.10	.06
313	John Harris	.10	.06
314	Buck Martinez	.10	.06
315	Burt Hooton	.10	.06
316	Steve Braun	.10	.06
317	Dick Ruthven	.10	.06
318	Mike Heath	.10	.06
319	Dave Rozema	.10	.06
320	Chris Chambliss	.15	.10
321	Chris Chambliss IA	.10	.06
322	Garry Hancock	.10	.06
323	Bill Lee	.10	.06
324	Steve Dillard	.10	.06
325	Jose Cruz	.15	.10
326	Pete Falcone	.10	.06
327	Joe Nolan	.10	.06
328	Ed Farmer	.10	.06
329	U.L. Washington	.10	.06
330	Rick Wise	.12	.07
331	Benny Ayala	.10	.06
332	Don Robinson	.10	.06
333	Brewers Future Stars Frank DiPino Marshall Edwards (R) Chuck Porter (R)	.12	.07
334	Aurelio Rodriguez	.10	.06
335	Jim Sundberg	.10	.06
336	Mariners (TL)(Glenn Abbott, Tom Paciorek)	.12	.07
337	Pete Rose AS	1.50	.90
338	Dave Lopes AS	.20	.10
339	Mike Schmidt AS	2.50	1.40
340	Dave Concepcion AS	.25	.12
341	Andre Dawson AS	1.50	.90
342a	George Foster AS (No Autograph)	.80	.50
342b	George Foster AS (Autograph)	.25	.15
343	Dave Parker AS	.25	.15
344	Gary Carter AS	.50	.30
345	Fernando Valenzuela AS	.25	.15
346	Tom Seaver AS	1.50	.90
347	Bruce Sutter AS	.25	.15
348	Derrel Thomas	.10	.06
349	George Frazier	.10	.06
350	Thad Bosley	.10	.06
351	Reds Future Stars Scott Brown (R) Geoff Combe (R) Paul Householder	.10	.06
352	Dick Davis	.10	.06
353	Jack O'Connor	.10	.06
354	Roberto Ramos	.10	.06
355	Dwight Evans	.40	.25
356	Denny Lewallyn	.10	.06
357	Butch Hobson	.10	.06
358	Mike Parrott	.10	.06
359	Jim Dwyer	.10	.06
360	Len Barker	.10	.06
361	Rafael Landestoy	.10	.06
362	Jim Wright	.10	.06
363	Bob Molinaro	.10	.06
364	Doyle Alexander	.10	.06
365	Bill Madlock	.25	.15
366	Padres (TL)(Juan Eichelberger, Luis Salazar)	.12	.07
367	Jim Kaat	.25	.12
368	Alex Trevino	.10	.06

369	Champ Summers	.10	.06		Bobby Johnson (R)			
370	Mike Norris	.10	.06		Dave Schmidt			
371	Jerry Don Gleaton	.10	.06	419	Steve Stone	.12	.07
372	Luis Gomez	.10	.06	420	George Hendrick	.12	.07
373	Gene Nelson	.10	.06	421	Mark Clear	.10	.06
374	Tim Blackwell	.10	.06	422	Cliff Johnson	.10	.06
375	Dusty Baker	.20	.10	423	Stan Papi	.10	.06
376	Chris Welsh	.10	.06	424	Bruce Benedict	.10	.06
377	Kiko Garcia	.10	.06	425	John Candelaria	.12	.07
378	Mike Caldwell	.10	.06	426	Orioles (TL) (Eddie	.50	.30
379	Rob Wilfong	.10	.06		Murray, Sammy		
380	Dave Stieb	.25	.15		Stewart)		
381	Red Sox Future Stars	.50	.28	427	Ron Oester	.10	.06
	Bruce Hurst			428	LaMarr Hoyt	.10	.06
	Dave Schmidt			429	John Wathan	.10	.06
	Julio Valdez			430	Vida Blue	.25	.15
382	Joe Simpson	.10	.06	431	Vida Blue IA	.15	.10
383a	Pascual Perez	18.00	10.00	432	Mike Scott	.25	.15
	(No position on front)			433	Alan Ashby	.10	.06
383b	Pascual Perez (Cor)	.20	.12	434	Joe Lefebvre	.10	.06
384	Keith Moreland	.10	.06	435	Robin Yount	4.50	3.00
385	Ken Forsch	.10	.06	436	Joe Strain	.10	.06
386	Jerry White	.10	.06	437	Juan Berenguer	.10	.06
387	Tom Veryzer	.10	.06	438	Pete Mackanin	.10	.06
388	Joe Rudi	.12	.07	439	Dave Righetti (R)	.60	.35
389	George Vukovich	.10	.06	440	Jeff Burroughs	.10	.06
390	Eddie Murray	3.50	2.50	441	Astros Future Stars	.15	.10
391	Dave Tobik	.10	.06		Danny Heep		
392	Rick Bosetti	.10	.06		Billy Smith (R)		
393	Al Hrabosky	.12	.07		Bobby Sprowl		
394	Checklist 265-396	.15	.06	442	Bruce Kison	.10	.06
395	Omar Moreno	.10	.06	443	Mark Wagner	.10	.06
396	Twins (TL) (Fernando	.12	.07	444	Terry Forster	.10	.06
	Arroyo, John Castino)			445	Larry Parrish	.10	.06
397	Ken Brett	.10	.06	446	Wayne Garland	.10	.06
398	Mike Squires	.10	.06	447	Darrell Porter	.10	.06
399	Pat Zachry	.10	.06	448	Darrell Porter IA	.10	.06
400	Johnny Bench	2.50	1.40	449	Luis Aguayo	.10	.06
401	Johnny Bench IA	1.50	.90	450	Jack Morris	1.25	.80
402	Bill Stein	.10	.06	451	Ed Miller	.10	.06
403	Jim Tracy	.10	.06	452	Lee Smith	14.00	7.50
404	Dickie Thon	.10	.06	453	Art Howe	.10	.06
405	Rick Reuschel	.12	.07	454	Rick Langford	.10	.06
406	Al Hollard	.10	.06	455	Tom Burgmeier	.10	.06
407	Danny Boone	.10	.06	456	Cubs (TL) (Bill Buckner	.20	.12
408	Ed Romero	.10	.06		Randy Martz)		
409	Don Cooper	.10	.06	457	Tim Stoddard	.10	.06
410	Ron Cey	.15	.10	458	Willie Montanez	.10	.06
411	Ron Cey IA	.10	.06	459	Bruce Berenyi	.10	.06
412	Luis Leal	.10	.06	460	Jack Clark	.25	.15
413	Dan Meyer	.10	.06	461	Rich Dotson	.10	.06
414	Elias Sosa	.10	.06	462	Dave Chalk	.10	.06
415	Don Baylor	.20	.12	463	Jim Kern	.10	.06
416	Marty Bystrom	.10	.06	464	Juan Bonilla	.10	.06
417	Pat Kelly	.10	.06	465	Lee Mazzilli	.10	.06
418	Rangers Future Stars	.12	.07	466	Randy Lerch	.10	.06
	John Butcher			467	Mickey Hatcher	.10	.06

468	Floyd Bannister	.10	.06
469	Ed Ott	.10	.06
470	John Mayberry	.12	.07
471	Royals Future Stars	.15	.10
	Atlee Hammaker (R)		
	Mike Jones (R)		
	Darryl Motley (R)		
472	Oscar Gamble	.12	.07
473	Mike Stanton	.10	.06
474	Ken Oberkfell	.10	.06
475	Alan Trammell	1.75	1.00
476	Brian Kingman	.10	.06
477	Steve Yeager	.10	.06
478	Ray Searage	.10	.06
479	Rowland Office	.10	.06
480	Steve Carlton	3.00	2.00
481	Steve Carlton IA	1.75	1.00
482	Glenn Hubbard	.10	.06
483	Gary Woods	.10	.06
484	Ivan DeJesus	.10	.06
485	Kent Tekulve	.10	.06
486	Yankees (TL) (Tommy	.25	.15
	John, Jerry Mumphrey)		
487	Bob McClure	.10	.06
488	Ron Jackson	.10	.06
489	Rick Dempsey	.12	.07
490	Dennis Eckersley	2.50	1.40
491	Checklist 397-528	.15	.06
492	Joe Price	.10	.06
493	Chet Lemon	.12	.07
494	Hubie Brooks	.50	.30
495	Dennis Leonard	.10	.06
496	Johnny Grubb	.10	.06
497	Jim Anderson	.10	.06
498	Dave Bergman	.10	.06
499	Paul Mirabella	.10	.06
500	Rod Carew	2.00	1.25
501	Rod Carew IA	1.00	.70
502	Braves Future Stars	5.00	3.00
	Steve Bedrosian (R)		
	Brett Butler (R)		
	Larry Owen (R)		
503	Julio Gonzalez	.10	.06
504	Rick Peters	.10	.06
505	Graig Nettles	.25	.15
506	Graig Nettles IA	.12	.07
507	Terry Harper	.10	.06
508	Jody Davis	.10	.06
509	Harry Spillman	.10	.06
510	Fernando Valenzuela	.25	.15
511	Ruppert Jones	.10	.06
512	Jerry Dybzinski	.10	.06
513	Rick Rhoden	.10	.06
514	Joe Ferguson	.10	.06
515	Larry Bowa	.15	.10
516	Larry Bowa IA	.10	.06
517	Mark Brouhard	.10	.06
518	Garth Iorg	.10	.06
519	Glenn Adams	.10	.06
520	Mike Flanagan	.15	.10
521	Billy Almon	.10	.06
522	Chuck Rainey	.10	.06
523	Gary Gray	.10	.06
524	Tom Hausman	.10	.06
525	Ray Knight	.15	.10
526	Expos (TL) (Warren	.15	.10
	Cromartie, Bill		
	Gullickson)		
527	John Henry Johnson	.10	.06
528	Matt Alexander	.10	.06
529	Allen Ripley	.10	.06
530	Dickie Noles	.10	.06
531	A's Future Stars	.10	.06
	Rich Bordi		
	Mark Budaska (R)		
	Kelvin Moore		
532	Toby Harrah	.10	.06
533	Joaquin Andujar	.15	.10
534	Dave McKay	.10	.06
535	Lance Parrish	.25	.15
536	Rafael Ramirez	.10	.06
537	Doug Capilla	.10	.06
538	Lou Piniella	.15	.10
539	Vern Ruhle	.10	.06
540	Andre Dawson	3.50	2.50
541	Barry Evans	.10	.06
542	Ned Yost	.10	.06
543	Bill Robinson	.10	.06
544	Larry Christenson	.10	.06
545	Reggie Smith	.15	.10
546	Reggie Smith IA	.10	.06
547	Rod Carew AS	.80	.50
548	Willie Randolph AS	.20	.12
549	George Brett AS	2.00	1.25
550	Bucky Dent AS	.15	.10
551	Reggie Jackson AS	1.50	.90
552	Ken Singleton AS	.12	.07
553	Dave Winfield AS	2.00	1.25
554	Carlton Fisk AS	.90	.60
555	Scott McGregor AS	.15	.10
556	Jack Morris AS	.50	.25
557	Rich Gossage AS	.15	.10
558	John Tudor	.15	.10
559	Indians (TL)(Bert	.25	.15
	Blyleven, Mike		
	Hargrove)		
560	Doug Corbett	.10	.06
561	Cardinals Future Stars	.10	.06
	Glenn Brummer		
	Luis DeLeon		
	Gene Roof		
562	Mike O'Berry	.10	.06
563	Ross Baumgarten	.10	.06
564	Doug DeCinces	.12	.07

565	Jackson Todd	.10	.06
566	Mike Jorgensen	.10	.06
567	Bob Babcock	.10	.06
568	Joe Pettini	.10	.06
569	Willie Randolph	.20	.12
570	Willie Randolph IA	.12	.07
571	Glenn Abbott	.10	.06
572	Juan Beniquez	.10	.06
573	Rick Waits	.10	.06
574	Mike Ramsey	.10	.06
575	Al Cowens	.10	.06
576	Giants (TL)(Vida Blue, Milt May)	.25	.15
577	Rick Monday	.15	.10
578	Shooty Babitt	.10	.06
579	Rick Mahler (R)	.20	.12
580	Bobby Bonds	.20	.12
581	Ron Reed	.10	.06
582	Luis Pujols	.10	.06
583	Tippy Martinez	.10	.06
584	Hosken Powell	.10	.06
585	Rollie Fingers	1.25	.80
586	Rollie Fingers IA	.60	.35
587	Tim Lollar	.10	.06
588	Dale Berra	.10	.06
589	Dave Stapleton	.10	.06
590	Al Oliver	.20	.12
591	Al Oliver IA	.12	.07
592	Craig Swan	.10	.06
593	Billy Smith	.10	.06
594	Renie Martin	.10	.06
595	Dave Collins	.10	.06
596	Damaso Garcia	.10	.06
597	Wayne Nordhagen	.10	.06
598	Bob Galasso	.10	.06
599	White Sox Future Stars Jay Loviglio Reggie Patterson (R) Leo Sutherland	.10	.06
600	Dave Winfield	5.00	3.00
601	Sid Monge	.10	.06
602	Freddie Patek	.10	.06
603	Rich Hebner	.10	.06
604	Orlando Sanchez	.10	.06
605	Steve Rogers	.10	.06
606	Blue Jays (TL)(John Mayberry, Dave Stieb)	.20	.12
607	Leon Durham	.10	.06
608	Jerry Royster	.10	.06
609	Rick Sutcliffe	.30	.18
610	Rickey Henderson	7.50	4.00
611	Joe Niekro	.10	.06
612	Gary Ward	.10	.06
613	Jim Gantner	.10	.06
614	Juan Eichelberger	.10	.06
615	Bob Boone	.25	.15
616	Bob Boone IA	.15	.10
617	Scott McGregor	.12	.07
618	Tim Foli	.10	.06
619	Bill Campbell	.10	.06
620	Ken Griffey	.35	.20
621	Ken Griffey IA	.20	.12
622	Dennis Lamp	.10	.06
623	Mets Future Stars Ron Gardenhire (R) Terry Leach (R) Tim Leary (R)	.30	.20
624	Ferguson Jenkins	.80	.50
625	Hal McRae	.20	.12
626	Randy Jones	.10	.06
627	Enos Cabell	.10	.06
628	Bill Travers	.10	.06
629	Johnny Wockenfuss	.10	.06
630	Joe Charboneau	.10	.06
631	Gene Tenace	.12	.07
632	Bryan Clark	.10	.06
633	Mitchell Page	.10	.06
634	Checklist 529-660	.15	.06
635	Ron Davis	.10	.06
636	Phillies (TL)(Steve Carlton, Pete Rose)	1.00	.60
637	Rick Camp	.10	.06
638	John Milner	.10	.06
639	Ken Kravec	.10	.06
640	Cesar Cedeno	.15	.10
641	Steve Mura	.10	.06
642	Mike Scioscia	.25	.15
643	Pete Vuckovich	.10	.06
644	John Castino	.10	.06
645	Frank White	.10	.06
646	Frank White IA	.10	.06
647	Warren Brusstar	.10	.06
648	Jose Morales	.10	.06
649	Ken Clay	.10	.06
650	Carl Yastrzemski	2.00	1.25
651	Carl Yastrzemski IA	1.25	.80
652	Steve Nicosia	.10	.06
653	Angels Future Stars Tom Brunansky (R) Luis Sanchez (R) Daryl Sconiers (R)	1.00	.60
654	Jim Morrison	.10	.06
655	Joel Youngblood	.10	.06
656	Eddie Whitson	.10	.06
657	Tom Poquette	.10	.06
658	Tito Landrum	.10	.06
659	Fred Martinez	.10	.06
660	Dave Concepcion	.25	.15
661	Dave Concepcion IA	.15	.10
662	Luis Salazar	.10	.06
663	Hector Cruz	.10	.06
664	Dan Spillner	.10	.06
665	Jim Clancy	.10	.06
666	Tigers (TL)(Steve	.15	.10

	Kemp, Dan Petry		
667	Jeff Reardon	2.50	1.40
668	Dale Murphy	1.50	.90
669	Larry Milbourne	.10	.06
670	Steve Kemp	.10	.06
671	Mike Davis	.10	.06
672	Bob Knepper	.10	.06
673	Keith Drumright	.10	.06
674	Dave Goltz	.10	.06
675	Cecil Cooper	.15	.10
676	Sal Butera	.10	.06
677	Alfredo Griffin	.10	.06
678	Tom Paciorek	.10	.06
679	Sammy Stewart	.10	.06
680	Gary Matthews	.12	.07
681	Dodgers Future Stars	2.00	1.25
	Mike Marshall (R)		
	Ron Roenicke		
	Steve Sax (R)		
682	Jesse Jefferson	.10	.06
683	Phil Garner	.12	.07
684	Harold Baines	1.25	.80
685	Bert Blyleven	.60	.35
686	Gary Allenson	.10	.06
687	Greg Minton	.10	.06
688	Leon Roberts	.10	.06
689	Larry Sorensen	.10	.06
690	Dave Kingman	.20	.12
691	Dan Schatzeder	.10	.06
692	Wayne Gross	.10	.06
693	Cesar Geronimo	.10	.06
694	Dave Wehrmeister	.10	.06
695	Warren Cromartie	.10	.06
696	Pirates (TL) (Bill	.20	.12
	Madlock, Buddy		
	Solomon)		
697	John Montefusco	.10	.06
698	Tony Scott	.10	.06
699	Dick Tidrow	.10	.06
700	George Foster	.25	.15
701	George Foster IA	.15	.10
702	Steve Renko	.10	.06
703	Brewers (TL)(Cecil	.25	.15
	Cooper, Pete Vuckovich)		
704	Mickey Rivers	.10	.06
705	Mickey Rivers IA	.10	.06
706	Barry Foote	.10	.06
707	Mark Bomback	.10	.06
708	Gene Richards	.10	.06
709	Don Money	.10	.06
710	Jerry Reuss	.12	.07
711	Mariners Future Stars	.80	.50
	Dave Edler (R)		
	Dave Henderson (R)		
	Reggie Walton (R)		
712	Denny Martinez	.50	.30
713	Del Unser	.10	.06

714	Jerry Koosman	.15	.10
715	Willie Stargell	1.25	.80
716	Willie Stargell IA	.60	.35
717	Rick Miller	.10	.06
718	Charlie Hough	.12	.07
719	Jerry Narron	.10	.06
720	Greg Luzinski	.20	.12
721	Greg Luzinski IA	.12	.07
722	Jerry Martin	.10	.06
723	Junior Kennedy	.10	.06
724	Dave Rosello	.10	.06
725	Amos Otis	.12	.07
726	Amos Otis IA	.10	.06
727	Sixto Lezcano	.10	.06
728	Aurelio Lopez	.10	.06
729	Jim Spencer	.10	.06
730	Gary Carter	1.25	.80
731	Padres Future Stars	.10	.06
	Mike Armstrong (R)		
	Doug Gwosdz (R)		
	Fred Kuhaulua		
732	Mike Lum	.10	.06
733	Larry McWilliams	.10	.06
734	Mike Ivie	.10	.06
735	Rudy May	.10	.06
736	Jerry Turner	.10	.06
737	Reggie Cleveland	.10	.06
738	Dave Engle	.10	.06
739	Joey McLaughlin	.10	.06
740	Dave Lopes	.15	.10
741	Dave Lopes IA	.10	.06
742	Dick Drago	.10	.06
743	John Stearns	.10	.06
744	Mike Witt (R)	.20	.12
745	Bake McBride	.10	.06
746	Andre Thornton	.15	.10
747	John Lowenstein	.10	.06
748	Marc Hill	.10	.06
749	Bob Shirley	.10	.06
750	Jim Rice	.50	.30
751	Rick Honeycutt	.12	.07
752	Lee Lacy	.10	.06
753	Tom Brookens	.10	.06
754	Joe Morgan	1.25	.80
755	Joe Morgan IA	.60	.35
756	Reds (TL) (Ken	.60	.35
	Griffey, Tom Seaver)		
757	Tom Underwood	.10	.06
758	Claudell Washington	.10	.06
759	Paul Splittorff	.12	.07
760	Bill Buckner	.20	.12
761	Dave Smith	.15	.10
762	Mike Phillips	.10	.06
763	Tom Hume	.10	.06
764	Steve Swisher	.10	.06
765	Gorman Thomas	.15	.10
766	Twins Future Stars	2.50	1.40

	Lenny Faedo (R)		
	Kent Hrbek (R)		
	Tim Laudner (R)		
767	Roy Smalley	.10	.06
768	Jerry Garvin	.10	.06
769	Richie Zisk	.10	.06
770	Rich Gossage	.30	.18
771	Rish Gossage IA	.15	.10
772	Bert Campaneris	.15	.10
773	John Denny	.10	.06
774	Jay Johnstone	.12	.07
775	Bob Forsch	.10	.06
776	Mark Belanger	.15	.10
777	Tom Griffin	.10	.06
778	Kevin Hickey	.10	.06
779	Grant Jackson	.10	.06
780	Pete Rose	3.50	2.00
781	Pete Rose IA	2.00	1.00
782	Frank Taveras	.10	.06
783	Greg Harris (R)	.35	.20
784	Milt Wllcox	.10	.06
785	Dan Driessen	.10	.06
786	Red Sox (TL) (Carney	.15	.10
	Lansford, Mike Torrez)		
787	Fred Stanley	.10	.06
788	Woodie Fryman	.10	.06
789	Checklist 661-792	.15	.06
790	Larry Gura	.10	.06
791	Bobby Brown	.10	.06
792	Frank Tanana	.15	.10

1982 Topps Traded

Patterned after Topps 1982 regular edition, this update set features players who changed teams during the season and a selection of rookies. Players are listed in alphabetical order and card numbers carry the letter "T". Cards measure 2-1/2" by 3-1/2". The production figures for this set are lower than the total cards produced in Topps regular edition.

		MINT	NR/MT
Complete Set (132)		310.00	185.00
Commons (1-132)		.35	.20
1T	Doyle Alexander	.35	.20
2T	Jesse Barfield	.80	.50
3T	Ross Baumgarten	.35	.20
4T	Steve Bedrosian	.60	.35
5T	Mark Belanger	.40	.25
6T	Kurt Bevacqua	.35	.20
7T	Tim Blackwell	.35	.20
8T	Vida Blue	.40	.25
9T	Bob Boone	.80	.50
10T	Larry Bowa	.40	.25
11T	Don Briggs	.35	.20
12T	Bobby Brown	.35	.20
13T	Tom Brunansky	1.25	.80
14T	Jeff Burroughs	.35	.20
15T	Enos Cabell	.35	.20
16T	Bill Campbell	.35	.20
17T	Bobby Castillo	.35	.20
18T	Bill Caudill	.35	.20
19T	Cesar Cedeno	.40	.25
20T	Dave Collins	.35	.20
21T	Doug Corbett	.35	.20
22T	Al Cowens	.35	.20
23T	Chili Davis	3.50	2.00
24T	Dick Davis	.35	.20
25T	Ron Davis	.35	.20
26T	Doug DeCinces	.35	.20
27T	Ivan DeJesus	.35	.20
28T	Bob Dernier	.35	.20
29T	Bo Diaz	.35	.20
30T	Roger Erickson	.35	.20
31T	Jim Essian	.35	.20
32T	Ed Farmer	.35	.20
33T	Doug Flynn	.35	.20
34T	Tim Foli	.35	.20
35T	Dan Ford	.35	.20
36T	George Foster	.40	.25
37T	Dave Frost	.35	.20
38T	Rich Gale	.35	.20
39T	Ron Gardenhire	.35	.20
40T	Ken Griffey	.75	.45
41T	Greg Harris	.50	.30
42T	Von Hayes	.80	.50
43T	Larry Herndon	.35	.20
44T	Kent Hrbek	4.50	3.00
45T	Mike Ivie	.35	.20
46T	Grant Jackson	.35	.20
47T	Reggie Jackson	14.00	7.50
48T	Ron Jackson	.35	.20
49T	Ferguson Jenkins	2.50	1.50
50T	Lamar Johnson	.35	.20
51T	Randy Johnson	.35	.20
52T	Jay Johnstone	.35	.20

53T	Mick Kelleher	.35	.20
54T	Steve Kemp	.35	.20
55T	Junior Kennedy	.35	.20
56T	Jim Kern	.35	.20
57T	Ray Knight	.40	.25
58T	Wayne Krenchicki	.35	.20
59T	Mike Krukow	.35	.20
60T	Duane Kuiper	.35	.20
61T	Mike LaCoss	.35	.20
62T	Chet Lemon	.35	.20
63T	Sixto Lezcano	.35	.20
64T	Dave Lopes	.40	.25
65T	Jerry Martin	.35	.20
66T	Renie Martin	.35	.20
67T	John Mayberry	.40	.25
68T	Lee Mazzilli	.35	.20
69T	Bake McBride	.35	.20
70T	Dan Meyer	.35	.20
71T	Larry Milbourne	.35	.20
72T	Edie Milner	.35	.20
73T	Sid Monge	.35	.20
74T	Jose Morales	.35	.20
75T	Keith Moreland	.35	.20
76T	John Montefusco	.35	.20
77T	Jim Morison	.35	.20
78T	Rance Mulliniks	.35	.20
79T	Steve Mura	.35	.20
80T	Gene Nelson	.35	.20
81T	Joe Nolan	.35	.20
82T	Dickie Noles	.35	.20
83T	Al Oliver	.40	.25
84T	Jorge Orta	.35	.20
85T	Tom Paciorek	.35	.20
86T	Larry Parrish	.35	.20
87T	Jack Perconte	.35	.20
88T	Gaylord Perry	2.50	1.50
89T	Rob Picciolo	.35	.20
90T	Joe Pittman	.35	.20
91T	Hosken Powell	.35	.20
92T	Mike Proly	.35	.20
93T	Greg Pryor	.35	.20
94T	Charlie Puleo (R)	.35	.20
95T	Shane Rawley	.35	.20
96T	Johnny Ray	.35	.20
97T	Dave Revering	.35	.20
98T	Cal Ripken	280.00	160.00
99T	Allen Ripley	.35	.20
100T	Bill Robinson	.35	.20
101T	Aurelio Rodriguez	.35	.20
102T	Joe Rudi	.40	.25
103T	Steve Sax	4.00	2.00
104T	Dan Schatzeder	.35	.20
105T	Bob Shirley	.35	.20
106T	Eric Show (R)	.40	.25
107T	Roy Smalley	.35	.20
108T	Lonnie Smith	.35	.20
109T	Ozzie Smith	28.00	18.00

110T	Reggie Smith	.40	.25
111T	Lary Sorensen	.35	.20
112T	Elias Sosa	.35	.20
113T	Mike Stanton	.35	.20
114T	Steve Stroughter	.35	.20
115T	Champ Summers	.35	.20
116T	Rick Sutcliffe	.60	.35
117T	Frank Tanana	.40	.25
117T	Frank Taveras	.35	.20
119T	Garry Templeton	.35	.20
120T	Alex Trevino	.35	.20
121T	Jerry Turner	.35	.20
122T	Ed Vande Berg	.35	.20
123T	Tom Veryzer	.35	.20
124T	Ron Washington	.35	.20
125T	Bob Watson	.35	.20
126T	Dennis Werth	.35	.20
127T	Eddie Whitson	.35	.20
128T	Rob Wilfong	.35	.20
129T	Bump Wills	.35	.20
130T	Gary Woods	.35	.20
131T	Butch Wynegar	.35	.20
132T	Checklist 1-132	.35	.20

1983 Topps

This 792-card set features two photos on the card fronts. A large color action shot and a small head shot located in a circle in the lower right corner. Cards measure 2-1/2" by 3-1/2". Subsets include Record Breakers (1-6), League Leaders, All-Stars, Team Leaders (TL) and a new category called Super Veterans (SV) with a horizontal format on the front.

	MINT	NR/MT
Complete Set (792)	175.00	105.00
Commons	.10	.06

1	Tony Armas (RB)	.15	.10
2	Rickey Henderson(RB)	1.75	.90
3	Greg Minton (RB)	.10	.06
4	Lance Parrish (RB)	.10	.06
5	Manny Trillo (RB)	.10	.06
6	John Wathan (RB)	.10	.06
7	Gene Richards	.10	.06
8	Steve Balboni	.10	.06
9	Joey McLaughlin	.10	.06
10	Gorman Thomas	.15	.10
11	Billy Gardner	.10	.06
12	Paul Mirabella	.10	.06
13	Larry Herndon	.10	.06
14	Frank LaCorte	.10	.06
15	Ron Cey	.15	.10
16	George Vukovich	.10	.06
17	Kent Tekulve	.10	.06
18	Kent Tekulve (SV)		
19	Oscar Gamble	.12	.07
20	Carlton Fisk	2.25	1.30
21	Orioles (TL)(Eddie Murray, Jim Palmer)	.70	.40
22	Randy Martz	.10	.06
23	Mike Heath	.10	.06
24	Steve Mura	.10	.06
25	Hal McRae	.20	.12
26	Jerry Royster	.10	.06
27	Doug Corbett	.10	.06
28	Bruce Bochte	.10	.06
29	Randy Jones	.12	.07
30	Jim Rice	.35	.20
31	Bill Gullickson	.15	.10
32	Dave Bergman	.10	.06
33	Jack O'Connor	.10	.06
34	Paul Householder	.10	.06
35	Rollie Fingers	1.25	.80
36	Rollie Fingers (SV)	.60	.35
37	Darrell Johnson	.10	.06
38	Tim Flannery	.10	.06
39	Terry Puhl	.10	.06
40	Fernando Valenzuela	.25	.15
41	Jerry Turner	.10	.06
42	Dale Murray	.10	.06
43	Bob Dernier	.10	.06
44	Don Robinson	.10	.06
45	John Mayberry	.12	.07
46	Richard Dotson	.10	.06
47	Dave McKay	.10	.06
48	Lary Sorensen	.10	.06
49	Willie McGee (R)	5.00	3.50
50	Bob Horner	.10	.06
51	Cubs (TL) (Leon Durham, Fergie Jenkins)	.35	.20
52	Onix Concepcion	.10	.06
53	Mike Witt	.10	.06
54	Jim Maler	.10	.06
55	Mookie Wilson	.15	.10
56	Chuck Rainey	.10	.06
57	Tim Blackwelll	.10	.06
58	Al Holland	.10	.06
59	Benny Ayala	.10	.06
60	Johnny Bench	2.50	1.25
61	Johnny Bench (SV)	1.25	.80
62	Bob McClure	.10	.06
63	Rick Monday	.12	.07
64	Bill Stein	.10	.06
65	Jack Morris	1.75	1.00
66	Bob Lillis	.10	.06
67	Sal Butera	.10	.06
68	Eric Show	.12	.07
69	Lee Lacy	.10	.06
70	Steve Carlton	2.50	1.25
71	Steve Carlton	1.25	.80
72	Tom Paciorek	.10	.06
73	Allen Ripley	.10	.06
74	Julio Gonzalez	.10	.06
75	Amos Otis	.15	.10
76	Rick Mahler	.12	.07
77	Hosken Powell	.10	.06
78	Bill Caudill	.10	.06
79	Mick Kelleher	.10	.06
80	George Foster	.25	.15
81	Yankees (TL) (Jerry Mumphrey, Dave Righetti)	.20	.12
82	Bruce Hurst	.25	.15
83	Ryne Sandberg (R)	60.00	38.00
84	Milt May	.10	.06
85	Ken Singleton	.12	.07
86	Tom Hume	.10	.06
87	Joe Rudi	.12	.07
88	Jim Gantner	.10	.06
89	Leon Roberts	.10	.06
90	Jerry Reuss	.12	.07
91	Larry Milbourne	.10	.06
92	Mike LaCoss	.10	.06
93	John Castino	.10	.06
94	Dave Edwards	.10	.06
95	Alan Trammell	1.50	.90
96	Dick Howser	.10	.06
97	Ross Baumgarten	.10	.06
98	Vance Law	.10	.06
99	Dickie Noles	.10	.06
100	Pete Rose	3.00	2.00
101	Pete Rose (SV)	1.50	.75
102	Dave Beard	.10	.06
103	Darrell Porter	.10	.06
104	Bob Walk	.10	.06
105	Don Baylor	.20	.12
106	Gene Nelson	.10	.06
107	Mike Jorgensen	.10	.06
108	Glenn Hoffman	.10	.06
109	Luis Leal	.10	.06
110	Ken Griffey	.30	.20

111	Expos (TL) (Al Oliver,	.20	.12
	Steve Rogers)		
112	Bob Shirley	.10	.06
113	Ron Roenicke	.10	.06
114	Jim Slaton	.10	.06
115	Chili Davis	.90	.55
116	Dave Cohmidt	.10	.06
117	Alan Knicely	.10	.06
118	Chris Welsh	.10	.06
119	Tom Brookens	.10	.06
120	Len Barker	.10	.06
121	Mickey Hatcher	.10	.06
122	Jimmy Smith	.10	.06
123	George Frazier	.10	.06
124	Marc Hill	.10	.06
125	Leon Durham	.12	.07
126	Joe Torre	.12	.07
127	Preston Hanna	.10	.06
128	Mike Ramsey	.10	.06
129	Checklist 1-132	.15	.06
130	Dave Stieb	.25	.15
131	Ed Ott	.10	.06
132	Todd Cruz	.10	.06
133	Jim Barr	.10	.06
134	Hubie Brooks	.25	.15
135	Dwight Evans	.40	.20
136	Willie Aikens	.10	.06
137	Woodie Fryman	.10	.06
138	Rick Dempsey	.10	.06
139	Bruce Berenyi	.10	.06
140	Willie Randolph	.15	.10
141	Indians (TL) (Toby	.20	.12
	Harrah, Rick Sutcliffe)		
142	Mike Caldwell	.10	.06
143	Joe Pettini	.10	.06
144	Mark Wagner	.10	.06
145	Don Sutton	.75	.45
146	Don Sutton (SV)	.35	.20
147	Rick Leach	.10	.06
148	Dave Roberts	.10	.06
149	Johnny Ray	.12	.07
150	Bruce Sutter	.20	.12
151	Bruce Sutter	.12	.07
152	Jay Johnstone	.12	.07
153	Jerry Koosman	.15	.10
154	Johnnie LeMaster	.10	.06
155	Dan Quisenberry	.15	.10
156	Billy Martin	.25	.15
157	Steve Bedrosian	.15	.10
158	Rob Wilfong	.10	.06
159	Mike Stanton	.10	.06
160	Dave Kingman	.15	.10
161	Dave Kingman (SV)	.10	.06
162	Mark Clear	.10	.06
163	Cal Ripken	25.00	15.00
164	Dave Palmer	.10	.06
165	Dan Driessen	.10	.06
166	John Pacella	.10	.06
167	Mark Brouhard	.10	.06
168	Juan Eichelberger	.10	.06
169	Doug Flynn	.10	.06
170	Steve Howe	.10	.06
171	Giants (TL) (Bill	.30	.20
	Lackey, Joe Morgan)		
172	Vern Ruhle	.10	.06
173	Jim Morrison	.10	.06
174	Jerry Ujdur	.10	.06
175	Bo Diaz	.10	.06
176	Dave Righetti	.20	.12
177	Harold Baines	.75	.45
178	Luis Tiant	.20	.12
179	Luis Tiant (SV)	.12	.07
180	Rickey Henderson	6.00	4.00
181	Terry Felton	.10	.06
182	Mike Fischin	.10	.06
183	Ed Vande Berg	.10	.06
184	Bob Clark	.10	.06
185	Tim Lollar	.10	.06
186	Whitey Herzog	.15	.10
187	Terry Leach	.10	.06
188	Rick Miller	.10	.06
189	Dan Schatzeder	.10	.06
190	Cecil Cooper	.15	.10
191	Joe Price	.10	.06
192	Floyd Rayford	.10	.06
193	Harry Spilman	.10	.06
194	Cesar Geronimo	.10	.06
195	Bob Stoddard	.10	.06
196	Bill Fahey	.10	.06
197	Jim Eisenreich (R)	1.00	.60
198	Kiko Garcia	.10	.06
199	Marty Bystrom	.10	.06
200	Rod Carew	2.00	1.25
201	Rod Carew (SV)	1.25	.80
202	Blue Jays (TL)(Damaso	.15	.10
	Garcia, Dave Stieb)		
203	Mike Morgan	.35	.20
204	Junior Kennedy	.10	.06
205	Dave Parker	.45	.28
206	Ken Oberkfell	.10	.06
207	Rick Camp	.10	.06
208	Dan Meyer	.10	.06
209	Mike Moore (R)	.80	.50
210	Jack Clark	.20	.12
211	John Denny	.10	.06
212	John Stearns	.10	.06
213	Tom Burgmeier	.10	.06
214	Jerry White	.10	.06
215	Mario Soto	.12	.07
216	Tony LaRussa	.20	.12
217	Tim Stoddard	.10	.06
218	Roy Howell	.10	.06
219	Mike Armstrong	.10	.06
220	Dusty Baker	.20	.12

221	Joe Niekro	.12	.07
222	Damaso Garcia	.10	.06
223	John Montefusco	.10	.06
224	Mickey Hivers	.10	.06
225	Enos Cabell	.10	.06
226	Enrique Romo	.10	.06
227	Chris Bando	.10	.06
228	Joaquin Andujar	.15	.10
229	Phillies (TL) (Steve Carlton, Bo Diaz)	.60	.35
230	Ferguson Jenkins	.75	.45
231	Ferguson Jenkins (SV)	.35	.20
232	Tom Brunansky	.25	.15
233	Wayne Gross	.10	.06
234	Larry Andersen	.10	.06
235	Claudell Washington	.12	.07
236	Steve Renko	.10	.06
237	Dan Norman	.10	.06
238	Bud Black (R)	.50	.30
239	Dave Stapleton	.10	.06
240	Rich Gossage	.30	.20
241	Rich Gossage (SV)	.15	.10
242	Joe Nolan	.10	.06
243	Duane Walker	.10	.06
244	Dwight Bernard	.10	.06
245	Steve Sax	.50	.30
246	George Bamberger	.10	.06
247	Dave Smith	.10	.06
248	Bake McBride	.10	.06
249	Checklist 133-264	.15	.06
250	Bill Buckner	.20	.12
251	Alan Wiggins (R)	.10	.06
252	Luis Aguayo	.10	.06
253	Larry McWilliams	.10	.06
254	Rick Cerone	.12	.07
255	Gene Garber	.10	.06
256	Gene Garber	.10	.06
257	Jesse Barfield	.15	.10
258	Manny Castillo	.10	.06
259	Jeff Jones	.10	.06
260	Steve Kemp	.10	.06
261	Tigers (TL) (Larry Herndon, Dan Petry)	.12	.07
262	Ron Jackson	.10	.06
263	Renie Martin	.10	.06
264	Jamie Quirk	.10	.06
265	Joel Youngblood	.10	.06
266	Paul Boris	.10	.06
267	Terry Francona	.10	.06
268	Storm Davis (R)	.25	.15
269	Ron Oester	.10	.06
270	Dennis Eckersley	1.50	.90
271	Ed Romero	.10	.06
272	Frank Tanana	.12	.07
273	Mark Belanger	.15	.10
274	Terry Kennedy	.10	.06
275	Ray Knight	.15	.10
276	Gene Mauch	.10	.06
277	Rance Mulliniks	.10	.06
278	Kevin Hickey	.10	.06
279	Greg Gross	.10	.06
280	Bert Blyleven	.45	.28
281	Andre Robertson	.10	.06
282	Reggie Smith	.30	.18
283	Reggie Smith (SV)	.10	.06
284	Jeff Lahti	.10	.06
285	Lance Parrish	.20	.12
286	Rick Langford	.10	.06
287	Bobby Brown	.10	.06
288	Joe Cowley	.10	.06
289	Jerry Dybzinski	.10	.06
290	Jeff Reardon	1.50	.90
291	Pirates (TL) (John Candelaria, Bill Madlock)	.25	.15
292	Craig Swan	.10	.06
293	Glenn Gulliver	.10	.06
294	Dave Engle	.10	.06
295	Jerry Remy	.10	.06
296	Greg Harris	.10	.06
297	Ned Yost	.10	.06
298	Floyd Chiffer	.10	.06
299	George Wright	.10	.06
300	Mike Schmidt	4.00	2.75
301	Mike Schmidt (SV)	2.50	1.50
302	Ernie Whitt	.10	.06
303	Miguel Dilone	.10	.06
304	Dave Rucker	.10	.06
305	Larry Bowa	.15	.10
306	Tom Lasorda	.15	.10
307	Lou Piniella	.20	.12
308	Jesus Vega	.10	.06
309	Jeff Leonard	.12	.07
310	Greg Luzinski	.20	.12
311	Glenn Brummer	.10	.06
312	Brian Kingman	.10	.06
313	Gary Gray	.10	.06
314	Ken Dayley (R)	.10	.06
315	Rick Burleson	.12	.07
316	Paul Splittorff	.12	.07
317	Gary Rajsich	.10	.06
318	John Tudor	.15	.10
319	Lenn Sakata	.10	.06
320	Steve Rogers	.10	.06
321	Brewers (TL) (Pete Vuckovich, Robin Yount)	.50	.30
322	Dave Van Gorder	.10	.06
323	Luis DeLeon	.10	.06
324	Mike Marshall	.12	.07
325	Von Hayes	.15	.10
326	Garth Iorg	.10	.06
327	Bobby Castillo	.10	.06
328	Craig Reynolds	.10	.06
329	Randy Niemann	.10	.06

330	Buddy Bell	.10	.06
331	Mike Krukow	.10	.06
332	Glenn Wilson (R)	.12	.07
333	Dave LaRoche	.10	.06
334	Dave LaRoche (SV)	.10	.06
335	Steve Henderson	.10	.06
336	Rene Lachemann	.10	.06
337	Tito Landrum	.10	.06
338	Bob Owchinko	.10	.06
339	Terry Harper	.10	.06
340	Larry Gura	.10	.06
341	Doug DeCinces	.12	.07
342	Atlee Hammaker	.10	.06
343	Bob Bailor	.10	.06
344	Roger LaFrancois	.10	.06
345	Jim Clancy	.10	.06
346	Joe Pittman	.10	.06
347	Sammy Stewart	.10	.06
348	Alan Bannister	.10	.06
349	Checklist 265-396	.15	.06
350	Robin Yount	4.00	2.75
351	Reds (TL) (Cesar Cedeno, Mario Soto)	.20	.12
352	Mike Scioscia	.15	.10
353	Steve Comer	.10	.06
354	Randy Johnson	.10	.06
355	Jim Bibby	.10	.06
356	Gary Woods	.10	.06
357	Len Matuszek (R)	.10	.06
358	Jerry Garvin	.10	.06
359	Dave Collins	.10	.06
360	Nolan Ryan	14.00	7.50
361	Nolan Ryan	7.50	4.00
362	Bill Almon	.10	.06
363	John Stuper	.10	.06
364	Brett Butler	1.25	.80
365	Dave Lopes	.15	.10
366	Dick Williams	.10	.06
367	Bud Anderson	.10	.06
368	Richie Zisk	.10	.06
369	Jesse Orosco	.10	.06
370	Gary Carter	1.00	.70
371	Mike Richardt	.10	.06
372	Terry Crowley	.10	.06
373	Kevin Saucier	.10	.06
374	Wayne Krenchicki	.10	.06
375	Pete Vuckovich	.12	.07
376	Ken Landreaux	.10	.06
377	Lee May	.10	.06
378	Lee May (SV)	.10	.06
379	Guy Sularz	.10	.06
380	Ron Davis	.10	.06
381	Red Sox (TL) (Jim Rice, Bob Stanley)	.20	.12
382	Bob Knepper	.10	.06
383	Ozzie Virgil	.10	.06
384	Dave Dravecky (R)	.60	.35
385	Mike Easler	.10	.06
386	Rod Carew AS	.75	.45
387	Bob Grich AS	.15	.10
388	George Brett AS	2.00	1.25
389	Robin Yount AS	1.50	.90
390	Reggie Jackson AS	1.50	.90
391	Rickey Henderson AS	1.75	1.00
392	Fred Lynn AS	.25	.15
393	Carlton Fisk AS	.75	.45
394	Pete Vuckovich AS	.15	.10
395	Larry Gura AS	.10	.06
396	Dan Quisenberry AS	.12	.07
397	Pete Rose AS	1.50	.90
398	Manny Trillo AS	.10	.06
399	Mike Schmidt AS	2.00	1.25
400	Dave Concepcion AS	.25	.15
401	Dale Murphy AS	.50	.30
402	Andre Dawson AS	.90	.55
403	Tim Raines AS	.40	.25
404	Gary Carter AS	.50	.30
405	Steve Rogers AS	.12	.07
406	Steve Carlton AS	1.50	.90
407	Bruce Sutter AS	.15	.10
408	Rudy May	.10	.06
409	Marvis Foley	.10	.06
410	Phil Niekro	.75	.45
411	Phil Niekro (SV)	.35	.20
412	Rangers (TL) (Buddy Bell, Charlie Hough)	.15	.10
413	Matt Keough	.10	.06
414	Julio Cruz	.10	.06
415	Bob Forsch	.10	.06
416	Joe Ferguson	.10	.06
417	Tom Hausman	.10	.06
418	Greg Pryor	.10	.06
419	Steve Crawford	.10	.06
420	Al Oliver	.20	.12
421	Al Oliver (R)	.12	.07
422	George Cappuzzello	.10	.06
423	Tom Lawless (R)	.10	.06
424	Jerry Augustine	.10	.06
425	Pedro Guerrero	.30	.20
426	Earl Weaver	.15	.10
427	Roy Lee Jackson	.10	.06
428	Champ Summers	.10	.06
429	Eddie Whitson	.10	.06
430	Kirk Gibson	.75	.45
431	Gary Gaetti (R)	.50	.30
432	Porfirio Altamirano	.10	.06
433	Dale Berra	.10	.06
434	Dennis Lamp	.10	.06
435	Tony Armas	.12	.07
436	Bill Campbell	.10	.06
437	Rick Sweet	.10	.06
438	Dave LaPoint	.10	.06
439	Rafael Ramirez	.10	.06
440	Ron Guidry	.35	.20

441	Astros (TL) (Ray Knight, Joe Niekro)	.15	.10
442	Brian Downing	.12	.07
443	Don Hood	.10	.06
444	Wally Backman	.15	.10
445	Mike Flanagan	.15	.10
446	Reid Nichols	.10	.06
447	Bryn Smith	.10	.06
448	Darrell Evans	.15	.10
449	Eddie Milner	.10	.06
450	Ted Simmons	.15	.10
451	Ted Simmons (SV)	.10	.06
452	Lloyd Moseby	.12	.07
453	Lamar Johnson	.10	.06
454	Bob Welch	.35	.20
455	Sixto Lezcano	.10	.06
456	Lee Elia	.10	.06
457	Milt Wilcox	.10	.06
458	Ron Washington	.10	.06
459	Ed Farmer	.10	.06
460	Roy Smalley	.10	.06
461	Steve Trout	.10	.06
462	Steve Nicosia	.10	.06
463	Gaylord Perry	.75	.45
464	Gaylord Perry (SV)	.35	.20
465	Lonnie Smith	.10	.06
466	Tom Underwood	.10	.06
467	Rufino Linares	.10	.06
468	Dave Goltz	.10	.06
469	Ron Gardenhire	.10	.06
470	Greg Minton	.10	.06
471	Royals (TL) (Vida Blue, Willie Wilson)	.20	.12
472	Gary Allenson	.10	.06
473	John Lowenstein	.10	.06
474	Ray Burris	.10	.06
475	Cesar Cedeno	.15	.10
476	Rob Picciolo	.10	.06
477	Tom Niedenfuer	.10	.06
478	Phil Garner	.12	.07
479	Charlie Hough	.12	.07
480	Toby Harrah	.10	.06
481	Scot Thompson	.10	.06
482	Tony Gwynn (R)	40.00	25.00
483	Lynn Jones	.10	.06
484	Dick Ruthven	.10	.06
485	Omar Moreno	.10	.06
486	Clyde King	.10	.06
487	Jerry Hairston	.10	.06
488	Alfredo Griffin	.10	.06
489	Tom Herr	.12	.07
490	Jim Palmer	2.00	1.25
491	Jim Palmer (SV)	1.25	.80
492	Paul Serna	.10	.06
493	Steve McCatty	.10	.06
494	Bob Brenly	.10	.06
495	Warren Cromartie	.10	.06
496	Tom Veryzer	.10	.06
497	Rick Sutcliffe	.25	.15
498	Wade Boggs (R)	40.00	25.00
499	Jeff Little	.10	.06
500	Reggie Jackson	3.00	1.75
501	Reggie Jackson (SV)	1.75	1.00
502	Braves (TL) (Dale Murphy, Phil Niekro)	.35	.20
503	Moose Haas	.10	.06
504	Don Werner	.10	.06
505	Garry Templeton	.10	.06
506	Jim Gott (R)	.40	.25
507	Tony Scott	.10	.06
508	Tom Filer	.10	.06
509	Lou Whitaker	.90	.55
510	Tug McGraw	.20	.12
511	Tug McGraw (SV)	.12	.07
512	Doyle Alexander	.10	.06
513	Fred Stanley	.10	.06
514	Rudy Law	.10	.06
515	Gene Tenace	.12	.07
516	Bill Virdon	.10	.06
517	Gary Ward	.10	.06
518	Bill Laskey	.10	.06
519	Terry Bulling	.10	.06
520	Fred Lynn	.25	.15
521	Bruce Benedict	.10	.06
522	Pat Zachry	.10	.06
523	Carney Lansford	.15	.10
524	Tom Brennan	.10	.06
525	Frank White	.10	.06
526	Checklist 397-528	.15	.06
527	Larry Biittner	.10	.06
528	Jamie Easterly	.10	.06
529	Tim Laudner	.10	.06
530	Eddie Murray	3.00	2.00
531	Athletics (TL)(Rickey Henderson, Rick Langford)	.60	.35
532	Dave Stewart	1.00	.60
533	Luis Salazar	.10	.06
534	John Butcher	.10	.06
535	Manny Trillo	.10	.06
536	Johnny Wockenfuss	.10	.06
537	Rod Scurry	.10	.06
538	Danny Heep	.10	.06
539	Roger Erickson	.10	.06
540	Ozzie Smith	3.00	1.75
541	Britt Burns	.10	.06
542	Jody Davis	.10	.06
543	Alan Fowlkes	.10	.06
544	Larry Whisenton	.10	.06
545	Floyd Bannister	.10	.06
546	Dave Garcia	.10	.06
547	Geoff Zahn	.10	.06
548	Brian Giles	.10	.06
549	Charlie Puleo	.10	.06

550	Carl Yastrzemski	2.50	1.50	605	Gary Roenicke	.10	.06
551	Carl Yastrzemski(SV)	1.25	.80	606	Bobby Cox	.10	.06
552	Tim Wallach	.35	.20	607	Charlie Leibrandt	.12	.07
553	Denny Martinez	.20	.12	608	Don Money	.10	.06
554	Mike Vail	.10	.06	609	Danny Darwin	.10	.06
555	Steve Yeager	.10	.06	610	Steve Garvey	.75	.45
556	Willie Upshaw	.10	.00	611	Bert Roberge	.10	.06
557	Rick Honeycutt	.10	.06	612	Steve Swisher	.10	.06
558	Dickie Thon	.10	.06	613	Mike Ivie	.10	.06
559	Pete Redfern	.10	.06	614	Ed Glynn	.10	.06
560	Ron LeFlore	.10	.06	615	Garry Maddox	.10	.06
561	Cardinals (R)(Joaquin	.15	.10	616	Bill Nahorodny	.10	.06
	Andujar, Lonnis Smith)			617	Butch Wynegar	.10	.06
562	Dave Rozema	.10	.06	618	LaMarr Hoyt	.10	.06
563	Juan Bonilla	.10	.06	619	Keith Moreland	.10	.06
564	Sid Monge	.10	.06	620	Mike Norris	.10	.06
565	Bucky Dent	.15	.10	621	Mets (TL) (Craig Swan,	.15	.10
566	Manny Sarmiento	.10	.06		Mookie Wilson)		
567	Joe Simpson	.10	.06	622	Dave Edler	.10	.06
568	Willie Hernandez	.12	.07	623	Luis Sanchez	.10	.06
569	Jack Perconte	.10	.06	624	Glenn Hubbard	.10	.06
570	Vida Blue	.20	.12	625	Ken Forsch	.10	.06
571	Mickey Klutts	.10	.06	626	Jerry Martin	.10	.06
572	Bob Watson	.25	.15	627	Doug Bair	.10	.06
573	Andy Hassler	.10	.06	628	Julio Valdez	.10	.06
574	Glenn Adams	.10	.06	629	Charlie Lea	.10	.06
575	Neil Allen	.10	.06	630	Paul Molitor	4.00	2.50
576	Frank Robinson	.35	.20	631	Tippy Martinez	.10	.06
577	Luis Aponte	.10	.06	632	Alex Trevino	.10	.06
578	David Green	.10	.06	633	Vicente Romo	.10	.06
579	Rich Dauer	.10	.06	634	Max Venable	.10	.06
580	Tom Seaver	2.50	1.50	635	Graig Nettles	.15	.10
581	Tom Seaver (SV)	1.25	.80	636	Graig Nettles (SV)	.10	.06
582	Marshall Edwards	.10	.06	637	Pat Corrales	.10	.06
583	Terry Forster	.10	.06	638	Dan Petry	.12	.07
584	Dave Hostetler	.10	.06	639	Art Howe	.10	.06
585	Jose Cruz	.15	.10	640	Andre Thornton	.12	.07
586	Frank Viola (R)	4.00	2.50	641	Billy Sample	.10	.06
587	Ivan DeJesus	.10	.06	642	Checklist 529-660	.15	.06
588	Pat Underwood	.10	.06	643	Bump Wills	.10	.06
589	Alvis Woods	.10	.06	644	Joe Lefebvre	.10	.06
590	Tony Pena	.15	.10	645	Bill Madlock	.20	.12
591	White Sox (TL)(LaMarr	.20	.12	646	Jim Essian	.10	.06
	Hoyt, Greg Luzinski)			647	Bobby Mitchell	.10	.06
592	Shane Rawley	.10	.06	648	Jeff Burroughs	.10	.06
593	Broderick Perkins	.10	.06	649	Tommy Boggs	.10	.06
594	Eric Rasmussen	.10	.06	650	George Hendrick	.12	.07
595	Tim Raines	1.00	.60	651	Angels (TL)(Rod Carew,	.30	.18
596	Randy Johnson	.10	.06		Mike Witt)		
597	Mike Proly	.10	.06	652	Butch Hobson	.10	.06
598	Dwayne Murphy	.10	.06	653	Ellis Valentine	.10	.06
599	Don Aase	.10	.06	654	Bob Ojeda	.20	.12
600	George Brett	4.00	2.75	655	Al Bumbry	.10	.06
601	Ed Lynch	.10	.06	656	Dave Frost	.10	.06
602	Rich Gedman	.10	.06	657	Mike Gates	.10	.06
603	Joe Morgan	1.25	.80	658	Frank Pastore	.10	.06
604	Joe Morgan (SV)	.60	.35	659	Charlie Moore	.10	.06

660 Mike Hargrove	.10	.06
661 Bill Russell	.12	.07
662 Joe Sambito	.10	.06
663 Tom O'Malley	.10	.06
664 Bob Molinaro	.10	.06
665 Jim Sundberg	.10	.06
666 Sparky Anderson	.20	.12
667 Dick Davis	.10	.06
668 Larry Christenson	.10	.06
669 Mike Squires	.10	.06
670 Jerry Mumphrey	.10	.06
671 Lenny Faedo	.10	.06
672 Jim Kaat	.20	.12
673 Jim Kaat (SV)	.12	.07
674 Kurt Bevacqua	.10	.06
675 Jim Beattie	.10	.06
676 Biff Pocoroba	.10	.06
677 Dave Revering	.10	.06
678 Juan Beniquez	.10	.06
679 Mike Scott	.15	.10
680 Andre Dawson	3.00	2.00
681 Dodgers (TL) (Pedro Guerrero, Fernando Valenzuela)	.20	.12
682 Bob Stanley	.10	.06
683 Dan Ford	.10	.06
684 Rafael Landestoy	.10	.06
685 Lee Mazzilli	.10	.06
686 Randy Lerch	.10	.06
687 U.L. Washington	.10	.06
688 Jim Wohlford	.10	.06
689 Ron Hassey	.10	.06
690 Kent Hrbek	.60	.35
691 Dave Tobik	.10	.06
692 Denny Walling	.10	.06
693 Sparky Lyle	.15	.10
694 Sparky Lyle (SV)	.10	.06
695 Ruppert Jones	.10	.06
696 Chuck Tanner	.10	.06
697 Barry Foote	.10	.06
698 Tony Bernazard	.10	.06
699 Lee Smith	3.50	2.00
700 Keith Hernandez	.25	.15
701 Batting Leaders	.20	.12
702 Home Run Leaders	.60	.35
703 Runs Batted In Leaders	.25	.15
704 Stolen Base Leaders	1.00	.70
705 Victory Leaders	.60	.35
706 Strikeout Leaders	.60	.35
707 ERA Leaders	.15	.10
708 Leading Firemen	.20	.12
709 Jimmy Sexton	.10	.06
710 Willie Wilson	.12	.07
711 Mariners (TL) (Jim Beattie, Bruce Bochte)	.10	.06
712 Bruce Kison	.10	.06
713 Ron Hodges	.10	.06

714 Wayne Nordhagen	.10	.06
715 Tony Perez	.60	.35
716 Tony Poroz (SV)	.35	.20
717 Scott Sanderson	.12	.07
718 Jim Dwyer	.10	.06
719 Rich Gale	.10	.06
720 Dave Concepcion	.25	.15
721 John Martin	.10	.06
722 Jorge Orta	.10	.06
723 Randy Moffitt	.10	.06
724 Johnny Grubb	.10	.06
725 Dan Spillner	.10	.06
726 Harvey Kuenn	.10	.06
727 Chet Lemon	.10	.06
728 Ron Reed	.10	.06
729 Jerry Morales	.10	.06
730 Jason Thompson	.10	.06
731 Al Williams	.10	.06
732 Dave Henderson	.25	.15
733 Buck Martinez	.10	.06
734 Steve Braun	.10	.06
735 Tommy John	.15	.10
736 Tommy John (SV)	.10	.06
737 Mitchell Page	.10	.06
738 Tim Foli	.10	.06
739 Rick Ownbey	.10	.06
740 Rusty Staub	.20	.12
741 Rusty Staub (SV)	.12	.07
742 Padres (TL) (Terry Kennedy, Tim Lollar)	.12	.07
743 Mike Torrez	.10	.06
744 Brad Mills	.10	.06
745 Scott McGregor	.10	.06
746 John Wathan	.10	.06
747 Fred Breining	.10	.06
748 Derrel Thomas	.10	.06
749 Jon Matlack	.10	.06
750 Ben Oglivie	.10	.06
751 Brad Havens	.10	.06
752 Luis Pujols	.10	.06
753 Elias Sosa	.10	.06
754 Bill Robinson	.10	.06
755 John Candelaria	.12	.07
756 Russ Nixon	.10	.06
757 Rick Manning	.10	.06
758 Aurelio Rodriguez	.10	.06
759 Doug Bird	.10	.06
760 Dale Murphy	1.25	.80
761 Gary Lucas	.10	.06
762 Cliff Johnson	.10	.06
763 Al Cowens	.10	.06
764 Pete Falcone	.10	.06
765 Bob Boone	.25	.15
766 Barry Bonnell	.10	.06
767 Duane Kuiper	.10	.06
768 Chris Speier	.10	.06

769	Checklist 661-792	.15	.06
770	Dave Winfield	5.00	3.00
771	Twins (TL) (Bobby Castillo, Kent Hrbek)	.20	.12
772	Jim Kern	.10	.06
773	Larry Hisle	.10	.06
774	Alan Ashby	.10	.06
775	Burt Hooton	.10	.06
776	Larry Parrish	.10	.06
777	John Curtis	.10	.06
778	Rich Hebner	.10	.06
779	Rick Waits	.10	.06
780	Gary Matthews	.12	.07
781	Rick Rhoden	.10	.06
782	Bobby Murcer	.15	.10
783	Bobby Murcer (SV)	.10	.06
784	Jeff Newman	.10	.06
785	Dennis Leonard	.10	.06
786	Ralph Houk	.10	.06
787	Dick Tidrow	.10	.06
788	Dane Iorg	.10	.06
789	Bryan Clark	.10	.06
790	Bob Grich	.12	.07
791	Gary Lavelle	.10	.06
792	Chris Chambliss	.15	.08

1983 Topps Traded

This 132-card update set is an extension of Topps regular 1983 edition in design and features cards of players traded during the regular season and rookies who joined their club during the season. Cards measure 2-1/2" by 3-1/2" and carry the suffix "T" after the card number.

	MINT	NR/MT
Complete Set (132)	75.00	45.00
Commons	.25	.15

1T	Neil Allen	.25	.15
2T	Bill Almon	.25	.15
3T	Joe Altobelli	.25	.15
4T	Tony Armas	.25	.15
5T	Doug Bair	.25	.15
6T	Steve Baker	.25	.15
7T	Floyd Bannister	.25	.15
8T	Don Baylor	.30	.20
9T	Tony Bernazard	.25	.15
10T	Larry Biittner	.25	.15
11T	Dann Bilardello	.25	.15
12T	Doug Bird	.25	.15
13T	Steve Boros	.25	.15
14T	Greg Brock (R)	.25	.15
15T	Mike Brown	.25	.15
16T	Tom Burgmeier	.25	.15
17T	Randy Bush (R)	.30	.18
18T	Bert Campaneris	.30	.18
19T	Ron Cey	.30	.18
20T	Chris Codiroli (R)	.25	.15
21T	Dave Collins	.25	.15
22T	Terry Crowley	.25	.15
23T	Julio Cruz	.25	.15
24T	Mike Davis	.25	.15
25T	Frank DiPino	.25	.15
26T	Bill Doran (R)	.75	.45
27T	Jerry Dybzinski	.25	.15
28T	Jamie Easterly	.25	.15
29T	Juan Eichelberger	.25	.15
30T	Jim Essian	.25	.15
31T	Pete Falcone	.25	.15
32T	Mike Ferraro	.25	.15
33T	Terry Forster	.25	.15
34T	Julio Franco (R)	6.50	3.75
35T	Rich Gale	.25	.15
36T	Kiko Garcia	.25	.15
37T	Steve Garvey	1.75	1.00
38T	Johnny Grubb	.25	.15
39T	Mel Hall (R)	1.00	.60
40T	Von Hayes	.25	.15
41T	Danny Heep	.25	.15
42T	Steve Henderson	.25	.15
43T	Keith Hernandez	.40	.25
44T	Leo Hernandez	.25	.15
45T	Willie Hernandez	.30	.18
46T	Al Holland	.25	.15
47T	Frank Howard	.25	.15
48T	Bobby Johnson	.25	.15
49T	Cliff Johnson	.25	.15
50T	Odell Jones	.25	.15
51T	Mike Jorgensen	.25	.15
52T	Bob Kearney	.25	.15
53T	Steve Kemp	.25	.15
54T	Matt Keough	.25	.15
55T	Ron Kittle (R)	.30	.18
56T	Mickey Klutts	.25	.15
57T	Alan Knicely	.25	.15

58T Mike Krukow	.25	.15
59T Rafael Landestoy	.25	.15
60T Carney Lansford	.25	.15
61T Joe Lefebvre	.25	.15
62T Bryan Little	.25	.15
63T Aurelio Lopez	.25	.15
64T Mike Madden	.25	.15
65T Rick Manning	.25	.15
66T Billy Martin	.35	.20
67T Lee Mazzilli	.25	.15
68T Andy McGaffigan	.25	.15
69T Craig McMurtry (R)	.35	.20
70T John McNamara	.25	.15
71T Orlando Mercado	.25	.15
72T Larry Milbourne	.25	.15
73T Randy Moffitt	.25	.15
74T Sid Monge	.25	.15
75T Jose Morales	.25	.15
76T Omar Moreno	.25	.15
77T Joe Morgan	3.00	1.75
78T Mike Morgan	.60	.35
79T Dale Murray	.25	.15
80T Jeff Newman	.25	.15
81T Pete O'Brien (R)	.60	.35
82T Jorge Orta	.25	.15
83T Alejandro Pena (R)	.60	.35
84T Pascual Perez	.25	.15
85T Tony Perez	1.75	1.00
86T Broderick Perkins	.25	.15
87T Tony Phillips (R)	7.50	4.00
88T Charlie Puleo	.25	.15
89T Pat Putnam	.25	.15
90T Jamie Quirk	.25	.15
91T Doug Rader	.25	.15
92T Chuck Rainey	.25	.15
93T Bobby Ramos	.25	.15
94T Gary Redus	.50	.30
95T Steve Renko	.25	.15
96T Leon Roberts	.25	.15
97T Aurelio Rodriguez	.25	.15
98T Dick Ruthven	.25	.15
99T Daryl Sconiers	.25	.15
100T Mike Scott	.30	.20
101T Tom Seaver	10.00	7.00
102T John Shelby (R)	.30	.18
103T Bob Shirley	.25	.15
104T Joe Simpson	.25	.15
105T Doug Sisk (R)	.25	.15
106T Mike Smithson (R)	.25	.15
107T Elias Sosa	.25	.15
108T Darryl Strawberry (R)	48.00	28.00
109T Tom Tellmann	.25	.15
110T Gene Tenace	.30	.18
111T Gorman Thomas	.30	.18
112T Dick Tidrow	.25	.15
113T Dave Tobik	.25	.15
114T Wayne Tolleson (R)	.25	.15
115T Mike Torrez	.25	.15
116T Manny Trillo	.25	.15
117T Steve Trout	.25	.15
118T Lee Tunnell (R)	.25	.15
119T Mike Vail	.25	.15
120T Ellis Valentine	.25	.15
121T Tom Veryzer	.25	.15
122T George Vukovich	.25	.15
123T Rick Waits	.25	.15
124T Greg Walker (R)	.30	.18
125T Chris Welsh	.25	.15
126T Len Whiethouse	.25	.15
127T Eddie Whitson	.25	.15
128T Jim Wohlford	.25	.15
129T Matt Young (R)	.30	.18
130T Joel Youngblood	.25	.15
131T Pat Zachry	.25	.15
132T Checklist 1-132	.30	.15

1984 Topps

This 792-card set has some of the same features of the 1983 set including the use of two photos on the card fronts, a large color action photo and a small head shot in the lower left corner. Cards measure 2-1/2" by 3-1/2". Key subsets include Highlights (HL) (1-6), League Leaders, All-Stars and Team Leaders. A new feature, Active Career Leaders, has been added to this set. A specially boxed glossy set, called Topps Tiffany, was also issued. Limited to 10,000 sets, the Tiffany Edition mirrors the regular issue except for the paper stock and the glossy coating. Those cards are valued at eight times the price of the redular edition.

	MINT	NR/MT
Complete Set (792)	80.00	45.00
Commons	.07	.04

1	Steve Carlton (HL)	1.00	.60
2	Rickey Henderson (HL)	.80	.50
3	Dan Quisenberry (HL)	.10	.06
4	Steve Carlton, Gaylord Perry, Nolan Ryan (HL)	1.25	.80
5	Bob Forsch, Dave Righetti, Mike Warren (HL)	.10	.06
6	Johnny Bench, Gaylord Perry, Carl Yastrzemski (HL)	.60	.35
7	Gary Lucas	.07	.04
8	Don Mattingly (R)	20.00	12.00
9	Jim Gott	.10	.06
10	Robin Yount	2.00	1.25
11	Twins (TL) (Kent Hrbek, Ken Schrom)	.12	.07
12	Billy Sample	.07	.04
13	Scott Holman	.07	.04
14	Tom Brookens	.07	.04
15	Burt Hooton	.07	.04
16	Omar Moreno	.07	.04
17	John Denny	.07	.04
18	Dale Berra	.07	.04
19	Ray Fontenot (R)	.07	.04
20	Greg Luzinski	.15	.10
21	Joe Altobelli	.07	.04
22	Bryan Clark	.07	.04
23	Keith Moreland	.07	.04
24	John Martin	.07	.04
25	Glenn Hubbard	.07	.04
26	Bud Black	.12	.07
27	Daryl Sconiers	.07	.04
28	Frank Viola	.50	.30
29	Danny Heep	.07	.04
30	Wade Boggs	4.00	2.75
31	Andy McGaffigan	.07	.04
32	Bobby Ramos	.07	.04
33	Tom Burgmeier	.07	.04
34	Eddie Milner	.07	.04
35	Don Sutton	.50	.30
36	Denny Walling	.07	.04
37	Rangers (TL) (Buddy Bell, Rick Honeycutt)	.12	.07
38	Luis DeLeon	.07	.04
39	Garth Iorg	.07	.04
40	Dusty Baker	.15	.10
41	Tony Bernazard	.07	.04
42	Johnny Grubb	.07	.04
43	Ron Reed	.07	.04
44	Jim Morrison	.07	.04
45	Jerry Mumphrey	.07	.04
46	Ray Smith	.07	.04
47	Rudy Law	.07	.04
48	Julio Franco	1.00	.60
49	John Stuper	.07	.04
50	Chris Chambliss	.10	.06
51	Jim Frey	.07	.04
52	Paul Splittorff	.10	.06
53	Juan Beniquez	.07	.04
54	Jesse Orosco	.07	.04
55	Dave Concepcion	.20	.12
56	Gary Allenson	.07	.04
57	Dan Schatzeder	.07	.04
58	Max Venable	.07	.04
59	Sammy Stewart	.07	.04
60	Paul Molitor	2.50	1.40
61	Chris Codiroli	.07	.04
62	Dave Hostetler	.07	.04
63	Ed Vande Berg	.07	.04
64	Mike Scioscia	.12	.07
65	Kirk Gibson	.35	.20
66	Astros (TL) (Jose Cruz, Nolan Ryan)	1.00	.60
67	Gary Ward	.07	.04
68	Luis Salazar	.07	.04
69	Rod Scurry	.07	.04
70	Gary Matthews	.07	.04
71	Leo Hernandez	.07	.04
72	Mike Squires	.07	.04
73	Jody Davis	.07	.04
74	Jerry Martin	.07	.04
75	Bob Forsch	.07	.04
76	Alfredo Griffin	.07	.04
77	Brett Butler	.35	.20
78	Mike Torrez	.07	.04
79	Rob Wilfong	.07	.04
80	Steve Rogers	.07	.04
81	Billy Martin	.20	.12
82	Doug Bird	.07	.04
83	Richie Zisk	.07	.04
84	Lenny Faedo	.07	.04
85	Atlee Hammaker	.07	.04
86	John Shelby	.07	.04
87	Frank Pastore	.10	.06
88	Rob Picciolo	.07	.04
89	Mike Smithson	.07	.04
90	Pedro Guerrero	.25	.15
91	Dan Spillner	.07	.04
92	Lloyd Moseby	.07	.04
93	Bob Knepper	.07	.04
94	Mario Ramirez	.07	.04
95	Aurelio Lopez	.07	.04
96	Royals (TL) (Larry Gura, Hal McRae)	.12	.07
97	LaMarr Hoyt	.07	.04
98	Steve Nicosia	.07	.04
99	Craig Lefferts (R)	.15	.10
100	Reggie Jackson	1.75	1.00
101	Porfirio Altamirano	.07	.04
102	Ken Oberkfell	.07	.04
103	Dwayne Murphy	.07	.04
104	Ken Dayley	.07	.04

105	Tony Armas	.10	.06
106	Tim Stoddard	.07	.04
107	Ned Yost	.07	.04
108	Randy Moffitt	.07	.04
109	Brad Wellman	.07	.04
110	Ron Guidry	.20	.12
111	Bill Virdon	.07	.04
112	Tom Niedenfuer	.07	.04
113	Kelly Paris	.07	.04
114	Checklist 1-132	.12	.05
115	Andre Thornton	.10	.06
116	George Bjorkman	.07	.04
117	Tom Veryzer	.07	.04
118	Charlie Hough	.10	.06
119	Johnny Wockenfuss	.07	.04
120	Keith Hernandez	.15	.10
121	Pat Sheridan (R)	.10	.06
122	Cecilio Guante	.07	.04
123	Butch Wynegar	.07	.04
124	Damaso Garcia	.07	.04
125	Britt Burns	.07	.04
126	Braves (TL) (Craig McMurtry, Dale Murphy)	.15	.10
127	Mike Madden	.07	.04
128	Rick Manning	.07	.04
129	Bill Laskey	.07	.04
130	Ozzie Smith	1.50	.90
131	Batting Leaders	.75	.45
132	Home Run Leaders	.75	.45
133	RBI Leaders Leaders	.30	.18
134	Stolen Base Leaders	.75	.45
135	Victory Leaders	.12	.07
136	Strikeout Leaders	.75	.45
137	ERA Leaders	.10	.06
138	Leading Firemen	.10	.06
139	Bert Campaneris	.12	.07
140	Storm Davis	.12	.07
141	Pat Corrales	.07	.04
142	Rich Gale	.07	.04
143	Jose Morales	.07	.04
144	Brian Harper (R)	1.00	.60
145	Gary Lavelle	.07	.04
146	Ed Romero	.07	.04
147	Dan Petry	.07	.04
148	Joe Lefebvre	.07	.04
149	Jon Matlack	.07	.04
150	Dale Murphy	.75	.45
151	Steve Trout	.07	.04
152	Glenn Brummer	.07	.04
153	Dick Tidrow	.07	.04
154	Dave Henderson	.15	.10
155	Frank White	.07	.04
156	A"s (TL) (Tim Conroy, Rickey Henderson)	.35	.20
157	Gary Gaetti	.12	.07
158	John Curtis	.07	.04
159	Darryl Cias	.07	.04
160	Mario Soto	.10	.06
161	Junior Ortiz (R)	.10	.06
162	Bob Ojeda	.07	.04
163	Lorenzo Gray	.07	.04
164	Scott Sanderson	.12	.07
165	Ken Singleton	.10	.06
166	Jamie Nelson	.07	.04
167	Marshall Edwards	.07	.04
168	Juan Bonilla	.07	.04
169	Larry Parrish	.07	.04
170	Jerry Reuss	.10	.06
171	Frank Robinson	.15	.10
172	Frank DiPino	.07	.04
173	Marvell Wynne (R)	.10	.06
174	Juan Berenguer	.07	.04
175	Graig Nettles	.10	.06
176	Lee Smith	.90	.55
177	Jerry Hairston	.07	.04
178	Bill Krueger	.10	.06
179	Buck Martinez	.07	.04
180	Manny Trillo	.07	.04
181	Roy Thomas	.07	.04
182	Darryl Strawberry	6.50	3.75
183	Al Williams	.07	.04
184	Mike O'Berry	.07	.04
185	Sixto Lezcano	.07	.04
186	Cardinals (TL)(Lonnie Smith, John Stuper)	.10	.06
187	Luis Aponte	.07	.04
188	Bryan Little	.07	.04
189	Tim Conroy (R)	.07	.04
190	Ben Oglivie	.07	.04
191	Mike Boddicker	.10	.06
192	Nick Esasky (R)	.10	.06
193	Darrell Brown	.07	.04
194	Domingo Ramos	.07	.04
195	Jack Morris	.75	.45
196	Don Slaught	.15	.10
197	Garry Hancock	.07	.04
198	Bill Doran	.30	.18
199	Willie Hernandez	.10	.06
200	Andre Dawson	1.75	1.00
201	Bruce Kison	.07	.04
202	Bobby Cox	.07	.04
203	Matt Keough	.07	.04
204	Bobby Meacham (R)	.07	.04
205	Greg Minton	.07	.04
206	Andy Van Slyke (R)	3.50	2.50
207	Donnie Moore	.07	.04
208	Jose Oquendo (R)	.20	.12
209	Manny Sarmiento	.07	.04
210	Joe Morgan	.60	.35
211	Rick Sweet	.07	.04
212	Broderick Perkins	.07	.04
213	Bruce Hurst	.15	.10
214	Paul Householder	.07	.04

215 Tippy Martinez	.07	.04	
216 White Sox (TL) (Richard Dotson Carlton Fisk)	.20	.12	
217 Alan Ashby	.07	.04	
218 Rick Waits	.07	.04	
219 Joe Simpson	.07	.04	
220 Fernando Valenzuela	.15	.10	
221 Cliff Johnson	.07	.04	
222 Rick Honeycutt	.07	.04	
223 Wayne Krenchicki	.07	.04	
224 Sid Monge	.07	.04	
225 Lee Mazzilli	.07	.04	
226 Juan Eichelberger	.07	.04	
227 Steve Braun	.07	.04	
228 John Rabb	.07	.04	
229 Paul Owens	.07	.04	
230 Rickey Henderson	4.00	2.75	
231 Gary Woods	.07	.04	
232 Tim Wallach	.20	.12	
233 Checklist 133-264	.12	.05	
234 Rafael Ramirez	.07	.04	
235 Matt Young	.12	.07	
236 Ellis Valentine	.07	.04	
237 John Castino	.07	.04	
238 Reid Nichols	.07	.04	
239 Jay Howell	.10	.06	
240 Eddie Murray	1.75	1.00	
241 Billy Almon	.07	.04	
242 Alex Trevino	.07	.04	
243 Pete Ladd	.07	.04	
244 Candy Maldonado	.25	.15	
245 Rick Sutcliffe	.15	.10	
246 Mets (TL) (Tom Seaver, Mookie Wilson)	.35	.20	
247 Onix Concepcion	.07	.04	
248 Bill Dawley (R)	.07	.04	
249 Jay Johnstone	.10	.06	
250 Bill Madlock	.15	.10	
251 Tony Gwynn	5.00	3.00	
252 Larry Christenson	.07	.04	
253 Jim Wohlford	.07	.04	
254 Shane Rawley	.07	.04	
255 Bruce Benedict	.07	.04	
256 Dave Geisel	.07	.04	
257 Julio Cruz	.07	.04	
258 Luis Sanchez	.07	.04	
259 Sparky Anderson	.10	.06	
260 Scott McGregor	.07	.04	
261 Bobby Brown	.07	.04	
262 Tom Candiotti (R)	.50	.30	
263 Jack Fimple	.07	.04	
264 Doug Frobel	.07	.04	
265 Donnie Hill (R)	.07	.04	
266 Steve Lubratich	.07	.04	
267 Carmelo Martinez (R)	.12	.07	
268 Jack O'Connor	.07	.04	
269 Aurelio Rodriguez	.07	.04	
270 Jeff Russell (R)	.35	.20	
271 Moose Haas	.07	.04	
272 Rick Dempsey	.10	.06	
273 Charlie Puleo	.07	.04	
274 Rick Monday	.10	.06	
275 Len Matuszek	.07	.04	
276 Angels (TL) (Rod Carew, Geoff Zahn)	.25	.15	
277 Eddie Whitson	.07	.04	
278 Jorge Bell	.60	.35	
279 Ivan DeJesus	.07	.04	
280 Floyd Bannister	.07	.04	
281 Larry Milbourne	.07	.04	
282 Jim Barr	.07	.04	
283 Larry Biittner	.07	.04	
284 Howard Bailey	.07	.04	
285 Darrell Porter	.07	.04	
286 Lary Sorensen	.07	.04	
287 Warren Cromartie	.07	.04	
288 Jim Beattie	.07	.04	
289 Randy Johnson	.07	.04	
290 Dave Dravecky	.12	.07	
291 Chuck Tanner	.07	.04	
292 Tony Scott	.07	.04	
293 Ed Lynch	.07	.04	
294 U.L. Washington	.07	.04	
295 Mike Flanagan	.15	.10	
296 Jeff Newman	.07	.04	
297 Bruce Berenyi	.07	.04	
298 Jim Gantner	.07	.04	
299 John Butcher	.07	.04	
300 Pete Rose	1.75	1.00	
301 Frank LaCorte	.07	.04	
302 Barry Bonnell	.07	.04	
303 Marty Castillo	.07	.04	
304 Warren Brusstar	.07	.04	
305 Roy Smalley	.07	.04	
306 Dodgers (TL)(Pedro Guerrero, Bob Welch)	.15	.10	
307 Bobby Mitchell	.07	.04	
308 Ron Hassey	.07	.04	
309 Tony Phillips	1.25	.80	
310 Willie McGee	.50	.30	
311 Jerry Koosman	.15	.10	
312 Jorge Orta	.07	.04	
313 Mike Jorgensen	.07	.04	
314 Orlando Mercado	.07	.04	
315 Bob Grich	.10	.06	
316 Mark Bradley	.07	.04	
317 Greg Pryor	.07	.04	
318 Bill Gullickson	.10	.06	
319 Al Bumbry	.07	.04	
320 Bob Stanley	.07	.04	
321 Harvey Kuenn	.07	.04	
322 Ken Schrom	.07	.04	
323 Alan Knicely	.07	.04	

324 Alejandro Pena	.20	.12
325 Darrell Evans	.15	.10
326 Bob Kearney	.07	.04
327 Ruppert Jones	.07	.04
328 Vern Ruhle	.07	.04
329 Pat Tabler	.10	.06
330 John Candelaria	.10	.06
331 Bucky Dent	.10	.06
332 Kevin Gross (R)	.15	.10
333 Larry Herndon	.07	.04
334 Chuck Rainey	.07	.04
335 Don Baylor	.15	.10
336 Mariners (TL) (Pat	.10	.06
Putnam, Matt Young)		
337 Kevin Hagen	.07	.04
338 Mike Warren	.07	.04
339 Roy Lee Jackson	.07	.04
340 Hal McRae	.15	.10
341 Dave Tobik	.07	.04
342 Tim Foli	.07	.04
343 Mark Davis	.07	.04
344 Rick Miller	.07	.04
345 Kent Hrbek	.30	.18
346 Kurt Bevacqua	.07	.04
347 Allan Ramirez	.07	.04
348 Toby Harrah	.07	.04
349 Bob Gibson	.07	.04
350 George Foster	.15	.10
351 Russ Nixon	.07	.04
352 Dave Stewart	.40	.25
353 Jim Anderson	.07	.04
354 Jeff Burroughs	.07	.04
355 Jason Thompson	.07	.04
356 Glenn Abbott	.07	.04
357 Ron Cey	.10	.06
358 Bob Dernier	.07	.04
359 Jim Acker (R)	.07	.04
360 Willie Randolph	.15	.10
361 Dave Smith	.07	.04
362 David Green	.07	.04
363 Tim Laudner	.07	.04
364 Scott Fletcher (R)	.12	.07
365 Steve Bedrosian	.10	.06
366 Padres (TL) (Dave	.10	.06
Dravecky, Terry		
Kennedy)		
367 Jamie Easterly	.07	.04
368 Hubie Brooks	.12	.07
369 Steve McCatty	.07	.04
370 Tim Raines	.50	.30
371 Dave Gumpert	.07	.04
372 Gary Roenicke	.07	.04
373 Bill Scherrer	.07	.04
374 Don Money	.07	.04
375 Dennis Leonard	.07	.04
376 Dave Anderson (R)	.10	.06
377 Danny Darwin	.10	.06

378 Bob Brenly	.07	.04
379 Checklist 265-396	.12	.05
380 Steve Garvey	.45	.28
381 Ralph Houk	.07	.04
382 Chris Hyman	.07	.04
383 Terry Puhl	.07	.04
384 Lee Tunnell	.07	.04
385 Tony Perez	.35	.20
386 George Hendrick AS	.10	.06
387 Johnny Ray AS	.07	.04
388 Mike Schmidt AS	1.00	.70
389 Ozzie Smith AS	.50	.30
390 Tim Raines AS	.25	.15
391 Dale Murphy AS	.30	.18
392 Andre Dawson AS	.50	.30
393 Gary Carter AS	.20	.12
394 Steve Rogers AS	.07	.04
395 Steve Carlton AS	.60	.35
396 Jesse Orosco AS	.07	.04
397 Eddie Murray AS	.50	.30
398 Lou Whitaker AS	.15	.10
399 George Brett AS	1.00	.60
400 Cal Ripken AS	2.00	1.25
401 Jim Rice AS	.15	.10
402 Dave Winfield AS	1.25	.80
403 Lloyd Moseby AS	.07	.04
404 Ted Simmons AS	.10	.06
405 LaMarr Hoyt AS	.07	.04
406 Ron Guidry AS	.15	.10
407 Dan Quisenberry AS	.07	.04
408 Lou Piniella	.10	.06
409 Juan Agosto (R)	.10	.06
410 Claudell Washington	.10	.06
411 Houston Jimenez	.07	.04
412 Doug Rader	.07	.04
413 Spike Owen (R)	.20	.12
414 Mitchell Page	.07	.04
415 Tommy John	.15	.10
416 Dane Iorg	.07	.04
417 Mike Armstrong	.07	.04
418 Ron Hodges	.07	.04
419 John Henry Johnson	.07	.04
420 Cecil Cooper	.12	.07
421 Charlie Lea	.07	.04
422 Jose Cruz	.12	.07
423 Mike Morgan	.07	.04
424 Dann Bilardello	.07	.04
425 Steve Howe	.07	.04
426 Orioles (TL)(Mike	1.25	.80
Boddicker, Cal Ripken)		
427 Rick Leach	.07	.04
428 Fred Breining	.07	.04
429 Randy Bush	.10	.06
430 Rusty Staub	.15	.10
431 Chris Bando	.07	.04
432 Charlie Hudson (R)	.07	.04
433 Rich Hebner	.07	.04

434 Harold Baines	.20	.12
435 Neil Allen	.07	.04
436 Rick Peters	.07	.04
437 Mike Proly	.07	.04
438 Biff Pocoroba	.07	.04
439 Bob Stoddard	.07	.04
440 Steve Kemp	.07	.04
441 Bob Lillis	.07	.04
442 Byron McLaughlin	.07	.04
443 Benny Ayala	.07	.04
444 Steve Renko	.07	.04
445 Jerry Remy	.07	.04
446 Luis Pujols	.07	.04
447 Tom Brunansky	.12	.07
448 Ben Hayes	.07	.04
449 Joe Pettini	.07	.04
450 Gary Carter	.40	.25
451 Bob Jones	.07	.04
452 Chuck Porter	.07	.04
453 Willie Upshaw	.07	.04
454 Joe Beckwith	.07	.04
455 Terry Kennedy	.07	.04
456 Cubs (TL) (Ferguson Jenkins, Keith Moreland)	.20	.12
457 Dave Rozema	.07	.04
458 Kiko Garcia	.07	.04
459 Kevin Hickey	.07	.04
460 Dave Winfield	3.00	1.75
461 Jim Maler	.07	.04
462 Lee Lacy	.07	.04
463 Dave Engle	.07	.04
464 Jeff Jones	.07	.04
465 Mookie Wilson	.10	.06
466 Gene Garber	.07	.04
467 Mike Ramsey	.07	.04
468 Geoff Zahn	.07	.04
469 Tom O'Malley	.07	.04
470 Nolan Ryan	7.50	4.50
471 Dick Howser	.07	.04
472 Mike Brown	.07	.04
473 Jim Dwyer	.07	.04
474 Greg Bargar	.07	.04
475 Gary Redus	.12	.07
476 Tom Tellmann	.07	.04
477 Rafael Landestoy	.07	.04
478 Alan Bannister	.07	.04
479 Frank Tanana	.10	.06
480 Ron Kittle	.10	.06
481 Mark Thurmond (R)	.07	.04
482 Enos Cabell	.07	.04
483 Ferguson Jenkins	.50	.30
484 Ozzie Virgil	.07	.04
485 Rick Rhoden	.07	.04
486 Yankees (TL) (Don Baylor, Ron Guidry)	.15	.10
487 Ricky Adams	.07	.04
488 Jesse Barfield	.15	.10
489 Dave Von Ohlen	.07	.04
490 Cal Ripken	7.50	4.25
491 Bobby Castillo	.07	.04
492 Tucker Ashford	.07	.04
493 Mike Norris	.07	.04
494 Chili Davis	.12	.07
495 Rollie Fingers	.50	.30
496 Terry Francona	.07	.04
497 Bud Anderson	.07	.04
498 Rich Gedman	.07	.04
499 Mike Witt	.07	.04
500 George Brett	3.00	2.00
501 Steve Henderson	.07	.04
502 Joe Torre	.10	.06
503 Elias Sosa	.07	.04
504 Mickey Rivers	.07	.04
505 Pete Vuckovich	.07	.04
506 Ernie Whitt	.07	.04
507 Mike LaCoss	.07	.04
508 Mel Hall	.35	.20
509 Brad Havens	.07	.04
510 Alan Trammell	.75	.45
511 Marty Bystrom	.07	.04
512 Oscar Gamble	.07	.04
513 Dave Beard	.07	.04
514 Floyd Rayford	.07	.04
515 Gorman Thomas	.10	.06
516 Expos (TL) (Charlie Lea, Al Oliver)	.12	.07
517 John Moses	.07	.04
518 Greg Walker	.07	.04
519 Ron Davis	.07	.04
520 Bob Boone	.20	.12
521 Pete Falcone	.07	.04
522 Dave Bergman	.07	.04
523 Glenn Hoffman	.07	.04
524 Carlos Diaz	.07	.04
525 Willie Wilson	.10	.06
526 Ron Oester	.07	.04
527 Checklist 397-528	.12	.05
528 Mark Brouhard	.07	.04
529 Keith Atherton	.07	.04
530 Dan Ford	.07	.04
531 Steve Boros	.07	.04
532 Eric Show	.07	.04
533 Ken Landreaux	.07	.04
534 Pete O'Brien	.15	.10
535 Bo Diaz	.07	.04
536 Doug Bair	.07	.04
537 Johnny Ray	.07	.04
538 Kevin Bass	.10	.06
539 George Frazier	.07	.04
540 George Hendrick	.10	.06
541 Dennis Lamp	.07	.04
542 Duane Kuiper	.07	.04
543 Craig McMurtry	.10	.06

544	Cesar Geronimo	.07	.04
545	Bill Buckner	.12	.07
546	Indians (TL) (Mike Hargrove, Lary Sorensen)	.07	.04
547	Mike Moore	.12	.07
548	Ron Jackson	.07	.04
549	Walt Terrell	.07	.04
550	Jim Rice	.15	.10
551	Scott Ullger	.07	.04
552	Ray Burris	.07	.04
553	Joe Nolan	.07	.04
554	Ted Power	.10	.06
555	Greg Brock	.07	.04
556	Joey McLaughlin	.07	.04
557	Wayne Tolleson	.07	.04
558	Mike Davis	.07	.04
559	Mike Scott	.12	.07
560	Carlton Fisk	1.50	.90
561	Whitey Herzog	.10	.06
562	Manny Castillo	.07	.04
563	Glenn Wilson	.07	.04
564	Al Holland	.07	.04
565	Leon Durham	.07	.04
566	Jim Bibby	.07	.04
567	Mike Heath	.07	.04
568	Pete Filson	.07	.04
569	Bake McBride	.07	.04
570	Dan Quisenberry	.10	.06
571	Bruce Bochy	.07	.04
572	Jerry Royster	.07	.04
573	Dave Kingman	.12	.07
574	Brian Downing	.10	.06
575	Jim Clancy	.07	.04
576	Giants (TL) (Atlee Hammaker, Jeff Leonard)	.10	.06
577	Mark Clear	.07	.04
578	Lenn Sakata	.07	.04
579	Bob James	.07	.04
580	Lonnie Smith	.12	.07
581	Jose DeLeon (R)	.10	.06
582	Bob McClure	.07	.04
583	Derrel Thomas	.07	.04
584	Dave Schmidt	.07	.04
585	Dan Driessen	.07	.04
586	Joe Niekro	.07	.04
587	Von Hayes	.10	.06
588	Milt Wilcox	.07	.04
589	Mike Easler	.07	.04
590	Dave Stieb	.12	.07
591	Tony LaRussa	.10	.06
592	Andre Robertson	.07	.04
593	Jeff Lahti	.07	.04
594	Gene Richards	.07	.04
595	Jeff Reardon	.60	.35
596	Ryne Sandberg	9.00	5.50
597	Rick Camp	.07	.04
598	Rusty Kuntz	.07	.04
599	Doug Sisk	.07	.04
600	Rod Carew	1.00	.70
601	John Tudor	.10	.06
602	John Wathan	.07	.04
603	Renie Martin	.07	.04
604	John Lowenstein	.07	.04
605	Mike Caldwell	.07	.04
606	Blue Jays (TL)(Lloyd Moseby, Dave Stieb)	.12	.07
607	Tom Hume	.07	.04
608	Bobby Johnson	.07	.04
609	Dan Meyer	.07	.04
610	Steve Sax	.25	.15
611	Chet Lemon	.07	.04
612	Harry Spilman	.07	.04
613	Greg Gross	.07	.04
614	Len Barker	.07	.04
615	Garry Templeton	.10	.06
616	Don Robinson	.07	.04
617	Rick Cerone	.07	.04
618	Dickie Noles	.07	.04
619	Jerry Dybzinski	.07	.04
620	Al Oliver	.12	.07
621	Frank Howard	.07	.04
622	Al Cowens	.07	.04
623	Ron Washington	.07	.04
624	Terry Harper	.07	.04
625	Larry Gura	.07	.04
626	Bob Clark	.07	.04
627	Dave LaPoint	.07	.04
628	Ed Jurak	.07	.04
629	Rick Langford	.07	.04
630	Ted Simmons	.10	.06
631	Denny Martinez	.15	.10
632	Tom Foley	.07	.04
633	Mike Krukow	.07	.04
634	Mike Marshall	.07	.04
635	Dave Righetti	.12	.07
636	Pat Putnam	.07	.04
637	Phillies (TL) (John Denny, Gary Matthews)	.10	.06
638	George Vukovich	.07	.04
639	Rick Lysander	.07	.04
640	Lance Parrish	.12	.07
641	Mike Richardt	.07	.04
642	Tom Underwood	.07	.04
643	Mike Brown	.07	.04
644	Tim Lollar	.07	.04
645	Tony Pena	.10	.06
646	Checklist 529-660	.12	.05
647	Ron Roenicke	.07	.04
648	Len Whitehouse	.07	.04
649	Tom Herr	.10	.06
650	Phil Niekro	.50	.30
651	John McNamara	.07	.04

652 Rudy May	.07	.04	
653 Dave Stapleton	.07	.04	
654 Bob Bailor	.07	.04	
655 Amos Otis	.10	.06	
656 Bryn Smith	.10	.06	
657 Thad Bosley	.07	.04	
658 Jerry Augustine	.07	.04	
659 Duane Walker	.07	.04	
660 Ray Knight	.10	.06	
661 Steve Yeager	.07	.04	
662 Tom Brennan	.07	.04	
663 Johnnie LeMaster	.07	.04	
664 Dave Stegman	.07	.04	
665 Buddy Bell	.07	.04	
666 Tigers (TL) (Jack Morris, Lou Whitaker)	.25	.15	
667 Vance Law	.07	.04	
668 Larry McWilliams	.07	.04	
669 Dave Lopes	.10	.06	
670 Rich Gossage	.20	.12	
671 Jamie Quirk	.07	.04	
672 Ricky Nelson	.07	.04	
673 Mike Walters	.07	.04	
674 Tim Flannery	.07	.04	
675 Pascual Perez	.10	.06	
676 Brian Giles	.07	.04	
677 Doyle Alexander	.07	.04	
678 Chris Speier	.07	.04	
679 Art Howe	.07	.04	
680 Fred Lynn	.15	.10	
681 Tom Lasorda	.10	.06	
682 Dan Morogiello	.07	.04	
683 Marty Barrett (R)	.20	.12	
684 Bob Shirley	.07	.04	
685 Willie Aikens	.07	.04	
686 Joe Price	.07	.04	
687 Roy Howell	.07	.04	
688 George Wright	.07	.04	
689 Mike Fischlin	.07	.04	
690 Jack Clark	.12	.07	
691 Steve Lake (R)	.07	.04	
692 Dickie Thon	.10	.06	
693 Alan Wiggins	.07	.04	
694 Mike Stanton	.07	.04	
695 Lou Whitaker	.50	.30	
696 Pirates (TL) (Bill Madlock, Rick Rhoden)	.12	.07	
697 Dale Murray	.07	.04	
698 Marc Hill	.07	.04	
699 Dave Rucker	.07	.04	
700 Mike Schmidt	3.50	2.50	
701 NL Active Batting Ldrs (Bill Madlock, Dave Parker, Pete Rose)	.35	.20	
702 NL Active Hit Leaders (Tony Perez, Pete Rose, Rusty Staub)	.35	.20	
703 NL Active HR Leaders (Dave Kingman, Tony Perez, Mike Schmidt)	.40	.25	
704 NL Active RBI Leaders (Al Oliver, Tony Perez, Rusty Staub)	.20	.12	
705 NL Active SB Leaders (Larry Bowa, Cesar Cedeno, Joe Morgan)	.25	.15	
706 NL Active Victory Ldrs (Steve Carlton, Fergie Jenkins, Tom Seaver)	.75	.45	
707 NL Active Strikeout Leaders (Steve Carlton, Nolan Ryan, Tom Seaver)	2.00	1.25	
708 NL Active ERA Leaders (Steve Carlton, Steve Rogers, Tom Seaver)	.75	.45	
709 NL Active Save Leaders (Gene Garber, Tug McGraw, Bruce Sutter)	.25	.15	
710 AL Active Batting Ldrs (George Brett, Rod Carew, Cecil Cooper)	.75	.45	
711 AL Active Hit Leaders (Bert Campaneris, Rod Carew, Reggie Jackson)	.80	.50	
712 AL Active HR Leaders (Reggie Jackson, Greg Luzinski, Graig Nettles)	.60	.35	
713 AL Active RBI Leaders (Reggie Jackson, Graig Nettles, Ted Simmons)	.60	.35	
714 AL Active SB Leaders (Bert Campaneris, Dave Lopes, Omar Moreno)	.20	.12	
715 AL Active Victory Ldrs (Tommy John, Jim Palmer, Don Sutton)	.35	.20	
716 AL Active Strikeout Leaders (Bert Blyleven, Jerry Koosman, Don Sutton)	.25	.15	
717 AL Active ERA Leaders (Rollie Fingers, Ron Guidry, Jim Palmer)	.40	.25	
718 AL Active Save Leaders (Rollie Ringers, Rich Gossage, Dan Quisenberry)	.25	.15	
719 Andy Hassler	.07	.04	
720 Dwight Evans	.25	.15	
721 Del Crandall	.07	.04	
722 Bob Welch	.15	.10	
723 Rich Dauer	.07	.04	
724 Eric Rasmussen	.07	.04	
725 Cesar Cedeno	.10	.06	

726	Brewers (TL) (Moose Haas, Ted Simmons)	.12	.07
727	Joel Youngblood	.07	.04
728	Tug McGraw	.12	.07
729	Gene Tenace	.10	.06
730	Bruce Sutter	.15	.10
731	Lynn Jones	.07	.04
732	Terry Crowley	.07	.04
733	Dave Collins	.07	.04
734	Odell Jones	.07	.04
735	Rick Burleson	.10	.06
736	Dick Ruthven	.07	.04
737	Jim Essian	.07	.04
738	Bill Schroeder	.07	.04
739	Bob Watson	.15	.10
740	Tom Seaver	1.25	.80
741	Wayne Gross	.07	.04
742	Dick Williams	.07	.04
743	Don Hood	.07	.04
744	Jamie Allen	.07	.04
745	Dennis Eckersley	.80	.50
746	Mickey Hatcher	.07	.04
747	Pat Zachry	.07	.04
748	Jeff Leonard	.10	.06
749	Doug Flynn	.07	.04
750	Jim Palmer	1.25	.80
751	Charlie Moore	.07	.04
752	Phil Garner	.10	.06
753	Doug Gwosdz	.07	.04
754	Kent Tekulve	.07	.04
755	Garry Maddox	.07	.04
756	Reds (TL)(Ron Oester, Mario Soto)	.10	.06
757	Larry Bowa	.10	.06
758	Bill Stein	.07	.04
759	Richard Dotson	.07	.04
760	Bob Horner	.10	.06
761	John Montefusco	.07	.04
762	Rance Mulliniks	.07	.04
763	Craig Swan	.07	.04
764	Mike Hargrove	.07	.04
765	Ken Forsch	.07	.04
766	Mike Vail	.07	.04
767	Carney Lansford	.10	.06
768	Champ Summers	.07	.04
769	Bill Caudill	.07	.04
770	Ken Griffey	.15	.10
771	Billy Gardner	.07	.04
772	Jim Slaton	.07	.04
773	Todd Cruz	.07	.04
774	Tom Gorman	.07	.04
775	Dave Parker	.25	.15
776	Craig Reynolds	.07	.04
777	Tom Paciorek	.07	.04
778	Andy Hawkins	.07	.04
779	Jim Sundberg	.07	.04
780	Steve Carlton	1.50	.90

781	Checklist 661-792	.12	.05
782	Steve Balboni	.07	.04
783	Luis Leal	.07	.04
784	Leon Roberts	.07	.04
785	Joaquin Andujar	.10	.06
786	Red Sox (TL) (Wade Boggs, Bob Ojeda)	.40	.25
787	Bill Campbell	.07	.04
788	Milt May	.07	.04
789	Bert Blyleven	.25	.15
790	Doug DeCinces	.10	.06
791	Terry Forster	.07	.04
792	Bill Russell	.12	.07

1984 Topps Traded

This 132-card update set is identical to the 1984 Topps regular edition. Cards measure 2-1/2" by 3-1/2" and the set features players traded during the season, rookies called up after the start of the season and new managers.

	MINT	NR/MT
Complete Set (132)	85.00	45.00
Commons	.20	.12

1T	Willie Aikens	.20	.12
2T	Luis Aponte	.20	.12
3T	Mike Armstrong	.20	.12
4T	Bob Bailor	.20	.12
5T	Dusty Baker	.35	.20
6T	Steve Balboni	.20	.12
7T	Alan Bannister	.20	.12
8T	Dave Beard	.20	.12
9T	Joe Beckwith	.20	.12
10T	Bruce Berenyi	.20	.12
11T	Dave Bergman	.20	.12
12T	Tony Bernazard	.20	.12

13T Yogi Berra	.80	.50
14T Barry Bonnell	.20	.12
15T Phil Bradley (R)	.30	.18
16T Ferd Breining	.20	.12
17T Bill Buckner	.25	.15
18T Ray Burris	.20	.12
19T John Butcher	.20	.10
20T Brett Butler	.80	.50
21T Enos Cabell	.20	.12
22T Bill Campbell	.20	.12
23T Bill Caudill	.20	.12
24T Bob Clark	.20	.12
25T Bryan Clark	.20	.12
26T Jaime Cocanower	.20	.12
27T Ron Darling (R)	2.50	1.40
28T Alvin Davis (R)	.75	.45
29T Ken Dayley	.20	.12
30T Jeff Dedmon (R)	.20	.12
31T Bob Dernier	.20	.12
32T Carlos Diaz	.20	.12
33T Mike Easler	.20	.12
34T Dennis Eckersley	4.00	2.50
35T Jim Essian	.20	.12
36T Darrell Evans	.35	.20
37T Mike Fitzgerald	.20	.12
38T Tim Foli	.20	.12
39T George Frazier	.20	.12
40T Rich Gale	.20	.12
41T Barbaro Garbey	.20	.12
42T Dwight Gooden (R)	24.00	14.00
43T Rich Gossage	.60	.35
44T Wayne Gross	.20	.12
45T Mark Gubicza (R)	1.00	.60
46T Jackie Gutierrez	.20	.12
47T Mel Hall	.40	.25
48T Toby Harrah	.20	.12
49T Ron Hassey	.25	.15
50T Rich Hebner	.20	.12
51T Willie Hernandez	.20	.12
52T Ricky Horton (R)	.20	.12
53T Art Howe	.25	.15
54T Dane Iorg	.20	.12
55T Brook Jacoby (R)	.35	.20
56T Mike Jeffcoat (R)	.25	.15
57T Dave Johnson	.25	.15
58T Lynn Jones	.20	.12
59T Ruppert Jones	.20	.12
60T Mike Jorgensen	.20	.12
61T Bob Kearney	.20	.12
62T Jimmy Key (R)	12.50	7.50
63T Dave Kingman	.25	.15
64T Jerry Koosman	.20	.12
65T Wayne Krenchicki	.20	.12
66T Rusty Kuntz	.20	.12
67T Rene Lachemann	.20	.12
68T Frank LaCorte	.20	.12
69T Dennis Lamp	.20	.12

70T Mark Langston (R)	12.50	7.50
71T Rick Leach	.20	.12
72T Craig Lefferts	.25	.15
73T Gary Lucas	.20	.12
74T Jerry Martin	.20	.12
75T Carmelo Martinez	.20	.12
76T Mike Mason	.20	.12
77T Gary Matthews	.25	.15
78T Andy McGaffigan	.20	.12
79T Larry Milbourne	.20	.12
80T Sid Monge	.20	.12
81T Jackie Moore	.20	.12
82T Joe Morgan	3.50	2.00
83T Graig Nettles	.40	.25
84T Phil Niekro	2.50	1.40
85T Ken Oberkfell	.20	.12
86T Mike O'Berry	.20	.12
87T Al Oliver	.25	.15
88T Jorge Orta	.20	.12
89T Amos Otis	.25	.15
90T Dave Parker	1.50	.90
91T Tony Perez	2.50	1.40
92T Gerald Perry (R)	.25	.15
93T Gary Pettis (R)	.25	.15
94T Rob Picciolo	.20	.12
95T Vern Rapp	.20	.12
96T Floyd Rayford	.20	.12
97T Randy Ready (R)	.30	.18
98T Ron Reed	.20	.12
99T Gene Richards	.20	.12
100T Jose Rijo (R)	10.00	6.50
101T Jeff Robinson (R)	.25	.15
102T Ron Romanick (R)	.20	.12
103T Pete Rose	12.50	7.50
104T Bret Saberhagen (R)	8.50	5.00
105T Juan Samuel (R)	.75	.45
106T Scott Sanderson	.25	.15
107T Dick Schofield (R)	.35	.20
108T Tom Seaver	8.50	5.50
109T Jim Slaton	.20	.12
110T Mike Smithson	.20	.12
111T Lary Sorensen	.20	.12
112T Tim Stoddard	.20	.12
113T Champ Summers	.20	.12
114T Jim Sundberg	.20	.12
115T Rick Sutcliffe	.40	.25
116T Craig Swan	.20	.12
117T Tim Teufel	.25	.15
118T Derrel Thomas	.20	.12
119T Gorman Thomas	.25	.15
120T Alex Trevino	.20	.12
121T Manny Trillo	.20	.12
122T John Tudor	.20	.12
123T Tom Underwood	.20	.12
124T Mike Vail	.20	.12
125T Tom Waddell	.20	.12
126T Gary Ward	.20	.12

		MINT	NR/MT
127T	Curt Wilkerson	.20	.12
128T	Frank Williams (R)	.20	.12
129T	Glenn Wilson	.20	.12
130T	Johnny Wockenfuss	.20	.12
131T	Ned Yost	.20	.12
132T	Checklist 1-132	.25	.12

1985 Topps

In this 792-card set Topps reverted to one large photo on the card front. Card backs are horizontal and printed in green and burgundy on a gray paper stock. All cards measure 2-1/2" by 3-1/2". Topps introduced several new subsets in 1985 including members of the 1984 U.S.A. Olympic Baseball Team and First Round Draft Picks. Topps also brought back the popular Fathers and Sons subset which last appeared in 1976. Other subsets include Record Breakers (RB) and All-Stars. For the second year in a row Topps produced a "glossy" ediiton called the Tiffany Set. Limited to 5,000 sets, the Tiffany edition is valued at five to six times the current price of the regular set.

		MINT	NR/MT
	Complete Set(792)	100.00	60.00
	Commons	.07	.04
1	Carlton Fisk (RB)	.50	.30
2	Steve Garvey (RB)	.25	.15
3	Dwight Gooden (RB)	.80	.50
4	Cliff Johnson (RB)	.10	.06
5	Joe Morgan (RB)	.20	.12
6	Pete Rose (RB)	.60	.35
7	Nolan Ryan (RB)	1.75	1.00
8	Juan Samuel (RB)	.10	.06

9	Bruce Sutter (RB)	.12	.07
10	Don Sutton (RB)	.20	.12
11	Ralph Houk	.07	.04
12	Dave Lopes	.10	.06
13	Tim Lollar	.07	.04
14	Chris Bando	.07	.04
15	Jerry Koosman	.10	.06
16	Bobby Meacham	.07	.04
17	Mike Scott	.12	.07
18	Mickey Hatcher	.07	.04
19	George Farzier	.07	.04
20	Chet Lemon	.07	.04
21	Lee Tunnell	.07	.04
22	Duane Kuiper	.07	.04
23	Bret Saberhagen	1.75	1.00
24	Jesse Barfield	.15	.10
25	Steve Bedrosian	.10	.06
26	Roy Smalley	.07	.04
27	Bruce Berenyl	.07	.04
28	Dann Bilardello	.07	.04
29	Odell Jones	.07	.04
30	Cal Ripken	5.00	3.00
31	Terry Whitfield	.07	.04
32	Chuck Porter	.07	.04
33	Tito Landrum	.07	.04
34	Ed Nunez (R)	.07	.04
35	Graig Nettles	.12	.07
36	Fred Breining	.07	.04
37	Reid Nichols	.07	.04
38	Jackie Moore	.07	.04
39	Johnny Wockenfuss	.07	.04
40	Phil Niekro	.25	.15
41	Mike Fischlin	.07	.04
42	Luis Sanchez	.07	.04
43	Andre David	.07	.04
44	Dickie Thon	.10	.06
45	Greg Minton	.07	.04
46	Gary Woods	.07	.04
47	Dave Rozema	.07	.04
48	Tony Fernandez (R)	.80	.50
49	Butch Davis	.07	.04
50	John Candelaria	.10	.06
51	Bob Watson	.20	.12
52	Jerry Dybzinski	.07	.04
53	Tom Gorman	.07	.04
54	Cesar Cedeno	.10	.06
55	Frank Tanana	.10	.06
56	Jim Dwyer	.07	.04
57	Pat Zachry	.07	.04
58	Orlando Mercado	.07	.04
59	Rick Waits	.07	.04
60	George Hendrick	.10	.06
61	Curt Kaufman	.07	.04
62	Mike Ramsey	.07	.04
63	Steve McCatty	.07	.04
64	Mark Bailey	.07	.04
65	Bill Buckner	.12	.07

66	Dick Williams	.07	.04
67	Rafael Santana (R)	.08	.05
68	Von Hayes	.10	.06
69	Jim Winn	.07	.04
70	Don Baylor	.15	.10
71	Tim Laudner	.07	.04
72	Rick Sutcliffe	.12	.07
73	Rusty Kuntz	.07	.04
74	Mike Krukow	.07	.04
75	Willie Upshaw	.07	.04
76	Alan Bannister	.07	.04
77	Joe Beckwith	.07	.04
78	Scott Fletcher	.07	.04
79	Rick Mahler	.07	.04
80	Keith Hernandez	.12	.07
81	Lenn Sakata	.07	.04
82	Joe Price	.07	.04
83	Charlie Moore	.07	.04
84	Spike Owen	.07	.04
85	Mike Marshall	.07	.04
86	Don Aase	.07	.04
87	David Green	.07	.04
88	Bryn Smith	.10	.06
89	Jackie Gutierrez	.07	.04
90	Rich Gossage	.15	.10
91	Jeff Burroughs	.07	.04
92	Paul Owens	.07	.04
93	Don Schulze	.07	.04
94	Toby Harrah	.07	.04
95	Jose Cruz	.12	.07
96	Johnny Ray	.07	.04
97	Pete Filson	.07	.04
98	Steve Lake	.07	.04
99	Milt Wilcox	.07	.04
100	George Brett	1.75	1.00
101	Jim Acker	.07	.04
102	Tommy Dunbar	.07	.04
103	Randy Lerch	.07	.04
104	Mike Fitzgerald	.07	.04
105	Ron Kittle	.10	.06
106	Pascual Perez	.10	.06
107	Tom Foley	.07	.04
108	Darnell Coles	.10	.06
109	Gary Roenicke	.07	.04
110	Alejandro Pena	.12	.07
111	Doug DeCinces	.10	.06
112	Tom Tellmann	.07	.04
113	Tom Herr	.10	.06
114	Bob James	.07	.04
115	Rickey Henderson	1.75	1.00
116	Dennis Boyd	.10	.06
117	Greg Gross	.07	.04
118	Eric show	.07	.04
119	Pat Corrales	.07	.04
120	Steve Kemp	.07	.04
121	Checklist 1-132	.10	.04
122	Tom Brunansky	.12	.07
123	Dave Smith	.07	.04
124	Rich Hebner	.07	.04
125	Kent Tekulve	.07	.04
126	Ruppert Jones	.07	.04
127	Mark Gubicza	.30	.18
128	Ernie Whitt	.07	.04
129	Gene Garber	.07	.04
130	Al Oliver	.12	.07
131	Buddy & Gus Bell	.10	.06
132	Dale & Yogi Berra	.20	.12
133	Bob & Ray Boone	.12	.07
134	Terry & Tito Francona	.07	.04
135	Bob & Terry Kennedy	.07	.04
136	Bill & Jeff Kunkel	.07	.04
137	Vance & Vern Law)	.07	.04
138	Dick Jr & Dick Schofield	.07	.04
139	Bob & Joel Skinner	.07	.04
140	Roy Jr & Roy Smalley	.07	.04
141	Dave & Mike Stenhouse	.07	.04
142	Dizzy & Steve Trout	.07	.04
143	Ossie Jr & Ozzie Virgil	.07	.04
144	Ron Gardenhier	.07	.04
145	Alvin Davis	.15	.10
146	Gary Redus	.07	.04
147	Bill Swaggerty	.07	.04
148	Steve Yeager	.07	.04
149	Dickie Noles	.07	.04
150	Jim Rice	.15	.10
151	Moose Haas	.07	.04
152	Steve Braun	.07	.04
153	Frank LaCorte	.07	.04
154	Argenis Salazar	.07	.04
155	Yogi Berra	.20	.12
156	Craig Reynolds	.07	.04
157	Tug McGraw	.10	.06
158	Pat Tabler	.07	.04
159	Carlos Diaz	.07	.04
160	Lance Parrish	.10	.06
161	Ken Schrom	.07	.04
162	Benny Distefano (R)	.07	.04
163	Dennis Eckersley	.40	.25
164	Jorge Orta	.07	.04
165	Dusty Baker	.10	.06
166	Keith Atherton	.07	.04
167	Rufino Linares	.07	.04
168	Garth Iorg	.07	.04
169	Dan Spillner	.07	.04
170	George Foster	.10	.06
171	Bill Stein	.07	.04
172	Jack Perconte	.07	.04
173	Mike Young	.07	.04
174	Rick Honeycutt	.07	.04
175	Dave Parker	.15	.10
176	Bill Schroeder	.07	.04
177	Dave Von Ohlen	.07	.04
178	Miguel Dilone	.07	.04
179	Tommy John	.12	.07

180	Dave Winfield	2.00	1.25
181	Roger Clemens (R)	24.00	14.00
182	Tim Flannery	.07	.04
183	Larry McWilliams	.07	.04
184	Carmen Castillo	.07	.04
185	Al Holland	.07	.04
186	Bob Lillis	.07	.04
187	Mike Waters	.07	.04
188	Greg Pryor	.07	.04
189	Warren Brusstar	.07	.04
190	Rusty Staub	.12	.07
191	Steve Nicosia	.07	.04
192	Howard Johnson	1.00	.60
193	Jimmy Key	2.00	1.25
194	Dave Stegman	.07	.04
195	Glenn Hubbard	.07	.04
196	Pete O'Brien	.10	.06
197	Mike Warren	.07	.04
198	Eddie Milner	.07	.04
199	Denny Martinez	.20	.12
200	Reggie Jackson	1.00	.70
201	Burt Hooton	.07	.04
202	Gorman Thomas	.10	.06
203	Bob McClure	.07	.04
204	Art Howe	.07	.04
205	Steve Rogers	.07	.04
206	Phil Garner	.10	.06
207	Mark Clear	.07	.04
208	Champ Summers	.07	.04
209	Bill Campbell	.07	.04
210	Gary Matthews	.07	.04
211	Clay Christiansen	.07	.04
212	George Vukovich	.07	.04
213	Billy Gardner	.07	.04
214	John Tudor	.10	.06
215	Bob Brenly	.07	.04
216	Jerry Don Gleaton	.07	.04
217	Leon Roberts	.07	.04
218	Doyle Alexander	.07	.04
219	Gerald Perry	.10	.06
220	Fred Lynn	.12	.07
221	Ron Reed	.07	.04
222	Hubie Brooks	.12	.07
223	Tom Hume	.07	.04
224	Al Cowens	.07	.04
225	Mike Boddicker	.10	.06
226	Juan Beniquez	.07	.04
227	Danny Darwin	.10	.06
228	Dion James	.15	.10
229	Dave LaPoint	.07	.04
230	Gary Carter	.30	.18
231	Dwayne Murphy	.07	.04
232	Dave Beard	.07	.04
233	Ed Jurak	.07	.04
234	Jerry Narron	.07	.04
235	Garry Maddox	.07	.04
236	Mark Thurmond	.07	.04
237	Julio Franco	.50	.30
238	Jose Rijo	1.75	1.00
239	Tim Teufel	.10	.06
240	Dave Stieb	.15	.10
241	Jim Frey	.07	.04
242	Greg Harris	.07	.04
243	Barbaro Garbey	.07	.04
244	Mike Jones	.07	.04
245	Chili Davis	.12	.07
246	Mike Norris	.07	.04
247	Wayne Tolleson	.07	.04
248	Terry Forster	.07	.04
249	Harold Baines	.25	.15
250	Jesse Orosco	.07	.04
251	Brad Gulden	.07	.04
252	Dan Ford	.07	.04
253	Sid Bream (R)	.30	.18
254	Pete Vuckovich	.10	.06
255	Lonnie Smith	.10	.06
256	Mike Stanton	.07	.04
257	Bryan Little	.07	.04
258	Mike Brown	.07	.04
259	Gary Allenson	.07	.04
260	Dave Righetti	.12	.07
261	Checklist 133-264	.10	.04
262	Greg Booker	.07	.04
263	Mel Hall	.15	.10
264	Joe Sambito	.07	.04
265	Juan Samuel	.15	.10
266	Frank Viola	.25	.15
267	Henry Cotto (R)	.10	.06
268	Chuck Tanner	.07	.04
269	Doug Baker	.07	.04
270	Dan Quisenberry	.10	.06
271	1968 #1 DP(Tim Foli)	.07	.04
272	1969 #1 DP (Jeff Burroughs)	.07	.04
273	1974 #1 DP (Bill Almon)	.07	.04
274	1976 #1 DP (Floyd Bannister)	.07	.04
275	1977 #1 DP (Harold Baines)	.20	.12
276	1978 #1 DP (Bob Horner)	.10	.06
277	1979 #1 DP (Al Chambers)	.07	.04
278	1980 #1 DP (Darryl Strawberry)	.90	.55
279	1981 #1 DP (Mike Moore)	.10	.06
280	1982 #1 DP (Shawon Dunston)	.60	.35
281	1983 #1 DP (Tim Belcher) (R)	1.00	.60
282	1984 #1 DP (Shawn Abner) (R)	.12	.07

283 Frank Mullins	.07	.04	
284 Marty Bystrom	.07	.04	
285 Dan Driessen	.07	.04	
286 Rudy Law	.07	.04	
287 Walt Terrell	.07	.04	
288 Jeff Kunkel (R)	.07	.04	
289 Tom Underwood	.07	.04	
290 Cecil Cooper	.10	.06	
291 Bob Welch	.10	.06	
292 Brad Komminsk	.07	.04	
293 Curt Young (R)	.10	.06	
294 Tom Nieto (R)	.07	.04	
295 Joe Niekro	.07	.04	
296 Ricky Nelson	.07	.04	
297 Gary Lucas	.07	.04	
298 Marty Barrett	.10	.06	
299 Andy Hawkins	.07	.04	
300 Rod Carew	.75	.45	
301 John Montefusco	.07	.04	
302 Tim Corcoran	.07	.04	
303 Mike Jeffcoat	.10	.06	
304 Gary Gaetti	.10	.06	
305 Dale Berra	.07	.04	
306 Rick Reuschel	.07	.04	
307 Sparky Anderson	.10	.06	
308 John Wathan	.07	.04	
309 Mike Witt	.07	.04	
310 Manny Trillo	.07	.04	
311 Jim Gott	.07	.04	
312 Marc Hill	.07	.04	
313 Dave Schmidt	.07	.04	
314 Ron Oester	.07	.04	
315 Doug Sisk	.07	.04	
316 John Lowenstein	.07	.04	
317 Jack Lazorko (R)	.07	.04	
318 Ted Simmons	.10	.06	
319 Jeff Jones	.07	.04	
320 Dale Murphy	.40	.25	
321 Ricky Horton	.07	.04	
322 Dave Stapleton	.07	.04	
323 Andy McGaffigan	.07	.04	
324 Bruce Bochy	.07	.04	
325 John Denny	.07	.04	
326 Kevin Bass	.10	.06	
327 Brook Jacoby	.10	.06	
328 Bob Shirley	.07	.04	
329 Ron Washington	.07	.04	
330 Leon Durham	.07	.04	
331 Bill Laskey	.07	.04	
332 Brian Harper	.30	.18	
333 Willie Hernandez	.10	.06	
334 Dick Howser	.07	.04	
335 Bruce Benedict	.07	.04	
336 Rance Mulliniks	.07	.04	
337 Billy Sample	.07	.04	
338 Britt Burns	.07	.04	
339 Danny Heep	.07	.04	
340 Robin Yount	2.00	1.25	
341 Floyd Rayford	.07	.04	
342 Ted Power	.07	.04	
343 Bill Russell	.10	.06	
344 Dave Henderson	.12	.07	
345 Charlie Lea	.07	.04	
346 Terry Pendleton (R)	3.50	2.50	
347 Rick Langford	.07	.04	
348 Bob Boone	.15	.10	
349 Domnigo Ramos	.07	.04	
350 Wade Boggs	2.50	1.40	
351 Juan Agosto	.07	.04	
352 Joe Morgan	.35	.20	
353 Julio Solano	.07	.04	
354 Andre Robertson	.07	.04	
355 Bert Blyleven	.20	.12	
356 Dave Meier	.07	.04	
357 Rich Bordi	.07	.04	
358 Tony Pena	.10	.06	
359 Pat Sheridan	.07	.04	
360 Steve Carlton	.80	.50	
361 Alfredo Griffin	.07	.04	
362 Craig McMurtry	.07	.04	
363 Ron Hodges	.07	.04	
364 Richard Dotson	.07	.04	
365 Danny Ozark	.07	.04	
366 Todd Cruz	.07	.04	
367 Keefe Cato	.07	.04	
368 Dave Bergman	.07	.04	
369 R.J. Reynolds (R)	.10	.06	
370 Bruce Sutter	.10	.06	
371 Mickey Rivers	.07	.04	
372 Roy Howell	.07	.04	
373 Mike Moore	.10	.06	
374 Brian Downing	.10	.06	
375 Jeff Reardon	.30	.18	
376 Jeff Newman	.07	.04	
377 Checklist 265-396	.10	.04	
378 Alan Wiggins	.07	.04	
379 Charles Hudson	.07	.04	
380 Ken Griffey	.12	.07	
381 Roy Smith	.07	.04	
382 Denny Walling	.07	.04	
383 Rick Lysaner	.07	.04	
384 Jody Davis	.07	.04	
385 Jose DeLeon	.07	.04	
386 Dan Gladden (R)	.25	.15	
387 Buddy Biancalana (R)	.07	.04	
388 Bert Roberge	.07	.04	
389 Rod Dedeaux (USA)	.07	.04	
390 Sid Akins (USA)(R)	.07	.04	
391 Flavio Alfaro (USA)(R)	.07	.04	
392 Don August (USA)(R)	.10	.06	
393 Scott Bankhead (USA) (R)	.30	.18	
394 Bob Caffrey (USA)(R)	.07	.04	
395 Mike Dunne (USA)(R)	.12	.07	

396	Gary Green (USA)(R)	.07	.04
397	John Hoover (USA)(R)	.07	.04
398	Shane Mack (USA)(R)	2.50	1.40
399	John Marzano(USA)(R)	.15	.10
400	Oddibe McDowell (USA) (R)	.12	.07
401	Mark McGwire (USA) (R)	22.00	11.00
402	Pat Pacillo (USA)(R)	.10	.06
403	Cory Snyder (USA)(R)	1.00	.70
404	Billy Swift (USA)(R)	3.50	2.00
405	Tom Veryzer	.07	.04
406	Len Whitehouse	.07	.04
407	Bobby Ramos	.07	.04
408	Sid Monge	.07	.04
409	Brad Wellman	.07	.04
410	Bob Horner	.10	.06
411	Bobby Cox	.07	.04
412	Bud Black	.10	.06
413	Vance Law	.07	.04
414	Gary Ward	.07	.04
415	Ron Darling	.25	.15
416	Wayne Gross	.07	.04
417	John Franco (R)	.50	.30
418	Ken Landreaux	.07	.04
419	Mike Caldwell	.07	.04
420	Andre Dawson	1.00	.60
421	Dave Rucker	.07	.04
422	Carney Lansford	.10	.06
423	Barry Bonnell	.07	.04
424	Al Nipper (R)	.07	.04
425	Mike Hargrove	.07	.04
426	Verne Ruhle	.07	.04
427	Mario Ramirez	.07	.04
428	Larry Andersen	.07	.04
429	Rick Cerone	.10	.06
430	Ron Davis	.07	.04
431	U.L. Washington	.07	.04
432	Thad Bosley	.07	.04
433	Jim Morrison	.07	.04
434	Gene Richards	.07	.04
435	Dan Petry	.07	.04
436	Willie Aikens	.07	.04
437	Al Jones	.07	.04
438	Joe Torre	.10	.06
439	Junior Ortiz	.07	.04
440	Fernando Valenzuela	.15	.10
441	Duane Walker	.07	.04
442	Ken Forsch	.07	.04
443	George Wright	.07	.04
444	Tony Phillips	.30	.18
445	Tippy Martinez	.07	.04
446	Jim Sundberg	.07	.04
447	Jeff Lahti	.07	.04
448	Derrel Thomas	.07	.04
449	Phil Bradley	.10	.06
450	Steve Garvey	.30	.18
451	Bruce Hurst	.12	.07
452	John Castino	.07	.04
453	Tom Waddell	.07	.04
454	Glenn Wilson	.07	.04
455	Bob Knepper	.07	.04
456	Tim Foli	.07	.04
457	Cecilio Guante	.07	.04
458	Randy Johnson	.07	.04
459	Charlie Leibrandt	.07	.04
460	Ryne Sandberg	5.00	3.00
461	Marty Castillo	.07	.04
462	Gary Lavelle	.07	.04
463	Dave Collins	.07	.04
464	Mike Mason	.07	.04
465	Bob Grich	.10	.06
466	Tony LaRussa	.10	.06
467	Ed Lynch	.07	.04
468	Wayne Krenchicki	.07	.04
469	Sammy Stewart	.07	.04
470	Steve Sax	.20	.12
471	Pete Ladd	.07	.04
472	Jim Essian	.07	.04
473	Tim Wallach	.12	.07
474	Kurt Kepshire	.07	.04
475	Andre Thornton	.10	.06
476	Jeff Stone	.07	.04
477	Bob Ojeda	.10	.06
478	Kurt Bevacqua	.07	.04
479	Mike Madden	.07	.04
480	Lou Whitaker	.30	.18
481	Dale Murray	.07	.04
482	Harry Spillman	.07	.04
483	Mike Smithson	.07	.04
484	Larry Bowa	.10	.06
485	Matt Young	.07	.04
486	Steve Balboni	.07	.04
487	Frank Williams	.07	.04
488	Joel Skinner	.07	.04
489	Bryan Clark	.07	.04
490	Jason Thompson	.07	.04
491	Rick Camp	.07	.04
492	Dave Johnson	.10	.06
493	Orel Hershiser (R)	1.75	1.00
494	Rich Dauer	.07	.04
495	Mario Soto	.10	.06
496	Donnie Scott	.07	.04
497	Gary Pettis	.10	.06
498	Ed Romero	.07	.04
499	Danny Cox	.07	.04
500	Mike Schmidt	2.50	1.50
501	Dan Schatzeder	.07	.04
502	Rick Miller	.07	.04
503	Tim Conroy	.07	.04
504	Jerry Willard	.07	.04
505	Jim Beattie	.07	.04
506	Franklin Stubbs (R)	.12	.07
507	Ray Fontenot	.07	.04

508	John Shelby	.07	.04
509	Milt May	.07	.04
510	Kent Hrbek	.15	.10
511	Lee Smith	.50	.30
512	Tom Brookens	.07	.04
513	Lynn Jones	.07	.04
514	Jeff Cornell	.07	.04
515	Dave Concepcion	.15	.10
516	Roy Lee Jackson	.07	.04
517	Jerry Martin	.07	.04
518	Chris Chambliss	.10	.06
519	Doug Rader	.07	.04
520	LaMarr Hoyt	.07	.04
521	Rick Dempsey	.07	.04
522	Paul Molitor	1.50	.90
523	Candy Maldonado	.10	.06
524	Rob Wilfong	.07	.04
525	Darrell Porter	.07	.04
526	Dave Palmer	.07	.04
527	Checklist 397-528	.10	.04
528	Bill Kruegar	.07	.04
529	Rich Gedman	.07	.04
530	Dave Dravecky	.10	.06
531	Joe Lefebvre	.07	.04
532	Frank DiPino	.07	.04
533	Tony Bernazard	.07	.04
534	Brian Dayett	.07	.04
535	Pat Putnam	.07	.04
536	Kirby Puckett (R)	28.00	18.00
537	Don Robinson	.07	.04
538	Keith Moreland	.07	.04
539	Aurelio Lopez	.07	.04
540	Claudell Washington	.07	.04
541	Mark Davis	.10	.06
542	Don Slaught	.07	.04
543	Mike Squires	.07	.04
544	Bruce Kison	.07	.04
545	Lloyd Moseby	.10	.06
546	Brent Gaff	.07	.04
547	Pete Rose	.70	.40
548	Larry Parrish	.07	.04
549	Mike Scioscia	.10	.06
550	Scott McGregor	.07	.04
551	Andy Van Slyke	.80	.50
552	Chris Codiroli	.07	.04
553	Bob Clark	.07	.04
554	Doug Flynn	.07	.04
555	Bob Stanley	.07	.04
556	Sixto Lezcano	.07	.04
557	Len Barker	.07	.04
558	Carmelo Martinez	.07	.04
559	Jay Howell	.10	.06
560	Bill Madlock	.15	.10
561	Darryl Motley	.07	.04
562	Houston Jimenez	.07	.04
563	Dick Ruthven	.07	.04
564	Alan Ashby	.07	.04
565	Kirk Gibson	.20	.12
566	Ed Vande Berg	.07	.04
567	Joel Youngblood	.07	.04
568	Cliff Johnson	.07	.04
569	Ken Oberkfell	.07	.04
570	Darryl Strawberry	1.25	.80
571	Charlie Hough	.10	.06
572	Tom Paciorek	.07	.04
573	Jay Tibbs (R)	.07	.04
574	Joe Altobelli	.07	.04
575	Pedro Guerrero	.12	.07
576	Jaime Cocanower	.07	.04
577	Chris Speier	.07	.04
578	Terry Francona	.07	.04
579	Ron Romanick	.07	.04
580	Dwight Evans	.20	.12
581	Mark Wagner	.07	.04
582	Ken Phelps	.07	.04
583	Bobby Brown	.07	.04
584	Kevin Gross	.07	.04
585	Butch Wynegar	.07	.04
586	Bill Scherrer	.07	.04
587	Doug Frobel	.07	.04
588	Bobby Castillo	.07	.04
589	Bob Dernier	.07	.04
590	Ray Knight	.10	.06
591	Larry Herndon	.07	.04
592	Jeff Robinson	.07	.04
593	Rick Leach	.07	.04
594	Curt Wilkerson	.07	.04
595	Larry Gura	.07	.04
596	Jerry Hairston	.07	.04
597	Brad Lesley	.07	.04
598	Jose Oquendo	.07	.04
599	Storm Davis	.07	.04
600	Pete Rose	1.00	.60
601	Tom Lasorda	.10	.06
602	Jeff Dedman	.07	.04
603	Rick Manning	.07	.04
604	Daryl Sconiers	.07	.04
605	Ozzie Smith	1.00	.60
606	Rich Gale	.07	.04
607	Bill Almon	.07	.04
608	Craig Lefferts	.10	.06
609	Broderick Perkins	.07	.04
610	Jack Morris	.45	.28
611	Ozzie Virgil	.07	.04
612	Mike Armstrong	.07	.04
613	Terry Puhl	.07	.04
614	Al Williams	.07	.04
615	Marvell Wynne	.07	.04
616	Scott Sanderson	.10	.06
617	Willie Wilson	.10	.06
618	Pete Falcone	.07	.04
619	Jeff Leonard	.10	.06
620	Dwight Gooden	4.00	2.50
621	Marvis Foley	.07	.04

622	Luis Leal	.07	.04
623	Greg Walker	.07	.04
624	Benny Ayala	.07	.04
625	Mark Langston	2.00	1.25
626	German Rivera	.07	.04
627	Eric Davis (R)	3.50	2.00
628	Rene Lacheman	.07	.04
629	Dick Schofield	.07	.04
630	Tim Raines	.25	.15
631	Bob Forsch	.07	.04
632	Bruce Bochte	.07	.04
633	Glenn Hoffman	.07	.04
634	Bill Dawley	.07	.04
635	Terry Kennedy	.07	.04
636	Shane Rawley	.07	.04
637	Brett Butler	.25	.15
638	Mike Pagliarulo (R)	.15	.10
639	Ed Hodge	.07	.04
640	Steve Henderson	.07	.04
641	Rod Scurry	.07	.04
642	Dave Owen	.07	.04
643	Johnny Grubb	.07	.04
644	Mark Huismann	.07	.04
645	Damaso Garcia	.07	.04
646	Scot Thompson	.07	.04
647	Rafael Ramirez	.07	.04
648	Bob Jones	.07	.04
649	Sid Fernandez	.30	.18
650	Greg Luzinski	.12	.07
651	Jeff Russell	.10	.06
652	Joe Nolan	.07	.04
653	Mark Brouhard	.07	.04
654	Dave Anderson	.07	.04
655	Joaquin Andujar	.10	.06
656	Chuck Cottier	.07	.04
657	Jim Slaton	.07	.04
658	Mike Stenhouse	.07	.04
659	Checklist 529-660	.10	.04
660	Tony Gwynn	2.50	1.40
661	Steve Crawford	.07	.04
662	Mike Heath	.07	.04
663	Luis Aguayo	.07	.04
664	Steve Farr (R)	.20	.12
665	Don Mattingly	3.50	2.50
666	Mike LaCoss	.07	.04
667	Dave Engle	.07	.04
668	Steve Trout	.07	.04
669	Lee Lacy	.07	.04
670	Tom Seaver	1.00	.70
671	Dane Iorg	.07	.04
672	Juan Berenguer	.07	.04
673	Buck Martinez	.07	.04
674	Atlee Hammaker	.07	.04
675	Tony Perez	.25	.15
676	Albert Hall (R)	.10	.06
677	Wally Backman	.07	.04
678	Joey McLaughlin	.07	.04
679	Bob Kearney	.07	.04
680	Jerry Reuss	.10	.06
681	Ben Oglivie	.07	.04
682	Doug Corbett	.07	.04
683	Whitey Herzog	.10	.06
684	Bill Doran	.10	.06
685	Bill Caudill	.07	.04
686	Mike easler	.07	.04
687	Bill Gullickson	.10	.06
688	Len Matuszek	.07	.04
689	Luis DeLeon	.07	.04
690	Alan Trammell	.40	.25
691	Dennis Rasmussen	.10	.06
692	Randy Bush	.07	.04
693	Tim Stoddard	.07	.04
694	Joe Carter (R)	6.50	3.75
695	Rick Rhoden	.07	.04
696	John Rabb	.07	.04
697	Onix Concepcion	.07	.04
698	Jorge Bell	.25	.15
699	Donnie Moore	.07	.04
700	Eddie Murray	1.25	.80
701	Eddie Murray AS	.40	.25
702	Damaso Garcia AS	.07	.04
703	George Brett AS	.90	.55
704	Cal Ripken AS	1.75	1.00
705	Dave Winfield AS	1.00	.60
706	Rickey Henderson AS	.75	.45
707	Tony Armas AS	.10	.06
708	Lance Parrish AS	.10	.06
709	Mike Boddicker AS	.10	.06
710	Frank Viola AS	.15	.10
711	Dan Quisenberry AS	.10	.06
712	Keith Hernandez AS	.12	.07
713	Ryne Sandberg AS	1.75	1.00
714	Mike Schmidt AS	1.00	.70
715	Ozzie Smith AS	.75	.45
716	Dale Murphy AS	.25	.15
717	Tony Gwynn AS	.80	.50
718	Jeff Leonard AS	.10	.06
719	Gary Carter AS	.15	.10
720	Rick Sutcliffe AS	.10	.06
721	Bob Knepper AS	.07	.04
722	Bruce Sutter AS	.10	.06
723	Dave Stewart	.35	.20
724	Oscar Gamble	.07	.04
725	Floyd Bannister	.07	.04
726	Al Bumbry	.07	.04
727	Frank Pastore	.07	.04
728	Bob Bailor	.07	.04
729	Don Sutton	.25	.15
730	Dave Kingman	.10	.06
731	Neil Allen	.07	.04
732	John McNamara	.07	.04
733	Tony Scott	.07	.04
734	John Henry Johnson	.07	.04
735	Garry Templeton	.10	.06

736	Jerry Mumphrey	.07	.04
737	Bo Diaz	.07	.04
738	Omar Moreno	.07	.04
739	Ernie Camacho	.07	.04
740	Jack Clark	.10	.06
741	John Butcher	.07	.04
742	Ron Hassey	.07	.04
743	Frank White	.10	.06
744	Doug Bair	.07	.04
745	Buddy Bell	.07	.04
746	Jim Clancy	.07	.04
747	Alex Trevino	.07	.04
748	Lee Mazzilli	.07	.04
749	Julio Cruz	.07	.04
750	Rollie Fingers	.25	.15
751	Kelvin Chapman	.07	.04
752	Bob Owchinko	.07	.04
753	Greg Brock	.07	.04
754	Larry Milbourne	.07	.04
755	Ken Singleton	.07	.04
756	Rob Picciolo	.07	.04
757	Willie McGee	.20	.12
758	Ray Burris	.07	.04
759	Jim Fanning	.07	.04
760	Nolan Ryan	6.00	4.00
761	Jerry Remy	.07	.04
762	Eddie Whitson	.07	.04
763	Kiko Garcia	.07	.04
764	Jamie Easterly	.07	.04
765	Willie Randolph	.12	.07
766	Paul Mirabella	.07	.04
767	Darrell Brown	.07	.04
768	Ron Cey	.10	.06
769	Joe Cowley	.07	.04
770	Carlton Fisk	.80	.50
771	Geoff Zahn	.07	.04
772	Johnnie LeMaster	.07	.04
773	Hal McRae	.15	.10
774	Dennis Lamp	.07	.04
775	Mookie Wilson	.10	.06
776	Jerry Royster	.07	.04
777	Ned Yost	.07	.04
778	Mike Davis	.07	.04
779	Nick Esasky	.07	.04
780	Mike Flanagan	.10	.06
781	Jim Gantner	.07	.04
782	Tom Niedenfuer	.07	.04
783	Mike Jorgensen	.07	.04
784	Checklist 661-792	.10	.04
785	Tony Armas	.07	.04
786	Enos Cabell	.07	.04
787	Jim Wohlford	.07	.04
788	Steve Comer	.07	.04
789	Luis Salazar	.07	.04
790	Ron Guidry	.15	.10
791	Ivan DeJesus	.07	.04
792	Darrell Evans	.12	.07

1985 Topps Traded

The 132-cards in this update set carry the "T" designation after the card numbers but otherwise, the set is identical to the Topps 1985 regular edition. The set contains players who were traded during the year and rookies who joined their clubs after this seaon began.

	MINT	NR/MT
Complete Set (132)	30.00	18.00
Commons	.15	.10

1T	Don Aase	.15	.10
2T	Bill Almon	.15	.10
3T	Benny Ayala	.15	.10
4T	Dusty Baker	.20	.12
5T	George Bamberger	.15	.10
6T	Dale Berra	.15	.10
7T	Rich Bordi	.15	.10
8T	Daryl Boston (R)	.40	.25
9T	Hubie Brooks	.25	.15
10T	Chris Brown (R)	.20	.12
11T	Tom Browning (R)	1.00	.70
12T	Al Bumbry	.15	.10
13T	Ray Burris	.15	.10
14T	Jeff Burroughs	.15	.10
15T	Bill Campbell	.15	.10
16T	Don Carman (R)	.15	.10
17T	Gary Carter	.75	.45
18T	Bobby Castillo	.15	.10
19T	Bill Caudill	.15	.10
20T	Rick Cerone	.15	.10
21T	Bryan Clark	.15	.10
22T	Jack Clark	.25	.15
23T	Pat Clements (R)	.15	.10
24T	Vince Coleman (R)	1.75	1.00
25T	Dave Collins	.15	.10
26T	Danny Darwin	.20	.12
27T	Jim Davenport	.15	.10
28T	Jerry Davis	.15	.10

29T	Brian Dayett	.15	.10
30T	Ivan DeJesus	.15	.10
31T	Ken Dixon	.15	.10
32T	Mariano Duncan (R)	1.00	.60
33T	John Felske	.15	.10
34T	Mike Fitzgerald	.15	.10
35T	Ray Fontenot	.15	.10
36T	Greg Gagne (R)	.50	.30
37T	Oscar Gamble	.20	.12
38T	Scott Garrelts (R)	.20	.12
39T	Bob Gibson	.15	.10
40T	Jim Gott	.20	.12
41T	David Green	.15	.10
42T	Alfredo Griffin	.20	.12
43T	Ozzie Guillen (R)	2.50	1.40
44T	Eddie Haas	.15	.10
45T	Terry Harper	.15	.10
46T	Toby Harrah	.15	.10
47T	Greg Harris	.15	.10
48T	Ron Hassey	.15	.10
49T	Rickey Henderson	5.00	3.00
50T	Steve Henderson	.15	.10
51T	George Hendrick	.20	.12
52T	Joe Hesketh (R)	.25	.15
53T	Teddy Higuera (R)	.35	.20
54T	Donnie Hill	.15	.10
55T	Al Holland	.15	.10
56T	Burt Hooton	.15	.10
57T	Jay Howell	.20	.12
58T	Ken Howell (R)	.15	.10
59T	LaMarr Hoyt	.15	.10
60T	Tim Hulett (R)	.15	.10
61T	Bob James	.15	.10
62T	Steve Jeltz (R)	.15	.10
63T	Cliff Johnson	.15	.10
64T	Howard Johnson	1.00	.60
65T	Ruppert Jones	.15	.10
66T	Steve Kemp	.15	.10
67T	Bruce Kison	.15	.10
68T	Alan Knicely	.15	.10
69T	Mike LaCoss	.15	.10
70T	Lee Lacy	.15	.10
71T	Dave LaPoint	.15	.10
72T	Gary Lavelle	.15	.10
73T	Vance Law	.15	.10
74T	Johnnie LeMaster	.15	.10
75T	Sixto Lezcano	.15	.10
76T	Tim Lollar	.15	.10
77T	Fred Lynn	.20	.12
78T	Billy Martin	.20	.12
79T	Ron Mathis	.15	.10
80T	Len Matuszek	.15	.10
81T	Gene Mauch	.15	.10
82T	Oddibe McDowell	.15	.10
83T	Roger McDowell	.30	.18
84T	John McNamara	.15	.10
85T	Donnie Moore	.15	.10
86T	Gene Nelson	.15	.10
87T	Steve Nicosia	.15	.10
88T	Al Oliver	.25	.15
89T	Joe Orsulak (R)	.60	.35
90T	Rob Picciolo	.15	.10
91T	Chris Pittaro	.15	.10
92T	Jim Presley (R)	.15	.10
93T	Rick Reuschel	.15	.10
94T	Bert Roberge	.15	.10
95T	Bob Rodgers	.15	.10
96T	Jerry Royster	.15	.10
97T	Dave Rozema	.15	.10
98T	Dave Rucker	.15	.10
99T	Vern Ruhl	.15	.10
100T	Paul Runge (R)	.15	.10
101T	Mark Salas (R)	.15	.10
102T	Luis Salazar	.15	.10
103T	Joe Sambito	.15	.10
104T	Rick Schu (R)	.15	.10
105T	Donnie Scott	.15	.10
106T	Larry Sheets (R)	.15	.10
107T	Don Slaught	.15	.10
108T	Roy Smalley	.15	.10
109T	Lonnie Smith	.15	.10
110T	Nate Snell	.15	.10
111T	Chris Speier	.15	.10
112T	Mike Stenhouse	.15	.10
113T	Tim Stoddard	.15	.10
114T	Jim Sundberg	.15	.10
115T	Bruce Sutter	.30	.15
116T	Don Sutton	.75	.45
117T	Kent Tekulve	.15	.10
118T	Tom Tellmann	.15	.10
119T	Walt Terrell	.15	.10
120T	Mickey Tettleton (R)	8.00	4.75
121T	Derrel Thomas	.15	.10
122T	Rich Thompson	.15	.10
123T	Alex Trevino	.15	.10
124T	John Tudor	.15	.10
125T	Jose Uribe (R)	.15	.10
126T	Bobby Valentine	.20	.12
127T	Dave Von Ohlen	.15	.10
128T	U.L. Washington	.15	.10
129T	Earl Weaver	.15	.10
130T	Eddie Whitson	.15	.10
131T	Herm Winningham (R)	.20	.12
132T	Checklist 1-132	.15	.10

1986 Topps

FERNANDO VALENZUELA

This set features 792-cards which measure 2-1/2" by 3-1/2". Card fronts consist of large color photos with team names in bold block letters above the photos while the player's name is printed under the photo. Card backs are horizontal. Topps honors Pete Rose with the first seven cards in the set and brings back the popular Turn Back The Clock series. Other subsets include Record Breakers, All-Stars and Team Leaders.

		MINT	NR/MT
Complete Set (792)		42.00	34.00
Commons		.05	.02
1	Pete Rose	1.25	.80
2	Pete Rose(1963-66)	.35	.20
3	Pete Rose(1967-70)	.35	.20
4	Pete Rose(1971-74)	.35	.20
5	Pete Rose(1975-78)	.35	.20
6	Pete Rose(1979-82)	.35	.30
7	Pete Rose(1983-85)	.35	.20
8	Dwayne Murphy	.05	.03
9	Roy Smith	.05	.03
10	Tony Gwynn	1.50	.90
11	Bob Ojeda	.07	.04
12	Jose Uribe	.10	.06
13	Bob Kearney	.05	.03
14	Julio Cruz	.05	.03
15	Eddie Whitson	.05	.03
16	Rick Schu	.05	.03
17	Mike Stenhouse	.05	.03
18	Brent Gaff	.05	.03
19	Rich Hebner	.05	.03
20	Lou Whitaker	.15	.10
21	George Bamberger	.05	.03
22	Duane Walker	.05	.03
23	Manny Lee (R)	.15	.10
24	Len Barker	.05	.03
25	Willie Wilson	.07	.04
26	Frank DiPino	.05	.03
27	Ray Knight	.10	.06
28	Eric Davis	.35	.20
29	Tony Phillips	.10	.06
30	Eddie Murray	.60	.35
31	Jamie Easterly	.05	.03
32	Steve Yeager	.05	.03
33	Jeff Lahti	.05	.03
34	Ken Phelps	.10	.06
35	Jeff Reardon	.20	.12
36	Tigers (Lance Parrish)	.10	.06
37	Mark Thurmond	.05	.03
38	Glenn Hoffman	.05	.03
39	Dave Rucker	.05	.03
40	Ken Griffey	.10	.06
41	Brad Wellman	.05	.03
42	Geoff Zahn	.05	.03
43	Dave Engle	.05	.03
44	Lance McCullers (R)	.10	.06
45	Damaso Garcia	.05	.03
46	Billy Hatcher	.05	.03
47	Juan Berenguer	.05	.03
48	Bill Almon	.05	.03
49	Rick Manning	.05	.03
50	Dan Quisenberry	.10	.06
51	Never Issued	.00	.00
52	Chris Welsh	.05	.03
53	Len Dykstra (R)	2.50	1.40
54	John Franco	.12	.07
55	Fred Lynn	.15	.10
56	Tom Niedenfuer	.05	.03
57a	Bobby Wine	.08	.05
57b	Bill Doran	.10	.06
58	Bill Krueger	.05	.03
59	Andre Thornton	.08	.05
60	Dwight Evans	.15	.10
61	Karl Best	.05	.03
62	Bob Boone	.12	.07
63	Ron Roenicke	.05	.03
64	Floyd Bannister	.05	.03
65	Dan Driessen	.05	.03
66	Cardinals Leaders	.08	.05
67	Carmelo Martinez	.07	.04
68	Ed Lynch	.05	.03
69	Luis Aguayo	.05	.03
70	Dave Winfield	1.00	.60
71	Ken Schrom	.05	.03
72	Shawon Dunston	.20	.12
73	Randy O'Neal	.05	.03
74	Rance Mulliniks	.05	.03
75	Jose DeLeon	.05	.03
76	Dion James	.05	.03
77	Charlie Leibrandt	.07	.04
78	Bruce Benedict	.05	.03
79	Dave Schmidt	.05	.03
80	Darryl Strawberry	.80	.50
81	Gene Mauch	.05	.03

82	Tippy Martinez	.05	.03
83	Phil Garner	.08	.05
84	Curt Young	.05	.03
85	Tony Perez	.20	.12
86	Tom Waddell	.05	.03
87	Candy Maldonado	.08	.05
88	Tom Nieto	.05	.03
89	Randy St. Claire	.05	.03
90	Garry Templeton	.08	.05
91	Steve Crawford	.05	.03
92	Al Cowens	.05	.03
93	Scot Thompson	.05	.03
94	Rick Bordi	.05	.03
95	Ozzie Virgil	.05	.03
96	Blue Jay Leaders	.08	.05
97	Gary Gaetti	.08	.05
98	Dick Ruthven	.05	.03
99	Buddy Biancalana	.05	.03
100	Nolan Ryan	3.50	2.00
101	Dave Bergman	.05	.03
102	Joe Orsulak	.15	.10
103	Luis Salazar	.05	.03
104	Sid Fernandez	.12	.07
105	Gary Ward	.05	.03
106	Ray Burris	.05	.03
107	Rafael Ramirez	.05	.03
108	Ted Power	.05	.03
109	Len Matuszek	.05	.03
110	Scott McGregor	.05	.03
111	Roger Craig	.05	.03
112	Bill Campbell	.05	.03
113	U.L. Washington	.05	.03
114	Mike Brown	.05	.03
115	Jay Howell	.08	.05
116	Brook Jacoby	.07	.04
117	Bruce Kison	.05	.03
118	Jerry Royster	.05	.03
119	Barry Bonnell	.05	.03
120	Steve Carlton	.90	.45
121	Nelson Simmons	.05	.03
122	Pete Filson	.05	.03
123	Greg Walker	.05	.03
124	Luis Sanchez	.05	.03
125	Dave Lopes	.08	.05
126	Mets Leaders	.10	.06
127	Jack Howell (R)	.10	.06
128	John Wathan	.05	.03
129	Jeff Dedmon	.05	.03
130	Alan Trammell	.25	.15
131	Checklist 1-132	.10	.03
132	Razor Shines	.05	.03
133	Andy McGaffigan	.05	.03
134	Carney Lansford	.10	.06
135	Joe Niekro	.05	.03
136	Mike Hargrove	.05	.03
137	Charlie Moore	.05	.03
138	Mark Davis	.07	.04
139	Daryl Boston	.08	.05
140	John Candelaria	.05	.03
141a	Bob Rogers	.05	.03
141b	Chuck Cottier	.05	.03
142	Bob Jones	.05	.03
143	Dave Van Gorder	.05	.03
144	Doug Sisk	.05	.03
145	Pedro Guerrero	.10	.06
146	Jack Perconte	.05	.03
147	Larry Sheets	.05	.03
148	Mike Heath	.05	.03
149	Brett Butler	.12	.07
150	Joaquin Andujar	.08	.05
151	Dave Stapleton	.05	.03
152	Mike Morgan	.08	.05
153	Ricky Adams	.05	.03
154	Bert Roberge	.05	.03
155	Bob Grich	.08	.05
156	White Sox Leaders	.07	.04
157	Ron Hassey	.05	.03
158	Derrel Thomas	.05	.03
159	Orel Hershiser	.25	.15
160	Chet Lemon	.05	.03
161	Lee Tunnell	.05	.03
162	Greg Gagne	.10	.06
163	Pete Ladd	.05	.03
164	Steve Balboni	.05	.03
165	Mike Davis	.05	.03
166	Dickie Thon	.05	.03
167	Zane Smith (R)	.20	.12
168	Jeff Burroughs	.05	.03
169	George Wright	.05	.03
170	Gary Carter	.25	.15
171	Never issued	.00	.00
172	Jerry Reed	.05	.03
173	Wayne Gross	.05	.03
174	Brian Snyder	.05	.03
175	Steve Sax	.12	.07
176	Jay Tibbs	.05	.03
177	Joel Youngblood	.05	.03
178	Ivan DeJesus	.05	.03
179	Stu Cliburn	.05	.03
180	Don Mattingly	1.25	.80
181	Al Nipper	.05	.03
182	Bobby Brown	.05	.03
183	Larry Andersen	.05	.03
184	Tim Laudner	.05	.03
185	Rollie Fingers	.20	.12
186	Astros Leaders	.10	.06
187	Scott Fletcher	.05	.03
188	Bob Dernier	.05	.03
189	Mike Mason	.05	.03
190	George Hendrick	.07	.04
191	Wally Backman	.05	.03
192	Milt Wilcox	.05	.03
193	Daryl Sconiers	.05	.03
194	Craig McMurtry	.05	.03

195	Dave Concepcion	.15	.10	251	Rich Dauer	.05	.03
196	Doyle Alexander	.05	.03	252	Bobby Castillo	.05	.03
197	Enos Cabell	.05	.03	253	Dann Bilardello	.05	.03
198	Ken Dixon	.05	.03	254	Ozzie Guillen	.25	.15
199	Dick Howser	.05	.03	255	Tony Armas	.05	.03
200	Mike Schmidt	1.50	.90	256	Kurt Kepshire	.05	.03
201	Vince Coleman (RB)	.10	.06	257	Doug DeCinces	.05	.03
202	Dwight Gooden (RB)	.25	.15	258	Tim Burke (R)	.10	.06
203	Keith Hernandez (RB)	.10	.06	259	Dan Pasqua (R)	.15	.10
204	Phil Niekro (RB)	.12	.07	260	Tony Pena	.08	.05
205	Tony Perez (RB)	.15	.10	261	Bobby Valentine	.05	.03
206	Pete Rose (RB)	.40	.25	262	Mario Ramirez	.05	.03
207	Fernando Valenzuela (RB)	.10	.06	263	Checklist 133-264	.10	.03
				264	Darren Daulton (R)	2.50	1.40
208	Ramon Romero	.05	.03	265	Ron Davis	.05	.03
209	Randy Ready	.05	.03	266	Keith Moreland	.05	.03
210	Calvin Schiraldi (R)	.10	.06	267	Paul Molitor	.80	.50
211	Ed Wojna	.05	.03	268	Mike Scott	.08	.05
212	Chris Speier	.05	.03	269	Dane Iorg	.05	.03
213	Bob Shirley	.05	.03	270	Jack Morris	.35	.20
214	Randy Bush	.05	.03	271	Dave Collins	.05	.03
215	Frank White	.07	.04	272	Tim Tolman	.05	.03
216	A's Leaders	.07	.04	273	Jerry Willard	.05	.03
217	Bill Scherrer	.05	.03	274	Ron Gardenhire	.05	.03
218	Randy Hunt	.05	.03	275	Charlie Hough	.08	.05
219	Dennis Lamp	.05	.03	276	Yankees Leaders	.10	.06
220	Bob Horner	.10	.06	277	Jaime Cocanower	.05	.03
221	Dave Henderson	.10	.06	278	Sixto Lezcano	.05	.03
222	Craig Gerber	.05	.03	279	Al Pardo	.05	.03
223	Atlee Hammaker	.05	.03	280	Tim Raines	.15	.10
224	Cesar Cedeno	.07	.04	281	Steve Mura	.05	.03
225	Ron Darling	.10	.06	282	Jerry Mumphrey	.05	.03
226	Lee Lacy	.05	.03	283	Mike Fischlin	.05	.03
227	Al Jones	.05	.03	284	Brian Dayett	.05	.03
228	Tom Lawless	.05	.03	285	Buddy Bell	.05	.03
229	Bill Gullickson	.08	.05	286	Luis DeLeon	.05	.03
230	Terry Kennedy	.05	.03	287	John Christensen (R)	.05	.03
231	Jim Frey	.05	.03	288	Don Aase	.05	.03
232	Rick Rhoden	.05	.03	289	Johnnie LeMaster	.05	.03
233	Steve Lyons (R)	.05	.03	290	Carlton Fisk	.60	.35
234	Doug Corbett	.05	.03	291	Tom Lasorda	.08	.05
235	Butch Wynegar	.05	.03	292	Chuck Porter	.05	.03
236	Frank Eufemia	.05	.03	293	Chris Chambliss	.08	.05
237	Ted Simmons	.08	.05	294	Danny Cox	.05	.03
238	Larry Parrish	.05	.03	295	Kirk Gibson	.10	.06
239	Joel Skinner	.05	.03	296	Gino Petralli	.05	.03
240	Tommy John	.10	.06	297	Tim Lollar	.05	.03
241	Tony Fernandez	.12	.07	298	Craig Reynolds	.05	.03
242	Rich Thompson	.05	.03	299	Bryn Smith	.07	.04
243	Johnny Grubb	.05	.03	300	George Brett	1.00	.70
244	Craig Lefferts	.08	.05	301	Dennis Rasmussen	.05	.03
245	Jim Sundberg	.05	.03	302	Greg Gross	.05	.03
246	Phillies TL (Carlton)	.30	.18	303	Curt Wardle	.05	.03
247	Terry Harper	.05	.03	304	Mike Gallego (R)	.10	.06
248	Spike Owen	.05	.03	305	Phil Bradley	.05	.03
249	Rob Deer (R)	.20	.12	306	Padres Leaders	.07	.04
250	Dwight Gooden	.60	.35	307	Dave Sax	.05	.03

308	Ray Fontenot	.05	.03
309	John Shelby	.05	.03
310	Greg Minton	.05	.03
311	Dick Schofield	.05	.03
312	Tom Filer	.05	.03
313	Joe DeSa	.05	.03
314	Frank Pastore	.05	.03
315	Mookie Wilson	.08	.05
316	Sammy Khalifa	.05	.03
317	Ed Romero	.05	.03
318	Terry Whitfield	.05	.03
319	Rick Camp	.05	.03
320	Jim Rice	.12	.07
321	Earl Weaver	.08	.05
322	Bob Forsch	.05	.03
323	Jerry Davis	.05	.03
324	Dan Schatzeder	.05	.03
325	Juan Beniquez	.05	.03
326	Kent Tekulve	.05	.03
327	Mike Pagliarulo	.08	.05
328	Pete O'Brien	.08	.05
329	Kirby Puckett	5.50	3.75
330	Rick Sutcliffe	.10	.06
331	Alan Ashby	.05	.03
332	Darryl Motley	.05	.03
333	Tom Henke (R)	.25	.15
334	Ken Oberkfell	.05	.03
335	Don Sutton	.20	.12
336	Indians Leaders	.08	.05
337	Darnell Coles	.05	.03
338	George Bell	.35	.20
339	Bruce Berenyi	.05	.03
340	Cal Ripken	3.00	2.00
341	Frank Williams	.05	.03
342	Gary Redus	.05	.03
343	Carlos Diaz	.05	.03
344	Jim Wohlford	.05	.03
345	Donnie Moore	.05	.03
346	Bryan Little	.05	.03
347	Teddy Higuera	.10	.06
348	Cliff Johnson	.05	.03
349	Mark Clear	.05	.03
350	Jack Clark	.08	.05
351	Chuck Tanner	.05	.03
352	Harry Spilman	.05	.03
353	Keith Atherton	.05	.03
354	Tony Bernazard	.05	.03
355	Lee Smith	.35	.20
356	Mickey Hatcher	.05	.03
357	Ed Vande Berg	.05	.03
358	Rick Dempsey	.05	.03
359	Mike LaCoss	.05	.03
360	Lloyd Moseby	.05	.03
361	Shane Rawley	.05	.03
362	Tom Paciorek	.05	.03
363	Terry Forster	.05	.03
364	Reid Nichols	.05	.03
365	Mike Flanagan	.08	.05
366	Reds Leaders	.10	.06
367	Aurelio Lopez	.05	.03
368	Greg Brock	.05	.03
369	Al Holland	.05	.03
370	Vince Coleman	.30	.18
371	Bell Stein	.05	.03
372	Ben Oglivie	.05	.03
373	Urbano Lugo (R)	.05	.03
374	Terry Francona	.05	.03
375	Rich Gedman	.05	.03
376	Bill Dawley	.05	.03
377	Joe Carter	1.50	.90
378	Bruce Bochte	.05	.03
379	Bobby Meacham	.05	.03
380	LaMarr Hoyt	.05	.03
381	Ray Miller	.05	.03
382	Ivan Calderon (R)	.20	.12
383	Chris Brown	.05	.03
384	Steve Trout	.05	.03
385	Cecil Cooper	.08	.05
386	Cecil Fielder (R)	9.00	6.00
387	Steve Kemp	.05	.03
388	Dickie Noles	.05	.03
389	Glenn Davis (R)	.15	.10
390	Tom Seaver	.60	.35
391	Julio Franco	.20	.12
392	John Russell	.05	.03
393	Chris Pittaro	.05	.03
394	Checklist 265-396	.10	.03
395	Scott Garrelts	.10	.06
396	Red Sox Leaders	.12	.07
397	Steve Buechele (R)	.25	.15
398	Earnie Riles (R)	.12	.07
399	Bill Swift	.30	.18
400	Rod Carew	.60	.35
401	Fernando Valenzuela (Clock)	.10	.06
402	Tom Seaver (Clock)	.25	.15
403	Willie Mays (Clock)	.30	.18
404	Frank Robinson (Clock)	.15	.10
405	Roger Maris (Clock)	.20	.12
406	Scott Sanderson	.08	.05
407	Sal Butera	.05	.03
408	Dave Smith	.05	.03
409	Paul Runge	.05	.03
410	Dave Kingman	.10	.06
411	Sparky Anderson	.08	.05
412	Jim Clancy	.05	.03
413	Tim Flannery	.05	.03
414	Tom Gorman	.05	.03
415	Hal McRae	.12	.07
416	Denny Martinez	.12	.07
417	R. J. Reynolds	.05	.03
418	Alan Knicely	.05	.03
419	Frank Wills	.05	.03
420	Von Hayes	.07	.04

421	Dave Palmer	.05	.03
422	Mike Jorgensen	.05	.03
423	Dan Spillner	.05	.03
424	Rick Miller	.05	.03
425	Larry McWilliams	.05	.03
426	Brewers Leaders	.05	.03
427	Joe Cowley	.05	.03
428	Max Venable	.05	.03
429	Greg Booker	.05	.03
430	Kent Hrbek	.15	.10
431	George Frazier	.05	.03
432	Mark Bailey	.05	.03
433	Chris Codiroli	.05	.03
434	Curt Wilkerson	.05	.03
435	Bill Caudill	.05	.03
436	Doug Flynn	.05	.03
437	Rick Mahler	.05	.03
438	Clint Hurdle	.05	.03
439	Rick Honeycutt	.05	.03
440	Alvin Davis	.10	.06
441	Whitey Herzog	.08	.05
442	Ron Robinson (R)	.05	.03
443	Bill Buckner	.08	.05
444	Alex Trevino	.05	.03
445	Bert Blyleven	.15	.10
446	Lenn Sakata	.05	.03
447	Jerry Don Gleaton	.05	.03
448	Herm Winningham	.05	.03
449	Rod Scurry	.05	.03
450	Graig Nettles	.08	.05
451	Mark Brown	.05	.03
452	Bob Clark	.05	.03
453	Steve Jeltz	.05	.03
454	Burt Hooton	.05	.03
455	Willie Randolph	.08	.05
456	Braves Leaders	.12	.07
457	Mickey Tettleton	1.00	.70
458	Kevin Bass	.07	.04
459	Luis Leal	.05	.03
460	Leon Durham	.05	.03
461	Walt Terrell	.05	.03
462	Domingo Ramos	.05	.03
463	Jim Gott	.07	.04
464	Ruppert Jones	.05	.03
465	Jesse Orosco	.05	.03
466	Tom Foley	.05	.03
467	Bob James	.05	.03
468	Mike Scioscia	.08	.05
469	Storm Davis	.05	.03
470	Bill Madlock	.12	.07
471	Bobby Cox	.05	.03
472	Joe Hesketh	.07	.04
473	Mark Brouhard	.05	.03
474	John Tudor	.08	.05
475	Juan Samuel	.05	.03
476	Ron Mathis	.05	.03
477	Mike Easler	.05	.03
478	Andy Hawkins	.05	.03
479	Bob Melvin (R)	.08	.05
480	Oddibe McDowell	.05	.03
481	Scott Bradley (R)	.05	.03
482	Rick Lysander	.05	.03
483	George Vukovich	.05	.03
484	Donnie Hill	.05	.03
485	Gary Matthews	.05	.03
486	Angels Leaders	.08	.05
487	Bret Saberhagen	.25	.15
488	Lou Thornton	.05	.03
489	Jim Winn	.05	.03
490	Jeff Leonard	.05	.03
491	Pascual Perez	.07	.04
492	Kelvin Chapman	.05	.03
493	Gene Nelson	.05	.03
494	Gary Roenicke	.05	.03
495	Mark Langston	.30	.18
496	Jay Johnstone	.05	.03
497	John Stuper	.05	.03
498	Tito Landrum	.05	.03
499	Bob Gibson	.05	.03
500	Rickey Henderson	1.00	.60
501	Dave Johnson	.05	.03
502	Glen Cook	.05	.03
503	Mike Fitzgerald	.05	.03
504	Denny Walling	.05	.03
505	Jerry Koosman	.08	.05
506	Bill Russell	.08	.05
507	Steve Ontiveros (R)	.05	.03
508	Alan Wiggins	.05	.03
509	Ernie Camacho	.05	.03
510	Wade Boggs	1.50	.90
511	Ed Nunez	.05	.03
512	Thad Bosley	.05	.03
513	Ron Washington	.05	.03
514	Mike Jones	.05	.03
515	Darrell Evans	.08	.05
516	Giants Leaders	.05	.03
517	Milt Thompson (R)	.20	.12
518	Buck Martinez	.05	.03
519	Danny Darwin	.07	.04
520	Keith Hernandez	.10	.06
521	Nate Snell	.05	.03
522	Bob Bailor	.05	.03
523	Joe Price	.05	.03
524	Darrell Miller	.05	.03
525	Marvell Wynne	.05	.03
526	Charlie Lea	.05	.03
527	Checklist 397-528	.10	.03
528	Terry Pendleton	.60	.35
529	Marc Sullivan	.05	.03
530	Rich Gossage	.12	.07
531	Tony LaRussa	.08	.05
532	Don Carman	.05	.03
533	Billy Sample	.05	.03
534	Jeff Calhoun	.05	.03

535 Toby Harrah	.05	.03
536 Jose Rijo	.30	.18
537 Mark Salas	.05	.03
538 Dennis Eckersley	.30	.18
539 Glenn Hubbard	.05	.03
540 Dan Petry	.07	.04
541 Jorge Orta	.05	.03
542 Don Schulze	.05	.03
543 Jerry Narron	.05	.03
544 Eddie Milner	.05	.03
545 Jimmy Key	.20	.12
546 Mariners Leaders	.08	.05
547 Roger McDowell	.10	.06
548 Mike Young	.05	.03
549 Bob Welch	.10	.06
550 Tom Herr	.07	.04
551 Dave LaPoint	.05	.03
552 Marc Hill	.05	.03
553 Jim Morrison	.05	.03
554 Paul Householder	.05	.03
555 Hubie Brooks	.10	.06
556 John Denny	.05	.03
557 Gerald Perry	.07	.04
558 Tim Stoddard	.05	.03
559 Tommy Dunbar	.05	.03
560 Dave Righetti	.08	.05
561 Bob Lillis	.05	.03
562 Joe Beckwith	.05	.03
563 Alejandro Sanchez	.05	.03
564 Warren Brusstar	.05	.03
565 Tom Brunansky	.10	.06
566 Alfredo Griffin	.05	.03
567 Jeff Barkley	.05	.03
568 Donnie Scott	.05	.03
569 Jim Acker	.05	.03
570 Rusty Staub	.08	.05
571 Mike Jeffcoat	.05	.03
572 Paul Zuvella	.05	.03
573 Tom Hume	.05	.03
574 Ron Kittle	.07	.04
575 Mike Boddicker	.08	.05
576 Expos Leaders	.15	.10
577 Jerry Reuss	.07	.04
578 Lee Mazzilli	.05	.03
579 Jim Slaton	.05	.03
580 Willie McGee	.12	.07
581 Bruce Hurst	.08	.05
582 Jim Gantner	.05	.03
583 Al Bumbry	.05	.03
584 Brian Fisher	.05	.03
585 Garry Maddox	.05	.03
586 Greg Harris	.05	.03
587 Rafael Santana	.05	.03
588 Steve Lake	.05	.03
589 Sid Bream	.08	.05
590 Bob Knepper	.05	.03
591 Jackie Moore	.05	.03

592 Frank Tanana	.08	.05
593 Jesse Barfield	.08	.05
594 Chris Bando	.05	.03
595 Dave Parker	.10	.06
596 Onix Concepcion	.05	.03
597 Sammy Stewart	.05	.03
598 Jim Presley	.05	.03
599 Rick Aguilera (R)	.50	.30
600 Dale Murphy	.25	.15
601 Gary Lucas	.05	.03
602 Mariano Duncan	.15	.10
603 Bill Laskey	.05	.03
604 Gary Pettis	.05	.03
605 Dennis Boyd	.05	.03
606 Royals Leaders	.10	.06
607 Ken Dayley	.05	.03
608 Bruce Bochy	.05	.03
609 Barbaro Garbey	.05	.03
610 Ron Guidry	.12	.07
611 Gary Woods	.05	.03
612 Richard Dotson	.05	.03
613 Roy Smalley	.05	.03
614 Rick Waits	.05	.03
615 Johnny Ray	.05	.03
616 Glenn Brummer	.05	.03
617 Lonnie Smith	.08	.05
618 Jim Pankovits	.05	.03
619 Danny Heep	.05	.03
620 Bruce Sutter	.10	.06
621 John Felski	.05	.03
622 Gary Lavelle	.05	.03
623 Floyd Rayford	.05	.03
624 Steve McCatty	.05	.03
625 Bob Brenly	.05	.03
626 Roy Thomas	.05	.03
627 Ron Oester	.05	.03
628 Kirk McCaskill (R)	.20	.12
629 Mitch Webster (R)	.15	.10
630 Fernando Valenzuela	.10	.06
631 Steve Braun	.05	.03
632 Dave Von Ohlen	.05	.03
633 Jackie Gutierrez	.05	.03
634 Roy Lee Jackson	.05	.03
635 Jason Thompson	.05	.03
636 Cubs Leaders	.12	.07
637 Rudy Law	.05	.03
638 John Butcher	.05	.03
639 Bo Diaz	.05	.03
640 Jose Cruz	.10	.06
641 Wayne Tolleson	.05	.03
642 Ray Searage	.05	.03
643 Tom Brookens	.05	.03
644 Mark Gubicza	.12	.07
645 Dusty Baker	.12	.07
646 Mike Moore	.08	.05
647 Mel Hall	.10	.06
648 Steve Bedrosian	.10	.06

649 Ronn Reynolds	.05	.03
650 Dave Stieb	.12	.07
651 Billy Martin	.12	.07
652 Tom Browning	.15	.10
653 Jim Dwyer	.05	.03
654 Ken Howell	.05	.03
655 Manny Trillo	.05	.03
656 Brian Harper	.12	.07
657 Juan Agosto	.05	.03
658 Rob Wilfong	.05	.03
659 Checklist 529-660	.10	.03
660 Steve Garvey	.25	.15
661 Roger Clemens	5.00	3.00
662 Bill Schroeer	.05	.03
663 Neil Allen	.05	.03
664 Tim Corcoran	.05	.03
665 Alejandro Pena	.08	.05
666 Rangers Leaders	.07	.04
667 Tim Teufel	.05	.03
668 Cecilio Guante	.05	.03
669 Ron Cey	.07	.04
670 Willie Hernandez	.07	.04
671 Lynn Jones	.05	.03
672 Rob Picciolo	.05	.03
673 Ernie Whitt	.05	.03
674 Pat Tabler	.05	.03
675 Claudell Washington	.05	.03
676 Matt Young	.05	.03
677 Nick Esasky	.05	.03
678 Dan Gladden	.05	.03
679 Britt Burns	.05	.03
680 George Foster	.08	.05
681 Dick Williams	.05	.03
682 Junior Ortiz	.05	.03
683 Andy Van Slyke	.35	.20
684 Bob McClure	.05	.03
685 Tim Wallach	.10	.06
686 Jeff Stone	.05	.03
687 Mike Trujillo	.05	.03
688 Larry Herndon	.05	.03
689 Dave Stewart	.15	.10
690 Ryne Sandberg	3.00	2.00
691 Mike Madden	.05	.03
692 Dale Berra	.05	.03
693 Tom Tellmann	.05	.03
694 Garth Iorg	.05	.03
695 Mike Smithson	.05	.03
696 Dodgers Leaders	.07	.04
697 Bud Black	.07	.04
698 Brad Komminsk	.05	.03
699 Pat Corrales	.05	.03
700 Reggie Jackson	.80	.50
701 Keith Hernandez AS	.10	.06
702 Tom Herr AS	.07	.04
703 Tim Wallach AS	.10	.06
704 Ozzie Smith AS	.20	.12
705 Dale Murphy AS	.15	.10

706 Pedro Guerrero AS	.10	.06
707 Willie McGee As	.10	.06
708 Gary Carter As	.15	.10
709 Dwight Gooden AS	.20	.12
710 John Tudor AS	.07	.04
711 Jeff Reardon AS	.15	.10
712 Don Mattingly AS	.40	.25
713 Damaso Garcia AS	.07	.04
714 George Brett AS	.50	.30
715 Cal Ripken AS	1.25	.80
716 Rickey Henderson AS	.40	.25
717 Dave Winfield AS	.35	.20
718 George Bell AS	.15	.10
719 Carlton Fisk AS	.20	.12
720 Bret Saberhagen AS	.12	.07
721 Ron Guidry AS	.12	.07
722 Dan Quisenberry AS	.08	.05
723 Marty Bystrom	.05	.03
724 Tim Hulett	.05	.03
725 Mario Soto	.07	.04
726 Orioles Leaders	.07	.04
727 David Green	.05	.03
728 Mike Marshall	.05	.03
729 Jim Beattie	.05	.03
730 Ozzie Smith	.75	.45
731 Don Robinson	.05	.03
732 Floyd Youmans (R)	.05	.02
733 Ron Romanick	.05	.03
734 Marty Barrett	.08	.05
735 Dave Dravecky	.08	.05
736 Glenn Wilson	.05	.03
737 Pete Vuckovich	.07	.04
738 Andre Robertson	.05	.03
739 Dave Rozema	.05	.03
740 Lance Parrish	.12	.07
741 Pete Rose	.50	.30
742 Frank Viola	.12	.07
743 Pat Sheridan	.05	.03
744 Lary Sorensen	.05	.03
745 Willie Upshaw	.05	.03
746 Denny Gonzalez	.05	.03
747 Rick Cerone	.07	.04
748 Steve Henderson	.05	.03
749 Ed Jurak	.05	.03
750 Gorman Thomas	.08	.05
751 Howard Johnson	.25	.15
752 Mike Krukow	.05	.03
753 Dan Ford	.05	.03
754 Pat Clements	.05	.03
755 Harold Baines	.10	.06
756 Pirates Leaders	.07	.04
757 Darrell Porter	.05	.03
758 Dave Anderson	.05	.03
759 Moose Haas	.05	.03
760 Andre Dawson	.60	.35
761 Don Slaught	.05	.03
762 Eric Show	.05	.03

763	Terry Puhl	.05	.03
764	Kevin Gross	.05	.03
765	Don Baylor	.10	.06
767	Jody Davis	.05	.03
768	Vern Ruhle	.05	.03
769	Harold Reynolds (R)	.25	.15
770	Vida Blue	.10	.06
771	John McNamara	.05	.03
772	Brian Downing	.08	.05
773	Greg Pryor	.05	.03
774	Terry Leach	.05	.03
775	Al Oliver	.08	.05
776	Gene Garber	.05	.03
777	Wayne Krenchicki	.05	.03
778	Jerry Hairston	.05	.03
779	Rick Reuschel	.07	.04
780	Robin Yount	1.00	.60
781	Joe Nolan	.05	.03
782	Ken Landreaux	.05	.03
783	Ricky Horton	.05	.03
784	Alan Bannister	.05	.03
785	Bob Stanley	.05	.03
786	Twins Leaders	.07	.04
787	Vance Law	.05	.03
788	Marty Castillo	.05	.03
789	Kurt Bevacqua	.05	.03
790	Phil Niekro	.15	.10
791	Checklsit 661-792	.10	.03
792	Charles Hudson	.05	.03

1986 Topps Traded

BARRY BONDS

The cards in this 132-card update set are identical to the 1986 Topps regular edition. Cards measure 2-1/2" by 3-1/2" and card numbers carry the letter "T". The set features players who were traded since the beginning of the year and a number of rookies who made their first Major League appearance during the 1986 season.

		MINT	NR/MT
Complete Set (132)		24.00	14.00
Commons		.07	.04
1T	Andy Allanson (R)	.10	.06
2T	Neil Allen	.07	.04
3T	Joaquin Andujar	.10	.06
4T	Paul Assenmacher (R)	.12	.07
5T	Scott Bailes (R)	.10	.06
6T	Don Baylor	.15	.10
7T	Steve Bedrosian	.10	.06
8T	Juan Beniquez	.07	.04
9T	Juan Berenguer	.07	.04
10T	Mike Bielecki (R)	.15	.10
11T	Barry Bonds (R)	10.00	6.50
12T	Bobby Bonilla (R)	1.75	1.00
13T	Juan Bonilla	.07	.04
14T	Rich Bordi	.07	.04
15T	Steve Boros	.07	.04
16T	Rick Burleson	.07	.04
17T	Bill Campbell	.07	.04
18T	Tom Candiotti	.15	.10
19T	John Cangelosi (R)	.10	.06
20T	Jose Canseco (R)	5.00	3.00
21T	Carmen Castillo	.07	.04
22T	Rick Cerone	.10	.06
23T	John Cerutti (R)	.10	.06
24T	Will Clark (R)	6.50	3.75
25T	Mark Clear	.07	.04
26T	Darnell Coles	.07	.04
27T	Dave Collins	.07	.04
28T	Tim Conroy	.07	.04
29T	Joe Cowley	.07	.04
30T	Joel Davis (R)	.07	.04
31T	Rob Deer	.12	.07
32T	John Denny	.07	.04
33T	Mike Easler	.07	.04
34T	Mark Eichhorn (R)	.12	.07
35T	Steve Farr	.07	.04
36T	Scott Fletcher	.07	.04
37T	Terry Forster	.07	.04
38T	Terry Francona	.07	.04
39T	Jim Fregosi	.07	.04
40T	Andres Galarraga (R)	2.50	1.40
41T	Ken Griffey	.15	.10
42T	Bill Gullickson	.10	.06
43T	Jose Guzman (R)	.35	.20
44T	Moose Haas	.07	.04
45T	Billy Hatcher	.15	.10
46T	Mike Heath	.07	.04
47T	Tom Hume	.07	.04
48T	Pete Incaviglia (R)	.35	.20
49T	Dane Iorg	.07	.04
50T	Bo Jackson (R)	3.50	2.50
51T	Wally Joyner (R)	1.00	.60
52T	Charlie Kerfeld (R)	.07	.04

53T Eric King (R)	.12	.07
54T Bob Kipper (R)	.10	.06
55T Wayne Krenchicki	.07	.04
56T John Kruk (R)	2.50	1.40
57T Mike LaCoss	.07	.04
58T Pete Ladd	.07	.04
59T Mike Laga	.07	.04
60T Hal Lanier	.07	.04
61T Dave LaPoint	.07	.04
62T Rudy Law	.07	.04
63T Rick Leach	.07	.04
64T Tim Leary	.10	.06
65T Dennis Leonard	.07	.04
66T Jim Leyland (R)	.20	.12
67T Steve Lyons	.07	.04
68T Mickey Mahler	.07	.04
69T Candy Maldonado	.15	.10
70T Roger Mason (R)	.12	.07
71T Bob McClure	.07	.04
72T Andy McGaffigan	.07	.04
73T Gene Michael	.07	.04
74T Kevin Mitchell (R)	1.25	.80
75T Omar Moreno	.07	.04
76T Jerry Mumphrey	.07	.04
77T Phil Niekro	.30	.18
78T Randy Niemann	.07	.04
79T Juan Nieves (R)	.15	.10
80T Otis Nixon (R)	.40	.25
81T Bob Ojeda	.10	.06
82T Jose Oquendo	.10	.06
83T Tom Paciorek	.07	.04
84T Dave Palmer	.07	.04
85T Frank Pastore	.07	.04
86T Lou Piniella	.10	.06
87T Dan Plesac (R)	.15	.10
88T Darrell Porter	.07	.04
89T Rey Quinones (R)	.08	.05
90T Gary Redus	.07	.04
91T Bip Roberts (R)	.40	.25
92T Billy Jo Robidoux	.07	.04
93T Jeff Robinson	.10	.06
94T Gary Roenicke	.07	.04
95T Ed Romero	.07	.04
96T Argenis Salazar	.07	.04
97T Joe Sambito	.07	.04
98T Billy Sample	.07	.04
99T Dave Schmidt	.07	.04
100T Ken Schrom	.07	.04
101T Tom Seaver	.75	.45
102T Ted Simmons	.12	.07
103T Sammy Stewart	.07	.04
104T Kurt Stillwell (R)	.15	.10
105T Franklin Stubbs	.10	.06
106T Dale Sveum	.15	.10
107T Chuck Tanner	.07	.04
108T Danny Tartabull (R)	.75	.45
109T Tim Teufel	.10	.06

110T Bob Tewksbury (R)	.60	.35
111T Andres Thomas (R)	.08	.05
112T Milt Thompson	.12	.07
113T Robby Thompson (R)	.80	.50
114T Jay Tibbs	.07	.04
115T Wayne Tolleson	.07	.04
116T Alex Trevino	.07	.04
117T Manny Trillo	.07	.04
118T Ed Vande Berg	.07	.04
119T Ozzie Virgil	.07	.04
120T Bob Walk	.07	.04
121T Gene Walter (R)	.07	.04
122T Claudell Washington	.07	.04
123T Bill Wegman (R)	.15	.10
124T Dick Williams	.07	.04
125T Mitch Williams (R)	.30	.18
126T Bobby Witt (R)	.30	.18
127T Todd Worrell (R)	.15	.10
128T George Wright	.07	.04
129T Ricky Wright	.07	.04
130T Steve Yeager	.07	.04
131T Paul Zuvella	.07	.04
132T Checklist	.07	.04

1987 Topps

This 792-card set features mostly action photos surrounded by wood grain borders that are similar to the 1962 Topps set. Card backs are horizontal with blue and yellow colors on a gray paper stock. Cards measure 2-1/2" by 3-1/2". Key subsets include Record Breakers, Turn Back The Clock, Team Leaders and All-Stars.

	MINT	NR/MT
Complete Set (792)	24.00	14.00
Commons	.05	.03

1	Roger Clemens (RB)	.50	.30
2	Jim Deshaies (RB)	.05	.03
3	Dwight Evans (RB)	.10	.06
4	Dave Lopes (RB)	.07	.04
5	Dave Righetti (RB)	.07	.04
6	Ruben Sierra (RB)	.25	.15
7	Todd Worrell (RB)	.07	.04
8	Terry Pendleton	.35	.20
9	Jay Tibbs	.05	.03
10	Cecil Cooper	.07	.04
11	Indians Leaders	.10	.06
12	Jeff Sellers	.05	.03
13	Nick Esasky	.05	.03
14	Dave Stewart	.10	.06
15	Claudell Washington	.07	.04
16	Pat Clements	.05	.03
17	Pete O'Brien	.05	.03
18	Dick Howser	.05	.03
19	Matt Young	.05	.03
20	Gary Carter	.15	.10
21	Mark Davis	.05	.03
22	Doug DeCinces	.05	.03
23	Lee Smith	.20	.12
24	Tony Walker	.05	.03
25	Bert Blyleven	.15	.10
26	Greg Brock	.05	.03
27	Joe Cowley	.05	.03
28	Rick Dempsey	.05	.03
29	Jimmy Key	.15	.10
30	Tim Raines	.15	.10
31	Braves Leaders	.05	.03
32	Tim Leary	.07	.04
33	Andy Van Slyke	.25	.15
34	Jose Rijo	.15	.10
35	Sid Bream	.08	.05
36	Eric King	.05	.03
37	Marvell Wynne	.05	.03
38	Dennis Leonard	.05	.03
39	Marty Barrett	.07	.04
40	Dave Righetti	.08	.05
41	Bo Diaz	.05	.03
42	Gary Redus	.05	.03
43	Gene Michael	.05	.03
44	Greg Harris	.05	.03
45	Jim Presley	.05	.03
46	Danny Gladden	.08	.05
47	Dennis Powell	.05	.03
48	Wally Backman	.05	.03
49	Terry Harper	.05	.03
50	Dave Smith	.05	.03
51	Mel Hall	.10	.06
52	Keith Atherton	.05	.03
53	Ruppert Jones	.05	.03
54	Bill Dawley	.05	.03
55	Tim Wallach	.10	.06
56	Brewers Leaders	.10	.06
57	Scott Nielsen	.05	.03
58	Thad Bosley	.05	.03
59	Ken Dayley	.05	.03
60	Tony Pena	.08	.05
61	Bobby Thigpen (R)	.20	.12
62	Bobby Meacham	.05	.03
63	Fred Toliver	.05	.03
64	Harry Spilman	.05	.03
65	Tom Browning	.10	.06
66	Marc Sullivan	.05	.03
67	Bill Swift	.15	.10
68	Tony LaRussa	.08	.05
69	Lonnie Smith	.07	.04
70	Charlie Hough	.05	.03
71	Mike Aldrete (R)	.08	.05
72	Walt Terrell	.05	.03
73	Dave Anderson	.05	.03
74	Dan Pasqua	.08	.05
75	Ron Darling	.10	.06
76	Rafael Ramirez	.05	.03
77	Bryan Oelkers	.05	.03
78	Tom Foley	.05	.03
79	Juan Nieves	.10	.06
80	Wally Joyner	.60	.35
81	Padres Leaders	.05	.03
82	Rob Murphy (R)	.08	.05
83	Mike Davis	.05	.03
84	Steve Lake	.05	.03
85	Kevin Bass	.08	.05
86	Nate Snell	.05	.03
87	Mark Salas	.05	.03
88	Ed Wojna	.05	.03
89	Ozzie Guillen	.10	.06
90	Dave Stieb	.10	.06
91	Harold Reynolds	.12	.07
92	Urbano Lugo	.05	.03
93	Jim Leyland	.10	.06
94	Calvin Schiraldi	.05	.03
95	Oddibe McDowell	.05	.03
96	Frank Williams	.05	.03
97	Glenn Wilson	.05	.03
98	Bill Scherrer	.05	.03
99	Darryl Motley	.05	.03
100	Steve Garvey	.20	.12
101	Carl Willis (R)	.08	.05
102	Paul Zuvella	.05	.03
103	Rick Aguilera	.12	.07
104	Billy Sample	.05	.03
105	Floyd Youmans	.05	.03
106	Blue Jays Leaders	.10	.06
107	John Butcher	.05	.03
108	Jim Gantner (Photo reversed)	.05	.03
109	R.J. Reynolds	.05	.03
110	John Tudor	.07	.04
111	Alfredo Griffin	.05	.03
112	Alan Ashby	.05	.03
113	Neil Allen	.05	.03

114	Billy Beane	.05	.03
115	Donnie Moore	.05	.03
116	Bill Russell	.07	.04
117	Jim Beattie	.05	.03
118	Bobby Valentine	.05	.03
119	Ron Robinson	.05	.03
120	Eddie Murray	.35	.20
121	Kevin Romine	.05	.03
122	Jim Clancy	.05	.03
123	John Kruk	.80	.50
124	Ray Fontenot	.05	.03
125	Bob Brenly	.05	.03
126	Mike Loynd (R)	.05	.03
127	Vance Law	.05	.03
128	Checklist 1-132	.06	.03
129	Rick Cerone	.05	.03
130	Dwight Gooden	.25	.15
131	Pirates Leaders	.07	.04
132	Paul Assenmacher	.05	.03
133	Jose Oquendo	.05	.03
134	Rich Yett (R)	.07	.04
135	Mike Easler	.05	.03
136	Ron Romanick	.05	.03
137	Jerry Willard	.05	.03
138	Roy Lee Jackson	.05	.03
139	Devon White (R)	.50	.30
140	Bret Saberhagen	.15	.10
141	Herm Winningham	.05	.03
142	Rick Sutcliffe	.08	.05
143	Steve Boros	.05	.03
144	Mike Scioscia	.07	.04
145	Charlie Kerfeld	.05	.03
146	Tracy Jones (R)	.08	.05
147	Randy Niemann	.05	.03
148	Dave Collins	.05	.03
149	Ray Searage	.05	.03
150	Wade Boggs	.50	.30
151	Mike LaCoss	.05	.03
152	Toby Harrah	.05	.03
153	Duane Ward (R)	.30	.18
154	Tom O'Malley	.05	.03
155	Eddie Whitson	.05	.03
156	Mariners Leaders	.05	.03
157	Danny Darwin	.05	.03
158	Tim Teufel	.05	.03
159	Ed Olwine	.05	.03
160	Julio Franco	.15	.10
161	Steve Ontiveros	.05	.03
162	Mike LaValliere	.10	.06
163	Kevin Gross	.05	.03
164	Sammy Khalifa	.05	.03
165	Jeff Reardon	.15	.10
166	Bob Boone	.12	.07
167	Jim Deshais	.10	.06
168	Lou Piniella	.08	.05
169	Ron Washington	.05	.03
170	Bo Jackson	1.25	.80

171	Chuck Cary	.05	.03
172	Ron Oester	.05	.03
173	Alex Trevino	.05	.03
174	Henry Cotto	.05	.03
175	Bob Stanley	.05	.03
176	Steve Buechele	.08	.05
177	Keith Moreland	.05	.00
178	Cecil Fielder	1.25	.80
179	Bill Wegman	.07	.04
180	Chris Brown	.05	.03
181	Cardinals Leaders	.10	.06
182	Lee Lacy	.05	.03
183	Andy Hawkins	.05	.03
184	Bobby Bonilla	.75	.45
185	Roger McDowell	.05	.03
186	Bruce Benedict	.05	.03
187	Mark Huismann	.05	.03
188	Tony Phillips	.07	.04
189	Joe Hesketh	.05	.03
190	Jim Sundberg	.05	.03
191	Charles Hudson	.05	.03
192	Cory Snyder	.08	.05
193	Roger Craig	.05	.03
194	Kirk McCaskill	.07	.04
195	Mike Pagliarulo	.05	.03
196	Randy O'Neal	.05	.03
197	Mark Bailey	.05	.03
198	Lee Mazzilli	.05	.03
199	Mariano Duncan	.07	.04
200	Pete Rose	.50	.30
201	John Cangelosi	.05	.03
202	Ricky Wright	.05	.03
203	Mike Kingery (R)	.08	.05
204	Sammy Stewart	.05	.03
205	Graig Nettles	.08	.05
206	Twins Leaders	.08	.05
207	George Frazier	.05	.03
208	John Shelby	.05	.03
209	Rich Schu	.05	.03
210	Lloyd Moseby	.05	.03
211	John Morris	.05	.03
212	Mike Fitzgerald	.05	.03
213	Randy Myers (R)	.30	.18
214	Omar Moreno	.05	.03
215	Mark Langston	.20	.12
216	B.J. Surhoff (R)	.15	.10
217	Chris Codiroli	.05	.03
218	Sparky Anderson	.08	.05
219	Cecilio Guante	.05	.03
220	Joe Carter	.50	.30
221	Vern Ruhle	.05	.03
222	Denny Walling	.05	.03
223	Charlie Liebrandt	.07	.04
224	Wayne Tolleson	.05	.03
225	Mike Smithson	.05	.03
226	Max Venable	.05	.03
227	Jamie Moyer	.08	.05

228	Curt Wilkerson	.05	.03
229	Mike Birkbeck (R)	.05	.03
230	Don Baylor	.10	.06
231	Giants Leaders	.07	.04
232	Reggie Williams	.05	.03
233	Russ Morman	.05	.03
234	Pat Sheridan	.05	.03
235	Alvin Davis	.07	.04
236	Tommy John	.10	.06
237	Jim Morrison	.05	.03
238	Bill Krueger	.05	.03
239	Juan Espino	.05	.03
240	Steve Balboni	.05	.03
241	Danny Heep	.05	.03
242	Rick Mahler	.05	.03
243	Whitey Herzog	.08	.05
244	Dickie Noles	.05	.03
245	Willie Upshaw	.05	.03
246	Jim Dwyer	.05	.03
247	Jeff Reed	.05	.03
248	Gene Walter	.05	.03
249	Jim Pankovits	.05	.03
250	Teddy Higuera	.08	.05
251	Rob Wilfong	.05	.03
252	Denny Martinez	.10	.06
253	Eddie Milner	.05	.03
254	Bob Tewksbury	.25	.15
255	Juan Samuel	.05	.03
256	Royals Leaders (Brett)	.20	.12
257	Bob Forsch	.05	.03
258	Steve Yeager	.05	.03
259	Mike Greenwell (R)	.50	.30
260	Vida Blue	.08	.05
261	Ruben Sierra	2.00	1.25
262	Jim Winn	.05	.03
263	Stan Javier	.05	.03
264	Checklist 133-264	.06	.03
265	Darrell Evans	.08	.05
266	Jeff Hamilton	.05	.03
267	Howard Johnson	.25	.15
268	Pat Corrales	.05	.03
269	Cliff Speck	.05	.03
270	Jody Davis	.05	.03
271	Mike Brown	.05	.03
272	Andres Galarraga	.50	.30
273	Gene Nelson	.05	.03
274	Jeff Hearron (R)	.05	.03
275	LaMarr Hoyt	.05	.03
276	Jackie Gutierrez	.05	.03
277	Juan Agosto	.05	.03
278	Gary Pettis	.10	.06
279	Dan Plesac	.08	.05
280	Jeffrey Leonard	.08	.05
281	Reds Leaders (Rose)	.20	.12
282	Jeff Calhuon	.05	.03
283	Doug Drabek (R)	.70	.40
284	John Moses	.05	.03
285	Dennis Boyd	.05	.03
286	Mike Woodard	.05	.03
287	Dave Von Ohlen	.05	.03
288	Tito Landrum	.05	.03
289	Bob Kipper	.05	.03
290	Leon Durham	.05	.03
291	Mitch Williams	.20	.12
292	Franklin Stubbs	.05	.03
293	Bob Rodgers	.05	.03
294	Steve Jeltz	.05	.03
295	Len Dykstra	.35	.20
296	Andres Thomas	.05	.03
297	Don Schulze	.05	.03
298	Terry Herndon	.05	.03
299	Joel Davis	.05	.03
300	Reggie Jackson	.50	.30
301	Luis Aquino	.05	.03
302	Bill Schroeder	.05	.03
303	Juan Berenguer	.07	.04
304	Phil Garner	.07	.04
305	John Franco	.10	.06
306	Red Sox Leaders	.20	.12
307	Lee Guetterman	.05	.03
308	Don Slaught	.05	.03
309	Mike Young	.05	.03
310	Frank Viola	.15	.10
311	Rickey Henderson (Clock)	.20	.12
312	Reggie Jackson (Clock)	.25	.15
313	Roberto Clemente (Clock)	.12	.07
314	Carl Yastrzemski (Clock)	.10	.06
315	Maury Wills (Clock)	.08	.05
316	Brian Fisher	.05	.03
317	Clint Hurdle	.05	.03
318	Jim Fregosi	.05	.03
319	Greg Swindell (R)	.40	.25
320	Barry Bonds	4.00	2.50
321	Mike Laga	.05	.03
322	Chris Bando	.05	.03
323	Al Newman	.05	.03
324	Dave Palmer	.05	.03
325	Garry Templeton	.08	.05
326	Mark Gubicza	.10	.06
327	Dale Sveum	.08	.05
328	Bob Welch	.08	.05
329	Ron Roenicke	.05	.03
330	Mike Scott	.08	.05
331	Mets Leaders	.20	.12
332	Joe Price	.05	.03
333	Ken Phelps	.05	.03
334	Ed Correa	.05	.03
335	Candy Maldonado	.08	.05
336	Allan Anderson	.07	.04
337	Darrell Miller	.05	.03
338	Tim Conroy	.05	.03

339	Donnie Hill	.05	.03	396	Tim Lollar	.05	.03
340	Roger Clemens	1.25	.80	397	Greg Walker	.05	.03
341	Mike Brown	.05	.03	398	Brad Havens	.05	.03
342	Bob James	.05	.03	399	Curt Ford (R)	.07	.04
343	Hal Lanier	.05	.03	400	George Brett	.50	.30
344	Joe Niekro	.05	.03	401	Billy Jo Robidoux	.05	.03
345	Andre Dawson	.30	.10	402	Mike Trujillo	.05	.03
346	Shawon Dunston	.15	.10	403	Jerry Royster	.05	.03
347	Mickey Brantley	.05	.03	404	Doug Sisk	.05	.03
348	Carmelo Martinez	.05	.03	405	Brook Jacoby	.05	.03
349	Storm Davis	.05	.03	406	Yankees Leaders	.25	.15
350	Keith Hernandez	.08	.05	407	Jim Acker	.05	.03
351	Gene Garber	.05	.03	408	John Mizerock	.05	.03
352	Mike Felder	.08	.05	409	Milt Thompson	.05	.03
353	Ernie Camacho	.05	.03	410	Fernando Valenzuela	.10	.06
354	Jamie Quirk	.05	.03	411	Darnell Coles	.07	.04
355	Don Carman	.05	.03	412	Eric Davis	.20	.12
356	White Sox Leaders	.05	.03	413	Moose Haas	.05	.03
357	Steve Fireovid (R)	.05	.03	414	Joe Orsulak	.08	.05
358	Sal Butera	.05	.03	415	Bobby Witt	.25	.15
359	Doug Corbett	.05	.03	416	Tom Nieto	.05	.03
360	Pedro Guerrero	.10	.06	417	Pat Perry (R)	.07	.04
361	Mark Thurmond	.05	.03	418	Dick Williams	.05	.03
362	Luis Quinones (R)	.07	.04	419	Mark Portugal (R)	.25	.15
363	Jose Guzman	.07	.04	420	Will Clark	2.50	1.40
364	Randy Bush	.07	.04	421	Jose DeLeon	.05	.03
365	Rick Rhoden	.05	.03	422	Jack Howell	.05	.03
366	Mark McGwire	1.75	1.00	423	Jaime Cocanower	.05	.03
367	Jeff Lahti	.05	.03	424	Chris Speier	.05	.03
368	John McNamara	.05	.03	425	Tom Seaver	.30	.18
369	Brian Dayett	.05	.03	426	Floyd Rayford	.05	.03
370	Fred Lynn	.08	.05	427	Ed Nunez	.05	.03
371	Mark Eichhorn	.08	.05	428	Bruce Bochy	.05	.03
372	Jerry Mumphrey	.05	.03	429	Tim Pyznarski (R)	.05	.03
373	Jeff Dedmon	.05	.03	430	Mike Schmidt	.80	.50
374	Glenn Hoffman	.05	.03	431	Dodgers Leaders	.08	.05
375	Ron Guidry	.10	.06	432	Jim Slaton	.05	.03
376	Scott Bradley	.05	.03	433	Ed Hearn	.05	.03
377	John Henry Johnson	.05	.03	434	Mike Fischlin	.05	.03
378	Rafael Santana	.05	.03	435	Bruce Sutter	.08	.05
379	John Russell	.05	.03	436	Andy Allanson	.05	.03
380	Rich Gossage	.10	.06	437	Ted Power	.05	.03
381	Expos Leaders	.05	.03	438	Kelly Downs (R)	.10	.06
382	Rudy Law	.05	.03	439	Karl Best	.05	.03
383	Ron Davis	.05	.03	440	Willie McGee	.10	.06
384	Johnny Grubb	.05	.03	441	Dave Leiper (R)	.07	.04
385	Orel Hershiser	.12	.07	442	Mitch Webster	.05	.03
386	Dickie Thon	.05	.03	443	John Felske	.05	.03
387	T.R. Bryden	.05	.03	444	Jeff Russell	.08	.05
388	Geno Petralli	.05	.03	445	Dave Lopes	.07	.04
389	Jeff Robinson	.05	.03	446	Chuck Finley (R)	.35	.20
390	Gary Matthews	.05	.03	447	Bill Almon	.05	.03
391	Jay Howell	.05	.03	448	Chris Bosio (R)	.25	.15
392	Checklist 265-396	.06	.03	449	Pat Dodson (R)	.07	.04
393	Pete Rose	.30	.18	450	Kirby Puckett	1.50	.90
394	Mike Bielecki	.08	.05	451	Joe Sambito	.05	.03
395	Damaso Garcia	.05	.03	452	Dave Henderson	.08	.05

453 Scott Terry (R)	.07	.04
454 Luis Salazar	.05	.03
455 Mike Boddicker	.08	.05
456 A's Leaders	.10	.06
457 Len Matuszak	.05	.03
458 Kelly Gruber (R)	.30	.18
459 Dennis Eckersley	.25	.15
460 Darryl Strawberry	.45	.28
461 Craig McMurtry	.05	.03
462 Scott Fletcher	.05	.03
463 Tom Candiotti	.10	.06
464 Butch Wynegar	.05	.03
465 Todd Worrell	.10	.06
466 Kal Daniels (R)	.15	.10
467 Randy St. Claire	.05	.03
468 George Bamberger	.05	.03
469 Mike Diaz (R)	.05	.03
470 Dave Dravecky	.08	.05
471 Ronn Reynolds	.05	.03
472 Bill Doran	.08	.05
473 Steve Farr	.05	.03
474 Jerry Narron	.05	.03
475 Scott Garrelts	.08	.05
476 Danny Tartabull	.40	.25
477 Ken Howell	.05	.03
478 Tim Laudner	.05	.03
479 Bob Sebra	.05	.03
480 Jim Rice	.10	.06
481 Phillies Leaders	.07	.04
482 Daryl Boston	.05	.03
483 Dwight Lowry	.05	.03
484 Jim Traber	.05	.03
485 Tony Fernandez	.08	.05
486 Otis Nixon	.15	.10
487 Dave Gumpert	.05	.03
488 Ray Knight	.07	.04
489 Bill Gullickson	.07	.04
490 Dale Murphy	.20	.12
491 Ron Karkovice (R)	.12	.07
492 Mike Heath	.05	.03
493 Tom Lasorda	.08	.05
494 Barry Jones	.05	.03
495 Gorman Thomas	.07	.04
496 Bruce Bochte	.05	.03
497 Dale Mohorcic (R)	.07	.04
498 Bob Kearney	.05	.03
499 Bruce Ruffin	.05	.03
500 Don Mattingly	.60	.35
501 Craig Lefferts	.07	.04
502 Dick Schofield	.05	.03
503 Larry Andersen	.05	.03
504 Mickey Hatcher	.05	.03
505 Bryn Smith	.07	.04
506 Orioles Leaders	.08	.05
507 Dave Stapleton	.05	.03
508 Scott Bankhead	.05	.03
509 Enos Cabell	.05	.03
510 Tom Henke	.10	.06
511 Steve Lyons	.05	.03
512 Dave Magadan (R)	.20	.12
513 Carmen Castillo	.05	.03
514 Orlando Mercado	.05	.03
515 Willie Hernandez	.07	.04
516 Ted Simmons	.08	.05
517 Mario Soto	.05	.03
518 Gene Mauch	.05	.03
519 Curt Young	.05	.03
520 Jack Clark	.08	.05
521 Rick Reuschel	.05	.03
522 Checklist 397-528	.06	.03
523 Earnie Riles	.05	.03
524 Bob Shirley	.05	.03
525 Phil Bradley	.05	.03
526 Roger Mason	.05	.03
527 Jim Wohlford	.05	.03
528 Ken Dixon	.05	.03
529 Alvaro Espinoza (R)	.10	.06
530 Tony Gwynn	.60	.35
531 Astros Leaders	.12	.07
532 Jeff Stone	.05	.03
533 Argenis Salazar	.05	.03
534 Scott Sanderson	.05	.03
535 Tony Armas	.05	.03
536 Terry Mulholland (R)	.50	.30
537 Rance Mulliniks	.05	.03
538 Tom Niedenfuer	.05	.03
539 Reid Nichols	.05	.03
540 Terry Kennedy	.05	.03
541 Rafael Belliard (R)	.10	.06
542 Ricky Horton	.05	.03
543 Dave Johnson	.05	.03
544 Zane Smith	.10	.06
545 Buddy Bell	.05	.03
546 Mike Morgan	.08	.05
547 Rob Deer	.10	.06
548 Bill Mooneyham (R)	.05	.03
549 Bob Melvin	.05	.03
550 Pete Incaviglia	.20	.12
551 Frank Wills	.05	.03
552 Larry Sheets	.05	.03
553 Mike Maddux (R)	.07	.04
554 Buddy Biancalana	.05	.03
555 Dennis Rasmussen	.05	.03
556 Angels Leaders	.08	.05
557 John Cerutti	.05	.03
558 Greg Gagne	.07	.04
559 Lance McCullers	.05	.03
560 Glenn Davis	.07	.04
561 Rey Quinones	.05	.03
562 Bryan Clutterbuck (R)	.05	.03
563 John Stefero	.05	.03
564 Larry McWilliams	.05	.03
565 Dusty Baker	.10	.06
566 Tim Hulett	.05	.03

567	Greg Mathews	.05	.03
568	Earl Weaver	.08	.05
569	Wade Rowdon (R)	.05	.03
570	Sid Fernandez	.05	.03
571	Ozzie Virgil	.05	.03
572	Pete Ladd	.05	.03
570	Hal McRae	.10	.00
574	Manny Lee	.07	.04
575	Pat Tabler	.05	.03
576	Frank Pastore	.05	.03
577	Dann Bilardello	.05	.03
578	Billy Hatcher	.05	.03
579	Rick Burleson	.05	.03
580	Mike Krukow	.05	.03
581	Cubs Leaders	.07	.04
582	Bruce Berenyi	.05	.03
583	Junior Ortiz	.05	.03
584	Ron Kittle	.07	.04
585	Scott Bailes	.05	.03
586	Ben Oglivie	.05	.03
587	Eric Plunk	.08	.05
588	Wallace Johnson	.05	.03
589	Steve Crawford	.05	.03
590	Vince Coleman	.10	.06
591	Spike Owen	.05	.03
592	Chris Welsh	.05	.03
593	Chuck Tanner	.05	.03
594	Rick Anderson	.05	.03
595	Keith Hernandez AS	.08	.05
596	Steve Sax AS	.08	.05
597	Mike Schmidt AS	.35	.20
598	Ozzie Smith AS	.12	.07
599	Tony Gwynn AS	.25	.15
600	Dave Parker AS	.10	.06
601	Darryl Strawberry AS	.20	.12
602	Gary Carter AS	.10	.06
603a	Dwight Gooden AS (No trademark on front)	.40	.25
603b	Dwight Gooden AS (Cor)	.15	.10
604	Fernando Valenzuela AS	.08	.05
605	Todd Worrell As	.07	.04
606a	Don Mattingly AS (No trademark on front)	.60	.35
606b	Don Mattingly AS	.20	.12
607	Tony Bernazard AS	.05	.03
608	Wade Boggs AS	.25	.15
609	Cal Ripken AS	.50	.30
610	Jim Rice AS	.08	.05
611	Kirby Puckett AS	.50	.30
612	George Bell AS	.10	.06
613	Lance Parrish AS	.08	.05
614	Rogers Clemens AS	.50	.30
615	Teddy Higuera AS	.08	.05
616	Dave Righetti AS	.08	.05
617	Al Nipper	.05	.03
618	Tom Kelly	.05	.03
619	Jerry Reed	.05	.03
620	Jose Canseco	1.75	1.00
621	Danny Cox	.05	.03
622	Glenn Braggs (R)	.10	.06
623	Kurt Stillwell	.07	.04
624	Tim Burke	.05	.03
625	Mookie Wilson	.00	.05
626	Joel Skinner	.05	.03
627	Ken Oberkfell	.05	.03
628	Bob Walk	.05	.03
629	Larry Parrish	.05	.03
630	John Candelaria	.05	.03
631	Tigers Leaders	.08	.05
632	Rob Woodward	.05	.03
633	Jose Uribe	.05	.03
634	Rafael Palmeiro (R)	2.00	1.25
635	Ken Schrom	.05	.03
636	Darren Daulton	.50	.30
637	Bip Roberts	.30	.18
638	Rich Bordi	.05	.03
639	Gerald Perry	.05	.03
640	Mark Clear	.05	.03
641	Domingo Ramos	.05	.03
642	Al Pulido	.05	.03
643	Ron Shepherd	.05	.03
644	John Denny	.05	.03
645	Dwight Evans	.12	.07
646	Mike Mason	.05	.03
647	Tom Lawless	.05	.03
648	Barry Larkin (R)	1.25	.80
649	Mickey Tettleton	.15	.10
650	Hubie Brooks	.08	.05
651	Benny Distefano	.05	.03
652	Terry Forster	.05	.03
653	Kevin Mitchell	.70	.40
654	Checklist 529-660	.06	.03
655	Jesse Barfield	.10	.06
656	Rangers Leaders	.07	.04
657	Tom Waddell	.05	.03
658	Robby Thompson	.30	.18
659	Aurelio Lopez	.05	.03
660	Bob Horner	.10	.06
661	Lou Whitaker	.12	.07
662	Frank DiPino	.05	.03
663	Cliff Johnson	.05	.03
664	Mike Marshall	.05	.03
665	Rod Scurry	.05	.03
666	Von Hayes	.07	.04
667	Ron Hassey	.05	.03
668	Juan Bonilla	.05	.03
669	Bud Black	.05	.03
670	Jose Cruz	.08	.05
671	Ray Soff	.05	.03
672	Chili Davis	.08	.05
673	Don Sutton	.12	.07
674	Bill Campbell	.05	.03
675	Ed Romero	.05	.03

676	Charlie Moore	.05	.03	733	Bill Caudill	.05	.03
677	Bob Grich	.07	.04	734	Bill Madlock	.10	.06
678	Carney Lansford	.08	.05	735	Rickey Henderson	.50	.30
679	Kent Hrbek	.10	.06	736	Steve Bedrosian	.08	.05
680	Ryne Sandberg	1.25	.80	737	Floyd Bannister	.05	.03
681	George Bell	.12	.07	738	Jorge Orta	.05	.03
682	Jerry Reuss	.05	.03	739	Chet Lemon	.05	.03
683	Gary Roenicke	.05	.03	740	Rich Gedman	.05	.03
684	Kent Tekulve	.05	.03	741	Paul Molitor	.35	.20
685	Jerry Hairston	.05	.03	742	Andy McGaffigan	.05	.03
686	Doyle Alexander	.05	.03	743	Dwayne Murphy	.05	.03
687	Alan Trammell	.20	.12	744	Roy Smalley	.05	.03
688	Juan Beniquez	.05	.03	745	Glenn Hubbard	.05	.03
689	Darrell Porter	.05	.03	746	Bob Ojeda	.05	.03
690	Dane Iorg	.05	.03	747	Johnny Ray	.05	.03
691	Dave Parker	.10	.06	748	Mike Flanagan	.07	.04
692	Frank White	.05	.03	749	Ozzie Smith	.35	.20
693	Terry Puhl	.05	.03	750	Steve Trout	.05	.03
694	Phil Niekro	.15	.10	751	Garth Iorg	.05	.03
695	Chico Walker	.05	.03	752	Dan Petry	.05	.03
696	Gary Lucas	.05	.03	753	Rick Honeycutt	.05	.03
697	Ed Lynch	.05	.03	754	Dave LaPoint	.05	.03
698	Ernie Whitt	.05	.03	755	Luis Aguayo	.05	.03
699	Ken Landreaux	.05	.03	756	Carlton Fisk	.30	.18
700	Dave Bergman	.05	.03	757	Nolan Ryan	1.50	.90
701	Willie Randolph	.08	.05	758	Tony Bernazard	.05	.03
702	Greg Gross	.05	.03	759	Joel Youngblood	.05	.03
703	Dave Schmidt	.05	.03	760	Mike Witt	.05	.03
704	Jesse Orosco	.05	.03	761	Greg Pryor	.05	.03
705	Bruce Hurst	.08	.05	762	Gary Ward	.05	.03
706	Rick Manning	.05	.03	763	Tim Flannery	.05	.03
707	Bob McClure	.05	.03	764	Bill Buckner	.08	.05
708	Scott McGregor	.05	.03	765	Kirk Gibson	.08	.05
709	Dave Kingman	.08	.05	766	Don Aase	.05	.03
710	Gary Gaetti	.05	.03	767	Ron Cey	.05	.03
711	Ken Griffey	.10	.06	768	Dennis Lamp	.05	.03
712	Don Robinson	.05	.03	769	Steve Sax	.12	.07
713	Tom Brookens	.05	.03	770	Dave Winfield	.50	.30
714	Dan Quisenberry	.07	.04	771	Shane Rawley	.05	.03
715	Bob Dernier	.05	.03	772	Harold Baines	.08	.05
716	Rick Leach	.05	.03	773	Robin Yount	.50	.30
717	Ed Vande Berg	.05	.03	774	Wayne Krenchicki	.05	.03
718	Steve Carlton	.40	.25	775	Joaquin Andujar	.07	.04
719	Tom Hume	.05	.03	776	Tom Brunansky	.08	.05
720	Richard Dotson	.05	.03	777	Chris Chambliss	.07	.04
721	Tom Herr	.05	.03	778	Jack Morris	.20	.12
722	Bob Knepper	.05	.03	779	Craig Reynolds	.05	.03
723	Brett Butler	.15	.10	780	Andre Thornton	.05	.03
724	Greg Minton	.05	.03	781	Atlee Hammaker	.05	.03
725	George Hendrick	.07	.04	782	Brian Downing	.07	.04
726	Frank Tanana	.07	.04	783	Willie Wilson	.07	.04
727	Mike Moore	.07	.04	784	Cal Ripken	1.25	.80
728	Tippy Martinez	.05	.03	785	Terry Francona	.05	.03
729	Tom Paciorek	.05	.03	786	Jimy Williams	.05	.03
730	Eric Show	.05	.03	787	Alejandro Pena	.08	.05
731	Dave Concepcion	.12	.07	788	Tim Stoddard	.05	.03
732	Manny Trillo	.05	.03	789	Dan Schatzeder	.05	.03

790	Julio Cruz	.05	.03
791	Lance Parrish	.12	.07
792	Checklist 661-792	.06	.03

1987 Topps Traded

This update set consists of 132-cards identical in design to those found in Topps regular 1987 edition. Cards measure 2-1/2" by 3-1/2" and card numbers are followed by the letter "T". The set features player's traded during the year and some up and coming rookie prospects not included in Topps regular set.

	MINT	NR/MT
Complete Set (132)	10.00	6.50
Commons	.05	.03

1T	Bill Almon	.05	.03
2T	Scott Bankhead	.05	.03
3T	Eric Bell (R)	.12	.07
4T	Juan Beniquez	.05	.03
5T	Juan Berenguer	.05	.03
6T	Greg Booker	.05	.03
7T	Thad Bosley	.05	.03
8T	Larry Bowa	.08	.05
9T	Greg Brock	.05	.03
10T	Bob Brower (R)	.05	.03
11T	Jerry Browne (R)	.12	.07
12T	Ralph Bryant (R)	.08	.05
13T	DeWayne Buice (R)	.05	.03
14T	Ellis Burks (R)	.60	.35
15T	Ivan Calderon	.12	.07
16T	Jeff Calhoun	.05	.03
17T	Casey Candaele	.05	.03
18T	John Cangelosi	.05	.03
19T	Steve Carlton	.50	.30

20T	Juan Castillo (R)	.05	.03
21T	Rick Cerone	.05	.03
22T	Ron Cey	.05	.03
23T	John Christensen	.08	.05
24T	Dave Cone (R)	1.50	.90
25T	Chuck Crim (R)	.07	.04
26T	Storm Davis	.07	.04
27T	Andre Dawson	.35	.20
28T	Rick Dempsey	.05	.03
29T	Doug Drabek	.30	.18
30T	Mike Dunne	.08	.05
31T	Dennis Eckersley	.35	.20
32T	Lee Elia	.05	.03
33T	Brian Fisher	.05	.03
34T	Terry Francona	.05	.03
35T	Willie Fraser (R)	.07	.04
36T	Billy Gardner	.05	.03
37T	Ken Gerhart (R)	.07	.04
38T	Danny Gladden	.10	.06
39T	Jim Gott	.08	.04
40T	Cecilio Guante	.05	.03
41T	Albert Hall	.05	.03
42T	Terry Harper	.05	.03
43T	Mickey Hatcher	.05	.03
44T	Brad Havens	.05	.03
45T	Neal Heaton	.05	.03
46T	Mike Henneman (R)	.25	.15
47T	Donnie Hill	.05	.03
48T	Guy Hoffman	.05	.03
49T	Brian Holton (R)	.12	.07
50T	Charles Hudson	.05	.03
51T	Danny Jackson (R)	.25	.15
52T	Reggie Jackson	.50	.30
53T	Chris James (R)	.12	.07
54T	Dion James	.05	.03
55T	Stan Jefferson (R)	.08	.05
56T	Joe Johnson (R)	.07	.04
57T	Terry Kennedy	.05	.03
58T	Mike Kingery	.08	.05
59T	Ray Knight	.10	.06
60T	Gene Larkin (R)	.15	.10
61T	Mike LaValliere	.10	.06
62T	Jack Lazorko	.05	.03
63T	Terry Leach	.05	.03
64T	Tim Leary	.10	.06
65T	Jim Lindeman (R)	.10	.06
66T	Steve Lombardozzi (R)	.15	.10
67T	Bill Long (R)	.12	.07
68T	Barry Lyons (R)	.12	.07
69T	Shane Mack	.60	.35
70T	Greg Maddux (R)	3.50	2.00
71T	Bill Madlock	.12	.07
72T	Joe Magrane (R)	.12	.07
73T	Dave Martinez (R)	.15	.10
74T	Fred McGriff (R)	4.00	2.50
75T	Mark McLemore (R)	.15	.10
76T	Kevin McReynolds	.12	.07

1988 Topps

This 792-card set features card fronts with large color photographs surrounded by a thin yellow line and a white border. Card backs are horizontal and printed in orange and black on a white card stock. Cards measure 2-1/2" by 3-1/2". Key subsets include Record Breakers, Turn Back The Clock, Team Leaders and All-Stars.

		MINT	NR/MT
Complete Set (792)		15.00	10.00
Commons		.05	.03

1	Vince Coleman (RB)	.08	.05
2	Don Mattingly (RB)	.15	.10
3	Mark McGwire (RB) (Er) (Spot behind left foot)	.50	.30
3b	Mark McGwire (RB) (Cor)	.20	.12
4a	Eddie Murray (RB) (Er) (No Record on front)	.35	.20
4b	Eddie Murray (RB) (Cor)	.12	.07
5	Joe & Phil Niekro (RB)	.12	.07
6	Nolan Ryan (RB)	.60	.35
7	Benito Santiago (RB)	.08	.05
8	Kevin Elster	.10	.06
9	Andy Hawkins	.05	.03
10	Ryne Sandberg	.75	.45
11	Mike Young	.05	.03
12	Bill Schroeder	.05	.03
13	Andres Thomas	.05	.03
14	Sparky Anderson	.08	.05
15	Chili Davis	.08	.05
16	Kirk McCaskill	.05	.03
17	Ron Oester	.05	.03
18a	Al Leiter (R) (Er)	.20	.12

77T	Dave Meads (R)	.10	.06
78T	Eddie Milner	.05	.03
79T	Greg Minton	.05	.03
80T	John Mitchell (R)	.08	.05
81T	Kevin Mitchell	.40	.25
82T	Charlie Moore	.05	.03
83T	Jeff Musselman (R)	.10	.06
84T	Gene Nelson	.05	.03
85T	Graig Nettles	.12	.07
86T	Al Newman	.05	.03
87T	Reid Nichols	.05	.03
88T	Tom Niedenfuer	.05	.03
89T	Joe Niekro	.08	.05
90T	Tom Nieto	.05	.03
91T	Matt Nokes (R)	.25	.15
92T	Dickie Noles	.05	.03
93T	Pat Pacillo	.05	.03
94T	Lance Parrish	.15	.10
95T	Tony Pena	.12	.07
96T	Luis Polonia (R)	.35	.20
97T	Randy Ready	.05	.03
98T	Jeff Reardon	.15	.10
99T	Gary Redus	.05	.03
100T	Jeff Reed	.05	.03
101T	Rick Rhoden	.05	.03
102T	Cal Ripken, Sr.	.08	.05
103T	Wally Ritchie	.08	.05
104T	Jeff Robinson	.10	.06
105T	Gary Roenicke	.05	.03
106T	Jerry Royster	.05	.03
107T	Mark Salas	.05	.03
108T	Luis Salazar	.05	.03
109T	Benny Santiago (R)	.35	.20
110T	Dave Schmidt	.05	.03
111T	Kevin Seitzer (R)	.20	.12
112T	John Shelby	.05	.03
113T	Steve Shields (R)	.05	.03
114T	John Smiley (R)	.40	.25
115T	Chris Speier	.05	.03
116T	Mike Stanley (R)	.35	.20
117T	Terry Steinbach (R)	.35	.20
118T	Les Straker (R)	.08	.05
119T	Jim Sundberg	.05	.03
120T	Danny Tartabull	.25	.15
121T	Tom Trebelhorn	.05	.03
122T	Dave Valle (R)	.12	.07
123T	Ed Vande Berg	.05	.03
124T	Andy Van Slyke	.25	.15
125T	Gary Ward	.05	.03
126T	Alan Wiggins	.05	.03
127T	Bill Wilkinson (R)	.07	.04
128T	Frank Williams	.05	.03
129T	Matt Williams (R)	3.00	1.75
130T	Jim Winn	.05	.03
131T	Matt Young	.05	.03
132T	Checklist 1T-132T	.06	.03

(Wrong Photo)		
18b Al Leiter (R) (Cor)	.10	.06
19 Mark Davidson (R)	.08	.05
20 Kevin Gross	.05	.03
21 Red Sox Leaders	.10	.06
22 Greg Swindell	.20	.12
23 Ken Landreaux	.05	.00
24 Jim Deshaies	.05	.03
25 Andres Galarraga	.15	.10
26 Mitch Williams	.10	.06
27 R.J. Reynolds	.05	.03
28 Jose Nunez (R)	.07	.04
29 Argenis Salazar	.05	.03
30 Sid Fernandez	.08	.05
31 Bruce Bochy	.05	.03
32 Mike Morgan	.05	.03
33 Rob Deer	.07	.04
34 Ricky Horton	.05	.03
35 Harold Baines	.08	.05
36 Jamie Moyer	.05	.03
37 Ed Romero	.05	.03
38 Jeff Calhoun	.05	.03
39 Gerald Perry	.05	.03
40 Orel Hershiser	.10	.06
41 Bob Melvin	.05	.03
42 Bill Landrum (R)	.08	.05
43 Dick Schofield	.05	.03
44 Lou Piniella	.08	.05
45 Kent Hrbek	.08	.05
46 Darnell Coles	.05	.03
47 Joaquin Andujar	.07	.04
48 Alan Ashby	.05	.03
49 Dave Clark	.05	.03
50 Hubie Brooks	.08	.05
51 Orioles Leaders (Eddie	.35	.20
Murray/Cal Ripken)		
52 Don Robinson	.05	.03
53 Curt Wilkerson	.05	.03
54 Jim Clancy	.05	.03
55 Phil Bradley	.05	.03
56 Ed Hearn	.05	.03
57 Tim Crews (R)	.08	.05
58 Dave Magadan	.10	.06
59 Danny Cox	.05	.03
60 Ricky Henderson	.35	.20
61 Mark Knudson (R)	.08	.05
62 Jeff Hamilton	.05	.03
63 Jimmy Jones	.05	.03
64 Ken Caminiti (R)	.35	.20
65 Leon Durham	.05	.03
66 Shane Rawley	.05	.03
67 Ken Oberkfell	.05	.03
68 Dave Dravecky	.07	.04
69 Mike Hart (R)	.05	.03
70 Roger Clemens	.60	.35
71 Gary Pettis	.07	.04
72 Dennis Eckersley	.20	.12
73 Randy Bush	.05	.03
74 Tom Lasorda	.08	.05
75 Joe Carter	.30	.18
76 Denny Martinez	.10	.06
77 Tom O'Malley	.05	.03
78 Dan Petry	.05	.03
79 Ernie Whitt	.05	.00
80 Mark Langston	.12	.07
81 Reds Leaders	.05	.03
82 Darrel Akerfelds (R)	.05	.02
83 Jose Oquendo	.05	.03
84 Cecilio Guante	.05	.03
85 Howard Johnson	.10	.06
86 Ron Karkovice	.05	.03
87 Mike Mason	.05	.03
88 Earnie Riles	.05	.03
89 Gary Thurman (R)	.10	.06
90 Dale Murphy	.12	.07
91 Joey Cora (R)	.12	.07
92 Len Matuszek	.05	.03
93 Bob Sebra	.05	.03
94 Chuck Jackson	.05	.03
95 Lance Parrish	.08	.05
96 Todd Benzinger (R)	.10	.06
97 Scott Garrelts	.07	.04
98 Rene Gonzales (R)	.12	.07
99 Chuck Finley	.12	.07
100 Jack Clark	.08	.05
101 Allan Anderson	.05	.03
102 Barry Larkin	.25	.15
103 Curt Young	.05	.03
104 Dick Williams	.05	.03
105 Jesse Orosco	.05	.03
106 Jim Walewander (R)	.05	.03
107 Scott Bailes	.05	.03
108 Steve Lyons	.05	.03
109 Joel Skinner	.05	.03
110 Teddy Higuera	.07	.04
111 Expos Leaders	.07	.04
112 Les Lancaster (R)	.10	.06
113 Kelly Gruber	.12	.07
114 Jeff Russell	.08	.05
115 Johnny Ray	.05	.03
116 Jerry Don Gleaton	.05	.03
117 James Steels (R)	.05	.03
118 Bob Welch	.08	.05
119 Robbie Wine (R)	.05	.03
120 Kirby Puckett	.70	.40
121 Checklist 1-132	.05	.03
122 Tony Bernazard	.05	.03
123 Tom Candiotti	.07	.04
124 Ray Knight	.07	.04
125 Bruce Hurst	.08	.05
126 Steve Jeltz	.05	.03
127 Jim Gott	.05	.03
128 Johnny Grubb	.05	.03
129 Greg Minton	.05	.03

130	Buddy Bell	.05	.03
131	Don Schulze	.05	.03
132	Donnie Hill	.05	.03
133	Greg Mathews	.05	.03
134	Chuck Tanner	.05	.03
135	Dennis Rasmussen	.05	.03
136	Brian Dayett	.05	.03
137	Chris Bosio	.07	.04
138	Mitch Webster	.05	.03
139	Jerry Browne	.08	.05
140	Jesse Barfield	.08	.05
141	Royals Leaders	.20	.12
	(George Brett/Bret Saberhagen)		
142	Andy Van Slyke	.15	.10
143	Mickey Tettleton	.10	.06
144	Don Gordon (R)	.05	.03
145	Bill Madlock	.08	.05
146	Donell Nixon (R)	.10	.06
147	Bill Buckner	.07	.04
148	Carmelo Martinez	.05	.03
149	Ken Howell	.05	.03
150	Eric Davis	.15	.10
151	Bob Knepper	.05	.03
152	Jody Reed (R)	.20	.12
153	John Habyan	.05	.03
154	Jeff Stone	.05	.03
155	Bruce Sutter	.08	.05
156	Gary Matthews	.05	.03
157	Atlee Hammaker	.05	.03
158	Tim Hulett	.05	.03
159	Brad Arnsberg (R)	.05	.03
160	Willie McGee	.10	.06
161	Bryn Smith	.05	.03
162	Mark McLemore	.05	.03
163	Dale Mohorcic	.05	.03
164	Dave Johnson	.07	.04
165	Robin Yount	.35	.20
166	Rick Rodriquez (R)	.08	.05
167	Rance Mulliniks	.05	.03
168	Barry Jones	.05	.03
169	Ross Jones (R)	.05	.03
170	Rich Gossage	.08	.05
171	Cubs Leaders	.08	.05
172	Lloyd McClendon (R)	.08	.05
173	Eric Plunk	.05	.03
174	Phil Garner	.07	.04
175	Kevin Bass	.07	.04
176	Jeff Reed	.05	.03
177	Frank Tanana	.07	.04
178	Dwayne Henry	.05	.03
179	Charlie Puleo	.05	.03
180	Terry Kennedy	.05	.03
181	Dave Cone	.35	.20
182	Ken Phelps	.05	.03
183	Tom Lawless	.05	.03
184	Ivan Calderon	.10	.06
185	Rick Rhoden	.05	.03
186	Rafael Palmeiro	.50	.30
187	Steve Kiefer	.05	.03
188	John Russell	.05	.03
189	Wes Gardner (R)	.00	.05
190	Candy Maldonado	.08	.05
191	John Cerutti	.05	.03
192	Devon White	.15	.10
193	Brian Fisher	.05	.03
194	Tom Kelly	.05	.03
195	Dan Quisenberry	.05	.03
196	Dave Engle	.05	.03
197	Lance McCullers	.05	.03
198	Franklin Stubbs	.05	.03
199	Dave Meads	.05	.03
200	Wade Boggs	.30	.18
201	Rangers Leaders	.07	.04
202	Glenn Hoffman	.05	.03
203	Fred Toliver	.05	.03
204	Paul O'Neill	.15	.10
205	Nelson Liriano (R)	.10	.06
206	Domingo Ramos	.05	.03
207	John Mitchell	.05	.03
208	Steve Lake	.05	.03
209	Richard Dotson	.05	.03
210	Willie Randolph	.08	.05
211	Frank DiPino	.05	.03
212	Greg Brock	.05	.03
213	Albert Bell	.05	.03
214	Dave Schmidt	.05	.03
215	Von Hayes	.05	.03
216	Jerry Reuss	.05	.03
217	Harry Spilman	.05	.03
218	Dan Schatzeder	.05	.03
219	Mike Stanley	.05	.03
220	Tom Henke	.08	.05
221	Rafael Belliard	.05	.03
222	Steve Farr	.05	.03
223	Stan Jefferson	.05	.03
224	Tom Trebelhorn	.05	.03
225	Mike Scioscia	.07	.04
226	Dave Lopes	.05	.03
227	Ed Correa	.05	.03
228	Wallace Johnson	.05	.03
229	Jeff Musselman	.05	.03
230	Pat Tabler	.05	.03
231	Pirates Leaders (Barry Bonds/Bobby Bonilla)	.25	.15
232	Bob James	.05	.03
233	Rafael Santana	.05	.03
234	Ken Dayley	.05	.03
235	Gary Ward	.05	.03
236	Ted Power	.05	.03
237	Mike Heath	.05	.03
238	Luis Polonia	.20	.12
239	Roy Smalley	.05	.03
240	Lee Smith	.15	.10
241	Damaso Garcia	.05	.03

242 Tom Niedenfuer	.05	.03
243 Mike Ryal	.05	.03
244 Jeff Robinson	.05	.03
245 Rich Gedman	.05	.03
246 Mike Campbell	.05	.03
247 Thad Bosley	.05	.03
248 Storm Davis	.05	.03
249 Mike Marshall	.05	.03
250 Nolan Ryan	1.00	.70
251 Tom Foley	.05	.03
252 Bob Brower	.05	.03
253 Checklist 133-264	.05	.03
254 Lee Elia	.05	.03
255 Mookie Wilson	.08	.05
256 Ken Schrom	.05	.03
257 Jerry Royster	.05	.03
258 Ed Nunez	.05	.03
259 Ron Kittle	.05	.03
260 Vince Coleman	.10	.06
261 Giants Leaders	.12	.07
262 Drew Hall	.05	.03
263 Glenn Braggs	.05	.03
264 Les Straker	.05	.03
265 Bo Diaz	.05	.03
266 Paul Assenmacher	.05	.03
267 Billy Bean (R)	.07	.04
268 Bruce Ruffin	.05	.03
269 Ellis Burks	.25	.15
270 Mike Witt	.05	.03
271 Ken Gerhart	.05	.03
272 Steve Ontiveros	.05	.03
273 Garth Iorg	.05	.03
274 Junior Ortiz	.05	.03
275 Kevin Seitzer	.10	.06
276 Luis Salazar	.05	.03
277 Alejandro Pena	.05	.03
278 Jose Cruz	.07	.04
279 Randy St. Claire	.05	.03
280 Pete Incaviglia	.08	.05
281 Jerry Hairston	.05	.03
282 Pat Perry	.05	.03
283 Phil Lombardi	.05	.03
284 Larry Bowa	.05	.03
285 Jim Presley	.05	.03
286 Chuck Crim	.05	.03
287 Manny Trillo	.05	.03
288 Pat Pacillo	.05	.03
289 Dave Bergman	.05	.03
290 Tony Fernandez	.08	.05
291 Astros Leaders	.07	.04
292 Carney Lansford	.07	.04
293 Doug Jones (R)	.20	.12
294 Al Pedrique (R)	.07	.04
295 Bert Blyleven	.12	.07
296 Floyd Rayford	.05	.03
297 Zane Smith	.07	.04
298 Milt Thompson	.05	.03

299 Steve Crawford	.05	.03
300 Don Mattingly	.35	.20
301 Bud Black	.08	.05
302 Jose Uribe	.07	.04
303 Eric Show	.05	.03
304 George Hendrick	.05	.03
305 Steve Sax	.12	.07
306 Billy Hatcher	.05	.03
307 Mike Trujillo	.05	.03
308 Lee Mazilli	.05	.03
309 Bill Long	.05	.03
310 Tom Herr	.05	.03
311 Scott Sanderson	.05	.03
312 Joey Meyer	.05	.03
313 Bob McClure	.05	.03
314 Jimy Williams	.05	.03
315 Dave Parker	.08	.05
316 Jose Rijo	.10	.06
317 Tom Nieto	.05	.03
318 Mel Hall	.08	.05
319 Mike Loynd	.05	.03
320 Alan Trammell	.15	.10
321 White Sox Leaders	.10	.06
322 Vicente Palacios (R)	.08	.05
323 Rick Leach	.05	.03
324 Danny Jackson	.08	.05
325 Glenn Hubbard	.05	.03
326 Al Nipper	.05	.03
327 Larry Sheets	.05	.03
328 Greg Cadaret (R)	.08	.05
329 Chris Speier	.05	.03
330 Eddie Whitson	.05	.03
331 Brian Downing	.05	.03
332 Jerry Reed	.05	.03
333 Wally Backman	.05	.03
334 Dave LaPoint	.05	.03
335 Claudell Washington	.05	.03
336 Ed Lynch	.05	.03
337 Jim Gantner	.05	.03
338 Brian Holton	.08	.05
339 Kurt Stillwell	.07	.04
340 Jack Morris	.15	.10
341 Carmen Castillo	.05	.03
342 Larry Andersen	.05	.03
343 Greg Gagne	.07	.04
344 Tony LaRussa	.08	.05
345 Scott Fletcher	.05	.03
346 Vance Law	.05	.03
347 Joe Johnson	.05	.03
348 Jim Eisenreich	.07	.04
349 Bob Walk	.05	.03
350 Will Clark	.50	.30
351 Cardinals Leaders	.08	.05
352 Billy Ripken (R)	.10	.06
353 Ed Olwine	.05	.03
354 Marc Sullivan	.05	.03
355 Roger McDowell	.05	.03

356	Luis Aguayo	.05	.03
357	Floyd Bannister	.05	.03
358	Rey Quinones	.05	.03
359	Tim Stoddard	.05	.03
360	Tony Gwynn	.35	.20
361	Greg Maddux	1.00	.60
362	Juan Castillo	.05	.03
363	Willie Fraser	.05	.03
364	Nick Esasky	.05	.03
365	Floyd Youmans	.05	.03
366	Chet Lemon	.05	.03
367	Tim Leary	.07	.04
368	Gerald Young (R)	.10	.06
369	Greg Harris	.05	.03
370	Jose Canseco	.50	.30
371	Joe Hesketh	.05	.03
372	Matt Williams	1.25	.80
373	Checklist 265-396	.05	.03
374	Doc Edwards	.05	.03
375	Tom Brunansky	.08	.05
376	Bill Wilkinson	.05	.03
377	Sam Horn	.10	.06
378	Todd Frohwirth (R)	.07	.04
379	Rafael Ramirez	.05	.03
380	Joe Magrane	.10	.06
381	Angels Leaders	.08	.05
382	Keith Miller (R)	.12	.07
383	Eric Bell	.05	.03
384	Neil Allen	.05	.03
385	Carlton Fisk	.25	.15
386	Don Mattingly AS	.15	.10
387	Willie Randolph AS	.08	.05
388	Wade Boggs AS	.15	.10
389	Alan Trammell AS	.10	.06
390	George Bell AS	.10	.06
391	Kirby Puckett AS	.25	.15
392	Dave Winfield AS	.20	.12
393	Matt Nokes AS	.08	.05
394	Roger Clemens AS	.25	.15
395	Jimmy Key AS	.08	.05
396	Tom Henke AS	.08	.05
397	Jack Clark AS	.08	.05
398	Juan Samuel AS	.05	.03
399	Tim Wallach AS	.08	.05
400	Ozzie Smith AS	.12	.07
401	Andre Dawson AS	.12	.07
402	Tony Gwynn AS	.15	.10
403	Tim Raines AS	.08	.05
404	Benny Santiago AS	.08	.05
405	Dwight Gooden AS	.12	.07
406	Shane Rawley AS	.05	.03
407	Steve Bedrosian AS	.07	.04
408	Dion James	.05	.03
409	Joel McKeon	.05	.03
410	Tony Pena	.07	.04
411	Wayne Tolleson	.05	.03
412	Randy Myers	.10	.06
413	John Christensen	.05	.03
414	John McNamara	.05	.03
415	Don Carman	.05	.03
416	Keith Moreland	.05	.03
417	Mark Ciardi (R)	.05	.03
418	Joel Youngblood	.05	.03
419	Scott McGregor	.05	.03
420	Wally Joyner	.15	.10
421	Ed Vande Berg	.05	.03
422	Dave Concepcion	.08	.05
423	John Smiley	.30	.18
424	Dwayne Murphy	.05	.03
425	Jeff Reardon	.20	.12
426	Randy Ready	.05	.03
427	Paul Kilgus (R)	.08	.05
428	John Shelby	.05	.03
429	Tigers Leaders	.08	.05
430	Glenn Davis	.10	.06
431	Casey Candaele	.05	.03
432	Mike Moore	.07	.04
433	Bill Pecota	.08	.05
434	Rick Aguilera	.08	.05
435	Mike Pagliarulo	.05	.03
436	Mike Bielecki	.07	.04
437	Fred Manrique (R)	.07	.04
438	Rob Ducey (R)	.08	.05
439	Dave Martinez	.08	.05
440	Steve Bedrosian	.07	.04
441	Rick Manning	.05	.03
442	Tom Bolton (R)	.12	.07
443	Ken Griffey	.08	.05
444	Cal Ripken Sr.	.08	.05
445	Mike Krukow	.05	.03
446	Doug DeCinces	.05	.03
447	Jeff Montgomery (R)	.50	.30
448	Mike Davis	.05	.03
449	Jeff Robinson	.05	.03
450	Barry Bonds	1.00	.60
451	Keith Atherton	.05	.03
452	Willie Wilson	.07	.04
453	Dennis Powell	.05	.03
454	Marvell Wynne	.05	.03
455	Shawn Hillegas (R)	.12	.07
456	Dave Anderson	.05	.03
457	Terry Leach	.05	.03
458	Ron Hassey	.05	.03
459	Yankees Leaders	.10	.06
460	Ozzie Smith	.25	.15
461	Danny Darwin	.05	.03
462	Don Slaught	.05	.03
463	Fred McGriff	.80	.50
464	Jay Tibbs	.05	.03
465	Paul Molitor	.30	.18
466	Jerry Mumphrey	.05	.03
467	Dan Aase	.05	.03
468	Darren Dalton	.20	.12
469	Jeff Dedmon	.05	.03

470	Dwight Evans	.10	.06	527	Steve Henderson	.05	.03
471	Donnie Moore	.05	.03	528	Checklist 397-528	.05	.03
472	Robby Thompson	.08	.05	529	Tim Burke	.05	.03
473	Joe Niekro	.05	.03	530	Gary Carter	.12	.07
474	Tom Brookens	.05	.03	531	Rich Yett	.05	.03
475	Pete Rose	.20	.12	532	Mike Kingery	.05	.03
476	Dave Stewart	.10	.06	533	John Farrell (R)	.08	.05
477	Jamie Quirk	.05	.03	534	John Wathan	.05	.03
478	Sid Bream	.05	.03	535	Ron Guidry	.10	.06
479	Brett Butler	.12	.07	536	John Morris	.05	.03
480	Dwight Gooden	.15	.10	537	Steve Buchele	.08	.05
481	Mariano Duncan	.05	.03	538	Bill Wegman	.05	.03
482	Mark Davis	.07	.04	539	Mike LaValliere	.07	.04
483	Rod Booker (R)	.05	.03	540	Bret Saberhagen	.15	.10
484	Pat Clements	.05	.03	541	Juan Beniquez	.05	.03
485	Harold Reynolds	.07	.04	542	Paul Noce (R)	.07	.04
486	Pat Keedy (R)	.05	.03	543	Kent Tekulve	.05	.03
487	Jim Pankovits	.05	.03	544	Jim Traber	.05	.03
488	Andy McGaffigan	.05	.03	545	Don Baylor	.08	.05
489	Dodgers Leaders	.07	.04	546	John Candelaria	.05	.03
490	Larry Parrish	.05	.03	547	Felix Fermin (R)	.07	.04
491	B.J. Surhoff	.07	.04	548	Shane Mack	.20	.12
492	Doyle Alexander	.05	.03	549	Braves Leaders	.10	.06
493	Mike Greenwell	.12	.07	550	Pedro Guerrero	.08	.05
494	Wally Ritchie	.05	.03	551	Terry Steinbach	.08	.05
495	Eddie Murray	.25	.15	552	Mark Thurmond	.05	.03
496	Guy Hoffman	.05	.03	553	Tracy Jones	.05	.03
497	Kevin Mitchell	.12	.07	554	Mike Smithson	.05	.03
498	Bob Boone	.08	.05	555	Brook Jacoby	.05	.03
499	Eric King	.05	.03	556	Stan Clarke	.05	.03
500	Andre Dawson	.25	.15	557	Craig Reynolds	.05	.03
501	Tim Birtsas	.07	.04	558	Bob Ojeda	.05	.03
502	Danny Gladden	.05	.03	559	Ken Williams (R)	.07	.04
503	Junior Noboa (R)	.08	.05	560	Tim Wallach	.10	.06
504	Bob Rodgers	.05	.03	561	Rick Cerone	.05	.03
505	Willie Upshaw	.05	.03	562	Jim Lindeman	.05	.03
506	John Cangelosi	.05	.03	563	Jose Guzman	.05	.03
507	Mark Gubicza	.10	.06	564	Frank Lucchesi	.05	.03
508	Tim Teufel	.05	.03	565	Lloyd Moseby	.05	.03
509	Bill Dawley	.05	.03	566	Charlie O'Brien (R)	.08	.05
510	Dave Winfield	.35	.20	567	Mike Diaz	.05	.03
511	Joel Davis	.05	.03	568	Chris Brown	.05	.03
512	Alex Trevino	.05	.03	569	Charlie Leibrandt	.05	.03
513	Tim Flannery	.05	.03	570	Jeffrey Leonard	.07	.04
514	Pat Sherdian	.05	.03	571	Mark Williamson (R)	.10	.06
515	Juan Nieves	.07	.04	572	Chris James	.05	.03
516	Jim Sundberg	.05	.03	573	Bob Stanley	.05	.03
517	Ron Robinson	.05	.03	574	Graig Nettles	.08	.05
518	Greg Gross	.05	.03	575	Don Sutton	.12	.07
519	Mariners Leaders	.07	.04	576	Tommy Hinzo (R)	.05	.03
520	Dave Smith	.05	.03	577	Tom Browning	.08	.05
521	Jim Dwyer	.05	.03	578	Gary Gaetti	.05	.03
522	Bob Patterson (R)	.07	.04	579	Mets Leaders	.08	.05
523	Gary Roenicke	.05	.03	580	Mark McGwire	.50	.30
524	Gary Lucas	.05	.03	581	Tito Landrum	.05	.03
525	Marty Barrett	.07	.04	582	Mike Henneman	.08	.05
526	Juan Berenguer	.05	.03	583	Dave Valle	.05	.03

584 Steve Trout	.05	.03
585 Ozzie Guillen	.08	.05
586 Bob Forsch	.05	.03
587 Terry Puhl	.05	.03
588 Jeff Parrett (R)	.10	.06
589 Geno Petralli	.05	.03
590 George Bell	.10	.06
591 Doug Drabek	.15	.10
592 Dale Sveum	.07	.04
593 Bob Tewksbury	.10	.06
594 Bobby Valentine	.05	.03
595 Frank White	.07	.04
596 John Kruk	.15	.10
597 Gene Garber	.05	.03
598 Lee Lacy	.05	.03
599 Calvin Schiraldi	.05	.03
600 Mike Schmidt	.50	.30
601 Jack Lazorko	.05	.03
602 Mike Aldrete	.05	.03
603 Rob Murphy	.05	.03
604 Chris Bando	.05	.03
605 Kirk Gibson	.08	.05
606 Moose Haas	.05	.03
607 Mickey Hatcher	.05	.03
608 Charlie Kerfeld	.05	.03
609 Twins Leaders	.08	.05
610 Keith Hernandez	.08	.05
611 Tommy John	.08	.05
612 Curt Ford	.05	.03
613 Bobby Thigpen	.10	.06
614 Herm Winningham	.05	.03
615 Jody Davis	.05	.03
616 Jay Aldrich	.05	.03
617 Oddibe McDowell	.05	.03
618 Cecil Fielder	.40	.25
619 Mike Dunne	.05	.03
620 Cory Snyder	.07	.04
621 Gene Nelson	.05	.03
622 Kal Daniels	.07	.04
623 Mike Flanagan	.07	.04
624 Jim Leyland	.08	.05
625 Frank Viola	.08	.05
626 Glenn Wilson	.05	.03
627 Joe Boever (R)	.08	.05
628 Dave Henderson	.07	.04
629 Kelly Downs	.07	.04
630 Darrell Evans	.08	.05
631 Jack Howell	.05	.03
632 Steve Shields	.05	.03
633 Barry Lyons	.05	.03
634 Jose DeLeon	.05	.03
635 Terry Pendleton	.20	.12
636 Charles Hudson	.05	.03
637 Jay Bell (R)	.60	.35
638 Steve Balboni	.05	.03
639 Brewers Leaders	.07	.04
640 Garry Templeton	.07	.04

641 Rick Honeycutt	.05	.03
642 Bob Dernier	.05	.03
643 Rocky Childress (R)	.08	.05
644 Terry McGriff	.05	.03
645 Matt Nokes	.10	.06
646 Checklist 529-660	.05	.03
647 Pascual Perez	.05	.03
648 Al Newman	.05	.03
649 DeWayne Buice	.05	.03
650 Cal Ripken	.60	.35
651 Mike Jackson (R)	.12	.07
652 Bruce Benedict	.05	.03
653 Jeff Sellers	.05	.03
654 Roger Craig	.05	.03
655 Len Dykstra	.25	.15
656 Lee Guetterman	.05	.03
657 Gary Redus	.05	.03
658 Tim Conroy	.05	.03
659 Bobby Meacham	.05	.03
660 Rick Reuschel	.05	.03
661 Nolan Ryan (Clock)	.50	.30
662 Jim Rice (Clock)	.08	.05
663 Ron Blomberg (Clock)	.05	.03
664 Bob Gibson (Clock)	.15	.10
665 Stan Musial (Clock)	.15	.10
666 Mario Soto	.05	.03
667 Luis Quinones	.05	.03
668 Walt Terrell	.05	.03
669 Phillies Leaders	.07	.04
670 Dan Plesac	.07	.04
671 Tim Laudner	.05	.03
672 John Davis (R)	.07	.04
673 Tony Phillips	.07	.04
674 Mike Fitzgerald	.05	.03
675 Jim Rice	.08	.05
676 Ken Dixon	.05	.03
677 Eddie Milner	.05	.03
678 Jim Acker	.05	.03
679 Darrell Miller	.05	.03
680 Charlie Hough	.07	.04
681 Bobby Bonilla	.20	.12
682 Jimmy Key	.07	.04
683 Julio Franco	.10	.06
684 Hal Lanier	.05	.03
685 Ron Darling	.05	.03
686 Terry Francona	.05	.03
687 Mickey Brantley	.05	.03
688 Jim Winn	.05	.03
689 Tom Pagnozzi (R)	.25	.15
690 Jay Howell	.05	.03
691 Dan Pasqua	.05	.03
692 Mike Birkbeck	.05	.03
693 Benny Santiago	.15	.10
694 Eric Nolte (R)	.08	.05
695 Shawon Dunston	.12	.07
696 Duane Ward	.05	.03
697 Steve Lombardozzi	.07	.04

698	Brad Havens	.05	.03
699	Padres Leaders	.15	.10
700	George Brett	.40	.25
701	Sammy Stewart	.05	.03
702	Mike Gallego	.05	.03
703	Bob Brenly	.05	.03
704	Dennis Boyd	.05	.03
705	Juan Samuel	.05	.03
706	Rick Mahler	.05	.03
707	Fred Lynn	.07	.04
708	Gus Polidor	.05	.03
709	George Frazier	.05	.03
710	Darryl Strawberry	.25	.15
711	Bill Gullickson	.07	.04
712	John Moses	.05	.03
713	Willie Hernandez	.05	.03
714	Jim Fregosi	.05	.03
715	Todd Worrell	.07	.04
716	Lenn Sakata	.05	.03
717	Jay Baller	.05	.03
718	Mike Felder	.05	.03
719	Denny Walling	.05	.03
720	Tim Raines	.08	.05
721	Pete O'Brien	.07	.04
722	Manny Lee	.05	.03
723	Bob Kipper	.05	.03
724	Danny Tartabull	.20	.12
725	Mike Boddicker	.05	.03
726	Alfredo Griffin	.05	.03
727	Greg Booker	.05	.03
728	Andy Allanson	.05	.03
729	Blue Jays Leaders	.12	.07
730	John Franco	.05	.03
731	Rick Schu	.05	.03
732	Dave Palmer	.05	.03
733	Spike Owen	.05	.03
734	Craig Lefferts	.05	.03
735	Kevin McReynolds	.08	.05
736	Matt Young	.05	.03
737	Butch Wynegar	.05	.03
738	Scott Bankhead	.05	.03
739	Daryl Boston	.05	.03
740	Rick Sutcliffe	.08	.05
741	Mike Easler	.05	.03
742	Mark Clear	.05	.03
743	Larry Herndon	.05	.03
744	Whitey Herzog	.08	.05
745	Bill Doran	.05	.03
746	Gene Larkin	.10	.06
747	Bobby Witt	.12	.07
748	Reid Nichols	.05	.03
749	Mark Eichhorn	.05	.03
750	Bo Jackson	.30	.18
751	Jim Morrison	.05	.03
752	Mark Grant	.05	.03
753	Danny Heep	.05	.03
754	Mike LaCoss	.05	.03

755	Ozzie Virgil	.05	.03
756	Mike Maddux	.05	.03
757	John Marzano	.05	.03
758	Eddie Williams (R)	.05	.03
759	A's Leaders (Canseco, McGwire)	.30	.18
700	Mike Scott	.07	.04
761	Tony Armas	.05	.03
762	Scott Bradley	.05	.03
763	Doug Sisk	.05	.03
764	Greg Walker	.05	.03
765	Neal Heaton	.05	.03
766	Henry Cotto	.05	.03
767	Jose Lind (R)	.20	.12
768	Dickie Noles	.05	.03
769	Cecil Cooper	.07	.04
770	Lou Whitaker	.08	.05
771	Ruben Sierra	.35	.20
772	Sal Butera	.05	.03
773	Frank Williams	.05	.03
774	Gene Mauch	.05	.03
775	Dave Stieb	.10	.06
776	Checklisst 661-792	.05	.03
777	Lonnie Smith	.07	.04
778a	Keith Comstock (White Team Letters)	2.00	1.25
778b	Keith Comstock (Blue Letters)	.05	.03
779	Tom Glavine (R)	3.00	1.75
780	Fernando Valenzuela	.08	.05
781	Keith Hughes (R)	.07	.04
782	Jeff Ballard (R)	.08	.05
783	Ron Roenicke	.05	.03
784	Joe Sambito	.05	.03
785	Alvin Davis	.05	.03
786	Joe Price	.05	.03
787	Bill Almon	.05	.03
788	Ray Searage	.05	.03
789	Indians Leaders	.12	.07
790	Dave Righetti	.08	.05
791	Ted Simmons	.08	.05
792	John Tudor	.08	.05

1988 Topps Traded

The cards in this 132-card set are identical to Topps regular 1988 edition. Measuring 2-1/2" by 3-1/2" teh cards feature players traded during the season and up and coming rookie prospects. The set also includes members of the 1988 U.S. Olympic Team (USA). Players are listed in alphabetical order and card numbers carry the "T" designation.

	MINT	NR/MT
Complete Set (132)	28.00	18.00
Commons	.06	.03

		MINT	NR/MT
1T	Jim Abbott (R)(USA)	6.50	3.75
2T	Juan Agosto	.06	.03
3T	Luis Alicea (R)	.15	.10
4T	Roberto Alomar (R)	9.00	5.50
5T	Brady Anderson (R)	1.25	.80
6T	Jack Armstrong (R)	.20	.12
7T	Don August	.06	.03
8T	Floyd Bannister	.06	.03
9T	Bret Barberie (R) (USA)	.40	.25
10T	Jose Bautista (R)	.07	.04
11T	Don Baylor	.10	.06
12T	Tim Belcher	.15	.10
13T	Buddy Bell	.06	.03
14T	Andy Benes (R)(USA)	3.00	2.00
15T	Damon Berryhill (R)	.15	.10
16T	Bud Black	.06	.03
17T	Pat Borders (R)	.40	.25
18T	Phil Bradley	.06	.03
19T	Jeff Branson (R)(USA)	.20	.12
20T	Tom Brunansky	.10	.06
21T	Jay Buhner (R)	1.00	.60
22T	Brett Butler	.12	.07
23T	Jim Campanis (R)(USA)	.20	.12
24T	Sil Campusano	.08	.05
25T	John Candelaria	.06	.03
26T	Jose Cecena (R)	.07	.04
27T	Rick Cerone	.06	.03
28T	Jack Clark	.08	.05
29T	Kevin Coffman (R)	.08	.05
30T	Pat Combs (R)(USA)	.20	.12
31T	Henry Cotto	.06	.03
32T	Chili Davis	.10	.06
33T	Mike Davis	.06	.03
34T	Jose DeLeon	.06	.03
35T	Richard Dotson	.06	.03
36T	Cecil Espy (R)	.15	.10
37T	Tom Filer	.06	.03
38T	Mike Fiore (R)(USA)	.10	.06
39T	Ron Gant (R)	3.00	2.00
40T	Kirk Gibson	.10	.06
41T	Rich Gossage	.12	.07
42T	Mark Grace (R)	3.00	2.00
43T	Alfredo Griffin	.06	.03
44T	Ty Griffin (R)(USA)	.10	.06
45T	Bryan Harvey (R)	1.75	1.00
46T	Ron Hassey	.06	.03
47T	Ray Hayward (R)	.06	.03
48T	Dave Henderson	.10	.06
49T	Tom Herr	.08	.05
50T	Bob Horner	.10	.06
51T	Ricky Horton	.06	.03
52T	Jay Howell	.06	.03
53T	Glenn Hubbard	.06	.03
54T	Jeff Innis (R)	.12	.07
55T	Danny Jackson	.08	.05
56T	Darrin Jackson (R)	.35	.20
57T	Roberto Kelly (R)	1.25	.80
58T	Ron Kittle	.08	.05
59T	Ray Knight	.08	.05
60T	Vance Law	.06	.03
61T	Jeffrey Leonard	.08	.05
62T	Mike Macfarlane (R)	.35	.20
63T	Scotti Madison (R)	.08	.05
64T	Kirt Manwaring (R)	.12	.07
65T	Mark Marquess (USA)	.06	.03
66T	Tino Martinez (R) (USA)	1.00	.60
67T	Billy Masse (R)(USA)	.12	.07
68T	Jack McDowell (R)	3.50	2.50
69T	Jack McKeon	.06	.03
70T	Larry McWilliams	.06	.03
71T	Mickey Morandini (R) (USA)	.60	.35
72T	Keith Moreland	.06	.03
73T	Mike Morgan	.08	.05
74T	Charles Nagy (R)(USA)	1.00	.60
75T	Al Nipper	.06	.03
76T	Russ Nixon	.06	.03
77T	Jesse Orosco	.06	.03
78T	Joe Orsulak	.06	.03
79T	Dave Palmer	.06	.03
80T	Mark Parent	.08	.05
81T	Dave Parker	.10	.06

82T	Dan Pasqua	.08	.05
83T	Melido Perez (R)	.40	.25
84T	Steve Peters (R)	.10	.06
85T	Dan Petry	.06	.03
86T	Gary Pettis	.06	.03
87T	Jeff Pico	.12	.07
88T	Jim Poole (H)(USA)	.15	.10
89T	Ted Power	.06	.03
90T	Rafael Ramirez	.06	.03
91T	Dennis Rasmussen	.06	.03
92T	Jose Rijo	.15	.10
93T	Earnie Riles	.06	.03
94T	Luis Rivera	.06	.03
95T	Doug Robbins (R)(USA)	.10	.06
96T	Frank Robinson	.10	.06
97T	Cookie Rojas	.06	.03
98T	Chris Sabo (R)	.75	.45
99T	Mark Salas	.06	.03
100T	Luis Salazar	.06	.03
101T	Rafael Santana	.06	.03
102T	Nelson Santovenia (R)	.10	.06
103T	Mackey Sasser (R)	.12	.07
104T	Calvin Schiraldi	.06	.03
105T	Mike Schooler (R)	.12	.07
106T	Scott Servais (R)(USA)	.20	.12
107T	Dave Silvestri (R) (USA)	.20	.12
108T	Don Slaught	.06	.03
109T	Joe Slusarski (R)(USA)	.25	.15
110T	Lee Smith	.20	.12
111T	Pete Smith (R)	.35	.20
112T	Jim Snyder	.06	.03
113T	Ed Sprague (R)(USA)	1.25	.80
114T	Pete Stanicek (R)	.10	.06
115T	Kurt Stillwell	.08	.05
116T	Todd Stottlemyre (R)	.40	.25
117T	Bill Swift	.15	.10
118T	Pat Tabler	.06	.03
119T	Scott Terry	.06	.03
120T	Mickey Tettleton	.15	.10
121T	Dickie Thon	.06	.03
122T	Jeff Treadway	.06	.03
123T	Willie Upshaw	.06	.03
124T	Robin Ventura (R) (USA)	10.00	6.50
125T	Ron Washington	.06	.03
126T	Walt Weiss (R)	.25	.15
127T	Bob Welch	.12	.07
128T	David Wells (R)	.20	.12
129T	Glenn Wilson	.06	.03
130T	Ted Wood (R)(USA)	.15	.10
131T	Dom Zimmer	.06	.03
132T	Checklist 1T-132T	.06	.03

1989 Topps

This 792-card set features standard size cards measuring 2-1/2" by 3-1/2". Card fronts consist of fll color photos with the players name listed in a banner below the photo. Card backs are horizontal and printed in light red and black. Key subsets include Record Breakers, All-Stars, Future Stars, Turn Back The Clock and First Round Draft Picks.

		MINT	NR/MT
Complete Set (792)		18.00	12.00
Commons		.05	.03

1	George Bell (RB)	.08	.05
2	Wade Boggs (RB)	.10	.06
3	Gary Carter (RB)	.08	.05
4	Andre Dawson (RB)	.08	.05
5	Orel Hershiser (RB)	.08	.05
6	Doug Jones (RB)	.05	.03
7	Kevin McReynolds (RB)	.07	.04
8	Dave Eiland (R)	.10	.06
9	Tim Teufel	.05	.03
10	Andre Dawson	.20	.12
11	Bruce Sutter	.08	.05
12	Dale Sveum	.05	.03
13	Doug Sisk	.05	.03
14	Tom Kelly	.05	.03
15	Robby Thompson	.12	.07
16	Ron Robinson	.05	.03
17	Brian Downing	.07	.04
18	Rick Rhoden	.05	.03
19	Greg Gagne	.05	.03
20	Steve Bedrosian	.07	.04
21	White Sox Leaders	.05	.03
22	Tim Crews	.05	.03
23	Mike Fitzgerald	.05	.03
24	Larry Andersen	.05	.03
25	Frank White	.05	.03
26	Dale Mohorcic	.05	.03
27	Orestes Destrade (R)	.25	.15

28	Mike Moore	.07	.04
29	Kelly Gruber	.08	.05
30	Dwight Gooden	.15	.10
31	Terry Francona	.05	.03
32	Dennis Rasmussen	.05	.03
33	B.J. Surhoff	.05	.03
34	Ken Williams	.05	.03
35	John Tudor	.05	.03
36	Mitch Webster	.05	.03
37	Bob Stanley	.05	.03
38	Paul Runge	.05	.03
39	Mike Maddux	.05	.03
40	Steve Sax	.08	.05
41	Terry Mulholland	.07	.04
42	Jim Eppard	.05	.03
43	Guillermo Hernandez	.05	.03
44	Jim Snyder	.05	.03
45	Kal Daniels	.07	.04
46	Mark Portugal	.05	.03
47	Carney Lansford	.08	.05
48	Tim Burke	.05	.03
49	Craig Biggio	.40	.25
50	George Bell	.12	.07
51	Angels Leaders	.05	.03
52	Bob Brenly	.05	.03
53	Reuben Sierra	.30	.18
54	Steve Trout	.05	.03
55	Julio Franco	.08	.05
56	Pat Tabler	.05	.03
57	Alejandro Pena	.07	.04
58	Lee Mazzilli	.05	.03
59	Mark Davis	.05	.03
60	Tom Brunansky	.07	.04
61	Neil Allen	.05	.03
62	Alfredo Griffin	.05	.03
63	Mark Clear	.05	.03
64	Alex Trevino	.05	.03
65	Rick Reuschel	.05	.03
66	Manny Trillo	.05	.03
67	Dave Palmer	.05	.03
68	Darrell Miller	.05	.03
69	Jeff Ballard	.05	.03
70	Mark McGwire	.40	.25
71	Mike Boddicker	.05	.03
72	John Moses	.05	.03
73	Pascual Perez	.05	.03
74	Nick Leyva	.05	.03
75	Tom Henke	.08	.05
76	Terry Blocker (R)	.08	.05
77	Doyle Alexander	.05	.03
78	Jim Sundberg	.05	.03
79	Scott Bankhead	.05	.03
80	Cory Snyder	.07	.04
81	Expos Leaders	.05	.03
82	Dave Leiper	.05	.03
83	Jeff Blauser	.12	.07
84	Bill Bene (#1 Pick)	.05	.03
85	Kevin McReynolds	.07	.04
86	Al Nipper	.05	.03
87	Larry Owen	.05	.03
88	Darryl Hamilton (R)	.30	.18
89	Dave LaPoint	.05	.03
90	Vince Coleman	.07	.04
91	Floyd Youmans	.05	.03
92	Jeff Kunkel	.05	.03
93	Ken Howell	.05	.03
94	Chris Speier	.05	.03
95	Gerald Young	.05	.03
96	Rick Cerone	.05	.03
97	Greg Mathews	.05	.03
98	Larry Sheets	.05	.03
99	Sherman Corbett (R)	.05	.03
100	Mike Schmidt	.50	.30
101	Les Straker	.05	.03
102	Mike Gallego	.05	.03
103	Tim Birtsas	.05	.03
104	Dallas Green	.05	.03
105	Ron Darling	.07	.04
106	Willie Upshaw	.05	.03
107	Jose DeLeon	.05	.03
108	Fred Manrique	.05	.03
109	Hipolito Pena (R)	.05	.03
110	Paul Molitor	.30	.18
111	Reds Leaders	.07	.04
112	Jim Presley	.05	.03
113	Lloyd Moseby	.05	.03
114	Bob Kipper	.05	.03
115	Jody Davis	.05	.03
116	Jeff Montgomery	.07	.04
117	Dave Anderson	.05	.03
118	Checklist 1-132	.05	.03
119	Terry Puhl	.05	.03
120	Frank Viola	.08	.05
121	Garry Templeton	.07	.04
122	Lance Johnson	.07	.04
123	Spike Owen	.05	.03
124	Jim Traber	.05	.03
125	Mike Krukow	.05	.03
126	Sid Bream	.05	.03
127	Walt Terrell	.05	.03
128	Milt Thompson	.05	.03
129	Terry Clark (R)	.07	.04
130	Gerald Perry	.05	.03
131	Dave Otto	.05	.03
132	Curt Ford	.05	.03
133	Bill Long	.05	.03
134	Don Zimmer	.05	.03
135	Jose Rijo	.12	.07
136	Joey Meyer	.05	.03
137	Geno Petralli	.05	.03
138	Wallace Johnson	.05	.03
139	Mike Flanagan	.07	.04
140	Shawon Dunston	.10	.06
141	Indians Leaders	.05	.03

142 Mike Diaz	.05	.03
143 Mike Campbell	.05	.03
144 Jay Bell	.08	.05
145 Dave Stewart	.10	.06
146 Gary Pettis	.05	.03
147 DeWayne Buice	.05	.03
148 Bill Pecota	.05	.03
149 Doug Dascenzo (R)	.10	.06
150 Fernando Valenzuela	.08	.05
151 Terry McGriff	.05	.03
152 Mark Thurmond	.05	.03
153 Jim Pankovits	.05	.03
154 Don Carman	.05	.03
155 Marty Barrett	.05	.03
156 Dave Gallagher (R)	.08	.05
157 Tom Glavine	.75	.45
158 Mike Aldrete	.05	.03
159 Pat Clements	.05	.03
160 Jeffrey Leonard	.07	.04
161 Gregg Olson (#1 Pick)	.35	.20
162 John Davis	.05	.03
163 Bob Forsch	.05	.03
164 Hal Lanier	.05	.03
165 Mike Dunne	.05	.03
166 Doug Jennings (R)	.08	.05
167 Steve Searcy (R)	.15	.10
168 Willie Wilson	.07	.04
169 Mike Jackson	.05	.03
170 Tony Fernandez	.08	.05
171 Braves Leaders	.05	.03
172 Frank Williams	.05	.03
173 Mel Hall	.08	.05
174 Todd Burns (R)	.12	.07
175 John Shelby	.05	.03
176 Jeff Parrett	.05	.03
177 Monty Fariss (#1 Pick)	.25	.15
178 Mark Grant	.05	.03
179 Ozzie Virgil	.05	.03
180 Mike Scott	.08	.05
181 Craig Worthington (R)	.07	.04
182 Bob McClure	.05	.03
183 Oddibe McDowell	.05	.03
184 John Costello	.05	.03
185 Claudell Washington	.05	.03
186 Pat Perry	.05	.03
187 Darren Daulton	.20	.12
188 Dennis Lamp	.05	.03
189 Kevin Mitchell	.12	.07
190 Mike Witt	.05	.03
191 Sil Campusano	.05	.03
192 Paul Mirabella	.05	.03
193 Sparky Anderson	.07	.04
194 Greg Harris (R)	.15	.10
195 Ozzie Guillen	.08	.05
196 Denny Walling	.05	.03
197 Neal Heaton	.05	.03
198 Danny Heep	.05	.03
199 Mike Schooler	.10	.06
200 George Brett	.35	.20
201 Blue Jays Leaders	.05	.03
202 Brad Moore (R)	.08	.05
203 Rob Ducey	.05	.03
204 Brad Havens	.05	.03
205 Dwight Evans	.12	.07
206 Roberto Alomar	1.00	.70
207 Terry Leach	.05	.03
208 Tom Pagnozzi	.08	.05
209 Jeff Bittiger (R)	.08	.05
210 Dale Murphy	.12	.07
211 Mike Pagliarulo	.05	.03
212 Scott Sanderson	.05	.03
213 Rene Gonzales	.08	.05
214 Charlie O'Brien	.05	.03
215 Kevin Gross	.05	.03
216 Jack Howell	.05	.03
217 Joe Price	.05	.03
218 Mike LaValliere	.05	.03
219 Jim Clancy	.05	.03
220 Gary Gaetti	.05	.03
221 Cecil Espy	.05	.03
222 Mark Lewis (#1 Pick)	.30	.18
223 Jay Buhner	.15	.10
224 Tony LaRussa	.07	.04
225 Ramon Martinez (R)	.50	.30
226 Bill Doran	.05	.03
227 John Farrell	.05	.03
228 Nelson Santovenia	.07	.04
229 Jimmy Key	.07	.04
230 Ozzie Smith	.20	.12
231 Padres Leaders	.15	.10
232 Ricky Horton	.05	.03
233 Gregg Jefferies (R)	.50	.30
234 Tom Browning	.08	.05
235 John Kruk	.15	.10
236 Charles Hudson	.05	.03
237 Glenn Hubbard	.05	.03
238 Eric King	.05	.03
239 Tim Laudner	.05	.03
240 Greg Maddux	.40	.25
241 Brett Butler	.10	.06
242 Ed Vande Berg	.05	.03
243 Bob Boone	.08	.05
244 Jim Acker	.05	.03
245 Jim Rice	.08	.05
246 Rey Quinones	.05	.03
247 Shawn Hillegas	.05	.03
248 Tony Phillips	.05	.03
249 Tim Leary	.05	.03
250 Cal Ripken	.60	.35
251 John Dopson (R)	.10	.06
252 Billy Hatcher	.05	.03
253 Jose Alvarez	.05	.03
254 Tom Lasorda	.07	.04
255 Ron Guidry	.08	.05

256 Benny Santiago	.10	.06
257 Rick Aguilera	.08	.05
258 Checklist 133-264	.05	.03
259 Larry McWilliams	.05	.03
260 Dave Winfield	.35	.20
261 Cardinals Leaders	.05	.03
262 Jeff Pico	.07	.04
263 Mike Felder	.05	.03
264 Rob Dibble	.20	.12
265 Kent Hrbek	.08	.05
266 Luis Aquino	.05	.03
267 Jeff Robinson	.05	.03
268 Keith Miller	.05	.03
269 Tom Bolton	.05	.03
270 Wally Joyner	.12	.07
271 Jay Tibbs	.05	.03
272 Ron Hassey	.05	.03
273 Jose Lind	.07	.04
274 Mark Eichhorn	.05	.03
275 Danny Tartabull	.15	.10
276 Paul Kilgus	.05	.03
277 Mike Davis	.05	.03
278 Andy McGaffigan	.05	.03
279 Scott Bradley	.05	.03
280 Bob Knepper	.05	.03
281 Gary Redus	.05	.03
282 Cris Carpenter (R)	.15	.10
283 Andy Allanson	.05	.03
284 Jim Leyland	.07	.04
285 John Candelaria	.05	.03
286 Darrin Jackson	.12	.07
287 Juan Nieves	.05	.03
288 Pat Sheridan	.05	.03
289 Ernie Whitt	.05	.03
290 John Franco	.05	.03
291 Mets Leaders	.12	.07
292 Jim Corsi (R)	.08	.05
293 Glenn Wilson	.05	.03
294 Juan Berenguer	.07	.04
295 Scott Flethcer	.05	.03
296 Ron Gant	.75	.45
297 Oswald Peraza (R)	.08	.05
298 Chris James	.05	.03
299 Steve Ellsworth (R)	.08	.05
300 Darryl Strawberry	.25	.15
301 Charlie Liebrandt	.05	.03
302 Gary Ward	.05	.03
303 Felix Fermin	.05	.03
304 Joel Youngblood	.05	.03
305 Dave Smith	.05	.03
306 Tracy Woodson	.05	.03
307 Lance McCullers	.05	.03
308 Ron Karkovice	.05	.03
309 Mario Diaz	.07	.04
310 Rafael Palmeiro	.25	.15
311 Chris Bosio	.08	.05
312 Tom Lawless	.05	.03
313 Denny Martinez	.10	.06
314 Bobby Valentine	.05	.03
315 Greg Swindell	.10	.06
316 Walt Weiss	.10	.06
317 Jack Armstrong	.08	.05
318 Gene Larkin	.05	.03
319 Greg Booker	.05	.03
320 Lou Whitaker	.08	.05
321 Red Sox Leaders	.05	.03
322 John Smiley	.12	.07
323 Gary Thurman	.05	.03
324 Bob Milacki (R)	.10	.06
325 Jesse Barfield	.08	.05
326 Dennis Boyd	.05	.03
327 Mark Lemke (R)	.15	.10
328 Rick Honeycutt	.05	.03
329 Bob Melvin	.05	.03
330 Eric Davis	.12	.07
331 Curt Wilkerson	.05	.03
332 Tony Armas	.05	.03
333 Bob Ojeda	.05	.03
334 Steve Lyons	.05	.03
335 Dave Righetti	.07	.04
336 Steve Balboni	.05	.03
337 Calvin Schiraldi	.05	.03
338 Jim Adduci	.05	.03
339 Scott Bailes	.05	.03
340 Kirk Gibsosn	.08	.05
341 Jim Deshaies	.07	.04
342 Tom Brookens	.05	.03
343 Gary Sheffield (R)	2.00	1.25
344 Tom Trebelhorn	.05	.03
345 Charlie Hough	.05	.03
346 Rex Hudler	.05	.03
347 John Cerutti	.05	.03
348 Ed Hearn	.05	.03
349 Ron Jones (R)	.08	.05
350 Andy Van Slyke	.15	.10
351 Giants Leaders	.05	.03
352 Rick Schu	.05	.03
353 Marvell Wynne	.05	.03
354 Larry Parrish	.05	.03
355 Mark Langston	.10	.06
356 Kevin Elster	.05	.03
357 Jerry Reuss	.05	.03
358 Ricky Jordan (R)	.15	.10
359 Tommy John	.08	.05
360 Ryne Sandberg	.50	.30
361 Kelly Downs	.05	.03
362 Jack Lazorko	.05	.03
363 Rich Yett	.05	.03
364 Rob Deer	.08	.05
365 Mike Henneman	.05	.03
366 Herm Winningham	.05	.03
367 Johnny Paredes (R)	.07	.04
368 Brian Holton	.05	.03
369 Ken Caminiti	.10	.06

370	Dennis Eckersley	.15	.10	427	Eric Show	.05	.03
371	Manny Lee	.05	.03	428	Craig Reynolds	.05	.03
372	Craig Lefferts	.05	.03	429	Twins Leaders	.05	.03
373	Tracy Jones	.05	.03	430	Mark Gubicza	.08	.05
374	John Wathan	.05	.03	431	Luis Rivera	.05	.03
375	Terry Pendleton	.15	.10	432	Chat Kreuter (R)	.12	.07
376	Steve Lombardozzi	.05	.03	433	Albert Hall	.05	.03
377	Mike Smithson	.05	.03	434	Ken Patterson (R)	.08	.05
378	Checklist 265-396	.05	.03	435	Len Dykstra	.25	.15
379	Tim Flannery	.05	.03	436	Bobby Meacham	.05	.03
380	Rickey Henderson	.30	.18	437	Andy Benes	.70	.40
381	Orioles Leaders	.05	.03	438	Greg Gross	.05	.03
382	John Smoltz (R)	.80	.50	439	Frank DiPino	.05	.03
383	Howard Johnson	.12	.07	440	Bobby Bonilla	.15	.10
384	Mark Salas	.05	.03	441	Jerry Reed	.05	.03
385	Von Hayes	.05	.03	442	Jose Oquendo	.05	.03
386	Andres Galarraga AS	.08	.05	443	Rod Nichols (R)	.08	.05
387	Ryne Sandberg AS	.25	.15	444	Moose Stubing	.05	.03
388	Bobby Bonilla AS	.10	.06	445	Matt Nokes	.08	.05
389	Ozzie Smith AS	.12	.07	446	Rob Murphy	.05	.03
390	Darryl Strawberry AS	.12	.07	447	Donell Nixon	.05	.03
391	Andre Dawson AS	.12	.07	448	Eric Plunk	.05	.03
392	Andy Van Slyke AS	.08	.05	449	Carmelo Martinez	.05	.03
393	Gary Carter AS	.08	.05	450	Roger Clemens	.45	.28
394	Orel Hershiser AS	.08	.05	451	Mark Davidson	.05	.03
395	Danny Jackson AS	.05	.03	452	Israel Sanchez	.05	.03
396	Kirk Gibson AS	.08	.05	453	Tom Prince	.05	.03
397	Don Mattingly AS	.15	.10	454	Paul Assenmacher	.05	.03
398	Julio Franco AS	.08	.05	455	Johnny Ray	.05	.03
399	Wade Boggs AS	.10	.06	456	Tim Belcher	.08	.05
400	Alan Trammell AS	.08	.05	457	Mackey Sasser	.05	.03
401	Jose Canseco AS	.15	.10	458	Donn Paul (R)	.10	.06
402	Mike Greenwell AS	.08	.05	459	Mariners Leaders	.05	.03
403	Kirby Puckett AS	.15	.10	460	Dave Stieb	.08	.05
404	Bob Boone AS	.08	.05	461	Buddy Bell	.05	.03
405	Roger Clemens AS	.15	.10	462	Jose Guzman	.05	.03
406	Frank Viola AS	.08	.05	463	Steve Lake	.05	.03
407	Dave Winfield AS	.12	.07	464	Bryn Smith	.05	.03
408	Greg Walker	.05	.03	465	Mark Grace	.75	.45
409	Ken Dayley	.05	.03	466	Chuck Crim	.05	.03
410	Jack Clark	.07	.04	467	Jim Walewander	.05	.03
411	Mitch Williams	.05	.03	468	Henry Cotto	.05	.03
412	Barry Lyons	.05	.03	469	Jose Bautista	.05	.03
413	Mike Kingery	.05	.03	470	Lance Parrish	.07	.04
414	Jim Fregosi	.05	.03	471	Steve Curry (R)	.08	.05
415	Rich Gossage	.08	.05	472	Brian Harper	.08	.05
416	Fred Lynn	.08	.05	473	Don Robinson	.05	.03
417	Mike LaCoss	.05	.03	474	Bob Rodgers	.05	.03
418	Bob Dernier	.05	.03	475	Dave Parker	.08	.05
419	Tom Filer	.05	.03	476	Jon Perlman	.05	.03
420	Joe Carter	.30	.18	477	Dick Schofield	.05	.03
421	Kirk McCaskill	.05	.03	478	Doug Drabek	.12	.07
422	Bo Diaz	.05	.03	479	Mike MacFarlane	.15	.10
423	Brian Fisher	.05	.03	480	Keith Hernandez	.07	.04
424	Luis Polonia	.08	.05	481	Chris Brown	.05	.03
425	Jay Howell	.05	.03	482	Steve Peters	.05	.03
426	Danny Gladden	.05	.03	483	Mickey Hatcher	.05	.03

484	Steve Shields	.05	.03
485	Hubie Brooks	.07	.04
486	Jack McDowell	.60	.35
487	Scott Lusader	.05	.03
488	Kevin Coffman	.05	.03
489	Phillies Leaders	.20	.12
490	Chris Sabo	.25	.15
491	Mike Birkbeck	.05	.03
492	Alan Ashby	.05	.03
493	Todd Benzinger	.05	.03
494	Shane Rawley	.05	.03
495	Candy Maldonado	.05	.03
496	Dwayne Henry	.05	.03
497	Pete Stanicek	.05	.03
498	Dave Valle	.05	.03
499	Don Heinkel (R)	.07	.04
500	Jose Canseco	.35	.20
501	Vance Law	.05	.03
502	Duane Ward	.05	.03
503	Al Newman	.05	.03
504	Bob Walk	.05	.03
505	Pete Rose	.15	.10
506	Kirt Manwaring	.05	.03
507	Steve Farr	.05	.03
508	Wally Backman	.05	.03
509	Bud Black	.05	.03
510	Bob Horner	.08	.05
511	Richard Dotson	.05	.03
512	Donnie Hill	.05	.03
513	Jesse Orosco	.05	.03
514	Chet Lemon	.05	.03
515	Barry Larkin	.20	.12
516	Eddie Whitson	.05	.03
517	Greg Brock	.05	.03
518	Bruce Ruffin	.05	.03
519	Yankees Leaders	.05	.03
520	Rick Sutcliffe	.07	.04
521	Mickey Tettleton	.08	.05
522	Randy Kramer (R)	.08	.05
523	Andres Thomas	.05	.03
524	Checklist 397-528	.05	.03
525	Chili Davis	.07	.04
526	Wes Gardner	.05	.03
527	Dave Henderson	.07	.04
528	Luis Medina (R)	.10	.06
529	Tom Foley	.05	.03
530	Nolan Ryan	.90	.55
531	Dave Hengel (R)	.07	.04
532	Jerry Browne	.07	.04
533	Andy Hawkins	.05	.03
534	Doc Edwards	.05	.03
535	Todd Worrell	.08	.05
536	Joel Skinner	.05	.03
537	Pete Smith	.20	.12
538	Juan Castillo	.05	.03
539	Barry Jones	.05	.03
540	Bo Jackson	.20	.12
541	Cecil Fielder	.30	.18
542	Todd Frohwirth	.05	.03
543	Damon Berryhill	.05	.03
544	Jeff Sellers	.05	.03
545	Mookie Wilson	.07	.04
546	Mark Williamson	.05	.03
547	Mark McLemore	.05	.03
548	Bobby Witt	.08	.05
549	Cubs Leaders	.05	.03
550	Orel Hershiser	.10	.06
551	Randy Ready	.05	.03
552	Greg Cadaret	.05	.03
553	Luis Salazar	.05	.03
554	Nick Esasky	.05	.03
555	Bert Blyleven	.08	.05
556	Bruce Fields	.05	.03
557	Keith Miller (R)	.08	.05
558	Dan Pasqua	.05	.03
559	Juan Agosto	.05	.03
560	Tim Raines	.08	.05
561	Luis Aguayo	.05	.03
562	Danny Cox	.05	.03
563	Bill Schroeder	.05	.03
564	Russ Nixon	.05	.03
565	Jeff Russell	.07	.04
566	Al Pedrique	.05	.03
567	David Wells	.12	.07
568	Mickey Brantley	.05	.03
569	German Jimenez (R)	.07	.04
570	Tony Gwynn	.25	.15
571	Billy Ripken	.05	.03
572	Atlee Hammaker	.05	.03
573	Jim Abbott (#1 Pick)	1.25	.80
574	Dave Clark	.05	.03
575	Juan Samuel	.05	.03
576	Greg Minton	.05	.03
577	Randy Bush	.05	.03
578	John Morris	.05	.03
579	Astros Leaders	.05	.03
580	Harold Reynolds	.05	.03
581	Gene Nelson	.05	.03
582	Mike Marshall	.05	.03
583	Paul Gibson (R)	.08	.05
584	Randy Velarde	.05	.03
585	Harold Baines	.08	.05
586	Joe Boever	.05	.03
587	Mike Stanley	.05	.03
588	Luis Alicea	.08	.05
589	Dave Meads	.05	.03
590	Andres Galarraga	.15	.10
591	Jeff Musselman	.05	.03
592	John Cangelosi	.05	.03
593	Drew Hall	.05	.03
594	Jimy Williams	.05	.03
595	Teddy Higuera	.07	.04
596	Kurt Stillwell	.05	.03
597	Terry Taylor (R)	.08	.05

598	Ken Gerhart	.05	.03	651	Tom Niedenfuer	.05	.03
599	Tom Candiotti	.07	.04	652	Rich Gedman	.05	.03
600	Wade Boggs	.25	.15	653	Tommy Barrett (R)	.07	.04
601	Dave Dravecky	.05	.03	654	Whitey Herzog	.07	.04
602	Devon White	.08	.05	655	Dave Magadan	.08	.05
603	Frank Tanana	.07	.04	656	Ivan Calderon	.08	.05
604	Paul O'Neill	.12	.07	657	Joe Magrane	.08	.05
605a	Bob Welch (Missing	3.00	1.75	658	R.J. Reynolds	.05	.03
	Major League Pitching			659	Al Leiter	.05	.03
	Record line)			660	Will Clark	.50	.30
605b	Bob Welch (Cor)	.08	.05	661	Dwight Gooden (Clock)	.10	.06
606	Rick Dempsey	.05	.03	662	Lou Brock (Clock)	.12	.07
607	Willie Ansley (R)	.15	.10	663	Hank Aaron (Clock)	.15	.10
	(#1 Pick)	.05	.03	664	Gil Hodges (Clock)	.10	.06
608	Phil Bradley	.05	.03	665	Tony Oliva (Clock)	.10	.06
609	Tigers Leaders	.05	.03	666	Randy St.Claire	.05	.03
610	Randy Myers	.07	.04	667	Dwayne Murphy	.05	.03
611	Don Slaught	.05	.03	668	Mike Bielecki	.07	.04
612	Dan Quisenberry	.05	.03	669	Dodgers Leaders	.08	.05
613	Gary Varsho (R)	.10	.06	670	Kevin Seitzer	.12	.07
614	Joe Hesketh	.05	.03	671	Jim Gantner	.05	.03
615	Robin Yount	.30	.18	672	Allan Anderson	.05	.03
616	Steve Rosenberg (R)	.07	.04	673	Don Baylor	.08	.05
617	Mark Parent	.05	.03	674	Otis Nixon	.07	.04
618	Rance Mulliniks	.05	.03	675	Bruce Hurst	.07	.04
619	Checklist 529-660	.05	.03	676	Ernie Riles	.05	.03
620	Barry Bonds	.75	.45	677	Dave Schmidt	.05	.03
621	Rick Mahler	.05	.03	678	Dion James	.05	.03
622	Stan Javier	.05	.03	679	Willie Fraser	.05	.03
623	Fred Toliver	.05	.03	680	Gary Carter	.10	.06
624	Jack McKeon	.05	.03	681	Jeff Robinson	.05	.03
625	Eddie Murray	.20	.12	682	Rick Leach	.05	.03
626	Jeff Reed	.05	.03	683	Jose Cecena	.05	.03
627	Greg Harris	.05	.03	684	Dave Johnson	.07	.04
628	Matt Williams	.40	.25	685	Jeff Treadway	.05	.03
629	Pete O'Brien	.05	.03	686	Scott Terry	.05	.03
630	Mike Greenwell	.10	.06	687	Alvin Davis	.07	.04
631	Dave Bergman	.05	.03	688	Zane Smith	.07	.04
632	Bryan Harvey	.35	.20	689	Stan Jefferson	.05	.03
633	Daryl Boston	.05	.03	690	Doug Jones	.07	.04
634	Marvin Freeman	.05	.03	691	Roberto Kelly	.25	.15
635	Willie Randolph	.07	.04	692	Steve Ontiveros	.05	.03
636	Bill Wilkinson	.05	.03	693	Pat Borders	.15	.10
637	Carmen Castillo	.05	.03	694	Les Lancaster	.05	.03
638	Floyd Bannister	.05	.03	695	Carlton Fisk	.20	.12
639	Athletics Leaders	.05	.03	696	Don August	.05	.03
640	Willie McGee	.08	.05	697	Franklin Stubbs	.05	.03
641	Curt Young	.05	.03	698	Keith Atherton	.05	.03
642	Argenis Salazar	.05	.03	699	Pirates Leaders	.05	.03
643	Louie Meadows (R)	.07	.04	700	Don Mattingly	.25	.15
644	Lloyd McClendon	.05	.03	701	Storm Davis	.05	.03
645	Jack Morris	.15	.10	702	Jamie Quirk	.05	.03
646	Kevin Bass	.07	.04	703	Scott Garrelts	.05	.03
647	Randy Johnson (R)	1.00	.60	704	Carlos Quintana (R)	.12	.07
648	Sandy Alomar Jr. (R)	.30	.18	705	Terry Kennedy	.05	.03
649	Stewart Cliburn	.05	.03	706	Pete Incaviglia	.07	.04
650	Kirby Puckett	.45	.28	707	Steve Jeltz	.05	.03

708	Chuck Finley	.10	.06
709	Tom Herr	.05	.03
710	Dave Cone	.20	.12
711	Candy Sierra (R)	.07	.04
712	Bill Swift	.08	.05
713	Ty Griffin (#1 Pick)	.08	.05
714	Joe Morgan	.08	.05
715	Tony Pena	.05	.03
716	Wayne Tolleson	.05	.03
717	Jamie Moyer	.05	.03
718	Glenn Braggs	.05	.03
719	Danny Darwin	.05	.03
720	Tim Wallach	.08	.05
721	Ron Tingley (R)	.08	.05
722	Todd Stottlemyre	.15	.10
723	Rafael Belliard	.05	.03
724	Jerry Don Gleaton	.05	.03
725	Terry Steinbach	.08	.05
726	Dickie Thon	.05	.03
727	Joe Orsulak	.05	.03
728	Charlie Puleo	.05	.03
729	Rangers Leaders	.05	.03
730	Danny Jackson	.07	.04
731	Mike Young	.05	.03
732	Steve Buechele	.08	.05
733	Randy Bockus (R)	.07	.04
734	Jody Reed	.05	.03
735	Roger McDowell	.05	.03
736	Jeff Hamilton	.05	.03
737	Norm Charlton (R)	.25	.15
738	Darnell Coles	.05	.03
739	Brook Jacoby	.05	.03
740	Dan Plesac	.05	.03
741	Ken Phelps	.07	.04
742	Mike Harkey (R)	.15	.10
743	Mike Heath	.05	.03
744	Roger Craig	.05	.03
745	Fred McGriff	.40	.25
746	German Gonzalez (R)	.07	.04
747	Wil Tejada	.05	.03
748	Jimmy Jones	.05	.03
749	Rafael Ramirez	.05	.03
750	Bret Saberhagen	.12	.07
751	Ken Oberkfell	.05	.03
752	Jim Gott	.05	.03
753	Jose Uribe	.05	.03
754	Bob Brower	.05	.03
755	Mike Scioscia	.07	.04
756	Scott Medvin (R)	.08	.05
757	Brady Anderson	.60	.35
758	Gene Walter	.05	.03
759	Brewers Leaders	.05	.03
760	Lee Smith	.12	.07
761	Dante Bichette (R)	.30	.18
762	Bobby Thigpen	.10	.06
763	Dave Martinez	.05	.03
764	Robin Ventura	1.25	.80

	(#1 Pick)		
765	Glenn Davis	.07	.04
766	Cecilio Guante	.05	.03
767	Mike Capel (R)	.08	.05
768	Bill Wegman	.05	.03
769	Junior Ortiz	.05	.03
770	Alan Trammell	.12	.07
771	Ron Kittle	.07	.04
772	Ron Oester	.05	.03
773	Keith Moreland	.05	.03
774	Frank Robinson	.10	.06
775	Jeff Reardon	.12	.07
776	Nelson Liriano	.05	.03
777	Ted Power	.05	.03
778	Bruce Benedict	.05	.03
779	Craig McMurtry	.05	.03
780	Pedro Guerrero	.08	.05
781	Greg Briley (R)	.12	.07
782	Checklist 661-792	.05	.03
783	Trevor Wilson (R)	.12	.07
784	Steve Avery (#1 Pick)	1.75	1.00
785	Ellis Burks	.10	.06
786	Melido Perez	.07	.04
787	Dave West (R)	.10	.06
788	Mike Morgan	.07	.04
789	Royals Leaders (Bo Jackson)	.15	.10
790	Sid Fernandez	.07	.04
791	Jim Lindeman	.05	.03
792	Rafael Santana	.05	.03

1989 Topps Traded

This update set contains 132-cards that are identical to the 1989 Topps regular issue. The featured players include those traded to new teams since the beginning of the year and a number of promising rookies. Cards measure 2-1/2" by 3-1/2" and numbers carry the "T" designation to distinguish it from the regular set.

		MINT	NR/MT
	Complete Set (132)	7.50	4.25
	Commons	.05	.03
1T	Don Aase	.05	.03
2T	Jim Abbott	1.00	.70
3T	Kent Anderson (R)	.12	.07
4T	Keith Atherton	.05	.03
5T	Wally Backman	.05	.03
6T	Steve Balboni	.05	.03
7T	Jesse Barfield	.08	.05
8T	Steve Bedrosian	.07	.04
9T	Todd Benzinger	.07	.04
10T	Geronimo Berroa (R)	.10	.06
11T	Bert Blyleven	.15	.10
12T	Bob Boone	.10	.06
13T	Phil Bradley	.05	.03
14T	Jeff Brantley (R)	.15	.10
15T	Kevin Brown (R)	.35	.20
16T	Jerry Browne	.05	.03
17T	Chuck Cary	.05	.03
18T	Carmen Castillo	.05	.03
19T	Jim Clancy	.05	.03
20T	Jack Clark	.08	.05
21T	Bryan Clutterbuck	.05	.03
22T	Jody Davis	.05	.03
23T	Mike Devereaux (R)	.30	.18
24T	Frank DiPino	.05	.03
25T	Benny Distefano	.05	.03
26T	John Dopson	.08	.05
27T	Len Dykstra	.25	.15
28T	Jim Eisenreich	.05	.03
29T	Nick Esasky	.05	.03
30T	Alvaro Espinoza	.08	.05
31T	Darrell Evans	.08	.05
32T	Junior Felix (R)	.12	.07
33T	Felix Fermin	.05	.03
34T	Julio Franco	.15	.10
35T	Terry Francona	.05	.03
36T	Cito Gaston	.08	.05
37T	Bob Geren (R) (Wrong Photo)	.25	.15
38T	Tom Gordon (R)	.15	.10
39T	Tommy Gregg (R)	.08	.05
40T	Ken Griffey	.10	.06
41T	Ken Griffey, Jr. (R)	6.00	3.75
42T	Kevin Gross	.05	.03
43T	Lee Guetterman	.05	.03
44T	Mel Hall	.10	.06
45T	Erik Hanson (R)	.25	.15
46T	Gene Harris (R)	.12	.07
47T	Andy Hawkins	.05	.03
48T	Rickey Henderson	.30	.18
49T	Tom Herr	.05	.03
50T	Ken Hill (R)	.50	.30
51T	Brian Holman (R)	.12	.07
52T	Brian Holton	.07	.04
53T	Art Howe	.05	.03
54T	Ken Howell	.05	.03
55T	Bruce Hurst	.08	.05
56T	Chris James	.05	.03
57T	Randy Johnson	.70	.40
58T	Jimmy Jones	.05	.03
59T	Terry Kennedy	.05	.03
60T	Paul Kilgus	.05	.03
61T	Eric King	.05	.03
62T	Ron Kittle	.05	.03
63T	John Kruk	.15	.10
64T	Randy Kutcher (R)	.07	.04
65T	Steve Lake	.05	.03
66T	Mark Langston	.10	.06
67T	Dave LaPoint	.05	.03
68T	Rick Leach	.05	.03
69T	Terry Leach	.05	.03
70T	Jim Levebvre	.05	.03
71T	Al Leiter	.05	.03
72T	Jeffrey Leonard	.05	.03
73T	Derek Lilliquist (R)	.08	.05
74T	Rick Mahler	.05	.03
75T	Tom McCarthy (R)	.08	.05
76T	Lloyd McClendon	.07	.04
77T	Lance McCullers	.05	.03
78T	Oddibe McDowell	.05	.03
79T	Roger McDowell	.05	.03
80T	Larry McWilliams	.05	.03
81T	Randy Milligan	.08	.05
82T	Mike Moore	.08	.05
83T	Keith Moreland	.05	.03
84T	Mike Morgan	.08	.05
85T	Jamie Moyer	.05	.03
86T	Rob Murphy	.05	.03
87T	Eddie Murray	.15	.10
88T	Pete O'Brien	.05	.03
89T	Gregg Olson	.25	.15
90T	Steve Ontiveros	.05	.03
91T	Jesse Orosco	.05	.03
92T	Spike Owen	.05	.03
93T	Rafael Palmeiro	.30	.18
94T	Clay Parker (R)	.10	.06
95T	Jeff Parrett	.05	.03
96T	Lance Parrish	.08	.05
97T	Dennis Powell	.05	.03
98T	Rey Quinones	.05	.03
99T	Doug Rader	.05	.03
100T	Willie Randolph	.08	.05
101T	Shane Rawley	.05	.03
102T	Randy Ready	.05	.03
103T	Bip Roberts	.12	.07
104T	Kenny Rogers (R)	.15	.10
105T	Ed Romero	.05	.03
106T	Nolan Ryan	1.75	1.00
107T	Luis Salazar	.05	.03
108T	Juan Samuel	.05	.03

		MINT	NR/MT
109T	Alex Sanchez (R)	.08	.05
110T	Deion Sanders (R)	1.50	.90
111T	Steve Sax	.10	.06
112T	Nick Esasky	.05	.03
113T	Dwight Smith (R)	.20	.12
114T	Lonnie Smith	.08	.05
115T	Billy Spiers (R)	.10	.06
116T	Kent Tekulve	.05	.03
117T	Walt Terrell	.05	.03
118T	Milt Thompson	.05	.03
119T	Dickie Thon	.05	.03
120T	Jeff Torborg	.05	.03
121T	Jeff Treadway	.05	.03
122T	Omar Vizquel (R)	.30	.18
123T	Jerome Walton (R)	.08	.05
124T	Gary Ward	.05	.03
125T	Claudell Washington	.05	.03
126T	Curt Wilkerson	.05	.03
127T	Eddie Williams	.05	.03
128T	Frank Williams	.05	.03
129T	Ken Williams	.05	.03
130T	Mitch Williams	.10	.06
131T	Steve Wilson (R)	.10	.06
132T	Checklist	.05	.03

1990 Topps

The 1990 Topps set consists of 792-cards and features multi-colored borders surrounding full color player photos. Cards measure 2-1/2" by 3-1/2". The set contains a special salute to Nolan Ryan (2-5), Record Breakers (6-9), All-Stars (385-407), Number One Draft Picks and a Turn Back The Clock subset.

	MINT	NR/MT
Complete Set (792)	20.00	12.50
Commons	.05	.03

		MINT	NR/MT
1	Nolan Ryan	.80	.50
2	Nolan Ryan (Mets)	.25	.15
3	Nolan Ryan (Angels)	.25	.15
4	Nolan Ryan (Astros)	.25	.15
5	Nolan Ryan (Rangers)	.25	.15
6	Vince Coleman (RB)	.07	.04
7	Rickey Henderson (RB)	.12	.07
8	Cal Ripken (RB)	.25	.15
9	Eric Plunk	.05	.03
10	Barry Larkin	.15	.10
11	Paul Gibson	.05	.03
12	Joe Girardi	.08	.05
13	Mark Williamson	.05	.03
14	Mike Fetters (R)	.10	.06
15	Teddy Higuera	.07	.04
16	Kent Anderson	.05	.03
17	Kelly Downs	.05	.03
18	Carlos Quintana	.10	.06
19	Al Newman	.05	.03
20	Mark Gubicza	.08	.05
21	Jeff Torborg	.05	.03
22	Bruce Ruffin	.05	.03
23	Randy Velarde	.05	.03
24	Joe Hesketh	.05	.03
25	Willie Randolph	.07	.04
26	Don Slaught	.05	.03
27	Rick Leach	.05	.03
28	Duane Ward	.05	.03
29	John Cangelosi	.05	.03
30	David Cone	.12	.07
31	Henry Cotto	.05	.03
32	John Farrell	.05	.03
33	Greg Walker	.05	.03
34	Tony Fossas (R)	.10	.06
35	Benito Santiago	.08	.05
36	John Costello	.05	.03
37	Domingo Ramos	.05	.03
38	Wes Gardner	.05	.03
39	Curt Ford	.05	.03
40	Jay Howell	.05	.03
41	Matt Williams	.25	.15
42	Jeff Robinson	.05	.03
43	Dante Bichette	.08	.05
44	Roger Salkeld (R) (#1 Pick)	.30	.18
45	Dave Parker	.08	.05
46	Rob Dibble	.08	.05
47	Brian Harper	.07	.04
48	Zane Smith	.07	.04
49	Tom Lawless	.05	.03
50	Glenn Davis	.05	.03
51	Doug Rader	.05	.03
52	Jack Daugherty (R)	.12	.07
53	Mike LaCoss	.05	.03
54	Joel Skinner	.05	.03
55	Darrell Evans	.07	.04
56	Franklin Stubbs	.05	.03

57 Greg Vaughn (R)	.30	.18
58 Keith Miller	.05	.03
59 Ted Power	.05	.03
60 George Brett	.25	.15
61 Deion Sanders	.40	.25
62 Ramon Martinez	.15	.10
63 Mike Pagliarulo	.05	.03
64 Danny Darwin	.05	.03
65 Devon White	.07	.04
66 Greg Litton (R)	.10	.06
67 Scott Sanderson	.05	.03
68 Dave Henderson	.07	.04
69 Todd Frohwirth	.05	.03
70 Mike Greenwell	.08	.05
71 Allan Anderson	.05	.03
72 Jeff Huson (R)	.10	.06
73 Bob Milacki	.05	.03
74 Jeff Jackson (R) (#1 Pick)	.20	.12
75 Doug Jones	.05	.03
76 Dave Valle	.05	.03
77 Dave Bergman	.05	.03
78 Mike Flanagan	.05	.03
79 Ron Kittle	.05	.03
80 Jeff Russell	.07	.04
81 Bob Rodgers	.05	.03
82 Scott Terry	.05	.03
83 Hensley Meulens	.10	.06
84 Ray Searage	.05	.03
85 Juan Samuel	.05	.03
86 Paul Kilgus	.05	.03
87 Rick Luecken (R)	.08	.05
88 Glenn Braggs	.05	.03
89 Clint Zavaras (R)	.10	.06
90 Jack Clark	.07	.04
91 Steve Frey	.05	.03
92 Mike Stanley	.05	.03
93 Shawn Hillegas	.05	.03
94 Herm Winningham	.05	.03
95 Todd Worrell	.07	.04
96 Jody Reed	.05	.03
97 Curt Schilling (R)	.30	.18
98 Jose Gonzalez	.07	.04
99 Rich Monteleone (R)	.08	.05
100 Will Clark	.35	.20
101 Shane Rawley	.05	.03
102 Stan Javier	.05	.03
103 Marvin Freeman	.05	.03
104 Bob Knepper	.05	.03
105 Randy Myers	.05	.03
106 Charlie O'Brien	.05	.03
107 Fred Lynn	.07	.04
108 Rod Nichols	.05	.03
109 Roberto Kelly	.15	.10
110 Tommy Helms	.05	.03
111 Ed Whited	.05	.03
112 Glenn Wilson	.05	.03

113 Manny Lee	.05	.03
114 Mike Bielecki	.05	.03
115 Tony Pena	.05	.03
116 Floyd Bannister	.05	.03
117 Mike Sharperson	.05	.03
118 Erik Hanson	.10	.06
119 Billy Hatcher	.05	.03
120 John Franco	.05	.03
121 Robin Ventura	.75	.45
122 Shawn Abner	.05	.03
123 Rich Gedman	.05	.03
124 Dave Dravecky	.05	.03
125 Kent Hrbek	.08	.05
126 Randy Kramer	.05	.03
127 Mike Devereaux	.08	.05
128 Checklist 1-132	.05	.03
129 Ron Jones	.05	.03
130 Bert Blyleven	.08	.05
131 Matt Nokes	.07	.04
132 Lance Blankenship	.05	.03
133 Ricky Horton	.05	.03
134 Earl Cunningham (R) (#1 Pick)	.15	.10
135 Dave Magadan	.07	.04
136 Kevin Brown	.10	.06
137 Marty Pevey (R)	.08	.05
138 Al Leiter	.05	.03
139 Greg Brock	.05	.03
140 Andre Dawson	.12	.07
141 John Hart	.05	.03
142 Jeff Wetherby (R)	.08	.05
143 Rafael Belliard	.05	.03
144 Bud Black	.07	.04
145 Terry Steinbach	.07	.04
146 Rob Richie (R)	.07	.04
147 Chuck Finley	.08	.05
148 Edgar Martinez	.35	.20
149 Steve Farr	.05	.03
150 Kirk Gibson	.07	.04
151 Rick Mahler	.05	.03
152 Lonnie Smith	.07	.04
153 Randy Milligan	.07	.04
154 Mike Maddux	.05	.03
155 Ellis Burks	.08	.05
156 Ken Patterson	.05	.03
157 Craig Biggio	.10	.06
158 Craig Lefferts	.05	.03
159 Mike Felder	.05	.03
160 Dave Righetti	.07	.04
161 Harold Reynolds	.05	.03
162 Todd Zeile (R)	.20	.12
163 Phil Bradley	.05	.03
164 Jeff Juden (R) (#1 Pick)	.25	.15
165 Walt Weiss	.05	.03
166 Bobby Witt	.08	.05
167 Kevin Appier (R)	.40	.25

168	Jose Lind	.05	.03
169	Richard Dotson	.05	.03
170	George Bell	.10	.06
171	Russ Nixon	.05	.03
172	Tom Lampkin	.05	.03
173	Tim Belcher	.07	.04
174	Jeff Kunkel	.05	.03
175	Mike Moore	.05	.03
176	Luis Quinones	.05	.03
177	Mike Henneman	.05	.03
178	Chris James	.05	.03
179	Brian Holton	.05	.03
180	Tim Raines	.08	.05
181	Juan Agosto	.05	.03
182	Mookie Wilson	.05	.03
183	Steve Lake	.05	.03
184	Danny Cox	.05	.03
185	Ruben Sierra	.20	.12
186	Dave LaPoint	.05	.03
187	Rick Wrona (R)	.08	.05
188	Mike Smithson	.05	.03
189	Dick Schofield	.05	.03
190	Rick Reuschel	.05	.03
191	Pat Borders	.05	.03
192	Don August	.05	.03
193	Andy Benes	.20	.12
194	Glenallen Hill	.10	.06
195	Tim Burke	.05	.03
196	Gerald Young	.05	.03
197	Doug Drabek	.12	.07
198	Mike Marshall	.05	.03
199	Sergio Valdez (R)	.10	.06
200	Don Mattingly	.25	.15
201	Cito Gaston	.05	.03
202	Mike Macfarlane	.05	.03
203	Mike Roesler (R)	.08	.05
204	Bob Dernier	.05	.03
205	Mark Davis	.05	.03
206	Nick Esasky	.05	.03
207	Bob Ojeda	.05	.03
208	Brook Jacoby	.05	.03
209	Greg Mathews	.05	.03
210	Ryne Sandberg	.35	.20
211	John Cerutti	.05	.03
212	Joe Orsulak	.05	.03
213	Scott Bankhead	.05	.03
214	Terry Francona	.05	.03
215	Kirk McCaskill	.05	.03
216	Ricky Jordan	.07	.04
217	Don Robinson	.05	.03
218	Wally Backman	.05	.03
219	Donn Pall	.05	.03
220	Barry Bonds	.70	.40
221	Gary Mielke (R)	.08	.05
222	Kurt Stillwell	.05	.03
223	Tommy Gregg	.05	.03
224	Delino DeShields (R)	.80	.50
225	Jim Deshaies	.05	.03
226	Mickey Hatcher	.05	.03
227	Kevin Tapani (R)	.20	.12
228	Dave Martinez	.05	.03
229	David Wells	.05	.03
230	Keith Hernandez	.07	.04
231	Jack McKeon	.05	.03
232	Darnell Coles	.05	.03
233	Ken Hill	.15	.10
234	Mariano Duncan	.05	.03
235	Jeff Reardon	.12	.07
236	Hal Morris (R)	.25	.15
237	Kevin Ritz (R)	.10	.06
238	Felix Jose (R)	.20	.12
239	Eric Show	.05	.03
240	Mark Grace	.20	.12
241	Mike Krukow	.05	.03
242	Fred Manrique	.05	.03
243	Barry Jones	.05	.03
244	Bill Schroeder	.05	.03
245	Roger Clemens	.35	.20
246	Jim Eisenreich	.05	.03
247	Jerry Reed	.05	.03
248	Dave Anderson	.05	.03
249	Mike Smith (R)	.08	.05
250	Jose Canseco	.30	.18
251	Jeff Blauser	.08	.05
252	Otis Nixon	.07	.04
253	Mark Portugal	.05	.03
254	Francisco Cabrera	.12	.07
255	Bobby Thigpen	.08	.05
256	Marvell Wynne	.05	.03
257	Jose DeLeon	.05	.03
258	Barry Lyons	.05	.03
259	Lance McCullers	.05	.03
260	Eric Davis	.10	.06
261	Whitey Herzog	.07	.04
262	Checklist 133-264	.05	.03
263	Mel Stottlemyre Jr (R)	.08	.05
264	Bryan Clutterbuck	.05	.03
265	Pete O'Brien	.05	.03
266	German Gonzalez	.05	.03
267	Mark Davidson	.05	.03
268	Rob Murphy	.05	.03
269	Dickie Thon	.05	.03
270	Dave Stewart	.10	.06
271	Chet Lemon	.05	.03
272	Bryan Harvey	.10	.06
273	Bobby Bonilla	.15	.10
274	Mauro Gozzo (R)	.10	.06
275	Mickey Tettleton	.08	.05
276	Gary Thurman	.05	.03
277	Lenny Harris	.05	.03
278	Pascual Perez	.05	.03
279	Steve Buechele	.07	.04
280	Lou Whitaker	.07	.04
281	Kevin Bass	.05	.03

282	Derek Lililquist	.05	.03
283	Albert Belle (R)	1.00	.60
284	Mark Gardner (R)	.15	.10
295	Willie McGee	.08	.05
286	Lee Guetterman	.05	.03
287	Vance Law	.05	.03
288	Greg Briley	.05	.03
289	Norm Charlton	.08	.05
290	Robin Yount	.25	.15
291	Dave Johnson	.05	.03
292	Jim Gott	.05	.03
293	Mike Gallego	.05	.03
294	Craig McMurtry	.05	.03
295	Fred McGriff	.30	.18
296	Jeff Ballard	.05	.03
297	Tom Herr	.05	.03
298	Danny Gladden	.05	.03
299	Adam Peterson	.05	.03
300	Bo Jackson	.20	.12
301	Don Aase	.05	.03
302	Marcus Lawton (R)	.12	.07
303	Rick Cerone	.05	.03
304	Marty Clary	.05	.03
305	Eddie Murray	.12	.07
306	Tom Niedenfuer	.05	.03
307	Bip Roberts	.08	.05
308	Jose Guzman	.05	.03
309	Eric Yelding (R)	.10	.06
310	Steve Bedrosian	.07	.04
311	Dwight Smith	.07	.04
312	Dan Quisenberry	.05	.03
313	Gus Polidor	.05	.03
314	Donald Harris (R) (#1 Pick)	.12	.07
315	Bruce Hurst	.07	.04
316	Carney Lansford	.07	.04
317	Mark Guthrie (R)	.10	.06
318	Wallace Johnson	.05	.03
319	Dion James	.05	.03
320	Dave Steib	.08	.05
321	Joe Morgan	.08	.05
322	Junior Ortiz	.05	.03
323	Willie Wilson	.05	.03
324	Pete Harnisch (R)	.15	.10
325	Robby Thompson	.07	.04
326	Tom McCarthy	.05	.03
327	Ken Williams	.05	.03
328	Curt Young	.05	.03
329	Oddibe McDowell	.05	.03
330	Ron Darling	.07	.04
331	Juan Gonzalez (R)	3.00	1.75
332	Paul O'Neill	.10	.06
333	Bill Wegman	.05	.03
334	Johnny Ray	.05	.03
335	Andy Hawkins	.05	.03
336	Ken Griffey, Jr.	2.00	1.25
337	Lloyd McClendon	.05	.03
338	Dennis Lamp	.05	.03
339	Dave Clark	.05	.03
340	Fernando Valenzuela	.08	.05
341	Tom Foley	.05	.03
342	Alex Trevino	.05	.03
343	Frank Tanana	.05	.03
344	George Canale (R)	.10	.06
345	Harold Baines	.08	.05
346	Jim Presley	.05	.03
347	Junior Felix	.07	.04
348	Gary Wayne (R)	.10	.06
349	Steve Finley (R)	.12	.07
350	Bret Saberhagen	.12	.07
351	Roger Craig	.05	.03
352	Bryn Smith	.05	.03
353	Sandy Alomar	.12	.07
354	Stan Belinda (R)	.12	.07
355	Marty Barrett	.05	.03
356	Randy Ready	.05	.03
357	Dave West	.05	.03
358	Andres Thomas	.05	.03
359	Jimmy Jones	.05	.03
360	Paul Molitor	.25	.15
361	Randy McCament (R)	.07	.04
362	Damon Berryhill	.05	.03
363	Dan Petry	.05	.03
364	Rolando Roomes	.07	.04
365	Ozzie Guillen	.07	.04
366	Mike Heath	.05	.03
367	Mike Morgan	.05	.03
368	Bill Doran	.05	.03
369	Todd Burns	.05	.03
370	Tim Wallach	.08	.05
371	Jimmy Key	.08	.05
372	Terry Kennedy	.05	.03
373	Alvin Davis	.05	.03
374	Steve Cummings (R)	.10	.06
375	Dwight Evans	.08	.05
376	Checklist 265-396	.05	.03
377	Mickey Weston (R)	.08	.05
378	Luis Salazar	.05	.03
379	Steve Rosenberg	.05	.03
380	Dave Winfield	.25	.15
381	Frank Robinson	.08	.05
382	Jeff Musselman	.05	.03
383	John Morris	.05	.03
384	Pat Combs	.10	.06
385	Fred McGriff AS	.15	.10
386	Julio Franco AS	.07	.04
387	Wade Boggs AS	.10	.06
388	Cal Ripken AS	.20	.12
389	Robin Yount AS	.15	.10
390	Ruben Sierra AS	.10	.06
391	Kirby Puckett AS	5	.10
392	Carlton Fisk AS	J	.06
393	Bret Saberhagen AS	.08	.05
394	Jeff Ballard AS	.05	.03

395	Jeff Russell AS	.05	.03
396	A. Bartlett Giamatti	.15	.10
397	Will Clark AS	.15	.10
398	Ryne Sandberg AS	.15	.10
399	Howard Johnson AS	.08	.05
400	Ozzie Smith AS	.10	.06
401	Kevin Mitchell AS	.08	.05
402	Eric Davis AS	.08	.05
403	Tony Gwynn AS	.10	.06
404	Craig Biggio AS	.07	.04
405	Mike Scott AS	.05	.03
406	Joe Magrane AS	.05	.03
407	Mark Davis AS	.05	.03
408	Trevor Wilson	.05	.03
409	Tom Brunansky	.07	.04
410	Joe Boever	.05	.03
411	Ken Phelps	.05	.03
412	Jamie Moyer	.05	.03
413	Brian DuBois (R)	.08	.05
414	Frank Thomas (R)	4.50	2.75
	(#1 Pick)		
415	Shawon Dunston	.10	.06
416	Dave Johnson (R)	.08	.05
417	Jim Gantner	.05	.03
418	Tom Browning	.07	.04
419	Beau Allred (R)	.12	.07
420	Carlton Fisk	.12	.07
421	Greg Minton	.05	.03
422	Pat Sheridan	.05	.03
423	Fred Oliver	.05	.03
424	Jerry Reuss	.05	.03
425	Bill Landrum	.05	.03
426	Jeff Hamilton	.05	.03
427	Carmen Castillo	.05	.03
428	Steve Davis (R)	.08	.05
429	Tom Kelly	.05	.03
430	Pete Incaviglia	.07	.04
431	Randy Johnson	.30	.18
432	Damaso Garcia	.05	.03
433	Steve Olin (R)	.12	.07
434	Mark Carreon	.05	.03
435	Kevin Seitzer	.08	.05
436	Mel Hall	.07	.04
437	Les Lancaster	.05	.03
438	Greg Myers	.05	.03
439	Jeff Parrett	.05	.03
440	Alan Trammell	.10	.06
441	Bob Kipper	.05	.03
442	Jerry Browne	.07	.04
443	Cris Carpenter	.08	.05
444	Kyle Abbott (R) (#1 Pick)	.20	.12
445	Danny Jackson	.05	.03
446	Dan Pasqua	.05	.03
447	Atlee Hammaker	.05	.03
448	Greg Gagne	.05	.03
449	Dennis Rasmussen	.05	.03
450	Rickey Henderson	.25	.15
451	Mark Lemke	.07	.04
452	Luis de los Santos (R)	.07	.04
453	Jody Davis	.05	.03
454	Jeff King (R)	.20	.12
455	Jeffrey Leonard	.05	.03
456	Chris Gwynn	.05	.03
457	Gregg Jefferies	.25	.15
458	Bob McClure	.05	.03
459	Jim Lefebvre	.05	.03
460	Mike Scott	.07	.04
461	Carlos Martinez (R)	.08	.05
462	Denny Walling	.05	.03
463	Drew Hall	.05	.03
464	Jerome Walton	.05	.03
465	Kevin Gross	.05	.03
466	Rance Mulliniks	.05	.03
467	Juan Nieves	.05	.03
468	Billy Ripken	.05	.03
469	John Kruk	.12	.07
470	Frank Viola	.08	.05
471	Mike Brumley	.05	.03
472	Jose Uribe	.05	.03
473	Joe Price	.05	.03
474	Rich Thompson	.05	.03
475	Bob Welch	.08	.05
476	Brad Komminsk	.05	.03
477	Willie Fraser	.05	.03
478	Mike LaValliere	.05	.03
479	Frank White	.05	.03
480	Sid Fernandez	.07	.04
481	Garry Templeton	.07	.04
482	Steve Carter	.05	.03
483	Alejandro Pena	.07	.04
484	Mike Fitzgerald	.05	.03
485	John Candelaria	.05	.03
486	Jeff Treadway	.05	.03
487	Steve Searcy	.05	.03
488	Ken Oberkfell	.05	.03
489	Nick Leyva	.05	.03
490	Dan Plesac	.05	.03
491	Dave Cochrane (R)	.10	.06
492	Ron Oester	.05	.03
493	Jason Grimsley (R)	.15	.10
494	Terry Puhl	.05	.03
495	Lee Smith	.10	.06
496	Cecil Espy	.05	.03
497	Dave Schmidt	.05	.03
498	Rick Schu	.05	.03
499	Bill Long	.05	.03
500	Kevin Mitchell	.10	.06
501	Matt Young	.05	.03
502	Mitch Webster	.05	.03
503	Randy St. Claire	.05	.03
504	Tom O'Malley	.05	.03
505	Kelly Gruber	.08	.05
506	Tom Glavine	.35	.20

507	Gary Redus	.05	.03	564	Tyler Houston (R) (#1 Pick)	.12	.07
508	Terry Leach	.05	.03				
509	Tom Pagnozzi	.08	.05	565	Scott Fletcher	.05	.03
510	Dwight Gooden	.12	.07	566	Mark Knudson	.05	.03
511	Clay Parker	.05	.03	567	Ron Gant	.30	.18
512	Gary Pettis	.05	.03	568	John Smiley	.10	.06
513	Mark Eichhorn	.05	.00	569	Ivan Calderon	.08	.05
514	Andy Allanson	.05	.03	570	Cal Ripken	.50	.30
515	Len Dykstra	.20	.12	571	Brett Butler	.08	.05
516	Tim Leary	.05	.03	572	Greg Harris	.05	.03
517	Roberto Alomar	.50	.30	573	Danny Heep	.05	.03
518	Bill Krueger	.05	.03	574	Bill Swift	.10	.06
519	Bucky Dent	.05	.03	575	Lance Parrish	.07	.04
520	Mitch Williams	.05	.03	576	Mike Dyer	.05	.03
521	Craig Worthington	.05	.03	577	Charlie Hayes (R)	.15	.10
522	Mike Dunne	.05	.03	578	Joe Magrane	.07	.04
523	Jay Bell	.10	.06	579	Art Howe	.05	.03
524	Daryl Boston	.05	.03	580	Joe Carter	.30	.18
525	Wally Joyner	.10	.06	581	Ken Griffey	.08	.05
526	Checklist 397-528	.05	.03	582	Rick Honeycutt	.05	.03
527	Ron Hassey	.05	.03	583	Bruce Benedict	.05	.03
528	Kevin Wickander (R)	.08	.05	584	Phil Stephenson (R)	.07	.04
529	Greg Harris	.05	.03	585	Kal Daniels	.05	.03
530	Mark Langston	.10	.06	586	Ed Nunez	.05	.03
531	Ken Caminiti	.08	.05	587	Lance Johnson	.05	.03
532	Cecilio Guante	.05	.03	588	Rick Rhoden	.05	.03
533	Tim Jones	.05	.03	589	Mike Aldrete	.05	.03
534	Louie Meadows	.05	.03	590	Ozzie Smith	.20	.12
535	John Smoltz	.30	.18	591	Todd Stottlemyre	.08	.05
536	Bob Geren	.05	.03	592	R.J. Reynolds	.05	.03
537	Mark Grant	.05	.03	593	Scott Bradley	.05	.03
538	Billy Spiers	.08	.05	594	Luis Sojo (R)	.15	.10
539	Neal Heaton	.05	.03	595	Greg Swindell	.08	.05
540	Danny Tartabull	.10	.06	596	Jose DeJesus	.05	.03
541	Pat Perry	.05	.03	597	Chris Bosio	.07	.04
542	Darren Daulton	.20	.12	598	Brady Anderson	.15	.10
543	Nelson Liriano	.05	.03	599	Frank Williams	.05	.03
544	Dennis Boyd	.05	.03	600	Darryl Strawberry	.20	.12
545	Kevin McReynolds	.07	.04	601	Luis Rivera	.05	.03
546	Kevin Hickey	.05	.03	602	Scott Garrelts	.05	.03
547	Jack Howell	.05	.03	603	Tony Armas	.05	.03
548	Pat Clements	.05	.03	604	Ron Robinson	.05	.03
549	Don Zimmer	.05	.03	605	Mike Scioscia	.05	.03
550	Julio Franco	.08	.05	606	Storm Davis	.05	.03
551	Tim Crews	.05	.03	607	Steve Jeltz	.05	.03
552	Mike Smith	.05	.03	608	Eric Anthony (R)	.50	.30
553	Scott Scudder (R)	.12	.07	609	Sparky Anderson	.07	.04
554	Jay Buhner	.08	.05	610	Pedro Guererro	.07	.04
555	Jack Morris	.12	.07	611	Walt Terrell	.05	.03
556	Gene Larkin	.05	.03	612	Dave Gallagher	.05	.03
557	Jeff Innis	.10	.06	613	Jeff Pico	.05	.03
558	Rafael Ramirez	.05	.03	614	Nelson Santovenia	.05	.03
559	Andy McGaffigan	.05	.03	615	Rob Deer	.07	.04
560	Steve Sax	.08	.05	616	Brian Holman	.05	.03
561	Ken Dayley	.05	.03	617	Geronimo Berroa	.05	.03
562	Chad Kreuter	.07	.04	618	Eddie Whitson	.05	.03
563	Alex Sanchez	.05	.03	619	Rob Ducey	.05	.03

620	Tony Castillo (R)	.07	.04	676	Randy Kutcher	.05	.03
621	Melido Perez	.07	.04	677	Jay Tibbs	.05	.03
622	Sid Bream	.05	.03	678	Kirt Manwaring	.05	.03
623	Jim Corsi	.05	.03	679	Gary Ward	.05	.03
624	Darrin Jackson	.07	.04	680	Howard Johnson	.08	.05
625	Roger McDowell	.05	.03	681	Mike Schooler	.05	.03
626	Bob Melvin	.05	.03	682	Dan Bilardello	.05	.03
627	Jose Rijo	.10	.06	683	Kenny Rogers	.05	.03
628	Candy Maldonado	.05	.03	684	Julio Machado (R)	.10	.06
629	Eric Hetzel	.08	.05	685	Tony Fernandez	.08	.05
630	Gary Gaetti	.05	.03	686	Carmelo Martinez	.05	.03
631	John Wetteland (R)	.25	.15	687	Tim Birtsas	.05	.03
632	Scott Lusader	.05	.03	688	Milt Thompson	.05	.03
633	Dennis Cook	.05	.03	689	Rich Yett	.05	.03
634	Luis Polonia	.07	.04	690	Mark McGwire	.30	.18
635	Brian Downing	.07	.04	691	Chuck Cary	.05	.03
636	Jesse Orosco	.05	.03	692	Sammy Sosa (R)	1.00	.60
637	Craig Reynolds	.05	.03	693	Calvin Schiraldi	.05	.03
638	Jeff Montgomery	.07	.04	694	Mike Stanton (R)	.15	.10
639	Tony LaRussa	.07	.04	695	Tom Henke	.08	.05
640	Rick Sutcliffe	.07	.04	696	B.J. Surhoff	.05	.03
641	Doug Strange (R)	.10	.06	697	Mike Davis	.05	.03
642	Jack Armstrong	.07	.04	698	Omar Vizquel	.08	.05
643	Alfredo Griffin	.05	.03	699	Jim Leyland	.07	.04
644	Paul Assenmacher	.05	.03	700	Kirby Puckett	.40	.25
645	Jose Oquendo	.05	.03	701	Bernie Williams (R)	.35	.20
646	Checklist 529-660	.05	.03	702	Tony Phillips	.05	.03
647	Rex Hudler	.05	.03	703	Jeff Brantley	.08	.05
648	Jim Clancy	.05	.03	704	Chip Hale (R)	.10	.06
649	Dan Murphy (R)	.08	.05	705	Claudell Washington	.05	.03
650	Mike Witt	.05	.03	706	Geno Petralli	.05	.03
651	Rafael Santana	.05	.03	707	Luis Aquino	.05	.03
652	Mike Boddicker	.05	.03	708	Larry Sheets	.05	.03
653	John Moses	.05	.03	709	Juan Berenguer	.05	.03
654	Paul Coleman (R) (#1 Pick)	.15	.10	710	Von Hayes	.05	.03
655	Gregg Olson	.10	.06	711	Rick Aguilera	.07	.04
656	Mackey Sasser	.05	.03	712	Todd Benzinger	.05	.03
657	Terry Mulholland	.05	.03	713	Tim Drummond (R)	.10	.06
658	Donell Nixon	.05	.03	714	Marquis Grissom (R)	1.00	.60
659	Greg Cadaret	.05	.03	715	Greg Maddux	.30	.18
660	Vince Coleman	.07	.04	716	Steve Balboni	.05	.03
661	Dick Howser (Clock)	.07	.04	717	Ron Karkovice	.05	.03
662	Mike Schmidt (Clock)	.15	.10	718	Gary Sheffield	.60	.35
663	Fred Lynn Clock)	.08	.05	719	Wally Whitehurst (R)	.10	.06
664	Johnny Bench (Clock)	.10	.06	720	Andres Galarraga	.15	.10
665	Sandy Koufax (Clock)	.15	.10	721	Lee Mazzilli	.05	.03
666	Brian Fisher	.05	.03	722	Felix Fermin	.05	.03
667	Curt Wilkerson	.05	.03	723	Jeff Robinson	.05	.03
668	Joe Oliver (R)	.15	.10	724	Juan Bell	.10	.06
669	Tom Lasorda	.07	.04	725	Terry Pendleton	.15	.10
670	Dennis Eckersley	.15	.10	726	Gene Nelson	.05	.03
671	Bob Boone	.08	.05	727	Pat Tabler	.05	.03
672	Roy Smith	.05	.03	728	Jim Acker	.05	.03
673	Joey Meyer	.05	.03	729	Bobby Valentine	.05	.03
674	Spike Owen	.05	.03	730	Tony Gwynn	.25	.15
675	Jim Abbott	.25	.15	731	Don Carman	.05	.03
				732	Ernie Riles	.05	.03

733	John Dopson	.05	.03
734	Kevin Elster	.05	.03
735	Charlie Hough	.05	.03
736	Rick Dempsey	.05	.03
737	Chris Sabo	.08	.05
738	Gene Harris	.05	.03
739	Dale Sveum	.05	.03
740	Jesse Barfield	.07	.04
741	Steve Wilson	.05	.03
742	Ernie Whitt	.05	.03
743	Tom Candiotti	.07	.04
744	Kelly Mann (R)	.08	.05
745	Hubie Brooks	.07	.04
746	Dave Smith	.05	.03
747	Randy Bush	.05	.03
748	Doyle Alexander	.05	.03
749	Mark Parent	.05	.03
750	Dale Murphy	.12	.07
751	Steve Lyons	.05	.03
752	Tom Gordon	.10	.06
753	Chris Speier	.05	.03
754	Bob Walk	.05	.03
755	Rafael Palmeiro	.20	.12
756	Ken Howell	.05	.03
757	Larry Walker (R)	.80	.50
758	Mark Thurmond	.05	.03
759	Tom Trebelhorn	.05	.03
760	Wade Boggs	.20	.12
761	Mike Jackson	.05	.03
762	Doug Dascenzo	.05	.03
763	Denny Martinez	.10	.06
764	Tim Teufel	.05	.03
765	Chili Davis	.08	.05
766	Brian Meyer	.08	.05
767	Tracy Jones	.05	.03
768	Chuck Crim	.05	.03
769	Greg Hibbard (R)	.15	.10
770	Cory Snyder	.07	.04
771	Pete Smith	.12	.07
772	Jeff Reed	.05	.03
773	Dave Leiper	.05	.03
774	Ben McDonald (R)	.40	.25
775	Andy Van Slyke	.15	.10
776	Charlie Leibrandt	.05	.03
777	Tim Laudner	.05	.03
778	Mike Jeffcoat	.05	.03
779	Lloyd Moseby	.05	.03
780	Orel Hershiser	.10	.06
781	Mario Diaz	.05	.03
782	Jose Alvarez	.05	.03
783	Checklist 661-792	.05	.03
784	Scott Bailes	.05	.03
785	Jim Rice	.08	.05
786	Eric King	.05	.03
787	Rene Gonzales	.08	.05
788	Frank DiPino	.05	.03
789	John Wathan	.05	.03

790	Gary Carter	.10	.06
791	Alvaro Espinoza	.05	.03
792	Gerald Perry	.05	.03

1990 Topps Traded

This 132-card set marks the tenth straight year that Topps issued an end-of-year Traded set. It also marks the first time the cards in the Traded Series were available in wax packs. Cards measure 2-1/2" by 3-1/2" and the set features a combination of players who were traded during the season and promising rookies.

		MINT	NR/MT
Complete Set (132)		7.00	4.50
Commons		.05	.03

1T	Darrel Akerfelds	.05	.03
2T	Sandy Alomar, Jr.	.12	.07
3T	Brad Arnsberg	.07	.04
4T	Steve Avery	.75	.45
5T	Wally Backman	.05	.03
6T	Carlos Baerga (R)	2.00	1.25
7T	Kevin Bass	.05	.03
8T	Willie Blair (R)	.15	.10
9T	Mike Blowers (R)	.08	.05
10T	Shawn Boskie (R)	.10	.06
11T	Daryl Boston	.05	.03
12T	Dennis Boyd	.05	.03
13T	Glenn Braggs	.05	.03
14T	Hubie Brooks	.08	.05
15T	Tom Brunansky	.08	.05
16T	John Burkett (R)	.40	.25
17T	Casey Candaele	.05	.03
18T	John Candelaria	.05	.03
19T	Gary Carter	.10	.06
20T	Joe Carter	.25	.15

21T	Rick Cerone	.05	.03	78T	Randy Myers	.07	.04

21T	Rick Cerone	.05	.03	78T	Randy Myers	.07	.04
22T	Scott Coolbaugh (R)	.08	.05	79T	Tim Naehring (R)	.20	.12
23T	Bobby Cox	.05	.03	80T	Junior Noboa	.05	.03
24T	Mark Davis	.08	.05	81T	Matt Nokes	.08	.05
25T	Storm Davis	.05	.03	82T	Pete O'Brien	.05	.03
26T	Edgar Diaz (R)	.10	.06	83T	John Olerud (R)	2.50	1.40
27T	Wayne Edwards (R)	.10	.06	84T	Greg Olson (R)	.10	.06
28T	Mark Eichhorn	.05	.03	85T	Junior Ortiz	.05	.03
29T	Scott Erickson (R)	.35	.20	86T	Dave Parker	.08	.05
30T	Nick Esasky	.05	.03	87T	Rick Parker	.10	.06
31T	Cecil Fielder	.30	.18	88T	Bob Patterson	.05	.03
32T	John Franco	.05	.03	89T	Alejandro Pena	.07	.04
33T	Travis Fryman (R)	1.25	.80	90T	Tony Pena	.08	.05
34T	Bill Gullickson	.08	.05	91T	Pascual Perez	.07	.04
35T	Darryl Hamilton	.12	.07	92T	Gerald Perry	.05	.03
36T	Mike Harkey	.15	.10	93T	Dan Petry	.05	.03
37T	Bud Harrelson	.05	.03	94T	Gary Pettis	.05	.03
38T	Billy Hatcher	.05	.03	95T	Tony Phillips	.05	.03
39T	Keith Hernandez	.08	.05	96T	Lou Pinella	.08	.05
40T	Joe Hesketh	.05	.03	97T	Luis Polonia	.08	.05
41T	Dave Hollins (R)	.75	.45	98T	Jim Presley	.05	.03
42T	Sam Horn	.10	.06	99T	Scott Radinsky (R)	.15	.10
43T	Steve Howard (R)	.10	.06	100T	Willie Randolph	.08	.05
44T	Todd Hundley (R)	.15	.10	101T	Jeff Reardon	.10	.06
45T	Jeff Huson	.05	.03	102T	Greg Riddoch	.05	.03
46T	Chris James	.05	.03	103T	Jeff Robinson	.05	.03
47T	Stan Javier	.05	.03	104T	Ron Robinson	.05	.03
48T	Dave Justice (R)	1.50	.90	105T	Kevin Romine	.05	.03
49T	Jeff Kaiser (R)	.08	.05	106T	Scott Ruskin (R)	.12	.07
50T	Dana Kiecker (R)	.12	.07	107T	John Russell	.05	.03
51T	Joe Klink	.05	.03	108T	Bill Sampen (R)	.12	.07
52T	Brent Knackert (R)	.12	.07	109T	Juan Samuel	.05	.03
53T	Brad Komminsk	.05	.03	110T	Scott Sanderson	.07	.04
54T	Mark Langston	.10	.06	111T	Jack Savage (R)	.10	.06
55T	Tim Layana (R)	.15	.10	112T	Dave Schmidt	.05	.03
56T	Rick Leach	.05	.03	113T	Red Schoendienst	.07	.04
57T	Terry Leach	.05	.03	114T	Terry Shumpert (R)	.15	.10
58T	Tim Leary	.08	.05	115T	Matt Sinatro	.05	.03
59T	Craig Lefferts	.05	.03	116T	Don Slaught	.05	.03
60T	Charlie Leibrandt	.05	.03	117T	Bryn Smith	.05	.03
61T	Jim Leyritz (R)	.15	.10	118T	Lee Smith	.12	.07
62T	Fred Lynn	.08	.05	119T	Paul Sorrento (R)	.30	.18
63T	Kevin Maas (R)	.15	.10	120T	Franklin Stubbs	.05	.03
64T	Shane Mack	.15	.10	121T	Russ Swan (R)	.10	.06
65T	Candy Maldonado	.07	.04	122T	Bob Tewksbury	.10	.06
66T	Fred Manrique	.05	.03	123T	Wayne Tolleson	.05	.03
67T	Mike Marshall	.05	.03	124T	John Tudor	.07	.04
68T	Carmelo Martinez	.05	.03	125T	Randy Veres (R)	.08	.05
69T	John Marzano	.05	.03	126T	Hector Villanueva (R)	.12	.07
70T	Ben McDonald	.30	.18	127T	Mitch Webster	.07	.04
71T	Jack McDowell	.35	.20	128T	Ernie Whitt	.05	.03
72T	John McNamara	.05	.03	129T	Frank Wills	.05	.03
73T	Orlando Mercado	.05	.03	130T	Dave Winfield	.25	.15
74T	Stump Merrill	.05	.03	131T	Matt Young	.05	.03
75T	Alan Mills (R)	.10	.06	132T	Checklist	.05	.03
76T	Hal Morris	.15	.10				
77T	Lloyd Moseby	.07	.04				

1991 Topps

This 792-card set marks Topps 40th Anniversary and the card fronts reflect that milestone with a special "Topps 40th" logo above the photo. As part of their celebration Topps randomly inserted into wax packs one of each card they issued since 1952. Card fronts feature full color player photos and different color borders with each team assigned the same border colors. Card backs are horizontal. Special subsets include Record Breakers, All-Stars, Number One Draft Picks and Future Stars.

		MINT	NR/MT
Complete Set (792)		18.50	12.50
Commons		.05	.03
1	Nolan Ryan	.60	.35
2	George Brett (RB)	.12	.07
3	Carlton Fisk (RB)	.08	.05
4	Kevin Maas (RB)	.07	.04
5	Cal Ripken (RB)	.20	.12
6	Nolan Ryan (RB)	.30	.18
7	Ryne Sandberg (RB)	.15	.10
8	Bobby Thigpen (RB)	.07	.04
9	Darrin Fletcher	.05	.03
10	Gregg Olson	.08	.05
11	Roberto Kelly	.12	.07
12	Paul Assenmacher	.05	.03
13	Mariano Duncan	.05	.03
14	Dennis Lamp	.05	.03
15	Von Hayes	.05	.03
16	Mike Heath	.05	.03
17	Jeff Brantley	.05	.03
18	Nelson Liriano	.05	.03
19	Jeff Robinson	.05	.03
20	Pedro Guerrero	.07	.04
21	Joe Morgan	.05	.03
22	Storm Davis	.05	.03
23	Jim Gantner	.05	.03
24	Dave Martinez	.05	.03
25	Tim Belcher	.07	.04
26	Luis Sojo	.07	.04
27	Bobby Witt	.08	.05
28	Alvaro Espinoza	.05	.03
29	Bob Walk	.05	.03
30	Gregg Jefferies	.15	.10
31	Colby Ward (R)	.09	.05
32	Mike Simms (R)	.10	.06
33	Barry Jones	.05	.03
34	Atlee Hammaker	.05	.03
35	Greg Maddux	.20	.12
36	Donnie Hill	.05	.03
37	Tom Bolton	.05	.03
38	Scott Bradley	.05	.03
39	Jim Neidlinger (R)	.10	.06
40	Kevin Mitchell	.08	.05
41	Ken Dayley	.05	.03
42	Chris Hoiles (R)	.20	.12
43	Roger McDowell	.05	.03
44	Mike Felder	.05	.03
45	Chris Sabo	.08	.05
46	Tim Drummond	.05	.03
47	Brook Jacoby	.05	.03
48	Dennis Boyd	.05	.03
49a	Pat Borders (Er) (40 stolen bases)	.20	.12
49b	Pat Borders (Cor)	.05	.03
50	Bob Welch	.08	.05
51	Art Howe	.05	.03
52	Francisco Oliveras	.05	.03
53	Mike Sharperson	.05	.03
54	Gary Mielke	.05	.03
55	Jeffrey Leonard	.05	.03
56	Jeff Parrett	.05	.03
57	Jack Howell	.05	.03
58	Mel Stottlemyre	.05	.03
59	Eric Yelding	.07	.04
60	Frank Viola	.08	.05
61	Stan Javier	.05	.03
62	Lee Guetterman	.05	.03
63	Milt Thompson	.05	.03
64	Tom Herr	.05	.03
65	Bruce Hurst	.07	.04
66	Terry Kennedy	.05	.03
67	Rick Honeycutt	.05	.03
68	Gary Sheffield	.30	.18
69	Steve Wilson	.05	.03
70	Ellis Burks	.08	.05
71	Jim Acker	.05	.03
72	Junior Ortiz	.05	.03
73	Craig Worthington	.05	.03
74	Shane Andrews (R) (#1 Pick)	.25	.15
75	Jack Morris	.12	.07
76	Jerry Browne	.05	.03
77	Drew Hall	.05	.03
78	Geno Petralli	.05	.03

79	Frank Thomas	1.50	.90
80	Fernando Valenzuela	.08	.05
81	Cito Gaston	.07	.04
82	Tom Galvine	.25	.15
83	Daryl Boston	.05	.03
84	Bob McClure	.05	.03
85	Jesse Barfield	.07	.04
86	Les Lancaster	.05	.03
87	Tracy Jones	.05	.03
88	Bob Tewksbury	.08	.05
89	Darren Dalton	.15	.10
90	Danny Tartabull	.12	.07
91	Greg Colbrunn (R)	.20	.12
92	Danny Jackson	.05	.03
93	Ivan Calderon	.07	.04
94	John Dopson	.05	.03
95	Paul Molitor	.20	.12
96	Trevor Wilson	.05	.03
97	Brady Anderson	.15	.10
98	Sergio Valdez	.05	.03
99	Chris Gwynn	.05	.03
100a	Don Mattingly (Er)	.50	.30
	(10 hits in 1990)		
100b	Don Mattingly (Cor)	.15	.10
	(101 hits in 1990)		
101	Ron Ducey	.05	.03
102	Gene Larkin	.05	.03
103	Tim Costo (R) (#1	.20	.12
	Pick)		
104	Don Robinson	.05	.03
105	Keith Miller	.05	.03
106	Ed Nunez	.05	.03
107	Luis Polonia	.07	.04
108	Matt Young	.05	.03
109	Greg Riddoch	.05	.03
110	Tom Henke	.07	.04
111	Andres Thomas	.05	.03
112	Frank DiPino	.05	.03
113	Carl Everett (R) (#1	.25	.15
	Pick)		
114	Lance Dickson (R)	.20	.12
115	Hubie Brooks	.07	.04
116	Mark Davis	.05	.03
117	Dion James	.05	.03
118	Tom Edens (R)	.08	.05
119	Carl Nichols	.05	.03
120	Joe Carter	.20	.12
121	Eric King	.05	.03
122	Paul O'Neill	.10	.06
123	Greg Harris	.05	.03
124	Randy Bush	.05	.03
125	Steve Bedrosian	.07	.04
126	Bernard Gilkey (R)	.25	.15
127	Joe Price	.05	.03
128	Travis Fryman	.50	.30
129	Mark Eichhorn	.05	.03
130	Ozzie Smith	.15	.10
131	Checklist 1	.05	.03
132	Jamie Quirk	.05	.03
133	Greg Briley	.05	.03
134	Kevin Elster	.05	.03
135	Jerome Walton	.05	.03
136	Dave Schmidt	.05	.03
137	Randy Ready	.05	.03
138	Jamie Moyer	.05	.03
139	Jeff Treadway	.05	.03
140	Fred McGriff	.25	.15
141	Nick Leyva	.05	.03
142	Curtis Wilkerson	.05	.03
143	John Smiley	.08	.05
144	Dave Henderson	.07	.04
145	Lou Whitaker	.07	.04
146	Dan Plesac	.05	.03
147	Carlos Baerga	.40	.25
148	Rey Palacios	.05	.03
149	Al Osuna (R)	.15	.10
150	Cal Ripken	.40	.25
151	Tom Browning	.08	.05
152	Mickey Hatcher	.05	.03
153	Bryan Harvey	.08	.05
154	Jay Buhner	.07	.04
155	Dwight Evans	.08	.05
156	Carlos Martinez	.05	.03
157	John Smoltz	.15	.10
158	Jose Uribe	.05	.03
159	Joe Boever	.05	.03
160	Vince Coleman	.07	.04
161	Tim Leary	.05	.03
162	Ozzie Canseco (R)	.12	.07
163	Dave Johnson	.05	.03
164	Edgar Diaz	.05	.03
165	Sandy Alomar	.10	.06
166	Harold Baines	.08	.05
167	Randy Tomlin (R)	.20	.12
168	John Olerud	.50	.30
169	Luis Aquino	.05	.03
170	Carlton Fisk	.12	.07
171	Tony LaRussa	.07	.04
172	Pete Incaviglia	.05	.03
173	Jason Grimsley	.05	.03
174	Ken Caminiti	.07	.04
175	Jack Armstrong	.05	.03
176	John Orton	.08	.05
177	Reggie Harris (R)	.10	.06
178	Dave Valle	.05	.03
179	Pete Harnisch	.08	.05
180	Tony Gwynn	.15	.10
181	Duane Ward	.05	.03
182	Junior Noboa	.05	.03
183	Clay Parker	.05	.03
184	Gary Green	.05	.03
185	Joe Magrane	.07	.04
186	Rod Booker	.05	.03
187	Greg Cadaret	.05	.03

188 Damon Berryhill	.05	.03
189 Daryl Irvine (R)	.10	.06
190 Matt Williams	.20	.12
191 Willie Blair	.08	.05
192 Rob Deer	.07	.04
193 Felix Fermin	.05	.03
194 Xavier Hernandez (R)	.10	.00
195 Wally Joyner	.10	.06
196 Jim Vatcher	.08	.05
197 Chris Nabholz (R)	.20	.12
198 R.J. Reynolds	.05	.03
199 Mike Hartley	.05	.03
200 Darryl Strawberry	.15	.10
201 Tom Kelly	.05	.03
202 Jim Leyritz	.05	.03
203 Gene Harris	.05	.03
204 Herm Winningham	.05	.03
205 Mike Perez (R)	.15	.10
206 Carlos Quintana	.08	.05
207 Gary Wayne	.05	.03
208 Willie Wilson	.07	.04
209 Ken Howell	.05	.03
210 Lance Parrish	.07	.04
211 Brian Barnes (R)	.15	.10
212 Steve Finley	.07	.04
213 Frank Wills	.05	.03
214 Joe Girardi	.05	.03
215 Dave Smith	.05	.03
216 Greg Gagne	.05	.03
217 Chris Bosio	.07	.04
218 Rick Parker	.05	.03
219 Jack McDowell	.20	.12
220 Tim Wallach	.08	.05
221 Don Slaught	.05	.03
222 Brian McRae (R)	.25	.15
223 Allan Anderson	.05	.03
224 Juan Gonzalez	1.00	.60
225 Randy Johnson	.25	.15
226 Alfredo Griffin	.05	.03
227 Steve Avery	.25	.15
228 Rex Hudler	.05	.03
229 Rance Mulliniks	.05	.03
230 Sid Fernandez	.07	.04
231 Doug Rader	.05	.03
232 Jose DeJesus	.05	.03
233 Al Leiter	.05	.03
234 Scott Erickson	.15	.10
235 Dave Parker	.08	.05
236 Frank Tanana	.05	.03
237 Rick Cerone	.05	.03
238 Mike Dunne	.05	.03
239 Darren Lewis (R)	.20	.12
240 Mike Scott	.07	.04
241 Dave Clark	.05	.03
242 Mike LaCoss	.05	.03
243 Lance Johnson	.07	.04
244 Mike Jeffcoat	.05	.03

245 Kal Daniels	.05	.03
246 Kevin Wickander	.05	.03
247 Jody Reed	.05	.03
248 Tom Gordon	.08	.05
249 Bob Melvin	.05	.03
250 Dennis Eckersley	.12	.07
251 Mark Lemke	.05	.03
252 Mel Rojas (R)	.10	.06
253 Garry Templeton	.07	.04
254 Shawn Boskie	.05	.03
255 Brian Downing	.05	.03
256 Greg Hibbard	.05	.03
257 Tom O'Malley	.05	.03
258 Chris Hammond (R)	.15	.10
259 Hensley Meulens	.08	.05
260 Harold Reynolds	.05	.03
261 Bud Harrelson	.05	.03
262 Tim Jones	.05	.03
263 Checklist 2	.05	.03
264 Dave Hollins	.25	.15
265 Mark Gubicza	.08	.05
266 Carmen Castillo	.05	.03
267 Mark Knudson	.05	.03
268 Tom Brookens	.05	.03
269 Joe Hesketh	.05	.03
270 Mark McGwire	.20	.12
271 Omar Olivares (R)	.10	.06
272 Jeff King	.10	.06
273 Johnny Ray	.05	.03
274 Ken Williams	.05	.03
275 Alan Trammell	.08	.05
276 Bill Swift	.08	.05
277 Scott Coolbaugh	.05	.03
278 Alex Fernandez (R)	.35	.20
279a Jose Gonzalez (Wrong Photo)	.20	.12
279b Jose Gonzalez (Cor	.05	.03
280 Bret Saberhagen	.10	.06
281 Larry Sheets	.05	.03
282 Don Carman	.05	.03
283 Marquis Grissom	.20	.12
284 Bill Spiers	.05	.03
285 Jim Abbott	.15	.10
286 Ken Oberkfell	.05	.03
287 Mark Grant	.05	.03
288 Derrick May	.12	.07
289 Tim Birtsas	.05	.03
290 Steve Sax	.08	.05
291 John Wathan	.05	.03
292 Bud Black	.05	.03
293 Jay Bell	.08	.05
294 Mike Moore	.05	.03
295 Rafael Palmeiro	.20	.12
296 Mark Williamson	.05	.03
297 Manny Lee	.05	.03
298 Omar Vizquel	.08	.05
299 Scott Radinsky	.08	.05

300 Kirby Puckett	.25	.15
301 Steve Farr	.05	.03
302 Tim Teufel	.05	.03
303 Mike Boddicker	.05	.03
304 Kevin Reimer	.12	.07
305 Mike Scioscia	.07	.04
306 Lonnie Smith	.07	.04
307 Andy Benes	.12	.07
308 Tom Pagnozzi	.07	.04
309 Norm Charlton	.08	.05
310 Gary Carter	.10	.06
311 Jeff Pico	.05	.03
312 Charlie Hayes	.07	.04
313 Ron Robinson	.05	.03
314 Gary Pettis	.05	.03
315 Roberto Alomar	.25	.15
316 Gene Nelson	.05	.03
317 Mike Fitzgerald	.05	.03
318 Rick Aguilera	.05	.03
319 Jeff McKnight	.05	.03
320 Tony Fernandez	.08	.05
321 Bob Rodgers	.05	.03
322 Terry Shumpert	.08	.05
323 Cory Snyder	.07	.04
324 Ron Kittle	.05	.03
325 Brett Butler	.08	.05
326 Ken Patterson	.05	.03
327 Ron Hassey	.05	.03
328 Walt Terrell	.05	.03
329 Dave Justice	.35	.20
330 Dwight Gooden	.10	.06
331 Eric Anthony	.15	.10
332 Kenny Rogers	.05	.03
333 Clipper Jones (R) (#1 Pick)	1.00	.60
334 Todd Benzinger	.05	.03
335 Mitch Williams	.05	.03
336 Matt Nokes	.05	.03
337 Keith Comstock	.05	.03
338 Luis Rivera	.05	.03
339 Larry Walker	.20	.12
340 Ramon Martinez	.12	.07
341 John Moses	.05	.03
342 Mickey Morandini	.12	.07
343 Jose Oquendo	.05	.03
344 Jeff Russell	.07	.04
345 Jose DeJesus	.05	.03
346 Jesse Orosco	.05	.03
347 Greg Vaughn	.12	.07
348 Todd Stottlemyre	.08	.05
349 Dave Gallagher	.05	.03
350 Glenn Davis	.05	.03
351 Joe Torre	.07	.04
352 Frank White	.05	.03
353 Tony Castillo	.05	.03
354 Sid Bream	.05	.03
355 Chili Davis	.07	.04
356 Mike Marshall	.05	.03
357 Jack Savage	.05	.03
358 Mark Parent	.05	.03
359 Chuck Cary	.05	.03
360 Tim Raines	.07	.04
361 Scott Garrelts	.05	.03
362 Hector Villanueva	.08	.05
363 Rick Mahler	.05	.03
364 Dan Pasqua	.05	.03
365 Mike Schooler	.05	.03
366 Checklist 3	.05	.03
367 Dave Walsh (R)	.10	.06
368 Felix Jose	.12	.07
369 Steve Searcy	.05	.03
370 Kelly Gruber	.08	.05
371 Jeff Montgomery	.07	.04
372 Spike Owen	.05	.03
373 Darrin Jackson	.07	.04
374 Larry Casian (R)	.08	.05
375 Tony Pena	.05	.03
376 Mike Harkey	.08	.05
377 Rene Gonzales	.08	.05
378 Wilson Alvarez (R)	.25	.15
379 Randy Velarde	.05	.03
380 Willie McGee	.08	.05
381 Jose Lind	.05	.03
382 Mackey Sasser	.05	.03
383 Pete Smith	.10	.06
384 Gerald Perry	.05	.03
385 Mickey Tettleton	.07	.04
386 Cecil Fielder (AS)	.12	.07
387 Julio Franco (AS)	.07	.04
388 Kelly Gruber (AS)	.07	.04
389 Alan Trammell (AS)	.08	.05
390 Jose Canseco (AS)	.12	.07
391 Rickey Henderson (AS)	.12	.07
392 Ken Griffey Jr. (AS)	.35	.20
393 Carlton Fisk (AS)	.08	.05
394 Bob Welch (AS)	.07	.04
395 Chuck Finley (AS)	.07	.04
396 Bobby Thigpen (AS)	.07	.04
397 Eddie Murray (AS)	.10	.06
398 Ryne Sandberg (AS)	.12	.07
399 Matt Williams (AS)	.10	.06
400 Barry Larkin (AS)	.10	.06
401 Barry Bonds (AS)	.25	.15
402 Darryl Strawberry(AS)	.10	.06
403 Bobby Bonilla (AS)	.08	.05
404 Mike Scoscia (AS)	.07	.04
405 Doug Drabek (AS)	.08	.05
406 Frank Viola (AS)	.08	.05
407 John Franco (AS)	.07	.04
408 Ernie Riles	.05	.03
409 Mike Stanley	.05	.03
410 Dave Righetti	.07	.04
411 Lance Blankenship	.05	.03
412 Dave Bergman	.05	.03

413	Terry Mulholland	.05	.03	470	Howard Johnson	.08	.05
414	Sammy Sosa	.20	.12	471	Mike Lieberthal (R)	.20	.12
415	Rick Sutcliffe	.07	.04		(#1 Pick)		
416	Randy Milligan	.07	.04	472	Kirt Manwaring	.05	.03
417	Bill Krueger	.05	.03	473	Curt Young	.05	.03
418	Nick Esasky	.05	.03	474	Phil Plantier (R)	.60	.35
419	Jeff Reed	.05	.03	475	Teddy Higuera	.07	.04
420	Bobby Thigpen	.07	.04	476	Glenn Wilson	.05	.03
421	Alex Cole	.08	.05	477	Mike Fetters	.05	.03
422	Rick Rueschel	.05	.03	478	Kurt Stillwell	.05	.03
423	Rafael Ramirez	.05	.03	479	Bob Patterson	.05	.03
424	Calvin Schiraldi	.05	.03	480	Dave Magadan	.07	.04
425	Andy Van Slyke	.12	.07	481	Eddie Whitson	.05	.03
426	Joe Grahe (R)	.15	.10	482	Tino Martinez	.12	.07
427	Rick Dempsey	.05	.03	483	Mike Aldrete	.05	.03
428	John Barfield	.05	.03	484	Dave LaPoint	.05	.03
429	Stump Merill	.05	.03	485	Terry Pendleton	.12	.07
430	Gary Gaetti	.05	.03	486	Tommy Greene	.15	.10
431	Paul Gibson	.05	.03	487	Rafael Bolliard	.05	.03
432	Delino DeShields	.20	.12	488	Jeff Manto	.08	.05
433	Pat Tabler	.05	.03	489	Bobby Valentine	.05	.03
434	Julio Machado	.07	.04	490	Kirk Gibson	.07	.04
435	Kevin Mass	.10	.06	491	Kurt Miller (R) (#1	.25	.15
436	Scott Bankhead	.05	.03		Pick)		
437	Doug Dascenzo	.05	.03	492	Ernie Whitt	.05	.03
438	Vicente Palacios	.05	.03	493	Jose Rijo	.08	.05
439	Dickie Thon	.05	.03	494	Chris James	.05	.03
440	George Bell	.08	.05	495	Charlie Hough	.05	.03
441	Zane Smith	.05	.03	496	Marty Barrett	.05	.03
442	Charlie O'Brien	.05	.03	497	Ben McDonald	.15	.10
443	Jeff Innis	.05	.03	498	Mark Salas	.05	.03
444	Glenn Braggss	.05	.03	499	Melido Perez	.05	.03
445	Greg Swindell	.08	.05	500	Will Clark	.20	.12
446	Craig Grebeck (R)	.10	.06	501	Mike Bielecki	.05	.03
447	John Burkett	.10	.06	502	Carney Lansford	.07	.04
448	Craig Lefferts	.05	.03	503	Roy Smith	.05	.03
449	Juan Berenguer	.05	.03	504	Julio Valera (R)	.08	.05
450	Wade Boggs	.15	.10	505	Chuck Finley	.08	.05
451	Neal Heaton	.05	.03	506	Darnell Coles	.05	.03
452	Bill Schroeder	.05	.03	507	Steve Jeltz	.05	.03
453	Lenny Harris	.05	.03	508	Mike York (R)	.05	.03
454	Kevin Appier	.12	.07	509	Glenallen Hill	.10	.06
455	Walt Weiss	.05	.03	510	John Franco	.05	.03
456	Charlie Leibrandt	.05	.03	511	Steve Balboni	.05	.03
457	Todd Handley	.10	.06	512	Jose Mesa	.05	.03
458	Brian Holman	.05	.03	513	Jerald Clark	.08	.05
459	Tom Trebelhorn	.05	.03	514	Mike Stanton	.05	.03
460	Dave Steib	.08	.05	515	Alvin Davis	.05	.03
461	Robin Ventura	.25	.15	516	Karl Rhodes (R)	.12	.07
462	Steve Frey	.05	.03	517	Joe Oliver	.08	.05
463	Dwight Smith	.07	.04	518	Cris Carpenter	.07	.04
464	Steve Buechele	.07	.04	519	Sparky Anderson	.07	.04
465	Ken Griffey	.07	.04	520	Mark Grace	.12	.07
466	Charles Nagy	.20	.12	521	Joe Orsulak	.05	.03
467	Dennis Cook	.05	.03	522	Stan Belinda	.07	.04
468	Tim Hulett	.05	.03	523	Rodney McCray (R)	.07	.04
469	Chet Lemon	.05	.03	524	Darrel Akerfelds	.05	.03

525 Willie Randolph	.07	.04
526 Moises Alou (R)	.35	.20
527 Checklist 4	.05	.03
528 Denny Martinez	.10	.06
529 Marc Newfield (R)	.60	.35
530 Roger Clemens	.25	.15
531 Dave Rhode (R)	.10	.06
532 Kirk McCaskill	.05	.03
533 Oddibe McDowell	.05	.03
534 Mike Jackson	.05	.03
535 Ruben Sierra	.15	.10
536 Mike Witt	.05	.03
537 Mike LaValliere	.05	.03
538 Bip Roberts	.08	.05
539 Scott Terry	.05	.03
540 George Brett	.20	.12
541 Domingo Ramos	.05	.03
542 Rob Murphy	.05	.03
543 Junior Felix	.07	.04
544 Alejandro Pena	.07	.04
545 Dale Murphy	.10	.06
546 Jeff Ballard	.05	.03
547 Mike Pagliarulo	.05	.03
548 Jaime Navarro	.10	.06
549 John McNamara	.05	.03
550 Eric Davis	.10	.06
551 Bob Kipper	.05	.03
552 Jeff Hamilton	.05	.03
553 Joe Klink	.05	.03
554 Brian Harper	.05	.03
555 Turner Ward (R)	.10	.06
556 Gary Ward	.05	.03
557 Wally Whitehurst	.05	.03
558 Otis Nixon	.07	.04
559 Adam Peterson	.05	.03
560 Greg Smith	.08	.05
561 Tim McIntosh	.12	.07
562 Jeff Kunkel	.05	.03
563 Brent Knackert	.08	.05
564 Dante Bichette	.08	.05
565 Craig Biggio	.10	.06
566 Craig Wilson (R)	.10	.06
567 Dwayne Henry	.05	.03
568 Ron Karkovice	.05	.03
569 Curt Schilling	.10	.06
570 Barry Bonds	.60	.35
571 Pat Combs	.07	.04
572 Dave Anderson	.05	.03
573 Rich Rodriguez (R)	.12	.07
574 John Marzano	.05	.03
575 Robin Yount	.20	.12
576 Jeff Kaiser	.05	.03
577 Bill Doran	.05	.03
578 Dave West	.05	.03
579 Roger Craig	.05	.03
580 Dave Stewart	.08	.05
581 Luis Quinones	.05	.03

582 Marty Clary	.05	.03
583 Tony Phillips	.07	.04
584 Kevin Brown	.10	.06
585 Pete O'Brien	.05	.03
586 Fred Lynn	.07	.04
587 Jose Offerman	.15	.10
588 Mark Whiten (R)	.30	.18
589 Scott Ruskin	.10	.06
590 Eddie Murray	.12	.07
591 Ken Hill	.10	.06
592 B.J. Surhoff	.05	.03
593 Mike Walker (R)	.08	.05
594 Rich Garces (R)	.12	.07
595 Bill Landrum	.05	.03
596 Ronnie Walden (R)	.12	.07
(#1 Pick)		
597 Jerry Don Gleaton	.05	.03
598 Sam Horn	.07	.04
599 Greg Myers	.05	.03
600 Bo Jackson	.15	.10
601 Bob Ojeda	.05	.03
602 Casey Candaele	.05	.03
603a Wes Chamberlain	.50	.30
(Wrong Photo)		
603b Wes Chamberlain (Cor)	.25	.15
604 Billy Hatcher	.05	.03
605 Jeff Reardon	.10	.06
606 Jim Gott	.05	.03
607 Edgar Martinez	.12	.07
608 Todd Burns	.05	.03
609 Jeff Torborg	.05	.03
610 Andres Galarraga	.12	.07
611 Dave Eiland	.07	.04
612 Steve Lyons	.05	.03
613 Eric Show	.05	.03
614 Luis Salazar	.05	.03
615 Bert Blyleven	.08	.05
616 Todd Zeile	.10	.06
617 Bill Wegman	.05	.03
618 Sil Campusano	.05	.03
619 David Wells	.05	.03
620 Ozzie Guillen	.07	.04
621 Ted Power	.05	.03
622 Jack Daugherty	.05	.03
623 Jeff Blauser	.08	.05
624 Tom Candiotti	.07	.04
625 Terry Steinbach	.07	.04
626 Gerald Young	.05	.03
627 Tim Layana	.05	.03
628 Greg Litton	.05	.03
629 Wes Gardner	.05	.03
630 Dave Winfield	.20	.12
631 Mike Morgan	.07	.04
632 Lloyd Moseby	.05	.03
633 Kevin Tapani	.08	.05
634 Henry Cotto	.05	.03
635 Andy Hawkins	.05	.03

636 Geronimo Pena (R)	.12	.07
637 Bruce Ruffin	.05	.03
638 Mike Macfarlane	.05	.03
639 Frank Robinson	.10	.06
640 Andre Dawson	.12	.07
641 Mike Henneman	.05	.03
642 Hal Morris	.10	.06
643 Jim Presley	.05	.03
644 Chuck Crim	.05	.03
645 Juan Samuel	.05	.03
646 Andujar Cedeno (R)	.15	.10
647 Mark Portugal	.05	.03
648 Lee Stevens	.07	.04
649 Bill Sampen	.05	.03
650 Jack Clark	.07	.04
651 Alan Mills	.05	.03
652 Kevin Romine	.05	.03
653 Anthony Telford (R)	.15	.10
654 Paul Sorrento	.08	.05
655 Erik Hanson	.08	.05
656 Checklist 5	.05	.03
657 Mike Kingery	.05	.03
658 Scott Aldred (R)	.10	.06
659 Oscar Azocar (R)	.12	.07
660 Lee Smith	.12	.07
661 Steve Lake	.05	.03
662 Rob Dibble	.07	.04
663 Greg Brock	.05	.03
664 John Farrell	.05	.03
665 Jim Leyland	.07	.04
666 Danny Darwin	.05	.03
667 Kent Anderson	.05	.03
668 Bill Long	.05	.03
669 Lou Pinella	.07	.04
670 Rickey Henderson	.15	.10
671 Andy McGaffigan	.05	.03
672 Shane Mack	.10	.06
673 Greg Olson	.05	.03
674 Kevin Gross	.07	.04
675 Tom Brunansky	.07	.04
676 Scott Chiamparino (R)	.10	.06
677 Billy Ripken	.05	.03
678 Mark Davidson	.05	.03
679 Bill Bathe	.05	.03
680 Dave Cone	.12	.07
681 Jeff Schaefer (R)	.08	.05
682 Ray Lankford (R)	.35	.20
683 Derek Lilliquist	.05	.03
684 Milt Cuyler (R)	.20	.12
685 Doug Drabek	.10	.06
686 Mike Gallego	.05	.03
687 John Cerutti	.05	.03
688 Rosario Rodriguez	.05	.03
689 John Kruk	.12	.07
690 Orel Hershiser	.10	.06
691 Mike Blowers	.05	.03
692 Efrain Valdez (R)	.10	.06

693 Francisco Cabrera	.05	.03
694 Randy Veres	.05	.03
695 Kevin Seitzer	.08	.05
696 Steve Olin	.05	.03
697 Shawn Abner	.05	.03
698 Mark Guthrie	.05	.03
699 Jim Lefebvre	.05	.03
700 Jose Canseco	.15	.10
701 Pascual Perez	.05	.03
702 Tim Naehring	.10	.06
703 Juan Agosto	.05	.03
704 Devon White	.08	.05
705 Robby Thompson	.08	.05
706 Brad Arnsberg	.05	.03
707 Jim Eisenreich	.05	.03
708 John Mitchell	.05	.03
709 Matt Sinatro	.05	.03
710 Kent Hrbek	.08	.05
711 Jose DeLeon	.05	.03
712 Ricky Jordan	.05	.03
713 Scott Scudder	.08	.05
714 Marvell Wynne	.05	.03
715 Tim Burke	.05	.03
716 Bob Geren	.05	.03
717 Phil Bradley	.05	.03
718 Steve Crawford	.05	.03
719 Kevin McReynolds	.07	.04
720 Cecil Fielder	.15	.10
721 Mark Lee (R)	.12	.07
722 Wally Backman	.05	.03
723 Candy Maldonado	.05	.03
724 David Segui (R)	.12	.07
725 Ron Gant	.15	.10
726 Phil Stephenson	.05	.03
727 Mookie Wilson	.05	.03
728 Scott Sanderson	.05	.03
729 Don Zimmer	.05	.03
730 Barry Larkin	.12	.07
731 Jeff Gray (R)	.12	.07
732 Franklin Stubbs	.05	.03
733 Kelly Downs	.05	.03
734 John Russell	.05	.03
735 Ron Darling	.07	.04
736 Dick Schofield	.05	.03
737 Tim Crews	.05	.03
738 Mel Hall	.07	.04
739 Russ Swan	.05	.03
740 Ryne Sandberg	.25	.15
741 Jimmy Key	.08	.05
742 Tommy Gregg	.05	.03
743 Bryn Smith	.05	.03
744 Nelson Santovenia	.05	.03
745 Doug Jones	.05	.03
746 John Shelby	.05	.03
747 Tony Fossas	.05	.03
748 Al Newman	.05	.03
749 Greg Harris	.05	.03

750	Bobby Bonilla	.10	.06
751	Wayne Edwards	.05	.03
752	Kevin Bass	.05	.03
763	Paul Marak (R)	.10	.06
754	Bill Pecota	.05	.03
755	Mark Langston	.08	.05
756	Jeff Huson	.05	.03
757	Mark Gardner	.10	.06
758	Mike Devereaux	.08	.05
759	Bobby Cox	.05	.03
760	Benny Santiago	.08	.05
761	Larry Andersen	.05	.03
762	Mitch Webster	.05	.03
763	Dana Kiecker	.05	.03
764	Mark Carreon	.05	.03
765	Shawon Dunston	.08	.05
766	Jeff Robinson	.05	.03
767	Dan Wilson (R) (#1 Pick)	.20	.12
768	Donn Paul	.05	.03
769	Tim Sherrill (R)	.08	.05
770	Jay Howell	.05	.03
771	Gary Redus	.05	.03
772	Kent Mercker	.10	.06
773	Tom Foley	.05	.03
774	Dennis Rasmussen	.05	.03
775	Julio Franco	.08	.05
776	Brent Mayne (R)	.10	.06
777	John Candelaria	.05	.03
778	Dan Gladden	.05	.03
779	Carmelo Martinez	.05	.03
780	Randy Myers	.05	.03
781	Darryl Hamilton	.08	.05
782	Jim Deshaies	.05	.03
783	Joel Skinner	.05	.03
784	Willie Fraser	.05	.03
785	Scott Fletcher	.05	.03
786	Eric Plunk	.05	.03
787	Checklist 6	.05	.03
788	Bob Milacki	.05	.03
789	Tom Lasorda	.07	.04
790	Ken Griffey Jr.	.75	.45
791	Mike Benjamin	.08	.05
792	Mike Greenwell	.10	.06

1991 Topps Stadium Club

This 600-card set marks Topps entrance into the upscale premium baseball card market. The set was released in two 300-card series and sold only in foil packs. Card fronts feature a high gloss, borderless design with full-bleed photos. Card backs include a small player photo, a player evaluation chart and biographical information. Cards measure 2-1/2" by 3-1/2".

		MINT	NR/MT
Complete Set (600)		210.00	125.00
Commons		.20	.12

1	Dave Stewart	.50	.30
2	Wally Joyner	.30	.18
3	Shawon Dunston	.25	.15
4	Darren Daulton	.80	.50
5	Will Clark	2.50	1.40
6	Sammy Sosa	1.75	1.00
7	Dan Plesac	.20	.12
8	Marquis Grissom	2.50	1.50
9	Erik Hanson	.25	.15
10	Geno Petralli	.20	.12
11	Jose Rijo	.25	.15
12	Carlos Quintana	.25	.15
13	Junior Ortiz	.20	.12
14	Bob Walk	.20	.12
15	Mike Macfarlane	.20	.12
16	Eric Yelding	.20	.12
17	Bryn Smith	.20	.12
18	Bip Roberts	.20	.12
19	Mike Scioscia	.20	.12
20	Mark Williamson	.20	.12
21	Don Mattingly	1.75	1.00
22	John Franco	.20	.12
23	Chet Lemon	.20	.12
24	Tom Henke	.20	.12

#	Player			#	Player		
25	Jerry Browne	.20	.12	82	Alvin Davis	.20	.12
26	Dave Justice	5.00	3.00	83	Tim Naehring	.30	.18
27	Mark Langston	.35	.20	84	Jay Bell	.25	.15
28	Damon Berryhill	.20	.12	85	Joe Magrane	.20	.12
29	Kevin Bass	.20	.12	86	Howard Johnson	.25	.15
30	Scott Fletcher	.20	.12	87	Jack McDowell	1.50	.90
31	Moises Alou	1.50	.90	88	Kevin Seitzer	.25	.15
32	Dave Valle	.20	.12	89	Bruce Ruffin	.20	.12
33	Jody Reed	.20	.12	90	Fernando Valenzuela	.25	.15
34	Dave West	.20	.12	91	Terry Kennedy	.20	.12
35	Kevin McReynolds	.25	.15	92	Barry Larkin	.90	.55
36	Pat Combs	.25	.15	93	Larry Walker	1.75	1.00
37	Eric Davis	.40	.25	94	Luis Salazar	.20	.12
38	Bret Saberhagen	.30	.18	95	Gary Sheffield	5.00	3.00
39	Stan Javier	.20	.12	96	Bobby Witt	.25	.15
40	Chuck Cary	.20	.12	97	Lonnie Smith	.20	.12
41	Tony Phillips	.20	.12	98	Bryan Harvey	.25	.15
42	Lee Smith	.30	.18	99	Mookie Wilson	.20	.12
43	Tim Teufel	.20	.12	100	Dwight Gooden	.40	.25
44	Lance Dickson	.30	.18	101	Lou Whitaker	.25	.15
45	Greg Litton	.20	.12	102	Ron Karkovice	.20	.12
46	Teddy Higuera	.20	.12	103	Jesse Barfield	.25	.15
47	Edgar Martinez	.50	.30	104	Jose DeJesus	.20	.12
48	Steve Avery	4.50	3.00	105	Benito Santiago	.25	.15
49	Walt Weiss	.20	.12	106	Brian Holman	.25	.15
50	David Segui	.25	.15	107	Rafael Ramirez	.20	.12
51	Andy Benes	.80	.50	108	Ellis Burks	.25	.15
52	Karl Rhodes	.20	.12	109	Mike Bielecki	.20	.12
53	Neal Heaton	.20	.12	110	Kirby Puckett	3.50	2.50
54	Danny Gladden	.20	.12	111	Terry Shumpert	.20	.12
55	Luis Rivera	.20	.12	112	Chuck Crim	.20	.12
56	Kevin Brown	.35	.20	113	Todd Benzinger	.20	.12
57	Frank Thomas	28.00	18.00	114	Brian Barnes	.30	.18
58	Terry Mulholland	.20	.12	115	Carlos Baerga	5.00	3.00
59	Dick Schofield	.20	.12	116	Kal Daniels	.20	.12
60	Ron Darling	.25	.15	117	Dave Johnson	.20	.12
61	Sandy Alomar, Jr.	.25	.15	118	Andy Van Slyke	.50	.30
62	Dave Stieb	.25	.15	119	John Burkett	.80	.50
63	Alan Trammell	.30	.18	120	Rickey Henderson	1.75	1.00
64	Matt Nokes	.20	.12	121	Tim Jones	.20	.12
65	Lenny Harris	.20	.12	122	Daryl Irvine	.25	.15
66	Milt Thompson	.20	.12	123	Ruben Sierra	1.25	.80
67	Storm Davis	.20	.12	124	Jim Abbott	1.50	.90
68	Joe Oliver	.20	.12	125	Daryl Boston	.20	.12
69	Andres Galarraga	.60	.35	126	Greg Maddux	2.00	1.25
70	Ozzie Guillen	.25	.15	127	Von Hayes	.20	.12
71	Ken Howell	.20	.12	128	Mike Fitzgerald	.20	.12
72	Garry Templeton	.20	.12	129	Wayne Edwards	.20	.12
73	Derrick May	1.25	.80	130	Greg Briley	.20	.12
74	Xavier Hernandez	.20	.12	131	Rob Dibble	.25	.15
75	Dave Parker	.25	.15	132	Gene Larkin	.20	.12
76	Rick Aguilera	.25	.15	133	David Wells	.20	.12
77	Robby Thompson	.25	.15	134	Steve Balboni	.20	.12
78	Pete Incaviglia	.20	.12	135	Greg Vaughn	1.00	.60
79	Bob Welch	.25	.15	136	Mark Davis	.20	.12
80	Randy Milligan	.25	.15	137	Dave Rohde	.25	.15
81	Chuck Finley	.25	.15	138	Eric Show	.20	.12

139	Bobby Bonilla	.70	.40
140	Dana Kiecker	.20	.12
141	Gary Pettis	.20	.12
142	Dennis Boyd	.20	.12
143	Mike Benjamin	.20	.12
144	Luis Polonia	.20	.12
145	Doug Jones	.20	.12
146	Al Newman	.20	.12
147	Alex Fernandez	2.50	1.40
148	Bill Doran	.20	.12
149	Kevin Elster	.20	.12
150	Len Dykstra	1.00	.60
151	Mike Gallego	.20	.12
152	Tim Belcher	.25	.15
153	Jay Buhner	.50	.30
154	Ozzie Smith	1.00	.70
155	Jose Canseco	1.75	1.00
156	Gregg Olson	.25	.15
157	Charlie O'Brien	.20	.12
158	Frank Tanana	.20	.12
159	George Brett	1.75	1.00
160	Jeff Huson	.20	.12
161	Kevin Tapani	.30	.18
162	Jerome Walton	.20	.12
163	Charlie Hayes	.20	.12
164	Chris Bosio	.20	.12
165	Chris Sabo	.25	.15
166	Lance Parrish	.25	.15
167	Don Robinson	.20	.12
168	Manuel Lee	.20	.12
169	Dennis Rasmussen	.20	.12
170	Wade Boggs	1.50	.90
171	Bob Geren	.20	.12
172	Mackey Sasser	.20	.12
173	Julio Franco	.35	.20
174	Otis Nixon	.25	.15
175	Bert Blyleven	.25	.15
176	Craig Biggio	.50	.30
177	Eddie Murray	1.00	.70
178	Randy Tomlin	.40	.25
179	Tino Martinez	.40	.25
180	Carlton Fisk	.80	.50
181	Dwight Smith	.20	.12
182	Scott Garrelts	.20	.12
183	Jim Gantner	.20	.12
184	Dickie Thon	.20	.12
185	John Farrell	.20	.12
186	Cecil Fielder	1.50	.90
187	Glenn Braggs	.20	.12
188	Allan Anderson	.20	.12
189	Kurt Stillwell	.20	.12
190	Jose Oquendo	.20	.12
191	Joe Orsulak	.20	.12
192	Ricky Jordan	.20	.12
193	Kelly Downs	.20	.12
194	Delino DeShields	1.50	.90
195	Omar Vizquel	.30	.18
196	Mark Carreon	.20	.12
197	Mike Harkey	.25	.15
198	Jack Howell	.20	.12
199	Lance Johnson	.20	.12
200	Nolan Ryan	14.00	9.00
201	John Marzano	.20	.12
202	Doug Drabek	.30	.18
203	Mark Lemke	.20	.12
204	Steve Sax	.25	.15
205	Greg Harris	.20	.12
206	B.J. Surhoff	.20	.12
207	Todd Burns	.20	.12
208	Jose Gonzalez	.20	.12
209	Mike Scott	.20	.12
210	Dave Magadan	.20	.12
211	Dante Bichette	.30	.18
212	Trevor Wilson	.20	.12
213	Hector Villanueva	.20	.12
214	Dan Pasqua	.20	.12
215	Greg Colbrunn (R)	.50	.30
216	Mike Jeffcoat	.20	.12
217	Harold Reynolds	.25	.15
218	Paul O'Neill	.25	.15
219	Mark Guthrie	.20	.12
220	Barry Bonds	6.50	3.75
221	Jimmy Key	.20	.12
222	Billy Ripken	.20	.12
223	Tom Pagnozzi	.25	.15
224	Bo Jackson	1.50	.90
225	Sid Fernandez	.25	.15
226	Mike Marshall	.20	.12
227	John Kruk	.75	.45
228	Mike Fetters	.20	.12
229	Eric Anthony	.80	.50
230	Ryne Sandberg	3.50	2.50
231	Carney Lansford	.20	.12
232	Melido Perez	.20	.12
233	Jose Lind	.20	.12
234	Darryl Hamilton	.30	.18
235	Tom Browning	.25	.15
236	Spike Owen	.20	.12
237	Juan Gonzalez	28.00	18.00
238	Felix Fermin	.20	.12
239	Keith Miller	.20	.12
240	Mark Gubicza	.25	.15
241	Kent Anderson	.20	.12
242	Alvaro Espinoza	.20	.12
243	Dale Murphy	.40	.25
244	Orel Hershiser	.30	.18
245	Paul Molitor	1.25	.80
246	Eddie Whitson	.20	.12
247	Joe Girardi	.20	.12
248	Kent Hrbek	.25	.15
249	Bill Sampen	.20	.12
250	Kevin Mitchell	.30	.18
251	Mariano Duncan	.20	.12
252	Scott Bradley	.20	.12

253 Mike Greenwell	.35	.20
254 Tom Gordon	.25	.15
255 Todd Zeile	.40	.25
256 Bobby Thigpen	.25	.15
257 Gregg Jefferies	1.50	.90
258 Kenny Rogers	.20	.12
259 Shane Mack	.40	.25
260 Zane Smith	.20	.12
261 Mitch Williams	.20	.12
262 Jim DeShaies	.20	.12
263 Dave Winfield	1.75	1.00
264 Ben McDonald	1.00	.60
265 Randy Ready	.20	.12
266 Pat Borders	.20	.12
267 Jose Uribe	.20	.12
268 Derek Lilliquist	.20	.12
269 Greg Brock	.20	.12
270 Ken Griffey, Jr.	20.00	12.50
271 Jeff Gray	.25	.15
272 Danny Tartabull	.40	.25
273 Dennis Martinez	.25	.15
274 Robin Ventura	3.50	2.00
275 Randy Myers	.20	.12
276 Jack Daugherty	.20	.12
277 Greg Gagne	.20	.12
278 Jay Howell	.20	.12
279 Mike LaValliere	.20	.12
280 Rex Hudler	.20	.12
281 Mike Simms (R)	.25	.15
282 Kevin Maas	.30	.18
283 Jeff Ballard	.20	.12
284 Dave Henderson	.20	.12
285 Pete O'Brien	.20	.12
286 Brook Jacoby	.20	.12
287 Mike Henneman	.20	.12
288 Greg Olson	.20	.12
289 Greg Myers	.20	.12
290 Mark Grace	1.50	.90
291 Shawn Abner	.20	.12
292 Frank Viola	.30	.18
293 Lee Stevens	.25	.15
294 Jason Grimsley	.25	.15
295 Matt Williams	1.25	.80
296 Ron Robinson	.20	.12
297 Tom Brunansky	.25	.15
298 Checklist	.20	.12
299 Checklist	.20	.12
300 Checklist	.20	.12
301 Darryl Strawberry	.75	.45
302 Bud Black	.20	.12
303 Harold Baines	.25	.15
304 Roberto Alomar	5.50	3.25
305 Norm Charlton	.25	.15
306 Gary Thurman	.20	.12
307 Mike Felder	.20	.12
308 Tony Gwynn	1.75	1.00
309 Roger Clemens	3.50	2.00
310 Andre Dawson	.90	.55
311 Scott Radinsky	.25	.15
312 Bob Melvin	.20	.12
313 Kirk McCaskill	.20	.12
314 Pedro Guerrero	.25	.15
315 Walt Terrell	.20	.12
316 Sam Horn	.20	.12
317 Wes Chamberlain (R)	.75	.45
318 Pedro Munoz (R)	.60	.35
319 Roberto Kelly	.50	.30
320 Mark Portugal	.20	.12
321 Tim McIntosh	.25	.15
322 Jesse Orosco	.20	.12
323 Gary Green	.20	.12
324 Greg Harris	.20	.12
325 Hubie Brooks	.25	.15
326 Chris Nabholz	.30	.18
327 Terry Pendleton	.60	.35
328 Eric King	.20	.12
329 Chili Davis	.25	.15
330 Anthony Telford	.25	.15
331 Kelly Gruber	.25	.15
332 Dennis Eckersley	.50	.30
333 Mel Hall	.25	.15
334 Bob Kipper	.20	.12
335 Willie McGee	.25	.15
336 Steve Olin	.20	.12
337 Steve Buechele	.20	.12
338 Scott Leius	.20	.12
339 Hal Morris	.30	.18
340 Jose Offerman	.25	.15
341 Kent Mercker	.25	.15
342 Ken Griffey	.25	.15
343 Pete Harnisch	.25	.15
344 Kirk Gibson	.25	.15
345 Dave Smith	.20	.12
346 Dave Martinez	.20	.12
347 Atlee Hammaker	.20	.12
348 Brian Downing	.20	.12
349 Todd Hundley	.25	.15
350 Candy Maldonado	.20	.12
351 Dwight Evans	.25	.15
352 Steve Searcy	.20	.12
353 Gary Gaetti	.20	.12
354 Jeff Reardon	.35	.20
355 Travis Fryman	10.00	6.50
356 Dave Righetti	.20	.12
357 Fred McGriff	2.50	1.50
358 Don Slaught	.20	.12
359 Gene Nelson	.20	.12
360 Billy Spiers	.20	.12
361 Lee Guetterman	.20	.12
362 Darren Lewis	.40	.25
363 Duane Ward	.20	.12
364 Lloyd Moseby	.20	.12
365 John Smoltz	1.25	.80
366 Felix Jose	.35	.20

367	David Cone	.40	.25
368	Wally Backman	.20	.12
369	Jeff Montgomery	.20	.12
370	Rich Garces (H)	.25	.15
371	Billy Hatcher	.20	.12
372	Bill Swift	.35	.20
373	Jim Eisenreich	.20	.12
374	Rob Ducey	.20	.12
375	Tim Crews	.20	.12
376	Steve Finley	.20	.12
377	Jeff Blauser	.25	.15
378	Willie Wilson	.20	.12
379	Gerald Perry	.20	.12
380	Jose Mesa	.20	.12
381	Pat Kelly (R)	.60	.35
382	Matt Merullo (R)	.25	.15
383	Ivan Calderon	.25	.15
384	Scott Chiamparino (R)	.25	.15
385	Lloyd McClendon	.20	.12
386	Dave Bergman	.20	.12
387	Ed Sprague	.50	.30
388	Jeff Bagwell (R)	8.50	5.50
389	Brett Butler	.25	.15
390	Larry Andersen	.20	.12
391	Glenn Davis	.20	.12
392	Alex Cole(Wrong Photo)	.20	.12
393	Mike Heath	.20	.12
394	Danny Darwin	.20	.12
395	Steve Lake	.20	.12
396	Tim Layana	.20	.12
397	Terry Leach	.20	.12
398	Bill Wegman	.20	.12
399	Mark McGwire	1.50	.90
400	Mike Boddicker	.20	.12
401	Steve Howe	.20	.12
402	Bernard Gilkey	.80	.50
403	Thomas Howard	.25	.15
404	Rafael Belliard	.20	.12
405	Tom Candiotti	.20	.12
406	Rene Gonzalez	.20	.12
407	Chuck McElroy	.20	.12
408	Paul Sorrento	.50	.30
409	Randy Johnson	1.25	.80
410	Brady Anderson	.50	.30
411	Dennis Cook	.20	.12
412	Mickey Tettleton	.25	.15
413	Mike Stanton	.25	.15
414	Ken Oberkfell	.20	.12
415	Rick Honeycutt	.20	.12
416	Nelson Santovenia	.20	.12
417	Bob Tewksbury	.20	.12
418	Brent Mayne	.25	.15
419	Steve Farr	.20	.12
420	Phil Stephenson	.20	.12
421	Jeff Russell	.20	.12
422	Chris James	.20	.12
423	Tim Leary	.20	.12
424	Gary Carter	.40	.25
425	Glenallen Hill	.25	.15
426	Matt Young	.20	.12
427	Sid Bream	.20	.12
428	Greg Swindell	.25	.15
429	Scott Aldred	.25	.15
430	Cal Ripken	4.50	2.75
431	Bill Landrum	.20	.12
432	Ernie Riles	.20	.12
433	Danny Jackson	.20	.12
434	Casey Candaele	.20	.12
435	Ken Hill	.50	.30
436	Jaime Navarro	.30	.18
437	Lance Blankenship	.20	.12
438	Randy Velarde	.20	.12
439	Frank DiPino	.20	.12
440	Carl Nichols	.20	.12
441	Jeff Robinson	.20	.12
442	Deion Sanders	1.75	1.00
443	Vincente Palacios	.20	.12
444	Devon White	.25	.15
445	John Cerutti	.20	.12
446	Tracy Jones	.20	.12
447	Jack Morris	.40	.25
448	Mitch Webster	.20	.12
449	Bob Ojeda	.20	.12
450	Oscar Azocar	.20	.12
451	Luis Aquino	.20	.12
452	Mark Whiten	1.25	.80
453	Stan Belinda	.20	.12
454	Ron Gant	1.75	1.00
455	Jose DeLeon	.20	.12
456	Mark Salas	.20	.12
457	Junior Felix	.20	.12
458	Wally Whitehurst	.20	.12
459	Phil Plantier (R)	5.00	3.00
460	Juan Berenguer	.20	.12
461	Franklin Stubbs	.20	.12
462	Joe Boever	.20	.12
463	Tim Wallach	.25	.15
464	Mike Moore	.25	.15
465	Albert Belle	4.50	2.75
466	Mike Witt	.20	.12
467	Craig Worthington	.20	.12
468	Jerald Clark	.25	.15
469	Scott Terry	.20	.12
470	Milt Cuyler	.25	.15
471	John Smiley	.30	.18
472	Charles Nagy	.75	.45
473	Alan Mills	.25	.15
474	John Russell	.20	.12
475	Bruce Hurst	.25	.15
476	Andujar Cedeno	1.25	.80
477	Dave Eiland	.20	.12
478	Brian McRae (R)	1.25	.80
479	Mike LaCoss	.20	.12
480	Chris Gwynn	.20	.12

481	Jamie Moyer	.20	.12
482	John Olerud	7.50	4.00
483	Efrain Valdez	.25	.15
484	Sil Campusano	.20	.12
485	Pascual Perez	.20	.12
486	Gary Redus	.20	.12
487	Andy Hawkins	.20	.12
488	Cory Snyder	.20	.12
489	Chris Hoiles	.80	.50
490	Ron Hassey	.20	.12
491	Gary Wayne	.20	.12
492	Mark Lewis	.35	.20
493	Scott Coolbaugh	.20	.12
494	Gerald Young	.20	.12
495	Juan Samuel	.20	.12
496	Willie Fraser	.20	.12
497	Jeff Treadway	.20	.12
498	Vince Coleman	.25	.15
499	Cris Carpenter	.20	.12
500	Jack Clark	.25	.15
501	Kevin Appier	1.50	.90
502	Rafael Palmeiro	1.50	.90
503	Hensley Meulens	.25	.15
504	George Bell	.40	.25
505	Tony Pena	.20	.12
506	Roger McDowell	.20	.12
507	Luis Sojo	.20	.12
508	Mike Schooler	.20	.12
509	Robin Yount	2.00	1.25
510	Jack Armstrong	.20	.12
511	Rick Cerone	.20	.12
512	Curt Wilkerson	.20	.12
513	Joe Carter	1.75	1.00
514	Tim Burke	.20	.12
515	Tony Fernandez	.25	.15
516	Ramon Martinez	.50	.30
517	Tim Hulett	.20	.12
518	Terry Steinbach	.25	.15
519	Pete Smith	.35	.20
520	Ken Caminiti	.25	.15
521	Shawn Boskie	.20	.12
522	Mike Pagliarulo	.20	.12
523	Tim Raines	.25	.15
524	Alfredo Griffin	.20	.12
525	Henry Cotto	.20	.12
526	Mike Stanley	.20	.12
527	Charlie Leibrandt	.20	.12
528	Jeff King	.25	.15
529	Eric Plunk	.20	.12
530	Tom Lampkin	.20	.12
531	Steve Bedrosian	.20	.12
532	Tom Herr	.20	.12
533	Craig Lefferts	.20	.12
534	Jeff Reed	.20	.12
535	Mickey Morandini	.50	.30
536	Greg Cadaret	.20	.12
537	Ray Lankford	3.00	2.00
538	John Candelaria	.20	.12
539	Rob Deer	.25	.15
540	Brad Arnsberg	.20	.12
541	Mike Sharperson	.20	.12
542	Jeff Robinson	.20	.12
543	Mo Vaughn	3.50	2.00
544	Jeff Parrett	.20	.12
545	Willie Randolph	.25	.15
546	Herm Winningham	.20	.12
547	Jeff Innis	.20	.12
548	Chuck Knoblauch	1.25	.80
549	Tommy Greene	1.25	.80
550	Jeff Hamilton	.20	.12
551	Barry Jones	.20	.12
552	Ken Dayley	.20	.12
553	Rick Dempsey	.20	.12
554	Greg Smith	.20	.12
555	Mike Devereaux	.30	.18
556	Keith Comstock	.20	.12
557	Paul Faries	.20	.12
558	Tom Glavine	2.50	1.40
559	Craig Grebeck (R)	.25	.15
560	Scott Erickson	.50	.30
561	Joel Skinner	.20	.12
562	Mike Morgan	.25	.15
563	Dave Gallagher	.20	.12
564	Todd Stottlemyre	.25	.15
565	Rich Rodriguez (R)	.25	.15
566	Craig Wilson (R)	.25	.15
567	Jeff Brantley	.25	.15
568	Scott Kamieniecki (R)	.30	.18
569	Steve Decker (R)	.25	.15
570	Juan Agosto	.20	.12
571	Tommy Gregg	.20	.12
572	Kevin Wickander	.20	.12
573	Jamie Quirk	.20	.12
574	Jerry Don Gleaton	.20	.12
575	Chris Hammond	.40	.25
576	Luis Gonzalez (R)	1.50	.90
577	Russ Swan	.20	.12
578	Jeff Conine (R)	2.00	1.25
579	Charlie Hough	.20	.12
580	Jeff Kunkel	.20	.12
581	Darrel Akerfelds	.20	.12
582	Jeff Manto (R)	.25	.15
583	Alejandro Pena	.25	.15
584	Mark Davidson	.20	.12
585	Bob MacDonald (R)	.25	.15
586	Paul Assenmacher	.20	.12
587	Dan Wilson (R)	.75	.45
588	Tom Bolton	.20	.12
589	Brian Harper	.20	.12
590	John Habyan	.20	.12
591	John Orton	.20	.12
592	Mark Gardner (R)	.25	.15
593	Turner Ward (R)	.30	.18
594	Bob Patterson	.20	.12

595	Edwin Nunez	.20	.12
596	Gary Scott	.30	.18
597	Scott Bankhead	.20	.12
598	Checklist	.20	.12
599	Checklist	.20	.12
600	Checklist	.20	.12

1991 Topps Traded

This 132-card set is identical in design to the 1991 Topps regular edition. The cards measure 2-1/2" by 3-1/2". Card fronts carry the "Topps 40th" logo in honor of Topps 40th Anniversary. The set contains card sof players who were traded during the years plus some promising rookie prospects and a 25-card Team USA subset.

		MINT	NR/MT
Complete Set (132)		12.00	7.50
Commons		.05	.03
1	Juan Agosto	.05	.03
2	Roberto Alomar	.25	.15
3	Wally Backman	.05	.03
4	Jeff Bagwell (R)	1.25	.80
5	Skeeter Barnes (R)	.10	.06
6	Steve Bedrosian	.07	.04
7	Derek Bell (R)	.30	.18
8	George Bell	.10	.06
9	Rafael Belliard	.05	.03
10	Dante Bichette	.08	.05
11	Bud Black	.05	.03
12	Mike Boddicker	.07	.04
13	Sid Bream	.05	.03
14	Hubie Brooks	.07	.04
15	Brett Butler	.10	.06

16	Ivan Calderon	.08	.05
17	John Candelaria	.05	.03
18	Tom Candiotti	.07	.04
19	Gary Carter	.10	.06
20	Joe Carter	.20	.12
21	Rick Cerone	.05	.03
22	Jack Clark	.07	.04
23	Vince Coleman	.07	.04
24	Scott Coolbaugh	.05	.03
25	Danny Cox	.05	.03
26	Danny Darwin	.05	.03
27	Chili Davis	.07	.04
28	Glenn Davis	.07	.04
29	Steve Decker (R)	.10	.06
30	Rob Deer	.07	.04
31	Rich DeLucia (R)	.12	.07
32	John Dettmer (R)(USA)	.20	.12
33	Brian Downing	.05	.03
34	Darren Dreifort (R) (USA)	1.00	.60
35	Kirk Dressendorfer (R)	.15	.10
36	Jim Essian	.05	.03
37	Dwight Evans	.08	.05
38	Steve Farr	.05	.03
39	Jeff Fassero (R)	.10	.06
40	Junior Felix	.08	.05
41	Tony Fernandez	.08	.05
42	Steve Finley	.08	.05
43	Jim Fregosi	.05	.03
44	Gary Gaetti	.05	.03
45	Jason Giambi (R)(USA)	.40	.25
46	Kirk Gibson	.07	.04
47	Leo Gomez (R)	.25	.15
48	Luis Gonzalez (R)	.35	.20
49	Jeff Granger (R)(USA)	.75	.45
50	Todd Greene (R)(USA)	.25	.15
51	Jeffrey Hammonds (R) (USA)	3.50	2.00
52	Mike Hargrove	.05	.03
53	Pete Harnisch	.10	.06
54	Rick Helling (R)(USA)	.75	.45
55	Glenallen Hill	.10	.06
56	Charlie Hough	.05	.03
57	Pete Incaviglia	.07	.04
58	Bo Jackson	.20	.12
59	Danny Jackson	.07	.04
60	Reggie Jefferson (R)	.20	.12
61	Charles Johnson (R) (USA)	1.25	.80
62	Jeff Johnson (R)	.20	.12
63	Todd Johnson (R)(USA)	.20	.12
64	Barry Jones	.05	.03
65	Chris Jones (R)	.15	.10
66	Scott Kamieniecki (R)	.12	.07
67	Pat Kelly (R)	.15	.10
68	Darryl Kile (R)	.30	.18
69	Chuck Knoblauch (R)	.25	.15

70	Bill Krueger	.05	.03
71	Scott Leius (R)	.10	.06
72	Donnie Leshnock (R) (USA)	.20	.12
73	Mark Lewis	.12	.07
74	Candy Maldonado	.07	.04
75	Jason McDonald (R) (USA)	.15	.10
76	Willie McGee	.08	.05
77	Fred McGriff	.25	.15
78	Billy McMillon (R) (USA)	.20	.12
79	Hal McRae	.08	.05
80	Dan Melendez (R)(USA)	.35	.20
81	Orlando Merced (R)	.30	.18
82	Jack Morris	.12	.07
83	Phil Nevin (R)(USA)	2.00	1.25
84	Otis Nixon	.07	.04
85	Johnny Oates	.05	.03
86	Bob Ojeda	.05	.03
87	Mike Pagliarulo	.05	.03
88	Dean Palmer (R)	.40	.25
89	Dave Parker	.08	.05
90	Terry Pendleton	.15	.10
91	Tony Phillips (R)(USA)	.15	.10
92	Doug Piatt (R)	.10	.06
93	Ron Polk (USA)	.05	.03
94	Tim Raines	.08	.05
95	Willie Randolph	.08	.05
96	Dave Righetti	.07	.04
97	Ernie Riles	.05	.03
98	Chris Roberts (R) (USA)	.80	.50
99	Jeff Robinsno (Angels)	.05	.03
100	Jeff Robinson (Orioles)	.05	.03
101	Ivan Rodriguez (R)	1.00	.60
102	Steve Rodriguez (R) (USA)	.15	.10
103	Tom Runnells	.05	.03
104	Scott Sanderson	.07	.04
105	Bob Scanlan (R)	.10	.06
106	Pete Schourek (R)	.12	.07
107	Gary Scott (R)	.12	.07
108	Paul Shuey (R)(USA)	.35	.20
109	Doug Simons (R)	.10	.06
110	Dave Smith	.05	.03
111	Cory Snyder	.07	.04
112	Luis Sojo	.07	.04
113	Kennie Steenstra (R) (USA)	.25	.15
114	Darryl Strawberry	.15	.10
115	Franklin Stubbs	.05	.03
116	Todd Taylor (R)(USA)	.20	.12
117	Wade Taylor (R)	.15	.10
118	Garry Templeton	.08	.05
119	Mickey Tettleton	.08	.05
120	Tim Teufel	.05	.03

121	Mike Timlin (R)	.12	.07
122	David Tuttle (R)(USA)	.15	.10
123	Mo Vaughn (R)	.35	.20
124	Jeff Ware (R)(USA)	.25	.15
125	Devon White	.07	.04
126	Mark Whiten	.35	.20
127	Mitch Williams	.09	.05
128	Craig Wilson (R)(USA)	.25	.15
129	Willie Wilson	.07	.03
130	Chris Wimmer (R) (USA)	.30	.18
131	Ivan Zweig (R)(USA)	.15	.10
132	Checklist	.05	.03

1992 Topps

This 792-card set is similar to the 1991 Topps regular edition. Card fronts feature large full color photos surrounded by muli-colored borders. Card backs are horizontal with the usual stats and bio's. Some card backs feature type printed over the an image of a ball park. Cards measure 2-1/2" by 3-1/2". Key subsets include Record Breakers (2-5), All-Stars, Top Prospects and Number One Draft Picks.

		MINT	NR/MT
Complete Set (792)		22.00	15.00
Commons		.05	.03
1	Nolan Ryan	.80	.50
2	Rickey Henderson (RB)	.12	.07
3	Jeff Reardon (RB)	.08	.05
4	Nolan Ryan (RB)	.60	.35
5	Dave Winfield (RB)	.12	.07
6	Brien Taylor (#1 Pick)	.80	.50
7	Jim Olander (R)	.10	.06

8	Bryan Hickerson (R)	.12	.07
9	John Farrell (R)	.10	.06
10	Wade Boggs	.15	.10
11	Jack McDowell	.20	.12
12	Luis Gonzalez	.12	.07
13	Mike Scioscia	.07	.04
14	Wes Chamberlain	.12	.07
15	Denny Martinez	.10	.06
16	Jeff Montgomery	.05	.03
17	Randy Milligan	.07	.04
18	Greg Cadaret	.05	.03
19	Jamie Quirk	.05	.03
20	Bip Roberts	.08	.05
21	Buck Rogers	.05	.03
22	Bill Wegman	.05	.03
23	Chuck Knoblauch	.20	.12
24	Randy Myers	.05	.03
25	Ron Gant	.12	.07
26	Mike Bielecki	.05	.03
27	Juan Gonzalez	1.00	.60
28	Mike Schooler	.05	.03
29	Mickey Tettleton	.07	.04
30	John Kruk	.12	.07
31	Bryn Smith	.05	.03
32	Chris Nabholz	.10	.06
33	Carlos Baerga	.30	.18
34	Jeff Juden	.12	.07
35	Dave Righetti	.05	.03
36	Scott Ruffcorn (R) (#1 Pick)	.35	.20
37	Luis Polonia	.07	.04
38	Tom Candiotti	.07	.04
39	Greg Olson	.05	.03
40	Cal Ripken	.35	.20
41	Craig Lefferts	.05	.03
42	Mike Macfarlane	.05	.03
43	Jose Lind	.05	.03
44	Rick Aguilera	.05	.03
45	Gary Carter	.08	.05
46	Steve Farr	.05	.03
47	Rex Hudler	.05	.03
48	Scott Scudder	.08	.05
49	Damon Berryhill	.05	.03
50	Ken Griffey, Jr.	1.25	.80
51	Tom Runnells	.05	.03
52	Juan Bell	.05	.03
53	Tommy Gregg	.05	.03
54	David Wells	.05	.03
55	Rafael Palmeiro	.15	.10
56	Charlie O'Brien	.05	.03
57	Donn Pall	.05	.03
58	Top Prospects-Catchers (Brad Ausmus (R) Jim Campanis, Dave Nilsson, Doug Robbins (R)	.20	.12
59	Mo Vaughn	.25	.15
60	Tony Fernandez	.08	.05

61	Paul O'Neill	.08	.05
62	Gene Nelson	.05	.03
63	Randy Ready	.05	.03
64	Bob Kipper	.05	.03
65	Willie McGee	.08	.05
66	Scott Stahoviak (R) (#1 Pick)	.20	.12
67	Luis Salazar	.05	.03
68	Marvin Freeman	.05	.03
69	Kenny Lofton (R)	.50	.30
70	Gary Gaetti	.05	.03
71	Erik Hanson	.07	.04
72	Eddie Zosky	.05	.03
73	Brian Barnes	.10	.06
74	Scott Leius	.07	.04
75	Bret Saberhagen	.08	.05
76	Mike Gallego	.05	.03
77	Jack Armstrong	.05	.03
78	Ivan Rodriguez	.20	.12
79	Jesse Orosco	.05	.03
80	David Justice	.30	.18
81	Ced Landrum	.05	.03
82	Doug Simons	.07	.04
83	Tommy Greene	.10	.06
84	Leo Gomez	.10	.06
85	Jose DeLeon	.05	.03
86	Steve Finley	.07	.04
87	Bob MacDonald	.07	.04
88	Darrin Jackson	.05	.03
89	Neal Heaton	.05	.03
90	Robin Yount	.25	.15
91	Jeff Reed	.05	.03
92	Lenny Harris	.05	.03
93	Reggie Jefferson	.10	.06
94	Sammy Sosa	.20	.12
95	Scott Bailes	.05	.03
96	Tom McKinnon (R) (#1 Pick)	.10	.06
97	Luis Rivera	.05	.03
98	Mike Harkey	.08	.05
99	Jeff Treadway	.05	.03
100	Jose Canseco	.20	.12
101	Omar Vizquel	.08	.05
102	Scott Kamieniecki	.08	.05
103	Ricky Jordan	.05	.03
104	Jeff Ballard	.05	.03
105	Felix Jose	.10	.06
106	Mike Boddicker	.05	.03
107	Dan Pasqua	.05	.03
108	Mike Timlin	.10	.06
109	Roger Craig	.05	.03
110	Ryne Sandberg	.30	.18
111	Mark Carreon	.05	.03
112	Oscar Azocar	.05	.03
113	Mike Greenwell	.08	.05
114	Mark Portugal	.05	.03
115	Terry Pendleton	.12	.07

116	Willie Randolph	.05	.03
117	Scott Terry	.05	.03
118	Chili Davis	.07	.04
119	Mark Gardner	.05	.03
120	Alan Trammell	.08	.05
121	Derek Bell	.20	.12
122	Gary Varsho	.05	.00
123	Bob Ojeda	.05	.03
124	Shawn Livsey (R) (#1 Pick)	.15	.10
125	Chris Hoiles	.08	.05
126	Top Prospects-1st Base Rico Brogna (R) John Jaha, Ryan Klesko(R) Dave Staton (R)	.60	.35
127	Carols Quintana	.07	.04
128	Kurt Stillwell	.05	.03
129	Melido Perez	.05	.03
130	Alvin Davis	.05	.03
131	Checklist 1	.05	.03
132	Eric Show	.05	.03
133	Rance Mulliniks	.05	.03
134	Darryl Kile	.10	.06
135	Von Hayes	.05	.03
136	Bill Doran	.05	.03
137	Jeff Robinson	.05	.03
138	Monty Fariss	.08	.05
139	Jeff Innis	.05	.03
140	Mark Grace	.12	.07
141	Jim Leyland	.07	.04
142	Todd Van Poppel (R)	.30	.18
143	Paul Gibson	.05	.03
144	Bill Swift	.08	.05
145	Danny Tartabull	.10	.06
146	Al Newman	.05	.03
147	Cris Carpenter	.05	.03
148	Anthony Young (R)	.15	.10
149	Brian Bohanon (R)	.10	.06
150	Roger Clemens	.30	.18
151	Jeff Hamilton	.05	.03
152	Charlie Leibrandt	.05	.03
153	Ron Karkovice	.05	.03
154	Hensley Meulens	.08	.05
155	Scott Bankhead	.05	.03
156	Manny Ramirez (R) (#1 Pick)	1.75	1.00
157	Keith Miller	.05	.03
158	Todd Frohwirth	.05	.03
159	Darrin Fletcher	.05	.03
160	Bobby Bonilla	.10	.06
161	Casey Candaele	.05	.03
162	Paul Faries	.05	.03
163	Dana Kiecker	.05	.03
164	Shane Mack	.08	.05
165	Mark Langston	.08	.05
166	Geronimo Pena	.05	.03
167	Andy Allanson	.05	.03
168	Dwight Smith	.05	.03
169	Chuck Crim	.05	.03
170	Alex Cole	.05	.03
171	Bill Plummer	.05	.03
172	Juan Berenguer	.05	.03
173	Brian Downing	.05	.03
174	Steve Frey	.05	.00
175	Orel Hershiser	.08	.05
176	Ramon Garcia (R)	.12	.07
177	Danny Gladden	.05	.03
178	Jim Acker	.05	.03
179	Top Prospects-2nd Base Cesar Bernhardt (R) Bobby DeJardin (R) Armando Moreno (R) Andy Stankiewicz	.15	.10
180	Kevin Mitchell	.08	.05
181	Hector Villanueva	.05	.03
182	Jeff Reardon	.08	.05
183	Brent Mayne	.07	.04
184	Jimmy Jones	.05	.03
185	Benny Santiago	.08	.05
186	Cliff Floyd (R) (#1 Pick)	2.00	1.25
187	Ernie Riles	.05	.03
188	Jose Guzman	.05	.03
189	Junior Felix	.05	.03
190	Glenn Davis	.05	.03
191	Charlie Hough	.05	.03
192	Dave Fleming (R)	.35	.20
193	Omar Oliveras	.08	.05
194	Eric Karros	.30	.18
195	David Cone	.10	.06
196	Frank Castillo	.05	.03
197	Glenn Braggs	.05	.03
198	Scott Aldred	.07	.04
199	Jeff Blauser	.07	.04
200	Len Dykstra	.15	.10
201	Buck Showalter	.07	.04
202	Rick Honeycutt	.05	.03
203	Greg Myers	.05	.03
204	Trevor Wilson	.05	.03
205	Jay Howell	.05	.03
206	Luis Sojo	.07	.04
207	Jack Clark	.07	.04
208	Julio Machado	.05	.03
209	Lloyd McClendon	.05	.03
210	Ozzie Guillen	.05	.03
211	Jeremy Hernandez (R)	.12	.07
212	Randy Velarde	.05	.03
213	Les Lancaster	.05	.03
214	Andy Mota (R)	.08	.05
215	Rich Gossage	.08	.05
216	Brent Gates (R) (#1 Pick)	.40	.25
217	Brian Harper	.05	.03
218	Mike Flanagan	.05	.03

219	Jerry Browne	.05	.03
220	Jose Rijo	.08	.05
221	Skeeter Barnes	.05	.03
222	Jaime Navarro	.08	.05
223	Mel Hall	.05	.03
224	Brett Barberie	.12	.07
225	Roberto Alomar	.30	.18
226	Pete Smith	.10	.06
227	Daryl Boston	.05	.03
228	Eddie Whitson	.05	.03
229	Shawn Boskie	.05	.03
230	Dick Schofield	.05	.03
231	Brian Drahman (R)	.10	.06
232	John Smiley	.08	.05
233	Mitch Webster	.05	.03
234	Terry Steinbach	.07	.04
235	Jack Morris	.10	.06
236	Bill Pecota	.05	.03
237	Jose Hernandez (R)	.08	.05
238	Greg Litton	.05	.03
239	Brian Holman	.05	.03
240	Andres Galarraga	.12	.07
241	Gerald Young	.05	.03
242	Mike Mussina	.40	.25
243	Alvaro Espinoza	.05	.03
244	Darren Daulton	.15	.10
245	John Smoltz	.12	.07
246	Jason Pruitt (R) (#1 Pick)	.12	.07
247	Chuck Finley	.08	.05
248	Jim Gantner	.05	.03
249	Tony Fossas	.05	.03
250	Ken Griffey	.07	.04
251	Kevin Elster	.05	.03
252	Dennis Rasmussen	.05	.03
253	Terry Kennedy	.05	.03
254	Ryan Bowen (R)	.12	.07
255	Robin Ventura	.25	.15
256	Mike Aldrete	.05	.03
257	Jeff Russell	.07	.04
258	Jim Lindeman	.05	.03
259	Ron Darling	.07	.04
260	Devon White	.07	.04
261	Tom Lasorda	.07	.04
262	Terry Lee	.05	.03
263	Bob Patterson	.05	.03
264	Checklist 2	.05	.03
265	Teddy Higuera	.05	.03
266	Roberto Kelly	.10	.06
267	Steve Bedrosian	.05	.03
268	Brady Anderson	.10	.06
269	Ruben Amaro (R)	.12	.07
270	Tony Gwynn	.15	.10
271	Tracy Jones	.05	.03
272	Jerry Don Gleaton	.05	.03
273	Craig Grebeck	.05	.03
274	Bob Scanlan	.07	.04
275	Todd Zeile	.10	.06
276	Shawn Green (R) (#1 Pick)	.25	.15
277	Scott Chiamparino	.05	.03
278	Darryl Hamilton	.08	.05
279	Jim Clancy	.05	.03
280	Carlos Martinez	.05	.03
281	Kevin Appier	.10	.06
282	John Wehner (R)	.08	.05
283	Reggie Sanders (R)	.20	.12
284	Gene Larkin	.05	.03
285	Bob Welch	.07	.04
286	Gilberto Reyes	.05	.03
287	Pete Schourek	.05	.03
288	Andujar Cedeno	.12	.07
289	Mike Morgan	.07	.04
290	Bo Jackson	.15	.10
291	Phil Garner	.05	.03
292	Ray Lankford	.15	.10
293	Mike Henneman	.05	.03
294	Dave Valle	.05	.03
295	Alonzo Powell	.07	.04
296	Tom Brunansky	.07	.04
297	Kevin Brown	.10	.06
298	Kelly Gruber	.07	.04
299	Charles Nagy	.12	.07
300	Don Mattingly	.20	.12
301	Kirk McCaskill	.05	.03
302	Joey Cora	.05	.03
303	Dan Plesac	.05	.03
304	Joe Oliver	.05	.03
305	Tom Glavine	.15	.10
306	Al Shirley (R) (#1 Pick)	.15	.10
307	Bruce Ruffin	.05	.03
308	Craig Shipley (R)	.08	.05
309	Dave Martinez	.05	.03
310	Jose Mesa	.05	.03
311	Henry Cotto	.05	.03
312	Mike LaValliere	.05	.03
313	Kevin Tapani	.08	.05
314	Jeff Huson	.05	.03
315	Juan Samuel	.05	.03
316	Curt Schilling	.10	.06
317	Mike Bordick	.12	.07
318	Steve Howe	.05	.03
319	Tony Phillips	.07	.04
320	George Bell	.08	.05
321	Lou Piniella	.07	.04
322	Tim Burke	.05	.03
323	Milt Thompson	.05	.03
324	Danny Darwin	.05	.03
325	Joe Orsulak	.05	.03
326	Eric King	.05	.03
327	Jay Buhner	.07	.04
328	Joel Johnson (R)	.10	.06
329	Franklin Stubbs	.05	.03

330	Will Clark	.20	.12
331	Steve Lake	.05	.03
332	Chris Jones	.05	.03
333	Pat Tabler	.05	.03
334	Kevin Gross	.05	.03
335	Dave Henderson	.07	.04
000	Greg Anthony (R) (#1 Pick)	.10	.10
337	Alejandro Pena	.05	.03
338	Shawn Abner	.05	.03
339	Tom Browning	.07	.04
340	Otis Nixon	.07	.04
341	Bob Geren	.05	.03
342	Tim Spehr (R)	.10	.06
343	Jon Vander Wal (R)	.10	.06
344	Jack Daugherty	.05	.03
345	Zane Smith	.05	.03
346	Rheal Cormier (R)	.15	.10
347	Kent Hrbek	.08	.05
348	Rick Wilkins (R)	.30	.18
349	Steve Lyons	.05	.03
350	Gregg Olson	.07	.04
351	Greg Riddoch	.05	.03
352	Ed Nunez	.05	.03
353	Braulio Castillo (R)	.08	.05
354	Dave Bergman	.05	.03
355	Warren Newson (R)	.08	.05
356	Luis Quinones	.05	.03
357	Mike Witt	.05	.03
358	Ted Wood	.08	.05
359	Mike Moore	.07	.04
360	Lance Parrish	.07	.04
361	Barry Jones	.05	.03
362	Javier Ortiz (R)	.08	.05
363	John Candelaria	.05	.03
364	Glenallen Hill	.08	.05
365	Duane Ward	.05	.03
366	Checklist 3	.05	.03
367	Rafael Belliard	.05	.03
368	Bill Kruegar	.05	.03
369	Steve Whitaker (R) (#1 Pick)	.15	.10
370	Shawon Dunston	.08	.05
371	Dante Bichette	.08	.05
372	Kip Gross	.08	.05
373	Don Robinson	.05	.03
374	Bernie Williams	.15	.10
375	Bert Blyleven	.08	.05
376	Chris Donnels (R)	.12	.07
377	Bob Zupcic (R)	.20	.12
378	Joel Skinner	.05	.03
379	Steve Chitren	.05	.03
380	Barry Bonds	.60	.35
381	Sparky Anderson	.07	.04
382	Sid Fernandez	.07	.04
383	Dave Hollins	.20	.12
384	Mark Lee	.05	.03

385	Tim Wallach	.08	.05
386	Will Clark (AS)	.12	.07
387	Ryne Sandberg (AS)	.15	.10
388	Howard Johnson (AS)	.07	.04
389	Barry Larkin (AS)	.08	.05
390	Barry Bonds (AS)	.20	.12
391	Ron Gant (AS)	.09	.05
392	Bobby Bonilla (AS)	.08	.05
393	Craig Biggio (AS)	.07	.04
394	Denny Martinez (AS)	.07	.04
395	Tom Glavine (AS)	.10	.06
396	Ozzie Smith (AS)	.10	.06
397	Cecil Fielder (AS)	.10	.06
398	Julio Franco (AS)	.07	.04
399	Wade Boggs (AS)	.10	.06
400	Cal Ripken (AS)	.15	.10
401	Jose Canseco (AS)	.12	.07
402	Joe Carter (AS)	.10	.06
403	Ruben Sierra (AS)	.10	.06
404	Matt Nokes (AS)	.07	.04
405	Roger Clemens (AS)	.12	.07
406	Jim Abbott (AS)	.08	.05
407	Bryan Harvey (AS)	.07	.04
408	Bob Milacki	.05	.03
409	Geno Petralli	.05	.03
410	Dave Stewart	.08	.05
411	Mike Jackson	.05	.03
412	Luis Aquino	.05	.03
413	Tim Teufel	.05	.03
414	Jeff Ware (#1 Pick)	.12	.07
415	Jim Deshaies	.05	.03
416	Ellis Burks	.08	.05
417	Allan Anderson	.05	.03
418	Alfredo Griffin	.05	.03
419	Wally Whitehurst	.05	.03
420	Sandy Alomar	.08	.05
421	Juan Agosto	.05	.03
422	Sam Horn	.05	.03
423	Jeff Fassero	.05	.03
424	Paul McClellan (R)	.10	.06
425	Cecil Fielder	.20	.12
426	Tim Raines	.07	.04
427	Eddie Taubensee (R)	.12	.07
428	Dennis Boyd	.05	.03
429	Tony LaRussa	.07	.04
430	Steve Sax	.07	.04
431	Tom Gordon	.07	.04
432	Billy Hatcher	.05	.03
433	Cal Eldred	.25	.15
434	Wally Backman	.05	.03
435	Mark Eichhorn	.05	.03
436	Mookie Wilson	.05	.03
437	Scott Servais	.08	.05
438	Mike Maddux	.05	.03
439	Chico Walker	.05	.03
440	Doug Drabek	.10	.06
441	Rob Deer	.07	.04

442	Dave West	.05	.03
443	Spike Owen	.05	.03
444	Tyrone Hill (R) (#1 Pick)	.25	.15
445	Matt Williams	.15	.10
446	Mark Lewis	.08	.05
447	David Segui	.07	.04
448	Tom Pagnozzi	.07	.04
449	Jeff Johnson	.07	.04
450	Mark McGwire	.20	.12
451	Tom Henke	.05	.03
452	Wilson Alvarez	.08	.05
453	Gary Redus	.05	.03
454	Darren Holmes	.07	.04
455	Pete O'Brien	.05	.03
456	Pat Combs	.07	.04
457	Hubie Brooks	.05	.03
458	Frank Tanana	.05	.03
459	Tom Kelly	.05	.03
460	Andre Dawson	.12	.07
461	Doug Jones	.05	.03
462	Rich Rodriguez	.07	.04
463	Mike Simms	.07	.04
464	Mike Jeffcoat	.05	.03
465	Barry Larkin	.10	.06
466	Stan Belinda	.05	.03
467	Lonnie Smith	.07	.04
468	Greg Harris	.05	.03
469	Jim Eisenreich	.05	.03
470	Pedro Guerrero	.07	.04
471	Jose DeJesus	.05	.03
472	Rich Rowland (R)	.10	.06
473	Top Prospects-3rd Base	.15	.10
	Frank Bolick (R)		
	Craig Paquette (R)		
	Tom Redington (R)		
	Paul Russo (R)		
474	Mike Rossiter (R) (#1 Pick)	.12	.07
475	Robby Thompson	.08	.05
476	Randy Bush	.05	.03
477	Greg Hibbard	.05	.03
478	Dale Sveum	.05	.03
479	Chito Martinez (R)	.15	.10
480	Scott Sanderson	.05	.03
481	Tino Martinez	.08	.05
482	Jimmy Key	.08	.05
483	Terry Shumpert	.05	.03
484	Mike Hartley	.05	.03
485	Chris Sabo	.08	.05
486	Bob Walk	.05	.03
487	John Cerutti	.05	.03
488	Scott Cooper	.12	.07
489	Bobby Cox	.05	.03
490	Julio Franco	.08	.05
491	Jeff Brantley	.05	.03
492	Mike Devereaux	.08	.05
493	Jose Offerman	.08	.05
494	Gary Thurman	.05	.03
495	Carney Lansford	.05	.03
496	Joe Grahe	.07	.04
497	Andy Ashby	.05	.03
498	Gerald Perry	.05	.03
499	Dave Otto	.05	.03
500	Vince Coleman	.07	.04
501	Rob Mallicoat (R)	.08	.05
502	Greg Briley	.05	.03
503	Pascual Perez	.05	.03
504	Aaron Sele (R) (#1 Pick)	2.00	1.25
505	Bobby Thigpen	.07	.04
506	Todd Benzinger	.05	.03
507	Candy Maldonado	.05	.03
508	Bill Gullickson	.05	.03
509	Doug Dascenzo	.05	.03
510	Frank Viola	.08	.05
511	Kenny Rogers	.05	.03
512	Mike Heath	.05	.03
513	Kevin Bass	.05	.03
514	Kim Batiste	.08	.05
515	Delino DeShields	.15	.10
516	Ed Sprague	.10	.06
517	Jim Gott	.05	.03
518	Jose Melendez	.05	.03
519	Hal McRae	.07	.04
520	Jeff Bagwell	.35	.20
521	Joe Hesketh	.05	.03
522	Milt Cuyler	.08	.05
523	Shawn Hillegas	.05	.03
524	Don Slaught	.05	.03
525	Randy Johnson	.15	.10
526	Doug Piatt	.05	.03
527	Checklist 4	.05	.03
528	Steve Foster (R)	.08	.05
529	Joe Girardi	.05	.03
530	Jim Abbott	.15	.10
531	Larry Walker	.12	.07
532	Mike Huff	.05	.03
533	Mackey Sasser	.05	.03
534	Benji Gil (R) (#1 Pick)	.35	.20
535	Dave Stieb	.07	.04
536	Willie Wilson	.05	.03
537	Mark Leiter	.08	.05
538	Jose Uribe	.05	.03
539	Thomas Howard	.08	.05
540	Ben McDonald	.12	.07
541	Jose Tolentino (R)	.08	.05
542	Keith Mitchell	.10	.06
543	Jerome Walton	.05	.03
544	Cliff Brantley (R)	.10	.06
545	Andy Van Slyke	.08	.05
546	Paul Sorrento	.08	.05
547	Herm Winningham	.05	.03
548	Mark Guthrie	.05	.03

549	Joe Torre	.07	.04
550	Darryl Strawberry	.15	.10
551	Top Prospects-SS	.75	.45
	Manny Alexander (R)		
	Alex Arias (R)		
	Wil Cordero (R)		
	Chipper Jones		
552	Dave Gallagher	.05	.03
553	Edgar Martinez	.10	.06
554	Donald Harris	.08	.05
555	Frank Thomas	1.50	.90
556	Storm Davis	.05	.03
557	Dickie Thon	.05	.03
558	Scott Garrelts	.05	.03
559	Steve Olin	.05	.03
560	Rickey Henderson	.15	.10
561	Jose Vizcaino	.05	.03
562	Wade Taylor	.05	.03
563	Pat Borders	.05	.03
564	Jimmy Gonzalez (R)	.10	.06
	(#1 Pick)		
565	Lee Smith	.10	.06
566	Bill Sampen	.05	.03
567	Dean Palmer	.15	.10
568	Bryan Harvey	.07	.04
569	Tony Pena	.05	.03
570	Lou Whitaker	.07	.04
571	Randy Tomlin	.08	.05
572	Greg Vaughn	.10	.06
573	Kelly Downs	.05	.03
574	Steve Avery	.20	.12
575	Kirby Puckett	.30	.18
576	Heathcliff Slocumb (R)	.10	.06
577	Kevin Seitzer	.07	.04
578	Lee Guetterman	.05	.03
579	Johnny Oates	.05	.03
580	Greg Maddux	.20	.12
581	Stan Javier	.05	.03
582	Vicente Palacios	.05	.03
583	Mel Rojas	.07	.04
584	Wayne Rosenthal (R)	.08	.05
585	Lenny Webster	.05	.03
586	Rod Nichols	.05	.03
587	Mickey Morandini	.08	.05
588	Russ Swan	.05	.03
589	Mariano Duncan	.05	.03
590	Howard Johnson	.08	.05
591	Top Prospects-OF	.35	.20
	Jacob Brumfield (R)		
	Jeromy Burnitz (R)		
	Alan Cockrell (R)		
	D.J. Dozier (R)		
592	Denny Neagle (R)	.12	.07
593	Steve Decker	.08	.05
594	Brian Barber (R)	.25	.15
	(#1 Pick)		
595	Bruce Hurst	.07	.04
596	Kent Mercker	.07	.04
597	Mike Magnante (R)	.10	.06
598	Jody Reed	.05	.03
599	Steve Searcy	.05	.03
600	Paul Molitor	.20	.12
601	Dave Smith	.05	.03
602	Mike Fetters	.05	.03
603	Luis Mercedes	.12	.07
604	Chris Gwynn	.05	.03
605	Scott Erickson	.10	.06
606	Brook Jacoby	.05	.03
607	Todd Stottlemyre	.07	.04
608	Scott Bradley	.05	.03
609	Mike Hargrove	.05	.03
610	Eric Davis	.08	.05
611	Brian Hunter (R)	.15	.10
612	Pat Kelly	.08	.05
613	Pedro Munoz	.10	.06
614	Al Osuna	.05	.03
615	Matt Merullo	.05	.03
616	Larry Andersen	.05	.03
617	Junior Ortiz	.05	.03
618	Top Prospects-OF	.30	.18
	Cesar Hernandez (R)		
	Steve Hosey (R)		
	Dan Peltier (R)		
	Jeff McNeely (R)		
619	Danny Jackson	.05	.03
620	George Brett	.25	.15
621	Dan Gakeler (R)	.10	.06
622	Steve Buechele	.05	.03
623	Bob Tewksbury	.05	.03
624	Shawn Estes (R)	.20	.12
	(#1 Pick)		
625	Kevin McReynolds	.07	.04
626	Chris Haney (R)	.10	.06
627	Mike Sharperson	.05	.03
628	Mark Williamson	.05	.03
629	Wally Joyner	.08	.05
630	Carlton Fisk	.10	.06
631	Armando Reynoso (R)	.12	.07
632	Felix Fermin	.05	.03
633	Mitch Williams	.05	.03
634	Manuel Lee	.05	.03
635	Harold Baines	.07	.04
636	Greg Harris	.05	.03
637	Orlando Merced	.12	.07
638	Chris Bosio	.05	.03
639	Wayne Housie (R)	.10	.06
640	Xavier Hernandez	.05	.03
641	David Howard	.05	.03
642	Tim Crews	.05	.03
643	Rick Cerone	.05	.03
644	Terry Leach	.05	.03
645	Deion Sanders	.12	.07
646	Craig Wilson	.07	.04
647	Marquis Grissom	.15	.10

648	Scott Fletcher	.05	.03
649	Norm Charlton	.07	.04
650	Jesse Barfield	.07	.04
651	Joe Olusarski	.07	.04
652	Bobby Rose	.07	.04
653	Dennis Lamp	.05	.03
654	Allen Watson (R)	.50	.30
	(#1 Pick)		
655	Brett Butler	.07	.04
656	Top Prospects-OF	.20	.12
	Rudy Pemberton (R)		
	Henry Rodriguez (R)		
	Lee Tinsley (R)		
	Gerald Williams (R)		
657	Dave Johnson	.05	.03
658	Checklist 5	.05	.03
659	Brian McRae	.12	.07
660	Fred McGriff	.25	.15
661	Bill Landrum	.05	.03
662	Juan Guzman	.25	.15
663	Greg Gagne	.05	.03
664	Ken Hill	.08	.05
665	Dave Haas (R)	.10	.06
666	Tom Foley	.05	.03
667	Roberto Hernandez (R)	.10	.06
668	Dwayne Henry	.05	.03
669	Jim Fregosi	.05	.03
670	Harold Reynolds	.05	.03
671	Mark Whiten	.12	.07
672	Eric Plunk	.05	.03
673	Todd Hundley	.08	.05
674	Mo Sanford (R)	.10	.06
675	Bobby Witt	.07	.04
676	Top Prospects-P	.40	.25
	Pat Mahomes (R)		
	Sam Militello (R)		
	Roger Salkeld		
	Turk Wendell (R)		
677	John Marzano	.05	.03
678	Joe Klink	.05	.03
679	Pete Incaviglia	.05	.03
680	Dale Murphy	.10	.06
681	Rene Gonzales	.07	.04
682	Andy Benes	.10	.06
683	Jim Poole	.08	.05
684	Trever Miller (R)	.10	.06
	(#1 Pick)		
685	Scott Livingstone (R)	.10	.06
686	Rich DeLucia	.07	.04
687	Harvy Pulliam (R)	.10	.06
688	Tim Belcher	.07	.04
689	Mark Lemke	.05	.03
690	John Franco	.05	.03
691	Walt Weiss	.05	.03
692	Scott Ruskin	.07	.04
693	Jeff King	.07	.04
694	Mike Gardiner	.07	.04
695	Gary Sheffield	.20	.12
696	Joe Boever	.05	.03
697	Mike Felder	.05	.03
698	John Habyan	.05	.03
699	Cito Gaston	.07	.04
700	Ruben Sierra	.15	.10
701	Scott Radinsky	.07	.04
702	Lee Stevens	.07	.04
703	Mark Wohlers (R)	.15	.10
704	Curt Young	.05	.03
705	Dwight Evans	.07	.04
706	Rob Murphy	.05	.03
707	Gregg Jefferies	.15	.10
708	Tom Bolton	.05	.03
709	Chris James	.05	.03
710	Kevin Maas	.08	.05
711	Ricky Bones (R)	.10	.06
712	Curt Wilkerson	.05	.03
713	Roger McDowell	.05	.03
714	Calvin Reese (R) (#1	.15	.10
	Pick)		
715	Craig Biggio	.08	.05
716	Kirk Dressendorfer	.08	.05
717	Ken Dayley	.05	.03
718	B.J. Surhoff	.05	.03
719	Terry Mulholland	.07	.04
720	Kirk Gibson	.07	.04
721	Mike Pagliarulo	.05	.03
722	Walt Terrell	.05	.03
723	Jose Oquendo	.05	.03
724	Kevin Morton	.05	.03
725	Dwight Gooden	.10	.06
726	Kirt Manwaring	.05	.03
727	Chuck McElroy	.05	.03
728	Dave Burba	.05	.03
729	Art Howe	.05	.03
730	Ramon Martinez	.10	.06
731	Donnie Hill	.05	.03
732	Nelson Santovenia	.05	.03
733	Bob Melvin	.05	.03
734	Scott Hatteberg (R)	.20	.12
	(#1 Pick)		
735	Greg Swindell	.07	.04
736	Lance Johnson	.05	.03
737	Kevin Reimer	.05	.03
738	Dennis Eckersley	.10	.06
739	Rob Ducey	.05	.03
740	Ken Caminiti	.07	.04
741	Mark Gubicza	.07	.04
742	Billy Spiers	.05	.03
743	Darren Lewis	.08	.05
744	Chris Hammond	.08	.05
745	Dave Magadan	.05	.03
746	Bernard Gilkey	.10	.06
747	Willie Banks	.08	.05
748	Matt Nokes	.05	.03
749	Jerald Clark	.05	.03

750	Travis Fryman	.25	.15
751	Steve Wilson	.05	.03
752	Billy Ripken	.05	.03
753	Paul Assenmacher	.05	.03
754	Charlie Hayes	.07	.04
755	Alex Fernandez	.20	.12
756	Gary Pettis	.05	.03
757	Rob Dibble	.07	.04
758	Tim Naehring	.07	.04
759	Jeff Torborg	.05	.03
760	Ozzie Smith	.15	.10
761	Mike Fitzgerald	.05	.03
762	John Burkett	.05	.03
763	Kyle Abbott	.10	.06
764	Tyler Green (R) (#1 Pick)	.20	.12
765	Pete Harnisch	.07	.04
766	Mark Davis	.05	.03
767	Kal Daniels	.05	.03
768	Jim Thome (R)	.25	.15
769	Jack Howell	.05	.03
770	Sid Bream	.05	.03
771	Arthur Rhodes	.12	.07
772	Garry Templeton	.05	.03
773	Hal Morris	.10	.06
774	Bud Black	.05	.03
775	Ivan Calderon	.07	.04
776	Doug Henry (R)	.12	.07
777	John Olerud	.35	.20
778	Tim Leary	.05	.03
779	Jay Bell	.08	.05
780	Eddie Murray	.12	.07
781	Paul Abbott (R)	.10	.06
782	Phil Plantier	.20	.12
783	Joe Magrane	.05	.03
784	Ken Patterson	.05	.03
785	Albert Belle	.30	.18
786	Royce Clayton	.20	.12
787	Checklist 6	.05	.03
788	Mike Stanton	.10	.06
789	Bobby Valentine	.05	.03
790	Joe Carter	.20	.12
791	Danny Cox	.05	.03
792	Dave Winfield	.20	.12

1992 Topps
Stadium Club

This is Topps second annual upscale premium baseball set and the design is similar to 1991 Stadium Club. The fronts feature full color action shots with the player's name and Stadium Club logo at the bottom of the card. Card backs include a small full color player photo. Cards measure 2-1/2" by 3-1/2" and the set was issued in three 300-card series. The set includes the Members Choice Subset (591-610) and three special First Round Draft Pick insert cards. The Draft Pick cards are included at the end of this checklist but are not part of the complete set price.

		MINT	NR/MT
Complete Set (900)		70.00	45.00
Commons		.10	.06
1	Cal Ripken	1.00	.60
2	Eric Yelding	.10	.06
3	Geno Petralli	.10	.06
4	Wally Backman	.10	.06
5	Milt Cuyler	.12	.07
6	Kevin Bass	.10	.06
7	Dante Bichette	.10	.06
8	Ray Lankford	.35	.20
9	Mel Hall	.10	.06
10	Joe Carter	.50	.30
11	Juan Samuel	.10	.06
12	Jeff Montgomery	.10	.06
13	Glenn Braggs	.10	.06
14	Henry Cotto	.10	.06
15	Deion Sanders	.30	.18
16	Dick Schofield	.10	.06
17	David Cone	.25	.15
18	Chili Davis	.10	.06
19	Tom Foley	.10	.06

20	Ozzie Guillen	.10	.06
21	Luis Salazar	.10	.06
22	Terry Steinbach	.10	.06
23	Chris James	.10	.06
24	Jeff King	.15	.10
25	Carlos Quintana	.12	.07
26	Mike Maddux	.10	.06
27	Tommy Greene	.20	.12
28	Jeff Russell	.10	.06
29	Steve Finley	.12	.07
30	Mike Flanagan	.12	.07
31	Darren Lewis	.15	.10
32	Mark Lee	.10	.06
33	Willie Fraser	.10	.06
34	Mike Henneman	.10	.06
35	Kevin Maas	.15	.10
36	Dave Hansen	.12	.07
37	Erik Hansen	.15	.10
38	Bill Doran	.10	.06
39	Mike Boddicker	.10	.06
40	Vince Coleman	.15	.10
41	Devon White	.15	.10
42	Mark Gardner	.12	.07
43	Scott Lewis	.10	.06
44	Juan Berenguer	.10	.06
45	Carney Lansford	.10	.06
46	Curt Wilkerson	.10	.06
47	Shane Mack	.20	.12
48	Bip Roberts	.10	.06
49	Greg Harris	.10	.06
50	Ryne Sandberg	1.00	.60
51	Mark Whiten	.20	.12
52	Jack McDowell	.60	.35
53	Jimmy Jones	.10	.06
54	Steve Lake	.10	.06
55	Bud Black	.10	.06
56	Dave Valle	.10	.06
57	Kevin Reimer	.10	.06
58	Rich Gedman	.10	.06
59	Travis Fryman	1.00	.70
60	Steve Avery	1.00	.70
61	Francisco de la Rosa (R)	.12	.07
62	Scott Hemond	.10	.06
63	Hal Morris	.15	.10
64	Hensley Muelens	.12	.07
65	Frank Castillo	.10	.06
66	Gene Larkin	.10	.06
67	Jose DeLeon	.10	.06
68	Al Osuna	.10	.06
69	Dave Cochrane	.15	.10
70	Robin Ventura	.75	.45
71	John Cerutti	.10	.06
72	Kevin Gross	.10	.06
73	Ivan Calderon	.10	.06
74	Mike Macfarlane	.10	.06
75	Stan Belinda	.10	.06
76	Shawn Hillegas	.10	.06
77	Pat Borders	.10	.06
78	Jim Vatcher	.10	.06
79	Bobby Rose	.10	.06
80	Roger Clemens	1.00	.60
81	Craig Worthington	.10	.06
82	Jeff Treadway	.10	.06
83	Jamie Quirk	.10	.06
84	Randy Bush	.10	.06
85	Anthony Young	.15	.10
86	Trevor Wilson	.10	.06
87	Jaime Navarro	.12	.07
88	Les Lancaster	.10	.06
89	Pat Kelly	.12	.07
90	Alvin Davis	.10	.06
91	Larry Anderson	.10	.06
92	Rob Deer	.10	.06
93	Mike Sharperson	.10	.06
94	Lance Parrish	.10	.06
95	Cecil Espy	.10	.06
96	Tim Spehr	.10	.06
97	Dave Stieb	.10	.06
98	Terry Mulholland	.10	.06
99	Dennis Boyd	.10	.06
100	Barry Larkin	.25	.15
101	Ryan Bowen	.20	.12
102	Felix Fermin	.10	.06
103	Luis Alicea	.10	.06
104	Tim Hulett	.10	.06
105	Rafael Belliard	.10	.06
106	Mike Gallego	.10	.06
107	Dave Righetti	.10	.06
108	Jeff Schaefer	.10	.06
109	Ricky Bones	.12	.07
110	Scott Erickson	.20	.12
111	Matt Nokes	.10	.06
112	Bob Scanlan	.10	.06
113	Tom Candiotti	.10	.06
114	Sean Berry	.20	.12
115	Kevin Morton	.12	.07
116	Scott Fletcher	.10	.06
117	B.J. Surhoff	.10	.06
118	Dave Magadan	.10	.06
119	Bill Gullickson	.10	.06
120	Marquis Grissom	.50	.30
121	Lenny Harris	.10	.06
122	Wally Joyner	.20	.12
123	Kevin Brown	.20	.12
124	Braulio Castillo (R)	.20	.12
125	Eric King	.10	.06
126	Mark Portugal	.12	.07
127	Calvin Jones (R)	.20	.12
128	Mike Heath	.10	.06
129	Todd Van Poppel	.80	.50
130	Benny Santiago	.15	.10
131	Gary Thurman	.10	.06
132	Joe Girardi	.10	.06
133	Dave Eiland	.10	.06

134 Orlando Merced	.30	.18
135 Joe Orsulak	.10	.06
136 John Burkett	.10	.06
137 Ken Dayley	.10	.06
138 Ken Hill	.15	.10
139 Walt Terrell	.10	.06
140 Mike Scioscia	.10	.06
141 Junior Felix	.10	.06
142 Ken Caminiti	.10	.06
143 Carlos Baerga	1.25	.80
144 Tony Fossas	.10	.06
145 Craig Grebeck	.10	.06
146 Scott Bradley	.10	.06
147 Kent Mercker	.12	.07
148 Derrick May	.20	.12
149 Jerald Clark	.10	.06
150 George Brett	1.00	.60
151 Luis Quinones	.10	.06
152 Mike Pagliarulo	.10	.06
153 Jose Guzman	.10	.06
154 Charlie O'Brien	.10	.06
155 Darren Holmes	.10	.06
156 Joe Boever	.10	.06
157 Rick Monteleone	.10	.06
158 Reggie Harris	.10	.06
159 Roberto Alomar	1.25	.80
160 Robby Thompson	.10	.06
161 Chris Hoiles	.20	.12
162 Tom Pagnozzi	.12	.07
163 Omar Vizquel	.15	.10
164 John Candiotti	.10	.06
165 Terry Shumpert	.10	.06
166 Andy Mota	.10	.06
167 Scott Bailes	.10	.06
168 Jeff Blauser	.10	.06
169 Steve Olin	.10	.06
170 Doug Drabek	.20	.12
171 Dave Bergman	.10	.06
172 Eddie Whitson	.10	.06
173 Gilberto Reyes	.10	.06
174 Mark Grace	.40	.25
175 Paul O'Neill	.15	.10
176 Greg Cadaret	.10	.06
177 Mark Williamson	.10	.06
178 Casey Candaele	.10	.06
179 Candy Maldonado	.10	.06
180 Lee Smith	.15	.10
181 Harold Reynolds	.10	.06
182 David Justice	1.50	.90
183 Lenny Webster	.10	.06
184 Donn Pall	.10	.06
185 Gary Alexander	.10	.06
186 Jack Clark	.12	.07
187 Stan Javier	.10	.06
188 Ricky Jordan	.10	.06
189 Franklin Stubbs	.10	.06
190 Dennis Eckersley	.25	.15

191 Danny Tartabull	.15	.10
192 Pete O'Brien	.10	.06
193 Mark Lewis	.15	.10
194 Mike Felder	.10	.06
195 Mickey Tettleton	.12	.07
196 Dwight Smith	.10	.06
197 Shawn Abner	.10	.06
198 Jim Leyritz	.10	.06
199 Mike Devereaux	.15	.10
200 Craig Biggio	.15	.10
201 Kevin Elster	.10	.06
202 Rance Mulliniks	.10	.06
203 Tony Fernandez	.10	.06
204 Allan Anderson	.10	.06
205 Herm Winningham	.10	.06
206 Tim Jones	.10	.06
207 Ramon Martinez	.20	.12
208 Teddy Higuera	.10	.06
209 John Kruk	.25	.15
210 Jim Abbott	.40	.25
211 Dean Palmer	.80	.50
212 Mark Davis	.10	.06
213 Jay Buhner	.10	.06
214 Jesse Barfield	.10	.06
215 Kevin Mitchell	.15	.10
216 Mike LaValliere	.10	.06
217 Mark Wohlers	.15	.10
218 Dave Henderson	.10	.06
219 Dave Smith	.10	.06
220 Albert Belle	1.25	.80
221 Spike Owen	.10	.06
222 Jeff Gray	.10	.06
223 Paul Gibson	.10	.06
224 Bobby Thigpen	.12	.07
225 Mike Mussina	1.75	1.00
226 Darrin Jackson	.10	.06
227 Luis Gonzalez	.20	.12
228 Greg Briley	.10	.06
229 Brent Mayne	.15	.10
230 Paul Molitor	.40	.25
231 Al Leiter	.10	.06
232 Andy Van Slyke	.25	.15
233 Ron Tingley	.10	.06
234 Bernard Gilkey	.20	.12
235 Kent Hrbek	.12	.07
236 Eric Karros	.75	.45
237 Randy Velarde	.10	.06
238 Andy Allanson	.10	.06
239 Willie McGee	.15	.10
240 Juan Gonzalez	4.00	2.50
241 Karl Rhodes	.20	.12
242 Luis Mercedes	.20	.12
243 Billy Swift	.20	.12
244 Tommy Gregg	.10	.06
245 David Howard	.10	.06
246 Dave Hollins	.75	.45
247 Kip Gross	.10	.06

248	Walt Weiss	.10	.06
249	Mackey Sasser	.10	.06
250	Cecil Fielder	.75	.45
251	Jerry Browne	.10	.06
252	Doug Dascenzo	.10	.06
253	Darryl Hamilton	.20	.12
254	Dan Bilardello	.10	.06
255	Luis Rivera	.10	.06
256	Larry Walker	.40	.25
257	Ron Karkovice	.10	.06
258	Bob Tewksbury	.10	.06
259	Jimmy Key	.12	.07
260	Bernie Williams	.20	.12
261	Gary Wayne	.15	.10
262	Mike Simms	.10	.06
263	John Orton	.15	.10
264	Marvin Freeman	.10	.06
265	Mike Jeffcoat	.10	.06
266	Roger Mason	.10	.06
267	Edgar Martinez	.20	.12
268	Henry Rodriquez	.15	.10
269	Sam Horn	.10	.06
270	Brian McRae	.20	.12
271	Kirt Manwaring	.10	.06
272	Mike Bordick	.15	.10
273	Chris Sabo	.10	.06
274	Jim Olander	.10	.06
275	Greg Harris	.10	.06
276	Dan Gakeler	.10	.06
277	Bill Sampen	.10	.06
278	Joel Skinner	.10	.06
279	Curt Schilling	.10	.06
280	Dale Murphy	.20	.12
281	Lee Stevens	.10	.06
282	Lonnie Smith	.10	.06
283	Manual Lee	.10	.06
284	Shawn Boskie	.10	.06
285	Kevin Seitzer	.12	.07
286	Stan Royer	.12	.07
287	John Dopson	.10	.06
288	Scott Bullett (R)	.30	.18
289	Ken Patterson	.10	.06
290	Todd Hundley	.15	.10
291	Tim Leary	.10	.06
292	Brett Butler	.15	.10
293	Gregg Olson	.15	.10
294	Jeff Brantley	.10	.06
295	Brian Holman	.15	.10
296	Brian Harper	.12	.07
297	Brian Bohanon	.10	.06
298	Checklist	.10	.06
299	Checklist	.10	.06
300	Checklist	.10	.06
301	Frank Thomas	5.00	3.50
302	Lloyd McClendon	.10	.06
303	Brady Anderson	.20	.12
304	Julio Valera	.10	.06
305	Mike Aldrete	.10	.06
306	Joe Oliver	.10	.06
307	Todd Stottlemyre	.12	.07
308	Rey Sanohoz (R)	.25	.15
309	Gary Sheffield	.60	.35
310	Andujar Cedeno	.20	.12
311	Kenny Rogers	.10	.06
312	Bruce Hurst	.12	.07
313	Mike Schooler	.10	.06
314	Mike Benjamin	.10	.06
315	Chuck Finley	.20	.12
316	Mark Lemke	.10	.06
317	Scott Livingstone	.15	.10
318	Chris Nabholz	.12	.07
319	Mike Humphreys	.12	.07
320	Pedro Guerrero	.12	.07
321	Willie Banks	.30	.18
322	Tom Goodwin	.25	.15
323	Hector Warner (R)	.20	.12
324	Wally Ritchie	.10	.06
325	Mo Vaughn	.80	.50
326	Jo Klink	.10	.06
327	Cal Eldred	.80	.50
328	Daryl Boston	.10	.06
329	Mike Huff	.10	.06
330	Jeff Bagwell	1.00	.60
331	Bob Milacki	.10	.06
332	Tom Prince (R)	.10	.06
333	Pat Tabler	.10	.06
334	Ced Landrum	.10	.06
335	Reggie Jefferson	.25	.15
336	Mo Sanford	.12	.07
337	Kevin Ritz	.12	.07
338	Gerald Perry	.10	.06
339	Jeff Hamilton	.10	.06
340	Tim Wallach	.12	.07
341	Jeff Huson	.12	.07
342	Jose Melendez	.10	.06
343	Willie Wilson	.10	.06
344	Mike Stanton	.12	.07
345	Joel Johnston	.10	.06
346	Lee Guetterman	.10	.06
347	Francisco Oliveras	.10	.06
348	Dave Burba (R)	.20	.12
349	Tim Crews	.10	.06
350	Scott Leius	.10	.06
351	Danny Cox	.10	.06
352	Wayne Housie (R)	.20	.12
353	Chris Donnels	.12	.07
354	Chris George	.15	.10
355	Gerald Young	.10	.06
356	Roberto Hernandez	.20	.12
357	Neal Heaton	.10	.06
358	Todd Frohwirth	.10	.06
359	Jose Vizcaino	.10	.06
360	Jim Thome	.75	.45
361	Craig Wilson	.20	.12

362 Dave Haas	.10	.06
363 Billy Hatcher	.10	.06
364 John Barfield	.10	.06
365 Luis Aquino	.10	.06
366 Charlie Leibrandt	.10	.06
367 Howard Farmer	.10	.06
368 Bryn Smith	.10	.06
369 Mickey Morandini	.20	.12
370 Jose Canseco	.50	.30
371 Jose Uribe	.10	.06
372 Bob MacDonald (R)	.15	.10
373 Luis Sojo	.10	.06
374 Craig Shipley (R)	.12	.07
375 Scott Bankhead	.10	.06
376 Greg Gagne	.10	.06
377 Scott Cooper	.40	.25
378 Jose Offerman	.20	.12
379 Billy Spiers	.10	.06
380 John Smiley	.15	.10
381 Jeff Carter (R)	.10	.06
382 Heathcliff Slocumb	.10	.06
383 Jeff Tackett	.15	.10
384 John Kiely (R)	.12	.07
385 John Vander Wal (R)	.15	.10
386 Omar Olivares	.10	.06
387 Ruben Sierra	.35	.20
388 Tom Gordon	.15	.10
389 Charles Nagy	.60	.35
390 Dave Stewart	.20	.12
391 Pete Harnisch	.20	.12
392 Tim Burke	.10	.06
393 Roberto Kelly	.25	.15
394 Freddie Benavides	.10	.06
395 Tom Glavine	.75	.45
396 Wes Chamberlain	.20	.12
397 Eric Gunderson	.10	.06
398 Dave West	.10	.06
399 Ellis Burks	.15	.10
400 Ken Griffey, Jr.	4.00	2.50
401 Thomas Howard	.12	.07
402 Juan Guzman	.80	.50
403 Mitch Webster	.10	.06
404 Matt Merullo	.12	.07
405 Steve Buechele	.12	.07
406 Danny Jackson	.10	.06
407 Felix Jose	.15	.10
408 Doug Piatt (R)	.12	.07
409 Jim Eisenreich	.10	.06
410 Bryan Harvey	.20	.12
411 Jim Austin (R)	.12	.07
412 Jim Poole	.10	.06
413 Glenallen Hill	.20	.12
414 Gene Nelson	.10	.06
415 Ivan Rodriguez	.75	.45
416 Frank Tanana	.10	.06
417 Steve Decker	.10	.06
418 Jason Grimsley	.10	.06

419 Tim Layana	.10	.06
420 Don Mattingly	.75	.45
421 Jerome Walton	.10	.06
422 Rob Ducey	.10	.06
423 Andy Benes	.25	.15
424 John Marzano	.10	.06
425 Gene Harris	.10	.06
426 Tim Raines	.20	.12
427 Bret Barberie	.20	.12
428 Harvey Pulliam	.12	.07
429 Cris Carpenter	.10	.06
430 Howard Johnson	.15	.10
431 Orel Hershiser	.15	.10
432 Brain Hunter	.15	.10
433 Kevin Tapani	.12	.07
434 Rick Reed	.10	.06
435 Ron Witmeyer (R)	.12	.07
436 Gary Gaetti	.10	.06
437 Alex Cole	.10	.06
438 Chito Martinez	.20	.12
439 Greg Litton	.10	.06
440 Julio Franco	.20	.12
441 Mike Munoz	.10	.06
442 Erik Pappas	.10	.06
443 Pat Combs	.10	.06
444 Lance Johnson	.10	.06
445 Ed Sprague	.20	.12
446 Mike Greenwell	.15	.10
447 Milt thompson	.10	.06
448 Mike Magnante (R)	.20	.12
449 Chris Haney	.15	.10
450 Robin Yount	.80	.50
451 Rafael Ramirez	.10	.06
452 Gino Minutelli	.10	.06
453 Tom Lampkin	.10	.06
454 Tony Perezchica	.10	.06
455 Dwight Gooden	.25	.15
456 Mark Guthrie	.12	.07
457 Jay Howell	.10	.06
458 Gary DiSarcina	.20	.12
459 John Smoltz	.40	.25
460 Will Clark	.80	.50
461 Dave Otto	.10	.06
462 Rob Maurer (R)	.15	.10
463 Dwight Evans	.15	.10
464 Tom Brunansky	.10	.06
465 Shawn Hare (R)	.20	.12
466 Geronimo Pena	.10	.06
467 Alex Fernandez	.80	.50
468 Greg Myers	.10	.06
469 Jeff Fassero	.10	.06
470 Len Dykstra	.35	.20
471 Jeff Johnson	.10	.06
472 Russ Swan	.10	.06
473 Archie Corbin (R)	.20	.12
474 Chuck McElroy	.10	.06
475 Mark McGwire	.50	.30

476 Wally Whitehurst	.10	.06	
477 Tim McIntosh	.20	.12	
478 Sid Bream	.10	.06	
479 Jeff Juden	.30	.18	
480 Carlton Fisk	.30	.18	
481 Jeff Plympton (R)	.15	.10	
482 Carlos Martinez	.10	.06	
483 Jim Gott	.10	.06	
484 Bob McClure	.10	.06	
485 Tim Teufel	.10	.06	
486 Vicente Palacios	.10	.06	
487 Jeff Reed	.10	.06	
488 Tony Phillips	.10	.06	
489 Mel Rojas	.12	.07	
490 Ben McDonald	.25	.15	
491 Andres Santana	.15	.10	
492 Chris Beasley (R)	.20	.12	
493 Mike Timlin	.12	.07	
494 Brian Downing	.10	.06	
495 Kirk Gibson	.12	.07	
496 Scott Sanderson	.10	.06	
497 Nick Esasky	.10	.06	
498 Johnny Guzman (R)	.25	.15	
499 Mitch Wiliams	.10	.06	
500 Kirby Puckett	1.25	.80	
501 Mike Harkey	.12	.07	
502 Jim Gantner	.10	.06	
503 Bruce Egloff	.12	.07	
504 Josias Manzanillo (R)	.15	.10	
505 Delino DeShields	.35	.20	
506 Rheal Cormier	.20	.12	
507 Jay Bell	.12	.07	
508 Rich Rowland (R)	.20	.12	
509 Scott Servais	.10	.06	
510 Terry Pendleton	.25	.15	
511 Rich DeLucia	.12	.07	
512 Warren Newson	.12	.07	
513 Paul Faries	.10	.06	
514 Kal Daniels	.10	.06	
515 Jarvis Brown (R)	.20	.12	
516 Rafael Palmeiro	.35	.20	
517 Kelly Downs	.10	.06	
518 Steve Chitren	.10	.06	
519 Moises Alou	.40	.25	
520 Wade Boggs	.50	.30	
521 Pete Schourek	.12	.07	
522 Scott Terry	.12	.07	
523 Kevin Appier	.25	.15	
524 Gary Redus	.10	.06	
525 George Bell	.20	.12	
526 Jeff Kaiser (R)	.20	.12	
527 Alvaro Espinoza	.10	.06	
528 Luis Polonia	.12	.07	
529 Darren Daulton	.35	.20	
530 Norm Charlton	.12	.07	
531 John Olerud	1.50	.90	
532 Dan Plesac	.10	.06	
533 Billy Ripken	.10	.06	
534 Rod Nichols	.10	.06	
535 Joey Cora	.10	.06	
536 Harold Baines	.20	.12	
537 Bob Ojeda	.10	.06	
538 Mark Leonard	.10	.06	
539 Danny Darwin	.10	.06	
540 Shawon Dunston	.15	.10	
541 Pedro Munoz	.15	.10	
542 Mark Gubicza	.12	.07	
543 Kevin Baez (R)	.15	.10	
544 Todd Zeile	.20	.12	
545 Don Slaught	.10	.06	
546 Tony Eusebio (R)	.15	.10	
547 Alonzo Powell	.15	.10	
548 Gary Pettis	.10	.06	
549 Brian Barnes	.15	.10	
550 Lou Whitaker	.15	.10	
551 Keith Mitchell	.15	.10	
552 Oscar Azocar	.10	.06	
553 Stu Cole (R)	.15	.10	
554 Steve Wapnick (R)	.15	.10	
555 Derek Bell	.60	.35	
556 Luis Lopez	.10	.06	
557 Anthony Telford	.15	.10	
558 Tim Mauser (R)	.20	.12	
559 Glenn Sutko (R)	.15	.10	
560 Darryl Strawberry	.30	.18	
561 Tom Bolton	.10	.06	
562 Cliff Young	.10	.06	
563 Bruce Walton (R)	.10	.06	
564 Chico Walker	.10	.06	
565 John Franco	.10	.06	
566 Paul McClellan	.10	.06	
567 Paul Abbott	.10	.06	
568 Gary Varsho	.10	.06	
569 Carlos Maldonado (R)	.15	.10	
570 Kelly Gruber	.12	.07	
571 Jose Oquendo	.10	.06	
572 Steve Frey	.10	.06	
573 Tino Martinez	.15	.10	
574 Bill Haselman	.10	.06	
575 Eric Anthony	.25	.15	
576 John Habyan	.10	.06	
577 Jeffrey McNeely	.40	.25	
578 Chris Bosio	.10	.06	
579 Joe Grahe	.12	.07	
580 Fred McGriff	.80	.50	
581 Rick Honeycutt	.10	.06	
582 Matt Williams	.35	.20	
583 Cliff Brantley (R)	.20	.12	
584 Rob Dibble	.12	.07	
585 Skeeter Barnes	.10	.06	
586 Greg Hibbard	.10	.06	
587 Randy Milligan	.10	.06	
588 Checklist 301-400	.10	.06	
589 Checklist 401-500	.10	.06	

590	Checklist 501-600	.10	.06
591	Frank Thomas (MC)	3.00	1.75
592	David Justice (MC)	.60	.35
593	Roger Clemens (MC)	.75	.45
594	Steve Avery (MC)	.50	.30
595	Cal Ripken (MC)	.80	.50
596	Barry Larkin (MC)	.20	.12
597	Jose Canseco (MC)	.35	.20
598	Will Clark (MC)	.50	.30
599	Cecil Fielder (MC)	.40	.25
600	Ryne Sandberg (MC)	.75	.45
601	Chuck Knoblauch (MC)	.25	.15
602	Dwight Gooden (MC)	.25	.15
603	Ken Griffey, Jr. (MC)	2.00	1.25
604	Barry Bonds (MC)	1.00	.60
605	Nolan Ryan (MC)	2.50	1.40
606	Jeff Bagwell (MC)	.60	.35
607	Robin Yount (MC)	.75	.45
608	Bobby Bonilla (MC)	.25	.15
609	George Brett (MC)	.75	.45
610	Howard Johnson (MC)	.25	.15
611	Esteban Beltre (R)	.15	.10
612	Mike Christopher (R)	.15	.10
613	Troy Afenir	.10	.06
614	Mariano Duncan	.10	.06
615	Doug Henry (R)	.20	.12
616	Doug Jones	.10	.06
617	Alvin Davis	.10	.06
618	Craig Lefferts	.10	.06
619	Kevin McReynolds	.12	.07
620	Barry Bonds	1.50	.90
621	Turner Ward	.10	.06
622	Joe Magrane	.10	.06
623	Mark Parent	.10	.06
624	Tom Browning	.12	.07
625	John Smiley	.12	.07
626	Steve Wilson	.10	.06
627	Mike Gallego	.10	.06
628	Sammy Sosa	.50	.30
629	Rico Rossy (R)	.15	.10
630	Royce Clayton	.40	.25
631	Clay Parker	.10	.06
632	Pete Smith	.15	.10
633	Jeff McKnight	.10	.06
634	Jack Daugherty	.10	.06
635	Steve Sax	.12	.07
636	Joe Hesketh	.10	.06
637	Vince Horsman (R)	.15	.10
638	Eric King	.10	.06
639	Joe Boever	.10	.06
640	Jack Morris	.20	.12
641	Arthur Rhodes	.15	.10
642	Bob Melvin	.10	.06
643	Rick Wilkins	.40	.25
744	Scott Scudder	.10	.06
645	Bip Roberts	.10	.06
646	Julio Valera	.10	.06
647	Kevin Campbell (R)	.15	.10
648	Steve Searcey	.10	.06
649	Scott Kamieniecki	.12	.07
650	Kurt Stillwell	.10	.06
651	Bob Welch	.12	.07
652	Andres Galarraga	.25	.15
653	Mike Jackson	.10	.06
654	Bo Jackson	.60	.35
655	Sid Fernandez	.12	.07
656	Mike Bielecki	.10	.06
657	Jeff Reardon	.15	.10
658	Wayne Rosenthal (R)	.15	.10
659	Eric Bullock	.10	.06
660	Eric Davis	.25	.15
661	Randy Tomlin	.12	.07
662	Tom Edens (R)	.20	.12
663	Rob Murphy	.10	.06
664	Leo Gomez	.15	.10
665	Greg Maddux	.50	.30
666	Greg Vaughn	.25	.15
667	Wade Taylor	.10	.06
668	Brad Arnsberg	.10	.06
669	Mike Moore	.10	.06
670	Mark Langston	.20	.12
671	Barry Jones	.10	.06
672	Bill Landrum	.10	.06
673	Greg Swindell	.12	.07
674	Wayne Edwards	.10	.06
675	Greg Olson	.10	.06
676	Bill Pulsipher (R)	.20	.12
677	Bobby Witt	.12	.07
678	Mark Carreon	.10	.06
679	Patrick Lennon	.20	.12
680	Ozzie Smith	.45	.28
681	John Briscoe	.12	.07
682	Matt Young	.10	.06
683	Jeff Conine	.30	.18
684	Phil Stephenson	.10	.06
685	Ron Darling	.10	.06
686	Bryan Hickerson (R)	.20	.12
687	Dale Sveum	.10	.06
688	Kirk McCaskill	.10	.06
689	Rich Amaral (R)	.20	.12
690	Danny Tartabull	.15	.10
691	Donald Harris	.20	.12
692	Doug Davis (R)	.12	.07
693	John Farrell	.12	.07
694	Paul Gibson	.10	.06
695	Kenny Lofton	1.00	.60
696	Mike Fetters	.10	.06
697	Rosario Rodriquez	.10	.06
698	Chris Jones	.10	.06
699	Jeff Manto	.12	.07
700	Rick Sutcliffe	.12	.07
701	Scott Bankhead	.10	.06
702	Donnie Hill	.10	.06
703	Todd Worrell	.10	.06

704	Rene Gonzales	.15	.10
705	Rick Cerone	.10	.06
706	Tony Pena	.10	.06
707	Paul Sorrento	.25	.15
708	Gary Scott	.15	.10
709	Junior Noboa	.10	.06
710	Wally Joyner	.20	.12
711	Charlie Hayes	.12	.07
712	Rich Rodriquez	.12	.07
713	Rudy Seanez	.12	.07
714	Jim Bullinger (R)	.15	.10
715	Jeff Robinson	.10	.06
716	Jeff Branson	.10	.06
717	Andy Ashby	.12	.07
718	Dave Burba	.12	.07
719	Rich Gossage	.12	.07
720	Randy Johnson	.60	.35
721	David Wells	.10	.06
722	Paul Kilgus	.10	.06
723	Dave Martinez	.10	.06
724	Denny Neagle	.12	.07
725	Andy Stankiewicz (R)	.20	.12
726	Rick Aguilera	.10	.06
727	Junior Noboa	.10	.06
728	Storm Davis	.10	.06
729	Don Robinson	.10	.06
730	Ron Gant	.40	.25
731	Paul Assenmacher	.10	.06
732	Mike Gardiner	.12	.07
733	Milt Hill (R)	.15	.10
734	Jeremy Hernandez (R)	.20	.12
735	Ken Hill	.15	.10
736	Xavier Hernandez	.10	.06
737	Gregg Jefferies	.40	.25
738	Dick Schofield	.10	.06
739	Ron Robinson	.10	.06
740	Sandy Alomar	.15	.10
741	Mike Stanley	.15	.10
742	Butch Henry (R)	.15	.10
743	Floyd Bannister	.10	.06
744	Brian Drahman (R)	.12	.07
745	Dave Winfield	.75	.45
746	Bob Walk	.10	.06
747	Chris James	.10	.06
748	Don Prybylinski (R)	.15	.10
749	Dennis Rasmussen	.10	.06
750	Rickey Henderson	.50	.30
751	Chris Hammond	.15	.10
752	Bob Kipper	.10	.06
753	Dave Rohde	.15	.10
754	Hubie Brooks	.10	.06
755	Bret Saberhagen	.15	.10
756	Jeff Robinson	.10	.06
757	Pat Listach (R)	.35	.20
758	Bill Wegman	.10	.06
759	John Wettland	.25	.15
760	Phil Plantier	.75	.45
761	Wilson Alvarez	.20	.12
762	Scott Aldred	.15	.10
763	Armando Reynoso (R)	.25	.15
764	Todd Benzinger	.10	.06
765	Kevin Mitchell	.15	.10
766	Gary Sheffield	.60	.35
767	Allan Anderson	.10	.06
768	Rusty Meacham (R)	.15	.10
769	Rick Parker	.10	.06
770	Nolan Ryan	4.00	2.50
771	Jeff Ballard	.10	.06
772	Cory Snyder	.12	.07
773	Denis Boucher	.12	.07
774	Jose Gonzalez	.10	.06
775	Juan Guerrero (R)	.20	.12
776	Scott Ruskin	.10	.06
778	Terry Leach	.10	.06
779	Carl Willis	.10	.06
780	Bobby Bonilla	.20	.12
781	Duane Ward	.10	.06
782	Joe Slusarski	.10	.06
783	David Segui	.15	.10
784	Kirk Gibson	.12	.07
785	Frank Viola	.12	.07
786	Keith Miller	.10	.06
787	Mike Morgan	.10	.06
788	Kim Batiste	.12	.07
789	Sergio Valdez (R)	.20	.12
790	Eddie Taubensee (R)	.20	.12
791	Jack Armstrong	.15	.10
792	Scott Fletcher	.10	.06
793	Steve Farr	.10	.06
794	Dan Pasqua	.10	.06
795	Eddie Murray	.40	.25
796	John Morris	.10	.06
797	Francisco Cabrera	.10	.06
798	Mike Perez	.25	.15
799	Ted Wood	.12	.07
800	Jose Rijo	.15	.10
801	Danny Gladden	.10	.06
802	Archi Ciafrocco (R)	.25	.15
803	Monty Fariss	.15	.10
804	Roger McDowell	.10	.06
805	Randy Myers	.12	.07
806	Kirk Dressendorfer	.20	.12
807	Zane Smith	.10	.06
808	Glenn Davis	.10	.06
809	Torey Lovullo	.12	.07
810	Andre Dawson	.40	.25
811	Bill Pecota	.10	.06
812	Ted Power	.10	.06
813	Willie Blair	.15	.10
814	Dave Fleming	.80	.50
815	Chris Gwynn	.10	.06
816	Jody Reed	.10	.06
817	Mark Dewey (R)	.15	.10
818	Kyle Abbott	.15	.10

819	Tom Henke	.10	.06
820	Kevin Seitzer	.10	.06
821	Al Newman	.10	.06
822	Tim Sherrill (R)	.15	.10
823	Chuck Crim	.12	.07
824	Darren Reed	.12	.07
825	Tony Gwynn	.60	.30
826	Steve Foster (R)	.20	.12
827	Steve Howe	.10	.06
828	Brook Jacoby	.10	.06
829	Rodney McCray (R)	.12	.07
830	Chuck Knoblauch	.30	.18
831	John Wehner	.12	.07
832	Scott Garrelts	.10	.06
833	Alejandro Pena	.10	.06
834	Jeff Parrett	.10	.06
835	Juan Bell	.10	.06
836	Lance Dickson	.15	.10
837	Darryl Kile	.60	.35
838	Efrain Valdez	.15	.10
839	Bob Zupcic (R)	.30	.18
840	George Bell	.15	.10
841	Dave Gallagher	.10	.06
842	Tim Belcher	.12	.07
843	Jeff Shaw	.15	.10
844	Mike Fitzgerald	.10	.06
845	Gary Carter	.30	.18
846	John Russell	.10	.06
847	Eric Hillman (R)	.20	.12
848	Mike Witt	.10	.06
849	Curt Wilkerson	.10	.06
850	Alan Trammell	.30	.18
851	Rex Hudler	.10	.06
852	Mike Walkden (R)	.15	.10
853	Kevin Ward (R)	.15	.10
854	Tim Naehring	.20	.12
855	Bill Swift	.20	.12
856	Damon Berryhill	.10	.06
857	Mark Eichhorn	.10	.06
858	Hector Villanueva	.10	.06
859	Jose Lind	.10	.06
860	Denny Martinez	.15	.10
861	Bill Krueger	.10	.06
862	Mike Kingery	.10	.06
863	Jeff Innis	.10	.06
864	Derek Lilliquist	.10	.06
865	Reggie Sanders	.75	.45
866	Ramon Garcia	.15	.10
867	Bruce Ruffin	.10	.06
868	Dickie Thon	.10	.06
869	Merlido Perez	.12	.07
870	Ruben Amaro	.12	.07
871	Alan Mills	.15	.10
872	Matt Sinatro	.10	.06
873	Eddie Zosky	.20	.12
874	Pete Incaviglia	.10	.06
875	Tom Candiotti	.10	.06

876	Bob Patterson	.10	.06
877	Neal Heaton	.10	.06
878	Terrel Hansen (R)	.20	.12
879	Dave Eiland	.10	.06
880	Von Hayes	.10	.06
881	Tim Scott (R)	.20	.12
882	Otis Nixon	.12	.07
883	Herm Winningham	.10	.06
884	Dion James	.10	.06
885	Dave Wainhouse	.15	.10
886	Frank DiPino	.10	.06
887	Dennis Cook	.10	.06
888	Jose Mesa	.10	.06
889	Mark Leiter	.10	.06
890	Willie Randolph	.12	.07
891	Craig Colbert (R)	.15	.10
892	Dwayne Henry	.10	.06
893	Jim Lindeman	.10	.06
894	Charlie Hough	.10	.06
895	Gil Heredia (R)	.20	.12
896	Scott Chiamparino	.15	.10
897	Lance Blankenship	.10	.06
898	Checklist	.10	.06
899	Checklist	.10	.06
900	Checklist	.10	.06
SP1	Chipper Jones	10.00	6.50
SP2	Brien Taylor	5.00	3.00
SP3	Phil Nevin	7.00	4.00

1992 Topps Traded

As in previous years this update set features 132-cards consisting of traded players and rookie prospects. The set is identical to the Topps regular issue except for the "T" designation on the card numbers. The key subset includes players from Team USA. All cards measure 2-1/2" by 3-1/2".

	MINT	NR/MT
Complete Set (132)	24.00	14.00
Commons	.05	.02

1	Willie Adams (USA)(R)	.20	.12
2	Jeff Alkire (USA)(R)	.75	.45
3	Felipe Alou	.05	.02
4	Moises Alou	.15	.10
5	Ruben Amaro	.08	.05
6	Jack Armstrong	.05	.02
7	Scott Bankhead	.05	.02
8	Tim Belcher	.07	.04
9	George Bell	.08	.05
10	Freddie Benavides	.05	.02
11	Todd Benzinger	.05	.02
12	Joe Boever	.05	.02
13	Ricky Bones	.10	.06
14	Bobby Bonilla	.12	.07
15	Hubie Brooks	.05	.02
16	Jerry Browne	.05	.02
17	Jim Bullinger	.08	.05
18	Dave Burba	.05	.02
19	Kevin Campbell (R)	.15	.10
20	Tom Candiotti	.05	.02
21	Mark Carreon	.05	.02
22	Gary Carter	.10	.06
23	Archi Cianfrocco (R)	.20	.12
24	Phil Clark	.08	.05
25	Chad Curtis (R)	.80	.50
26	Eric Davis	.08	.05
27	Tim Davis (USA)(R)	.40	.25
28	Gary DiSarcina	.07	.04
29	Darren Dreifort (USA)	1.00	.60
30	Mariano Duncan	.05	.02
31	Mike Fitzgerald	.05	.02
32	John Flaherty (R)	.12	.07
33	Darrin Fletcher	.05	.02
34	Scott Fletcher	.05	.02
35	Ron Fraser (USA)	.10	.06
36	Andres Galarraga	.07	.04
37	Dave Gallagher	.05	.02
38	Mike Gallego	.05	.02
39	Nomar Garciaparra(USA)	.35	.20
40	Jason Giambi (USA)	.75	.45
41	Dan Gladden	.05	.02
42	Rene Gonzales	.05	.02
43	Jeff Granger (USA)	.80	.50
44	Rick Greene (USA)(R)	.25	.15
45	Jeffrey Hammonds (USA)	1.50	.90
46	Charlie Hayes	.07	.04
47	Von Hayes	.05	.02
48	Rick Helling (USA)	1.25	.80
49	Butch Henry (R)	.12	.07
50	Carlos Hernandez	.08	.05
51	Ken Hill	.10	.06
52	Butch Hobson	.05	.02
53	Vince Horsman (R)	.12	.07
54	Pete Incaviglia	.05	.02
55	Gregg Jefferies	.25	.15
56	Charles Johnson (USA)	1.00	.60
57	Doug Jones	.05	.02
58	Brian Jordan (R)	.60	.35
59	Wally Joyner	.08	.05
60	Daron Kirkreit (USA)	.50	.30
61	Bill Krueger	.05	.02
62	Gene Lamont	.05	.02
63	Jim Lefebvre	.05	.02
64	Danny Leon (R)	.10	.06
65	Pat Listach (R)	.50	.30
66	Kenny Lofton	1.00	.60
67	Dave Martinez	.05	.02
68	Derrick May	.10	.06
69	Kirk McCaskill	.05	.02
70	Chad McConnell (USA)	.40	.25
71	Kevin McReynolds	.07	.04
72	Rusty Meacham	.08	.05
73	Keith Miller	.05	.02
74	Kevin Mitchell	.08	.05
75	Jason Moler (USA)	.40	.25
76	Mike Morgan	.05	.02
77	Jack Morris	.10	.06
78	Calvin Murray (USA)	.60	.35
79	Eddie Murray	.12	.07
80	Randy Myers	.05	.02
81	Denny Neagle	.08	.05
82	Phil Nevin (USA)	1.75	1.00
83	Dave Nilsson	.15	.10
84	Junior Ortiz	.05	.02
85	Donovan Osborne	.35	.20
86	Bill Pecota	.05	.02
87	Melido Perez	.08	.05
88	Mike Perez	.05	.02
89	Hipolito Pichardo (R)	.15	.10
90	Willie Randolph	.07	.04
91	Darren Reed	.05	.02
92	Bip Roberts	.05	.02
93	Chris Roberts (USA)	.60	.35
94	Steve Rodriquez (USA)	.15	.10
95	Bruce Ruffin	.05	.02
96	Scott Ruskin	.05	.02
97	Bret Saberhagen	.10	.06
98	Rey Sanchez (R)	.20	.12
99	Steve Sax	.07	.04
100	Curt Schilling	.10	.06
101	Dick Schofield	.05	.02
102	Gary Scott	.07	.04
103	Kevin Seitzer	.05	.02
104	Frank Seminara (R)	.15	.10
105	Gary Sheffield	.30	.18
106	John Smiley	.08	.05
107	Cory Snyder	.05	.02
108	Paul Sorrento	.10	.06
109	Sammy Sosa	.25	.15
110	Matt Stairs (R)	.12	.07
111	Andy Stankiewicz	.12	.07
112	Kurt Stillwell	.05	.02
113	Rick Sutcliffe	.05	.02

114	Bill Swift	.10	.06
115	Jeff Tackett	.08	.05
116	Danny Tartabull	.10	.06
117	Eddie Taubensee	.08	.05
118	Dickie Thon	.05	.02
119	Michael Tucker (USA)	1.50	.90
120	Scooter Tucker (R)	.12	.07
121	Marc Valdes (USA)	.40	.25
122	Julio Valera	.05	.02
123	Jason Varitek (USA)	1.25	.80
124	Ron Villone (USA)	.30	.18
125	Frank Viola	.07	.04
126	B.J. Wallace (USA)	.80	.50
127	Dan Walters (R)	.15	.10
128	Craig Wilson (USA)	.12	.07
129	Chris Wimmer (USA)	.15	.10
130	Dave Winfield	.30	.18
131	Herm Winningham	.05	.02
132	Checklist	.05	.02

1993 Topps

This cards in this 825-card set were issued in two series and feature full color photos on the card fronts framed by a white border. The player's name appears in a color bar below the photo while the team name is centered at the bottom. Card backs include a color photo, personal data and complete stats. The set includes random gold inserts valued at 6 to10 times the price of the player's regular card. All cards measure 2-1/2" by 3-1/2".

	MINT	NR/MT
Complete Set (825)	34.00	22.00
Commons	.05	.02

1	Robin Yount	.20	.12
2	Barry Bonds	.50	.30
3	Ryne Sandberg	.30	.18
4	Roger Clemens	.30	.18
5	Tony Gwynn	.15	.10
6	Jeff Tackett	.08	.05
7	Pete Incaviglia	.05	.02
8	Mark Wohlers	.10	.06
9	Kent Hrbek	.05	.02
10	Will Clark	.20	.12
11	Eric Karros	.20	.12
12	Lee Smith	.10	.06
13	Esteban Beltre	.07	.04
14	Greg Briley	.05	.02
15	Marquis Grissom	.15	.10
16	Dan Plesac	.05	.02
17	Dave Hollins	.10	.06
18	Terry Steinbach	.05	.02
19	Ed Nunez	.05	.02
20	Tim Salmon	1.50	.90
21	Luis Salazar	.05	.02
22	Jim Eisenreich	.05	.02
23	Todd Stottlemyre	.05	.02
24	Tim Naehring	.05	.02
25	John Franco	.05	.02
26	Skeeter Barnes	.05	.02
27	Carlos Garcia	.12	.07
28	Joe Orsulak	.05	.02
29	Dwayne Henry	.05	.02
30	Fred McGriff	.20	.12
31	Derek Lilliquist	.05	.02
32	Don Mattingly	.15	.10
33	B.J. Wallace	.30	.18
34	Juan Gonzalez	1.00	.60
35	John Smoltz	.10	.06
36	Scott Servais	.05	.02
37	Lenny Webster	.05	.02
38	Chris James	.05	.02
39	Roger McDowell	.05	.02
40	Ozzie Smith	.12	.07
41	Alex Fernandez	.08	.05
42	Spike Owen	.05	.02
43	Ruben Amaro	.08	.05
44	Kevin Seitzer	.05	.02
45	Dave Fleming	.25	.15
46	Eric Fox	.07	.04
47	Bob Scanlan	.05	.02
48	Bert Blyleven	.07	.04
49	Brian McRae	.08	.05
50	Roberto Alomar	.25	.15
51	Mo Vaughn	.15	.10
52	Bobby Bonilla	.12	.07
53	Frank Tanana	.05	.02
54	Mike LaValliere	.05	.02
55	Mark McLemore	.05	.02
56	Chad Mottola (R)	.75	.45
57	Norm Charlton	.05	.02

58	Jose Melendez	.05	.02
59	Carlos Martinez	.05	.02
60	Roberto Kelly	.10	.06
61	Gene Larkin	.05	.02
62	Rafael Belliard	.05	.02
63	Al Osuna	.05	.02
64	Scott Chiamparino	.05	.02
65	Brett Butler	.07	.04
66	John Burkett	.08	.05
67	Felix Jose	.08	.05
68	Omar Vizquel	.05	.02
69	John Vander Wal	.07	.04
70	Roberto Hernandez	.05	.02
71	Ricky Bones	.07	.04
72	Jeff Grotewold	.05	.02
73	Mike Moore	.05	.02
74	Steve Buechele	.05	.02
75	Juan Guzman	.20	.12
76	Kevin Appier	.10	.06
77	Junior Felix	.05	.02
78	Greg Harris	.05	.02
79	Dick Schofield	.05	.02
80	Cecil Fielder	.20	.12
81	Lloyd McClendon	.05	.02
82	David Segui	.07	.04
83	Reggie Sanders	.15	.10
84	Kurt Stillwell	.05	.02
85	Sandy Alomar	.07	.04
86	John Habyan	.05	.02
87	Kevin Reimer	.05	.02
88	Mike Stanton	.05	.02
89	Eric Anthony	.10	.06
90	Scott Erickson	.08	.05
91	Craig Colbert	.05	.02
92	Tom Pagnozzi	.07	.04
93	Pedro Astacio	.15	.10
94	Lance Johnson	.05	.02
95	Larry Walker	.10	.06
96	Russ Swan	.05	.02
97	Scott Fletcher	.05	.02
98	Derek Jeter (R)	.35	.20
99	Mike Williams	.10	.06
100	Mark McGwire	.15	.10
101	Jim Bullinger	.05	.02
102	Brian Hunter	.10	.06
103	Jody Reed	.05	.02
104	Mike Butcher	.05	.02
105	Gregg Jefferies	.15	.10
106	Howard Johnson	.08	.05
107	John Kiely	.08	.05
108	Jose Lind	.05	.02
109	Sam Horn	.05	.02
110	Barry Larkin	.12	.07
111	Bruce Hurst	.07	.04
112	Brian Barnes	.07	.04
113	Thomas Howard	.07	.04
114	Mel Hall	.07	.04
115	Robby Thompson	.05	.02
116	Mark Lemke	.05	.02
117	Eddie Taubensee	.05	.02
118	David Hulse (R)	.12	.07
119	Pedro Munoz	.08	.05
120	Ramon Martinez	.10	.06
121	Todd Worrell	.05	.02
122	Joey Cora	.05	.02
123	Moises Alou	.12	.07
124	Franklin Stubbs	.05	.02
125	Pete O'Brien	.05	.02
126	Bob Ayrault	.07	.04
127	Carney Lansford	.05	.02
128	Kal Daniels	.05	.02
129	Joe Drake	.05	.02
130	Jeff Montgomery	.05	.02
131	Dave Winfield	.20	.12
132	Preston Wilson (R)	.50	.30
133	Steve Wilson	.05	.02
134	Lee Guetterman	.05	.02
135	Mickey Tettleton	.07	.04
136	Jeff King	.07	.04
137	Alan Mills	.05	.02
138	Joe Oliver	.05	.02
139	Gary Gaetti	.05	.02
140	Gary Sheffield	.15	.10
141	Dennis Cook	.05	.02
142	Charlie Hayes	.05	.02
143	Jeff Huson	.05	.02
144	Kent Mercker	.05	.02
145	Eric Young	.10	.06
146	Scott Leius	.05	.02
147	Bryan Hickerson	.08	.05
148	Steve Finley	.05	.02
149	Rheal Cormier	.07	.04
150	Frank Thomas	1.50	.90
151	Archi Cianfrocco	.12	.07
152	Rich DeLucia	.05	.02
153	Greg Vaughn	.10	.06
154	Wes Chamberlain	.10	.06
155	Dennis Eckersley	.12	.07
156	Sammy Sosa	.15	.10
157	Gary DiSarcina	.07	.04
158	Kevin Koslofski	.08	.05
159	Doug Linton	.08	.05
160	Lou Whitaker	.07	.04
161	Chad McConnell	.15	.10
162	Joe Hesketh	.05	.02
163	Tim Wakefield	.10	.06
164	Leo Gomez	.08	.05
165	Jose Rijo	.08	.05
166	Tim Scott	.05	.02
167	Steve Olin	.07	.04
168	Kevin Maas	.08	.05
169	Kevin Rogers	.05	.02
170	David Justice	.25	.15
171	Doug Jones	.05	.02

172	Jeff Reboulet	.08	.05
173	Andres Galarraga	.12	.07
174	Randy Velarde	.05	.02
175	Kirk McCaskill	.05	.02
176	Darren Lewis	.07	.04
177	Lenny Harris	.05	.02
178	Jeff Fassero	.05	.02
179	Ken Griffey, Jr.	1.25	.80
180	Darren Daulton	.12	.07
181	John Jaha	.10	.06
182	Ron Darling	.05	.02
183	Greg Maddux	.15	.10
184	Damion Easley	.12	.07
185	Jack Morris	.15	.10
186	Mike Magnante	.07	.04
187	John Dopson	.05	.02
188	Sid Fernandez	.07	.04
189	Tony Phillips	.05	.02
190	Doug Drabek	.10	.06
191	Sean Lowe (R)	.20	.12
192	Bob Milacki	.05	.02
193	Steve Foster	.05	.02
194	Jerald Clark	.07	.04
195	Pete Harnisch	.08	.05
196	Pat Kelly	.08	.05
197	Jeff Frye	.05	.02
198	Alejandro Pena	.05	.02
199	Junior Ortiz	.05	.02
200	Kirby Puckett	.25	.15
201	Jose Uribe	.05	.02
202	Mike Scioscia	.05	.02
203	Bernard Gilkey	.10	.06
204	Dan Pasqua	.05	.02
205	Gary Carter	.10	.06
206	Henry Cotto	.05	.02
207	Paul Molitor	.15	.10
208	Mike Hartley	.05	.02
209	Jeff Parrett	.05	.02
210	Mark Langston	.08	.05
211	Doug Dascenzo	.05	.02
212	Rick Reed	.05	.02
213	Candy Maldonado	.05	.02
214	Danny Darwin	.05	.02
215	Pat Howell	.08	.05
216	Mark Leiter	.05	.02
217	Kevin Mitchell	.08	.05
218	Ben McDonald	.12	.07
219	Bip Roberts	.05	.02
220	Benito Santiago	.08	.05
221	Carlos Baerga	.25	.15
222	Bernie Williams	.10	.06
223	Roger Pavlik	.10	.06
224	Sid Bream	.05	.02
225	Matt Williams	.15	.10
226	Willie Banks	.08	.05
227	Jeff Bagwell	.20	.12
228	Tom Goodwin	.08	.05
229	Mike Perez	.07	.04
230	Carlton Fisk	.15	.10
231	John Wetteland	.07	.04
232	Tino Martinez	.08	.05
233	Rick Greene	.12	.07
234	Tim McIntosh	.10	.06
235	Mitch Williams	.05	.02
236	Kevin Campbell	.07	.04
237	Jose Vizcaino	.05	.02
238	Chris Donnels	.07	.04
239	Mike Bodicker	.05	.02
240	John Olerud	.40	.25
241	Mike Gardiner	.05	.02
242	Charlie O'Brien	.05	.02
243	Rob Deer	.07	.04
244	Denny Neagle	.07	.04
245	Chris Sabo	.07	.04
246	Gregg Olson	.07	.04
247	Frank Seminara	.08	.05
248	Scott Scudder	.07	.04
249	Tim Burke	.05	.02
250	Chuck Knoblauch	.15	.10
251	Mike Bielecki	.05	.02
252	Xavier Hernandez	.05	.02
253	Jose Guzman	.07	.04
254	Cory Snyder	.05	.02
255	Orel Hershiser	.10	.06
256	Wil Cordero	.15	.10
257	Luis Alicea	.05	.02
258	Mike Schooler	.05	.02
259	Craig Grebeck	.05	.02
260	Duane Ward	.05	.02
261	Bill Wegman	.05	.02
262	Mickey Morandini	.07	.04
263	Vince Horsman	.08	.05
264	Paul Sorrento	.08	.05
265	Andre Dawson	.12	.07
266	Rene Gonzales	.07	.04
267	Keith Miller	.05	.02
268	Derek Bell	.10	.06
269	Todd Steverson (R)	.25	.15
270	Frank Viola	.07	.04
271	Wally Whitehurst	.05	.02
272	Kurt Knudsen	.10	.06
273	Dan Walters	.08	.05
274	Rick Sutcliffe	.05	.02
275	Andy Van Slyke	.12	.07
276	Paul O'Neill	.12	.07
277	Mark Whiten	.15	.10
278	Chris Nabholz	.07	.04
279	Todd Burns	.05	.02
280	Tom Glavine	.15	.10
281	Butch Henry	.05	.02
282	Shane Mack	.08	.05
283	Mike Jackson	.05	.02
284	Henry Rodriquez	.08	.05
285	Bob Tewksbury	.05	.02

#	Player			#	Player		
286	Ron Karkovice	.05	.02	343	Doug Henry	.05	.02
287	Mike Gallego	.05	.02	344	Jack McDowell	.15	.10
288	Dave Cochrane	.05	.02	345	Harold Baines	.07	.04
289	Jesse Orosco	.05	.02	346	Chuck McElroy	.05	.02
290	Dave Stewart	.08	.05	347	Luis Sojo	.05	.02
291	Tommy Greene	.10	.06	348	Andy Stankiewicz	.07	.04
292	Rey Sanchez	.10	.06	349	Hipolito Pichardo	.10	.06
293	Rob Ducey	.05	.02	350	Joe Carter	.20	.12
294	Brent Mayne	.07	.04	351	Ellis Burks	.07	.04
295	Dave Stieb	.08	.05	352	Pete Schourek	.05	.02
296	Luis Rivera	.05	.02	353	Buddy Groom (R)	.10	.06
297	Jeff Innis	.05	.02	354	Jay Bell	.05	.02
298	Scott Livingstone	.07	.04	355	Brady Anderson	.12	.07
299	Bob Patterson	.05	.02	356	Freddie Benavides	.05	.02
300	Cal Ripken	.30	.18	357	Phil Stephenson	.05	.02
301	Cesar Hernandez	.08	.05	358	Kevin Wickander	.05	.02
302	Randy Myers	.05	.02	359	Mike Stanley	.08	.05
303	Brook Jacoby	.05	.02	360	Ivan Rodriguez	.15	.10
304	Melido Perez	.07	.04	361	Scott Bankhead	.05	.02
305	Rafael Palmeiro	.15	.10	362	Luis Gonzalez	.08	.05
306	Damon Berryhill	.05	.02	363	John Smiley	.08	.05
307	Dan Serafini (R)	.25	.15	364	Trevor Wilson	.05	.02
308	Darryl Kile	.05	.02	365	Tom Candiotti	.05	.02
309	J.T. Bruett	.08	.05	366	Craig Wilson	.08	.05
310	Dave Righetti	.05	.02	367	Steve Sax	.07	.04
311	Jay Howell	.05	.02	368	Delino DeShields	.12	.07
312	Geronimo Pena	.05	.02	369	Jaime Navarro	.08	.05
313	Greg Hibbard	.05	.02	370	Dave Valle	.05	.02
314	Mark Gardner	.05	.02	371	Mariano Duncan	.05	.02
315	Edgar Martinez	.10	.06	372	Rod Nichols	.05	.02
316	Dave Nilsson	.10	.06	373	Mike Morgan	.05	.02
317	Kyle Abbott	.07	.04	374	Julio Valera	.05	.02
318	Willie Wilson	.05	.02	375	Wally Joyner	.08	.05
319	Paul Assenmacher	.05	.02	376	Tom Henke	.05	.02
320	Tim Fortugno	.05	.02	377	Herm Winningham	.05	.02
321	Rusty Meacham	.08	.05	378	Orlando Merced	.08	.05
322	Pat Borders	.07	.04	379	Mike Munoz	.07	.04
323	Mike Greenwell	.08	.05	380	Todd Hundley	.07	.04
324	Willie Randolph	.07	.04	381	Mike Flannigan	.05	.02
325	Bill Gullickson	.05	.02	382	Tim Belcher	.07	.04
326	Gary Varsho	.05	.02	383	Jerry Browne	.05	.02
327	Tim Hulett	.07	.04	384	Mike Benjamin	.07	.04
328	Scott Ruskin	.07	.04	385	Jim Leyritz	.05	.02
329	Mike Maddux	.05	.02	386	Ray Lankford	.15	.10
330	Danny Tartabull	.10	.06	387	Devon White	.05	.02
331	Kenny Lofton	.20	.12	388	Jeremy Hernandez	.08	.05
332	Gino Petralli	.05	.02	389	Brian Harper	.05	.02
333	Otis Nixon	.08	.05	390	Wade Boggs	.15	.10
334	Jason Kendall (R)	.25	.15	391	Derrick May	.08	.05
335	Mark Portugal	.05	.02	392	Travis Fryman	.20	.12
336	Mike Pagliarulo	.05	.02	393	Ron Gant	.12	.07
337	Kirk Manwaring	.05	.02	394	Checklist I-132	.05	.02
338	Bob Ojeda	.05	.02	395	Checklist 133-264	.05	.02
339	Mark Clark	.08	.05	396	Checklist 265-396	.05	.02
340	John Kruk	.07	.04	397	George Brett	.25	.15
341	Mel Rojas	.05	.02	398	Bobby Witt	.07	.04
342	Erik Hanson	.05	.02	399	Daryl Boston	.05	.02

400	Bo Jackson	.15	.10
401	McGriff/Thomas	.60	.35
402	Sandberg/Baerga	.20	.12
403	Sheffield/E. Martinez	.10	.06
404	Larkin/Fryman	.15	.10
405	Van Slyke/Griffey Jr.	.40	.25
406	L. Walker/Puckett	.15	.10
407	B. Bonds/J. Carter	.20	.12
408	Daulton/Harper	.07	.04
409	G. Maddux/Clemens	.20	.12
410	Glavine/Fleming	.12	.07
411	L. Smith/Eckersley	.10	.06
412	Jamie McAndrew	.05	.02
413	Pete Smith	.08	.05
414	Juan Guerrero	.08	.05
415	Todd Frohwirth	.07	.04
416	Randy Tomlin	.08	.05
417	B.J. Surhoff	.05	.02
418	Jim Gott	.05	.02
419	Mark Thompson (R)	.12	.07
420	Kevin Tapani	.07	.04
421	Curt Schilling	.08	.05
422	J.T. Snow (R)	.75	.45
423	1993 Prospects (Klesko)	.40	.25
424	John Valentin	.15	.10
425	Joe Girardi	.05	.02
426	Nigel Wilson	.75	.45
427	Bob MacDonald (R)	.20	.12
428	Todd Zeile	.08	.05
429	Milt Cuyler	.07	.04
430	Eddie Murray	.12	.07
431	Rich Amaral (R)	.15	.10
432	Pete Young (R)	.15	.10
433	Bailey/Schmidt (R)	.20	.12
434	Jack Armstrong	.05	.02
435	Willie McGee	.08	.05
436	Greg Harris	.05	.02
437	Chris Hammond	.07	.04
438	Ritchie Moody (R)	.12	.07
439	Bryan Harvey	.07	.04
440	Ruben Sierra	.20	.12
441	D. Lemon/T. Pridy (R)	.20	.12
442	Kevin McReynolds	.08	.05
443	Terry Leach	.05	.02
444	David Nied	.60	.35
445	Dale Murphy	.10	.06
446	Luis Mercedes	.08	.05
447	Keith Shepherd (R)	.20	.12
448	Ken Caminiti	.05	.02
449	James Austin (R)	.15	.10
450	Darryl Strawberry	.15	.10
451	1993 Prospects (Gates)	.35	.20
452	Bob Wickman	.20	.12
453	Victor Cole	.05	.02
454	John Johnstone (R)	.10	.06
455	Chili Davis	.07	.04
456	Scott Taylor (R)	.15	.10
457	Tracy Woodson	.05	.02
458	David Wells	.05	.02
459	Derek Wallace (R)	.20	.12
460	Randy Johnson	.15	.10
461	Steve Reed (R)	.15	.10
462	Felix Fermin	.05	.02
463	Scott Aldred	.08	.05
464	Greg Colbrunn	.10	.06
465	Tony Fernandez	.07	.04
466	Mike Felder	.05	.02
467	Lee Stevens	.05	.02
468	Matt Whiteside (R)	.12	.07
469	Dave Hansen	.05	.02
470	Rob Dibble	.07	.04
471	Dave Gallagher	.05	.02
472	Chris Gwynn	.05	.02
473	Dave Henderson	.07	.04
474	Ozzie Guillen	.05	.02
475	Jeff Reardon	.08	.05
476	Voisard/Scalzitti (R)	.20	.12
477	Jimmy Jones	.05	.02
478	Greg Cadaret	.05	.02
479	Todd Pratt (R)	.12	.07
480	Pat Listach	.20	.12
481	Ryan Luzinsky (R)	.40	.25
482	Darren Reed	.05	.02
483	Brian Griffiths (R)	.20	.12
484	John Wehner	.05	.02
485	Glenn Davis	.05	.02
486	Eric Wedge (R)	.12	.07
487	Jesse Hollins (R)	.20	.12
488	Manuel Lee	.05	.02
489	Scott Fredrickson (R)	.15	.10
490	Omar Olivares	.05	.02
491	Shawn Hare	.20	.12
492	Tom Lampkin	.05	.02
493	Jeff Nelson	.05	.02
494	1993 Prospects (Young)	.35	.20
495	Ken Hill	.08	.05
496	Reggie Jefferson	.10	.06
497	Petersen/Brown (R)	.20	.12
498	Bud Black	.05	.02
499	Chuck Crim	.05	.02
500	Jose Canseco	.15	.10
501	Johnny Oates	.05	.02
502	Butch Hobson	.05	.02
503	Buck Rodgers	.05	.02
504	Gene Lamont	.05	.02
505	Mike Hargrove	.05	.02
506	Sparky Anderson	.07	.04
507	Hal McRae	.07	.04
508	Phil Garner	.05	.02
509	Tom Kelly	.05	.02
510	Buck Showalter	.05	.02
511	Tony LaRussa	.07	.04
512	Lou Piniella	.05	.02
513	Toby Harrah	.05	.02

514	Cito Gaston	.07	.04	571	Dave Mlicki	.08	.05
515	Greg Swindell	.07	.04	572	Trevor Hoffman (R)	.20	.12
516	Alex Arias	.10	.06	573	John Patterson	.07	.04
517	Bill Pecota	.05	.02	574	Shawn Warren (R)	.10	.06
518	Benji Grigsby (R)	.20	.12	575	Monty Fariss	.08	.05
519	David Howard	.08	.05	576	1993 Prospects	.60	.35
520	Charlie Hough	.05	.02	577	Tim Costo	.15	.10
521	Kevin Flora (R)	.15	.10	578	Dave Magadan	.05	.02
522	Shane Reynolds (R)	.20	.12	579	N. Garrett/Bates (R)	.20	.12
523	Doug Bochtler (R)	.15	.10	580	Walt Weiss	.05	.02
524	Chris Hoiles	.08	.05	581	Chris Haney	.07	.04
525	Scott Sanderson	.05	.02	582	Shawn Abner	.05	.02
526	Mike Sharperson	.05	.02	583	Marvin Freeman	.05	.02
527	Mike Fetters	.05	.02	584	Casey Candaele	.05	.02
528	Paul Quantrill	.08	.05	585	Ricky Jordan	.07	.04
529	1993 Prospects (Jones)	.40	.25	586	Jeff Tabaka (R)	.12	.07
530	Sterling Hitchcock (R)	.40	.25	587	Manny Alexander	.15	.10
531	Joe Millette (R)	.15	.10	588	Mike Trombley	.07	.04
532	Tom Brunansky	.07	.04	589	Carlos Hernandez	.15	.10
533	Frank Castillo	.05	.02	590	Cal Eldred	.30	.18
534	Randy Knorr	.05	.02	591	Alex Cole	.05	.02
535	Jose Oquendo	.05	.02	592	Phil Plantier	.15	.10
536	Dave Haas	.05	.02	593	Brett Merriman (R)	.15	.10
537	Hutchins/Turner (R)	.20	.12	594	Jerry Nielsen (R)	.15	.10
538	Jimmy Baron (R)	.15	.10	595	Shawon Dunston	.08	.05
539	Kerry Woodson (R)	.25	.15	596	Jimmy Key	.05	.02
540	Ivan Calderon	.07	.04	597	Gerald Perry	.05	.02
541	Denis Boucher	.05	.02	598	Rico Brogna	.10	.06
542	Royce Clayton	.12	.07	599	Nunez/Robinson (R)	.15	.10
543	Reggie Williams (R)	.15	.10	600	Bret Saberhagen	.10	.06
544	Steve Decker	.08	.05	601	Craig Shipley	.05	.02
545	Dean Palmer	.12	.07	602	Henry Mercedes	.10	.06
546	Hal Morris	.10	.06	603	Jim Thome	.15	.10
547	Ryan Thompson	.20	.12	604	Rod Beck	.08	.05
548	Lance Blankenship	.05	.02	605	Chuck Finley	.08	.05
549	Hensley Meulens	.08	.05	606	J. Owens (R)	.20	.12
550	Scott Radinsky	.05	.02	607	Dan Smith	.15	.10
551	Eric Young	.12	.07	608	Bill Doran	.05	.02
552	Jeff Blauser	.05	.02	609	Lance Parrish	.05	.02
553	Andujar Cedeno	.12	.07	610	Denny Martinez	.08	.05
554	Arthur Rhodes	.10	.06	611	Tom Gordon	.07	.04
555	Terry Mulholland	.05	.02	612	Bryon Mathews (R)	.12	.07
556	Darryl Hamilton	.08	.05	613	Joel Adamson (R)	.15	.10
557	Pedro Martinez	.20	.12	614	Brian Williams	.10	.06
558	R. Whitman/Skeels (R)	.25	.15	615	Steve Avery	.15	.10
559	Jamie Arnold (R)	.20	.12	616	1993 Prospects	.35	.20
560	Zane Smith	.05	.02	617	Craig Lefferts	.05	.02
561	Matt Nokes	.05	.02	618	Tony Pena	.05	.02
562	Bob Zupcic	.08	.05	619	Billy Spiers	.05	.02
563	Shawn Boskie	.05	.02	620	Todd Benzinger	.05	.02
564	Mike Timlin	.08	.05	621	Kotarski/Boyd (R)	.20	.12
565	Jerald Clark	.07	.04	622	Ben Rivera	.08	.05
566	Rod Brewer	.05	.02	623	Al Martin	.20	.12
567	Mark Carreon	.05	.02	624	Sam Militello	.15	.10
568	Andy Benes	.10	.06	625	Rick Aguilera	.05	.02
569	Shawn Barton (R)	.12	.07	626	Dan Gladden	.05	.02
570	Tim Wallach	.07	.04	627	Andres Berumen (R)	.15	.10

628 Kelly Gruber	.07	.04
629 Cris Carpenter	.07	.04
630 Mark Grace	.12	.07
631 Jeff Brantley	.05	.02
632 Chris Widger (R)	.15	.10
633 Three Russians	.15	.10
634 Mo Sanford	.05	.02
635 Albert Belle	.25	.15
636 Tim Teufel	.05	.02
637 Greg Myers	.05	.02
638 Brian Bohanon	.05	.02
639 Mike Bordick	.08	.05
640 Dwight Gooden	.12	.07
641 Leahy/Baugh (R)	.15	.10
642 Milt Hill	.05	.02
643 Luis Aquino	.05	.02
644 Dante Bichette	.05	.02
645 Bobby Thigpen	.07	.04
646 Rich Scheid (R)	.12	.07
647 Brian Sackinsky (R)	.15	.10
648 Ryan Howblitzel	.12	.07
649 Tom Marsh	.10	.06
650 Terry Pendleton	.12	.07
651 Rafael Bournigal (R)	.10	.06
652 Dave West	.05	.02
653 Steve Hosey	.15	.10
654 Gerald Williams	.15	.10
655 Scott Cooper	.10	.06
656 Gary Scott	.07	.04
657 Mike Harkey	.07	.04
658 1993 Prospects (Nieves)	.35	.20
659 Ed Sprague	.08	.05
660 Alan Trammell	.10	.06
661 Alston/Case (R)	.20	.12
662 Donovan Osborne	.12	.07
663 Jeff Gardner	.08	.05
664 Calvin Jones	.15	.10
665 Darrin Fletcher	.05	.02
666 Glenallen Hill	.08	.05
667 Jim Rosenbohm (R)	.10	.06
668 Scott Leius	.05	.02
669 Kip Vaughn (R)	.15	.10
670 Julio Franco	.08	.05
671 Dave Martinez	.05	.02
672 Kevin Bass	.05	.02
673 Todd Van Poppel	.20	.12
674 Mark Gubicza	.07	.04
675 Tim Raines	.07	.04
676 Rudy Seanez	.08	.05
677 Charlie Leibrandt	.05	.02
678 Randy Milligan	.05	.02
679 Kim Batiste	.08	.05
680 Craig Biggio	.08	.05
681 Darren Holmes	.05	.02
682 John Candelaria	.05	.02
683 Stafford/Christian (R)	.20	.12
684 Pat Mahomes	.25	.15
685 Bob Walk	.05	.02
686 Russ Springer	.15	.10
687 Tony Sheffield (R)	.12	.07
688 Dwight Smith	.05	.02
689 Eddie Zosky	.08	.05
690 Bien Figueroa	.10	.06
691 Jim Tatum (R)	.12	.07
692 Chad Kreuter	.07	.04
693 Rich Rodriquez	.07	.04
694 Shane Turner	.12	.07
695 Kent Bottenfield	.08	.05
696 Jose Mesa	.05	.02
697 Darrell Whitmore (R)	.25	.15
698 Ted Wood	.07	.04
699 Chad Curtis	.15	.10
700 Nolan Ryan	.75	.45
701 1993 Prospects(Piazza)	2.50	1.40
702 Tim Pugh (R)	.15	.10
703 Jeff Kent	.20	.12
704 Goodrich/D. Figueroa(R)	.12	.07
705 Bob Welch	.07	.04
706 Sherard Clinkscales (R)	.12	.07
707 Donn Paul	.05	.02
708 Greg Olson	.05	.02
709 Jeff Juden	.08	.05
710 Mike Mussina	.25	.15
711 Scott Chiamparino	.07	.04
712 Stan Javier	.05	.02
713 John Doherty	.05	.02
714 Kevin Gross	.05	.02
715 Greg Gagne	.05	.02
716 Steve Cooke	.20	.12
717 Steve Farr	.05	.02
718 Jay Buhner	.07	.04
719 Butch Henry	.08	.05
720 David Cone	.10	.06
721 Rick Wilkins	.05	.02
722 Chuck Carr	.12	.07
723 Kenny Felder (R)	.20	.12
724 Guillermo Valesquez(R)	.08	.05
725 Billy Hatcher	.05	.02
726 Venezaile/Kendrena(R)	.20	.12
727 Jonathan Hurst	.12	.07
728 Steve Frey	.05	.02
729 Mark Leonard	.05	.02
730 Charles Nagy	.10	.06
731 Donald Harris	.15	.10
732 Travis Buckley (R)	.15	.10
733 Tom Browning	.07	.04
734 Anthony Young	.08	.05
735 Steve Shifflett	.10	.06
736 Jeff Russell	.05	.02
737 Wilson Alvarez	.08	.05
738 Lance Painter (R)	.15	.10
739 Dave Weathers (R)	.15	.10
740 Len Dykstra	.15	.10
741 Mike Devereaux	.07	.04

742	1993 Prospects(Arocha)	.25	.15
743	Dave Landaker (R)	.15	.10
744	Chris George	.12	.07
745	Eric Davis	.08	.05
746	Strittmatter/Rogers (R)	.20	.12
747	Carl Willis	.05	.02
748	Stan Belinda	.05	.02
749	Scott Kamieniecki	.07	.04
750	Rickey Henderson	.15	.10
751	Eric Hillman	.08	.05
752	Pat Hentgen	.10	.06
753	Jim Corsi	.05	.02
754	Brian Jordan	.15	.10
755	Bill Swift	.08	.05
756	Mike Henneman	.05	.02
757	Harold Reynolds	.05	.02
758	Sean Berry	.10	.06
759	Charlie Hayes	.05	.02
760	Luis Polonia	.07	.04
761	Darrin Jackson	.07	.04
762	Mark Lewis	.07	.04
763	Rob Maurer	.08	.05
764	Willie Greene	.15	.10
765	Vince Coleman	.07	.04
766	Todd Revenig (R)	.12	.07
767	Rich Ireland (R)	.10	.06
768	Mike Macfarlane	.05	.02
769	Francisco Cabrera	.05	.02
770	Robin Ventura	.15	.10
771	Kevin Ritz	.07	.04
772	Chito Martinez	.08	.05
773	Cliff Brantley	.07	.04
774	Curtis Leskanic (R)	.12	.07
775	Chris Bosio	.07	.04
776	Jose Offerman	.10	.06
777	Mark Guthrie	.05	.02
778	Don Slaught	.05	.02
779	Rich Monteleone	.05	.02
780	Jim Abbott	.12	.07
781	Jack Clark	.07	.04
782	Mendoza/Roman (R)	.15	.10
784	Jeff Branson	.05	.02
785	Kevin Brown	.08	.05
786	1993 Prospects	.20	.12
787	Mike Matthews (R)	.15	.10
788	Mackey Sasser	.05	.02
789	Jeff Conine	.12	.07
790	George Bell	.10	.06
791	Pat Rapp	.15	.10
792	Joe Boever	.05	.02
793	Jim Poole	.05	.02
794	Andy Ashby	.07	.04
795	Deion Sanders	.15	.10
796	Scott Brosius	.05	.02
797	Brad Pennington	.10	.06
798	Greg Blosser	.30	.18
799	Jim Edmonds (R)	.15	.10

800	Shawn Jeter	.12	.07
801	Jesse Levis	.08	.05
802	Phil Clark	.08	.05
803	Ed Pierce (R)	.15	.10
804	Jose Valentin (R)	.15	.10
805	Terry Jorgensen	.10	.06
806	Mark Hutton	.15	.10
807	Troy Neel	.15	.10
808	Bret Boone	.20	.12
809	Cris Colon	.10	.06
810	Domingo Martinez (R)	.20	.12
811	Javy Lopez	.60	.35
812	Matt Walbeck (R)	.15	.10
813	Dan Wilson	.12	.07
814	Scooter Tucker	.07	.04
815	Billy Ashley	.50	.30
816	Tim Laker (R)	.12	.07
817	Bobby Jones	.35	.20
818	Brad Brink (R)	.10	.06
819	William Pennyfeather	.15	.10
820	Stan Royer	.07	.04
821	Doug Brocail	.08	.05
822	Kevin Rogers	.05	.02
823	Checklist	.05	.02
824	Checklist	.05	.02
825	Checklist	.05	.02

1993 Topps Traded

The cards in this update set consist of rookies and players traded during the 1993 season, including members of the expansion Marlins and Rockies plus Team USA. The cards are identical to the Topps regular issue except the card numbers carry the "T" designation. All cards measure 2-1/2" by 3-1/2".

	MINT	NR/MT
Complete Set (132)	15.00	10.00
Commons	.05	.02

1	Barry Bonds	.50	.30
2	Rich Renteria	.05	.02
3	Aaron Sele	.80	.50
4	Carlton Loewer(R)(USA)	.30	.18
5	Erik Pappas	.12	.07
6	Greg McMichael (R)	.20	.12
7	Freddie Benavides	.05	.02
8	Kirk Gibson	.08	.05
9	Tony Fernandez	.05	.02
10	Jay Gainer (R)	.20	.12
11	Orestes Destrade	.08	.05
12	A.J. Hinch (R)(USA)	.30	.18
13	Bobby Munoz	.10	.06
14	Tom Henke	.05	.02
15	Rob Butler	.08	.05
16	Gary Wayne	.08	.05
17	David McCarty	.30	.18
18	Walt Weiss	.05	.02
19	Todd Helton (R)(USA)	.60	.35
20	Mark Whiten	.20	.12
21	Ricky Gutierrez	.10	.06
22	Dustin Hermanson (USA)	.25	.15
23	Sherman Obando (R)	.12	.07
24	Mike Piazza	5.00	3.00
25	Jeff Russell	.05	.02
26	Jason Bere	1.00	.60
27	Jack Voight (R)	.15	.10
28	Chris Bosio	.07	.04
29	Phil Hiatt	.15	.10
30	Matt Beaumont(R)(USA)	.30	.18
31	Andres Galarraga	.12	.07
32	Greg Swindell	.07	.04
33	Vinny Castilla	.08	.05
34	Pat Clougherty(R)(USA)	.25	.15
35	Greg Briley	.07	.04
36	Dallas Green	.05	.02
	Davey Johnson		
37	Tyler Green	.10	.06
38	Craig Paquette	.08	.05
39	Danny Sheaffer (R)	.12	.07
40	Jim Converse (R)	.15	.10
41	Terry Harvey (R)(USA)	.25	.15
42	Phil Plantier	.20	.12
43	Doug Saunders (R)	.12	.07
44	Benito Santiago	.08	.05
45	Dante Powell (R)(USA)	.40	.25
46	Jeff Parrett	.05	.02
47	Wade Boggs	.15	.10
48	Paul Molitor	.15	.10
49	Turk Wendell	.08	.05
50	David Wells	.05	.02
51	Gary Sheffield	.15	.10
52	Kevin Young	.15	.10
53	Nelson Liriano	.05	.02
54	Greg Maddux	.20	.12
55	Derek Bell	.15	.10
56	Matt Turner (R)	.12	.07
57	Charlie Nelson(R)(USA)	.25	.15
58	Mike Hampton	.10	.06
59	Troy O'Leary (R)	.15	.10
60	Benji Gil	.20	.12
61	Mitch Lyden (R)	.10	.06
62	J.T. Snow	.75	.45
63	Damon Buford	.08	.05
64	Gene Harris	.05	.02
65	Randy Myers	.07	.04
66	Felix Jose	.07	.04
67	Todd Dunn (R)(USA)	.30	.18
68	Jimmy Key	.08	.05
69	Pedro Castellano	.07	.04
70	Mark Merila (R)(USA)	.25	.15
71	Rich Rodriguez	.05	.02
72	Mat Mieske	.07	.04
73	Pete Incaviglia	.05	.02
74	Carl Everett	.15	.10
75	Jim Abbott	.12	.07
76	Luis Aquino	.05	.02
77	Rene Arocha (R)	.25	.15
78	Jon Shave (R)	.10	.06
79	Todd Walker (R)(USA)	.75	.45
80	Jack Armstrong	.05	.02
81	Jeff Richardson	.05	.02
82	Blas Minor	.07	.04
83	Dave Winfield	.20	.12
84	Paul O'Neill	.10	.06
85	Steve Reich (R)(USA)	.25	.15
86	Chris Hammond	.05	.02
87	Hilly Hathaway (R)	.15	.10
88	Fred McGriff	.30	.18
89	Dave Telgheder (R)	.10	.06
90	Richie Lewis (R)	.12	.07
91	Brent Gates	.25	.15
92	Andre Dawson	.15	.10
93	Andy Barkett (R)(USA)	.25	.15
94	Doug Drabek	.08	.05
93	Joe Klink	.05	.02
96	Willie Blair	.08	.05
97	Danny Graves (R)(USA)	.30	.18
98	Pat Meares (R)	.15	.10
99	Mike Lansing (R)	.20	.12
100	Marcos Armas (R)	.25	.15
101	Darren Grass(R)(USA)	.25	.15
102	Chris Jones	.07	.04
103	Ken Ryan (R)	.25	.15
104	Ellis Burks	.08	.05
105	Roberto Kelly	.10	.06
106	Dave Magadan	.05	.02
107	Paul Wilson (R)(USA)	.40	.25
108	Rob Natal	.07	.04
109	Paul Wagner	.20	.12
110	Jeromy Burnitz	.25	.15
111	Monty Fariss	.05	.02
112	Kevin Mitchell	.08	.05
113	Scott Pose (R)	.12	.07

114	Dave Stewart	.12	.07
115	Russ Johnson (R)(USA)	.30	.18
116	Armando Reynoso	.05	.02
117	Geronimo Berroa	.05	.02
118	Woody Williams (R)	.12	.07
119	Tim Bogar (R)	.12	.07
120	Bob Scafa (R)(USA)	.30	.18
121	Henry Cotto	.05	.02
122	Gregg Jefferies	.15	.10
123	Norm Charlton	.05	.02
124	Bret Wagner (R)(USA)	.40	.25
125	David Cone	.08	.05
126	Daryl Boston	.05	.02
127	Tim Wallach	.05	.02
128	Mike Martin (R)(USA)	.25	.15
129	John Cummings (R)	.20	.12
130	Ryan Bowen	.10	.06
131	John Powell (R)(USA)	.50	.30
132	Checklist	.05	.02

1993 Topps Stadium Club

The cards in this premium set feature full-bleed, full-color action photos on the card fronts and are similar in design to the 1992 Stadium Club set. The player's name appears on the bottom of the card under a Stadium Club logo. Card backs contain another full color photo. The set includes Members Choice cards (MC). Random limited insert cards called Fist Day Production cards were distributed in Stadium Club foil packs. Those cards are valued at 25 X to 50 X the value of the player's regular Stadium Club card listed below. All cards measure 2-1/2" by 3-1/2".

		MINT	NR/MT
Complete Set (750)		55.00	32.50
Commons		.08	.05
1	Pat Borders	.08	.05
2	Greg Maddux	.25	.15
3	Daryl Boston	.08	.05
4	Bob Ayrault	.08	.05
5	Tony Phillips	.12	.07
6	Damion Easley	.20	.12
7	Kip Gross	.08	.05
8	Jim Thome	.12	.07
9	Tim Belcher	.08	.05
10	Gary Wayne	.08	.05
11	Sam Militello	.15	.10
12	Mike Magnante	.08	.05
13	Tim Wakefield	.20	.12
14	Tim Hulett	.10	.06
15	Rheal Comier	.10	.06
16	Juan Guerrero	.12	.07
17	Rich Gossage	.10	.06
18	Tim Laker (R)	.20	.12
19	Darrin Jackson	.08	.05
20	Jack Clark	.10	.06
21	Roberto Hernandez	.10	.06
22	Dean Palmer	.35	.20
23	Harold Reynolds	.08	.05
24	Dan Plesac	.08	.05
25	Brent Mayne	.08	.05
26	Pat Hentgen	.15	.10
27	Luis Sojo	.08	.05
28	Ron Gant	.15	.10
29	Paul Gibson	.08	.05
30	Bip Roberts	.08	.05
31	Mickey Tettleton	.10	.06
32	Randy Velarde	.08	.05
33	Brian McRae	.12	.07
34	Wes Chamberlain	.12	.07
35	Wayne Kirby	.12	.07
36	Rey Sanchez	.08	.05
37	Jesse Orosco	.08	.05
38	Mike Stanton	.08	.05
39	Royce Clayton	.20	.12
40	Cal Ripken Jr.	.75	.45
41	John Dopson	.08	.05
42	Gene Larkin	.08	.05
43	Tim Raines	.12	.07
44	Randy Myers	.10	.06
45	Clay Parker	.08	.05
46	Mike Scioscia	.08	.05
47	Pete Incaviglia	.08	.05
48	Todd Van Poppel	.40	.25
49	Ray Lankford	.20	.12
50	Eddie Murray	.20	.12
51	Barry Bonds	1.25	.80
52	Gary Thurman	.08	.05

53	Bob Wickman	.35	.20	110	Pete Harnisch	.10	.06
54	Joey Cora	.08	.05	111	Kent Mercker	.10	.06
55	Kenny Rogers	.08	.05	112	Scott Fletcher	.08	.05
56	Mike Devereaux	.10	.06	113	Rex Hudler	.08	.05
57	Kevin Seitzer	.08	.05	114	Chico Walker	.08	.05
58	Rafael Belliard	.08	.05	115	Rafael Palmeiro	.25	.15
59	David Wells	.08	.05	116	Mark Leiter	.08	.05
60	Mark Clark	.15	.10	117	Pedro Munoz	.12	.07
61	Carlos Baerga	.75	.45	118	Jim Bullinger	.08	.05
62	Scott Brosius	.08	.05	119	Ivan Calderon	.08	.05
63	Jeff Grotewald	.08	.05	120	Mike Timlin	.10	.06
64	Rick Wrona	.08	.05	121	Rene Gonzalez	.08	.05
65	Kurt Knudson	.08	.05	122	Greg Vaughn	.20	.12
66	Lloyd McClendon	.08	.05	123	Mike Flannigan	.08	.05
67	Omar Vizquel	.08	.05	124	Mike Hartley	.08	.05
68	Jose Vizcaino	.08	.05	125	Jeff Montgomery	.08	.05
69	Rob Ducey	.08	.05	126	Mike Gallego	.08	.05
70	Casey Candaele	.08	.05	127	Don Slaught	.08	.05
71	Ramon Martinez	.12	.07	128	Charlie O'Brien	.08	.05
72	Todd Hundley	.08	.05	129	Jose Offerman	.12	.07
73	John Marzano	.08	.05	130	Mark Wohlers	.12	.07
74	Derek Parks	.12	.07	131	Eric Fox	.15	.10
75	Jack McDowell	.40	.25	132	Doug Strange	.12	.07
76	Tim Scott	.08	.05	133	Jeff Frye	.12	.07
77	Mike Mussina	.50	.30	134	Wade Boggs	.30	.18
78	Delino DeShields	.15	.10	135	Lou Whitaker	.12	.07
79	Chris Bosio	.10	.06	136	Craig Grebeck	.08	.05
80	Mike Bordick	.10	.06	137	Rich Rodriquez	.08	.05
81	Rod Beck	.12	.07	138	Jay bell	.12	.07
82	Ted Power	.08	.05	139	Felix Fermin	.08	.05
83	John Kruk	.20	.12	140	Dennis Martinez	.10	.06
84	Steve Shifflett	.12	.07	141	Eric Anthony	.15	.10
85	Danny Tartabull	.12	.07	142	Roberto Alomar	.75	.45
86	Mike Greenwell	.10	.06	143	Darren Lewis	.12	.07
87	Jose Melendez	.08	.05	144	Mike Blowers	.08	.05
88	Craig Wilson	.12	.07	145	Scott Bankhead	.08	.05
89	Melvin Nieves	.75	.45	146	Jeff Reboulet	.10	.06
90	Ed Sprague	.10	.06	147	Frank Viola	.10	.06
91	Willie McGee	.12	.07	148	Bill Pecota	.08	.05
92	Joe Orsulak	.08	.05	149	Carlos Hernandez	.10	.06
93	Jeff King	.10	.06	150	Bobby Witt	.10	.06
94	Dan Pasqua	.08	.05	151	Sid Bream	.08	.05
95	Brian Harper	.10	.06	152	Todd Zeile	.10	.06
96	Joe Oliver	.08	.05	153	Dennis Cooke	.08	.05
97	Shane Turner	.12	.07	154	Brian Bohanon	.08	.05
98	Lenny Harris	.08	.05	155	Pat Kelly	.10	.06
99	Jeff Parrett	.08	.05	156	Milt Cuyler	.10	.06
100	Luis Polonia	.08	.05	157	Juan Bell	.10	.06
101	Kent Bottenfield	.08	.05	158	Randy Milligan	.08	.05
102	Albert Belle	.75	.45	159	Mark Gardner	.10	.06
103	Mike Maddux	.08	.05	160	Pat Tabler	.08	.05
104	Randy Tomlin	.12	.07	161	Jeff Reardon	.12	.07
105	Andy Stankiewicz	.10	.06	162	Ken Patterson	.08	.05
106	Rico Rossy	.08	.05	163	Bobby Bonilla	.15	.10
107	Joe Hesketh	.08	.05	164	Tony Pena	.08	.05
108	Dennis Powell	.12	.07	165	Greg Swindell	.10	.06
109	Derrick May	.20	.12	166	Kirk McCaskill	.08	.05

167	Doug Drabek	.12	.07
168	Franklin Stubbs	.08	.05
169	Ron Tingley	.08	.05
170	Willie Banks	.12	.07
171	Sergio Valdez	.12	.07
172	Mark Lemke	.08	.05
173	Robin Yount	.40	.25
174	Storm Davis	.08	.05
175	Dan Walters	.15	.10
176	Steve Farr	.08	.05
177	Curt Wilkerson	.08	.05
178	Luis Alicea	.08	.05
179	Russ Swan	.08	.05
180	Mitch Williams	.08	.05
181	Wilson Alvarez	.20	.12
182	Carl Willis	.08	.05
183	Craig Biggio	.10	.06
184	Sean Berry	.12	.07
185	Trevor Wilson	.08	.05
186	Jeff Tackett	.08	.05
187	Ellis Burks	.10	.06
188	Jeff Branson	.08	.05
189	Matt Nokes	.08	.05
190	John Smiley	.12	.07
191	Dan Gladden	.08	.05
192	Mike Boddicker	.08	.05
193	Roger Pavlik	.20	.12
194	Paul Sorrento	.12	.07
195	Vince Coleman	.10	.06
196	Gary DiSarcina	.10	.06
197	Rafael Bournigal (R)	.15	.10
198	Mike Schooler	.08	.05
199	Scott Ruskin	.08	.05
200	Frank Thomas	3.50	2.00
201	Kyle Abbott	.10	.06
202	Mike Perez	.12	.07
203	Andre Dawson	.20	.12
204	Bill Swift	.15	.10
205	Alejandro Pena	.08	.05
206	Dave Winfield	.40	.25
207	Andujar Cedeno	.12	.07
208	Terry Steinbach	.08	.05
209	Chris Hammond	.08	.05
210	Todd Burns	.08	.05
211	Hipolito Pichardo	.08	.05
212	John Kelly	.08	.05
213	Tim Teufel	.08	.05
214	Lee Gutterman	.08	.05
215	Geronimo Pena	.08	.05
216	Brett Butler	.12	.07
217	Bryan Hickerson	.12	.07
218	Rick Trlicek	.08	.05
219	Lee Stevens	.08	.05
220	Roger Clemens	.50	.30
221	Carlton Fisk	.15	.10
222	Chili Davis	.10	.06
223	Walt Terrell	.08	.05
224	Jim Eisenreich	.08	.05
225	Ricky Bones	.10	.06
226	Henry Rodriquez	.12	.07
227	Ken Hill	.12	.07
228	Rick Wilkins	.15	.10
229	Ricky Jordan	.08	.05
230	Bernard Gilkey	.15	.10
231	Tim Fortungo	.10	.06
232	Geno Petralli	.08	.05
233	Jose Rijo	.12	.07
234	Jim Leyritz	.08	.05
235	Kevin Campbell	.08	.05
236	Al Osuna	.08	.05
237	Pete Smith	.12	.07
238	Pete Schourek	.10	.06
239	Moises Alou	.15	.10
240	Donn Pall	.08	.05
241	Denny Neagle	.10	.06
242	Dan Peltier	.12	.07
243	Scott Scudder	.08	.05
244	Juan Guzman	.40	.25
245	Dave Burba	.08	.05
246	Rick Sutcliffe	.08	.05
247	Tony Fossas	.08	.05
248	Mike Munoz	.10	.06
249	Tim Salmon (R)	3.50	2.00
250	Rob Murphy	.08	.05
251	Roger McDowell	.08	.05
252	Lance Parrish	.08	.05
253	Cliff Brantley	.10	.06
254	Scott Leius	.08	.05
255	Carlos Martinez	.08	.05
256	Vince Horsman	.12	.07
257	Oscar Azocar	.08	.05
258	Craig Shipley	.08	.05
259	Ben McDonald	.15	.10
260	Jeff Brantley	.08	.05
261	Damon Berryhill	.08	.05
262	Joe Grahe	.08	.05
263	Dave Hansen	.08	.05
264	Rich Amaral	.12	.07
265	Tim Pugh (R)	.25	.15
266	Dion James	.08	.05
267	Frank Tanana	.08	.05
268	Stan Belinda	.08	.05
269	Jeff Kent	.20	.12
270	Bruce Ruffin	.08	.05
271	Xavier Hernandez	.08	.05
272	Darrin Fletcher	.12	.07
273	Tino Martinez	.12	.07
274	Benito Santiago	.12	.07
275	Scott Radinsky	.08	.05
276	Mariano Duncan	.08	.05
277	Kenny Lofton	.60	.35
278	Dwight Smith	.10	.06
279	Joe Carter	.50	.30
280	Tim Jones	.08	.05

281	Jeff Huson	.08	.05
282	Phil Plantier	.40	.25
283	Kirby Puckett	.75	.45
284	Johnny Guzman	.08	.05
285	Mike Morgan	.08	.05
286	Chris Sabo	.10	.06
287	Matt Williams	.25	.15
288	Checklist	.08	.03
289	Checklist	.08	.03
290	Checklist	.08	.03
291	Dennis Eckersley (MC)	.12	.07
292	Eric Karros (MC)	.25	.15
293	Pat Listach (MC)	.10	.06
294	Andy Van Slyke (MC)	.15	.10
295	Robin Ventura (MC)	.20	.12
296	Tom Glavine (MC)	.20	.12
297	Juan Gonzalez (MC)	1.50	.90
298	Travis Fryman (MC)	.30	.18
299	Larry Walker (MC)	.15	.10
300	Gary Sheffield (MC)	.20	.12
301	Chuck Finley	.12	.07
302	Luis Gonzalez	.12	.07
303	Darryl Hamilton	.15	.10
304	Bien Figueroa	.10	.06
305	Ron Darling	.08	.05
306	Jonathon Hurst	.10	.06
307	Mike Sharperson	.08	.05
308	Mike Christopher	.08	.05
309	Marvin Freeman	.08	.05
310	Jay Buhner	.10	.06
311	Butch Henry	.10	.06
312	Greg Harris	.08	.05
313	Darren Daulton	.25	.15
314	Chuck Knoblauch	.15	.10
315	Greg Harris	.08	.05
316	John Franco	.08	.05
317	John Wehner	.08	.05
318	Donald Harris	.12	.07
319	Benito Santiago	.12	.07
320	Larry Walker	.25	.15
321	Randy Knorr	.12	.07
322	Ramon Martinez	.12	.07
323	Mike Stanley	.12	.07
324	Bill Wegman	.08	.05
325	Tom Candiotti	.08	.05
326	Glenn Davis	.08	.05
327	Chuck Crim	.08	.05
328	Scott Livingstone	.08	.05
329	Eddie Taubensee	.10	.06
330	George Bell	.12	.07
331	Edgar Martinez	.12	.07
332	Paul Assenmacher	.08	.05
333	Steve Hosey	.25	.15
334	Mo Vaughn	.30	.18
335	Bret Saberhagen	.12	.07
336	Mike Trombley	.12	.07
337	Mark Lewis	.10	.06
338	Terry Pendleton	.15	.10
339	Dave Hollins	.25	.15
340	Jeff Conine	.15	.10
341	Bob Tewksbury	.08	.05
342	Billy Ashley	.70	.40
343	Zane Smith	.08	.05
344	John Wetteland	.10	.06
345	Chris Hoiles	.12	.07
346	Frank Castillo	.08	.05
347	Bruce Hurst	.10	.06
348	Kevin McReynolds	.10	.06
349	Dave Henderson	.08	.05
350	Ryan Bowen	.12	.07
351	Sid Fernandez	.10	.06
352	Mark Whiten	.25	.15
353	Nolan Ryan	2.75	1.60
354	Rick Aguilera	.08	.05
355	Mark Langston	.12	.07
356	Jack Morris	.12	.07
357	Rob Deer	.10	.06
358	Dave Fleming	.25	.15
359	Lance Johnson	.10	.06
360	Joe Millette	.10	.06
361	Wil Cordero	.25	.15
362	Chito Martinez	.10	.06
363	Scott Servais	.08	.05
364	Bernie Williams	.15	.10
365	Pedro Martinez	.25	.15
366	Ryne Sandberg	.75	.45
367	Brad Ausmus	.12	.07
368	Scott Cooper	.12	.07
369	Rob Dibble	.10	.06
370	Walt Weiss	.08	.05
371	Mark Davis	.08	.05
372	Orlando Merced	.15	.10
373	Mike Jackson	.10	.06
374	Kevin Appier	.15	.10
375	Esteban Beltre	.12	.07
376	Joe Slusarski	.10	.06
377	William Suero	.12	.07
378	Pete O'Brien	.08	.05
379	Alan Embree	.15	.10
380	Lenny Webster	.08	.05
381	Eric Davis	.12	.07
382	Duane Ward	.10	.06
383	John Habyan	.08	.05
384	Jeff Bagwell	.35	.20
385	Ruben Amaro	.10	.06
386	Julio Valera	.08	.05
387	Robin Ventura	.25	.15
388	Archi Cianfrocco	.12	.07
389	Skeeter Barnes	.10	.06
390	Tim Costo	.15	.10
391	Luis Mercedes	.12	.07
392	Jeremy Hernandez	.10	.06
393	Shawon Dunstan	.10	.06
394	Andy Van Slyke	.15	.10

395	Kevin Maas	.10	.06
396	Kevin Brown	.12	.07
397	J.T. Bruett	.15	.10
398	Darryl Strawberry	.20	.12
399	Tom Pagnozzi	.10	.06
400	Sandy Alomar Jr.	.12	.07
401	Keith Miller	.08	.05
402	Rich DeLucia	.08	.05
403	Shawn Abner	.08	.05
404	Howard Johnson	.12	.07
405	Mike Benjamin	.08	.05
406	Roberto Mejia (R)	.60	.35
407	Mike Butcher	.10	.06
408	Deion Sanders	.25	.15
409	Todd Stottlemyre	.08	.05
410	Scott Kamieniecki	.08	.05
411	Doug Jones	.08	.05
412	John Burkett	.12	.07
413	Lance Blankenship	.08	.05
414	Jeff Parrett	.08	.05
415	Barry Larkin	.15	.10
416	Alan Trammell	.15	.10
417	Mark Kiefer	.08	.05
418	Gregg Olson	.10	.06
419	Mark Grace	.20	.12
420	Shane Mack	.12	.07
421	Bob Walk	.08	.05
422	Curt Schilling	.12	.07
423	Erik Hanson	.08	.05
424	George Brett	.50	.30
425	Reggie Jefferson	.12	.07
426	Mark Portugal	.10	.06
427	Ron Karkovice	.08	.05
428	Matt Young	.08	.05
429	Troy Neel	.35	.20
430	Hector Fajardo	.10	.06
431	Dave Righetti	.08	.05
432	Pat Listach	.20	.12
433	Jeff Innis	.08	.05
434	Bob McDonald	.08	.05
435	Brian Jordan	.25	.15
436	Jeff Blauser	.12	.07
437	Mike Myers (R)	.20	.12
438	Frank Seminara	.10	.06
439	Rusty Meacham	.10	.06
440	Greg Briley	.08	.05
441	Derek Lilliquist	.08	.05
442	John Vander Wal	.08	.05
443	Scott Erickson	.20	.12
444	Bob Scanlan	.08	.05
445	Todd Frohwirth	.08	.05
446	Tom Goodwin	.15	.10
447	William Pennyfeather	.12	.07
448	Travis Fryman	.60	.35
449	Mickey Morandini	.10	.06
450	Greg Olson	.08	.05
451	Trevor Hoffman	.15	.10
452	Dave Magadan	.08	.05
453	Shawn Jeter	.15	.10
454	Andres Galarraga	.15	.10
455	Ted Wood	.10	.06
456	Freddie Benavides	.08	.05
457	Junior Felix	.08	.05
458	Alex Cole	.08	.05
459	John Orton	.10	.06
460	Eddie Zosky	.10	.06
461	Dennis Eckersley	.15	.10
462	Lee Smith	.15	.10
463	John Smoltz	.12	.07
464	Ken Caminiti	.08	.05
465	Melido Perez	.08	.05
466	Tom Marsh	.10	.06
467	Jeff Nelson	.10	.06
468	Jesse Levis	.10	.06
469	Chris Nabholz	.10	.06
470	Mike Macfarlane	.08	.05
471	Reggie Sanders	.25	.15
472	Chuck McElroy	.08	.05
473	Kevin Gross	.08	.05
474	Matt Whiteside (R)	.20	.12
475	Cal Eldred	.25	.15
476	Dave Gallagher	.08	.05
477	Len Dykstra	.25	.15
478	Mark McGwire	.30	.18
479	David Segui	.10	.06
480	Mike Henneman	.08	.05
481	Bret Barberie	.08	.05
482	Steve Sax	.10	.06
483	David Valle	.08	.05
484	Danny Darwin	.08	.05
485	Devon White	.12	.07
486	Eric Plunk	.08	.05
487	Jim Gott	.08	.05
488	Scooter Tucker	.10	.06
489	Omar Olivares	.08	.05
490	Greg Myers	.08	.05
491	Brian Hunter	.15	.10
492	Kevin Tapani	.10	.06
493	Rich Monteleone	.08	.05
494	Steve Buechele	.08	.05
495	Bo Jackson	.25	.15
496	Mike LaValliere	.08	.05
497	Mark Leonard	.08	.05
498	Daryl Boston	.08	.05
499	Jose Canseco	.35	.20
500	Brian Barnes	.12	.07
501	Randy Johnson	.25	.15
502	Tim McIntosh	.10	.06
503	Cecil Fielder	.35	.20
504	Derek Bell	.25	.15
505	Kevin Koslofski	.10	.06
506	Darren Holmes	.12	.07
507	Brady Anderson	.12	.07
508	John Valentin	.20	.12

509	Jerry Browne	.08	.05
510	Fred McGriff	.60	.35
511	Pedro Astacio	.30	.18
512	Gary Gaetti	.08	.05
513	John Burke (R)	.40	.25
514	Doc Gooden	.15	.10
515	Thomas Howard	.10	.06
516	Darrell Whitmore (R)	.80	.50
517	Ozzie Guillen	.10	.06
518	Darryl Kile	.25	.15
519	Rich Rowland	.10	.06
520	Carlos Delgado	2.00	1.25
521	Doug Henry	.10	.06
522	Greg Colbrunn	.12	.07
523	Tom Gordon	.10	.06
524	Ivan Rodriquez	.30	.18
525	Kent Hrbek	.10	.06
526	Eric Young	.15	.10
527	Rod Brewer	.08	.05
528	Eric Karros	.30	.18
529	Marquis Grissom	.20	.12
530	Rico Brogna	.12	.07
531	Sammy Sosa	.25	.15
532	Bret Boone	.20	.12
533	Luis Rivera	.08	.05
534	Hal Morris	.12	.07
535	Monty Fariss	.08	.05
536	Leo Gomez	.12	.07
537	Wally Joyner	.12	.07
538	Tony Gwynn	.30	.18
539	Mike Williams	.12	.07
540	Juan Gonzalez	2.00	1.25
541	Ryan Klesko	.75	.45
542	Ryan Thompson	.25	.15
543	Chad Curtis	.25	.15
544	Orel Hershiser	.15	.10
545	Carlos Garcia	.20	.12
546	Bob Welch	.08	.05
547	Vinny Castilla	.10	.06
548	Ozzie Smith	.30	.18
549	Luis Salazar	.08	.05
550	Mark Guthrie	.10	.06
551	Charles Nagy	.20	.12
552	Alex Fernandez	.35	.20
553	Mel Rojas	.10	.06
554	Orestes Destrade	.10	.06
555	Mark Gubicza	.10	.06
556	Steve Finley	.08	.05
557	Don Mattingly	.50	.30
558	Rickey Henderson	.35	.20
559	Tommy Greene	.20	.12
560	Arthur Rhodes	.10	.06
561	Alfredo Griffin	.08	.05
562	Will Clark	.40	.25
563	Bob Zupcic	.12	.07
564	Chuck Carr	.20	.12
565	Henry Cotto	.08	.05
566	Bill Spiers	.08	.05
567	Jack Armstrong	.08	.05
568	Kurt Stillwell	.08	.05
569	David McCarty	.70	.40
570	Joe Vitiello	.60	.35
571	Gerald Williams	.15	.10
572	Dale Murphy	.10	.07
573	Scott Aldred	.10	.06
574	Bill Gullickson	.08	.05
575	Bobby Thigpen	.08	.05
576	Glenallen Hill	.15	.10
577	Dwayne Henry	.08	.05
578	Calvin Jones	.12	.07
579	Al Martin	.40	.25
580	Ruben Sierra	.20	.12
581	Andy Benes	.15	.10
582	Anthony Young	.10	.06
583	Shawn Boskie	.08	.05
584	Scott Pose (R)	.25	.15
585	Mike Piazza (R)	5.00	3.00
586	Donovan Osborne	.20	.12
587	James Austin	.08	.05
588	Checklist	.08	.03
589	Checklist	.08	.03
590	Checklist	.08	.03
591	Ken Griffey Jr. (MC)	1.75	1.00
592	Ivan Rodriguez (MC)	.15	.10
593	Carlos Baerga (MC)	.50	.30
594	Fred McGriff (MC)	.50	.30
595	Mark McGwire (MC)	.40	.25
596	Roberto Alomar (MC)	.50	.30
597	Kirby Puckett (MC)	.40	.25
598	Marquis Grissom (MC)	.15	.10
599	John Smoltz (MC)	.12	.07
600	Ryne Sandberg (MC)	.40	.25
601	Wade Boggs	.30	.18
602	Jeff Reardon	.12	.07
603	Billy Ripken	.08	.05
604	Bryan Harvey	.12	.07
605	Carlos Quintana	.08	.05
606	Greg Hibbard	.08	.05
607	Ellis Burks	.12	.07
608	Greg Swindell	.10	.06
609	Dave Winfield	.40	.25
610	Charlie Hough	.08	.05
611	Storm Davis	.08	.05
612	Jody Reed	.08	.05
613	Mark Williamson	.08	.05
614	Phil Plantier	.50	.30
615	Jim Abbott	.20	.12
616	Dante Bichette	.15	.10
617	Mark Eichhorn	.08	.05
618	Gary Sheffield	.35	.20
619	Richie Lewis (R)	.20	.12
620	Joe Girardi	.08	.05
621	Jaime Navarro	.10	.06
622	Willie Wilson	.08	.05

623 Scott Fletcher	.08	.05
624 Bud Black	.10	.06
625 Tom Brunansky	.10	.06
626 Steve Avery	.35	.20
627 Paul Molitor	.30	.18
628 Gregg Jefferies	.25	.15
629 Dave Stewart	.15	.10
630 Javy Lopez	1.25	.80
631 Greg Gagne	.08	.05
632 Roberto Kelly	.20	.12
633 Mike Fetters	.08	.05
634 Ozzie Canseco	.08	.05
635 Jeff Russell	.08	.05
636 Pete Incaviglia	.08	.05
637 Tom Henke	.08	.05
638 Chipper Jones	1.50	.90
639 Jimmy Key	.12	.07
640 Dave Martinez	.08	.05
641 Dave Stieb	.08	.05
642 Milt Thompson	.08	.05
643 Alan Mills	.10	.06
644 Tony Fernandez	.10	.06
645 Randy Bush	.08	.05
646 Joe Magrane	.08	.05
647 Ivan Calderon	.08	.05
649 John Olerud	1.25	.80
650 Tom Glavine	.40	.25
651 Julio Franco	.12	.07
652 Armando Reynoso	.08	.05
653 Felix Jose	.10	.06
654 Ben Rivera	.08	.05
655 Andre Dawson	.20	.12
656 Mike Harkey	.10	.06
657 Kevin Seitzer	.08	.05
658 Lonnie Smith	.08	.05
659 Norm Charlton	.08	.05
660 David Justice	.75	.45
661 Fernando Valenzuela	.08	.05
662 Dan Wilson	.12	.07
663 Mark Gardner	.10	.06
664 Doug Dascenzo	.08	.05
665 Greg Maddux	.30	.18
666 Harold Baines	.10	.06
667 Randy Myers	.10	.06
668 Harold Reynolds	.08	.05
669 Candy Maldonado	.08	.05
670 Al Leiter	.08	.05
671 Jerald Clark	.08	.05
672 Doug Drabek	.15	.10
673 Kirk Gibson	.10	.06
674 Steve Reed (R)	.15	.10
675 Mike Felder	.08	.05
676 Ricky Gutierrez	.12	.07
677 Spike Owen	.08	.05
678 Otis Nixon	.10	.06
679 Scott Sanderson	.08	.05
680 Mark Carreon	.08	.05

681 Troy Percival	.12	.07
682 Kevin Stocker	1.25	.80
683 Jim Converse (R)	.25	.15
684 Barry Bonds	1.50	.90
685 Greg Gohr	.15	.10
686 Tim Wallach	.10	.06
687 Matt Mieske	.15	.10
688 Robby Thompson	.15	.10
689 Brien Taylor	.75	.45
690 Kirt Manwaring	.08	.05
691 Mike Lansing (R)	.30	.18
692 Steve Decker	.10	.06
693 Mike Aldrette	.08	.05
694 Kevin Mitchell	.12	.07
695 Phil Hiatt	.35	.20
696 Tony Tarasco (R)	.60	.35
697 Benji Gil	.50	.30
698 Jeff Juden	.12	.07
699 Kevin Reimer	.08	.05
700 Andy Ashby	.10	.06
701 John Jaha	.25	.15
702 Tim Bogar (R)	.20	.12
703 David Cone	.12	.07
704 Willie Greene	.25	.15
705 David Hulse (R)	.35	.20
706 Cris Carpenter	.08	.05
707 Ken Griffey Jr.	3.00	1.75
708 Steve Bedrosian	.08	.05
709 Dave Nilsson	.12	.07
710 Paul Wagner	.25	.15
711 B.J. Surhoff	.08	.05
712 Rene Arocha (R)	.40	.25
713 Manual Lee	.08	.05
714 Brian Williams	.10	.06
715 Sherman Obando (R)	.25	.15
716 Terry Mulholland	.08	.05
717 Paul O'Neil	.15	.10
718 David Nied	.80	.50
719 J.T. Snow (R)	1.00	.70
720 Nigel Wilson	1.00	.70
721 Mike Bielecki	.08	.05
722 Kevin Young	.40	.25
723 Charlie Leibrandt	.08	.05
725 Jon Shave (R)	.20	.12
726 Steve Cooke	.30	.18
727 Domingo Martinez (R)	.50	.30
728 Todd Worrell	.08	.05
729 Jose Lind	.08	.05
730 Jim Tatum (R)	.25	.15
731 Mike Hampton	.12	.07
732 Mike Draper	.12	.07
733 Henry Mercedes	.10	.06
734 John Johnstone (R)	.25	.15
735 Mitch Webster	.08	.05
736 Russ Springer	.15	.10
737 Rob Natal	.12	.07
738 Steve Howe	.08	.05

739	Darrell Sherman (R)	.30	.18
740	Pat Mahomes	.20	.12
741	Alex Arias	.08	.05
742	Damon Buford	.12	.07
743	Charlie Hayes	.12	.07
744	Guillermo Velasquez	.12	.07
745	Checklist	.08	.05
746	Frank Thomas (MC)	2.50	1.50
747	Barry Bonds (MC)	.75	.45
748	Roger Clemens (MC)	.40	.25
749	Joe Carter (MC)	.40	.25
750	Greg Maddux (MC)	.30	.18
BC1	Robin Yount	4.00	2.50
BC2	George Brett	5.00	3.00
BC3	David Nied	4.00	2.50
BC4	Nigel Wilson	5.00	3.00
BC5	Charlie Hough	3.00	1.75
___	Clark/McGwire	4.50	2.75
___	Gooden/Mattingly	4.00	2.50
___	Sandberg/Thomas	15.00	10.00
___	Griffey Jr./Strawberry	8.50	5.00

1993 Topps Finest

The cards in this high-quality set mark Topps entrance in the super-premium category. The full-color glossy card fronts feature action photos printed on high grade paper stock. The headline "Basebal's Finest" appears across the top. The player's name is printed in a horizontal box next to a Topps logo below the photograph. The only subset is All-Stars (84-116). Topps also produced a limited version of the set called Refractors which are valued at 5X to 8X the prices listed below. Those cards were inserted randomly in Topps Finest packs. All cards measure 2-1/2" by 3-1/2".

		MINT	NR/MT
Complete Set (199)		550.00	375.00
Commons		2.00	1.25
1	David Justice	10.00	6.50
2	Lou Whitaker	2.00	1.25
3	Bryan Harvey	2.00	1.25
4	Carlos Garcia	3.50	2.00
5	Sid Fernandez	2.00	1.25
6	Brett Butler	2.00	1.25
7	Scott Cooper	2.50	1.50
8	B.J. Surhoff	2.00	1.25
9	Steve Finley	2.00	1.25
10	Curt Schilling	2.50	1.50
11	Jeff Bagwell	8.50	5.00
12	Alex Cole	2.00	1.25
13	John Olerud	15.00	10.00
14	John Smiley	2.00	1.25
15	Bip Roberts	2.00	1.25
16	Albert Belle	10.00	6.50
17	Duane Ward	2.00	1.25
18	Alan Trammell	3.00	1.75
19	Andy Benes	2.50	1.50
20	Reggie Sanders	3.50	2.00
21	Todd Zeile	2.50	1.50
22	Rick Aguilera	2.00	1.25
23	Dave Hollins	5.00	3.00
24	Jose Rijo	2.50	1.50
25	Matt Williams	4.00	2.50
26	Sandy Alomar	2.50	1.50
27	Alex Fernandez	3.50	2.00
28	Ozzie Smith	5.00	3.00
29	Ramon Martinez	2.50	1.50
30	Bernie Williams	2.50	1.50
31	Gary Sheffield	4.00	2.50
32	Eric Karros	3.50	2.00
33	Frank Viola	2.00	1.25
34	Kevin Young	3.50	2.00
35	Ken Hill	2.50	1.50
36	Tony Fernandez	2.00	1.25
37	Tim Wakefield	2.50	1.50
38	John Kruk	3.50	2.00
39	Chris Sabo	2.50	1.50
40	Marquis Grissom	3.50	2.00
41	Glenn Davis	2.00	1.25
42	Jeff Montgomery	2.00	1.25
43	Kenny Lofton	8.50	5.00
44	John Burkett	2.50	1.50
45	Darryl Hamilton	2.50	1.50
46	Jim Abbott	4.50	2.75
47	Ivan Rodriquez	5.00	3.00
48	Eric Young	2.50	1.50
49	Mitch Williams	2.00	1.25
50	Harold Reynolds	2.00	1.25
51	Brian Harper	2.00	1.25
52	Rafael Palmeiro	3.50	2.00

53	Brett Saberhagen	2.50	1.50	110	Ken Griffey Jr. (AS)	40.00	26.00
54	Jeff Conine	3.00	1.75	111	Cecil Fielder (AS)	8.50	5.00
55	Ivan Calderon	2.00	1.25	112	Kirby Puckett (AS)	15.00	10.00
56	Juan Guzman	6.00	3.75	113	Doc Gooden (AS)	3.00	1.75
57	Carlos Baerga	12.00	7.50	114	Barry Larkin (AS)	3.00	1.75
58	Charles Nagy	2.50	1.50	115	David Cone (AS)	2.50	1.50
59	Wally Joyner	2.50	1.50	116	Juan Gonzalez (AS)	32.00	20.00
60	Charlie Hayes	2.00	1.25	117	Kent Hrbek	2.00	1.25
61	Shane Mack	2.50	1.50	118	Tim Wallach	2.00	1.25
62	Pete Harnisch	2.50	1.50	119	Craig Biggio	2.00	1.25
63	George Brett	10.00	6.50	120	Roberto Kelly	2.50	1.50
64	Lance Johnson	2.00	1.25	121	Gregg Olson	2.00	1.25
65	Ben McDonald	3.00	1.75	122	Eddie Murray	3.50	2.00
66	Bobby Bonilla	2.50	1.50	123	Wil Cordero	3.50	2.00
67	Terry Steinbach	2.00	1.25	124	Jay Buhner	2.00	1.25
68	Ron Gant	3.50	2.00	125	Carlton Fisk	3.00	1.75
69	Doug Jones	2.00	1.25	126	Eric Davis	2.50	1.50
70	Paul Molitor	7.50	4.00	127	Doug Drabek	2.50	1.50
71	Brady Anderson	2.50	1.50	128	Ozzie Guillen	2.00	1.25
72	Chuck Finley	2.50	1.50	129	John Wetteland	2.00	1.25
73	Mark Grace	4.50	2.75	130	Andres Galarraga	3.00	1.75
74	Mike Devereaux	2.00	1.25	131	Ken Caminiti	2.00	1.25
75	Tony Phillips	2.50	1.50	132	Tom Candiotti	2.00	1.25
76	Chuck Knoblauch	2.50	1.50	133	Pat Borders	2.00	1.25
77	Tony Gywnn	7.00	4.00	134	Kevin Brown	2.50	1.50
78	Kevin Appier	3.00	1.75	135	Travis Fryman	8.50	5.00
79	Sammy Sosa	4.00	2.50	136	Kevin Mitchell	2.50	1.50
80	Mickey Tettleton	2.50	1.50	137	Greg Swindell	2.00	1.25
81	Felix Jose	2.00	1.25	138	Benito Santiago	2.50	1.50
82	Mark Langston	2.50	1.50	139	Reggie Jefferson	2.50	1.50
83	Gregg Jefferies	3.50	2.00	140	Chris Bosio	2.00	1.25
84	Andre Dawson (AS)	3.50	2.00	141	Deion Sanders	5.00	3.00
85	Greg Maddux (AS)	7.50	4.00	142	Scott Erickson	2.50	1.50
86	Rickey Henderson(AS)	6.00	3.75	143	Howard Johnson	2.50	1.50
87	Tom Glavine (AS)	7.50	4.00	144	Orestes Destrade	2.00	1.25
88	Roberto Alomar (AS)	15.00	10.00	145	Jose Guzman	2.00	1.25
89	Darryl Strawberry(AS)	3.00	1.75	146	Chad Curtis	3.50	2.00
90	Wade Boggs (AS)	7.00	4.00	147	Cal Eldred	3.50	2.00
91	Bo Jackson (AS)	3.50	2.00	148	Willie Green	2.50	1.50
92	Mark McGwire (AS)	6.00	3.75	149	Tommy Greene	3.00	1.75
93	Robin Ventura (AS)	5.00	3.00	150	Erik Hanson	2.00	1.25
94	Joe Carter (AS)	8.50	5.00	151	Bob Welch	2.00	1.25
95	Lee Smith (AS)	2.50	1.50	152	John Jaha	2.50	1.50
96	Cal Ripken (AS)	18.00	12.00	153	Harold Baines	2.50	1.50
97	Larry Walker (AS)	3.00	1.75	154	Randy Johnson	4.50	2.75
98	Don Mattingly (AS)	10.00	6.50	155	Al Martin	3.50	2.00
99	Jose Canseco (AS)	6.00	3.75	156	J.T. Snow	8.50	5.00
100	Dennis Eckersley (AS)	2.50	1.50	157	Mike Mussina	10.00	6.50
101	Terry Pendleton (AS)	3.00	1.75	158	Ruben Sierra	3.00	1.75
102	Frank Thomas (AS)	48.00	30.00	159	Dean Palmer	3.50	2.00
103	Barry Bonds (AS)	20.00	13.50	160	Steve Avery	10.00	6.50
104	Roger Clemens (AS)	12.50	7.50	161	Julio Franco	2.00	1.25
105	Ryne Sandberg (AS)	15.00	10.00	162	Dave Winfield	10.00	6.50
106	Fred McGriff (AS)	10.00	6.50	163	Tim Salmon	25.00	15.00
107	Nolan Ryan (AS)	40.00	26.00	164	Tom Henke	2.00	1.25
108	Will Clark (AS)	10.00	6.50	165	Mo Vaughn	5.00	3.00
109	Pat Listach (AS)	2.50	1.50	166	John Smoltz	2.50	1.50

167	Danny Tartabull	2.50	1.50
168	Delino DeShields	3.50	2.00
169	Charlie Hough	2.00	1.25
170	Paul O'Neill	2.50	1.50
171	Darren Daulton	3.50	2.00
172	Jack McDowell	5.00	3.00
173	Junior Felix	2.00	1.25
174	Jimmy Key	2.50	1.50
175	George Bell	2.50	1.50
176	Mike Stanton	2.00	1.25
177	Len Dykstra	5.00	3.00
178	Norm Charlton	2.00	1.25
179	Eric Anthony	2.50	1.50
180	Rob Dibble	2.00	1.25
181	Otis Nixon	2.00	1.25
182	Randy Myers	2.00	1.25
183	Tim Raines	2.50	1.50
184	Orel Hershiser	2.50	1.50
185	Andy Van Slyke	3.00	1.75
186	Mike Lansing	3.00	1.75
187	Ray Lankford	3.50	2.00
188	Mike Morgan	2.00	1.25
189	Moises Alou	3.50	2.00
190	Edgar Martinez	2.50	1.50
191	John Franco	2.00	1.25
192	Robin Yount	8.50	5.00
193	Bob Tewksbury	2.00	1.25
194	Jay Bell	2.50	1.50
195	Luis Gonzalez	2.50	1.50
196	Dave Fleming	4.00	2.50
197	Mike Greenwell	2.50	1.50
198	David Nied	7.50	4.00
199	Mike Piazza	50.00	35.00

UPPER DECK

1989 Upper Deck

Dave Stieb

This 800-card set marks Upper Deck's entrance into the baseball card field. The cards, which measure 2-1/2" by 3-1/2", feature full color photographs on both the card fronts and card backs. The backs also contain a small hologram that makes the card counterfeit-proof. The first 26-cards are "Star Rookies". A high-number series, (701-800) was released later in the year and consists of additional rookies and traded players. The complete set prices includes values for both the low and high number series.

		MINT	NR/MT
Complete Set (800)		135.00	75.00
Commons (1-800)		.10	.06

1	Ken Griffey, Jr (R)	60.00	42.00
2	Luis Medina (R)	.12	.07
3	Tony Chance (R)	.12	.07
4	Dave Otto (R)	.10	.06
5	Sandy Alomar, Jr. (R)	.40	.25
6	Rolando Roomes (R)	.12	.07
7	David West (R)	.15	.10
8	Cris Carpenter (R)	.20	.12
9	Gregg Jefferies	1.50	.90
10	Doug Dascenzo	.12	.07
11	Ron Jones (R)	.10	.06
12	Luis de los Santos (R)	.10	.06
13	Gary Sheffield (R)	8.50	5.00
14	Mike Harkey (R)	.30	.18
15	Lance Blankenship (R)	.20	.12
17	John Smoltz (R)	4.50	2.75
18	Ramon Martinez (R)	2.00	1.25
19	Mark Lemke (R)	.25	.15
20	Juan Bell (R)	.12	.07
21	Rey Palacios (R)	.12	.07
22	Felix Jose (R)	.75	.45
23	Van Snider (R)	.10	.06
24	Dante Bichette (R)	1.00	.60
25	Randy Johnson (R)	3.00	1.75
26	Carlos Quintana (R)	.20	.12
27	Checklist 1-26	.10	.06
28	Mike Schooler (R)	.12	.07
29	Randy St. Claire	.10	.06
30	Jerald Clark (R)	.20	.12
31	Kevin Gross	.10	.06
32	Dan Firova (R)	.10	.06
33	Jeff Calhoun (R)	.10	.06
34	Tommy Hinzo (R)	.12	.07
35	Ricky Jordan (R)	.20	.12
36	Larry Parrish	.10	.06
37	Bret Saberhagen	.25	.15
38	Mike Smithson	.10	.06
39	Dave Dravecky	.10	.06
40	Ed Romero	.10	.06
41	Jeff Musselman	.10	.06

42 Ed Hearn	.10	.06
43 Rance Mulliniks	.10	.06
44 Jim Eisenreich	.10	.06
45 Sil Campusano (R)	.15	.08
46 Mike Krukow	.10	.06
47 Paul Gibson	.10	.06
48 Mike LaCoss	.10	.06
49 Larry Herndon	.10	.06
50 Scott Garretts	.10	.06
51 Dwayne Henry	.12	.07
52 Jim Acker	.10	.06
53 Steve Sax	.10	.06
54 Pete O'Brien	.10	.06
55 Paul Runge	.10	.06
56 Rick Rhoden	.10	.06
57 John Dopson (R)	.15	.08
58 Casey Candaele	.10	.06
59 Dave Righetti	.10	.06
60 Joe Hesketh	.10	.06
61 Frank DiPino	.10	.06
62 Tim Laudner	.10	.06
63 Jamie Moyer	.10	.06
64 Fred Toliver	.10	.06
65 Mitch Webster	.10	.06
66 John Tudor	.10	.06
67 John Gangelosi	.10	.06
68 Mike Devereaux	.35	.20
69 Brian Fisher	.10	.06
70 Mike Marshall	.10	.06
71 Zane Smith	.10	.06
72a Brian Holton (Wrong Photo)	1.50	.90
72b Brian Holton (Cor)	.10	.06
73 Jose Guzman	.10	.06
74 Rick Mahler	.10	.06
75 John Shelby	.10	.06
76 Jim Deshaies	.10	.06
77 Bobby Meacham	.10	.06
78 Bryn Smith	.10	.06
79 Joaquin Andujar	.10	.06
80 Richard Dotson	.10	.06
81 Charlie Lea	.10	.06
82 Calvin Schiraldi	.10	.06
83 Les Straker	.10	.06
84 Les Lancaster	.10	.06
85 Allan Anderson	.10	.06
86 Junior Ortiz	.10	.06
87 Jesse Orosco	.10	.06
88 Felix Fermin	.10	.06
89 Dave Anderson	.10	.06
90 Rafael Belliard	.10	.06
91 Franklin Stubbs	.10	.06
92 Cecil Espy	.10	.06
93 Albert Hall	.10	.06
94 Tim Leary	.10	.06
95 Mitch Williams	.10	.06
96 Tracy Jones	.10	.06
97 Danny Darwin	.10	.06
98 Gary Ward	.10	.06
99 Neal Heaton	.10	.06
100 Jim Pankovitz	.10	.06
101 Bill Doran	.10	.06
102 Tim Wallach	.12	.07
103 Joe Magrane	.12	.07
104 Ozzie Virgil	.10	.06
105 Alvin Davis	.10	.06
106 Tom Brookens	.10	.06
107 Shawon Dunston	.15	.08
108 Tracy Woodson	.10	.06
109 Nelson Liriano	.10	.06
110 Devon White	.10	.06
111 Steve Balboni	.10	.06
112 Buddy Bell	.10	.06
113 German Jimenez (R)	.12	.07
114 Ken Dayley	.10	.06
115 Andres Galarraga	.50	.30
116 Mike Scioscia	.10	.06
117 Gary Pettis	.10	.06
118 Ernie Whitt	.10	.06
119 Bob Boone	.15	.08
120 Ryne Sandberg	2.00	1.25
121 Bruce Benedict	.10	.06
122 Hubie Brooks	.12	.07
123 Mike Moore	.10	.06
124 Wallace Johnson	.10	.06
125 Bob Horner	.10	.06
126 Chili Davis	.10	.06
127 Manny Trillo	.10	.06
128 Chet Lemon	.10	.06
129 John Cerutti	.10	.06
130 Orel Hershiser	.15	.08
131 Terry Pendleton	.50	.30
132 Jeff Blauser	.15	.10
133 Mike Fitzgerald	.10	.06
134 Henry Cotto	.10	.06
135 Gerald Young	.12	.07
136 Luis Salazar	.10	.06
137 Alejandro Pena	.10	.06
138 Jack Howell	.10	.06
139 Tony Fernandez	.12	.07
140 Mark Grace	1.50	.90
141 Ken Caminiti	.12	.07
142 Mike Jackson	.10	.06
143 Larry McWilliams	.10	.06
144 Andres Thomas	.10	.06
145 Nolan Ryan	5.00	3.50
146 Mike Davis	.10	.06
147 DeWayne Buice	.10	.06
148 Jody Davis	.10	.06
149 Jesse Barfield	.12	.07
150 Matt Nokes	.12	.07
151 Jerry Reuss	.10	.06
152 Rick Cerone	.10	.06
153 Storm Davis	.10	.06

154	Marvell Wynne	.10	.06
155	Will Clark	1.75	1.00
156	Luis Aguayo	.10	.06
157	Willie Upshaw	.10	.06
158	Randy Bush	.10	.06
159	Ron Darling	.12	.07
160	Kal Daniels	.10	.06
161	Spike Owen	.10	.06
162	Luis Polonia	.12	.07
163	Kevin Mitchell	.20	.12
164	Dave Gallagher (R)	.12	.07
165	Benito Santiago	.15	.08
166	Greg Gagne	.10	.06
167	Ken Phelps	.10	.06
168	Sid Fernandez	.12	.07
169	Bo Diaz	.10	.06
170	Cory Snyder	.10	.06
171	Eric Show	.10	.06
172	Rob Thompson	.12	.07
173	Marty Barrett	.10	.06
174	Dave Henderson	.10	.06
175	Ozzie Guillen	.12	.07
176	Barry Lyons	.10	.06
177	Kevin Torve (R)	.12	.07
178	Don Slaught	.10	.06
179	Steve Lombardozzi	.10	.06
180	Chris Sabo (R)	.75	.45
181	Jose Uribe	.10	.06
182	Shane Mack	.20	.12
183	Ron Karkovice	.10	.06
184	Todd Benzinger	.10	.06
185	Dave Stewart	.15	.08
186	Julio Franco	.20	.12
187	Ron Robinson	.10	.06
188	Wally Backman	.10	.06
189	Randy Velarde	.10	.06
190	Joe Carter	1.25	.80
191	Bob Welch	.12	.07
192	Kelly Paris	.10	.06
193	Chris Brown	.10	.06
194	Rick Reuschel	.10	.06
195	Roger Clemens	2.00	1.25
196	Dave Concepcion	.10	.06
197	Al Newman	.10	.06
198	Brook Jacoby	.10	.06
199	Mookie Wilson	.10	.06
200	Don Mattingly	1.00	.70
201	Dick Schofield	.10	.06
202	Mark Gubicza	.12	.07
203	Gary Gaetti	.10	.06
204	Dan Pasqua	.10	.06
205	Andre Dawson	.60	.35
206	Chris Speier	.10	.06
207	Kent Tekulve	.10	.06
208	Rod Scurry	.10	.06
209	Scott Bailes	.10	.06
210	Rickey Henderson	1.25	.80
211	Harold Baines	.12	.07
212	Tony Armas	.10	.06
213	Kent Hrbek	.12	.07
214	Darrin Jackson	.12	.07
215	George Brett	1.25	.80
216	Rafael Santana	.12	.07
217	Andy Allanson	.10	.06
218	Brett Butler	.15	.08
219	Steve Jeltz	.10	.06
220	Jay Buhner	.35	.20
221	Bo Jackson	.75	.45
222	Angel Salazar	.10	.06
223	Kirk McCaskill	.10	.06
224	Steve Lyons	.10	.06
225	Bert Blyleven	.12	.07
226	Scott Bradley	.10	.06
227	Bob Melvin	.10	.06
228	Ron Kittle	.10	.06
229	Phil Bradley	.10	.06
230	Tommy John	.12	.07
231	Greg Walker	.10	.06
232	Juan Berenguer	.10	.06
233	Pat Tabler	.10	.06
234	Terry Clark (R)	.10	.06
235	Rafael Palmeiro	1.00	.60
236	Paul Zuvella	.10	.06
237	Willie Randolph	.12	.07
238	Bruce Fields	.10	.06
239	Mike Aldrete	.10	.06
240	Lance Parrish	.10	.06
241	Greg Maddux	1.50	.90
242	John Moses	.10	.06
243	Melido Perez	.12	.07
244	Willie Wilson	.10	.06
245	Mark McLemore	.10	.06
246	Von Hayes	.10	.06
247	Matt Williams	1.25	.80
248	John Candelaria	.10	.06
249	Harold Reynolds	.12	.07
250	Greg Swindell	.15	.08
251	Juan Agosto	.10	.06
252	Mike Felder	.10	.06
253	Vince Coleman	.12	.07
254	Larry Sheets	.10	.06
255	George Bell	.20	.12
256	Terry Steinbach	.12	.07
257	Jack Armstrong (R)	.20	.12
258	Dickie Thon	.10	.06
259	Ray Knight	.10	.06
260	Darryl Strawberry	.60	.35
261	Doug Sisk	.10	.06
262	Alex Trevino	.10	.06
263	Jeff Leonard	.10	.06
264	Tom Henke	.12	.07
265	Ozzie Smith	.50	.30
266	Dave Bergman	.10	.06
267	Tony Phillips	.12	.07

268	Mark Davis	.10	.06
269	Kevin Elster	.10	.06
270	Barry Larkin	.40	.25
271	Manny Lee	.10	.06
272	Tom Brunansky	.15	.08
273	Craig Biggio (R)	.75	.45
274	Jim Gantner	.10	.06
275	Eddie Murray	.60	.35
276	Jeff Reed	.10	.06
277	Tim Teufel	.10	.06
278	Rick Honeycutt	.10	.06
279	Guillermo Hernandez	.10	.06
280	John Kruk	.40	.25
281	Luis Alicea (R)	.15	.08
282	Jim Clancy	.10	.06
283	Billy Ripken	.10	.06
284	Craig Reynolds	.10	.06
285	Robin Yount	1.00	.70
286	Jimmy Jones	.10	.06
287	Ron Oester	.10	.06
288	Terry Leach	.10	.06
289	Dennis Eckersley	.40	.25
290	Alan Trammell	.30	.18
291	Jimmy Key	.15	.10
292	Chris Bosio	.12	.07
293	Jose DeLeon	.10	.06
294	Jim Traber	.10	.06
295	Mike Scott	.10	.06
296	Roger McDowell	.10	.06
297	Garry Templeton	.10	.06
298	Doyle Alexander	.10	.06
299	Nick Esasky	.10	.06
300	Mark McGwire	1.25	.80
301	Darryl Hamilton (R)	.50	.30
302	Dave Smith	.10	.06
303	Rick Sutcliffe	.10	.06
304	Dave Stapleton	.10	.06
305	Alan Ashby	.10	.06
306	Pedro Guerrero	.12	.07
307	Ron Guidry	.12	.07
308	Steve Farr	.10	.06
309	Curt Ford	.10	.06
310	Claudell Washington	.10	.06
311	Tom Prince	.10	.06
312	Chad Kreuter (R)	.35	.20
313	Ken Oberkfell	.10	.06
314	Jerry Browne	.10	.06
315	R.J. Reynolds	.10	.06
316	Scott Bankhead	.10	.06
317	Milt Thompson	.10	.06
318	Mario Diaz	.10	.06
319	Bruce Ruffin	.10	.06
320	Dave Valle	.10	.06
321a	Gary Varsho (Wrong Photo)	1.25	.80
321b	Gary Varsho (R) (Cor)	.12	.07
322	Paul Mirabella	.10	.06
323	Chuck Jackson	.10	.06
324	Drew Hall	.10	.06
325	Don August	.10	.06
326	Israel Sanchez (R)	.12	.07
327	Denny Walling	.10	.06
328	Joel Skinner	.10	.06
329	Danny Tartabull	.30	.18
330	Tony Pena	.12	.07
331	Jim Sundberg	.10	.06
332	Jeff Robinson	.10	.06
333	Odibbe McDowell	.10	.06
334	Jose Lind	.10	.06
335	Paul Kilgus	.10	.06
336	Juan Samuel	.10	.06
337	Mike Campbell	.10	.06
338	Mike Maddux	.10	.06
339	Darnell Coles	.10	.06
340	Bob Dernier	.10	.06
341	Rafael Ramirez	.10	.06
342	Scott Sanderson	.10	.06
343	B.J. Surhoff	.10	.06
344	Billy Hatcher	.10	.06
345	Pat Perry	.10	.06
346	Jack Clark	.12	.07
347	Gary Thurman	.10	.06
348	Timmy Jones (R)	.12	.07
349	Dave Winfield	1.00	.60
350	Frank White	.10	.06
351	Dave Collins	.10	.06
352	Jack Morris	.40	.25
353	Eric Plunk	.10	.06
354	Leon Durham	.10	.06
355	Ivan DeJesus	.10	.06
356	Brian Holman (R)	.20	.12
357a	Dale Murphy (Photo Reversed)	35.00	20.00
357b	Dale Murphy (Cor)	.40	.25
358	Mark Portugal	.12	.07
359	Andy McGaffigan	.10	.06
360	Tom Glavine	2.50	1.40
361	Keith Moreland	.10	.06
362	Todd Stottlemyre	.20	.12
363	Dave Leiper	.12	.07
364	Cecil Fielder	1.25	.80
365	Carmelo Martinez	.10	.06
366	Dwight Evans	.12	.07
367	Kevin McReynolds	.12	.07
368	Rich Gedman	.10	.06
369	Len Dykstra	.50	.30
370	Jody Reed	.10	.06
371	Jose Canseco	1.25	.80
372	Rob Murphy	.10	.06
373	Mike Henneman	.10	.06
374	Walt Weiss	.12	.07
375	Rob Dibble (R)	.40	.25
376	Kirby Puckett	2.00	1.25
377	Denny Martinez	.25	.15

378	Ron Gant	1.25	.80
379	Brian Harper	.10	.06
380	Nelson Santovenia (R)	.12	.07
381	Lloyd Moseby	.10	.06
382	Lance McCullers	.10	.06
383	Dave Stieb	.12	.07
384	Tony Gwynn	1.25	.80
385	Mike Flanagan	.10	.06
386	Bob Ojeda	.12	.07
387	Bruce Hurst	.12	.07
388	Dave Magadan	.12	.07
389	Wade Boggs	1.25	.80
390	Gary Carter	.25	.15
391	Frank Tanana	.10	.06
392	Curt Young	.10	.06
383	Jeff Treadway	.10	.06
384	Darrell Evans	.12	.07
385	Glenn Hubbard	.10	.06
386	Chuck Cary	.10	.06
387	Frank Viola	.12	.07
388	Jeff Parrett	.10	.06
389	Terry Blocker (R)	.10	.06
400	Dan Gladden	.10	.06
401	Louie Meadows (R)	.12	.07
402	Tim Raines	.15	.10
403	Joey Meyer	.10	.06
404	Larry Andersen	.10	.06
405	Rex Hudler	.10	.06
406	Mike Schmidt	2.00	1.25
407	John Franco	.10	.06
408	Brady Anderson (R)	1.00	.60
409	Don Carman	.10	.06
410	Eric Davis	.35	.20
411	Bob Stanley	.10	.06
412	Pete Smith	.20	.12
413	Jim Rice	.15	.08
414	Bruce Sutter	.12	.07
415	Oil Can Boyd	.10	.06
416	Ruben Sierra	.80	.50
417	Mike LaValliere	.10	.06
418	Steve Buechele	.10	.06
419	Gary Redus	.10	.06
420	Scott Fletcher	.10	.06
421	Dale Sveum	.10	.06
422	Bob Knepper	.10	.06
423	Luis Rivera	.10	.06
424	Ted Higuera	.10	.06
425	Kevin Bass	.10	.06
426	Ken Gerhart	.10	.06
427	Shane Rawley	.10	.06
428	Paul O'Neill	.20	.12
429	Joe Orsulak	.12	.07
430	Jackie Gutierrez	.10	.06
431	Gerald Perry	.10	.06
432	Mike Greenwell	.20	.12
433	Jerry Royster	.10	.06
434	Ellis Burks	.20	.12

435	Ed Olwine	.10	.06
436	Dave Rucker	.10	.06
437	Charlie Hough	.10	.06
438	Bob Walk	.10	.06
439	Bob Brower	.10	.06
440	Barry Bonds	3.00	1.75
441	Tom Foley	.10	.06
442	Rob Deer	.12	.07
443	Glenn Davis	.12	.07
444	Dave Martinez	.10	.06
445	Bill Wegman	.10	.06
446	Lloyd McClendon	.10	.06
447	Dave Schmidt	.10	.06
448	Darren Daulton	.50	.30
449	Frank Williams	.10	.06
450	Don Aase	.10	.06
451	Lou Whitaker	.12	.07
452	Goose Gossage	.12	.07
453	Ed Whison	.10	.06
454	Jim Walewander	.10	.06
455	Damon Berryhill	.10	.06
456	Tim Burke	.10	.06
457	Barry Jones	.10	.06
458	Joel Youngblood	.10	.06
459	Floyd Youmans	.10	.06
460	Mark Salas	.10	.06
461	Jeff Russell	.10	.06
462	Darrell Miller	.10	.06
463	Jeff Kunkel	.10	.06
464	Sherman Corbett (R)	.12	.07
465	Curtis Wilkerson	.10	.06
466	Bud Black	.10	.06
467	Cal Ripken, Jr.	2.50	1.40
468	John Farrell	.10	.06
469	Terry Kennedy	.10	.06
470	Tom Candiotti	.12	.07
471	Roberto Alomar	5.00	3.50
472	Jeff Robinson	.10	.06
473	Vance Law	.10	.06
474	Randy Ready	.10	.06
475	Walt Terrell	.10	.06
476	Kelly Downs	.10	.06
477	Johnny Paredes (R)	.10	.06
478	Shawn Hillegas	.10	.06
479	Bob Brenly	.10	.06
480	Otis Nixon	.12	.07
481	Johnny Ray	.10	.06
482	Geno Petralli	.10	.06
483	Stu Cliburn	.10	.06
484	Pete Incaviglia	.10	.06
485	Brian Downing	.12	.07
486	Jeff Stone	.10	.06
487	Carmen Castillo	.10	.06
488	Tom Niedenfuer	.10	.06
489	Jay Bell	.25	.15
490	Rick Schu	.10	.06
491	Jeff Pico (R)	.12	.07

492 Mark Parent (R)	.10	.06
493 Eric King	.10	.06
494 Al Nipper	.10	.06
495 Andy Hawkins	.10	.06
496 Daryl Boston	.10	.06
497 Ernie Riles	.10	.06
498 Pascual Perez	.10	.06
499 Bill Long	.10	.06
500 Kirt Manwaring	.10	.06
501 Chuck Crim	.10	.06
502 Candy Maldonado	.10	.06
503 Dennis Lamp	.10	.06
504 Glenn Braggs	.10	.06
505 Joe Price	.10	.06
506 Ken Williams	.10	.06
507 Bill Pecota	.10	.06
508 Rey Quinones	.10	.06
509 Jeff Bittiger (R)	.12	.07
510 Kevin Seitzer	.15	.08
511 Steve Bedrosian	.10	.06
512 Todd Worrell	.15	.08
513 Chris James	.10	.06
514 Jose Oquendo	.10	.06
515 David Palmer	.10	.06
516 John Smiley	.15	.08
517 Dave Clark	.10	.06
518 Mike Dunne	.10	.06
519 Ron Washington	.10	.06
520 Bob Kipper	.10	.06
521 Lee Smith	.20	.12
522 Juan Castillo	.10	.06
523 Don Robinson	.10	.06
524 Kevin Romine	.10	.06
525 Paul Molitor	1.00	.60
526 Mark Langston	.20	.12
527 Donnie Hill	.10	.06
528 Larry Owen	.10	.06
529 Jerry Reed	.10	.06
530 Jack McDowell	2.00	1.25
531 Greg Matthews	.10	.06
532 John Russell	.10	.06
533 Don Quisenberry	.10	.06
534 Greg Gross	.10	.06
535 Danny Cox	.10	.06
536 Terry Francona	.10	.06
537 Andy Van Slyke	.30	.18
538 Mel Hall	.12	.07
539 Jim Gott	.10	.06
540 Doug Jones	.10	.06
541 Craig Lefferts	.10	.06
542 Mike Boddicker	.10	.06
543 Greg Brock	.10	.06
544 Atlee Hammaker	.10	.06
545 Tom Bolton	.10	.06
546 Mike Macfarlane (R)	.30	.18
547 Rich Renteria (R)	.12	.07
548 John Davis	.10	.06

549 Floyd Bannister	.10	.06
550 Mickey Brantley	.10	.06
551 Duane Ward	.10	.06
552 Dan Petry	.10	.06
553 Mickey Tettleton	.15	.08
554 Rick Leach	.10	.06
555 Mike Witt	.10	.06
556 Sid Bream	.10	.06
557 Bobby Witt	.15	.08
558 Tommy Herr	.10	.06
559 Randy Milligan	.12	.07
560 Jose Cecena (R)	.10	.06
561 Mackey Sasser	.10	.06
562 Carney Lansford	.10	.06
563 Rick Aguilera	.10	.06
564 Ron Hassey	.10	.06
565 Dwight Gooden	.50	.30
566 Paul Assenmacher	.10	.06
567 Neil Allen	.10	.06
568 Jim Morrison	.10	.06
569 Mike Pagliarulo	.10	.06
570 Ted Simmons	.12	.07
571 Mark Thurmond	.10	.06
572 Fred McGriff	1.50	.90
573 Wally Joyner	.30	.18
574 Jose Bautista (R)	.12	.07
575 Kelly Gruber	.12	.07
576 Cecilio Guane	.10	.06
577 Mark Davidson	.10	.06
578 Bobby Bonilla	.35	.20
579 Mike Stanley	.10	.06
580 Gene Larkin	.10	.06
581 Stan Javier	.10	.06
582 Howard Johnson	.30	.18
583a Mike Gallego (Photo Reversed On Back)	1.00	.70
583b Mike Gallego (Cor)	.10	.06
584 David Cone	.30	.18
585 Doug Jennings (R)	.12	.07
586 Charlie Hudson	.10	.06
587 Dion James	.10	.06
588 Al Leiter	.10	.06
589 Charlie Puleo	.10	.06
590 Roberto Kelly	.50	.30
591 Thad Bosley	.10	.06
592 Pete Stanicek	.10	.06
593 Pat Borders (R)	.40	.25
594 Bryan Harvey (R)	.75	.45
595 Jeff Ballard	.10	.06
596 Jeff Reardon	.15	.10
597 Doug Drabek	.20	.12
598 Edwin Correa	.10	.06
599 Keith Atherton	.10	.06
600 Dave LaPoint	.10	.06
601 Don Baylor	.15	.08
602 Tom Pagnozzi	.12	.07
603 Tim Flannery	.10	.06

604	Gene Walter	.10	.06
605	Dave Parker	.15	.08
606	Mike Diaz	.10	.06
607	Chris Gwynn	.10	.06
608	Odell Jones	.10	.06
609	Carlton Fisk	.50	.30
610	Jay Howell	.10	.06
611	Tim Crews	.10	.06
612	Keith Hernandez	.12	.07
613	Willie Fraser	.10	.06
614	Jim Eppard	.10	.06
615	Jeff Hamilton	.10	.06
616	Kurt Stillwell	.10	.06
617	Tom Browning	.12	.07
618	Jeff Montgomery	.10	.06
619	Jose Rijo	.15	.08
620	Jamie Quirk	.10	.06
621	Willie McGee	.15	.08
622	Mark Grant	.10	.06
623	Bill Swift	.20	.12
624	Orlando Mercado	.10	.06
625	John Costello (R)	.12	.07
626	Jose Gonzalez	.10	.06
627a	Bill Schroder (Wrong Photo)	1.00	.70
627b	Bill Schroder (Cor)	.10	.06
628a	Fred Manrique (Wrong Photo On Back)	.25	.15
628b	Fred Manrique (Cor)	.10	.06
629	Ricky Horton	.10	.06
630	Dan Plesac	.10	.06
631	Alfredo Griffin	.10	.06
632	Chuck Finley	.15	.08
633	Kirk Gibson	.12	.07
634	Randy Myers	.10	.06
635	Greg Minton	.10	.06
636	Herm Winningham	.10	.06
637	Charlie Leibrandt	.10	.06
638	Tim Birtsas	.10	.06
639	Bill Buckner	.12	.07
640	Danny Jackson	.12	.07
641	Greg Booker	.10	.06
642	Jim Presley	.10	.06
643	Gene Nelson	.10	.06
644	Rod Booker	.10	.06
645	Dennis Rasmussen	.10	.06
646	Juan Nieves	.10	.06
647	Bobby Thigpen	.12	.07
648	Tim Belcher	.12	.07
649	Mike Young	.10	.06
650	Ivan Calderon	.12	.07
651	Oswaldo Peraza (R)	.12	.07
652a	Pat Sheridan (No Position On Front)	24.00	12.00
652b	Pat Sheridan (Cor)	.10	.06
653	Mike Morgan	.10	.06
654	Mike Heath	.10	.06
655	Jay Tibbs	.10	.06
656	Fernando Valenzuela	.12	.07
657	Lee Mazzilli	.10	.06
658	Frank Viola (CY)	.15	.08
659	Jose Canseco (MVP)	.50	.30
660	Walt Weiss (ROY)	.12	.07
661	Orel Hershiser (CY)	.15	.08
662	Kirk Gibson (MVP)	.12	.07
663	Chris Sabo (ROY)	.12	.07
664	Dennis Eckersley(ALCS)	.15	.08
665	Orel Hershiser (NLCS)	.15	.08
666	Kirk Gibson (WS)	.12	.07
667	Orel Hershiser (WS)	.15	.08
668	Wally Joyner (CL)	.10	.06
669	Nolan Ryan (CL)	.80	.50
670	Jose Canseco (CL)	.40	.25
671	Fred McGriff (CL)	.30	.18
672	Dale Murphy (CL)	.15	.08
673	Paul Molitor (CL)	.15	.08
674	Ozzie Smith (CL)	.15	.08
675	Ryne Sandberg (CL)	.40	.25
676	Kirk Gibson (CL)	.12	.07
677	Andres Galarraga (CL)	.12	.07
678	Will Clark (CL)	.40	.25
679	Cory Snyder (CL)	.10	.06
680	Alvin Davis (CL)	.10	.06
681	Darryl Strawberry(CL)	.20	.12
682	Cal Ripken (CL)	.60	.35
683	Tony Gwynn (CL)	.25	.15
684	Mike Schmidt (CL)	.60	.35
685	Andy Van Slyke (CL)	.12	.07
686	Ruben Sierra (CL)	.20	.12
687	Wade Boggs (CL)	.25	.15
688	Eric Davis (CL)	.15	.08
689	George Brett (CL)	.25	.15
690	Alan Trammell (CL)	.12	.07
691	Frank Viola (CL)	.12	.07
692	Harold Baines (CL)	.12	.07
693	Don Mattingly (CL)	.25	.15
694	Checklist 1-100	.10	.06
695	Checklist 101-200	.10	.06
696	Checklist 201-300	.10	.06
697	Checklist 301-400	.10	.06
698	Checklist 401-500	.10	.06
699	Checklist 501-600	.10	.06
700	Checklist 601-700	.10	.06
701	Checklist 701-800	.10	.06
702	Jessie Barfield	.10	.06
703	Walt Terrell	.10	.06
704	Dickie Thon	.10	.06
705	Al Leiter	.10	.06
706	Dave LaPoint	.10	.06
707	Charlie Hayes (R)	.60	.35
708	Andy Hawkins	.10	.06
709	Mickey Hatcher	.10	.06
710	Lance McCullers	.10	.06
711	Ron Kittle	.10	.06

712	Bert Blyleven	.12	.07
713	Rick Dempsey	.10	.06
714	Ken Williams	.10	.06
715	Steve Rosenberg (R)	.12	.07
716	Joe Skalski (R)	.10	.06
717	Spike Owen	.10	.06
718	Todd Burns	.10	.06
719	Kevin Gross	.10	.06
720	Tommy Herr	.10	.06
721	Rob Ducey	.10	.06
722	Gary Green (R)	.12	.07
723	Gregg Olson (R)	1.25	.80
724	Greg Harris (R)	.20	.12
725	Craig Worthington (R)	.12	.07
726	Thomas Howard (R)	.20	.12
727	Dale Mohorcic	.10	.06
728	Rich Yett	.10	.06
729	Mel Hall	.12	.07
730	Floyd Youmans	.10	.06
731	Lonnie Smith	.10	.06
732	Wally Backman	.10	.06
733	Trevor Wilson (R)	.20	.12
734	Jose Alvarez (R)	.12	.07
735	Bob Milacki (R)	.12	.07
736	Tom Gordon (R)	.25	.15
737	Wally Whitehurst (R)	.12	.07
738	Mike Aldrete	.10	.06
739	Keith Miller	.10	.06
740	Randy Milligan	.10	.06
741	Jeff Parrett	.10	.06
742	Steve Finley (R)	.50	.30
743	Junior Felix (R)	.15	.10
744	Pete Harnisch (R)	.70	.40
745	Bill Spiers (R)	.20	.12
746	Hensley Meulens (R)	.12	.07
747	Juan Bell	.10	.06
748	Steve Sax	.12	.07
749	Phil Bradley	.10	.06
750	Rey Quinones	.12	.07
751	Tommy Gregg (R)	.10	.06
752	Kevin Brown (R)	.60	.35
753	Derek Lilliquist (R)	.12	.07
754	Todd Zeile (R)	1.25	.80
755	Jim Abbott (R)	4.00	2.75
756	Ozzie Canseco (R)	.25	.15
757	Nick Esasky	.10	.06
758	Mike Moore	.10	.06
759	Rob Murphy	.10	.06
760	Rick Mahler	.10	.06
761	Fred Lynn	.12	.07
762	Kevin Blankenship (R)	.12	.07
763	Eddie Murray	.50	.30
764	Steve Searcy (R)	.12	.07
765	Jerome Walton (R)	.20	.12
766	Erik Hanson (R)	.60	.35
767	Bob Boone	.15	.08
768	Edgar Martinez	.50	.30
769	Jose DeJesus (R)	.15	.08
770	Greg Briley (R)	.15	.08
771	Steve Peters (R)	.12	.07
772	Rafael Palmeiro	1.00	.60
773	Jack Clark	.12	.07
774	Nolan Ryan	4.00	2.75
775	Lance Parrish	.10	.06
776	Joe Girardi (R)	.15	.08
777	Willie Randolph	.12	.07
778	Mitch Williams	.12	.07
779	Dennis Cook (R)	.12	.07
780	Dwight Smith (R)	.15	.08
781	Lenny Harris (R)	.15	.10
782	Torey Lovullo (R)	.12	.07
783	Norm Charlton (R)	.30	.18
784	Chris Brown	.10	.06
785	Todd Benzinger	.10	.06
786	Shane Rawley	.10	.06
787	Omar Vizquel (R)	.40	.25
788	LaVel Freeman (R)	.10	.06
789	Jeffrey Leonard	.10	.06
790	Eddie Williams (R)	.10	.06
791	Jamie Moyer	.10	.06
792	Bruce Hurst	.12	.07
793	Julio Franco	.20	.12
794	Claudell Washington	.10	.06
795	Jody Davis	.10	.06
796	Odibbe McDowell	.10	.06
797	Paul Kilgus	.10	.06
798	Tracy Jones	.10	.06
799	Steve Wilson (R)	.12	.07
800	Pete O'Brien	.12	.07

1990 Upper Deck

Darren Daulton

Upper Deck follows up their premier issue with another 800-card set. The cards measure 2-1/2" by 3-1/2" and feature full color photos on the front and back. With this edition Upper Deck introduces their Heroes Of Baseball Inserts. 10 special Reggie Jackson Heroes cards were inserted randomly into the company's foil packs. Those cards are listed at the end of this checklist. Upper Deck issued a separate high-number series (701-800) at mid-season featuring rookies and traded players. Those card values are included in the complete set price below.

		MINT	NR/MT
Complete Set (800)		32.00	20.00
Commons (1-800)		.05	.02

1	Star Rookie Checklist	.05	.02
2	Randy Nosek (R)	.08	.05
3	Tom Drees (R)	.05	.02
4	Curt Young	.08	.05
5	Devon White (CL)	.05	.02
6	Luis Salazar	.05	.02
7	Von Hayes (CL)	.05	.02
8	Jose Bautista	.08	.05
9	Marquis Grissom (R)	1.50	.90
10	Orel Hershiser (CL)	.07	.04
11	Rick Aguilera	.05	.02
12	Benito Santiago (CL)	.07	.04
13	Deion Sanders (R)	1.75	1.00
14	Marvell Wynne	.05	.02
15	David West	.05	.02
16	Bobby Bonilla (CL)	.08	.05
17	Sammy Sosa (R)	1.50	.90
18	Steve Sax (CL)	.07	.04
19	Jack Howell	.05	.02
20	Mike Schmidt (SP)	.60	.35
21	Robin Ventura (R)	2.00	1.25
22	Brian Meyer (R)	.12	.07
23	Blaine Beatty (R)	.10	.06
24	Ken Griffey Jr. (CL)	.50	.30
25	Greg Vaughn (R)	.60	.35
26	Xavier Hernandez (R)	.15	.07
27	Jason Grimsley (R)	.15	.07
28	Eric Anthony (R)	.75	.45
29	Tim Raines (CL)	.07	.04
30	David Wells	.07	.04
31	Hal Morris (R)	.30	.18
32	Bo Jackson (CL)	.20	.12
33	Kelly Mann (R)	.12	.07
34	Nolan Ryan (SP)	1.00	.60
35	Scott Service (R)	.10	.06
36	Mark McGwire (CL)	.20	.12
37	Tino Martinez (R)	.40	.25
38	Chili Davis	.07	.04
39	Scott Sanderson	.05	.02
40	Kevin Mitchell (CL)	.08	.05
41	Lou Whitaker (CL)	.07	.04
42	Scott Coolbaugh (R)	.07	.04
43	Jose Cano (R)	.08	.05
44	Jose Vizcaino (R)	.20	.12
45	Bob Hamelin (R)	.20	.12
46	Jose Offerman (R)	.35	.20
47	Kevin Blankenship	.05	.02
48	Kirby Puckett (CL)	.25	.15
49	Tommy Greene (R)	.80	.50
50	Will Clark (SP)	.25	.15
51	Rob Nelson (H)	.07	.04
52	Chris Hammond (R)	.30	.18
53	Joe Carter (CL)	.15	.08
54a	Ben McDonald (No Rookie Logo) (R)	14.00	8.00
54b	Ben McDonald (Cor)	1.25	.70
55	Andy Benes (R)	.80	.50
56	John Olerud (R)	4.50	2.75
57	Roger Clemens (CL)	.25	.15
58	Tony Armas	.05	.02
59	George Canale (R)	.10	.06
60a	Mickey Tettleton (CL) (Lists Jamie Weston)	2.00	1.00
60b	Mickey Tettleton (CL) (Lists Mickey Weston)	.08	.05
61	Mike Stanton (R)	.20	.12
62	Dwight Gooden (CL)	.10	.06
63	Kent Mercker (R)	.20	.12
64	Francisco Cabrera (R)	.12	.07
65	Steve Avery (R)	1.75	1.00
66	Jose Canseco	.50	.30
67	Matt Merullo (R)	.10	.06
68	Vince Coleman (CL)	.07	.04
69	Ron Karkovice	.05	.02
70	Kevin Maas (R)	.20	.12
71	Dennis Cook	.05	.02
72	Juan Gonzalez (R)	10.00	7.00
73	Andre Dawson (CL)	.10	.06
74	Dean Palmer (R)	1.50	.90
75	Bo Jackson (SP)	.25	.15
76	Rob Richie (R)	.07	.04
77	Bobby Rose (R)	.15	.08
78	Brian DuBois (R)	.10	.06
79	Ozzie Guillen (CL)	.07	.04
80	Gene Nelson	.05	.02
81	Bob McClure	.05	.02
82	Julio Franco (CL)	.08	.05
83	Greg Minton	.05	.02
84	John Smoltz (CL)	.15	.08
85	Willie Fraser	.05	.02
86	Neal Heaton	.05	.02
87	Kevin Tapani (R)	.25	.15
88	Mike Scott (CL)	.07	.04
89a	Jim Gott (Wrong Photo)	4.00	2.50
89b	Jim Gott (Cor)	.07	.04
90	Lance Johnson (R)	.08	.05
91	Robin Yount (CL)	.15	.07
92	Jeff Parrett	.05	.02
93	Julio Machado (R)	.08	.05
94	Ron Jones	.05	.02

95 George Bell (CL)	.08	.05
96 Jerry Reuss	.05	.02
97 Brian Fisher	.05	.02
08 Kevin Ritz (R)	.10	.06
99 Barry Larkin (CL)	.10	.06
100 Checklist 1-100	.05	.02
101 Gerald Perry	.05	.02
102 Kevin Appier (R)	1.25	.80
103 Julio Franco	.15	.08
104 Craig Biggio	.15	.08
105 Bo Jackson	.30	.18
106 Junior Felix	.08	.05
107 Mike Harkey (R)	.10	.06
108 Fred McGriff	.50	.30
109 Rick Sutcliffe	.07	.04
110 Pete O'Brien	.05	.02
111 Kelly Gruber	.07	.04
112 Pat Borders	.07	.04
113 Dwight Evans	.07	.04
114 Dwight Gooden	.15	.08
115 Kevin Batiste	.12	.07
116 Eric Davis	.15	.08
117 Kevin Mitchell	.12	.07
118 Ron Oester	.05	.02
119 Brett Butler	.10	.06
120 Danny Jackson	.07	.04
121 Tommy Gregg	.05	.02
122 Ken Caminiti	.07	.04
123 Kevin Brown	.25	.15
124 George Brett	.50	.30
125 Mike Scott	.05	.02
126 Cory Snyder	.05	.02
127 George Bell	.15	.08
128 Mark Grace	.25	.15
129 Devon White	.08	.05
130 Tony Fernandez	.07	.04
131 Dan Aase	.05	.02
132 Rance Mulliniks	.05	.02
133 Marty Barrett	.05	.02
134 Nelson Liriano	.05	.02
135 Mark Carreon (R)	.07	.04
136 Candy Maldonado	.05	.02
137 Tim Birtsas	.05	.02
138 Tom Brookens	.05	.02
139 John Franco	.05	.02
140 Mike LaCoss	.05	.02
141 Jeff Treadway	.05	.02
142 Pat Tabler	.05	.02
143 Darrell Evans	.07	.04
144 Rafael Ramirez	.05	.02
145 Oddibe McDowell	.05	.02
146 Brian Downing	.05	.02
147 Curtis Wilkerson	.05	.02
148 Ernie Whitt	.05	.02
149 Bill Schroeder	.05	.02
150 Domingo Ramos	.05	.02
151 Rick Honeycutt	.05	.02

152 Don Slaught	.05	.02
153 Mitch Webster	.05	.02
154 Tony Phillips	.05	.02
155 Paul Kilgus	.05	.02
156 Ken Griffey, Jr.	6.00	3.50
157 Gary Sheffield	.80	.50
158 Wally Backman	.05	.02
159 B.J. Surhoff	.05	.02
160 Louie Meadows	.05	.02
161 Paul O'Neill	.15	.08
162 Jeff McKnight (R)	.15	.08
163 Alvaro Espinoza (R)	.12	.07
164 Scott Scudder (R)	.15	.08
165 Jeff Reed	.05	.02
166 Gregg Jefferies	.50	.30
167 Barry Larkin	.20	.12
168 Gary Carter	.10	.06
169 Robby Thompson	.05	.02
170 Rolando Roomes	.05	.02
171 Mark McGwire	.60	.35
172 Steve Sax	.07	.04
173 Mark Williamson	.05	.02
174 Mitch Williams	.05	.02
175 Brian Holton	.05	.02
176 Rob Deer	.07	.04
177 Tim Raines	.07	.05
178 Mike Felder	.05	.02
179 Harold Reynolds	.07	.04
180 Terry Francona	.05	.02
181 Chris Sabo	.12	.07
182 Darryl Strawberry	.30	.18
183 Willie Randolph	.07	.04
184 Billy Ripken	.05	.02
185 Mackey Sasser	.05	.02
186 Todd Benzinger	.05	.02
187 Kevin Elster	.05	.02
188 Jose Uribe	.05	.02
189 Tom Browning	.07	.04
190 Keith Miller	.05	.02
191 Don Mattingly	.40	.25
192 Dave Parker	.07	.04
193 Roberto Kelly	.25	.15
194 Phil Bradley	.05	.02
195 Ron Hassey	.05	.02
196 Gerald Young	.05	.02
197 Hubie Brooks	.05	.02
198 Bill Doran	.05	.02
199 Al Newman	.05	.02
200 Checklist 101-200	.05	.02
201 Terry Puhl	.05	.02
202 Frank DiPino	.05	.02
203 Jim Clancy	.05	.02
204 Bob Ojeda	.05	.02
205 Alex Trevino	.05	.02
206 Dave Henderson	.05	.02
207 Henry Cotto	.05	.02
208 Rafael Belliard	.05	.02

209	Stan Javier	.05	.02
210	Jerry Reed	.05	.02
211	Doug Dascenzo	.07	.04
212	Andres Thomsa	.05	.02
213	Greg Maddux	.40	.25
214	Mike Schooler	.05	.02
215	Lonnie Smith	.05	.02
216	Jose Rijo	.08	.05
217	Greg Gagne	.05	.02
218	Jim Gantner	.05	.02
219	Allan Anderson	.05	.02
220	Rick Mahler	.05	.02
221	Jim Deshaies	.05	.02
222	Keith Hernandez	.07	.04
223	Vince Coleman	.07	.04
224	David Cone	.20	.12
225	Ozzie Smith	.25	.15
226	Matt Nokes	.05	.02
227	Barry Bonds	1.50	.90
228	Felix Jose	.35	.20
229	Dennis Powell	.05	.02
230	Mike Gallego	.05	.02
231	Shawon Dunston	.08	.05
232	Ron Gant	.50	.30
233	Omar Vizquel	.08	.05
234	Derek Lilliquist	.05	.02
235	Erik Hanson	.15	.10
236	Kirby Puckett	.75	.45
237	Bill Spiers	.08	.05
238	Dan Gladden	.05	.02
239	Bryan Clutterbuck (R)	.07	.04
240	John Moses	.05	.02
241	Ron Darling	.07	.04
242	Joe Magrane	.07	.04
243	Dave Magadan	.07	.04
244	Pedro Guerrero	.07	.04
245	Glenn Davis	.07	.04
246	Terry Steinbach	.07	.04
247	Fred Lynn	.07	.04
248	Gary Redus	.05	.02
249	Kenny Williams	.05	.02
250	Sid Bream	.05	.02
251	Bob Welch	.07	.04
252	Bill Buckner	.07	.04
253	Carney Lansford	.07	.04
254	Paul Molitor	.40	.25
255	Jose DeJesus	.05	.02
256	Orel Hershiser	.10	.06
257	Tom Brunansky	.07	.04
258	Mike Davis	.05	.02
259	Jeff Ballard	.05	.02
260	Scott Terry	.05	.02
261	Sid Fernandez	.07	.04
262	Howard Johnson	.12	.07
263	Kirk Gibson	.07	.04
264	Kevin McReynolds	.07	.04
265	Cal Ripken, Jr.	1.00	.60
267	Ozzie Guillen	.07	.04
268	Jim Traber	.05	.02
269	Bobby Thigpen	.07	.04
270	Joe Orsulak	.05	.02
271	Bob Boone	.08	.05
272	Dave Stewart	.08	.05
273	Tim Wallach	.08	.05
274	Luis Aquino	.05	.02
275	Mike Moore	.05	.02
276	Tony Pena	.07	.04
277	Eddie Murray	.20	.12
278	Milt Thompson	.05	.02
279	Alejandro Pena	.05	.02
280	Ken Dayley	.05	.02
281	Carmen Castillo	.05	.02
282	Tom Henke	.05	.02
283	Mickey Hatcher	.05	.02
284	Roy Smith	.07	.04
285	Manny Lee	.05	.02
286	Dan Pasqua	.05	.02
287	Larry Sheets	.05	.02
288	Garry Templeton	.05	.02
289	Eddie Williams	.05	.02
290	Brady Anderson	.20	.12
291	Spike Owen	.05	.02
292	Storm Davis	.05	.02
293	Chris Bosio	.07	.04
294	Jim Eisenreich	.05	.02
295	Don August	.05	.02
296	Jeff Hamilton	.05	.02
297	Mickey Tettleton	.07	.04
298	Mike Scioscia	.05	.02
299	Kevin Hickey	.05	.02
300	Checklist 201-300	.05	.02
301	Shawn Abner	.05	.02
302	Kevin Bass	.05	.02
303	Bip Roberts	.08	.05
304	Joe Girardi	.08	.05
305	Danny Darwin	.05	.02
306	Mike Heath	.05	.02
307	Mike Macfarlane	.07	.04
308	Ed Whitson	.05	.02
309	Tracy Jones	.05	.02
310	Scott Fletcher	.05	.02
311	Darnell Coles	.05	.02
312	Mike Brumley	.05	.02
313	Bill Swift	.12	.07
314	Charlie Hough	.05	.02
315	Jim Presley	.05	.02
316	Luis Polonia	.07	.04
317	Mike Morgan	.05	.02
318	Lee Guetterman	.05	.02
319	Jose Oquendo	.07	.04
320	Wayne Tollenson	.05	.02
321	Jody Reed	.05	.02
322	Damon Berryhill	.05	.02
323	Roger Clemens	.75	.45
266	Cal Ripken, Jr.	1.00	.60

324	Ryne Sandberg	.75	.45
325	Benito Santiago	.10	.06
326	Bret Saberhagen	.10	.06
027	Lou Whitaker	.07	.04
328	Dave Gallagher	.05	.02
329	Mike Pagliarulo	.05	.02
330	Doyle Alexander	.05	.02
331	Jeffrey Leonard	.05	.02
332	Torey Lovullo	.05	.02
333	Pete Incaviglia	.05	.02
334	Rickey Henderson	.45	.28
335	Rafael Palmeiro	.35	.20
336	Ken Hill (R)	.30	.18
337	Dave Winfield	.50	.30
338	Alfredo Griffin	.05	.02
339	Andy Hawkins	.05	.02
340	Ted Power	.05	.02
341	Steve Wilson	.05	.02
342	Jack Clark	.07	.04
343	Ellis Burks	.10	.06
344	Tony Gwynn	.40	.25
345	Jerome Walton	.10	.06
346	Roberto Alomar	1.25	.80
347	Carlos Martinez (R)	.10	.06
348	Chet Lemon	.05	.02
349	Willie Wilson	.05	.02
350	Greg Walker	.05	.02
351	Tom Bolton	.05	.02
352	German Gonzalez	.07	.04
353	Harold Baines	.07	.04
354	Mike Greenwell	.10	.06
355	Ruben Sierra	.35	.20
356	Andres Galarraga	.25	.15
357	Andre Dawson	.20	.12
358	Jeff Brantley (R)	.12	.07
359	Mike Bielecki	.05	.02
360	Ken Oberkfell	.05	.02
361	Kurt Stillwell	.05	.02
362	Brian Holman	.07	.04
363	Kevin Seitzer	.07	.04
364	Alvin Davis	.05	.02
365	Tom Gordon	.10	.06
366	Bobby Bonilla	.20	.12
367	Carlton Fisk	.20	.12
368	Steve Carter (R)	.08	.05
369	Joel Skinner	.05	.02
370	John Cangelosi	.05	.02
371	Cecil Espy	.05	.02
372	Gary Wayne (R)	.10	.06
373	Jim Rice	.08	.05
374	Mike Dyer (R)	.08	.05
375	Joe Carter	.30	.18
376	Dwight Smith	.08	.05
377	John Wetteland (R)	.35	.20
378	Ernie Riles	.05	.02
379	Otis Nixon	.07	.04
380	Vance Law	.05	.02
381	Dave Bergman	.05	.02
382	Frank White	.05	.02
383	Scott Bradley	.05	.02
384	Israel Sanchez	.05	.02
385	Gary Pettis	.05	.02
386	Donn Pall	.08	.05
387	John Smiley	.10	.06
388	Tom Candiotti	.07	.04
389	Junior Ortiz	.05	.02
390	Steve Lyons	.05	.02
391	Brian Harper	.05	.02
392	Fred Manrique	.05	.02
393	Lee Smith	.12	.07
394	Jeff Kunkel	.05	.02
395	John Tudor	.05	.02
397	Terry Kennedy	.05	.02
398	Lloyd McClendon	.05	.02
399	Craig Lefferts	.05	.02
400	Checklist 301-400	.05	.02
401	Keith Moreland	.05	.02
402	Rich Gedman	.05	.02
403	Jeff Robinson	.05	.02
404	Randy Ready	.05	.02
405	Rick Cerone	.05	.02
406	Jeff Blauser	.05	.02
407	Larry Anderson	.05	.02
408	Joe Boever	.05	.02
409	Felix Fermin	.05	.02
410	Glenn Wilson	.05	.02
411	Rex Hudler	.05	.02
412	Mark Grant	.05	.02
413	Dennis Martinez	.10	.06
414	Darrin Jackson	.05	.02
415	Mike Aldrete	.05	.02
416	Roger McDowell	.05	.02
417	Jeff Reardon	.15	.08
418	Darren Daulton	.25	.15
419	Tim Laudner	.05	.02
420	Don Carman	.05	.02
421	Lloyd Moseby	.05	.02
422	Doug Drabek	.10	.06
423	Lenny Harris	.05	.02
424	Jose Lind	.05	.02
425	Dave Johnson (R)	.10	.06
426	Jerry Browne	.05	.02
427	Eric Yelding (R)	.15	.08
428	Brad Komminsk	.07	.04
429	Jody Davis	.05	.02
430	Mariano Duncan	.07	.04
431	Mark Davis	.05	.02
432	Nelson Santovenia	.05	.02
433	Bruce Hurst	.07	.04
434	Jeff Huson (R)	.10	.06
435	Chris James	.05	.02
436	Mark Guthrie (R)	.12	.07
437	Charlie Hayes	.07	.04
438	Shane Rawley	.05	.02

439	Dickie Thon	.05	.02
440	Juan Berenguer	.05	.02
441	Kevin Romine	.05	.02
442	Bill Landrum	.05	.02
443	Todd Frohwirth	.05	.02
444	Craig Worthington	.05	.02
445	Fernando Valenzuela	.07	.04
446	Joey Belle (R)	2.50	1.50
447	Ed Whited (R)	.08	.05
448	Dave Smith	.05	.02
449	Dave Clark	.05	.02
450	Juan Agosto	.05	.02
451	Dave Valle	.05	.02
452	Kent Hrbek	.07	.04
453	Von Hayes	.05	.02
454	Gary Gaetti	.05	.02
455	Greg Briley	.05	.02
456	Glenn Braggs	.05	.02
457	Kirt Manwaring	.05	.02
458	Mel Hall	.07	.04
459	Brook Jacoby	.05	.02
460	Pat Sheridan	.05	.02
461	Rob Murphy	.05	.02
462	Jimmy Key	.05	.02
463	Nick Esasky	.05	.02
464	Rob Ducey	.05	.02
465	Carlos Quintana	.07	.04
466	Larry Walker (R)	1.75	1.00
467	Todd Worrell	.07	.04
468	Kevin Gross	.05	.02
469	Terry Pendleton	.20	.12
470	Dave Martinez	.05	.02
471	Gene Larkin	.05	.02
472	Len Dykstra	.30	.18
473	Barry Lyons	.05	.02
474	Terry Mulholland	.15	.08
475	Chip Hale (R)	.10	.06
476	Jesse Barfield	.05	.02
477	Dan Plesac	.05	.02
478a	Scott Garrelts (Wrong Photo)	2.00	1.25
478b	Scott Garrelts (Cor)	.10	.06
479	Dave Righetti	.05	.02
480	Gus Polidor	.07	.04
481	Mookie Wilson	.05	.02
482	Luis Rivera	.05	.02
483	Mike Flanagan	.05	.02
484	Dennis "Oil Can" Boyd	.05	.02
485	John Cerutti	.05	.02
486	John Costello	.05	.02
487	Pascual Perez	.05	.02
488	Tommy Herr	.05	.02
489	Tom Foley	.05	.02
490	Curt Ford	.05	.02
491	Steve Lake	.05	.02
492	Tim Teufel	.05	.02
493	Randy Bush	.05	.02
494	Mike Jackson	.05	.02
495	Steve Jeltz	.05	.02
496	Paul Gibson	.05	.02
497	Steve Balboni	.05	.02
498	Bud Black	.07	.04
499	Dale Sveum	.05	.02
500	Checklist 401-500	.05	.02
501	Timmy Jones	.05	.02
502	Mark Portugal	.05	.02
503	Ivan Calderon	.08	.05
504	Rick Rhoden	.05	.02
505	Willie McGee	.08	.05
506	Kirk McCaskill	.05	.02
507	Dave LaPoint	.05	.02
508	Jay Howell	.05	.02
509	Johnny Ray	.05	.02
510	Dave Anderson	.05	.02
511	Chuck Crim	.05	.02
512	Joe Hesketh	.05	.02
513	Dennis Eckersley	.20	.12
514	Greg Brock	.05	.02
515	Tim Burke	.05	.02
516	Frank Tanana	.05	.02
517	Jay Bell	.07	.04
518	Guillermo Hernandez	.05	.02
519	Randy Kramer	.07	.04
520	Charles Hudson	.05	.02
521	Jim Corsi	.08	.05
522	Steve Rosenberg	.05	.02
523	Cris Carpenter	.05	.02
524	Matt Winters (R)	.08	.05
525	Melido Perez	.07	.04
526	Chris Gwynn	.05	.02
527	Bert Blyleven	.10	.06
528	Chuck Cary	.05	.02
529	Daryl Boston	.05	.02
530	Dale Mohorcic	.05	.02
531	Geronimo Berroa	.07	.04
532	Edgar Martinez	.30	.18
533	Dale Murphy	.15	.08
534	Jay Buhner	.08	.05
535	John Smoltz	.50	.30
536	Andy Van Slyke	.15	.08
537	Mike Henneman	.05	.02
538	Miguel Garcia (R)	.10	.06
539	Frank Williams	.05	.02
540	R.J. Reynolds	.05	.02
541	Shawn Hillegas	.05	.02
542	Walt Weiss	.05	.02
543	Greg Hibbard (R)	.25	.15
544	Nolan Ryan	1.75	1.00
545	Todd Zeile	.25	.15
546	Hensley Meulens	.10	.06
547	Tim Belcher	.07	.04
548	Mike Witt	.05	.02
549	Greg Cadaret	.05	.02
550	Franklin Stubbs	.05	.02

551	Tony Castillo (R)	.15	.08
552	Jeff Robinson	.05	.02
553	Steve Olin (R)	.15	.10
554	Alan Trammell	.10	.06
555	Wade Boggs	.40	.25
556	Will Clark	.60	.35
557	Jeff King (R)	.15	.10
558	Mike Fitzgerald	.05	.02
559	Ken Howell	.05	.02
560	Bob Kipper	.05	.02
561	Scott Bankhead	.05	.02
562a	Jeff Innis (Wrong Photo)	2.00	1.25
562b	Jeff Innis (Cor)	.12	.07
563	Randy Johnson	.50	.30
564	Wally Whithurst	.05	.02
565	Gene Harris (R)	.08	.05
566	Norm Charlton	.07	.04
567	Robin Yount	.40	.25
568	Joe Oliver (R)	.20	.12
569	Mark Parent	.05	.02
570	John Farrell	.05	.02
571	Tom Glavine	.75	.45
572	Rod Nichols	.07	.04
573	Jack Morris	.20	.12
574	Greg Swindell	.07	.04
575	Steve Searcy	.08	.05
576	Ricky Jordan	.07	.04
577	Matt Williams	.50	.30
578	Mike LaValliere	.05	.02
579	Bryn Smith	.05	.02
580	Bruce Ruffin	.05	.02
581	Randy Myers	.05	.02
582	Rick Wrona (R)	.10	.06
583	Juan Samuel	.05	.02
584	Les Lancaster	.05	.02
585	Jeff Musselman	.05	.02
586	Rob Dibble	.12	.07
587	Eric Show	.05	.02
588	Jesse Orosco	.05	.02
589	Herm Winningham	.05	.02
590	Andy Allanson	.05	.02
591	Dion James	.05	.02
592	Carmelo Martinez	.05	.02
593	Luis Quinones	.07	.04
594	Dennis Rasmussen	.05	.02
595	Rich Yett	.05	.02
596	Bob Walk	.05	.02
597	Andy McGaffigan	.05	.02
598	Billy Hatcher	.05	.02
599	Bob Knepper	.05	.02
600	Checklist 501-600	.05	.02
601	Joey Cora	.07	.04
602	Steve Finley	.12	.07
603	Kal Daniels	.05	.02
604	Gregg Olson	.12	.07
605	Dave Steib	.07	.04
606	Kenny Rogers (R)	.10	.06
607	Zane Smith	.05	.02
608	Bob Geren (R)	.10	.06
609	Chad Kreuter	.08	.05
610	Mike Smithson	.05	.02
611	Jeff Wetherby (R)	.12	.07
612	Gary Mielke (R)	.08	.05
613	Pete Smith	.10	.06
614	Jack Daugherty (R)	.10	.06
615	Lance McCullers	.05	.02
616	Don Robinson	.05	.02
617	Jose Guzman	.05	.02
618	Steve Bedrosian	.05	.02
619	Jamie Moyer	.05	.02
620	Atlee Hammaker	.05	.02
621	Rick Luecken (R)	.10	.06
622	Greg W. Harris	.05	.02
623	Pete Harnisch	.10	.06
624	Jerald Clark	.07	.04
625	Jack McDowell	.50	.30
626	Frank Viola	.08	.05
627	Ted Higuera	.05	.02
628	Marty Pevey (R)	.08	.05
629	Bill Wegman	.05	.02
630	Eric Plunk	.05	.02
631	Drew Hall	.05	.02
632	Doug Jones	.05	.02
633	Geno Petralli	.05	.02
634	Jose Alvarez	.05	.02
635	Bob Milacki	.07	.04
636	Bobby Witt	.08	.05
637	Trevor Wilson	.08	.05
638	Jeff Russell	.05	.02
639	Mike Krukow	.05	.02
640	Rick Leach	.05	.02
641	Dave Schmidt	.05	.02
642	Terry Leach	.05	.02
643	Calvin Schiraldi	.05	.02
644	Bob Melvin	.05	.02
645	Jim Abbott	.40	.25
646	Jaime Navarro (R)	.25	.15
647	Mark Langston	.10	.06
648	Juan Nieves	.05	.02
649	Damaso Garcia	.05	.02
650	Charlie O'Brien	.05	.02
651	Eric King	.05	.02
652	Mike Boddicker	.05	.02
653	Duane Ward	.05	.02
654	Bob Stanley	.05	.02
655	Sandy Alomar, Jr.	.12	.07
656	Danny Tartabull	.15	.08
657	Randy McCament	.05	.02
658	Charlie Leibrandt	.05	.02
659	Dan Quisenberry	.05	.02
660	Paul Assenmacher	.05	.02
661	Walt Terrell	.05	.02
662	Tim Leary	.05	.02

663	Randy Milligan	.07	.04
664	Bo Diaz	.05	.02
665	Mark Lemke	.05	.02
666	Jose Gonzalez	.05	.02
667	Chuck Finley —	.10	.06
668	John Kruk	.15	.10
000	Dick Ochiofield	.03	.02
670	Tim Crews	.05	.02
671	John Dopson	.05	.02
672	John Orton (R)	.10	.06
673	Eric Hetzel	.08	.05
674	Lance Parrish	.05	.02
675	Ramon Martinez	.25	.15
676	Mark Gubicza	.07	.04
677	Greg Litton	.05	.02
678	Greg Matthews	.05	.02
679	Dave Dravecky	.05	.02
680	Steve Farr	.05	.02
681	Mike Deveraux	.12	.07
682	Ken Griffey, Sr.	.10	.06
683a	Mickey Weston (Jamie)	2.00	1.25
683b	Mickey Weston (Cor)	.10	.06
684	Jack Armstrong	.07	.04
685	Steve Buechele	.05	.02
686	Bryan Harvey	.12	.07
687	Lance Blankenship	.05	.02
688	Dante Bichette	.05	.02
689	Todd Burns	.05	.02
690	Dan Petry	.05	.02
691	Kent Anderson (R)	.08	.05
692	Todd Stottlemyre	.08	.05
693	Wally Joyner	.15	.08
694	Mike Rochford	.08	.05
695	Floyd Bannister	.05	.02
696	Rick Reuschel	.05	.02
697	Jose DeLeon	.05	.02
698	Jeff Montgomery	.05	.02
699	Kelly Downs	.05	.02
700a	Checklist 601-700 (Jamie Weston Listed)	3.00	1.50
700b	Checklist 601-700 (Mickey Weston Listed)	.12	.07
701	Jim Gott	.05	.02
702	Rookie Threats	.80	.50
	Delino DeShields		
	Larry Walker		
	Marquis Grissom		
703	Alejandro Pena	.05	.02
704	Willie Randolph	.07	.04
705	Tim Leary	.05	.02
706	Chuck McElroy (R)	.20	.12
707	Gerald Perry	.05	.02
708	Tom Brunansky	.07	.04
709	John Franco	.05	.02
710	Mark Davis	.05	.02
711	Dave Justice (R)	3.50	2.00
712	Storm Davis	.05	.02
713	Scott Ruskin (R)	.20	.12
714	Glenn Braggs	.05	.02
715	Kevin Bearse (R)	.10	.06
716	Jose Nunez (R)	.12	.07
717	Tim Layana (R)	.15	.08
718	Greg Myers (R)	.15	.08
719	Pete O'Brien	.05	.02
720	John Candelaria	.05	.02
721	Craig Grebeck (R)	.25	.15
722	Shawn Boskie (R)	.15	.08
723	Jim Leyritz (R)	.15	.08
724	Bill Sampen (R)	.12	.07
725	Scott Radinsky (R)	.25	.15
726	Todd Hundley (R)	.20	.12
727	Scott Hemond (R)	.12	.07
728	Lenny Webster (R)	.10	.06
729	Jeff Reardon	.15	.08
730	Mitch Webster	.05	.02
731	Brian Bohanon (R)	.10	.06
732	Rick Parker (R)	.12	.07
733	Terry Shumpert (R)	.15	.08
734a	Nolan Ryan (6th No Hitter)	7.50	4.00
734b	Nolan Ryan (6th No Hitter/300 Win)	1.50	.90
735	John Burkett (R)	.75	.45
736	Derrick May (R)	1.25	.70
737	Carlos Baerga (R)	3.50	2.00
738	Greg Smith (R)	.10	.06
739	Joe Kraemer (R)	.08	.05
740	Scott Sanderson	.05	.02
741	Hector Villanueva (R)	.12	.07
742	Mike Fetters (R)	.12	.07
743	Mark Gardner (R)	.20	.12
744	Matt Nokes	.05	.02
745	Dave Winfield	.50	.30
746	Delino DeShields (R)	1.25	.70
747	Dann Howitt (R)	.15	.08
748	Tony Pena	.05	.02
749	Oil Can Boyd	.05	.02
750	Mike Benjamin (R)	.10	.06
751	Alex Cole (R)	.25	.15
752	Eric Gunderson (R)	.12	.07
753	Howard Farmer (R)	.10	.06
754	Joe Carter	.35	.20
755	Ray Lankford (R)	1.25	.70
756	Sandy Alomar, Jr.	.15	.08
757	Alex Sanchez (R)	.10	.06
758	Nick Esasky	.05	.02
759	Stan Belinda (R)	.20	.12
760	Jim Presley	.05	.02
761	Gary DiSarcina (R)	.25	.15
762	Wayne Edwards (R)	.10	.06
763	Pat Combs (R)	.10	.06
764	Mickey Pina (R)	.08	.05
765	Wilson Alvarez (R)	.80	.50
766	Dave Parker	.07	.04

1991 Upper Deck

This 800-card set features color photos on both the card fronts and backs. The cards measure 2-1/2" by 3-1/2". The first 26-cards belong to the Star Rookies Subset. Special insert cards include a Michael Jordan Bonus card, a 9-card Heroes of Baseball set featuring Nolan Ryan, a 9-card Hank Aaron Heroes of Baseball Set, 4-Hall of Fame Heroes, and 18- Silver Sluggers. All of these inserts are listed at the end of this checklist. A high-number series (701-800) includes additional rookies and traded players. The complete set price below includes the high number series but not the special Jordan card or Heroes sets.

		MINT	NR/MT
Complete Set (800)		26.00	16.00
Commons		.05	.02

767	Mike Blowers (R)	.10	.06
768	Tony Phillips	.07	.04
769	Pascual Perez	.05	.02
770	Gary Pettis	.05	.02
771	Fred Lynn	.07	.04
772	Mel Rojas (R)	.25	.15
773	David Segui (R)	.20	.12
774	Gary Carter	.10	.06
775	Rafael Valdez (R)	.12	.07
776	Glenallen Hill (R)	.20	.12
777	Keith Hernandez	.07	.04
778	Billy Hatcher	.05	.02
779	Marty Clary (R)	.10	.06
780	Candy Maldonado	.05	.02
781	Mike Marshall	.05	.02
782	Billy Jo Robidoux (R)	.10	.06
783	Mark Langston	.10	.06
784	Paul Sorrento (R)	.50	.30
785	Dave Hollins (R)	1.25	.70
786	Cecil Fielder	.40	.25
787	Matt Young	.05	.02
788	Jeff Huson	.07	.04
789	Lloyd Moseby	.05	.02
790	Ron Kittle	.05	.02
791	Hubie Brooks	.05	.02
792	Craig Lefferts	.05	.02
793	Kevin Bass	.05	.02
794	Bryn Smith	.05	.02
795	Juan Samuel	.05	.02
796	Sam Horn (R)	.15	.08
797	Randy Myers	.05	.02
798	Chris James	.05	.02
799	Bill Gullickson	.05	.02
800	Checklist 701-800	.05	.02
BH1	Reggie Jackson (Hero)	3.50	2.00
BH2	Reggie Jackson (Hero)	3.50	2.00
BH3	Reggie Jackson (Hero)	3.50	2.00
BH4	Reggie Jackson (Hero)	3.50	2.00
BH5	Reggie Jackson (Hero)	3.50	2.00
BH6	Reggie Jackson (Hero)	3.50	2.00
BH7	Reggie Jackson (Hero)	3.50	2.00
BH8	Reggie Jackson (Hero)	3.50	2.00
BH9	Reggie Jackson (Hero)	3.50	2.00
	Reggie Jackson (Cover)	5.00	3.00
	Heroes Checklist	3.50	2.00
	Reggie Jackson (Hero) (Autographed)	400.00	200.00
1	Star Rookie Checklist	.05	.02
2	Phil Plantier (R)	.90	.55
3	D.J. Dozier (R)	.12	.07
4	Dave Hansen (R)	.15	.08
5	Maurice Vaughn (R)	.75	.45
6	Leo Gomez (R)	.15	.10
7	Scott Aldred (R)	.10	.06
8	Scott Chiamparino (R)	.10	.06
9	Lance Dickson (R)	.20	.12
10	Sean Berry (R)	.20	.12
11	Bernie Williams (R)	.40	.25
12	Brian Barnes (R)	.12	.07
13	Narciso Elvira (R)	.10	.06
14	Mike Gardiner (R)	.15	.08
15	Greg Colbrunn (R)	.20	.12
16	Bernard Gilkey (R)	.35	.20
17	Mark Lewis (R)	.15	.10
18	Mickey Morandini (R)	.20	.12
19	Charles Nagy (R)	1.00	.70
20	Geronimo Pena (R)	.12	.07

21	Henry Rodriguez (R)	.25	.15
22	Scott Cooper (R)	.40	.25
23	Andujar Cedeno (R)	.35	.20
24	Eric Karros (R)	1.25	.70
25	Steve Decker (R)	.10	.06
26	Kevin Belcher (R)	.12	.07
27	Jeff Conine (R)	.10	.06
28	Dave Stewart (TC)	.05	.02
29	Carlton Fisk (TC)	.05	.02
30	Rafael Palmeiro (TC)	.05	.02
31	Chuck Finley (TC)	.05	.02
32	Harold Reynolds (TC)	.05	.02
33	Bret Saberhagen (TC)	.05	.02
34	Gary Gaetti (TC)	.05	.02
35	Scott Leius	.10	.06
36	Neal Heaton	.05	.02
37	Terry Lee (R)	.10	.06
38	Gary Redus	.05	.02
39	Barry Jones	.05	.02
40	Chuck Knoblauch (R)	.60	.35
41	Larry Andersen	.05	.02
42	Darryl Hamilton	.10	.06
43	Mike Greenwell (TC)	.05	.02
44	Kelly Gruber (TC)	.05	.02
45	Jack Morris (TC)	.05	.02
46	Sandy Alomar Jr. (TC)	.05	.02
47	Gregg Olson (TC)	.05	.02
48	Dave Parker (TC)	.05	.02
49	Roberto Kelly (TC)	.05	.02
50	Top Prospect Checklist	.05	.02
51	Kyle Abbott	.15	.08
52	Jeff Juden (R)	.25	.15
53	Todd Van Poppel (R)	1.00	.60
54	Steve Karsay (R)	.75	.45
55	Chipper Jones (R)	1.75	1.00
56	Chris Johnson (R)	.12	.08
57	John Ericks	.15	.08
58	Gary Scott (R)	.10	.06
59	Kiki Jones	.10	.06
60	Wilfredo Cordero (R)	.80	.05
61	Royce Clayton	.60	.35
62	Tim Costo (R)	.40	.25
63	Roger Salkeld	.30	.18
64	Brook Fordyce (R)	.15	.08
65	Mike Mussina (R)	2.00	1.25
66	Dave Staton (R)	.30	.18
67	Mike Lieberthal (R)	.30	.18
68	Kurt Miller (R)	.50	.30
69	Dan Peltier (R)	.15	.08
70	Greg Blosser	.30	.18
71	Reggie Sanders (R)	1.25	.70
72	Brent Mayne	.10	.06
73	Rico Brogna	.10	.06
74	Willie Banks	.20	.12
75	Len Brutcher (R)	.08	.05
76	Pat Kelly (R)	.30	.18
77	Chris Sabo (TC)	.05	.02
78	Ramon Martinez (TC)	.07	.04
79	Matt Williams (TC)	.07	.04
80	Roberto Alomar (TC)	.15	.08
81	Glenn Davis (TC)	.05	.02
82	Ron Gant (TC)	.08	.05
83	Cecil Fielder (Feat)	.15	.08
84	Orlando Merced (R)	.50	.00
85	Domingo Ramos	.05	.02
86	Tom Bolton	.05	.02
87	Andres Santana	.10	.06
88	John Dopson	.05	.02
89	Kenny Williams	.05	.02
90	Marty Barrett	.05	.02
91	Tom Pagnozzi	.07	.04
92	Carmelo Martinez	.05	.02
93	Bobby Thigpen (Save)	.08	.05
94	Barry Bonds (TC)	.25	.15
95	Gregg Jefferies (TC)	.05	.02
96	Tim Wallach (TC)	.05	.02
97	Len Dykstra (TC)	.05	.02
98	Pedro Guerrero (TC)	.05	.02
99	Mark Grace (TC)	.05	.02
100	Checklist 1-100	.05	.02
101	Kevin Elster	.05	.02
102	Tom Brookens	.05	.02
103	Mackey Sasser	.05	.02
104	Felix Fermin	.05	.02
105	Kevin McReynolds	.07	.04
106	Dave Steib	.07	.04
107	Jeffrey Leonard	.05	.02
108	Dave Henderson	.05	.02
109	Sid Bream	.05	.02
110	Henry Cotto	.05	.02
111	Shawon Dunston	.08	.05
112	Mariano Duncan	.05	.02
113	Joe Girardi	.05	.02
114	Billy Hatcher	.05	.02
115	Greg Maddux	.25	.15
116	Jerry Browne	.05	.02
117	Juan Samuel	.05	.02
118	Steve Olin	.07	.04
119	Alfredo Griffin	.05	.02
120	Mitch Webster	.05	.02
121	Joel Skinner	.05	.02
122	Frank Viola	.08	.05
123	Cory Snyder	.05	.02
124	Howard Johnson	.10	.06
125	Carlos Baerga	.75	.45
126	Tony Fernandez	.07	.04
127	Dave Stewart	.08	.05
128	Jay Buhner	.08	.05
129	Mike LaValliere	.05	.02
130	Scott Bradley	.05	.02
131	Tony Phillips	.05	.02
132	Ryne Sandberg	.40	.25
133	Paul O'Neill	.08	.05
134	Mark Grace	.15	.10

135	Chris Sabo	.10	.06	192	Walt Weiss	.05	.02
136	Ramon Martinez	.12	.07	193	Jose Oquendo	.05	.02
137	Brook Jacoby	.05	.02	194	Carney Lansford	.07	.04
138	Candy Maldonado	.05	.02	195	Jeff Huson	.05	.02
139	Mike Scioscia	.05	.02	196	Keith Miller	.05	.02
140	Chris James	.05	.02	197	Eric Yelding	.05	.02
141	Craig Worthington	.05	.02	198	Ron Darling	.07	.04
142	Manny Lee	.05	.02	199	John Kruk	.12	.07
143	Tim Raines	.07	.04	200	Checklist 101-200	.05	.02
144	Sandy Alomar, Jr.	.08	.05	201	John Shelby	.05	.02
145	John Olerud	.80	.50	202	Bob Geren	.05	.02
146	Ozzie Canseco	.08	.05	203	Lance McCullers	.05	.02
147	Pat Borders	.05	.02	204	Alvaro Espinoza	.05	.02
148	Harold Reynolds	.05	.02	205	Mark Salas	.05	.02
149	Tom Henke	.05	.02	206	Mike Pagliarulo	.05	.02
150	R.J. Reynolds	.05	.02	207	Jose Uribe	.05	.02
151	Mike Gallego	.05	.02	208	Jim Deshaies	.05	.02
152	Bobby Bonilla	.15	.08	209	Ron Karkovice	.05	.02
153	Terry Steinbach	.07	.04	210	Rafael Ramirez	.05	.02
154	Barry Bonds	.75	.45	211	Donnie Hill	.05	.02
155	Jose Canseco	.30	.18	212	Brian Harper	.05	.02
156	Gregg Jeffries	.15	.10	213	Jack Howell	.05	.02
157	Matt Williams	.12	.07	214	Wes Gardner	.05	.02
158	Craig Biggio	.08	.05	215	Tim Burke	.05	.02
159	Daryl Boston	.05	.02	216	Doug Jones	.05	.02
160	Ricky Jordan	.05	.02	217	Hubie Brooks	.07	.04
161	Stan Belinda	.05	.02	218	Tom Candiotti	.07	.04
162	Ozzie Smith	.15	.08	219	Gerald Perry	.05	.02
163	Tom Brunansky	.07	.04	220	Jose DeLeon	.05	.02
164	Todd Zeile	.10	.06	221	Wally Whitehurst	.05	.02
165	Mike Greenwell	.08	.05	222	Alan Mills	.08	.05
166	Kal Daniels	.05	.02	223	Alan Trammell	.10	.06
167	Kent Hrbek	.07	.04	224	Dwight Gooden	.15	.08
168	Franklin Stubbs	.05	.02	225	Travis Fryman (R)	2.00	1.25
169	Dick Schofield	.05	.02	226	Joe Carter	.20	.12
170	Junior Ortiz	.05	.02	227	Julio Franco	.08	.05
171	Hector Villanueva	.05	.02	228	Craig Lefferts	.05	.02
172	Dennis Eckersley	.20	.12	229	Gary Pettis	.05	.02
173	Mitch Williams	.05	.02	230	Dennis Rasmussen	.05	.02
174	Mark McGwire	.30	.18	231	Brian Downing	.05	.02
175	Fernando Valenzuela	.05	.02	232	Carlos Quintana	.08	.05
176	Gary Carter	.08	.05	233	Gary Gaetti	.05	.02
177	Dave Magadan	.05	.02	234	Mark Langston	.10	.06
178	Robby Thompson	.05	.02	235	Tim Wallach	.08	.05
179	Bob Ojeda	.05	.02	236	Greg Swindell	.08	.05
180	Ken Caminiti	.07	.04	237	Eddie Murray	.15	.08
181	Don Slaught	.05	.02	238	Jeff Manto	.08	.05
182	Luis Rivera	.05	.02	239	Lenny Harris	.05	.02
183	Jay Bell	.05	.02	240	Jesse Orosco	.05	.02
184	Jody Reed	.05	.02	241	Scott Lusader	.05	.02
185	Wally Backman	.05	.02	242	Sid Fernandez	.07	.04
186	Dave Martinez	.05	.02	243	Jim Leyritz	.10	.06
187	Luis Polonia	.05	.02	244	Cecil Fielder	.25	.15
188	Shane Mack	.10	.06	245	Darryl Strawberry	.20	.12
189	Spike Owen	.05	.02	246	Frank Thomas	5.00	3.00
190	Scott Bailes	.05	.02	247	Kevin Mitchell	.10	.06
191	John Russell	.05	.02	248	Lance Johnson	.05	.02

249	Rick Rueschel	.05	.02
250	Mark Portugal	.05	.02
251	Derek Lilliequest	.05	.02
252	Brian Holman	.08	.05
253	Rafael Valdez	.08	.05
254	B.J. Surhoff	.05	.02
255	Tony Gwynn	.20	.12
256	Andy Van Slyke	.12	.07
257	Todd Stottlemyre	.07	.04
258	Jose Lind	.05	.02
259	Greg Myers	.05	.02
260	Jeff Ballard	.05	.02
261	Bobby Thigpen	.05	.02
262	Jimmy Kremers (R)	.08	.05
263	Robin Ventura	.50	.30
264	John Smoltz	.25	.15
265	Sammy Sosa	.08	.05
266	Gary Sheffield	.40	.25
267	Lenny Dykstra	.20	.12
268	Bill Spiers	.05	.02
269	Charlie Hayes	.05	.02
270	Brett Butler	.08	.05
271	Bip Roberts	.05	.02
272	Rob Deer	.07	.04
273	Fred Lynn	.07	.04
274	Dave Parker	.07	.04
275	Andy Benes	.15	.08
276	Glenallen Hill	.08	.05
277	Steve Howard (R)	.08	.05
278	Doug Drabek	.12	.07
279	Joe Oliver	.05	.02
280	Todd Benzinger	.05	.02
281	Eric King	.05	.02
282	Jim Presley	.05	.02
283	Ken Patterson	.05	.02
284	Jack Daugherty	.05	.02
285	Ivan Calderon	.07	.04
286	Edgar Diaz (R)	.08	.05
287	Kevin Bass	.05	.02
288	Don Carman	.05	.02
289	Greg Brock	.05	.02
290	John Franco	.05	.02
291	Joey Cora	.05	.02
292	Bill Wegman	.05	.02
293	Eric Show	.05	.02
294	Scott Bankhead	.05	.02
295	Garry Templeton	.05	.02
296	Mickey Tettleton	.07	.04
297	Luis Sojo	.08	.05
298	Jose Rijo	.10	.06
299	Dave Johnson	.05	.02
300	Checklist 201-300	.05	.02
301	Mark Grant	.05	.02
302	Pete Harnisch	.10	.06
303	Greg Olson	.10	.06
304	Anthony Telford	.10	.06
305	Lonnie Smith	.05	.02
306	Chris Hoiles	.20	.12
307	Bryn Smith	.05	.02
308	Mike Devereaux	.10	.06
309	Milt Thompson	.05	.02
310	Bob Melvin	.05	.02
311	Luis Salazar	.05	.02
312	Ed Whitson	.05	.02
313	Charlie Hough	.05	.02
314	Dave Clark	.05	.02
315	Eric Gunderson	.07	.04
316	Dan Petry	.05	.02
317	Dante Bichette	.05	.02
318	Mike Heath	.05	.02
319	Damon Berryhill	.05	.02
320	Walt Terrell	.05	.02
321	Scott Fletcher	.05	.02
322	Dan Plesac	.05	.02
323	Jack McDowell	.30	.18
324	Paul Molitor	.25	.15
325	Ozzie Guillen	.07	.04
326	Gregg Olson	.08	.05
327	Pedro Guerrero	.05	.02
328	Bob Milacki	.05	.02
329	John Tudor	.05	.02
330	Steve Finley	.07	.04
331	Jack Clark	.07	.04
332	Jerome Walton	.05	.02
333	Andy Hawkins	.05	.02
334	Derrick May	.25	.15
335	Roberto Alomar	.60	.35
336	Jack Morris	.12	.07
337	Dave Winfield	.20	.12
338	Steve Searcy	.05	.02
339	Chili Davis	.05	.02
340	Larry Sheets	.05	.02
341	Ted Higuera	.05	.02
342	David Segui	.10	.06
343	Greg Cadaret	.05	.02
344	Robin Yount	.20	.12
345	Nolan Ryan	.90	.55
346	Ray Lankford	.40	.25
347	Cal Ripken, Jr.	.60	.35
348	Lee Smith	.10	.06
349	Brady Anderson	.15	.10
350	Frank DiPino	.05	.02
351	Hal Morris	.12	.07
352	Deion Sanders	.35	.20
353	Barry Larkin	.15	.08
354	Don Mattingly	.25	.05
355	Eric Davis	.10	.06
356	Jose Offerman	.10	.06
357	Mel Rojas	.08	.05
358	Rudy Seanez (R)	.10	.06
359	Oil Can Boyd	.05	.02
360	Nelson Liriano	.05	.02
361	Ron Gant	.25	.15
362	Howard Farmer	.08	.05

363	David Justice	.60	.35
364	Delino DeShields	.30	.18
365	Steve Avery	.50	.30
366	David Cone	.12	.07
367	Lou Whitaker	.07	.04
368	Von Hayes	.05	.02
369	Frank Tanana	.05	.02
370	Tim Teufel	.05	.02
371	Randy Myers	.05	.02
372	Roberto Kelly	.20	.12
373	Jack Armstrong	.07	.04
374	Kelly Gruber	.07	.04
375	Kevin Maas	.08	.05
376	Randy Johnson	.25	.15
377	David West	.05	.02
378	Brent Knackert (R)	.10	.06
379	Rick Honeycutt	.05	.02
380	Kevin Gross	.05	.02
381	Tom Foley	.05	.02
382	Jeff Blauser	.05	.02
383	Scott Ruskin	.05	.02
384	Andres Thomas	.05	.02
385	Dennis Martinez	.10	.06
386	Mike Henneman	.05	.02
387	Felix Jose	.10	.06
388	Alejandro Pena	.05	.02
389	Chet Lemon	.05	.02
390	Craig Wilson (R)	.10	.06
391	Chuck Crim	.07	.04
392	Mel Hall	.07	.04
393	Mark Knudson	.05	.02
394	Norm Charlton	.05	.02
395	Mike Felder	.05	.02
396	Tim Layana	.05	.02
397	Steve Frey	.07	.04
398	Bill Doran	.05	.02
399	Dion James	.05	.02
400	Checklist 301-400	.05	.02
401	Ron Hassey	.05	.02
402	Don Robinson	.05	.02
403	Gene Nelson	.05	.02
404	Terry Kennedy	.05	.02
405	Todd Burns	.05	.02
406	Roger McDowell	.05	.02
407	Bob Kipper	.05	.02
408	Darren Daulton	.20	.12
409	Chuck Cary	.05	.02
410	Bruce Ruffin	.05	.02
411	Juan Berenguer	.05	.02
412	Gary Ward	.05	.02
413	Al Newman	.05	.02
414	Danny Jackson	.05	.02
415	Greg Gagne	.05	.02
416	Tom Herr	.05	.02
417	Jeff Parrett	.05	.02
418	Jeff Reardon	.10	.06
419	Mark Lemke	.05	.02
420	Charlie O'Brien	.05	.02
421	Willie Randolph	.07	.04
422	Steve Bedrosian	.05	.02
423	Mike Moore	.05	.02
424	Jeff Brantley	.07	.04
425	Bob Welch	.07	.04
426	Terry Mulholland	.05	.02
427	Willie Blair	.12	.07
428	Darrin Fletcher	.08	.05
429	Mike Witt	.05	.02
430	Joe Boever	.05	.02
431	Tom Gordon	.07	.04
432	Pedro Munoz (R)	.25	.15
433	Kevin Seitzer	.07	.04
434	Kevin Tapani	.08	.05
435	Bret Saberhagen	.08	.05
436	Ellis Burks	.08	.05
437	Chuck Finley	.10	.06
438	Mike Boddicker	.05	.02
439	Francisco Cabrera	.05	.02
440	Todd Hundley	.10	.06
441	Kelly Downs	.05	.02
442	Dann Howitt	.08	.05
443	Scott Garrelts	.05	.02
444	Rickey Henderson	.25	.15
445	Will Clark	.30	.18
446	Ben McDonald	.20	.12
447	Dale Murphy	.12	.07
448	Dave Righetti	.05	.02
449	Dickie Thon	.05	.02
450	Ted Power	.05	.02
451	Scott Coolbaugh	.05	.02
452	Dwight Smith	.07	.04
453	Pete Incaviglia	.05	.02
454	Andre Dawson	.20	.12
455	Ruben Sierra	.20	.12
456	Andres Galarraga	.15	.10
457	Alvin Davis	.05	.02
458	Tony Castillo	.05	.02
459	Pete O'Brien	.05	.02
460	Charlie Leibrandt	.05	.02
461	Vince Coleman	.07	.04
462	Steve Sax	.08	.05
463	Omar Oliveras (R)	.15	.08
464	Oscar Azocar (R)	.10	.06
465	Joe Magrane	.07	.04
466	Karl Rhodes (R)	.15	.10
467	Benito Santiago	.08	.05
468	Joe Klink (R)	.10	.06
469	Sil Campusano	.05	.02
470	Mark Parent	.05	.02
471	Shawn Boskie	.07	.04
472	Kevin Brown	.12	.07
473	Rick Sutcliffe	.07	.04
474	Rafael Palmeiro	.20	.12
475	Mike Harkey	.10	.06
476	Jaime Navarro	.10	.06

477	Marquis Grissom	.30	.18	534	Julio Valera	.07	.04
478	Marty Clary	.05	.02	535	Glenn Davis	.05	.02
479	Greg Briley	.05	.02	536	Larry Walker	.30	.18
480	Tom Glavine	.30	.18	537	Pat Combs	.07	.04
481	Lee Guetterman	.05	.02	538	Chris Nabholz	.15	.10
482	Rex Hudler	.05	.02	539	Kirk McCaskill	.05	.02
483	Dave LaPoint	.05	.02	540	Randy Ready	.05	.02
484	Terry Pendleton	.15	.10	541	Mark Gubicza	.07	.04
485	Jesse Barfield	.07	.04	542	Rick Aguilera	.05	.02
486	Jose DeJesus	.05	.02	543	Brian McRae (R)	.40	.25
487	Paul Abbott (R)	.10	.06	544	Kirby Puckett	.35	.20
488	Ken Howell	.05	.02	545	Bo Jackson	.25	.15
489	Greg W. Harris	.05	.02	546	Wade Boggs	.20	.12
490	Roy Smith	.05	.02	547	Tim McIntosh	.10	.06
491	Paul Assenmacher	.05	.02	548	Randy Milligan	.07	.04
492	Geno Petralli	.05	.02	549	Dwight Evans	.07	.04
493	Steve Wilson	.05	.02	550	Billy Ripken	.05	.02
494	Kevin Reimer	.08	.05	551	Erik Hanson	.07	.04
495	Bill Long	.05	.02	552	Lance Parrish	.05	.02
496	Mike Jackson	.05	.02	553	Tino Martinez	.10	.06
497	Oddibe McDowell	.05	.02	554	Jim Abbott	.20	.12
498	Bill Swift	.10	.06	555	Ken Griffey, Jr.	1.50	.90
499	Jeff Treadway	.05	.02	556	Milt Cuyler	.10	.06
500	Checklist 401-500	.05	.02	557	Mark Leonard (R)	.10	.06
501	Gene Larkin	.05	.02	558	Jay Howell	.05	.02
502	Bob Boone	.08	.05	559	Lloyd Moseby	.05	.02
503	Allan Anderson	.05	.02	560	Chris Gwynn	.05	.02
504	Luis Aquino	.05	.02	561	Mark Whiten (R)	.40	.25
505	Mark Guthrie	.05	.02	562	Harold Baines	.07	.04
506	Joe Orsulak	.05	.02	563	Junior Felix	.05	.02
507	Dana Kiecker (R)	.10	.06	564	Darren Lewis (R)	.20	.12
508	Dave Gallagher	.05	.02	565	Fred McGriff	.30	.18
509	Greg W. Harris	.05	.02	566	Kevin Appier	.15	.10
510	Mark Williamson	.05	.02	567	Luis Gonzalez (R)	.50	.30
511	Casey Candaele	.05	.02	568	Frank White	.05	.02
512	Mookie Wilson	.05	.02	569	Juan Agosto	.05	.02
513	Dave Smith	.05	.02	570	Mike Macfarlane	.05	.02
514	Chuck Carr (R)	.35	.20	571	Bert Blyleven	.10	.06
515	Glenn Wilson	.05	.02	572	Ken Griffey, Sr.	.25	.15
516	Mike Fitzgerald	.05	.02	573	Lee Stevens	.05	.02
517	Devon White	.05	.02	574	Edgar Martinez	.15	.10
518	Dave Hollins	.30	.18	575	Wally Joyner	.12	.07
519	Mark Eichhorn	.05	.02	576	Tim Belcher	.07	.04
520	Otis Nixon	.07	.04	577	John Burkett	.12	.07
521	Terry Shumpert	.10	.06	578	Mike Morgan	.05	.02
522	Scott Erickson	.15	.10	579	Paul Gibson	.05	.02
523	Danny Tartabull	.12	.07	580	Jose Vizcaino	.05	.02
524	Orel Hershiser	.10	.06	581	Duane Ward	.05	.02
525	George Brett	.30	.18	582	Scott Sanderson	.05	.02
526	Greg Vaughn	.10	.06	583	David Wells	.05	.02
527	Tim Naehring	.10	.06	584	Willie McGee	.08	.05
528	Curt Schilling	.08	.05	585	John Cerutti	.05	.02
529	Chris Bosio	.07	.04	586	Danny Darwin	.05	.02
530	Sam Horn	.05	.02	587	Kurt Stillwell	.05	.02
531	Mike Scott	.05	.02	588	Rich Gedman	.05	.02
532	George Bell	.10	.06	589	Mark Davis	.05	.02
533	Eric Anthony	.20	.12	590	Bill Gullickson	.05	.02

591	Matt Young	.05	.02	648	Jeff Russell	.05	.02
592	Bryan Harvey	.08	.05	649	Chuck Malone (R)	.12	.07
593	Omar Vizquel	.05	.02	650	Steve Buechele	.05	.02
594	Scott Lewis (R)	.12	.07	651	Mike Benjamin	.07	.04
595	Dave Valle	.05	.02	652	Tony Pena	.07	.04
596	Tim Crews	.05	.02	653	Trevor Wilson	.07	.04
597	Mike Bielecki	.05	.02	654	Alex Cole	.10	.06
598	Mike Sharperson	.05	.02	655	Roger Clemens	.35	.20
599	Dave Bergman	.05	.02	656	Mark McGwire (Bash)	.20	.12
600	Checklist 501-600	.05	.02	657	Joe Grahe (R)	.20	.12
601	Steve Lyons	.05	.02	658	Jim Eisenreich	.07	.04
602	Bruce Hurst	.08	.05	659	Dan Gladden	.05	.02
603	Donn Pall	.05	.02	660	Steve Farr	.05	.02
604	Jim Vatcher (R)	.10	.06	661	Bill Sampen	.07	.04
605	Dan Pasqua	.05	.02	662	Dave Rohde (R)	.10	.06
606	Kenny Rogers	.05	.02	663	Matt Nokes	.07	.04
607	Jeff Schulz (R)	.08	.05	664	Mike Simms (R)	.08	.05
608	Brad Arnsberg (R)	.10	.06	665	Moises Alou (R)	.50	.30
609	Willie Wilson	.05	.02	666	Mickey Hatcher	.05	.02
610	Jamie Moyer	.05	.02	667	Jimmy Key	.07	.04
611	Ron Oester	.05	.02	668	John Wetteland	.10	.06
612	Dennis Cook	.05	.02	669	John Smiley	.10	.06
613	Rick Mahler	.05	.02	670	Jim Acker	.05	.02
614	Bill Landrum	.05	.02	671	Pascual Perez	.05	.02
615	Scott Scudder	.05	.02	672	Reggie Harris (FC)	.12	.07
616	Tom Edens (R)	.10	.06	673	Matt Nokes	.05	.02
617	1917 Revisited	.08	.05	674	Rafael Novoa (R)	.08	.05
618	Jim Gantner	.05	.02	675	Hensley Meulens	.08	.05
619	Darrel Akerfelds (R)	.10	.06	676	Jeff M. Robinson	.05	.02
620	Ron Robinson	.05	.02	677	Carlton Fisk/Robin	.20	.12
621	Scott Radinsky	.15	.08		Ventura (New Comiskey)		
622	Pete Smith	.10	.06	678	Johnny Ray	.05	.02
623	Melido Perez	.07	.04	679	Greg Hibbard	.05	.02
624	Jerald Clark	.07	.04	680	Paul Sorrento	.12	.07
625	Carlos Martinez	.05	.02	681	Mike Marshall	.05	.02
626	Wes Chamberlain (R)	.25	.15	682	Jim Clancy	.05	.02
627	Bobby Witt	.08	.05	683	Rob Murphy	.05	.02
628	Ken Dayley	.05	.02	684	Dave Schmidt	.05	.02
629	John Barfield (R)	.08	.05	685	Jeff Gray (R)	.12	.07
630	Bob Tewksbury	.05	.02	686	Mike Hartley	.08	.05
631	Glenn Braggs	.05	.02	687	Jeff King	.07	.04
632	Jim Neidlinger (R)	.08	.05	688	Stan Javier	.05	.02
633	Tom Browning	.07	.04	689	Bob Walk	.05	.02
634	Kirk Gibson	.07	.04	690	Jim Gott	.05	.02
635	Rob Dibble	.10	.06	691	Mike LaCoss	.05	.02
636	R. Henderson/L. Brock	.50	.30	692	John Farrell	.05	.02
637	Jeff Montgomery	.07	.04	693	Tim Leary	.05	.02
638	Mike Schooler	.05	.02	694	Mike Walker (R)	.08	.05
639	Storm Davis	.05	.02	695	Eric Plunk	.05	.02
640	Rich Rodriguez (R)	.10	.06	696	Mike Fetters	.08	.05
641	Phil Bradley	.05	.02	697	Wayne Edwards	.05	.02
642	Kent Mercker	.07	.04	698	Tim Drummond	.07	.04
643	Carlton Fisk	.15	.08	699	Willie Fraser	.05	.02
644	Mike Bell (R)	.10	.06	700	Checklist 601-700	.05	.02
645	Alex Fernandez	.50	.30	701	Mike Heath	.05	.02
646	Juan Gonzalez	1.75	1.00	702	Rookie Threats	.50	.30
647	Ken Hill	.10	.06		Jeff Bagwell		

	Luis Gonzalez		
	Karl Rhodes		
703	Jose Mesa	.05	.02
704	Dave Smith	.05	.02
705	Danny Darwin	.05	.02
706	Rafael Belliard	.05	.02
707	Rob Murphy	.05	.02
708	Terry Pendleton	.12	.07
709	Mike Pagilarulo	.05	.02
710	Sid Bream	.05	.02
711	Junior Felix	.05	.02
712	Dante Bichette	.05	.02
713	Kevin Gross	.05	.02
714	Luis Sojo	.05	.02
715	Bob Ojeda	.05	.02
716	Julio Machado	.05	.02
717	Steve Farr	.05	.02
718	Franklin Stubbs	.05	.02
719	Mike Boddicker	.05	.02
720	Willie Randolph	.07	.04
721	Willie McGee	.08	.05
722	Chili Davis	.07	.04
723	Danny Jackson	.07	.04
724	Cory Snyder	.05	.02
725	MVP Lineup	.20	.12
	George Bell		
	Andre Dawson		
	Ryne Sandberg		
726	Rob Deer	.07	.04
727	Rich DeLucia (R)	.12	.07
728	Mike Perez (R)	.20	.12
729	Mickey Tettleton	.07	.04
730	Mike Blowers	.05	.02
731	Gary Gaetti	.05	.02
732	Brett Butler	.08	.05
733	Dave Parker	.07	.04
734	Eddie Zosky	.10	.06
735	Jack Clark	.07	.04
736	Jack Morris	.12	.07
737	Kirk Gibson	.07	.04
738	Steve Bedrosian	.05	.02
739	Candy Maldonado	.05	.02
740	Matt Young	.05	.02
741	Rich Garces (R)	.15	.10
742	George Bell	.10	.06
743	Deion Sanders	.25	.15
744	Bo Jackson	.25	.15
745	Luis Mercedes (R)	.20	.12
746	Reggie Jefferson	.25	.15
747	Pete Incaviglia	.05	.02
748	Chris Hammond	.10	.06
749	Mike Stanton	.07	.04
750	Scott Sanderson	.05	.02
751	Paul Faries (R)	.08	.05
752	Al Osuna (R)	.10	.06
753	Steve Chitren (R)	.12	.07
754	Tony Fernandez	.07	.04

755	Jeff Bagwell (R)	2.00	1.25
756	Kirk Dressendorfer (R)	.20	.12
757	Glenn Davis	.05	.02
758	Gary Carter	.10	.06
759	Zane Smith	.05	.02
760	Vance Law	.05	.02
761	Denis Boucher (R)	.15	.10
762	Turner Ward (R)	.12	.07
763	Roberto Alomar	.40	.25
764	Albert Belle	.50	.30
765	Joe Carter	.25	.15
766	Pete Schourek (R)	.20	.12
767	Heathcliff Slocumb	.08	.05
768	Vince Coleman	.07	.04
769	Mitch Williams	.05	.02
770	Brian Downing	.05	.02
771	Dana Allison (R)	.08	.05
772	Pete Harnisch	.10	.06
773	Tim Raines	.08	.05
774	Darryl Kile (R)	.35	.20
775	Fred McGriff	.30	.18
776	Dwight Evans	.08	.05
777	Joe Slusarski (R)	.12	.07
778	Dave Righetti	.05	.02
779	Jeff Hamilton	.05	.02
780	Ernest Riles	.05	.02
781	Ken Dayley	.05	.02
782	Eric King	.05	.02
783	Devon White	.05	.02
784	Beau Allred	.05	.02
785	Mike Timlin (R)	.12	.07
786	Ivan Calderon	.07	.04
787	Hubie Brooks	.07	.04
788	Juan Agosto	.05	.02
789	Barry Jones	.05	.02
790	Wally Backman	.05	.02
791	Jim Presley	.05	.02
792	Charlie Hough	.05	.02
793	Larry Andersen	.05	.02
794	Steve Finley	.07	.04
795	Shawn Abner	.05	.02
796	Jeff M. Robinson	.05	.02
797	Joe Bitker (R)	.07	.04
798	Eric Show	.05	.02
799	Bud Black	.07	.04
800	Checklist 701-800	.05	.02
___	Michael Jordan (SP)	10.00	7.00
	BH10 Nolan Ryan (Hero)	.80	.50
	BH11 Nolan Ryan (Hero)	.80	.50
	BH12 Nolan Ryan (Hero)	.80	.50
	BH13 Nolan Ryan (Hero)	.80	.50
	BH14 Nolan Ryan (Hero)	.80	.50
	BH15 Nolan Ryan (Hero)	.80	.50
	BH16 Nolan Ryan (Hero)	.80	.50
	BH17 Nolan Ryan (Hero)	.80	.50
	BH18 Nolan Ryan (Hero)	.80	.50

____Nolan Ryan (Cover)	3.50	2.50
____Nolan Ryan Checklist	.80	.50
____Nolan Ryan (Signed)	600.00	325.00
BH19 Hank Aaron (Hero)	.80	.50
BH20 Hank Aaron (Hero)	.80	.50
BH21 Hank Aaron (Hero)	.80	.50
BH22 Hank Aaron (Hero)	.80	.50
BH23 Hank Aaron (Hero)	.80	.50
BH24 Hank Aaron (Hero)	.80	.50
BH25 Hank Aaron (Hero)	.80	.50
BH26 Hank Aaron (Hero)	.80	.50
BH27 Hank Aaron (Hero)	.80	.50
____Hank Aaron (Cover)	3.50	2.50
____Hank Aaron Checklist	.80	.50
____Hank Aaron (Signed)	350.00	200.00
HOF1a Harmon Killebrew	12.00	8.00
HOF1b (Hero) (Signed)	125.00	60.00
HOF2a Gaylord Perry (Hero)	12.00	8.00
HOF2b (Signed)	100.00	50.00
HOF3a Ferguson Jenkins	12.00	8.00
HOF3b (Hero) (Signed)	100.00	50.00
HOF4 Hall of Fame Cover	12.00	8.00
SS1 Julio Franco	.75	.45
SS2 Allan Trammell	.80	.50
SS3 Rickey Henderson	2.00	1.25
SS4 Jose Canseco	2.50	1.40
SS5 Barry Bonds	4.50	2.75
SS6 Eddie Murray	1.25	.70
SS7 Kelly Gruber	.75	.45
SS8 Ryne Sandberg	3.50	2.00
SS9 Darryl Strawberry	1.25	.70
SS10 Ellis Burks	.80	.50
SS11 Lance Parrish	.75	.45
SS12 Cecil Fielder	2.50	1.40
SS13 Matt Williams	1.00	.60
SS14 Dave Parker	.80	.50
SS15 Bobby Bonilla	1.00	.60
SS16 Don Robinson	.75	.45
SS17 Benito Santiago	.75	.45
SS18 Barry Larkin	1.00	.60

1991 Upper Deck Final Edition

Patterned after Upper Deck's 1991 regular edition, this 100-card boxed set includes additional rookies and traded players. New subsets include Diamond Skills (1-21) and All-Stars (80-99). The standard-size cards measure 2-1/2" by 3-1/2" and card numbers on the back carry the "F" designation.

	MINT	NR/MT
Complete Set (100)	10.00	6.50
Commons	.05	.02

		MINT	NR/MT
1	Diamond Skills (CL) Ryan Klesko/Deion Sanders	.50	.30
2	Pedro Martinez (R)	.80	.50
3	Lance Dickson	.12	.07
4	Royce Clayton	.25	.15
5	Scott Bryant (R)	.15	.10
6	Dan Wilson (R)	.40	.25
7	Dmitri Young (R)	1.25	.70
8	Ryan Klesko (R)	1.75	1.00
9	Tom Goodwin (R)	.25	.15
10	Rondell White (R)	1.25	.70
11	Reggie Sanders	.40	.25
12	Todd Van Poppel	.30	.18
13	Arthur Rhodes (R)	.20	.12
14	Eddie Zosky	.10	.06
15	Gerald Williams (R)	.35	.20
16	Robert Eenhorn (R)	.12	.07
17	Jim Thome (R)	.60	.35
18	Marc Newfield (R)	1.00	.60
19	Kerwin Moore (R)	.25	.15
20	Jeff McNeely (R)	.50	.30
21	Frankie Rodriguez (R)	1.00	.60
22	Andy Mota (R)	.12	.07
23	Chris Haney (R)	.15	.08

24	Kenny Lofton (R)	1.75	1.00
25	Dave Nilsson (R)	.30	.18
26	Derek Bell (R)	.60	.35
27	Frank Castillo (R)	.15	.08
28	Candy Maldonado	.05	.02
29	Chuck McElroy	.07	.04
30	Chito Martinez (R)	.20	.12
31	Steve Howe	.05	.02
32	Freddie Benavides (R)	.08	.05
33	Scott Kamienieck (R)	.12	.07
34	Denny Neagle (R)	.12	.07
35	Mike Humphreys (R)	.15	.10
36	Mike Remlinger (R)	.10	.06
37	Scott Coolbaugh	.05	.02
38	Darren Lewis	.10	.06
39	Thomas Howard (R)	.10	.06
40	John Candelaria	.05	.02
41	Todd Benzinger	.05	.02
42	Wilson Alvarez	.10	.06
43	Patrick Lennon (R)	.20	.12
44	Rusty Meacham (R)	.15	.08
45	Ryan Bowen (R)	.20	.12
46	Rick Wilkins (R)	.75	.45
47	Ed Sprague	.15	.10
48	Bob Scanlan (R)	.12	.07
49	Tom Candiotti	.05	.02
50	Dennis Martinez	.10	.06
51	Oil Can Boyd	.05	.02
52	Glenallen Hill	.08	.05
53	Scott Livingstone (R)	.25	.15
54	Brian Hunter (R)	.20	.12
55	Ivan Rodriguez (R)	1.25	.70
56	Keith Mitchell (R)	.15	.10
57	Roger McDowell	.05	.02
58	Otis Nixon	.07	.04
59	Juan Bell	.07	.04
60	Bill Krueger	.05	.02
61	Chris Donnels (R)	.08	.05
62	Tommy Greene	.25	.15
63	Doug Simons (R)	.10	.06
64	Andy Ashby (R)	.12	.07
65	Anthony Young (R)	.20	.12
66	Kevin Morton (R)	.15	.10
67	Bret Barberie	.12	.07
68	Scott Servais	.10	.06
69	Ron Darling	.05	.02
70	Vincente Palacios	.05	.02
71	Tim Burke	.05	.02
72	Gerald Alexander (R)	.10	.06
73	Reggie Jefferson	.20	.12
74	Dean Palmer	.35	.20
75	Mark Whiten	.35	.15
76	Randy Tomlin (R)	.15	.10
77	Mark Wohlers (R)	.25	.15
78	Brook Jacoby	.05	.02
79	All-Star Checklist	.40	.25
	Ken Griffey Jr/ Ryne Sandberg		

80	Jack Morris (AS)	.10	.06
81	Sandy Alomar, Jr. (AS)	.07	.04
82	Cecil Fielder (AS)	.15	.08
83	Roberto Alomar (AS)	.25	.15
84	Wade Boggs (AS)	.15	.10
85	Cal Ripken, Jr. (AS)	.40	.25
86	Rickey Henderson (AS)	.15	.08
87	Ken Griffey, Jr. (AS)	.50	.30
88	Dave Henderson (AS)	.05	.02
89	Danny Tartabull (AS)	.08	.05
90	Tom Glavine (AS)	.20	.12
91	Benito Santiago (AS)	.08	.05
92	Will Clark (AS)	.20	.12
93	Ryne Sandberg (AS)	.25	.15
94	Chris Sabo (AS)	.07	.04
95	Ozzie Smith (AS)	.10	.06
96	Ivan Calderon (AS)	.07	.04
97	Tony Gwynn (AS)	.15	.08
98	Andre Dawson (AS)	.10	.06
99	Bobby Bonilla (AS)	.08	.05
100	Checklist	.05	.02

1992 Upper Deck

This 800-card set is styled after previous Upper Deck issues and includes five major subsets; Star Rookies, Top Prospects, Bloodlines, Diamond Skills and Diamond Debuts. This edition contains two 9-card Heroes of Baseball insert sets.The first features Ted Williams, the second Johnny Bench and Joe Morgan. A 4-card Hall of Fame Heroes Insert set was randomly packed in high-number foil packs. All cards measure 2-1/2" by 3-1/2". The high-number series (701-800) was released later in the season. Those cards are included in the Complete Set Price below. The Heroes Inserts are priced at the end of this checklist but are not included in the Complete Set Price.

		MINT	NR/MT
Complete Set (800)		24.00	14.00
Commons		.05	.02
1	Star Rookie Checklist (R. Klesko/J. Thome)	.25	.15
2	Royce Clayton	.20	.12
3	Brian Jordan (R)	.40	.25
4	Dave Fleming	.35	.20
5	Jim Thome	.30	.18
6	Jeff Juden	.12	.07
7	Roberto Hernandez	.10	.06
8	Kyle Abbott (R)	.12	.07
9	Chris George (R)	.10	.06
10	Rob Maurer (R)	.12	.07
11	Donald Harris (R)	.10	.06
12	Ted Wood (R)	.08	.05
13	Patrick Lennon	.10	.06
14	Willie Banks	.10	.06
15	Roger Salkeld	.15	.10
16	Wilfredo Cordero	.20	.12
17	Arthur Rhodes	.10	.06
18	Pedro Martinez	.30	.18
19	Andy Ashby	.08	.05
20	Tom Goodwin	.08	.05
21	Braulio Castillo (R)	.12	.07
22	Todd Van Poppel	.25	.15
23	Brian Williams (R)	.15	.10
24	Ryan Klesko	.50	.30
25	Kenny Lofton	.40	.25
26	Derek Bell	.20	.12
27	Reggie Sanders	.20	.12
28	Winfield's 400th	.15	.08
29	Dave Justice (CL)	.15	.08
30	Rob Dibble (CL)	.07	.04
31	Craig Biggio (CL)	.07	.04
32	Eddie Murray (CL)	.08	.05
33	Fred McGriff (CL)	.10	.06
34	Willie McGee (CL)	.07	.04
35	Shawon Dunston (CL)	.07	.04
36	Delino DeShields (CL)	.08	.05
37	Howard Johnson (CL)	.07	.04
38	John Kruk (CL)	.05	.02
39	Doug Drabek (CL)	.07	.04
40	Todd Zeile (CL)	.07	.04
41	Steve Avery (Playoff)	.10	.06
42	Jeremy Hernandez (R)	.10	.06
43	Doug Henry (R)	.12	.07
44	Chris Donnels	.05	.02
45	Mo Sanford	.08	.05
46	Scott Kamieniecki	.07	.04
47	Mark Lemke	.05	.02
48	Steve Farr	.05	.02
49	Francisco Oliveras	.05	.02
50	Ced Landrum	.08	.05
51	Top Prospect Checklist	.25	.15
	Rondell White/Craig Griffey)		
52	Eduardo Perez (R)	1.00	.60
53	Tom Nevers	.08	.05
54	David Zancanaro (R)	.15	.08
55	Shawn Green (R)	.25	.15
56	Mark Wohlers	.15	.08
57	Dave Nilsson	.12	.07
58	Dmitri Young	.40	.25
59	Ryan Hawblitzel (R)	.15	.10
60	Raul Mondesi	.35	.20
61	Rondell White	.50	.30
62	Steve Hosey	.20	.12
63	Manny Ramirez (R)	1.50	.70
64	Marc Newfield	.50	.30
65	Jeromy Burnitz	.30	.18
66	Mark Smith (R)	.30	.18
67	Joey Hamilton (R)	.25	.15
68	Tyler Green (R)	.20	.12
69	John Farrell (R)	.15	.10
70	Kurt Miller	.15	.10
71	Jeff Plympton (R)	.10	.06
72	Dan Wilson	.12	.07
73	Joe Vitiello (R)	.50	.30
74	Rico Brogna	.10	.06
75	David McCarty (R)	.80	.50
76	Bob Wickman (R)	.30	.18
77	Carlos Rodriquez (R)	.12	.07
78	Jim Abbott (School)	.10	.06
79	Ramon & Pedro Martinez	.12	.07
80	Kevin & Keith Mitchell	.08	.05
81	Sandy & Roberto Alomar	.15	.10
82	Cal Jr. & Billy Ripken	.20	.12
83	Tony & Chris Gwynn	.15	.08
84	Dwight Gooden & Gary Sheffield	.20	.12
85	Ken, Ken Jr. & Craig Griffey	.60	.35
86	Jim Abbott (CL)	.10	.06
87	Frank Thomas (CL)	.50	.30
88	Danny Tartabull (CL)	.07	.04
89	Scott Erickson (CL)	.07	.04
90	Rickey Henderson (CL)	.12	.07
91	Edgar Martinez (CL)	.08	.05
92	Nolan Ryan (CL)	.50	.30
93	Ben McDonald (CL)	.08	.05
94	Ellis Burks (CL)	.07	.04
95	Greg Swindell (CL)	.05	.02
96	Cecil Fielder (CL)	.12	.07
97	Greg Vaughn (CL)	.07	.04
98	Kevin Maas (CL)	.07	.04
99	Dave Stieb (CL)	.05	.02
100	Checklist 1-100	.05	.02
101	Joe Oliver	.05	.02
102	Hector Villanueva	.05	.02
103	Ed Whitson	.05	.02

104 Danny Jackson	.07	.04
105 Chris Hammond	.07	.04
106 Ricky Jordan	.05	.02
107 Kevin Bass	.05	.02
108 Darrin Fletcher	.05	.02
109 Junior Ortiz	.05	.02
110 Tom Bolton	.05	.02
111 Jeff King	.07	.04
112 Dave Magadan	.05	.02
113 Mike LaValliere	.05	.02
114 Hubie Brooks	.05	.02
115 Jay Bell	.08	.05
116 David Wells	.05	.02
117 Jim Leyritz	.05	.02
118 Manuel Lee	.05	.02
119 Alvaro Espinoza	.05	.02
120 B. J. Surhoff	.05	.02
121 Hal Morris	.10	.06
122 Shawon Dunston	.08	.05
123 Chris Sabo	.07	.04
124 Andre Dawson	.15	.08
125 Eric Davis	.08	.05
126 Chili Davis	.07	.04
127 Dale Murphy	.08	.05
128 Kirk McCaskill	.05	.02
129 Terry Mulholland	.05	.02
130 Rick Aguilera	.05	.02
131 Vince Coleman	.05	.02
132 Andy Van Slyke	.10	.06
133 Gregg Jefferies	.12	.07
134 Barry Bonds	.50	.30
135 Dwight Gooden	.12	.07
136 Dave Stieb	.07	.04
137 Albert Belle	.25	.15
138 Teddy Higuera	.05	.02
139 Jesse Barfield	.05	.02
140 Pat Borders	.05	.02
141 Bip Roberts	.05	.02
142 Rob Dibble	.07	.04
143 Mark Grace	.12	.07
144 Barry Larkin	.12	.07
145 Ryne Sandberg	.30	.18
146 Scott Erickson	.10	.06
147 Luis Polonia	.07	.04
148 John Burkett	.05	.02
149 Luis Sojo	.05	.02
150 Dickie Thon	.05	.02
151 Walt Weiss	.05	.02
152 Mike Scioscia	.05	.02
153 Mark McGwire	.15	.10
154 Matt Williams	.12	.07
155 Rickey Henderson	.15	.08
156 Sandy Alomar, Jr.	.07	.04
157 Brian McRae	.10	.06
158 Harold Baines	.05	.02
159 Kevin Appier	.10	.06
160 Felix Fermin	.05	.02

161 Leo Gomez	.08	.05
162 Craig Biggio	.07	.04
163 Ben McDonald	.12	.07
164 Randy Johnson	.20	.12
165 Cal Ripken, Jr.	.35	.20
166 Frank Thomas	1.25	.70
167 Delino Deshields	.15	.10
168 Greg Gagne	.05	.02
169 Ron Karkovice	.05	.02
170 Charlie Leibrandt	.05	.02
171 Dave Righetti	.05	.02
172 Dave Henderson	.05	.02
173 Steve Decker	.08	.05
174 Darryl Strawberry	.15	.10
175 Will Clark	.20	.12
176 Ruben Sierra	.15	.10
177 Ozzie Smith	.12	.07
178 Charles Nagy	.15	.10
179 Gary Pettis	.05	.02
180 Kirk Gibson	.07	.04
181 Randy Milligan	.05	.02
182 Dave Valle	.05	.02
183 Chris Hoiles	.08	.05
184 Tony Phillips	.05	.02
185 Brady Anderson	.10	.06
186 Scott Fletcher	.05	.02
187 Gene Larkin	.05	.02
188 Lance Johnson	.05	.02
189 Greg Olson	.05	.02
190 Melido Perez	.05	.02
191 Lenny Harris	.05	.02
192 Terry Kennedy	.05	.02
193 Mike Gallego	.05	.02
194 Willie McGee	.08	.05
195 Juan Samuel	.05	.02
196 Jeff Huson	.05	.02
197 Alex Cole	.07	.04
198 Ron Robinson	.05	.02
199 Joel Skinner	.05	.02
200 Checklist 101-200	.05	.02
201 Kevin Reimer	.05	.02
202 Stan Belinda	.05	.02
203 Pat Tabler	.05	.02
204 Jose Guzman	.05	.02
205 Jose Lind	.05	.02
206 Spike Owen	.05	.02
207 Joe Orsulak	.07	.04
208 Charlie Hayes	.05	.02
209 Mike Devereaux	.08	.05
210 Mike Fitzgerald	.05	.02
211 Willie Randolph	.07	.04
212 Rod Nichols	.05	.02
213 Mike Boddicker	.05	.02
214 Bill Spiers	.05	.02
215 Steve Olin	.07	.04
216 David Howard (R)	.10	.06
217 Gary Varsho	.05	.02

218	Mike Harkey	.08	.05
219	Luis Aquino	.05	.02
220	Chuck McElroy	.05	.02
221	Doug Drabek	.10	.06
222	Dave Winfield	.20	.12
223	Rafael Palmeiro	.08	.05
224	Joe Carter	.20	.12
225	Bobby Bonilla	.10	.06
226	Ivan Calderon	.07	.04
227	Gregg Olson	.08	.05
228	Tim Wallach	.07	.04
229	Terry Pendleton	.12	.07
230	Gilberto Reyes	.05	.02
231	Carlos Baerga	.25	.15
232	Greg Vaughn	.08	.05
233	Bret Saberhagen	.08	.05
234	Gary Sheffield	.15	.10
235	Mark Lewis	.08	.05
236	George Bell	.10	.06
237	Danny Tartabull	.10	.06
238	Willie Wilson	.05	.02
239	Doug Dascenzo	.05	.02
240	Bill Pecota	.05	.02
241	Julio Franco	.08	.05
242	Ed Sprague	.07	.04
243	Juan Gonzalez	1.00	.60
244	Chuck Finley	.10	.06
245	Ivan Rodriguez	.20	.12
246	Lenny Dykstra	.07	.04
247	Deion Sanders	.12	.07
248	Dwight Evans	.07	.04
249	Larry Walker	.10	.06
250	Billy Ripken	.05	.02
251	Mickey Tettleton	.07	.04
252	Tony Pena	.05	.02
253	Benito Santiago	.08	.05
254	Kirkby Puckett	.25	.15
255	Cecil Fielder	.20	.12
256	Howard Johnson	.08	.05
257	Andujar Cedeno	.10	.06
258	Jose Rijo	.08	.05
259	Al Osuna	.05	.02
260	Todd Hundley	.07	.04
261	Orel Hershiser	.10	.06
262	Ray Lankford	.15	.08
263	Robin Ventura	.20	.12
264	Felix Jose	.08	.05
265	Eddie Murray	.12	.07
266	Kevin Mitchell	.08	.05
267	Gary Carter	.10	.06
268	Mike Benjamin	.07	.04
269	Dick Schofield	.05	.02
270	Jose Uribe	.05	.02
271	Pete Incaviglia	.05	.02
272	Tony Fernandez	.07	.04
273	Alan Trammell	.08	.05
274	Tony Gwynn	.15	.10
275	Mike Greenwell	.08	.05
276	Jeff Bagwell	.25	.15
277	Frank Viola	.08	.05
278	Randy Myers	.05	.02
279	Ken Caminiti	.05	.02
280	Bill Doran	.05	.02
281	Dan Pasqua	.05	.02
282	Alfredo Griffin	.05	.02
283	Jose Oquendo	.05	.02
284	Kal Daniels	.05	.02
285	Bobby Thigpen	.07	.04
286	Robby Thompson	.05	.02
287	Mark Eichhorn	.05	.02
288	Mike Felder	.05	.02
289	Dave Gallagher	.05	.02
290	Dave Anderson	.05	.02
291	Mel Hall	.07	.04
292	Jerald Clark	.05	.02
293	Al Newman	.05	.02
294	Rob Deer	.07	.04
295	Matt Nokes	.05	.02
296	Jack Armstrong	.05	.02
297	Jim Deshaies	.05	.02
298	Jeff Innis	.05	.02
299	Jeff Reed	.05	.02
300	Checklist 201-300	.05	.02
301	Lonnie Smith	.05	.02
302	Jimmy Key	.07	.04
303	Junior Felix	.05	.02
304	Mike Heath	.05	.02
305	Mark Langston	.10	.06
306	Greg W. Harris	.05	.02
307	Brett Butler	.08	.05
308	Luis Rivera	.05	.02
309	Bruce Ruffin	.05	.02
310	Paul Faries	.05	.02
311	Terry Leach	.05	.02
312	Scott Brosius (R)	.10	.06
313	Scott Leius	.05	.02
314	Harold Reynolds	.05	.02
315	Jack Morris	.12	.07
316	David Segui	.07	.04
317	Bill Gullickson	.05	.02
318	Todd Frohwirth	.05	.02
319	Mark Leiter (FC)	.05	.02
320	Jeff M. Robinson	.05	.02
321	Gary Gaetti	.05	.02
322	John Smoltz	.15	.08
323	Andy Benes	.10	.06
324	Kelly Gruber	.07	.04
325	Jim Abbott	.15	.08
326	John Kruk	.10	.06
327	Kevin Seitzer	.07	.04
328	Darrin Jackson	.05	.02
329	Kurt Stillwell	.05	.02
330	Mike Maddux	.05	.02
331	Dennis Eckersley	.15	.08

332 Dan Gladden	.05	.02	389 Jeff Treadway	.05	.02
333 Jose Canseco	.15	.10	390 Scott Bradley	.05	.02
334 Kent Hrbek	.07	.04	391 Mookie Wilson	.05	.02
335 Ken Griffey, Sr.	.07	.04	392 Jimmy Jones	.05	.02
336 Greg Swindell	.07	.04	393 Candy Maldonado	.05	.02
337 Trevor Wilson	.07	.04	394 Eric Yelding	.05	.02
338 Sam Horn	.05	.02	395 Tom Henke	.05	.02
339 Mike Henneman	.05	.02	396 Franklin Stubbs	.05	.02
340 Jerry Browne	.05	.02	397 Milt Thompson	.05	.02
341 Glenn Braggs	.05	.02	398 Mark Carreon	.05	.02
342 Tom Glavine	.15	.10	399 Randy Velarde	.05	.02
343 Wally Joyner	.08	.05	400 Checklist 301-400	.05	.02
344 Fred McGriff	.20	.12	401 Omar Vizquel	.07	.04
345 Ron Gant	.12	.07	402 Joe Boever	.05	.02
346 Ramon Martinez	.10	.06	403 Bill Krueger	.05	.02
347 Wes Chamberlain	.12	.07	404 Jody Reed	.05	.02
348 Terry Shumpert	.05	.02	405 Mike Schooler	.05	.02
349 Tim Teufel	.05	.02	406 Jason Grimsley	.05	.02
350 Wally Backman	.05	.02	407 Greg Myers	.05	.02
351 Joe Girardi	.05	.02	408 Randy Ready	.05	.02
352 Devon White	.05	.02	409 Mike Timlin	.07	.04
353 Greg Maddux	.20	.12	410 Mitch Williams	.05	.02
354 Ryan Bowen	.08	.05	411 Garry Templeton	.05	.02
355 Roberto Alomar	.25	.15	412 Greg Cadaret	.05	.02
356 Don Mattingly	.20	.12	413 Donnie Hill	.05	.02
357 Pedro Guerrero	.05	.02	414 Wally Whitehurst	.05	.02
358 Steve Sax	.08	.05	415 Scott Sanderson	.05	.02
359 Joey Cora	.05	.02	416 Thomas Howard	.08	.05
360 Jim Gantner	.05	.02	417 Neal Heaton	.05	.02
361 Brian Barnes	.08	.05	418 Charlie Hough	.05	.02
362 Kevin McReynolds	.07	.04	419 Jack Howell	.05	.02
363 Bret Barberie	.10	.06	420 Greg Hibbard	.05	.02
364 David Cone	.10	.06	421 Carlos Quintana	.08	.05
365 Dennis Martinez	.10	.06	422 Kim Batiste	.08	.05
366 Brian Hunter	.10	.06	423 Paul Molitor	.20	.12
367 Edgar Martinez	.10	.06	424 Ken Griffey, Jr.	1.00	.60
368 Steve Finley	.07	.04	425 Phil Plantier	.20	.12
369 Greg Briley	.05	.02	426 Denny Neagle	.08	.05
370 Jeff Blauser	.05	.02	427 Von Hayes	.05	.02
371 Todd Stottlemyre	.05	.02	428 Shane Mack	.08	.05
372 Luis Gonzalez	.08	.05	429 Darren Daulton	.15	.10
373 Rick Wilkins	.05	.02	430 Dwayne Henry	.07	.04
374 Darryl Kile	.10	.06	431 Lance Parrish	.05	.02
375 John Olerud	.35	.20	432 Mike Humphreys	.08	.05
376 Lee Smith	.10	.06	433 Tim Burke	.05	.02
377 Kevin Maas	.08	.05	434 Bryan Harvey	.07	.04
378 Danta Bichette	.05	.02	435 Pat Kelly	.10	.06
379 Tom Pagnozzi	.05	.02	436 Ozzie Guillen	.05	.02
380 Mike Flanagan	.05	.02	437 Bruce Hurst	.07	.04
381 Charlie O'Brien	.05	.02	438 Sammy Sosa	.15	.10
382 Dave Martinez	.05	.02	439 Dennis Rasmussen	.05	.02
383 Keith Miller	.05	.02	440 Ken Patterson	.05	.02
384 Scott Ruskin	.05	.02	441 Jay Buhner	.07	.04
385 Kevin Elster	.05	.02	442 Pat Combs	.07	.04
386 Alvin Davis	.05	.02	443 Wade Boggs	.15	.08
387 Casey Candaele	.05	.02	444 George Brett	.25	.15
388 Pete O'Brien	.05	.02	445 Mo Vaughn	.20	.12

446	Chuck Knoblauch	.12	.07	503	Tony Fossas	.05	.02
447	Tom Candiotti	.05	.02	504	Cory Snyder	.05	.02
448	Mark Portugal	.05	.02	505	Matt Young	.05	.02
449	Mickey Morandini	.07	.04	506	Allan Anderson	.05	.02
450	Duane Ward	.05	.02	507	Mark Lee	.05	.02
451	Otis Nixon	.07	.04	508	Gene Nelson	.05	.02
452	Bob Welch	.07	.04	509	Mike Pagliarulo	.05	.02
453	Rusty Meacham	.08	.05	510	Rafael Belliard	.05	.02
454	Keith Mitchell	.08	.05	511	Jay Howell	.05	.02
455	Marquis Grissom	.15	.10	512	Bob Tewksbury	.05	.02
456	Robin Yount	.25	.15	513	Mike Morgan	.05	.02
457	Harvey Pulliam	.08	.05	514	John Franco	.05	.02
458	Jose DeLeon	.05	.02	515	Kevin Gross	.05	.02
459	Mark Gubicza	.07	.04	516	Lou Whitaker	.07	.04
460	Darryl Hamilton	.05	.02	517	Orlando Merced	.10	.06
461	Tom Browning	.07	.04	518	Todd Benzinger	.05	.02
462	Monty Fariss	.07	.04	519	Gary Redus	.05	.02
463	Jerome Walton	.05	.02	520	Walt Terrell	.05	.02
464	Paul O'Neill	.10	.06	521	Jack Clark	.07	.04
465	Dean Palmer	.15	.08	522	Dave Parker	.07	.04
466	Travis Fryman	.30	.18	523	Tim Naehring	.08	.05
467	John Smiley	.08	.05	524	Mark Whiten	.15	.10
468	Lloyd Moseby	.05	.02	525	Ellis Burks	.08	.05
469	John Wehner (R)	.10	.06	526	Frank Castillo	.08	.05
470	Skeeter Barnes	.05	.02	527	Brian Harper	.05	.02
471	Steve Chitren	.05	.02	528	Brook Jacoby	.05	.02
472	Kent Mercker	.05	.02	529	Rick Sutcliffe	.07	.04
473	Terry Steinbach	.07	.04	530	Joe Klink	.05	.02
474	Andres Galarraga	.12	.07	531	Terry Bross	.05	.02
475	Steve Avery	.20	.12	532	Jose Offerman	.10	.06
476	Tom Gordon	.07	.04	533	Todd Zeile	.08	.05
477	Cal Eldred	.25	.15	534	Eric Karros	.25	.15
478	Omar Olivares	.08	.05	535	Anthony Young	.10	.06
479	Julio Machado	.05	.02	536	Milt Cuyler	.08	.05
480	Bob Milacki	.05	.02	537	Randy Tomlin	.08	.05
481	Les Lancaster	.05	.02	538	Scott Livingstone	.08	.05
482	John Candelaria	.05	.02	539	Jim Eisenreich	.05	.02
483	Brian Downing	.05	.02	540	Don Slaught	.05	.02
484	Roger McDowell	.05	.02	541	Scott Cooper	.15	.08
485	Scott Scudder	.05	.02	542	Joe Grahe	.08	.05
486	Zane Smith	.05	.02	543	Tom Brunansky	.07	.04
487	John Cerutti	.05	.02	544	Eddie Zosky	.07	.04
488	Steve Buechele	.05	.02	545	Roger Clemens	.25	.15
489	Paul Gibson	.05	.02	546	David Justice	.25	.15
490	Curtis Wilkerson	.05	.02	547	Dave Stewart	.08	.05
491	Marvin Freemen	.05	.02	548	David West	.05	.02
492	Tom Foley	.05	.02	549	Dave Smith	.05	.02
493	John Berenguer	.05	.02	550	Dan Plesac	.05	.02
494	Ernest Riles	.05	.02	551	Alex Fernandez	.20	.12
495	Sid Bream	.05	.02	552	Bernard Gilkey	.12	.07
496	Chuck Crim	.05	.02	553	Jack McDowell	.20	.12
497	Mike Macfarlane	.05	.02	554	Tino Martinez	.08	.05
498	Dale Sveum	.05	.02	555	Bo Jackson	.15	.10
499	Storm Davis	.05	.02	556	Bernie Williams	.12	.07
500	Checklist 401-500	.05	.02	557	Mark Gardner	.08	.05
501	Jeff Reardon	.10	.06	558	Glenallen Hill	.07	.04
502	Shawn Abner	.05	.02	559	Oil Can Boyd	.05	.02

560	Chris James	.05	.02
561	Scott Servais	.07	.04
562	Rey Sanchez (R)	.12	.07
563	Paul McClellan (R)	.10	.06
564	Andy Mota	.07	.04
565	Darren Lewis	.10	.06
566	Jose Melendez (R)	.10	.06
567	Tommy Greene	.12	.07
568	Rich Rodriguez	.07	.04
569	Heathcliff Slocumb	.07	.04
570	Joe Hesketh	.05	.02
571	Carlton Fisk	.12	.07
572	Erik Hanson	.07	.04
573	Wilson Alvarez	.07	.04
574	Rheal Cormier	.10	.06
575	Tim Raines	.07	.04
576	Bobby Witt	.08	.05
577	Roberto Kelly	.12	.07
578	Kevin Brown	.12	.07
579	Chris Nabholz	.08	.05
580	Jesse Orosco	.05	.02
581	Jeff Brantley	.07	.04
582	Rafael Ramirez	.05	.02
583	Kelly Downs	.05	.02
584	Mike Simms	.05	.02
585	Mike Remlinger	.07	.04
586	Dave Hollins	.20	.12
587	Larry Andersen	.05	.02
588	Mike Gardiner	.07	.04
589	Craig Lefferts	.05	.02
590	Paul Assenmacher	.05	.02
591	Bryn Smith	.05	.02
592	Donn Pall	.05	.02
593	Mike Jackson	.05	.02
594	Scott Radinsky	.05	.02
595	Brian Holman	.07	.04
596	Geronimo Pena	.05	.02
597	Mike Jeffcoat	.05	.02
598	Carlos Martinez	.05	.02
599	Geno Petralli	.05	.02
600	Checklist 501-600	.05	.02
601	Jerry Don Gleaton	.05	.02
602	Adam Peterson	.05	.02
603	Craig Grebeck	.05	.02
604	Mark Guthrie	.05	.02
605	Frank Tanana	.05	.02
606	Hensley Meulens	.07	.04
607	Mark Davis	.05	.02
608	Eric Plunk	.05	.02
609	Mark Williamson	.05	.02
610	Lee Guetterman	.05	.02
611	Bobby Rose	.08	.05
612	Bill Wegman	.05	.02
613	Mike Hartley	.05	.02
614	Chris Beasley (R)	.10	.06
615	Chris Bosio	.05	.02
616	Henry Cotto	.05	.02
617	Chico Walker (R)	.10	.06
618	Russ Swan	.05	.02
619	Bob Walk	.05	.02
620	Billy Swift	.10	.06
621	Warren Newson	.05	.02
622	Steve Bedrosian	.05	.02
623	Ricky Bones	.08	.05
624	Kevin Tapani	.07	.04
625	Juan Guzman	.25	.15
626	Jeff Johnson	.08	.05
627	Jeff Montgomery	.05	.02
628	Ken Hill	.08	.05
629	Gary Thurman	.05	.02
630	Steve Howe	.05	.02
631	Jose DeJesus	.05	.02
632	Bert Blyleven	.08	.05
633	Jaime Navarro	.10	.06
634	Lee Stevens	.05	.02
635	Pete Harnisch	.08	.05
636	Bill Landrum	.05	.02
637	Rich DeLucia	.05	.02
638	Luis Salazar	.05	.02
639	Rob Murphy	.05	.02
640	Diamond Skills (CL) (Jose Canseco/Rickey Henderson)	.15	.10
641	Roger Clemens (DS)	.15	.10
642	Jim Abbott (DS)	.08	.05
643	Travis Fryman (DS)	.15	.08
644	Jesse Barfield (DS)	.05	.02
645	Cal Ripken, Jr. (DS)	.20	.12
646	Wade Boggs (DS)	.12	.07
647	Cecil Fielder (DS)	.12	.07
648	Rickey Henderson (DS)	.12	.07
649	Jose Canseco (DS)	.12	.07
650	Ken Griffey, Jr. (DS)	.50	.30
651	Kenny Rogers	.05	.02
652	Luis Mercedes	.10	.06
653	Mike Stanton	.07	.04
654	Glenn Davis	.07	.04
655	Nolan Ryan	.75	.45
656	Reggie Jefferson	.12	.07
657	Javier Ortiz (R)	.12	.07
658	Greg A. Harris	.05	.02
659	Mariano Duncan	.05	.02
660	Jeff Shaw	.05	.02
661	Mike Moore	.05	.02
662	Chris Haney	.07	.04
663	Joe Slusarski	.08	.05
664	Wayne Housie (R)	.10	.06
665	Carlos Garcia	.15	.10
666	Bob Ojeda	.05	.02
667	Bryan Hickerson (R)	.10	.06
668	Tim Belcher	.07	.04
669	Ron Darling	.07	.04
670	Rex Hudler	.05	.02
671	Sid Fernandez	.07	.04

672	Chito Martinez	.12	.07
673	Pete Schourek	.10	.06
674	Armando Reynoso (R)	.12	.07
675	Mike Mussina	.35	.20
676	Kevin Morton	.08	.05
677	Norm Charlton	.07	.04
678	Danny Darwin	.05	.02
679	Eric King	.05	.02
680	Ted Power	.05	.02
681	Barry Jones	.05	.02
682	Carney Lansford	.05	.02
683	Mel Rojas	.07	.04
684	Rick Honeycutt	.05	.02
685	Jeff Fassero (R)	.10	.06
686	Cris Carpenter	.05	.02
687	Tim Crews	.05	.02
688	Scott Terry	.05	.02
689	Chris Gwynn	.05	.02
690	Gerald Perry	.05	.02
691	John Barfield	.05	.02
692	Bob Melvin	.05	.02
693	Juan Agosto	.05	.02
694	Alejandro Pena	.05	.02
695	Jeff Russell	.05	.02
696	Carmelo Martinez	.05	.02
697	Bud Black	.07	.04
698	Dave Otto	.05	.02
699	Billy Hatcher	.05	.02
700	Checklist 601-700	.05	.02
701	Clemente Nunez (R)	.20	.12
702	Rookie Threats	.15	.10
	(Clark/Jordan/Osborne)		
703	Mike Morgan	.05	.02
704	Keith Miller	.05	.02
705	Kurt Stillwell	.05	.02
706	Damon Berryhill	.05	.02
707	Von Hayes	.05	.02
708	Rick Sutcliffe	.07	.04
709	Hubie Brooks	.05	.02
710	Ryan Turner (R)	.20	.12
711	Barry Bonds/Andy	.20	.12
	Van Slyke (CL)		
712	Jose Rijo (DS)	.08	.05
713	Tom Glavine (DS)	.12	.07
714	Shawon Dunston (DS)	.08	.05
715	Andy Van Slyke (DS)	.10	.06
716	Ozzie Smith (DS)	.10	.06
717	Tony Gwynn (DS)	.12	.07
718	Will Clark (DS)	.12	.07
719	Marquis Grissom (DS)	.12	.07
720	Howard Johnson (DS)	.08	.05
721	Barry Bonds (DS)	.25	.15
722	Kirk McCaskill	.05	.02
723	Sammy Sosa	.15	.10
724	George Bell	.10	.06
725	Gregg Jefferies	.12	.07
726	Gary DiSarcina	.10	.06
727	Mike Bordick	.10	.06
728	Eddie Murray (400 HR)	.12	.07
729	Alvin Davis	.05	.02
730	Mike Bielecki	.05	.02
731	Calvin Jones (R)	.12	.07
732	Jack Morris	.12	.07
733	Frank Viola	.08	.05
734	Dave Winfield	.20	.12
735	Kevin Mitchell	.08	.05
736	Billy Swift	.10	.06
737	Dan Gladden	.05	.02
738	Mike Jackson	.05	.02
739	Mark Carreon	.05	.02
740	Kirt Manwaring	.05	.02
741	Randy Myers	.05	.02
742	Kevin McReynolds	.07	.04
743	Steve Sax	.08	.05
744	Wally Joyner	.08	.05
745	Gary Sheffield	.15	.10
746	Danny Tartabull	.08	.05
747	Julio Valera	.05	.02
748	Danny Neagle	.08	.05
749	Lance Blankenship	.05	.02
750	Mike Gallego	.05	.02
751	Bret Saberhagen	.08	.05
752	Ruben Amaro	.08	.05
753	Eddie Murray	.12	.07
754	Kyle Abbott	.07	.04
755	Bobby Bonilla	.10	.06
756	Eric Davis	.08	.05
757	Eddie Taubensee (R)	.12	.07
758	Andres Galarraga	.07	.04
759	Pete Incaviglia	.05	.02
760	Tom Candiotti	.05	.02
761	Tim Belcher	.07	.04
762	Ricky Bones	.08	.05
763	Bip Roberts	.05	.02
764	Pedro Munoz	.10	.06
765	Greg Swindell	.07	.04
766	Kenny Lofton	.35	.20
767	Gary Carter	.10	.06
768	Charlie Hayes	.05	.02
769	Dickie Thon	.05	.02
770	Donovan Osborne (CL)	.08	.05
771	Bret Boone (R)	.25	.15
772	Archi Cianfrocco (R)	.20	.12
773	Mark Clark (R)	.20	.12
774	Chad Curtis (R)	.40	.25
775	Pat Listach (R)	.30	.18
776	Pat Mahomes (R)	.30	.18
777	Donovan Osborne	.15	.10
778	John Patterson (R)	.10	.06
779	Andy Stankiewicz (R)	.12	.07
780	Turk Wendell (R)	.20	.12
781	Bill Krueger	.05	.02
782	Rickey Henderson	.15	.08
	Grand Theft)		

783	Kevin Seitzer	.07	.04
784	Dave Martinez	.05	.02
785	John Smiley	.08	.05
786	Matt Stairs (R)	.12	.07
787	Scott Scudder	.05	.02
788	John Wetteland	.08	.05
789	Jack Armstrong	.07	.04
790	Ken Hill	.08	.05
791	Dick Schofield	.05	.02
792	Mariano Duncan	.05	.02
793	Bill Pecota	.05	.02
794	Mike Kelly (R)	1.25	.80
795	Willie Randolph	.07	.04
796	Butch Henry	.05	.02
797	Carlos Hernandez	.05	.02
798	Doug Jones	.05	.02
799	Melido Perez	.07	.04
800	Checklist 701-800	.07	.04
BH28	Ted Williams (Hero)	.80	.50
BH29	Ted Williams (Hero)	.80	.50
BH30	Ted Williams (Hero)	.80	.50
BH31	Ted Williams (Hero)	.80	.50
BH32	Ted Williams (Hero)	.80	.50
BH33	Ted Williams (Hero)	.80	.05
BH34	Ted Williams (Hero)	.80	.50
BH35	Ted Williams (Hero)	.80	.50
BH36	Ted Williams (Hero)	.80	.50
____	Ted Williams (Cover)	3.50	2.00
BH37	Johnny Bench/Joe Morgan (Hero)	.80	.50
BH38	Johnny Bench/Joe Morgan (Hero)	.80	.50
BH39	Johnny Bench/Joe Morgan (Hero)	.80	.50
BH40	Johnny Bench/Joe Morgan (Hero)	.80	.50
BH41	Johnny Bench/Joe Morgan (Hero)	.80	.50
BH42	Johnny Bench/Joe Morgan (Hero)	.80	.50
BH43	Johnny Bench/Joe Morgan (Hero)	.80	.50
BH44	Johnny Bench/Joe Morgan (Hero)	.80	.50
BH45	Johnny Bench/Joe Morgan (Hero)	.80	.50
____	Bench/Morgan (Cover)	4.00	2.75
HOF5	Vida Blue (Hero)	4.00	2.75
HOF6	Lou Brock (Hero)	8.00	5.50
HOF7	Rollie Fingers (Hero)	7.00	4.50
HOF8	Blue/Brock/Fingers	8.00	5.50

1993 Upper Deck

For the first time Upper Deck divided their baseball set into two series, each with 420-cards. Card fronts feature full color action photos framed by a white border. Upper Deck appears in white type across the top with the player's name, team and position centered under the photo. Card backs include another full color action shot and a stats box. The set includes numerous subsets including Star Rookies, Community Heroes (CH) and Teammates (41-55), Top Prospects (421-449), Inside The Numbers (450-470), Team Stars (471-485), Award Winners (486-499) and Diamond Debuts (500-510). All cards measure 2-1/2" by 3-1/2".

		MINT	NR/MT
Complete Set (840)		46.00	30.00
Commons		.05	.02
1	Star Rookie (CL)	.75	.45
2	Mike Piazza (R)	3.00	1.75
3	Rene Arocha (R)	.40	.25
4	Willie Greene (R)	.25	.15
5	Manny Alexander (R)	.12	.07
6	Dan Wilson	.10	.06
7	Dan Smith (R)	.25	.15
8	Kevin Rogers	.10	.06
9	Nigel Wilson (R)	.75	.45
10	Joe Vitko (R)	.25	.15
11	Tim Costo	.15	.10
12	Alan Embree (R)	.20	.12
13	Jim Tatum (R)	.15	.10
14	Cris Colon	.08	.05
15	Steve Hosey	.20	.12
16	Sterling Hitchcock (R)	.40	.25
17	Dave Mlicki	.10	.06
18	Jessie Hollins (R)	.15	.10
19	Bobby Jones	.35	.20

#	Name	Price 1	Price 2
20	Kurt Miller	.10	.06
21	Melvin Nieves	.40	.25
22	Billy Ashley	.50	.30
23	J.T. Snow (R)	.80	.50
24	Chipper Jones	.75	.45
25	Tim Salmon	2.00	1.25
26	Tim Pugh (R)	.20	.12
27	Dave Nied	.40	.25
28	Mike Trombley	.10	.06
29	Javy Lopez	.75	.45
30	Checklist	.07	.04
31	Jim Abbott (CH)	.10	.06
32	Dale Murphy (CH)	.10	.06
33	Tony Pena (CH)	.06	.03
34	Kirby Puckett (CH)	.15	.10
35	Harold Reynolds (CH)	.06	.03
36	Cal Ripken, Jr. (CH)	.20	.12
37	Nolan Ryan (CH)	.50	.30
38	Ryne Sandberg (CH)	.20	.12
39	Dave Stewart (CH)	.07	.04
40	Dave Winfield (CH)	.12	.07
41	Checklist	.12	.07
42	R. Alomar/J. Carter	.20	.12
43	Brew Crew	.20	.12
44	Iron And Steal	.15	.10
45	Young Tribe	.20	.12
46	Motown Mashers	.12	.07
47	Yankee Pride	.12	.07
48	Boston Cy Sox	.15	.10
49	Bash Brothers	.15	.10
50	Twin Titles	.15	.10
51	Southside Sluggers	.60	.35
52	Latin Stars	.30	.18
53	Lethal Lefties	.10	.06
54	Royal Family	.10	.06
55	Pacific Sox	.25	.15
56	George Brett	.25	.15
57	Scott Cooper	.12	.07
58	Mike Maddux	.05	.02
59	Rusty Meacham	.08	.05
60	Wilfredo Cordero	.25	.15
61	Tim Teufel	.05	.02
62	Jeff Montgomery	.05	.02
63	Scott Livingstone	.07	.04
64	Doug Dascenzo	.05	.02
65	Bret Boone	.15	.10
66	Tim Wakefield (R)	.15	.10
67	Curt Schilling	.05	.02
68	Frank Tanana	.05	.02
69	Lenny Dykstra	.07	.04
70	Derek Lilliquist	.05	.02
71	Anthony Young	.08	.05
72	Hipolito Pichardo (R)	.12	.07
73	Rod Beck (R)	.15	.10
74	Kent Hrbek	.05	.02
75	Tom Glavine	.20	.12
76	Kevin Brown	.10	.06
77	Chuck Finley	.08	.05
78	Bob Walk	.05	.02
79	Rheal Cormier	.08	.05
80	Rick Sutcliffe	.05	.02
81	Harold Baines	.07	.04
82	Lee Smith	.10	.06
83	Geno Petralli	.05	.02
84	Jose Oquendo	.05	.02
85	Mark Gubicza	.07	.04
86	Mickey Tettleton	.07	.04
87	Bobby Witt	.07	.04
88	Mark Lewis	.07	.04
89	Kevin Appier	.07	.04
90	Mike Stanton	.05	.02
91	Rafael Belliard	.05	.02
92	Kenny Rogers	.05	.02
93	Randy Velarde	.05	.02
94	Luis Sojo	.05	.02
95	Mark Leiter	.05	.02
96	Jody Reed	.05	.02
97	Pete Harnisch	.08	.05
98	Tom Candiotti	.05	.02
99	Mark Portugal	.05	.02
100	Dave Valle	.05	.02
101	Shawon Dunston	.08	.05
102	B.J. Surhoff	.05	.02
103	Jay Bell	.05	.02
104	Sid Bream	.05	.02
105	Checklist 1-105	.05	.02
106	Mike Morgan	.05	.02
107	Bill Doran	.05	.02
108	Lance Blankenship	.05	.02
109	Mark Lemke	.05	.02
110	Brian Harper	.05	.02
111	Brady Anderson	.10	.06
112	Bip Roberts	.05	.02
113	Mitch Williams	.05	.02
114	Craig Biggio	.07	.04
115	Eddie Murray	.15	.10
116	Matt Nokes	.05	.02
117	Lance Parrish	.05	.02
118	Bill Swift	.10	.06
119	Jeff Innis	.05	.02
120	Mike LaValliere	.05	.02
121	Hal Morris	.08	.05
122	Walt Weiss	.05	.02
123	Ivan Rodriquez	.20	.12
124	Andy Van Slyke	.10	.06
125	Roberto Alomar	.35	.20
126	Robby Thompson	.07	.04
127	Sammy Sosa	.12	.07
128	Mark Langston	.10	.06
129	Jerry Browne	.05	.02
130	Chuck McElroy	.05	.02
131	Frank Viola	.08	.05
132	Leo Gomez	.08	.05
133	Ramon Martinez	.10	.06

134	Don Mattingly	.20	.12
135	Roger Clemens	.30	.18
136	Rickey Henderson	.20	.12
137	Darren Daulton	.15	.10
138	Ken Hill	.08	.05
139	Ozzie Guillen	.05	.02
140	Jerald Clark	.00	.06
141	Dave Fleming	.12	.07
142	Delino DeShields	.12	.07
143	Matt Williams	.12	.07
144	Larry Walker	.15	.10
145	Ruben Sierra	.12	.07
146	Ozzie Smith	.15	.10
147	Chris Sabo	.08	.05
148	Carlos Hernandez	.08	.05
149	Pat Borders	.07	.04
150	Orlando Merced	.08	.05
151	Royce Clayton	.12	.07
152	Kurt Stillwell	.05	.02
153	Dave Hollins	.15	.10
154	Mike Greenwell	.08	.05
155	Nolan Ryan	.80	.50
156	Felix Jose	.08	.05
157	Junior Felix	.05	.02
158	Derek Bell	.15	.10
159	Steve Buechele	.05	.02
160	John Burkett	.05	.02
161	Pat Howell (R)	.10	.06
162	Milt Cuyler	.08	.05
163	Terry Pendleton	.12	.07
164	Jack Morris	.05	.02
165	Tony Gwynn	.15	.10
166	Deion Sanders	.15	.10
167	Mike Deavereaux	.07	.04
168	Ron Darling	.07	.04
169	Orel Hershiser	.10	.06
170	Mike Jackson	.05	.02
171	Doug Jones	.05	.02
172	Dan Walters	.08	.05
173	Darren Lewis	.08	.05
174	Carlos Baerga	.25	.15
175	Ryne Sandberg	.35	.20
176	Gregg Jefferies	.15	.10
177	John Jaha (R)	.20	.12
178	Luis Polonia	.07	.04
179	Kirt Manwaring	.05	.02
180	Mike Magnante	.07	.04
181	Billy Ripken	.05	.02
182	Mike Moore	.05	.02
183	Eric Anthony	.15	.10
184	Lenny Harris	.05	.02
185	Tony Pena	.05	.02
186	Mike Felder	.05	.02
187	Greg Olson	.05	.02
188	Rene Gonzales	.08	.05
189	Mike Bordick	.08	.05
190	Mel Rojas	.05	.02
191	Todd Frohwirth	.07	.04
192	Darryl Hamilton	.08	.05
193	Mike Fetters	.07	.04
194	Omar Olivares	.05	.02
195	Tony Phillips	.05	.02
196	Paul Sorrento	.10	.06
197	Trevor Wilson	.05	.02
198	Kevin Gross	.05	.02
199	Ron Karkovice	.05	.02
200	Brook Jacoby	.05	.02
201	Mariano Duncan	.05	.02
202	Dennis Cook	.05	.02
203	Daryl Boston	.05	.02
204	Mike Perez	.10	.06
205	Manuel Lee	.05	.02
206	Steve Olin	.08	.05
207	Charlie Hough	.05	.02
208	Scott Scudder	.05	.02
209	Charlie O'Brien	.05	.02
210	Checklist 106-210	.05	.02
211	Jose Vizcaino	.05	.02
212	Scott Leius	.05	.02
213	Kevin Mitchell	.12	.07
214	Brian Barnes	.07	.04
215	Pat Kelly	.10	.06
216	Chris Hammond	.08	.05
217	Rob Deer	.08	.05
218	Cory Snyder	.05	.02
219	Gary Carter	.10	.06
220	Danny Darwin	.05	.02
221	Tom Gordon	.08	.05
222	Gary Sheffield	.15	.10
223	Joe Carter	.25	.15
224	Jay Buhner	.08	.05
225	Jose Offerman	.10	.06
226	Jose Rijo	.08	.05
227	Mark Whiten	.12	.07
228	Randy Milligan	.05	.02
229	Bud Black	.05	.02
230	Gary DiSarcina	.08	.05
231	Steve Finley	.05	.02
232	Dennis Martinez	.10	.06
233	Mike Mussina	.35	.20
234	Joe Oliver	.07	.04
235	Chad Curtis	.15	.10
236	Shane Mack	.10	.06
237	Jaime Navarro	.08	.05
238	Brian McRae	.08	.05
239	Chili Davis	.07	.04
240	Jeff King	.07	.04
241	Dean Palmer	.15	.10
242	Danny Tartabull	.08	.05
243	Charles Nagy	.10	.06
244	Ray Lankford	.15	.10
245	Barry Larkin	.12	.07
246	Steve Avery	.20	.12
247	John Kruk	.07	.04

248	Derrick May	.15	.10
249	Stan Javier	.05	.02
250	Roger McDowell	.05	.02
251	Dan Gladden	.05	.02
252	Wally Joyner	.10	.06
253	Pat Listach	.15	.10
254	Chuck Knoblauch	.12	.07
255	Sandy Alomar, Jr.	.08	.05
256	Jeff Bagwell	.25	.15
257	Andy Stankiewicz	.08	.05
258	Darrin Jackson	.07	.04
259	Brett Butler	.08	.05
260	Joe Orsulak	.05	.02
261	Andy Benes	.12	.07
262	Kenny Lofton	.30	.18
263	Robin Ventura	.20	.12
264	Ron Gant	.15	.10
265	Ellis Burks	.08	.05
266	Juan Guzman	.20	.12
267	Wes Chamberlain	.10	.06
268	John Smiley	.08	.05
269	Franklin Stubbs	.05	.02
270	Tom Browning	.07	.04
271	Dennis Eckersley	.12	.07
272	Carlton Fisk	.12	.07
273	Lou Whitaker	.07	.04
274	Phil Plantier	.20	.12
275	Bobby Bonilla	.10	.06
276	Ben McDonald	.10	.06
277	Bob Zupcic	.12	.07
278	Terry Steinbach	.07	.04
279	Terry Mulholland	.05	.02
280	Lance Johnson	.05	.02
281	Willie McGee	.08	.05
282	Bret Saberhagen	.10	.06
283	Randy Myers	.05	.02
284	Randy Tomlin	.08	.05
285	Mickey Morandini	.08	.05
286	Brian Williams	.10	.06
287	Tino Martinez	.08	.05
288	Jose Melendez	.08	.05
289	Jeff Huson	.07	.04
290	Joe Grahe	.07	.04
291	Mel Hall	.07	.04
292	Otis Nixon	.07	.04
293	Todd Hundley	.08	.05
294	Casey Candaele	.05	.02
295	Kevin Seitzer	.05	.02
296	Eddie Taubensee	.08	.05
297	Moises Alou	.20	.12
298	Scott Radinsky	.05	.02
299	Thomas Howard	.08	.05
300	Kyle Abbott	.08	.05
301	Omar Vizquel	.07	.04
302	Keith Miller	.05	.02
303	Rick Aguilera	.05	.02
304	Bruce Hurst	.08	.05
305	Ken Caminiti	.07	.04
306	Mike Pagliarulo	.05	.02
307	Frank Seminara	.08	.05
308	Andre Dawson	.15	.10
309	Jose Lind	.05	.02
310	Joe Boever	.05	.02
311	Jeff Parrett	.05	.02
312	Alan Mills	.08	.05
313	Kevin Tapani	.08	.05
314	Daryl Kile	.10	.06
315	Checklist 211-315	.05	.02
316	Mike Sharperson	.05	.02
317	John Orton	.07	.04
318	Bob Tewksbury	.05	.02
319	Xavier Hernandez	.05	.02
320	Paul Assenmacher	.05	.02
321	John Franco	.07	.04
322	Mike Timlin	.07	.04
323	Jose Guzman	.05	.02
324	Pedro Martinez	.20	.12
325	Bill Spiers	.05	.02
326	Melido Perez	.08	.05
327	Mike Macfarlane	.05	.02
328	Ricky Bones	.08	.05
329	Scott Bankhead	.05	.02
330	Rich Rodriguez	.08	.05
331	Geronimo Pena	.05	.02
332	Bernie Williams	.10	.06
333	Paul Molitor	.15	.10
334	Roger Mason	.05	.02
335	David Cone	.10	.06
336	Randy Johnson	.15	.10
337	Pat Mahomes	.12	.07
338	Erik Hanson	.07	.04
339	Duane Ward	.05	.02
340	Al Martin	.25	.15
341	Pedro Munoz	.10	.06
342	Greg Colbrunn	.10	.06
343	Julio Valera	.05	.02
344	John Olerud	.40	.25
345	George Bell	.10	.06
346	Devon White	.07	.04
347	Donovan Osborne	.12	.07
348	Mark Gardner	.07	.04
349	Zane Smith	.05	.02
350	Wilson Alvarez	.07	.04
351	Kevin Koslofski (R)	.20	.12
352	Roberto Hernandez	.08	.05
353	Glenn Davis	.05	.02
354	Reggie Sanders	.15	.10
355	Ken Griffey, Jr.	1.25	.70
356	Marquis Grissom	.15	.10
357	Jack McDowell	.20	.12
358	Jimmy Key	.08	.05
359	Stan Belinda	.05	.02
360	Gerald Williams	.12	.07
361	Sid Fernandez	.07	.04

362	Alex Fernandez	.15	.10
363	John Smoltz	.15	.10
364	Travis Fryman	.30	.18
365	Jose Canseco	.15	.10
366	David Justice	.30	.18
367	Pedro Astacio	.20	.12
000	Tim Delcher	.07	.01
369	Steve Sax	.08	.05
370	Gary Gaetti	.05	.02
371	Jeff Frye (R)	.10	.06
372	Bob Wickman	.20	.12
373	Ryan Thompson	.20	.12
374	David Hulse (R)	.15	.10
375	Cal Eldred	.25	.15
376	Ryan Klesko	.40	.25
377	Damion Easley	.15	.10
378	John Kiely (R)	.12	.07
379	Jim Bullinger (R)	.12	.07
380	Brian Bohanon	.05	.02
381	Rod Brewer	.05	.02
382	Fernando Ramsey (R)	.12	.07
383	Sam Militello	.25	.15
384	Arthur Rhodes	.10	.06
385	Eric Karros	.25	.15
386	Rico Brogna	.08	.05
387	John Valentin	.15	.10
388	Kerry Woodson	.10	.06
389	Ben Rivera	.10	.06
390	Matt Whiteside (R)	.15	.10
391	Henry Rodriquez	.10	.06
392	John Wetteland	.08	.05
393	Kent Mercker	.05	.02
394	Bernard Gilkey	.12	.07
395	Doug Henry	.10	.06
396	Mo Vaughn	.20	.12
397	Scott Erickson	.10	.06
398	Bill Gullickson	.05	.02
399	Mark Guthrie	.05	.02
400	Dave Martinez	.05	.02
401	Jeff Kent	.15	.10
402	Chris Hoiles	.10	.06
403	Mike Henneman	.05	.02
404	Chris Nabholz	.07	.04
405	Tom Pagnozzi	.08	.05
406	Kelly Gruber	.07	.04
407	Bob Welch	.07	.04
408	Frank Castillo	.05	.02
409	John Dopson	.05	.02
410	Steve Farr	.05	.02
411	Henry Cotto	.05	.02
412	Bob Patterson	.05	.02
413	Todd Stottlemyre	.07	.04
414	Greg Harris	.05	.02
415	Denny Neagle	.08	.05
416	Bill Wegman	.05	.02
417	Willie Wilson	.07	.04
418	Terry Leach	.05	.02
419	Willie Randolph	.07	.04
420	Checklist (316-420)	.05	.02
421	Top Prospect Checklist	.20	.12
422	Pete Janicki (R)	.10	.06
423	Todd Jones	.05	.02
424	Mike Neill	.20	.12
425	Carlos Delgado	1.75	1.00
426	Jose Oliva	.12	.07
427	Tyrone Hill	.15	.10
428	Dmitri Young	.40	.25
429	Derrick Wallace (R)	.25	.15
430	Michael Moore (R)	.40	.25
431	Cliff Floyd	2.00	1.25
432	Calvin Murray	.35	.20
433	Manny Ramirez	1.25	.80
434	Marc Newfield	.30	.18
435	Charles Johnson	.50	.30
436	Butch Huskey	.30	.18
437	Brad Pennington	.12	.07
438	Ray McDavid (R)	.50	.30
439	Chad McConnell	.25	.15
440	Midre Cummings (R)	.50	.30
441	Benji Gil	.25	.15
442	Frank Rodriguez	.35	.20
443	Chad Motolla (R)	1.00	.70
444	John Burke (R)	.50	.30
445	Michael Tucker	.75	.45
446	Rick Greene	.15	.10
447	Rich Becker	.15	.10
448	Mike Robertson	.12	.07
449	Derek Jeter (R)	.60	.35
450	Checklist	.30	.18
451	Jim Abbott	.10	.06
452	Jeff Bagwell	.15	.10
453	Jason Bere	.50	.30
454	Delino DeShields	.08	.05
455	Travis Fryman	.20	.12
456	Alex Gonzalez	.50	.30
457	Phil Hiatt	.15	.10
458	Dave Hollins	.10	.06
459	Chipper Jones	.40	.25
460	David Justice	.20	.12
461	Ray Lankford	.10	.06
462	David McCarty	.20	.12
463	Mike Mussina	.20	.12
464	Jose Offerman	.08	.05
465	Dean Palmer	.10	.06
466	Geronimo Pena	.05	.02
467	Eduardo Perez	.25	.15
468	Ivan Rodriguez	.10	.06
469	Reggie Sanders	.10	.06
470	Bernie Williams	.07	.04
471	Checklist	.30	.18
472	Strike Force	.25	.15
473	Red October	.08	.05
474	Four Corners	.20	.12
475	Shooting Stars	.10	.06

476 Giant Sticks	.30	.18
477 Boyhood Friends	.10	.06
478 Rock Solid	.40	.25
479 Inaugural Catch	.10	.06
480 Steel City Champs	.08	.05
481 Les Grandes Etolles	.12	.07
482 Runnin' Redbirds	.05	.02
483 Ivy Leaguers	.15	.10
484 Big Apple Power	.12	.07
485 Hammers & Nails	.15	.10
486 Barry Bonds (AW)	.30	.18
487 Dennis Eckersley (AW)	.07	.04
488 Greg Maddux (AW)	.10	.06
489 Dennis Eckersley (AW)	.07	.04
490 Eric Karros (AW)	.15	.10
491 Pat Listach (AW)	.07	.04
492 Gary Sheffield (AW)	.10	.06
493 Mark McGwire (AW)	.10	.06
494 Gary Sheffield (AW)	.10	.06
495 Edgar Martinez(AW)	.07	.04
496 Fred McGriff (AW)	.10	.06
497 Juan Gonzalez (AW)	.50	.30
498 Darren Daulton (AW)	.08	.05
499 Cecil Fielder (AW)	.10	.06
500 Checklist	.12	.07
501 Tavo Alvarez	.08	.05
502 Rod Bolton	.07	.04
503 John Cummings (R)	.25	.15
504 Brent Gates	.25	.15
505 Tyler Green	.10	.06
506 Jose Martinez (R)	.15	.10
507 Troy Percival	.07	.04
508 Kevin Stocker	.60	.35
509 Matt Walbeck (R)	.20	.12
510 Rondell White	.50	.30
511 Billy Ripken	.05	.02
512 Mike Moore	.05	.02
513 Jose Lind	.05	.02
514 Chito Martinez	.08	.05
515 Jose Guzman	.05	.02
516 Kim Batiste	.05	.02
517 Jeff Tackett	.05	.02
518 Charlie Hough	.05	.02
519 Marvin Freeman	.05	.02
520 Carlos Martinez	.07	.04
521 Eric Young	.10	.06
522 Pete Incaviglia	.05	.02
523 Scott Fletcher	.05	.02
524 Orestes Destrade	.08	.05
525 Checklist (421-525)	.05	.02
526 Ellis Burks	.07	.04
527 Juan Samuel	.05	.02
528 Dave Magadan	.05	.02
529 Jeff Parrett	.05	.02
530 Bill Krueger	.05	.02
531 Frank Bolik	.07	.04
532 Alan Trammell	.10	.06

533 Walt Weiss	.05	.02
534 David Cone	.08	.05
535 Greg Maddux	.20	.12
536 Kevin Young	.30	.18
537 Dave Hansen	.05	.02
538 Alex Cole	.05	.02
539 Greg Hibbard	.05	.02
540 Gene Larkin	.05	.02
541 Jeff Reardon	.08	.05
542 Felix Jose	.07	.04
543 Jimmy Key	.08	.05
544 Reggie Jefferson	.08	.05
545 Gregg Jefferies	.15	.10
546 Dave Stewart	.12	.07
547 Tim Wallach	.07	.04
548 Spike Owen	.05	.02
549 Tommy Greene	.15	.10
550 Fernando Valenzuela	.07	.04
551 Rich Amaral	.10	.06
552 Bret Barberie	.07	.04
553 Edgar Martinez	.10	.06
554 Jim Abbott	.15	.10
555 Frank Thomas	2.00	1.25
556 Wade Boggs	.15	.10
557 Tom Henke	.05	.02
558 Milt Thompson	.05	.02
559 Lloyd McClendon	.05	.02
560 Vinny Castilla	.07	.04
561 Ricky Jordan	.05	.02
562 Andujar Cedeno	.10	.06
563 Greg Vaughn	.12	.07
564 Cecil Fielder	.20	.12
565 Kirby Puckett	.35	.20
566 Mark McGwire	.15	.10
567 Barry Bonds	.75	.45
568 Jody Reed	.05	.02
569 Todd Zeile	.07	.04
570 Mark Carreon	.05	.02
571 Joe Girardi	.05	.02
572 Luis Gonzalez	.10	.06
573 Mark Grace	.20	.12
574 Rafael Palmeiro	.20	.12
575 Darryl Strawberry	.15	.10
576 Will Clark	.25	.15
577 Fred McGriff	.30	.18
578 Kevin Reimer	.05	.02
579 Dave Righetti	.05	.02
580 Juan Bell	.07	.04
581 Jeff Brantley	.05	.02
582 Brian Hunter	.10	.06
583 Tim Naehring	.08	.05
584 Glenallen Hill	.08	.05
585 Cal Ripken Jr.	.60	.35
586 Albert Belle	.30	.18
587 Robin Yount	.25	.15
588 Chris Bosio	.07	.04
589 Pete Smith	.08	.05

590	Chuck Carr	.20	.12	647	Charlie Hayes	.07	.04
591	Jeff Blauser	.08	.05	648	Jim Deshaies	.05	.02
592	Kevin McReynolds	.07	.04	649	Dan Pasqua	.05	.02
593	Andres Galarraga	.15	.10	650	Mike Maddux	.05	.02
594	Kevin Maas	.08	.05	651	Domingo Martinez (R)	.30	.18
595	Eric Davis	.10	.06	652	Greg McMichael (R)	.20	.12
596	Brian Jordan	.20	.12	653	Eric Wedge (R)	.12	.07
597	Tim Raines	.08	.05	654	Mark Whiten	.20	.12
598	Rick Wilkins	.10	.06	655	Roberto Kelly	.12	.07
599	Steve Cooke	.20	.12	656	Julio Franco	.08	.05
600	Mike Gallego	.05	.02	657	Gene Harris	.05	.02
601	Mike Munoz	.08	.05	658	Paul Schourek	.07	.04
602	Luis Rivera	.05	.02	659	Mike Bielecki	.05	.02
603	Junior Ortiz	.05	.02	660	Ricky Gutierrez	.10	.06
604	Brent Mayne	.07	.04	661	Chris Hammond	.05	.02
605	Luis Alicea	.05	.02	662	Tim Scott	.05	.02
606	Damon Berryhill	.05	.02	663	Norm Charlton	.05	.02
607	Dave Henderson	.05	.02	664	Doug Drabek	.10	.06
608	Kirk McCaskill	.05	.02	665	Dwight Gooden	.12	.07
609	Jeff Fassero	.05	.02	666	Jim Gott	.05	.02
610	Mike Harkey	.07	.04	667	Randy Myers	.07	.04
611	Francisco Cabrera	.05	.02	668	Darren Holmes	.08	.05
612	Rey Sanchez	.05	.02	669	Tim Spehr	.05	.02
613	Scott Servais	.05	.02	670	Bruce Ruffin	.05	.02
614	Darren Fletcher	.05	.02	671	Bobby Thigpen	.05	.02
615	Felix Fermin	.05	.02	672	Tony Fernandez	.05	.02
616	Kevin Seitzer	.05	.02	673	Darrin Jackson	.05	.02
617	Bob Scanlan	.05	.02	674	Gregg Olson	.07	.04
618	Billy Hatcher	.05	.02	675	Rob Dibble	.07	.04
619	John Vander Wal	.05	.02	676	Howard Johnson	.08	.05
620	Joe Hesketh	.05	.02	677	Mike Lansing (R)	.25	.15
621	Hector Villanueva	.05	.02	678	Charlie Leibrandt	.05	.02
622	Randy Milligan	.05	.02	679	Kevin Bass	.05	.02
623	Tony Tarasco (R)	.40	.25	680	Hubie Brooks	.05	.02
624	Russ Swan	.05	.02	681	Scott Brosius	.05	.02
625	Willie Wilson	.05	.02	682	Randy Knorr	.08	.05
626	Frank Tanana	.05	.02	683	Dante Bichette	.08	.05
627	Pete O'Brien	.05	.02	684	Bryan Harvey	.07	.04
628	Lenny Webster	.05	.02	685	Greg Gohr	.08	.05
629	Mark Clark	.08	.05	686	Willie Banks	.08	.05
630	Checklist (526-630)	.05	.02	687	Robb Nen	.12	.07
631	Alex Arias	.05	.02	688	Mike Scioscia	.05	.02
632	Chris Gwynn	.05	.02	689	John Farrell	.05	.02
633	Tom Bolton	.05	.02	690	John Candelaria	.05	.02
634	Greg Briley	.05	.02	691	Damon Buford	.08	.05
635	Kent Bottenfield	.05	.02	692	Todd Worrell	.05	.02
636	Kelly Downs	.05	.02	693	Pat Hentgen	.25	.15
637	Manuel Lee	.05	.02	694	John Smiley	.08	.05
638	Al Leiter	.05	.02	695	Greg Swindell	.07	.04
639	Jeff Gardner	.05	.02	696	Derek Bell	.15	.10
640	Mike Gardiner	.05	.02	697	Terry Jorgensen	.08	.05
641	Mark Gardner	.05	.02	698	Jimmy Jones	.05	.02
642	Jeff Branson	.05	.02	699	David Wells	.05	.02
643	Paul Wagner	.20	.12	700	Dave Martinez	.05	.02
644	Sean Berry	.12	.07	701	Steve Bedrosian	.05	.02
645	Phil Hiatt	.15	.10	702	Jeff Russell	.05	.02
646	Kevin Mitchell	.08	.05	703	Joe Magrane	.05	.02

704 Matt Mieski	.10	.06
705 Paul Molitor	.25	.15
706 Dale Murphy	.12	.07
707 Steve Howe	.05	.02
708 Greg Gagne	.05	.02
709 Dave Eiland	.05	.02
710 David West	.05	.02
711 Luis Aquino	.05	.02
712 Joe Orsulak	.05	.02
713 Eric Plunk	.05	.02
714 Mike Felder	.05	.02
715 Joe Klink	.05	.02
716 Lonnie Smith	.05	.02
717 Monty Fariss	.05	.02
718 Craig Lefferts	.05	.02
719 John Habyan	.05	.02
720 Willie Blair	.07	.04
721 Darnell Coles	.05	.02
722 Mark Williamson	.05	.02
723 Bryn Smith	.05	.02
724 Greg W. Harris	.05	.02
725 Graeme Lloyd (R)	.15	.10
726 Cris Carpenter	.05	.02
727 Chico Walker	.05	.02
728 Tracy Woodson	.05	.02
729 Jose Uribe	.05	.02
730 Stan Javier	.05	.02
731 Jay Howell	.05	.02
732 Freddie Benavides	.05	.02
733 Jeff Reboulet	.08	.05
734 Scott Sanderson	.05	.02
735 Checklist (631-735)	.05	.02
736 Archi Cianfrocco	.08	.05
737 Daryl Boston	.05	.02
738 Craig Grebeck	.05	.02
739 Doug Dascenzo	.05	.02
740 Gerald Young	.05	.02
741 Candy Maldonado	.05	.02
742 Joey Cora	.05	.02
743 Don Slaught	.05	.02
744 Steve Decker	.07	.04
745 Blas Minor	.07	.04
746 Storm Davis	.05	.02
747 Carlos Quintana	.05	.02
748 Vince Coleman	.08	.05
749 Todd Burns	.05	.02
750 Steve Frey	.05	.02
751 Ivan Calderon	.05	.02
752 Steve Reed (R)	.15	.10
753 Danny Jackson	.05	.02
754 Jeff Conine	.15	.10
755 Juan Gonzalez	1.50	.90
756 Mike Kelly	.30	.18
757 John Doherty	.10	.06
758 Jack Armstrong	.05	.02
759 John Wehner	.05	.02
760 Scott Bankhead	.05	.02

761 Jim Tatum	.10	.06
762 Scott Pose (R)	.15	.10
763 Andy Ashby	.08	.05
764 Ed Sprague	.00	.05
765 Harold Baines	.08	.05
766 Kirk Gibson	.08	.05
767 Troy Neel	.20	.12
768 Dick Schofield	.05	.02
769 Dickie Thon	.05	.02
770 Butch Henry	.05	.02
771 Junior Felix	.05	.02
772 Ken Ryan (R)	.30	.18
773 Trevor Hoffman	.15	.10
774 Phil Plantier	.20	.12
775 Bo Jackson	.20	.12
776 Benito Santiago	.08	.05
777 Andre Dawson	.20	.12
778 Bryan Hickerson	.08	.05
779 Dennis Moeller	.08	.05
780 Ryan Bowen	.08	.05
781 Eric Fox	.08	.05
782 Joe Kmak	.08	.05
783 Mike Hampton	.08	.05
784 Darrell Sherman (R)	.20	.12
785 J.T. Snow	.60	.35
786 Dave Winfield	.25	.15
787 Jim Austin	.08	.05
788 Craig Shipley	.05	.02
789 Greg Myers	.05	.02
790 Todd Benzinger	.05	.02
791 Corey Snyder	.05	.02
792 David Segui	.05	.02
793 Armando Reynoso	.05	.02
794 Chili Davis	.07	.04
795 Dave Nilsson	.10	.06
796 Paul O'Neill	.10	.06
797 Jerald Clark	.07	.04
798 Jose Mesa	.08	.05
799 Brian Holman	.05	.02
800 Jim Eisenreich	.05	.02
801 Mark McLemore	.05	.02
802 Luis Sojo	.05	.02
803 Harold Reynolds	.05	.02
804 Dan Plesac	.05	.02
805 Dave Stieb	.05	.02
806 Tom Brunansky	.05	.02
807 Kelly Gruber	.05	.02
808 Bob Ojeda	.05	.02
809 Dave Burba	.05	.02
810 Joe Boever	.05	.02
811 Jeremy Hernandez	.05	.02
812 Angels (CL) (Salmon)	.60	.35
813 Astros (CL) (Bagwell)	.12	.07
814 Athletics (CL)	.05	.02
815 Blue Jays (CL)(Alomar)	.25	.15
816 Braves (CL) (Avery)	.12	.07
817 Brewers (CL)	.05	.02

818	Cardinals (CL)	.05	.02
819	Cubs (CL)	.05	.02
820	Dodgers (CL)	.05	.02
821	Expos (CL)	.05	.02
822	Giants (CL)	.05	.02
823	Indians (CL) (Belle)	.20	.12
824	Mariners (CL)	.05	.02
825	Marlins (CL)(Wilson)	.30	.18
826	Mets (CL)	.05	.02
827	Orioles (CL)	.05	.02
828	Padres (CL)	.05	.02
829	Phillies (CL)	.05	.02
830	Pirates (CL)	.05	.02
831	Rangers (CL)(Gonzalez)	.50	.30
832	Red Sox (CL)	.05	.02
833	Reds (CL)	.05	.02
834	Rockies (CL) (Nied)	.20	.12
835	Royals (CL)	.05	.02
836	Tigers (CL) (Fryman)	.15	.10
837	Twins (CL)	.05	.02
838	White Sox (CL)	.08	.05
839	Yankess (CL)	.05	.02
840	Checklist (736-840)	.05	.02
BC	Willie Mays Heroes(ea)	1.00	.70

1993 Upper Deck Home Run Heroes

The cards in this limited insert set were issued randomly in 1993 Upper Deck Jumbo packs. The card fronts feature full-color action photos with the headline "Home Run Heroes printed vertically along the side of the card. The player's name appears in a baseball bat under his photo. The crd numbers are preceed by the letters "HR". All cards measure 2-1/2" by 3-1/2".

		MINT	NR/MT
Complete Set (28)		22.00	12.00
Commons		.50	.30
1	Juan Gonzalez	4.50	2.75
2	Mark McGwire	1.50	.90
3	Cecil Fielder	1.50	.90
4	Fred McGriff	2.00	1.25
5	Albert Belle	2.00	1.25
6	Barry Bonds	3.00	1.75
7	Joe Carter	1.75	1.00
8	Darren Daulton	.75	.45
9	Ken Griffey, Jr.	6.00	3.75
10	Dave Hollins	1.25	.80
11	Ryne Sandberg	3.00	2.00
12	George Bell	.75	.50
13	Danny Tartabull	.75	.50
14	Mike Devereaux	.50	.30
15	Greg Vaughn	.75	.50
16	Larry Walker	1.00	.70
17	David Justice	2.00	1.25
18	Terry Pendleton	.75	.45
19	Eric Karros	1.75	1.00
20	Ray Lankford	.75	.45
21	Matt Williams	1.25	.80
22	Eric Anthony	.75	.45
23	Bobby Bonilla	.75	.45
24	Kirby Puckett	3.00	2.00
25	Mike Macfarlane	.50	.30
26	Tom Brunansky	.50	.30
27	Paul O'Neill	.75	.45
28	Gary Gaetti	.50	.30

1993 Upper Deck Triple Crown

These limited insert cards were distributed randomly in Upper Deck Series I Hobby Foil packs. The card design includes a full-color action shot of the player with a small Crown-type logo in the lower corner next to the headline "Triple Crown Contenders." The player's name is printed under the headline. Card numbers contain the prefix TC. All cards measure 2-1/2" by 3-1/2"

		MINT	NR/MT
Complete Set (10)		34.00	20.00
Commons		1.75	1.00
1	Barry Bonds	6.00	3.75
2	Jose Canseco	3.00	1.75
3	Will Clark	3.00	1.75
4	Ken Griffey, Jr.	8.00	5.00
5	Fred McGriff	3.50	2.00
6	Kirby Puckett	4.00	2.75
7	Cal Ripken, Jr.	5.00	3.00
8	Gary Sheffield	3.00	1.75
9	Frank Thomas	10.00	6.50
10	Larry Walker	1.75	1.00

9	Eric Karros	1.50	.90
10	Delino DeShields	.75	.45
11	Will Clark	2.00	1.25
12	Albert Belle	3.00	1.75
13	Ken Griffey Jr.	9.00	5.75
14	Howard Johnson	.75	.45
15	Cal Ripken Jr.	4.00	2.50
16	Fred McGriff	3.00	1.75
17	Darren Daulton	1.25	.80
18	Andy Van Slyke	.75	.45
19	Nolan Ryan	8.00	5.00
20	Wade Boggs	1.50	.90
21	Barry Larkin	1.00	.70
22	George Brett	3.00	1.75
23	Cecil Fielder	2.00	1.25
24	Kirby Puckett	3.00	1.75
25	Frank Thomas	10.00	6.50
26	Dan Mattingly	2.50	1.50
___	Cover Card	3.50	2.00

1993 Upper Deck Walter Looss Set

The cards in this insert set feature the work of noted sports photographer Walter Looss. The full-bleed, full-color fronts consist of action shots with the words Walter Looss Collection printed across the bottom. The cards were available randomly in Upper Deck Series I Retail packs. All cards measure 2-1/2" by 3-1/2".

		MINT	NR/MT
Complete Set (26)		32.00	20.00
Commons		.75	.45
1	Tim Salmon	6.00	3.75
2	Jeff Bagwell	2.50	1.50
3	Mark McGwire	1.50	.90
4	Roberto Alomar	4.50	2.75
5	Steve Avery	2.50	1.50
6	Paul Molitor	2.00	1.25
7	Ozzie Smith	2.00	1.25
8	Mark Grace	1.25	.80

1993 Upper Deck Fifth Anniversary

The cards in this limited insert set were distributed randomly in Upper Deck Series II hobby packs. The framed full color action photos on the card fronts also include an Upper Deck Fifth Anniversary logo. All cards measure 2-1/2" by 3-1/2".

		MINT	NR/MT
Complete Set (15)		22.00	15.00
Commons		.80	.50
1	Ken Griffey Jr.	8.50	5.00
2	Gary Sheffield	1.50	.90
3	Roberto Alomar	3.50	2.00
4	Jim Abbott	1.00	.70

		MINT	NR/MT
5	Nolan Ryan	6.00	3.75
6	Juan Gonzalez	6.00	3.75
7	David Justice	2.00	1.25
8	Carlos Baerga	2.50	1.50
9	Reggie Jackson	2.00	1.25
10	Eric Karros	1.25	.80
11	Chipper Jones	1.75	1.00
12	Ivan Rodriquez	1.25	.80
13	Pat Listach	.80	.50
14	Frank Thomas	9.00	5.75
15	Tim Salmon	4.00	2.75

		MINT	NR/MT
19	John Smoltz	.75	.45
20	Frank Thomas	9.00	5.75

1993 Upper Deck Future Heroes

The cards in this limited insert set are a continuation of Upper Decks Heroes Series and are numbered accordingly. The cards were distributed randomly in Upper Deck Series II packs. Card fronts feature an full-color action photo of the player whith his name printed in a design that resembles torn paper just under his photo. A Future Heroes logo is printed in the top corner. All cards measure 2-1/2" by 3-1/2".

		MINT	NR/MT
Complete Set (10)		15.00	10.00
Commons		.75	.45
55	Roberto Alomar	1.50	.90
56	Barry Bonds	2.50	1.50
57	Roger Clemens	1.25	.80
58	Juan Gonzalez	3.00	1.75
59	Ken Griffey Jr.	4.00	2.75
60	Mark McGwire	1.00	.70
61	Kirby Puckett	1.25	.90
62	Frank Thomas	5.00	3.00
63	Checklist	.75	.45
64	Art Title Card	.75	.45

1993 Upper Deck Clutch Performers

The cards in this limited insert set were issued randomly in Upper Deck Series II Jumbo packs. The card fronts consist of full color action shots of the player with his name printed under his photo and just above a horizontal box containing the words "Clutch Performers". The player's in the set were chosen by Reggie Jackson who offers comentary on each selection. The card numbers are preceeded by the prefix "R". All cards measure 2-1/2" by 3-1/2".

		MINT	NR/MT
Complete Set (20)		32.00	18.50
Commons		.75	.45
1	Roberto Alomar	3.00	1.75
2	Wade Boggs	1.25	.80
3	Barry Bonds	5.00	3.00
4	Jose Canseco	1.75	1.00
5	Joe Carter	3.00	1.75
6	Will Clark	2.50	1.50
7	Roger Clemens	3.00	1.75
8	Dennis Eckersley	.75	.45
9	Cecil Fielder	2.00	1.25
10	Juan Gonzalez	7.00	4.00
11	Ken Griffey Jr.	8.00	5.00
12	Rickey Henderson	1.50	.90
13	Barry Larkin	1.00	.70
14	Don Mattingly	3.00	1.75
15	Fred McGriff	3.50	2.00
16	Terry Pendleton	1.00	.70
17	Kirby Puckett	3.50	2.00
18	Ryne Sandberg	3.50	2.00

1993 Upper Deck Then & Now

These limited full-color holograms were packaged randomly in Upper Deck

Series Hobby Foil packs. The card numbers include the prefix TN. All cards measure 2-1/2" by 3-1/2".

		MINT	NR/MT
	Complete Set (18)	70.00	40.00
	Commons	.75	.45
1	Wade Boggs	1.75	1.00
2	George Brett	2.50	1.50
3	Rickey Henderson	2.00	1.25
4	Cal Ripken	5.00	3.00
5	Nolan Ryan	10.00	6.50
6	Ryne Sandberg	5.00	3.00
7	Ozzie Smith	2.00	1.25
9	Dave Winfield	3.50	2.00
10	Dennis Eckersley	.75	.45
11	Tony Gwynn	1.75	1.00
12	Howard Johnson	.75	.45
13	Don Mattingly	3.00	1.75
14	Eddie Murray	1.25	.80
15	Robin Yount	2.50	1.50
16	Mickey Mantle	15.00	10.00
17	Willie Mays	10.00	6.50
18	Reggie Jackson	6.00	3.75

1993 Upper Deck On Deck

These insert cards were issued one per Upper Deck Series II Jumbo pack. The full-bleed, full-color cards contain a fascimile autograph. The letter "D" preceeds the card numbers. All cards measure 2-1/2" by 3-1/2".

		MINT	NR/MT
	Complete Set (25)	20.00	12.50
	Commons	.50	.30
1	Jim Abbott	.75	.45
2	Roberto Alomar	2.00	1.25
3	Carlos Baerga	2.00	1.25
4	Albert Belle	2.00	1.25
5	Wade Boggs	.75	.45
6	George Brett	1.50	.90
7	Jose Canseco	1.00	.70
8	Will Clark	1.50	.90
9	Roger Clemens	1.50	.90

10	Dennis Eckersley	.50	.30
11	Cecil Fielder	1.00	.70
12	Juan Gonzalez	3.50	2.00
13	Ken Griffey Jr.	5.00	3.00
14	Tony Gwynn	.75	.45
15	Bo Jackson	.75	.45
16	Chipper Jones	1.50	.90
17	Eric Karros	.75	.45
18	Mark McGwire	1.00	.70
19	Kirby Puckett	1.50	.90
20	Nolan Ryan	5.00	3.00
21	Tim Salmon	3.00	1.75
22	Ryne Sandberg	1.50	.90
23	Darryl Strawberry	1.00	.70
24	Frank Thomas	6.50	3.75
25	Andy Van Slyke	.50	.30

1993 Upper Deck SP

This 290-card set marks the first Super Premium brand from The Upper Deck Company. The full-bleed, full-color card fronts feature action photos of the players. Their names are printed in gold creating an arch at the top of the card. An Upper Deck SP stamp appears in the lower corner. Key subsets include All-Stars (AS)(1-18) and a 20-card foil insert set called. Premier Prospects (P)(271-290). All cards measure 2-1/2" by 3-1/2".

		MINT	NR/MT
	Complete Set (290)	80.00	48.00
	Commons	.10	.06
1	Roberto Alomar (AS)	.75	.45
2	Wade Boggs (AS)	.30	.18
3	Joe Carter (AS)	.50	.30
4	Ken Griffey Jr. (AS)	4.00	2.50
5	Mark Langston (AS)	.12	.07

6	John Olerud (AS)	1.00	.70
7	Kirby Puckett (AS)	.75	.45
8	Cal Ripken Jr. (AS)	.80	.50
9	Ivan Rodriguez (AS)	.30	.18
10	Barry Bonds (AS)	1.25	.80
11	Darren Daulton (AS)	.15	.10
12	Marquis Grissom (AS)	.20	.12
13	David Justice (AS)	.75	.45
14	John Kruk (AS)	.12	.07
15	Barry Larkin (AS)	.15	.10
16	Terry Mulholland (AS)	.12	.07
17	Ryne Sandberg (AS)	.75	.45
18	Gary Sheffield (AS)	.30	.18
19	Chad Curtis	.25	.15
20	Chili Davis	.12	.07
21	Gary DiSarcina	.10	.06
22	Damion Easley	.20	.12
23	Chuck Finley	.12	.07
24	Luis Polonia	.10	.06
25	Tim Salmon	3.50	2.00
26	J.T. Snow	1.50	.90
27	Russ Springer	.12	.07
28	Jeff Bagwell	.40	.25
29	Craig Biggio	.12	.07
30	Ken Caminiti	.10	.06
31	Andujar Cedeno	.15	.10
32	Doug Drabek	.15	.10
33	Steve Finley	.10	.06
34	Luis Gonzalez	.15	.10
35	Pete Harnisch	.12	.07
36	Darryl Kile	.20	.12
37	Mike Bordick	.12	.07
38	Dennis Eckersley	.15	.10
39	Brent Gates	.40	.25
40	Rickey Henderson	.35	.20
41	Mark McGwire	.30	.18
42	Craig Poquette	.12	.07
43	Ruben Sierra	.20	.12
44	Terry Steinbach	.10	.06
45	Todd Van Poppel	.35	.20
46	Pat Borders	.10	.06
47	Tony Fernandez	.10	.06
48	Juan Guzman	.35	.20
49	Pat Hentgen	.50	.30
50	Paul Molitor	.40	.25
51	Jack Morris	.12	.07
52	Ed Sprague	.12	.07
53	Duane Ward	.10	.06
54	Devon White	.12	.07
55	Steve Avery	.35	.20
56	Jeff Blauser	.12	.07
57	Ron Gant	.20	.12
58	Tom Glavine	.40	.25
59	Greg Maddux	.30	.18
60	Fred McGriff	.75	.45
61	Terry Pendleton	.15	.10
62	Deion Sanders	.25	.15
63	John Smoltz	.12	.07
64	Cal Eldred	.20	.12
65	Darryl Hamilton	.15	.10
66	John Jaha	.20	.12
67	Pat Listach	.15	.10
68	Jaime Navarro	.10	.06
69	Kevin Reimer	.10	.06
70	B.J. Surhoff	.10	.06
71	Greg Vaughn	.15	.10
72	Robin Yount	.40	.25
73	Rene Arocha	.40	.25
74	Bernard Gilkey	.12	.07
75	Gregg Jefferies	.20	.12
76	Ray Lankford	.20	.12
77	Tom Pagnozzi	.10	.06
78	Lee Smith	.12	.07
79	Ozzie Smith	.30	.18
80	Bob Tewksbury	.10	.06
81	Mark Whiten	.25	.15
82	Steve Buechele	.10	.06
83	Mark Grace	.25	.15
84	Jose Guzman	.10	.06
85	Derrick May	.20	.12
86	Mike Morgan	.10	.06
87	Randy Myers	.12	.07
88	Kevin Roberson	.30	.18
89	Sammy Sosa	.20	.12
90	Rick Wilkins	.12	.07
91	Brett Butler	.12	.07
92	Eric Davis	.12	.07
93	Orel Hershiser	.12	.07
94	Eric Karros	.25	.15
95	Ramon Martinez	.15	.10
96	Raul Mondesi	.25	.15
97	Jose Offerman	.12	.07
98	Mike Piazza	7.50	4.00
99	Darryl Strawberry	.15	.10
100	Moises Alou	.15	.10
101	Wil Cordero	.25	.15
102	Delino DeShields	.15	.10
103	Darrin Fletcher	.12	.07
104	Ken Hill	.12	.07
105	Mike Lansing	.30	.18
106	Dennis Martinez	.10	.06
107	Larry Walker	.20	.12
108	John Wetteland	.12	.07
109	Rod Beck	.10	.06
110	John Burkett	.12	.07
111	Will Clark	.35	.20
112	Royce Clayton	.15	.10
113	Darren Lewis	.12	.07
114	Willie McGee	.12	.07
115	Bill Swift	.15	.10
116	Robby Thompson	.15	.10
117	Matt Williams	.25	.15
118	Sandy Alomar Jr.	.12	.07
119	Carlos Baerga	.75	.45

120	Albert Belle	.75	.45	177	Mickey Morandini	.12	.07
121	Reggie Jefferson	.12	.07	178	Curt Schilling	.12	.07
122	Kenny Lofton	.40	.25	179	Kevin Stocker	1.25	.80
123	Wayne Kirby	.12	.07	180	Mitch Williams	.10	.06
124	Carlos Martinez	.10	.06	181	Stan Belinda	.10	.06
125	Charles Nagy	.15	.10	182	Jay Bell	.12	.07
126	Paul Sorrento	.12	.07	183	Steve Cooke	.25	.15
127	Rich Amaral	.12	.07	184	Carlos Garcia	.20	.12
128	Jay Buhner	.12	.07	185	Jeff King	.12	.07
129	Norm Charlton	.10	.06	186	Orlando Merced	.15	.10
130	Dave Fleming	.25	.15	187	Don Slaught	.10	.06
131	Erik Hanson	.10	.06	188	Andy Van Slyke	.15	.10
132	Randy Johnson	.30	.18	189	Kevin Young	.35	.20
133	Edgar Martinez	.15	.10	190	Kevin Brown	.12	.07
134	Tino Martinez	.12	.07	191	Jose Canseco	.35	.20
135	Omar Vizquel	.10	.06	192	Julio Franco	.12	.07
136	Bret Barberie	.12	.07	193	Benji Gil	.40	.25
137	Chuck Carr	.20	.12	194	Juan Gonzalez	3.00	1.75
138	Jeff Conine	.15	.10	195	Tom Henke	.10	.06
139	Orestes Destrade	.12	.07	196	Rafael Palmeiro	.20	.12
140	Chris Hammond	.10	.06	197	Dean Palmer	.30	.18
141	Bryan Harvey	.12	.07	198	Nolan Ryan	3.50	2.00
142	Benito Santiago	.15	.10	199	Roger Clemens	.50	.30
143	Walt Weiss	.10	.06	200	Scott Cooper	.15	.10
144	Derrell Whitmore	.80	.50	201	Andre Dawson	.25	.15
145	Tim Bogar	.15	.10	202	Mike Greenwell	.12	.07
146	Bobby Bonilla	.15	.10	203	Carlos Quintana	.10	.06
147	Jeromy Burnitz	.40	.25	204	Jeff Russell	.10	.06
148	Vince Coleman	.12	.07	205	Aaron Sele	3.00	1.75
149	Dwight Gooden	.15	.10	206	Mo Vaughn	.30	.18
150	Todd Hundley	.10	.06	207	Frank Viola	.10	.06
151	Howard Johnson	.12	.07	208	Rob Dibble	.10	.06
152	Eddie Murray	.25	.15	209	Roberto Kelly	.15	.10
153	Brett Saberhagen	.15	.10	210	Kevin Mitchell	.12	.07
154	Brady Anderson	.12	.07	211	Hal Morris	.12	.07
155	Mike Devereaux	.10	.06	212	Joe Oliver	.10	.06
156	Jeffrey Hammonds	2.50	1.50	213	Jose Rijo	.12	.07
157	Chris Hoiles	.12	.07	214	Bip Roberts	.10	.06
158	Ben McDonald	.15	.10	215	Chris Sabo	.12	.07
159	Mark McLemore	.10	.06	216	Reggie Sanders	.25	.15
160	Mike Mussina	.60	.35	217	Dante Bichette	.12	.07
161	Gregg Olson	.10	.06	218	Jerald Clark	.10	.06
162	David Segui	.12	.07	219	Alex Cole	.10	.06
163	Derek Bell	.20	.12	220	Andres Galarraga	.15	.10
164	Andy Benes	.15	.10	221	Joe Girardi	.10	.06
165	Archi Cianfrocco	.15	.10	222	Charlie Hayes	.12	.07
166	Ricky Gutierrez	.12	.07	223	Roberto Mejia	.60	.35
167	Tony Gwynn	.35	.20	224	Armando Reynoso	.10	.06
168	Gene Harris	.10	.06	225	Eric Young	.20	.12
169	Trevor Hoffman	.20	.12	226	Kevin Appier	.12	.07
170	Ray McDavid	.75	.45	227	George Brett	.50	.30
171	Phil Plantier	.25	.15	228	David Cone	.12	.07
172	Mariano Duncan	.10	.06	229	Phil Hiatt	.25	.15
173	Lenny Dykstra	.25	.15	230	Felix Jose	.12	.07
174	Tommy Greene	.20	.12	231	Wally Joyner	.15	.10
175	Dave Hollins	.30	.18	232	Mike Macfarlane	.10	.06
176	Pete Incaviglia	.10	.06	233	Brian McRae	.15	.10

234	Jeff Montgomery	.10	.06
235	Rob Deer	.12	.07
236	Cecil Fielder	.35	.20
237	Travis Fryman	.60	.35
238	Mike Henneman	.10	.06
239	Tony Phillips	.12	.07
240	Mickey Tettleton	.12	.07
241	Alan Trammell	.20	.12
242	David Wells	.10	.06
243	Lou Whitaker	.12	.07
244	Rick Aguilera	.10	.06
245	Scott Erickson	.15	.10
246	Brian Harper	.12	.07
247	Kent Hrbek	.10	.06
248	Chuck Knoblauch	.15	.10
249	Shane Mack	.15	.10
250	David McCarty	.75	.45
251	Pedro Munoz	.12	.07
252	Dave Winfield	.40	.25
253	Alex Fernandez	.30	.18
254	Ozzie Guillen	.10	.06
255	Bo Jackson	.25	.15
256	Lance Johnson	.10	.06
257	Ron Karkovice	.10	.06
258	Jack McDowell	.30	.18
259	Tim Raines	.12	.07
260	Frank Thomas	5.00	3.00
261	Robin Ventura	.30	.18
262	Jim Abbott	.20	.12
263	Steve Farr	.10	.06
264	Jimmy Key	.12	.07
265	Don Mattingly	.40	.25
266	Paul O'Neill	.15	.10
267	Mike Stanley	.12	.07
268	Danny Tartabull	.12	.07
269	Bob Wickman	.30	.18
270	Bernie Williams	.15	.10
271	Jason Bere (P)	2.50	1.40
272	Roger Cedeno (P)	1.25	.80
273	Johnny Damon (P)	1.00	.60
274	Russ Davis (P)	1.50	.90
275	Carlos Delgado (P)	3.00	1.75
276	Carl Everett (P)	.50	.30
277	Cliff Floyd (P)	7.00	4.00
278	Alex Gonzalez (P)	2.50	1.40
279	Derek Jeter (P)	2.00	1.25
280	Chipper Jones (P)	2.50	1.50
281	Javy Lopez (P)	2.00	1.25
282	Chad Mottola (P)	2.50	1.40
283	Marc Newfield (P)	1.50	.90
284	Eduardo Perez (P)	2.50	1.50
285	Manny Ramirez (P)	3.50	2.00
286	Todd Steverson (P)	.60	.35
287	Michael Tucker (P)	1.25	.80
288	Allen Watson (P)	1.50	.90
289	Rondell White (P)	2.00	1.25
290	Dmitri Young (P)	1.50	.90

1993 Upper Deck SP Platinum Power

These limited insert cards were issued randomly in Upper Deck SP foil packs. The cards feature full color fronts and gold foil stamping with isolated action shots of the player superimposed over a background that resembles a blueprint for a baseball diamond and the words Platinum Power. The player's name appears in an arch above his picture. All cards measure 2-1/2" by 3-1/2".

		MINT	NR/MT
Complete Set (20)		180.00	100.00
Commons		5.00	3.00
1	Albert Belle	10.00	6.50
2	Barry Bonds	15.00	10.00
3	Joe Carter	8.50	5.00
4	Will Clark	7.50	4.50
5	Darren Daulton	5.00	3.00
6	Cecil Fielder	7.50	4.50
7	Ron Gant	5.00	3.00
8	Juan Gonzalez	18.00	12.00
9	Ken Griffey Jr.	20.00	13.50
10	Dave Hollins	5.00	3.00
11	David Justice	10.00	6.50
12	Fred McGriff	10.00	6.50
13	Mark McGwire	7.50	4.50
14	Dean Palmer	5.00	3.00
15	Mike Piazza	32.00	20.00
16	Tim Salmon	20.00	13.50
17	Ryne Sandberg	10.00	6.50
18	Gary Sheffield	6.50	3.75
19	Frank Thomas	25.00	16.00
20	Matt Williams	6.00	3.50

1994 Upper Deck Collector's Choice I

The cards in this set measure 2-1/2" by 3-1/2" and come in both vertical and horizontal formats. The fronts consist of full-color action shots printed on a glossy paper stock and framed by a white border. The player's name and position appear in the lower corner in white type next to a small silhouette of a player. The words "Collectors Choice " and the Upper Deck logo are printed in the top corner. The flip side contains another full color photo, personal data and statistics. Key subsets include Draft Picks (21-30) and Top Performers (TP)(306-315).

		MINT	NR/MT
Complete Set (320)		18.50	12.50
Commons		.05	.02

1	Rich Becker	.10	.06
2	Greg Blosser	.15	.10
3	Midre Cummings	.25	.15
4	Carlos Delgado	.75	.45
5	Steve Dreyer (R)	.15	.10
6	Carl Everett	.10	.06
7	Cliff Floyd	1.25	.80
8	Alex Gonzalez	.40	.25
9	Shawn Green	.10	.06
10	Butch Huskey	.15	.10
11	Mark Hutton	.10	.06
12	Miguel Jimenez	.15	.10
13	Steve Karsay	.25	.15
14	Marc Newfield	.25	.15
15	Luis Ortiz	.10	.06
16	Manny Ramirez	.80	.50
17	Johnny Ruffin	.05	.02
18	Scott Stahoviak	.08	.05
19	Salomon Torres	.20	.12
20	Gabe White	.12	.07
21	Brian Anderson (R)	.15	.10
22	Wayne Gomez (R)	.15	.10
23	Jeff Granger	30	18
24	Steve Soderstrom (R)	.15	.10
25	Trot Nixon (R)	1.00	.60
26	Kirk Presley (R)	.75	.45
27	Matt Brunson (R)	.15	.10
28	Brooks Kieschnick (R)	.80	.50
29	Billy Wagner (R)	.25	.15
30	Matt Drews (R)	.15	.10
31	Kurt Abbott (R)	.40	.25
32	Luis Alicea	.05	.02
33	Roberto Alomar	.30	.18
34	Sandy Alomar Jr.	.08	.05
35	Moises Alou	.12	.07
36	Wilson Alvarez	.10	.06
37	Rich Amaral	.08	.05
38	Eric Anthony	.12	.07
39	Luis Aquino	.05	.02
40	Jack Armstrong	.05	.02
41	Rene Arocha	.10	.06
42	Rich Aude (R)	.25	.15
43	Brad Ausmus	.05	.02
44	Steve Avery	.20	.12
45	Bob Ayrault	.08	.05
46	Willie Banks	.08	.05
47	Bret Barberie	.05	.02
48	Kim Batiste	.05	.02
49	Rod Beck	.08	.05
50	Jason Bere	.75	.45
51	Sean Berry	.10	.06
52	Dante Bichette	.08	.05
53	Jeff Blauser	.08	.05
54	Mike Blowers	.05	.02
55	Tim Bogar	.10	.06
56	Tom Bolton	.05	.02
57	Ricky Bones	.05	.02
58	Bobby Bonilla	.10	.06
59	Bret Boone	.12	.07
60	Pat Borders	.05	.02
61	Mike Bordick	.07	.04
62	Daryl Boston	.05	.02
63	Ryan Bowen	.08	.05
64	Jeff Branson	.08	.05
65	George Brett	.25	.15
66	Steve Buechele	.05	.02
67	Dave Burba	.05	.02
68	John Burkett	.08	.05
69	Jeromy Burnitz	.20	.12
70	Brett Butler	.07	.04
71	Rob Butler	.08	.05
72	Ken Caminiti	.05	.02
73	Cris Carpenter	.05	.02
74	Vinny Castilla	.05	.02
75	Andujar Cedeno	.10	.06
76	Wes Chamberlain	.10	.06
77	Archi Cianfrocco	.08	.05

78	Dave Clark	.05	.02
79	Jerald Clark	.05	.02
80	Royce Clayton	.10	.06
81	David Cone	.10	.06
82	Jeff Conine	.12	.07
83	Steve Cooke	.10	.06
84	Scott Cooper	.12	.07
85	Joey Cora	.05	.02
86	Tim Costo	.12	.07
87	Chad Curtis	.15	.10
88	Ron Darling	.05	.02
89	Danny Darwin	.05	.02
90	Rob Deer	.05	.02
91	Jim Deshaies	.05	.02
92	Delino DeShields	.10	.06
93	Rob Dibble	.05	.02
94	Gary DiSarcina	.07	.04
95	Doug Drabek	.10	.06
96	Scott Erickson	.10	.06
97	Rikkert Faneyte (R)	.15	.10
98	Jeff Fassero	.05	.02
99	Alex Fernandez	.20	.12
100	Cecil Fielder	.20	.12
101	Dave Fleming	.15	.10
102	Darrin Fletcher	.07	.04
103	Scott Fletcher	.05	.02
104	Mike Gallego	.05	.02
105	Carlos Garcia	.10	.06
106	Jeff Gardner	.05	.02
107	Brent Gates	.20	.12
108	Benji Gil	.20	.12
109	Bernard Gilkey	.10	.06
110	Chris Gomez	.12	.07
111	Luis Gonzalez	.10	.06
112	Tom Gordon	.08	.05
113	Jim Gott	.05	.02
114	Mark Grace	.15	.10
115	Tommy Greene	.12	.07
116	Willie Greene	.20	.12
117	Ken Griffey Jr.	1.25	.80
118	Bill Gullickson	.05	.02
119	Ricky Gutierrez	.07	.04
120	Juan Guzman	.20	.12
121	Chris Gwynn	.05	.02
122	Tony Gwynn	.15	.10
123	Jeffrey Hammonds	.40	.25
124	Erik Hanson	.05	.02
125	Gene Harris	.05	.02
126	Greg Harris	.05	.02
127	Bryan Harvey	.08	.05
128	Billy Hatcher	.05	.02
129	Hilly Hathaway	.08	.05
130	Charlie Hayes	.07	.04
131	Rickey Henderson	.15	.10
132	Mike Henneman	.05	.02
133	Pat Hentgen	.10	.06
134	Roberto Hernandez	.07	.04
135	Orel Hershiser	.08	.05
136	Phil Hiatt	.12	.07
137	Glenallen Hill	.08	.05
138	Ken Hill	.08	.05
139	Eric Hillman	.05	.02
140	Chris Hoiles	.08	.05
141	Dave Hollins	.15	.10
142	David Hulse	.08	.05
143	Todd Hundley	.07	.04
144	Pete Incaviglia	.05	.02
145	Danny Jackson	.05	.02
146	John Jaha	.10	.06
147	Domingo Jean	.12	.07
148	Gregg Jefferies	.15	.10
149	Reggie Jefferson	.10	.06
150	Lance Johnson	.05	.02
151	Bobby Jones	.20	.12
152	Chipper Jones	.60	.35
153	Todd Jones	.08	.05
154	Brian Jordan	.10	.06
155	Wally Joyner	.08	.05
156	David Justice	.25	.15
157	Ron Karkovice	.05	.02
158	Eric Karros	.15	.10
159	Jeff Kent	.12	.07
160	Jimmy Key	.08	.05
161	Mark Kiefer	.05	.02
162	Darryl Kile	.10	.06
163	Jeff King	.08	.05
164	Wayne Kirby	.08	.05
165	Ryan Klesko	.25	.15
166	Chuck Knoblauch	.12	.07
167	Chad Kreuter	.08	.05
168	John Kruk	.12	.07
169	Mark Langston	.10	.06
170	Mike Lansing	.12	.07
171	Barry Larkin	.10	.06
172	Manuel Lee	.05	.02
173	Phil Leftwich (R)	.12	.07
174	Darren Lewis	.08	.05
175	Derek Lilliquist	.05	.02
176	Jose Lind	.05	.02
177	Albie Lopez	.12	.07
178	Javier Lopez	.50	.30
179	Torey Lovullo	.05	.02
180	Scott Lydy	.08	.05
181	Mike Macfarlane	.05	.02
182	Shane Mack	.08	.05
183	Greg Maddux	.20	.12
184	Dave Magadan	.05	.02
185	Joe Magrane	.05	.02
186	Kirt Manwaring	.05	.02
187	Al Martin	.15	.10
188	Pedro A. Martinez	.15	.10
189	Pedro J. Martinez (R)	.15	.10
190	Ramon Martinez	.08	.05
191	Tino Martinez	.08	.05

192	Don Mattingly	.15	.10
193	Derrick May	.12	.07
194	David McCarty	.15	.10
195	Ben McDonald	.10	.06
196	Roger McDowell	.05	.02
197	Fred McGriff	.25	.15
198	Mark McLemore	.05	.02
199	Greg McMichael	.08	.05
200	Jeff McNeely	.12	.07
201	Brian McRae	.10	.06
202	Pat Meares	.08	.05
203	Roberto Mejia	.12	.07
204	Orlando Merced	.10	.06
205	Jose Mesa	.05	.02
206	Blas Minor	.05	.02
207	Angel Miranda	.05	.02
208	Paul Molitor	.15	.10
209	Raul Mondesi	.10	.06
210	Jeff Montgomery	.07	.04
211	Mickey Morandini	.08	.05
212	Mike Morgan	.05	.02
213	Jamie Moyer	.05	.02
214	Bobby Munoz	.10	.06
215	Troy Neel	.12	.07
216	Dave Nilsson	.07	.04
217	John O'Donoghue	.07	.04
218	Paul O'Neill	.08	.05
219	Jose Offerman	.08	.05
220	Joe Oliver	.05	.02
221	Greg Olson	.05	.02
222	Donovan Osborne	.10	.06
223	Jayhawk Owens	.10	.06
224	Mike Pagliarulo	.05	.02
225	Craig Paquette	.07	.04
226	Roger Pavlik	.10	.06
227	Brad Pennington	.07	.04
228	Eduardo Perez	.30	.18
229	Mike Perez	.08	.05
230	Tony Phillips	.07	.04
231	Hipolito Pichardo	.05	.02
232	Phil Plantier	.15	.10
233	Curtis Pride (R)	.60	.35
234	Tim Pugh	.08	.05
235	Scott Radinsky	.05	.02
236	Pat Rapp	.08	.05
237	Kevin Reimer	.05	.02
238	Armando Reynoso	.07	.04
239	Jose Rijo	.08	.05
240	Cal Ripken Jr.	.30	.18
241	Kevin Roberson	.15	.10
242	Kenny Rogers	.05	.02
243	Kevin Rogers	.05	.02
244	Mel Rojas	.05	.02
245	John Roper	.07	.04
246	Kirk Rueter	.25	.15
247	Scott Ruffcorn	.12	.07
248	Ken Ryan	.15	.10
249	Nolan Ryan	.80	.50
250	Bret Saberhagen	.08	.05
251	Tim Salmon	1.00	.60
252	Reggie Sanders	.10	.06
253	Curt Schilling	.08	.05
254	David Segui	.07	.04
255	Aaron Sele	.60	.35
256	Scott Servais	.05	.02
257	Gary Sheffield	.15	.10
258	Ruben Sierra	.12	.07
259	Don Slaught	.05	.02
260	Lee Smith	.08	.05
261	Cory Snyder	.05	.02
262	Paul Sorrento	.08	.05
263	Sammy Sosa	.15	.10
264	Bill Spiers	.05	.02
265	Mike Stanley	.08	.05
266	Dave Staton	.15	.10
267	Terry Steinbach	.05	.02
268	Kevin Stocker	.30	.18
269	Todd Stottlemyre	.05	.02
270	Doug Strange	.05	.02
271	Bill Swift	.08	.05
272	Kevin Tapani	.05	.02
273	Tony Tarasco	.15	.10
274	Julian Tavarez	.08	.05
275	Mickey Tettleton	.07	.04
276	Ryan Thompson	.10	.06
277	Chris Turner	.10	.06
278	John Valentin	.10	.06
279	Todd Van Poppel	.15	.10
280	Andy Van Slyke	.08	.05
281	Mo Vaughn	.15	.10
282	Robin Ventura	.15	.10
283	Frank Viola	.07	.04
284	Jose Vizcaino	.05	.02
285	Omar Vizquel	.08	.05
286	Larry Walker	.12	.07
287	Duane Ward	.05	.02
288	Allen Watson	.40	.25
289	Bill Wegman	.05	.02
290	Turk Wendell	.07	.04
291	Lou Whitaker	.07	.04
292	Devon White	.08	.05
293	Rondell White	.20	.12
294	Mark Whiten	.15	.10
295	Darrell Whitmore	.15	.10
296	Bob Wickman	.12	.07
297	Rick Wilkins	.08	.05
298	Bernie Williams	.10	.06
299	Matt Williams	.15	.10
300	Woody Williams	.10	.06
301	Nigel Wilson	.30	.18
302	Dave Winfield	.15	.10
303	Anthony Young	.07	.04
304	Eric Young	.08	.05
305	Todd Zeile	.08	.05

306	J. Burkett/T. Glavine J. McDowell (TP)	.15	.10
307	Randy Johnson (TP)	.20	.12
308	Randy Myers (TP)	.05	.02
309	Jack McDowell (TP)	.20	.12
310	Mike Piazza (TP)	1.25	.80
311	Barry Bonds (TP)	.00	.10
312	Andres Galarraga (TP)	.12	.07
313	Juan Gonzalez/ Barry Bonds (TP)	.60	.35
314	Albert Belle (TP)	.20	.12
315	Kenny Lofton (TP)	.15	.10
316	Checklist (1-64)	.05	.02
317	Checklist (65-128)	.05	.02
318	Checklist (129-192)	.05	.02
319	Checklist (193-256)	.05	.02
320	Checklist (257-320)	.05	.02

Hot Off The Presses
(1994 Card Sets)

1994 Donruss I

This 330-card set is the first of two series of 1994 Donruss Baseball. The card fronts feature full-bleed, full-color action shots with the player's name and position printed in gold type in a color stripe across the bottom of the card. The team logo appears in a block in the lower corner of the card just below the Donruss logo. The card backs contain another full color photo, personal data and stats. Limited inserts include a continuation of the Elite Series. Those cards are listed at the end of this checklist but are not included in the complete set price below. All cards measure 2-1/2" by 3-1/2".

		MINT	NR/MT
Complete Set (330)		20.00	12.50
Commons		.07	.04

1	Nolan Ryan	1.50	.90
2	Mike Piazza	3.00	1.75
3	Moises Alou	.15	.10
4	Ken Griffey Jr.	2.00	1.25
5	Gary Sheffield	.15	.10
6	Roberto Alomar	.35	.20
7	John Kruk	.12	.07
8	Gregg Olson	.07	.04
9	Gregg Jefferies	.15	.10
10	Tony Gwynn	.20	.12
11	Chad Curtis	.20	.12
12	Craig Biggio	.08	.05
13	John Burkett	.10	.06
14	Carlos Baerga	.40	.25
15	Robin Yount	.25	.15
16	Dennis Eckersley	.10	.06
17	Dwight Gooden	.10	.06
18	Ryne Sandberg	.50	.30
19	Rickey Henderson	.20	.12
20	Jack McDowell	.20	.12
21	Jay Bell	.08	.05
22	Kevin Brown	.08	.05
23	Robin Ventura	.20	.12
24	Paul Molitor	.25	.15
25	David Justice	.40	.25
26	Rafael Palmeiro	.20	.12
27	Cecil Fielder	.20	.12
28	Chuck Knoblauch	.10	.06
29	Dave Hollins	.20	.12
30	Jimmy Key	.08	.05
31	Mark Langston	.10	.06
32	Darryl Kile	.10	.06
33	Ruben Sierra	.15	.10
34	Ron Gant	.15	.10
35	Ozzie Smith	.15	.10
36	Wade Boggs	.20	.12
37	Marquis Grissom	.15	.10
38	Will Clark	.20	.12
39	Kenny Lofton	.25	.15
40	Cal Ripken Jr.	.50	.30
41	Steve Avery	.20	.12
42	Mo Vaughn	.20	.12
43	Brian McRae	.10	.06
44	Mickey Tettleton	.08	.05
45	Barry Larkin	.12	.07
46	Charlie Hayes	.07	.04
47	Kevin Appier	.12	.07
48	Robby Thompson	.08	.05
49	Juan Gonzalez	1.25	.80
50	Paul O'Neill	.10	.06
51	Marcos Armas (R)	.15	.10
52	Mike Butcher	.08	.05
53	Ken Caminiti	.07	.04
54	Pat Borders	.07	.04
55	Pedro Munoz	.10	.06
56	Tim Belcher	.07	.04
57	Paul Assenmacher	.07	.04
58	Damon Berryhill	.07	.04
59	Rickey Bones	.07	.04
60	Rene Arocha	.10	.06
61	Shawn Boskie	.07	.04
62	Pedro Astacio	.10	.06
63	Frank Bolick	.07	.04
64	Bud Black	.07	.04
65	Sandy Alomar Jr.	.08	.05
66	Rich Amaral	.08	.05
67	Luis Aquino	.07	.04
68	Kevin Baez	.08	.05
69	Mike Devereaux	.08	.05
70	Andy Ashby	.08	.05
71	Larry Andersen	.07	.04
72	Steve Cooke	.12	.07
73	Mario Diaz	.07	.04
74	Rob Deer	.07	.04
75	Bobby Ayala	.08	.05
76	Freddie Benavides	.07	.04
77	Stan Belinda	.07	.04
78	John Doherty	.07	.04

79	Willie Banks	.10	.06	136	Jerald Clark	.07	.04
80	Spike Owen	.07	.04	137	Billy Brewer	.10	.06
81	Mike Bordick	.08	.05	138	Dan Gladden	.07	.04
82	Chili Davis	.08	.05	139	Eddie Guardado	.10	.06
83	Luis Gonzalez	.10	.06	140	Checklist	.07	.04
84	Ed Sprague	.08	.05	141	Scott Hemond	.07	.04
85	Jeff Reboulet	.10	.06	142	Steve Frey	.07	.04
86	Jason Bere	.75	.45	143	Xavier Hernandez	.08	.05
87	Mark Hutton	.15	.10	144	Mark Eichhorn	.07	.04
88	Jeff Blauser	.08	.05	145	Ellis Burks	.10	.06
89	Cal Eldred	.15	.10	146	Jim Leyritz	.07	.04
90	Bernard Gilkey	.10	.06	147	Mark Lemke	.07	.04
91	Frank Castillo	.07	.04	148	Pat Listach	.10	.06
92	Jim Gott	.07	.04	149	Donovan Osborne	.10	.06
93	Greg Colbrunn	.10	.06	150	Glenallen Hill	.08	.05
94	Jeff Brantley	.07	.04	151	Orel Hershiser	.08	.05
95	Jeremy Hernandez	.08	.05	152	Darrin Fletcher	.08	.05
96	Norm Charlton	.07	.04	153	Royce Clayton	.12	.07
97	Alex Arias	.07	.04	154	Derek Lilliquist	.07	.04
98	John Franco	.07	.04	155	Mike Felder	.07	.04
99	Chris Hoiles	.10	.06	156	Jeff Conine	.15	.10
100	Brad Ausmus	.08	.05	157	Ryan Thompson	.12	.07
101	Wes Chamberlain	.10	.06	158	Ben McDonald	.12	.07
102	Mark Dewey	.10	.06	159	Ricky Gutierrez	.08	.05
103	Benji Gil	.20	.12	160	Terry Mulholland	.08	.05
104	John Dopson	.07	.04	161	Carlos Garcia	.12	.07
105	John Smiley	.08	.05	162	Tom Henke	.07	.04
106	David Nied	.35	.20	163	Mike Greenwell	.08	.05
107	George Brett	.40	.25	164	Thomas Howard	.07	.04
108	Kirk Gibson	.08	.05	165	Joe Girardi	.07	.04
109	Larry Casian	.08	.05	166	Hubie Brooks	.07	.04
110	Checklist	.07	.04	167	Greg Gohr	.10	.06
111	Brent Gates	.25	.15	168	Chip Hale	.08	.05
112	Damion Easley	.08	.05	169	Rick Honeycutt	.07	.04
113	Pete Harnisch	.08	.05	170	Hilly Hathaway	.10	.06
114	Danny Cox	.07	.04	171	Todd Jones	.10	.06
115	Kevin Tapani	.08	.05	172	Tony Fernandez	.07	.04
116	Roberto Hernandez	.08	.05	173	Bo Jackson	.12	.07
117	Domingo Jean	.20	.12	174	Bobby Munoz	.12	.07
118	Sid Bream	.07	.04	175	Greg McMichael	.10	.06
119	Doug Henry	.08	.05	176	Graeme Lloyd	.12	.07
120	Omar Olivares	.07	.04	177	Tom Pagnozzi	.07	.04
121	Mike Harkey	.08	.05	178	Derrick May	.12	.07
122	Carlos Hernandez	.08	.05	179	Pedro Martinez	.15	.10
123	Jeff Fassero	.07	.04	180	Ken Hill	.08	.05
124	Dave Burba	.07	.04	181	Bryan Hickerson	.08	.05
125	Wayne Kirby	.08	.05	182	Jose Mesa	.07	.04
126	John Cummings	.12	.07	183	Dave Fleming	.10	.06
127	Bret Barberie	.07	.04	184	Henry Cotto	.07	.04
128	Todd Hundley	.08	.05	185	Jeff Kent	.12	.07
129	Tim Hulett	.08	.05	186	Mark McLemore	.07	.04
130	Phil Clark	.08	.05	187	Trevor Hoffman	.10	.06
131	Danny Jackson	.07	.04	188	Todd Pratt	.08	.05
132	Tom Foley	.07	.04	189	Blas Minor	.07	.04
133	Donald Harris	.10	.06	190	Charlie Leibrandt	.07	.04
134	Scott Fletcher	.07	.04	191	Tony Pena	.07	.04
135	Johnny Ruffin	.08	.05	192	Larry Luebbers (R)	.12	.07

193	Greg Harris	.07	.04
194	David Cone	.10	.06
195	Bill Gullickson	.07	.04
196	Brian Harper	.08	.05
197	Steve Karsay	.25	.15
198	Greg Myers	.08	.05
199	Mark Portugal	.08	.05
200	Pat Hentgen	.12	.07
201	Mike LaValliere	.07	.04
202	Mike Stanley	.08	.05
203	Kent Mercker	.07	.04
204	Dave Nilsson	.08	.05
205	Erik Pappas	.08	.05
206	Mike Morgan	.07	.04
207	Roger McDowell	.07	.04
208	Mike Lansing	.10	.06
209	Kirt Manwaring	.07	.04
210	Randy Milligan	.07	.04
211	Erik Hanson	.07	.04
212	Orestes Destrade	.10	.06
213	Mike Maddux	.07	.04
214	Alan Mills	.08	.05
215	Tim Mauser	.10	.06
216	Ben Rivera	.08	.05
217	Don Slaught	.07	.04
218	Bob Patterson	.07	.04
219	Carlos Quintana	.08	.05
220	Checklist	.07	.04
221	Hal Morris	.10	.06
222	Darren Holmes	.10	.06
223	Chris Gwynn	.07	.04
224	Chad Kreuter	.10	.06
225	Mike Hartley	.07	.04
226	Scott Lydy	.10	.06
227	Eduardo Perez	.35	.20
228	Greg Swindell	.08	.05
229	Al Leiter	.07	.04
230	Scott Radinsky	.07	.04
231	Bob Wickman	.15	.10
232	Otis Nixon	.08	.05
233	Kevin Reimer	.07	.04
234	Geronimo Pena	.07	.04
235	Kevin Roberson	.12	.07
236	Jody Reed	.07	.04
237	Kirk Rueter	.50	.30
238	Willie McGee	.08	.05
239	Charles Nagy	.10	.06
240	Tim Leary	.07	.04
241	Carl Everett	.10	.06
242	Charlie O'Brien	.07	.04
243	Mike Pagliarulo	.07	.04
244	Kerry Taylor	.10	.06
245	Kevin Stocker	.60	.35
246	Joel Johnston	.07	.04
247	Geno Petralli	.07	.04
248	Jeff Russell	.07	.04
249	Joe Oliver	.07	.04
250	Robert Mejia	.15	.10
251	Chris Haney	.10	.06
252	Bill Krueger	.07	.04
253	Shane Mack	.08	.05
254	Terry Steinbach	.07	.04
255	Luis Polonia	.08	.05
256	Eddie Taubensee	.07	.04
257	Dave Stewart	.10	.06
258	Tim Raines	.10	.06
259	Bernie Williams	.10	.06
260	John Smoltz	.12	.07
261	Kevin Seitzer	.07	.04
262	Bob Tewksbury	.07	.04
263	Bob Scanlan	.07	.04
264	Henry Rodriquez	.10	.06
265	Tim Scott	.07	.04
266	Scott Sanderson	.07	.04
267	Eric Plunk	.07	.04
268	Edgar Martinez	.10	.06
269	Charlie Hough	.07	.04
270	Joe Orsulak	.07	.04
271	Harold Reynolds	.07	.04
272	Tim Teufel	.07	.04
273	Bobby Thigpen	.07	.04
274	Randy Tomlin	.08	.05
275	Gary Redus	.07	.04
276	Ken Ryan	.15	.10
277	Tim Pugh	.10	.06
278	Jayhawk Owens	.10	.06
279	Phil Hiatt	.12	.07
280	Alan Trammell	.12	.07
281	Dave McCarty	.20	.12
282	Bob Welch	.07	.04
283	J.T. Snow	.50	.30
284	Brian Williams	.08	.05
285	Devon White	.08	.05
286	Steve Sax	.08	.05
287	Tony Tarasco	.20	.12
288	Bill Spiers	.07	.04
289	Allen Watson	.30	.18
290	Checklist	.07	.04
291	Jose Vizcaino	.07	.04
292	Darryl Strawberry	.12	.07
293	John Wetteland	.10	.06
294	Bill Swift	.10	.06
295	Jeff Treadway	.07	.04
296	Tino Martinez	.10	.06
297	Richie Lewis	.10	.06
298	Bret Saberhagen	.10	.06
299	Arthur Rhodes	.10	.06
300	Guillermo Velasquez	.08	.05
301	Milt Thompson	.07	.04
302	Doug Strange	.07	.04
303	Aaron Sele	.75	.45
304	Bip Roberts	.07	.04
305	Bruce Ruffin	.07	.04
306	Jose Lind	:07	.04

		MINT	NR/MT
307	David Wells	.07	.04
308	Bobby Witt	.08	.05
309	Mark Wohlers	.10	.06
310	B.J. Surhoff	.07	.04
311	Mark Whiten	.15	.10
312	Turk Wendell	.08	.05
313	Raul Mondesi	.15	.10
314	Brian Turang (R)	.15	.10
315	Chris Hammond	.07	.04
316	Tim Bogar	.10	.06
317	Brad Pennington	.08	.05
318	Tim Worrell	.10	.06
319	Mitch Williams	.07	.04
320	Rondell White	.50	.30
321	Frank Viola	.08	.05
322	Manny Ramirez	.80	.50
323	Gary Wayne	.10	.06
324	Mike Macfarlane	.07	.04
325	Russ Springer	.10	.06
326	Tim Wallach	.08	.05
327	Salomon Torres	.30	.18
328	Omar Vizquel	.10	.06
329	Andy Tomberlin (R)	.15	.10
330	Chris Sabo	.08	.05
E37	Frank Thomas	150.00	90.00
E38	Tony Gwynn	50.00	32.00
E39	Tim Salmon	100.00	60.00
E40	Albert Belle	60.00	38.00
E41	John Kruk	30.00	18.50
E42	Juan Gonzalez	100.00	60.00

1994 Donruss
Special Edition

The cards in this insert set were issued one per pack in 1994 Donruss baseball packs. The cards feature full-color action photos with gold accents. All cards measure 2-1/2" by 3-1/2".

		MINT	NR/MT
Complete Set (50)		28.00	18.00
Commons		.20	.12
1	Nolan Ryan	2.50	1.40
2	Mike Piazza	6.00	3.50
3	Moises Alou	.25	.15
4	Ken Griffey Jr.	3.50	2.00
5	Gary Sheffield	.30	.18
6	Roberto Alomar	.80	.50
7	John Kruk	.30	.18
8	Gregg Olson	.20	.12
9	Gregg Jefferies	.35	.20
10	Tony Gwynn	.40	.25
11	Chad Curtis	.35	.20
12	Craig Biggio	.20	.12
13	John Burkett	.25	.15
14	Carlos Baerga	1.00	.60
15	Robin Yount	.75	.45
16	Dennis Eckersley	.25	.15
17	Dwight Gooden	.25	.15
18	Ryne Sandberg	.90	.55
19	Rickey Henderson	.50	.30
20	Jack McDowell	.50	.30
21	Jay Bell	.25	.15
22	Kevin Brown	.25	.15
23	Robin Ventura	.60	.35
24	Paul Molitor	.60	.35
25	David Justice	1.00	.60
26	Rafael Palmeiro	.30	.18
27	Cecil Fielder	.50	.30
28	Chuck Knoblauch	.25	.15
29	Dave Hollins	.40	.25
30	Jimmy Key	.25	.15
31	Mark Langston	.25	.15
32	Darryl Kile	.30	.18
33	Ruben Sierra	.30	.18
34	Ron Gant	.30	.18
35	Ozzie Smith	.35	.20
36	Wade Boggs	.40	.25
37	Marquis Grissom	.30	.18
38	Will Clark	.60	.35
39	Kenny Lofton	.60	.35
40	Cal Ripken Jr.	1.25	.80
41	Steve Avery	.50	.30
42	Mo Vaughn	.60	.35
43	Brian McRae	.25	.15
44	Mickey Tettleton	.20	.12
45	Barry Larkin	.30	.18
46	Charlie Hayes	.20	.12
47	Kevin Appier	.35	.20
48	Robby Thompson	.20	.12
49	Juan Gonzalez	2.50	1.40
50	Paul O'Neill	.25	.15

1994 Donruss I Diamond Kings

The cards in this insert set feature the work of noted Hall of Fame artist Dick Perez and were distributed randomly in Donruss packs. The full-color fronts consist of artist renderings of some of the top stars of the game. All cards measure 2-1/2" by 3-1/2".

		MINT	NR/MT
Complete Set (14)		28.00	18.00
Commons		1.50	.90

1	Barry Bonds	6.50	3.75
2	Mo Vaughn	2.00	1.25
3	Steve Avery	2.50	1.50
4	Tim Salmon	7.50	4.00
5	Rick Wilkins	1.50	.90
6	Brian Harper	1.50	.90
7	Andres Galarraga	2.00	1.25
8	Albert Belle	5.00	3.00
9	John Kruk	2.50	1.50
10	Ivan Rodriquez	2.50	1.50
11	Tony Gwynn	3.50	2.00
12	Brian McRae	2.00	1.25
13	Bobby Bonilla	2.00	1.25
14	Ken Griffey Jr.	10.00	6.50

1994 Donruss I Decade Dominators

The cards in this limited insert set were randomly distributed in all Donruss packs. The fronts feature full-color action shots with the headline "Dominators" printed across the bottom in bold type just above the player's name and his accomplishment.

		MINT	NR/MT
Complete Set (10)		38.00	22.00
Commons		2.50	1.50

1	Cecil Fielder	3.50	2.00
2	Barry Bonds	6.50	3.75
3	Fred McGriff	5.00	3.00
4	Matt Williams	2.50	1.50
5	Joe Carter	4.00	2.50
6	Juan Gonzalez	8.50	5.00
7	Jose Canseco	7.50	2.00
8	Ron Gant	2.50	1.50
9	Ken Griffey Jr.	10.00	6.50
10	Mark McGwire	3.50	2.00

1994 Donruss MVP's

These limited inserts consist of full-color fronts with an MVP logo printed on the card. They were inserted randomly in Donruss packs and measure 2-1/2" by 3-1/2".

		MINT	NR/MT
Complete Set (14)		35.00	22.00
Commons		.80	.50

1	David Justice	5.00	3.00
2	Mark Grace	2.00	1.25
3	Jose Rijo	.80	.50
4	Andres Galarraga	1.50	.90
5	Bryan Harvey	1.00	.60
6	Jeff Bagwell	3.50	2.00
7	Mike Piazza	12.00	7.50
8	Moises Alou	1.25	.80
9	Bobby Bonilla	1.00	.60
10	Lenny Dykstra	2.50	1.50
11	Jeff King	.80	.50
12	Greg Jefferies	1.75	1.00
13	Tony Gwynn	3.00	1.75
14	Barry Bonds	6.50	3.75

1994 Donruss Spirit Of The Game

The cards in this limited insert set were distributed randomly in Donruss packs and feature full-color action shots on the card fronts with a "Spirit of the Game" headline printed across the front. All cards measure 2-1/2" by 3-1/2"

		MINT	NR/MT
Complete Set (5)		38.00	24.00
Commons		6.00	3.75
1	John Olerud	6.00	3.75
2	Barry Bonds	7.00	4.00
3	Ken Griffey jr.	10.00	6.50
4	Mike Piazza	12.50	7.50
5	Juan Gonzalez	8.50	5.00

1994 Donruss Anniversary

The cards in this 10-card insert set were distributed randomly in Donruss hobby packs. The cards measure 2-1/2" by 3-1/2".

		MINT	NR/MT
Complete Set (10)		32.00	20.00
Commons		2.50	1.50
1	Don Mattingly	4.50	2.75
2	Joe Carter	2.50	1.50
3	Cal Ripken Jr.	6.00	3.75
4	Ryne Sandberg	5.00	3.00
5	Robin Yount	4.00	2.50
6	Nolan Ryan	8.00	5.00
7	Tony Gwynn	2.50	1.50
8	Wade Boggs	2.50	1.50
9	Rickey Henderson	2.50	1.50
10	George Brett	5.00	3.00

1994 Fleer

The cards in this set were issued in a single series and feature full-color action photos on the card fronts framed by a white border. A team logo appears in the top corner while the player's name and position are printed in gold foil in a semi-circle around the team logo. The flip side consists of another full color photo along with personal data and stats. Tim Salmon is featured in a limited 12-card metalized insert set. Those cards were distributed randomly in all Fleer pack types and are not included in the complete set price below but are listed and the end of this checklist. All cards measure 2-1/2" by 3-1/2".

		MINT	NR/MT
Complete Set (720)		50.00	32.00
Commons		.05	.02
1	Brady Anderson	.10	.06
2	Harold Baines	.08	.05
3	Mike Devereaux	.07	.04
4	Todd Frohwirth	.05	.02
5	Jeffrey Hammonds	.60	.35
6	Chris Hoiles	.08	.05
7	Tim Hulett	.08	.05
8	Ben McDonald	.10	.06
9	Mark McLemore	.05	.02
10	Alan Mills	.07	.04
11	Jamie Moyer	.05	.02
12	Mike Mussina	.25	.15
13	Gregg Olson	.07	.04
14	Mike Pagliarulo	.05	.02
15	Brad Pennington	.07	.04
16	Jim Poole	.05	.02
17	Harold Reynolds	.05	.02
18	Arthur Rhodes	.08	.05
19	Cal Ripken Jr.	.30	.18

20	David Segui	.07	.04
21	Rick Sutcliffe	.05	.02
22	Fernando Valenzuela	.05	.02
23	Jack Voight	.07	.04
24	Mark Williamson	.05	.02
25	Scott Bankhead	.05	.02
26	Roger Clemens	.25	.15
27	Scott Cooper	.12	.07
28	Danny Darwin	.05	.02
29	Andre Dawson	.12	.07
30	Rob Deer	.05	.02
31	John Dopson	.05	.02
32	Scott Fletcher	.05	.02
33	Mike Greenwell	.08	.05
34	Greg Harris	.05	.02
35	Billy Hatcher	.05	.02
36	Bob Melvin	.05	.02
37	Tony Pena	.05	.02
38	Paul Quantrill	.07	.04
39	Carlos Quintana	.07	.04
40	Ernest Riles	.05	.02
41	Jeff Russell	.05	.02
42	Ken Ryan (R)	.25	.15
43	Aaron Sele	.75	.45
44	John Valentin	.08	.05
45	Mo Vaughn	.15	.10
46	Frank Viola	.07	.04
47	Bob Zupcic	.08	.05
48	Mike Butcher	.08	.05
49	Rod Correia	.08	.05
50	Chad Curtis	.20	.12
51	Chili Davis	.07	.04
52	Gary DiSarcina	.07	.04
53	Damion Easley	.07	.04
54	Jim Edmonds	.10	.06
55	Chuck Finley	.10	.06
56	Steve Frey	.05	.02
57	Rene Gonzales	.05	.02
58	Joe Grahe	.05	.02
59	Hilly Hathaway	.10	.06
60	Stan Javier	.05	.02
61	Mark Langston	.10	.06
62	Phil Leftwich	.15	.10
63	Torey Lovullo	.05	.02
64	Joe Magrane	.05	.02
65	Greg Myers	.05	.02
66	Ken Patterson	.05	.02
67	Eduardo Perez	.80	.50
68	Luis Polonia	.07	.04
69	Tim Salmon	1.00	.60
70	J.T. Snow	.60	.35
71	Ron Tingley	.08	.05
72	Julio Valera	.05	.02
73	Wilson Alvarez	.10	.06
74	Tim Belcher	.05	.02
75	George Bell	.08	.05
76	Jason Bere	.75	.45
77	Rod Bolton	.05	.02
78	Ellis Burks	.08	.05
79	Joey Cora	.05	.02
80	Alex Fernandez	.20	.12
81	Craig Grebeck	.05	.02
82	Ozzie Guillen	.05	.02
83	Roberto Hernandez	.08	.05
84	Bo Jackson	.15	.10
85	Lance Johnson	.05	.02
86	Ron Karkovice	.05	.02
87	Mike LaValliere	.05	.02
88	Kirk McCaskill	.05	.02
89	Jack McDowell	.20	.12
90	Warren Newson	.05	.02
91	Dan Pasqua	.05	.02
92	Scott Radinsky	.05	.02
93	Tim Raines	.08	.05
94	Steve Sax	.07	.04
95	Jeff Schwarz	.10	.06
96	Frank Thomas	1.50	.90
97	Robin Ventura	.15	.10
98	Sandy Alomar Jr.	.08	.05
99	Carlos Baerga	.25	.15
100	Albert Belle	.25	.15
101	Mark Clark	.08	.05
102	Jerry DiPoto	.07	.04
103	Alvaro Espinoza	.05	.02
104	Felix Fermin	.05	.02
105	Jeremy Hernandez	.07	.04
106	Reggie Jefferson	.10	.06
107	Wayne Kirby	.08	.05
108	Tom Kramer	.10	.06
109	Mark Lewis	.07	.04
110	Derek Lilliquist	.05	.02
111	Kenny Lofton	.20	.12
112	Candy Maldonado	.05	.02
113	Jose Mesa	.05	.02
114	Jeff Mutis	.08	.05
115	Charles Nagy	.12	.07
116	Bob Ojeda	.05	.02
117	Junior Ortiz	.05	.02
118	Eric Plunk	.05	.02
119	Manny Ramirez	.80	.50
120	Paul Sorrento	.10	.06
121	Jim Thome	.20	.12
122	Jeff Treadway	.05	.02
123	Bill Wertz	.10	.06
124	Skeeter Barnes	.05	.02
125	Milt Cuyler	.08	.05
126	Eric Davis	.10	.06
127	John Doherty	.08	.05
128	Cecil Fielder	.15	.10
129	Travis Fryman	.25	.15
130	Kirk Gibson	.08	.05
131	Dan Gladden	.05	.02
132	Greg Gohr	.08	.05
133	Chris Gomez	.10	.06

134	Bill Gullickson	.05	.02
135	Mike Henneman	.05	.02
136	Kurt Knudsen	.05	.02
137	Chad Kreuter	.08	.05
138	Bill Krueger	.05	.02
139	Scott Livingstone	.05	.02
140	Bob MacDonald	.07	.04
141	Mike Moore	.05	.02
142	Tony Phillips	.07	.04
143	Mickey Tettleton	.07	.04
144	Alan Trammell	.10	.06
145	David Wells	.05	.02
146	Lou Whitaker	.08	.05
147	Kevin Appier	.15	.10
148	Stan Belinda	.05	.02
149	George Brett	.25	.15
150	Billy Brewer	.08	.05
151	Hubie Brooks	.05	.02
152	David Cone	.10	.06
153	Gary Gaetti	.05	.02
154	Greg Gagne	.05	.02
155	Tom Gordon	.08	.05
156	Mark Gubicza	.05	.02
157	Chris Gwynn	.05	.02
158	John Habyan	.05	.02
159	Chris Haney	.08	.05
160	Phil Hiatt	.12	.07
161	Felix Jose	.08	.05
162	Wally Joyner	.10	.06
163	Jose Lind	.05	.02
164	Mike Macfarlane	.05	.02
165	Mike Magnante	.08	.05
166	Brent Mayne	.05	.02
167	Brian McRae	.10	.06
168	Kevin McReynolds	.05	.02
169	Keith Miller	.05	.02
170	Jeff Montgomery	.07	.04
171	Hipolito Pichardo	.07	.04
172	Rico Rossy	.08	.05
173	Juan Bell	.05	.02
174	Ricky Bones	.05	.02
175	Cal Eldred	.15	.10
176	Mike Fetters	.05	.02
177	Darryl Hamilton	.10	.06
178	Doug Henry	.08	.05
179	Mike Ignasiak	.10	.06
180	John Jaha	.10	.06
181	Pat Listach	.05	.02
182	Graeme Lloyd	.12	.07
183	Matt Mieske	.10	.06
184	Angel Miranda	.07	.04
185	Jaime Navarro	.07	.04
186	Dave Nilsson	.07	.04
187	Troy O'Leary	.10	.06
188	Jesse Orosco	.05	.02
189	Kevin Reimer	.05	.02
190	Kevin Seitzer	.05	.02
191	Bill Spiers	.05	.02
192	B.J. Surhoff	.05	.02
193	Dickie Thon	.05	.02
194	Jose Valentin	.10	.06
195	Greg Vaughn	.12	.07
196	Bill Wegman	.05	.02
197	Robin Yount	.25	.15
198	Rick Aguilera	.05	.02
199	Willie Banks	.08	.05
200	Bernardo Brito	.05	.02
201	Larry Casian (R)	.10	.06
202	Scott Erickson	.10	.06
203	Eddie Guardado	.10	.06
204	Mark Guthrie	.10	.06
205	Chip Hale	.07	.04
206	Brian Harper	.07	.04
207	Mike Hartley	.07	.04
208	Kent Hrbek	.07	.04
209	Terry Jorgensen (R)	.15	.10
210	Chuck Knoblauch	.12	.07
211	Gene Larkin	.05	.02
212	Shane Mack	.08	.05
213	David McCarty	.25	.15
214	Pat Meares	.10	.06
215	Pedro Munoz	.08	.05
216	Derek Parks	.08	.05
217	Kirby Puckett	.25	.15
218	Jeff Reboulet	.08	.05
219	Kevin Tapani	.07	.04
220	Mike Trombley	.07	.04
221	George Tsamis	.10	.06
222	Carl Willis	.05	.02
223	Dave Winfield	.25	.15
224	Jim Abbott	.15	.10
225	Paul Assenmacher	.05	.02
226	Wade Boggs	.15	.10
227	Russ Davis	.30	.18
228	Steve Farr	.05	.02
229	Mike Gallego	.05	.02
230	Paul Gibson	.05	.02
231	Steve Howe	.05	.02
232	Dion James	.05	.02
233	Domingo Jean	.20	.12
234	Scott Kamieniecki	.05	.02
235	Pat Kelly	.08	.05
236	Jimmy Key	.08	.05
237	Jim Leyritz	.05	.02
238	Kevin Maas	.08	.05
239	Don Mattingly	.20	.12
240	Rich Monteleone	.05	.02
241	Bobby Munoz	.08	.05
242	Matt Nokes	.05	.02
243	Paul O'Neill	.10	.06
244	Spike Owen	.05	.02
245	Melido Perez	.05	.02
246	Lee Smith	.10	.06
247	Mike Stanley	.08	.05

248	Danny Tartabull	.10	.06
249	Randy Velarde	.05	.02
250	Bob Wickman	.20	.12
251	Bernie Williams	.10	.06
252	Mike Aldrete	.05	.02
253	Marcos Armas	.20	.12
254	Lance Blankenship	.03	.02
255	Mike Bordick	.08	.05
256	Scott Brosius	.05	.02
257	Jerry Browne	.05	.02
258	Ron Darling	.05	.02
259	Kelly Downs	.05	.02
260	Dennis Eckersley	.12	.07
261	Brent Gates	.20	.12
262	Goose Gossage	.07	.04
263	Scott Hemond	.05	.02
264	Dave Henderson	.05	.02
265	Rick Honeycutt	.05	.02
266	Vince Horsman	.08	.05
267	Scott Lydy	.08	.05
268	Mark McGwire	.15	.10
269	Mike Mohler	.12	.07
270	Troy Neel	.20	.12
271	Edwin Nunez	.05	.02
272	Craig Paquette	.08	.05
273	Ruben Sierra	.12	.07
274	Terry Steinbach	.05	.02
275	Todd Van Poppel	.25	.15
276	Bob Welch	.05	.02
277	Bobby Witt	.07	.04
278	Rich Amaral	.08	.05
279	Mike Blowers	.05	.02
280	Bret Boone	.15	.10
281	Chris Bosio	.07	.04
282	Jay Buhner	.08	.05
283	Norm Charlton	.05	.02
284	Mike Felder	.05	.02
285	Dave Fleming	.12	.07
286	Ken Griffey Jr.	1.25	.80
287	Erik Hanson	.05	.02
288	Bill Haselman	.07	.04
289	Brad Holman	.05	.02
290	Randy Johnson	.15	.10
291	Tim Leary	.05	.02
292	Greg Litton	.05	.02
293	Dave Magadan	.05	.02
294	Edgar Martinez	.10	.06
295	Tino Martinez	.08	.05
296	Jeff Nelson	.07	.04
297	Erik Platenberg (R)	.12	.07
298	Mackey Sasser	.05	.02
299	Brian Turang	.08	.05
300	Dave Valle	.05	.02
301	Omar Vizquel	.08	.05
302	Brian Bohanon	.05	.02
303	Kevin Brown	.10	.06
304	Jose Canseco	.15	.10
305	Mario Diaz	.05	.02
306	Julio Franco	.08	.05
307	Juan Gonzalez	1.00	.60
308	Tom Henke	.05	.02
309	David Hulse	.08	.05
310	Manuel Lee	.05	.02
311	Craig Lefferts	.05	.02
312	Charlie Leibrandt	.05	.02
313	Rafael Palmeiro	.15	.10
314	Dean Palmer	.20	.12
315	Roger Pavlik	.15	.10
316	Dan Peltier	.10	.06
317	Geno Petralli	.05	.02
318	Gary Redus	.05	.02
319	Ivan Rodriquez	.15	.10
320	Kenny Rogers	.05	.02
321	Nolan Ryan	.75	.45
322	Doug Strange	.05	.02
323	Matt Whiteside	.08	.05
324	Roberto Alomar	.25	.15
325	Pat Borders	.05	.02
326	Joe Carter	.20	.12
327	Tony Castillo	.08	.05
328	Darnell Coles	.05	.02
329	Danny Cox	.05	.02
330	Mark Eichhorn	.05	.02
331	Tony Fernandez	.05	.02
332	Alfredo Griffin	.05	.02
333	Juan Guzman	.15	.10
334	Rickey Henderson	.15	.10
335	Pat Hentgen	.10	.06
336	Randy Knorr	.08	.05
337	Al Leiter	.05	.02
338	Paul Molitor	.20	.12
339	Jack Morris	.08	.05
340	John Olerud	.30	.18
341	Dick Schofield	.05	.02
342	Ed Sprague	.08	.05
343	Dave Stewart	.10	.06
344	Todd Stottlemyre	.05	.02
345	Mike Timlin	.07	.04
346	Duane Ward	.05	.02
347	Turner Ward	.07	.04
348	Devon White	.08	.05
349	Woody Williams	.10	.06
350	Steve Avery	.20	.12
351	Steve Bedrosian	.05	.02
352	Rafael Belliard	.05	.02
353	Damon Berryhill	.05	.02
354	Jeff Blauser	.08	.05
355	Sid Bream	.05	.02
356	Francisco Cabrera	.05	.02
357	Marvin Freeman	.05	.02
358	Ron Gant	.15	.10
359	Tom Glavine	.20	.12
360	Jay Howell	.05	.02
361	David Justice	.25	.15

362	Ryan Klesko	.40	.25
363	Mark Lemke	.05	.02
364	Javier Lopez	75	45
365	Greg Maddux	.20	.12
366	Fred McGriff	.25	.15
367	Greg McMichael	.10	.06
368	Kent Mercker	.05	.02
369	Otis Nixon	.07	.04
370	Greg Olson	.05	.02
371	Bill Pecota	.05	.02
372	Terry Pendleton	.12	.07
373	Deion Sanders	.12	.07
374	Pete Smith	.08	.05
375	John Smoltz	.12	.07
376	Mike Stanton	.05	.02
377	Tony Tarasco	.25	.15
378	Mark Wohlers	.10	.06
379	Jose Bautista	.05	.02
380	Shawn Boskie	.05	.02
381	Steve Buechele	.05	.02
382	Frank Castillo	.05	.02
383	Mark Grace	.15	.10
384	Jose Guzman	.05	.02
385	Mike Harkey	.07	.04
386	Greg Hibbard	.05	.02
387	Glenallen Hill	.08	.05
388	Steve Lake	.05	.02
389	Derrick May	.12	.07
390	Chuck McElroy	.05	.02
391	Mike Morgan	.05	.02
392	Randy Myers	.07	.04
393	Dan Plesac	.05	.02
394	Kevin Roberson	.15	.10
395	Rey Sanchez	.07	.04
396	Ryne Sandberg	.30	.18
397	Bob Scanlan	.05	.02
398	Dwight Smith	.07	.04
399	Sammy Sosa	.15	.10
400	Jose Vizcaino	.05	.02
401	Rick Wilkins	.12	.07
402	Willie Wilson	.05	.02
403	Eric Yelding	.05	.02
404	Bobby Ayala	.07	.04
405	Jeff Branson	.07	.04
406	Tom Browning	.07	.04
407	Jacob Brumfield (R)	.12	.07
408	Tim Costo	.12	.07
409	Rob Dibble	.05	.02
410	Willie Greene	.15	.10
411	Thomas Howard	.05	.02
412	Roberto Kelly	.15	.10
413	Bill Landrum	.05	.02
414	Barry Larkin	.12	.07
415	Larry Luebbers (R)	.10	.06
416	Kevin Mitchell	.08	.05
417	Hal Morris	.10	.06
418	Joe Oliver	.05	.02
419	Tim Pugh	.08	.05
420	Jeff Reardon	.08	.05
421	Jose Rijo	.08	.05
422	Bip Roberts	.05	.02
423	John Roper	.07	.04
424	Johnny Ruffin	.05	.02
425	Chris Sabo	.07	.04
426	Juan Samuel	.05	.02
427	Reggie Sanders	.15	.10
428	Scott Service	.05	.02
429	John Smiley	.08	.05
430	Jerry Spradlin (R)	.10	.06
431	Kevin Wickander	.05	.02
432	Freddie Benavides	.05	.02
433	Dante Bichette	.10	.06
434	Willie Blair	.07	.04
435	Daryl Boston	.05	.02
436	Kent Bottenfield	.07	.04
437	Vinny Castilla	.05	.02
438	Jerald Clark	.05	.02
439	Alex Cole	.05	.02
440	Andres Galarraga	.12	.07
441	Joe Girardi	.05	.02
442	Greg Harris	.05	.02
443	Charlie Hayes	.08	.05
444	Darren Holmes	.08	.05
445	Chris Jones	.08	.05
446	Roberto Mejia (R)	.30	.18
447	David Nied	.40	.25
448	J. Owens (R)	.15	.10
449	Jeff Parrett	.05	.02
450	Steve Reed	.08	.05
451	Armando Reynoso	.07	.04
452	Bruce Ruffin	.05	.02
453	Mo Sanford	.05	.02
454	Danny Sheaffer	.08	.05
455	Jim Tatum	.08	.05
456	Gary Wayne	.08	.05
457	Eric Young	.10	.06
458	Luis Aquino	.05	.02
459	Alex Arias	.05	.02
460	Jack Armstrong	.05	.02
461	Bret Barberie	.05	.02
462	Ryan Bowen	.08	.05
463	Chuck Carr	.12	.07
464	Jeff Conine	.15	.10
465	Henry Cotto	.05	.02
466	Orestes Destrade	.08	.05
467	Chris Hammond	.05	.02
468	Bryan Harvey	.08	.05
469	Charlie Hough	.05	.02
470	Joe Klink	.05	.02
471	Richie Lewis	.08	.05
472	Bob Natal	.08	.05
473	Pat Rapp	.10	.06
474	Rich Renteria	.05	.02
475	Rich Rodriguez	.05	.02

476	Benito Santiago	.08	.05	533	Sean Berry	.10	.06
477	Gary Sheffield	.15	.10	534	Greg Colbrunn	.08	.05
478	Matt Turner	.10	.06	535	Delino DeShields	.10	.06
479	David Weathers	.10	.06	536	Jeff Fassero	.05	.02
480	Walt Weiss	.05	.02	537	Darrin Fletcher	.07	.04
481	Darrell Whitmore	.25	.15	538	Cliff Floyd	1.50	.90
482	Eric Anthony	.12	.07	539	Lou Frazier	.08	.05
483	Jeff Bagwell	.15	.10	540	Marquis Grissom	.15	.10
484	Kevin Bass	.05	.02	541	Butch Henry	.07	.04
485	Craig Biggio	.08	.05	542	Ken Hill	.07	.04
486	Ken Caminiti	.05	.02	543	Mike Lansing	.10	.06
487	Andújar Cedeno	.10	.06	544	Brian Looney (R)	.12	.07
488	Chris Donnels	.05	.02	545	Dennis Martinez	.10	.06
489	Doug Drabek	.10	.06	546	Chris Nabholtz	.07	.04
490	Steve Finley	.05	.02	547	Randy Ready	.05	.02
491	Luis Gonzalez	.10	.06	548	Mel Rojas	.05	.02
492	Pete Harnisch	.08	.05	549	Kirk Rueter (R)	.20	.12
493	Xavier Hernandez	.07	.04	550	Tim Scott	.07	.04
494	Doug Jones	.05	.02	551	Jeff Shaw	.08	.05
495	Todd Jones	.08	.05	552	Tim Spehr	.08	.05
496	Darryle Kile	.12	.07	553	John Vander Wal	.05	.02
497	Al Osuna	.05	.02	554	Larry Walker	.12	.07
498	Mark Portugal	.07	.04	555	John Wetteland	.08	.05
499	Scott Servais	.05	.02	556	Rondell White	.30	.18
500	Greg Swindell	.08	.05	557	Tim Bogar	.10	.06
501	Eddie Taubensee	.07	.04	558	Bobby Bonilla	.10	.06
502	Jose Uribe	.05	.02	559	Jeromy Burnitz	.20	.12
503	Brian Williams	.08	.05	560	Sid Fernandez	.05	.02
504	Billy Ashley	.50	.30	561	John Franco	.05	.02
505	Pedro Astacio	.12	.07	562	Dave Gallagher	.05	.02
506	Brett Butler	.07	.04	563	Dwight Gooden	.10	.06
507	Tom Candiotti	.05	.02	564	Eric Hillman	.05	.02
508	Omar Daal	.08	.05	565	Todd Hundley	.07	.04
509	Jim Gott	.05	.02	566	Jeff Innis	.05	.02
510	Kevin Gross	.05	.02	567	Darrin Jackson	.05	.02
511	Dave Hansen	.05	.02	568	Howard Johnson	.08	.05
512	Carlos Hernandez	.05	.02	569	Bobby Jones	.15	.10
513	Orel Hershiser	.08	.05	570	Jeff Kent	.10	.06
514	Eric Karros	.15	.10	571	Mike Maddux	.05	.02
515	Pedro Martinez	.15	.10	572	Jeff McKnight	.07	.04
516	Ramon Martinez	.08	.05	573	Eddie Murray	.12	.07
517	Roger McDowell	.05	.02	574	Charlie O'Brien	.05	.02
518	Raul Mondesi	.20	.12	575	Joe Orsulak	.05	.02
519	Jose Offerman	.08	.05	576	Bret Saberhagen	.10	.06
520	Mike Piazza	1.50	.90	577	Pete Schourek	.07	.04
521	Jody Reed	.05	.02	578	Dave Telgheder	.10	.06
522	Henry Rodriquez	.08	.05	579	Ryan Thompson	.12	.07
523	Mike Sharperson	.05	.02	580	Anthony Young	.07	.04
524	Cory Snyder	.05	.02	581	Ruben Amaro	.05	.02
525	Darryl Strawberry	.15	.10	582	Larry Andersen	.05	.02
526	Rick Trlicek	.05	.02	583	Kim Batiste	.05	.02
527	Tim Wallach	.07	.04	584	Wes Chamberlain	.10	.06
528	Mitch Webster	.05	.02	585	Darren Daulton	.15	.10
529	Steve Wilson	.05	.02	586	Mariano Duncan	.05	.02
530	Todd Worrell	.05	.02	587	Lenny Dykstra	.15	.10
531	Moises Alou	.10	.06	588	Jim Eisenreich	.05	.02
532	Brian Barnes	.05	.02	589	Tommy Greene	.12	.07

590	Dave Hollins	.15	.10
591	Pete Incaviglia	.05	.02
592	Danny Jackson	.05	.02
593	Ricky Jordan	.05	.02
594	John Kruk	.12	.07
595	Roger Mason	.05	.02
596	Mickey Morandini	.08	.05
597	Terry Mulholland	.07	.04
598	Todd Pratt	.08	.05
599	Ben Rivera	.08	.05
600	Curt Schilling	.10	.06
601	Kevin Stocker	.40	.25
602	Milt Thompson	.05	.02
603	David West	.05	.02
604	Mitch Williams	.05	.02
605	Jay Bell	.08	.05
606	Dave Clark	.05	.02
607	Steve Cooke	.12	.07
608	Tom Foley	.05	.02
609	Carlos Garcia	.15	.10
610	Joel Johnston	.05	.02
611	Jeff King	.08	.05
612	Al Martin	.20	.12
613	Lloyd McClendon	.05	.02
614	Orlando Merced	.10	.06
615	Blas Minor	.07	.04
616	Denny Neagle	.07	.04
617	Mark Petkovsek (R)	.10	.06
618	Tom Prince	.07	.04
619	Don Slaught	.05	.02
620	Zane Smith	.05	.02
621	Randy Tomlin	.08	.05
622	Andy Van Slyke	.10	.06
623	Paul Wagner	.15	.10
624	Tim Wakefield	.15	.10
625	Bob Walk	.05	.02
626	Kevin Young	.15	.10
627	Luis Alicea	.05	.02
628	Rene Arocha	.10	.06
629	Rod Brewer	.05	.02
630	Rheal Cormier	.07	.04
631	Bernard Gilkey	.10	.06
632	Lee Guetterman	.05	.02
633	Gregg Jefferies	.15	.10
634	Brian Jordan	.15	.10
635	Les Lancaster	.05	.02
636	Ray Lankford	.15	.10
637	Rob Murphy	.05	.02
638	Omar Olivares	.05	.02
639	Jose Oquendo	.05	.02
640	Donovan Osborne	.08	.05
641	Tom Pagnozzi	.05	.02
642	Erik Pappas	.07	.04
643	Geronimo Pena	.05	.02
644	Mike Perez	.07	.04
645	Gerald Perry	.05	.02
646	Ozzie Smith	.15	.10
647	Bob Tewksbury	.05	.02
648	Allen Watson	.40	.25
649	Mark Whiten	.15	.10
650	Tracy Woodson	.05	.02
651	Todd Zeile	.10	.06
652	Andy Ashby	.05	.02
653	Brad Ausmus	.07	.04
654	Billy Bean	.08	.05
655	Derek Bell	.15	.10
656	Andy Benes	.10	.06
657	Doug Brocail	.07	.04
658	Jarvis Brown	.10	.06
659	Archi Cianfrocco	.08	.05
660	Phil Clark	.08	.05
661	Mark Davis	.05	.02
662	Jeff Gardner	.05	.02
663	Pat Gomez	.05	.02
664	Ricky Gutierrez	.08	.05
665	Tony Gwynn	.15	.10
666	Gene Harris	.05	.02
667	Kevin Higgins	.08	.05
668	Trevor Hoffman	.12	.07
669	Pedro Martinez	.08	.05
670	Tim Mauser	.10	.06
671	Melvin Nieves (R)	.60	.35
672	Phil Plantier	.15	.10
673	Frank Seminara	.07	.04
674	Craig Shipley	.05	.02
675	Kerry Taylor	.12	.07
676	Tim Teufel	.05	.02
677	Guillermo Velasquez	.07	.04
678	Wally Whitehurst	.05	.02
679	Tim Worrell	.08	.05
680	Rod Beck	.08	.05
681	Mike Benjamin	.05	.02
682	Todd Benzinger	.05	.02
683	Bud Black	.05	.02
684	Barry Bonds	.35	.20
685	Jeff Brantley	.05	.02
686	Dave Burba	.05	.02
687	John Burkett	.10	.06
688	Mark Carreon	.05	.02
689	Will Clark	.20	.12
690	Royce Clayton	.12	.07
691	Bryan Hickerson	.08	.05
692	Mike Jackson	.05	.02
693	Darren Lewis	.08	.05
694	Kirt Manwaring	.05	.02
695	Dave Martinez	.05	.02
696	Willie McGee	.08	.05
697	John Patterson	.05	.02
698	Jeff Reed	.05	.02
699	Kevin Rogers	.05	.02
700	Scott Sanderson	.05	.02
701	Steve Scarsone	.10	.06
702	Bill Swift	.10	.06
703	Robby Thompson	.08	.05

704	Matt Williams	.15	.10
705	Trevor Wilson	.05	.02
706	R. Gant, D. Justice, F. McGriff	.20	.12
		.05	.02
707	P. Molitor, J. Olerud	.20	.12
708	M. Mussina, J. McDowell	.20	.12
709	A. Trammell, L. Whitaker	.10	.06
710	J. Gonzalez, R. Palmeiro	.30	.18
711	B. Butler, T. Gwynn	.10	.06
712	K. Puckett, C. Knoblauch	.15	.10
713	E. Karros, M. Piazza	1.00	.60
714	Checklist	.05	.02
715	Checklist	.05	.02
716	Checklist	.05	.02
717	Checklist	.05	.02
718	Checklist	.05	.02
719	Checklist	.05	.02
720	Checklist	.05	.02
___	Tim Salmon (ea)	3.50	2.00
___	Tim Salmon (Signed)	150.00	80.00

1994 Fleer
Rookie Sensations

The cards in this insert set were randomly distributed in Fleer Cello packs. The cards feature full color action photos on the fronts with the headline "Rookie Sensations". All cards measure 2-1/2" by 3-1/2".

		MINT	NR/MT
	Complete Set (20)	75.00	45.00
	Commons	1.00	.60
1	Rene Arocha	1.25	.80
2	Jason Bere	7.00	4.00
3	Jeromy Burnitz	2.00	1.25
4	Chuck Carr	1.50	.90
5	Jeff Conine	2.00	1.25
6	Steve Cooke	1.50	.90
7	Cliff Floyd	10.00	6.50
8	Jeffrey Hammonds	5.00	3.00
9	Wayne Kirby	1.00	.60
10	Mike Lansing	1.25	.80
11	Al Martin	4.00	2.50
12	Greg McMichael	1.25	.80

13	Troy Neel	2.50	1.50
14	Mike Piazza	15.00	10.00
15	Armando Reynoso	1.00	.60
16	Kirk Rueter	1.50	.90
17	Tim Salmon	10.00	6.50
18	Aaron Sele	7.00	4.00
19	J.T. Snow	7.50	4.50
20	Kevin Stocker	8.50	5.00

1994 Fleer
All-Stars

The cards in this set feature full-color action photos on the fronts with an American Flag covering the top third of the background. A logo in the shape of a star appears in the lower corner of the card front while the player's name is printed in gold foil across the bottom. The cards were randomly inserted in Fleer packs and measure 2-1/2" by 3-1/2".

		MINT	NR/MT
	Complete Set (50)	40.00	26.00
	Commons	.60	.35
1	Roberto Alomar	3.00	1.75
2	Carlos Baerga	3.00	1.75
3	Albert Belle	3.00	1.75
4	Wade Boggs	2.50	1.50
5	Joe Carter	2.50	1.50
6	Scott Cooper	1.25	.80
7	Cecil Fielder	2.50	1.50
8	Travis Fryman	5.00	3.00
9	Juan Gonzalez	8.00	5.00
10	Ken Griffey Jr.	10.00	6.50
11	Pat Hentgen	1.00	.60
12	Randy Johnson	1.50	.90

13	Jimmy Key	.60	.35
14	Mark Langston	.80	.50
15	Jack McDowell	2.50	1.50
16	Paul Molitor	3.50	2.00
17	Jeff Montgomery	.60	.35
18	Mike Mussina	3.50	2.00
19	John Olerud	6.00	3.75
20	Kirby Puckett	3.50	2.00
21	Cal Ripken Jr.	5.00	3.00
22	Ivan Rodriguez	1.50	.90
23	Frank Thomas	12.50	7.50
24	Greg Vaughn	1.25	.80
25	Duane Ward	.60	.35
26	Steve Avery	2.50	1.50
27	Rod Beck	.60	.35
28	Jay Bell	.60	.35
29	Andy Benes	.80	.50
30	Jeff Blauser	.60	.35
31	Barry Bonds	5.00	3.00
32	Bobby Bonilla	1.00	.60
33	John Burkett	.80	.50
34	Darren Daulton	1.50	.90
35	Andres Galarraga	1.25	.80
36	Tom Glavine	2.50	1.50
37	Mark Grace	1.50	.90
38	Marquis Grissom	1.50	.90
39	Tony Gwynn	2.50	1.50
40	Bryan Harvey	.75	.45
41	Dave Hollins	2.00	1.25
42	David Justice	3.00	1.75
43	Darryl Kile	.80	.50
44	John Kruk	1.25	.80
45	Barry Larkin	1.25	.80
46	Terry Mulholland	.60	.35
47	Mike Piazza	18.00	12.00
48	Ryne Sandberg	5.00	3.00
49	Gary Sheffield	1.25	.80
50	John Smoltz	1.25	.80

1994 Fleer Award Winners

The 6-cards in this insert set were randomly distributed in all Fleer packs. The cards feature three full-color photos on the fronts, a large action shot, a smaller inset photo and a close-up head shot in the top corner. The player's name is printed in gold foil across the bottom next to the "Award Winners" logo. All cards measure 3-1/2" by 2-1/2".

	MINT	NR/MT
Complete Set (6)	50.00	35.00
Commons	2.00	1.25

		MINT	NR/MT
1	Frank Thomas	15.00	10.00
2	Barry Bonds	6.50	3.75
3	Jack McDowell	3.00	1.75
4	Greg Maddux	2.00	1.25
5	Tim Salmon	10.00	6.50
6	Mike Piazza	18.00	12.50

1994 Fleer League Leaders

The cards in this set consist of two images on the card fronts, a full-color action shot in the foreground and a black and white shot in the background. The player's name and League Leader appear along the border under the photo while his achievement is printed vertically beside his picture. The cards were randomly inserted in all Fleer pack types. All cards measure 2-1/2" by 3-1/2".

	MINT	NR/MT
Complete Set (12)	24.00	14.00
Commons	1.00	.60

		MINT	NR/MT
1	John Olerud	3.50	2.00
2	Albert Belle	3.50	2.00
3	Rafael Palmeiro	1.50	.90
4	Kenny Lofton	2.50	1.50
5	Jack McDowell	2.50	1.50
6	Kevin Appier	1.00	.60
7	Andres Galarraga	1.25	.70
8	Barry Bonds	4.50	2.75
9	Lenny Dykstra	2.50	1.50
10	Chuck Carr	1.00	.60
11	Tom Glavine	2.00	1.25
12	Greg Maddux	2.00	1.25

1994 Fleer Major League Prospects

The cards in this 35-card insert set feature full-color action photos on the card fronts with a large team logo printed behind the photograph. The player's name appears in gold under his photo below the headline "Major League Prospect." The cards were issued randomly in all types of Fleer packs. All cards measure 2-1/2" by 3-1/2".

1994 Fleer Lumber Company

This 10-card limited insert set features a full-bleed design with full-color action photos on the fronts. The cards were only available in Fleer 21-card packs. All cards measure 2-1/2" by 3-1/2".

		MINT	NR/MT
Complete Set (10)		40.00	28.00
Commons		1.50	.90
1	Albert Belle	3.50	2.00
2	Barry Bonds	6.00	3.75
3	Ron Gant	1.50	.90
4	Juan Gonzalez	8.50	5.00
5	Ken Griffey Jr.	10.00	6.50
6	David Justice	5.00	3.00
7	Fred McGriff	4.50	2.75
8	Rafael Palmeiro	1.50	.90
9	Frank Thomas	12.00	7.50
10	Matt Williams	1.50	.90

		MINT	NR/MT
Complete Set (35)		60.00	38.00
Commons		.50	.30
1	Kurt Abbott	1.00	.60
2	Brian Anderson	1.25	.80
3	Rich Aude	.80	.50
4	Cory Baily	1.75	1.00
5	Danny Bautista	.50	.30
6	Marty Cordova	.50	.30
7	Tripp Cromer	1.50	.90
8	Midre Cummings	1.25	.80
9	Carlos Delgado	3.50	2.00
10	Steve Dreyer	.75	.45
11	Steve Dunn	.50	.30
12	Jeff Granger	2.50	1.50
13	Tyrone Hill	1.50	.90
14	Denny Hocking	1.00	.60
15	John Hope	.50	.30
16	Butch Huskey	1.25	.60
17	Miguel Jimenez	.80	.50
18	Chipper Jones	3.50	2.00
19	Steve Karsay	3.50	2.00
20	Mike Kelly	2.50	1.50
21	Mike Lieberthal	2.00	1.25
22	Albie Lopez	.80	.50

23	Jeff McNeely	1.25	.80
24	Dan Miceli	1.75	1.00
25	Nate Minchey	.75	.45
26	Marc Newfield	1.75	1.00
27	Darren Oliver	1.25	.80
28	Luis Ortiz	.50	.30
29	Curtis Pride	2.00	1.25
30	Roger Salkeld	1.25	.80
31	Scott Sanders	.80	.50
32	Dave Staton	1.50	.90
33	Salomon Torres	2.50	1.50
34	Steve Trachel	.80	.50
35	Chris Turner	1.25	.80

1994 Fleer
Team Leaders

The cards in this insert set consist of two full-color images on the card fronts, an action photo and a close-up picture. The team logo appears in the top corner while the player's name, team and position appear in gold in a small box under the pictures. The cards were available randomly in all Fleer packs. All cards measure 2-1/2" by 3-1/2".

		MINT	NR/MT
Complete Set (28)		30.00	18.50
Commons		.75	.45

1	Cal Ripken Jr.	3.50	2.00
2	Mo Vaughn	1.50	.90
3	Tim Salmon	5.00	3.00
4	Frank Thomas	8.50	5.00
5	Carlos Baerga	4.50	2.75
6	Cecil Fielder	2.50	1.50
7	Brian McRae	1.00	.60

8	Greg Vaughn	.75	.45
9	Kirby Puckett	3.00	1.50
10	Don Mattingly	2.50	1.50
11	Mark McGwire	1.25	.80
12	Ken Griffey Jr.	7.50	4.50
13	Juan Gonzalez	6.00	3.75
14	Paul Molitor	2.50	1.50
15	David Justice	3.00	1.50
16	Ryne Sandberg	3.50	2.00
17	Barry Larkin	1.00	.60
18	Andres Galarraga	.75	.45
19	Gary Sheffield	1.25	.80
20	Jeff Bagwell	1.25	.80
21	Mike Piazza	10.00	6.50
22	Marquis Grissom	1.00	.60
23	Bobby Bonilla	.75	.45
24	Lenny Dykstra	1.25	.80
25	Jay Bell	.75	.45
26	Gregg Jefferies	1.00	.60
27	Tony Gwynn	1.50	.90
28	Will Clark	2.50	1.50

1994 Fleer
Smoke N' Heat

The cards in this insert set are all-foil, metalized cards that feature some of the top pitchers in the Major Leagues. The fronts consist of full-color action shots superimposed over a background that says "Smoke 'N Heat". The player's name and team appear in gold under his photograph. The cards were inserted randomly in all Fleer pack types and each measures 2-1/2" by 3-1/2".

		MINT	NR/MT
Complete Set (12)		26.00	16.00
Commons		.75	.45

1	Roger Clemens	3.50	2.00
2	David Cone	1.00	.60
3	Juan Guzman	2.50	1.50
4	Pete Harnisch	.75	.45
5	Randy Johnson	2.00	1.25
0	Mark Langston	1.25	.00
7	Greg Maddux	2.50	1.50
8	Mike Mussina	4.50	2.75
9	Jose Rijo	.75	.45
10	Nolan Ryan	8.00	5.00
11	Curt Schilling	1.00	.60
12	John Smoltz	1.25	.80

1994 Fleer
Golden Moments

The 10-special cards in this insert set were distributed exclusively in Fleer's 23-card packs. The fronts consist of full-bleed, full-color photos. All cards measure 2-1/2" by 3-1/2".

		MINT	NR/MT
Complete Set (10)		25.00	15.00
Commons		.75	.45

1	Mark Whiten	1.50	.90
2	Carlos Baerga	2.00	1.25
3	Dave Winfield	2.50	1.50
4	Ken Griffey Jr.	5.00	3.00
5	Bo Jackson	2.00	1.25
6	George Brett	3.00	1.75
7	Nolan Ryan	5.00	3.00
8	Fred McGriff	2.50	1.50
9	Frank Thomas	6.00	3.75
10	J. Abbott, C. Bosio, D. Kile	.75	.45

1994 Fleer
Pro Visions

These limited art cards feature full-bleed, full color portraits on the card fronts. The player's name is stamped in gold in the lower corner of the card front. The cards were randomly inserted in all Fleer pack types. The cards measure 2-1/2" by 3-1/2".

		MINT	NR/MT
Complete Set (9)		16.00	10.00
Commons		.75	.45

1	Darren Daulton	.75	.45
2	John Olerud	3.00	1.75
3	Matt Williams	1.00	.60
4	Carlos Baerga	2.50	1.50
5	Ozzie Smith	.75	.45
6	Juan Gonzalez	4.00	2.50
7	Jack McDowell	2.00	1.25
8	Mike Piazza	5.00	3.00
9	Tony Gwynn	1.50	.90

1994 Fleer Ultra I

The cards in this series consist of a full-bleed design on three sides along with full-color action player photos on the card fronts. The player's name, team, position and the Ultra logo are printed in gold foil stamping below the photograph. A gold foil border runs across the bottom of the card. The horizontal card backs contain a montage of three full-color player photos and a box containing statistics. Limited inserts include random cards of Phillies stars Darren Daulton and John Kruk. Those cards are listed at the end of this checklist but are not included in the complete set price below. All cards measure 2-1/2" by 3-1/2".

		MINT	NR/MT
Complete Set (300)		25.00	15.00
Commons		.10	.06
1	Jeffrey Hammonds	.75	.45
2	Chris Hoiles	.15	.10
3	Ben McDonald	.15	.10
4	Mark McLemore	.10	.06
5	Alan Mills	.10	.06
6	Jamie Moyer	.10	.06
7	Brad Pennington	.12	.07
8	Jim Poole	.10	.06
9	Cal Ripken Jr.	.75	.45
10	Jack Voight	.12	.07
11	Roger Clemens	.50	.30
12	Danny Darwin	.10	.06
13	Andre Dawson	.15	.10
14	Scott Fletcher	.10	.06
15	Greg Harris	.10	.06
16	Billy Hatcher	.10	.06
17	Jeff Russell	.10	.06
18	Aaron Sele	1.00	.60
19	Mo Vaughn	.25	.15
20	Mike Butcher	.15	.10
21	Rod Correia	.15	.10
22	Steve Frey	.10	.06
23	Phil Leftwich	.50	.30
24	Torey Lovullo	.10	.06
25	Ken Patterson	.10	.06
26	Eduardo Perez	1.00	.60
27	Tim Salmon	2.00	1.25
28	J.T. Snow	1.00	.60
29	Chris Turner	.25	.15
30	Wilson Alvarez	.12	.07
31	Jason Bere	1.00	.60
32	Joey Cora	.10	.06
33	Alex Fernandez	.25	.15
34	Roberto Hernandez	.12	.07
35	Lance Johnson	.10	.06
36	Ron Karkovice	.10	.06
37	Kirk McCaskill	.10	.06
38	Jeff Schwarz	.12	.07
39	Frank Thomas	3.00	1.75
40	Sandy Alomar Jr.	.12	.07
41	Albert Belle	.60	.35
42	Felix Fermin	.10	.06
43	Wayne Kirby	.12	.07
44	Tom Kramer	.15	.10
45	Kenny Lofton	.40	.25
46	Jose Mesa	.10	.06
47	Eric Plunk	.10	.06
48	Paul Sorrento	.15	.10
49	Jim Thome	.30	.18
50	Bill Wertz	.12	.07
51	John Doherty	.10	.06
52	Cecil Fielder	.30	.18
53	Travis Fryman	.50	.30
54	Chris Gomez	.12	.07
55	Mike Henneman	.10	.06
56	Chad Kreuter	.15	.10
57	Bob MacDonald	.10	.06
58	Mike Moore	.10	.06
59	Tony Phillips	.12	.07
60	Lou Whitaker	.15	.10
61	Kevin Appier	.20	.12
62	Greg Gagne	.10	.06
63	Chris Gwynn	.10	.06
64	Bob Hamelin	.20	.12
65	Chris Haney	.12	.07
66	Phil Hiatt	.25	.15
67	Felix Jose	.12	.07
68	Jose Lind	.10	.06
69	Mike Macfarlane	.10	.06
70	Jeff Montgomery	.12	.07
71	Hipolito Pichardo	.10	.06
72	Juan Bell	.10	.06
73	Cal Eldred	.25	.15
74	Darryl Hamilton	.15	.10
75	Doug Henry	.12	.07
76	Mike Ignasiak	.12	.07
77	John Jaha	.20	.12
78	Graeme Lloyd	.15	.10
79	Angel Miranda	.10	.06
80	Dave Nilsson	.12	.07
81	Troy O'Leary	.25	.15
82	Kevin Reimer	.10	.06
83	Willie Banks	.15	.10
84	Larry Casian	.12	.07
85	Scott Erickson	.15	.10
86	Eddie Guardado	.20	.12
87	Kent Hrbek	.12	.07
88	Terry Jorgensen	.15	.10
89	Chuck Knoblauch	.20	.12
90	Pat Meares	.20	.12
91	Mike Trombley	.15	.10
92	Dave Winfield	.40	.25

93	Wade Boggs	.30	.18
94	Scott Kamieniecki	.10	.06
95	Pat Kelly	.12	.07
96	Jimmy Key	.12	.07
97	Jim Leyritz	.10	.06
98	Bobby Munoz	.15	.10
99	Paul O'Neill	.15	.10
100	Melido Perez	.10	.06
101	Mike Stanley	.12	.07
102	Danny Tartabull	.15	.10
103	Bernie Williams	.15	.10
104	Kurt Abbott (R)	.35	.20
105	Mike Bordick	.12	.07
106	Ron Darling	.10	.06
107	Brent Gates	.50	.30
108	Miguel Jimenez	.15	.10
109	Steve Karsay	.75	.45
110	Scott Lydy	.12	.07
111	Mark McGwire	.25	.15
112	Troy Neel	.30	.18
113	Craig Paquette	.12	.07
114	Bob Welch	.10	.06
115	Bobby Witt	.12	.07
116	Rich Amaral	.12	.07
117	Mike Blowers	.10	.06
118	Jay Buhner	.15	.10
119	Dave Fleming	.20	.12
120	Ken Griffey Jr.	3.00	1.75
121	Tino Martinez	.12	.07
122	Marc Newfield	.20	.12
123	Ted Power	.10	.06
124	Mackey Sasser	.10	.06
125	Omar Vizquel	.12	.07
126	Kevin Brown	.15	.10
127	Juan Gonzalez	2.50	1.50
128	Tom Henke	.10	.06
129	David Hulse	.15	.10
130	Dean Palmer	.30	.18
131	Roger Pavlik	.25	.15
132	Ivan Rodriquez	.25	.15
133	Kenny Rogers	.10	.06
134	Doug Strange	.10	.06
135	Pat Borders	.10	.06
136	Joe Carter	.50	.30
137	Darnell Coles	.10	.06
138	Pat Hentgen	.25	.15
139	Al Leiter	.10	.06
140	Paul Molitor	.40	.25
141	John Olerud	1.25	.80
142	Ed Sprague	.15	.10
143	Dave Stewart	.15	.10
144	Mike Timlin	.12	.07
145	Duane Ward	.10	.06
146	Devon White	.12	.07
147	Steve Avery	.35	.20
148	Steve Bedrosian	.10	.06
149	Damon Berryhill	.10	.06
150	Jeff Blauser	.12	.07
151	Tom Glavine	.35	.20
152	Chipper Jones	1.00	.60
153	Mark Lemke	.10	.06
154	Fred McGriff	.50	.30
155	Greg McMichael	.20	.12
156	Deion Sanders	.20	.10
157	John Smoltz	.20	.12
158	Mark Wohlers	.15	.10
159	Jose Bautiste (R)	.20	.12
160	Steve Buechele	.10	.06
161	Mike Harkey	.12	.07
162	Greg Hibbard	.10	.06
163	Chuck McElroy	.10	.06
164	Mike Morgan	.10	.06
165	Kevin Roberson	.30	.18
166	Ryne Sandberg	.75	.45
167	Jose Vizcaino	.10	.06
168	Rick Wilkins	.20	.12
169	Willie Wilson	.10	.06
170	Willie Greene	.20	.12
171	Roberto Kelly	.15	.10
172	Larry Luebbers (R)	.15	.10
173	Kevin Mitchell	.15	.10
174	Joe Oliver	.10	.06
175	John Roper	.12	.07
176	Johnny Ruffin	.10	.06
177	Reggie Sanders	.25	.15
178	John Smiley	.12	.07
179	Jerry Spradlin (R)	.20	.12
180	Freddie Benavides	.10	.06
181	Dante Bichette	.25	.15
182	Willie Blair	.12	.07
183	Kent Bottenfield	.10	.06
184	Jerald Clark	.10	.06
185	Joe Girardi	.10	.06
186	Roberto Mejia (R)	.60	.35
187	Steve Reed	.10	.06
188	Armando Reynoso	.12	.07
189	Bruce Ruffin	.10	.06
190	Eric Young	.15	.10
191	Luis Aquino	.10	.06
192	Bret Barberie	.10	.06
193	Ryan Bowen	.12	.07
194	Chuck Carr	.20	.12
195	Orestes Destrade	.12	.07
196	Richie Lewis	.12	.07
197	Dave Magadan	.10	.06
198	Bob Natal	.12	.07
199	Gary Sheffield	.30	.18
200	Matt Turner (R)	.25	.15
201	Darrell Whitmore (R)	.80	.50
202	Eric Anthony	.20	.12
203	Jeff Bagwell	.35	.20
204	Andujar Cedeno	.15	.10
205	Luis Gonzalez	.15	.10
206	Xavier Hernandez	.12	.07

207	Doug Jones	.10	.06	264	Rene Arocha	.25	.15
208	Darryl Kile	.25	.15	265	Richard Batchelor (R)	.15	.10
209	Scott Servais	.10	.06	266	Gregg Jefferies	.30	.18
210	Greg Swindell	.12	.07	267	Brian Jordan	.20	.12
211	Brian Williams	.12	.07	268	Jose Oquendo	.10	.06
212	Pedro Astacio	.20	.12	269	Donovan Osborne	.15	.10
213	Brett Butler	.12	.07	270	Eric Pappas	.12	.07
214	Omar Daal	.12	.07	271	Mike Perez	.12	.07
215	Jim Gott	.10	.06	272	Bob Tewksbury	.10	.06
216	Raul Mondesi	.25	.15	273	Mark Whiten	.25	.15
217	Jose Offerman	.12	.07	274	Todd Zeile	.15	.10
218	Mike Piazza	3.00	1.75	275	Andy Ashby	.10	.06
219	Cory Snyder	.10	.06	276	Brad Ausmus	.12	.07
220	Tim Wallach	.10	.06	277	Phil Clark	.15	.10
221	Todd Worrell	.10	.06	278	Jeff Gardner	.10	.06
222	Moises Alou	.15	.10	279	Ricky Gutierrez	.12	.07
223	Sean Berry	.15	.10	280	Tony Gwynn	.30	.18
224	Wil Cordero	.20	.12	281	Tim Mauser	.12	.07
225	Jeff Fassero	.10	.06	282	Scott Sanders	.12	.07
226	Darrin Fletcher	.12	.07	283	Frank Seminara	.12	.07
227	Cliff Floyd	2.50	1.50	284	Wally Whitehurst	.10	.06
228	Marquis Grissom	.20	.12	285	Rod Beck	.20	.12
229	Ken Hill	.12	.07	286	Barry Bonds	1.00	.60
230	Mike Lansing	.15	.10	287	Dave Burba	.10	.06
231	Kirk Rueter (R)	.20	.12	288	Mark Carreon	.10	.06
232	John Wetteland	.12	.07	289	Royce Clayton	.15	.10
233	Rondell White	.60	.35	290	Mike Jackson	.10	.06
234	Tim Bogar	.12	.07	291	Darren Lewis	.12	.07
235	Jeromy Burnitz	.40	.25	292	Kirt Manwaring	.10	.06
236	Dwight Gooden	.15	.10	293	Dave Martinez	.10	.06
237	Todd Hundley	.12	.07	294	Bill Swift	.20	.12
238	Jeff Kent	.20	.12	295	Salomon Torres	.40	.25
239	Josias Manzanillo (R)	.15	.10	296	Matt Williams	.30	.18
240	Joe Orsulak	.10	.06	297	Checklist	.10	.03
241	Ryan Thompson	.25	.15	298	Checklist	.10	.03
242	Kim Batiste	.10	.06	299	Checklist	.10	.03
243	Darren Daulton	.25	.15	300	Checklist	.10	.03
244	Tommy Greene	.15	.10	___	Darren Daulton (ea)	1.50	.90
245	Dave Hollins	.25	.15	___	John Kruk (ea)	1.25	.80
246	Pete Incaviglia	.10	.06	___	Darren Daulton (Auto)	75.00	45.00
247	Danny Jackson	.10	.06	___	John Kruk (Auto)	60.00	35.00
248	Ricky Jordan	.10	.06				
249	John Kruk	.20	.12				
250	Mickey Morandini	.12	.07				
251	Terry Mulholland	.12	.07				
252	Ben Rivera	.12	.07				
253	Kevin Stocker (R)	.80	.50				
254	Jay Bell	.15	.10				
255	Steve Cooke	.25	.15				
256	Jeff King	.12	.07				
257	Al Martin	.30	.18				
258	Danny Miceli	.12	.07				
259	Blas Minor	.10	.06				
260	Don Slaught	.10	.06				
261	Paul Wagner	.20	.12				
262	Tim Wakefield	.15	.10				
263	Kevin Young	.30	.18				

1994 Fleer Ultra I Award Winners

	MINT	NR/MT
Complete Set (25)	70.00	48.00
Commons	.75	.45

1	Ivan Rodriguez	1.50	.90
2	Don Mattingly	3.50	2.00
3	Roberto Alomar	4.00	2.50
4	Robin Ventura	1.50	.90
5	Omar Vizquel	.75	.45
6	Ken Griffey Jr.	8.00	5.00
7	Kenny Lofton	4.00	2.50
8	Devon White	.75	.45
9	Mark Langston	.75	.45
10	Kirt Manwaring	.75	.45
11	Mark Grace	1.25	.80
12	Robby Thompson	.75	.45
13	Matt Williams	2.50	1.50
14	Jay Bell	.75	.45
15	Barry Bonds	6.50	3.75
16	Marquis Grissom	1.25	.80
17	Larry Walker	1.00	.60
18	Greg Maddux	2.50	1.50
19	Frank Thomas	10.00	6.50
20	Barry Bonds	6.50	3.75
21	Paul Molitor	3.00	1.75
22	Jack McDowell	3.00	1.75
23	Greg Maddux	2.50	1.50
24	Tim Salmon	6.00	3.50
25	Mike Piazza	12.00	7.00

1994 Fleer Ultra I RBI Kings

		MINT	NR/MT
Complete Set (12)		50.00	38.00
Commons		2.00	1.25
1	Albert Belle	3.50	2.00
2	Frank Thomas	12.50	7.50
3	Joe Carter	3.00	1.75
4	Juan Gonzalez	8.00	5.00
5	Cecil Fielder	3.00	1.75
6	Carlos Baerga	3.50	2.00
7	Barry Bonds	6.50	3.75
8	David Justice	5.00	3.00
9	Ron Gant	2.00	1.25
10	Mike Piazza	12.00	7.00
11	Matt Williams	2.50	1.50
12	Darren Daulton	2.00	1.25

1994 Fleer Ultra I Home Run Kings

		MINT	NR/MT
Complete Set (12)		50.00	38.00
Commons		2.00	1.25
1	Juan Gonzalez	8.50	5.00
2	Ken Griffey Jr.	10.00	6.50
3	Frank Thomas	12.50	7.50
4	Albert Belle	3.50	2.00
5	Rafael Palmeiro	2.00	1.25
6	Joe Carter	3.00	1.75
7	Barry Bonds	6.50	3.75
8	David Justice	5.00	3.00
9	Matt Williams	2.50	1.50
10	Fred McGriff	3.50	2.00
11	Ron Gant	2.00	1.25
12	Mike Piazza	12.00	7.00

1994 Fleer Ultra I League Leaders

		MINT	NR/MT
Complete Set (10)		18.00	12.00
Commons		.75	.45
1	John Olerud	4.00	2.50
2	Rafael Palmeiro	2.00	1.25
3	Kenny Lofton	3.50	2.00
4	Jack McDowell	3.00	1.75
5	Randy Johnson	2.00	1.25
6	Andres Galarraga	1.25	.80
7	L:enny Dykstra	2.50	1.50
8	Chuck Carr	1.00	.60
9	Tom Glavine	2.00	1.25
10	Jose Rijo	.75	.45

1994 Fleer Ultra I Second Year Standouts

		MINT	NR/MT
Complete Set (10)		55.00	40.00
Commons		1.25	.80
1	Jason Bere	6.00	3.75
2	Brent Gates	4.50	2.75
3	Jeffrey Hammonds	3.50	2.00
4	Tim Salmon	12.00	7.00
5	Aaron Sele	5.00	3.00
6	Chuck Carr	1.25	.80
7	Jeff Conine	2.00	1.25
8	Greg McMichael	1.25	.80
9	Mike Piazza	18.00	12.00
10	Kevin Stocker	7.50	4.50

1994 Fleer Ultra I Ultra Firemen

		MINT	NR/MT
Complete Set (10)		10.00	6.50
Commons		.75	.45
1	Jeff Montgomery	1.00	.60
2	Duane Ward	.75	.45
3	Tom Henke	.75	.45
4	Roberto Hernandez	.75	.45
5	Dennis Eckersley	2.00	1.25
6	Randy Myers	.75	.45
7	Rod Beck	1.25	.80
8	Bryan Harvey	1.50	.90
9	John Wetteland	1.00	.60
10	Mitch Williams	.75	.45

1994 Pinnacle I

The cards in this premium set consist of full-color action photos on the card fronts with a high-gloss, UV coated finish. The flip side features another full-color photo along with personal data and statistics. All cards measure 2-1/2" by 3-1/2".

		MINT	NR/MT
Complete Set (270)		28.00	18.00
Commons		.10	.06
1	Frank Thomas	3.50	2.00
2	Carlos Baerga	.75	.45
3	Sammy Sosa	.25	.15
4	Tony Gwynn	.30	.18
5	John Olerud	1.25	.80
6	Ryne Sandberg	.75	.45
7	Moises Alou	.15	.10
8	Steve Avery	.30	.18
9	Tim Salmon	2.00	1.25
10	Cecil Fielder	.30	.18
11	Greg Maddux	.30	.18
12	Barry Larkin	.20	.12
13	Mike Devereaux	.12	.07
14	Charlie Hayes	.12	.07
15	Albert Belle	.75	.45
16	Andy Van Slyke	.15	.10
17	Mo Vaughn	.25	.15
18	Brian McRae	.15	.10
19	Cal Eldred	.25	.15
20	Craig Biggio	.12	.07
21	Kirby Puckett	.75	.45
22	Derek Bell	.30	.18
23	Don Mattingly	.30	.18
24	John Burkett	.20	.12
25	Roger Clemens	.50	.30
26	Barry Bonds	1.25	.80
27	Paul Molitor	.40	.25
28	Mike Piazza	4.50	2.75
29	Robin Ventura	.35	.20
30	Jeff Conine	.25	.15

31	Wade Boggs	.30	.18
32	Dennis Eckersley	.15	.10
33	Bobby Bonilla	.15	.10
34	Lenny Dykstra	.25	.15
35	Manny Alexander	.12	.07
36	Ray Lankford	.20	.12
37	Greg Vaughn	.15	.10
38	Chuck Finley	.12	.07
39	Todd Benzinger	.10	.06
40	David Justice	.75	.45
41	Rob Dibble	.10	.06
42	Tom Henke	.10	.06
43	David Nied	.50	.30
44	Sandy Alomar Jr.	.12	.07
45	Pete Harnisch	.12	.07
46	Jeff Russell	.10	.06
47	Terry Mulholland	.12	.07
48	Kevin Appier	.20	.12
49	Randy Tomlin	.12	.07
50	Cal Ripken Jr.	.75	.45
51	Andy Benes	.15	.10
52	Jimmy Key	.12	.07
53	Kirt Manwaring	.10	.06
54	Kevin Tapani	.10	.06
55	Jose Guzman	.10	.06
56	Todd Stottlemyre	.10	.06
57	Jack McDowell	.35	.20
58	Orel Hershiser	.12	.07
59	Chris Hammond	.10	.06
60	Chris Nabholz	.10	.06
61	Ruben Sierra	.20	.12
62	Doc Gooden	.15	.10
63	John Kruk	.20	.12
64	Omar Vizquel	.12	.07
65	Tim Naehring	.12	.07
66	Dwight Smith	.12	.07
67	Mickey Tettleton	.12	.07
68	J.T. Snow	.75	.45
69	Greg McMichael	.20	.12
70	Kevin Mitchell	.15	.10
71	Kevin Brown	.15	.10
72	Scott Cooper	.20	.12
73	Jim Thome	.25	.15
74	Joe Girardi	.10	.06
75	Eric Anthony	.15	.10
76	Orlando Merced	.15	.10
77	Felix Jose	.12	.07
78	Tommy Greene	.20	.12
79	Bernard Gilkey	.15	.10
80	Phil Plantier	.25	.15
81	Danny Tartabull	.12	.07
82	Trevor Wilson	.10	.06
83	Chuck Knoblauch	.15	.10
84	Rick Wilkins	.15	.10
85	Devon White	.12	.07
86	Lance Johnson	.10	.06
87	Eric Karros	.25	.15
88	Gary Sheffield	.30	.18
89	Wil Cordero	.25	.15
90	Ron Darling	.10	.06
91	Darren Daulton	.25	.15
92	Joe Orsulak	.10	.06
93	Steve Cooke	.25	.15
94	Darryl Hamilton	.15	.10
95	Aaron Sele	.60	.35
96	John Doherty	.10	.06
97	Gary DiSarcina	.10	.06
98	Jeff Blauser	.12	.07
99	John Smiley	.12	.07
100	Ken Griffey Jr.	2.50	1.50
101	Dean Palmer	.30	.18
102	Felix Fermin	.10	.06
103	Jerald Clark	.10	.06
104	Doug Drabek	.12	.07
105	Curt Schilling	.12	.07
106	Jeff Montgomery	.12	.07
107	Rene Arocha	.20	.12
108	Carlos Garcia	.20	.12
109	Wally Whitehurst	.10	.06
110	Jim Abbott	.25	.15
111	Royce Clayton	.15	.10
112	Chris Hoiles	.12	.07
113	Mike Morgan	.10	.06
114	Joe Magrane	.10	.06
115	Tom Candiotti	.10	.06
116	Ron Karkovice	.10	.06
117	Ryan Bowen	.12	.07
118	Rod Beck	.15	.10
119	John Wetteland	.12	.07
120	Terry Steinbach	.10	.06
121	Dave Hollins	.25	.15
122	Jeff Kent	.20	.12
123	Ricky Bones	.12	.07
124	Brian Jordan	.20	.12
125	Chad Kreuter	.12	.07
126	John Valentin	.12	.07
127	Hilly Hathaway	.15	.10
128	Wilson Alvarez	.12	.07
129	Tino Martinez	.12	.07
130	Rodney Bolton	.10	.06
131	David Segui	.12	.07
132	Wayne Kirby	.12	.07
133	Eric Young	.15	.10
134	Scott Servais	.10	.06
135	Scott Radinsky	.10	.06
136	Bret Barberie	.10	.06
137	John Roper	.10	.06
138	Ricky Gutierrez	.12	.07
139	Bernie Williams	.15	.10
140	Bud Black	.10	.06
141	Jose Vizcaino	.10	.06
142	Gerald Williams	.15	.10
143	Duane Ward	.10	.06
144	Danny Jackson	.10	.06

145	Allen Watson	.60	.35
146	Scott Fletcher	.10	.06
147	Delino DeShields	.15	.10
148	Shane Mack	.12	.07
149	Jim Eisenreich	.10	.06
150	Troy Neel	.40	.25
151	Jay Bell	.15	.10
152	B.J. Surhoff	.10	.06
153	Mark Whiten	.25	.15
154	Mike Henneman	.10	.06
155	Todd Hundley	.12	.07
156	Greg Myers	.10	.06
157	Ryan Klesko	.50	.30
158	Dave Fleming	.20	.12
159	Mickey Morandini	.12	.07
160	Blas Minor	.10	.06
161	Reggie Jefferson	.15	.10
162	David Hulse	.12	.07
163	Greg Swindell	.12	.07
164	Roberto Hernandez	.12	.07
165	Brady Anderson	.15	.10
166	Jack Armstrong	.10	.06
167	Phil Clark	.15	.10
168	Melido Perez	.10	.06
169	Darren Lewis	.12	.07
170	Sam Horn	.10	.06
171	Mike Harkey	.12	.07
172	Juan Guzman	.25	.15
173	Bob Natal	.12	.07
174	Deion Sanders	.30	.18
175	Carlos Quintana	.10	.06
176	Mel Rojas	.12	.07
177	Willie Banks	.12	.07
178	Ben Rivera	.12	.07
179	Kenny Lofton	.30	.18
180	Leo Gomez	.12	.07
181	Roberto Mejia (R)	.75	.45
182	Mike Perez	.12	.07
183	Travis Fryman	.60	.35
184	Ben McDonald	.15	.10
185	Steve Frey	.12	.07
186	Kevin Young	.30	.18
187	Dave Magadan	.10	.06
188	Bobby Munoz	.15	.10
189	Pat Rapp	.15	.10
190	Jose Offerman	.12	.07
191	Vinny Castilla	.10	.06
192	Ivan Calderon	.10	.06
193	Ken Caminiti	.10	.06
194	Benji Gil	.25	.15
195	Chuck Carr	.15	.10
196	Derrick May	.20	.12
197	Pat Kelly	.12	.07
198	Jeff Brantley	.10	.06
199	Jose Lind	.10	.06
200	Steve Buechele	.10	.06
201	Wes Chamberlain	.15	.10
202	Eduardo Perez	1.00	.60
203	Bret Saberhagen	.12	.07
204	Gregg Jefferies	.25	.15
205	Darrin Fletcher	.12	.07
206	Kent Hrbek	.10	.06
207	Kim Batiste	.10	.06
208	Jeff King	.12	.07
209	Donovan Osborne	.15	.10
210	Dave Nilsson	.12	.07
211	Al Martin	.30	.18
212	Mike Moore	.10	.06
213	Sterling Hitchcock	.30	.18
214	Geronimo Pena	.10	.06
215	Kevin Higgins	.12	.07
216	Norm Charlton	.10	.06
217	Don Slaught	.10	.06
218	Mitch Williams	.10	.06
219	Derek Lilliquist	.10	.06
220	Armando Reynoso	.12	.07
221	Kenny Rogers	.10	.06
222	Doug Jones	.10	.06
223	Luis Aquino	.10	.06
224	Mike Oquist (R)	.25	.15
225	Darryl Scott (R)	.25	.15
226	Kurt Abbott (R)	.35	.20
227	Andy Tomberlin (R)	.15	.10
228	Norberto Martin (R)	.25	.15
229	Pedro Castellano	.10	.06
230	Curtis Pride (R)	.60	.35
231	Jeff McNeely	.25	.15
232	Scott Lydy	.12	.07
233	Darren Oliver (R)	.30	.18
234	Danny Bautista (R)	.15	.10
235	Butch Huskey	.25	.15
236	Chipper Jones	.75	.45
237	Eddie Zambrano (R)	.20	.12
238	Domingo Jean (R)	.60	.35
239	Javier Lopez (R)	.80	.50
240	Nigel Wilson	.60	.35
241	Drew Denson (R)	.25	.15
242	Raul Mondesi	.25	.15
243	Luis Ortiz (R)	.25	.15
244	Manny Ramirez	1.00	.60
245	Greg Blosser	.30	.18
246	Rondell White	.40	.25
247	Steve Karsay	.60	.35
248	Scott Stahoviak	.15	.10
249	Jose Valentin	.12	.07
250	Marc Newfield	.35	.20
251	Keith Kessinger (R)	.60	.35
252	Carl Everett	.25	.15
253	John O'Donoghue	.12	.07
254	Turk Wendell	.12	.07
255	Scott Ruffcorn	.25	.15
256	Tony Tarasco	.35	.20
257	Andy Cook (R)	.20	.12
258	Matt Mieske	.15	.10

259	Luis Lopez (R)	.40	.25
260	Ramon Caraballo (R)	.25	.15
261	Salomon Torres	.50	.30
262	Brooks Kieschnick (R)	1.00	.60
263	Daron Kirkreit (R)	.40	.25
264	Bill Wagner (R)	.50	.30
265	Matt Drews (R)	.40	.25
266	Scott Christman (R)	.35	.20
267	Torii Hunter (R)	.25	.15
268	Jamey Wright (R)	.20	.12
269	Jeff Granger (R)	1.00	.60
270	Trot Nixon (R)	1.25	.80

1994 Pinnacle I
Rookie Team
Pinnacle

The cards in this limited insert set were distributed randomly in Pinnacle foil packs. The cards depict full-color action photos on players on each side. The headline" Rookie Team Pinnacle" is printed acxross the top. All cards measure 2-1/2" by 3-1/2".

		MINT	NR/MT
Complete Set (9)		325.00	200.00
Commons		12.00	7.00
1	C.arlos Delgado Javier Lopez	75.00	45.00
2	Bob Hamelin J.R. Phillips	15.00	10.00
3	Keith Kessinger Jon Shave	12.00	7.00
4	Butch Huskey Luis Ortiz	18.00	12.00
5	Kurt Abbott Chipper Jones	35.00	20.00
6	Manny Ranirez Rondell White	80.00	50.00
7	Cliff Floyd Jeffrey Hammonds	100.00	60.00
8	Marc Newfield Nigel Wilson	40.00	25.00
9	Mark Hutton Salomon Torres	20.00	14.00

1994 Pinnacle I
Run Creators

The cards in this limited insert set were packed randomly in Pinnacle packs and feature full-color action photos on the fronts and a smaller color picture on the flip side. The headline "Run Creators" appears in bold type on the card fronts. All cards measure 2-1/2" by 3-1/2".

		MINT	NR/MT
Complete Set (22)		75.00	48.00
Commons		.75	.45
1	John Olerud	4.50	2.75
2	Frank Thomas	12.50	7.50
3	Ken Griffey Jr.	10.00	6.50
4	Paul Molitor	3.00	1.75
5	Rafael Palmeiro	2.00	1.25
6	Roberto Alomar	5.00	3.00
7	Juan Gonzalez	8.50	5.00
8	Albert Belle	4.50	2.75
9	Travis Fryman	6.00	3.50
10	Rickey Henderson	2.50	1.50
11	Tony Phillips	.75	.45
12	Mo Vaughn	1.50	.90
13	Tim Salmon	6.00	3.75
14	Kenny Lofton	4.50	2.75
15	Carlos Baerga	5.00	3.00
16	Greg Vaughn	1.00	.60
17	Jay Buhner	.75	.45
18	Chris Hoiles	.75	.45
19	Mickey Tettleton	.75	.45
20	Kirby Puckett	3.50	2.00
21	Danny Tartabull	.75	.45
22	Devon White	.75	.45

1994 Pinnacle I
Tribute Series I

The cards in this limited 9-card insert set pays tribute to players who's special achievements or milestones made news during the 1993 season. The card fronts include a photo of the player while his achievement is mentioned on the card backs. All cards measure 2-1/2" by 3-1/2".

		MINT	NR/MT
	Complete Set (9)	38.00	24.00
	Commons	2.50	1.50
1	Paul Molitor	3.50	2.00
2	Jim Abbott	2.50	1.50
3	Dave Winfield	4.50	2.75
4	Bo Jackson	3.50	2.00
5	Dave Justice	5.00	3.00
6	Lenny Dykstra	3.00	1.75
7	Mike Piazza	10.00	6.50
8	Barry Bonds	6.50	3.75
9	Randy Johnson	2.50	1.50

1994 Score I

The cards in this series feature full-color player photos on the card fronts with a smaller color shot on the card backs. The player's name, position and team name appear in two small horizontal boxes under a corner of the player's photo on the front. The backs also include personal data and statistics. This is the first of two series of 1994 Score baseball. All cards measure 2-1/2" by 3-1/2".

	MINT	NR/MT
Complete Set (330)	16.00	10.00
Commons	.05	.02

1	Barry Bonds	.50	.30
2	John Olerud	.35	.20
3	Ken Griffey Jr	1.25	.80
4	Jeff Bagwell	.25	.15
5	John Burkett	.12	.07
6	Jack McDowell	.20	.12
7	Albert Belle	.25	.15
8	Andres Galarraga	.12	.07
9	Mike Mussina	.20	.12
10	Will Clark	.20	.12
11	Travis Fryman	.20	.12
12	Tony Gwynn	.15	.10
13	Robin Yount	.20	.12
14	Dave Magadan	.05	.02
15	Paul O'Neill	.10	.06
16	Ray Lankford	.12	.07
17	Damion Easley	.07	.04
18	Andy Van Slyke	.08	.05
19	Brian McRae	.08	.05
20	Ryne Sandberg	.25	.15
21	Kirby Puckett	.25	.15
22	Doc Gooden	.15	.10
23	Don Mattingly	.20	.12
24	Kevin Mitchell	.10	.06
25	Roger Clemens	.25	.15
26	Eric Karros	.20	.12
27	Juan Gonzalez	.80	.50
28	John Kruk	.10	.06
29	Gregg Jefferies	.12	.07
30	Tom Glavine	.20	.12
31	Ivan Rodriquez	.15	.10
32	Jay Bell	.08	.05
33	Randy Johnson	.15	.10
34	Darren Daulton	.15	.10
35	Rickey Henderson	.20	.12
36	Eddie Murray	.15	.10
37	Brian Harper	.07	.04
38	Delino DeShields	.10	.06
39	Jose Lind	.05	.02
40	Benito Santiago	.08	.05
41	Frank Thomas	1.50	.90
42	Mark Grace	.12	.07
43	Roberto Alomar	.25	.15
44	Andy Benes	.10	.06
45	Luis Polonia	.05	.02
46	Brett Butler	.07	.04
47	Terry Steinbach	.05	.02
48	Craig Biggio	.07	.04
49	Greg Vaughn	.10	.06
50	Charlie Hayes	.07	.04
51	Mickey Tettleton	.07	.04
52	Jose Rijo	.08	.05
53	Carlos Baerga	.25	.15
54	Jeff Blauser	.07	.04
55	Leo Gomez	.07	.04
56	Bob Tewksbury	.05	.02
57	Mo Vaughn	.15	.10

58	Orlando Merced	.08	.05	115	Jeff Treadway	.05	.02
59	Tino Martinez	.08	.05	116	Ricky Jordan	.05	.02
60	Lenny Dykstra	.20	.12	117	Mike Henneman	.05	.02
61	Jose Canseco	.15	.10	118	Willie Blair	.08	.05
62	Tony Fernandez	.05	.02	119	Doug Henry	.05	.02
63	Donovan Osborne	.10	.06	120	Gerald Perry	.05	.02
64	Ken Hill	.08	.05	121	Greg Myers	.05	.02
65	Kent Hrbek	.05	.02	122	John Franco	.05	.02
66	Bryan Harvey	.08	.05	123	Roger Mason	.05	.02
67	Wally Joyner	.08	.05	124	Chris Hammond	.05	.02
68	Derrick May	.12	.07	125	Hubie Brooks	.05	.02
69	Lance Johnson	.05	.02	126	Kent Mercker	.05	.02
70	Willie McGee	.08	.05	127	Jim Abbott	.12	.07
71	Mark Langston	.10	.06	128	Kevin Bass	.05	.02
72	Terry Pendleton	.10	.06	129	Rick Aguilera	.05	.02
73	Joe Carter	.20	.12	130	Mitch Webster	.05	.02
74	Barry Larkin	.10	.06	131	Eric Plunk	.05	.02
75	Jimmy Key	.08	.05	132	Mark Carreon	.05	.02
76	Joe Girardi	.05	.02	133	Dave Stewart	.12	.07
77	B.J. Surhoff	.05	.02	134	Willie Wilson	.05	.02
78	Pete Harnisch	.08	.05	135	Dave Fleming	.15	.10
79	Lou Whitaker	.08	.05	136	Jeff Tackettt	.05	.02
80	Cory Snyder	.05	.02	137	Geno Petralli	.05	.02
81	Kenny Lofton	.20	.12	138	Gene Harris	.05	.02
82	Fred McGriff	.25	.15	139	Scott Bankhead	.05	.02
83	Mike Greenwell	.08	.05	140	Trevor Wilson	.05	.02
84	Mike Perez	.07	.04	141	Alvaro Espinoza	.05	.02
85	Cal Ripken Jr.	.30	.18	142	Ryan Bowen	.08	.05
86	Don Slaught	.05	.02	143	Mike Moore	.05	.02
87	Omar Visquel	.08	.05	144	Bill Pecota	.05	.02
88	Curt Schilling	.08	.05	145	Jaime Navarro	.07	.04
89	Chuck Knoblauch	.12	.07	146	Jack Daugherty	.05	.02
90	Moises Alou	.12	.07	147	Bob Wickman	.12	.07
91	Greg Gagne	.05	.02	148	Chris Jones	.05	.02
92	Bret Saberhagen	.10	.06	149	Todd Stottlemyre	.05	.02
93	Ozzie Guillen	.05	.02	150	Brian Williams	.07	.04
94	Matt Williams	.15	.10	151	Chuck Finley	.08	.05
95	Chad Curtis	.15	.10	152	Lenny Harris	.05	.02
96	Mike Harkey	.07	.04	153	Alex Fernandez	.12	.07
97	Devon White	.07	.04	154	Candy Maldonado	.05	.02
98	Walt Weiss	.05	.02	155	Jeff Montgomery	.07	.04
99	Kevin Brown	.08	.05	156	David West	.05	.02
100	Gary Sheffield	.15	.10	157	Mark Williamson	.05	.02
101	Wade Boggs	.15	.10	158	Milt Thompson	.05	.02
102	Orel Hershiser	.08	.05	159	Ron Darling	.05	.02
103	Tony Phillips	.07	.04	160	Stan Belinda	.05	.02
104	Andujar Cedeno	.10	.06	161	Henry Cotto	.05	.02
105	Bill Spiers	.05	.02	162	Mel Rojas	.05	.02
106	Otis Nixon	.05	.02	163	Doug Strange	.05	.02
107	Felix Fermin	.05	.02	164	Rene Arocha	.10	.06
108	Bip Roberts	.05	.02	165	Tim Hulett	.05	.02
109	Dennis Eckersley	.10	.06	166	Steve Avery	.15	.10
110	Dante Bichette	.08	.05	167	Jim Thome	.15	.10
111	Ben McDonald	.12	.07	168	Tom Browning	.07	.04
112	Jim Poole	.05	.02	169	Mario Diaz	.05	.02
113	John Dopson	.05	.02	170	Steve Reed	.05	.02
114	Rob Dibble	.05	.02	171	Scott Livingstone	.05	.02

172	Chris Donnels	.05	.02
173	John Jaha	.10	.06
174	Carlos Hernandez	.05	.02
175	Dion James	.05	.02
176	Bud Black	.05	.02
177	Tony Castillo	.05	.02
178	Jose Guzman	.05	.02
179	Torey Lovullo	.05	.02
180	John Vander Wal	.05	.02
181	Mike LaValliere	.05	.02
182	Sid Fernandez	.05	.02
183	Brent Mayne	.05	.02
184	Terry Mulholland	.07	.04
185	Willie Banks	.07	.04
186	Steve Cooke	.12	.07
187	Brent Gates	.20	.12
188	Erik Pappas	.07	.04
189	Bill Hasselman	.05	.02
190	Fernando Valenzuela	.05	.02
191	Gary Redus	.05	.02
192	Danny Darwin	.05	.02
193	Mark Portugal	.07	.04
194	Derek Lilliquist	.05	.02
195	Charlie O'Brien	.05	.02
196	Matt Nokes	.05	.02
197	Danny Sheaffer	.07	.04
198	Bill Gullickson	.05	.02
199	Alex Arias	.05	.02
200	Mike Fetters	.05	.02
201	Brian Jordan	.10	.06
202	Joe Grahe	.05	.02
203	Tom Candiotti	.05	.02
204	Jeremy Stanton	.10	.06
205	Mike Stanton	.05	.02
206	David Howard	.05	.02
207	Darren Holmes	.05	.02
208	Rick Honeycutt	.05	.02
209	Danny Jackson	.05	.02
210	Rich Amaral	.07	.04
211	Blas Minor	.05	.02
212	Kenny Rogers	.05	.02
213	Jim Leyritz	.05	.02
214	Mike Morgan	.05	.02
215	Dan Gladden	.05	.02
216	Randy Velarde	.05	.02
217	Mitch Williams	.05	.02
218	Hipolito Pichardo	.05	.02
219	Dave Burba	.05	.02
220	Wilson Alvarez	.08	.05
221	Bob Zupcic	.08	.05
222	Francisco Cabrera	.05	.02
223	Julio Valera	.05	.02
224	Paul Assenmacher	.05	.02
225	Jeff Branson	.05	.02
226	Todd Frohwirth	.05	.02
227	Armando Reynoso	.07	.04
228	Rich Rowland	.07	.04
229	Freddie Benavides	.05	.02
230	Wayne Kirby	.07	.04
231	Darryl Kile	.12	.07
232	Skeeter Barnes	.05	.02
233	Ramon Martinez	.08	.05
234	Tom Gordon	.08	.05
235	Dave Gallagher	.05	.02
236	Ricky Bones	.05	.02
237	Larry Andersen	.05	.02
238	Pat Meares	.08	.05
239	Zane Smith	.05	.02
240	Tim Leary	.05	.02
241	Phil Clark	.08	.05
242	Danny Cox	.05	.02
243	Mike Jackson	.05	.02
244	Mike Gallego	.05	.02
245	Lee Smith	.10	.06
246	Todd Jones	.07	.04
247	Steve Bedrosian	.05	.02
248	Troy Neel	.15	.10
249	Jose Bautista	.07	.04
250	Steve Frey	.05	.02
251	Jeff Reardon	.08	.05
252	Stan Javier	.05	.02
253	Mo Sanford	.05	.02
254	Steve Sax	.07	.04
255	Luis Aquino	.05	.02
256	Domingo Jean	.20	.12
257	Scott Servais	.05	.02
258	Brad Pennington	.05	.02
259	Dave Hansen	.05	.02
260	Goose Gossage	.07	.04
261	Jeff Fassero	.05	.02
262	Junior Ortiz	.05	.02
263	Anthony Young	.07	.04
264	Chris Bosio	.05	.02
265	Ruben Amaro Jr.	.05	.02
266	Mark Eichhorn	.05	.02
267	Dave Clark	.05	.02
268	Gary Thurman	.05	.02
269	Les Lancaster	.05	.02
270	Jamie Moyer	.05	.02
271	Ricky Gutierrez	.07	.04
272	Greg Harris	.05	.02
273	Mike Benjamin	.05	.02
274	Gene Nelson	.05	.02
275	Damon Berryhill	.05	.02
276	Scott Radinsky	.05	.02
277	Mike Aldrete	.05	.02
278	Jerry DiPoto	.05	.02
279	Chris Haney	.07	.04
280	Richie Lewis	.07	.04
281	Jarvis Brown	.12	.07
282	Juan Bell	.05	.02
283	Joe Klink	.05	.02
284	Graeme Lloyd	.08	.05
285	Casey Candaele	.05	.02

286	Bob MacDonald	.05	.02
287	Mike Sharperson	.05	.02
288	Gene Larkin	.05	.02
289	Brian Barnes	.05	.02
290	David McCarty	.20	.12
291	Jeff Innis	.05	.02
292	Bob Patterson	.05	.02
293	Ben Rivera	.07	.04
294	John Habyan	.05	.02
295	Rich Rodriquez	.05	.02
296	Edwin Nunez	.05	.02
297	Rod Brewer	.05	.02
298	Mike Timlin	.05	.02
299	Jesse Orasco	.05	.02
300	Gary Gaetti	.05	.02
301	Todd Benzinger	.05	.02
302	Jeff Nelson	.05	.02
303	Rafael Belliard	.05	.02
304	Matt Whiteside	.05	.02
305	Vinny Castilla	.05	.02
306	Matt Turner	.08	.05
307	Eduardo Perez	.25	.15
308	Joel Johnston	.05	.02
309	Chris Gomez	.12	.07
310	Pat Rapp	.10	.06
311	Jim Tatum	.05	.02
312	Kirk Rueter	.25	.15
313	John Flaherty	.07	.04
314	Tom Kramer	.10	.06
315	Mark Whiten	.15	.10
316	Chris Bosio	.05	.02
317	Orioles (CL)	.10	.04
318	Red Sox (CL)	.08	.03
319	Angels (CL)	.08	.03
320	White Sox (CL)	.08	.03
321	Indians (CL)	.08	.03
322	Tigers (CL)	.08	.03
323	Royals (CL)	.08	.03
324	Brewers (CL)	.08	.03
325	Twins (CL)	.08	.03
326	Yankees (CL)	.08	.03
327	Athletics (CL)	.08	.03
328	Mariners (CL)	.08	.03
329	Rangers (CL)	.08	.03
330	Blue Jays (CL)	.08	.03

1994 Score 1 Dream Team

The cards in this limited insert set were issued randomly in Score packs. The card fronts feature player photos fromed by borders at the top and bottom and are borderless on the sides. Dream Team appears in a small horizontal box above the photo while the player's name is printed in a small box under his photo. All cards measure 2-1/2" by 3-1/2".

		MINT	NR/MT
Complete Set (10)		40.00	28.00
Commons		1.50	.90
1	Mike Mussina	8.50	5.50
2	Tom Glavine	5.00	3.00
3	Don Mattingly	7.50	4.50
4	Carlos Baerga	8.00	5.00
5	Barry Larkin	2.50	1.50
6	Matt Wiliams	3.50	2.00
7	Juan Gonzalez	12.00	7.00
8	Andy Van Slyke	2.00	1.25
9	Larry Walker	2.50	1.50
10	Mike Stanley	1.50	.90

1994 Score I Gold Stars

These insert cards feature full-bleed, full-color action photos on the card fromts. The words "Gold Star" is printed in a small triangle below his photo. The player's name appears in a small box under the triangle. The cards were issued randomly in Score hobby packs. All cards measure 2-1/2" by 3-1/2".

		MINT	NR/MT
Complete Set (30)		80.00	50.00
Commons		1.50	.90

1	Barry Bonds	8.00	5.00
2	Orlando Merced	1.75	1.00
3	Mark Grace	3.00	1.75
4	Darren Daulton	3.50	2.00
5	Jeff Blauser	1.50	.90
6	Deion Sanders	3.00	1.75
7	John Kruk	2.50	1.50
8	Jeff Bagwell	5.00	3.00
9	Gregg Jefferies	3.50	2.00
10	Matt Williams	4.00	2.50
11	Andres Galarraga	2.50	1.50
12	Jay Bell	1.50	.90
13	Mike Piazza	18.00	12.00
14	Ron Gant	2.50	1.50
15	Barry Larkin	2.00	1.25
16	Tom Glavine	5.00	3.00
17	Len Dykstra	4.00	2.50
18	Fred McGriff	7.00	4.00
19	Andy Van Slyke	1.50	.90
20	Gary Sheffield	3.50	2.00
21	John Burkett	2.00	1.25
22	Dante Bichette	1.50	.90
23	Tony Gwynn	5.00	3.00
24	David Justice	7.50	4.50
25	Marquis Grissom	3.00	1.75
26	Bobby Bonilla	1.50	.90
27	Larry Walker	2.50	1.50
28	Brett Butler	1.50	.90
29	Robby Thompson	1.50	.90
30	Jeff Conine	3.00	1.75

1994 Topps I

The cards in this set feature full-color action photos on the fronts framed by a thin multi-colored line next to the photo and a wider white border outside. The player's name is printed in script under his picture while his team name and position appear in a horizontal color bar under his name. The horizontal card backs contain another full-color shot along with personal data, statistical and highlights. The only subset on note is All-Stars (AS)(384-394). Gold cards of each player were inserted randomly in Topps packs. Those cards are valued at 3X to 5X the book price listed below. All cards measure 2-1/2" by 3-1/2".

		MINT	NR/MT
Complete Set (396)		16.00	10.00
Commons		.05	.02

1	Mike Piazza	1.25	.80
2	Bernie Williams	.10	.06
3	Kevin Rogers	.05	.02
4	Paul Carey	.10	.06
5	Ozzie Guillen	.05	.02
6	Derrick May	.10	.06
7	Jose Mesa	.05	.02
8	Todd Hundley	.07	.04
9	Chris Haney	.07	.04
10	John Olerud	.35	.20
11	Andujar Cedeno	.10	.06
12	John Smiley	.08	.05
13	Phil Plantier	.20	.12
14	Willie Banks	.07	.04
15	Jay Bell	.08	.05
16	Doug Henry	.05	.02
17	Lance Blankenship	.05	.02
18	Greg Harris	.05	.02
19	Scott Livingstone	.05	.02
20	Bryan Harvey	.08	.05
21	Wil Cordero	.20	.12
22	Roger Pavlik	.20	.12
23	Mark Lemke	.05	.02
24	Jeff Nelson	.05	.02
25	Todd Zeile	.08	.05
26	Billy Hatcher	.05	.02
27	Joe Magrane	.05	.02
28	Tony Longmire	.08	.05
29	Omar Daal	.08	.05
30	Kirk Manwaring	.05	.02
31	Melido Perez	.05	.02
32	Tim Hulett	.08	.05
33	Jeff Schwarz	.10	.06
34	Nolan Ryan	.75	.45
35	Jose Guzman	.05	.02
36	Felix Fermin	.05	.02
37	Jeff Innis	.05	.02
38	Brent Mayne	.05	.02
39	Huck Flener (R)	.15	.10
40	Jeff Bagwell	.15	.10
41	Kevin Wickander	.05	.02
42	Ricky Gutierrez	.07	.04

43	Pat Mahomes	.08	.05
44	Jeff King	.08	.05
45	Cal Eldred	.12	.07
46	Craig Paquette	.07	.04
47	Richie Lewis	.07	.04
48	Tony Phillips	.07	.04
49	Armando Reynoso	.00	.00
50	Moises Alou	.10	.06
51	Manuel Lee	.05	.02
52	Otis Nixon	.05	.02
53	Billy Ashley	.20	.12
54	Mark Whiten	.15	.10
55	Jeff Russell	.05	.02
56	Chad Curtis	.12	.07
57	Kevin Stocker	.40	.25
58	Mike Jackson	.05	.02
59	Matt Nokes	.05	.02
60	Chris Bosio	.05	.02
61	Damon Buford	.08	.05
62	Tim Belcher	.07	.04
63	Glenallen Hill	.08	.05
64	Bill Wertz	.08	.05
65	Eddie Murray	.12	.07
66	Tom Gordon	.08	.05
67	Alex Gonzalez	.25	.15
68	Eddie Taubensee	.05	.02
69	Jacob Brumfield	.08	.05
70	Andy Benes	.10	.06
71	Rich Becker	.10	.06
72	Steve Cooke	.20	.12
73	Billy Spiers	.05	.02
74	Scott Brosius	.05	.02
75	Alan Trammell	.10	.06
76	Luis Aquino	.05	.02
77	Jerald Clark	.05	.02
78	Mel Rojas	.07	.04
79	1994 Prospects (Cameron/Clark/ McClure)	.25	.15
80	Jose Canseco	.15	.10
81	Greg McMichael	.10	.06
82	Brian Turang (R)	.10	.06
83	Tom Urbani	.05	.02
84	Garret Anderson	.08	.05
85	Tony Pena	.05	.02
86	Ricky Jordan	.05	.02
87	Jim Gott	.05	.02
88	Pat Kelly	.08	.05
89	Bud Black	.05	.02
90	Robin Ventura	.15	.10
91	Rick Sutcliffe	.05	.02
92	Jose Bautista	.08	.05
93	Bob Ojeda	.05	.02
94	Phil Hiatt	.12	.07
95	Tim Pugh	.08	.05
96	Randy Knorr	.07	.04
97	Todd Jones	.08	.05
98	Ryan Thompson	.12	.07
99	Tim Mauser	.08	.05
100	Kirby Puckett	.30	.18
101	Mark Dewey	.07	.04
102	B.J. Surhoff	.05	.02
103	Sterling Hitchcock	.25	.15
104	Alex Arias	.05	.02
105	David Wells	.05	.02
106	Daryl Boston	.05	.02
107	Mike Stanton	.05	.02
108	Gary Redus	.05	.02
109	Delino DeShields	.10	.06
110	Lee Smith	.10	.06
111	Greg Litton	.05	.02
112	Frank Rodriquez	.25	.15
113	Russ Springer	.07	.04
114	Mitch Williams	.05	.02
115	Eric Karros	.15	.10
116	Jeff Brantley	.05	.02
117	Jack Voight	.07	.04
118	Jason Bere	.40	.25
119	Kevin Roberson	.15	.10
120	Jimmy Key	.08	.05
121	Reggie Jefferson	.10	.06
122	Jeromy Burnitz	.15	.10
123	Billy Brewer	.10	.06
124	Willie Canale	.07	.04
125	Greg Swindell	.07	.04
126	Hal Morris	.10	.06
127	Brad Ausmus	.07	.04
128	George Tsamis	.10	.06
129	Denny Neagle	.05	.02
130	Pat Listach	.10	.06
131	Steve Karsay	.25	.15
132	Bret Barberie	.05	.02
133	Mark Leiter	.05	.02
134	Greg Colbrunn	.07	.04
135	David Nied	.25	.15
136	Dean Palmer	.12	.07
137	Steve Avery	.15	.10
138	Bill Haselman	.05	.02
139	Tripp Cromer	.08	.05
140	Frank Viola	.07	.04
141	Rene Gonzales	.05	.02
142	Curt Schilling	.08	.05
143	Tim Wallach	.05	.02
144	Bobby Munoz	.10	.06
145	Brady Anderson	.10	.06
146	Rod Beck	.08	.05
147	Mike LaValliere	.05	.02
148	Greg Hibbard	.05	.02
149	Kenny Lofton	.20	.12
150	Doc Gooden	.12	.07
151	Greg Gagne	.05	.02
152	Ray McDavid	.20	.12
153	Chris Donnels	.05	.02
154	Dan Wilson	.08	.05

155	Todd Stottlemyre	.05	.02
156	David McCarty	.20	.12
157	Paul Wagner	.15	.10
158	1994 Prospects	..50	.30
	(Jeter/Miller/Neal)		
159	Mike Fetters	.05	.02
160	Scott Lydy	.08	.05
161	Darrell Whitmore	.15	.10
162	Bob MacDonald	.05	.02
163	Vinny Castilla	.05	.02
164	Denis Boucher	.07	.04
165	Ivan Rodriquez	.15	.10
166	Ron Gant	.12	.07
167	Tim Davis	.10	.06
168	Steve Dixon	.08	.05
169	Scott Fletcher	.05	.02
170	Terry Mulholland	.07	.04
171	Greg Myers	.05	.02
172	Brett Butler	.07	.04
173	Bob Wickman	.12	.07
174	Dave Martinez	.05	.02
175	Fernando Valenzuela	.05	.02
176	Craig Grebeck	.05	.02
177	Shawn Boskie	.05	.02
178	Albie Lopez	.12	.07
179	Butch Huskey	.15	.10
180	George Brett	.30	.18
181	Juan Guzman	.15	.10
182	Eric Anthony	.10	.06
183	Rob Dibble	.05	.02
184	Craig Shipley	.05	.02
185	Kevin Tapani	.05	.02
186	Marcus Moore	.20	.12
187	Graeme Lloyd	.08	.05
188	Mike Bordick	.07	.04
189	Chris Hammond	.05	.02
190	Cecil Fielder	.15	.10
191	Curtis Leskanic	.07	.04
192	Lou Frazier	.07	.04
193	Steve Dreyer (R)	.12	.07
194	Javy Lopez	.50	.30
195	Edgar Martinez	.10	.06
196	Allen Watson	.20	.12
197	John Flaherty	.05	.02
198	Kurt Stillwell	.05	.02
199	Danny Jackson	.05	.02
200	Cal Ripken Jr.	.30	.18
201	Mike Bell (R)	.20	.12
202	Alan Benes (R)	.35	.20
203	Matt Farmer (R)	.20	.12
204	Jeff Granger	.35	.20
205	Brooks Kieschnick (R)	.80	.50
206	Jeremy Lee (R)	.15	.10
207	Charles Peterson (R)	.15	.10
208	Andy Rice (R)	.20	.12
209	Billy Wagner (R)	.35	.20
210	Kelly Wunsch (R)	.15	.10
211	Tom Candiotti	.05	.02
212	Domingo Jean	.15	.10
213	John Burkett	.08	.05
214	George Bell	.08	.05
215	Dan Plesac	.05	.02
216	Manny Ranirez	.75	.45
217	Mike Maddux	.05	.02
218	Kevin McReynolds	.05	.02
219	Pat Borders	.05	.02
220	Doug Drabek	.10	.06
221	Larry Luebbers (R)	.10	.06
222	Trevor Hoffman	.10	.06
223	Pat Meares	.10	.06
224	Danny Miceli	.08	.05
225	Greg Vaughn	.10	.06
226	Scott Hemond	.05	.02
227	Pat Rapp	.08	.05
228	Kirk Gibson	.07	.04
229	Lance Painter	.08	.05
230	Larry Walker	.12	.07
231	Benji Gil	.15	.10
232	Mark Wohlers	.08	.05
233	Rich Amaral	.07	.04
234	Erik Pappas	.07	.04
235	Scott Cooper	.10	.06
236	Mike Butcher	.08	.05
237	1994 Prospects	.60	.35
	(Curtis Pride)		
238	Kim Batiste	.05	.02
239	Paul Assenmacher	.05	.02
240	Will Clark	.20	.12
241	Jose Offerman	.08	.05
242	Todd Frohwirth	.05	.02
243	Tim Raines	.08	.05
244	Rick Wilkins	.12	.07
245	Bret Saberhagen	.08	.05
246	Thomas Howard	.05	.02
247	Stan Belinda	.05	.02
248	Rickey Henderson	.15	.10
249	Brian Williams	.08	.05
250	Barry Larkin	.10	.06
251	Jose Valentin	.07	.04
252	Lenny Webster	.05	.02
253	Blas Minor	.05	.02
254	Tim Teufel	.05	.02
255	Bobby Witt	.07	.04
256	Walt Weiss	.05	.02
257	Chad Kreuter	.08	.05
258	Roberto Mejia	.20	.12
259	Cliff Floyd	1.00	.60
260	Julio Franco	.05	.02
261	Rafael Belliard	.05	.02
262	Marc Newfield	.20	.12
263	Gerald Perry	.05	.02
264	Ken Ryan	.20	.12
265	Chili Davis	.07	.04
266	Dave West	.05	.02

267	Royce Clayton	.10	.06	323	Pete Incaviglia	.05	.02
268	Pedro Martinez	.10	.06	324	Alan Mills	.05	.02
269	Mark Hutton	.12	.07	325	Jody Reed	.05	.02
270	Frank Thomas	1.50	.90	326	Rich Monteleone	.05	.02
271	Brad Pennington	.07	.04	327	Mark Carreon	.05	.02
272	Mike Harkey	.07	.04	328	Donn Pall	.05	.02
273	Candy Alomar Jr.	.00	.06	329	Matt Walbeck	.12	.07
274	Dave Gallagher	.05	.02	330	Charles Nagy	.12	.07
275	Wally Joyner	.10	.06	331	Jeff McKnight	.10	.06
276	Rick Trlicek	.05	.02	332	Jose Lind	.05	.02
277	Al Osuna	.05	.02	333	Mike Timlin	.05	.02
278	Calvin Reese	.07	.04	334	Doug Jones	.05	.02
279	Kevin Higgins	.07	.04	335	Kevin Mitchell	.10	.06
280	Rick Aguilera	.05	.02	336	Luis Lopez	.15	.10
281	Orlando Merced	.10	.06	337	Shane Mack	.08	.05
282	Mike Mohler	.10	.06	338	Randy Tomlin	.08	.05
283	John Jaha	.10	.06	339	Matt Mieske	.10	.06
284	Robb Nen	.08	.05	340	Mark McGwire	.15	.10
285	Travis Fryman	.25	.15	341	Nigel Wilson	.30	.18
286	Mark Thompson	.08	.05	342	Dan Gladden	.05	.02
287	Mike Lansing	.08	.05	343	Mo Sanford	.05	.02
288	Craig Lefferts	.05	.02	344	Sean Berry	.08	.05
289	Damon Berryhill	.05	.02	345	Kevin Brown	.08	.05
290	Randy Johnson	.15	.10	346	Greg Olson	.05	.02
291	Jeff Reed	.05	.02	347	Dave Magadan	.05	.02
292	Danny Darwin	.05	.02	348	Rene Arocha	.10	.06
293	J.T. Snow	.50	.30	349	Carlos Quintana	.05	.02
294	Tyler Green	.12	.07	350	Jim Abbott	.15	.10
295	Chris Hoiles	.08	.05	351	Gary DiSarcina	.07	.04
296	Roger McDowell	.05	.02	352	Ben Rivera	.07	.04
297	Spike Owen	.05	.02	353	Carlos Hernandez	.07	.04
298	Salomon Torres	.20	.12	354	Darren Lewis	.08	.05
299	Wilson Alvarez	.08	.05	355	Harold Reynolds	.05	.02
300	Ryne Sandberg	.30	.18	356	Scott Ruffcorn	.15	.10
301	Derek Lilliquist	.05	.02	357	Mark Gubicza	.05	.02
302	Howard Johnson	.08	.05	358	Paul Sorrento	.08	.05
303	Greg Cadaret	.05	.02	359	Anthony Young	.07	.04
304	Pat Hentgen	.10	.06	360	Mark Grace	.15	.10
305	Craig Biggio	.08	.05	361	Rob Butler	.08	.05
306	Scott Service	.05	.02	362	Kevin Bass	.05	.02
307	Melvin Nieves	.30	.18	363	Eric Helfand	.08	.05
308	Mike Trombley	.07	.04	364	Derek Bell	.12	.07
309	Carlos Garcia	.12	.07	365	Scott Erickson	.08	.05
310	Robin Yount	.30	.18	366	Al Martin	.15	.10
311	Marcos Armas	.10	.06	367	Ricky Bones	.05	.02
312	Rich Rodriquez	.05	.02	368	Jeff Branson	.07	.04
313	Justin Thompson	.10	.06	369	1994 Prospects	.35	.20
314	Danny Sheaffer	.07	.04		(Arias/Bell/Giambi)		
315	Ken Hill	.08	.05	370	Benito Santiago	.08	.05
316	1994 Prospects	.50	.30	371	John Doherty	.05	.02
	(Ogea/Wade)			372	Joe Girardi	.05	.02
317	Cris Carpenter	.05	.02	373	Tim Scott	.05	.02
318	Jeff Blauser	.07	.04	374	Marvin Freeman	.05	.02
319	Ted Power	.05	.02	375	Deion Sanders	.12	.07
320	Ozzie Smith	.15	.10	376	Roger Salkeld	.12	.07
321	John Dopson	.05	.02	377	Bernard Gilkey	.10	.06
322	Chris Turner	.10	.06	378	Tom Fossas	.05	.02

		MINT	NR/MT
379	Mark McLemore	.05	.02
380	Darren Daulton	.15	.10
381	Chuck Finley	.08	.05
382	Mitch Webster	.05	.02
383	Gerald Williams	.10	.06
384	Frank Thomas/Fred McGriff (AS)	.75	.45
385	Roberto Alomar/Robby Thompson (AS)	.20	.12
386	Wade Boggs/Matt Williams(AS)	.15	.10
387	Cal Ripken/Jeff Blauser (AS)	.20	.12
388	Lenny Dykstra/Ken Griffey Jr. (AS)	.50	.30
389	David Justice/Juan Gonzalez (AS)	.40	.25
390	Albert Belle/Barry Bonds (AS)	.35	.20
391	Mike Piazza/Mike Stanley (AS)	.60	.35
392	Greg Maddux/Jack McDowell (AS)	.20	.12
393	Tom Glavine/Jimmy Key (AS)	.15	.10
394	Myers/Montgomery	.07	.04
395	Checklist	.05	.02
396	Checklist	.05	.02

1994 Topps Stadium Club I

The cards in this series feature full-bleed, full-color action photos on the fronts with the player's name and Stadium Club insignia printed in the lower portion of the card fronts. The backs contain another full-color action shot along with personal data and stats. The only subset of note is the 35+ Home Run Club (35+)(258-268). All cards measure 2-1/2" by 3-1/2".

		MINT	NR/MT
Complete Set (270)		30.00	20.00
Commons		.10	.06
1	Robin Yount	.40	.25
2	Rick Wilkins	.25	.15
3	Steve Scarsone	.20	.12
4	Gary Sheffield	.25	.15
5	George Brett	.50	.30
6	Al Martin	.05	.20
7	Joe Oliver	.10	.06
8	Stan Belinda	.10	.06
9	Denny Hocking	.30	.18
10	Roberto Alomar	.50	.30
11	Luis Polonia	.10	.06
12	Scott Hemond	.10	.06
13	Jody Reed	.10	.06
14	Mel Rojas	.12	.07
15	Junior Ortiz	.10	.06
16	Harold Baines	.12	.07
17	Brad Pennington	.12	.07
18	Jay Bell	.15	.10
19	Tom Henke	.10	.06
20	Jeff Branson	.12	.07
21	Roberto Meja	.60	.35
22	Pedro Munoz	.15	.10
23	Matt Nokes	.10	.06
24	Jack McDowell	.35	.20
25	Cecil Fielder	.30	.18
26	Tony Fossas	.10	.06
27	Jim Eisenreich	.10	.06
28	Anthony Young	.12	.07
29	Chuck Carr	.25	.15
30	Jeff Treadway	.10	.06
31	Chris Nabholz	.12	.07
32	Tom Candiotti	.10	.06
33	Mike Maddux	.10	.06
34	Nolan Ryan	2.00	1.25
35	Luis Gonzalez	.20	.12
36	Tim Salmon	1.75	1.00
37	Mark Whiten	.30	.18
38	Roger McDowell	.10	.06
39	Royce Clayton	.20	.12
40	Troy Neel	.40	.25
41	Mike Harkey	.12	.07
42	Darrin Fletcher	.12	.07
43	Wayne Kirby	.12	.07
44	Rich Amaral	.15	.10
45	Robb Nen	.15	.10
46	Tim Teufel	.10	.06
47	Steve Cooke	.30	.18
48	Jeff McNeely	.35	.20
49	Jeff Montgomery	.12	.07
50	Skeeter Barnes	.10	.06
51	Scott Stahoviak	.12	.07
52	Pat Kelly	.12	.07
53	Brady Anderson	.20	.12
54	Mariano Duncan	.10	.06
55	Brian Bohanon	.10	.06
56	Jerry Spradlin	.20	.12
57	Ron Karkovice	.10	.06
58	Jeff Gardner	.10	.06
59	Bobby Bonilla	.15	.10

60 Tino Martinez	.15	.10
61 Todd Benzinger	.10	.06
62 Steve Trachsel	.15	.10
63 Brian Jordan	.25	.15
64 Steve Bedrosian	.10	.06
65 Brent Gates	.50	.30
66 Shawn Green	.25	.15
67 Sean Berry	.15	.10
68 Joe Klink	.10	.06
69 Fernando Valenzuela	.10	.06
70 Andy Tomberlin	.15	.10
71 Tony Pena	.10	.06
72 Eric Young	.15	.10
73 Chris Gomez	.20	.12
74 Paul O'Neill	.15	.10
75 Ricky Gutierrez	.12	.07
76 Brad Holman	.12	.07
77 Lance Painter	.12	.07
78 Mike Butcher	.15	.10
79 Sid Bream	.10	.06
80 Sammy Sosa	.30	.18
81 Felix Fermin	.10	.06
82 Todd Hundley	.12	.07
83 Kevin Higgins	.15	.10
84 Todd Pratt	.12	.07
85 Ken Griffey Jr.	3.00	1.75
86 John O'Donoghue	.12	.07
87 Rick Renteria	.10	.06
88 John Burkett	.15	.10
89 Jose Vizcaino	.10	.06
90 Kevin Seitzer	.10	.06
91 Bobby Witt	.12	.07
92 Chris Turner	.15	.10
93 Omar Vizquel	.12	.07
94 David Justice	.75	.45
95 David Segui	.12	.04
96 Dave Hollins	.25	.15
97 Doug Strange	.10	.06
98 Jerald Clark	.10	.06
99 Mike Moore	.10	.06
100 Joey Cora	.10	.06
101 Scott Kamieniecki	.12	.07
102 Andy Benes	.15	.10
103 Chris Bosio	.10	.06
104 Rey Sanchez	.12	.07
105 John Jaha	.20	.12
106 Otis Nixon	.12	.07
107 Rickey Henderson	.30	.18
108 Jeff Bagwell	.25	.15
109 Gregg Jefferies	.25	.15
110 Trio (Blue Jays)	.40	.25
111 Trio (Braves)	.50	.30
112 Trio (Rangers)	.50	.30
113 Greg Swindell	.12	.07
114 Bill Haselman	.12	.07
115 Phil Plantier	.30	.18
116 Ivan Rodriquez	.30	.18
117 Kevin Tapani	.12	.07
118 Mike LaValliere	.10	.06
119 Tim Costo	.20	.12
120 Mickey Morandini	.12	.07
121 Brett Butler	.12	.07
122 Tom Pagnozzi	.12	.07
123 Ron Gant	.20	.12
124 Damion Easley	.12	.07
125 Dennis Eckersley	.15	.10
126 Matt Mieske	.15	.10
127 Cliff Floyd	4.00	2.50
128 Julian Tavarez	.20	.12
129 Arthur Rhodes	.15	.10
130 Dave West	.10	.06
131 Tim Naehring	.12	.07
132 Freddie Benavides	.10	.06
133 Paul Assenmacher	.10	.06
134 David McCarty	.30	.18
135 Jose Lind	.10	.06
136 Reggie Sanders	.25	.15
137 Don Slaught	.10	.06
138 Andujar Cedeno	.15	.10
139 Rob Deer	.10	.06
140 Mike Piazza	3.00	1.75
141 Moises Alou	.15	.10
142 Tom Foley	.10	.06
143 Benny Santiago	.15	.10
144 Sandy Alomar	.12	.07
145 Carlos Hernandez	.12	.07
146 Luis Alicea	.10	.06
147 Tom Lampkin	.10	.06
148 Ryan Klesko	.50	.30
149 Juan Guzman	.30	.18
150 Scott Servais	.10	.06
151 Tony Gwynn	.30	.18
152 Tim Wakefield	.20	.12
153 David Nied	.50	.30
154 Chris Haney	.12	.07
155 Danny Bautista	.15	.10
156 Randy Velarde	.10	.06
157 Darrin Jackson	.10	.06
158 J.R. Phillips	.50	.30
159 Greg Gagne	.10	.06
160 Luis Aquino	.10	.06
161 John Vander Wal	.10	.06
162 Randy Myers	.12	.07
163 Ted Power	.10	.06
164 Scott Brosius	.10	.06
165 Len Dykstra	.40	.25
166 Jacob Brumfield	.15	.10
167 Bo Jackson	.25	.15
168 Eddie Taubensee	.10	.06
169 Carlos Baerga	.75	.45
170 Tim Bogar	.15	.10
171 Jose Canseco	.30	.18
172 Greg Blosser	.20	.12
173 Chili Davis	.12	.07

174	Randy Knorr	.12	.07
175	Mike Perez	.12	.07
176	Henry Rodriquez	.15	.10
177	Brian Turang	.15	.10
178	Roger Pavlik	.25	.15
179	Aaron Sele	.75	.45
180	F. McGriff/G. Sheffield	.30	.18
181	T. Salmon/J.T. Snow	1.25	.80
182	Roberto Hernandez	.12	.07
183	Jeff Reboulet	.12	.07
184	John Doherty	.10	.06
185	Danny Sheaffer	.15	.10
186	Bip Roberts	.10	.06
187	Denny Martinez	.15	.10
188	Darryl Hamilton	.20	.12
189	Eduardo Perez	1.00	.60
190	Pete Harnisch	.12	.07
191	Rich Gossage	.12	.07
192	Mickey Tettleton	.12	.07
193	Lenny Webster	.10	.06
194	Lance Johnson	.10	.06
195	Don Mattingly	.40	.25
196	Gregg Olson	.12	.07
197	Mark Gubicza	.10	.06
198	Scott Fletcher	.10	.06
199	Jon Shave	.20	.12
200	Tim Mauser	.15	.10
201	Jeromy Burnitz	.35	.20
202	Rob Dibble	.10	.06
203	Will Clark	.35	.20
204	Steve Buechele	.10	.06
205	Brian Williams	.12	.07
206	Carlos Garcia	.20	.12
207	Mark Clark	.15	.10
208	Rafael Palmeiro	.30	.18
209	Eric Davis	.15	.10
210	Pat Meares	.15	.10
211	Chuck Finley	.15	.10
212	Jason Bere	.75	.45
213	Gary DiSarcina	.12	.07
214	Tony Fernandez	.10	.06
215	B.J. Surhoff	.10	.06
216	Lee Guetterman	.10	.06
217	Tim Wallach	.12	.07
218	Kirt Manwaring	.10	.06
219	Albert Belle	.70	.40
220	Doc Gooden	.20	.12
221	Archi Cianfrocco	.15	.10
222	Terry Mulholland	.12	.07
223	Hipolito Pichardo	.10	.06
224	Kent Hrbek	.12	.07
225	Craig Grebeck	.10	.06
226	Todd Jones	.12	.07
227	Mike Bordick	.12	.07
228	John Olerud	1.25	.80
229	Jeff Blauser	.12	.07
230	Alex Arias	.10	.06
231	Bernard Gilkey	.15	.10
232	Denny Neagle	.10	.06
233	Pedro Borbon	.15	.10
234	Dick Schofield	.10	.06
235	Matias Carrillo (R)	.20	.12
236	Juan Bell	.10	.06
237	Mike Hampton	.15	.10
238	Barry Bonds	1.25	.80
239	Cris Carpenter	.10	.06
240	Eric Karros	.25	.15
241	Greg McMichael	.20	.12
242	Pat Hentgen	.25	.15
243	Tim Pugh	.15	.10
244	Vinny Castilla	.12	.07
245	Charlie Hough	.10	.06
246	Bobby Munoz	.20	.12
247	Kevin Baez	.12	.07
248	Todd Frohwirth	.10	.06
249	Charlie Hayes	.15	.10
250	Mike Macfarlane	.10	.06
251	Danny Darwin	.10	.06
252	Ben Rivera	.12	.07
253	Dave Henderson	.10	.06
254	Steve Avery	.40	.25
255	Tim Belcher	.12	.07
256	Dan Plesac	.10	.06
257	Jim Thome	.25	.15
258	Albert Belle (35+)	.50	.30
259	Barry Bonds (35+)	1.00	.60
260	Ron Gant (35+)	.15	.10
261	Juan Gonzalez (35+)	1.25	.80
262	Ken Griffey Jr. (35+)	1.75	1.00
263	David Justice (35+)	.60	.35
264	Fred McGriff (35+)	.40	.25
265	Rafael Palmeiro (35+)	.20	.12
266	Mike Piazza (35+)	2.50	1.50
267	Frank Thomas (35+)	2.00	1.25
268	Matt Williams (35+)	.20	.12
269	Checklist (1-135)	.10	.06
270	Checklist (136-270)	.10	.06

1994 Stadium Club Super Team Inserts

The team cards in this limtied insert set were distributed randomly in Topps Stadium Club foil packs and are part of a Stadium Club prize promotion. Cards of teams winning division titles, the League Championship Series and the World Series could be redeemed for prizes. The cards measure 2-1/2" by 3-1/2".

		MINT	NR/MT
Complete Set (28)		400.00	250.00
Commons		5.00	3.00
1	Atlanta Braves	75.00	48.00
2	Chicago Cubs	8.00	5.00
3	Cincinnati Reds	6.00	3.75
4	Colorado Rockies	6.00	3.75
5	Florida Marlins	6.00	3.75
6	Houston Astros	15.00	10.00
7	Los Angeles Dodgers	12.00	7.50
8	Montreal Expos	10.00	6.50
9	New York Mets	5.00	3.00
10	Philadelphia Phillies	40.00	28.00
11	Pittsburgh Pirates	5.00	3.00
12	St. Louis Cardinals	6.00	3.75
13	San Diego Padres	5.00	3.00
14	San Francisco Giants	60.00	38.00
15	Baltimore Orioles	25.00	15.00
16	Boston Red Sox	5.00	3.00
17	California Angels	6.00	3.75
18	Chicago White Sox	60.00	38.00
19	Cleveland Indians	6.00	3.75
20	Detroit Tigers	5.00	3.00
21	Kansas City Royals	6.00	3.75
22	Milwaukee Braves	5.00	3.00
23	Minnesota Twins	5.00	3.00
24	New York Yankees	15.00	10.00
25	Oakland Athletics	5.00	3.00
26	Seattle Mariners	12.00	7.50
27	Texas Rangers	8.50	5.50
28	Toronto Blue Jays	70.00	45.00

The ⓒNFIDENT ⓒLLECTOR™

KNOWS THE FACTS

Each volume packed with valuable information that
no collector can afford to be without

THE OVERSTREET COMIC BOOK
GRADING GUIDE, 1st Edition
by Robert M. Overstreet and Gary M. Carter   76910-7/$12.00 US/$15.00 Can

THE OVERSTREET COMIC BOOK
PRICE GUIDE COMPANION, 6th Edition
by Robert M. Overstreet   76911-5/$6.00 US/$8.00 Can

• • •

FINE ART
Identification and Price Guide, 2nd Edition
by Susan Theran   76924-7/$20.00 US/$24.00 Can

QUILTS
Identification and Price Guide, 1st Edition
by Liz Greenbacker and Kathleen Barach   76930-1/$14.00 US/$17.00 Can

ORIGINAL COMIC ART
Identification and Price Guide, 1st Edition
by Jerry Weist   76965-4/$15.00 US/$18.00 Can

ART DECO
Identification and Price Guide, 2nd Edition
by Tony Fusco   77012-1/$16.00 US/$19.00 Can

COLLECTIBLE MAGAZINES
Identification and Price Guide, 1st Edition
by David K. Henkel   76926-3/$15.00 US/$17.50 Can